SAMULNORI

Master Drummers and Dancers from Korea

四物놀이

"A complete theatrical experience"

New York Times

▶ For further Information please contact SamulNori Hanullim
163-25 Hyehwa-dong Jongro-gu Seoul, Korea 110-530
Phone 82-2-765-7951 Fax 82-2-744-3417

Photo • Park Seung - U (Art Space)

PAYE

PERFORMING ARTS YEARBOOK FOR EUROPE

THE DEFINITIVE AND INDISPENSABLE DIRECTORY

2000

10th edition – completely revised

Editor Karin Junker

Consultant Editor Ana Laura Lopez de la Torre

Arts Publishing International Ltd

the publishers of

Music, Opera, Dance and Drama in Asia, the Pacific and North America.

International Arts Manager magazine

Published in 1999 in Great Britain by Arts Publishing International Ltd,
Lime Wharf, Vyner Street, London E2 9DJ, England, Tel: (+44 20) 8709 9050
Fax: (+44 20) 8709 9080 E-Mail: post@api.co.uk

ISBN 1-873463-24-3
Performing Arts Yearbook for Europe 2000 (pbk) £45.00 (UK incl. P&P)

Printed in Great Britain by Perfectaprint, Byfleet, Surrey

© Paul Maurer / Photo Courtesy Arquitectonica, Miami

Auditorium de Dijon, Dijon, France

© Georg Anderhub

Lucerne Culture and Congress Center, Lucerne, Switzerland

KIBBUTZ CONTEMPORARY DANCE COMPANY

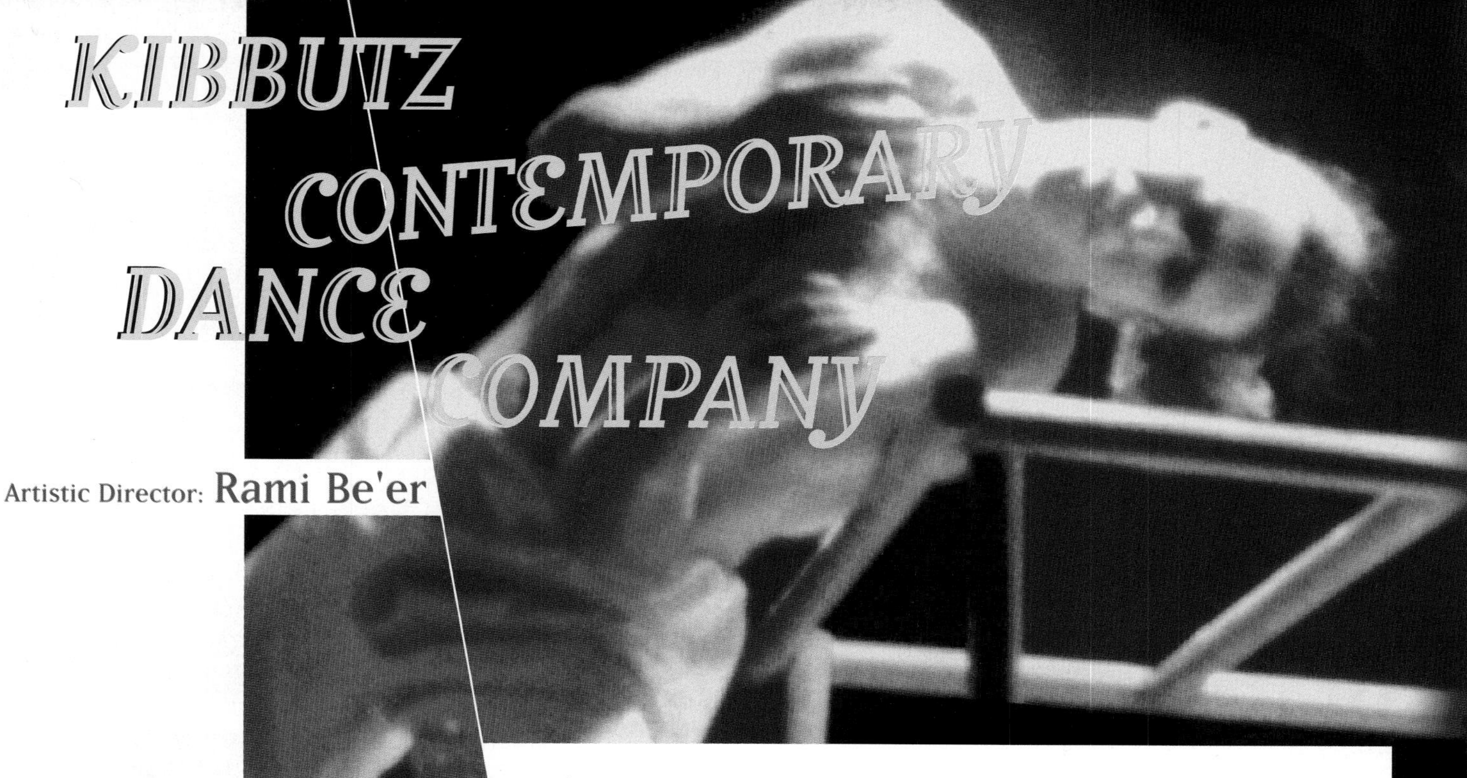

Artistic Director: Rami Be'er

"...phantasmagoric images of fear, compulsion and, ultimately transcendence, multiplied into infinity...combined with extraordinary lighting..."

Sylviane Gold "Newsday" 26.2.98

Founder & Artistic Adviser: Yehudit Arnon
General Manager: Dan Rudolf

להקת המחול הקיבוצית

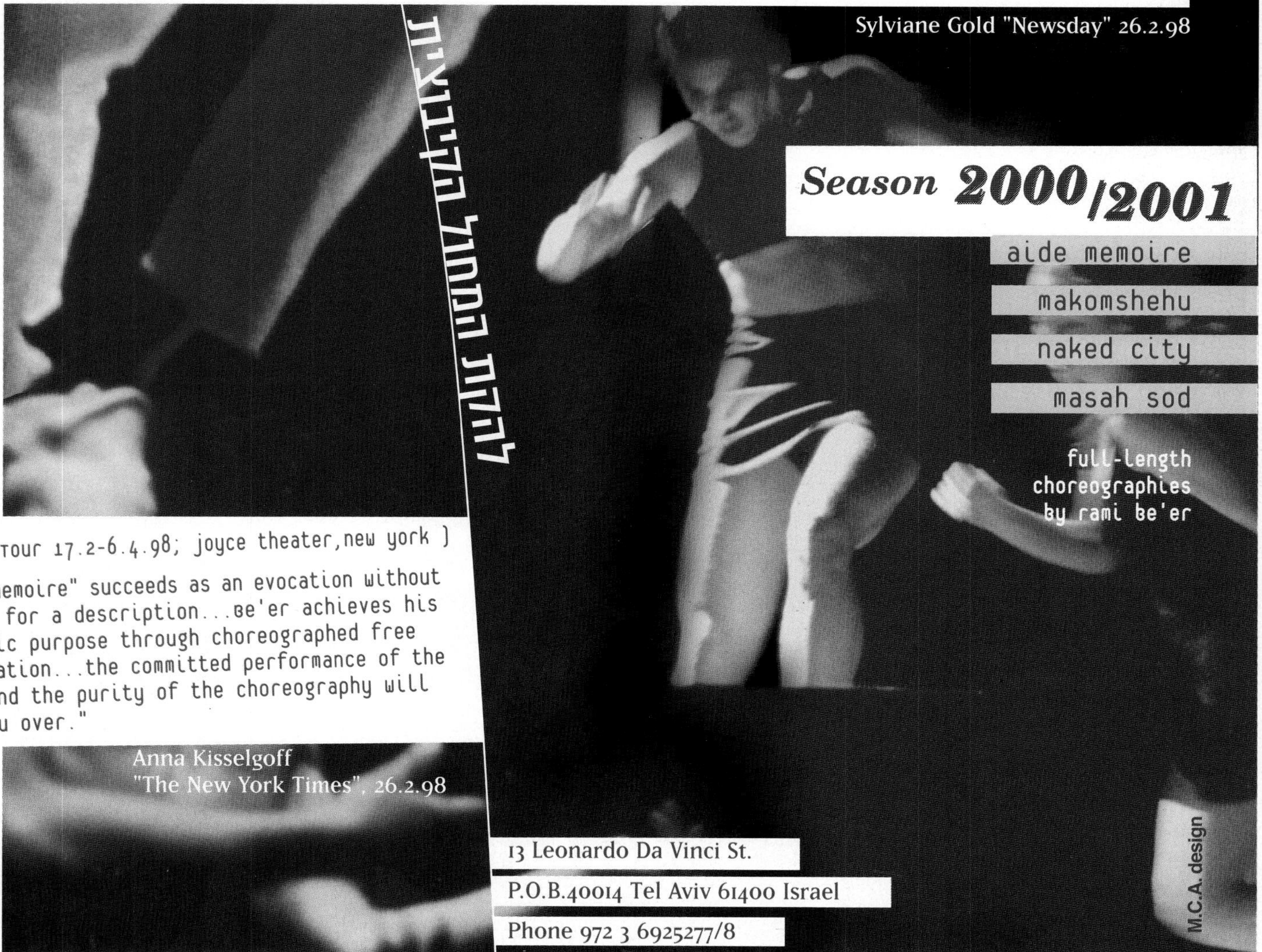

Season 2000/2001

aide memoire
makomshehu
naked city
masah sod

full-length choreographies by rami be'er

(u.s.a tour 17.2-6.4.98; joyce theater, new york)

"aide memoire" succeeds as an evocation without trying for a description...be'er achieves his dramatic purpose through choreographed free association...the committed performance of the cast and the purity of the choreography will win you over."

Anna Kisselgoff
"The New York Times", 26.2.98

13 Leonardo Da Vinci St.
P.O.B.40014 Tel Aviv 61400 Israel
Phone 972 3 6925277/8
Fax 972 3 6925279
M. Phone 972 53 345693
E-mail dan@kba.org.il

M.C.A. design

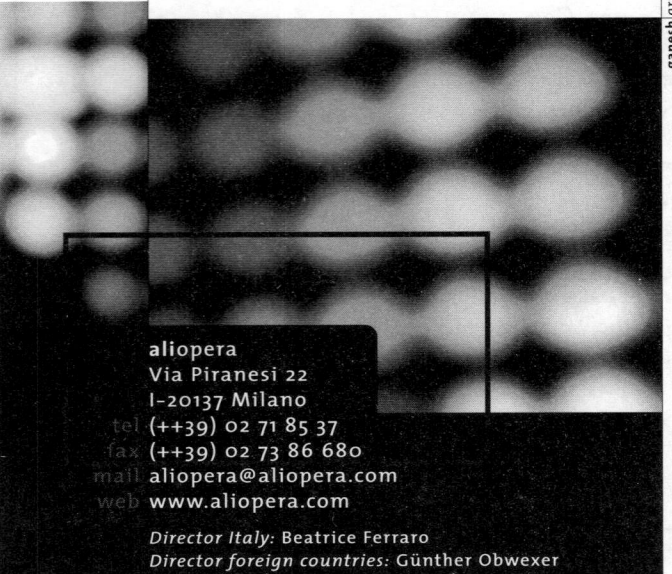

Foreword

There is a popular saying in French which comforts the conservative streak in all of us: "Plus ça change, plus c'est la même chose" i.e. the more things change, the more they stay the same. But at the turn of the century - for some also the millennium - I think most of us would really like a real change in the state of affairs, what with the scare of globalization, genetically modified foodstuffs, global warming, increasing fanaticism and violence of all kinds, to mention but a few of the worries that grew out of the latter part of the 20th century.

Some things, however, because they unquestionably contribute to the quality of human existence need to be preserved - which doesn't mean they cannot be added to or invigorated by fresh initiative. Such indeed should, to my mind, be the approach to our culture: due respect for the heritage we have received from the past and determined efforts to maintain a high level of cultural activity and creativity. And that is not so easy as it sounds!. But at the Council of Europe we still endeavour to give substance to that belief.

In September last year we launched a new campaign entitled "Europe, a common heritage" which aims once again at raising public awareness and appreciation of the natural and man-made environment and of the duties we have towards the legacy received from past generations. Also, through our programmes devoted to cultural policies, new technologies and training and assistance in cultural administration, we are constantly striving to maintain and improve the conditions for creativity in our own times and for the future.

Over the years I have come to regard PAYE as a key partner in this approach. As the principal provider of up-to-date and reliable information about those who organize and perform the works of our heritage and new creations, PAYE remains one of those services that should never disappear. So long life in this new century!

Raymond Weber
Director of Education
Culture & Sport
Council of Europe

Foreword

It is a pleasure and an honour, soon after taking up my new duties in the European Commission, to be given the chance to welcome your new edition of the Performing Arts Yearbook for Europe.

The wealth and diversity of existing as well as of new cultural forms of expression in Europe can only be strengthened, promoted and widely disseminated through quality publications such as this one. I am sure that the PAYE, with its innovative and creative approach, will continue to be an important forum for receiving and disseminating information on cultural issues.

The Commission, despite its limitations in terms of finance and human resources, will continue to encourage such initiatives, which are very much in line with its efforts to reach out to all European citizens and support their cultural expressions through its actions and programmes. Cultural organisations and operators at all levels have an important role to play in ensuring, together with the Commission, that prime consideration is given to Europe's unique cultural character and to the aspirations of its people when they launch and implement cultural initiatives and activities.

It is very much with this in mind that the new <Culture 2000> programme will try to live up to the expectations it has created and to attain its first and foremost objective, to encompass and promote Europe's past and present cultural wealth and diversity through real partnerships and networks at all levels for the benefit of as many citizens in this continent of ours. As in previous yearbooks, this year's edition tries to demonstrate just that - the importance of both past and present cultural expressions in our everyday life.

Viviane Reding
Commissioner with responsibility for Information, Communication and Culture - European Commission

SVENSKA KONSERTBYRÅN
SWEDISH CONCERT BUREAU

Conductor
Roberto Abbado *Sc*
B Tommy Andersson *W*
Gary Berkson *W excl US*
Ivor Bolton *SE*
Martyn Brabbins *SE*
Nicholas Cleobury *S + N + SF*
Russell Harris *W*
Elgar Howarth *S + N + SF*
Gérard Korsten *SE*
Paul Mägi *V*
Andrew Parrott *SE*
Vladimir Ponkin *Sc + SF*
Cecilia Rydinger Alin *W*
En Shao *SE*
Petter Sundkvist *W*
Jean-Pierre Wallez *SE*
Christopher Warren-Green *Sc + SF*
Niklas Willén *Sc + SF*
Martin Yates *W*

Piano
Helge Antoni *SE*
Arnaldo Cohen *Sc + SF*
Anders Kilström *W*
Evgeny Kissin *SE*
Bengt-Åke Lundin *W*
Mikhail Rudy *SE*
Grigory Sokolov *SE*

Violin
Karen Gomyo *Sc*
Daniel Hope *SE*
Karl-Ove Mannberg *W*
György Pauk *SE*
Tobias Ringborg *W*
Leon Spierer *S + SF + N*
Jean Pierre Wallez *SE*
Christopher Warren-Green *Sc + SF*

Viola
Lars Anders Tomter *SE*

Cello
Michaela Fukačová *SE*
Mischa Maisky *SE*
Mats Rondin *W*

Flute
James Galway *SE*

Clarinet
Michel Lethiec *SE*
Håkan Rosengren *W*

French Horn
Ib Lanzky-Otto *W*

Guitar
Per Skareng *W*

Director/Producer (Opera)
Wilhelm Carlsson *W*

Soprano
Gunnel Bohman *W*
Amelie Fleetwood *W*
Karin Ingebäck *W*
Charlotta Larsson *W*
Lisa Larsson *SE*
Katarina Nilsson *W*
Sara Olsson W
Gitta-Maria Sjöberg *W excl DK + G + CH + A*
Anita Soldh *W*
Gunilla Stephen-Kallin *W*
Tua Åberg *W*

Mezzo-Soprano
Anette Bod *W*
Martina Dike *W*
Marianne Eklöf *W*
Malena Ernman *W*
Kristina Hammarström *W*
Doris Soffel *SE*

Contralto
Anna Larsson *W*

Tenor
Jonas Degerfeldt *W*
Göran Eliasson *W*
Staffan Galli *W*
Lars-Erik Jonsson *W*
Jan Kyhle *W*
Neil Mackie *SE + N*
Nils Olsson *W excl G + A + CH*
Mathias Zachariassen *Sc + SF*

Baritone
Carl Johan/Loa Falkman *W*
Marcus Jupither *W*
Anders Larsson *W*
Peter Mattei *W*

Bass Baritone
Lars Arvidson *W*
John Erik Eleby *W*

String Quartet
Chilingirian Quartet *SE*
Hagen Quartet *Sc + SF*
The Lindsays *SE*
Shostakovich Quartet *SE*
Tale Quartet *W*
Vellinger String Quartet *SE*
Vilnius Quartet *SE*
Wihan Quartet *SE*

Chamber Orchestra
Chamber Orchestra of Lithuania / S Sondeckis *Sc*
London Chamber Orchestra / Christopher Warren-Green *Sc + SF*
I Fiamminghi / R Werthen *Sc + SF*

DK	*Denmark*
Sc	*Scandinavia*
N	*Norway*
G	*Germany*
SF	*Finland*
A	*Austria*
CH	*Switzerland*
SE	*Sweden*
W	*World*

Svenska Konsertbyrån AB

Member of the International Artist Managers' Association Ltd

KERSTIN HAMMARSTRÖM, Managing Director ANN BRAATHEN, Artist Manager
Jungfrugatan 45 S-114 44 Stockholm, Sweden Tel +46 8 665 80 88 Fax +46 8 665 80 66
E-mail info@svenskakonsertbyran.se Web www.svenskakonsertbyran.se

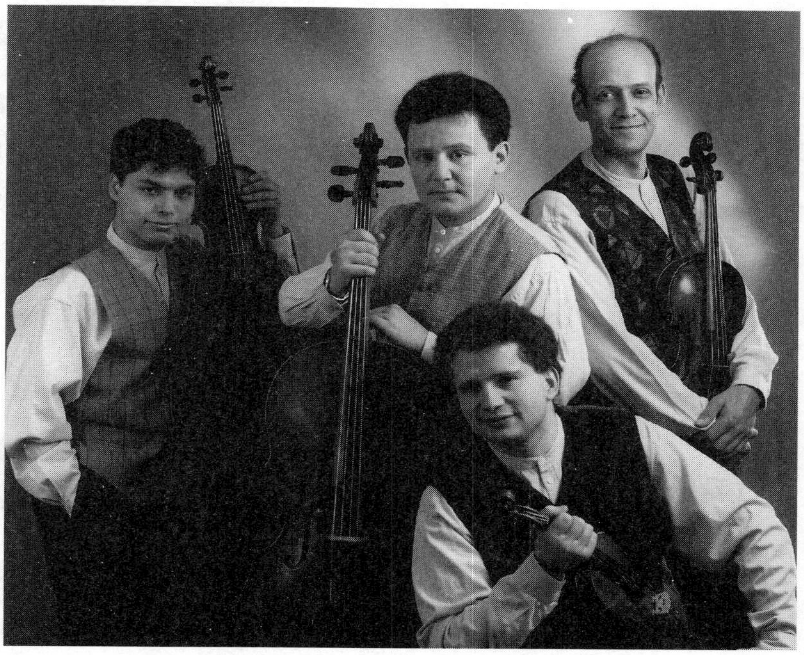

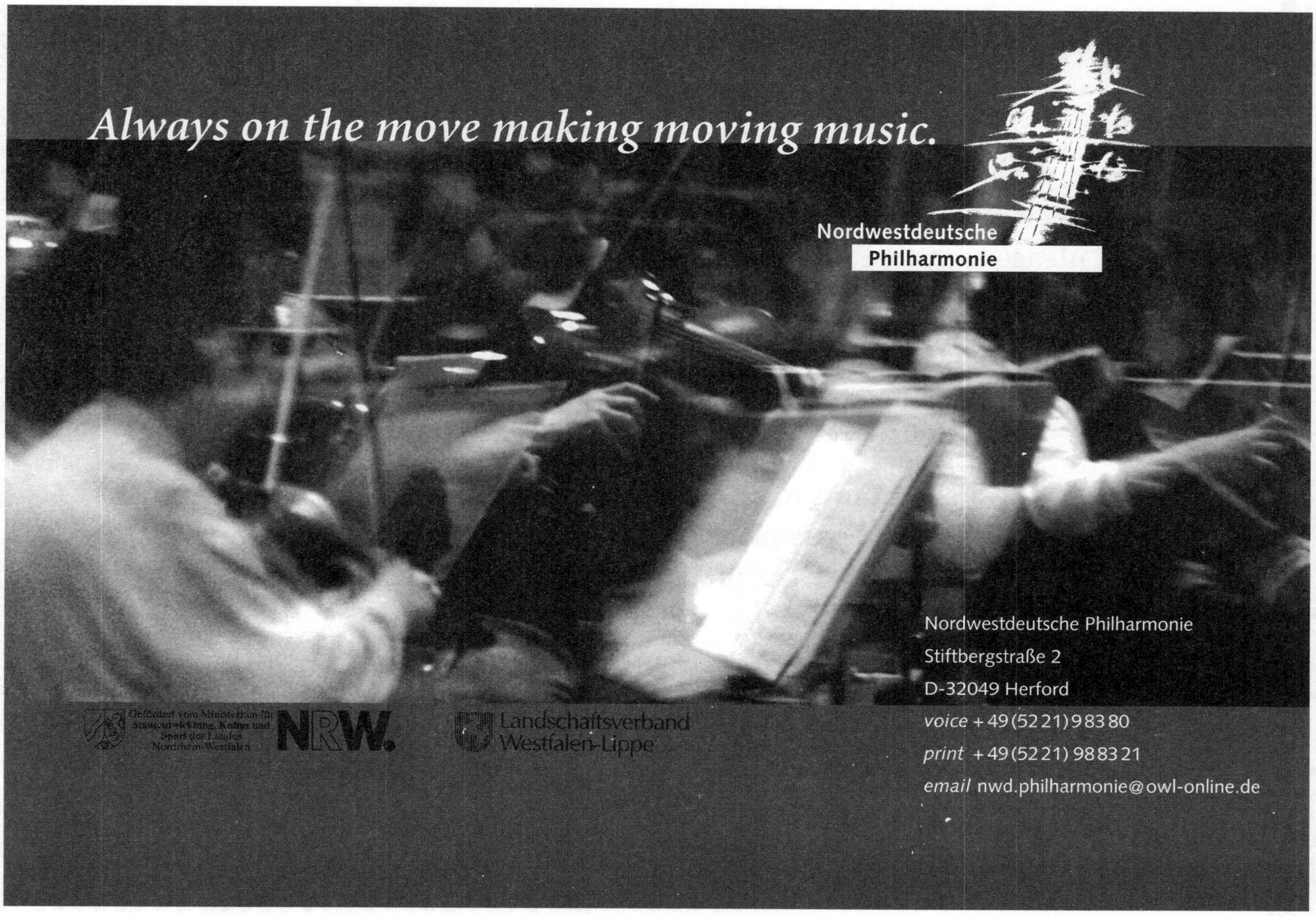

Always on the move making moving music.
Nordwestdeutsche Philharmonie
NRW.
Landschaftsverband Westfalen-Lippe
Nordwestdeutsche Philharmonie
Stiftbergstraße 2
D-32049 Herford
voice +49 (5221) 98380
print +49 (5221) 988321
email nwd.philharmonie@owl-online.de

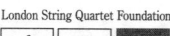

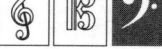

Performing Arts Yearbook for Europe 2000

Contents

- **Customer Service, see page 170, 272, 648, 740**
- **International Arts Manager (IAM) magazine see page 83, 377, 656**
- **Music, Opera, Dance and Drama in Asia, the Pacific and North America see page 366, 640**

Reference Section

Indexes

Introduction to the PAYE

As with the previous editions of the yearbook, the bulk of this publication is given over to a directory of performing arts companies and services throughout Europe. To get the most from the book, you should read the chapter entitled **How to use the PAYE**. The emphasis of the **PAYE** remains on major and medium scale professional companies (whether subsidised at national, regional or local level). It includes some of the more notable smaller scale subsidised companies, usually chosen after consultation with ministry officials or other experts in each country. The commercial West End Theatres in London and the boulevard théâtre privé in Paris are also included, because of their role in presenting products derived from the subsidised sector, particularly in London.
We have also included some young people's and children's theatre companies. To obtain information on other children's/YPT companies, and on theatre in education companies, youth theatres and orchestras which have not been included, readers are advised to contact the national centres of ASSITEJ, the ITI, UNIMA and the Federation des Jeunesse Musicales etc. Many of these are listed in the section of PAYE on **National Organisations**, but in case of difficulty, the international headquarters of these networks are listed in the section on **Supra-National Organisations**.

Every editon of the **PAYE** is the result of a team effort and we are extremely grateful for the support of contributors keeping us up-to-date with changes and new developments in their countries. The **PAYE** depends on their support and we would like to encourage comments and information from individuals and organisations as to how we can make it an even more useful publication for the performing arts business.

Please write to us or let us know at our email-address at:
paye@api.co.uk

Special thanks goes to Ana Laura Lopez de la Torre, Consultant Editor, without whose experience, knowledge and generosity this book would not have been possible.

Karin Junker
Editor

How to use the PAYE

Ordering of entries within section
The ordering of entries varies from section to section.
The rubric at the beginning of each section explains how that section has been ordered.

Languages
Wherever possible, we have retained the title of companies in the language in which it was presented to us i.e. their original language. In the case of Russian or Slav languages, etc, a transliteration is given. English translations of company names are generally provided for the more uncommon or lesser-used languages in the international arena (eg Finnish, Hungarian, Polish, Serbian, Croation, Swedish, Russian etc).
As the PAYE is intended for an international readership, cities are generally shown in their original language (eg Firenze for Florence, Köln for Cologne, Torino for Turin, and Wien for Vienna). However anglicised versions are used for the Russian or Slav countries etc. and for countries which are bi-lingual. Thus the capital of Belgium is referred to as Brussels rather than Brussel (Dutch) or Bruxelles (French), and Antwerpen is referred to as Antwerp.

Index
The index of editorial entries at the back of the Performing Arts Yearbook for Europe will enable you to identify on which page an entry for an organisation appears (eg. Gmundner Festspiele, Gmunden, p.n).

Telephoning
The direct dialling code prefix for each country is listed at the beginning of the entries relating to that country within each section. It is possible to dial most of the organisations listed in the PAYE directly, though telephone and fax communications with some Eastern European countries can still be a time consuming business.
The area/city code is included in the entries. Please remember, when dialling a number from within a country you are often required to add a digit before the area/city code. In many instances this is a zero: eg when dialling Glasgow from London or Birmingham you would dial 0141 followed by the number.
In some of the larger arts organisations, especially in Germany or Austria, the number given is followed by a hyphen and then a zero or another number, eg 1234-0. This simply denotes that the number given will enable you to reach the general switchboard, but most individuals in that organisation will have their own direct line, which is likely to be two, three or even four digits after the hyphen.
Each country has its own international access code prefix to enable you to dial directly. The requirement to add this code is indicated in the listings by the + sign before the country code. If you wanted to dial Hungary (country code 36), you would use the international access code before dialling the country code and the direct number. For most countries this code is (00), but for example, if you are phoning from the United States, you would need to dial (011) before the country code. Please contact your local operator if in doubt.

the Silk and Bamboo Ensemble

Contact: Dr. Yuan-Yuan Lee, Director, Concert & Lecture Division,
Chinese Music Society of North America,
PO Box 5275, Woodridge IL 60517-0275 USA. Tel: 630-910-1551. FAX: 630-910-1561.

Performing Arts Yearbook for Europe 2000

Table de Matières

• **Service Clièntele, voir pages 170, 272, 648, 740**

• **International Arts Manager (IAM) magazine voir page 83, 377, 656**

• **Music, Opera, Dance and Drama in Asia, the Pacific and North America voir page 366, 640**

Rubriques

Index

Introduction au PAYE

Comme les éditions précédentes de notre guide annuel, la grande majorité des exemplaires publiés est distribuée à travers l'Europe, de l'Atlantique à l'Oural, à un éventail de compagnies et de services directement liés aux arts du spectacle. Afin d'utiliser au mieux notre guide, nous vous conseillons de lire le chapitre intitulé **Comment utiliser le PAYE**.
Le **PAYE** répertorie principalement les compagnies professionnelles de grande et de moyenne envergure (subventionnées aussi bien au niveau local que, régional ou national). Certaines compagnies de plus petite taille figurent également dans le guide, ces dernières ayant été choisies aprés consultation auprès des ministères ou auprès d'experts nationaux. Les théâtres commerciaux du West End de Londres et les théâtres privés de boulevard à Paris sont également inclus parce qu'ils présentent des spectacles produits par le secteur subventionné, surtout à Londres.
Cette édition comprend également les coordonnées de compagnies de théâtre pour enfants et jeune public les plus connues. Pour obtenir plus d'information sur les autres compagnies pour enfants, les théâtres éducatifs, les théâtres ou orchestres de jeunes ne figurant pas dans le guide, nous vous conseillons de contacter les centres nationaux de l'ASSITEJ, l'ITI, l'UNIMA, la Fédération des jeunesses musicales etc. Vous trouverez la liste de ces centres dans notre section **Organisations Nationales**; en cas de problème renseignez-vous auprès des bureaux internationaux de ces organismes, répertoriés dans la section **Organisations Supranationales**.

Chaque édition du **PAYE** résulte d'un vrais travail d'équipe et nous sommes très reconnaissants du soutient que certains d'entre vous nous apportent en nous indiquant les changements et les évolutions de leur pays. Le **PAYE** est dépendant de ce type de soutient et nous aimerions encourager la venue de commentaires et d'informations provenant de personnes isolées ou d'organisations. Par conséquent,
les commentaires ou suggestions visant à rendre le **PAYE** plus utile pour les compagnies des arts du spectacle sont toujours les bienvenues. Vous pouvez nous transmettre vos informations par e-mail à l'adresse suivante: paye@api.co.uk.

Special remerciement à Ana Laura Lopez de la Torre, Éditeur Adjoint, sans l'expérience, la connaissance et la générosité de celle-ci, la réalisation de ce livre n'aurait jamais été possible.

Karin Junker
Rédactrice

Comment utiliser le PAYE

Ordre des Parutions
L'ordre des parutions varie d'une section à l'autre.
Au début de chaque section, la rubrique explique comment s'organise chaque section.

Langues
Autant que possible, nous avons gardé le nom des organismes dans la langue dans laquelle il nous a été présenté, c'est-à-dire dans leur langue d'origine. Dans le cas du Russe ou des langues Slaves, etc.. une traduction est fournie. En général, une traduction anglaise est fournie pour les langues plus rares et moins employées comme par exemple le finnois, le hongrois, le polonnais, le serbe, le croate, le suédois, le russe etc....
Comme le PAYE est destiné aux lecteurs internationaux, nous avons essayé de garder le nom d'orgine des villes (ex: Firenze pour Florence et Wien pour Vienna). Pourtant une version anglaise est donnée pour les pays slaves et pour les pays bilingues. Ainsi la capitale de la Belgique est "Brussels" plutôt que "Brussel" (flamand) ou "Bruxelles" (français), et "Antwerpen" signifie "Antwerp".

L'Index
L'index des parutions à la fin du Performing Arts Yearbook for Europe vous permettra de retrouver les pages où se trouvent les renseignements concernant chaque organisme (ex. Gmundner Festspiele, Gmunden, p.n).

Téléphone
L'indicatif pour chaque pays est donné au début de chaque section.
Il est possible d'appeler directement la plupart des organismes répertoriés dans le PAYE. Pourtant, il existe toujours des problèmes de communication (téléphone et télécopie) avec certains pays d'Europe de l'Est.
L'Indicatif local est inclus dans le numéro de chaque organisme. Quand vous composez un numéro dans le pays lui-même, il est souvent nécessaire d'ajouter un chiffre devant l'indicatif de la ville ou de la région. Souvent ce chiffre supplémentaire est un zéro, par exemple en téléphonant à Glasgow de Londres, ou de Birmingham, il est nécessaire de composer le 0141 suivi du numéro.
Dans le cas d'organismes plus grands, surtout en Allemagne et Autriche, le numéro est suivi d'un tiret, puis d'un zéro ou d'un autre numéro, par exemple, 1234-0. Ce numéro est celui du standard mais la majorité des membres de cette organisme aura une ligne directe qui se composera probablement de 2,3 ou même 4 chiffres après le tiret.
Chaque pays a son propre indicatif d'accès qui vous permet de téléphoner directement à l'étranger. Le signe + avant l'indicatif du pays indique les cas où il est nécessaire de composer cet indicatif. Par exemple, en téléphonant en Hongrie des pays suivants, il est nécessaire de composer les indicatifs d'accès ci-dessous avant de composer l'indicatif du pays et le numéro (00).

Ombra

A stage performance

An italian style performance, based in Federico García Lorca's life. With *Ombra*, La Fura continues penetrating into the conventional parametres of Italian style theatre whilst maintaining the company's own language and provoking new stimulus for the spectator. The simultaneity of a visual language such as video, the black voice of the Blues and the art of flamenco dancing are intermixed with the texts extracted and adapted from the works of the poet and author, F.G. Lorca.

LA FURA DELS BAUS

La Fura dels Baus: Hansel Cereza, Miki Espuma, Pep Gatell, Jurgën Müller, Alex Ollé, Carlos Padrissa, Pera Tantiñá.

Furamobil

Urban Action

The moving machine show. Sculpture/Device. The public are the actors.

The **Furamobil** is La Fura's new invention. Is an hybrid device that tries to mix a variety of world show aspects. It is a machine that creates a show, an sculpture that becomes an stage, a performance in wich the actors are the audience, where the actor-audience can feel, for a minutes, to be a creator and the center of attention and where the essencial is the participants feelings.

OBS

A Furan language show created for non conventional venues

Live Music. 3-D Projections. A total interaction with the audience. Movile sets. An action-packed tragic comedy.

Contact:
La Fura dels Baus
De la Ciència, 21.
08850 Gavà. Barcelona.
Phone: (34) 93 662 40 47
Fax: (34) 93 662 40 49
Email: lafura@lafura.com
http://www.lafura.com

Touring:
International: Rosa Arnaiz
Spain, Latinoamerica, Portugal: Elena Blanco
Catalonia and France: Martina Gatell

La Fura dels Baus is a company funded by:

Generalitat de Catalunya
Departament
de Cultura

SOPRANOS

- Paula Almerares (Z/G)
- Pamela Armstrong (Z/G)
- Ainhoa Arteta (WG/JV)
- Kathleen Battle (MK)
- Maria Bayo (Z/G)
- • Isabel Bayrakdarian (KA)
- Harolyn Blackwell (KB)
- Eva Maria Bundschuh (Z/G)
- Amy Burton (WG/JV)
- Kristine Ciesinski (WG)
- Paula Delligatti (KB)
- Mireille Delunsch (KA)
- Giusy Devinu (Z/G)
- Mary Dunleavy (Z/G)
- Nina Edwards (Z/G)
- Rebecca Evans (KA)
- Stefka Evstatieva (Z/G)
- Tiziana Fabbricini (Z/G)
- Ruth Falcon (KB)
- Elena Filipova (Z/G)
- Renée Fleming (AT)
- Nuccia Focile (Z/G)
- Nicolle Foland (JV)
- Cristina Gallardo-Domas (Z/G)
- Mechthild Gessendorf (Z/G)
- Gwynne Geyer (EC)
- Jane Giering-De Haan (WG/JV)
- Sheri Greenawald (WG/JV)
- Andrea Gruber (AT)
- Maria Guleghina (Z/G)
- Nicole Heaston (Z/G)
- Hei-Kyung Hong (JV)
- Ying Huang (MK/WG)
- Karen Huffstodt (Z/G)
- Carla Maria Izzo (KA)
- Carolyn James (Z/G)
- Dame Gwyneth Jones (Z/G)
- Isabelle Kabatu (EC)
- Elena Kelessidi (Z/G)
- Dawn Kotoski (MH)
- Dame Felicity Lott (JV)
- Emily Magee (Z/G)
- Catherine Malfitano (MH/WG)
- • Audra McDonald (AT)
- Alwyn Mellor (KB)
- • Marina Mescheriakova (JV)
- Aprile Millo (Z/G)
- Mary Mills (Z/G)
- Nelly Miricioiu (Z/G)
- Inva Mula (KA)
- Anna Netrebko (JV)
- • Susan Neves (Z/G)
- Simone Nold (KA)
- Elizabeth Norberg-Schulz (JV)
- Maureen O'Flynn (KB/WG)
- • Gianna Queni (KA)
- Sondra Radvanovsky (EC)
- Deborah Riedel (JV)
- Dorothea Röschmann (KA)
- Andrea Rost (JV)
- Ana María Sánchez (EC)
- Christine Schäfer (AT)
- Patricia Schuman (EC)
- Nadine Secunde (Z/G)
- Marina Shaguch (KA)
- Elisabeth Söderström (JV)
- Cheryl Studer (Z/G)
- • Xiu Wei Sun (Z/G)
- Sharon Sweet (Z/G)
- Ruth Ann Swenson (Z/G)
- Iano Tamar (Z/G)
- • Dimitra Theodossiou (Z/G)
- Lynette Tapia (WG)
- Sylvie Valayre (Z/G)
- Zvetelina Vassileva (EC)
- Veronica Villarroel (Z/G)
- Deborah Voigt (AT)
- • Linda Watson (Z/G)
- • Jennifer Welch (EC)
- Janet Williams (Z/G)
- • Carol Wilson (Z/G)
- Sally Wolf (EC)
- Margaret Jane Wray (Z/G)
- Carol Yahr (Z/G)

MEZZO-SOPRANOS

- Graciela Araya (Z/G)
- Kimberly Barber (JV)
- Norine Burgess (EC)
- Zheng Cao (KA)
- Judith Christin (KB)
- Katherine Ciesinski (KB)
- Beth Clayton (EC)
- Diane Curry (EC)
- Luciana D'Intino (Z/G)
- Ruxandra Donose (JV)
- Judith Forst (Z/G)
- Sara Fulgoni (KA)
- Sonia Ganassi (Z/G)
- Jane Gilbert (WG)
- Susan Graham (AT)
- Denyce Graves (JV)
- Elizabeth Grohowski (EC)
- Jill Grove (KA)
- Eugenie Grunewald (KB)
- Charlotte Hellekant (JV)
- Marilyn Horne (RDS/MJC)
- • Katarina Karnéus (KB)
- ▲ Marjana Lipovšek (MK)
- Nancy Maultsby (JV/WG)
- Irina Mishura (JV)
- Sheila Nadler (KA)
- Carmen Oprisanu (EC)
- Nadia Pelle (Z/G)
- • Pettia Petrova (Z/G)
- Florence Quivar (KB)
- Gloria Scalchi (Z/G)
- Carolyn Sebron (Z/G)
- Rinat Shaham (KA)
- Stefania Toczyska (Z/G)
- Laura Tucker (Z/G)
- Violeta Urmana (Z/G)
- Victoria Vergara (Z/G)
- Frederica von Stade (JV)
- Sandra Walker (EC)
- Dolora Zajick (EC)

TENORS

- Gianni Abbagnato (KA)
- Marcelo Alvarez (Z/G)
- Francisco Araiza (DS)
- • Octavio Arevalo (Z/G)
- Vladimir Bogachov (EC)
- José Bros (EC)
- Steven Cole (EC)
- • James Cornelison (KB)
- Richard Croft (WG/JV)
- José Cura (Z/G)
- Fernando De La Mora (EC)
- Ian DeNolfo (Z/G)
- Franco Farina (Z/G)
- Clifton Forbis (WG)
- Bruce Ford (KA)
- Walter Fraccaro (EC)
- Paul Frey (Z/G)
- Anthony Dean Griffey (JV/AT)

2000/2001 70th Anniversary Season

The Creative Source for the Performing Arts

Francesco Grollo (Z/G)
Paul Groves (JV)
• Cesar Gutierrez (Z/G)
Marcus Haddock (WG)
Jerry Hadley (KB)
Thomas Harper (Z/G)
Ben Heppner (WG)
Emil Ivanov (Z/G)
Peter Kazaras (JV)
James King (Z/G)
David Kuebler (KB)
Richard Margison (Z/G)
David Miller (Z/G)
Michael Myers (EC)
Stuart Neill (JV)
Stanford Olsen (KB)
John Osborn (WG)
Alfredo Portilla (EC)
Neil Rosenshein (WG)
Gabriel Sade (Z/G)
Michael Schade (EC)
Neil Shicoff (AT)
John Short (Z/G)
• Antonio Siragusa (Z/G)
• Thomas Studebaker (KB)
Michael Sylvester (Z/G)
Martin Thompson (JV/WG)
• Gregory Turay (AT)
Ramón Vargas (Z/G)
Raymond Very (KB)
Jon Villars (AT)
• Rolando Villazon (Z/G)
• Dario Volonté (Z/G)
Joseph Wolverton (KB)
• Endrik Wottrich (KB)

COUNTERTENORS

David Daniels (AT)
Bejun Mehta (KA)

BARITONES

Russell Braun (EC)
Victor Braun (Z/G)
Vladimir Chernov (AT)
Dwayne Croft (JV)
• Alfredo Daza (Z/G)
Claudio Desderi (JV)
• Franck Ferrari (Z/G)
Richard Paul Fink (Z/G)
Tom Fox (KB)
Roberto Frontali (Z/G)
Paolo Gavanelli (Z/G)
• Robert Gardner (WG)
Rodney Gilfry (KB)
John Hancock (KB)
Kim Josephson (KB)
• Mariusz Kwiecien (WG)
Jean Philippe Lafont (Z/G)
Jorge Lagunes (EC)
Jeff Mattsey (KB)
Kurt Ollmann (KB)
Bruno Pola (Z/G)
Michele Porcelli (Z/G)
Vladimir Redkin (Z/G)
Christopher Robertson (JV)
Jochen Schmeckenbecher (KB)
Roberto Servile (Z/G)
Richard Stilwell (WG/JV)
Eduard Tumagian (Z/G)
LeRoy Villanueva (EC)
Vittorio Vittelli (Z/G)
• James Westman (KA)

BASS-BARITONES

Simone Alaimo (EC)
• Scott Altman (KB)
Alfonso Antoniozzi (Z/G)
Jay Baylon (JV)
Richard Bernstein (KB)
• Patrick Carfizzi (KB/WG)
Alan Held (Z/G)
• Mark McCrory (KB)
Monte Pederson (Z/G)
Dale Travis (KB)

BASSES

Raymond Aceto (WG/JV)
Simone Alberghini (Z/G)
Carlo Colombara (Z/G)
Franz Hawlata (AT)
Matthias Hölle (Z/G)
Dimitri Kavrakos (EC)
Kevin Langan (EC)
John Macurdy (Z/G)
Eric Owens (Z/G)
David Pittsinger (EC)
Samuel Ramey (JV/AT)
Kurt Rydl (Z/G)
Roberto Scandiuzzi (Z/G)
Erwin Schrott (Z/G)
Franz-Joseph Selig (Z/G)
Egils Silins (JV)
John Tomlinson (Z/G)
Barseg Tumanyan (Z/G)

• First CAMI Season
▲ Concerts Only

DESIGNERS

Gianni Quaranta (EC)
Dada Saligeri (EC)
Michael Scott (Z/G)

STAGE DIRECTORS

Christopher Alden (WG)
Grischa Asagaroff (EC)
Tito Capobianco (Z/G)
Robert Carsen (EC)
Giulio Chazalettes (EC)
Liviu Ciulei (EC)
John Copley (WG)
Frank Corsaro (EC)
Sonja Frisell (EC)
Colin Graham (WG)
Marthe Keller (WG)
Lotfi Mansouri (EC)
Fabrizio Melano (WG)
Hans Nieuwenhuis (WG)
Jean-Pierre Ponnelle (Estate) (RW)
John Schlesinger (RW/EC)
Graziella Sciutti (EC)

DUO RECITALISTS

Sharon Isbin &
Gaudencio Thiago de Mello (DS)
Latin Guitar & Percussion

Celin & Pepe Romero (DS)
Guitar Duo

Columbia Artists Management Inc.
Vocal Artists

COLUMBIA ARTISTS MANAGEMENT INC.

NEW YORK
165 West 57th Street, New York, NY 10019-2276
Telephone: (212) 841-9500
Fax: (212) 841-9744
E-mail: cami@cami.com

MANAGERIAL ROSTER

(KA)	**Karen Ashley** Fax: (212) 841-9687	(212) 841-9541 ashley@cami.com
(KB)	**Ken Benson** Fax: (212) 841-9687	(212) 841-9545 kbenson@cami.com
(MJC)	**Mary Jo Connealy** Fax: (212) 841-9517	(212) 841-9513 connealy@cami.com
(EC)	**Elizabeth Crittenden** Fax: (212) 841-9557	(212) 841-9682 crittend@cami.com
(WG)	**William G. Guerri** Fax: (212) 841-9516	(212) 841-9680 guerri@cami.com
(MH)	Matthew A. Horner Fax: (212) 841-9557	(212) 841-9556 mhorner@cami.com
(MK)	**Michaela Kurz** Fax: (212) 841-9747	(212) 841-9539 mkurz@cami.com
(AM)	Andreas Melinat Fax: (212) 841-9557	(212) 841-9551 amelinat@cami.com
(DP)	Denise A. Pineau Fax: (212) 841-9517	(212) 841-9527 dpineau@cami.com
(RDS)	**R. Douglas Sheldon** Fax: (212) 841-9734	(212) 841-9512 dsheldon@cami.com
(AT)	**Alec C. Treuhaft** Fax: (212) 841-9557	(212) 841-9713 treuhaft@cami.com
(JV)	**Jeffrey D. Vanderveen** Fax: (212) 841-9516	(212) 841-9548 vander@cami.com
(RW)	**Ronald A. Wilford** Fax: (212) 841-9719	(212) 841-9502 rwilford@cami.com
(Z/G)	**Bruce Zemsky** Fax: (212) 841-9742	(212) 841-9648 bzemsky@cami.com
(Z/G)	**Alan Green** Fax: (212) 841-9742	(212) 841-9649 agreen@cami.com

2000/2001 70th Anniversary Season

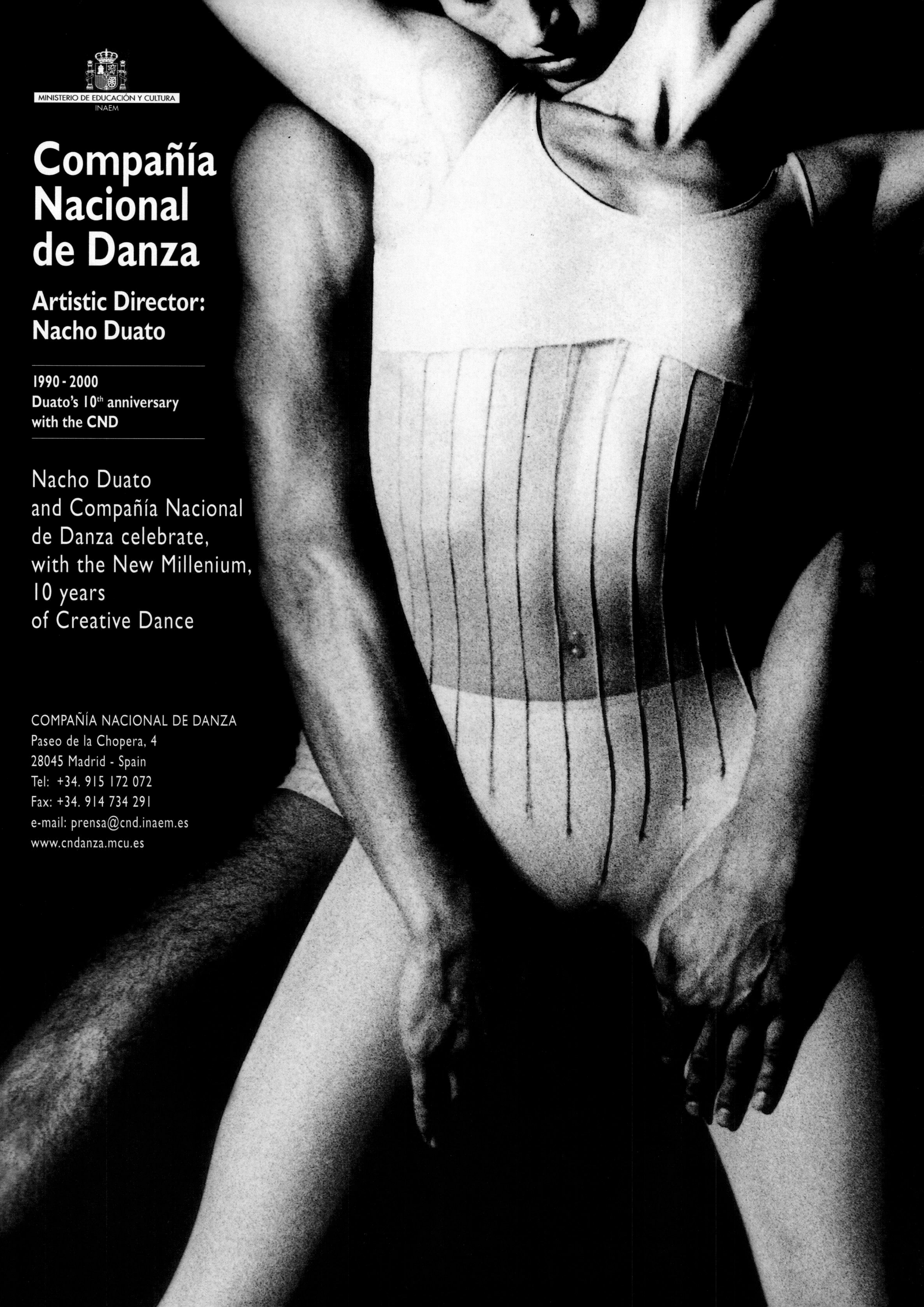
MINISTERIO DE EDUCACIÓN Y CULTURA
INAEM
Compañía Nacional de Danza
Artistic Director: Nacho Duato
1990 - 2000
Duato's 10th anniversary with the CND
Nacho Duato and Compañía Nacional de Danza celebrate, with the New Millenium, 10 years of Creative Dance
COMPAÑÍA NACIONAL DE DANZA
Paseo de la Chopera, 4
28045 Madrid - Spain
Tel: +34. 915 172 072
Fax: +34. 914 734 291
e-mail: prensa@cnd.inaem.es
www.cndanza.mcu.es

HRA

ARTIST MANAGEMENT HELGE RUDOLF AUGSTEIN
HELGE AUGSTEIN & STEFAN HAHN
SEBASTIANSPLATZ 3 / D - 80331 MÜNCHEN
TEL ~49 (0)89 26024 333 / FAX ~49 (0)89 26024344
MOBILE ~49 (0)172 6423344 / EMAIL: AgenturHRA@aol.com

MEMBER OF VERBAND DER DEUTSCHEN KONZERTDIREKTIONEN
AND ASSOCIATION EUROPÉENNE DES AGENTS ARTISTIQUES

conductors:

JÖRG-PETER WEIGLE *
EKKEHARD KLEMM **
ULRICH WINDFUHR **

instrumental:

cello:

NATALIA GUTMAN *

piano:

ELISO VIRSALADZE (ELISSO WIRSSALADZE) *
MICHAEL KORSTICK *
ALEXEI LUBIMOV *
PETER ORTH *

vocal:

soprano:

BARBARA HENDRICKS **
YING HUANG
DAME FELICITY LOTT
MARGARET MARSHALL *
CHRISTINE SCHÄFER

mezzo-soprano:

ANN MURRAY

tenor:

PHILIP LANGRIDGE
KEITH LEWIS
KOBIE VAN RENSBURG **

baritone:

OLAF BAR **

** = WORLD*
*** = DIVERS COUNTRIES including GERMANY*
unless indicated representation refers to Germany only
in some cases representation may be limited to recital and concert

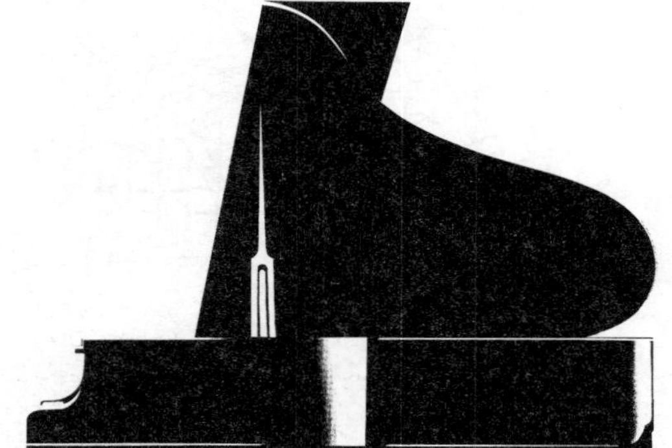

Deutsch

Performing Arts Yearbook for Europe 2000

Inhalt

• **Kundendienst, siehe Seiten 170, 272, 648, 740**

• **International Arts Manager (IAM) magazine siehe Seite 83, 377, 658**

• **Music, Opera, Dance and Drama in Asia, the Pacific and North America siehe Seite 366, 640**

Rubriken

Index

Einleitung zum PAYE

Wie in den anderen jährlichen Ausgaben besteht der Hauptteil des **PAYE** aus einer Übersicht kultureller Einrichtungen und Organisationen im Bereich der Musik und darstellenden Kunst in Europa. Um die im PAYE enthaltenen Informationen am besten zu nutzen, lesen Sie bitte das Kapitel **Hinweise zur Benutzung des PAYE**.
Im Mittelpunkt des **PAYE** stehen mittlere und größere professionelle Gruppen oder kulturelle Einrichtungen in Europa (auf nationaler, regionaler oder örtlicher Ebene subventioniert). Es sind auch einige kleinere Einrichtungen/Organisationen eingetragen worden, die uns auf Grund ihres Namens und ihrer besonderen Subventionszuschüsse von Fachleuten in den jeweiligen Ländern signalisiert wurden. Die privaten West End Theater in London und die privaten Boulevardtheater in Paris sind auch eingetragen, weil sie 'subventionierte Arbeit' aufführen.
Wir haben ebenfalls einige Kinder- und Jugendtheater eingeschlossen. Um Informationen über nicht aufgeführte Kindertheater, Jugendorchester usw. zu erhalten, wenden Sie sich bitte an die Geschäftsstellen der ASSITEJ, des ITIs, des UNIMA und der Federation des Jeunesse Musicales usw. Viele dieser Organisationen haben Geschäftsstellen in den einzelnen Ländern und sind deshalb im PAYE unter **Nationale Organisationen** zu finden. Falls diese Organisationen in Ihrem Land keine Zweigstelle haben sollten, können Sie sich an die Hauptgeschäftsstellen wenden, die Sie in der Rubrik **Übernationale Organisationen** finden.

Bitte haben Sie Verständnis dafür, daß Solisten, Duos und/oder Trios aus Platzgründen nicht aufgeführt werden können. Auch möchte ich noch einmal daran erinnern, daß alle redaktionellen Einträge kostenlos sind; scheuen Sie sich also nicht, uns über Ihre Organisation zu informieren.

Ich freue mich, daß wir jetzt auch auf CD-Rom verfügbar sind und glaube, daß dies die Benutzung des **PAYE** noch einfacher machen wird.

Wir sind natürlich für alle Anregungen sehr dankbar. Schreiben Sie uns! Oder benutzen Sie unsere neue Email-Anschrift: **paye@api.co.uk**

Besonders danken wir Ana Laura Lopez de la Torre, unserer Redaktionberaterin, für ihre Erfahrung, ihr Wissen und ihre Großzügigkeit. Ohne sie wäre dieses Buch nicht möglich gewesen.

Karin Junker
Redakteurin

Hinweise zur Benutzung des PAYE

Anordnung der Einträge
Die Anordnung der Einträge in den verschiedenen Rubriken des Jahrbuches ist unterschiedlich. Am Anfang einer jeden Rubrik wird kurz erklärt, wie diese gegliedert ist.

Sprache
Wo es möglich war, haben wir die Namen der Organisationen in der Landessprache gehalten. Es gibt allerdings englische Übersetzungen slawischer Namen. In der Regel finden Sie englische Übersetzungen aller im internationalen Raum wenig verbreiteten Sprachen (z.B. Finnisch, Schwedisch, Ungarisch, Polnisch, Serbisch, Kroatisch, Russisch usw.)
Da das PAYE sich an eine internationale Leserschaft wendet, erscheinen fast alle Städtenamen in der Landessprache (z.B. Firenze anstatt Florenz, Torino anstatt Turin, Köln anstatt Cologne, Wien anstatt Vienna). Allerdings benutzen wir die englische Variante für russische und andere slawische Städtenamen sowie Städtenamen zweisprachiger Länder, d.h. die Hauptstadt Belgiens heißt im PAYE Brussels und nicht Brussel (Flämisch) oder Bruxelles (Französisch). Antwerpen heißt Antwerp.

Index
Der Index am Ende des PAYE ermöglicht schnelles Auffinden von Informationen über eine bestimmte Organisation, (z.B. Gmundner Festspiele, Gmunden, p.n).

Telefonieren
Die internationale Vorwahl für jedes Land steht am Anfang der für das Land aufgeführten Einträge.
Es ist möglich, die meisten der aufgeführten Organisationen direkt anzuwählen (bei Telefonanrufen in die osteuropäischen Länder braucht man aber noch ein bißchen Geduld).
Die Vorwahlnummer für die jeweilige Stadt finden Sie bei jedem Eintrag. Bitte achten Sie bei Telefonaten innerhalb eines Landes darauf, daß Sie eine Ziffer vor der Stadtvorwahlnummer wählen. In vielen Fällen wählt man die Ziffer - 0 -, z.B. bei Telefonanrufen aus London oder Birmingham in Glasgow wählt man -0141 vor der Rufnummer. In manchen Fällen wählt man eine andere Ziffer, z.B. in Spanien wählt man -9. Also, um eine Rufnummer in Barcelona aus Madrid zu wählen, wählt man -93 vor der Rufnummer.
Einige der größeren Kulturorganisationen, vor allem in Deutschland und Österreich, haben eine zentrale Rufnummer. In der Regel finden Sie aber die Durchwahlnummenr für die verschiedenen Abteilungen innerhalb der Organisation in dem Eintrag.

Jedes Land hat seine eigene Landesvorwahl, die am Anfang der jeweiligen Sektion angegeben ist. Das Kennzeichnen '+' besagt, daß man die internationale Vorwahlnummer wählen muß. Wenn man zum Beispiel Ungarn (Landesvorwahl 36) anrufen will, würde man vor der 36 und der eigentlichen Nummer die internationale Vorwahl wählen. Für die meisten Länder ist diese Vorwahl (00), aber wenn man zum Beispiel von den Vereinigten Staaten anruft, ist es die (011)

"THE BEST CONCERT HALL IN THE COUNTRY"

Daily Telegraph

Symphony Hall
International Convention Centre
Broad Street
Birmingham B1 2EA
England

Director:
Andrew Jowett
0121 200 2000

OVER 200 CONCERTS A YEAR

HOME OF THE
CITY OF BIRMINGHAM
SYMPHONY ORCHESTRA

THE WORLD'S FINEST VISITING
ORCHESTRAS AND MUSICIANS

POPULAR MUSIC AND VARIETY OF
ALL KINDS

LOCAL MUSICIANS AND
YOUNG ARTISTS

BOX OFFICE
0121 212 3333

»Opera House of the Year«

Opernwelt critic's poll, September 1998

Klaus Zehelein *General Director*
Pamela Rosenberg *Co-Director*
Lothar Zagrosek *General Music Director*

1999/2000 season

New Productions

Die Fledermaus
by Johann Strauß
Conductor Marc Albrecht
Director Tilman Knabe
Premiere January 22, 2000

The Tales of Hoffmann
by Jacques Offenbach
Conductor Lothar Zagrosek
Director Joachim Schlömer
Premiere July 9, 2000

The Ring Cycle
by Richard Wagner

Das Rheingold
Conductor Lothar Zagrosek
Director Joachim Schlömer
Premiere March 12, 1999

Die Walküre
Conductor Lothar Zagrosek
Director Christof Nel
Premiere July 4, 1999

Siegfried
Conductor Lothar Zagrosek
Director Jossi Wieler
Premiere November 14, 1999

Götterdämmerung
Conductor Lothar Zagrosek
Director Peter Konwitschny
Premiere March 12, 2000

Other Productions in the 1999/2000 Repertory

Alcina, Aufstieg und Fall der Stadt Mahagonny, Il Barbiere di Siviglia, Boris Godunov, Così fan tutte, Die Entführung aus dem Serail, Der Freischütz, Hänsel und Gretel, L'Incoronazione di Poppea, The Love of the Three Oranges, Pique Dame, Rigoletto, Tosca, La Traviata, Turandot, Wozzeck

Staatsoper Stuttgart

Box Office: Oberer Schloßgarten 6, D-70173 Stuttgart
Telephone ticket sales: +49-711-20 20 90
Ticket fax: +49-711-20 20 920
E-mail: tickets@staatstheater-stuttgart.de
Visit our website at: http://www.staatstheater.stuttgart.de

Staatsoper Stuttgart

Performing Arts Yearbook for Europe 2000

Indice

- **Servizio Cliente, vedere pagina 170, 272, 648, 740**
- **International Arts Manager (IAM) magazine vedere pagina 83, 377**
- **Music, Opera, Dance and Drama in Asia, the Pacific and North America vedere pagina 366, 640**

Sezioni di consultazione

Indici

Introduzione al PAYE

Come per le precedenti edizioni, gran parte della pubblicazione è dedicata ad una serie di organizzazioni e servizi che operano in Europa nel campo artistico. Per usare al meglio le informazioni contenute nel volume dovreste consultare il capitolo intitolato **Guida all'Uso del PAYE**.
Di rilievo per il **PAYE** rimangono le maggiori e le medie organizzazioni professionali sovvenzionate a livello nazionale, regionale o locale. Sono incluse anche alcune tra le più rilevanti piccole aziende/compagnie che ricevono sovvenzioni; la loro scelta è avvenuta dopo aver consultato ministeri o altri esperti in ogni nazione. Sono stati inoltre inclusi i Teatri commerciali del West End di Londra e i Boulevard Theatres Prives di Parigi, per via del notevole ruolo svolto nella produzione di spettacoli sovvenzionati, particolarmente a Londra.
Abbiamo anche incluso le più famose compagnie di teatro per bambini e ragazzi. Per avere ulteriori informazioni su altre compagnie di teatro per bambini e ragazzi, e su orchestre giovanili, che non sono state incluse, i lettori sono pregati di mettersi in contatto con l'UNIMA, l'ASSITEJ, l'ITI, la Federation des Jeunesse Musicales, ecc. Gran parte di queste organizzazioni sono elencate nel **PAYE** nella sezione **National Organisations**, ma in caso di difficoltà potrete trovare le loro sedi principali elencate nella sezione **Supranational Organisations**.

Ogni edizione del **PAYE** é il risultato di un lavoro di gruppo e perció la nostra gratitudine va a tutti co loro che hanno contribuito a tenerci informati sui cambiamenti e nuovi sviluppi nei loro paesi. Basandosi sulla collaborazione, il **PAYE** incoraggia commenti ed informazioni forniti sia da singolicheda organizzazioni affinche sia una pubblicazione sempre piú utile nel settore delle arti sceniche.

Non esitate a scrivere e contatarci su: **paye@api.co.uk**

Un ringraziamento speciale va a Ana Laura Lopez de la Torre, Consulente Editoriale, senza la cui esperienza, consapevolezza e generosita, questo libro non sarebbe stato possibile.

Karin Junker
Redatrice

Guida all'uso del PAYE

Ordine delle entrate all'interno di ogni sezione
L'ordine delle entrate varia da sezione a sezione ed é spiegato dalla rubrica all'inizio di ogni paragrafo.

Lingue
Dove é stato possibile abbiamo mantenuto i nomi delle organizzazioni nella lingua originale. Per quanto riguarda la Russia, i Paesi dell'Est Europeo ecc. i nomi sono stati traslitterati in inglese. Sono stati inoltre tradotti - in inglese – anche i nomi di tutte quelle organizzazioni di Paesi le cui lingue sono meno comuni o meno usate nel panorama internazionale (Finlandese, Ungherese, Polacco, Serbo, Croato, Svedese, Russo, ecc).
Dal momento che PAYE é stato pensato per un pubblico internazionale, le cittá sono generalmente indicate nella loro lingua madre (ad es. London per Londra, Köln per Colonia, Paris per Parigi e Wien per Vienna). Per quanto riguarda la Russia, i Paesi dell'Est ecc., e per quelle Nazioni che sono bilingue i nomi sono stati inglesizzati.
Per esempio la capitale del Belgio é indicata come Brussels anziché Brussel (fiammingo) o Bruxelles (francese), ed Antwerpen (Anversa) é indicata come Antwerp.

Indice
L'indice delle entrate editoriali situato alla fine del Performing Arts Yearbook for Europe vi permetterá di trovare su quale pagina appare l'entrata di una organizzazione (es. Gmundner Festspiele, Gmunden, p.n).

Telefono
All'inizio di ogni Nazione ed in ogni sezione é indicato il prefisso diretto nazionale.
Si puó telefonare o trasmettere dei fax direttamente a gran parte delle organizzazioni elencate nel PAYE. Per quanto riguarda alcuni Paesi dell'Est Europeo é ancora difficile comunicare in tempi brevi. Il prefisso della cittá é incluso nelle varie entrate. Ricordatevi ogni volta che fate un numero dalla stessa nazione di aggiungere lo zero o il prefisso corretto della zona o della cittá. Ad esempio chiamando Glasgow da Londra o da Birmingham dovrete comporre il prefisso 0141 seguito dal numero di telefono.
In molte delle maggiori organizzazioni, specialmente in Germania ed in Austria, il numero dato é spesso seguito da un trattino e da uno zero, es:1234-0. Questo indica semplicemente che il numero dato é quello del centralino; gran parte delle associazioni o del personale che vi lavora ha una linea diretta e ció é indicato da due, tre o quattro numeri dopo il trattino.
Ogni Paese ha un suo proprio codice che vi permette di accedere direttamente alle altre Nazioni ed é indicato da un + che dovrá essere preceduto dai numeri qui elencati. Se per esempio volete chiamare in Ungheria (prefisso nazionale +36) da un delle seguenti nazioni, dovete usare questi prefissi internazionali prima di quello nazionale e del numero diretto. Per la maggior parte delle nazioni il numero é (00), ma dagli Stati Uniti per esempio, dovete comporre lo (011) prime del prefisso nazionale. Nel dubbio contattate la vostra compagnia telefonica.

Performing Arts Yearbook for Europe 2000

Contenido

- **Servicio al consumidor, ver páginas 170, 272, 648**
- **International Arts Manager (IAM) magazine ver página 83, 377**
- **Music, Opera, Dance and Drama in Asia, the Pacific and North America ver página 366, 640**

Secciones

Indices

Introducción al PAYE

Como en sus ediciones anteriores, la mayor parte de esta publicación está dedicada al listado de compañías europeas de artes escénicas y otros servicios relacionados. Para sacar el máximo partido a esa información, remitimos al lector al capítulo **Como utilizar el PAYE**.
El énfasis sigue estando en compañías profesionales - públicas y privadas - de gran y mediana escala (generalmente subvencionadas a nivel nacional, regional o local). Incluye también algunas compañías más pequeñas a destacar, según el consejo de expertos en cada país. Los teatros comerciales del West End en Londres y los teatros privados del Boulevard en Paris están incluidos por el papel que desempeñan en la presentación de producciones procedentes del sector privado, especialmente en Londres.
También hemos incluido las compañías más notables de teatro para jóvenes o niños. Para obtener información sobre otras compañías juveniles e infantiles que no aparecen en el **PAYE**, aconsejamos al lector que se ponga en contacto con los centros nacionales de ASSITEJ, ITI, UNIMA y la Fédération des Jeunesses Musicales. Estas organizaciones se encuentran en la sección **Organizaciones Nacionales**, pero en caso de dificultad, las oficinas centrales internacionales están en la sección **Organizaciones Supranacionales**.

Cada nueva edición del **PAYE** es el resultado de un esfuerzo colectivo, y estamos enormemente agradecidos a todos aquellos que nos ayudan manteniéndonos informados de los cambios y desarrollos del sector en sus países. El **PAYE** depende de su colaboración, y nos gustaría alentar todo tipo de comentarios y contribuciones para que el **PAYE** siga siendo un instrumento útil en el mercado de las artes escénicas.

Le agradecemos el envío de cualquier comentario o sugerencia que pueda contribuir a mejorar esta publicación, a nuestra dirección electrónica: **paye@api.co.uk**

Un agradecimiento especial para Ana Laura Lopez de la Torre, Editora de Consulta, sin cuya experiencia, conocimientos y generosidad este libro no hubiera sido posible.

Karin Junker
Editora

Como utilizar el PAYE

Orden de información dentro de cada sección
El orden de información dentro de una sección varía en cada caso. La rúbrica al principio de cada sección explica como se ha ordenado la misma.

Idiomas
Donde ha sido posible, hemos mantenido los nombres de las compañías en la lengua en que se nos ha proporcionado, es decir, en su lengua original. En el caso de las lenguas rusas o eslavas, etc, se proporciona una traducción del nombre original.
Generalmente se da una traducción inglesa de las lenguas menos conocidas o menos utilizadas en el foro internacional (p.e. finlandés, húngaro, polaco, serbio, croata, sueco, ruso, etc.).
Dada la naturaleza internacional de los lectores a los que va dirigida esta publicación, las ciudades están nombradas por lo general en su lengua original (por ejemplo, Firenze para Florencia, Köln para Colonia, Wien para Viena). Sin embargo se utiliza la version inglesa para los países nordicos, eslavos etc y para países bilingües. Así, se nombra a la capital de Bélgica como Brussels (inglés) en vez de Brussel (holandés) o Bruxelles (francés), y a Antwerpen se refiere como Antwerp (inglés).

Indice
El índice que aparece al final del Performing Arts Yearbook for Europe le permitirá identificar las páginas en donde aparecen la información de una organización (por ejemplo Gmundner Festspiele, Gmunden, página x).

Teléfonos
Los prefijos nacionales se encuentran al principio de la información de cada país, dentro de las diferentes secciones. Se puede llamar directamente a la mayoría de las organizaciones que están listadas en el PAYE, aunque frecuentemente ponerse en contacto con algunos países de Europa Oriental exige mucho tiempo.
El prefijo de la región/ciudad está incluído en la información de cada entrada editorial. Recuerde, al marcar un número desde dentro de un país a menudo hace falta añadir una cifra antes del prefijo. En muchos casos es un cero, por ejemplo para marcar Glasgow desde Londres o Birmingham el número es precedido por 0141.
En algunas de las organizaciones de mayor tamaño, sobre todo en Alemania o Austria, el número dado es seguido por un guión y luego un cero u otro número, por ejemplo 1234-0. Esto significa simplemente que el número dado le permitirá alcanzar la central, pero que existe una línea directa para la mayoría de las personas en esta organización, que se constituirá probablemente de dos, tres o cuatro cifras después del guión.
Cada país tiene su propio prefijo internacional que le permitirá marcar directamente. La necesidad de añadir este prefijo es indicado en la información de cada país con el símbolo + antes del prefijo nacional. Para llamar a Hungría (prefijo nacional 36) desde la mayor parte de los países, es necesario discar (00). Sin embargo esto puede variar de acuerdo al pais desde el que se llama. Si por ejemplo desea llamar a Hungría desde los Estados Unidos, el prefijo internacional a discar es (011), seguido del prefijo nacional (36), y finalmente, del número deseado. En caso de duda, consulte con la operadora local.

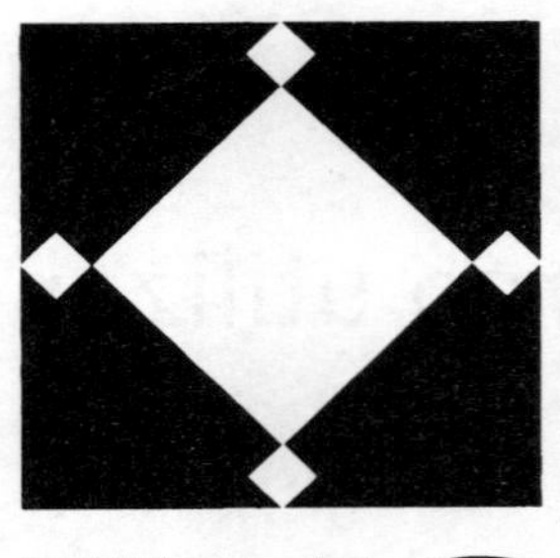

IMG *Artists*

IMG ARTISTS EUROPE IS PROUD TO ANNOUNCE REPRESENTATION OF THE FOLLOWING ARTISTS AND ORCHESTRAS

CONDUCTORS
David Charles Abell
Kees Bakels
Jiri Belohlavek
Peter Bergamin
Matthew Best
Iona Brown
Justin Brown
Michael Christie
William Christie
Jonathan Darlington
Thomas Dausgaard
Sachio Fujioka
János Fürst
Sir John Eliot Gardiner
Alan Gilbert
Manfred Honeck *UK + France*
Marek Janowski
Mariss Jansons
Lü Jia
Andrew Litton
Jerzy Maksymiuk
John Nelson
Paolo Olmi
Kazushi Ono
Chean See Ooi
Eiji Oue *excl Germany, Austria & Switzerland*
Antonio Pappano UK
Libor Pešek
Michel Plasson
Julian Reynolds
En Shao
Vassily Sinaisky
Dmitry Sitkovetsky
David Stern
Yuri Temirkanov
Yan Pascal Tortelier
Bramwell Tovey
Tamás Vásáry
Franz Welser-Möst
Barry Wordsworth
Long Yu
Benjamin Zander
Jaap van Zweden *excl Holland*

PIANISTS
Dmitri Alexeev
Leif Ove Andsnes
Boris Berezovsky
Yefim Bronfman
Michel Dalberto
Barry Douglas
Jonathan Gilad
Jeffrey Kahane
Zoltán Kocsis
Momo Kodama
Lang Lang
Alexander Melnikov
Tamás Vásáry

VIOLINISTS
Joshua Bell
Sarah Chang
Pamela Frank
Ilya Gringolts
Hilary Hahn
Leila Josefowicz
Jack Liebeck
Cho-Liang Lin
Vadim Repin
Nadja Salerno-Sonnenberg
Dmitry Sitkovetsky
Kyoko Takezawa
Nikolaj Znaider *UK & Sundry*

CELLISTS
Lynn Harrell
Julian Lloyd Webber
Alisa Weilerstein

FLUTE
James Galway OBE

SAXOPHONE
John Harle

CHAMBER MUSIC
Emerson String Quartet *UK*
I Salonisti
Kennedy/Lynn Harrell
Zephyr

SOLO PERCUSSION
Evelyn Glennie

PERCUSSION DUO
Safri Duo

VOCAL ENSEMBLE
The King's Singers

STAGE PRODUCERS
David Alden
Robert Carsen
Jonathan Miller
Francisco Negrin
David Pountney
Olivier Tambosi *UK and Sundry*

DANCE COMPANIES / ATTRACTIONS
Adventures in Motion Pictures/Swan Lake
On application
Bill T. Jones / Arnie Zane Dance Co.
Les Ballets Trockadero de Monte Carlo
Miami City Ballet
Parsons Dance Company
Trinity Irish Dance
Urban Bush Women
Darcy Bussell By special arrangement

VOCALISTS

Soprano
Norah Amsellem *excl France, Italy & Spain*
Lada Biriucov
Barbara Bonney
Laura Claycomb
Elizabeth Connell
Majella Cullagh
Lynne Dawson
Renée Fleming *UK*
Nancy Gustafson
Alison Hagley
Soile Isokoski *UK*
Lyuba Kazarnovskaya
Solveig Kringelborn
Rosa Mannion
Alessandra Marc
Karita Mattila
Marie McLaughlin
Miah Persson
Patricia Racette
Deborah Riedel
Christine Schäfer
Ellen Shade
Ana Camelia Stefanescu
Rosalind Sutherland
Camilla Tilling
Dawn Upshaw
Carol Vaness
Deborah Voigt *UK*
Lillian Watson
Deborah York
Ruth Ziesak

Mezzo Soprano
Stephanie Blythe
Sally Bruce-Payne
Sally Burgess
Beth Clayton
Alice Coote
Emma Curtis
Joyce DiDonato
Susan Graham *UK & Sundry*
Monica Groop *UK*
Charlotte Hellekant
Anne Howells
Catherine Keen Europe *(excl Italy) & Australia*
Jennifer Larmore
Lorraine Hunt Lieberson

Emer McGilloway
Diana Montague
Anne Sofie von Otter
Anne-Marie Owens
Susan Parry
Patricia Risley
Nathalie Stutzmann *UK*
Elizabeth Vaughan
Anne Wilkens

Tenor
Wolfgang Ablinger-Sperrhacke
Paul Austin Kelly
Kim Begley
Yann Beuron *UK*
Jan Blinkhof *UK & Sundry*
Richard Coxon
John Daszak
Ryland Davies
Jorge Elias
Julian Gavin
Gordon Gietz
Christopher Gillett
Jerry Hadley
John Horton Murray
Donald Kaasch
Jonas Kaufmann *UK & Sundry*
David Kuebler *UK*
Keith Lewis
Alexander Oliver
Tom Randle
David Rendall
Rafael Rojas
Michael Schade *UK & Sundry*
Nicholas Sears
Jeffrey Stewart
Kurt Streit
Christopher Ventris
Carlo Ventre

Baritone
Olaf Bär *UK & Sundry*
Jeffrey Black
Russell Braun *UK & Sundry*
Morten Ernst Lassen
Hakan Hagegard
Thomas Hampson
Dietrich Henschel *UK & Sundry*
Ashley Holland
Jason Howard
Phillip Joll
Anthony Michaels-Moore
Leigh Melrose
Timothy Noble
Brett Polegato
Gino Quilico
Stephen Roberts
Roberto Scaltriti UK & Sundry
Andreas Schmidt UK
William Shimell
Riccardo Simonetti
Paul Whelan

Bass-Baritone / Bass
Clive Bayley
Nathan Berg
Matthew Best
Stafford Dean
Michael Druiett
Phillip Ens
Gerald Finley
Michael George
Eric Halfvarson
Franz Hawlata UK & France
Panajotis Iconomou
Samuel Ramey
Willard White

ACCOMPANISTS
Helmut Deutsch UK & Sundry
Julius Drake

ORCHESTRAS

General Management
Czech National Symphony Orchestra/
Paul Freeman
Malaysian Philharmonic Orchestra/
Kees Bakels
New European Strings/
Dmitry Sitkovetsky
Norwegian Chamber Orchestra/
Iona Brown
Oslo Philharmonic Orchestra/
Mariss Jansons
The Hague Residentie Orchestra/
Jaap van Zweden
St Petersburg Philharmonic/
Yuri Temirkanov
Sinfonia Varsovia/
Krzysztof Penderecki

Touring Representation
IMG Artists also organises tours and/or appearances for the following orchestras and ensembles in various countries

Academy of St Martin in the Fields
Bavarian Radio Symphony Orchestra
Berliner Symphoniker
Belgian National Orchestra
Bolshoi Opera Orchestra
BBC Concert Orchestra
BBC Philharmonic Orchestra
BBC Symphony Orchestra
Budapest Symphony Orchestra
Czech National Symphony Orchestra
Dallas Symphony Orchestra
English Concert
English String Orchestra
English Symphony Orchestra
European Union Youth Orchestra
Gustav Mahler Jugend Orchester
Hungarian National Philharmonic Orchestra
The Johann Strauss Orchestra of Vienna
The King's Consort
Kirov Opera & Ballet
Kirov Orchestra
La Scala Philharmonic Orchestra
Leipzig Gewandhaus Orchestra
Lithuanian Chamber Orchestra
London Mozart Players
The London Philharmonic
London Symphony Orchestra
Mahler Chamber Orchestra
Moscow Philharmonic Orchestra
Moscow Radio Symphony Orchestra
Moscow State Symphony Orchestra
National Youth Orchestra of Great Britain
New European Strings
Orchestra of the Age of Enlightenment
Orchestre National de France
Orchestre de Paris
Orchestre Philharmonique de Radio France
Pittsburgh Symphony Orchestra
Polish Chamber Orchestra
Polish National Radio Symphony Orchestra
Rhineland Philharmonic Orchestra
Rotterdam Philharmonic Orchestra
Royal Concertgebouw Orchestra
Royal Liverpool Philharmonic Orchestra
Royal Opera House Orchestra
Royal Philharmonic Orchestra
Royal Scottish National Orchestra
Russian Symphony Orchestra
Russian State Philharmonic Orchestra
Russian Symphony Orchestra
San Francisco Symphony Youth Orchestra
Sofia Philharmonic Orchestra
Stavanger Symphony Orchestra
Strasbourg Philharmonic
Ukraine National Symphony Orchestra
Ulster Orchestra
Vienna Philharmonic
Vienna Radio Symphony Orchestra
Vienna Symphony Orchestra
Warsaw Philharmonic Orchestra

IMG Artists, First Floor, 616 Chiswick High Road
London W4 5RX
Tel: +44 20 8233 5800
Fax: +44 20 8233 5801
E-Mail: artistseurope@imgworld.com

Stephen Wright, *Managing Director*
Tom Graham, *Director, Vocal Division*
Nicholas Mathias, *Director, Artist Management*
Anthony Howard, *Director, Orchestral Tours*
Kathryn Enticott, *Associate Director, Artist Management*
Joan Cruickshank, *Associate Director, Orchestral Tours*
Gillian Newson, *Associate Director, Dance Division*
Wray Armstrong, *Special Consultant*

IMG Artists, 54 Avenue Marceau
75008 Paris
France
Tel: +33 1 44 31 44 31
Fax: +33 1 44 31 44 45
E-Mail: artistsparis@imgworld.com
Stephen Wright, *Managing Director*
Gilles Demonet, *Director, Orchestral Tours*
Philippe Etourneau, *Director, Artist Management*
VÈronique Jourdain, *Consultant, Artist Management*
Peter Wiggins, *Director, Vocal Division*

IMG Artists, 825 7th Avenue
New York, NY 10019
USA
Tel: +1 212 489 8300
Fax: +1 212 246 1596
E-Mail: artistsny@imgworld.com

Edna Landau, *Managing Director*

IMG Artists Asia, Level 61, Tower 2
PETRONAS Twin Towers
Kuala Lumpur City Centre
50088 Kuala Lumpur
Malaysia
Tel: +60 3 266 2166
Fax: +60 3 262 6634
E-Mail: artistsasia@imgworld.com

Ian Smallbone, *Director*

IMG Artists in Europe is part of **IMG Artists worldwide** and a division of the **IMG Group of Companies** (Mark H. McCormack, Chairman and CEO).

bregenz festival

july 20 - august 23, 2000

Performance on the floating stage 2000

Giuseppe Verdi

Un ballo in maschera

Conductor **Marcello Viotti**
Director **Richard Jones** and **Antony McDonald**
Designs **Richard Jones** and **Antony McDonald**
Lighting **Wolfgang Göbbel**
Choreography **Philippe Giraudeau**

Vienna Symphony Orchestra
Moscow Chamber Choir
Bregenz Festival Chorus

Revival july 21, 2000
22 performances until august 20, 2000
Floating stage

Opera indoors 2000

Nikolai Rimski-Korsakow

The golden cockerel

Opera in three acts by Nikolai Rimski-Korsakow. Text by W. I. Belsky after a fairy tale by Alexander Puschkin. In German and Russian.

Conductor **Vladimir Fedoseyev**
Director **David Pountney**
Set Designs **Sue Huntley, Donna Muir**
Light Design **Mimi Jordan Sherin**

Vienna Symphony Orchestra
Moscow Chamber Choir

First night july 20, 2000
july 23, 27, 30 / august 3
Festspielhaus

More informations and bookings for all events including orchestra concerts, contemporary music, theatre
Bregenz Festival, P. O. Box 311, A-6901 Bregenz, Tickets **0043 5574 407-6**, Fax 0043 5574 407-400, e-mail: info@bregenzerfestspiele.com, www.bregenzerfestspiele.com, Photo: Richard Hörmann / Archiv Vorarlberg Tourismus

P e r o n i s i v e s t e
e f a s

per lo spettacol

Peroni puts on new clothes and is noticed more and more. A ne
Peroni s'habille de neuf et occupe de plus en plus le devant de la scène. Un nouv
Peroni se viste de nuevo para
Peroni zeigt sich von neuer Seite und tritt imm

PERONI SUD SRL
Via Vittorio Emanuele, 67/h
95131 Catania
Tel. 0039-095-322855
Fax 0039-095-314035

SPAGNA
PERONIS ESPA
Parque Empr. Casablanca 11
Av. del Dr. S. Ochoa, 33 Local 3F
28100 Alcobendas (Madrid)
Tel. 0034-91-8463710
Fax 0034-91-8463719

FRANCIA
S.A.R.L. PERONI SPA
14/18 Rue Francis de Pressensé
93210 La Plaine St. Denis
Tel. 0033-01-49460845
Fax 0033-01-49460262

SVIZZERA
PERONI S.A.
Via Dufor, 2 - 6901 Lugano
Tel. 0041-91-9227156
Fax 0041-91-9227157

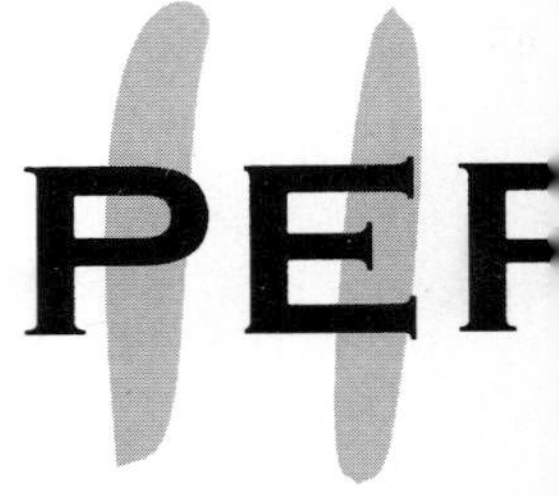

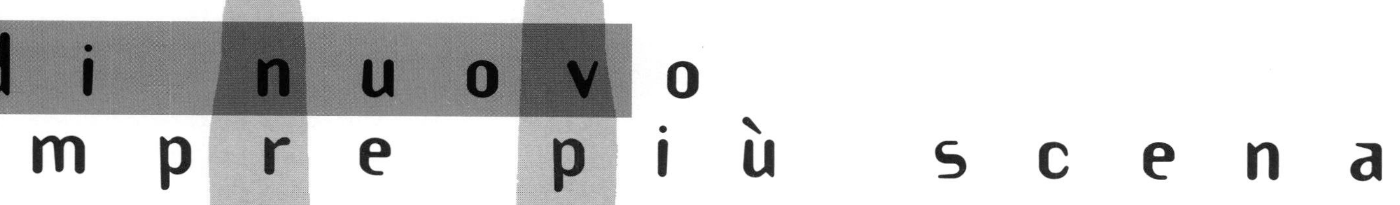

un nuovo marchio
el duemila

o for the year 2000
ogo pour le spectacle de l'an 2000
siempre más escena. Un nuevo logotipo para el espectáculo del 2000
rh in Szene. Ein neues Logo für das Schauspiel im Jahr 2000

PERONI SPA
21013 Gallarate (VA)
Via Monte Leone 93
Tel: 0039-0331-756811
Fax: 0039-0331-776260

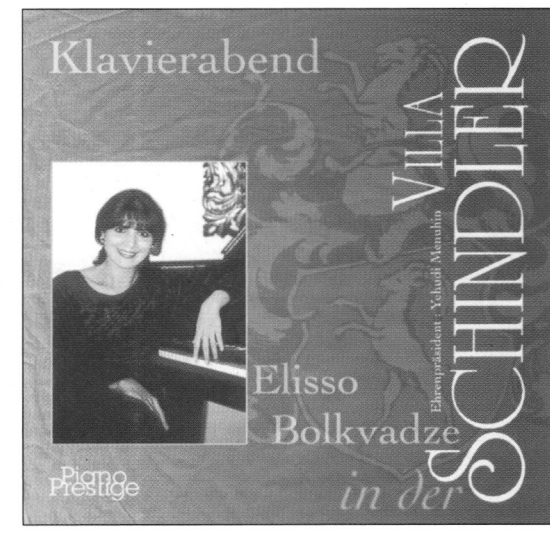

233 years of symphonic tradition

Bergen Philharmonic Orchestra welcomes Simone Young as Chief Conductor and Music Director for the seasons 1999-2002.

Bergen Philharmonic Orchestra

- Founded in 1765, the BPO is one of the world´s oldest orchestras
- Situated in Edvard Grieg´s home town
- 94 musicians of international standing
- One of Norway´s two national orchestras
- Important guest conductors after 1945: Leopold Stokowski, Ernest Ansermet, Pierre Monteux, Eugene Ormandy, John Barbirolli, Rafael Kubelik
- Recordings for BIS, Virgin, Chandos, Sony Japan, Simax
- Music directors of the last decade: Aldo Ceccato and Dmitri Kitayanko

Bergen Philharmonic Orchestra
General Manager: Lorentz Reitan

For more information, please contact:
BPO - Liv Hege Tveit
Edvard Griegs Plass 1
N-5015 Bergen, Norway
Tel.: +47 55 21 62 65/55 21 61 00
Fax: +47 55 31 85 34

Internet, from February 1999: www.harmonien.no
E-mail: post.harmonien.no

AG BYRAENE AG1

Performing Arts Yearbook for Europe 2000

目次

Performing Arts Yearbook for Europe 2000

はじめに

今までの版と同じく、本書の大半はヨーロッパにおける舞台芸術団体とサービスの要覧に当てられています。本書を最大限に活用していただくために、まず「PAYEの使い方」の章をお読みください。

PAYEでは引き続き、大、中規模のプロの団体（国、地域、地方等、助成の拠出レベルに拘わらず）を中心に掲載しています。 小規模ながら有名な助成対象団体もいくつか含まれますが、その選択にあたっては、ほとんどの場合、それぞれ拠点国の政府担当者あるいは専門家の意見を参考にしています。本書にはロンドンのウェストエンド、パリのブールバールにある商業劇場も含まれていますが、これは、特にロンドンにおいて、作品上演に助成対象セクターが大きな役割を占めているためです。

ここにはまた、いくつかの児童、青年劇団も含まれています。これら以外の児童、青年劇団、教育劇団、青年オーケストラについては、ASSITEJ、ITI、UNIMA、Federation des Jeunesse Musicales等の全国センターにお問い合わせ下さい。これらの団体の大半は国家団体のセクションに掲載されていますが、何らかの理由で連絡できなかった場合に備え、超国家団体のセクションにはこれらのネットワークの国際本部が掲載されています。

テレックス番号の記載は中止し、かわりにEメールアドレスとワールド・ワイド・ウェッブ／インターネット・アドレスを掲載しました。本書刊行時にはさらに多くの団体がネットに参加していることと思われます。ネット上のアドレスの掲載を希望する団体は次のEメールアドレスまでご連絡ください。**paye@api.co.uk**

PAYEに対する評価はさらに高まっています。舞台芸術ビジネスにより役立つ出版物を作成するためのご意見、ご希望をお待ちしております。

最後に、編集顧問のアナ・ラウラ・ロペス氏に特別の感謝の意を表わしたいと思います。氏の豊富な知識と経験なしにこの年鑑はありえませんでした。

カリン・ユンカー

PAYE

PAYEの使い方

掲載分野内におけるエントリー順序

エントリーの記載順序はセクション毎に異なります。各セクションの冒頭にある説明をお読み下さい。

言語

団体名は可能な限り、編集部に提出された名称一原語を使用しました。ロシア語、スラブ語の場合には翻訳名が記載されています。国際的に見て使用頻度が少ない言語の団体名（フィンランド語、ハンガリー語、ポーランド語、セルビア語、クロアチア語、スウェーデン語、ロシア語）の大半には英訳が併記されています。

PAYEは国際的な読者層を対象としているため、大半の都市名は原語の綴りで記載しました（例：FlorenceではなくFirenze、TurinではなくTorino、ViennaではなくWien)。但し、ロシア、スラブ系言語、あるいは二ヵ国語が通用している国における都市名は英語の綴りを用いています。従って、ベルギーの首都はBurussel（ドイツ語）やBruxelles（フランス語）ではなくBrussels（英語）、また、AntwerpenではなくAntwerpの綴りを採用しました。

索引

ヨーロッパ舞台芸術年鑑の最後には団体名の索引があり、エントリー団体や組織の掲載されたページが識別できるようになっています（例：Gmundner Festspiele、Gmunden p.xx)。

電話番号

直通ダイヤル用の国別コード番号は各セクションの該当国の頭に記載されています。

PAYEに掲載された団体、組織の大半へは直接ダイヤルすることが可能ですが、東ヨーロッパのいくつかの国への電話、ファックスには時間を要するかもしれません。

地域／都市コードはそれぞれのエントリー毎に記載されています。同じ国から電話するときは、記載されている地域／都市コードの前に一桁の数字を加えなくてはならない場合が多いのでご留意下さい。この数字は大半の場合0です。例えば、グラスゴーあるいはロンドンからバーミンガムに電話するときは、まず0141、それに続いて相手先の番号をダイヤルします。国によっては0ではなく他の数字の場合があります。

大規模な団体、特にドイツやオーストリアの団体では、1234-0のように、-が含まれた番号が記載されている場合があります。記載されている番号は交換台の番号で、各デスクに直接電話する場合は-の後に2、3、4桁の番号を続けてダイヤルします。

国際回線をにつながるためのコード番号は国ごとに異なります。このコード番号が必要であることは＋で示されています。例えば海外からハンガリー（国別コード番号は36）に電話する場合、ほとんどの国ではコード番号36の前に（00）をダイヤルしますが、アメリカからの場合は最初に（011）をダイヤルします。コード番号等については自国のオペレーターにご確認ください。

Elizabeth Day
MEDIA RELATIONS
& MARKETING
Publicity is crucial
Composers
Ensembles
Events
Festivals
Performers
Record Companies
For appropriate & effective
P.R. Solutions
ELIZABETH DAY
TEL: 0171 286 5390
15 GROVE COURT, CIRCUS ROAD
LONDON NW8 9EN

Marinus Komst, timpani player of the Royal Concertgebouw Orchestra.

Performing Arts Yearbook for Europe 2000

目录

• **Customer Service, see page 170, 272, 648, 740**

• **International Arts Manager (IAM) magazine see page 83, 377, 656**

• **Music, Opera, Dance and Drama in Asia, the Pacific and North America see page 366, 640**

参考部分

索引

如何使用《年鉴》

一部分中条目的顺序排列

每部分中条目的顺序排列是不同的。每部分开头的标题解释该部分排列顺序。

语言

我们尽可能将公司称号保留为最初介绍给我们的语言，即其本国语言。俄罗斯或斯拉夫等语言则有音译。公司的英文译名通常用于国际舞台中不那么普遍和较少使用的语言中（如芬兰文、匈牙利文、波兰文、塞尔维亚文、克罗地亚文、瑞典文、俄文等等）。

由于《年鉴》是针对国际读者的，城市通常以原文出现（如：佛罗伦萨为Firenze，科隆为Köln，图林为Torino，维也纳为Wien）。然而，俄罗斯和斯拉夫等国家以及双语国家则使用了英语化的名称。因而，比利时首都被称为Brussels而不是Brussel荷兰文）或Bruxelles（法文），安特卫普被叫做Antwerp。

索引

《欧洲表演艺术年鉴》后面的编目索引可使你找到某一机构出现的页数（例如：Gmundner Festspiele, Gmunden, p.n）。

打电话

各国的直拨号码前缀列在每一部分与该国相关的条目的开头。

《年鉴》所列多数机构是可能直拨的，虽然与某些东欧国家的电话、传真往来仍旧可以是件很花时间的事。

条目中包括了地区及城市的代码。请记住，在某一国内拨一个号码时常常要在地区及城市的代码前加一个数字。其中许多是加零：例如，从伦敦或伯明翰拨格拉斯哥时要拨0141，然后拨电话号码，有时情况则不同

某些较大的艺术机构，特别是在德国和奥地利，所给的号码后面有一个连字符，然后是零或另一个数字，如1234-0。这仅表明所给号码可使您打到总机，但那一机构的多数个人会有自己的直线，这有可能在连字符后面有两位、三位或者四位数字。

各国均有自己的国际通行号码前缀以使你可直接拨号。名录中如需增加这一代码则在国家代码前以“十”号表示。例如，如你要从下列任何国家拨匈牙利（国家代号36），你在拨国家代码和号码前要使用这些国际通行代码：

大部份国家的代码是(00)。但例如从美国打往其他国家，便需在国家代号前拨(011)。如有疑问，请联络你本地的接线员。

Performing Arts Yearbook for Europe 2000

简介

与前五版的年鉴一样，此刊物的大部分篇幅为全欧洲表演艺术公司和服务项目的名录。为了最好地利用此书，应阅读“如何使用《欧洲表演艺术年鉴》”一章。

《年鉴》的重点仍为主要的和中型的专业公司（不论是受国家、地区或当地补贴）。它包括一些较著名的规模较小的受补助公司，这通常是与各国的部门官员或其他专家协商后选定的。商业性的伦敦West End的剧院和巴黎的私人剧院大街由于上演来自受补助部门的作品（特别是在伦敦）也被包括在内。

我们还收入了一些青年和儿童剧院。有关其它未包括在内的儿童和青年剧院公司和教育剧院公司、青年剧院及交响乐团的信息，我们建议读者们与ASSITEJ、ITI、UNIMA及“青年音乐家协会”(Federation des Jeunesse Musicales)的全国中心联系。其中许多列于《年鉴》的“国家机构”部分中，但如有问题，这些网络的国际总部还列于“超国家机构”部分中。

我们给两个部分重新取名，即“歌剧和音乐剧院”及“交响乐团和乐队”两部分，以反映活跃于这些领域的组织的广泛性。

《年鉴》的目录、简介和标题除五种主要欧洲语言之外首次使用了中文、日文和朝鲜文。

我们决定不再列出电传号码，而是使用电子邮件地址和World Wide Web及英特网地址。我肯定有许多在本刊付印时还没联网的组织现在已“入网了”；因此，假如您想要我们列出贵机构的地址，请通过下址告诉我们**paye@api.co.uk**

《年鉴》的声誉越来越好。我们随时欢迎大家对如使它变得对表演艺术行业更为有用提出意见和建议。

Karin Junker

Performing Arts Yearbook for Europe 2000

차례

• Customer Service, see page 170, 272, 648, 740

• International Arts Manager (IAM) magazine see page 83, 377, 656

• Music, Opera, Dance and Drama in Asia, the Pacific and North America see page 366, 640

참고

색인

Performing Arts Yearbook for Europe 2000

서문

지난5년간의 연감에서처럼, 올해도 이 책의 대부분은 전 유럽에 있는 퍼포밍 아트 단체들 및 서비스 인명록을 주로 다루고 있습니다. 독자들은 이 책을 보다 더 잘 이용하기 위해서 "PAYE 이용법"을 먼저 읽기 바랍니다.

이번에도 PAYE는 계속해서 대, 중규모의 전문적인 단체들을(그들이 전국적인 차원에서 보조금을 받는 단체이거나 아니면 지역적인 차원에서 보조금을 받는 단체이거나 상관없이) 중점적으로 다루고 있습니다. 그러나 보조금을 받고 운영되는 단체로서 규모는 작지만 유명한 몇몇 단체들도 포함되었습니다. 이들은 주로 해당국가의 담당 공무원이나 전문가들의 자문을 받은 후 추천된 단체들입니다. 런던의 상업적 웨스트엔드 극장들과 파리의 개인극장들 역시 포함되었습니다. 이것은 보조금을 받는 상품을 공연하는 데 이들이, 특히 런던에 있는 극장들이, 담당하는 역할이 인정되었기 때문입니다.

몇몇 청소년 및 어린이 극장 단체들 또한 포함되었습니다. 여기 포함되지 않은 어린이/청소년 극장 단체들, 교육 단체들의 극장, 청소년 극장/오케스트라 등에 대한 정보는, ASSITEJ, ITI, UNIMA, Federation des Jeunesse Musicales 등과 같은 조직의 국내 센터에 문의하십시오. 이들 조직들의 대부분이 PAYE의 "National Organisation (국내 조직)" 부문의 리스트에 열거되어 있습니다. 그러나 문제가 있을 경우는 이들 네트워크의 국제본부가 나와있는 "Supranational Organisations (범국가 조직)" 부문을 참조하십시오.

텔렉스 번호 대신에 전자 우편 주소 및 WWW/인터네트 주소를 포함하기로 결정했습니다. 저는 이 책을 편집할 당시보다 현재 더 많은 조직들이 "네트워크에 연결되어" 있을 것이라고 확신합니다. 귀사의 네트워크 주소가 기재되기를 원하시면 **paye@api.co.uk**로 연락을 주십시오.

PAYE의 위상은 계속해서 높아지고 있습니다. 이 책을 퍼포밍 아트 비즈니스를 위한 더욱 더 유익한 책자로 만들 수 있도록 귀하의 귀중한 논평이나 의견을 보내주시면 감사하겠습니다.

Karin Junker

PAYE

PAYE 이용법

부문 내의 명단 열거 순서

열거 순서는 부문마다 다르다. 각 부문의 시작에 나와있는 표제에 그 부문이 어떤 순서로 열거되어 있는지 설명되어 있다.

언어

가능한 한 단체명은 편집자에게 소개된 언어로, 즉 각기 해당 언어로 기재되었다. 러시아나 슬라브 언어들의 경우에는, 번역이 나와있다. 국제 무대에서 자주 통용되지 않거나 자주 사용되지 않는 언어에서는 (예: 핀란드어, 헝가리어, 폴란드어, 세르비아어, 크로아티아어, 스웨덴어, 러시아어 등) 일반적으로 단체명의 영어번역이 기재되었다. PAYE는 국제 독자층을 겨냥하기 때문에, 도시명은 보통 각기 해당 언어로 나와있다 (예: Florence는 Firenze, Cologne은 Köln, Turin은 Torino, Vienna는 Wien). 그러나 러시아나 슬라브 국가들 그리고 공용어가 둘인 국가들에 대해서는 영어화된 이름들이 적용되었다, 그래서 벨기에의 수도는 Brussel (네덜란드어)나 Bruxelles (불어) 대신에 Brussels 그리고 Antwerpen은 Antwerp로 기재되었다.

색인

PAYE의 뒤에 나와 있는 편집 명단 색인을 이용하면, 찾는 조직이 몇 페이지에 기재되어 있는지 알 수 있다 (예: Gmundner Festspiele, Gmunden, 페이지수).

전화통화

각 국의 직통국제번호는 각 부문의 숫자별 명단의 시작에 기재되어 있다.

PAYE에 실린 대부분의 조직은 전화로 연결된다. 그러나 아직도 몇몇 동유럽 국가에 전화를 하거나 팩스를 보내려면 시간이 많이 걸릴 수 있다.

지역/도시 번호는 명단에 포함되어 있다. 국내 장거리 전화일 경우는, 자주 지역/도시 번호 앞에 한 자리 수를 더 붙이는 것에 주의해야 한다. 일반적으로 '0' 을 붙인다: 즉 런던이나 버밍엄에서 글래스고로 전화를 할 때는 041을 돌리고 번호를 돌린다. 그러나 이 앞에 붙는 숫자가 다른 곳도 있다.

규모가 큰 예술 조직체들의 명단에는, 특히 독일과 오스트리아 조직체들의 명단에는 번호 뒤에 하이픈이 있고 다시 '0' 이나 다른 번호가 따른다 (예: 1234-0). 이 예의 번호를 돌리면 단순히 중앙 교환실로 연결된다. 그러나 조직체 내의 대부분의 직원들은 개인 직통선으로 연결되어 있기 때문에, 하이픈 뒤에 두 자리 어떤 때는 세 자리 숫자가 붙어 있다.

나라마다 국제직통전화를 할 때 시작하는 번호가 다르다. 국제번호 앞에 '+' 가 붙어 있는 것은 이 국제전화 시작번호를 먼저 돌려야 한다는 것을 의미한다. 예를 들어 아래 중의 한 국가에서 헝가리 (국제번호 36)로 전화를 하려면, 헝가리 국제번호와 전화를 하고자 하는 곳의 번호를 돌리기 전에 먼저 발신국가의 국제전화 시작번호를 돌려야 한다: 대부분의 국가는 시작번호 (00)을 사용하지만, 예를 들어 미국에서 국제전화를 할 경우 국가번호 전에 (011)을 돌려야 한다. 확실하지 않은 경우는 지역 교환에 문의한다.

TEATRO COMUNALE DI BOLOGNA

ENTE AUTONOMO

>>>>>>>>>>>>>>>>>>>> STAGIONE 1999 - 2000 <<<<<<<<<<<<<<<<<<

27 NOVEMBRE
2,5,7,9,12,14,16,19,21 DICEMBRE 1999

Allestimento del Teatro Comunale di Bologna

TOSCA*

Musica di GIACOMO PUCCINI

Interpreti principali:
Daniela Dessì/Elmira Veda,Vincenzo La Scola/Alfredo Portilla, Ruggero Raimondi/Alan Titus, Enrico Turco/Marco Vinco, Mauro Utzeri/Alessandro Busi, Enrico Cossutta/Stefano Consolini

DANIELE GATTI maestro conc. e dir.
PAOLO ARRIVABENI (21/12) altro direttore
ALBERTO FASSINI regia
WILLIAM ORLANDI scene e costumi
PIERO MONTI maestro del coro

11,13,15,16,18,26,28,30 APRILE
2 MAGGIO 2000

Coproduzione con il Teatro Massimo di Palermo

LA VOIX HUMAINE

Musica di FRANCIS POULENC
(Société anonyme ed. RICORDI, Paris)

Interprete Raina Kabaivanska

CHRISTIAN BADEA maestro conc. e dir.
ROBERTO POLASTRI (18/04, 2/05) altro dir.

Coproduzione con «Ravenna Festival»

I PAGLIACCI

Parole e Musica di RUGGERO LEONCAVALLO
(Ed. CASA MUSICALE SONZOGNO, Milano)

Interpreti principali:
José Cura/Giorgio Merighi, Daniela Dessì/Simona Baldolini, Alberto Mastromarino/Marco Chingari, Dalibor Jenis

CHRISTIAN BADEA maestro conc. e dir.
ROBERTO POLASTRI (18/04, 2/05) altro dir.
LILIANA CAVANI regia
DANTE FERRETTI scene
GABRIELLA PESCUCCI costumi
PIERO MONTI maestro del coro

4,6,8,10,13,15,17,19,20 FEBBRAIO 2000

Allestimento dell'Opéra di Lille

PELLÉAS ET MÉLISANDE

Musica di CLAUDE DEBUSSY
(Ed. Durand S.A - rappr. CASA MUSICALE SONZOGNO di Piero Ostali, Milano)

Interpreti principali:
William Joyner/Tracey Welborn, Lucio Gallo/Gaetan Laperrière, Nicolaj Ghiaurov/Eldar Aliev, Marina Domashenko/Cassandra Riddle, Debora Beronesi/Claudia Nicole Bandera

VLADIMIR JUROWSKI maestro conc. e dir.
ROBERTO POLASTRI (15/02) altro dir.
PIER'ALLI regia, scene e costumi
PIERO MONTI maestro del coro

L'opera si rappresenta in lingua originale con aopratitoli in italiano

30 MAGGIO, 1,3,4,8,11,13,14 GIUGNO 2000

Allestimento della «De Nederlandse Opera» di Amsterdam

WOZZECK

Musica di ALBAN BERG
(Universal Edition, Wien rappr. per l'Italia CASA RICORDI, Milano)

Interpreti principali:
Jürgen Linne, Edward Cook, Benedikt Kobel, Sergio Bertocchi, Johann Werner Prein, Pierre Lefebvre, Maria Russo, Annette Elster

DANIELE GATTI maestro conc. e dir.
WILLY DECKER regia
WOLFGANG GUSSMANN scene e costumi
PIERO MONTI maestro del coro

L'opera si rappresenta, senza intervalli, in lingua originale con sopratitoli in italiano

15,16,18,19,21,22,24,26 MARZO 2000

Allestimento del Teatro «Romolo Valli» di Reggio Emilia

SALOME*

Musica di RICHARD STRAUSS
(Ed. Musicali Fürstner/ Schott - rappr. CASA MUSICALE SONZOGNO di Piero Ostali, Milano)

Interpreti principali:
Wolfgang Neumann, Chris Merritt, Julia Juon, Susan Anthony/Anna-Katrin Behnke, Jürgen Linne, Matthias Klink

DANIELE GATTI maestro conc. e dir.
PIER LUIGI PIZZI regia, scene e costumi
LUCA VEGGETTI coreografia

L'opera si rappresenta in lingua originale con sopratitoli in italiano

24,25,27,28,29,30 GIUGNO, 1,2 LUGLIO 2000

Allestimento del Teatro «A. Rendano» di Cosenza

LA NOTTE DI UN NEVRASTENICO

Musica di NINO ROTA
(Ed. CASA RICORDI, Milano)

Interpreti principali:
Simone Alberghini/Domenico Colaianni, Luca Canonici/Valter Borin,Alida Ferrarini, Mario Bolognesi

ZOLTÁN PESKÓ maestro conc. e dir.
ROBERTO POLASTRI (1,2/07) altro dir.
PIERA DEGLI ESPOSTI regia
PASQUALE GROSSI scene e costumi
PIERO MONTI maestro del coro

Nuovo allestimento

GIANNI SCHICCHI

Musica di GIACOMO PUCCINI
(Ed. CASA RICORDI, Milano)

Interpreti principali:
Bruno Praticò, Alida Ferrarini, Cinzia De Mola, Luca Canonici, Mario Bolognesi, Adelina Scarabelli, Massimiliano Gagliardo, Simone Alberghini, Alessandro Patalini, Tiziana Tramonti, Domenico Colaianni, Gastone Sarti

ZOLTÁN PESKÓ maestro conc.e dir.
ROBERTO POLASTRI (1,2/07) altro dir.
MARCO GANDINI regia
PASQUALE GROSSI scene e costumi

*** *L'allestimento sarà utilizzato nell'ambito della collaborazione fra il Teatro Comunale ed i Teatri di Tradizione dell'Emilia Romagna***

>>>>>>>>>>>>> <<<<<<<<<<<<

STAGIONE D'OPERA

>>>>>>>>>>>>> <<<<<<<<<<<<

ORCHESTRA E CORO DEL TEATRO COMUNALE DI BOLOGNA

PLAYBILLS, POSTERS AND PRINTS
FROM THE GREEN ROOM
TURANDOT
MUSICA DI G. PUCCINI
EDIZIONI RICORDI

LATE ENTRIES

All phone numbers in Portugal changed after some sections had gone to print; for all Portuguese entries in all sections before Festivals (p.387), add 2 before the existing city code

Baroque Opera Festival, The
Warsaw Chamber Opera, Nowogrodzka 49, 00-695 **Warszawa**, Poland
Tel: 48 22-628 3096 Fax: 48 22-827 3926/629 3233

boilerhouse
The Gateway Theatre, Elm Ros, **Edinburgh (Scotland)** EH4 7AH, United Kingdom
Tel: 44 131-317 3966
E-Mail: boiler@dircon.co.uk

Calouste Gulbenkian Foundation
Lisboa, Portugal
Tel: 351 21-782 3000 Fax: 351 21-793 7296
Comments: new phone and fax numbers for entries in National Organisations, Orchestras and Choirs, see entries in those sections for full details

Circus Ronaldo
c/o Frans Brood Productions, Muinklaan 10, 9000 **Gent**, Belgium
Tel: 32 9-234 1212 Fax: 32 9-265 9650
Internet: www.fransbrood.com
E-Mail: frabro@agoranet.be
Arts types: circus, street theatre

Compañía María Pagés
Avsa. Rosario Manzaneque,1, 28250 **Torrelodones**, Spain
Tel: 34 1-859 1914 Fax: 34 1-859 3601
E-Mail: oficina@mariapages.com
director: María Pagés
Comments: updated information for entry on page 201

CONCEPTS Theatre Network
University College Scarborough, Filey Road, **Scarborough** YO11 3AZ, United Kingdom
Tel: 44 1723-362 392 Fax: 44 1723-370 815
Internet: www.ucscarb.ac.uk/ucsscar/concepts1.html
E-Mail: nicolar@ucscarb.ac.uk
contact Noel Witts; secretariat Gerald Lidstone
Role & Services: international network of educational and professional theatre organisations across Europe
Comments: also branches in Sofia, Bulgaria and in Sibiu, Romania; secretariat: Tel: +44 20-7919 7426, Fax: +44 20-7919 7413, E-mail: g.lidstone@gold.ac.uk

Concerto Copenhagen
16 Gammeltoftsgade, 1355 **Copenhagen** K, Denmark
Tel: 45 3313 5570/5580 Fax: 45 3313 5540
Internet: www.coco.dk
E-Mail: info@coco.dk
artistic director Lars Ulrik Mortensen; production manager Anja Reiff; business manager Nicolai Gjessing
Comments: updated information for entry on page 260

Crimea Symphonic Orchestra
Iekaterinskaia 13, 334202 **Yalta**, Ukraine
Tel: 380 654-325 070 Fax: 380 654-321 034
E-Mail: bruno@cinquegrani.fsnet.co.uk
music director & principal conductor Alexej Guljanizki (Russia); associate conductor Bruno Cinquegrani (Italy); orchestra manager Vladimir Noskov
Comments: updated information for entry on page 250

ENCATC (European Network of Cultural Administration Training Centres)
c/o KIT, Vestergade 5, 1456 **Copenhagen** K, Denmark
Tel: 45 3315 8214 Fax: 45 3332 8182
E-Mail: encatc@artecnet.com
coordinator of ENCATC Isabelle Schwarz
Role & Services: independent network of training institutions and individuals professionally involved in the cultural management training and related sectors;
Comments: 82 members from 22 European countries; publishes Directory of Cultural Administration Training Programmes in Europe

Euro-Bulgarian Cultural Centre
Al. Stamboliiski Str. 17, **Sofia**, Bulgaria
Tel: 359 2-988 0084 Fax: 359 2-988 0084
Internet: www.culture-link.nat.bg
E-Mail: cip@culture-link.nat.bg
director Yavor Koinakov
Role & Services: to support the interaction of and the mutual understanding between arts and culture in Bulgaria and the other European countries; the Centre works in the field of all arts forms

Europa&Baltikum
c/o J. Schiek, Hittorfstr. 45, 48149 **Münster**, Germany
chairman Jazeps Kukulis; artistic director Inga Suta
Role & Services: presentations and promotions base for Latvian/Baltic politics, culture, literature, art and music, artists and musicians; promotes Cultural Exchange Project and Festival Europa&Baltikum (administrator J. Kukulis) in Germany, concerts, concert lectures, lectures and exhibitions in Germany and neighbouring states etc.
Comments: see also entry for Jauna Kulturas Sabiedriba

European Festival of Contemporary Dance in Moscow
Moscow Academic Stanislavsky and Nemirovich-Danchenko Music Theatre, 17B Dmitrovka str., 103009 **Moscow**, Russia
Tel: 7 095-229 0649 Fax: 7 095-229 0048
director Vladimir G Urin
Period/frequency: October, biennial (2001) *Second Address:* Director Michael Kahn-Ackermann, Goethe Institut Moskau, Leninskij Prospekt 95a, 117313 Moscow, Russia, Tel: +7 095-936 2461, Fax: +7 095-936 2232

Events-Co
Rua D. Luis de Ataíde 265,
2785-589 **São Domingos de Rana (Lisboa)**, Portugal
Tel: 351 21-452 8807 Fax: 351 21-452 8900
E-Mail: events.co@ip.pt
production manager: Hubert Dombrecht

International Seiler Piano Competition
Steffen Seiler e.V. zur Förderung der Klaviermusik, Schwarzacherstr. 40, 97318 **Kitzingen**, Germany
Tel: 49 9321-93311 Fax: 49 9321-36367
Internet: www.seiler-pianos.de
E-Mail: info@seiler-pianos.de
contact Kurt Schäfer, Ursula Seiler
Dates: June 2001 *Awards:* cash, total 80k DM

Internationales Seiler Klavierfestival
Steffen Seiler e.V. zur Förderung der Klaviermusik, Schwarzacherstr. 40, 97318 **Kitzingen**, Germany
Tel: 49 9321-93311 Fax: 49 9321-36367
Internet: www.seiler-pianos.de
E-Mail: info@seiler-pianos.de
contact Kurt Schäfer, Ursula Seiler

Irish Music Rights Organisation, The
Copyright House, Pembroke Row, Lower Baggot Street, **Dublin** 2, Ireland, Republic of
Tel: 353 1-661 4844 Fax: 353 1-661 3789
Internet: www.imro.ie
E-Mail: info@imro.ie
ceo Adrian Gaffmy; director of distribution Eoin Colley

Jauna Kulturas Sabiedriba
New Culture Society
c/o I. Kruss, Ropazu 58 – 8, 1006 **Riga**, Latvia
Tel: 371 2-554 812
promotion, information, press Jazeps Kukulis;

Karamba Experience
Ollends Lodge Heydon, **Norwich**, NR 11 6RB
Tel: 44 1603-872 402 Fax: 44 1603-879 053
E-Mail: karamba@gn.apc.org
director: Gary Newland

Königer Management Group
Fichter Str. 8, 71032 **Böblingen**, Germany
Tel: 49 7031-499 952 Fax: 49 7031-499 999
Geschäftsführer: Franz Königer, Herr Schubach

Market Place, Armagh Theatre & Arts Centre, The
Market Street, **Armagh (Northern Ireland)** BT61 7AT, United Kingdom
Tel: 44 28-3752 1805 Fax: 44 28-3751 0180
E-Mail: armagh.arts@dnet.co.uk
arts manager Kate Bond; technical office Patrick Dalgety
Comments: due to open in March 2000; no other email address, phone or fax numbers were available at the time of going to print

Milton Keynes Theatre
Marlborough, **Central Milton Keynes** MK9 3NZ, United Kingdom
Tel: 44 1908-547 500 Fax: 44 1908-547 647
E-Mail: michaellynas@theambassadors.com
chief executive Michael Lynas

Molteni
Dufourstr 97, 8008 **Zürich**, Switzerland
Tel: 41 1-383 8050
Fax: 41 1-383 8050
Internet: www.moltenitanzt.ch
E-Mail: molteni@moltenitanzt.ch

ÖKS (Österreichischer Kultur-Service)
Stiftgasse 6, 1070 **Wien**, Austria
Tel: 43 1-523 5781 Fax: 43 1-523 8933
Internet: www.oks.at
E-Mail: oks@oks.ac.at
Geschäftsführer Dr Michael Wimmer

Robert Fox Ltd
6 Beauchamp Place,
London SW3 1NG, United Kingdom
Tel: 44 20-7584 6855 Fax: 44 20-7225 1638
E-Mail: rf@robertfoxltd.com
managing director Robert Fox

School of Physical Theatre
Waterhouse Studios 3 Mills, 3 Mill Lane,
London, E3 3DU, United Kingdom
Tel: 44 20-8215 3350 Fax: 44 20-8215 3482
administrator: Lin Grist
Comments: also based in Canada, see entry in MOD (MUC Productions)

SFX Entertainment, Inc
650 Madison Avenue, **New York**, NY 10022, United States of America
Tel: 1 212-838 3100 Fax: 1 212-319 6517
Internet: www.sfx.com
E-Mail: first.lastname@sfx.com

Sinfonia 21
14 Prince's Gardens, **London** SW7 1NA, United Kingdom
Tel: 44 20-7584 2759 Fax: 44 20-7581 0970
Internet: www.sinfonia21.co.uk
E-Mail: info@sinfonia21.co.uk
princ. conductor Martyn Brabbins; chief executive Oliver Rivers
Size: 3-40 *Comments:* chamber ensemble with a commitment to contemporary music and experience in touring; updated information for entry on page 256

Sirius Record Company
El Venizelu 21, 15451 **Athens**, Greece
Tel: 30 1-677 5579/724 0242 Fax: 30 1-677 4787
E-Mail: siriosgr@odenet.gr
contact Vasiadis Haris
Format: CDs *Own and distributed labels:* own: Sirius

Skinning the Cat Aerail Theatre Company Limited
Woolston House, 3 Tettley Street, **Bradford**, BD1 2NP, United Kingdom
Tel: 44 1274-770 300 Fax: 44 1274-770 352
E-Mail: skcats@globalnet.co.uk
artistic director: Becky Truman

Sozio-kulturelles Zentrum St Spiritus
Lange Str. 49, 17489 **Greifswald**, Germany
Tel: 49 3834-3463 Fax: 49 3834-894 344
director Brigitte Schöpf
Comments: promoter of contemporary dance events

Tacheles
Oranienburgerstrasse 54-56 A, 10117 **Berlin**, Germany
Tel: 49 30-282 6185 Fax: 49 30-282 3130
Internet: www.tacheles.de
E-Mail: buero@tacheles.de
Vorstand Bettina Hertrampf, Peter Langbauer; pr Meike Janssen
Venue type: multi-purpose *Capacity:* up to 350
Art types: drama, dance, music

tanzraum
c/o Ensemble Theater Erlangen, Wasserturmstr. 16, 91054 **Erlangen**, Germany
Tel: 49 9131-862 984 Fax: 49 9131-862 104
director Hartmut Henne;
Date: 2-11 February 2001 *Frequency:* biennial (2001)
Comments: festival co-organised by Stadttheater Fürth (q.v.), Tafelhalle Nürnberg (q.v.), Theater Nürnberg (q.v.)

Vladimir Boys Choir
c/o Prof Eduard Markin, ul. Georgievskaya d. 2-A, 600002 **Vladimir**, Russia
Tel: 7 922-325 495/322 771/326 725
Fax: 7 922-232 723/233 917
E-Mail: mark@mark.vladimir.ru
contact Prof Eduard Markin
Type: boys choir *Repertoire:* ranging from the time of Peter the Great to the classics of the 20th C

Vladimir Chamber Choir
c/o Prof Eduard Markin, ul. Georgievskaya d. 2-A, 600002 **Vladimir**, Russia
Tel: 7 922-325 495/322 771/326 725 Fax: 7 922-232 723/233 917
E-Mail: mark@mark.vladimir.ru
contact Prof Eduard Markin

Vladimir Symphony Orchestra
c/o Prof Eduard Markin, ul. Georgievskaya d. 2-A, 600002 **Vladimir**, Russia
Tel: 7 922-325 495/322 771/326 725
Fax: 7 922-232 723/233 917
E-Mail: mark@mark.vladimir.ru
contact Prof Eduard Markin; director Artyom Markin

Wilton's Music Hall
Grace's Alley, Ensign Street, **London** E1 8JB, United Kingdom
Tel: 44 20-7702 9555 Fax: 44 20-7702 9555
Internet: www.broomhill.demon.co.uk
E-Mail: opera@broomhill.demon.co.uk
artistic director Broomhill Opera Marc Dornford-May;
Comment: updated information for entry on page 525

Wurre Wurre
c/o Frans Brood Productions, Muinklaan 10, 9000 **Gent**, Belgium
Tel: 32 9-234 1212 Fax: 32 9-265 9650
Internet: www.fransbrood.com
E-Mail: frabro@agoranet.be
artistic directors Tom Roos, Philip De Martelaere

Very Special Arts (VSA)
Suite 700, 1300 Connecticut Ave. **Washington DC** 20036, United States of America
Tel: 1 202-628 2800 Fax: 1 202-737 0735
Internet: www.vsarts.org
E-Mail: info@vsarts.org

LEONID KUZMIN

Pianist

"Leonid Kuzmin – Remember the name and hold your breath!"
LOS ANGELES TIMES

E, A, G Sharp, Co.

www.eagsharp.com
eagsharp@eagsharp.com

235 West 102 Street - Suite 16 J
New York, N.Y. 10025

Phone (212) 864 6020
Fax (212) 864 6934

PAYE

Don't fight over copies buy more!

Performing Arts Yearbook For Europe 2000

The definitive guide for Europe containing contact details for 14,000 arts organisations and their senior personnel in more than 50 European countries.

It is essential for you:

to discover how countries and regions fund the performing arts... to contact organisations and colleagues around the world... to keep track of changes and developments in your sector... source new ideas, new venues.... to help you plan tours... to improve your public relations programmes.

As an added bonus a free cd-rom is included, offering quick search capabilities, label printing and much much more all at your fingertips!

Order more copies,

simply photocopy and complete this form

PAYE 2000 (plus free cd-rom)

No. of copies ________ @ £45 UK

No. of copies ________ @ £53 Rest of The World

* all prices include post and packaging

☐ **Please debit my: Mastercard/Amex/Visa/Diners club/Eurocard for £ ________ Sterling**

Card No: ☐☐☐☐☐☐☐☐☐☐☐☐☐☐☐☐

Expiry Date: ☐☐☐☐

Billing Address (if different from your contact address)

____

____

☐ **I enclose a cheque (drawn on a British bank) or Eurocheque for £ ________ Sterling**

☐ **I wish to pay by bank transfer (including all charges) to:**

bank: National Westminster Bank plc

branch: Law Courts, Temple Bar Branch,
P.O.B. 10720,
217 The Strand,
London, WC2R 1AL, England

bank code: 60-80-08

account no: 04259505

account name: Arts Publishing International Ltd., subscription account

It is essential that you send the remittance advice for this bank transfer

Name: ______________________________

Job Title: ______________________________

Organisation: ______________________________

____

Address: ______________________________

____

____

Country: ______________________________

Phone: ______________________________

Fax: ______________________________

Email: ______________________________

Please send this form with payment to:

The Subscriptions Department, Arts Publishing International Ltd., Lime Wharf, Vyner Street, London E2 9DJ

For immediate service please:

Phone: (+44) 181 709 9050

Fax: (+44) 181 709 9080 or Email : subs@api.co.uk

Hsepaye ex.99

I would like to thank the following individuals and organisations which have helped with their time and information. The **PAYE** depends on contributors keeping us up-to-date with changes and new developments and I am extremely grateful for their support.

Special thanks go to
Nika Babaian (N.A.B. Artists Management, Armenia)
Milan Babjak (Art Agency MBM, Slovakia)
Victor Bublitchi (Asociatia Republicana Interarta, Moldova)
Aida Cengic (Open Society Foundation, Bosnia & Herzegovina)
Sînziana Dragos (Cultural Counsellor, Embassy of Romania, London)
Ahmet Erenli (International Istanbul Music Festival)
Júlia Gábor (Hungarian Centre of the ITI)
Victoria Gordievskaya (St Petersburg Mussorgsky Opera & Ballet Theatre)
Valéry Khasanov (Russian Centre of the ITI)
Levan Khetaguri (Stichting Caucasus Foundation, Georgia)
Anu Kivilo (Open Estonia Foundation)
Mojca Kranjc (Slovene National Theatre Drma Ljubljana)
Anneli Kurki (Finnish Theatre Information Centre)
Margaret Majewska (Polish Centre of the ITI)
Dr Juliana Menclová (Ministry of Culture, Slovakia)
Prof Alex Mikhnevich (Belarussian Institute of Cultural Studies)
Andras Mikle (IAG Europe, Hungary)
Nicolas Nicolaou (Ministry of Education & Culture, Cyprus)
Woijciech Nowak (Warsaw Philharmonic Orchestra)
Mevlüt Özhan (Turkish UNIMA)
Vida Pabarjkaede (Ministry of Culture, Lithuania)
Mirka Potucková (Czech Theatre Institute)
Ruta Pruseviciene (Lithuanian National Philharmonic Society)
Misha Rachlevsky (Chamber Orchestra Kremlin)
Pritt Raud (Tantsuinfo Keskus Eestis, Estonia)
Ana Rousseva (Appolonia Arts Foundation, Bulgaria)
Silvana Sebic (Rimi Co d.o.o., Croatia)
Diana Selecka (Slovak Republic Theatre Institute)
Jahangir Selimkhanov (Open Society Institute)
Mojmír Sobotka (Czech Music Information Centre)
Janina Tiskina (Ministry of Culture, Latvia)
Dr Vasil S. Tole (Theatre of Opera and Ballet)
Jacek Urbaniak (Poland)

This edition would not have been possible without:

Martin Huber, Publisher and Managing Director of Arts Publishing International Ltd
Stefan Braun, Deputy Editor
Ana Laura Lopez de la Torre, Consultant Editor
Marion Qazi, Editorial Administrator
Richard Poole, Advertising Director
Peter Lynch, Advertising Executive
Christine Hoffmann, Subscription Manager
Shizuka Yokomizo, Editor MOD Asia
Wiebke Morgan, Advertisers' Index Editor

Last, but definitely not least, the following people deserve a special mention for their "input" and hard work on the phones:
Angeliki Avgitidou, Paola Bottini, Carol Beigneux, Isabel Caleya, Carlos Chirinos, Ella Gibbs, Jaime Gili, Sarah Kersley, Amy Plant, Giovanni Porfido, Marta Rivero, Jimmy Robert, Elisabetta Sale, Andreas Steinmann, Grace Surman, Gary Winters

Very Special Thanks also go to
Alan Drew, **Loraine Holmes** and **Tom Shaw** at **Xinc** and to everybody at **Perfectaprint**

Many, many thanks to all the above
Karin Junker
Editor

CONDUCTORS

Petr Altrichter
Principal Conductor: Royal Liverpool Philharmonic Orchestra
Guest Conductor: Prague Symphony Orchestra
Music Director: Südwestdeutsche Philharmonie

Stephen Cleobury
Director of Music: King's College, Cambridge
Chief Conductor: BBC Singers

Simon Halsey
Chorus Director: City of Birmingham Symphony Chorus
Principal Conductor: City of Birmingham Touring Opera
Principal Guest Conductor: Netherlands Radio Choir
Artistic Director: BBC National Chorus of Wales
Principal Guest Conductor: Sydney Philharmonia Choirs
Conductor: European Voices

***Ton Koopman**
Artistic Director: Amsterdam Baroque Orchestra
Principal Conductor: Netherlands Radio Chamber Orchestra

Stephen Layton
Director: Polyphony
Principal Guest Conductor: Danish National Radio Choir
Artistic Director: Holst Singers
Director of Music: Temple Church, London

Grant Llewellyn
Conductor in Residence: BBC National Orchestra of Wales

Edward Warren

DIRECTOR / SOLOIST

Monica Huggett, *baroque violin*

Martin Roscoe, *piano*

SINGERS

Paul Agnew, *tenor*

Rogers Covey-Crump, *tenor*

Charles Daniels, *tenor*

Peter Harvey, *baritone*

David James, *counter-tenor*

Emma Kirkby, *soprano*

VIOLIN

***Isabelle Faust**

BAROQUE VIOLIN

Monica Huggett

GUITAR

***Julian Bream**

PIANO

***Andrei Gavrilov**

Artur Pizarro

Martin Roscoe

PIANO DUO

Martin Roscoe and Peter Donohoe
(in association with Askonas Holt, managers of Peter Donohoe)

PERIOD KEYBOARD

***Ton Koopman**
harpsichord/organ

RECORDERS

Pamela Thorby

STRING QUARTETS

Duke Quartet

Endellion String Quartet

Eroica Quartet

PIANO TRIO

****Trio Wanderer**

CHOIRS

European Voices
Conductor: Simon Halsey

Polyphony
Director: Stephen Layton

VOCAL ENSEMBLES

The Hilliard Ensemble

The Tallis Scholars
Director: Peter Phillips

INSTRUMENTAL ENSEMBLES

Palladian Ensemble

***Sequentia**

Sonnerie

Steve Martland Band

ORCHESTRAS

***Amsterdam Baroque Orchestra**
Director: Ton Koopman

***Franz Liszt Chamber Orchestra**
Director: János Rolla

General management except where marked
*UK and Sundry Territories
**UK, Scandinavia and Australia

SPECIAL PROJECTS

The Hilliard Ensemble with Jan Garbarek

The Tallis Scholars with Sting

Directors:

Nigel Brown
Chairman

James Brown
Managing

John Bickley

Elizabeth Jones

Tony Puckridge

John Willan

Artist Managers:

Chris Loake

Sibylle Mager

Anne-Marie Norman

Hilary Perrott

Lucy Rice

Events Manager:

Helen Poole

Finance:

Zoe Owen

Administration:

Kika Challis

Hannah Pettit

HAZARD
CHASE

Richmond House,
16-20 Regent Street,
Cambridge CB2 1DB.
United Kingdom

Tel: (01223) 312400
Fax: (01223) 460827

info@hazardchase.co.uk

www.hazardchase.co.uk

Member of the International Artist Managers' Association & North American Performing Arts Managers & Agents

ProMúsica

DIRECCIÓN ARTÍSTICA:
Ricardo de Quesada
Xavier Güell

SEASON 1999 | 2000

THE SYMPHONIC WORLD II
Barcelona - Auditori de Barcelona

November

Orchestre National du Capitole de Toulouse

Michel Plasson

Russian National Orchestra

Mijail Pletnev - Nikolai Lugansky

February

Süddeutscher Runfunk Stuttgart

Heinrich Schiff

London Philharmonic Orchestra

Kurt Masur - Michel Beroff

Budapest Festival Orchestra

Ivan Fischer

March

English Chamber Orchestra

Jeffrey Tate

April

Ivo Pogorelich

May

Wiener Oktett

Rosa Torres-Pardo

Chamber Orchestra of Europe

Paavo Berglund

Orchestre Philharmonique de Radio France

Myung-Whun Chung

THE SYMPHONIC° WORLD I
Bilbao, Euskalduna

January

Süddeutscher Runfunk Stuttgart

Heinrich Schiff

March

English Chamber Orchestra

Jeffrey Tate

May

Chamber Orchestra of Europe

Paavo Berglund

June

Bayerischer Runfunk

Lorin Maazel

THE SYMPHONIC WORLD I
Coruña. Palacio de la Ópera

November

Russian National Orchestra

Mijail Pletnev - Nikolai Lugansky

February

London Philharmonic Orchestra

Kurt Masur - Michel Beroff

April

Junge Deutsche Philharmonie

Steven Sloane - Frank Peter Zimmermann

THE SYMPHONIC WORLD V
Madrid. Auditorio Nacional de Música. Sala Sinfónica

ASOCIACIÓN CULTURAL Y ARTÍSTICA PROMUSICA

Capitán Haya, 22, 2° - 28020
Madrid, España
Tel: 34+91+597.15.54
Fax: 34+91+556.95.80
Email: p_musica@teleline.es

November

Orchestre National du Capitole de Toulouse

Sociedad Coral de Bilbao

Michel Plasson

Russian National Orchestra

Mijail Pletnev -

Nikolai Lugansky

February

Süddeutscher Runfunk Stuttgart

Heinrich Schiff

London Philharmonic Orchestra

Kurt Masur - Michel Beroff

Budapest Festival Orchestra

Ivan Fischer

March

English Chamber Orchestra

Jeffrey Tate

April

Ivo Pogorelich

May

Wiener Oktett

Rosa Torres-Pardo

Chamber Orchestra of Europe

Paavo Berglund

Orchestre Philharmonique de Radio France

Myung-Whun Chung

THE MUSIC OF OUR TIME IV
Madrid. Auditorio Nacional de Música

January

ENSEMBLE MODERN

THOMAS ADÈS

February

PROYECTO GERHARD

GLORIA ISABEL RAMOS TRIANO

KLANG FORUM WIEN

SYLVAIN CAMBRELING

ROSEMARY HARDY

March

ANANDA SUKARLAN

PROYECTO GERHARD

PETER RUNDEL

April

PROYECTO GERHARD

ERNEST MARTÍNEZ IZQUIERDO

May

PROYECTO GERHARD

CORO DE LA COMUNIDAD DE MADRID

JOSÉ RAMÓN ENCINAR

PILAR JURADO - CARLOS ÁLVAREZ

June

PROYECTO GERHARD

JOSÉ LUIS TEMES

KARLHEINZ STOCKHAUSEN

THE SYMPHONIC WORLD III
Palma de Mallorca. Auditorium de Palma

February

Süddeutscher Runfunk Stuttgart

Heinrich Schiff

Budapest Festival Orchestra

Ivan Fischer

March

English Chamber Orchestra

Jeffrey Tate

Junge Deutsche Philharmonie

Steven Sloane - Frank Peter Zimmerman

May

Wiener Orktett

Rosa Torres - Pardo

Chamber Orchestra of Europe

Paavo Berglund

THE SYMPHONIC WORLD III
Sevilla. Teatro de la Maestranza

February

Süddeutscher Runfunk Stuttgart

Heinrich Schiff

Orquesta Festival de Budapest

Ivan Fischer

March

English Chamber Orchestra

Jeffrey Tate

May

Chamber Orchertra Europe

Paavo Berglund

Orchestre Philharmonique de Radio France

Myung-Whun Chung

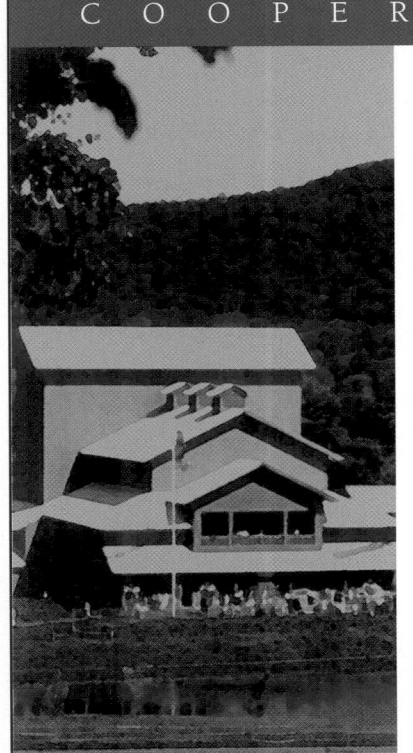

Performing Arts Yearbook for Europe 2000
Reference Section

The accuracy and the comprehensiveness of the **Performing Arts Yearbook for Europe** benefit from the cooperation of individuals and organisations in providing corrections and extra information to existing entries, and in providing information about new companies and organisations.

Information about new entries, changes of detail and other material will be gratefully received and should be sent to:

The Editor, Performing Arts Yearbook for Europe, Arts Publishing International Ltd, Lime Wharf, Vyner Sreet, London E2 9DJ, England, tel: (+44 20) 8709 9050; fax: (+44 20) 8709 9080, email: paye@api.co.uk.

*Please always include your name, the full company name and address and phone and fax number. Please feel welcome to use our **customer service page**, on page 170.*

Entries are free, but are included at the Editor's discretion.

Pan European Governmental Institutions

Commission of the European Communities
Commission des Communautés Européennes
Rue de la Loi 200, 1049 **Brussels**
Tel: 32 2-299 1111 Fax: 32 2-295 0138
Internet: europea.eu.int
commissioner of education and culture Vivianne Reding; director-general of education and culture Spyridon Pappas; head of cultural action division Enrica Varese; head of audio-visual division Jacques Delmoly; director of cultural division and audiovisual policy Jean-Michel Baer
Comments: The European Communities can offer financial support to cultural activities that fulfill certain other Community objectives; These include enhancing a region's social or economic infrastructure, strengthening ties between European countries and regions or furthering links between the EC and Central and Eastern Europe or the Africa Caribbean Pacific (ACP) countries; Bread and Circuses commissioned by Informal European Theatre Movement (IETM, q.v.) and written and researched by Simon Kirby and Louise Scott offers further information on the various schemes, how to apply and what to expect; a new programme called Culture 2000 will replace the Comission's existing funding programmes (Kaleidoscope, Raphael and Ariane); the aim of the new funding programme, beginning in Jan. 2000, is to encourage cooperation between cultural organisations and institutions of the member states

Council of Europe
Conseil de l'Europe
67075 **Strasbourg** Cedex
Tel: 33 3-8841 2000/2173 (culture)/2685 (director) Fax: 33 3-8841 2781
Internet: culture.coe.fr
E-Mail: vera.boltho@coe.ind
director education, culture & sport Raymond Weber (3-8841 2685); culture Vera Boltho (3-8841 2685)
Role & Services: European cultural policies
Comments: alternative e-mail: raymond.weber@coe.ind

Comittee on Culture, Youth, Education, Media and Sport
Comission de la Culture, de la Jeunesse, de l'Education, des medias et des Sports
c/o European Parliament, Rue Wiertz, 1047 **Brussels**
Tel: 32 2-284 3553 Fax: 32 2-284 9071
Internet: www.europarl.eu.int
E-Mail: mhouben@europarl.eu.int
president Giuseppe Gargani; vice presidents Vasco Graca Moura, Ulpu Iivari, Georgio Ruffolo; head of division Mignon Houben
Comments: office in Strasbourg: Tel: 33 3-8817 2447, Fax: 33 3-8817 5061

United Nations Educational, Scientific and Cultural Organisation (UNESCO)
7 place de Fontenoy, 75352 **Paris** 07 SP
Tel: 33 1-4568 1000 Fax: 33 1-4567 1690/4568 5592 (culture)
Internet: www.unesco.org
E-Mail: t.wagner@unesco.org
programme specialist in promotion of artistic creation T. Wagner (33 1-4568 4325)

•*Comments:* for full details of the role and cultural policies of these organisations refer to More Bread and Circuses – Who does what in Europe, published by the Informal European Theatre Meeting (IETM) and the Arts Council of England, London (q.v.)

National and Regional Ministries of Culture and Funding Agencies

Ministries of Culture and Funding Agencies
Information on ministry addresses etc. has been provided by the countries concerned. In federal countries such as Austria and Switzerland, and semi-federal nations, e.g.. Spain or Italy, we have included the addresses of ministries or government departments at a regional level. It was also thought appropriate to include the Regional Arts Boards (RABs) in the UK and the Directions Regionales des Affaires Culturelles (DRACs) in France. The headquarters of some key organisations that promote their national culture, e.g. the British Council, Goethe Institute and Swedish Institute, are included as they may be able to provide financial or other assistance on occasions. Readers will find the British addresses of these and similar organisations in the revised edition of *More Bread and Circuses* published by the Arts Council of England and IETM (see address in UK section and in Supranational Section). A start has been made on listing the cultural departments of the major cities within each country. **Within country the ministries and funding agencies are ordered alphabetically within descending order of government tier.**

Ministères des Affaires Culturelles, mécénes et sponsors
Les renseignements sur les ministères etc. ont été fournis par les pays en question. Dans le cas des pays fédéraux comme l'Autriche et la Suisse, et les nations semi-fédérales comme l'Espagne et l'Italie, les adresses des ministères et des départements gouvernementaux sont données au niveau régional. On pourra aussi trouver les noms des 'Regional Arts Association' (RAA) pour le Royaume Uni et des 'Directions Régionales des Affaires Culturelles' (DRAC) pour la France. Les sièges de quelques organisations clés qui assurent la promotion des cultures nationales comme le British Council, l'Institut Goette et l'Institut Suédois sont inclus parce qu'il est possible qu'ils fournissent une aide financière ou autre. Nos lecteurs trouveront entre autres les adresses en Grande-Bretagne de ces organisations dans l'édition revue et corrigée de *More Bread and Circusses* publié par le 'Arts Council of England' et IETM (cf adresses dans la section 'UK' et 'Supranational Organisations). Une liste des services culturels des plus grandes villes de chaque pays est en cours, mais n'est pas achevée.ce jour. **Pour chaque pays, les ministères et les agences de fonds sont classés par ordre alphabétique dans l'ordre décroissant de leurs liens gouvernementaux.**

Kultusministerien und Förderungseinrichtungen
Die Informationen über Namen und Adressen von Kultusministerien usw. wurden von Quellen der jeweiligen Länder zur Verfügung gestellt. In Ländern mit föderativer Struktur, z.B. Österreich und Schweiz, und in denen mit halb-föderativer Struktur, z.B. Italien, haben wir die Adressen von regionalen Ministeriums- und Regierungsabteilungen aufgenommen. Es erschien zweckmäßig, auch die Regional Arts Boards (RABs) im Vereinigten Königreich und die Directions Regionales des Affaires Culturelles (DRACs) in Frankreich zu verzeichnen. Die Geschäftsstellen einiger Schlüsselorganisationen, die nationale Kultur fördern, z.B. das British Council, das Goethe-Institut, und das Svenska institutet, werden in diesem Kapitel ebenfalls aufgeführt, weil diese Institutionen gelegentlich finanzielle oder sonstige Unterstützung gewähren können. Die britischen Adressen dieser und ähnlicher Organisationen finden Sie in der neuen Ausgabe der vom Arts Council und IETM (Die Adressen finden Sie im 'UK'- bzw. 'Supranational Organisations' Kapitel) herausgegebenen Veröffentlichung *More Bread and Circuses*. Wir haben auch versucht, die Kulturämter der größeren Städte einzuschließen. Das Verzeichnis ist aufgrund mangelnder Kooperationsbereitschaft leider nicht vollständig. **Die Ministerien und Förderungseinrichtungen sind innerhalb aller Staaten alphabetisch nach Rangwichtigkeit geordnet.**

Ministeri ed assessorati alla Cultura
Le informazioni riguardanti gli indirizzi dei ministeri sono state fornite dai Paesi stessi. Nelle Federazioni come l'Austria e la Svizzera e nelle Nazioni semi-federali come la Spagna e l'Italia abbiamo incluso gli indirizzi dei Ministeri e degli Assessorati regionali. Sono stati inclusi inoltre il Regional Arts Boards (RABs) per il Regno Unito, le Directions Regionales des Affaires Culturelles (DRACs) per la Francia, ecc. Le sedi principali di alcune organizzazioni che promuovono la propria cultura nazionale, come ad esempio il British Council, il Goethe Institut e l'Istituto Svedese sono state inserite in relazione al fatto che possono finanziare iniziative culturali o dare assistenza se necessario. I lettori troveranno gli indirizzi inglesi, riguardanti queste e simili associazioni, nell'edizione del *More Bread and Circuses pubblicata dall'Arts Council e IETM (cfr indirizzi nelle sezione 'UK' e 'Supranational Organisations'). Si é iniziato ad elencare, inoltre, i dipartimenti culturali delle maggiori province e cittá di ogni singola Nazione. Questa lista é attualmente incompleta.*
All'interno di ogni Nazione, i Ministeri, gli Assessorati, ecc. sono stati elencati in ordine gerarchico ed in ordine alfabetico (Regione/Provincia/Comune).

Ministerios de Cultura y Organizaciones responsables para becas y ayudas
Las direcciones de los ministerios, organizaciones etc fueron facilitadas por los propios países. Para los países federales como Austria y Suiza, y en países semifederales como España e Italia, se han incluido las direcciones de los ministerios o departamentos gubernamentales a nivel regional. También se consideró pertinente incluir las Regional Arts Boards (RABs) en Gran Bretaña y Directions Regionales des Affaires Culturelles (DRACs) en Francia. Se han incluido las sedes centrales de algunas organizaciones claves que promocionan su cultura nacional – por ejemplo se han incluido el British Council, Goethe Institute y Swedish Institute porque ocasionalmente ofrecen alguna ayuda financiera o de otro tipo. Las direcciones británicas de éstas o semejantes organizaciones se pueden encontrar en la edición revisada de *More Bread and Circuses*, publicada por el Arts Council of England (vea dirección en la sección británica). Se ha empezado a listar las áreas de cultura de los municipios más grandes de cada país. Por el momento, esta lista está incompleta.
Dentro de cada pais, los ministerios y organizaciones responsables para becas están ordenados alfabéticamente siguiendo un orden descendente encabezado por el nivel gubernamental.

Ministries of Culture and Funding Agencies (정부 문화부 및 기금제공 재단)

부서의 주소 및 기타 정보는 관계 국가가 제공했다. 호주와 스위스 같은 연방 국가들이나, 스페인 이탈리아 같은 반연방 국가들편에는 주정부 차원의 부서나 관청들의 주소가 포함되었다. 영국의 지역예술이사회(RABs: Regional Arts Boards) 및 프랑스의 지역문화담당이사회(DRACs: Directions Regionales des Affaires Culturelles) 등도 역시 포함되는 것이 적당하다고 결정되었다. 그 밖에 영국문화원, 독일문화원, 스웨덴문화원 등과 같은 각 국가의 주요 문화장려조직들 역시 문화 행사를 재정적으로나 어떤 다른 형태로 지원할 수 있기 때문에 그들 본부가 포함되었다. 이들 조직 및 이들과 비슷한 역할을 하는 조직들의 영국 내 주소는 영국예술원(Arts Council of England)과 IETM가 발행한 'More Bread and Circuses' 개정판에 나와 있다 (영국편 및 범국가편에 실린 주소 참조). 각 국가의 주요 도시 문화부 역시 기재가 시작되었다. **리스트는 국가별로 정부위계에 따라 알파벳순으로 기재되었다.**

文化部和资助机构
有关该部的地址等资料已由各有关国家提供。在如奥地利和瑞士这样的联邦国家及如西班牙或意大利这样的半联邦国家，我们已经收集了该部或政府部门的地区性地址。我们也认为将英国的地区艺术 委员会(RABs)和法国的文化事务地区总部(DRACs)包括在内是适宜的。一些发扬它们本国文化的主要机构的总部，例如英国文化委员会(British Council)、歌德学院(Goethe Institute)和瑞典学院(Swedish Institute)也包括在内，因为它们可能对有关活动能够提供资金或其它方面的协助。读者将会在由英格兰艺术委员会(Arts Council of England)和IETM（地址见英国章节及超国家章节）出版的“More Bread and Circuses”的修订版中找到这些机构或者其它类似机构在英国的地址。现在已经开始将各国主要城市的文化部门列入名单中。**在每个国家中这些文化部门和资助机构是按字母顺序及按政府级别高低来排列的。**

文化省と財団
文化省の住所等の情報は各国により提供されたものです。オーストリア、.スイス等の連邦国、スペイン、イタリア等の準連邦国では地方レベルの省庁や政府部門の住所も掲載しました。また、英国の地方芸術委員会（Regional Arts Boards-RAB）とフランスの文化地方委員会（Directions Regionales des Affaires Culturelles-DRAC）も含めることが適切であると判断しました。ブリティッシュ・カウンシル、ゲーテ協会、スウェーデン協会等、各国の文化を促進する主要団体も財務的、その他の支援を提供することがあるため、それぞれの本拠地が掲載されています。イングランド芸術委員会（Arts Council of England）とIETMが出版している「More Bread and Circuses」改訂版（英国と超国家的団体の章を参照）には、ここ掲載された英国の団体、それ以外の類似団体の住所が載っています。リストはそれぞれの国の主要都市にある文化関連省庁から始まっています。**国別リストは政府レベルの上から下へ記載され、同じレベル内ではアルファベット順になっています。**

ALBANIA (+355)

Ministry of Culture, Youth and Sports
Ministria e Kulturës, Rinisë dhe Sporteve
Bulevardi Dÿshmorÿt e Kombit, **Tirana**
Tel: 42-23236/50387 Fax: 42-32488
minister of culture Edi Rama (tel/fax: 42-32488); vice-minister Kreshnik Tartari (tel/fax: 42-23682); director of foreign relations department Petraq Buka; director of arts department Vangjush Valla (tel/fax: 42-22493); director of culture deparment Virgjill Muçi

Albanian Music Council, The
Rr. Sitki 6ifio, Pallatet 9 kate, Shkalla2, Ap. 4, **Tirana**
Tel: 42-74127/30203 Fax: 42-30203
E-Mail: root@tob.tirana/al
president Dr Vasil S Tole
Comments: member of I.M.C-UNESCO

Cultural Section – Municipality of Tirana
Bashkia e Tiranÿs, Sheshi Skÿnderbej, **Tirana**
director Shaqir Rexhvelaj

ANDORRA (+376)

Departament de Culture Ministeri de Turisme i Culture
62-64 Carrér Prat de la Creu, **Andorra la Vella**
Tel: 875 708 Fax: 826 707
E-Mail: cultura.gov@andorra
minister Enric Pusal Areny; directora Cristina Marti Torres
Role & Services: government department with main responsibility for financing the arts and national heritage *Comments:* award 2 literary prizes annually

ARMENIA (+374)

Ministry of Culture, Youth and Sport of Armenia
5, Toumanian St, 375010 **Yerevan**
Tel: 2-529 349/523 922 Fax: 2-523 930
minister of culture, youth and sport Roland Sharoyan

Department of Information & Publishing by the Armenian Government
89 Terian Street, 375009 **Yerevan**
Tel: 2-528 660 Fax: 2-506 756
E-Mail: info@arminco.com
director Harutyun Karapetian

Yerevan Council Department of Sports and Culture
1/3 Pavstos Byuzand Street, 375010 **Yerevan**
Tel: 2-529 863
chief of department Ara Yerinjakian

AUSTRIA (+43)

• Federal

Bundeskanzleramt Sektion II (Kunstangelegenheiten)
Schottengasse 1, 1014 **Wien**
Tel: 1-53120-0 Fax: 1-5312 07620
Internet: www.bmwf.gv.at
Bundeskanzler Dr Victor Klima; Staatssekretär Dr Peter Wittmann; Sektionschef Dr Andreas Mailath-Pokorny

Office for foreign cultural relations
Büro für kulturelle Auslandsbeziehungen (Oberösterreich)
Landeskulturzentrum Ursulinenhof, Landstr. 31, 4020 **Linz**
Tel: 732-7720 5474 Fax: 732-7720 4804
Leiter Dr. Aldemar Schiffkorn

• Regional

Provincial Government of Burgenland – Department 7 / Culture, Science and Archive
Burgenländische Landesregierung – Abteilung 7 / Kultur, Wissenschaft und Archiv
Europaplatz 1, 7000 **Eisenstadt**
Tel: 2682-600 Fax: 2682-600 2058
E-Mail: josef.tiefenbach@bgld.gv.at
Leiter der Abt. Kultur, Wissenschaft und Archiv Hofrat Dr. Johann Seedoch
Comments: see also Promoters

Provincial Government of Carinthia – Culture Dept.
Kärntner Landesregierung – Kulturabteilung
Paradeisergasse 7, 9021 **Klagenfurt**
Tel: 463-5363 0502 Fax: 463-5363 0500
Leiter der Kulturabteilung Dr Gerhard Baumann

Provincial Government of Lower Austria
Niederösterreichische Landesregierung – Abt. Kultur und Wissenschaft
Landhausplatz 1, 3109 **St Pölten**
Tel: 2742-200-0 Fax: 2742-200 3029
Internet: www.noel.gv./service/k
E-Mail: post.servicestelle2@noel.gv.at
Leiter der Abt Kultur und Wissenschaft Univ-Doz Dr. Georg Schmitz

Provincial Government of Upper Austria – Culture Dept.
Oberösterreichische Landeskulturdirektion
Spittelwiese 4, 4020 **Linz**
Tel: 732-7720 5480 (Landeskulturdirektion)
Fax: 732-7720 1786
Internet: www.ooe.gv.at
Leitung W. Hofrat Mag. Manfred Mohr; Fachbereich Kulturförderung Dr Paul Stepanek; Fachbereich Veranstaltungen Hofrat Dr Reinhard Mattes; Fachbereich Wissenschaft und Denkmalpflege Erwin Garstenauer; Institut für Volkskultur Dr. Alexander Jalkotzy

Provincial Government of Salzburg (Dept 12)
Salzburger Landesregierung (Abt. 12)
Franziskanergasse 5a, 5010 **Salzburg**
Tel: 662-8042-0/2282/2248/2249
Fax: 662-8042 2919
Internet: www.land-sbg.gv.at/kultur-sport
E-Mail: post@kultur.land-sbg.gv.at
Leiter der Abteilung Kultur und Sport Herbert Werner
Comments: other email: herbert.werner@land-sbg.gv.at

Provincial Government of Styria – Culture & Arts Dept.
Kulturabteilung der Steiermärkischen Landesregierung
Trautmannsdorfgasse 2, 8011 **Graz**
Tel: 316-877 4320/21 Fax: 316-877 3156
E-Mail: manfred.glawogger@stm.k.gv.at
Leiter der Kulturabteilung Hofrat Dr. Manfred Glawogger

Provincial Government of Tyrol – Culture Dept.
Tiroler Landesregierung – Kulturabteilung
Sillgasse 8, 6020 **Innsbruck**
Tel: 512-508-0/3752 Fax: 512-508 3755
E-Mail: kultur@tirol.gv.at
Leiter der Kulturabteilung Dr Christoph Mader; Leiter Musikreferat Mag Walter Meixner; Leiter Bildende Kunst Dr Magdalena Hörmann
Role & Services: funding for resident artists in Tyrol or works closely connected to Tyrol

Provincial Government of Vorarlberg – Culture Dept.
Vorarlberger Landesregierung – Kultur
Römerstraße 15, 6901 **Bregenz**
Tel: 5574-5112 2305 Fax: 5574-5112 2196
Internet: www.vorarlberg.at
E-Mail: Kunrich.Gehrer@vlr.gv.at
Leiter der Kulturabteilung Kunrich Gehrer
Comments: alternative internet: www.vol.at/Landesregierung/

• Municipal

City of Vienna – Cultural Department
Wien – Kulturabteilung, Amt der Landesregierung
Friedrich-Schmidt-Platz 5, 1082 **Wien**
Tel: 1-4000 84711 Fax: 1-4000 998 007
Internet: www.wien.gv.at
E-Mail: post@m07.magwien.gv.at
Leiter Dr Bernhard Denscher

AZERBAIDZHAN (+994)

Ministry of Culture of the Azerbaidzhan Republic
Government House, Azadlyg Square 1, 370016 **Baku**
Tel: 12-934 398 Fax: 12-935 605
minister Polad Byul-Byul Oglu

BELARUS (+375)

Belarus Republic Culture Ministry
Ministjerstvo Kultury Respubliki Bjelaruss
prosp. Mashjerova 11, 220004 **Minsk**
Tel: 172-234 574 Fax: 172-235 825
minister Aljexandr Sosnowsky
Comments: Dept of International Relations: Tel: 172-226 440

BELGIUM (+32)

Please note: general elections were held in June 1999; so changes may have occured

Ministry of the French Community of Belgium
Ministère de la Communauté française de Belgique
Boulevard Leopold II, 44, 1080 **Brussels**
Tel: 2-413 2311 Fax: 2-413 3443
secrétaire général Henry Ingberg

Ministry of Culture: Administrative Directorate for the Promotion and Dissemination of the Arts
Ministère de la Culture: Direction d'Administration de la Promotion des Arts de la Scène
Espace 27 Septembre, Boulevard Leopold II, 44, 1080 **Brussels**
Tel: 2-413 2311 Fax: 2-413 3443
Internet: www.cfwb.be
directeur général de la culture Martine Lahaye (tel: 413 2405); directeur d' administration de la promotion des arts de la scéne Christine Guillaume (tel: 413 2509)
Role & Services: admininstration in charge of culture, communication, health, infrastructure & public service

Cabinet of the Minister of Culture for the French Community of Belgium
Cabinet de la Culture et de l' Education Permanente de la Communatuté Française de Belgique
21-23 Bld du Régent, 1000 **Brussels**
Tel: 2-506 3411 Fax: 2-511 8859
E-Mail: hermand@csub.be
ministre de la culture Charles Picqué

General Commissariat for the French Community for Belgium
Commissariat général pour la Communauté française de Belgique
2 Place Sainctete, 1080 **Brussels**
Tel: 2-421 8211 Fax: 2-421 8787
Internet: www.cfwb.be/cgri
E-Mail: cgri@cfwb.be
commissaire général Philippe Suimen
Role & Services: finance and promote abroad the artistic activities of the French community (Brussels & Wallonie)

Cabinet of the Flemish Minister for Culture, Family and Welfare
Kabinet van de Vlaamse Minister van Cultuur, Gezin en Welzijn
Martelaarsplein 7, 1000 **Brussels**
Tel: 2-227 2811 Fax: 2-227 2805
E-Mail: luc.martens@vlanderen.be
minister of culture Luc Martens
Role & Services: finance and promote cultural activities for the Flemish community, such as theater, opera, orchestra, literature, etc

Ministry of the Flemish Community: Department of social welfare, health and culture – Cultural administration
Ministerie van de Vlaamse Gemeenschap: Departement welzijn, volksgezondheid en cultuur – Administratie Cultuur
Parochiaanstraat 15, 1000 **Brussels**
Tel: 2-553 3111 Fax: 2-553 6969
Internet: www.vlaandern.be/ned/sites/cultuur/cultur_s.htm
head of cultural administration Jos Van Rilfaer (6868); division head: music, dance, literature & performing arts Robert Elsen (6902); head, visual arts and museums Jan Verlinden (6842); community education and libraries Gilbert Van Houtven (4245); youth t.b.a.
Role & Services: ministry of culture, responsible for the arts in the Flemish community of Belgium

Government of the German-speaking Community
Regierung der Deutschsprachigen Gemeinschaft
Abteilung Kulturelle Angelegenheiten, Klötzerbahn 32, 4700 **Eupen**
Tel: 87-744 075 Fax: 87-557 021/055
minister for education, culture and tourism Bernd Gentges; cultural counsellor Roger Heck

Cabinet of the minister of the region of Brussels
Cabinet du Ministre de la Région Bruxelloise
Avenue Louise 54, BP 10, 1050 **Brussels**
Tel: 2-517 1200 Fax: 2-511 9442
E-Mail: eholland@gosuin.irisnet.be
ministre de la culture, de la rénovation, du tourisme, de l'aide aux personnes et du sport Didier Gosuin; attachés culturels Jacques Steurs, Sandra Preud'Homme
Role & Services: finance and promote artistic activities of and for the region of Brussels

French Commission of the Community of Brussels
Commission Communautaire française
Bruxelles-Capital
102-103 Bd Waterloo, 1000 **Brussels**
Tel: 2-542 8211 Fax: 2-542 8390
ministre chargé de la culture Didier Gosuin (517 1200); directeur général ad interim Philippe Debacker; conseiller chef de service pour la culture Luc Legrand; conseiller chef du service socio-culturel Philippe Legrain; conseiller théâtre Yollande Rossen
Role & Services: finance and promote artistic activities of and for the region of Brussels

Ministry of the German speaking Community
Ministerium der Deutschsprachigen Gemeinschaft
Abteilung Kulturelle Angelegenheiten
Gospert 1-5, 4700 **Eupen**
Tel: 87-596 300 Fax: 87-556 476
ministre chargé de la culutre Bernd Gentges; ministre-président Karl-Heinz Lambertz; chef de service du départment des affaires culturelles Herbert Lennertz

Brabant Province – Cultural Service
Direction D'Administration de la Culture, du Sport et de la Jeunesse – Brabant Wallon
Bâtiment Folon, 25 chaussée des Nerviens, 1300 **Wavre**
Tel: 10-236 340 Fax: 10-236 327
E-Mail: pbw.culture@skynet.be
directeur d'administration Mr. Piersotte; chef du service de l'inspection Thierry Marchal; chef du service de l'administration, événements cult Philippe van Cranem
Role & Services: finance and promote local artistic activities; organization of cultural events: Dance Dense (biennial, next 2000), international Festival – Performances (biennial)

Province of Hainaut – Cultural
ServiceProvince de Hainaut – Service culturel
Rue A. Warocqué 83, 7100 **La Louvière**
Tel: 64-229 258 Fax: 64-225 089
directeur général Jacques Lanotte; chef du service provincial des arts de la scène Michel Tanner
Role & Services: finance & promote local artistic activities

Province of Liège – Cultural Service
Province de Liège – Service culturel
Rue des Croisiers 15, 4000 **Liège**
Tel: 4-232 8686 Fax: 4-232 8694
E-Mail: culture@prov-liege.be
direction générale de la culture, de la jeunesse et de sports Claude Deregowski

Province of Luxembourg – Cultural Service
Province de Luxembourg – Service de la diffusion et de l'animation culturelle
Palais Abbatial, 6870 **Saint Hubert**
Tel: 61-612 201 Fax: 61-613 289
chef de service de l'administration Christiane Toussaint
Role & Services: finance and promote local artistic and cultural activities in the province of Luxembourg

Province of Namur – Cultural Service
Province de Namur – Service de la Culture
Avenue Reine Astrid 22a, 5000 **Namur**
Tel: 81-729 750 Fax: 81-729 761
directeur André Lambotte; secteur formation Francis Tonon; secteur audiovisuel Patrick Van Hoecke; secteur animation Jean-François de Coster; section théâtre Marie-Noël Vandermensbrugghe; section musique Anne Dereine
Role & Services: finance and promote local artistic activities *Comments:* address for André Lambotte: 4 Avenue Golenvaux, 5000 Namur, tel: 229 014, fax: 221 779; address for Marie-Noël Vandermensbrugghe: rue des Brasseurs, 177, tel: 224 088

Province of Antwerp – Cultural Service
Provincie Antwerpen – Provinciale Cultuurdienst
Koningin Elisabethlei 22, 2018 **Antwerp**
Tel: 3-240 5011/2-406 403 Fax: 3-240 6470
head of the cultural service Dirk Berkvens

Flemish Cultural Center of Brabant
Provincie Vlaams Brabant
52 Diestefteenweg, 3010 **Leuven**
Tel: 16-267 011 Fax: 16-267 676
Internet: www.vl-brabant.be
cultural consultant Jo Rombouts; arts consultant Egide Gabau; coordinator Piet Fonger
Role & Services: finance and promote cultural activities for the province of Brabant

Province Limburg – Cultural Service
Provincie Limburg – Directie Cultuur
Universiteitslaan 1, 3500 **Hasselt**
Tel: 11-237 513 Fax: 11-237 510
Internet: www.limburg.be
E-Mail: cbm@limburg.be
director Jean Pierre De Waal
Role & Services: finance and promote cultural activities for the province of Limburg

Province East-Flanders – Department of Arts, Museums & Cultural Heritage
Provincie Bestuur Oost-Vlaanderen – Dienst 91 Kunst & Cultuur en 92 Monumentenzorg en Cultuur Patrimonium
2 Welsonplein, 9000 **Gent**
Tel: 9-267 7200 Fax: 9-267 7299
E-Mail: kunst.en.cultur@oost-vlaanderen.be
cultureel adviseur Andrea de Kegel
Role & Services: promote cultural activities in the province East-Flanders

Province of West-Flanders – Cultural Service
Provincie West-Vlaanderen – Provinciale dienst voor Cultuur
Koning Leopold III laan 41, 8200 **Bruges**
Tel: 50-403 111 Fax: 50-403 100
E-Mail: bb:province@west_vlanderen.be
president Lodo Valcke
Role & Services: promote cultural activities in the province West-Flanders

Stedelyke Dienst voor Cultuur
A.C.T. Brugse Vrije, Burg 11, 8000 **Bruges**
Tel: 50-448 272 Fax: 50-448 280
director Freddy Smoaders
Role & Services: promote local cultural activities

BOSNIA & HERZEGOVINA (+387)

Ministry of Education, Science, Culture, and Sports of Federation of Bosnia-Herzegovina
Mak Dizdar Str 3, 71000 **Sarajevo**
Tel: 71-663 691/664 594/663 757 Fax: 71-663 693/664 381
minister Fahrudin Rizvanbegovic; deputy for culture Asaf Dzanic
Comments: Please contact the embassy in your country if you have problems in contacting this organisation; also has office in Mostar

Ministry of Education, Science, Culture, and Sports of Federation of Bosnia-Herzegovina
Adema Buca 34, 88000 **Mostar**
Tel: 88-580 011/012/013/014 Fax: 88-580 011/012/013/014
minister Fahrudin Rizvanbegovic; deputy for culture Asaf Dzanic
Comments: Please contact the embassy in your country if you have problems in contacting this organisation; also has office in Sarajevo

BULGARIA (+359)

Ministry of Culture of Bulgaria
17 Al.Stamboliisky Blvd, 1000 **Sofia**
Tel: 2-86111 Fax: 2-981 8145
minister of culture Emma Moskova; vice ministers Nikolai Poliakov, Panteley Tzankov, Maria Roussinova; secretary general Velitchka Filipova; theatre centre director Stefan Jankov; book centre director Svetozar Jekov; music and dance centre director Momtchil Gueorguiev; director, centre for museum and art gallery Zonja Drajeva; director, centre for films Dimitar Dereliev

CROATIA (+385)

Ministry of Culture of Croatia
Ministarstvo kulture
Trg burze 6, 10000 **Zagreb**
Tel: 1-456 9000 Fax: 1-461 0489
minister Bozo Biskupic

CYPRUS (+357)

Ministry of Education and Culture
Corner of Thoukydides and Kimon Streets, 1434 **Nicosia**
Tel: 2-800 601 Fax: 2-426 349
E-Mail: roc1@cytanet.com.cy
minister Ouranios Ioannides

Cultural Services of the Ministry of Education & Culture
20 Byron Avenue, 1437 **Nicosia**
Tel: 2-302 442/571/919 Fax: 2-673 565
acting director Stelios A Hadjistyllis; senior cultural officer Eleni S Nikita; cultural officers A George Moleskis, Pavlos Paraskeva, Eleni Papademetriou

CZECH REPUBLIC (+420)

Ministry of Culture of the Czech Republic
Ministerstvo kultury Ceské republiky
PB 214, 164 41 **Praha** 6
Tel: 2-5708 5111 Fax: 2-2432 3053
Internet: www.mkcr.cz
E-Mail: durtj@mkcr.cz
minister of culture Pavel Dostal; head of dept of arts Pavla Petrova (tel: 2-2432 0059, email: petrovap@mkcr.cz); responsible for theatre Natasa Zichova (tel: 2-5708 5213, email: zichova@mkcr.cz); responsible for music Anna Chorvàtovà (tel: 2-2431 0559, email: chorvata@mkcr.cz)
Role & Services: central state administration department dealing with performing arts (music, theatre, dance, ballet, mime etc.), visual arts, art education, museums, galleries, national heritage, matters of churches and religious societies, media (radio and TV broadcasting, press incl. non-periodicals, publishing, literature and libraries, copyright) *Comments:* visiting address: Milady Horàkové 139, 164 41 Praha 6

DENMARK (+45)

• Federal

Ministry for Cultural Affairs
Kulturministeriet
Nybrogade 2, Postbox 2140, 1015 **Copenhagen** K
Tel: 3392 3370 Fax: 3391 3388
Internet: www.kulturnet.dk
E-Mail: min@kum.dk
minister for culture Elsebeth Gerner Nielsen; permanent undersecretary & head of department Susan Marker

Danish Cultural Institute
Det Danske Kulturinstitut
Kultorvet 2, 1175 **Copenhagen** K
Tel: 3313 5448 Fax: 3315 1091
Internet: www.dankultur.dk
E-Mail: dankultur@dankultur.dk
secretary general Finn Andersen
Role & Services: independent institution under the Danish Ministry of Cultural Affairs which aims to inform about Danish life and promote cultural cooperation; it has offices in Brussels, Hannover, Edinburgh, Vienna, Kecskemét, Gdynia, Riga, Tallinn and Vilnius
Comments: main international operator for the Danish Ministry of Culture

• Regional Councils

Role & Services: Denmark is divided into 275 local authority areas, each of which is administered by a democratically elected council ('Borough Council', where appropriate), assembled in 14 counties, each of which is administered by a county council. Two councils, the City of Copenhagen and the Borough of Frederiksberg, are responsible for both municipal and county administration in their areas.

Århus Amtsråd
Lyseng Allé 1, 8270 **Højbjerg**
Tel: 8944 6666 Fax: 8944 6990(culture dept)
amtsskoledirektør Bo Johannsen; director of culture Lars Vildbrad
Role & Services: regional authority responsible for education and cultural matters

County Council of Bornholm – Dept. of Culture & Social Affairs
Bornholms Amtsråd
Ullasvej 23, 3700 **Rønne**
Tel: 5695 6000 Fax: 5695 7397
Internet: www.bornholm.dk/amtet
forvaltningschef Sinn Lykkegaard
Role & Services: regional authority responsible for education and cultural matters

Frederiksberg kommune
Kulturdirektoratet, Frederiksberg Rådhus, 2000 **Frederiksberg**
Tel: 3819 2121 Fax: 3888 0409
E-Mail: raadhyset@frederiksberg.dk
kulturdirektør Ivar Koed
Role & Services: regional authority responsible for education and cultural matters

Frederiksborg County
2 Kongens Vænge, 3400 **Hillerød** PK
Tel: 4820 5000 Fax: 4820 5399
E-Mail: jam@fa.dk
director Jan Magnussen
Role & Services: regional authority responsible for education, industry and cultural matters

Fyns Amt
Ørbækvej 100, 5220 **Odense** SØ
Tel: 6556 1000 Fax: 6556 1056
Internet: www.fyns-amt.dk
E-Mail: fyns-amt@fyns-amt.dk
direcør Keld Brondbjerg; head director Max Rasmussen
Role & Services: regional authority responsible for education and cultural matters

County of Copenhagen, Cultural Department
Stationsparken 27, 2600 **Glostrup**
Tel: 4322 2222/2354 Fax: 4322 2350 (culture dept.)
Internet: www.kbhamt.dk
head of cultural department Henning Thomsen; head of cultural division Jens Nielsen
Role & Services: regional authority responsible for education and cultural matters

Nordjyllands Amt
Niels Bohrsvej 30, 9220 **Aalborg** Ø
Tel: 9635 1000 Fax: 9815 7177 (culture dept.)
E-Mail: wg@nja.dk
amtsskoledirektør Peter Korsbü
Role & Services: regional authority responsible for education and cultural matters

Ribe Amt
Sorsigvej 35, 6760 **Ribe**
Tel: 7542 4200 Fax: 7542 4911
Internet: www.ribeamt.dk
E-Mail: ribeamt@ribeamt.dk
county director Bent Peter Larsen; administration: education and cultural, disability, childrens' and adults', pay and personnel, building depts, staff course centre Kirsten Kornum; cultural matters: cultural advisor Oyrite Andersen
Role & Services: the county of Ribe spends DDK 10m a year on facilities as the West Jutland Symphony Orchestra, museums, drama, Esbjerg Ensemble, The New Opera, various cultural projects

Ringkjøbing Amtsråd
Østergade 41, 6950 **Ringkøbing**
Tel: 9675 3000 Fax: 9675 3080 (culture dept.)
Internet: www.ringamt.dk
E-Mail: ringkjoebing-amt@rangamt.dk
direktør Hans Christen Vestergaard
Role & Services: regional authority responsible for education and cultural matters

Roskilde Amt/Amtsgarden
Postboks 170, Køgevej 80, 4000 **Roskilde**
Tel: 4632 3232 Fax: 4632 0483
Internet: www.ar.dk
E-Mail: uktmj@ra.dk
forvaltningschef Ole Hvidesten-Rasmussen
Role & Services: regional authority responsible for education and cultural matters

Sønderjyllands Amtsråd
Skelbækvej 2, 6200 **Aabenraa**
Tel: 7433 5050 Fax: 7433 5151
Internet: www.sja.dk
E-Mail: amtet@sja.dk
forvaltningschef Lars Creutz; kontorchef Kern Haurum Pedersen; vicekontorchef Erling Jørgensen; vicekontorchef Finn Degn; kontorchef Karsten Sauer (udd.); kontorchef Gunnar Lausten (spec.)
Role & Services: regional authority responsible for education and cultural matters

Storstrøms Amtsråd
Parkvej 37, 4800 **Nykøbing** F
Tel: 5482 3232 Fax: 5482 2182
E-Mail: stoa@ff.stam.dk
amtsskoledirektør Hans Stige Hansen
Role & Services: regional authority responsible for education and cultural matters

Vejle Amt
Damhaven 12, 7100 **Vejle**
Tel: 7583 5333 Fax: 7943 4365
Internet: www.vejleamt.dk
E-Mail: vejleamt@vejleamt.dk
amtsskoledirektør Pelle Lund

Vestajællands Amtsråd
Alléen 15, 4180 **Sorø**
Tel: 5787 2533 Fax: 5787 2025
Internet: www.vestamt.dk
E-Mail: vestamt@vestamt.dk
head directør Bent Michaelson

Viborg Amt
Skottenborg 26, 8800 **Viborg**
Tel: 8727 1700 Fax: 8662 3933
E-Mail: viborgamt@vibamt.dk
county director of administration Niels Högberg

ESTONIA (+372)

• Federal

Ministry of Culture of the Republic of Estonia
Kultuuriministeerium
Suur-Karja 23, 10140 **Tallinn**
Tel: 6-282 222 Fax: 6-282 200
Internet: www.kul.ee
E-Mail: Min@kul.ee
minister Signe Kivi; secretary Monika Grigor

• Regional

Council of Culture and Education of Harju County Government
Harju Maavalitsuse Kultuuri-ja haridusosakond
Roosikarantsi 12, 10119 **Tallinn**
Tel: 2-666 984
head of department Enn Kasemaa

Council of Education of Hiiumaa Country Government
Hiiu Maavalitsuse haridusosakond
Leigeri väljak 5, 92401 **Kärdla**
Tel: 46-31128
E-Mail: haridus@mv.hiiumaa.ee
head of department Ermo Mäeots

Council of Education of Ida-Virumaa County Government
Ida-Viru Maavalitsuse Kultuuriosakond
Keskväljak 1, 41531 **Jõhvi**
Tel: 33-21204
E-Mail: leo@ivmv.ee
director Leo Raidma

Department of Culture of Järva County Government
Järva Maavalitsuse Kultuuriosakond
Rüütli 25, 72713 **Paide**
Tel: 38-59624
head of department Aivo Toomistu

Department of Culture of Jõgeva County Government
Jõgeva Maavalitsuse Kultuuriosakond
Suur 3, 48306 **Jõgeva**
Tel: 77-66342
E-Mail: arne@jogevamv.ee
head of department Arne Tegelmann

Department of Culture of Pärnu County Government
Pärnu Maavalitsuse Kultuuriosakond
Akadeemia 2, 80088 **Pärnu**
Tel: 44-79768
head of department Aet Maatee

Department of Culture of Põlva County Government
Põlva Maavalitsuse Kultuuriosakond
Kesk 20, 63308 **Põlva**
Tel: 79-94618
head of department Peeter Aas

Department of Education of Rapla County Government
Rapla Maavalitsuse Haridusosakond
Tallinna mnt. 14, 79513 **Rapla**
Tel: 48-55538
E-Mail: marju@raplamv.ee
culture counsellor Marju Sarv

Department of Culture of Saaremaa County
Saare Maavalitsuse Kutluuriosakond
Lossi 1, 93816 **Kuressaare**
Tel: 45-33441
director Lea Kuldsepp

Department of Education & Culture of Tartumaa County
Tartumaa hariduse-ja kultuuriosakond
Riia 15, 51014 **Tartu**
Tel: 7-305 261
head of department Peep Laanes

Department of Culture of Valga County Government
Valga Maavalitsuse Kultuuri- ja haridusosakond
Kesk 12, 68203 **Valga**
Tel: 76-66120
Internet: www.valgamv.ee
head of culture department Valeri Talu

Department of Culture and Education of Viljandi County Government
Viljandi Maavalitsuse Kultuuri- ja haridusosakond
Vabaduse plats 2, 71020 **Viljandi**
Tel: 43-30439
E-Mail: gunnar@viljandimaa.ee
head of culture department Gunnar Leets

Department of Culture and Education of Lääne-Virumaa County Government
Lääne-Viru Maavalitsuse Kultuuri- ja haridusosakond
Kreutzwaldi 5, 44314 **Rakvere**
Tel: 32-43727
E-Mail: jaan@l-virumv.ee
head of department Jaan Kulver

Department of Culture and Sport of Võru County Government
Võru Maavalitsuse Kultuuri- ja Spordiosakond
Jüri 12, 65620 **Voru**
Tel: 78-68301 Fax: 78-68302
E-Mail: peeter@mv.werro.ee
head of department Peeter Laurson

Department of Culture and Education of Lääne County Government
Lääne Maavalitsuse haridus- ja kultuuriosakond
Sadama 28, 90502 **Haapsalu**
Tel: 47-44182
head of department Ly Pukspuu

• Municipal

Department of Culture of Kohtla Järve City Government
Kohtla-Järve Linnavalitsuse Kultuuriosakond
Keskallee 19, 30321 **Kohtla-Järve**
Tel: 33-78560
head of department Artur Seppern

Department of Culture of Pärnu City Government
Pärnu Linnavalitsuse kultuuri- ja spordiamet
Nikolai 8, 80002 **Pärnu**
Tel: 44-41252 Fax: 44-44167
head of department Andrus Haugas

City Council of Culture of Tallinn
Tallinna kultuuriamet
Vabaduse väljak 10b, 10141 **Tallinn**
Tel: 6-404 606/8 Fax: 6-404 612
Internet: linn.tallinn.ee
director Ene Vohu

Department of Culture & Sports of Tartu City Government
Tartu Linnavalitsuse kultuuri-ja spordiosakond
Kalevi 24, 51010 **Tartu**
Tel: 7-432 252
head of department Vello Lauring

FAROE ISLANDS (+298)

Ministry of Education & Culture
Falkavegur 6, Box 3279, 110 **Tórshavn**
Tel: 355 050 (culture) Fax: 355 055
E-Mail: umms@umms.fo
minister of education & culture Signar Á Brúnni; director of the department of culture and research Jóannes Dalsgaard

FINLAND (+358)

• Federal

Ministry of Education
Opetusministeriö
Meritullinkatu 10, PO Box 293, 00171 **Helsinki**
Tel: 9-134 171 Fax: 9-135 9335
Internet: www.minedu.fi
minister of culture Suvi Lindén (fax 1341 6978); counsellor for cultural affairs (European integration) Risto Kivelä; counsellor for cultural affairs (visual arts, crafts and design) Kari Poutasuo; planning officer Mikko Cortés-Tellez; senior adviser Leena Laaksonen; officer, cultural affairs (drama) Helena Suomela; officer, cultural affairs (literature, dance, children's culture) Mervi Tiensuu-Nylund; officer, cultural affairs (music) Marja-Liisa Morri; director, department of culture Rauno Anttila (fax: 1341 6987); special government advisor (media culture, copyright affairs) Jukka Liedes
Comments: is led by 2 ministers, one mainly responsible for education and science, one mainly responsible for cultural affairs, for the planning and implementation of cultural policies; the supervision of central government arts administration: the Arts Council of Finland and regional Arts Councils; the supervision of state cultural institutes; copyright questions and matters relating to audiovisual culture

Arts Council of Finland
Taiteen Keskustoimikunta
Maneesikatu 7, PO Box 293, 00171 **Helsinki**
Tel: 9-134 171 Fax: 9-1341 7069
Internet: www.minedu.fi/artcoun
E-Mail: eija.ristimaki@minedu.fi
secretary general, central arts council Jarmo Malkavaara (email: jarmo.malkavaara@minedu.fi); chairperson Risto Ruohonen; secretary, national council for dance Sanna Rekola (tel: 9-1733 6512, email: srekola@fng.fi); secretary, national council for music Marja-Leena Häkkinen (marja-leena.hakkinen@siba.fi); secretary, national council for theatre Leena Hyvärinen (9-185 3363); information unit Ritva Mitchell (9-1341 7382)
Comments: with the 9 national Arts Councils (NACs), which include dance, music and theatre, and 13 regional Arts Councils it is part of the system responsible for the planning and implementation of arts policies under the supervision of the Ministry of Education; its 9 members are the chairs of the NACs and 4 others appointed by the Council of State;
acts as an arms-length body in matters relating to awarding state grants to artists and as a permanent expert and advisory body to the Ministry concerning the planning and implementing of arts policies; it ensures cooperation between the NACs and proposes appropriations to be included in Finland's arts budget; its Research and Information Unit carries out cultural policy research and international cooperation; Unit also maintains cultural policy library; the NACs award annual state grants to artists.

• Regional Arts Councils

Role & Services: The task of the 13 Regional Arts Councils (RACs) is to foster the arts and culture at the regional level. They monitor the development of cultural life at that level and maintain contacts with and promote cooperation between regional arts institutions and organisations. They award grants to artists and grant subsidies to various cultural organisations and events. They do not financially support theatres, orchestras or museums which receive state subsidies from the central government and are maintained by municipalities. Finnish provinces are not autonomous regions, and provincial government is only an extension of central government administration. RACs, however, have independent decision making power within the limits of the appropriations they receive from the state budget. The role of RACs within the system of public cultural policies seems to be to a greater extent the promotion of professional arts and artists, and less the promotion of cultural activities and amateur arts

Regional Arts Council for Central Finland
Keski-Suomen läänin taidetoimikunta
Pl. 41, 40101 **Jyväskylä**
Tel: 20-517 141 Fax: 20-517 4232
Internet:
www.intermin.fi/sm/laanit/ks/taide.htm
E-Mail: tiina.nurminen@kslh.intermin.fi
general secretary Tiina Nurminen

Regional Arts Council for Häme
Hämeen taidetoimikunta
PL 150, Birger Jaarlinkatu 15, 13101 **Hämeenlinna**
Tel: 20-516 2043 Fax: 20-516 2045
Internet: www.tavastia.sci.fi
E-Mail: taideposti@tavastia.sci.fi
general secretary Osmo Vuorenoja (email: osmo.vuorenoja@eslh.intermin.fi)

Arts Council of North Savo
Kuninkaankatu 15, 70100 **Kuopio**
Tel: 17-262 5330 Fax: 17-262 5408
Internet:
www.mediacenter.kuopio.fi/pstaidetoimi-unntn
E-Mail: arja.laitinen@nic.fi
general secretary Arja Laitinen; secretary Tuula Koistinen (email: tuula.koistinen.nic.fi)
Role & Services: award grants to artists in Northern Savo region, grants are for 1,3 or 5 years; allocate subsidies to artists, organisations and associations operating in Northern Savo region

Arts Council of Southeast Finland
Kaakkois-Suomen taidetoimikunta
Salpausselänkatu 22, PO Box 301, 45101 **Kouvola**
Tel: 20-516 4094 Fax: 5-311 5273
Internet:
www.intermin.fi/suom/laanit/eslh/sivistys/z-tt-nk.htm
E-Mail: matti.nieminen@eslh.intermin.fi
general secretary Matti Nieminen
Role & Services: award grants to artists and other financial support to art societies and festivals, can also promote international art contacts

Arts Council of Lapland
Lapin läänin taidetoimikunta
PL 8278, 96101 **Rovaniemi**
Tel: 16-327 7200 Fax: 16-310 663
E-Mail: lapin.taidetoimikunta@crossroads.fi
general secretary Kari Laine
Comments: visiting address: Rovakatu 29, 96101 Rovaniemi

Arts Council of Etelä-Savo
Vuorikatu 3A, 50100 **Mikkeli**
Tel: 20-516 6020 Fax: 20-516 6031
Internet:
www.intermin.fi/sm/laanit/mlh/ttkkoti1.htm
E-Mail: raimo.manninen@pp.kolumbus.fi
general secretary Raimo Manninen

Arts Council of North Karelia
Pohjois-Karjalan taidetoimikunta
PL 90, Torikatu 36 B, 80101 **Joensuu**
Tel: 20-516 8028 Fax: 20-516 8030
E-Mail: eila.nevalainen@islh.intermin.fi
general secretary Eila Nevalainen
Role & Services: to foster the arts and culture at a regional level; it monitors the development of cultural life and promotes cooperation between regional arts institutions and organisations; it awards grants to artists, cultural organisations and events

Regional Arts Council for the Province of Oulu
Oulun läänin taidetoimikunta
PO Box 293, 90109 **Oulu**
Tel: 20-517 181 Fax: 8-311 0735
Internet: www.intermin.fi/sm/laanit/olh/taide
E-Mail: maija.kotilainen@olh.intermin.fi
general secretary Marja-Riitta Vainikkala
Role & Services: to follow, promote, and evaluate the development of the arts in the province, promote the artistic work of professional artists, and the international cultural co-operation in the region, maintain contact with the regional arts and cultural organisations, institutions, and the regional government, initiate projects to promote the arts in the province

Arts Council of Turku Region, The
Varsinais-Suomen taidetoimikunta
Itäinen Rantakatu 42, Box 51, 20801 **Turku**
Tel: 20-517 2131/50-351 3310 Fax: 20-517 2138
E-Mail: maria.merikanto@lslh.intermin.fi
general secretary Maria Merikanto
Role & Services: promoting arts in Turku region

Arts Council of Uusimaa
Uudenmaan taidetoimikunta
PL 110, 00521 **Helsinki**
Tel: 20-516 3146 Fax: 20-516 3138
Internet:
www.intermin.fi/sm/laanit/ulh/taide.htm
E-Mail: liisa.heinonen@eslh.intermin.fi
secretary general Liisa Heinonen; chairman of the council Hannes Markkula; regional artists Irmeli Kokko, Esa Laaksonen, Katja Tukiainen; art producers Irmeli Kokko, Esa Laaksonen
Role & Services: increase regional equality in the area of culture in the area; safeguard and improve the position of professional artists; promote amateur activities in the area of arts; activate municipalities, groups and individuals; express views on the part of the province in the nationwide cultural debate
Comments: alternative email:
artinfo@ulh.kuvernet.kuvernet.mailnet.fi

Regional Arts Council of Vaasa
Vaasan läänin taidetoimikunta
POB 200, Wolffintie 35, 65101 **Vaasa**
Tel: 6-317 1116 Fax: 6-317 1119
secretary general Reia Nummatärva; co-ordinator Helena Escola (323 6147)
Role & Services: promotes the rights of regional artists; annually funds individuals and organisations; close contact with regional artists

FRANCE (+33)

• Federal

Ministère de la Culture et de la Communication
3 rue de Valois, 75001 **Paris**
Tel: 1-4015 8000 Fax: 1-4261 3577
ministre Catherine Trautmann; directeur du cabinet Marc Sadaoui; chef de cabinet Christophe Castaner; chargée de la presse et de la communication de la ministre Marylène Courivaud (tel: 4015 8026, fax: 4015 8050); contact bureau du cabinet, service documentation Laurence Nicod (tel: 4015 8778); pr Beatrice Clerc-Bastide; documentation service Jean-Paul Ciret

Ministère de la Culture et de la Communication
Direction de l'Administration Générale, 3 rue de Valois, 75001 **Paris**
Tel: 1-4015 8000/8418 Fax: 1-4015 8002
E-Mail: jaudon@culture.fr
directeur Frédérique Scanvic; directeur adjoint Christophe Vallet; responsable de mission Chantal Jaudon (8062); adjointe Elisabeth Nadaud (8372)
Comments: two institutions are directly related to this direction: Centre national d' art et de Culture Georges Pompidou [président Jean-Jacques Aillagon, directeur général Guillaume Cerutti (4478 1233)]; Ecole nationale du patrimoine [directeur Jean-Pierre Bady (4441 1641)]; alternative e-mail: pascale.marie@culture.fr

Ministère de la Culture et de la Communication (DMDTS)
Direction de la Musique, de la Danse, du Théâtre et des Spectacles, 53 rue Saint Dominique, 75007 **Paris**
Tel: 1-4015 8884 Fax: 1-4015 8980/8993
directeur Dominique Wallon; communication et information Nicole Gasser
Comments: the result of a merger between Direction de la Musique et de la Danse and the Direction du Théâtre et des Spectacles; further details were not available at time of going to print

Ministère de la Culture et de la Communication
Département des Affaires Internationales, 12 rue de Louvois, 75002 **Paris**
Tel: 1-4015 3727 Fax: 1-4015 3740
chef du département Alain Lombard; chef adjoint, chargé des affaires financières Louis Poulhès; secrétaire général Philippe Albou; communication Laurent Maillaud (4015 3715); documentation Christine Poirié (4015 3754)
Role & Services: co-ordinates and develops the ministry's international work in promoting French culture and art; works directly with the minister's cabinet

Ministère de la Culture et de la Communication
Département de l'Information et de la Communication, 3 rue de Valois, 75001 **Paris**
Tel: 1-4015 8689/8751 Fax: 1-4015 8172
E-Mail: marouani@valois.culture.fr
chef de département Jean Paul Ciret (4015 8120); chargée de mission Brigitte Olivier (4015 8294); press office Sophie Bazerolle, Marjorie Lecointre
Comments: publishes a newsletter (bimonthly, free), contact: Paul Henri Doro (tel: 1-4015 8365, email: doro@valoris.culture.fr); and two yearbooks: Festivals et expositions (May) and Saison Culturelle (October)

Association Française d'Action Artistique (AFAA)
1 bis avenue de Villars, 75327 **Paris** Cedex 07
Tel: 1-5369 8300 Fax: 1-5369 3300
Internet: www.afaa.asso.fr
director Olivier Poivre-D'Arvor; secrétaire général Claude Mathis; chef des services administratifs Pierre Bonzi; responsable de la musique, danse et de la théâtre Jean-Marc Granet-Bouffartigue; responsable des arts plastiques Marie-Paule Serre; responsable du théâtre José-Emmanuel Gonçalvès; chargée de l'information Claire Magnac
Role & Services: defends and promotes French culture abroad, finances foreign tours by French companies, encourages visits from foreign companies, encourages coproductions with French companies *Comments:* attached to the Ministère des Affaires Etrangères working with the Ministère de la Culture and to the Ministère de la coopération, also works with the French Institutes, Alliances Française and Embassies abroad

Fonds pour la Création Musicale (FCM)
141 rue la Fayette, 75010 **Paris**
Tel: 1-4878 5060 Fax: 1-4596 0697
directeur Bruno Boutleux; chargée de mission pour les programmes disques, vidéos et l'etranger Isabelle Boivin; chargé de mission pour le spectacle vivant, les festivals et formation Denis Turmel
Role & Services: supports actions in the field of diffusion and performing arts and artists' formation; protects the general interest and helps the structures in needs

• Dir. Regionales des Affaires Culturelles (DRACs)

Role & Services: DRACs under the authority of French administrative préfectures at regional and departmental level, are charged with the implementation of ministerial priorities as adapted to the needs of each region, and the promotion of state cultural activity. DRACs also serve in advisory capacity, working with local groups and others active in local cultural affairs to ensure coherent public involvement in cultural development of the region. Their role involves all areas of cultural activity within the ministry including subsidies, museums, public readings, music, dance, theatre, visual arts, art education, cinema and the cultural environment in general. The director of each DRAC is directly in charge of all the functions listed above.

Direction Régionale des Affaires Culturelles d'Alsace
Palais du Rhin, 2 place de la République, 67082 **Strasbourg** Cedex
Tel: 3-8815 5700/71 Fax: 3-8875 6095
E-Mail: catherine.marco@culture.fr
directeur Jean-Luc Bredel; théâtre et action culturelle Frantz Delplanque; musique et danse Sophie Mège; information, documentation et communication Catherine Marco; assistante Annie Höckel

Direction Régionale des Affaires Culturelles Aquitaine
54 rue Magendie, 33074 **Bordeaux** Cedex
Tel: 5-5795 0202 Fax: 5-5795 0125
E-Mail: m.parisot@culture.fr
directeur Jean-Michel Perthod; théâtre et action culturelle Jean-René Girard; musique et danse Patrick Le Dauphin-Dubourg; communication et documentation Martine Parisot
Comments: see also Promoters

Direction Régionale des Affaires Culturelles d'Auvergne
4 rue Pascal, BP 378,
63010 **Clermont-Ferrand** Cedex 1
Tel: 4-7341 2700 Fax: 4-7341 2769
E-Mail: ricard@culture.fr
directeur Dominique Paillarse; affaires générales et financières Patrice Ducher; livre et lecture Caroline Durand; arts plastiques Stéphane Doré; théâtre et action culturelle Daniel Poignant; musique et danse Philippe Bucherer; communication presse Marie-Claire Ricard; documentation Jean-Luc Lascar
Comments: see also Promoters

Direction Régionale des Affaires Culturelles de Basse-Normandie
13 Bis rue St Ouen, 14052 **Caen** Cedex 04
Tel: 2-3138 3940 Fax: 2-3123 8465
E-Mail: girot@bnormand.culture.fr
directeur régional des affaires culturelles Elisabeth Gautier-Desvaux (3138 3942); action culturelle et théâtre Gérard Brision (3138 3948); communication, information et documentation Jocelyne Girot (3138 3961); musique et danse Gérard Baille (3138 3976); programmation, coordination, contrôle de gestion Lionel Béziel (3138 3968) *Comments:* see also Promoters

Direction Régionale des Affaires Culturelles de Bourgogne
Hôtel Chartraire de Montigny, 41 rue Vannerie, 21000 **Dijon**
Tel: 3-8068 5050 Fax: 3-8068 5099/8031 6862
E-Mail: bourgogne@bourgogn.culture.fr
directeur t.b.a.; théâtre et action culturelle Ghislain Mille; musique et danse Mireille Pic; attachée principale adjointe au directeur Marie-Josèphe Gaillard; communication Stéphanie Augeyre *Comments:* see also Promoters

Direction Régionale des Affaires Culturelles de Bretagne
Hôtel de Blossac, 6 rue du Chapitre, 35044 **Rennes** Cedex
Tel: 2-9929 6767 Fax: 2-9929 6799
E-Mail: pichon@bretagne.culture.fr
directeur Raymond Lachat; musique et danse Anne-Christine Micheu; communication et documentation Hervé Musse; théâtre et spectacle Bernadette Rousseaux
Comments: other email: musse@bretagne.culture.fr; see also Promoters

Direction Régionale des Affaires Culturelles du Centre
6 rue de la manufacture, 45043 **Orléans** Cedex 1
Tel: 2-3878 8500 Fax: 2-3878 8599
E-Mail: drac.centre@wanadoo.fr
directeur Alain Marais; coordination action culturelle Mr Normand; théâtre et action culturelle Kattel Pouessen; musique et danse Joël Forgues; communication Jean-Louis Gauthier
Comments: see also Promoters

Direction Régionale des Affaires Culturelles de Champagne-Ardenne
3 rue du Faubourg Saint-Antoine,
51037 **Chalons-en-Champagne** Cedex
Tel: 3-2670 3650 Fax: 3-2670 4371
E-Mail: rollet@culture.fr
directeur Richard Lagrange; théâtre & action culturelle Marie-Claire Riou; musique & danse Michel Louis Richard
Comments: see also Promoters

Direction Régionale des Affaires Culturelles de Corse
19 Cours Napoléon, BP 301, 20181 **Ajaccio** Cedex 1
Tel: 4-9551 5213/5215 Fax: 4-9521 2069
E-Mail: pierre.berthier@culture.fr
directeur Pierre Berthier (9551 5212); action culturelle et spectacles vivants Marie-Jeanne Nicoli; communication, information Matthieu Coti
Comments: see also Promoters

Direction Régionale des Affaires Culturelles de Franche-Comté
7 rue Charles Nodier, 25043 **Besançon** Cedex
Tel: 3-8165 7200 Fax: 3-8165 7272
directrice Madame De Boisjolly; théâtre et action culturelle Dominique Daeschler; musique et danse Jean-Marc Vernier; communication Françoise Josseron
Comments: see also Promoters

Direction Régionale des Affaires Culturelles de Haute-Normandie
2 rue Saint-Sever, 76032 **Rouen** Cédex
Tel: 2-3563 6160 Fax: 2-3572 8460
E-Mail: xerri@hnormand.culture.fr
director Sylvane Tarst-Gillery; adjoint au directeur Thierry Delamare; secrétaire générale Isabelle Revol; conseillère pour le théâtre François Bauer; conseillère pour l'action culturelle Sophie Bardet; conseiller pour la musique et la danse Jérôme Alexandre; chargée de communication Natacha Xerri
Comments: see also Promoters

Direction Régionale des Affaires Culturelles de l'Ile de France
98, rue de Charonne, 75011 **Paris**
Tel: 1-5606 5000 Fax: 1-5606 5248
directeur Alain Van Der Malière; directrice adjoint Anne-Marie Le Guérel; action culturelle Yvette Masson; musique et danse Pierre Costes, Catherine Reflé; théâtre Yves Chevallier, Edithe Rappoport, Brigitte Perrault
Comments: see also Promoters

Direction Régionale des Affaires Culturelles de Languedoc-Roussillon
Hôtel de Grave, 5 rue Salle l'Evêque, BP 20 51,
34024 **Montpellier** Cedex 1
Tel: 4-6702 3200 Fax: 4-6702 3204
E-Mail: eid@languedo.culture.fr
directeur Michel Fontes; théâtre Jean-Claude Loubière; musique et danse François-Victor Lepargneur; chargée communication Jakline Eid;
action culturelle Isabel Martinez
Comments: see also Promoters

Direction Régionale des Affaires Culturelles du Limousin
6 rue Haute de la Comédie, 87036 **Limoges** Cedex
Tel: 5-5545 6645 Fax: 5-5545 6644
directeur Jean-Luc Massy; théâtre et action culturelle Richard Madjarev; musique et danse Fabrice Linon; centre d'information et de documentation communication, accueil Catherine Catinus
Comments: see also Promoters

Direction Régionale des Affaires Culturelles de Lorraine
6 place de Chambre, 57045 **Metz** Cedex 1
Tel: 3-8756 4100 Fax: 3-8775 2828
E-Mail: silistrini@culture.fr
directeur Jacques Charlot; théâtre, cinéma, audiovisuel René Peilloux; musique et danse François Derudder; communication Isabelle Wagner; documentation t.b.a.; arts plastiques Jacques Bayle
Comments: see also Promoters

Direction Régionale des Affaires Culturelles de Midi-Pyrénées
Place Alphonse Jourdain, 56 rue du Taur, BP 811, 31080 **Toulouse** Cedex 6
Tel: 5-6230 3100 Fax: 5-6123 1271
E-Mail: kowalewski@culture.fr
directeur Didier Deschamps; adjoint au directeur Pierre-Jean Dupuy; responsable financier Françoise Mezergues; théâtre Jean-Michel Treguer; action culturelle Francis Luttiau; musique et danse Francis Barascou; communication et information Anne-Françoise Kowalewski; conseillers musées Charles Chaettel, Martine Jaoul
Comments: see also Promoters

Direction régionale des Affaires Culturelles de Nord-Pas-de-Calais
Hôtel Scrive, 1 rue du Lombard, 59800 **Lille**
Tel: 3-2006 8758 Fax: 3-2074 0720
E-Mail: yves.ledun@nord.culture.fr
directeur Richard Martineau; musique et danse Marc Le Bourhis; théâtre et action culturelle Denis Decelerck; documentation Nicole Moussarie; info. Yves Ledun
Comments: see also Promoters

Direction Régionale des Affaires Culturelles des Pays de la Loire
BP 63518, 1 rue Stanislas Baudry, 44035 **Nantes** Cedex 01
Tel: 2-4014 2300/2323 (centre d'info et documentation)
Fax: 2-4014 2301
E-Mail: ecormier@culture.fr (theatre)
directeur Michel Clement; adjointe au directeur chargée de l'aménagement culturel du territoire et service de coordination Chantal Dagault; service des affaires financières et générales Loic Brosseau; service communication Elisabeth Hodebourge de Verbois; responsable du centre d'information et de documentation générale Anne de Chanterac; conseiller pour l'action culturelle, le théâtre et le cinéma Elysabeth Cormier; conseiller pour la musique et la danse t.b.a. *Comments:* other e-mail: ruellan@culture.fr (music & dance); see also Promoters

Direction Régionale des Affaires Culturelles de Picardie
5, rue Henry Daussy, 80044 **Amiens** Cedex 1
Tel: 3-2297 3300 Fax: 3-2297 3356
E-Mail: maunier@picardie.culture.fr
directeur Yves Martial; musique et danse Christine Dogny; théâtre et action culturelle Fabrice Morio; communication Michel Maunier; arts plastiques Coline Le Neün; service livres et lecture t.b.a.
Comments: see also Promoters

Direction Régionale des Affaires Culturelles de Poitou-Charentes
Hôtel de Rochefort, 102 Grand'Rue, BP 553,|86020 **Poitiers** Cedex
Tel: 5-4936 3030 Fax: 5-4988 3202
E-Mail: duvigneau@culture.fr
directeur Jean-Pierre Pottier; théâtre et action culturelle Jean Claude Senechal; musique et danse Pierre Blanc; adjointe au directeur Claudine Trougnov; chargée de communication Madame Duvigneau
Comments: see also Promoters

Direction Régionale des Affaires Culturelles de Provence-Alpes-Côte d'Azur
23 Bld du Roi René, 13617 **Aix-en-Provence** Cedex 1
Tel: 4-4216 1900 Fax: 4-4238 0322
E-Mail: ledoux@provence.culture.fr (documentation)
directeur François de Banes Gardonne; théâtre et action culturelle Yves Olivier; musique et danse André Santelli; communication Alain Bez; documentation Mr Ledoux
Comments: see also Promoters

Direction Régionale des Affaires Culturelles de Rhône-Alpes
Le Grenier d'Abondance, 6 quai Saint-Vincent, 69283 **Lyon** Cedex 01
Tel: 4-7200 4400/49 (commun.) Fax: 4-7200 4330
E-Mail: kneubuhler@culture.fr
directeur Abraham Bengio; adjoint au directeur Pierre Sigaud; théâtre Mr Roussel; action culturelle Benoît Guillemont; musique et danse Laure Marcel-Berlioz, Laurent Van Kote; communication Michel Kneubühler; arts plastiques Marie-Claude Jeune, Alain Rérat
Comments: see also Promoters

GEORGIA (+995)

Ministry of Culture of Georgia
37 Rustaveli ave., 380008 **Tbilisi**
Tel: 32-932 255/987 430 Fax: 32-999 037
minister Valerian Asatiani; deputy minister Nino Kobakhidze; secretary Tina Tushkadze
Role & Services: central state administration department dealing with performing arts (music, theatre, dance, ballet, mime, etc), visual arts, art education, museums, galleries, libraries, national heritage, matters of churches

GERMANY (+49)

• Federal

Federal Government Commissioner for Cultural Affairs and the Media
Beauftragten der Bundesregierung für Anglegenheiten der Kultur und der Medien
c/o Bundesministerium des Innern, Postfach 170290, 53108 **Bonn**
Tel: 228-681-0 (switchboard)/562 096 (press)
Fax: 228-681 4665/561 808 (press)
E-Mail: posteingang@bmi.bund400.de
Staatsminister Dr Michael Naumann
Comments: visiting address: Graurheindorfer Str. 198, 53117 Bonn

Federal Ministry of Education and Research
Bundesministerium für Bildung und Forschung
53170 **Bonn**
Tel: 228-57-0 Fax: 228-572 094/573 601
E-Mail: bmbf@bmbf.bund400.de
Ministerin Edelgard Bulmahn; Persönliche Referentin Klaudia Seltmann; Leiter des Referates Öffentlichkeitsarbeit Dr. Irina Ehrhardt; Pressesprecherin Sabine Baun
Comments: visiting address: Heinemannstr 2, 53175 Bonn

Secretariat of the Standing Conference of the Ministers of Education and Cultural Affairs of the Federal States
Sekretariat der Ständigen Konferenz der Kultusminister der Länder
Postfach 2240, 53012 **Bonn**
Tel: 228-5010 Fax: 228-501 777
Internet: www.kmk.org
E-Mail: presse@kmk.org
Generalsekretär Prof. Dr. Erich Thies
Role & Services: coordinating cultural policy on a national level with the aim of representing the common interests of the cultural ministries of the Länder
Comments: visiting address: Lennéstr. 6, 53113 Bonn

Goethe-Institut
Postfach 190419, 80604 **München**
Tel: 89-159 210 Fax: 89-1592 1450
Internet: www.goethe.de
E-Mail: ZV@goethe.de
Präsident Prof. Hilmar Hoffmann; Generalsekretär Dr. Joachim Sartorius
Role & Services: promotes a wider knowledge abroad of the German language and fosters cultural cooperation with other countries *Comments:* there are 135 Goethe-Institut centres in 76 countries and 18 within Germany; visiting address: Dachauer Str. 122, 80637 München; postal address: Helene-Weber-Allee 1, 80637 München

• Regional

Baden-Württemberg Ministry for Science, Research and Arts
Baden-Württemberg Ministerium für Wissenschaft, Forschung und Kunst
Königstraße 46, 70173 **Stuttgart**
Tel: 711-279-0 Fax: 711-279 3080
Internet: www.mwk-bw.de
E-Mail: wissenschaftsministerium@mwk-bw.de
Minister Klaus von Trotha

Bavarian State Ministry for Science, Research and Arts
Bayerisches Staatsministerium für Wissenschaft, Forschung und Kunst
Salvatorstr. 2, 80333 **München**
Tel: 89-218 601 Fax: 89-2186 2800
Internet: www.stmokwk.bayern.de
E-Mail: poststelle@stmokwk.bayern.de
Staatsminister Hans Zehetmair

Senate Administration for Science, Research and Culture
Senatsverwaltung für Wissenschaft, Forschung und Kultur
Brunnenstr. 188-190, 10119 **Berlin**
Tel: 30-902 280 Fax: 30-90228-450
Internet: www.berlin.de
E-Mail: senwfk@berlin.snafu.de
Senator Peter Radunski; Pressesprecher Kultur Axel Wallrabenstein; Wissenschaft Kerstin Schneider

Ministry for Science, Research and Culture, Brandenburg
Ministerium für Wissenschaft, Forschung und Kultur des Landes, Brandenburg
Dortustr. 36, 14467 **Potsdam**
Tel: 331-866 4560 Fax: 331-866 4545
Internet: www.brandenburg.de/land/mwfk
E-Mail: mwfk@mwfk.brandenburg.de
Minister Steffen Reiche; Staatssekretär Prof. Dr. Friedrich Buttler; Abteilungsleiter Kultur Dr. Wilhelm Neufeldt; Pressesprecher Martin Gorholt

Ministry for Education and Science Research
Senator für Bildung und Wissenschaft
Rembertiring 8-12, 28195 **Bremen**
Tel: 421-361 4777 Fax: 421-361 4176
Minister Willi Lemke; Staatsrat Rainer Köttgen

Hamburg State Board for Culture
Kulturbehörde der Freien und Hansestadt Hamburg
Postfach 303081, 20310 **Hamburg**
Tel: 40-42824-0 Fax: 40-42824-209
Internet: www.hamburg.de
E-Mail: pressestelle@kb.hamburg.de
Senatorin Dr Christina Weiss
Comments: visiting address: Hohe Bleichen 22, 20354 Hamburg

Ministry for Science and Arts, Hessen
Hessisches Ministerium für Wissenschaft und Kunst
Rheinstraße 23-25, 65185 **Wiesbaden**
Tel: 611-323 551 Fax: 611-323 550
Internet: www.hmwk.hessen.de
E-Mail: pressestelle@hmwk.hessen.de
Staatsministerin Ruth Wagner; Staatssekretär Frank E. Portz; Abteilungsleiter Kultur MinDir Dr. Konrad Schacht

Ministerium für Bildung, Wissenschaft und Kultur Mecklenburg-Vorpommern
Werderstraße 124, 19055 **Schwerin**
Tel: 385-588-0/588 7040 Fax: 385-588 7087
Internet: www.kultus-mv.de
E-Mail: presse@kultus-mv.de
Leiter der Abteilung Kultur Reiner Lorenz (MDgt)

Lower Saxony Ministry for Science and Culture
Niedersächsisches Ministerium für Wissenschaft und Kultur
Leibnitzufer 9, 30169 **Hannover**
Tel: 511-120 (switchboard)/2604 (press) Fax: 511-120 2605
E-Mail: markus.hoppe@mwk.niedersachsen.de
Minister Thomas Oppermann

Minister for Work, Social Affairs, Urban Development, Culture and Sport
Ministerium für Arbeit, Soziales und Stadtentwicklung, Kultur und Sport
Breite Str. 31, 40213 **Düsseldorf**
Tel: 211-861 850 Fax: 211-8618 54444
Ministerin Ilse Brusis; Staatsekretär Dr Hans-Jürgen Baedeker; Kultur, Kirchen, Regionale Kulturförderung Theater, Musik, Kunst
Role & Services: support of cultural activities; consultation of theatres, orchestras, free artists, dance activities

Rhineland-Palatinate Ministry of Culture, Youth, Family and Women
Ministerium für Kultur, Jugend, Familie und Frauen Rheinland-Pfalz
Mittlere Bleiche 61, 55116 **Mainz**
Tel: 6131-160 Fax: 6131-162 878
Staatsministerin Dr Rose Götte

Ministry for Education, Culture and Science, Saarland
Ministerium für Bildung, Kultur und Wissenschaft
Postfach 102452, 66024 **Saarbrücken**
Tel: 681-503-0 Fax: 681-503 291
Internet: www.mbkw.saarland.de
E-Mail: presse@mbkw.saarland.de
Minister Henner Wittling
Comments: visiting address: Hohenzollernstrasse 60, 66117 Saarbrücken

Saxon Ministry of Science and Art
Sächsisches Staatsministerium für Wissenschaft und Kunst
Postfach 100920, 01076 **Dresden**
Tel: 351-564 6020 (presse)/6000 (minister)/6450 (kunst)
Fax: 351-564 6004 (minister)/6225 (press)
Internet: www.smwk.de
E-Mail: presse@smwk.sachsen.de
Staatsminister Prof. Dr. Hans Joachim Meyer; Leiter der Abteilung Kunst Dr. Reiner Zimmermann
Comments: visiting address: Wigardstrasse 17, 01097 Dresden

Kultusministerium des Landes Sachsen-Anhalt
Turmschanzenstr. 32, 39114 **Magdeburg**
Tel: 391-56701/3638 (pressestelle)
Fax: 391-567 3695/3775 (pressestelle)
E-Mail: brigitte.deckstein@mk.uni-magdeburg.de
Kultusminister Dr. Gerd Harms; Staatssekretäre Dr. Wolfgang Eichler, Dr. Bodo Richter; Pressesprecherin Dr. Brigitte Deckstein

Ministry of Education, Science, Research and Culture Schleswig-Holstein
Ministerin für Bildung, Wissenschaft, Forschung und Kultur des Landes Schleswig-Holstein
Brunswiker Straße 16-22, 24105 **Kiel**
Tel: 431-988 5707 (press)
Fax: 431-988 5815 (press)
Ministerin Ute Erdsiek-Rave

Ministry for Science, Research and Culture – Culture dept.
Thüringer Ministerium für Wissenschaft, Forschung und Kultur – Abteilung Kultur
Postfach 672, 99013 **Erfurt**
Tel: 361-379 1101 Fax: 361-379 1109
Internet: www.thueringen.de
E-Mail: tmwfk@+z.tu-ilmenau
Abteilungsleiter Dr Rolf Lettmann; Minister Dr Gerd Schuchardt; Staatssekretär Martina Heppt; Abteilungsleiter Forschung Dr Hermann Hamacher; Abteilungsleiter Hochschulen Dr Werner von Trützschler; Zentralabteilung Dr Harald Dörig
Comments: visiting address: Juri-Gagarin – Ring 158, 99084 Erfurt

• Municipal

Cultural Department Chemnitz
Stadt Chemnitz/Kulturamt, 09106 **Chemnitz**
Tel: 371-488 4101 Fax: 371-488 4199
E-Mail: a41@post.stadt-chemnitz.de
Amtsleiterin Petra Borges; Verwaltungsleiterin Angela Klebert; Abteilungsleiter (Abteilung Kunst – und Kulturförderung) Bernd Ruscher
Comments: visiting address: Bahnhofstr. 53, 09111 Chemnitz

Dortmund, Kulturbüro der Stadt
Kleppingstr. 21-23, 44122 **Dortmund**
Tel: 231-502 2419 Fax: 231-502 2497
E-Mail: kulturbuero.do@online.de
Kulturdezernent Dr. Gerhard Langemeyer; Geschäftsführer der Kulturbetriebe und Leiter des Kulturbüros Kurt Eichler; stellv. Leiter des Kulturbüros Egon Schefers; Internationale Kulturarbeit Burkhard Rinsche; Programmleitung Claudia Kokoschka

Department for Culture, Youth and Sports
Landeshauptstadt Dresden Stadtverwaltung – Dezernat für Kultur und Jugend
Königsstraße 15, 01097 **Dresden**
Tel: 351-488 8900 Fax: 351-488 8903
Bürgermeister für Kultur, Jugend und Sport Jörg Stüdemann

Düsseldorf – Kulturamt, Stadtverwaltung
40200 **Düsseldorf**
Tel: 211-899 6101 Fax: 211-892 9043(Kulturamt)/9002 (Kulturdezernent)
Kulturdezernent Hans-Heinrich Grosse-Brockhoff; Referent des Kulturdezernenten Hans-Georg Lohe; Leiterin des Kulturamtes Marianne Schirge; Leiterin Kunstraum Düsseldorf Ulla Lux; Künstlerfördeung u. internationaler Künstleraustausch Karin Rauers
Comments: visiting address: Amt 41, 40200 Düsseldorf

Cultural Department for the City of Erfurt
Kulturdirektion der Stadt Erfurt
Fischmarkt 27, 99084 **Erfurt**
Tel: 361-655 1601 Fax: 361-655 1609
Internet: www.erfurt.de
Kulturdirektor Herr Bornmann; Kulturbeigeordneter Herr Kaiser

Cultural Department for the City of Essen
Kulturbüro der Stadt Essen
Hollestr. 3 (Gildehof Center), 45121 **Essen**
Tel: 201-884 1210 Fax: 201-888 8454
Internet: www.essen.de.emg
E-Mail: touristikcenter@essen.de
Decernent für Bildung, Kultur und Wirtschaft Dr. Oliver Scheytt

Magistrat der Stadt Frankfurt, Amt für Wissenschaft und Kunst
Brückenstr. 3-7, 60594 **Frankfurt am Main**
Tel: 69-2123 5435 Fax: 69-2123 5435
Internet: www.frankfurt.de
E-Mail: mussmann.amt41@stadt-frankfurt.de
Kulturdezernent t.b.a.; Leiter des Kulturamts Frank Mußmann

Cultural Department for the City of Köln
Köln, Kulturdezernat der Stadt
Richartzstr. 2-4, 50667 **Köln**
Tel: 221-2212 2322 Fax: 221-2212 4141
Internet: kulturamt.köln.line.de
Kulturdezernentin Marie Hüllenkremer; Leiter des Kulturamts Jürgen Nordt; Musikreferentin Renate Liesmann; Theaterreferent Gisela Deckard-Kolvenbach

Leipzig Stadt Dezernat Kultur
Stadt Leipzig Dezernat Kultur, 04092 **Leipzig**
Tel: 341-123 4209 Fax: 341-123 4205
Beigeordneter für Kultur Georg Girardet
Role & Services: support cultural activities

München, Kulturreferat der Landeshauptstadt
Bugstr. 4, 80313 **München**
Tel: 89-2332 4380(Musik)/8561 (Darstellende Kunst)
Fax: 89-2332 1563
Internet: www.muenchen.de
Kulturreferent Prof. Dr. Julian Nida-Rümelin; Leiterin des Fachgebietes Musik Annelise Riedl; Leiter des Fachgebietes Darstellende Kunst Werner Schmitz

Cultural Department for the City of Potsdam
Stadtverwaltung der Landeshauptstadt Postdam Kulturamt
Hegelallee 9, 14461 **Potsdam**
Tel: 331-289 1950 Fax: 331-289 3342
Leiter des Kulturamtes Martin Schmidt-Roßleben; Abteilungsleiterin der Abteilung 412 Frau Faber-Schmidt

Stuttgart, Kulturamt der Landeshauptstadt
Eichstr. 9, 70173 **Stuttgart**
Tel: 711-216 7775/2850
Fax: 711-216 7628
Leiter Dr Wolfgang Ostberg; Leiter der Presse- und Öffentlichkeitsarbeit Dr. Roland Haas

GIBRALTAR (+350)

Ministry of Culture
310 Main Street, **Gibraltar**
Tel: 41687 Fax: 52589
E-Mail: minculture@gibnyrex.gi
minister for education, culture and youth affairs Hon. Dr Bernard Linares; director of culture Manolo Galliano; cultural officer Mercy Taylor
Role & Services: organises the Gibraltar Spring Festival, Gibraltar Drama Festival and Gibraltar National Week and Annual Open Art Exhibition *Comments:* owns Ince's Hall Theatre Complex; responsiblity for main cultural centre (John Mackintosh Hall); see also Venues

GREECE (+30)

Ministry of Culture
Ypourgeio Politismou
Bouboulinas 20-22, 106 82 **Athens**
Tel: 1-820 1100 (switchboard)/820 1648/49 (minister)/820 1632/34/35 (gen. sec.)/820 1637/1372/1325/1326/1319/1321 (press office)
Fax: 1-820 1373 (press office)/1337 (minister)/27/20
E-Mail: minister@culture.gr or press@culture.gr
minister of culture Elisavet Papazoè; secretary general Lina Mendoni; administration director Anna Karpouzi; financial director t.b.a.; antiquities director Parlama Liana; director of byzantinian monuments I Kakouris; press office Sofia Tarantou, Anna Andira, Froso Mantziou; fine arts director P Polychronopoulos; cultural relations director Alkistis Soulogiannis; EU division head D Diakides; Letters Directorate K Koroulis; archeological museums director Eo Zervoudaki; legal department Dr D Papapetropoulos
Comments: directorates for fine arts, folk culture, cultural centres and Byzantine Antiquities are at : Ermou 17, 105 63 Athens (tel: 1-323 6198, fax: 1-322 2245). Directorates for cultural relations, classical antiquities, cultural events and EU division are at Karytsi Square 10-12, 105 61 Athens (tel: 1-323 2922); Letters Directorate and legal department are at Metsovou 5, 106 82 Athens (tel: 1-825 3701/2, fax: 1-825 3693)

HUNGARY (+36)

Ministry of National Culture & Heritage
Nemzeti Kulturális Örökség Minisztériuma
POB 1, 1884 **Budapest**
Tel: 1-302 0600 Fax: 1-302 3002
Internet: www.mkm.hu
minister of culture József Hámori; political secretary of state Attila Várhegyi; managing secretary of state Gergely Pröhle; deputy secretary of state (culture) Zsolt Visy; deputy secretary of state (international relations) Jozsef Pal; deputy secretary of state (preservation of monuments) Geza Entz; deputy secretary of state (churches) Zsolt Semjen; deputy secretary of state (finances) Laszlo Baan; deputy secretary of state (performing arts) Janos Devich
Comments: visiting address: Szalay u. 10-14, 1055 Budapest

Chancellery – the Prime Minister's Office
Kossuth ter 4, 1055 **Budapest**
Tel: 1-268 3000 Fax: 1-268 3050
minister of the chancellery Istvan Stumpf; secretary of state (political) Laszlo Bogar; secretary of state (managing) Bela Bartfai; deputy secretary of state (ministries) Peter Szerdahelyi; director (ministry of NCH) Endre Pordan

ICELAND (+354)

Please note: general elections were held in May 1999; so changes may have occurred

Ministry of Education, Science and Culture
Menntamálaráduneytid
Sölvhólsgata 4, 150 **Reykjavík**
Tel: 560 9500 Fax: 562 3068
Internet: www.mrn.stjr.is
E-Mail: postur@mrn.stjr.is
minister Bjorn Bjarnason; secretary general Mrs Gudridur Sigurdardottir; head of department of cultural affairs Arni Gunnarsson; head of department of administration Kristin Jonsdottir; head of division of arts and museums Karitas H Gunnarsdóttir; special adviser on music and museums Thorgeir Olafsson; special adviser on visual arts and literature t.b.a.

IRELAND Republic of (+353)

Department of Arts, Heritage, Gaeltacht and the Islands
Dún Aimhirgin, 43-49 Mespil Road, **Dublin** 4
Tel: 1-667 0788/0803 (press office) Fax: 1-667 0826
Internet: www.ealga.irlgov.ie
E-Mail: pressinfo@ealga.irlgov.ie
minister Síle de Valera; minister of state Éamon Ó Cuív; secretary Tadhg S. Ó hÉalaithe; assistant principal Seamus Lwnem; press officer Cian O'Lináin
Role & Services: responsible for arts, culture and the promotion of the cultural, social and economic welfare of the Gaeltacht areas and the preservation and extension of the use of Irish as a vernacular language

Arts Council, The
An Chomhairle Ealaíon
70 Merrion Square, **Dublin** 2
Tel: 1-618 0200 Fax: 1-676 1302/661 0349
Internet: www.artscouncil.ie
E-Mail: info@artscouncil.ie
director/registrar of Aosdána Patricia Quinn; artform director Dermot McLaughlin; drama & opera officer Phelim Donlon; visual arts officer Oliver Dowling; literature officer Sinéad MacAodha; local arts development officer (arts centres/festivals/community arts) Susan Coughlan; development director Mary Cloake; finance & capital officer David McConnell; communications and film officer Mary Hyland; youth arts & dance officer, Gaye Tanham; communications executive Liz Powell; music officer Maura Eaton
Role & Services: to stimulate public interest in and promote the knowledge, appreciation and practice of the arts; an independent autonomous state body which acts as the development agency for the arts in Ireland; it is the primary source of support for the individual artist; also to provide advice to government on artistic matters, also provides financial assistance to individuals and organisations, for artistic purposes

ITALY (+39)

• Federal

Ministero dei Beni e delle Attivita Culturali – Dipartimento dello Spettacolo
via della Ferratella in Laterano 51, 00184 **Roma**
Tel: 06-77321 (switchboard) Fax: 06-7049 2602
E-Mail: osservatorio.spettacolo@pcm.it
ministro Giovanna Melandri; capo dipartimento Rossana Rummo

Direzione Generale Relazioni Culturali – Uff. III
c/o Ministero degli Affari Esteri, Piazzale della Farnesina 1, 00194 **Roma**
Tel: 06-3691-1 Fax: 06-3691 8552
capoufficio Patrizio Fondi; vice Manuela Ruosi; uff. stampa Silvia Giampaola

• Regional

Abruzzo Regional Council – Cultural Promotion Service
Giunta Regionale Abruzzo – Servizio Promozione Culturale
Via Roio 12, Palazzo Dragonetti, 67100 **L'Aquila**
Tel: 0862-3631 (switchboard) Fax: 0862-364 421
Internet: www.regione.abruzzo.it
assessore promozione culturale Stefania Pezzopane; dirigente del servizio promozione culturale Angelo Piccirillo; dirigente uff. attività Marcello Verderosa

Basilicata Regional Council – Cultural Councillor's Office
Giunta Regionale Basilicata – Dipartimento Cultura e Formazione
Corso Umberto I 28, 85100 **Potenza**
Tel: 0971-448 111 (switchboard) Fax: 0971-448 082
direttore generale Sign.a Cecilia Salvia; assessore Signor Sabino Altobello; segretaria particolare dell'assessore Sign.a Marisa Gabriele

Autonomous Province of Bolzano – Department for Italian education and culture
Provincia Autonoma di Bolzano – Ripartizione cultura italiana
Via del Ronco 2, 39100 **Bolzano**
Tel: 0471-991 200 Fax: 0471-991 209
Internet: www.provincia.bz.it/ (cultura)
E-Mail: antonio.lampis@provincia.bz.it
assessore dott. Luigi Cigolla; direttore di ripartizione dott. Antonio Lampis
Comments: contact information dott. Luigi Cigolla: via Duca d'Aosta 59, 39100 Bolzano, Tel: 0471-995 860, Fax: 0471-995 699

Calabria Region – Department for Sport, Leisure and Entertainment
Regione Calabria – Assessorato allo Sport, Tempo Libero e Spettacolo
Via Spasari (Galleria Mancuso) N8, 88100 **Catanzaro**
Tel: 0961-741 657
assessore al turismo e spettacolo Antonella Freno

Campania Regional Council – Department for Public Education and Culture
Giunta Regionale Della Campania - Istruzione e Cultura
Centro Direzionale Isola A/6, 80143 **Napoli**
Tel: 081-796 6502 Fax: 081-796 6526
capo settore Dott. Giancarlo D'Alessandro

Emilia-Romagna Regional Council – Culture
Giunta Regionale Emilia-Romagna – Assessorato Cultura
viale Aldo Moro 30, 40127 **Bologna**
Tel: 051-283 760/61 Fax: 051-283 299
Internet: www.regione.emilia-romagna.it
E-Mail: davoli@regione.emilia-romagna.it
assessore Lorenza Davoli; direttore generale Alessandro Chili; capo servizio cultura Giovanni Serpe
: alternative e-mail: segr-ass-cultura@arcelo.regione.emilia-romagna.it

Istituto per i Beni Artistici, Culturali e Naturali Della Regione Emilia-Romagna
Via Farini 17, 40124 **Bologna**
Tel: 051-217 442 (direzione)/411 (switchboard)
Fax: 051-232 599
Internet: www.ibc.regione.emilia-romagna.it
E-Mail: ibc@iperbole.bologna.it
presidente Prof Ezio Raimondi; direttore Dott. Nazzareno Pisauri

Friuli-Venezia Giulia Regional Council – Regional Directorate for Education and Culture
Regione Autonoma Friuli-Venezia Giulia – Direzione regionale dell'Istruzione e della Cultura
via S. Francesco 37, 34133 **Trieste**
Tel: 040-377 1111 Fax: 040-377 5275
Internet: www.regione.fug.it
E-Mail: istruzione@regione.fug.it
direttore regionale Dott. Giuliano Abate (368 042/377 5261); direttore del servizio della attività culturali Dott. Nicolò Molea (377 5253); direttore del servizio dei beni culturali Dott. Andrea Balanza (377 5274); direttore del servizio della istruzione e della ricerca Claudio Sepin (377 5271); direttore sostututor del servizio per le lingue regionali e minoritarie Dott. Adriana Janezic (377 5273)
Comments: press office: P.zza Unità d'Italiana, 34100 Trieste, Tel: 040-377 3524, Fax: 040-377 3519; press officer Dario Cociani

Lazio Regional Council – Dept for Culture, Tourism, Performing Arts and Sport
Giunta Regionale Lazio – Assessorarato alle Politiche per la Promozione della Cultura del Turismo, dello Spettacolo e dello Sport
via Rosa Raimondi Garibaldi 7, 00147 **Roma**
Tel: 06-5168-1 Fax: 06-5168 4059
assessore Dott. Pasquale Donato (5168 5000); dirigente settore attività culturali Enzo Ciarravano (5168 6846); dirigente ufficio attività culturali connesse con i rapporti internazionali Dott. Anna Maria Cambria (5168 4718)

Liguria Regional Council – Department for Tourism, Culture, Sport & Leisure Time)
Giunta Regionale Liguria – Assessorato al Turismo, Cultura Sport e Tempo Libero
via Ravasco 10, 16121 **Genova**
Tel: 010-548 5775/5553 Fax: 010-570 4216
Internet: www.regione.liguria.it
E-Mail: baratti@regione.liguria.it
direttore generale Dott. ssa Silvana Monari (548 4963); promozione culturale Anna Fioretti (548 5255)

Lombardy Regional Council – General Management for Culture
Giunta Regionale Lombardia – Direzione Generale Cultura
Piazza 4 Novembre 5, 20124 **Milano**
Tel: 02-67651 (switchboard)/6765 2696 (dir. gen.)
Fax: 02-6765 2704
Internet: www.reteculturale.regione.lombardia.it
E-Mail: petraroiap@regione.lombardia.it
direttore generale direzione cultura Pietro Petraroia; promozione culturale e spettacolo Luica Bianchi; uff. comunicazione Donata Corelli

Marche Regional Council – Cultural Councillors Office
Giunta Regione Marche – Assessorato alla Cultura
via Gentile da Fabriano 9, 60125 **Ancona**
Tel: 071-806 2282/3/69 Fax: 071-806 2410
Internet: www.regione.marche.it
E-Mail: gino.troli@regione.marche.it
assessore Gino Troli; responsabile servizio beni e attività culturali Dott. Eustacchio Montemurro; responsabile ufficio attivita culturali Dott. Angelo de Angelis; responsabile centro regionale beni culturali Mario Canti

Molise Region – Cultural Councillor's Office
Regione Molise – Assessorato alla Cultura
via Toscana 15, 86100 **Campobasso**
Tel: 0874-481 456/429 477
Fax: 0874-429 479
assessore Nicola Jacobacci; responsabile cultura Dott. Giuseppe D'Agostino

Piedmont Regional Council – Cultural Councillor's Office
Giunta Regionale del Piemonte – Assessorato alla Cultura
via Antonio Meucci 1, 10121 **Torino**
Tel: 011-432 4407 Fax: 011-432 2009
E-Mail: spettacolo@regione.piemonte.it
direttore settore promozione attività culturali D.ssa Rita Marchiori (432 4407); dirigente promozione attività culturali D.ssa Marilena Damberto (432 4560); dirigente settore spettacolo Amanzio Borio (432 4062)

Puglia Regional Council – Department for Culture
Giunta Regionale Puglia – Assessorato Cultura
via Venezia 13, 70121 **Bari**
Tel: 080-558 9745 Fax: 080-540 6634
assessore cultura, sport e turismo Giuseppe Semeraro; coordinatore settore cultura Gaetano Volpe

Sardinia Regional Council – Department for Public Education, Fine Arts, Information, Sport & Entertainment
Giunta Regionale Sardegna – Assessorato Pubblica Istruzione, Beni Culturali, Informazione, Sport e Spettacolo
Viale Trieste N50, 09123 **Cagliari**
Tel: 070-606 5011 Fax: 070-606 5002
direttore generale Ettore Gasperini (606 5011); coordinatore di servizio Augusto Fadda; coordinatore settore informazione sport e spettacolo Franco Sardi (606 4960)

Sicily Regional Council – Department for Education & Culture
Giunta Regionale Sicilia – Assessorato Beni Culturali, Ambientali e Pubblica Istruzione
via delle Croci 8, 90139 **Palermo**
Tel: 091-696 1823/4 Fax: 091-696 1739/1650
assessore regionale Salvatore Morinello; direttore Dott. Giuseppe Grado (696 1785); dirigente coordinatore iniziative culturali teatrali e musicali D.ssa Maria Luigia Agria (696 1815)

Tuscany Regional Council – Department for Education & Culture
Giunta Regionale Toscana – Dipartimento Politiche Formative e Beni culturali
via Farini 8, 50121 **Firenze**
Tel: 055-438 2111 Fax: 055-438 2600
Internet: www.regione.toscana.it
coordinatore Dott.ssa Rossella Dini (438 2629); assessore cultura, spetacolo e comunicazione Franco Cazzola (tel: 438 2702/1, fax: 438 2700)

Autonomous Province of Trento – Department for Cultural Activities
Provincia Autonoma di Trento – Servizio Attivitá Culturali
via Romagnosi N5, 38100 **Trento**
Tel: 0461-496 917 Fax: 0461-495 080
Internet: www.provincia.tn.it/
E-Mail: serv.att.cult@provincia.tn.it
assessore Claudio Molinari; dirigente servizio attività culturali Gianluigi Bozza

Umbria Regional Council – Cultural Councillor's Office
Giunta Regionale dell'Umbria – Assessorato alla Cultura
Centro Direzionale Fontivegge, via M. Angeloni 63, 06124 **Perugia**
Tel: 075-504 5412/5483 Fax: 075-504 5568
assessore alla cultura Giampiero Bocci; direttore istruzione e cultura Ciro Becchetti

Valle D'Aosta Regional Council – Department of Education, Cultural Services
Regione Autonoma Valle D'Aosta – Assessorato della Pubblica Istruzione e Cultura
piazza Deffeyes 1, 11100 **Aosta**
Tel: 0165-273 111 Fax: 0165-236 200
assessore alla cultura Ennio Pastoret (273 278); coordinatore cultura Alessio Betemps (273 818/19); dirigente attività culturali Elmo Domaine (273 432)

Veneto Regional Council – Department of Culture, Information and Immigration
Giunta Regionale Veneto – Direzione Cultura, Informazione e Flussi Migratori
Palazzo Sceriman, Lista di Spagna Cannaregio 168, 30121 **Venezia**
Tel: 041-279 2689 Fax: 041-279 2685
Internet: www.regione.venteto.it
E-Mail: dir.cultura@mail.regione.veneto.it
assessore cultura On. Giancarlo Galan; dirigente regionale Dott. Angelo Tabaro

• Regional

Provincial Administration of Bari – Department of Culture & Communication
Amministrazione Provinciale – Assessorato alla Cultura, Tutela beni Culturali, Attività Artistiche e Comunicazione
Via Spalato 19, 70121 **Bari**
Tel: 080-541 2360/558 0884 Fax: 080-558 8147
assessore William Formicola; diririgente cultura Pietro Centrone

Province of Bologna – Department for Culture, Sports and Leisure
Provincia di Bologna – Assessorato Cultura, Turismo, Sport e Tempo Libero
Via De' Castagnoli 3, 40126 **Bologna**
Tel: 051-218 458/459 Fax: 051-218 755/760
Internet: www.provincia.bologna.it/platea
E-Mail: platea@provincia.bologna.it
assessore Prof. Marco Macciantelli; dirigente del settore Dott. Pasquale Petrucci

Province of Cagliari – Department of Culture, Sports, Tourism and Performing Arts
Provincia di Cagliari – Assessorato beni Culturali, Sport, Turismo e Spettacolo
Via Cadello, 9, 09121 **Cagliari**
Tel: 070-40921 (switchboard)/2721/2732
Fax: 070-409 2807/521 034
presidente Nicola Scano; assessore Adriano Salis; dirigente Dott. Iosto Tuveri

Provincial Administration of Florence – Department for Culture
Amministrazione Provinciale di Firenze – Assessorato alla Cultura
Via Cavour, 11, 50129 **Firenze**
Tel: 055-27601 (switchboard)/276 0200 (office)/0346 (press) Fax: 055-276 0451
assessore Elisabetta Del Lungo (276 0200); dirigente Dott. Alessandro Belisario (276 0420)

Provincial Administration of Genova – Department for Culture
Assessorato al Patrimonio Culturale dell' Entroterra e Del Mare
P.le Mazzini 2, 16122 **Genova**
Tel: 010-54991 Fax: 010-549 9244
Internet: www.provincia.genova.it
E-Mail: cultura@mbox-provincia.genova.it
assessore alla cultura Gualtiero Schiaffino; dirigente D.ssa Mirella Rossini (549 9633)
Comments: the Cultural Department of Theatres and International Relations (Assesorato alla Cultura, Rapporti con i Teatri, Iniziative per il Giubileo e Relazioni Internazionali, Assesore: Gabriela Airaldi) is also based at the same address; alternative e-mail: schiaffino@mbox.provincia.genova.it

Provincial Administration of Milano – Department for Culture
Amministrazione Provinciale di Milano – Assessorato alla Cultura
Via Guicciardini 6, 20129 **Milano**
Tel: 02-7740 2926/2921/2966 (pr) Fax: 02-7740 2918
Internet: www.provincia.milano.it
E-Mail: r.bugnoli@provincia.milano.it
assessore cultura e beni culturali Dott. Gianni Verga; direttore servizi culturali Giuseppe Manzoni; president Ombretta Colli

Provincial Administration of Modena – Department of Culture
Amministrazione Provinciale – Assessorato alla Cultura
Via Yacopo Barozzi 340, 41100 **Modena**
Tel: 059-209 557/556 Fax: 059-224 866
Internet: www.provincia.modena.it
assessore alla cultura Mario Lugli; capo settore Ubaldo Fraulini; responsabile cultura Lauretta Longagnani

Provincial Administration of Palermo – Department of Cultural Activity, Public Education and Performing Arts
Amministrazione Provinciale di Palermo – Settore Attività Culturali
Via Maqueda 100, 90134 **Palermo**
Tel: 091-662 8567/6 Fax: 091-662 8548
E-Mail: propal@tin.it
assessore alla cultura Tommaso Romano; presidente Francesco Musotto; responsabile alla cultura Maria Navetta
Comments: the Settore Attiuità Culturali is in charge of the entertainment along with the Assessore al Turismo e Spettacolo (sig. Liborio Polizzi), also in charge of the Provincial Library (director: Arch. Director Rosabla Mirenda)

Province of Ravenna – Department for Cultural Activity Research University
Provincia di Ravenna – Assessorato di Beni e Attività Culturali Ricerca Università
Via Garatoni 6, 48100 **Ravenna**
Tel: 0544-212 885 Fax: 0544-35727
E-Mail: procultura@provincia.ra.it
assessore Avv. Paolo Gambi; dirigente Dott. Gianfranco Casadio; responsabile Dott. Rosella Cantarelli

Provincial Administration of Roma – Department for Culture
Amministrazione Provinciale – Settore Cultura
Via Petroselli N47, 00187 **Roma**
Tel: 06-6766 4745/95 Fax: 06-678 0212
E-Mail: gpietroboni@provincia.roma.it
assessore alla cultura, beni culturali e spettacolo Paola Guerci; dirigente servizio e attività culturali Giuliana Pietroboni
Role & Services: deal with all aspect of culture

Provincial Administration of Torino – Department for Culture
Amministrazione Provinciale – Assessorato Risorse Naturali e Culturali
Via Gaudenzio Ferrari, 1, 10123 **Torino**
Tel: 011-861 3630/3615/3650 (ass.)
Fax: 011-861 3611
E-Mail: picchi@provincia.torino.it
dirigente servizio cultura Dott. ssa Patrizia Picchi; assessor Alle Risorse; culturali Walter Giuliano
Role & Services: they are developing a cultural network, new eco-museums and eco-sites; also working on the Museo del passante Ferroviario di Bussoleno (Museum of the railway track of Bussoleno) with France

Provincial Administration of Venezia – Department for Culture
Amministrazione Provinciale – Assessorato alla Cultura e Beni Culturali
Palazzo ca' Corner – S.Marco 2662, 30124 **Venezia**
Tel: 041-529 0511/550 Fax: 041-529 0589
Internet: www.provincia.venezia.it/bbcc-pve
E-Mail: bbcc-pve@provincia.venezia.it
assessore t.b.a.; assessore alla cultural e istruzione Andrea Ferrazzi; dirigente del servizio beni culturali Gloria Vidali

• Municipal

City Council of Arezzo – Culture Department
Comune di Arezzo – Servizio Cultura
Via Veneto 33/14, 52100 **Arezzo**
Tel: 0575-377 253/255 Fax: 0575-377 251
Internet: www.arezzo.net
E-Mail: cultura@ats.it
responsabile aspetti economici e artisticii Manuela Fabbrini; direttore artistico Aldo Tarabella

City Council of Bari – Department of Culture
Comune di Bari – Assessorato alla Cultura, Turismo per il Mediterraneo
Via Argiro 33, 70122 **Bari**
Tel: 080-577 2337/8 Fax: 080-524 3381
assessore Simeone Dicagno Abbrescia; direttore ripartizione Giuseppe Parisi

City Council of Bologna – Department of Culture
Comune di Bologna – Assessorato alla Cultura
Via Oberdan 24, 40126 **Bologna**
Tel: 051-204 633/730/731 Fax: 051-268 636
Internet: www.comune.bologna.it
E-Mail: cultura@comune.bologna.it
assess. Prof. Roberto Grandi; assess. cultura Marina Deserti; responsabile spettacolo Cheti Corsini (204 680)

City Council of Cagliari – Department of Culture
Comune di Cagliari – Assessorato alla Cultura
Piazza Alcide De Gasperi 43, 09125 **Cagliari**
Tel: 070-677 8368 Fax: 070-677 8497
assessore attività culturali Dott. Gianni Filippini; dirigente settore spettacolo Dott. Bruno Soriga

City Council of Florence – Department for Culture
Comune di Firenze – Assessorato alla Cultura
Via Ghibellina N. 30, 50122 **Firenze**
Tel: 055-262 5965/66/67 Fax: 055-262 5952
Internet: www.comune.fi.it
E-Mail: asscult@comune.fi.it
assess. Rosa Maria Di Giorgio; dir. Sergio De Carieini

City Council of Genova – Department of Culture
Comune di Genova – Assessorato alla Cultura e Settacolo
Largo Pertini, 4, 16121 **Genova**
Tel: 010-557 4729/30 Fax: 010-557 4708
E-Mail: asscultura@comune.genova.it
assessore cultura e spettacolo Ruggero Pierantoni; direttore uff. spettacolo Guido Gandino (557 4249)
Comments: Promozione città, Turismo, Sport Palazzo Serra Geracé, Via Sottoripa 5, 16126 Genova, assessore: Carlo Repetti

City Council of Milan – Department for Culture and Museums
Comune di Milano – Settore Cultura e Musei
Via T.Marino 7, 20121 **Milano**
Tel: 02-8646 0239 (assessore)/878 600 (direttore)
Fax: 02-869 0330 (assessore)/878 007 (direttore)
assessore Dott. Salvatore Carrubba (8646 0239/890 0378); direttore di settore Stefania Yahier (878 600); assistente di settore D.ssa Rossana Ferro (869 2901); responsabile relazioni esterne Dott. Sergio Mauri (875 176/6208 5222); ufficio San Maurizio – Musica (concert series + festival) Carla Macchi (862 418); ufficio spettacoli Maria Silvana Foti (8646 4094/6208 3636)

City Council of Modena – Department of Culture
Comune di Modena – Assessorato alla Cultura
Via Galaverna 8, 41100 **Modena**
Tel: 059-206 111/788 (assessore secretary)
Fax: 059-206 877
Internet: www.comune.modena.it
E-Mail: duretti@comune.modena.it
assessore Dott. Gianni Cottafavi; capo settore cultura Carlo Artioli; direttore Galleria Civica Walter Guadagnini

City Council of Palermo – Department for Culture
Comune di Palermo – Assessorato alla Cultura
Villa Trabbia, Via Salinas 3, 90141 **Palermo**
Tel: 091-740 5932/30 Fax: 091-740 5900/31
assessore Laura Iacovoni; capo ripartizione Ermanno Cascio (tel: 740 5901/14)

City Council of Ravenna – Department for Culture
Comune di Ravenna – Assessorato alle Istituzioni Culturali e Spettacolo
Via Mario Gordini 27, 48100 **Ravenna**
Tel: 0544-482 257 Fax: 0544-482 298
E-Mail: assculturacomra@racine.ra.it
capo area culturale Donatino Domini; assessore Dr. Alberto Cassani

City Council of Rome – Department for Culture
Comune di Roma – Assessorato alle Politiche Culturali
Piazza Campitelli 7, 00186 **Roma**
Tel: 06-67101 (switchboard) Fax: 06-6710 3118/679 7826
Internet: www.comune.roma.it
assessore Gianni Borgna (6710 3100/2997); dirigente superiore reggente Dott. Antonio Calicchia; sovrintendente Prof. Eugenio La Rocca (6710 3887)

City Council of Sassan – Department of Culture
Comune di Sassari – Assessorato alla Cultura
Viale Dante 1, 07100 **Sassari**
Tel: 079-283 0902/4 Fax: 079-283 0920
assessore Antonietta Duce; dirigente servizi educativi e culturali Francesca Chessa; responsabile servizi culturali Mariangela Valentini

City Council of Torino – Department for Culture
Comune di Torino – Assessorato per la Cultura
Via San Francesco da Paola 3, 10123 **Torino**
Tel: 011-442 4717/18/35/97 Fax: 011-442 4776
Internet: www.comune.torino.it/infocultura
E-Mail: vetrina@comune.torino.it
direttore divisione cultura Fausto Sorba; responsabile ufficio manifestazioni Maurizio Florio; dirigente servizi generali Vittorio Manganelli; dirigente arti musicali Paola Grassi Reverdini; assessore cultura Ugo Perone

City Council of Venice – Department for Culture
Comune di Venezia – Assessore alla Cultura e Pubblica Istruzione
San Marco 4089, Palazzo Cavalli, 30124 **Venezia**
Tel: 041-274 8346 Fax: 041-274 8582 (segreteria assessore)
Internet: www.comune.venezia.it
E-Mail: assessore.cultura.pi@comune.venezia.it
assessore Mara Rumiz; direttore Prof. Giandomenico Ravanelli; dirigente cultura Sandro Mescola (tel: 274 7613)
Comments: other address: Assessorato alla Cultura e Pubblica Istruzione, Corte Cantarina, San Marco, Tel: 041-274 7605/7603 (press office)

LATVIA (+371)

Please note: general elections were held in October 1999; so changes may have occurred

Ministry of Culture of the Republic of Latvia
Latvijas Republikas Kulturas ministrija
11a Kr. Valdemara, 1364 **Riga**
Tel: 7-224 772 Fax: 7-227 916
E-Mail: intercontact@km.gov.lv
minister Karina Petersone
Role & Services: the Ministry of Culture is in charge of the State's cultural policy and administration; promotes and develops international cultural relations, the practical part of cultural co-operation *Comments:* department for Foreign Relations (7-336 040), department of cultural policy (7-320 896)

Ministry of Foreign Affairs of the Republic of Latvia
Latvijas Republikas Arlietu ministrija
36 Brivibas Blvd., 1395 **Riga**
Tel: 7-016 210 Fax: 7-828 121/282 882
minister Valdis Birkavs
Role & Services: the Ministry of Foreign Affairs is the coordinating body which carries out the foreign policy; the Ministry analyses international situations and matters of economical, cultural and scientific co-operation; the Ministry participates in creating the foreign policy and strategy of Latvia

Culture Department of Riga City
Rigas pilsetas Kulturas parvalde
Kr. Valdemara 5, 1010 **Riga**
Tel: 7-320 941/398 Fax: 7-326 035
Internet: www.rcc.lv
E-Mail: rdkp@latnet.lv
head of department Rolands Jurasevskis
Comments: municipal institution, which implements municipal functions in the field of management and administration of cultural activities; see also Festivals and Promoters

LIECHTENSTEIN (+423)

Principality of Liechtenstein
Landesverwaltung Liechtenstein
Regierungsgebäude, 9490 **Vaduz**
Tel: 236 6111 Fax: 236 6022
Ministerin (responsible for culture and sport) Dr. Andrea Willi
Comments: Präsident des Fürstlich Liechtensteinischen Kulturbeirats: Arnold Kind, Großfeldweg 358, 9491 Ruggell

LITHUANIA (+370)

Ministry of Culture of the Republic of Lithuania
Lietuvos Respublikos kulturos ministerija
Basanaviciaus 5, 2683 **Vilnius**
Tel: 2-619 486/621 830/623 093/221 425 Fax: 2-623 120
E-Mail: CULTURE@MUZA.lt
minister Arunas Beksta; viceminister INA MARCIULIONYTE; head of department of arts Ona Servaite
Comments: 2-221 425 (music section), 2-623 817 (theatre section), 2-220 055 (foreign relations)

Lithuanian Board of Culture and Art
Lietuvos kulturos ir meno taryba
J. Basanaviciaus 5, 2683 **Vilnius**
Tel: 2-618 584 Fax: 2-623 120
chairperson Alfredas Bumblauskas
Role & Services: advisory body under the Ministry of Culture

LUXEMBOURG (+352)

Ministry of Culture
Ministère de la Culture
20 Montée de la Pétrusse, 2912 **Luxembourg**
Tel: 478 6610 Fax: 402 427
ministre Mme. Erna Hennicot-Schoepges; director Guy Dockendorf
Role & Services: promote national cultural events in Luxembourg

MACEDONIA (+389)

Ministry of Culture
Ilidenska bb, 91000 **Skopje**
Tel: 91-220 823 Fax: 91-225 810
minister Slobodan Unkovski

MALTA (+356)

Ministry of Education and National Culture – Department of Culture
230 Republic Street, **Valletta** CMR 02
Tel: 248 006/247 913/245 168/232 515
Fax: 241 964
minister of education Dr Louis Galea; parliamentary secretary for youth & sport Jesmond Mugliett; chairman of the Manoel Theatre Management Committee John Lowell; permanent secretary Frederic Fearne; director of culture Joseph J Mifsud
Comments: the head office of the Ministry of Education & National Culture is situated in the Education Building, Floriana

MOLDOVA (+373)

Moldovan Ministry of Culture
Ministerul Culturii al Republicii Moldova
Piata Marii Adunari Nationale, 1,
2033 **Chisinau**
Tel: 2-233 986 Fax: 2-232 388
minister Ghenadie Ciobanu

MONACO (+377)

Direction des Affaires Culturelles de la Principauté de Monaco
Winter Palace, 4 Boulevard des Moulins,
98000 **Monaco**
Tel: 9315 8303 Fax: 9350 6694
directeur des affaires culturelles Rainier Rocchi

NETHERLANDS (+31)

Ministry of Education, Culture and Science
Ministerie van Onderwijs, Cultuur en Wetenschappen
PO Box 25000, 2700 LZ **Zoetermeer**
Tel: 79-323 2323 Fax: 79-323 2320
Internet: www.minocw.nl
state secretary of cultural affairs Dr F. Rick van der Bloeg; head, arts directorate M W B Asscher; head, performing arts George Lawson; head, dance and music-theatre unit G A Hoogerbrug; head, music unit A W F den Haring

Council for Culture
Raad voor Cultuur
PO Box 61243, 2506 AE **Den Haag**
Tel: 70-310 6686 Fax: 70-361 4727
E-Mail: cultuur@cultuur.nl
chairman J Jessurun; general secretary Dr J A Brandenbarg; theatre & dance Paul Broekhoff; music & music theatre Neil van der Linden
Role & Services: The Raad voor Cultuur (Council for Culture) is legally the advisor to the government on culture and cultural policy *Comments:* Second address: R J Schimmelpennincklaan 3, 2517 JN Den Haag

NORWAY (+47)

• Federal

Royal Norwegian Ministry of Cultural Affairs
Det Kongelige Kulturdepartement
Akersgaten 59, PO Box 8030 DEP, 0030 **Oslo**
Tel: 2224 9090 Fax: 2224 8038
Internet: www.dep.no/kd/
minister of cultural affairs Anne Enger Lahnstein; state secretary Per Kristian Skulberg; political advisor Vanja Stenslie Krakk; secretary general Per Haga (2224 7808); director general, department of culture Kjell Myhren; director general, department of media and copyright Helge Sønneland (2224 8002); director general, department of sport policy Hans B Skaset (2224 8050); director general, department of administrative affairs Henning Gorholt (2224 7810)
head of information Berit Griebenow (2224 7809)

Norwegian Council for Cultural Affairs
Norsk Kulturråd
Grev Wedels Plass 1, 0151 **Oslo**
Tel: 2247 8330 Fax: 2233 4042
Internet: www.kulturrad.no
E-Mail: kultur@kulturrad.no
director Ole Jacob Bull; deputy director Guri Skjeldal
Role & Services: administers the Norwegian Cultural Fund, which is part of the public purse; advisory body to the Ministry of Cultural Affairs
Comments: the Council particularly allocates funds to a number of non-institutionalised and creative activites, i.e. initiative which is not covered by ordinary subsidy arrangements at local and national levels

• Regional

Akerhus County Municipality – Dept. of Culture
Akershus fylkeskommune – Kulturavdelingen
Schweigaardsgt. 4, 0185 **Oslo**
Tel: 2205 5460 Fax: 2205 5434
regional cultural head Inge Hasselberg

Aust-Agder County Municipality – Sector for Regional Development, Dept. of Culture
Aust-Agder fylkeskommune – Sektor for regional utvikling, kuturavdelingen
Fylkeshuset, 4809 **Arendal**
Tel: 3701 7300 Fax: 3701 7365
regional cultural head Per Norstrøm
Comments: visiting address: Ragnvald Bakstads Vei 1, 4838 Arendal

Buskerud County Municipality – Dept. of Culture
Buskerud fylkeskommune – Kulturavdalingen
Haugesgt. 89, 3020 **Drammen**
Tel: 3280 8500 Fax: 3280 8672
regional cultural head Åse Klundelien

Finnmark County Municipality – Dept. of Culture
Finnmark fylkeskommune – Kulturavdelingen
Fylkeshuset, Henry Karlsens Pl. 1, 9815 **Vadsø**
Tel: 7896 2000 Fax: 7896 2372
regional cultural head Elsa Jonassen

Hedmar County Municipality – Sector for Regional Development, Dept. of Culture
Hedmar fylkeskommune – Sektor for regional utvikling, kuturavdelingen
Parkagata 64, 2325 **Hamar**
Tel: 6254 4000 Fax: 6254 2225
Internet: www.hedmark/s.kommune.no
regional cultural head Hanne Warhausg Soeberg

Hordaland County Municipality – Sector for Regional Development, Dept. of Culture
Hordaland fylkeskommune – Sektor for regional utvikling, kuturavdelingen
Fylkeshuset, Postboks 7900, 5020 **Bergen**
Tel: 5523 9000 Fax: 5523 9209
regional cultural head Aasmund Mjeldheim

Møre and Romsdal County Municipality – Dept. of Culture
Møre og Romsdal fylkeskommune – Kulturavdelingen
Julsundveien 49, 6412 **Molde**
Tel: 7125 8000/8833 Fax: 7125 8837
E-Mail: arvid.blindheim@mor.fylke.org
regional cultural head Arvid Blindheim

Nord-Trøndelag County Municipality – Dept. of Culture
Nord-Trøndelag fylkeskommune – Kulturavdelingen
Selmakergata 2, 7735 **Steinkjer**
Tel: 7414 1000/1143 Fax: 7414 1200
regional cultural head Ragnhild Kvalø

Nordland County Municipality – Dept. of Culture
Nordland fylkeskommune – Kulturavdelingen
Fylkeshuset, Prinsensgt 100, 8048 **Bodö**
Tel: 7553 1240 Fax: 7553 1250
director of cultural affairs Aaslaug Vaa (email: aaslaug.vaa@nfk.telemax.no); deputy director Stig Olsen (email: stig.olsen@nfk.telemax.no)

Øppland County Municipality – Sector for Regional Development, Dept. of Culture
Øppland fylkeskommune – Sektor for regional utvikling, kuturavdelingen
Kirkegt. 76, 2600 **Lillehammer**
Tel: 6128 9370/9000 Fax: 6128 9491
E-Mail: postmottak@oppland-f.kommune.no
regional cultural head Frode Sannum

Oslo City Council – Dept. for Culture and Education
Oslo kommune – Byrads avdeling for kultur og utdannelse
Rådhuset, 0037 **Oslo**
Tel: 2286 1600 Fax: 2286 1272
head of cultural affairs Ann Britt Lindsøe

Østfold County Municipality – Section of Trade & Culture
Østfold fylkeskommune – Avdeling for noering og kultur, kulturavdelingen
Postboks 220, 1702 **Sarpsborg**
Tel: 6911 7000 Fax: 6911 7062
Internet: www.ostfold-f.kommune.no.
E-Mail: mail@ostfold-f.kommune.no
regional cultural head Odd Raeng; contact Jan Petter Olsen

Rogaland County Municipality – Sector for Regional Development, Dept. of Culture
Rogaland fylkeskommune – Sektor for regional utvikling, kuturavdelingen
Peder Klowes gate 27, 4001 **Stavanger**
Tel: 5151 6870/6851 Fax: 5151 6674
head of culture department Roald Håland; senior executive officer/sport Hans Olavsandvoll; senior executive officer/music t.b.a.; culture heritage officers Solveig Thomassen, Ingebjøvg Reigstad, Jan Auestad; senior architects Ole S Trodahl, Anne Midtrod; county culture heritage officer Egil Harald Grude; senior executive officer/youth Malfrid Roen

Sogn and Fjordane County Municipality – Dept. of Culture
Sogn og Fjordane fylkeskommune – Kulturavdelingen
Postboks 173, 6801 **Førde**
Tel: 5782 5000 Fax: 5782 5050
regional cultural head Lidvin M Osland; administration director Trond Ueland

Sør-Trøndelag County Municipality – Dept. of Culture
Sør-Trøndelag fylkeskommune – Kulturavdelingen
Erling Skakkes gate 14, 7013 **Trondheim**
Tel: 7386 6000/6241 Fax: 7386 6046
E-Mail: knut.moller@fylkeshuset.sor-trondelag-f.post.no
regional cultural head Knut Møller

Telemark County Municipality – Dept. of Culture
Telemark fylkeskommune – kulturseksjonen
Fylkeshuset, 3706 **Skien**
Tel: 3558 4272 Fax: 3552 0154
regional cultural head t.b.a.; contact: regional director Lars Nicolaysen

Troms County Municipality – Dept. of Culture
Troms fylkeskommune – Kulturavdelingen
Strandveien 13, 9296 **Tromsø**
Tel: 7762 3000 Fax: 7762 3367
regional cultural head Nina Badendyck; interim head of culture Judith Romuld
Role & Services: department of culture in the county of Troms; international cooperation in the northern regions of Norway, Sweden, Finland and Russia

Vest-Agder County Municipality – Section of Trade and Culture
Vest-Agder fylkeskommune – Avdeling for noering samferdsel og kultur, kulturavdelingen
Postboks 770, 4666 **Kristiansand**
Tel: 3807 4500 Fax: 3807 4504
regional cultural head Anne Tore Hageland

Vestfold County Municipality – Sector for Regional Development, Dept. of Culture
Vestfold fylkeskommune – Sektor for regional utvikling, kuturavdelingen
Svend Foynsgt. 9, 3126 **Tønsberg**
Tel: 3334 4000 Fax: 3331 5905
E-Mail: bente.i.solberg@fadm.vestfold-f.kommune.no
head of cultural department Bente Lie Solberg

POLAND (+48)

• Federal

Ministry of Culture and Art
Ministerstwo Kultury i Sztuki
ul. Krakowskie Przedmiescie 15/17, 00-071 **Warszawa**
Tel: 22-620 0231 Fax: 22-826 1992 (minister)
minister of culture Andrzej Zakrzewski (tel: 22-826 5750); department of international cultural affairs Anna Niewiadomska (tel: 22-826 7331, fax: 826 1922); cultural activity promotion department director Agnieszka Komar-Morawska (tel: 22-826 7545/828 3789, fax: 22-827 3958)

• Regional

In 1999 as a result of an administrative reform Poland was divided into 16 big regions (voivodships); each of them is administered by a democratically elected council headed by a marshal (marszalek); councils are responsible for matters of common interest, among others culture

Kujawsko-Pomorski Regional Council – Marshal Office
Urzad Marszalkowski Województwa Kujawsko-Pomorskiego
Plac Teatralny 2, 87-100 **Toru**
Tel: 56-621 8390/622 2977 Fax: 56-621 0485

Lódzki Regional Council – Marshal Office
Urzad Marszalkowski Województwa Lódzkiego
ul. Sienkiewicza 3, 90-113 **Lódz**
Tel: 42-633 5176/630 1796 Fax: 42-633 8312

Low Silesia Regional Council – Marshal Office
Urzad Marszalkowski Województwa Dolnoslaskiego
Pl. Powstanców Slaskich 1, 50-951 **Wroclaw**
Tel: 71-343 5524 Fax: 71-343 5524

Lubelski Regional Council – Marshal Office
Urzad Marszalkowski Województwa Lubelskiego
ul. Spokojna 4, 20-914 **Lublin**
Tel: 81-532 6770 Fax: 81-532 6770

Lubuski Regional Council – Marshal Office
Urzad Marszalkowski Województwa Lubuskiego
ul. Podgórna 7, 65-057 **Zielona Góra**
Tel: 68-320 2037 Fax: 68-327 1429

Malopolski Regional Council – Marshal Office
Urzad Marszalkowski Województwa Malopolskiego
ul. Basztowa 22, 31-156 **Kraków**
Tel: 12-616 0229/422 9666 Fax: 12-421 5798

Mazovia Regional Council – Marshal Office
Urzad Marszalkowski Województwa Mazowieckiego
Pl. Bankowy 3/5, 00-950 **Warszawa**
Tel: 90-224 920 Fax: 22-620 1374

Opolski Regional Council – Marshal Office
Urzad Marszalkowski Województwa Opolskiego
ul. Piastowska 14, 45-082 **Opole**
Tel: 77-454 5137 Fax: 77-452 4265

Podkarpacki Regional Council – Marshal Office
Urzad Marszalkowski Województwa Podkarpackiego
ul. Bieszczadzka 1, 38-400 **Krosno**
Tel: 13-432 0313 Fax: 13-432 1335

Podlaski Regional Council – Marshal Office
Urzad Marszalkowski Województwa Podlaskiego
ul. Mickiewicza 3, 15-213 **Bialystok**
Tel: 85-732 4216 Fax: 85-732 0668

Pomorski Regional Council – Marshal Office
Urzad Marszalkowski Województwa Pomorskiego
ul. Okopowa 21/27, 80-810 **Gdansk**
Tel: 58-301 1412/307 7633 Fax: 58-301 8771

Silesia Regional Council – Marshal Office
Urzad Marszalkowski Województwa Slaskiego
ul. Jagiellonska 25, 40-032 **Katowice**
Tel: 32-255 5518 Fax: 32-256 4276

Swietokrzyski Regional Council – Marshal Office
Urzad Marszalkowski Województwa Swietokrzyskiego
al. IX Wieków Kielc 3, 25-955 **Kielce**
Tel: 41-342 1549 Fax: 41-344 5265

Warminsko-Mazurski Regional Council – Marshal Office
Urzad Marszalkowski Województwa Warminsko-Mazurskiego
al. Pilsudskiego 7/9, 10-959 **Olsztyn**
Tel: 89-523 2552 Fax: 89-523 2552

Wielkopolski Regional Council – Marshal Office
Urzad Marszalkowski Województwa Wielkopolskiego
Al. Niepodleglosci 16/18, 60-967 **Poznan**
Tel: 61-852 6007/854 1988 Fax: 61-854 1219

Zachodniopomorski Regional Council – Marshal Office
Urzad Marszalkowski Województwa Zachodniopomorskiego
ul. Waly Chrobrego 4, 70-502 **Szczecin**
Tel: 91-430 3368 Fax: 91-434 4994

PORTUGAL (+351)

• Federal

Ministry of Culture
Ministèrio da Cultura
Palácio Nacional da Ajuda, Calçada da Ajuda 3° andar, 1300 **Lisboa**
Tel: 1-361 4500 Fax: 1-364 9872
Internet: www.min-cultura.pt
minister of culture Prof. Dr. Manuel Marja Carrilho; secretary of state of the culture Drª Catarina Vaz Pinto

Secretary of State for Culture – General Direction for Cultural Activities
Secretaria de Estado da Cultura – Expeçaõ-Geral de Actividades Culturais
Palácio Foz, Praça dos Restauradores, Apartado 2616, 1269-139 **Lisboa** Codex
Tel: 1-321 2500 Fax: 1-321 2564/38
general-director Carlos Pedros Fernandez
Role & Services: protects the authors and performing rights; has an anti-piracy program; has incentive and aid programs for artistic productions on music, theatre, dance, plastic and stage arts; sets competitions and festivals; assigns scholarships to authors and artists and allowances to theatre companies and orchestras; runs the Oporto Classical Orchestra

Secretary of State for Culture – Office of International Cultural Relations
Secretaria de Estado da Cultura – Gabinete das Relações Culturais Internacionais
Rua s Pedro de Alcântara, 45-2°, 1269-139 **Lisboa** Codex
Tel: 1-346 8819/347 3923/342 9009/346 8819
Fax: 1-342 4605
directora Patricia Salvacão Barreto

Instituto Português das Artes do Espetaculo
Av. Concelheiro Fernando de Sousa 21A,
1070-072 **Lisboa**
Tel: 1-382 5200 Fax: 1-382 5207
E-Mail: ipae@meganet.pt
president Ana Marin; head of theatre Carlos Pimenta; head of dance Gil Mendo; head of music José Luis Maia; touring dept Rosa Matos; training dept Teresa Duarte; information center Maria Verissimo; technical dept Rosa Sousa
Role & Services: funding and promotion of professional performing arts in Portugal

Calouste Gulbenkian Foundation
Fundação Calouste Gulbenkian Serviço de Animação Artistica e Educação pela Arte (ACARTE)
Rua Dr. Nicolau de Bettencourt, 1067 **Lisboa** Codex
Tel: 1-793 5131 (music dept)
Fax: 1-793 5139/795 5206 (ACARTE)
Internet: www.telepac.pt/earte/gulbenkian
E-Mail: musica@gulbenkian.pt
chairman of the board of trustees Dr. Vitor de sa Machado; director, music department Dr. Luis Pereira Leal; assistant director, music department Carlos Ede Pontes Leça; director, department of animation, artistic creation and education through art (ACARTE) Yvette Centeno; assessors Domingos Morais, Maria de Assis Swinnerton; France branch Prof. Dr. António Coimbra Martins; international department Dr João Pedro Garcia; United Kingdom branch Ben Whitaker
Role & Services: supports culture extensively within Portugal and can also provide aid for Portuguese culture in other countries; has London and Paris offices providing aid to UK and France cultural activities; runs the Ballet Gulbenkian (q.v.), Orquestra Gulbenkian (q.v.), 1200- and 344-seat venues (q.v.), Gulbenkian choir, three festivals: in October, annual Early Music Festival, in May, annual Contemporary Music Festival, from October-May Great Orchestras from the world – invites the most prestigious orchestras to play, 2 major museums, and the largest network of libraries in Portugal; also organises concerts throughout Portugal; decentralisation programme *Comments:* accounts for approx 25% of arts funding in Portugal; see also Choirs, Dance, Venues, Festivals, Promoters, Orchestras

Instituto Camões
Campo Grande 56, 6° e 7° Andar, 1794-103 **Lisboa**
Tel: 1-795 5470 Fax: 1-795 6113/793 7675
Internet: www.instituto-camoes.pt
E-Mail: geral@instituto-camões.pt
president Dr. Jorge Couto; vice -presidents Drª de Bertina Sousa Gomes, Drª Ana Paula Zagarias; chief of publications, documentation and education division Dr. Mario Filipe
Comments: operates around the world, teaching Portuguese and diffusing Portuguese culture through more than 150 offices; publishes a monthly magazine

• Regional

Regional Cultural Delegation – Centre
Delegaçào Regional Da Cultura do Centro
Rua Gomes Freire de Andrade no.28, 3000-204 **Coimbra**
Tel: 39-701 391 Fax: 39-701 3178
E-Mail: cultura.centro@mail.telepac.pt
chairman Dr Anna Pires

Regional Cultural Delegation – Alentejo
Delegaçào Regional Da Cultura do Alentejo
Rua de Burgos no. 5 Apartado 235, 7003 **Evora** Codex
Tel: 66-741 964/963 Fax: 66-744 839
chairman Dra. Ana Maria de Mira Borges

Regional Cultural Delegation – Algarve
Delegaçào Regional Da Cultura do Algarve
Rua de Portugal no. 58, 8000-281 **Faro**
Tel: 89-805 773 Fax: 89-805 482
E-Mail: geral@kultalg.pt
chairman Dr. Joaõ Ventura

Regional Agency of the Secretary of State for Culture – North – Villa Real
Delegaçào Regional Da Cultura do Norte
Edificio da Cruz Vermelha, Av Aureliano Berrigas, 5000-413 **Vila Real**
Tel: 59-330 770 Fax: 59-330 779
chairman Dr. Jorge Ginja
Role & Services: represent the Secretary of State for Culture in the Northern Region of Portugal, coordinates the action of the local branches of SEC and support local cultural initiatives

Secretaria Regional de Educação e Cultura
Rua de Sé, 168, 9700 **Angra do Heroismo (Terceira, Azores)**
Tel: 95-216 191 Fax: 95-401 089
director Dr. Luis Fagundes Duarte

Madeira regional government -Dept for Culture
Direcçaõ Regional dos Asuntos Culturais
Rua dos Ferreiros 165, 9004-520 **Funchal (Madeira)**
Tel: 91-233 164 Fax: 91-230 341
regional secretary João Carlos Nunes de Abreu; director for culture Dr. João Henrique da Silva
Comments: see also Festivals

ROMANIA (+40)

Ministry of Culture
Piata Presei Libere 1, Sector 1, **Bucharest**
Tel: 1-223 1530/37/40/44
Fax: 1-222 6282 (dep. for international cultural relations)
minister Ion Caramitru (tel: 1-222 3338/3255, fax: 1- 223 4951); secretary of state (international cultural relations, literature) Maria Berza (tel: 1-222 3329, fax: 1-222 4837); secretary of state (performing arts, national minorities) Hunor Kelemen (tel: 1-223 0346); director, department of international cultural relations Vladimir Simon (tel: 1-222 3356, fax: 1-222 6282); director, historical monuments department Dan Nicolae (tel: 1-222 3215)
Role & Services: promotes main events in Romania, directs 41 local cultural inspectors jointly with local authorities, still subsidises almost all Romanian cultural organisations

RUSSIA (+7)

Ministry of Culture of the Russian Federation
Ministerstvo Kultury Rossistoi Federatsii
Kitaiskii pr. 7, 103693 **Moscow**
Tel: 095-925 2881 (minister)/0608/923 9351 (dept of foreign affairs) Fax: 095-925 2881
minister Vladimir Egorov

Cultural Committee of the St Petersburg Regional Administration
Komitet po kulture administratsii
Sankt-Peterburgskoi oblasti
Smolnii proezd 9, 193331 **St Petersburg**
Tel: 812-276 1420 Fax: 812-276 1846
chairman Vladimir Bogush

Main Cultural Direction of the St Petersburg Municipal Committee
Komitet po kulture goroda Sankt-Peterburga
Nevskii pr 40, 191011 **St Petersburg**
Tel: 812-312 2471 Fax: 812-110 5515
director Vladimir Jakovlev; theatre department Leonid Satst (tel/fax: 812-311 2148); history of culture department Liubov Agoshkova (tel/fax: 812-311 0723); international department Alexey Polikin (tel/fax: 812-311 7751); cinema department Boris Prokofiev (tel: 812-310 4187)
Comments: Foreign Relations Department of Culture Committee of Mayor's office: Tel: 812-311 7111/7751, Fax: 812-110 5993

Moscow Government Committee of Culture
Komitet po kulture pravitelstva Moskvy
Neglinnaya 8/10, 103031 **Moscow**
Tel: 095-921 9864 Fax: 095-928 9915
chairman Igor Bugayev

Cultural Direction of the Ekaterinburg Region
Upravlenie kultury Ekaterinburgsroi oblasti
ul. Myalysheva 46, 620219 **Ekaterinburg**
Tel: 3432-516 735
minister of culture of the Ekaterinburg Region Natalia Vetrova

Cultural Direction of the Nizhni Novgorod Region Administration
Upravlenie kultury Administratsii
Nizhegorodskoi oblasti
Kreml, 603082 **Nizhni Novgorod**
Tel: 8312-390 868/390 670
director Mikhail Groshev

Cultural Direction of the Novosibirsk Region
Upravlenie kultury Novosibirskoi oblasti
Krasni pr. 18, 630011 **Novosibirsk**
Tel: 3832-235 245
Fax: 3832-236 342
chairman Nikolai Tetenko

SAN MARINO (+378)

State Secretary for Education, Social Affairs, Culture and Justice
Segreteria di Stato per la Pubblica Istruzione gli Affari Sociali, gli Istituti Culturali e la Giustizia
Contrada Omerelli, 23, 47890 **San Marino**
Tel: 0549-882 250
Fax: 0549-882 301
E-Mail: segr.pub-istr@omniway.sm
segretario di stato Dott Sante Canducci; segretario particolare AvvElisabetta Lonfernini; coordinatore di Dipartimento Dott Paolo Mancini
Role & Services: responsible for education, leisure, memberships, theatre, culture, music, museums and libraries

Office of Social Activities and Culture
Ufficio Attività Sociali e Culturali
Contrada Omagnano 20, 47890 **San Marino**
Tel: 0549-882 452 (switchboard)
Fax: 0549-882 300
head of culture and performing arts Manlio Gozi; head of social affairs dott. ssa Marilena Stefanoni; head of administration Fausta Casadei; managing director dott. ssa Gemma Cavalleri

SLOVAKIA (+421)

Please note: changes have occurred to the telephone numbers within the whole country; new numbers have been provided where possible, however, some changes may have occurred after this section had gone to print

• Federal

Ministry of Culture of the Slovak Republic
Ministerstvo kultúry SR
Dobrovicova 12, 813 31 **Bratislava 1**
Tel: 7-539 1111
Fax: 7-531 9669
Internet: www.culture.gov.sk
E-Mail: mksr@culture.gov.sk
minister of culture Milan Knazko; state secretary Milan Gacík; general director of the art section Darina Kárová; director of foreign relations department Zuzana Bugánová
Comments: visiting address: Dobrovicova 12, 813 31 Bratislava, Tel: 7-5926 6495/5292 3295, Fax: 7-5296 8140

• Regional

Regional Council in Banská Bystrica
Krajsky úrad Banská Bystrica
Nám. L. Stúra 1, 975 41 **Banská Bystrica**
Tel: 88-423 1605/413 6460 (cultural department)
Fax: 88-413 6558/423 1515 (cultural department)
head of the regional council in Banská Bystrica Pavol Seckár; director of the department of culture Eva Chylová

Regional Council in Bratislava
Krajsky úrad Bratislava
Staromestská 6, 814 71 **Bratislava**
Tel: 7-5443 1050/5441 7077 (cultural department)
Fax: 7-5443 1282
head of the regional council of Bratislava Branislav Longauer; director of the department of culture Milan Kristofovic

Regional Council in Kosice
Krajsky úrad Kosice
Komenského 52, 041 26 **Kosice**
Tel: 95-600 1001/1185 (cultural department)
Fax: 65-633 6718/7134 (cultural department)
head of the regional council in Kosice Stefan Vranovsky; director of the department of culture Milan Biath

Regional Council in Nitra
Krajsky úrad Nitra
Stefánikova 69, 949 80 **Nitra**
Tel: 87-522 879/549 200/229/111 (cultural department)
Fax: 87-515 329/522 337/528 929 (cultural department)
head of the regional council in Nitra Peter Missík; director of the department of culture Ivan Gontko

Regional Council in Presov
Krajsky úrad Presov
Nám. Mieru 2, 080 73 **Presov**
Tel: 91-708 2200/2204/711 561 (cultural department)
Fax: 91-721 423/711 561 (cultural department)
head of the regional council in Presov Jozef Polacko; director of the department of culture Jozef Zajac

Regional Council in Trencín
Krajsky úrad Trencín
Hviezdoslavova 3, 911 49 **Trencín**
Tel: 831-434 397/513 415/436 821 (cultural department)
Fax: 831-441 017
head of the regional council in Trencín Dominik Gahér; director of the department of culture Eva Gazdíková

Regional Council in Trnava
Krajsky úrad Trnava
Kollárova 8, 917 77 **Trnava**
Tel: 805-551 2611/556 4111/4285 (cultural department)
Fax: 805-551 2320
head of the regional council in Trnava Martin Pado; director of the department of culture Lubica Malá

Regional Council in Zilina
Krajsky úrad Zilina
Janka Krála 4, 010 40 **Zilina**
Tel: 89-651 402/677 7111/7504/7505 (cultural dept.)
Fax: 89-651 428/677 7424/7453 (cultural department)
head of the regional council in Zilina Anton Straka; director of the department of culture Pavol Kuzma

SLOVENIA (+386)

Ministry of Culture of the Republic of Slovenia
Ministrstvo za kulturo
Cankarjeva 5, 1000 **Ljubljana**
Tel: 61-178 5900
Fax: 61-178 5901/2
Internet: www.sigov.si/mk
minister Jozef Skolc; state secretary Majda Sirca; undersecretary, international dept Marjutka Hafner; undersecretary for programme Ivan Pal; counsellor for the performing arts Simon Kardum; counsellor to the minister for music, opera and ballet Sonja Kralj

Ministry of Foreign Affairs of the Republic of Slovenia – Department of International Cultural Relations
Ministrstvo za zunanje zadeve Republike Slovenije – Sektor za mednarodne odnose v kulturi
Gregorciceva 25, 1000 **Ljubljana**
Tel: 61-178 2302 Fax: 61-178 2393
state undersecretary Tanja Orel-Sturm; counsellor to the government Tatjana Kovacic
Role & Services: deals with international cultural, educational and scientific cooperation

SPAIN (+34)

• Federal

Ministry of Education and Culture
Ministerio de Educación y Cultura
Plaza del Rey 1, 28004 **Madrid**
Tel: 91-701 7000 (culture)/8000 (education)
Fax: 91-701 7003 (culture)/7005 (education)
Internet: www.mec.es
E-Mail: informa.admini@sgt.mcu.es
ministro de educación y cultura Mariano Rajoy; subsecretario de educación y cultura Ana Maria Pastor; secretario de estado de cultura Miguel Angel Cortez Martín

National Institute for Scenic Arts and Music – INAEM
Instituto Nacional de las Artes Escénicas y de la Música – INAEM
Plaza del Rey 1, 28004 **Madrid**
Tel: 91-701 7014 Fax: 91-532 3179
Internet: www.mec.es
E-Mail: informa@inaem.mcu.es
director general Andrés Ruiz Tarazona; subdirector de departamento dramático Eduardo Galán; subdirector música y danza Juan José Herrera de la Muela; secretario general inaem Carlos de la Torre-Lluch
Role & Services: government department responsible for funding the performing arts

• Regional

Please note: in 1999 there were regional and provinical elections in all regions; so changes may have occurred

Andalucía Region – Regional Directorate of Cultural Promotion
Andalucía Región – Dirección General de Fomento y Promoción Cultural de la Consejería de Cultura; Junta de Andalucía
Calle Levilles nº 17, 41071 **Sevilla**
Tel: 95-455 5525/38 Fax: 95-455 5527
Internet: www.junta-andalucia.es/cultura
E-Mail: epgpc@retemail.es
directora general Elena Angulo Aranburu (95-455 9875); consejera de cultura Carmen Calvo Poyato; jefe de servicio de programas Adela Real Montero; empresa pública de gestión de programas culturales Elena Angula Aranburu; circuito andaluz de música Enrique Gamex (email: cam@epgpc.com)
Role & Services: promoters of performing arts, visual arts and literature in Andalucia; specialised Centres: Centro Andaluz de la Danza, Centro Andaluz del Teatro; Orquesta Joven de Andalucía

Aragón Region – General Directorate of Culture and Heritage
Aragón Región – Dirección General de Cultura y Patrimonio
Edificio Pignatelli, Paseo María Agustín 36, 50071 **Zaragoza**
Tel: 976-714 915/7 Fax: 976-714 808
Internet: www.aragon.net
E-Mail: info@correo.aragon.net
director general de cultura y patrimonio Domingo Buesa Conde; coordinador de exposiciones Fernando Moles; jefe de servicio de acción cultural Agustín Azaña Lorenzo; coordinador general José Luis Melendo
Role & Services: gives literary awards and grants, funds and coordinates Festivales de Aragon
Comments: see also Festivals

Asturias Region – Regional Directorate of Cultural Action
Asturias Región – Consejería de Cultura del Principado de Asturias
Plaza del Sol 8, 33071 **Oviedo**
Tel: 98-5106 710/106 700
Fax: 98-5106 731/732
consejero Francisco Javier, Fernandez Ballina; directora regional de cultura t.b.a.
Role & Services: government department responsible for the performing arts, education, sports youth, women and culture in Asturias

Basque County Region – Directorate of Creation & Cultural Production: Cultural Department
País Vasco Región – Dirección de Creación y Difusión Cultural: Departamento de Cultura
C/ Duque de Wellington 2, 01010 **Vitoria-Gasteiz**
Tel: 945-019 466 Fax: 945-019 535
Internet: www.euskadi.net
E-Mail: Difusion@ej-ev.es
director Ricardo Bilbao; director partrimonio Eduardo Estrade; director deportes Xavier Leibar; director juventud José Luis Madrazo

Canarias Region – General Directorate of Culture
Canarias Región – Dirección General de Cultura
Plaza de los Derechos Humanos s/n, Edificio Usos Múltiples 1, 5ª planta,
35003 **Las Palmas de Gran Canaria**
Tel: 928-380 000 Fax: 928-363 681
Internet: www.cultura.siscom.es.
E-Mail: bgalvau@seleue.siscom.es
director general Horacio Umpierrez Sánchez; viceconsejero de cultura Angel Marrero Alayon
Role & Services: management and production of scenic and performance arts; performing arts are coordinated by SOCAEN (Sociedad Canaria de las Artes Escénicas y de la Música)

Cantabria Region – General Directorate of Culture
Cantabria Región – Dirección General de Cultura
Pasaje de Peña 2, 1º, 39008 **Santander**
Tel: 942-207 420/1 Fax: 942-217 666
director general de cultura Fernando Castillo Gutiérrez; consejero Francisco Javier López Marcano
Role & Services: government department responsible for heritage, culture and sports *Comments:* responsible for the management of venue: Palacio de Festivales de Cantabria, 1600 (see Venues)

Castilla-La Mancha Region: General Directorate of Education & Culture
Castilla-La Mancha Región: Consejería de Educación y Cultura
Plaza del Cardenal Siliceo s/n, 45071 **Toledo**
Tel: 925-267 400/445 (teatro)/482 (dance, music)
Fax: 925-267 508
Internet: www.jccm.es
E-Mail: gavinete.eduycultoria@jcm.es
director general de cultura Mª Angeles Diaz Vieco; teatro Emilio Recio; música y danza Ana Muñoz; director general de enseñanza universitaria, investigacion y desarrollo educativo Jenacio Gavira Toma; director general de educación Angel Altisen Peñas

Castilla & León Region – General Directorate of Heritage and Cultural Promotion: Performing Arts Section
Castilla y León Región – Dirección General de Patrimonio y Promoción Cultural, Sección de Música y Artes Escénicas; Junta de Castilla y Léon: Consejería de Educación y Cultura
Monasterio Nuestra Señora de Prado, Autovía Puente Colgante s/n, 47014 **Valladolid**
Tel: 983-411 503/696 Fax: 983-411 568
E-Mail: gloria.sanchez@svac.dgppc.cec.jcil.es
director general de patrimonio y promoción cultural Javier Toquero Mateo; servicio de acción cultural Amparo Gómez Merino; jefa de sección del departamento de música y artes escénicas Gloria Sánchez Calvo
Role & Services: organizes courses for the performing arts; responsible for programming of Red de Teatros de Castilla y León (Network of Theatres of Castilla & León)
Comments: publications: Memoria Anual de la Red de Teatro, Libro Blanco de las Artes Escénicas de Castilla y León, Propuestas para una Crisis

Catalan Consortium for the External Promotion of Culture (COPEC)
Consorci Catalá de Promoció Exterior de la Cultura (COPEC)
Portal de Santa Madrona, 6-8, 08001 **Barcelona**
Tel: 93-316 2780 Fax: 93-316 2789
Internet: www.copec.es
E-Mail: copec@correu.gencat.es
director Valentí Sallas
Role & Services: autonomous body formed by the Department of Culture of the Generalitat of Catalonia to promote Catalan culture abroad, also office in London, see entry under United Kingdom

Catalunya Region – General Directorate of Cultural Promotion: Culture Department; Autonomous Government of Catalunya
Cataluña Región – Direcció General de Promoció Cultural: Departament de Cultura; Generalitat de Catalunya
Portal de Santa Madrona 6 y 8, 08001 **Barcelona**
Tel: 93-316 2780 Fax: 93-316 2781
Internet: www.diba.es/escenari/
E-Mail: kultiso@correu.gencat.es
general director of cultural promotion Vicente Villatoro; general subdirector of cultural promotion Rosa Pascual
Role & Services: government department responsible for cultural activities; gives awards to Catalan literature and grants

Extremadura Region – General Directorate of Culture and National Heritage
Extremadura Región – Consejería de Cultura y Patrimonio; Comunidad Autónoma de Extremadura
Almendralejo 14, 06800 **Mérida**
Tel: 924-381 222 Fax: 924-381 313
consejero Francisco Muñoz Ramírez; director general centro dramatico y musical Carmelo Sayago
Role & Services: government department responsible for performing arts & music; gives grants for dance & music, manages Sala Trajano, see also Venues

Galicia Region – General Directorate of Cultural Promotion
Galicia Región – Dirección General de Promoción Cultural
Edificio Administrativo San Caetano s/n, bloque 3, 2°, 15771 **Santiago de Compostela**
Tel: 981-544 816 Fax: 981-544 887
Internet: www.xunta.es
E-Mail: castillayleon@redteatros.inaem.sarenet.es
director general Omero José Mª Pérez Quintana (tel: 981-544 886); subdirector Javier Senin Fernández
Role & Services: give funding for cultural activities
Comments: alternative e-mail: cg112110@xunta.es

Galician Institute for Music and the Performing Arts
Instituto Galego das Artes Escénica e Musicais (IGAEM)
Pavillón de Galicia. San Lázaro s/n, 15703 **Santiago de Compostela**
Tel: 981-577 126/8 Fax: 981-577 127
Internet: www.xunta.es
E-Mail: secretaria@igaem.com
presidente José Mª García;
gerente Aníbal Otero Fernández
Role & Services: gives grants for courses in theatre, music and dance; it has a theatre company (Centro Dramático Galego) and Ballet Galego Rey de Viana
Comments: autonomous organisation with commercial status affiliated with the Consellería de Cultura de la Xunta de Galicia; Centro de Documentación tel: 981-581 777

La Rioja Region – Council of Education, Culture, Sport and Youth: Cultural Promotion
La Rioja Región: Consejería de Educación, Cultura, Deportes y Juventud: Promoción Cultural
Portales 2, 26071 **Logroño**
Tel: 941-291 100 Fax: 941-291 261
director general Domingo Rivera Canobellas; consejero Luis Angel Alegre Galilea

Murcia Region – General Directorate of Culture
Murcia Región – Dirección General de Cultura
Gran Vía Francisco Salcillo 42, Edificio Galerías, 30005 **Murcia**
Tel: 968-362 000 Fax: 968-201 162
director general de cultura Miguel Angel Centenero Gallego; consejero Fernando de la Cierva Carrasco; secretary general Maria Pedro Reverte García
Comments: performing arts funding body; organises courses in music; youth orchestras

Navarra Region – General Directorate of Culture: Príncipe de Viana Institute
Navarra Región – Dirección General de Cultura: Inistitución Príncipe de Viana
Calle Santo Domingo Nº 8, 31001 **Pamplona**
Tel: 948-426 500 Fax: 948-223 906
Internet: www.cfnavarra.es
E-Mail: yosesper@cfnavarra.es
director general Tomás Yerro; director patrimonio histórico Carlos Idoate Ezquieta; director acción cultural José Ortega García
Role & Services: organizes Festival de Teatro y Danza 'Escena' (May), Semana Música Antigua (Sept), Festivales de Navarra

Palma de Mallorca Comission for Culture and Heritage
Comisió de Cultura i Patrimoni
Centre Cultural de la Misericòrdia, Via Roma, 1, 07012 **Palma de Mallorca**
Tel: 971-368 390 Fax: 971-717 066
E-Mail: cultura@cim.net
conseller del departamento de cultura, educación y deportes Manuel Ferrer Massanet; director general de deportes Ventura Blach; director general de política lingüística Jaume Gill; director general de planificación y centros Rafael Bosch; director general de ordenación e innovación Miquel Esvert
Role & Services: coordination of cultural activities in Mallorca

Valencia Region – General Directorate of Cultural Promotion
Valencia Región – Consellería de Cultura Educació i Ciència, Dirección General de Promoción Cultural
Avda Campanar 32, 46015 **Valencia**
Tel: 96-386 6500/3213
Fax: 96-386 6574 (prom. cult.)/394 2184 (teatros)
Internet: www.cult.gva.es
director general de promoción cultural Consuelo Ciscar Casaban; conseller Manuel Tarancón Fandos
Comments: Institut Valencia d'Arts Esceniques, Cinematografía i Música, Plaza del Ayuntamiento 17, 46002 Valencia; tel: 96-351 2336; fax: 96-352 5079; see also Festivals

• Provincial

Barcelona Provincial Government – Culture Department
Oficina de Difusió Artistica – Area de Cultura de la Diputació de Barcelona
c/Montalegre 7, 08001 **Barcelona**
Tel: 93-402 2565 Fax: 93-402 2819
Internet: www.diba.es/escenari

E-Mail: src.oda@diba.es
director Francesc Vila
Role & Services: public services organisation which promotes theatre, music, dance and opera in towns in the province of Barcelona; main services and activities are management of a permanent circuit of professional shows (theatre, music, dance and opera); preparation and maintenance of an on line data-base on shows in Catalonia; advice to towns on organising shows and management of facilities for promoting the arts

Basque Country Region – Administrative Council for Alava: Department of Culture
País Vasco Región – Diputación Foral de Alava: Departamento de Cultura
Plaza de la Provincia 5-3ª, 01001 **Vitoria-Gasteiz**
Tel: 945-181 818 Fax: 945-181 947
Internet: www.jet.es/paginasjet.htm
E-Mail: cazkuespaña@alava.es
director general de cultura Ramon Rabaneda
Role & Services: give grants for dance and music; organizes literary competitions; organizes performing arts workshops; early music and organ festivals

Madrid Region – Cultural Council
Madrid Región: Consejería de Cultura
Plaza de España 8, 28008 **Madrid**
Tel: 91-580 2505 Fax: 91-580 2565
Internet: www.comadrid.es
consejero de cultura Alicia Moreno Espert; director general promoción cultura José Manuel Pérez Aguilar; danza & música t.b.a.; asesor de teatro t.b.a.; prensa Mercedes Calvo

Basque Country Region – Administrative Council for Vizcaya: Department of Culture
País Vasco Región – Diputación Foral de Vizcaya: Departamento de Cultura
Alameda de Recalde 30,2°, 48009 **Bilbao**
Tel: 94-420 7700 Fax: 94-420 8792
Internet: www.bizkaia.net
diputado general de cultura Ana Madariaga
Role & Services: gives grants for theatre and dance

• Municipal

Barcelona Municipal Government – Institute of Culture
Ayuntament de Barcelona – Instituto de Cultura de Barcelona
Palau de la Virreina, Ramblas, 99, 08002 **Barcelona**
Tel: 93-301 7775 Fax: 93-317 1240/301 6100
Internet: www.bcn.es
E-Mail: infoicub@intercom.es
regidor de cultura (local minister for culture) Ferrán Mascarell; director/manager Jordi Martí Grau; presidente de l'auditori Joaquim de Nadal
Role & Services: runs 12 municipal museums, one municipal theatre, a summer festival, the Barcelona Symphony Orchestra, organizes the 12 Prizes of Barcelona, the Summer Festival, Festival de Teatro Grec and directly participates in most of cultural activities and venues of the city; manages cultural resources and equipment, makes decisions on arts subsidy
Comments: see also Orchestras, Venues and Festivals

Bilbao Municipal Government – Culture and Tourism Department
Ayuntamiento de Bilbao – Area de Cultura y Turismo
Plaza Ernesto Ercoreca s/n, 5° Planta, 48007 **Bilbao**
Tel: 94-420 4420 Fax: 94-420 4403
Internet: www.bilbao.net
E-Mail: cultura@ayto.bilbao.net
concejal de cultura (town councellor for culture) José Luis Sabas; directora Ana Elejalde Lorente; animación Amaya Aguirrezábal, Fernando Perez
Role & Services: municipal arts funding and promotional body *Comments:* organizes Fiesta de Bilbao, and Festival Int. de Musica Tropical

Las Palmas Municipal Government – Culture Department
Ayuntamiento de Las Palmas – Consejo Municipal de Cultura y Fiestas Populares
León y Castillo 330, 35007 **Las Palmas de Gran Canaria**
Tel: 928-446 022 Fax: 928-446 043/368 993
E-Mail: cultura@laspalmasgc.es
departamento de eventos culturales Mª Soledad Castro Sánchez, Mª del Rosario de León Fernández; departamento de artes escénicas Adela Martín Hinojal, Mª Soledad García Abraham; interventor-delegado Santiago Rodríguez Cárdenes; administrador del teatro pérez galdós Juan Molero
Comments: owner of Teatro Pérez Galdós (tel 928-361 509); organizes Festival de Otoño (Oct/Nov); see alsoVenues

Madrid Municipal Government – Cultural Department
Ayuntamiento de Madrid – Concejalía del Area de Cultura
Conde Duque 9-11, 28015 **Madrid**
Tel: 91-588 5821/540 4010 Fax: 91-588 5839
Internet: www.munimadrid.es/
E-Mail: 4teniente@munimadrid.es
concejal de cultura y educación Mª Jesus Freile
Role & Services: responsible for cultural programming; organizes festival Veranos de la Villa, and Fiestas de San Isidro *Comments:* gives awards for arts

Málaga Municipal Government – Cultural Activities Department
Ayuntamiento de Málaga – Area Cultura, Educación y Turismo
Alameda Principal 23, 4°, Edificio Archivo Municipal, 29001 **Málaga**
Tel: 952-220 023/043 Fax: 952-220 033
concejal de cultura, educación y turismo Antonio M. Garrido Moraga; director area de cultura Juan Ignacio Montañez; director turismo Francisco Game
Comments: owners of Teatro Municipal Miguel de Cervantes with own orchestra; Orquesta Ciudad de Malaga, director gerente Benjamin Esparza Gil (tel: 952-222 805); see Orchestras

Murcia Municipal Government – Culture Department
Ayuntamiento de Murcia – Fomento y Promoción Cultural
Palacio Almudí, Plano de San Francisco 8, 30004 **Murcia**
Tel: 968-211 024/210 815 Fax: 968-222 238/216 248
concejal de cultura Antonio González Barnés; jefe de servicio de museos y actividades culturales Manuel Fernández-Delgado (952-221 099); jefe de servicio Mª Luisa Feral Noguera
Comments: exhibition hall and conference hall; owners of Teatro Romea and Museo Ciencia y Agua

Palma de Mallorca Municipal Government – Culture Department
Ayuntament de Palma de Mallorca – Area de Cultura
c/ Almudaina 7° A, 07001 **Palma de Mallorca**
Tel: 971-727 744/714 745 Fax: 971-716 474
Internet: www.palma.es
E-Mail: cultura@a-palma.es
regidora cultura y juventud Carmen Feliú Alvarez de Sotomayor; director de arte Luis Socías Cerda; coordinador de espectaculos José Gabriel Pomar Ordinas
Comments: the Department of Youth publishes the magazine – Te Interesa

Seville Municipal Government – Culture Department
Ayuntamiento de Sevilla – Area de Cultura
c/ El Silencio 1, 41001 **Sevilla**
Tel: 95-450 5622/23/24/25 Fax: 95-450 5640
Internet: www.sevilla.org
E-Mail: serscultura@sitrantor.es
delegada de cultura Paola Vivancos; director Manuel Zid Pérez; jefa de servicio Natalia Laguarda; teatro Juan Victor Rodríguez Yagüe (Lope de Vega), Guadalupe Tempestini (Sala Alameda); música y danza José Sánchez; jefe de servicios, archivo, biblioteca y hemeroteca municipal Alfonso Braojos; seccion del libro y educación – Concepción Padial Marín; educación Andrés Iglesias
Role & Services: organises festivals and local cultural activities; publishes 'El siglo que viene'
Comments: see also Venues and Drama

Valencia Municipal Government – Cultural Department
Ayuntamiento de Valencia – Area de Cultura
Pl de Ayuntamiento 1, 46002 **Valencia**
Tel: 96-352 5478 ext 1200 Fax: 96-352 9871
concejal delegado Ferias y Fiestas Alfonso Grau Alonso; concejal delegado de cultura Mª José Alcón Miguel
Comments: exhibition hall Las Atarazanas; organizes festivals and competitions: Certamen de Bandas de Musica (July), Expotoven (December), Feria de Juliol (July)

Valladolid Municipal Government – Cultural Department (Music, Theatre and Dance)
Ayuntamiento de Valladolid – Fundación Municipal de Cultura (Música, Teatro y Danza)
Torrecilla 5, 47003 **Valladolid**
Tel: 983-426 246 Fax: 983-426 254
Internet: www.fmcva.org
E-Mail: fmcva@fmcva.org
concesal de cultura Alberto Gutierrez; teatro, música y danza Mario Pérez Tápanes; gerente de la fundación municipal de cultura t.b.a.
Comments: organises Muestra Int del Teatro (Nov) and Muestra Int de la Danza (May)

Zaragoza Municipal Government – Culture Department
Ayuntamiento de Zaragoza – Servicio de Cultura
Torreón de Fortea, Calle Torrenueva 25, 50003 **Zaragoza**
Tel: 976-721 400 Fax: 976-200 260
E-Mail: cultura-mye@ayto-zaragoza.es
teniente alcalde Verónica López Fontagne; director del area de cultura Rafeal Ordónez Fernandez; gerente sociedad municipal zaragoza cultural José Luis Azón
Comments: Owner of Teatro Principal c/Coso 57, 50001 Zaragoza, and Museo Pablo Gargallo, Museo del Foro de Caesar Augusta (Tel 976-292 622/296 090)

SWEDEN (+46)

Ministry of Culture
Kultur departementet
103 33 **Stockholm**
Tel: 8-405 1000 Fax: 8-216 819/3
minister for cultur Marita Ulvskog; minister Ulrica Messing; secretaries of state Ann-Christin Nykvist, Lena Nyberg; press secretaries Hans Ånell, Ursula Berge; political advisors Gunilla Thorgren, Refik Sener
Role & Services: decisions regarding cultural policies

Swedish National Council for Cultural Affairs
Statens kulturråd
Långa Raden 4, Skeppsholmen, PO Box 7843, 103 98 **Stockholm**
Tel: 8-679 7260 Fax: 8-611 1349
Internet: www.kur.se
E-Mail: statens.kulturrad@kur.se
director Göran Lannegren; information department Per Sveson; information assistant Kennet Gabrielsson
Role & Services: the Council has the central responsibility for application of the State's cultural policies; its tasks include co-ordinating, advising, distributing grants etc.

Swedish Institute, The
Svenska Institutet
Hamngatan 27, Box 7434, 103 91 **Stockholm**
Tel: 8-789 2000 Fax: 8-207 248
Internet: www.si.se
E-Mail: si@si.se
director general Erland Ringborg; responsible for performing arts Hans Lepp; director of information & marketing Lisbeth Lüfberg
Role & Services: the Swedish institute is a public agency concerned with disseminating knowledge about Sweden abroad and promoting exchanges with other countries in culture, education, research and other sectors of public life

Federation of Swedish County Councils
Box 70491, 107 26 **Stockholm**
Tel: 8-702 4300 Fax: 8-702 4590
E-Mail: landstemgsforbundet@if.se
head of section for regional development Martin Andreaf; policy analysts Anders Lemegik; executive director Monica Sundström; information department director Erik Trillkott; directors international affairs Lars Öhrman, Elmire af Geijerstam
Role & Services: the Federation of Swedish County Councils represents the governmental, professional and employer-related interest of its members: the 18 county councils and 2 regional Municipalities & 1 municipality of Gothenburg, Malmö and Gotland;
it works to uphold and develop the county councils' role as directly-elected, democratic bodies at the regional level. Effort to inform and shape public opinion, to monitor professional developments and disseminate information are important elements of the Federation's work; it is also the central employers' organisation for the county councils
Comments: as a representative for the regional level in Sweden the Federation has six nominated political representatives in the committee of the Regions (CoR) of the European Union; cultural affairs are organised as a part of the work of the Federation's Section for Regional Development

• County Councils

The County Councils are responsible for matters of common interest which are too extensive and too costly for individual municipalities to manage. This mainly concerns health care, which is the County Councils' major task, but also public transport, culture, higher and secondary education, tourism, the environment, support for business and industry and regional growth and development. The County Councils' funding of cultural activities amounts to approximately SEK 1 billion per year in the form of grants to regional cultural institutions and various popular movements and organisations.

Blekinge County Council
Landstinget i Blekinge
Wämö Centre, 371 81 **Karlskrona**
Tel: 455-88000 Fax: 455-80250
E-Mail: landstinget.blekinge@ltblekinge.se
culture secretary Ylva Haasum

Dalarna County Council – Culture Department
Landstinget Dalarna – Utbildnings och kulturnämndens
Box 712, 791 29 **Falun**
Tel: 23-490 000 Fax: 23-490 220
E-Mail: landstinget.dalarna@ltdalarna.se
head of cultural section Åke Sundberg

Gävleborg County Council – Culture Department
Landstinget i Gävleborgs – Utbildnings och kulturnämndens
Kyrkogatan 4, 801 18 **Gävle**
Tel: 26-155 700/986 (culture dept)
Fax: 26-183 731
E-Mail: lt@lg.se
head of department Åsa Viren
Role & Services: Department is responsible for arts and culture in the area of Gävleborg

Halland County Council – Cultural Department
Landstinget i Halland – Utbildnings och kulturnämnden
PO Box 517, 301 80 **Halmstad**
Tel: 35-134 800 Fax: 35-135 444
E-Mail: landstinget.halland@cfv.lthalland.se
head of section for culture and art Ingemar Andréasson
Role & Services: deals with regional culture in the county of Halland

Jämtland County Council – Culture Dept
Jämtlands läns Landsting – Kulturenheten
zä Tagränd
PO Box 602, 832 23 **Frösön**
Tel: 63-147 500 Fax: 63-147 515
E-Mail: jamtlands.lans.landsting@jll.se
head of department Hans Nordmark
Role & Services: The Kulturenheten deals with regional culture in the county of Jämtland

Jönköping County Council – Culture Department
Landstinget i Jönköpings län – Utbildnings och kulurnämndens
Box 1024, 551 11 **Jönköping**
Tel: 36-324 000 Fax: 36-166 599
E-Mail: landstinget@kansli.ltkpg.se
head of culture Goy Persson
Role & Services: deals with culture in the region of Jönköping

Kalmar County Council – Culture Department
Landstinget i Kalmar län – Utbildnings-och kulturförvaltningen
PO Box 601, 391 26 **Kalmar**
Tel: 480-84000 Fax: 480-84197
E-Mail: landstinget@ltkalmar.se
head of culture Ulf Bexell

Kronoberg County Council
Landstinget Kronoberg
Allmän kultur, 351 88 **Växjö**
Tel: 470-588 500 Fax: 470-588 530
E-Mail: landstinget@ltkronoberg.se
head of culture Jan-Gustav Gustafsson

Norrbotten County Council – Culture Department
Landsting i Norrbottens läns Kultur – Ochutbildningsförvaltningen
Robertsviksgatan 7, 971 89 **Luleå**
Tel: 920-78000/78255 Fax: 920-78027
Internet: www.nll.se
E-Mail: jan.henriksson@nll.se
secretary of cultural affairs Jan Henriksson; cultural assistant Jenny Nilsson
Role & Services: the County Council and its cultural board are responsible for the cultural policy in the region, and is the financial resource for all regional activities; provide information through regional database: http://www.nll.se/arcticult future plans include an expansion of this database to involve other countries in the Barent Region
Comments: the county of Norrbotten is the most northern region of Sweden and consists of 1/4 of Sweden; strong cultural exchange with the Barent Euro Arctic Region, Scotland, Greece

Örebro County Council – Culture Department
Örebro läns Landsting – Utbildnings och kulturnämndens
Box 1613, 701 16 **Örebro**
Tel: 19-157 000 Fax: 19-611 8132
E-Mail: orebroll@orebroll.se
head of cultural section Toni Eriksson

Östergötland County Council – Culture Department
Landstinget i Östergötland – Utbildnings och kulturnämndens
581 91 **Linköping**
Tel: 13-227 000 Fax: 13-227 100
E-Mail: landstinget@lio.se
head of culture/education department Margreta Jonsson
Comments: libraries, schools, culture, communications

Region Skåne – Kultur Skåne
Box 267, 216 23 **Landskrona**
Tel: 418-454 581 Fax: 418-454 599
Internet: www.skane.se
E-Mail: chris.marschall@skane.se
head of cultural affairs Chris Marschall; cultural assistant Cecilia Palmkvist (454 581)
Role & Services: supports regional and international arts projects

Culture and Education Department of Stockholm County Council
Landstinget i Stockholms Län Kultur och Utbildningsnämndens
Ormbergsvägen 6, Box 9099, 102 72 **Stockholm**
Tel: 8-737 2500 Fax: 8-645 1002
E-Mail: hans.ullström@kun.sll.se
manager of cultural department Anders Hansen

Culture and Education Department of Uppsala County Council
Kultur & Utbildning, Landstinget i Uppsala län
Box 26074, 750 26 **Uppsala**
Tel: 18-176 000 Fax: 18-176 539
E-Mail: solweig.ekstrom@adm.ku.lul.se
head of department Solweig Ekström; secretaries of cultural affairs Andreas Bjersby, Louise Bown, Annika Elnarsson, Åke Forsgren, Helen Lind, Maria Bergren
Comments: alternative e-mail: andreas.bjersby@kultur.kult.lul.se

Culture Department of Värmland County Council
Landstinget i Värmlands län – Utbildnings-och kulturnämndens
651 82 **Karlstad**
Tel: 54-194 000/215 (culture department)
Fax: 54-194 298/058 (culture department)
E-Mail: anders.petterson@regional.leu.se
head of regional department Anders Pettersson

Culture Department of Västerbottens County Council
Landstinget i Västerbottens län – Utbildnings-och kulturnämndens
901 89 **Umeå**
Tel: 90-785 7000 Fax: 90-136 570
E-Mail: ann.landstrom.lt@vll.se
head of cultural department Ann Landstrom

Culture Department of Västernorrland County Council
Landstinget i Västernorrlands län – Utbildnings-och kulturnämndens
871 85 **Härnösand**
Tel: 611-80000 (general)/80350 (culture)
Fax: 611-80152 (culture)
E-Mail: landstinget.vasternorrland@lvn.se
head of cultural department Christer Nylén

Västmanland County Coucil – Culture Department
Landstinget i Västmanland län – Utbildnings-och kulturnämndens
721 51 **Västerås**
Tel: 21-173 000 Fax: 21-174 546
E-Mail: landstingets.kansli.myndighetsbrevlada@ltvastmanland.se
head of culture department Christer Olsson

West Sweden County Council – Culture Department
Landstinget Skarborgs kulturnämnd Västra Götalands Läs County Council
Box 764, 451 26 **Udderalla**
Tel: 522-670 800
Fax: 522-670 805
E-Mail: khristin.quentzer@vgrageiun.se
head manager of culture Khristin Quentzer

• Municipal Councils

Municipality of Gotland – Culture Department
Kung Magnus väg 16, 621 81 **Visby**
Tel: 498-269 000 Fax: 498-215 520
E-Mail: gotlands_kommun@gotland.se
head of culture Ulla Pettersson

Stockholm City Council
Ragnar Östbergs Plan 1, 105 35 **Stockholm**
Tel: 8-508 29000 Fax: 8-508 29940
contact Birgitta Rydell

SWITZERLAND (+41)

Please note: parlamentiary elections were held in October 1999; so changes may have occurred

• Federal

Federal Office of Culture
Bundesamt für Kultur
Hallwylstrasse 15, 3003 **Bern**
Tel: 31-322 9266
Fax: 31-322 9273
Internet: www.kultur-schweiz.admin.ch
E-Mail: regula.schatzmann@bak.admin.ch
director David Streiff (31-322 9261); head of information Regula Schatzmann-Brawand (tel:31-322 7985)
Role & Services: the Swiss Federal Office of Culture is the government instrument for all basic questions of cultural policy; it is divided into three fields: the promotion of culture, the Swiss National Library and the Swiss National Museum; its duties are to encourage cultural activity: fine art, design, cinema, conservation of historic monuments, socio-cultural events, questions of language and minorities and youth

Arts Council of Switzerland
Pro Helvetia – Schweizer Kulturstiftung
Hirschengraben 22, 8024 **Zürich**
Tel: 1-267 7171 Fax: 1-267 7106
Internet: www.pro-helvetia.ch
E-Mail: phmail@pro-helvetia.ch
director Bernard Cathomas; vice director Rolf Keller; head of theatre and dance Barbara Suthoff; Abteilungsleiter visuelle Künste Christoph Eggenberger; Abteilungsleiter Literatur und Geisteswissenschaften Erica Benz; Abteilungsleiter Musik Thomas Gartmann; Abteilungsleiter Kommunikation Michael Guggenheimer; Abteilungsleiter Réseaux Thomas Laely
Role & Services: government funded arts council responsible for promotion and encouragement of Swiss arts both in and out of Switzerland

Culture and Sport Office of Solothurn Canton
Amt für Kultur und Sport des Kantons Solothurn
Rathaus, 1509 **Solothurn**
Tel: 326-272 978 Fax: 326-277 685
E-Mail: franziska.ruprecht@aio.ktso.ch
Vorsteher Rainer W. Walter

Culture Office – Department of the Interior and Military Ministery of St. Gallen Canton
Amt für Kultur – Department für Inneres und Militär des Kantons St. Gallen
Regierungsgebäude, 9001 **St Gallen**
Tel: 71-229 3213 Fax: 71-229 3805
E-Mail: walter.lendi@dim-asku.sg.ch
Leiter Dr Walter Lendi

• Regional

Education Department of Jura Canton
Département de l'Education du Canton de Jura
2 rue du 24-Septembre, 2800 **Delémont**
Tel: 32-420 5400 Fax: 32-420 5001
Internet: www.jura.ch
délégué aux affaires culturelles & chef du patrimoine Michel Hauser (tel: 32-465 7400, fax: 32-465 7499, e-mail: Michel.hauser@jura.ch)

Public Education Department of Geneva Canton
Département de l'Instruction Publique du Canton de Genève
Case postale 3925, 1211 **Genève** 3
Tel: 22-319 2111/2753 (culture) Fax: 22-319 3443
délégué aux affaires culturelles Jean Pierre Ballenegger

Public Education Department of Neuchâtel Canton
Département de l'Instruction Publique et des Affaires Culturelles
Chateau, 2001 **Neuchâtel**
Tel: 32-889 6900 Fax: 32-889 6282
E-Mail: Secretariat.DIPAC@he.ch
secrétaire général Daniel Ruedin

Department of Education, Culture and Sport – Valais Canton
Département de l'éducation, de la culture et du sport
3, place de la Planta, 1950 **Sion**
Tel: 27-606 4000 Fax: 27-606 4004
délégué aux affaires culturelles Karl Salzgeber; chef de département Serge Sierro
Role & Services: support of cultural activity in the canton of Valais

Cultural Advice Service of Vaud Canton
Service des activités culturelles du Canton de Vaud
8 rue de la Barre, 1014 **Lausanne**
Tel: 21-316 3300 Fax: 21-316 3306
E-Mail: brigitte.waridel@dfj.vd.ch
chef de service des activités culturelles Brigitte Waridel
Role & Services: responsibility for and surveillance of cultural institutions in the Canton; financial aid for cultural creation and promotion in the Canton

Department for Cultural Affairs of Fribourg Canton
Département des affaires culturelles du Canton de Fribourg
rue de l'Hôpital 1, 1700 **Fribourg**
Tel: 26-305 1206 (main)/81 (culture) Fax: 26-3051 20614
Internet: www.fribourg-culture.ch
E-Mail: bergerg@etat.fr.ch
responsable des affaires culturelles Gérald Berger
Role & Services: the department supervises all the canton's cultural services and provides grants to performers whose work is thought worth supporting

Education and Cultural Affairs Department of Thurgau Canton
Département für Erziehung und Kultur des Kantons Thurgau
Regierungsgebäude, 8510 **Frauenfeld**
Tel: 52-724 2268 Fax: 52-724 2956
E-Mail: hboehlen@klik.ch
Departementchefin Freni Schawalder; Departementssekretär Heinrich Lang; Leiter Fachstelle für Kultur Kurt Künzler

Education and Culture Department of Ticino Canton – Cultural Division
Dipartimento dell'Istruzione e della Cultura – Divisione Della Cultura
Viale S. Franscini, 30a, 6501 **Bellinzona**
Tel: 91-814 1300 Fax: 92-814 1309
E-Mail: dic-dc@ti.ch
direttore Dino Jauch; aggiunto direttore Lorenzo Sganzini
Role & Services: coordinates the management of the Cantonali cultural institutions and supervises sponsoring policy of cultural activities

Education Department of Nidwalden
Bildungsdirektion Nidwalden
Marktgasse 3, 6371 **Stans**
Tel: 41-618 7413 Fax: 41-618 7345
E-Mail: bildungsdirektion.nidwalden@bluven.ch
Vorsteher und Sekretär Dr. Christoph Mylaeus; Regierungsrat Dr. Victor Furrer

Education and Culture Department of Basel regional Canton
Erziehungs- u. Kulturdirektion des Kantons Basel-Landschaft – Abteilung Kulturelles
Rheinstrasse 31, 4410 **Liestal**
Tel: 61-925 5067/5111 (switchboard) Fax: 61-925 6930
Leiter der Kulturabteilung Niklaus Ullrich

Education and Culture Department of Greater Appenzell Canton
Erziehungs- und Kulturdirektion des Kantons Appenzell-Ausserahoden
Regierungsgebäude, 9102 **Herisau**
Tel: 71-353 6111 Fax: 71-353 6497
E-Mail: Richard.Kunz@ed.ar.ch
Direktionssekretär und Kulturbeauftragter Richard Kunz

Education Department of Aargau Canton
Erziehungsdepartement des Kantons Aargau
Regierungsgebäude, 5001 **Aarau**
Tel: 62-835 3535 Fax: 62-835 2009
Internet: www.ag.ch
Chef der Abt. Kulturpflege Dr. André François Moosbrugger

Education Department of Basel City Canton
Erziehungsdepartement des Kantons Basel-Stadt
Münsterplatz 2, Postfach, 4001 **Basel**
Tel: 61-267 8413 Fax: 61-267 6842
Leiter Ressort Kultur Andreas Spillmann

Education Department of Inner Appenzell Canton
Erziehungsdirektion des Kantons Appenzell-Innerrhoden
Sekretariat, Hauptgasse 51, 9050 **Appenzell**
Tel: 71-788 9361 Fax: 71-788 9369
E-Mail: ferdinand.bischofberger@ed.ai.admin.ch
Departementssekretär und Schulinspektor Ferdinand Bischofberger; Kulturbeauftragter Konservator Roland Inauen

Office of Culture
Amt für Kultur (AK) – Office de la cultur (OC)
Sulgeneckstrasse 70, 3005 **Bern**
Tel: 31-633 8777 Fax: 31-633 8780
Internet: www.erz.be.ch
E-Mail: erzbe@erz.be.ch
Vorsteher Anton Ryf (31-633 8773); Wissenschaftliche Mitarbeiterin Anina Barandun (31-633 8772); Abteilung Kulturförderung (dtsprachig) Beatrice Stadelmann (31-633 8767); section des activités culturelles (partie francophone) Walter Wenger (31-633 8768)
Comments: visiting address: Sulgeneckstrasse 19, 3007 Bern (Sekretariat)

Education Department of Glarus Canton
Erziehungsdirektion des Kantons Glarus
Kulturelle Angelegenheiten, Freulerpalast, 8752 **Näfels**
Tel: 55-612 4010 Fax: 55-612 5232
Beaufragter für Kulturelle Angelegenheiten Dr Jürg Davatz
Role & Services: promotion of culture

Education Department of Graubünden Canton
Erziehungs-, Kultur und Umweltschutzdepartement des Kantons Graubünden
Quaderstrasse 17, 7000 **Chur**
Tel: 81-257 2714 Fax: 81-257 2151
E-Mail: Florin.Caviezel@kms.gr.ch
Beauftragter für Kultur-und Medienfragen Florin Caviezel

Education Department of Lucerne Canton
Erziehungsdepartement des Kantons Luzern
Bahnhofstr 18, 6002 **Luzern**
Tel: 41-228 5111 Fax: 41-210 0573
Internet: www.ekdluzern.ch
E-Mail: dhuber@ekdLuzern.ch
Vorsteher der Gruppe Kultur u. Jugendförderung Daniel Huber (tel:228 5205); head of department Dr. Ulrich Fassler
Role & Services: dealing with culture and education

Education Department of Oberwald Canton
Erziehungsdepartement des Kantons Obwalden
Postfach 1254, 6061 **Sarnen**
Tel: 41-666 6243 (culture dept.) Fax: 41-660 2727
E-Mail: bkd@o.w.ch
Kulturbeauftragte Beatrice Stadelmann
Comments: visiting address: Brünigstrasse 178, 6060 Sarnen

Education Department of Schaffhausen Canton
Erziehungsdepartement des Kantons Schaffhausen
Herrenacker 3, 8201 **Schaffhausen**
Tel: 52-632 7111 Fax: 52-632 7600
E-Mail: raphael.rohner@ktsh.ch
Departementssekretär Dr. Raphaël Rohner

Education Department of Schwyz Canton
Erziehungsdepartement des Kantons Schwyz
Bahnhofstrasse 15, 6430 **Schwyz**
Tel: 41-819 1901 Fax: 41-819 1917
E-Mail: hans.steine@sz.ch
Departementssekretär Hans Steinegger
Role & Services: Bereich Kulturförderung tel: 41-819 1901 (Hans Steinegger)

Education Department of Uri Canton – Bureau for Cultural Affairs
Erziehungsdirektion des Kantons Uri – Amt für Kultur
Klausenstr. 4, 6460 **Altdorf**
Tel: 41-875 2050 Fax: 41-875 2087
E-Mail: ds.ed@ur.ch
Vorsteher Dr. Rolf Aebersold; Regierungsrat Dr. Stadler

Education and Culture Department of Zug Canton
Direktion für Bildung und Kultur des Kantons Zug
Baarerstrasse 19, 6304 **Zug**
Tel: 41-728 3184 Fax: 41-728 3189
E-Mail: regula.koch@dbk.zg.ch
Kulturbeauftragte Regula Koch

Department of Home Justice and Affairs Zürich Canton – Department of Cultural Funding
Direktion des Juntiz und des Innern – Fachstelle Kultur
Kasper-Escher-Haus, 8090 **Zürich**
Tel: 1-259 2552/1 Fax: 1-259 4276
E-Mail: susanna.tanner@zh.ch
Leiterin Abteilung Fachstelle Kultur Susanna Tanner

TURKEY (+90)

Ministry of Culture
Kültür Bakanligi
Atatürk Bulvari, N° 9, Opera Karsisi, Ulus, **Ankara**
Tel: 312-324 0926/0322
Fax: 312-311 1431
minister of culture Istemihan Talay

UKRAINE (+380)

Ministry of Culture and Arts of the Ukraine
19 Ivana Franka St. , 252030 **Kiev** 30
Tel: 44-226 2645/224 4911/225 7336 (music)/224 7911 (theatre)/225 5274 (foreign relations dept)
Fax: 44-225 3257
minister Dmytro Ostapenko

UNITED KINGDOM (+44)

Department for Culture, Media & Sport
2-4 Cockspur Street, **London** SW1Y 5DH
Tel: 20-7211 6212/6000 (switchboard)
Fax: 20-7211 6230/70 (press office)
Internet: www.culture.gov.uk
secretary of state for Culture, Media & Sport Chris Smith; minister for arts Alan Howarth; minister for sport Kate Hoey; minister for film and tourism Janet Anderson; parliamentary private secretary Fiona MacTaggart; special advisers Andy Burnham, John Newbign
Role & Services: government department with main responsibility for financing the arts, chiefly via the Arts Council of England; the Department for Culture, Media & Sport is also responsible for the administration of the National Lottery

NESTA – National Endowment for Science, Technology and the Arts
2-4 Cockspur Street, **London** SW1Y 5DH
Tel: 20-7861 9670 Fax: 20-7861 9675
Internet: www.nesta.org.uk
E-Mail: nesta@nesta.org.uk
chairman Lord Puttnam; board of trustees Carol Vorderman, Dr Christopher Evans OBE, Sir Martin Rees, Dame Bridget Ogilvie, David Wardell, Francois Matarasso, Genista McIntosh, Janice Kirkpatrick, Clive Gillinson, Catherine McKeever
Role & Services: set up to help talented individuals in science, technology and the arts

National Foundation for Youth Music, The
c/o The Foundling Museum, 40 Brunswick Square, **London** WC1N 1AU
Tel: 20-7713 0024
Fax: 20-7713 6973
chief executive Christina Coker; educational consultant John Stevens; marketing consultant Helena Doliveria

British Council
Arts Division, 10 Spring Gardens,
London SW1A 2BN
Tel: 20-7930 8466 Fax: 20-7839 6347
Internet: www.britishcouncil.org/
director Paul Smith; head, performing arts John Kieffer (7389 3074); head, film and tv Paul Howson (7389 3068); head, visual arts Andrea Rose (7389 3055); head, literature Dr Alastair Niven (7389 3169); head arts promotion Mike Winter (7389 3104); head, design Christopher Wade (7389 3161)
Role & Services: responsible for the dissemination of British culture to other countries, including financial assistance to tours/visits by British artists and organisations

Arts Council of England
14 Great Peter Street, **London** SW1P 3NQ
Tel: 20-7333 0100
Fax: 20-7973 6590
Internet: www.artscouncil.org.uk
E-Mail: joe.meaney@artscouncil.org.uk (press office)
chairman Gerry Robinson; chief executive Peter Hewitt; executive director communications Wendy Andrews; executive director arts Kim Evans; drama director Anna Stapleton; director broadcasting t.b.a.; executive director planning and resources Graham Long; dance Hilary Carty; education and training Pauline Tambling; literature Gary McKeone; music t.b.a.; touring Kate Devey; visual arts and architecture Marjorie Allthorpe-Guyton
Role & Services: the ACE is the key funding body for the arts in England; a fully independent, non-political organisation, it is responsible for fostering the arts across the nation through the judicious distribution of public money from central government and revenue generated by the National Lottery
Comments: ACE aims to help the people of Engalnd enjoy and participate in the arts by funding a range of theatres, galleries and exhibitions, film and literature projects, orchestras, opera, dance and touring companies as well as individual creative artists;
ACE underwent major restructuring during 1999, no further information available at time of going to print

Scottish Arts Council
12 Manor Place, **Edinburgh (Scotland)** EH3 7DD
Tel: 131-226 6051
Fax: 131-225 9833
Internet: www.sac.org.uk
E-Mail: administrator.SAC@artsfb.org.uk
director Tessa Jackson; deputy director Barclay Price; performing arts (drama & dance) David Taylor; performing arts (music) Nod Knowles; combined arts (inc. festivals) Jim Tough; director of finance and administration Graham Berry; senior press and media officer Susan Gavaghan
Role & Services: main channel of government aid and national lottery funding and development to the arts in Scotland; also offer information and advice; information help desk tel: 131-240 2443/2444

Arts Council of Wales
Cyngor Celfyddydau Cymru
9 Museum Place, **Cardiff (Wales)** CF1 3NX
Tel: 29-2037 6500 Fax: 29-2022 1447
Internet: www.ccc-acw.org.uk
E-Mail: information@ccc-acw.org.uk
chief executive Joanna Weston; artform development director Michael Baker; access development director Sandra Wynne; planning and public affairs director t.b.a.; finance and resources director Rhys Parry; lottery director Robert Edge; international art manager Yvette Vaughan Jones
Role & Services: main channel of government aid and lottery funding to the arts in Wales
Comments: alternative internet for Wales art international: www.wai.org.uk

National Assembly for Wales – Culture and Recreation Division
Cynulliad Cenedlaethol Cymru – Culture and Recreation Division
Cathays Park, **Cardiff (Wales)** CF10 3NQ
Tel: 29-2082 6092 (head of culture & recreation div.)/6043 (head of arts & sports)
Fax: 29-2082 6112
assembly secretary (education and training) Tom Middlehurst; head of culture and recreation division D R Thomas (email: russell.thomas@wales.gsi.gov.uk); head of arts and sports branch G Hallett (email: gerry.hallett@wales.gsi.gov.uk)
Role & Services: the Culture and Recreation Division is responsible for taking forward the National Assembly for Wales' policy on the Arts, Sports, Museums, Library, Lottery, Welsh Language, Broadcasting and Film, amongst others; this is achieved, in the main, through the sponsorship of Assembly Sponsored Public Bodies e.g. Arts Council of Wales

Arts Council of Northern Ireland
MacNeice House, 77 Malone Road,
Belfast (Northern Ireland) BT9 6AQ
Tel: 28-9038 5200
Fax: 28-9066 1715
Internet: www.artscouncil-ni.org/
E-Mail: publicaffairs@artscouncil-ni.org
chief executive Brian Ferran; public affairs officer Damian Smyth; dance & drama officer Imelda Foley
Role & Services: main channel of government aid to the arts in N. Ireland and administrative centre for National Lottery Arts Funds in N. Ireland

Visiting Arts
11 Portland Place, **London** W1N 4EJ
Tel: 20-7389 3019
Fax: 20-7389 3016
Internet: www.britcoun.org/visitingarts
E-Mail: office@visitingarts.demon.co.uk
chairman Richard Lambert; director Terry Sandell OBE; deputy director Camilla Edwards; assistant directors Nelson Fernandez, Melissa Naylor
Role & Services: promotes and facilitates the inward flow of foreign arts into England, Scotland, Wales and Northern Ireland in the context of the contribution they can make to cultural relations, cultural awareness and fostering mutually beneficial international arts contacts and activities at national, regional, local and institutional levels; it does this through consultancy, information and advice giving and awarding of grants
Comments: is a joint venture of the Arts Council of England, the Scottish Arts Council, the Arts Council of Northern Ireland, the Crafts Council, the Foreign and Commonwealth Office, The British Council

Foundation for Sport and the Arts
PO Box 20, **Liverpool** L13 1HB
Tel: 151-259 5505 Fax: 151-230 0664
chairman Tim Rice; deputy chairman The Lord Brabazon of Tara; secretary to the trustees Grattan Endicott OBE; administrator Jean Beynon
Role & Services: to reinforce what is already happening, to increase the use of existing facilities, to modernise current buildings or where appropriate construct new, and to assist projects that are already underway; hopes to encourage outstanding initiative, enterprise and creativity; has roughly £5million per annum available for the arts from contributory element in the remittances of clients (betting on the results of football matches) of the pools' clients; working party makes recommendations after examining applications *Comments:* ability to fund extremely small local organisations has led to very heavy numbers of applications and, to a degree, concentration recently on more modest levels of grant aid

• Regional Arts Boards

English Regional Arts Boards
5 City Road, **Winchester** SO23 8SD
Tel: 1962-851 063 Fax: 1962-842 033
Internet: www.arts.org.uk
E-Mail: info@erab.org.uk
chief executive Christopher Gordon; PA/administrator Carolyn Nixson
Role & Services: Information, co-ordination and liaison services for the 10 Regional Arts Boards in England, national and international representation of their interests

East Midlands Arts
Mountfields House, Epinal Way, **Loughborough** LE11 OQE
Tel: 1509-218 292 Fax: 1509-262 214
Internet: www.arts.org.uk
E-Mail: info@em-arts.co.uk
chief executive t.b.a.; head of arts Helen Flach; planning & resources Michaela Butter; head of management services Bharat Pandya
Role & Services: the arts development agency for the counties of Derbyshire (below the High Peak District), Nottinghamshire, Lincolnshire, Leicestershire, Rutland and Northamptonshire; the overall objectives of the Board are to promote quality, increase access, develop the arts economy and operate effectively; as a result of its constitution they are not able to give grants to students in full time education

Eastern Arts Board
Cherry Hinton Hall, Cherry Hinton Road, **Cambridge** CB1 8DW
Tel: 1223-215 355 Fax: 1223-248 075
Internet: www.arts.org.uk
E-Mail: info@eastern-arts.co.uk
chief executive Andrea Stark; director (performing arts) Sue Grace; director (business & resources) Lesley Thompson; director (planning and development) Fred Brookes; director (visual and media arts) Rosy Greenlees; director (information and communications) Jane Moss
Role & Services: regional arts development agency for the east of England: Bedfordshire, Cambridgeshire, Essex, Hertfordshire, Norfolk and Suffolk, and the unitary authorities of Luton, Peterborough, Southend-on-Sea and Thurroch; provides: advice and information on all aspects of arts development including national lottery; grants, bursaries and schemes relating to all performing and visual art forms; welcomes enquiries from international companies interested in touring in the region

London Arts Board
Elme House, 133 Long Acre, Covent Garden, **London** WC2E 9AF
Tel: 20-7240 1313 Fax: 20-7670 2400
Internet: www.arts.org.uk/lab
chief executive Sue Robertson; director (arts) Greg Hilty; director of external & strategic relations Jennifer Edwards; principal music officer Andrew McKenzie; principal dance officer Jacqueline Rose; principal combined arts officer Paula Brown; principal theatre officer Sue Timothy; principal literature officer John Hampson; principal visual arts & crafts officer, Holly Tebbutt; press & media Purba Choudhury; research & information Adrienne Hedge
Role & Services: the London Arts Board is responsible for encouraging assisting and funding the arts and their development in the Greater London Area in a variety of ways; the London Arts Board regrets that it is unable to support students in full-time education *Comments:* all e-mails are: firstname.surname@lonab.co.uk, minicom 20-7670 2450

North West Arts Board
Manchester House, 22 Bridge Street, **Manchester** M3 3AB
Tel: 161-834 6644 Fax: 161-834 6969
Internet: www.arts.org.uk
E-Mail: nwarts-info@mcr1.poptel.org.uk
chief executive Sue Harrison; director of performing arts Hilary Garnham; deputy chief executive Aileen McEvoy; director visual arts and media Howard Rifkin; director communications & research Theresa Griffin; director finance & internal services Roger Goddard; dance officer Anne Clayton; music officer Debra King; drama officer Ian Tabbron; touring officer Maureen Jordan; interdisciplinary arts & festivals officer Nick Chapman; administrator drama/touring Kirsten Fussing; administrator dance/interdisciplinary arts & festivals Jill Godfrey; information officer Ian Gasse; administrator music Andrew Korn; pa to arts directorate Josephine Gannon
Role & Services: North West Arts Board is the regional arts development agency for Cheshire, Greater Manchester, Lancashire, Merseyside, the High Peak district of Derbyshire and the unitary authorities of Blackburn with Darwen, Blackpool, Halton and Warrington; it is one of the ten regional arts boards in England and part of the national arts funding system; the Board works to support and develop the arts in the north-west through a series of funding, advice, information and other services and by working with a range of strategic partners across the region

Northern Arts
9/10 Osborne Terrace, Jesmond, **Newcastle upon Tyne** NE2 1NZ
Tel: 191-281 6334 Fax: 191-281 3276
Internet: www.arts.org.uk
E-Mail: nab@norab.demon.co.uk
chief executive Andrew Dixon; deputy chief executive Paul Rubinstein; head of visual arts James Bustard; head of film, media & literature Janice Campbell; head of performing arts Brian Debnam; head of regional development Reuben Kench; head of finance Pete O'Hara; press & pr officer Jo Beddows; lottery & resources coordinator Rachel Bottomley; education officer Shirley Campbell; finance & resources officer Dianne Coaten; literature officer Chrissie Glazebrook; lottery officer capital Diane Fisher-Naylor; resource development officer Jane Robinson; visual arts officer t.b.a.; performing arts officers Mark Monument, Mark Mulqueen; northern production fund administrator t.b.a.
Role & Services: to promote access to the arts, art in education, art development and individual artists; also promote and strengthen the arts ecconomy and promote the value of the arts *Comments:* covers Teeside, Cumbria, County Durham, Tyne & Wear and Northumberland

South East Arts
Union House, Eridge Road, **Tunbridge Wells** TN4 8HF
Tel: 1892-507 200 Fax: 1892-549 383
Internet: www.arts.org.uk
E-Mail: info@seab.co.uk
chief executive Felicity Harvest; director of performing arts Dermot O'Brien; performing arts officer (drama) Judith Hibberd; performing arts officer (music) Jonathan Dabner; director of visual and media arts Margaret O'Brien; director of resource Clive Russell; director strategy & external affairs Debra Reay; research & information officer Jill Hogan; dance & live arts officer Sian Prime; combined arts officer Paul Ackerley
Role & Services: South East Arts Board is the regional art development agency for Kent, Surrey, East Sussex, West Sussex and the unitary authorities of Brighton & Hove and Medway; the mission is to develop, support, lobby for and promote the arts of the highest quality and widest range for the benefit of people living, working, being educated in or visiting the south east of England; offer funding, advice, information and other services and collaborate with a range of strategic partners throughout the region

South West Arts
Bradninch Place, Gandy Street, **Exeter** EX4 3LS
Tel: 1392-218 188 Fax: 1392-413 554
Internet: www.swa.co.uk
E-Mail: info@swa.co.uk
chief executive Nick Capaldi; performing arts administrators Ouvrielle Holmes, Sarah Homes
Role & Services: aims to raise awareness, stimulate investment, enhance quality & improve access to the arts through funding information, working with private & public sector and widely advocating the arts of the South West *Comments:* covers: the unitary authority areas of Bristol, Bath and North East Somerset, South Glouchestershire, North Somerset, Torbay and Plymouth and the counties of Cornwall, Devon, Dorset, Gloucestershire and Somerset

Southern Arts Board
13 St Clement Street, **Winchester** SO23 9DQ
Tel: 1962-855 099
Fax: 1962-861 186
Internet: www.arts.org.uk
E-Mail: info@southernarts.co.uk
chief executive director Robert Hutchison; deputy executive director Stephen Boyce; director arts (arts unit) Sarah Maxfield; music officer David Everett; theatre officer Nicolas Young; dance officer Sally Abbott; combine arts officer Joanna Day; information and marketing officer Paul Clough; capital projects officer Peter Taylor; communications officer Juliet Mills
Role & Services: the arts development agency for Buckinghamshire, south east Dorset, Hampshire, Isle of Wight, Oxfordshire and Wiltshire

West Midlands Arts
82 Granville Street, **Birmingham** B1 2LH
Tel: 121-631 3121 Fax: 121-643 7239
Internet: www.west-midlands.arts.org.uk
E-Mail: info@west-midlands-arts.co.uk
chief executive Sally Luton; director of management services Sharon Neal; director of performing & combined arts Kate Organ; director of policy and resources Beverley Parker; director of visual arts, crafts and media Caroline Foxhall; music officer Val Birchall; drama officer Alison Gagen; dance officer Anouk Perinpanayagam; combined arts officer Stephanie Edmunds; executive officer Martin Turner
Role & Services: Regional Arts Board for the West Midlands (Herefordshire, Worcestershire, Staffordshire, Warwickshire and Shropshire, Stoke on Trent, Telford and Wrekin, and the metropolitan districts of Birmingham, Coventry, Dudley, Sandwell, Solihull, Walsall and Wolverhampton); West Midlands Arts provides funding, advice, information and planning to help develop the arts, crafts and media of the region

Yorkshire Arts
21 Bond Street, **Dewsbury** WF13 1AX
Tel: 1924-455 555 Fax: 1924-466 522
Internet: www.arts.org.uk
E-Mail: info@yarts.co.uk
chief executive Roger Lancaster; head of performing arts James Beirne; director of corporate affairs Andy Carver; communications officers Sally Brown, Jill Foggin; director of management services Alan Wallace; drama officer t.b.a.; music officer Andrew Cleaton; dance officer Mileva Drljaca; director of arts Nima Poovaya-Smith; head of communications Mary Wright; head of visual & media arts Adrian Friedli; head of regional development Toby Hyam
Role & Services: a policy led development agency based on a partnership approach with a wide range of public, private and voluntary sector agencies operating within a broad cultural context; it hopes to promote the arts in society by developing public appreciation of the arts and by improving public access to, and the quality of, the arts

Arts Council of Wales, North Wales Office
Swyddfa Gogledd Cymru
36 Princes' Drive, **Colwyn Bay (Wales)** LL29 8LA
Tel: 1492-533 440/532 288 (minicom) Fax: 1492-533 677
Role & Services: the Arts Council of Wales is the national organisation with specific responsibility for the funding and development of the arts in Wales; ACW also distributes the National Lottery funds in Wales
Comments: ACW work through the medium of both Welsh and English

Arts Council of Wales, Mid & West Wales Office
6 Gardd Llydaw, Jacksons Lane, **Camarthen (Wales)** SA31 1QD
Tel: 1267-234 248 Fax: 1267-233 084
head of Mid & West Wales Office Mererid Hopwood; access development officer Amanda Loosemore; scheme administrator Margaret James
Role & Services: regional office of the Arts Council of Wales (q.v.) covering Carmarthen, Ceredigion, Pembrokeshire, Neath/Port Talbot, Swansea and Powys; with specific responsibilty for funding and developing the arts in its area

VATICAN CITY (+39)

Pontifica Council for Culture
Pontificio Consiglio della Cultura
Piazza San Calisto 16, 00120 **Città del Vaticano**
Tel: 6-6988 7321 Fax: 6-6988 7368/7165
Internet: www.vatican.va
E-Mail: cultura@cultr.va
president Cardinal Paul Poupard; secretary Father Bernard Ardura
Role & Services: Its two sections, Faith and Culture and Dialogue with Cultures facilitate cooperation among cultural departments of the Catholic Church, international organisations, universities and cultural centres through research, cultural promotion, meetings, publications and representation at cultural events; coordinates the Pontifical Academies; coordinates 7 of the pontifical academies; publishes the trilingual (French, English, Spanish) magazine Cultures and Faith – quarterly

YUGOSLAVIA (+381)

Federal Ministry of Foreign Affairs
Department for International Cultural and Educational Cooperation, Kneza Milosa 24-26, **Belgrade**
Tel: 11-683 585 Fax: 11-684 848
director Dr. Stanislav Stojanovic

Serbia Ministry of Culture
Nemanjina 11, 11000 **Belgrade**
Tel: 11-657 347/682 966 Fax: 11-683 854
minister Dr. Nada Popovic-Perisic

Montenegro Ministry of Culture
Njegoseva 2, 81000 **Podgorica**
Tel: 81-24847 Fax: 81-24164
minister t.b.a.

Supra-National Organisations and Networks

Supra-National Organisations and Networks
We have included a wide range of networks that we think will be of interest to those working in the performing arts. For a comprehensive list of networks covering the whole cultural sector, readers are referred to *Networking in Europe?* published by the Arts Council of England. **The organisations and networks are listed alphabetically. The phone number includes the country code**

Organisations Supra-nationales et Réseaux
Une large gamme de réseaux que nous estimons intéressante pour ceux qui travaillent dans le monde des Arts Vivants est inclue. Pour une liste complète de réseaux, qui englobe tout le secteur culturel, nos lecteurs sont priés de se reporter à *Networking in Europe?* publié par le Arts Council of England. **Les organisations et les réseaux sont classés par ordre alphabétique. L'indicatif du pays est compris dans le numéro de téléphone.**

Übernationale Organisationen und Netzwerke
Wir haben in diesem Kapitel eine Reihe von Organisationen und Netzwerken vorgestellt, die unserer Meinung nach interessant für Berufstätige im Bereich der Musik und darstellenden Kunst sind. Ein umfassendes Verzeichnis von europäischen Netzwerken im kulturellen Bereich finden Sie in der vom British Council herausgegebenen Veröffentlichung *Networking in Europe?* **Die Organisationen sind alphabetisch geordnet. Die Telefonnummern enthalten die Landesvorwahl.**

Organizzazioni 'Sopranazionali' e networks
Sono stati inclusi numerosi networks che pensiamo possano interessare chi opera nel settore artistico. Per un elenco completo di networks riguardanti l'ambito culturale, i lettori possono riferirsi a *Networking in Europe?* che sarà pubblicato dall'Arts Council in Inglaterra
Le organizzazioni ed i networks sono in ordine alfabetico. I numeri di telefono includono il prefisso nazionale

Organizaciones supranacionales y organizaciones vinculadas internacionalmente
Se ha incluido una amplia gama de organizaciones vinculadas internacionalmente que prometen ser de interés para todo tipo de empresarios relacionados con las artes escénicas y musicales. Para una lista completa de semejantes organizaciones que cubran todo el sector cultural, remitimos al lector a *Networking in Europe?*, guía publicada por el Arts Council of England.
Las organizaciones se encuentran en orden alfabético. El prefijo del país está incluido en el número de teléfono.

Supra-National Organisations and Networks (범국가 조직 및 네트워크)
공연 예술 관계인들에게 관심이 있을 광범위한 네트워크가 포함되었다. 전 문화 부문을 커버하는 포괄적인 네트워크 리스트는 영국예술원이 발행한 'Networking in Europe?'을 참조하시오. **리스트는 알파벳순으로 기재되었다. 전화번호는 국제번호를 포함한다.**

超国家机构和网络
我们已经将我们认为那些从事表演艺术的人士感兴趣的一系列广泛的网络包括在内。欲阅囊括整个文化部门网络的综合性名单的读者请阅由英格兰艺术委员会(Arts Council of England)出版的《欧洲网络?》(Networking in Europe?)。**这些机构和网络是按字母顺序排列的。电话码包括了该国家区号。**

超国家団体とネットワーク
本書には舞台芸術の領域に関わる人々に関心が高いと思われる広範なネットワークを収めました。すべての文化領域を網羅するネットワーク・リストはイングランド芸術委員会（Arts Council of England）発行の「Networking in Europe?」をご参照下さい。団体とネットワークはアルファベット順に記載されています。**電話番号には国コードも含まれます。**

ASEAN COCI-Singapore
c/o Ministry of Information and the Arts, 37th Floor, PSA Building, **Singapore** 119963, Singapore
Tel: 65 375 7743 Fax: 65 376 7870
chairman Mr Choo Whatt Bin
Role & Services: to promote effective cooperation in culture and information to enhance mutual understanding and solidarity among the ASEAN member countries, as well as furthering regional development; to accelerate cultural development in the region through joint endeavours in order to strengthen the foundation of a prosperous and peaceful ASEAN community; to promote better understanding and appreciation of the ASEAN cultures, the similarities, diversities and the traditional as well as present ties among the peoples of ASEAN, and to enable such efforts to be shared by them

ASEAN Secretariat
Jalan Sisingaramangaraja, 78 Kebayoranbaru, **Jakarta** 12110, Indonesia
Tel: 62-21 726 2991/724 3372
Fax: 62-21 739 8234/724 3504
E-Mail: public@asean.or.id
contacts Rodolfo Seferino Jr., Vic Albornoz Lactaoen
Role & Services: co-ordinates annual ASEAN Festival for Performing Arts that rotates around the 6 member countries

Asia-Europe Foundation (ASEF)
No.1 Nassim Hill, **Singapore** 258466, Singapore
Fax: 65 838 4719
Internet: www.asef.org
E-Mail: info@asef.org
executive director prof. Tommy Koh; deputy executive director Pierre Barroux; director (Intellectual Exchange) Duncan Jackman; director (People-to-People Exchange) Urich Niemann; director (culture exchange) Cai Rongsheng; public affairs Peggy Kek

Asia/Pacific Cultural Centre for UNESCO (ACCU)
6 Fukuro-machi, Shinjuku-ku, **Tokyo** 162-8484, Japan
Tel: 81 3-3269 4435 Fax: 81 3-3269 4510
Internet: www.accu.or.jp
E-Mail: general@accu.or.jp
president Kazuo Suzuki; secretary Kazuko Yoshitomi
Role & Services: a non-profitmaking organisation for Asia/Pacific regional activities established in 1971; in line with the principles of UNESCO, ACCU has since been working for the promotion of mutual understanding and cultural cooperation among peoples in Asia and the Pacific by implementing various programmes in the fields of culture, book development and literacy; its activities have focused on joint programmes of UNESCO Member States in Asia and the Pacific based on their various cultural and educational needs, and devised as practical ways of cooperation; it is not a funding organisation

Asian Council for People's Culture (ACPC)
13, Madre Selva St., Roxas District, **Quezon City** 1103, Philippines
Tel: 63 2-373 4932 Fax: 63 2-412 1954
E-Mail: acpc@mnl.sequel.net
executive director Aries R. Clemeno; programme directror Al Santos; regional coordinator Lisa Takayama; administrator Ofelia Asuncion
Role & Services: a network of cultural organizations in the Asia-Pacific region established in 1985 with the aim of promoting multi-cultural exchanges among community artists; it's main production is Cry of Asia which brings together musicians, dancers, and theatre artists from 10 Asia-Pacific countries; Cry of Asia has performed in more than 50 cities in Europe and Asia and gained enthusiastic reviews; also provides Regional Trainning Programme which aims to revitalize Asian indigenous cultural expressions and traditions as a medium for advocacy on contemporary issues

Asian Council for People's Culture (ACPC)
13, Madre Selva St., Roxas District, **Quezon City** 1103, Philippines
Tel: 63 2-373 4932 Fax: 63 2-412 1954
E-Mail: acpc@mnl.sequel.net
executive director Aries R. Clemeno; programme directror Al Santos; regional coordinator Lisa Takayama; administrator Ofelia Asuncion
Role & Services: a network of cultural organizations in the Asia-Pacific region established in 1985 with the aim of promoting multi-cultural exchanges among community artists; it's main production is Cry of Asia which brings together musicians, dancers, and theatre artists from 10 Asia-Pacific countries; Cry of Asia has performed in more than 50 cities in Europe and Asia and gained enthusiastic reviews; also provides Regional Trainning Programme which aims to revitalize Asian indigenous cultural expressions and traditions as a medium for advocacy on contemporary issues

Asian Dancers Association Japanese Office
Asia Buyohka Kyokai Nihonkyoku
Sakakibara Gakuen, 5-8-12 Ueno, Taito-ku, **Tokyo** 110-0005, Japan
Tel: 81 3-3831 4083/3511 Fax: 81 3-3833 6178
director Kiitsu Sakakibara

Association Internationale de la Recherche et de la Création Artistique Contemporaine (AIRCAC)
International Association for Research and Contemporary Artistic Creation
90 Boulevard Murat, 75016 **Paris**, France
Tel: 33 1-4651 5571 Fax: 33 1-4743 1099
directeur artistique Francesco Agnello
Role & Services: promote artists in the field of music, dance and theatre and painting in France and world-wide

Association Internationale du Théâtre pour l'Enfance et la Jeunesse (ASSITEJ)
International Association of Theatre for Children and Young People
c/o The VCA Arts House, 204 St Kilda Road, Southbank, **Melbourne** VIC 3006, Australia
Tel: 61 3-9686 9644 Fax: 61 3-9682 3844
Internet: www.assitej.org
E-Mail: ypaa@vicnet.net.au
world president Michael FitzGerald; executive officer Niclas Malmcrona (Assitej Sweden)
Role & Services: promotes contacts and exchange of experience of those involved in theatre for children and young people, and promotes study tours and engagements for producing companies travelling abroad; ASSITEJ has national centres in many countries, which provide a forum to bring together all those interested in this area of theatre; A triennial international congress is organised (next in 1999 in Trømso, Norway)

Association of European Cities of Culture 2000 (AECC)
30-36 Boulevard Anspach, Anspach Centre, 1000 **Brussels**, Belgium
E-Mail: Ginnalia@aecc.by.com
co-ordinator Ginnalia Cogliandro

Association of European Performers' Organisations (AEPO)
28 rue de la Loi, 1040 **Brussels**, Belgium
Tel: 32 2-280 1934 Fax: 32 2-230 3507
E-Mail: aepo@compuserve.com
general secretary Xavier Blanc (Spedidam Paris); membre de l'association Eric Edwine
Role & Services: non profit-making association of European performers' organisations; represents performers' rights in most European countries; maintains contact with the European Union, participates as observer in WIPO meetings (World Intellectual Property Organisation, Geneva) as N.G.O. and is observer in the working group on Mass Media (MM-S-PR) at the Council of Europe

Association of International Directors of Opera (AIDO)
c/o Bayrische Theaterakademie, Prinzregentenpl. 12, 81675 **München**, Germany
Tel: 49 89-2185 2802 Fax: 49 89-2185 2804
contact: Generalsekretariat Christine Reif
Role & Services: an informal network of opera managers in more than 20 major opera houses; It exists to exchange information on issues of mutual concern, especially fees for artists, and to provide a forum for contact between directors of different opera houses; An annual general assembly is organised

Australasian Classical Music Managers' Association (ACMMA)
c/o Jenifer Eddy Artists' Management, Suite 11, 596 St Kilda Road, **Melbourne** VIC 3004, Australia
Tel: 61 3-9525 2700 Fax: 61 3-9529 5410
E-Mail: jean@compuserve.com
chairman Noël Pelly

Australasian Mechanical Copyright Owners Society (AMCOS)
Locked Bag 3456, **St Leonards** NSW 2065, Australia
Tel: 61 2-9935 7700 Fax: 61 2-9935 7709
Internet: www.amcos.com.au
E-Mail: info@amcos.com.au
company secretary Britten Sutcliffe (e-mail: britten@amcos.com.au)
Role & Services: administering mechanical and synchronisation rights in music, and serving the interests of music publishers and their writers throughout Australasia; all AMCOS licences are administered by the Australasian Performing Right Association (APRA)
Comments: visiting address: 6-12 Atchison Street, St Leonards, NSW 2065

Australasian Performing Right Association (APRA)
Locked Bag 3565, **St Leonards** NSW 2067, Australia
Tel: 61 2-9935 7900 Fax: 61 2-9935 7999
E-Mail: apra@apra.com.au
chief executive Brett Cottle; director of international relations Scot Morris
Role & Services: APRA is a music copyright collection agency which works on behalf of composers and music publishers

Australia Latin America Foundation (ALAF)
9 Telopea Street, **Redfern** NSW 2016, Australia
Tel: 61 2-9310 3716 Fax: 61 2-9699 9099
executive director Justin Macdonnell; manager Latin America Mario Estrella
Role & Services: to initiate, promote and encourage educational, scientific and cultural exchange between Australia and the countries of Latin America and specifically to: further the study, appreciation, practise and development of Australian arts and society in Latin America and of Latin American arts and society in Australia

Caucasian Arts Managers Network – CAMN
45 Chavchavadze av., 380079 **Tbilisi**, Georgia
Tel: 32-250 089/294 306
Fax: 32-294 306
Internet: www.AZERINET.COM/CAMN
E-Mail: SCF@lingua.edu.ge
chairman of the board Levan Khetaguri
Role & Services: the aims of CAMN are: information bank, exchange of ideas and experience, networking, professional links, mobility, common cultural space for management in the region, directory, exchange of practical training programmes, international cultural cooperation
Comments: the board representatives are from five countries: Georgia, Armenia, Azerbeijan, Russia and Kirgistan; alternativel E-mail: luri@lingua.edu.ge

Centre D'Information de Recherche Culturelle et de Liaison en Europe (CIRCLE)
Cultural Information & Research Centres Liaison in Europe
c/o InterArts Observatory, Rambla de Catalunya 81 pral, 08008 **Barcelona**, Spain
Tel: 34 93-487 7022 Fax: 34 93-487 2644
E-Mail: interart@pangea.org
secretary general Cas Smithuijsen
Role & Services: aims to provide a bridge between policy-makers and researchers by disseminating information on cultural issues; publications include the Handbook of Cultural Affairs in Europe, Professional Managers for the Arts and Culture Training of Cultural Administrators and Arts Managers in Europe, Human Rights and Cultural Policies in a Changing Europe, Harmony or Confusion for Culture in Europe: The impact of the Single Market and Maastricht Treaty, and a quarterly newsletter, Circular
Comments: secretary general Cas Smithuijsen is also the director of Boekman Foundation, Amsterdam (see entry in Services)

Centre Européen de la Culture
European Cultural Centre
Villa Moynier, 120 b rue de Lausanne, 1202 **Genève**, Switzerland
Tel: 41 22-732 2803
Fax: 41 22-738 4012
Internet: www.europeans.ch
E-Mail: cecge@vtx.ch
president Jean-Fred Bourquin
Role & Services: stimulates collaboration and joint ventures and participates in the establishment of a network of European cultural and scientific organisations; it acts as a coordinating body for associations, cultural centres, foundations, public and private institutions; as a meeting place for exchange of ideas, a forum for research and reflection, and an information centre comprising documentation on cultural Europe, the regions, and federalism; the centre aims to facilitate dialogue between cultures
Comments: a non-governmental organisation (NGO)

Centre for Performance Research (CPR)
8 Science Park, **Aberystwyth (Wales)** SY23 3AH, United Kingdom
Tel: 44 1970-622 133
Fax: 44 1970-622 132
Internet: www.aber.ac.uk/~cprwww
E-Mail: cprwww@aber.ac.uk
artistic director Richard Gough; producer Judie Christie
Role & Services: multi-faceted theatre organisation committed to promoting a wider understanding of theatre in its broadest sense, both in its theory and practice and creating exchange and development opportunities for theatre practitioners, students and academics and interested members of the public from the UK and beyond; The CPR produces innovative performance work; arranges conferences; stages workshops; mounts master-classes, lectures and demonstrations; collaborates and exchanges with theatre companies of international significance; promotes tours; publishes and distributes theatre books and runs a multi-cultural theatre reference library; organise an international voice project (annually), also publishes the journal Performance Research
Comments: extensive video and sound archive available (members only), see also under Promoters

Confédération Internationale des Sociétés d'Auteurs et Compositeurs (CISAC)
11 rue Kepler, 75116 **Paris**, France
Tel: 33 1-5357 3400
Fax: 33 1-5357 3410
E-Mail: cisac@cisac.org
secrétaire général Eric Batisde
Role & Services: confederation of societies representing the interests of authors of works

Confederation of Australasian Performing Arts Presenters (CAPAP)
c/o Adelaide Festival of Arts, PO Box 8116, Station Arcade, **Adelaide** SA 5000, Australia
Tel: 61 8-8216 4444 Fax: 61 8-8216 4455
E-Mail: afa@adelaidefestival.net.au
chair Nicholas Heyward
Role & Services: the communications network of the major presenters of international work; includes the major festivals, the larger arts centers and presenting organizations among its members

Conseil International de la Danse
International Dance Council
UNESCO, 1 rue Miollis, 75732 **Paris** Cedex 15, France
Tel: 33 1-4568 4953 Fax: 33 1-4306 8798
president Jean-Albert Cartier; vice-presidents Jean Robin, Susanne Egri (Italy), Vladimir Vassiliev (Russia); secrétaire général Nicole Luc-Maréchal, Arlet Bon
Role & Services: aims to promote all it can be of benefit to dance through the world, in accordance with the objectives of UNESCO and in particular to: protect the dance heritage; encourage the creation of documentation dance centres; promote creation and research; incite the setting up of national dance committes; promote the creation and dissemination of choreographic works; incite and encourage the organization of congresses, festivals, dance competitions; promote the knowledge of dance in general education; encourage the training of performers and choreographers; act in close co-operation with UNESCO
Comments: there is no council in England; see also Nat. Organisations (France)

Conseil International de la Musique
International Music Council
UNESCO, 1 rue Miollis, 75732 **Paris** Cedex 15, France
Tel: 33 1-4568 2550 Fax: 33 1-4306 8798
Internet: www.unesco.org/imc
E-Mail: imc_cim@compuserve.com
president Frans de Ruiter; secretary general Guy Huot
Role & Services: serves as an umbrella organisation for music throughout the world via national committees in 70 countries and 30 associated international member organisations and networks; fosters international co-operation between countries and regions, and organises a general assembly every two years around October, International Music Day; advisory body to UNESCO, with its members and with UNESCO organises and co-ordinates music projects worldwide

Consortium for the Co-ordination of European Performance and Theatre Studies (CONCEPTS)
c/o Drama Department, Goldsmith's College, University of London, Lewisham Way, New Cross, **London** SE14 6NW, United Kingdom
Tel: 44 20-7919 7424
Fax: 44 20-7919 7413
E-Mail: g.lidstone@gold.ac.uk
secretariat Gerald Lidstone; chairman Noel Witts
Role & Services: a network of educational institutions and professional theatre organisations across Europe interested in promoting co-operation through joint projects with a European perspective in all aspects of European Performing Arts (live and recorded), in particular in the areas of professional training, higher education, production, performance, criticism and research; members in all European countries, including Eastern Europe, also members in India, Australia, USA and Latin America

Coordination Européenne des Producteurs Independants (CEPI)
European Coordination of Independent Producers
Widenmayer Str 32, 80538 **München**, Germany
Tel: 49 89-2121 4747 Fax: 49 89-2121 4777
Internet: www.cepi.de
E-Mail: mail@cepi.de
président Jorge Arqué; secretaries general Jacques Peskine
Role & Services: network of tv producers associations set up to encourage contact between independent producers across Europe; It aims to provide a unified lobby to represent its members' interests

Delegation of the European Commission
Europa House, 9-15 Sanban-cho, Chiyoda-ku, **Tokyo** 102-0075, Japan
Tel: 81 3-3239 0441 Fax: 81 3-3261 5194
Internet: jpn.cec.eu.int

Eucrea Europe – European Association for Creativity by and with Disabled People
Bonner Platz 1/V, 80803 **München**, Germany
Tel: 49 89-307 992-17
Fax: 49 89-3079 9222
Internet: www.rabu-medien.de
E-Mail: info@abu-medien.de
president Dr. Peter Radtke
Role & Services: EUCREA: promoting co-operation on an equal basis between disabled and non-disabled artists; among the main aims of the network are: to stimulate a policy of equal opportunities for disabled artists; to raise awareness about the contribution of disabled artists to the current art scence; to facilitate the integration of disabled people's artwork in mainstream cultural venues *Comments:* has national commitees in each member state of the European Communities; EUCREA promotes and supports networking and initiatives that extend the potential for people with disablities to be involved with the arts; EUCREA also organises conferences, arts projects, festivals and functions as an agency for disabled artists; see also National Organsations

Euro-Citizen-Action-Service (ECAS)
53 Rue de la Concorde, 1050 **Brussels**, Belgium
Tel: 32 2-548 0490
Fax: 32 2-548 0499
Internet: www.ecas.org
E-Mail: admin@ecas.org
director Tony Venables; financial manager Ann Hespe
Role & Services: informs and advises citizen's associations on their European strategy, in order to strengthen their voice with the EU's institutions it is a non-profit association independent of commercial interests and national or European authorities; it has 180 member associations in social welfare and culture, civil liberties, health, environment etc. and hosts a number of European associations; member organisations must be independent of governments, political parties or industry – they may receive money from the public purse or private sector, but their policy must not be influenced as a result; publishes a monthly magazine 'The News Flash'; organises conferences, publishes guides, organises press conferences and European Telephone Hotlines; publishes a guide on 'Funding for NGO's'

EUROLYRICA, Association Internationale de Promotion de l'art Lyrique
1 rue des Dominicains, 4000 **Liège**, Belgium
Tel: 32 4-221 4720/232 4207
Fax: 32 4-221 0201
Internet: www.eurolyrica.be
E-Mail: info@eurolyrica.be
administrateur delegué Jean-Louis Grinda; president Francesco Ernani; communication Régine Didden
Role & Services: Eurolyrica (previously AITL and OETL – Organisation Européenne des Théâtre Lyriques) established in 1996 to collect and exchange information on experiences, projects and productions between opera houses, and to promote joint collaboration; it organises a biennial congress and an annual general assembly; promotes lyric arts in Europe

EuroMusica-Centro Europeo per la musica e il Teatro musicale
c/o Casa Malipiero, Foresto Vecchio 8, 31011 **Asolo (TV)**, Italy
Tel: 39 0423-950 966/73
Fax: 39 0423-950 970
Internet: www.euromusica.net
E-Mail: euromusica@filippin.it
president Salvatore Epifanio; vice-president Ferruccio Bresolin; general secretary Attilio Zamperoni; artistic director maestro Francesco Bencivenga
Role & Services: one of the main objectives is to examine the relationship between government funded and private sector in art
Comments: masterclasses, competitions, technical and artistic course on all aspects of the theatre world

Europa Cantat
European Federation of Young Choirs
c/o Bayerische Musikakademie, Kurfürstenstr 19, 87616 **Marktoberdorf**, Germany
Tel: 49 8342-961 826
Fax: 49 8342-40370
Internet: www.intro.ch/ec/
E-Mail: modmusik@compuserve.com
secretary general Gustav Adolf Rabus (Germany); president Noël Minet (Belgium)
Role & Services: exists to encourage links between young people's choirs through the organisation of international events and exchanges and courses on aspects of choir training and conducting; membership consists of national choral organisations, choirs and individual members all over Europe
Comments: in 1998/99 there will be international singing weeks in several European countries; further activities include: European Youth Choir, European Academy for Young Choral Conductors, International Study Tours for choral conductors, European Parliament of Young Musicians and festival EUROPA CANTAT, next: 21-30 July 2000 in Nevers, France

Europe Jazz Network
Via Amalasunta 7, 48100 **Ravenna**, Italy
Tel: 39 0544-405 666/408 030
Fax: 39 0544-405 656
Internet: www.ejn.it
E-Mail: ejn@ejn.it
president Gianbattista Tofoni (I); vice president Huub van Riel (NL); secretary general & press officer Sandra Costantini (I); board of directors Reiner Michalke (D), Markus Baumer (CH)
Role & Services: non-profit association of promoters, musicians' associations, artistic directors, consultants of music programmes in Europe working mainly in the field of jazz and improvised music
Comments: part of EFAH-FEAP; organisers of festival Musica in Gioco; see also Festivals

European Association for Tourism and Leisure Education (ATLAS)
Katholieke Universiteit Brabant, Postbus 90153, 5000 LE **Tilburg**, Netherlands
Tel: 31 13-466 2313
Fax: 31 13-466 8314
Internet: www.atlas-euro.org
E-Mail: richards@kub.nl
contact Dr Greg Richards
Role & Services: association of higher education institutions throughout Europe which exists to promote the teaching of tourism, leisure and the arts throughout Europe; it encourages exchanges between staff and students, promotes links between professional bodies in tourism, leisure and the arts and promotes transnational research; involved in research on cultural tourism in 9 EC countries funded by DGXXIII of the European Commission; publication 'Cultural Tourism in Europe' available; also hold conference; has database on cultural tourism attractions

European Association of Artist Managers (Association Européenne des Agents Artistiques)
Apollolaan 181, 1077 AT
Amsterdam, Netherlands
Tel: 31 20-664 3151
Fax: 31 20-675 2426
E-Mail: alferink@worldonline.nl
president Pieter Alferink; board members Maria Bruzzese, Liliane Weinstadt, Dr. Hans-Dieter Göhre; general secretary Irene A M Van Affelen-Van Saemsfoort
Role & Services: an association of 120 concert agents etc representing more than 3,500 artists worldwide; it provides a forum to promote the interests of its members; next general assembly in Bukarest in 2000 *Comments:* publish a directory of artists jointly with IAMA (International Artists' Managers Association) [q.v.]

European Association of Event Centres (EVVC)
Europäischer Verband der Veranstaltungs-Centren e.V. (EVVC)
c/o Messe Berlin, Messedamm 22, 14055 **Berlin**, Germany
Tel: 49 30-3038 5800
Fax: 49 30-3038 5802
Internet: www.evvc.de
E-Mail: info@evvc.de
President Matthias Fuchs; Vice-President Karl Joachim Kierey; Contact: Head Office Ulrike Wenk
Role & Services: umbrella organisation of event centres in Germany and surrounding countries; promotes and coordinates general exchange of information between members; offers aid and active support; gathers relevant information; publishes magazines; organises training seminars; go-between between members and concert/tour promoters, as well as the general public *Comments:* approx. 270 members; membership is open to the authorities financially responsible for municipal, sports and multipurpose centres and like facilities or the managers of such facilities; general working assembly held once a year at a different venue

European Association of Theatre Audience Organisations e.V.
Europäische Arbeitsgemeinschaft der Theaterbesucherorganisationen (EATO)
Kufsteiner Str 10, 10825 **Berlin**, Germany
Tel: 49 30-854 6085
Fax: 49 30-8572 8789
E-Mail: Dkramarz@t-online.de
Präsident Dr. Joachim Kramarz (Berlin); Vizepräsidenten Dr. André Gottrau (Luzern), Erich Wolf (Wien)
Role & Services: a forum for the major organisations concerned with theatre audience development and ticket subscriptions in Germany, Austria, Netherlands and Switzerland; smaller organisations are also associated with the network

European Association of Youth Orchestras (EAYO)
Association Européenne des Orchestres de Jeunes
c/o Anneke van Nes, Otterswijk 13, 7701 PC **Dedemsvaart**, Netherlands
Tel: 31 523-638 435
Fax: 31 523-638 437
E-Mail: avnesjon@inn.nl
president Anneke van Nes; vice-president Christopher Nurse
Role & Services: aims to bring together young musicians, whose common interest in live music leads to mutual respect and understanding and the acceptance of international co-operation; EAYO aims to establish better musical, social and cultural links throughout Europe and provides information, advice, contacts and project development
Comments: UK contact: Frances Williams, 1 Coulson Close, Milton, Cambridge CB4 4ZE; tel. +44 1223-863124, fax +44 1480-425803; EAYO is an associate member of IMC and a full member of EMC

European Broadcasting Union (EBU)
Union Européenne de Radio-Télévision
Ancienne Route 17a,
1218 **Grand-Saconnex (Genève)**, Switzerland
Tel: 41 22-717 2111 Fax: 41 22-747 4000
Internet: www.ebu.ch
E-Mail: ebu@ebu.ch
president Professor Albert Scharf (ARD/BR, Germany); vice presidents Xavier Gouyou-Beauchamps (France Télévision), Boris Bergant (RTVSLO, Slovenia), Will Wyatt (BBC); secretary general Dr Jean-Bernard Münch; director radio Thomas Alexanderson; director, television Gaetano Stucchi; director, legal affairs Dr Werner Rumphorst; director, technical dept. Philip Laven; director of operations Henri Perez
Role & Services: with 68 active members in 49 countries, is the world's largest professional association of national broadcasters; it runs the Eurovision and Euroradio transmission networks, negotiates broadcasting rights for top sports events, lobbies on behalf of public service broadcasting, and works with and on behalf of its members in the programme, legal and technical fields

European Committee for Business, Arts and Culture (CEREC)
Comité européen pour le rapprochement de l'économie et de la culture (CEREC)
c/o Admical, Rue Girardon, 75018 **Paris**, France
Tel: 33 1-4255 2001 Fax: 33 1-4255 7132
Internet: www.cerec.org
E-Mail: contact@cerec.org
managing director Virginie Seghers; coordinator Nathalie Sauvanet; president Colin Tweedy; treasurer Luc Debrue
Role & Services: exists to promote partnerships between the private sector and the arts to their mutual benefit throughout Europe, encourages communication and co-operation between member organisations, represents them at a European level and provides information and services to raise awareness of the extent and importance of business support for the arts; acts as secretariat for the national associations at European level – organises meetings seminars, conferences for members and supporters; Cerec does not itself provide grants for arts organisations nor does it seek business sponsorship for art groups; it encourages the creation of national arts sponsorship associations in countries where they do not exist; it currently has members in Austria, Belgium, Denmark, France, Germany, Greece, Israel, Italy, Ireland, the Netherlands, Portugal, Spain, Sweden and the UK
Comments: it was set up with start-up funds from the European Commission and is now funded by its network associatons and business supporters; publications: Business Support in Europe, Patronage & Heritage; gives an annual award for a business company, in association with The Financial Times and ABSA

European Conference of Promoters of New Music
Union Européenne des Organisateurs de Musique Nouvelle
c/o Gaudeamus, Swammerdamstraat 38, 1091 RV **Amsterdam**, Netherlands
Tel: 31 20-694 7349 Fax: 31 20-694 7258
Internet: www.xs4all.nl/~ecpnm
E-Mail: ecpnm@xs4all.nl
secretary general Henk Heuvelmans
Role & Services: European network of organisations concerned with the promotion of 20th century music, especially music composed since 1950; an annual calendar of events is produced

European Conference of Symphony Orchestras (ECSO)
c/o Richard Bächi, Schirmensee 5,
8714 **Feldbach**, Switzerland
Tel: 41 55-244 3828 Fax: 41 55-244 3808
E-Mail: rbachi@dplanet.ch
president Richard Bächi
Role & Services: aims to provide a forum for orchestral managers and directors of concert halls to discuss issues of mutual concern

European Federation of National Youth Orchestras (EFNYO)
Van Limburg Stirumstraat 20a,
1051 BB **Amsterdam**, Netherlands
Tel: 31 20-688 5700 Fax: 31 20-688 5545
Internet: www.rnw.nl/efnyo
E-Mail: efnyo@njo.nl
president Arthur van Dijk
Role & Services: federation of 14 European pre-professional youth orchestras; is currently developing its project 'Symphonic Variations of Europe' to take place in August 2000 in Utrecht and Berlin; these series of concerts will bring together all members of the Federation to celebrate youh, education and culture in Europe; the orchestras will give a representative survey of 20th century music by commissioning a composer from each of the fourteen countries involved

European Festivals Association
Association Européenne des Festivals
120B rue de Lausanne, 1202 **Genève**, Switzerland
Tel: 41 22-738 6873 Fax: 41 22-738 4012
Internet: www.eurofestivals.efa.ch
E-Mail: geneva@eurofestivals.efa.ch
president Frans De Ruiter;
secretary general Tamás Klenjánszky
Role & Services: to maintain and develop the high artistic level of the 75 festivals and 7 national festival associations in membership, and their representative role in the cultural life of Europe; An annual publication, Festivals, gives dates and major attractions planned at each of the festivals

European Forum for the Arts and Heritage
EFAH/FEAP, 53 rue de la Concorde,
1050 **Brussels**, Belgium
Tel: 32 2-514 1945 Fax: 32 2-514 2265
Internet: www.eurplace.org/orga/efah/index.html
E-Mail: efah@innet.be
coordinator Marie-Louise Lule; executive president Ferdinand Richard; membership officer Florence Berteletti-Kemp
Role & Services: is a European cultural forum; identify and highlight the needs of the European artistic community to European decision makers, and to thereby participate in those decision making procedures; to improve the exchange of information on the arts and heritage in Europe, between the cultural sector and those invloved in cultural policy making; to act as consultant in the fields of arts and heritage to European, national and regional policy and decision making bodies
Comments: works with the Council of Europe, UNESCO and eastern European states; publishes 4 times a year Culture Alert , a source of up-to-date information on issues affecting the cultural sector in Europe; three categories of membership: Full membership – for cultural organisations that have members of their own, Associate membership – for cultural organisations that do not have a membership structure, Subscribers – for any organisation or individual who wishes to receive Culture Alert

European Forum of Worldwide Music Festivals (EFWMF)
c/o Sfinks, Jan Frans Willemsstraat 10a,
2530 **Boechout**, Belgium
Tel: 32 3-455 6944 Fax: 32 3-454 1162
Internet: www.sfinks.be/efwmf
E-Mail: pdegroote@sfinks.be
contacts Katrien Verhuyck, Patrick de Groote
Role & Services: association of artistic directors of independent festivals in Europe; a network of thirty five major European festivals in the area of world, ethnic, traditional and roots music in fifteen Europena countries *Comments:* also organize Worldwide Music Expo – WOMEX (tradefair, conference and showcases, annual event)

European Institute of Cultural Routes
Tour Jacob, Plateau du Rham, 2427 **Luxembourg**, Luxembourg
Tel: 352 241 250 Fax: 352 241 176
Internet: culture.coe.fr-routes
E-Mail: institut@culture-routes.lu
director Michel Thomas-Penette
Role & Services: joint initiative of the Council of Europe and the Grand Duchy of Luxembourg, which aims to promote the Cultural Routes programme, led by the Council of Europe's Directorate of Education, Culture and Sport

European League of Institutes of the Arts (ELIA)
Waterlooplein 219, 1001 PG **Amsterdam**, Netherlands
Tel: 31 20-620 3936 Fax: 31 20-620 5616
Internet: www.elia.ahk.nl
E-Mail: elia@elia.ahk.nl
executive director Carla Delfos; office manager Niels Gladdines; documentalists Isolde Landman, Katinka Nieuwendijk, Bregtje van Dam
Role & Services: to promote international cooperation between students and teachers of academic institutes of arts throughout Europe and to help promote all kinds of artistic and cultural exchanges and projects; advice and support for smaller scale networks, projects, masterclasses, workshops and events; a political lobby supporting policies and measures that encourage art and culture; more than 280 members from all fields of the arts; the League has established a database of Institutes of the Arts

European Mime Federation
Féderation Européenne de l'Art du Mime
Herengracht 174, 1016 BR **Amsterdam**, Netherlands
Tel: 31 20-422 6623 Fax: 31 20-422 6624
E-Mail: emf@mapa.nl
president Frits Vogels; director Ide van Heiningen; office manager Yolande Hezemans; office assistant Bettina Lorsheÿd
Role & Services: The EMF is a network-organisation of professional artists and pedagogues in the field of mime and movement theatre; main purpose is to promote and support international exchange, co-operation and development of professional expertise and to represent the interests of the discipline on an international level; membership is open to all individuals and organsations professionally engaged in mime and movement theatre *Comments:* the EMF publishes a quarterly newsletter: 'State of Mime', EMF membership can be obtained by faxing to EMF; costs: EURO 47.50 yearly, and State of Mime is free

European Music School Union (EMU)
Europäische Musikschul-Union
General Sekretariat, c/o Liechtensteinische Musikschule, St. Florinsgasse 1, 9490 **Vaduz**, Liechtenstein
Tel: 41 423-232 4620 Fax: 41 423-232 4642
E-Mail: louis.vogt@lms.llv.li
president Josef Frommelt; contact Louis Vogt
Role & Services: commited to enhancing the status of music schools across europe and to finding solutions for pedagogical, political and other problems through co-operation with other European music organisations including the EYFC, ISME, and IMC; organises music camps, conferences, meetings; organises European Youth Music Festival; collates and distributes infomation on music education throughout Europe; emphasis on music schools *Comments:* there are presidential elections in Oct 99; after which the presidency will no longer be in Lichtenstein; at the time of going to print no further information was available

European Network of Cultural Centres
c/o Council of Europe, Cultural Policy and Action Division, 67075 **Strasbourg** Cedex, France
Tel: 33 3-8841 3824 Fax: 33 3-8841 3782
Internet: www.coe.fr/culture
E-Mail: mercedes.giovinazzo@coe.fr
head of cultural policy and action division Vera Baltho; director of education, culture and sport Raymond Weber
Role & Services: aims to promote cultural co-operation between networks in Europe; at the inaugural meeting organised by the Council of Europe at Arc-et-Senans in 1988, and attended by centres nominated by member countries, it was agreed that groups of centres with common features should form specific networks, which would be brought together annually at a General Forum; the networks or groups that have been established or are under consideration include: centres specialising in theatre; centres specialising in the application of the new technologies in artistic creation; centres occupying historical monuments or premises of great architectural value; residential centres for creative talent, artists, writers, etc; Euro-Sud Centres

European Network of Information Centres for the Performing Arts
Réseau Européen des Centres d'Information du Spectacle Vivant
c/o VTI, Sainctelettesquare 19, 1000 **Brussels**, Belgium
Tel: 32 2-201 0906 Fax: 32 2-203 0502
Internet: www.enicpa.org
E-Mail: info@vti.be
network coordinator Caroline Derycke
Role & Services: the goal of the network is to gather and to make available to involved professionals on the widest possible basis all information on the performing arts, not only within Europe but also outside; The network has so far published the International Festival Guide and European Venue Guide, both available on-line on the Internet *Comments:* alternative internet: www.ecna.org/enicpa.html

European Opera Network
33, route du Rhin, 67000 **Strasbourg**, France
Tel: 33 3-8834 1808 Fax: 33 3-8834 1025
E-Mail: european-network@wanadoo.fr
president Rudolph Berger; pr Sophie Bertaut; consultant Virpri Nurmi
Role & Services: association of European opera companies; EON provides a wide variety of services that help to improve communication and cooperation among European opera companies, and with opera companies around the world; EON provides members with access to information and resources on a world-wide basis through its link to OPERA America, the service organisation for opera companies in the United States and Canada, as well as for companies in South America, Australia, New Zealand, and Asia, offering members a variety of meetings, publications and databases

European Theatre Convention
Delegation pour la Convention Théâtrale Européenne
c/o Koninklijke Vlaamse Schouwburg, Rue Delaunoy 58, 1080 **Brussels**, Belgium
Tel: 32 2-412 7040 Fax: 32 2-412 7068
Internet: www.etc-centre.org
E-Mail: cte@kvs.be
president Daniel Benoin (Comedie de Saint-Etienne); vice-presidents Peter Wahlqvist (Stockholms Stadsteater), Domenec Reixach (Teatre Nacional de Catalunya); general secretary Lieven Struye (Koninklijke Vlaamse Schouwburg); general delegate Patricia Canellis
Role & Services: created in 1988, the European Theatre Convention is a network of 31 theatres institutions from 16 European countries that have established a close cooperation in the field of contemporary writing; the ETC's programmes include: Public of European theatres, staff exchanges, coproductions, publications, newsletters, workshops, school exchanges and colloquia; furthermore, the Convention organises a festival every two years in a different city, coproduces the Bonner Biennale (Germany), and publishes a catalogue of selected contemporary plays from all over Europe; also organises the annual European Theatre Forum in Saint-Etienne (France)

European Union of Music Competitions for Youth (EMCY)
Postfach 662205, 81219 **München**, Germany
Tel: 49 89-871 002-50 (EMCY-Rohlfs)/002-41 (EMCY-van der Linden) Fax: 49 89-871 002-90
Internet: www.deutscher-musikrat.de/jumu.htm
E-Mail: jumu.emcy@t-online.de
Secretary General Dr. Eckart Rohlfs; Executive Secretary Eleonore van der Linden
Role & Services: promote music education and musical training at a European level through national and international music competitions for young amateurs, pupils and students; promote collaboration among organisers of member competitions concerning exchange of information; stimulate the interest of national and European authorities and of the general public concerning musical education, training and promotion of young musical talent; stimulate foundation of music competitions for youth in countries where these do not exist; cooperate with international youth competitions, festivals and organisations, spec. member organisations of European Music Council; special promotion programmes for prizewinners of national and international competitions in Europe: annual competitions 'European Music Prize for Youth', European Music Academy, Bonn (annual, international seminar), European Summer Academy in cooperation with the Hindemith Foundation (bi-annual, chamber music seminar), European Concerts; other events serving further education and meetings of prizewinners, jury members, organizers etc. on European level
Comments: visiting address: EMCY c/o Jugend musiziert, Trimburgstr. 2, 81249 München

European Video Services (EVS)
Vidéo Les beaux jours
BP 77, 67067 **Strasbourg** Cedex, France
Tel: 33 3-8823 8651 Fax: 33 3-8823 8655
Directeur Georges Heck; Président Alain Walther
Role & Services: a network of organisations representing and promoting different aspects of creative video who have joined forces to create a co-ordinated forum for the exchange of information and critical discourse throughout Europe; annual forum; publishes a news letter twice yearly *Comments:* EVS's activities were suspended during 1999, although Vidéo Les beaux jours is still active; visiting address: 31, rue Kageneck, 67000 Strasbourg

Federation for Asian Cultural Promotion (FACP), The
Asia Bunka Sokushin Renmei
Hikarigaoka, 6-1-1-909, Nerima-ku,
Tokyo 179-0072, Japan
Tel: 81 3-3977 4816 Fax: 81 3-3977 4816
chairperson Kang Suk-heung; vice chairperson Carrillo Gantner; secretary-general Tadashi Yokoyama
Role & Services: its objectives are to assist professional artists, promoters, impresarios, groups, companies and other organisations in or related to the arts in Asia and the Pacific region and to assemble and provide information regularly to members on cultural activities and the performing arts

Fédération Internationale des Jeunesses Musicales (FIJM)
International Federation of 'Jeunesses Musicales'
10 rue Royale, 1000 **Brussels**, Belgium
Tel: 32 2-513 9774 Fax: 32 2-514 4755
Internet: www.jmi.net
E-Mail: mail@jmi.net
secretary general Dag Franzen
Role & Services: created in 1945 to enable young people to develop through music accross all boundaries; it has a network of national organisations in more than 50 countries; the FIJM runs a World Orchestra and a World Youth Choir (in collaboration with the IFMC) and co-ordinates international activities such as international touring, festivals and music camps

Fédération Internationale des Musiciens
International Federation of Musicians
21 Bis rue Victor Massé, 75009 **Paris**, France
Tel: 33 1-4526 3123 Fax: 33 1-4526 3157
E-Mail: FIMparis@compuserve.com
president John Morton; general secretary Jean Vincent
Role & Services: established in 1948 to protect and further the economic, social and artistic interests of musicians worldwide and to promote the international exchange of musicians, it provides a forum for trade unions representing the music profession in 46 countries including Russia & provinces, South American countries, Africa

Fédération Mondiale des Concours Internationaux de Musique
World Federation of International Music Competitions
104 rue de Carouge, 1205 **Genève**, Switzerland
Tel: 41 22-321 3620 Fax: 41 22-781 1418
Internet: music-competitions.org
E-Mail: fmcim@iprolink.ch
president Renate Ronnefeld; secretary general Jacques Haldenwang; executive secretary Lottie Chalut
Role & Services: co-ordinates and promotes the activities of 107 major music competitions throughout the world, and publishes an annual calendar of competitions

Felix Meritis Foundation, The
European Centre for Arts and Science
Keizersgracht 324, 1016 EZ **Amsterdam**, Netherlands
Tel: 31 20-626 2321 Fax: 31 20-624 9368
Internet: www.felix.meritis.nl
E-Mail: felix@felix.meritis.nl
director Steve Austen
Role & Services: a European centre for the Arts and Science with internationalisation as its mission; a breeding ground for various international initiatives and projects in the fields of arts, science and cultural policy; its aim is being established by means of mobility, programmes, exchanges, co-production and international cooperation; its strength lies in the cooperation with several prominent organisations/institutions and personalities at home and abroad; such cooperation has led to the creation of strong networks which open the doors to the expertise available all over Europe
Comments: the Felix Meritis building is a monument from the Age of Enlightenment; from its inception the building has been a centre for arts and science; in keeping with its tradition it is a fitting place to stimulate the artistic, creative and scientific process with an international and interdisciplinary approach

Fundación Instituto Internacional de Teatro del Mediterráneo (IITM)
C/Ricardo de la Vega, 18, 28028 **Madrid**, Spain
Tel: 34 91-355 5867/64994 Fax: 34 91-726 3711
Internet: www.iitm.org
E-Mail: iitm-es@iitm.org
director José Monleón; presidente Salvador Távora; presidente hon. Rafael Alberti
Role & Services: help to develop the expression of the mediterranean performing arts; promote projects that help the theatre exchange and solidarity between mediterranean culture, research, information, publications, coproductions, cooperation, educational programs and all types of activities that develops the aims of the organization *Comments:* the IITM network has bases in: Albania, Algeria, Austria, Bosnia, Bulgaria, Corsica, Croatia, Egypt, Slovenia, Spain, France, Greece, Israel, Italy, Lebanon, Macedonia, Morocco, Moldova, Palestine, Portugal, Romania, Tunisia, Turkey, Yugoslavia

Groupement Européen des Sociétés d'Auteurs et Compositeurs (GESAC)
23 rue Montoyer, 1000 **Brussels**, Belgium
Tel: 32 2-511 4454 Fax: 32 2-514 5662
E-Mail: gesac@skynet.be
secrétaire général Véronique Desbrosses; président-fondateur Jean-Loup Tournier (SACEM, France)
Role & Services: European grouping of 24 EU and Switzerland and Norway national societies, constituted January 1991; its main object is to collaborate with the EC authorities to ensure legislation offering the highest level of protection to creators of works, involving for instance the length of period of protection and reproduction *Comments:* GESAC is an associate member of the Confederation International des Sociétés d'Auteurs et Compositeurs (q.v.) and an associate member of the Bureau International des Sociétés gérant les droits d'enregistrement et de reproduction mechanique (BIEM)

Informal European Theatre Meeting (IETM)
Saincteletteesquare 19, 1000 **Brussels**, Belgium
Tel: 32 2-201 0915 Fax: 32 2-203 0226
Internet: www.ietm.org
E-Mail: ietm@ietm.org
network coordinator Mary Ann De Vlieg; assistant Fanny Bouquerel
Role & Services: an international network of performing arts professionals with a commitment to innovative theatre and dance; it exists to facilitate collaborations and the exchange of information and ideas between members; IETM holds an Annual Plenary Meeting; an annual Forum Meeting (for members only), East-West meetings, 4 mediterranean meetings (to promote permanent links with the new Europe and the mediterranean countries) and various satellite meetings on specific topics; meetings and discussions are devoted to cross-border cooperation, information exchange, cultural policy matters, and reflection on international developments in the performing arts; IETM produces a newsletter and its publication programme includes studies and policy documents including 'More Bread and Circuses: Who does What for the Arts in Europe' (1995); membership is open to organisations professionally involved in the innovative contemporary performing arts; currently over four hundred organisations in over 40 different countries actively participate in the life of the network

Institute for International Relations (IRMO)
Ljudevita Farkasa Vukotinovica br. 2, PO Box 303, 10000 **Zagreb**, Croatia
Tel: 385 1-482 6522 Fax: 385 1-482 8361
Internet: www.culturelink.hr
E-Mail: clink@mairmo.irmo.hr
head of culture and communication department & coordinator of the Culturelink Network Biserka Cvjeticanin; senior research fellow at IRMO Nada Svob-Dokic
Role & Services: an independent, non-governmental research organisation engaged in the interdisciplinary study of developmental processes, international relations and cooperation; The Culture and Communication department coordinates the work of Culturelink, a worldwide network for research and cooperation in cultural development; Areas of research/activities: cultural development, cultural policies, and cultural cooperation, especially North-South and East-West cooperation, mass media and communications; Documentation, databases, Culturelink bulletin (quarterly), sponsored by UNESCO and the Council of Europe

International Alliance of Orchestra Associations (IAOA)
c/o Teatrarnas Riksforbund-TR (Association of Swedish Theatres and Orchestras), PO Box 1778,
111 87 **Stockholm**, Sweden
Tel: 46 8-440 8370 Fax: 46 8-440 8389
E-Mail: musik.teater@teatrarnasriks.se
president Betty Webster (executive director, Orchestras Canada); vice-president Libby McNamara (director, Association of British Orchestras q.v.); secretary Claes W. Englund (director, Teatrarnas Riksforbund, Sweden)
Role & Services: the Alliance aims to foster the development and interests of orchestras worldwide, working together on issues such as taxes, copyright, performing rights, management and conductor training

International Amateur Theatre Association (IATA)
IATA Secretariat, Vesterbrogade 175,
1800 **Frederiksberg** C, Denmark
Tel: 45 3122 2245 Fax: 45 3325 2553
Internet: home2.inet.tele.dk/aitaiata
E-Mail: aitaiata@post2.tele.ak
president Thomas Hauger; administrator Tina M Jakobsen
Role & Services: established in 1952, this UNESCO-affiliated organisation aims to propagate and protect dramatic art by all amateur theatrical groups devoted, without remuneration, to artistic and cultural aims; to co-ordinate the action of members in their purpose of enriching human experience and education through the medium of theatre; and to facilitate international exchange between all groups belonging to amateur theatre

International Artist Managers' Association (IAMA)
4 Addison Bridge Place,
London W14 8XP, United Kingdom
Tel: 44 20-7610 4884 Fax: 44 20-7610 4994
E-Mail: iama@easynet.co.uk
executive director Richard Steele; administration manager Patrick Vincent; membership development manager Wiebke Morgan
Role & Services: the leading worldwide association for classical music artist managers and concert agents; the Association provides professional support on behalf of its members and their artists at national, regional and international levels *Comments:* publishes annual Directory of Artists in 1999 jointly with European Association of Artist Managers (q.v.); regular Newsletter; and International Guide; co-organises professional conferences and seminars; tax, legal and hotel helplines for members

International Association of Entertainment Lawyers
13, rue Alphonse Lauryens Neuville, 75117 **Paris**, France
Tel: 33 1-4318 5500 Fax: 33 1-4417 6868
Internet: www.iael.org
président Julian Turton; secrétaire Eric Lauvraux
Role & Services: professional association of lawyers and business executives with over 200 members in 25 countries; specialise in performing arts law

International Association of German-speaking theatres
Internationale Arbeitsgemeinschaft deutschsprachiger Theater
Hirschengraben 8, 3011 **Bern**, Switzerland
Tel: 41 31-381 8020 Fax: 41 31-381 4410
secretary Notar Roland Morgenegg
Role & Services: members are Deutsche Bühnenverein, Theatererhalterverband österreichischer Bundesländer und Städte, Wiener Bühnenverein, Schweizerische Bühnenverband

International Association of Music Information Centres (IAMIC)
Stiftgasse 29, 1070 **Wien**, Austria
Tel: 43 1-52104/55 Fax: 43 1-52104/99
Internet: www.iamic.ie
E-Mail: office@iamic.at
secretary Matthias Finkentey
Role & Services: IAMIC is a worldwide network of organisations promoting new music; each Music Information Centre is responsible for documenting and promoting the music of its own country or region, as well as co-operating internationally with other centres and international organisations on issues of common concern; the centres are open to the public and have extensive resources to offer; also large libraries of sheet music and sound archives, some centres maintain up-to-date collections of biographical and research material, many issue publications and recordings
Comments: IAMIC is a member of the International Music Council of UNESCO; members of IAMIC are active in more than thirty countries internationally

International Association of Theatre Critics
Association Internationale des Critiques de Théâtre (AICT)
6 rue de Braque, 75003 **Paris**, France
Tel: 33 1-4627 4630 Fax: 33 1-4627 1608
president Georges Banu; secretary general Michel Vais; treasurer/contact Irene Sadowska Guillon
Role & Services: the association provides a forum worldwide for theatre critics and others who write about theatre; It organises a biennial congress, regular conferences, annual young critics' seminars and issues publications; regularly collaborate with the European Prize for Theatres, taking place every year in Taormina (Italy); collaborates with various festivals in Europe including Eastern Europe
Comments: it publishes a quarterly newsletter

International Confederation of Music Publishers (ICMP)
Confédération Internationale des Éditeurs de Musique
47 rue de Turbigo, 75003 **Paris**, France
Tel: 33 1-4272 3899 Fax: 33 1-4272 3805
E-Mail: 101374.25@compuserve.com
general director Jenny Vacher-Desvernais; lawyer Anne-Sophée De Pinsun
Role & Services: represents the interests of its 25 member organisations worldwide; federates the International Federation of Serious Music Publishers (IFSMP) and the International Federation of Popular Music Publishers (IFPMP); European national publishers are grouped in the European Committee of the Confederation

International Confederation of Societies of Authors & Composers (CISAC), The
Regional Office Asia-Pacific, 77A Duxton Road, **Singapore** 089536, Singapore
Tel: 65 225 5025 Fax: 65 725 5153
E-Mail: ang-kt@cisacap.com.sg
director Ang Kwee Tiang
Role & Services: deals with music copyrights

International Council for Traditional Music
Center for Ethnomusicology, Columbia University, **New York** NY 10027, United States of America
Tel: 1 212-678 0332 Fax: 1 212-678 2513
Internet: www.music.columbia.edu/~ictm
E-Mail: ictm@compuserve.com
secretary general Dieter Christensen
Role & Services: supports research and performance of traditional music, organises conferences and publishes a yearbook for traditional music

International Federation for Choral Music (IFCM)
Villa Gadea, 03590 **Altea**, Spain
Tel: 34 96-584 5213 Fax: 34 96-584 5213
Internet: www.choralnet.org
E-Mail: jcwilkens@compuserve.com
president Eskil Hemberg, Sweden; vice president Europe Thomas Rabbow, Germany; secretary general Jean-Claude Wilkens, Spain
Role & Services: to promote friendship and understanding among the peoples of the world through choral music and to assist choral music attain its due recognition in the world's musical life; The official representative of choral music at the International Music Council of UNESCO (q.v.); publish International Choral Bulletin – a quarterly in four languages, World Choral Census, an annual compendium of choral organisations, festivals, competitions and publishers
Comments: organise World Symposium on Choral Music: 2002 in Minneapolis

International Federation for Theatre Research (IFTR)
Fédération Internationale pour la Recherche Théâtrale (FIRT)
School of Drama, Samuel Beckett Centre, Trinity College, **Dublin** 2, Ireland (Republic of)
Tel: 353 1-608 1550 Fax: 353 1-679 3488
Internet: www.tcd.ie/iftr
E-Mail: bsnglton@tcd.ie
president Prof Josette Féral; joint secretary general – English Dr. Brian Singleton; joint secretary general – French Christiane Page; treasurer Prof Martin Dreier; membership secretary Kay McDonnell
Role & Services: promotes international liaison between organisations and individuals concerned with theatre research, and organises international conferences and symposia; publishes Theatre Research International

International Federation of Actors
Fédération Internationale des Acteurs/Internationaler Schauspielerverband/ Federación International de Actores
Guild House, Upper St Martin's Lane, **London** WC2H 9EG, United Kingdom
Tel: 44 20-7379 0900 Fax: 44 20-7379 8260
Internet: www.Fia-actors.com
E-Mail: FiaLondon@compuserve.com
general secretary Katherine Sand; administrator Marie-José Albertini-Dassa; president Tomas Bolme
Role & Services: a forum for 78 trade unions and professional associations in 57 countries concerned with the rights of performers (actors, dancers, opera performers, variety and circus performers, and those working in film, broadcasting and the recording industry); it promotes the exchange of information on issues affecting performers and on their experiences through publications, and the convening of conferences and seminars; it also organises solidarity action in support of any of its affiliate member unions that become involved in industrial disputes or experience problems related to performers' rights; it represents its members towards most international fora including WIPO, UNESCO, ILO and the European Commission

International Federation of Festival Organizations (FIDOF)
4230 Stansbury Avenue, #105, **Sherman Oaks** CA 91423, United States of America
Tel: 1 818-789 7596 Fax: 1 818-784 9141
E-Mail: moreno@gateway.net
founder and president Prof. Armando Moreno; secretary general Mario Moreno (email: mm412@aol.com)
Role & Services: an international non-profit organization servicing and coordinating information about festivals and cultural events from around the world. FIDOF provides a valuable network of co-ordination and information as an ideal forum for the exchange of concepts, cultural events and know-how. *Comments:* Membership includes all major festivals of international and national prominence as well as festival related parties such as: corporate sponsors, record and television companies, managers, agents, impresarios, music publishers, artists, songwriters etc.

International Federation of the Phonographic Industry (IFPI)
54 Regent Street, **London** W1R 5PJ, United Kingdom
Tel: 44 20-7878 7900 Fax: 44 20-7878 7950
Internet: www.ifpi.org
E-Mail: info@ifpi.org
chairman of the board David G Fine; director general Nicholas Garnett; director of European affairs Frances Moore; director of communications Catrin Hughes
Role & Services: represents some 1300 record producers in over 70 countries around the world, including some of the major international ones; IFPI campaigns for the introduction, improvement and enforcement of copyright and related rights legislation, and coordinates the music industry's anti-piracy activities

International Federation of the Phonographic Industry – IFPI (Asian Regional Office)
Room 3705, Hopewell Centre, 183 Queen's Road East, Wanchai, **Hong Kong**, China
Tel: 852 2866 6862 Fax: 852 2865 6326/2866 6869
regional director (Asia) J C Giouw; deputy director Sean Mok
Role & Services: record association

International Federation of the Phonographic Industry (IFPI) – European Office
Square de Meeus 19, 1050 **Brussels**, Belgium
Tel: 32 2-511 9208 Fax: 32 2-502 3077
Internet: www.ifpi.org
E-Mail: euroinfo@ifpi.org.be
director Francis Moore; legal advisor Olivia Regnier; office manager Beryl Reuland; international trade Stephan Krawczyk; media relations/manager Adrian Strain
Role & Services: international recording industries representation to the E.U.

International Festivals & Events Association Europe (IFEA)
c/o Netherlands Board of Tourism, PO Box 458, 2260 MG **Leadschendan**, Netherlands
Tel: 31 70-370 5296 Fax: 31 70-320 1654
E-Mail: ewinkel@net.nl
chairman Hanne Söndergaard; administrator Lotte Dige; pr Hanna Soenger
Role & Services: promotes cooperation between managers, organisers, producers, PR directors, fundraisers, and sponsors of the performing arts; IFEA Europe has 90 members from 19 different countries, and is the European affiliate of IFEA World (a non-profit organisation with more than 2200 festivals, special events, and events suppliers worldwide); the primary service of IFEA Europe is to create network opportunities for professional producers of festivals and events; produces conferences, publish magazines, newsletters, textbooks and directories
Comments: focus on the management, marketing and production side of festivals and events

International Festivals & Events Association – World Headquarters
PO Box 2950, 115 E. Railroad Avenue, # 302, **Port Angeles** WA 98362-0336, United States of America
Tel: 1 360-457 3141 Fax: 1 360-452 4695
Internet: www.ifea.com
E-Mail: bruce@ifea.com
president Bruce Skinner; secretary Teresa MacDonald
Comments: see also International Festivals & Events Association – Europe

International Managers Forum (IMF)
1 Glenthorne Mews, 115A Glenthorne Road, **London** W6 0LJ, United Kingdom
Tel: 44 20-7741 2555 Fax: 44 20-7741 4856
Internet: www.imf-uk.org
E-Mail: office@imf-uk.org
general secretary James Fisher
Role & Services: organisation which represents the interests of music managers

International Music Centre/Internationales Musikzentrum (IMZ)
Centre International de la Musique (IMZ)
Speisinger Str. 121-127, 1230 **Wien**, Austria
Tel: 43 1-889 0315 Fax: 43 1-889 0315-77
Internet: www.imz.at
E-Mail: office@imz.at
president Adrienne Clarkson; secretary general Franz Patay; database managers Martin C Mandlmayr; editor in chief Monika Gelbmann
Role & Services: forum for discussion of issues related to the performance and dissemination of music through the technical media (broadcasting, film, recordings, etc); its membership comprises broadcasting organisations producing and programming audiovisual music productions, artists, agents, producers and distributors, organises congresses, seminars, screenings and competitions; monthly bulletin 'Music in the Media'; International database of audiovisual productions on music and dance

International Society for Contemporary Music (ISCM)
Société Internationale pour la Musique Contemporaine
c/o Gaudeamus, Swammerdamstraat 38, 1091 RV **Amsterdam**, Netherlands
Tel: 31 20-694 7349 Fax: 31 20-694 7258
Internet: www.xs4all.nl/~iscm
E-Mail: iscm@xs4all.nl
secretary general Henk Heuvelmans; president Arne Mellnäs
Role & Services: forum for the promotion of modern music with branches in more than 48 countries worldwide; The ISCM organises a competition for new works, ISCM World Music Days, in a different country each year; in 1999 the ISCM World Music Days will take place in Romania (Bucharest and Cluj) from September 25 until October 2, contact: ISCM Romanian Section, Cal. Victoriei 141, sector 1, 71102 Bucharest, Romania

International Society for Music Education (ISME)
ICRME, University of Reading, Bulmershe Court, **Reading** RG6 1HY, United Kingdom
Tel: 44 118-931 8846 Fax: 44 118-931 8846/935 2080
Internet: www.isme.org
E-Mail: e.smith@reading.ac.uk
secretary general Joan Therens; administrator Elizabeth Smith
Role & Services: aims to stimulate music education throughout the world as an integral part of general education; organises biennial conferences and issues the 'International Journal of Music Education' and other publications; ISME has seven commissions which organise specialist seminars, usually held immediately prior to the International Conference; their task is to gather, collate and disseminate information on developments in their specialised fields

International Society for the Performing Arts Foundation (ISPA)
PO Box 909, **Rye** NY 10580, United States of America
Tel: 1 914-921 1550 Fax: 1 914-921 1593
Internet: www.ispa.org
E-Mail: info@ispa.org
executive director David G. Watson (e-mail: dwatson@ispa.org)
Role & Services: to provide services in education and international business exchange at the highest level for perfoming arts executives of concert and performance halls, festivals, orchestras, dance and theatre companies, competitions, artist managers, consultants and cultural ministries around the world; Members participate in international meetings twice annually and share information and expertise by publications and internet
Comments: the International Society for the Performing Arts (ISPA) is a subsidiary of the Foundation and currently has 700 members from 50 countries; visiting address: 17 Purdy Avenue, Rye, NY 10580, United States of America

International Society for the Performing Arts Foundation (ISPA)
European Chapter c/o Arts Publishing International Ltd, Lime Wharf, Vyner Street, **London** E2 9DJ, United Kingdom
Tel: 44 20-8709 9050 Fax: 44 20-8709 9080
E-Mail: mph@api.co.uk
contact Martin Huber
Role & Services: to provide services in education and international business exchange at the highest level for perfoming arts executives of concert and performance halls, festivals, orchestras, dance and theatre companies, competitions, artist managers, consultants and cultural ministries around the world; Members participate in international meetings twice annually and share information and expertise by publications and internet
Comments: the International Society for the Performing Arts (ISPA) is a subsidiary of the Foundation and currently has 700 members from 50 countries; visiting address: 17 Purdy Avenue, Rye, NY 10580, United States of America

International Theatre Institute (ITI)
Institut International du Théâtre
UNESCO, 1 rue Miollis, 75732
Paris Cedex 15, France
Tel: 33 1-4568 2650/1 Fax: 33 1-4566 5040
Internet: iti-worldwide.org
E-Mail: iti@unesco.org
secretary general André-Louis Perinetti; assistant executive Jennifer Walpole
Role & Services: is an international non-governmental organisation, created by UNESCO in 1948 to promote the international exchange of knowledge in the performing arts and to stimulate creation and increase co-operation between people in the theatre; There are now 95 ITI centres around the world and many of these provide a valuable resource and point of entry to the theatre scene and organisations in their own countries; They can often suggest the most appropriate individuals and organisations for overseas visitors to contact. At an international level, ITI promotes a Theatre of Nations Festival, organises a World Congress every 3 years (next 2000), created celebrates World Theatre Day and International Dance Day, organises seminars and publishes reports and newletters; The ITI is concerned with all aspects of theatre and has permanent international committees for dance, music theatre, playwrights, theatre education, theatre publications, dramatic theatre, cultural identity and development, etc. Organisations such as ASSITEJ, OISTAT, SIBMAS and UNIMA (all referred to elsewhere in this section) are affiliated to the ITI

International Ticketing Association (INTIX)
Suite 722, 250 West 57th Street, **New York** NY 10107, United States of America
Tel: 1 212-581 0600 Fax: 1 212-581 0885
Internet: www.intix.org
E-Mail: info@intix.org
president Patricia Spira; chairman of European management committee Richard Brundle; exbit manager Ann Marie Sinnott
Role & Services: to provide the definite resource and forum for the international ticketing industry

Japan Center, Pacific Basin Arts Communication (PARC)
Kokusai Butai Geijutsu Kohryu Center
3A, 7-3-12 Roppongi, Minato-ku,
Tokyo 106-0032, Japan
Tel: 81 3-3423 7018 Fax: 81 3-3423 7597
E-Mail: parc@jah.ne.jp
chairman Takeomi Nagayama; secretary general Tadao Nakane; vice secretary Shuji Sota
Comments: see National Organisations, Japan

Nordic Music Committee (NOMUS)
Nybrokajen 11, 111 48 **Stockholm**, Sweden
Tel: 46 8-407 1720/21
Fax: 46 8-407 1650
Internet: www.norden.org
E-Mail: gen.secr@nomus.org
secretary general Johan Falk
Role & Services: as the official expert committee for music of the Nordic Council of Ministers (Copenhagen Denmark) NOMUS acts as an advisory body in Nordic musical affairs, subsidises commissioned works, concerts, tours and conferences within the five Nordic countries and publishes 'Nordic Sounds', an English-language magazine dealing with Nordic musical life, and a yearbook of Nordic music organizations and institutions (NOMUS-Katalogen); NOMUS is also prize committee for the annual Nordic Council Music Prize of DKK 350000

Nordisk Copyright Bureau (NCB)
Société représentant des droits de reproduction mécaniques Les Pays Nordiques
Frederiksgade 17, PO box 3064,
1021 **Copenhagen** K, Denmark
Tel: 45 3336 8700 Fax: 45 3336 4690
Internet: www.ncb.dk
E-Mail: ncb@ncb.dk
managing director Thorkil Emborg
Role & Services: member of GESAC (Groupement Européen des Sociétes d'Auteurs et Compositeurs) (q.v.) & BIEM, CISAC
Comments: represents mechanical rights for Denmark, Sweden, Norway, Finland, Iceland, Lithuania and Estonia

Open Society Institute – Budapest
October 6, V. 12, 1051 **Budapest**, Hungary
Tel: 36 1-327 3100 Fax: 36 1-327 3101
Internet: www.osi.hu/art
E-Mail: dgavrilova@osi.hu
performing arts network programme Ms Dessilava; executive director Katalin Koncz
Role & Services: a network of foundations established in Eastern and Central Europe with the objective to fostering the evolution of a pluralistic and open society; the foundations support programmes across a wide range of fields including health, education, art and culture; there are more than 25 foundations in former communist countries each with their own trustees and cultural programme, foundations also established in Haiti and South Africa

OPERA America
1156 15th Street, Suite 810,
Washington DC 20005-1704, United States of America
Tel: 1 202-293 4446 Fax: 1 202-393 0735
Internet: www.operaam.org
E-Mail: frontdesk@operaam.org (for general inquiries)
president and chief executive officer Marc A Scorca (marc@operaam.org); director of finance and administration Harris Povich (harris@operaam.org); media & audience relations Sam Smith (sam@operaam.org); director of operations Eve Smith (eve@operaam.org)
Role & Services: a not-for-profit service organization; founded to support the professional opera companies of North America, it since has expanded to include allied international companies; other producing, presenting, and educational institutions, and others; provides a variety of informatonal, technical, and financial services to its members and serves as a resource to the media, funders, government agencies, and the general public; OPERA America seeks to promote opera as an exciting and accessible art form to all segments of society; see European Opera Network *Comments:* see also Services and National Organisations (MOD)

Organisation Internationale des Scénographes, Techniciens et Architects de Théâtre (OISTAT)
International Organisation of Scenographers, Theatre Architects and Technicians
General Secretariat, PO Box 15172,
1001 MD **Amsterdam**, Netherlands
Tel: 74-250 5095 Fax: 26-445 7235
Internet: www.oistat.nl
E-Mail: c.lievaart@inter.nl.net
general secretary Chris Lievaart; assistant to the general secretary Karin Winkelsesser (email: 100430.3035@compuserve.com)
Role & Services: to establish and maintain an international exchange of Scenography, Theatre Architecture and Technology together with other relevant and related areas of theatrical technical development
Comments: In any one country only one organisation can be a member of OISTAT; the members of each national organisation are automatically members of OISTAT, hence total membership 20,000 (from 36 countries)

Pearle* Performing Arts Employers Associations League Europe
Herengracht 62, 1015 BP **Amsterdam**, Netherlands
Tel: 31 20-620 9000 Fax: 31 20-638 5151
E-Mail: cno@xs4all.nl
executive officer Rudolf Wolfensberger; personal assistant Cornélie Kars
Role & Services: members are the leading performing arts employers' organisations in all Western European countries and a growing number in Eastern Europe; PEARLE acts as a forum for exchanging information of relevance to members, in addition to serving as the body to make representations to the European Commission and any other authorities whose deliberations may affect the work of the performing arts in Europe; observer status with WIPO (World Intellectual Property Organisation); member of EEN (European Employers' Network) facilitated by UNICE (Union of Industrial and Employers Confederations of Europe); registered as an employers' organization by ILO (International Labour Office) with observer status at the International Labour Conference; established by the European Commission as the Social Dialogue Committee Performing Arts together with European Entertainment Alliance, representing FIM (International Federation of Musicians), FIA (International Federation of Actors) and MEI (Media Entertainment International)

Pegasus Foundation
c/o European Parliament, EAS 255, Rue Belliard, 135A, 1047 **Brussels**, Belgium
Tel: 32 2-284 2361/3695
Fax: 32 2-284 9009
E-Mail: jpegasus@europol.eu.int
president Fernand Herman, MPE; executive president Eugenio Belloni; consultants Christina Hazard
Role & Services: promotes, disseminates and supports all activities whose goal is to develop the perception of a European cultural identity; wishes to find common ground between the worlds of business, culture and European institutions; promotes European identity through education projects & cultural heritage targeted at youth

Rencontres, Les
25 rue Deparcieux, 75014 **Paris**, France
Tel: 33 1-4538 7013 Fax: 33 1-4538 7013
Internet: www.les-rencontres.org
E-Mail: rencontr@club-internet.fr
chairman Roger Tropeano
Role & Services: Network of elected representatives of European towns and regions; aimed at creating a strong exchange of ideas and actions in the cultural field; the association also publishes a directory of the cultural local administration in Europe containing information about 200 cities and regions with contact names and addresses, the cultural policy of each municipality and more

Réseau Européen des Centres de Formation d'Administrateurs Culturels (ENCATC)
European Network of Cultural Administration Training Centres (ENCATC)
c/o KIT, Vestergade n° 5,
1456 **Copenhagen** K, Denmark
Tel: 45 3315 8214 Fax: 45 3332 8182
Internet: www.artecnet.com/encatc/
E-Mail: encatc@artecnet.com
president Herwig Pöschl; secretary Brigitte Remer; treasurer Mickäel Quine; co-ordinator Isabelle Schwarz; vice-president Lidia Varbanova
Role & Services: an independent network of training institutions and individuals professionally involved in the cultural management training and related sectors; it aims at developing the training of cultural administrators in Europe and the co-operation between centres organising such a training; Its objectives are: facilitating the exchange of information between centres, providing opportunities for training the trainers, identifying and supporting areas of research which are of common interest to its members, advising European bodies on training policies in the field of cultural administration and management, representing the interest of European cultural administration training centres at a European level; ENCATC has established working groups on issues related to arts administration and cultural management and produced an interactive database with information on all network members; it organises summer schools and theatrical sessions and produces newsletters and various relevant publications
Comments: currently has 82 members from 24 European countries

Service Centre for International Cultural Activities, The Netherlands
Herengracht 609, 1017 CE **Amsterdam**, Netherlands
Tel: 20-520 0510 Fax: 20-520 0504
Internet: post@sicasica.nl
E-Mail: www.sicasica.nl
contact Inez Boogaarts
Role & Services: promotes the exchange of information and documentation between different cultural sectors, to improve coordination, and to encourage exchanges of expertise and experience within the field of international culture; also the European cultural contact point for The Netherlands

Société Internationale des Bibliothèques et Musées des Arts du Spectacle (SIBMAS)
International Society of Libraries and Museums of the Performing Arts
c/o Membership Secretary & Treasurer Georg Geldner, Österreichisches Theatermuseum, Lobkowitzplatz 2,
1010 **Wien**, Austria
Tel: 43 1-512 8800 ext 32
Fax: 43 1-512 8800 45
E-Mail: georg-geldner@theatermuseum.at
membership secretary & treasurer Georg Geldner; president Noëlle Guibert; secretary general Willem Rodenhuis
Role & Services: SIBMAS is intended for museum and library staff and others concerned with the collection, organisation or dissemination of information about the performing arts; It exists to provide a forum for discussion, to promote research and to facilitate the international exchange of contacts and information about performing arts collections; It organises a biennial international congress (Sept. 2000: Paris), it collates and edits the International Directory of Performing Arts Collections and sends out to members regular information in the SIBMAS/FIRT Bulletin; It has set up a committee to monitor and develop automated cataloguing systems for performing arts collections; It contributes to the International Bibliography of Theatre and the World Encyclopedia of Contemporary Theatre

Societies Council for the Administration of Performers' Rights (SCAPR)
c/o SAMI, Döbelnsgatan 3,
111 40 **Stockholm**, Sweden
Tel: 46 8-453 3400
Fax: 46 8-453 3440
E-Mail: info@sami.se
chairman t.b.a.; secretary Bjorn Juell-Sundbye (Denmark); contact Raija Lindblad
Role & Services: joint forum for societies that are related through bilateral agreements to settle rights of performers in different countries; issues information and guidelines regarding rights of performers; responsible for IPD (the International Performers' Database)
Comments: the chairman rotates and is always the managing director of the society of the country where each conference is held

Southeast Asian Ministers of Education Organisation (SEAMO)
30 Orange Grove Road,
Singapore 258-352, Singapore
Tel: 65 737 9044 Fax: 65 734 2753
Role & Services: primary aim to improve educational standards, but has also become active in a wide range of cultural programs

Trans Europe Halles – Association of Independent Cultural Centres
18 rue Etienne Dolet,
93400 **St Ouen**, France
Tel: 33 1-4011 6414
Fax: 33 1-4011 6414
Internet: www.teh.net
E-Mail: teh@teh.net
secretary Philippe Grombeer; chairman Cor Schlösser; coordinator of T.E.H Fazette Bordage
Role & Services: a European network of multi-media centres concerned with exchanges and international co-operation in new developments in all forms of creativity and cultural production, including music, drama, dance, festivals, workshops, etc.; all cultural centres in the network occupy converted industrial buildings; T.E.H is also a member of the European Forum for the Arts and Heritage and the Forum of European Cultural Networks

UNESCO Principal Office for Asia and the Pacific
920, Daiakarn Bldg., Sukhumvit Road,
Bangkok 10110, Thailand
Tel: 66 2-391 0577/0879
Fax: 66 2-391 0866
Internet:
www.education.unesco.org/proap/new/main.htm
E-Mail: culture.asia-pacific@unesco.org
director Victor Ordonez; regional advisor for culture in Asia & the Pacific Richard Engelhardt
Role & Services: prospective studies, standard-setting action, training technical support and advisory services to the Member States in the fields of heritage, culture resource management, cultural activities and tourism; Alternative internet: www.unescobkk.org/culture

Union des Théâtres de l'Europe
c/o Odéon-Théâtre de l'Europe, 1 Place Paul Claudel,
75006 **Paris**, France
Tel: 33 1-4441 3664
Fax: 33 1-4329 3188
Internet: www.ute-net.org
E-Mail: ute@ute-net.org
fondateur Giorgio Strehler; président Gábor Zsámbéki; directeur Eli Malka
Role & Services: European network uniting sixteen major theatres in Europe to develop common cultural actions, extending beyond national and linguistical boundaries, open to all theatres sharing similar ideals; among the UTE activities: annual Festival, presenting shows of the member theatres; workshops for young directors and young actors conducted by leading European directors; exhibitions of European set designers; productions, co-productions and exchanges between the member theatres, colloquia and publications; the member theatres are: Odéon – Théâtre de l'Europe (Paris), Piccolo Teatro – Teatro d'Europa (Milan), Teatre Lliure (Barcelone), Deutsches Theater und Kammerspiele (Berlin), Kungliga Dramatiska Teatern (Stockholm), Katona József Színház (Budapest), Düsseldorfer Schauspielhaus (Düsseldorf), Royal Shakespeare Company (Stratford Upon Avon), Teatrul Bulandra (Bucharest), Maly Teatr (Saint-Petersburg), Stary Teatr (Krakow), Teatro di Roma (Rome), TNS (Strasbourg), National Theatre of Finland (Helsinki), National Theatre of Northern Greece (Thessaloniki), Teatro de la Abadia (Madrid)

Union Internationale de la Marionnette (UNIMA)
International Union of the Marionnette
UNIMA, BP 249,
08103 **Charleville-Mezieres** Cédex, France
Tel: 33 3-2433 7250
Fax: 33 3-2433 7269
Internet: www.unima.org
E-Mail: sgi@unima.org
general secretary Jacques Felix
Role & Services: non-governmental organisation affiliated to UNESCO bringing together people and puppeters from around the world who contribute to the development of the art of puppetry; it's main objectives are to encourage and facilitate contact and exchange between practitioners from every continent, to act as a medium for the promotion, dissemination and support of the development of the art of puppetry
Comments: organises congresses, conferences, festivals, exhibitions and competitions, or else grants UNIMA patronage for these; currently compiling a World Encyclopedia of Puppetry Arts

Web Art Garden (WAG)
Uk office, 46C Montpellier Spa Road,
Cheltenham GL50 1UL, United Kingdom
Tel: 44 1242-578 033
Fax: 44 1242-578 033
E-Mail: sdreeeve@compuserve.com
contact Sandra Reeve
Role & Services: independent, non-profit intercultural network concerned with cultural, environmental and educational issues in the fields of visual and performing arts
Comments: organises ACE (Arts, Culture, Environment) project around World Environment Day (5 June 1999)

World Association for Symphonic Bands and Ensembles
c/o Felix Hauswirth, Dorfstrasse 84b,
6332 **Hagendorn**, Switzerland
Tel: 41 41-780 3602 Fax: 41 41-780 3602
E-Mail: felix.hauswirth@swissonline.ch
president Felix Hauswirth
Comments: at present 1000 members from 50 countries, next conference in 2001 in Luzern, Switzerland

World Dance Alliance – Europe
Erkrather Straße 30, 40233 **Düsseldorf**, Germany
Tel: 49 211-172 7010
Fax: 49 211-172 7017
E-Mail: tanzhausnrw@t-online.de
President Marc Jonkers (Netherlands); Executive Director & Chair of Board of Directors Bertram Müller (Germany)
Role & Services: mission is to serve as a primary voice and support group for dance in Europe

World Dance Alliance International
5524 Chippewa St., 2W, **St Louis** MO 63109,
United States of America
Tel: 1 314-352 1135 Fax: 1 314-352 1755
E-Mail: wolz@aol.com
international director Carl Wolz; president of the Asia-Pacific-Centre Mr Miki Wakamatsu; president of the Americas-Centre Grant Strate; president of the Europe-Centre Marc Jonkers

National Organisations and Resource Centres

National Organisations and Resource Centres
We have sought to provide addresses of some of the key organisations involved with the performing arts in each country. Some of these are better resourced than others and the level of advice and help they provide often reflects this fact. Where there are gaps it is usually because information was not supplied. **Within country the organisations are ordered alphabetically.**

Organisations Nationales et Centres de Documentation
Nous avons cherché à fournir les adresses de quelques organisations importantes qui s'occupent des Arts Vivants dans chaque pays. Certaines de ces organisations disposent de plus de ressources que d'autres et les possibilités d'aide ou de conseil offerts s'en ressentent souvent. Les lacunes dans cette rubrique représentent généralement un manque d'informations fournies par les différentes organisations. **Pour chaque payes les organisations sont classés par ordres alphabétique.**

Nationale Organisationen, Forschungs- und Dokumentationszentren
In diesem Kapitel haben wir versucht, für jedes Land Schlüsselorganisationen aus dem Bereich der darstellenden Künste aufzuführen. Manchen Organisationen stehen bessere Geld- und Informationsquellen zur Verfügung als anderen. Dies spiegelt sich oft in der Qualität der gebotenen Zusammenarbeit und Hilfe wider. Lücken im Kapitel entstehen durch Mangel an bereitgestellten Informationen. **Die Organisationen sind innerhalb der Staaten alphabetisch verzeichnet.**

Organizzazioni Nazionali e Centri di Ricerca
Si é cercato di provvedere a fornire gli indirizzi delle principali organizzazioni che agiscono nel campo artistico in ogni singolo Paese. Alcune associazioni hanno fornito piú dettagli di altre specificando di che cosa si occupano e quindi dando al lettore un'idea dell'aiuto e dei consigli che puó ricevere da ogni singola associazione. Laddove non vengono date altre informazioni all'infuori dell'indirizzo é perché tali organizzazioni non hanno provveduto a farlo. **Le organizzazioni sono ordinate alfabeticamente.**

Organizaciones nacionales y centros de recursos y documentación
Se han incluido las direcciones de algunas de las organizaciones claves vinculadas con las artes escénicas y musicales en cada país. El hecho de que alguna de estas organizaciones cuente con más recursos que otras se ve reflejado a menudo en el nivel de ayuda ofrecido. En los casos en los que hay una falta de datos se debe generalmente a que la información no fue facilitada. **Las organizaciones se encuentran por orden alfabético dentro de cada país.**

National Organisations and Resource Centres (**국내 조직 및 자원 센타**)
각 국가의 주요 공연 예술 관계 조직들의 주소를 제공하기 위해 노력했다. 이들 중 어떤 조직체들은 다른 조직체들보다 많은 정보를 제공한다. 그 차이점은 그들이 제공한 충고나 지원 정도를 반영한다. 빈칸은 일반적으로 정보가 제공되지 않았기 때문이다. **리스트는 국가별로 알파벳순으로 기재되었다.**

国家机构和资源中心
我们已经尽量提供各国从事表演艺术的一些主要机构的地址。某些机构比其它机构的资源丰富，这通常可以由它们提供的咨询和帮助反映出来。存在的差距通常是因为缺乏信息。**在每个国家里机构是按字母顺序排列的。**

国家団体とリソースセンター
ここではそれぞれの国で舞台芸術に関わるいくつかの主要団体の住所を掲載しました。これらの団体は財源の豊かさという意味において差があり、個々の団体が提供するアドバイスや支援のレベルの差は多くの場合、財政の差に由来しています。情報にばらつきがありますが、これはその提供量に起因します。**リストは国別で、一国内ではアルファベット順に記載されています。**

ALBANIA (+355)

Albanian Civil Society Foundation
Rr Asim Vokshi, Vila 137, **Tirana**
Tel: 42-33067 Fax: 42-33067
E-Mail: rolanda@acsf.tirana.al
executive director Rolanda Dhimitri

Albanian NGOs Forum
Rr Jani Vreto, nr. 14, **Tirana**
Tel: 42-30893
E-Mail: spahiu@angof.tirana.al
executive director Artan Spahiu

Albanian section of EPTA, The
Liceu Artistik Jordan Misja, Rr. Elbasanit, **Tirana**
Tel: 42-23743
chairman Takuina Truja

Albanian section of Frederik Shopen, The
Bulevardi Dÿshmorÿt e Kombit, Pall. 62/1, Ap. 6, **Tirana**
Tel: 42-20607
chairman Prof Spiro Theodhosi
Role & Services: international music association

Albanian section of RILM, The
Rr Sitki Cico, Pallatet 9 kate, Shkalla 2, Ap. 4, **Tirana**
Tel: 42-30203 Fax: 42-30203
secretary Prof Dr Shpÿtim Kushta
Comments: the RilM Abstract Literature of Music-New York; Secretary Prof Dr Shpÿtim Kushta: Kavaja, street nr. 4, Tirana

Albautor
Rr. Gjik Kuqali, P.4/1, ap. 9, **Tirana**
Tel: 42-24803
chairman Neshat Tozaj
Role & Services: the Albanian association of rights in music

AMIA – Albanian Music Information Agency
ASHIM – Agjensia Shqiptare e Informacionit Muzikor
c/o Dr Vasil S Tole, Sitkci Cico, App 4, **Tirana**
Tel: 42-74127
E-Mail: root@tob.tirana.al
chief of AMIA Dr Vasil S Tole

Fondacioni Fan Noli
Tirana
executive director Dhimitÿr Anagnosti

Institute of Folk Culture – Academy of Sciences, The
Kont Urani, street nr. 3, **Tirana**
Tel: 42-22323/24555 Fax: 42-24555
general director Prof Afÿrdita Onuzi

Music foundation Dhora Leka
Rr Durrÿsit, Pallati 240, Shkalla 8, ap. 66, **Tirana**
Tel: 42-30715 Fax: 42-30715
president Dhora Leka

New Albanian Music
Academy of Arts, Nÿnÿ Tereza, street, **Tirana**
Tel: 42-62899
president Aleksander Peci
Comments: member of the European conference Promotors of New Music

Pan-Albanian Union of Music Professionals
L9, Rr Muhamet Gjollesha, P.54/11/22, **Tirana**
Tel: 42-37012 Fax: 42-25488

SOROS foundation – Albania
óapajev Gjokutaj
Pallati 23/1, **Tirana**
Tel: 42-34621/35856/34223 Fax: 42-35855
executive director Pjetÿr Bogdani
Role & Services: aims to foster the evolution of a pluralistic and open society

Tonin Harapi
Rr Myslym Shyri, P. 12, Shkalla 5, Ap. 38, **Tirana**
Tel: 42-34557
chairman Prof Kozma Lara
Role & Services: music association

ARMENIA (+374)

Armenian Little Singers International Association
26-39 Kievian Street, 375033 **Yerevan**
Tel: 2-563 616/232 920 Fax: 2-151 059
president Tigran Hekekian

Armenian Musical Assembly
Aram Khachaturian House-Museum,
3 Plekhanov Street, 375000 **Yerevan**
Tel: 2-589 418/534 108 Fax: 2-151 795
president Levon Chaushian

Armenian Section of Union Internationale de la Marionnette (UNIMA)
24-18 Kievian Street, 375033 **Yerevan**
Tel: 2-272 961/582 867 Fax: 2-151 795 (AT&T)
E-Mail: ngoc@moon.yerphi.am
president Armen Safarian

Armenian State Philharmony
13a Khandjian Street, 375010 **Yerevan**
Tel: 2-566 705/790
Fax: 2-562 324
director Laert Movsesian

CADENCE Chamber Music Centre
4-4 Azatoutian Street, 375037 **Yerevan**
Tel: 2-254 493/525 840
Fax: 2-151 431/525 840
Internet: www.arminco.com/homepages/nab
E-Mail: nbart@arminco.com
president Nika Babaian
Role & Services: support of young musicians, organisation of their debuts and concerts; training, masterclasses, competitions and festivals; publishing of scores of Armenian composers; booklets, posters and other advertising material; assistance and consultancy for CD-productions; audio and video recordings; exchanges *Comments:* public, non-government, nonprofit organisation

Composers and Musicologists' Union of Armenia
25 Demirchian Street, 375002 **Yerevan**
Tel: 2-524 292/525 337 Fax: 2-151 431
chairman Robert Amirkhanian

International Cultural Centre
5 Tumanian Street, 375001 **Yerevan**
Tel: 2-520 479/523 930
Fax: 2-390 7223
chairman Samvel Mayrapetian; director Martin Adoian

International League – Music of Intellectuals
4-12 Azatoutian Street, 375037 **Yerevan**
Tel: 2-254 483 Fax: 2-151 795
vice-president Edouard Sadoyan

Musical Society of Armenia
15 Sayat-Nova Street, 375001 **Yerevan**
Tel: 2-580 423
Fax: 2-521 355/525 826
president David Kazarian

AUSTRIA (+43)

Association internationale du théâtre pour l'enfance et la jeunesse (ASSITEJ) Austria
Pfeilgasse 8/3, 1080 **Wien**
Tel: 1-4038 79413
Fax: 1-4038 9360
Vorsitzender Ernst Reepmaker
Role & Services: promotes theatre for children and adolescents; network/coordinating organisation for children's theatre in Austria; promotion of events and festivals

Austrian Business Committee for the Arts – Initiativen Wirtschaft für Kunst
Kärntner Straße 8/6, 1010 **Wien**
Tel: 1-512 7800 Fax: 1-513 8956
Internet: www.iwk.at
E-Mail: office@iwk.at
Geschäftsführung Mag. Brigitte Kössner
Role & Services: business sponsorship support group, member of CEREC (q.v.), the official sponsoring organisation of the European community; offering information, advice, the organisation of international seminars & symposia and annual Austrian art sponsorship award MAECENAS to the best art sponsorship projects of Austrian companies
Comments: publications on cultural sponsoring

Austrian Centre of Union Internationale de la Marionette (UNIMA)
UNIMA Zentrum Osterrreich
Springergasse 22/8, 1020 **Wien**
Tel: 1-212 9644
Präsident Helga Ruso-Pawslka (c/o Stadtgemeinde Mistelbach, Hauptplatz 6, 2130 Mistelbach, tel: 2572-251 5253) ; Sekretariat Michael Freismuth

Austrian Music Council
Österreichischer Musikrat
Stiftgasse 29, 1070 **Wien**
Tel: 1-52104-50
Fax: 1-52104-99
E-Mail: mica@mica at
Präsident Franz Welser-Möst; Sekretär Matthias Finkentey

Austrian Section of the International Society for Contemporary Music
Internationale Gesellschaft für Neue Musik – Sektion Österreich
Stiftgasse 29, 1070 **Wien**
Tel: 1-521 0441
Fax: 1-521 0449
Präsident Lothar Knessl; Geschäftsführung Maria Skodak
Role & Services: to promote contemporary Austrian music and composers; takes part in exchange programmes at national/international level; member of ISCM (q.v) *Comments:* founder of ISCM; elections for new board to be held in March/April 2000

Austrian Theatre Museum – International Theatre Institute (ITI)
Österreichisches Theater museum – Internationales Theater Institut (ITI)
Lobkovitzplatz 2, 1010 **Wien**
Tel: 1-5128 80030 (centre)/317 0699 (music theatre)
Fax: 1-5128 80045 (centre)/ 310 8292 (music theatre)
Internet: info.wien.at/d/mus/mus02023.htm
E-Mail: heidi.herda@theatermuseum.at
Präsident Dr Helga Dostal; Vizepräsident Prof. Dr Wolfgang Greisenegger; Secretary Heidi Herda
Role & Services: runs and attends congresses, seminars and other conferences; edits publications; offers grants/scholarships; follows and coordinates Austrian theatre activities and international information exchange; maintains contact between educational theatre institutions, the audio-visual media and all other ITI centres in the world that follow the same or similar objectives

Austro-Mechana Gesellschaft zur Wahrnehmung Mechanisch Musikalischer Urheberechte mbH
Baumannstrasse 10, 1031 **Wien**
Tel: 1-71787 Fax: 1-712 7136
E-Mail: waltraud.schmidt@aume.telecom.at
Direktor Dr Helmut Steinmetz
Role & Services: member of Groupement Européen des Sociétés d'Auteurs et Compositeurs (q.v.)
Comments: additional e-mail: office@aume.at

Gewerkschaft KMfB -Sektion Bühnenangehörige
Maria Theresien-Strasse 11, 1090 **Wien**
Tel: 1-31316/83840 Fax: 1-3131 67992
E-Mail: Sabine_Sahab@kmfb.oegb.or.at
Vorsitzender der Gewerkschaft KMfB Ernst Körmer; Präsident Fritz Peschke; Zentralsekretär der Gewerkschaft KMfB Thomas Linzbauer (Thomas_Linzbauer@kmfb.oegb.or.at); Präsident Sektion Bühenangehörige Prof. Fritz Peschke; Sekretärin Sektion Bühenangehörige Mag. Sabine Sahab
Role & Services: union for performers engaged by a theatre; supports members in legal affairs, negotiates collective agreements for theatres and new work legislation laws

Independent Theatre Association of Austria
Interessengemeinschaft Freie Theaterarbeit
Pfeilgasse 8/3, 1080 **Wien**
Tel: 1-403 8794 Fax: 1-408 9360
E-Mail: igft@magnet.at
Geschäftsführung Dr. Juliane Alton; Mitgliederbetreuung Andrea Wälzl
Role & Services: the aim of the Association is the improvement of the cultural, political, social and legal status of independent theatre artists and groups in Austria and to support and facilitate communication and collaboration between them; in addition to its cultural and information services, IG FREIE THEATERARBEIT provides a social fund for independent theatre artists through yearly subsidies from the Department of Arts at the Federal Chancellary of Austria
Comments: IG FREIE THEATERARBEIT issues a newsletter for its members every two months; it also publishes a catalogue of independent theatre artists and groups in Austria every year

International Federation of the Phonographic Industry (IFPI)
Schreyvogelgasse 2/5, 1010 **Wien**
Tel: 1-535 6035 Fax: 1-535 5191
E-Mail: ifpi@ifpi.at
President Chris Wemcken; Treasurer Manfred Lappe; General manager Dr. Franz Medwenitsch

Jeunesse Österreich
Musikalische Jugend Österreichs
PO Box 45, Lothringerstraße 20, 1037 **Wien**
Tel: 1-710 3616 (admin)/505 6356 (box office)
Fax: 1-710 3616/17 (admin)/505 8277 (box office)
Internet: www.jeunesse.at
E-Mail: mail@jeunesse.at
General Secretary Matthias Naske (e-mail: m.naske@jeunesse.at); Concerts Administration Alexandra Tscheitschonig (e-mail: a.tscheitschonig@jeunesse.at), Antonia Schmidt-Chiari (e-mail: a.schmidt-chiari@jeunesse.at); Marketing Catharina Jürs (e-mail: c.juers@jeunesse.at); Dramaturgy Dr. Astrid Schramek (e-mail: a.schramek@jeunesse.at); Press Albert Seitlinger (a.seitlinger@jeunesse.at)
Role & Services: promoting classical music for a youth audience; see also Promoters *Comments:* visiting address: Bosendorferstraße 12, 1010 Wien; alternative e-mail: tickets@jeunesse.at (box office)

Kultur Kontakt
Spittelberggasse 3, 1070 **Wien**
Tel: 1-523 8765 Fax: 1-523 876 520
Internet: www.kulturkontakt.or.at/kk
E-Mail: kk@kulturkontakt.or.at
contact Annemarie Türk
Role & Services: aim to promote cultural and educational cooperation between Austria and Central and Eastern European countries

Music Information Center Austria (MICA)
Musik Informations Zentrum Österreich
Stiftgasse 29, 1070 Wien
Tel: 1-52104-0 Fax: 1-521 0459
Internet: www.mica.at
E-Mail: office@mica.at
Messen & Pop/Rock Mario Rossori, Daniela Gütermann; Jazz Helge Hinteregger; Contemporary Bernhard Günther, Günther Leucht, Eva Wirlitsch-Essl; Information Management Wolfgang Sturm, Markus Glaser; PR Edith Schweitzer
Role & Services: worldwide information about and promotion of actual Austrian music (contemporary, jazz, pop); workshops for musicians, composers etc.; online database and shop with CDs & books from Austria *Comments:* member of IAMIC (q.v.)

Österreichische Gesellschaft für Musik
Hanuschgasse 3, 1010 **Wien**
Tel: 1-512 3143 Fax: 1-512 4299
Direktor Dr Walburga Litschauer
Role & Services: information on and promotion of contemporary music and composers; links between universities of music and auditors *Comments:* reports, books etc, on symposions, workshops etc

Österreichischer Bundestheaterverband
Goethegasse 1, 1010 **Wien**
Tel: 1-51444/2955-60
Fax: 1-51444/2952
Internet: www.oebthv.gv.at
Geschäftsführer (Bundestheater Holding) Dr Georg Springer; Geschäftsführer (Theaterservice GmbH) Dr. Josef Kirchberger

Österreichischer Tanzrat
Lehargasse 9-11, 1060 **Wien**
Tel: 1-581 4576 Fax: 1-581 4576
Präsident Prof. Karl Musil

Society for Music Theatre
Gesellschaft für Musiktheater
Türkenstrasse 19, 1090 **Wien**
Tel: 1-317 0699 Fax: 1-310 8292
Präsident Prof. Franz Eugen Dostal
Role & Services: music theatre committee and dance committee of the Austrian centre of the ITI; training courses in ballet education: Ballettpädagogik (Russian School) at Ballett-Zentrum Wolfsegg every August; more than 100 concerts (chamber & vocal) between October and June)
Comments: see also Festivals

Staatlich Genehmigte Gesellschaft der Autoren, Komponisten und Musikverleger (AKM)
Baumannstraße 8-10, 1030 **Wien**
Tel: 1-71714 Fax: 1-7171 4107
Internet: www.akm.co.at
E-Mail: ingrid.waldingbredt@akm.co.at
Generaldirektor Manfred Brunner
Role & Services: copyright society, member of CISAC

AZERBAIDZHAN (+994)

Artists' Union
Khagany St. 19, 370000 **Baku**
Tel: 12-936 230
chairman Khalilov Farhad Kurban Oglu

Azerbaidzhan Union of Composers
M Mukhtarov St. 6, 370001 **Baku**
Tel: 12-926 575
chairman Kuliyev Tofik Alekper Oglu

Musicians' Union
Arts St. 9, 370000 **Baku**
Tel: 12-926 704
chairman Badalbayli Farhad Shamsi Oglu

Theatre Union
Khagany St. 10, 370000 **Baku**
Tel: 12-931 703
president Turabov Gasan Sattar Oglu

BELARUS (+375)

Art Union National Academic Opera and Ballet Grand Theatre of the Republic of Belarus, The
Tvorchjeskoje Objedinjenije Nacionalnyj Akadjemichjeskij Bolshoj Tjeatr Rjespubliki Bjelaruss
Pl Parizhskoj Kommuny 1, 220029 **Minsk**
Tel: 172-340 652 Fax: 172-340 646
director Anatolij Kirijenko

Belarus Centre of the ITI
26 av. Skorina, 220030 **Minsk**
Tel: 172-277 528
Fax: 172-271 376/366 982
secretary general Antonina Mikhaltsova

Belarussian Cultural Fund
Bjeloruskij Fond Kultury
Komunalnaja nab. 6b, 220005 **Minsk**
Tel: 172-344 203 Fax: 172-345 034
director Vladimir A Gilep

Belarussian Cultural Studies Institute
Bjeloruskij Institut Probljem Kultury
ul. Kalinovskogo 12, 220086 **Minsk**
Tel: 172-641 733 Fax: 172-641 733
rector Arnold E Mikhnjevich

Republican Center of National Culture
Rjespublikanskij Cjentr Nacionalnoj Kultury
ul. Janki Kupaly 21-107, 220030 **Minsk**
Tel: 172-292 134 Fax: 172-292 134
director Victor I Matiushenko

BELGIUM (+32)

Association Belge des Scénographes, Techniciens et Architectes de Théâtre (ABSTAT)
Rue de Flandre, 46, 1000 **Brussels**
Tel: 2-513 3333 Fax: 2-502 6159
co-directrices Monique Duren, Anne Molitor
Role & Services: represents the interests of scenographers, technicians and theatre architects in Belgium; documentation centre on dance and theatre (drama)

Belgian Centre of the Association du théâtre pour l'enfance et la jeunesse (ASSITEJ)
321, Avenue de la Couronne, 1050 **Brussels**
Tel: 2-648 3458 Fax: 2-640 9712
E-Mail: ctej@skynet.be
chairman Hadi El Gammal; secretary Anneliese Simon; vice-chairman Alain Moreau; treasurer Thierry Hellin; financial & administrative director Benoît Scutnaire; public relations officer Anne Jaspard
Role & Services: includes the Association Chambre des Théâtres pour l'enfance et la jeunesse; promotes young peoples theatre; organises the Festival Noël au Théâtre, festival of theatre for children in December every year
Comments: publishes Le Petit Cyrano and Les Carnets de la CTEJ; see also Publications

Belgian Centre of the International Theatre Institute (ITI) – Flanders Community
Centre Belge de l'Institut International du Theatre – Communauté Flanders
Minderbroedersstraat 24, 2018 **Anvers**
Tel: 3-238 5177 Fax: 3-288 8402
Internet: users.skynet.be/iti.vlaams.centrum
E-Mail: vlaams.centrum@skynet.be
président Jaak Van Schoor; vice-président Roger Rennenberg; secrétaire genérale Mark Hermans

Belgian Centre of the International Theatre Institute (ITI) – French Community
Centre Belge de l'Institut International du Theatre – Communauté française
Archives et Musée de la Littérature,
Blvd de l'Empereur 4, 1000 **Brussels**
Tel: 2-519 5576 Fax: 2-519 5583
E-Mail: leclercq.nicole.iit@writeme.com
président Jacques de Decker; secrétaire genérale Nicole Leclercq
Role & Services: information resource for foreigners and nationals on Belgian and foreign theatre; encourage contact between theatre associations in the french-speaking community and common activity
Comments: publishes the Annuaire Mondial du Théâtre; see also Publications (France and Belgium); see also SIBMAS (centre belge) q.v.; Diffusion Belgians Lansman, 63 Rue Royale, 7141 Carnieres Morlauner, Tel: 64-447 511, Fax: 64-443 102

Belgian Music Information Centre
Centre Belge de Documentation Musicale (CeBeDeM)
Rue d'Arlon 75-77, 1040 **Brussels**
Tel: 2-230 9430/37
Fax: 2-231 1800 (fao CeBeDeM)/230 9437
Internet: www.arcadis.be/cebedem
E-Mail: 101573.3644@compuserve.com
director Dr Diana von Volborth
Role & Services: promotion and performance of the works of Belgian contemporary composers; services: sheet music library, recording library, reading and listening room, loan department, publishing and reproduction department, sales and rent department, promotion department *Comments:* CeBeDeM is a member of IAMIC (q.v.) and so affiliated to IAML (International Association of Music Libraries, Archives and Documentation Centres); see also SABAM (q.v.)

Belgian Section of the International Society for Contemporary Music (ISCM)
Section Belge de la Société Internationale pour la Musique Contemporaine
22 Langeheide, 3040 **Huldenberg**
Tel: 16-471 376
président André Laporte; vice président Christian Renard
Role & Services: promote Belgian contemporary music worldwide

Belgian Video Federation
3 Place de l'Alma Bte 5, 1200 **Brussels**
Tel: 2-779 4174 Fax: 2-779 1669
Internet: users.skynet.be/sky38852
E-Mail: bvf@bvf-ifbi.be
president Rob Jonkmans; director Marcel Heymans
Role & Services: represents the video industry in Belgium

Centrale Générale des Services Publics (CGSP)
Place Fontainas 9-11, 1000 **Brussels**
Tel: 2-508 5811 Fax: 2-508 5902
secrétaire général Nicolas Donato (section française); general secretary Laurette Muylaert (flemish section ACOD)
Role & Services: to defend the interests of workers in cultural areas; makes collective agreements on behalf of its members; comprises the 3 federations of musicians, actors and technicians; member of International Federation of Actors, and Musicians *Comments:* see also ACOD (flemish section)

Centre Belge de la SIBMAS – Communauté française Archives et Musée de la Littérature
Blvd de l'Empereur 4, 1000 **Brussels**
Tel: 2-519 5576 Fax: 2-519 5583
E-Mail: leclercq.nicole.iit@writeme.com
présidente Nicole Leclercq; secrétaire Yves Bruyn
Role & Services: establish contacts between libraries specialised in performing arts

Centre de la Marionnette de la Communauté française de Belgique
Rue Saint-Martin, 47, 7500 **Tournai**
Tel: 69-889 135 Fax: 69-840 069
président Claude Michez; coordination Francis Houtteman
Role & Services: exhibitions on puppet theatre; library

Christian Union of Communications and Culture
Syndicat Chrétien de Communications et de la Culture (SCCC)
Pastorijstraat 23, 2060 **Antwerp**
Tel: 3-271 0026/272 0304 Fax: 3-231 3885
general & cultural secretary Jean-Paul Van der Vurst
Role & Services: trade union *Comments:* member of International Federation of Musicians, the International Federation of Actors and ISETU/FISTAV/MEI

Conseil de la Musique de la Communauté Française
c/o Le Botanique, 236 rue Royale, 1210 **Brussels**
Tel: 2-209 1090/91 Fax: 2-219 6660/209 1099
Internet: www.datanet.be/conseildelamusique
E-Mail: cecile.grevisse@skynet.be
president Robert Wangermee; secrétaire général Georges Dumortier; coordinatrice Cécile Grévisse; coordinateur Marc Jacobs; rédacteur consonance dissonance Piérre Hacha; responsable presse et promotion Ivo Ghizzardi
Role & Services: organises the Fête de la Musique; organise conferences, colloquia, present festival, publish magazines and guides
Comments: see also Publications

Contredanse
46 rue de Flandre, 1000 **Brussels**
Tel: 2-502 0327 Fax: 2-513 8739
Internet: user.skynet.be/contredanse
E-Mail: contredanse@skynet.be
administration Michel Cheval; responsable documentation dance Claire Destrée; responsable publications et centre de documentation Béatrice Menet; directrice artistique Patricia Kuypers; centre de documentation Françoise Irkhine
Role & Services: documents and stimulates dance choreography within the French speaking community in Belgium; biannual publication Nouvelles de danse en Communauté française de Belgique *Comments:* dance library and documentation centre; see also Publications (Nouvelles de Danse & Guide de la Danse)

Europees Figurenteatercentrum
Trommelstraat 1, 9000 **Gent**
Tel: 9-223 1215 Fax: 9-225 4545
E-Mail: eftc.gent@skynet.be
general coordinator Freek Neirynck (Bomastraat 47, 9000 Gent); secretary Myriam Bodenghier
Role & Services: information and exhibition centre for puppet theatre and puppet theatre festivals, video archives, library *Comments:* see also Festivals

Flemish Section of the Algemene Centrale Openbare Diensten (ACOD)
Place Fontainas 9-11, 1000 **Brussels**
Tel: 2-508 5811 Fax: 2-508 5840
general secretary Laurette Muylaert; general secretary of the French Section (CGSP) Nicolas Donato
Role & Services: defends the interests of workers in cultural areas, makes collective agreements on behalf of its members; comprises the 3 federations of musicians, actors and technicians; member of International Federation of Actors, Musicians and Audio-Visual workers *Comments:* see also Centrale Générale des Services Publics (q.v. France Nat. Org)

Flemish Theatre Institute
Vlaams Theater Instituut
Saincteletttesquare 19, 1000 **Brussels**
Tel: 2-201 0906 Fax: 2-203 0205
Internet: www.vti.be
E-Mail: info@vti.be
directeur Klaas Thüdemans
Role & Services: centre for research, documentation, advice and promotion for performing arts *Comments:* publishes the magazine CARNET in co-operation with the Theater Instituut Nederland

Fondation Promethea
60 rue de la Concorde, 1050 **Brussels**
Tel: 2-513 7827 Fax: 2-502 2657
director Chantal Pirlot
Role & Services: cultural business sponsorship support group

Foundation for the Promotion of Arts
Stichting voor Kunstpromotie
Handelskaai 14, 1000 **Brussels**
Tel: 2-219 4080 Fax: 2-219 0462
Internet: www.stichting-kunstpromotie.be
E-Mail: info@stichting-kunstpromotie.be
directeur Luc Delrue
Role & Services: event management, fundraising, sponsorship consultancy, advise companies based in Belgium and the Netherlands on projects, audit

French Speaking Section of the Belgian Centre of Union Internationale de la Marionnette (UNIMA)
Section Francophone du Centre Belge de l'UNIMA
Rue des Houlpays 58, 4020 **Jupille sur Meuse**
Tel: 4-370 1025 Fax: 4-370 1025
président Georges Vetters; secrétaire gral Hubert Roman

International Federation of the Phonographic Industry (IFPI)
3 Place de l'Alma, Bte 5, 1200 **Brussels**
Tel: 2-779 4174 Fax: 2-779 1669
E-Mail: besf@skynet.be
président Dirk de Clippeleir; director Marcel Heymans
Role & Services: represents the Phonographic Industry in Belgium *Comments:* alternative E-mail: ifpi@bof-ifpi.be

Jeunesses Musicales International
10 rue Royale, 1000 **Brussels**
Tel: 2-513 9774 Fax: 2-514 4755
Internet: www.JMInternational.org
E-Mail: mail@jmi.net
general secretary Dag Franzen
Role & Services: to enable young people to develop through music across all boundaries; to stimulate contacts between member countries- members in 50 countries *Comments:* q.v. Promoters

Maison du Spectacle – la Bellone
Rue de Flandre 46, 1000 **Brussels**
Tel: 2-513 3333 Fax: 2-502 6159
Internet: www.best.be/bellone
E-Mail: bellone@ontonet.be
co-directrices Anne Molitor, Monique Duren
Role & Services: library, reference and information centre available for everyone connected with the arts (music, dance, drama); provide a rehearsal room; exhibitions; publications *Comments:* home of numerous associations working in the performing arts; see also ABSTAT (q.v)

Societé Belge des Auteurs, Compositeurs et Editeurs (SABAM)
Rue d'Arlon 75-77, 1040 **Brussels**
Tel: 2-286 8211 Fax: 2-231 1800/230 0589
Internet: www.sabam.be
directeur général Jacques Lion; president Jacques Leduc; administrateurs délégués Paul Louka (Francophone), Roger Van Ransbeek (Flemish); directeur financier Luc Van Oycke; directeur grands droits Christophe Depareter; directeur doc. et repartition Patrick de Vulder; PR J.P.Desmet
Role & Services: represents authors, composers etc and collects the royalties in both communities and worldwide; collects and redistributes royalties *Comments:* see also National Organisations: CeBedem

Société des Auteurs et Compositeurs Dramatiques Délégation Belgique (SACD)
87, Rue du Prince Royal, 1050 **Brussels**
Tel: 2-551 0320 Fax: 2-551 0325
E-Mail: 100602.2206@compuserve.com
délégué général pour la Belgique Frederic Young; conseiller juridique Tanguy Roosen; chargée des affaires européennes Cécile Despingre
Role & Services: collecting rights society (theatre, opera, ballet, audiovisual)
Comments: delegation of the French SACD

Société Philharmonique de Bruxelles
rue Baron Horta 11, 1000 **Brussels**
Tel: 2-507 8410 Fax: 2-511 7977
E-Mail: sofil@ibm.net
président Jean-Pierre de Bandt; directeur général Paul Dujardin; directeur artistique Christian Renard
Role & Services: organise concerts mainly in the Palais des Beaux Arts and in the Conservatoire Royal de Musique and also in churches; organises over 250 concerts per year, all repertory: from the middle ages to contemporary; also organises three cycles of concerts of traditional music and jazz; artists in residence

Théâtre et Publics
Place du XX Août, 16, 4000 **Liège**
Tel: 4-223 4598 Fax: 4-221 1867
président Willy Legras; directeur Max Parfondry; librarian Alain Chevalier
Role & Services: information and liaison centre for international theatre, workshops; training centre for actors

Union des Artistes
Rue Marché-aux-Herbes 105, BP 33, 1000 **Brussels**
Tel: 2-513 5780 Fax: 2-513 5780
président Bernard Marbaix; vice-présidents Jacques Monseu, Luc de Meulenaere; secrétaire générale trésoriere Anne Carpriau
Role & Services: safeguards moral and financial welfare of over 500 working artists in Belgium; publishes Le Bulletin De L'Union Des Artistes *Comments:* office opening hrs: Monday, Tuesday, Thursday 10 am – 12 am

Vlaams Theater Instituut
Brussels
Comments: see under Flemish Theatre Institute

Vlaamse Directies voor Podiumkunsten
Sainctelettesquare 19, 1000 **Brussels**
Tel: 2-203 6296 Fax: 2-201 1727
E-Mail: vdp@ibm.net
president Stefaan De Ruyck; coordinator Liesbeth Dejonghe
Role & Services: performing arts employers association

Wallonie-Bruxelles Musiques
13 Bld. Adolphe Max , Boite 6, 1000 **Brussels**
Tel: 2-218 6209 Fax: 2-218 3424
Internet: www.wbm.be
E-Mail: wbm@arcadis.be
coordinator Patrick Printz; assistant Sylvie Andre; project manager Liliane Graziani
Role & Services: promotion on an international scale of the artists, producers, publishers, distributors of the french-speaking community of Belgium; runs a documentation centre, publishes guides, brochures, records, etc.

BOSNIA & HERZEGOVINA (+387)

Music Youth Sarajevo/Jeunesses Musicales Sarajevo
Mis Irbina 10, 71000 **Sarajevo**
Tel: 71-665 713 Fax: 71-665 713
E-Mail: muzomlsa@soros.org.ba
secretary Slavica Spoljaric

Open Society Fund Bosnia-Herzegovina
Dzenetica ~ikma 2/II, 71000 **Sarajevo**
Tel: 71-472 580/444 488 Fax: 71-472 580/444 488
E-Mail: aida@soros.org.ba
director, cultural programme Aida Cengic

BULGARIA (+359)

Bulgarian Centre of the International Theatre Institute (ITI)
Centre Bulgare de l'Institut International du Theatre
12 Place Narodno sabranie, 1000 **Sofia**
Tel: 2-738 288 Fax: 2-443 290
president Iskra Radeva; secretary N Kolewska-Kourteva

Bulgarian Centre of Union Internationale de la Marionette (UNIMA)
Petar Schmidt Str. , bl. 50/B, 1408 **Sofia**
contact Slavcho Malenov

Bulgarian Section of International Music Council
Union of Bulgarian Composers, 2 Ivan Vazov Str., 1000 **Sofia**
Tel: 2-874 547
secretary general Victor Tchoutchkov

Bulgarian Section of Jeunesses Musicales
56 Alabin St, 1040 **Sofia**
Tel: 2-880 853 Fax: 2-884 283
vice-president Plamen Djurov

Bulgarian Writers Association
136 Rakovski Str., 1000 **Sofia**
Tel: 2-981 2976
president Ivan Teofilov

Centre Bulgare de l'IIT
12 Place Narodno sabranie, 1000 **Sofia**
Tel: 2-738 288 Fax: 2-443 290
president Iskra Radeva

International Foundation St. Cyril and Methodius
19 Oborishte Str., 1504 **Sofia**
Tel: 2-943 4185/430 001/464 131 Fax: 2-446 027
E-Mail: SMFND@Cserv.MGU.BG
president acad. Petar Kenderov; secretary general Michail Tachev
Role & Services: to help young people, working in the sphere of art, culture, science and education, providing them with long and short-term scholarships for study and post-graduate specializations abroad; exchange of cultural and educational programmes; charity activities

MUSICAUTOR – Bulgarian Society for Performing and Mechanical Rights
73, Vassal Levski Blvd, 1000 **Sofia**
Tel: 2-980 1035/870 986 Fax: 2-980 0253
E-Mail: musautor@ttm.bg
president Plamen Djurov; managing director Mariana Lazarova
Role & Services: collective administration of performing, broadcasting and mechanical rights on musical works
Comments: member of CISAC (q.v.) and BIEM

Open Society Foundation
PO Box 114, 1414 **Sofia**
Tel: 2-919 329 Fax: 2-951 6348
Internet: www.osf.acad.bg
executive director Gueorgui Guentchev
Role & Services: the foundation exists to finance numerous educational and cultural initiatives by Bulgarians at home and abroad; it aims to establish new contacts and channels of information in the social sciences, economics, state and economic management and education *Comments:* founded in April 1990 by George Soros; visiting address: 1 Balsha Str., 1408 Sofia

Union of Bulgarian Actors
12 Narodno Sabranie Square, 1000 **Sofia**
Tel: 2-870 725/880 440
Fax: 2-883 301
president Stefan Iliev
Role & Services: about 5000 members; publishes Theatre magazine, a joint publication with the Ministry of Culture, and the Gestus Theatre Bulletin, concerned with issues like social security, copyright, rates and fees, a social statue for artists; member of International Federation of Actors

Union of Bulgarian Artists
6 Shipka Str., 1000 **Sofia**
Tel: 2-43351/446 115 Fax: 2-946 0212
president Hristo Haralampiev

Union of Bulgarian Composers
2 Ivan Vazov Str., 1000 **Sofia**
Tel: 2-881 560/874 547 Fax: 2-874 378
E-Mail: ubc@mail.bol.bg
president Prof. Victor Tchoutchkov; secretary general Velislav Zaimov

Union of Bulgarian Filmmakers
67 Dondukov Str., 1504 **Sofia**
Tel: 2-946 1068 Fax: 2-874 378
president Pavel Vassev

Union of Bulgarian Musicians and Dancers (UBMD)
12 Vitosha Str., 1000 **Sofia**
Tel: 2-987 1410/5259
president Prof. Jenny Zaharieva

Union of Bulgarian Writers
5 Angel Kanchev Str., 1000 **Sofia**
Tel: 2-880 031/685 Fax: 2-874 757
president Nikolay Haitov

CROATIA (+385)

Association of Orchestral and Chamber Musicians of Croatia
Hrvatska udruga orkestralnih i komornih umjetnika
Ilica 42, 10000 **Zagreb**
Tel: 1-484 7570 Fax: 1-484 7570
president Goran Koncar; general secretary Ivan Tocilj

Centre for Dramatic Art
Centar za dramsku umjetnost
Hebrangova 21, 10000 **Zagreb**
Tel: 1-485 4821/23/6455 Fax: 1-485 6455
Internet: www.soros.hr/cda.htm
E-Mail: cdu@zamir.net
president of the board Vjeran Zuppa

Croatian Association of Composers
Hrvatsko drustvo skladatelja
Berislaviceva 9, 10000 **Zagreb**
Tel: 1-487 2370 Fax: 1-487 2372
president Adalbert Markovic; general secretary Dr. Ivo Jozipovic
Comments: organisers of Music Biennale Zagreb, international festival of contemporary music, see also Festivals

Croatian Association of Musicians
Hrvatsko drustvo glazbenih umjetnika
Ilica 42, 10000 **Zagreb**
Tel: 1-484 7569/7568
Fax: 1-484 7568
president Andelko Ramuscak; secretary Leandra Golik

Croatian Association of Theatre Artists
Hrvatsko drustvo dramskih umjetnika
Ilica 42, 10000 **Zagreb**
Tel: 1-484 7552 Fax: 1-484 7568
president Zlatko Vitez; secretary Katarina Bahunek

Croatian Association of Theatre Critics and Theoreticians
Hrvatsko drustvo kazalisnih kritcara i teatrologa
Ilica 42/II, 10000 **Zagreb**
Tel: 1-484 7552 Fax: 1-484 7568
president Antonija Bogner Saban

Croatian Centre of International Association of Theatre Critics (AICT)
Hrvatski centar AICT
Ilica 42/II, 10000 **Zagreb**
Tel: 1-484 7552 Fax: 1-484 7568
president Antonija Bogner Saban

Croatian Centre of International Federation of Actors (FIA)
Hrvatski centar FIA
Ilica 42/II, 10000 **Zagreb**
Tel: 1-484 7552 Fax: 1-484 7568
Croatian representative Relija Basic

Croatian Centre of the Association du théâtre pour l'enfance et la jeunesse (ASSITEJ)
Hrvatski centar – ASSITEJ
Medvescak bb, 10000 **Zagreb**
Tel: 1-468 3374/3/52/70
Fax: 1-468 3370
president Ivica Simic

Croatian Centre of the International Theatre Institute (ITI)
B. Magovca bb, pp 499, 10010 **Zagreb**
Tel: 1-660 1626 Fax: 1-660 1619
Internet: www.tel.hr/hc-iti-teatar
E-Mail: hc-iti@zg.tel.hr
president Sanja Nikcevic

Croatian Centre of Union Internationale de la Marionnette (UNIMA)
Hrvatski centar UNIMA
Magovca b.b., pp 499, B., 10010 **Zagreb**
Tel: 1-660 1626 Fax: 1-660 1619
president Zvonko Festini

Croatian Copyright Agency
Hrvatska autorska agencija
Preradoviceva 25, 10000 **Zagreb**
Tel: 1-481 1055/034/129 Fax: 1-481 7122
director Dorde Podna

Croatian Cultural Society
Matica Hrvatska
Ulica Matice Hrvatske 2, 10000 **Zagreb**
Tel: 1-481 9310 Fax: 1-481 9319
president Josip Bratulic; contact Alma Cavlek Kovac
Role & Services: promotes national and cultural identity of the Croatian people in all fields of artistic, scientific and spiritual creative work
Comments: founded in 1842

Croatian Music Institute
Hrvatski glazbeni zavod
Gunduliceva 6, 10000 **Zagreb**
Tel: 1-481 9322 Fax: 1-481 9322
president Andre Mohorovicic

Croatian Union of Workers in Culture
Hrvatski sindikat djelatnika u kulturi
Trg M. Tita 4, 10000 **Zagreb**
Tel: 1-425 988
president Vlatko Dulic; secretary Ferdo Boban

Music Information Centre
Muzicki informativni centar Koncertne direkcije Zagreb (KDZ)
Kneza Mislava 18, 10000 **Zagreb**
Tel: 1-461 1797 Fax: 1-461 1792
contact Ivan Zivanovic

Music Youth of Croatia
Hrvatska glazbena mladez
Trg Stjepana Radicá 4, 10000 **Zagreb**
Tel: 1-611 1579/1566 Fax: 1-611 1566
Internet: www.tel.hr/hgm-jmc
E-Mail: hfm-jme@zg.tel.hr.
general secretary Janjanin Krkljes;
president Naima Balic

CYPRUS (+357)

Actors Union of Cyprus
PO Box 25018, 1307 **Nicosia**
Tel: 2-849 849 Fax: 2-849 859
chairman Pantelis Papaconstantinou; secretary general Lea Maleni
Role & Services: protection of the rights of its members (employment, industrial relations, intellectual property); promotion of the work of its members; development of Cypriot Performing Arts internationally; organisation of meetings, seminars etc. for the enhancement of drama activity in Cyprus *Comments:* current membership 130 (stage, cinema and TV actors)

Cypriot Centre of Union Internationale de la Marionette (UNIMA)
52, Amaranthe House, 37 J.F. Kennedy Street, 3106 **Limassol**
Tel: 5-589 715 Fax: 5-581 711
E-Mail: sitas@spidernet.com.cy
representative Amaranth Sitas

Cyprus Centre of the Association du théâtre pour l'enfance et la jeunesse (ASSITEJ)
3 Kitiou Str, Kaimakli, 1021 **Nicosia**
Tel: 2-439 309 Fax: 2-439 309
president Monika Vassiliou
Role & Services: promotion and development of the theatre for children and young people, by professional and/or amateur groups

Cyprus Centre of the International Theatre Institute (ITI)
38 Regaena Street, 1010 **Nicosia**
Tel: 2-674 920 Fax: 2-680 822
E-Mail: ccoiti@cylink
director Nicos Shiafkalis
Role & Services: providing contact with theatre officials, cultural authorities, festival organisers, producers etc.; providing information about theatre in Cyprus, organising conferences, seminars etc.; works closely with Theatre Organisation of Cyprus

Cyprus Chamber of Fine Arts
2 Isaakios Komnenos Street, 1016 **Nicosia**
Tel: 2-753 177 Fax: 2-765 118
president Xenia Panteli; secretary general Antros Efstathiou; vice-president Aristidis Anastasiades
Role & Services: promotion of arts in Cyprus, artistic communication among its members and the development of cooperation; protection of its members' rights and interests; representation of Cyprus at international level; publication of arts newsletters *Comments:* membership is open to artists from visual arts including theatre and TV set designers; organise the annual Festival of Arts in Cyprus

Cyprus Classic Guitar Association
Arch. Kyprianou 9, 2059 Strovolos, **Nicosia**
Tel: 2-495 532 Fax: 2-673 565
chairman Christos Savvopoulos
Role & Services: to promote and develop the classic guitar compositon and performance activity within Cyprus and abroad; to organise concerts, seminars, masterclasses and meetings in those fields

Cyprus Music Committee – Cyprus Centre of the International Music Council
PO Box 24326, 1703 **Nicosia**
Tel: 2-336 106 Fax: 2-441 213
chairman Lenia Serghi
Role & Services: promotes and provides infrastructure for musical activities in Cyprus; cooperates in the administration of various projects with other national music committees; organises seminars, lectures, conferences, concerts and other cultural events

Cyprus PEN Centre
PO Box 23836, 1686 **Nicosia**
Tel: 2-358 028 Fax: 2-351 116
E-Mail: armidaco@spidernet.com.cy
chairman Panos Ioannides
Role & Services: to promote mutual understanding and cooperation among writers in Cyprus and abroad and promote Greek-Cypriot literature; it operates in close cooperation with PEN International, UNESCO and other cultural associations; publishes Cypriot literature in translation, with grants provided by the Ministry of Education and Culture of Cyprus

Cyprus Professional Association of Teachers of Dance
6 Ipparchou Street, 3027 **Limassol**
Tel: 5-355 156 Fax: 5-342 547
president Froso Hadjigeorghiou
Role & Services: to lobby for a legal framework for the teaching of Ballet and Dance; to organise events to raise the standard of classical and modern dance in Cyprus; to promote Dance activities in Cyprus and abroad

Greek Cultural Society of Cyprus
Archbishop Kyprianos Square, 1060 **Nicosia**
Tel: 2-430 008/421 041 Fax: 2-430 667
president Dr Costas Hadjistephanou
Role & Services: to promote and study Greek-Cypriot culture and to enhance cultural relations between Greece and Cyprus; annual publication Philological Cyprus

Music and Fine Arts Fund
PO Box 23414, 1683 **Nicosia**
Tel: 2-781 368 Fax: 2-780 589
E-Mail: poseidon@spidernet.com.cy
president Michalis Kolokasides
Role & Services: to promote and develop Classical Music and Fine Arts

National Society of Greek Cypriot Authors
30 A. Papadiamanti Street, 2123 **Aglantzia**
Tel: 2-334 608/487 792/500 Fax: 2-332 491/486 092
chairman Dr Georgios Ioannides
Role & Services: to forge ties among Greek authors internationally; to promote greek letters; to promote and protect the intellectual rights of its members; organises publications, exhibitions and lectures

Playwrights' Society of Cyprus
Foyer of Letters and Arts, 15 Heroon Street, 1105 **Nicosia**
Tel: 2-774 804 Fax: 2-449 080
chairwoman Nitsa Thalassinou
Role & Services: promotion of Cypriot theatre writing in Cyprus and abroad; protection of the interests of Cypriot playwrights, screenwriters and translators; the creation and enhancement of the ties between Cypriot playwrights and screenwriters with authors abroad
Comments: membership is open to Cypriot residents, playwrights and screenwriters (cinema and TV) with produced, performed or broadcasted work

Society of Cypriot Studies
30 A. Papadiamanti Street, 2123 **Aglantzia**
Tel: 2-334 608/487 792/500
Fax: 2-332 491/486 092
chairman Dr Georgios Ioannides
Role & Services: to conduct and publish studies about Cypriot culture and civilization from ancient to modern times; main areas of study are letters, art, architechture, history and culture

CZECH REPUBLIC (+420)

Antonín Dvorák Society
Spolecnost Antonína Dvoráka
Ke Karlovu 20, 120 00 **Praha** 2
Tel: 2-298 214 Fax: 2-298 214
president Jan Hanus; chairman Radoslav Kapil

Arts Association (ARTES)
Umelecké sdruzení (ARTES)
Senovázné nám. 23, 112 82 **Praha** 1
Tel: 2-2414 2363 Fax: 2-2414 2262
chairman Dalimil Klapka

Association for Protection of Authors Rights
Ochranny svaz autorsky (OSA)
Trída Cs. armády 20, 160 56 **Praha** 6
Tel: 2-2031 5111 Fax: 2-312 3073
chairman Dr. Josef Slanina
Role & Services: mechanical and performing right society

Association for Sacred Music
Spolecnost pro duchovní hudbu
Kolejní 4, 160 00 **Praha** 6
Tel: 2-2018 1710 Fax: 2-2018 1710
honarary president Petr Eben; chairman MUDr. Jaroslav Eliá; vice chairman Jan Hanus

Association of Actors
Herecká Asociace
Senovázne nám. 23, 112 82 **Praha** 1
Tel: 2-2414 2672/2434
Fax: 2-2414 2690
president Jan Teply; secretary Ladislava Chalupova
Role & Services: member of International Federation of Actors

Association of Concerts and Theatre Agencies
Associace koncertních a divadelních agentur
c/o Peitho Artists Agency, Ronkova 1831/6, 180 00 **Praha** 8
Tel: 2-684 5819 Fax: 2-684 5820
Internet: www.vol.cz/peitho
E-Mail: peitho@mbox.vol.cz
president Dr Petr Hosna

Association of Czech Music Artists and Scientists
Asociace hudebních umelcu a vedcu
Radlická 99, 150 00 **Praha** 5
Tel: 2-531 271
chairman Jiri Hlaváè
Comments: includes more special societies

Association of Professional Puppeteers
Sdruzeni profesionalnich loutkaru
Moskevska 18, 460 31 **Liberec** 4
Tel: 48-510 7616 Fax: 48-510 7616
E-Mail: naive.theatre@oasanet.cz
chairman Stanislav Doubrava
Comments: contact: Divadelni ustav, Celetna 17, 110 00 Praha 1, tel: 2-2480 9131, fax: 2-2481 1452)

Association of Professional Theatres in Czech Republic
Asociace profesionalnich divadel CR
Ostrovní 1, 112 30 **Praha** 1
chairman Mojmir Weimann (National Theatre Brno); secretary Arlena Zbornikova (tel: 19-723 7222)
Comments: secretary Arlena Zbornikova, Prokopova 14, 304 11 Plzen

Association of Theatre Designers
Asociace Scénografú
Celetná 17, 110 00 **Praha** 1
Tel: 2-2480 9138
Fax: 2-2481 1452
chairman doc. Miroslav Melena

Bohuslav Martinu Institute
Besední 3, 118 00 **Praha** 1
Tel: 2-5731 3104
Fax: 2-5731 3104
Internet: www.vol.cz/SDMUSIC/MARTINU
E-Mail: martinu@martinu.cz
president Viktor Kalabis; director PhDr Ales Brezina
Comments: also includes Bohuslav Martinù Study Centrum; see also Promoters

Confederation of Arts and Culture (KUK)
Konfederace umení a kultury (KUK)
Senovázné nám 23, 112 82 **Praha** 1
Tel: 2-2414 2721/2555
Fax: 2-2414 2512
president Adriena Jirková;
secretary Miroslava Bohunková

Czech Centre of International Federation of the Phonographic Industry (IFPI)
IFPI-CR Mezinárodní federace fonografického prumyslu – Národní skupina CR
Senovázné nám. 23, 112 82 **Praha** 1
Tel: 2-2414 2373 Fax: 2-2414 2374
E-Mail: ifpicr@ifpicr.cz
secretary Ing. Vratislav Safár
Comments: Telex: 122410

Czech Centre of the Association du théâtre pour l'enfance et la jeunesse (ASSITEJ)
Divadelní ústav, Celetná 17, 110 00 **Praha** 1
Tel: 2-2481 2754/2480 9132 Fax: 2-232 6100
E-Mail: foreign.dpt@czech-theatre.cz
chairman Vladimir Hulec; secretary Alena Kulhankova

Czech Centre of the International Amateur Theatre Association (AITA-IATA)
ARTAMA, Kresomyslova 7, 140 16 **Praha** 4
Tel: 2-6121 5684-7 Fax: 2-6121 5688
E-Mail: artama@anet.cz
president Lenka Laznovska

Czech Centre of the International Association of Theatre Critics (AICT)
Divadelní ústav, Celetná 17, 110 00 **Praha** 1
Tel: 2-2481 2754/2480 9132 Fax: 2-232 6100
E-Mail: foreign.dpt@czech-theatre.cz
chairman Barbara Topolova; secretary Mirka Potucková

Czech Centre of the International Federation for Theatre Research (FIRT)
Divadelní ústav, Kabinet pro studium ceského divadla, Celetná 17, 110 00 **Praha** 1
Tel: 2-2480 9133 Fax: 2-2481 1452
E-Mail: kabinet.du@czech-theatre.cz
contact Dr Eva Sormová

Czech Centre of the International Federation of Actors (FIA)
Herecka asociac FIA
Senovazné nám 223, 112 82 **Praha** 1
Tel: 2-2414 2672/2434 Fax: 2-2414 2690
president Jan Teply; secretary Ladislava Chalupova

Czech Centre of the International Organisation of Scenographers, Theatre Architects and Technicians (OISTAT)
Divadelní ústav, Celetná 17, 110 00 **Praha** 1
Tel: 2-2481 2754/2480 9132 Fax: 2-232 6100
E-Mail: foreign.dpt@czech-theatre.cz
chairman Jaroslav Malina; secretary Mirka Potuckova

Czech Centre of the International Society of Libraries and Museums for the Performing Arts (SIBMAS)
Divadelní ústav, Celetná 17, 110 00 **Praha** 1
Tel: 2-2480 9141 Fax: 2-2481 1452/232 6100
E-Mail: knihovna.du@czech-theatre.cz
chairman Jarmila Svobodová; contact Helena Hantáková

Czech Centre of the International Theatre Institute (ITI)
Divadelní ústav, Celetná 17, 110 00 **Praha** 1
Tel: 2-2481 2754/2480 9111/9132 Fax: 2-2481 1452/232 6100
Internet: www.divadlo.cz
E-Mail: divadelni.ustav@czech-theatre.cz
chairman Helena Albertová; secretary Mirka Potucková
Comments: alternative e-mail: foreign.dpt@czech-theate.cz

Czech Centre of Union Internationale de la Marionette (UNIMA)
Divadelní ústav, Celetná 17, 110 00 **Praha** 1
Tel: 2-2480 9131/2481 2754 Fax: 2-232 6100
E-Mail: foreign.dpt@czech-theatre.cz
chairman Nina Maliková; contact Alena Kulhánkova

Czech Händel Society
Ceská Händlova spolecnost
Na Maninách 11/795, 170 00 **Praha** 7
Tel: 2-6671 2203 Fax: 2-6671 2203
chairman Pavel Polka; secretary Ondrej Macek

Czech Jazz Society
Ceská jazzová spolecnost
U druzstva Ideál 6, 140 00 **Praha** 4
Tel: 2-6121 1890 Fax: 2-6121 1890
chairman Frantisek Kop

Czech Literary Fund
Nadace Cesky literární fond
Pod Nuselskymi schody 3, 120 00 **Praha** 2
Tel: 2-691 1908/1362 Fax: 2-691 1375
Internet: www.nclf.cz
E-Mail: nclf@vol.cz
director Ing. Michal Novotny

Czech Music Council
Ceská hudební rada
c/o Divadelní ustav, Celetná 17, 110 00 **Praha** 1
Tel: 2-2480 9138 Fax: 2-2431 1212
E-Mail: dohnalova@email.cz
president Prof PhDr Ivan Polednák, Dr. Sc.; secretary Dr Lenka Dohnalová
Comments: alternative e-mail: dohnalova@lorien.site.cas.cz

Czech Music Fund
Nadace Cesky hudební fond
Besední 3, 118 00 **Praha** 1
Tel: 2-573 2008 Fax: 2-534 234
E-Mail: his@vol.cz
director Miroslav Drozd

Czech Music Information Centre
Hudebni informacní stredisko
Besední 3, 118 00 **Praha** 1
Tel: 2-573 2008 Fax: 2-539 720
Internet: www.musica.cz
E-Mail: his@vol.cz
executive manager PhDr. Miroslav Pudlák

Czech Music Society
Ceská hudební spolecnost
Janáckovo nábr, 59, 150 00 **Praha** 5
Tel: 2-5731 9679/531 582 Fax: 2-531 582
chairman Miloslava Smetácková
Comments: includes more special societies (B. Smetana, L. Janácek, V.Novák, J. Suk, Z. Fibich, J.B. Foerster, Orff, Music Education, Music Ecology, Music Therapy, Early Music and others)

Czech Society of Chamber Music
Cesky spolek pro komorní hudbu
Alsovo nábr. 12, 110 00 **Praha** 1
Tel: 2-2489 3224 Fax: 2-2489 3248
secretary PhDr Bohumila Benesová

Dance Association
Tanecní sdruzeni CR
Celetná 17, 110 00 **Praha** 1
Tel: 2-2480 9111 Fax: 2-2481 1452
contact Zdenek Prokes; secretary Jana Holenová

Folklore Association of the Czech Republic
Folklórní sdruzení Ceské republiky
Senovázné nám 24, 110 00 **Praha** 1
Tel: 2-2410 2218/2303/2343 Fax: 2-2421 4647
Internet: www.win1250/fos/index.htm
E-Mail: foscr@adam.cz
chairman PhDr. Frantisek Synek

Franz Schubert Society
Petr Matuszek, U Kríze 3, 158 00 **Praha** 5
Tel: 2-651 8382/0603-271 861
foreign contacts RnDr. Petr Pokorny (tel: 2-523 8305)

Friends of Music Circles
Kruhy prátel hudby
c/o Nadace Cesky hudebni fond, Besedni 3, 118 00 **Praha** 1
Tel: 2-573 2008/5732 3860 Fax: 2-534 234
Internet: www.musica.cz/nchf
E-Mail: czmic@login.cz
Comments: c. 200 members in different towns; alternative E-mail: his@vol.cz

Fryderyk Chopin Society in the Czech Republic
Spoleènost Fryderyka Chopina v Ceské republice
Hlavní tr. 47, 353 01 **Mariánské Lázne**
Tel: 165-622 617 Fax: 165-622 617
president Ivan Klánsk; secretary Halka Jelínková

Hába Information Centre
U druzstva Práce 59, 140 00 **Praha** 4
Tel: 2-4446 6716
chairman Dipl. Ing. Jan Andreska
Role & Services: information about the Czech Composer Alois Hába

IASPM – Czech Branch
IASPM – èeská sekce
c/o Ústav hudební vedy FFMU, Arna Nováka 1, 660 88 **Brno**
Tel: 5-4112 1434
Internet: www.phil.muni.cz/musi/iaspm
E-Mail: iaspm@phil.muni.cz
president Jirí Fukac; general secretary Ales Opekar
Role & Services: studies in popular music

Information and Advisory Centre for the Local Culture Department of Amateurs' Art (IPOS-ARTAMA)
Kresomyslova 7, PO Box 2, 140 16 **Praha** 4
Tel: 2-6121 5684-7 Fax: 2-6121 5688
E-Mail: artama@ipos-mk.cz
chairman Dr. Vítezslava Srámková (tel: 2-6121 5681)

Information and Advisory Centre for the Local Culture (IPOS)
PO Box 12, 120 21 **Praha** 2
Tel: 2-2252 7432 Fax: 2-2252 1629
Internet: www.ipos-mk.cz
E-Mail: ipos@ipos-mk.cz
director PhDr Miroslav Smolik (tel: 2-2251 3660)
Role & Services: information and advisory centre with statistics on culture in the region
Comments: visiting address: Blanická 4

Intergram
Na porící 27, 110 00 **Praha** 1
Tel: 2-231 1392/72/0435 Fax: 2-232 3341
director Jirí Novotny (tel: 2-231 1392)
Role & Services: independent association of performing artists and producers of sound and sound-picture records

Leos Janácek Foundation
Komenského nám.8, 602 00 **Brno**
Tel: 5-4221 1022 Fax: 5-4221 1022
chairman Prof. Adolf Sykora; secretary PhDr. Alena Nemcová

Mahler 2000
Konviktská 5, 110 00 **Praha** 1
Tel: 2-2209 2331 Fax: 2-2209 2330
Internet: www.arcodiva.cz
E-Mail: arcodiva@login.cz
president PhDr. Jiri Tilec
Role & Services: support of young artists, G.Mahler memory

Mozart Society in the Czech Republic
Mozartova obec v Ceske republice
Mozartova 169 (Bertramka), 150 00 **Praha** 5
president Dr Tomislav Volek (tel: 2-472 5690); secretary Mag. Marketa Kozinová (tel/fax: 2-885 921)

Music Youth of the Czech Republic
Hudební mládez Ceské republiky
Radlická 99, 150 00 **Praha** 5
Tel: 2-531 320
honorary president Frantiek Kovarîèek; secretary Jana Klimtová

Society for Electroacoustic Music
Spolecnost pro elektroakustickou hudbu
Radlická 99, 150 00 **Praha** 5
Tel: 2-537 374/401 4083 Fax: 2-401 4083
chairman Rudolf Ruzicka (tel: 5-4122 0174); manager Mgr. Tatjana Bublíková-Odstrcilová; secretary PhDr. Lenka Dohnalová (e-mail: dohnalova@email.cz)

Study Centre of the Bohuslav Martinu Institute
Besední 3, 118 00 **Praha** 1
Tel: 2-531 157/5731 3104/5732 0008 ext 525
Fax: 2-531 157
director PhDr. Ales Brezina
Comments: visiting address: nám. Kinskych 3, Praha 5

Theatre Community
Divadelní obec
Celetná 17, 110 00 **Praha** 1
Tel: 2-2481 7180 Fax: 2-2481 8184
chairman Marie Reslova (tel: 2-2480 9124)

Theatre Institute
Divadelni ústav
Celetná 17, 110 00 **Praha** 1
Tel: 2-2480 9111/2481 2754 Fax: 2-2481 1452/232 6100
Internet: www.czech-theatre.cz
E-Mail: divadelni.ustav@czech-theatre.cz
director Dr Ondrej Cerny; edition department Jana Patocková; theatre documentation Zuzana Jindrová; theatre library Jarmila Svobodová; theatre bibliography Mirka Prikrylová; theatre institute videothéque and Kylian videothéque Helena Brotánkova; foreign department and centre of international non-governmental organisations Mirka Potucková; department for Czech theatre studies Eva Sormová
Role & Services: centre of Czech theatre documentation and information, theatre library, videothéque of theatre performances, photoarchives, publishing house for theatrical literature, research centre for Czech theatre, national centre of international non-government organisations from the theatre field *Comments:* publish: Czech Theatre (review on the Czech theatre published in English once a year) editor Jana Patocková; Year-book (list of the theatre artists and theatre first performances during the season – with indexes) editor Zuzana Jindrová; Divadelní revue – Theatre revue (theoretical-historical theatre quarterly) editor Vladimír Just and Infoservice of Theatre Institute – bulletin with all theatre information from Czech Republic and abroad (published 10 times a year), editor Ondrej Svoboda; alternative internet: www.divadlo.cz; alternative e-mail: divadelni.ustav@divadlo.cz

Union of Authors and Performers
Svaz autoru a interpretu
Besední 3, 118 00 **Praha** 1
Tel: 2-5732 0008/5732 0064 Fax: 2-534 234/539 720
E-Mail: czmic@login.cz
chairman Jirí Vondrácek; secretary Marie Kounovská
Comments: pop music, contemporary music, sacred music, Musica ludaica festival

Union of Czech Vocal Choirs
Unie ceskych peveckych sboru
c/o M. Slechtová, Mezibranská 11, 110 00 **Praha** 1
Tel: 2-2221 1755/531 344 Fax: 2-531 343
president PadDr. Jirí Kolár; secretary Marcela Slechtová

Union of Employees in Cultural Institutions
OS pracovníku kulturních zarízení
Senovázné nám. 23, 112 82 **Praha** 1
Tel: 2-2414 2372/2674
secretary Milos Jandak

Union of Orchestra Musicians of the Czech Republic
Unie orchestrálních hudebníku CR
Senovázné nám 23, 112 82 **Praha** 1
Tel: 2-2414 2673 Fax: 2-2414 2673
president Ivan Pazour; secretary Robert Bezdek

Union of the Music Theatre
Jednota hudebního divadla
Divadelní ustav, Celetná 17, 110 00 **Praha** 1
Tel: 2-402 2548 Fax: 2-402 2548
Internet: www.divadlo.cz/jhd
chairman Josef Herman; contact K Vltave 18, 143 00 Praha 4, Modrany

Union of Theatre Artists
Odborová asociace divadelníku
Senovazné nám. 23, 112 82 **Praha** 1
Tel: 2-2414 2555
Fax: 2-2414 2512
chairman Václav Velík

DENMARK (+45)

Association of Danish Regional Symphony Orchestras
Landsdelsorkestrenes Samråd
Ny Kongensgade 13, 1472 **Copenhagen** K
Tel: 3393 0040 Fax: 3393 0040
Internet: www.symphony.dk
E-Mail: ls@webpartner.dk
chairman Sonja Refslund Skrumsager; general secretary Elna Barsøe
Role & Services: members are 5 main Danish symphony orchestras

Association of Danish Scenographers
KGS. Nytorv 21, 1050 **Copenhagen** K
Tel: 3314 3355 Fax: 3314 3303
E-Mail: sds@scenograf.dk
contact Jakob Pelch

Association of Danish Stage Directors
KGS. Nytorv 21, 1050 **Copenhagen** K
Tel: 3314 3355 Fax: 3314 3303
E-Mail: faf@kulturel.dk
contact Susanne Baigaard

Association of Danish Theatre Managers
Dansk Teatres Fællesorganisation
Rialto Teater, Box 723, Smollegade 2, 2000 **Frederiksberg**
Tel: 3888 0111 Fax: 3888 0100
chairman Anders Ahnfelt Roenne
Role & Services: aims to represent the interests of the managers of major Danish theatres, negotiate collective agreements, organises annual seminars etc

Copenhagen International Theatre (KIT)
Verstergade 5, 3rd Floor, 1456 **Copenhagen** K
Tel: 3315 1564 Fax: 3332 8182
Internet: www.kit.dk
E-Mail: info@kit.dk
artistic director Trevor Davies; accountant Jørgen Poemann; programme co-ordinator Katrean Verwitt; press officer Hans Christian Gimble
Role & Services: worldwide contact to other festival organizers and professional non-established dance, theatre and performance groups; presenter of international guest performances and festivals of dance, theatre, music and new circus *Comments:* it is funded by The Danish Theatre Council, The City of Copenhagen and The County of Copenhagen; festivals and projects are based on the collaboration with numerous international partners

Copy-Dan
Oistirfålled Torv 10, 2100 **Copenhagen** Ø
Tel: 3544 1400 Fax: 3544 1414
Internet: www.copydan.dk
E-Mail: copydan@copydan.dk
managing director & manager (tv and press copy) Litten Hansen; managers Sven Karnov(cable tv), Niels Holm Svendsen(copy and education), Kirsten Kierkegaard(visual art)
Role & Services: copyright collection society, owned by 45 organisations representing the copyright owners (producers, publishers, composers, authors, artists etc)

Danish Actors Association
Dansk Skuespillerforbund
Sankt Knuds Vej 26, 1903 **Frederiksberg** C
Tel: 3324 2200 Fax: 3324 8159
E-Mail: skuespil@Post7.tele.dk
president Henrik Petersen
Comments: union for actors, opera singers, dancers & choreographers

Danish ASSITEJ – Danish Centre of the Association du Théâtre pour l'enfance et la jeunesse (ASSITEJ)
Suomisvej 2, 2nd floor, 1927 **Frederiksberg** C
Tel: 3530 4409 Fax: 3530 4401
Internet: www.assitej.dk
E-Mail: assitej@vip.cybercity.dk
secretariat Peter Manscher
Role & Services: to promote children's theatre; organise festivals, exchanges and seminars

Danish Center for Culture and Development (DCCD)
Vestergade 5, 1456 **Copenhagen** K
Tel: 3317 9700 Fax: 3317 9701
Internet: www.dccd.dk
E-Mail: info@dccd.dk
director Olaf Gerlach Hansen
Role & Services: established to strengthen cultural cooperation between Denmark and the non-Western world through festivals, information activities, networking, support of projects, etc; provides an entry point into Denmark with regards to the promotion of non-Western arts and culture, and has interest to facilitate information concerning: projects that could be presented in Denmark, projects in search of a Danish partner, the improvement of cultural cooperation between the Western and non-Western world (information, fundraising, networking, dialogue, research etc)
Comments: see also Festivals

Danish Centre of International Federation of the Phonographic Industry (IFPI)
St. Strandstræde 9, 1255 **Copenhagen** K
Tel: 3391 9111 Fax: 3391 9973
E-Mail: ybahner@eurolaw.com
chairman Stefan Fryland; secretary, legal adviser Johan Schlüter

Danish Centre of the International Theatre Institute (ITI)
Dansk ITI og Teaterunion
Vesterbrogade 26, 3rd Floor, 1620 **Copenhagen** V
Tel: 3386 1210 Fax: 3324 0157
Internet: www.image.dk/~perditu
E-Mail: dititu@image.dk
manager Jan G. Christiansen; president Heino Byrgesen
Role & Services: for all theatre professionals, both employees and employers; publishes theatre yearbook; biennial nordic drama prize, and nordic theatre congress/festival in turn with the other four nordic countries

Danish Centre of Union Internationale de la Marionette (UNIMA)
Sintrupvej 11A, 8220 **Brabrand**
Tel: 8624 0572 Fax: 8624 0593
Internet: hjem.get2net.dk/unima
E-Mail: refleksion@post7.tele.dk
secretaire Bjarne Sandborg

Danish Council of Performing Artists' Organisation
Fællesrådet for Udøvende Kunstnere
Sankt Hans Torv 26, 2200 **Copenhagen** N
Tel: 3537 0649 Fax: 3537 0649
chairman Ejvind Callesen
Role & Services: liaison agency composed of professional organisations whose members' profession is artistic performance; the main task is to contribute to maintenance/enforcement, promotion and development – nationally and internationally – of the rights that are held by persons whose profession is artistic performance

Danish Film and TV Workers' Union
Kongens Nytorv 21, 1050 **Copenhagen** K
Tel: 3314 3355 Fax: 3314 3303
Internet: www.filmtv.dk
E-Mail: faf@filmtv.dk
general secretary Susanne Bækgaard

Danish Jazz Center/ The JAZZPAR Prize
Borupvej 66, 4683 **Rønnede**
Tel: 5671 1567 Fax: 5671 1749
E-Mail: jazzcent@inet.uni2.dk
director Arnvid Meyer; accountant Karen Meyer; manager Cim Meyer

Danish Music Council (Danish Section of the International Music Council)
Statens Musikråd
Vesterbrogade 24, 1620 **Copenhagen** V
Tel: 3325 1055 Fax: 3324 2242
Internet: www.musikraad.dk
E-Mail: sm@musikraad.dk
general secretary Erik Skovgaard Pedersen; chairman Lennart Ricard
Role & Services: to promote music in Denmark and advise and assist public authorities and institutions in musical matters

Danish Music Information Centre
Dansk Musik Informations Center MIC
16 Gråbrødretorv, 1154 **Copenhagen** K
Tel: 3311 2066 Fax: 3332 2016
Internet: www.mic.dk
E-Mail: mic@mic.dk
director Anette Faaborg; chief librarian Bendt Viinholt Nielsen; chairman Lennart Ricard
Role & Services: provides information on Danish music and musical activities in all genres; works for Danish music and Danish musicians and bands in Denmark and abroad

Danish Music Publishers' Association
Dansk Musikforlæggerforening
Maarkaervej 13, 2630 **Taastrup**
Tel: 4399 9400 Fax: 4399 9407
chairman John Rasmussen; secretary Hans-Ulrik Barfoed (fax: 7555 2316)
Role & Services: represents the major Danish music publishers; private foundation, owned by its members; looks after members' interests, gives advice on contracts, rights etc *Comments:* member of KODA (q.v.), Nordisk Copyright Bureau (q.v.), COPY-DAN (q.v.) , the Nordic Music Publishers Association and the International Music Publishers' Association (q.v.)

Danish Musician's Union
Dansk Musiker Forbund
Sankt Hans Torv 26, 2200 **Copenhagen** N
Tel: 3524 0240 Fax: 3524 0250
E-Mail: dmf@dmf.dk
chairman Anders Laursen; secretary Jens Slumpstrup
Role & Services: Union of all professional musicians; help with taxation; legal advice; organise master classes; band doctor consultation; promotion tour for upcoming bands; discount on CD-Production; workshops; instrument insurance

Danish Performing Right Society
KODA Selskabet til Forvaltning af Internationale Kompositionsrettigheter
Landemaerket 23-25, PO Box 2154, 1016 **Copenhagen** K
Tel: 3330 6300 Fax: 3330 6330
Internet: www.koda.dk
E-Mail: info@koda.dk
directeur général Niels Bak
Role & Services: member of Groupement Européen des Sociétés d'Auteurs et Compositeurs (q.v.)

Danish Section of Jeunesses Musicales
Landsorganisationen Musik og Ungdom
Enghavevej 40, 1674 **Copenhagen** V
Tel: 3386 3086 Fax: 3386 3087
E-Mail: musik-ungdom@post1.tele.dk
president Jens Ole Petersen; secretary general Pia Dahl
Role & Services: aim to encourage interest in music for young audience – concerts with professional musicians for young people; courses and workshops for young, amateur musicians

Danish Theatre Union
Dansk Teaterforbund
Sankt Knuds Vej 26, 1903 **Frederiksberg** C
Tel: 3324 2200 Fax: 3324 8159
E-Mail: skuespio@post7.tele.dk
Role & Services: umbrella organisation for Danish Actors Association and Danish Association for Theatre Technicians (e-mail: tef@tef.dk)

Dansens Hus
Hørsholmsgade 20, 2200 **Copenhagen** N
Tel: 3583 0609 Fax: 3582 0620
Internet: www.kulturnet.dk/homes/dh
E-Mail: dansens.hus@image.dk
administrator Kristina Sloth
Role & Services: provides rehearsal facilities and daily classes for professional dancers and dance companies; information on dance events in Denmark; run annual Copenhagen Dance Seminar – 3 weeks of classes with guest teachers

Dansk Artist Union
Vendersgade 24, 1363 **Copenhagen** K
Tel: 3332 6677 Fax: 3333 7330
Internet: www.artisten.dk
E-Mail: artisten@artisten.dk
president Nick Olander; general secretary Andy Filipsen
Role & Services: represents professional artists, entertainers, singers, soloists, bands etc. in pop, rock, jazz, ballads, show, variety and circus – including 80% of professional recording artists in Denmark, whose recordings are currently on sale; is a member of IFA, Copy-Dan, Gramex, the Danish Confederation of Trade Unions (LO); negotiates collective agreements; gives judicial assistance; advises on contracts; ensures right holders individual remuneration; works for the preservation of exclusive rights; works against internet piracy; organises courses, master classes; administrates its own state recognised unemployment fund and projects; more than 80% of the union's right holders have assigned to the union the sole authority to administer their rights

Gramex
Gl. Kongevej 11-13, 2nd Floor, 1610 **Copenhagen** V
Tel: 3385 3200 Fax: 3385 3215
Internet: www.gramex.dk
E-Mail: gramex@gramex.dk
managing director Bjørn Juell-Sundbye; chairman Stefan Fryland
Role & Services: independent organisation for the administration of neighbouring rights; Gramex is approved by the Danish Ministry of Culture(q.v.) and collects and distributes renumeration paid when phonograms are played publicly; Gramex is also appointed as national IRSC agency

Musica Nova (Danish section of the ISCM)
Grabrodretorv 16, 1154 **Copenhagen** K
Tel: 3393 0024 Fax: 3393 0024
E-Mail: iscm-dk@get2net.dk
administrator Einar Kanding

National Society for the Promotion of Drama, The
Danmarks Teaterforeninger
Suomisvej 2, 2. sal, 1927 **Frederiksberg** C
Tel: 3535 4846
Fax: 3530 4401
Internet: www.dk-teaterforeninger.dk
E-Mail: date@image.dk
president Jorten Hvidtfelt
Role & Services: central organization of 80 local theatre associations *Comments:* aim to publish surveys on touring performances for all audience ages; to promote an interest in the theatre art of to-day and of the future by organizing seminars on theatre, by producing newsletters, study guides, pamphlets and reports on activities and events; cooperate with related associations outside Denmark with a view to exchanging experiences

Union of Theatre Technicians in Denmark
Teaterteknikerforbundet
Sankt Knuds Vej 23A, 1903 **Frederiksberg** C
Tel: 3386 2626 Fax: 3386 2627
Internet: www.tef.dk
E-Mail: tef@tef.dk
president Gorm Friborg

ESTONIA (+372)

2.tants – independent dance organisation
Sõltumatu tantsuorganisatsioon 2.tants
Rataskaevu 10, 10123 **Tallinn**
Tel: 6-269 094 Fax: 6-269 099
contact Priit Raud
Role & Services: promoting contemporary Estonian dance

Centre of Dance Information in Estonia (TIKE)
Tantsuinfo Keskus Eestis
Rataskaevu 10, 10123 **Tallinn**
Tel: 6-269 098 Fax: 6-269 099
executive director Priit Raud
Role & Services: to develop mutual understanding and extend collaboration between dance fields; to develop dance activities; to look after the general interests of dance in Estonia; to arrange dance courses and workshops; publishes Tantsu INFO leaflet and other titles; not-for-profit organisation

CIOFF-Estonia
c/o ERKA, Suur-Karja 23, 10140 **Tallinn**
Tel: 2-442 927 Fax: 6-313 486
Internet: www.kul.ee/cioff.html
chairman Ingrid Rüütel; secretary Anne Ojalo

Cultural Endowment Estonia
Kultuurkapital
Suur-karja 23, 10140 **Tallinn**
Tel: 2-446 922 Fax: 2-446 983
Internet: www.ee/Kulka/
director Avo Viiol; public relations Ainiki Väljataga

Estonian Amateur Theatre Association
Eesti Harrastusteatrite Liit
Vene 6, 10123 **Tallinn**
Tel: 2-601 591 Fax: 2-601 591
chairman Jaan Urvet; secretary Piret Viisimaa

Estonian Authors Society
Eesti Autorite Ühing
Toompuiestee 7, 10142 **Tallinn**
Tel: 6-460 272 Fax: 6-460 273
Internet: www.eauthors.ee
chairman Mikk Targo; managing director Kalev Ratus
Role & Services: organisation of Estonion composers and musicologists

Estonian Centre of the Association du théâtre pour l'enfance et la jeunesse (ASSITEJ)
PO Box 3242, **Tallinn**
Tel: 2-450 959 Fax: 2-450 959
secretary Hiie Fluss

Estonian Centre of the International Theatre Institute (ITI)
ITI Eesti Keskus
c/o Eesti Teatriliit, Uus 5, 66403 **Tallinn**
Tel: 2-443 584
chairman Priit Pedajas; secretary Kadi Herkül

Estonian Choral Society
Eesti Kooriühing
Suur-Karja 23, 10140 **Tallinn**
Tel: 2-449 147 Fax: 2-449 147
Internet: www.kul.ee/koor.html
chairman Ants Soots
Role & Services: organisation of choirs and wind bands; publish information leaflet

Estonian Composers Union
Eesti Heliloojate Liit
Lauteri 7, 10145 **Tallinn**
Tel: 6-454 968
chairman Lepo Sumera
Role & Services: organisation of Estonion composers and musicologists

Estonian Cultural Foundation
Eesti Kultuurifond
Olevimägi 14, 10123 **Tallinn**
Tel: 6-411 242 Fax: 6-411 220
chairman Sirje Endre
Role & Services: cultural funding in Estonia

Estonian Drama Agency
Eesti Näitemänguagentuur
Suur-Karja 23, 10140 **Tallinn**
Tel: 6-282 344 Fax: 6-282 342
Internet: www.kul.ee/agency.html
E-Mail: ena@teleport.ee
director Külli Holsting
Role & Services: promotion of Estonian plays and playwrights, assisting theatres and authors in trading with rights of perfomance

Estonian Folk Dance and Folk Music Society
Eesti Rahvatantsu ja Rahvamuusika Selts
Suur-Karja 23, 10140 **Tallinn**
Tel: 2-445 909
chairman Valdo Rebane; secretary Helena Kalbus
Role & Services: organisation of Estonian folk dance and folk music groups

Estonian Music Council
Eesti Muusikanõukogu
Suur-Karja 23, 10140 **Tallinn**
Tel: 6-449 931 Fax: 6-449 931
Internet: www.kul.ee/emc/
E-Mail: emn@kul.ee
president Prof Peep Lassmann; secretary Kadri Ruudi
Role & Services: representative body of musicians; links musical institutions in Estonia

Estonian Music Foundation
Eesti Muusikafond
Lauteri 7, 10145 **Tallinn**
Tel: 6-466 536
director Raimo Kangro

Estonian Music Information Centre
Eesti Muusika Infokeskus
Lauteri 7, 10145 **Tallinn**
Tel: 6-454 395 Fax: 6-454 395
E-Mail: emik@zzz.ee
director Mare Põldmäe

Estonian National Culture Foundation
Eesti Rahvuskultuuri Fond
A. Weizenbergi 20A -13, 10150 **Tallinn**
Tel: 6-419 162 Fax: 6-419 163
E-Mail: post@erkf.ee
chairman Eri Klas; executive director Toivo Toomemets
Role & Services: cultural funding in Estonia

Estonian Performing Arts Information Centre
Eesti Teatri ja Tantsu Infokeskus
Rataskaevu 10, 10123 **Tallinn**
Tel: 6-269 090 Fax: 6-269 099
director Kristiina Garancis

Estonian Stage Productions (ESP)
Rataskaevu 10, 10123 **Tallinn**
Tel: 6-269 090 Fax: 6-269 099
managing director Valdo Kask; assistant Katrin Vingel
Role & Services: developing theatre exchange between Estonia and other countries; organise Baltoscandal festival (q.v.)

Estonian Theatre Union
Eesti Teatriliit
Uus 5, 66403 **Tallinn**
Tel: 2-446 868 Fax: 2-443 584
chairman Tõnu Tepandi; secretary Helgi Toom
Role & Services: organisation of Estonian professional theatre people

Open Estonia Foundation
Avatud Eesti Fond
Estonia pst. 3/5, 10143 **Tallinn**
Tel: 6-313 791 Fax: 6-313 796
Internet: www.oef.org.ee
E-Mail: anu@oef.org.ee
director Mall Hellam; culture programme manager Anu Kilvio
Role & Services: financial contribution to Estonian education and culture

FAROE ISLANDS (+298)

Association of Classical Musicians
Yrkisfelag fyri klassikar tónleikarar
Børkugøtu 21, 100 **Tórshavn**
Tel: 316 462/311 818 Fax: 316 991
E-Mail: martin@umms.fo
contact Martin Mouritsen

Society of Faroese Composers
Felagið Føroysk Tónaskøld
Reynagøta 12, 100 **Tórshavn**
Tel: 314 815 Fax: 314 825
E-Mail: summar@olivant.fo
contact Pauli í Sandagerøi

FINLAND (+358)

Association of Finnish Operas
Suomen Oopperaliitto/Finlands Operaförbund
Teatterikulma, Meritullinkatu 33, 00170 **Helsinki**
Tel: 9-135 7170 Fax: 9-135 7190/2-244 4104
1st chairman Kirsti Ala-Harja; 2nd chairman Hilkka Lirho

Association of Finnish Symphony Orchestras
Suomen Sinfoniaorkesterit ry
Uudenmaankatu 36 D 21, 00120 **Helsinki**
Tel: 9-2709 1411/14
Fax: 9-621 4414
Internet: www.sinfoniaorkesterit.fi
E-Mail: kai.amberla@sinfoniaorkesterit.fi
executive director Kai Amberla; secretary Elina Tuomola
Role & Services: established in 1965; main purpose is to promote and develop orchestral life in Finland and to look after the interests of member orchestras; association now has 28 member orchestras; operations can be divided as follows: a) communications and consultation with various departments of government b) acting as an expert body of orchestras c) training: seminars, workshops, conferences d) information, publishing, statistics and research e) international public relations f) upkeep of a central library for orchestral materials *Comments:* publish Finnish Symphony Orchestras Concert Calender (Suomen Sinfoniaorkesterit Konserttikalenteri free twice year)

Association of Finnish Theatres
Suomen Teatteriliitto
Meritullinkatu 33, 00170 **Helsinki**
Tel: 9-135 7452 Fax: 9-135 7462
Internet: www.kolumbus.fi/teatteriliito
E-Mail: teatteriliitto@teatteriliitto.fi
chief executive officer Matti A Holopainen; legal counsel Anita Prusila
Role & Services: association of 39 professional theatres; joint interest and employer organisation for Finnish professional drama theatres and opera

Central Union of Finnish Theatre Employees
Suomen Teatterityöntekijäin Yhteisjärjestö STY
Meritullinkatu 33, 00170 **Helsinki**
Tel: 9-135 6369/67
Fax: 9-135 6658
managing director Raimo Söder
Role & Services: trade union in the field of theatre, dance and audiovisual arts; member of ISETU-FISTAV

Finland Festivals
Uudenmaankatu 36 D 21, 00120 **Helsinki**
Tel: 9-612 6760/61 Fax: 9-6126 7610
Internet: www.festivals.fi/
E-Mail: info@mail.festivals.fi
general manager Tuomo Tirkkonen; marketing secretary Riitta Kerman
Role & Services: promotes some 58 Finnish festivals, produces an annual guide in English

Finland Swedish Folk Dance Organization
Finlands Svenska Folkdansring
Kaserngatan 28, 00130 **Helsinki**
Tel: 9-638 081 Fax: 9-636 513
E-Mail: folkdansringen@fsf.inet.fi
president Eivor Wallinvirta
Role & Services: coordinate the folk-dance activities in the Swedish-speaking parts of Finland; encourage interests in and knowledge of folk-dances and games; create understanding of folk music and folk costumes; promote cooperation with similar organizations in Scandinavia and worldwide

Finnish Centre of the Association du théâtre pour l'enfance et la jeunesse (ASSITEJ)
Suomen Assitej Keskus
Meritullinkatu 33, 2.krs., 00170 **Helsinki**
Tel: 9-135 7641/693 551
Fax: 9-135 5522/693 878
E-Mail: katariina.metsalampi@kulttuuri.hel.fi
president Marjaana Castrén; vice-president Katariina Metsälampi
Role & Services: study and promotion of theatre for young people; organise seminars and festivals
Comments: in March 2000 BRAVO! – Festival presents new theatre makers from Helsinki and 8 other first class performances from the other cultural cities of Europe 2000

Finnish Centre of Union Internationale de la Marionette (UNIMA)
Pispalan valtatie 30, 33250 **Tampere**
Tel: 3-212 2474 Fax: 3-213 3209
Internet: www.sgic.fi/~unima
E-Mail: unima@sgic.fi
president Mansi Stycz; secretary Anna-Liisa Tarvainen
Role & Services: publishes yearly bulletins and papers with information on Finnish and foreign puppetry, events and training opportunities, collects data and information, organizes training and education for Finnish puppeteers and promotes international contacts and cooperation within the field of puppet theatres

Finnish Composer's Copyright Society (TEOSTO)
Lauttasaarentie 1, 00200 **Helsinki**
Tel: 9-681 011 Fax: 9-677 134
Internet: www.teosto.fi
E-Mail: publicrelations.kalle.jamsen@teosto.fi
managing director Jaakko Fredman; deputy managing director Jaakko Eskola; head of general licensing Satu Kangas; public relations officer Kalle Jämsen; head of broadcasting licensing, NCB department Katri Sipilä
Role & Services: member of Groupement Européen des Sociétés d'Auteurs et Compositeurs (q.v.)

Finnish Cultural Foundation, The
Suomen Kulttuurirahasto
SKR, PO Box 203, 00121 **Helsinki**
Tel: 9-602 144 Fax: 9-640 474
Internet: www.skr.fi
E-Mail: info@skr.fi
secretary general Paabo Hohti; cultural manager Eiga Kurka
Role & Services: to advance cultural life in Finland by funding Finnish arts and research *Comments:* visiting address: Bulevardi 5A, 00121 Helsinki

Finnish Folklore Association
PO Box 132, 00101 **Helsinki**
Tel: 9-441 803 Fax: 9-441 803
E-Mail: suom@kansantanssinyst.fi
secretary Rtva Sabelli
Role & Services: to maintain the folk dances, music, costumes and traditions; participates in international co-operation through membership in Nordlek (organisation for Nordic co-operation) and Folklore Suomi Finland (co-ordinating organisation and national committee representing IVO and CIOFF) *Comments:* Tanhuviesti magazine and secretary fax: +358 9-660 651

Finnish Group of IFPI, The
Yrjönkatu 3, 00120 **Helsinki**
Tel: 9-6803 4050 Fax: 9-6803 4055
E-Mail: ifpi@ifpi.fi
secretary/director Arto Alaspää; president Mr Vasilij Kokljuschkin

Finnish Music Information Centre
Lauttasaarentie 1, 00200 **Helsinki**
Tel: 9-6810 1313/1311 (music library) Fax: 9-682 0770
Internet: www.fimic.fi
E-Mail: info@mic.teosto.fi
executive director Pekka Hako (6810 1252); information manager Anni Heino (6810 1316); executive producer/non-classical music Jari Muikku (9-6810 1315)
Role & Services: promote Finnish composers and compositions all around the world; publish information material; answer enquiries and maintain sound and press cutting archives; hire, lend and sell unpublished sheet music

Finnish Music Publishers' Association
Lastenkodinkatu 7, 00180 **Helsinki**
Tel: 9-562 2055 Fax: 9-562 2045
Internet: www.musiikkikustantajat.fi
E-Mail: info@musiikkikustantajat.fi
general manager Pekka Sipilä

Finnish Musicians' Union
Suomen Muusikkojen liitto
Pieni Roobertinkatu 16, 00120 **Helsinki**
Tel: 9-6803 4070 Fax: 9-6803 4087
Internet: www.musicfinland.com/sml
E-Mail: sml@musicfinland.com
director Raimo Vikström
Role & Services: trade union for musicians in Finland

Finnish Performing Music Promotion Centre (ESEK)
Esittävän Säveltaiteen Edistämiskeskus
Pieni Roobertinkatu 16, 00120 **Helsinki**
Tel: 9-6803 4040 Fax: 9-6803 4033
Internet: www.gramex.fi
E-Mail: leena.hirvonen@gramex.fi
secretary general Leena Hirvonen
Role & Services: with Gramex, the Copyright Society of Performing Artists and Producers of Phonograms in Finland aims to influence the professional capacities of Finnish artists, the quality and quantity of Finnish phonogram production, and the international competitive position of Finnish performing music; priority areas are: supporting phonogram production; supporting opportunities for performing; supporting and providing courses, master classes; publishing professional literature; supporting audiovisual music program production; takes care of performing music export projects within the framework of cultural agreements and cultural exchange programmes; information on Finnish performing artists

Finnish Playwrights Union
Suomen Näytelmäkirjailijaliitto
PO Box 168, 00171 **Helsinki**
Tel: 9-135 6191 Fax: 9-135 6171
E-Mail: pirjo.westman@sunklo.fi
director Pirjo Westman; president/chairman Saara Kesävuori
Role & Services: responsible for handling contracts between authors/playwrights and theatres, television, radio and films; holds a vast collection of Finnish drama in their library *Comments:* visiting address: Vironkatu 12 B 13, 00170 Helsinki

Finnish Theatre Information Centre
Teatterin Tiedotuskeskus ry
Teatterikulma, Meritullinkatu 33, 00170 **Helsinki**
Tel: 9-135 5550/7861
Fax: 9-135 5522
Internet: www.teatteri.org
E-Mail: tinfo@teatteri.org
director Riitta Seppälä; assistant director Anneli Kurki
Role & Services: Functions as the Finnish Centre of the ITI and the Nordic Theatre Union; the objective of the centre is to promote Finnish theatre and international exchange in the theatre arts; the centre gives information on Finnish theatre to individuals and organizations in Finland and abroad, and on international theatre to Finnish theatre people; publishes an English and French language theatre magazine called Finnish Theatre and a Finnish language newsletter, yearly Finnish Theatre Statistics, Theatre calendar, Finnish Theatre Directory

Foundation for the Promotion of Finnish Music (LUSES)
Lauttasaarentie 1, 00200 **Helsinki**
Tel: 9-6810 1252 Fax: 9-682 0770
chairman Paavo Suokko
Role & Services: the Foundation supports promotion of Finnish composers and their works (e.g. record production and sheet music)

Information Center for Dance in Finland
Alexander Theatre, Bulevardi 23-27, 00180 **Helsinki**
Tel: 9-612 1812 Fax: 9-612 1824
Internet: www.kaapeli.fi/~tanssi
E-Mail: tanssi@kaapeli.fi
president Jyri Pulkkinen; administrator Johanna Laakkonen; information officer Iiris Autio; editor Minna Tawast
Role & Services: domestic & foreign dance information; publishes Tanssi magazine quarterly; publishes information on Finnish dance in other languages; services for dancers in transition; promotes Finnish dance

Society of Finnish Composers
Suomen Säveltäjät ry
Runeberginkatu 15A 11, 00100 **Helsinki**
Tel: 9-445 589 Fax: 9-440 181
Internet: personal.eunel.fi/pp/compose
E-Mail: Saveltajat@compose.pp.fi
president Mikko Heiniö; secretary Annu Mikkonen; leader of the activities Tapio Tuomela
Role & Services: informing members, representing them in organisations and cultural life; information leaflets and member meetings; catalogue of finished compositions each year; organising a competition for composers (every 3rd year) and a competition for ensembles playing contemporary music (every 3rd year); taking care of administration of two foundations which give granst for promoting Finnish contemporary music

Theatre Centre
Teatterikeskus
Teatterikulma, Meritullinkatu 33, 00170 **Helsinki**
Tel: 9-135 7613 Fax: 9-135 5522
Internet: teatterikeskus.fi
E-Mail: teatterikeskus@teatterikeskus.fi
director Riitta Aarniokoski
Role & Services: organization of theatre and dance groups

TNL – Workers Theatre Association
Työväen Näyttämöiden Liitto
Meritullinkatu 33, 00170 **Helsinki**
Tel: 9-135 7083 Fax: 9-135 7061
E-Mail: tnl@saunalahti.fi
managing director Eeva-Sisko Artell
Role & Services: association of professional and amateur theatres

Union of Finnish Actors
Suomen Näyttelijäliitto
Arkadiankatu 12 A 18, 00100 **Helsinki**
Tel: 9-495 355/387
Fax: 9-448 501
general secretary Tuire Lankinen
Role & Services: member of International Federation of Actors

Union of Finnish Dance Artists
Suomen Tanssitaiteilijain Liitto-Finlands Danskonstnärförbund r.y.
Meritullinkatu 33, 00170 **Helsinki**
Tel: 9-135 7295 Fax: 9-135 7268
Internet: www.kaapeli.fi/~sttl/
E-Mail: sttl@kaapeli.fi
chairman Timo Sokura; secretary Ulla Tenhunen
Role & Services: main tasks of the union are to negotiate agreement on the terms of working for dancers, teachers and choreographers, to arrange dance courses, to give juridical help to its members and to take care of its members copyrights and arrange dance performances

FRANCE (+33)

Association for the Development of Industrial & Commercial Patronage (ADMICAL)
Association pour le Developpement du Mecenat Industriel et Commercial (ADMICAL)
16 rue Girardon, 75018 **Paris**
Tel: 1-4255 2001 Fax: 1-4255 7132
Internet: www.admica.org
E-Mail: contact@admical.org
président Jacques Rigaud; déléguée générale Virginie Seghers; délégué à l'information Lionel Bertinet; chargées de mission Nathalie Sauvanet, Julie Le Roy
Role & Services: Association for business sponsorship; promotion of business sponsorship in France, especially in arts, humanities and environment; to inform, counsel and train companies; each year Admical give awards for business companies; numerous publications on sponsorship issues in French; Admical holds the secretaryship of the CEREC (European Committee for Business arts 2 culture) until June 2000, coordinator: Nathalie Sauvanet

Bureau Export de la Musique Francaise
33 rue de Surène, 75008 **Paris**
Tel: 1-4312 9570 Fax: 1-4312 9579
E-Mail: burex@club-internet.fr
director Jean-François Michel; operational manager Patrice Hourbette
Role & Services: to promote professional French music abroad; centre of information and advice

Centre de Documentation de la Musique Contemporaine (CDMC)
Cité de la Musique, 16 Place de la Fontaine aux Lions, 75019 **Paris**
Tel: 1-4715 4715 Fax: 1-4715 4989
Internet: www.cdmc.asso.fr
directrice Marianne Lyon; documentalistes Corinne Monceau, Isabelle Gauchet; administration et promotion Katherine Vayne; accueil ventes et cdmc etranger Sylvie Chaput; web master Marie Frenay
Role & Services: contemporary music information centre

Centre National de la Danse
1, rue Victor-Hugo, 93507 **Pantin**
Tel: 1-4183 2727 Fax: 1-4840 3366
Internet: www.centredanse.fr
E-Mail: cnd@wanadoo.fr
président Anne Chiffert; directeur général Michel Sala
Role & Services: the centre national de la danse has been created by the French Ministry of Culture; it is organised in four departments corresponding to its missions; Maison des compagnies et des spectacles, 9, rue Geoffroy-l'Asnier, 75004 Paris, Tel: 1-4274 4422, Fax: 1-4029 0646, director: Daniel Gillet; Institut de pédagogie et de recherche chorégraphiques, 12-14, rue Lèchevin, 75011 Paris, Tel: 1-4805 0745, Fax: 1-4805 0710, director: Anne-Marie Reynaud, 40 ter, rue Vaubecour, 69002 Lyon, Tel: 4-7256 1070, Fax: 4-7256 1072, associate director for Lyon Bernadette Leguil; Département des métiers, 9, rue Geoffroy-l'Asnier, 75004 Paris, Tel: 1-4274 5861, Fax: 1-4029 0646, director Thierry Jopeck; Département du développement de la culture chorégraphique, 1, rue Victor-Hugo, 93507 Pantin cedex, Tel: 1-4183 2726, Fax: 1-4840 3366, director Claire Rousier *Comments:* the departments are located in several places but they should all be in Pantin in 2001; see also Venues and Promoters

Centre National du Théâtre (CNT)
6 Rue de Braque, 75003 **Paris**
Tel: 1-4461 8485 Fax: 1-4461 8486
E-Mail: documentation@cnt.asso.fr
directeur Jacques Baillon; chargée de mission outil pédagogique Danièle Naudin; chargé de mission Vincent Gatel; documentaliste Marie-Pierre Bianchi
Role & Services: documentation and information centre of theatrical activities supported by the Ministry of Culture *Comments:* alternative E-mail: cnt@cnt.asso.fr

Chambre des Directeurs de Théâtres Lyriques de France
41 rue de Colisée, 75008 **Paris**
Tel: 1-5396 9288 Fax: 1-5396 9296
président pierre Medecin; trésorier Elie Bankhalter; délégation permanente Laure Sylvestre
Role & Services: organise annual auditions for young opera singers; represent the profession of directors of lyric theater

Federation of Music Schools, The
Fédération Française de L' Enseignement Musical (FFEM)
12, rue Vivienne, 75002 **Paris**
Tel: 1-4261 0555 Fax: 1-4261 1331
président Alfred Herzog; vice-présidents Jean Simon, Pura Benichet, Jean-Philippe Dejussieu; secretaire de direction Brigitte Molard
Role & Services: FFEM is a member and administrator of the National Music Committee; by its statutes it has the duty to represent the entirety of its adherent institutions nationally and internationally; promote the musical teaching in France *Comments:* member of EMU, a non-governmental organisation regrouping 20 National Federations of music schools

French Centre of the Association du théâtre pour l'enfance et la jeunesse (ASSITEJ)
98 Boulevard Kellermann, 75013 **Paris**
Tel: 1-5380 3022 Fax: 1-5380 3022
président Maurice Yendt
Role & Services: provide national, international and institutional information to young people about theatre

French Centre of the International Theatre Institute (ITI) – Centre Français du Théâtre
10 Chaussée d'Antin, 75009 **Paris**
Tel: 1-4770 3984 Fax: 1-4246 4219
Internet: iti-worldwide.org
E-Mail: secretariat@iti-worldwide.org
president Pierre Santini; secretaires général Rodolphe Fouano, Iatine Bouhouhou
Role & Services: organises exchanges between French and foreign professionals (theatre, opera & dance); publishes a Review: Action-Théâtre, 4 times a year; this is the French section of the ITI and is attached to UNESCO; represent the Trade Union of living art professions; publishes a review: Action – Théâtre, 3 times a year *Comments:* hosting the World Congress of ITI in year 2000; 90 countries are represented in the International Theatre Institute

French Committee for Dance (UNESCO)
Comité Français du Conseil International de la Danse (UNESCO)
M. Jean Robin, 33, rue de la République, 60700 **Pont-Ste-Maxence**
Tel: 3-4472 0877
president Jean Robin; sécretaire générale Jocelyne Meunier
Role & Services: French national dance organisation; information service
Comments: includes 35 dance associations

French Federation of International Music Festivals (FFFIM)
Fèdération française des festivals internationaux de Musique (FFFIM)
3, bis rue Léonel de Moustier, 25000 **Besançon**
Tel: 3-8125 0585 Fax: 3-8181 5215
président Philippe Toussaint; président d'honneur Guy Ramona; secrétaire Daniel Linuesa; trésorier Henré de Colombel; administration Yvette Cussey; attacheé de presse Colette Chaunu
Role & Services: unites 62 festivals in France; aims to attract a younger audience and also international audience; to promote the cultural and economic role of these festivals *Comments:* contact for european festivals: L'Association Europeenne des Festivals de Musique, 122, rue de Lausanne, 1211 Genève 21, Switzerland, Tel: +41 22-732 2803; see also Festivals

French Trade Union of Performing Artists (SFA)
Syndicat Français des Artistes Interprètes
21 bis, Rue Victor Massé, 75009 **Paris**
Tel: 1-5325 0909 Fax: 1-5325 0901
E-Mail: SFA75@aol.com
délégation générale Catherine Alméras, Xavier Timmel, Jimmy Schuman, Tonys Fouqueray, Pierre Grimaldi, Michel Gautherin
Role & Services: a trade union which defends the social and moral rights of professional actors, dancers, singers, puppeteers, variety and circus artists

Hors les Murs – Association for the Promotion and Development of Street Arts and Circus
Hors les Murs – Association Nationale pour la Promotion et le Développement des Arts de la Rue et des Arts de la Piste
68 rue de la Folie Méricourt, 75011 **Paris**
Tel: 1-5528 1010 Fax: 1-5528 1011
Internet: www.horslesmurs.asso.fr
E-Mail: info@horslesmurs.asso.fr
administrateur Frédéric Cardon; directeur Jean-Luc Baillet; responsable du centre du ressources Catherine Charpin; chargé de mission rue et cirque Stèphane Simonin; relations publiques Patricia Demé
Role & Services: documentation, publishing, gathering of information and evalutation, coordination of surveys and consulting; Hors les Murs assists street artists and professional networks in requests for financial support and in developing contacts with other artists or public institutions; provides information about different practical aspects of artistic work in outdoor spaces and publishes Rue de la Folie Newsletter (quarterly), Goliath-Directory (biennial), International directory of circus arts (biennial) and Arts de la Piste Newsletter (for circus) quarterly *Comments:* the association is supported by the theatre and performance department of the French Ministry of Culture

Jeunesses Musicales de France
20 rue Geoffroy l'Asnier, 75004 **Paris**
Tel: 1-4461 8686 Fax: 1-4461 8688
E-Mail: jmf_jbf@club-internet.fr
président Jean Loup Tournier; directeur Robert Berthier; administration Didier Gobillot; international affairs Martin Beyer
Role & Services: organiser of concerts & young artists
Comments: see also Promoters; other E-mail: info@j-musi-fr.org

L'Itinéraire
Fondation Avicenne, 27D Boulevard Jourdan, 75690 **Paris** Cedex 14
Tel: 1-4416 1460/4581 4461 Fax: 1-4416 1462
président Michael Levinas; administratrice Marielle Thierry
Role & Services: organises contemporary music concerts (electro-acoustic as well as chamber ensembles)
Comments: organises colloquiums, seminars and has publishing activity

Musique Française d'Aujourd'hui (MFA)
30, rue Ballu, 75009 **Paris**
Tel: 1-4715 4877 Fax: 1-4715 4879
general coordination Claudine Pellerin
Role & Services: offers financial support in the elaboration of discs of contemporary music, classical and jazz

National Music Committee – French Section of the International Music Council (CNM)
Comite National de la Musique (CNM)
252 rue du Faubourg St Honore, 75008 **Paris**
Tel: 1-4563 4858 Fax: 1-4563 4858
sécretaire général Jacques Masson-Forestier; président Pierre Henry
Role & Services: French section of the International Music Council of UNESCO

National Office of Touring (ONDA)
Office National de Diffusion Artistique (ONDA)
13 bis rue Henry Monnier, 75009 **Paris**
Tel: 1-4280 2822 Fax: 1-4874 1603
E-Mail: onda@club-internet.fr
présidente Michèle Puybasset; directeur Fabien Jannelle; secrétaire géneral Christophe Blandin-Estournet; conseillers Sonia Brenot, Solange Dondi, Jean-Pierre Lacoste; chargée de mission: jeune public, jeunes compagnies, auteurs contemporains Françoise Girard; chargée de mission: information nationale et internationale Giusi Tinella; chargée de mission: musiques actuelles Sylvie Teste; attaché d'aministration Pierre Kechkeguian; attachée à l'information (fichiers) Thérèse Gintzburger; chargée de l'accueil Emmanuelle Bastien
Role & Services: supports live performance of contemporary work: dance, theatre, music in France

Organisation Française des Techniciens du Spectacle Vivant (OFTSV)
Centre Français de L'Oistat, 92, Avenue Galliéni, 93170 **Bagnolet**
Tel: 1-4972 9218 Fax: 1-4972 9218
président Etienne Bisson; vice-président Michel Day; secrétaire général Alain Girot; trésorier Marc Morange
Role & Services: represents technicians from the performing arts; defends and takes decisions on a European level for the French technicians, it is a centre of research, it represents France at meetings of the OISTAT; financed by its members; the OFTSV has representatives in 18 regions of France

Permanent Conference of French Orchestras (COPOF)
Conférence Permanente des Orchestres Français (COPOF)
48, rue Monsieur Le Prince, 75006 **Paris**
Tel: 1-4354 1580 Fax: 1-4354 3801
président Ivan Renard; vice-présidents Rose Lowry, Philippe Fanjas; secrétaire général Daniel Feugas
Role & Services: Association in charge of the permanent coordination of French orchestras; study office on rights and law (taxes, social matters, legal status and musicians' contracts); regular meeting sessions on relevant topics with orchestra managers. Musicians' representatives included in a consultative comittee; 24 members

Prolyrica
11 bis, rue Ballu, 75442 **Paris** Cedex 09
Tel: 1-4023 4550 Fax: 1-4526 7428
Internet: www.sacol.fr
manager Elisabeth Martinoty
Role & Services: new department of the SACD for promotion in France and abroad and in the area of lyric drama by contemporary French composers

RESEAU AGEC
5, rue Gaspar Monge Futuroscope, 86130 **Jaunay-Clan**
Tel: 5-4988 0720 Fax: 5-4988 1260
president Thierry Lucas; treasurer Patrick Berthelot; secretary Luc Jambais
Role & Services: development and reinforcement of the existing structures and plans in the cultural sector; the goal of the AGEC network is the economic development of the cultural & artistic sector *Comments:* benefit from the support of the ministry of Arts

Société Civile des Auteurs Multimedia (SCAM)
5, avenue Velasquez, 75008 **Paris**
Tel: 1-5669 5858 Fax: 1-5669 5859
Internet: www.scam.fr
E-Mail: communication@scam.fr
délégué général Laurent Duvillier; adjointe au délégué général Béatrice de Vallavieille; directrice de la communication Eve-Marie Cloquet
Role & Services: member of CISAC; its purpose is to exercise and administer in all countries all the rights relating to the reproduction or performance, of its members' works, and the collection and distribution of royalties *Comments:* Montreal address: 5186 Chemin Côte des Neiges, Montréal PQ H3T 1X8, tel: +1-514 738 8877, fax: +1-514 342 4615; Belgian address: Rue du Prince Royal, 87, 1050 Bruxelles, tel: +32 2-551 0321, fax: +32 2-551 0325

Société civile pour l'exercise des Droits des Producteurs Phonographiques (SCPP)
159 Avenue Charles de Gaulle, 92521 **Neuilly-sur-Seine** Cedex
Tel: 1-4640 1000 Fax: 1-4640 1317
directeur général gérant Marc Guez; directeur administratif et financier Jacques Chesnais; directrice juridique Natalie Piaskowski; relations publiques Frédéric Campo
Role & Services: collectively manages music producers' rights and redistributes sound and audiovisual copyrights to its members

Société de Perception et de Distribution des Droits des Artistes Interprètes de la Musique et de la Danse (SPEDIDAM)
16 rue Amélie, 75343 **Paris** Cedex 07
Tel: 1-4418 5858 Fax: 1-4418 5859/83 (legal)/51 (cultural)
président gérant Antony Marschutz; directeur aux affaires juridiques et internationales Xavier Blanc; directeur adjoint à la culture et la communication François Lubrano; directeur financier et administratif François Nowak
Role & Services: collecting society for performing artists and musicians, protects the rights of artists whose names do not appear on recorded formats & all performing artists even independent

Société des Auteurs, Compositeurs et Editeurs de Musique (SACEM)
225, Avenue Charles de Gaulle, 92521 **Neuilly-sur-Seine** Cedex
Tel: 1-4715 4715 Fax: 1-4745 1294
Internet: www.sacem.org
E-Mail: sacemdac@dial.oleane.com
président du conseil d'administration Jacques Demarny; président du directoire Jean-Loup Tournier; directeur général adjoint Thierry Desurmont; directeur délégué Alain Izard; directrice adjointe Catherine Kerr-Vignale; directeur adjoint Claude Gaillard; conseiller auprés du président du directoire Jacques Blache; déléguée à la communication Madame Claude Clerc; conseillère auprés du président du directoire Angelika Schouler
Role & Services: member of Groupement Européen des Sociétés d'Auteurs et Compositeurs ISAC (q.v.)

Société pour l'Administration du Droit de Reproduction Mécanique des Auteurs, Compositeurs et Editeurs (SDRM)
16 place de la Fontaine aux Lyons, 75019 **Paris**
Tel: 1-4715 4715 Fax: 1-4715 4975 (video)/4971 (audio)
Internet: www.sacem.org.
E-Mail: sacemdac@dial.oleane.com
directeur général Jean-Loup Tournier; directeur du département des droits phonographiques et vidéo Catherine Kerr-Vignale
Role & Services: member of Groupement Européen des Sociétés d'Auteurs et Compositeurs (q.v.); the SDRM has 2 departments: video and audio; the main office is situated with the SACEM, 225 Av. Charles de Gaulle, 92521 Neuilly-sur-Seine

Society for the Administration of the Rights of Performing Artists and Musicians
Société pour l'Administration des Droits des Artistes et Musiciens Interprètes (ADAMI)
10 A rue de la Paix, 75002 **Paris**
Tel: 1-4015 1000 Fax: 1-4015 1030
président Pierre Santini; directeur gérant Jean-Claude Voltaire; directeur de l'Action Artistique François Chenais; secrétaire général Mme Catherine Almeras
Role & Services: collecting society for performing artists and musicians, protects the rights of artists whose names appear on recorded formats *Comments:* ADAMI is a society which manages the intellectual copyrights for artists/performers (singers, musicians, conductors, comedians, dancers...all those whose recorded performance is broadcast) and is an essential collective management tool for each of these professional categories – collective management is becoming increasingly important in the context of the international performance market and the development of multimedia products

Syndicat des Entreprises Artistiques et Culturelles (SYNDEAC)
8 rue Blanche, 75009 **Paris**
Tel: 1-4453 7210 Fax: 1-4453 7212
président Jean Parthenay; deléguée nationale Christine Langrand
Role & Services: employers' organisation of public theatres in France, 980 members

Syndicat National de l'Edition Phonographique (SNEP)
27 rue du docteur Lancereaux, 75008 **Paris**
Tel: 1-4413 6666 Fax: 1-5376 0733/0730
président Paul-René Albertini; directeur gral Hervé Rony
Role & Services: member of the International Federation of the Phonographic Industry (q.v.)

Syndicat National des Petites Structures de Spectacle (SYNAPSS)
Théatre de la mainate, 36 rue Bichat, 75010 **Paris**
Tel: 1-4887 8248
Role & Services: representative of venues under 300 seats

Syndicat National des Producteurs et Organisateurs de Spectacles (SYNPOS)
23, boulevard des Capucines, 75002 **Paris**
Tel: 1-4265 7313 Fax: 1-4265 7323
déléguée générale Colette Chardon; président Gérard Louvin
Role & Services: represents and defends the rights of the producers and those organising performances

THEMAA, Association Nationale des Théâtres de Marionnettes
23, bis rue du Cloître St Etienne, 10000 **Troyes**
Tel: 3-2542 5911
présidente Sylvie Baillon
Role & Services: aims at promoting the art of puppetry, develop the professional practice, support the amateurs and obtain the creation of permanent venues or production places at a national international and also regional level *Comments:* publishes the revue MÛ, l'autre continent du Théâtre, quarterly, info on the revue: c/o Everlyne Lecucq, 18 rue de Gergovie, 75014 Paris, Tel/Fax: 1-4545 7663

Union Internationale de la Marionnette (UNIMA)
National & International Centre of UNIMA
Jacques Félix, Secrétaire Général, 7, place Wilson Churchill, BP 249, 08103 **Charleville-Mézières**
Tel: 3-2433 7250 Fax: 3-2433 7269
Internet: www.ardennes.com/asso/iim
E-Mail: sgi@unima.org
secrétaire général Jacques Félix; directrice Margareta Niculescu; director of puppet institue Roman Paska
Role & Services: UNIMA is the international union for marionettes/puppets; it is a non-governmental organisation attached to the UNESCO; it was first founded in 1929, and refounded in 1959; it has centres in 80 different countries, 8000 members; centre of information, research, education (Institut international de Marionnettes) and school – Ecole Supérieure Nationale des Arts de la Martionnettes (ESNAM) *Comments:* also organises Festival Mondial des Théâtres de Marionnettes (q.v.); visiting address: 7, place Wilson Churchill

Union Nationale des Compositeurs
Secretariat, 10 rue de Marmes, 92410 **Ville d'Avray**
Tel: 1-4750 4428 Fax: 1-4750 5390
president Pierre Ancelin

Union Syndicale de la Production Audiovisuelle (USPA)
5 rue Cernuschi, 75017 **Paris**
Tel: 1-4053 2300 Fax: 1-4053 2323
délégué général Jacques Peskine; secrétaire général Patrice Laumé
Role & Services: aims to answer technical, administrative and professional questions producers face in their daily activity; to represent the common interest of companies in France and abroad; to encourage everything which reinforces the identity and marketshare of French TV producers

GEORGIA (+995)

Georgian Centre of the International Theatre Institute (ITI)
45 Chavchavadze av., 380008 **Tbilisi**
Tel: 32-227 524 Fax: 32-294 306
E-Mail: ITI-Georgia@hotmail.com
president Avtandil Varsimashvili; secretary general Dr. Levan Khetaguri

Georgian Musical Society
22 Rustaveli Ave., 380008 **Tbilisi**
Tel: 32-934 353/998 609/999 243
Fax: 32-990 037/998 406
chairman Paata Burchuladze; co-chairman Manana Akhmeteli; chairman's assistant Madona Zakareishvili

Georgian Philharmonic Society
136 Agmashenebeli Ave., 380002 **Tbilisi**

International Bureau for Caucasian Cultural Programmes
45 Chavchavadze av., 380062 **Tbilisi**
Tel: 32-294 306 Fax: 32-294 306/231 196
E-Mail: IBCCP@lingua.edu.ge
director IBCCP Georgia Levan Dadiani; director IBCCP Azerbaijan Jahangir Selimkhanov (email: jselimkhanov@OSI-AZ-org); director IBCCP Armenia Arthur Gukasyan (email: aghukasyan@hotmail.com)
Role & Services: for all arts types; bureau coordinates educational programmes, managment training centre, information centre, festivals centre, publishing house, etc *Comments:* see also Promoters

International Centre of Playwriting
17 Atoneli str., **Tbilisi**
Tel: 32-984 207
E-Mail: IPC_Georgia@hotmail.com
honorary director Levan Khetaguri; coordinator Maka Vasadze

Managers Association of Georgia
54 Chavchavadze av., 380079 **Tbilisi**
Tel: 32-225 126 Fax: 32-939 124
E-Mail: lmgebrishvili@hotmail.com
coordinator Ketevan Kordzakhia; chairman Iuri Mgebrishvili

Open Society Georgian Foundation
11 Moseshvili, 380079 **Tbilisi**
Tel: 32-250 463/938 999 Fax: 32-291 052
E-Mail: office@osgf.ge
director Michael Chachkhunashvili

Stichting Caucasus Foundation
45 Chavchavadze av., 380062 **Tbilisi**
Tel: 32-294 306 Fax: 32-294 306/231 196
E-Mail: SCF@lingua.edu.ge
president Levan Khetaguri; chairman Steve Austen; programme coordinator Iuri Mgebrishvili
Role & Services: supports Caucasian countries in the process of cultural integration with European countries, sets up and implements programmes and events in art and culture for professional artists
Comments: regional programmes coordinated by IBCCP (International Bureau for Caucasian Cultural Programmes), educational programmes, management training centre, information centre; office in the Netherlands: secretary Henk van Silfhout, Koxhorn 32-3 EW Amsterdam; see also Promoters

Theatre Workers Union
11a Leonidze st., 380007 **Tbilisi**
Tel: 32-999 643/967/998 085
chairman Giga Lordkipanidze; assistant Anzor Kutateladze

Union of Composers
123 Agmashenebeku str., 380064 **Tbilisi**
Tel: 32-967 506/954 164 Fax: 32-959 513
chairman Nodar Gabunia; secretary Nugzar Vatsadze; referent Nino Meskhi

Union of Writers
13 Machabeli St., 380007 **Tbilisi**
Tel: 32-995 796/998 490
chairman Tamaz Tsivtsivadze

GERMANY (+49)

Association of German Concert Agents
Verband der Deutschen Konzertdirektionen eV
Widenmayerstr. 32, 80538 **München**
Tel: 89-212 147-123 Fax: 89-212 147-74
Präsident Michael Russ (tel: 711-163 5311)
Role & Services: the objectives are: representation of the general economic interest of German concert agents and promotion of solidarity according to traditional values of the trade

Bund der Theatergemeinden eV
Bonner Talweg 10, 53113 **Bonn**
Tel: 228-915 031 Fax: 228-915 0345
Geschäftsführer Roswitha Kleinwächter; Präsident Josef Reimers
Role & Services: federation of theatre audiences (31 organisations & 11 youth organisations) with 151,369 members

Bundesverband Freier Theater e.V.
Güntherstr. 65, 44143 **Dortmund**
Tel: 231-5575 2116 Fax: 231-5575 2129
Internet: www.th-net.de/buft
E-Mail: buft_@t-online.de
Vorsitzender Stefan Kuntz; Stellvertreter Matze Schmidt, Klaus Maier, Stefan Klehenz, Peter Bischoff, Ines Schulze
Role & Services: federal organisation for theatre-groups, mainly not subsidised by the state; members are regional organisations

Bundesvereinigung Sozio-Kultureller Zentren e.V.
Weberstr. 59a, 53113 **Bonn**
Tel: 228-242 0210 Fax: 228-242 0212
E-Mail: bvsozkul@aol.com
Geschäftsführer Gerd Spieckermann; Vorstandsmitglieder Rainer Bode, Andreas Kämpf, Berndt Urban, Stefanie Duncker, Frank Eckhardt, Grit Hannefort, Klaus Nagel, Michael Wegener
Role & Services: to promote socio-cultural centres in Germany (alternative culture venues)
Comments: promotion of 375 centres in Germany

Children and Youth Theatre Centre in the Federal Republic of Germany
Kinder und Jugendtheaterzentrum in der Bundesrepublik Deutschland
Schützenstrasse 12, 60311 **Frankfurt am Main**
Tel: 69-296 661 Fax: 69-292 354
Internet: www.f.shuttle.de/kjtz
E-Mail: zentrum@kjtz.f.shuttle.de
Leiter Dr. Gerd Taube; Stellv. Leiter Henning Fangauf
Role & Services: the centre aims to develop children's and young people's theatre and its inclusion in all fields of youth welfare work: education and continuation of studies, national & international exchange, information & documentation and the promotion of authors are four focal points of the programme *Comments:* The centre is member of BKJ (Federal Association for Cultural Youth Education), EU NET ART (European Network of Arts Organisations for Children and Young People), SIBMAS (q.v.) and national representative of INTERPLAY; cooperates with Goethe-Institut

Cultural Initiative of German Industry
Kulturkreis der Deutschen Wirtschaft im BDI e.V
Haus der Wirtschaft, Mühlendamm/Ecke Breite Str., 10178 **Berlin**
E-Mail: kulturkreis@dbi-online.de
Direktor Dr. Ludger Hünnekens; Vorstandsvorsitzender Dr. Arend Oetker
Role & Services: business support group, cultural activities *Comments:* they recently moved; at time of going to print the new telephone no. was still not known

Deutsche Orchestervereinigung eV in der DAG (DOV)
Postfach 130263, 20102 **Hamburg**
Tel: 40-410 6061 Fax: 40-410 6034
Internet: www.dov.org
E-Mail: contact@dov.org
Geschäftsführer Prof. Dr. Rolf Dünnwald
Comments: visiting address: Heimhuder Str 5, 20148Hamburg

Deutscher Berufsverband für Tanzpädagogik eV
Hollestrasse 1, 45127 **Essen**
Tel: 201-228 883 Fax: 201-226 444
1. Vorsitzender Ulrich Roehm; 2. Vorsitzender Prof. Martin Puttke

Deutscher Bühnenverein – Bundesverband Deutscher Theater e.V
St. Apern-Straße 17-21, 50667 **Köln**
Tel: 221-208 120 Fax: 221-208 1228
Internet: www.buehnenverein.de
E-Mail: debue@buehnenverein.de
Geschäftsführender Direktor Rolf Bolwin
Role & Services: association for venues; umbrella organisation of German theatre and cultural orchestras; the objective is to maintain and support variety of theatre in Germany *Comments:* see also Publications

Deutsches Forum für Figurentheater u. Puppenspielkunst e.V
Hattinger Str. 467, 44795 **Bochum**
Tel: 234-47720/29 Fax: 234-47735
Internet: www.dfp-idena.de
E-Mail: info@dfp-idena.de
Leitung Annette Dabs-Baucks; Wissenschaftliche Mitarbeit Anke Meyer; Sekretariat Elke Citrich
Role & Services: the Forum was founded to guide the development of the art of puppet-theatre; its services include: documentation, research and communication; the Forum aims to promote figure and puppet-theatre nationwide *Comments:* also organises the international festival Figurentheater der Nationen (biennial) and the competition for the Fritz-Wortelmann prize of the city of Bochum for amateur-figure-theatre; see also Festivals and Competitions

EUCREA Germany
Friedensallee 45, 22765 **Hamburg**
Tel: 40-3990 2212 Fax: 40-390 8895
project coordinator Jutta Schubert
Role & Services: membership consists not only of individual artists and groups, but also of organisations and institutions of handicapped people; organises and supports artistic and cultural activities of people with handicaps, e.g. national and international festivals; supplies information concerning activities, possibilities of performances and exhibitions; arranges contacts; promotes exchange of ideas and information. Since April 98 has been able to offer a special mediating agency – EUCREA-Agency *Comments:* see also Supranational Organisations and Agents & Producers

GEDOK – Verband der Gemeinschaften der Künstlerinnen und Kunstfreunde e.V.
Einern 29, 42279 **Wuppertal**
Tel: 202-524 642/520 223/0172-640 3376 (mobile)
Fax: 202-522 539
Internet: www.gedok.de.
E-Mail: GEDOK.Ma.Wpt@-t-online.de
Präsidentin Dr. Renate Massman
Role & Services: GEDOK is concerned with the arts in general, playing particular attention to the interests of women artists regardless of their areas of creativity; the goal is to support the artistic work of women, promote gifted young women artists and assist them; help organise art exhibitions, readings, concerts etc.; also awards two prizes *Comments:* not-for-profit organisation; approx. 4500 members in Germany and Austria, subdivided into 23 regional groups

Genossenschaft Deutscher Bühnen-Angehöriger (GDBA)
Postfach 130270, 20102 **Hamburg**
Tel: 40-445 185/443 870 Fax: 40-459 352
Präsident Hans Herdlein
Role & Services: member of International Federation of Actors *Comments:* visiting address: Feldbrunnenstraße 74, 20148 Hamburg; see also Publications

German Centre of the Association du théâtre pour l'enfance et la jeunesse (ASSITEJ)
Schützenstrasse 12, 60311 **Frankfurt am Main**
Tel: 69-291 538 Fax: 69-292 354
Internet: www.f.shuttle.de
E-Mail: aff@kjtz.f.shuttle.de
Vorsitzender Prof. Wolfgang Schneider; Geschäftsführer Eckhard Mittelstädt
Role & Services: supports professional Children and Youth Theatre in Germany, organises meetings, edits publications

German Centre of the International Theatre Institute (ITI)
Postfach 41 11 28, 12121 **Berlin**
Tel: 30-791 1777 Fax: 30-791 1874
Internet: users.aol.com/itigermany/
E-Mail: itigermany@aol.com
Geschäftsführer Martin Roeder-Zerndt; Acting Präsident Manfred Beilharz; Assistant Direktor Thomas Engel; Vice Präsident Jurgen Schitthelm
Role & Services: the German ITI develops and supports international cultural co-operation by providing information services, by organising international encounters, specialists' conferences, theatre festivals (i.e. Theater der Welt in Germany) (q.v.), and workshops centred around various aspects of the performing arts; ITI Germany regularly publishes newsletters (Impulse), papers, and books; publishes newsletter Impulse
Comments: visiting address: Schloßstr. 48, 12165 Berlin

German Centre of Union Internationale de la Marionette (UNIMA)
c/o Die Schaubude/Puppentheater Berlin, Greifswalder Str 81-84, 10405 **Berlin**
Tel: 30-428 6059 Fax: 30-423 4310
Internet: www.schaubude.bkv.org
E-Mail: info@bkv.org
Künstlerische Leitung der Schaubude Sylvia Brendenal; UNIMA Vorsitzender Dr. Christian Noack
Comments: see also Puppetry

German Cultural Council
Deutscher Kulturrat
Weberstr. 59a, 53113 **Bonn**
Tel: 228-201 350 Fax: 228-201 3521
Internet: www.kulturrat.de
E-Mail: post@kulturrat.de
Geschäftsführer Olaf Zimmermann
Role & Services: often known as the German Arts Council, it is a pressure group coordinating the policies of its different section members in relation to the federal government; it is not a funding agency

German Dance Council
Deutscher Tanzrat/Deutscher Ballettrat eV
Bonner Künstlerhaus, Graurheindorfer Str 23, 53111 **Bonn**
Tel: 228-633 578 Fax: 228-633 578
Präsidentin Iskra Zankova
Role & Services: represents the interests of professional dancers, choreographers and dance teachers in the field of educational and cultural politics, as well as for tax, social and legal queries; offers and organises conferences and seminars; has own publications; offers councilling with regard to questions on professional dancing

German Music Council
Deutscher Musikrat e.V.
Weberstr. 59, 53113 **Bonn**
Tel: 228-2091-0 Fax: 228-2091-200
Internet: www.deutscher-musikrat.de
E-Mail: deutscher-musikrat.bonn@t-online.de
Präsident Prof. Dr. Franz Müller-Heuser; Generalsekretär Dr. Marlene Wartenberg
Role & Services: at present the GMC comprises 91 member organisations and institutions, 16 state councils (Landesmusikräte), honorary and indvidual members; the Council represents about 8 million citizens, who as professionals, amateurs and laymen are engaged in music; the main aim of the Council as the central organisation for all fields of music is to urge the political and educational authorities as well as public opinion to secure an adequate role and place for music in education and society and to contribute to the further development of music culture; for the realization of its tasks the GMC cooperates with the responsible Ministries of the Federal Government and the Länder, with regional and municipal bodies and other institutions *Comments:* see also Publications

German Music Foundation (DSM)
Deutsche Stiftung Musikleben
Herrengraben 3, 20459 **Hamburg**
Tel: 40-3767 7150 Fax: 40-3767 7151
E-Mail: dsm@dsm-hamburg.de
Chairman of the Board of Trustees Erhard Bouillon; Präsident Irene Schulte-Hillen; Programme Planning Heike Siebel; Office Management Saskia Egger; PR Esther Schulte; Secretary Teli Taylan
Role & Services: projects to promote talents in classical music throughout Germany; concert series Foyer for Young Artists; fund for precious string instruments in cooperation with the federal government, which are lent to young musicians in an annual competition; individual support for the highly gifted young musicians; support in the activities of the Germany Music Council (esp. competition youth plays music, federal youth orchestra of Germany)

German Music Information Centre/ Germany Music Council
Deutsches Musikinformationszentrum
Deutscher Musikrat, Weberstraße 59, 53113 **Bonn**
Tel: 228-209 1180 Fax: 228-209 1280
Internet: www.miz.org
E-Mail: miz.dmr@t-online.de
Vorsitzender des Beratungsausschusses Prof. Dr. Joachim-Felix Leonhard; Geschäftsführung Margot Wallscheid
Role & Services: central clearing house for information on musical life in Germany, from traditional and contemporary art music to rock, pop, jazz and folk music; its task is to collect, present and communicate information on all aspects of musical life, from education and training to amateur music-making and professional performance, and from musical events to the media and business worlds *Comments:* database accessible via the Internet; reference library with Internet workplaces open to the public; MIC triennially edits the Musik Almanach, the central reference book with facts and figures on musical life in Germany

German National Group of International Federation of the Phonographic Industry (IFPI)
Grelckstrasse 36, 22529 **Hamburg**
Tel: 40-589 7470 Fax: 40-5897 4747
Internet: www.ifpi.de
E-Mail: name@phono.de
Präsident Wolf-D. Gramatke; Geschäftsführer Peter Zombik, Dr Martin Schaefer
Role & Services: Internationaler Verband der Tonträgerhersteller

German Performing Rights Society
Gesellschaft für musikalische Aufführung und mechanische Vervielfältigungsrechte (GEMA)
Rosenheimer Str. 11, 81667 **München**
Tel: 89-480 0300 Fax: 89-4800 3969
Aufsichtsrat (Vorsitz) Christian Bruhn; Vorstand und Generaldirektor Prof. Dr. Reinhold Kreile; Kommunikation und Öffentlichkeitsarbeit Dr. Hans-Herwig Geyer; Vorstand Prof. Dr. Jürgen Becker
Role & Services: looking after German and foreign performing rights in the German music sector
Comments: second address: Bayreuther Str. 37, 10787 Berlin, tel: 30-212 4500, fax: 30-2124 5950

German Section of Jeunesses Musicales
Marktplatz 12, 97990 **Weikersheim**
Tel: 7934-280 Fax: 7934-8526
Internet: www.JeunessesMusicales.de
E-Mail: weikersheim@JeunessesMusicales.de
Präsident Prof Martin Christoph Redel; Generalsekretär Thomas Rietschel

German Section of the International Society for Contemporary Music (ISCM)
Gesellschaft für Neue Musik – Sektion Bundesrepublik Deutschland der ISCM
Postfach 102461, 50464 **Köln**
Tel: 221-952 0215 Fax: 221-952 0216
E-Mail: musiktexte@t-online.de
Präsident Ernst Albrecht Stiebler; Vizepräsident Armin Köhler; Schriftführerin Gisela Gronemeyer
Role & Services: to promote new music in Germany

Institut für Neue Musik und Musikerziehung eV
Olbrichweg 15, 64287 **Darmstadt**
Tel: 6151-46667 Fax: 6151-46647
E-Mail: inst_musik@aol.com
Geschäftsführung Dr Susanne Ziegler; 1. Vorsitzender Prof. Dr. Rudolf Frisius
Role & Services: organises a conference, including concerts, seminars and instrument classes once a year, always around Easter.

Interessengemeinschaft der Städte mit Theatergastspielen (INTHEGA)
Geschäftsstelle im Bürgerhaus Bergischer Löwe, Konrad-Adenauer-Platz, 51465 **Bergisch Gladbach**
Tel: 2202-459 280 Fax: 2202-459 281
E-Mail: theater@bergischgladbach.de
Präsident Michael Haensel (Theater im Pfalzbau, Ludwigshafen); Geschäftsführerin Marion Grundmann (Bürgerhaus Bergischer Löwe, Bergisch Gladbach)
Comments: a service for cultural departments and associations in towns without own theatres; INTHEGA is member of Deutscher Bühnenverein and cooperating with the Community of German-speaking Theatres on tour

Internationales Musikinstitut Darmstadt (IND)
Nieder-Ramstädter Strasse 190, 64285 **Darmstadt**
Tel: 6151-132 416/7/133 093 (library) Fax: 6151-132 405
Direktor Solf Schaefer
Role & Services: information centre for contemporary music *Comments:* international holiday courses for NEW music; biennial

Mime Centre Berlin
Schönhauser Allee 73, 10437 **Berlin**
Tel: 30-4465 1860 Fax: 30-4465 1862
Internet: www.mimecentrum.de
E-Mail: info@mimecentrum.de
Director Thilo Wittenbecher; Public relations Marc Pohl
Role & Services: research – further training – documentation centre for mime and physical theatre; organising workshops, support performance projects, bring together artists, research on Meyerholds Biomechanics; member of European Mime Federation and IETM; video archive; small schedule theatre 'The Lab'
Comments: work centres around theatre in movement

Rat für Darstellende Künste im Deutschen Kulturrat (Theaterrat)
c/o Deutscher Bühnenverein -Bundesverband deutscher Theater, St. Apern Str. 17-21, 50667 **Köln**
Tel: 221-208 120 Fax: 221-208 1228
Internet: www.buehnenrerein.de
Sprecher Rolf Bolwin, Hans Härtlein; Stellvertreter Michael Schindhelm; Barbara Wollenberg, Eskra Zankova
Role & Services: umbrella organisation with 26 members (dance and theatre organisations)

Tanztendenz München e.V.
Lindwurmstr 88/V, 80337 **München**
Tel: 89-721 1015 Fax: 89-721 2249
E-Mail: tanzmuc@aol.com
Geschäftsführer Ulrich Rogun; Presse-und Öffentlichkeitsarbeit Tanja Irle
Role & Services: cooperation of professional free-lance choreographers (living and working in Munich); production centre *Comments:* information centre; international exchange, event Kostprobe (short-choreographies); publisher: dance calendar (list of all dance events in Munich)

Verband Deutsche Puppentheater e.V.
Geschäftsstelle, Moorweg 1, 21337 **Lüneburg**
Tel: 4131-84415 Fax: 4131-84415
Internet: www.figurentheater.de
E-Mail: VDPeV@aol.com
1. Vorsitzende Jörg Dreismann; Geschäftsführer Marianne Schoppan; Beisitzer Andreas Wahler
Role & Services: organisation of German professional puppet theatres, 130 members, publishes biannual specialist magazine; mobile exhibition; calendar of events; statistics of productions

Vereinigung Deutscher Opernchöre und Bühnentänzer e.V.
Opera Chorus Singers and Stage Dancers Guild of Germany
Kaiserstraße 39, 80801 **München**
Tel: 89-343 559 Fax: 89-343 560
Executive Director Stefan Meuschel; Legal Adviser Bruno Lehmann; Chairman of the Board Winfried Knoll
Role & Services: the purpose of the association is the advocacy, the aid and the advising of its members (including the copyright-protection); promotes the new recruits; an independent trade union federation

GREECE (+30)

Association For Business Support of Arts – OMEPO
19 Solonos Street, 106 71 **Athens**
Tel: 1-361 3907 Fax: 1-361 1085
chairperson Marlene Georgiades
Role & Services: promotion of the arts and culture through private enterprise, sponsorship and support
Comments: during 1999 Omepo suspended its activities in protest for the 20% tax imposed on sponsorship funds

Centre for Contempory Music Research (KSYME)
Phaneromenis 19, 155 62 **Athens**
Tel: 1-651 8895/654 4224 Fax: 1-651 8895
chairman John G. Papaioannou; director Stefanos Vassiliades
Role & Services: music education, research, composition, performances in concerts, festivals, seminars, international conferences: as relating principally to music (but also in collaboration with other arts) both traditional and Avant-Garde/contempory, using advanced scientific technological methods; conservation of archives of tradtional music

Greek Actors' Union
Somateion Hellenon Ethopoeon
Caningos 33, 106 82 **Athens**
Tel: 1-383 3742/381 1369
Fax: 1-380 8651
chair Anna Fonsou; secretary general Andreas Varouchas; public relations Antella Merminga
Role & Services: the protection and promotion of the economic, artistic, professional and social rights of actors; the promotion of theatric decentralisation and the support of theatrical experimentation and research; the protection of copyright, intellectual property and royalties of its members; administration of SHEE pension fund, organisation of seminars, workshops and drama performances *Comments:* member of International Federation of Actors

Greek Centre of International Federation of the Phonographic Industry (IFPI) / Association of Greek Producers of Phonogram
c/o MINOS EMI, Mesogion 245-247, 154 51 **Athens**
Tel: 1-679 2500 Fax: 1-675 6561
chairman Kostas Bourmas; vice-chairmen Ion Stamboulis, Yiannis Petridis; secretary general Dimitris Yarmenitis
Role & Services: member of the International Federation of the Phonographic Industry

Greek Centre of the Association du théâtre pour l'enfance et la jeunesse (ASSITEJ)
Theatro Porta, Mesoghion 59, 115 26 **Athens**
Tel: 1-724 0056 Fax: 1-724 0056
E-Mail: mporta@otenet.gr
president Xenia Kalogeropoulu
Role & Services: to promote children's and youth theatre; to facilitate communication among artists and people employed and interested in youth theatre; to organise seminars, conferences, festivals, etc.; manages the children's theatre library in Athens

Greek Centre of Union Internationale de la Marionette (UNIMA)
34, Psaroudaki Str, 106 45 **Athens**
Tel: 1-832 3714/861 4902 Fax: 1-832 3714
chairwoman Mina Sarri; secretary gral Stathis Markopoulos
Role & Services: enhancement and promotion of puppet-theatre as art and technique; the centre organises seminars, meetings, conferences, exhibitions and workshops among puppeteers; it is also responsible for the publication of the 'To Nima ' (The String) magazine

Greek Directors' Guild (Theatre, Cinema, TV)
Enosi Hellenon Skenotheton
Possitsa Street 11, 106 83 **Athens**
Tel: 1-822 3205 Fax: 1-821 1390
president Panayiotis Simonetatos; general secretary Giorgos Mulonas; international relations Panos Papakyriakopoulos
Role & Services: the support of its members in protecting and promoting their professional interests and intellectual property; support to its members in promoting their artistic interests and creative pursuits; the organisation of conferences, cultural events and seminars; the administration of its extensive film library and film club; publications concerning the history of audio-visual creation and filmographies
Comments: member of FERA and FISTAV

Greek Playwrights Society
Etaireia Hellenon Theatrikon Syggrafeon
Asklipiou 33, 106 80 **Athens**
Tel: 1-361 2766/7507 Fax: 1-361 4219
president Melpo Zarokosta
Role & Services: protection of copyright of the works of its members; legal assistance in royalties collection, copyright and intellectual property related matters; promotion of Modern Greek drama worldwide
Comments: est. 1908; current membership 460

Greek Section of Jeunesses Musicales
Stratigou Kallari 52, 154 52 **Athens-Psychico**
Tel: 1-671 2332 Fax: 1-231 4888
president Domini Sarris; vice-president Marilena Kerameus
Role & Services: the initiation of children and young people into music; to help young and talented music artists with studies and promotion of their work
Comments: organise 5-6 concerts per year and 10 concerts in schools in Crete; participate in World Youth Orchestra

Greek Union of Shadow Theatre
George 6, 106 77 **Athens**
Tel: 1-382 0586 Fax: 1-382 0586
Internet: surf.to/panos
chairman Dagiakos Yiannis
Role & Services: to provide representation and assistance to its members; promotion of the traditional art of shadow theatre (karaghiozis) through the organisation of conferences, exhibitions, performances and lectures; campaign for the establishment of a national shadow theatre and train new talent in the art
Comments: organise for the coming season: an exhibition of figures and sets from performers past and new, a series of lectures on the history of karaghiozis and a 26-episode documentary series to be presented on national TV about the origins and development of shadow theatre

Hellenic Centre of the International Theatre Institute (ITI)
9 Lyssiou Str., 105 56 **Athens**
president Aliki Bacopoulou-Halls; secretary general Lia Karavia
Role & Services: role is (a) to contribute to international collaboration on the development of theatre arts and (b) to promote Greek theatre arts, in all artistic and technical matters; activities include the organisation of international and local seminars, symposia, conferences, cultural exchanges; emphasis on promoting women's interests and in particular the international development of women playwrights *Comments:* 700 members, publish THESPIS and regular news bulletins; collection of information on Greek theatre (festivals, companies, publications etc); all members are theatre/music/dance professionals, many of whom are interested in collaborations with foreign artists and exchange visits; changed address, new telephone and fax numbers not available at time of going to print

Hellenic Society for the Protection of Intellectual Property (AEPI)
Fragoklissias & Samou 51, Amaroussio, 151 25 **Athens**
Tel: 1-685 7494/6 Fax: 1-685 1576
president George Mouzakis; managing director George Galanakis; general manager George Krippas; manager of legal and international affairs Peter Xanthopoulos; public relations Mary Fasoulaki
Role & Services: the protection of composers', authors', publishers' and performers' economic rights and intellectual property *Comments:* AEPI is a member of: CISAC (Confederation Internationale des Societes d'Auteurs et Compositeurs); BIEM (Bureau International des Societes Gerant les Droits d'Enregistrement et de Reproduction Mechanique); GESAC (Groupement Europeen des Societes d'Auteurs et Compositeurs)

International Music Section – Greek Section
Ethnikon Symvoulion Mousikis
Kallidromiou 18, 114 72 **Athens**
Tel: 1-360 3139 Fax: 1-361 8464
president Apostolos Kostios; general secretary Evi Mika-Sampson
Role & Services: co-ordination and consultation in matters of music policy; research and information gathering and dissemination; Greek representative in UNESCO's general council

Music Composers and Lyricists Union of Greece (EMSE)
Zoodochou Pigis 38-40, 106 81 **Athens**
Tel: 1-384 1548/382 8022 Fax: 1-382 8022
chairman Lefteris Papadopoulos; vice-chairman Christos Leontis; secretary general Theodoros Derveniotis; legal advisor and general manager George C Despotopoulos
Role & Services: to represent Greek composers and lyricists nationally and internationally; to protect their intellectual property; to collect royalties for performance, reproduction and other use of their work

Society of Authors of Dramatic & Audiovisual works (SADA)
Charilaou Trikoupi 46, 106 80 **Athens**
Tel: 1-361 8368/8371 Fax: 1-363 2127
Internet: www.sadamail.hol.gr
chairman of the board Giorgos Mylonas; general manager & head of legal department Stelios Kokolinakis; assistant general manager Kalliopi Sana
Role & Services: represents directors and scriptwriters; administers and manages the intellectual property of its members; the collection and distribution of royalties to its members for use of their intellectual property for broadcasting, public performance, copy (public and private) etc.; protection of related rights of its members

Union of Greek Singers
10 Sapfous Street, 105 53 **Athens**
Tel: 1-321 4916/0566 Fax: 1-321 1614
chairman Kostas Tournas; vice chairman Manolis Mitsias; treasurer Hatzikotaki Agni; secretary Kostas Skondras
Role & Services: main aim of U.G.S is to provide assistance to its members in legal matters (labour and contract disputes, tax matters, copyright infringements etc.); secondary objective is to promote their work internationally and be a point of contact between its members and overseas organisations, agents etc.; it also organises events consistent with its aims and role
Comments: member of International Federation of Actors

HUNGARY (+36)

ARTISJUS/ Agency for Theatre and Literature
PO Box 593, 1539 **Budapest**
Tel: 1-488 2706 (theatre)/342 0791 (music)
Fax: 1-488 2708 (theatre)/322 1267 (music)
theatre department – head Anita Kenedi; music department – head Adrienne Hartai
Comments: visiting address: Mészáros u. 15-17, 1016 Budapest; other address: Andrássy út 29, 1061 Budapest

Artpool Art Research Centre
Liszt Frerenc tér 10, 1061 **Budapest** VI
Tel: 1-268 0114 Fax: 1-321 0833
Internet: www.artpool.hu
E-Mail: artpool@artpool.hu
managing director Júlia Klaniczay; art director György Galántai
Role & Services: centre of documentation of Hungarian neo avant garde, international non-traditional and performance art

Association of Alternative Theatres
Rumbach Sebestyén utca 9, 1075 **Budapest** VII
Tel: 1-269 6610 Fax: 1-269 6609
E-Mail: rs9theater@compuserve.com
director Katalin Lábán
Role & Services: represents the interests of 40 members; arranges annual festivals of alternative theatres

Association of Hungarian Artistic Agencies
Magyarországi Müvészeti Ügynökségek Szövetsége
Rákóczi ut. 65, 1081 **Budapest**
Tel: 1-210 1249/333 2337
Fax: 1-333 2075
E-Mail: budfest@elender.hu
president Zsofia Zimanyi; general secretary Ildiko Gedenyi
Comments: organise occassional events

Association of Hungarian Choirs and Orchestras (KOTA)
102 Vigadó Irodaház, Vörösmartu tér 1, 1051 **Budapest**
Tel: 1-318 4918 Fax: 1-318 4906
president Gabor Baross; vice president Ágnes Vadasz
Role & Services: supports and coordinates semi-professional musical activities *Comments:* organisers of international choir competition

Association of Hungarian Concert Promoters
Magyar Hangversenyrendezök Egyesülete
Bathory 10, 1055 **Budapest**
Tel: 1-312 0857 Fax: 1-312 0857
president Kalman Strem

Association of Hungarian Music and Art Schools
Rottenbiller utca 16-22, 1074 **Budapest** VII
Tel: 1-352 1547/8 Fax: 1-352 1547/8
president Lázsló Némes; executive secretary Zsuzsanna Kollarik

Association of Hungarian Record Companies
Magyar Hanglemezkiadók Szövetsége (MAHASZ)
Falk Miksa 24/26, 1055 **Budapest**
Tel: 1-266 3076 Fax: 1-353 0008
president Laszlo Pasztor (1-131 2528/132 7707); managing director Dr Agnes Musinger; treasurer Miklós Deák

Association of Hungarian Symphony Orchestras
Magyar Szimfonikus Zenekarok Szövetsége
Városligeti fasor 38, 1068 **Budapest**
Tel: 1-342 8927 Fax: 1-342 8372
president Peter Popa

Budapest Music Centre
Lonyay utca 41, 1093 **Budapest** IX
Tel: 1-216 7896 Fax: 1-326 7895
Internet: www.bmc.hu/
E-Mail: musiccenter@bmc.hu
director László Göz
Role & Services: record publishing; cultural management; dissemination of information on Hungarian music; Hungarian musical database

C3 Centre for Culture and Communication
Országhaz utca 9, 1014 **Budapest**
Tel: 1-214 6856 Fax: 1-214 6872
Internet: www.c3.hu
E-Mail: info@c3.hu
director Miklós Peternák
Role & Services: introducing and developing technological trends in art and culture *Comments:* part of Soros Foundations

Contemporary Dance Theatre Association (CDTA)
Kortárs Táncszínházi Egyesület
Körösy J. u. 17, 1117 **Budapest**
Tel: 1-209 4016 Fax: 1-209 4016
E-Mail: kortanc@elender.hu
secretary Beáta Barda; intern. affairs Beatrice Rossi, György Szabó
Role & Services: the CDTA was formed in 1990 by the initiative of Hungarian artists, pedagogues and organizers working in the field of contemporary dance as a response to the growing needs of Hungary's dance community; the aim of the CDTA is to serve these independent artists working among difficult circumstances and to encourage their development; the main activity fields of CDTA is the representation of interests and lobby; contacts with the national and international fields; information service; documentation and resources, organising festivals and platforms

Dance Forum
Táncfórum
Corvin ter. 8, 1011 **Budapest**
Tel: 1-201 8779 Fax: 1-201 5128
E-Mail: tforum@mail.c3.hu
director Tibor Galambos
Role & Services: an institute providing venues and forum for young performers and choreographers, new and small/contemporary, alternative avantgarde dance groups; also classical ballet, folk dance, jazz dance

Forum of Hungarian Musicians
Magyar Muzsikusok Foruma
Vörösmarty ter.1, 1051 **Budapest**
Tel: 1-267 3316 Fax: 1-267 3316
president Jozsef Tothpal
Comments: postal address:
Vörösmarty tér 1, 1051 Budapest

Hungarian Actors' Society
Városligeti fasor 38, 1068 **Budapest**
Tel: 1-342 0146 Fax: 1-342 0146
president Tamás Végvári; secretary general Ágnes Nánássy
Comments: see also Hungarian Theatre Society

Hungarian Art Festival Federation
Magyar Müvészeti Fesztiválok Szövetsége
POB 80, 1366 **Budapest**
Tel: 1-318 8165 Fax: 1-318 8165
executive secretary Gabor Palfy; president András Lukovics
Comments: visiting address: Vörösmarty ter 1, 1051 Budapest

Hungarian Centre of International Amateur Theatre Association (IATA)
Magyar M velödési Intézet
Pf. 33, 1951 **Budapest**
Tel: 1-201 3766 Fax: 1-201 5764
Hungarian representative Lajos Máté
Comments: representative's address: Lajos Máté, Corvin tér 8, 1011 Budapest

Hungarian Centre of the Association du théâtre pour l'enfance et la jeunesse (ASSITEJ)
c/o Budapest Bábszínház, Andrássy út 69, 1062 **Budapest**
Tel: 1-322 5051/321 5200 Fax: 1-342 4765
president Judit Nyilassy; managing secretary János Meczner

Hungarian Centre of the International Theatre Institute (ITI)
PO Box 23, 1253 **Budapest**
Tel: 1-212 5247 Fax: 1-212 5247
E-Mail: itihun@freemail.c3.hu
president András Nagy; vice-president Janos Novak
Comments: Hungarian member-representative of ITI; visiting address: Krisztina Krt 57, 1016 Budapest

Hungarian Centre of Union Internationale de la Marionette (UNIMA)
Hungarian member of the Excom Dr Dezsö Szilágyi, c/o Budapest Bábszínház (Budapest Puppet Theatre), Andrássy út 69, 1062 **Budapest**
Tel: 1-351 1323 Fax: 1-342 4765
secretary Eva Mogyorósi

Hungarian Composers' Union
Magyar Zeneszerzök Egyesülete
PO Box 228, 1364 **Budapest**
Tel: 1-338 4139 Fax: 1-338 4139
president Máté Hollós; secretary Irene Bacskai; director Irén Bácskai
Comments: visiting address: Vörösmarty ter 1, 1051 Budapest

Hungarian Cultural Association
Magyar Kulturális Szövetség
Miklós tér 1., 1035 **Budapest**
Tel: 1-368 7228 Fax: 1-368 7228
Internet: www.port.hu/kultural/mksz/index_bd.htm
E-Mail: krisar@mksz
president József Zelnik

Hungarian Dancers' Association
Magyar Táncmüvészek Szövetsége
PO Box 21, 1406 **Budapest**
Tel: 1-342 9865 Fax: 1-342 9865
Internet: www.elender.hu/~danceass
E-Mail: danceass@elender.hu
president Gyula Harangozo; co-president Ferenc Sebö; managing directors Jenö Löcsei, Jolan Török
Comments: visiting address: Városligeti Fasor 38, 1068 Budapest

Hungarian Film & TV Artists' Association
Magyar Film és TV Müvészek Szövetsége
PO Box 21, 1406 **Budapest**
Tel: 1-342 4760
Fax: 1-342 4760
secretary general Gergely Horvath-Z, László Lugossy; president György Illes; managing director Krisztina Hermann
Comments: visiting address: Városligeti fasor 38, 1068 Budapest

Hungarian Institute of Culture
Magyar Müvelödési Intézet
Corvin tér 8, 1011 **Budapest** I
Tel: 1-201 3766/5782 Fax: 1-201 5764
Internet: www.mmi.hu
E-Mail: mmi@mmi.hu
director András Földiák (tel: 1-201 5053); deputy director Erika Borbáth (tel: 1-214 3524); head department of performing & visual arts Péter Lágler (tel: 1-201 4892); head department of folk arts Éva Héra (tel: 1-201 4492); head professional house of folk dancers Annamária Neuwirth (tel: 1-212-2883); head of international section Dorottya Lukácsy (tel: 1-212 5782); head research library & information centre Mária Hargitai (tel: 1-201 8973)
Role & Services: support non-formal cultural education around Hungary

Hungarian Music Council
Magyar Zenei Tanács
PO Box 47, 1364 **Budapest**
Tel: 1-318 4243/317 9598 Fax: 1-317 8267
Internet: www.c3.hu/~hmic/
E-Mail: hmic@mail.c3.hu
president Adrienne Csengery; general secretary Éva Csébfalvy; vice-president László Gyimesi
Role & Services: Hungarian member of the International Music Council (UNESCO) *Comments:* visiting address: Vörösmarty tér 1, 1051 Budapest

Hungarian Section of Jeunesses Musicales
Ifjú Zenebarátok Magyarországi Szervezete
c/o Interart Fesztiválcenter, Vörösmarty tér 1, 1051 **Budapest**
Tel: 1-317 5291 Fax: 1-317 9910
president Beáta Schanda; secretary general Eszter Fehér

Hungarian Theatre Institute and Museum
Országos Színházttörténeti Múzeum és Intézet
Krisztina krt. 57, 1013 **Budapest**
Tel: 1-375 2372/5190/1184 Fax: 1-375 1184
director Dr. Péter Müller

Hungarian Theatre Society
Magyar Színházi Társaság
Városligeti fasor 38, 1068 **Budapest**
Tel: 1-342 0146 Fax: 1-342 0146
managing director Márta Vajda
Comments: umbrella organisation for Hungarian Actors' Society (q.v.), Hungarian Directors' Society and Hungarian Playwrights Society

Hungarian Theatre Workers` Union
Szinhazi Dolgozók Szakszervezete
Városligeti fasor 38, 1068 **Budapest**
Tel: 1-342 9944 Fax: 1-342 9944
president Antal Konrád; secretary Sándor Döme
Comments: member of International Federation of Actors

Hungarian Writers Union, Playwrights` Section
Bajza u. 18, 1062 **Budapest**
Tel: 1-322 0631 Fax: 1-321 3419
president Károly Szakonyi

Hungary National Commision for UNESCO
Szalay Utca 10-14-/108 Oktatási Miniszterium, 1054 **Budapest** V
Tel: 1-269 1723 Fax: 1-331 5326
E-Mail: mihaly.rozsa@mkm.x400gw.itb.hu
chairman György Enyedi; secretary Mihály Rózsa

Institute of Contemporary Arts
Vasmü út 12, 2400 **Dunaúsváros**
Tel: 25-404 690 Fax: 25-312 220
Internet: www.ica-d.hu
E-Mail: ica-d@dunanet.hu
general dir. Janos Szoboszlai; artistic dir. Livia Páldi
Role & Services: multi-functional, organises and coordinates international art projects; cooperation with artists and theoreticians

Interart Festivalcenter – National Centre of International Music Competitions and Festivals
Vörösmarty tér 1, PO Box 80, 1366 **Budapest**
Tel: 1-266 3108 Fax: 1-317 9910
director Beáta Schanda

Union of Hungarian Puppeteers
Magyar Bábjátékos Egyesület
Corvin tér 1, 1011 **Budapest**
Tel: 1-375 5190 Fax: 1-375 1184
president Gábor Siklósi; secretary Mária Bánhidi

World Association of Hungarian Musicians and Dancers
Benczúr Utca, 15, 1068 **Budapest** VI
Tel: 1-268 1059 Fax: 1-351 7950
president Zsolt Durkó; secretary Ibolya Csikós
Role & Services: coordinates activities of Hungarian artists throughout the world

ICELAND (+354)

Association of Icelandic Musicians
Félag Íslenskra Hljómlistarmanna
Raudagerdi 27, 108 **Reykjavík**
Tel: 588 8255 Fax: 588 8215
Internet: www.fih.is
E-Mail: fih@fih.is
chairman and manager Björn Arnason
Role & Services: Icelandic musicians union, main aim is to provide legal assistance to its members as well as general guidance

Association of Icelandic Stage, Film and TV Directors
Félag leikstjóra a islandi
Lindargötu 6, 101 **Reykjavík**
Tel: 562 1025/553 9590
Fax: 562 7706
E-Mail: leikstjorar@ismennt.is
chairman Pétur Einarsson
Role & Services: negotiate contracts with theatres, TV & radio for its members; aims to further the profession through seminars & discussions; to protect the royalty rights of its members

Association of Mixed Choirs
Samband blandadra kóra
Söngskólinn í Reykjavík, Hverfisgata 45, 101 **Reykjavík**
Tel: 552 7366 Fax: 552 5966
head Gardar Cortes

Federation of Icelandic Artists
Bandalag Íslenskra Listamanna
PO Box 637, 121 **Reykjavík**
Tel: 552 2620 Fax: 564 4717
president Hjálmar H. Ragnarsson
Role & Services: to be a collective force in promoting the Arts in the country; to guard the artists' interests and strengthen co-operation between them; to be an adviser and intermediary in cultural and artistic matters for the Ministry of Culture and Parliament; 1950 members
Comments: established 1928

Iceland Music Information Centre (MIC)
Íslensk Tónverkamidstöd (ITM)
Sídumúla 34, 108 **Reykjavík**
Tel: 568 3122 Fax: 568 3124
Internet: www.mic.is
E-Mail: icemic@vortex.is
director Bergthora Jonsdottir
Role & Services: archive of all Icelandic classical music recordings and sheet music some of which are published; Information on Icelandic music, compositions,composers, performers, festivals and icelandic music life in general

Icelandic Actors Association
Felag Islenskra Leikara
Lindargötu 6, 101 **Reykjavík**
Tel: 552 6040 Fax: 562 7706
Internet: www.actors-union.is
E-Mail: office@actors-union.is
president Edda Thorarinsdöttir; secretary June E Clark
Role & Services: union for performing artists. Member of International Federation of Actors

Icelandic Centre of International Federation of the Phonographic Industry (IFPI)
Samband Hljómplötuframleidenda
Fonogrambolagens Förbund
PO Box 150, 172 **Seltjarnarnes**
Tel: 561 8065 Fax: 561 8066
E-Mail: sfh@islandia.is
secretary & legal adviser Gunnar Gudmundsson
Comments: member of the International Federation of the Phonographic Industry

Icelandic Centre of the Association du théâtre pour l'enfance et la jeunesse (ASSITEJ)
Moguleikhùsid, Laugavegur 105, 105 **Reykjavík**
Tel: 562 2669 Fax: 562 2669
E-Mail: ml@islandia.is
contact Pêtur Eggerz

Icelandic Centre of Union Internationale de la Marionette (UNIMA)
UNIMA Iceland
Blonduhlid 10, 105 **Reykjavík**
Tel: 552 5098 Fax: 552 5098
president Margret Kolka; secretary Helga Steffensen; treasurer Sigrun Jonsdottir

Icelandic Theatre Union – Centre of the International Theatre Institute (ITI)
Leiklistarsamband Islands
c/o National Theatre of Iceland, Lindargata 7, 101 **Reykjavík**
Tel: 551 1204 Fax: 561 1200
president Stefan Baldursson; secretary general Torhallur Sigurdsson
Role & Services: 'Theater in Iceland' is published bi-annually

Performing Right Society of Iceland
Samband tónskálda og eigenda flutningsréttar (STEF)
Laufásvegur 40, 101 **Reykjavík**
Tel: 561 6173 Fax: 562 6273
Internet: www.listis.is/stef/
E-Mail: stef@stef.is
director Eiríkur Tómasson; chairman Kjartan Olafsson

SFH
PO Box 150, 172 **Seltjarnarnes**
Tel: 561 8065 Fax: 561 8066
contact Gunnar Gudmundsson
Role & Services: independent organisation for the administration of neighbouring rights

Society of Icelandic Composers – Iceland Section of the International Society for Contemporary Music (ISCM)
Tónskáldafelag Islands
Laufásvegur 40, 101 **Reykjavík**
Tel: 552 4972 Fax: 562 6273
E-Mail: tonskald@centrum.is
president Kjartan Olafsson
Role & Services: protects and furthers the artistic and economic rights of Icelandic composers; its president is a member of the Nordic Composers Council *Comments:* Tonskaldafelag Islands holds biennial festival of contemporary music: Dark Music Days Festival (q.v.)

IRELAND Republic of (+353)

Association of Irish Choirs
Drinan Str., **Cork**
Tel: 21-312 296 Fax: 21-962 457
E-Mail: cnc@iol.ie
administration Barbara Heas
Role & Services: established in 1980; national organisation which provides for the needs of amateur Irish Choirs and their conductors; register of nationwide choirs; organises regional courses and an annual summer school for choral conducters and teachers; organises the Irish Youth Choir (mixed, 17-29 years); publishes Choral music; issues a newsletter for members

Association of Irish Composers – Irish Section of the International Society for Contemporary Music
Copyright House, Pembroke Row, **Dublin** 2
Tel: 1-496 1484 Fax: 1-496 1484
E-Mail: aic@tinet.ie
executive director John Mclachlan
Role & Services: the AIC is the representative body for composers and contemporary music in Ireland; it promotes and fosters Irish contemporary music and obtains support and recognition for composers and their work both in Ireland and internationally
Comments: AIC is funded by IMRO (the Irish Music Rights Organisation) and the Arts Council/An Chomhairle Ealaíon

Contemporary Music Centre
95 Lower Baggot Street, **Dublin** 2
Tel: 1-661 2105 Fax: 1-676 2639
Internet: www.cmc.ie
E-Mail: info@cmc.ie
director Eve O'Kelly; information and outreach manager Jonathan Grimes
Role & Services: promotes and documents Irish contemporary music

Cothú – The Business Council for the Arts
64 Lower Mount Street, **Dublin** 2
Tel: 1-676 6966 Fax: 1-676 6997
chief executive Bridget Ruden; chairman Kevin J Kelly; director of programmes Sharon Stanfords
Role & Services: Cothú's mission is to foster and encourage creative partnership between business and the arts for the mutual benefit of the partners and of the wider community;
to promote and encourage arts sponsorship Cothú runs the Arts Sponsor of the Year Awards; publishes the National Arts Sponsorship Survey; engages in research and provides ongoing sponsorship advice to business, the PR industry and arts organisations;
Cothú is the most important provider of managment and business training to the arts community in Ireland; the training is provided under the INFORM programme which provides access free of charge, to training courses run by member companies, for arts managers and administrators;
Cothú also organises a programme of social and cultural events to develop contacts between business and the arts

Early Music Organisation of Ireland
Kilballyquilty, Carrick-on-Suir, **Waterford**
Tel: 51-646 286 Fax: 51-646 286
chair Siobhán Armstrong; secretary Maura Uí Chróinín; treasurer Lindsay Armstrong
Role & Services: founded in 1986, The Early Music Organisation of Ireland is a non-profit making all-Ireland organisation; it supports performance and educational opportunities in all areas of early music and provides an Irish forum and information point for people interested in early music; the definition of early music is broad, with an emphasis on historically informed performance; EMOI produces a quarterly newsletter called Early Music Ireland and a Register of Early Music in Ireland; EMOI is also currently organising a vocal and instrumental tuition scheme

Irish Actors Equity Group
S.I.P.T.U., Liberty Hall, **Dublin** 1
Tel: 1-874 0081 Fax: 1-874 3691
E-Mail: equity@siptu.ie
group secretary Gerard Browne; president Robert Carrickford
Role & Services: the only performers trade union for stage, screen, radio, tv and cabaret in Ireland

Irish Centre of the Association du théâtre pour l'enfance et la jeunesse (ASSITEJ)
c/o Graffiti Theatre Company, The Weightmaster's House, 2 Church Street, Shandon, **Cork**
Tel: 21-397 111 Fax: 21-397 110
E-Mail: graffiti@tinet.ie
contact Emelie FitzGibbon

Irish Centre of the International Theatre Institute (ITI)
c/o Steve Wilmer, Beckett Centre, Trinity College, Dublin University, **Dublin** 2
Tel: 1-608 1441/702 1239 Fax: 1-679 3488
contact Steve Wilmer
Role & Services: liaises between Irish and international theatre organisations, practitioners and scholars

Irish Recorded Music Association (IRMA)
IRMA House, Corrig Avenue 1, **Dun Laoghaire**
Tel: 1-280 6571 Fax: 1-280 6579
Internet: www.iol.ie/~ppiltd/
E-Mail: info@PPiltd.com
chairman Dennis Woods; secretary Riobard Mac Górían; director general Dick Doyle

Irish Traditional Music Archive
Taisce Cheol Dúchais Éireann
63 Merrion Square, **Dublin** 2
Tel: 1-661 9699
Fax: 1-662 4585
Internet: www.itma.ie
director Nicholas Carolan
Role & Services: collection, preservation, organisation, and provision of access to the materials of Irish traditional music; provision of public access, advice to researchers, information service etc.

Music Network
Coach House, Dublin Castle, **Dublin** 2
Tel: 1-671 9429/30
Fax: 1-671 9430
E-Mail: info@musicnet.ie
chief executive John O'Kane; performance programme manager Catherine Carey; PR manager Assumpta Lawless; regional development manager Orla Moloney; research & resourcing manager Peter Mangan
Role & Services: national organisation established and funded by the Irish Arts Council with a brief to develop music in the regions; runs a series of 14-16 nationwide concert tours of classical, jazz and traditional music (totalling 150 performances) integrated with educational activities and also works in the field of regional promoter development and support; offers a comprehensive computerised information service which is also available in publication form as The Irish Music Handbook and the Directory of Musicians in Ireland; through it's regional development programme Music County 2000 it also aims to facilitate long terms plans for music development, access and participation at local level; see also entry under Promoters
Comments: patron: President of Ireland, Mary McAleese

ITALY (+39)

Association of Italian Traditional Theatres
Associazione Teatri Italiani di Tradizione (ATIT)
via di Villa Patrizi 10, 00161 **Roma**
Tel: 06-884 731 (switchboard)/73253 (secretary)
Fax: 06-440 4254
presidente Alfonso Malaguti; vice presidente Angela Cauzzi

Associazione dei Fonografici Italiani (AFI)
Via Vittor Pisani 10, 20124 **Milano**
Tel: 02-669 6263 Fax: 02-670 5059
Internet: www.afi.mi.it
E-Mail: afi@afi.mi.it
presidente Franco Bixio
Role & Services: promote and protect the rights of the independent musical producers

Associazione Nazionale Enti Lirici e Sinfonici (ANELS)
via di Villa Patrizi 10, 00161 **Roma**
Tel: 06-884 731 (switchboard)/73253 (secretary)
Fax: 06-440 4254
presidente Lorenzo Jorio

Associazione Nazionale Esercizi Teatrali (ANET)
Via di Villa Patrizi 10, 00161 **Roma**
Tel: 06-884 731 (switchboard)
Fax: 06-440 4254
presidente Giovanni Lippi; vice presidente Lucio Mirra, Franco Ghizzo; componenti consiglio direttivo Luigi Foscale, Carmelo Grassi, Elio Schiavoni

CIDIM – Comitato Nazionale Italiano Musica (UNESCO)
Largo di Torre Argentina, 11, 00186 **Roma**
Tel: 06-681 9061 Fax: 06-6819 0651
Internet: www.cidim.it
E-Mail: cidim.italia@flashnet.it
president Francesco Agnello; responsabile annuario Patrizia Cea
Role & Services: gives information on all aspects of musical life in Italy; promotes young Italian artists in Italy and abroad; annual magazine 'Fonti Musicali Italiane' with Italian Society of Musicology, editors of Annuario Musicale and of the only data bank for music in Italy *Comments:* member of the International Music Council

Comitato Lombardia Europa Musica 2000 (CLEM)
c/o CAMTAM, Villa Olmo, Via Cantoni 1,22100 **Como**
Tel: 031-571 150 Fax: 031-570 540
E-Mail: camtam@galactica.it
direttore artistico Italo Gomez
Role & Services: organises and promotes musical activities in Lombardy, including Il Canto delle Pietre, medieval music festival, collaborates with other European cultural organisations on festivals outside Italy *Comments:* registered office: Via Cavur 66, 26900 Lodi

Entertainment Information Federation
Federazione Informazione Spettacolo e Telecomunicazioni – FISTEL
Via Palestro 30, 00185 **Roma**
Tel: 06-492 171 Fax: 06-445 7330
E-Mail: fistelnaz@cisl.it
segretario generale Fulvio Giacomassi; responsible settore artistico Romolo Barbona
Role & Services: performing arts trade union, looking after the needs of people employed in the field of cultural productions, entertainments and telecommunication

Federation of Theatre, Music, Dance & Film Festivals
Federazione di Festival di Teatro, Musica, Danza e Cinema (FEDERFESTIVAL)
via di Villa Patrizi 10, 00161 **Roma**
Tel: 06-880 2402 Fax: 06-440 4254
presidente Gisella Belgeri

Federazione Industria Musicale Italiana (FIMI) / Italian Centre of International Federation of the Phonographic Industry(IFPI)
Largo Augusto 3, 20122 **Milano**
Tel: 02-795 879 Fax: 02-799 673
Internet: www.fimi.it
E-Mail: enzo.mazza@fimi.it
presidente Alberto Poyaghi; direttore generale Enzo Mazza

Fourth Area
Quarta Area
Via di Villa Patrizi 10, 00161 **Roma**
Tel: 06-884 731 (switchboard)/73255 (secretary)
Fax: 06-440 4254
presidente Monica Gattini Bernabó; vice presidente vicario Renato Quaglia; vice presidente Angelo Curti

General Association of Italian Entertainment
Associazione Generale Italiana Dello Spettacolo (AGIS)
via di Villa Patrizi 10, 00161 **Roma**
Tel: 06-884 731 (switchboard) Fax: 06-440 4257
presidente Giorgio van Straten; segretario generale Paolo Manca; capo ufficio stampa Luigi Filippi; 06-884 731 (switchboard)/73261 (secretary)

International Association of Dance Teachers
Associazione Nazionale Insegnanti di Danza (ANID)
via A. Gramsci 36, 00197 **Roma**
Tel: 06-323 0263 Fax: 06-361 1889
presidente Anna Maria Cerullo
Role & Services: aims to promote dance; awards annual prizes; ANID also organises follow ups for dance teachers; open Monday-Wednesday + Friday only, from 10.00 to 14.00

International Society for Contemporary Music – Italian Section
Societa Italiana Musica Contemporanea (SIMC)
via F Juvara 11, 20129 **Milano**
Tel: 02-7060 0837 Fax: 02-7060 0837
presidente Giuseppe Garbarino; segretario Vittorio Fellegara

Italian Actors Society
Sindacato Attori Italiani (SAI)
via Ofanto, 18, 00198 **Roma**
Tel: 06-841 7303/1288 Fax: 06-854 6780
Internet: cgil.it/sai-slc
E-Mail: sai-slc@cgil.it
segretario generale Massimo Ghini; segretario aggiunto Massimo Cestaro; segretario nazionale Nicoletta Rizzi
Comments: part of the FIA (International Federation of Actors)

Italian Association of Authors and Editors
Societá Italiana degli Autori ed Editori (SIAE)
Viale della Letteratura n° 30, 00144 **Roma**
Tel: 06-59901 (switchboard) Fax: 06-5964 7052/50
Internet: www.siea.it
presidente t.b.a.; direzione generale Francesco Chirighigno; capo ufficio stampa Sapo Matteucci (tel: 599 0695/7, fax: 599 0093, email: press@siae.it)
Role & Services: member of Groupement Européen des Sociétés d'Auteurs et Compositeurs (q.v.); member of Confederation Internationale des Sociétés d'Auteurs et Compositeurs.S.I.A.E has 800 agencies and 45 branches, coordinated by 14 regional head offices, and is linked to 100 copyright societies over the five continents by reciprocal representation contracts; among S.I.A.E s functions are : the issue of licences and authorizations for the economic utilization of protected works; the collection, distribution and payment to the persons entitled to the profits derived from the works entrusted to it for protection; the S.I.A.E also edits numerous publications of a juridicial, economic and social nature

Italian Association of Concert Activity
Associazione Italiana Attivita Musical (AIAM)
via di Villa Patrizi 10, 00161 **Roma**
Tel: 06-884 731 (switchboard)/73253 (secretary)
Fax: 06-440 4254
presidente Francesco Agnello; vice presidenti Lucio Fupo, Gianni Antonioni

Italian Association of Dance Activities (AIAD)
Associazione Italiana Attivita di Danza (AIAD)
via di Villa Patrizi 10, 00161 **Roma**
Tel: 06-884 731 (switchboard)/73253 (secretary)
Fax: 06-440 4254
presidente Riccardo Bozzi; vice presidente Paola Leoni

Italian Association of Representatives of Concert & Entertainment Artists (ARIACS)
Associazione dei Rappresentanti Italiani degli Artisti di Concerti e Spettacoli (ARIACS)
ORIA snc, Via Savoia Cavalleria, 10, 20143 **Milano**
Tel: 02-466 239
presidente Denise Petriccione; consiglieri Raffaella Coletti, Giuseppe Oldani, Ettore Volontieri
Comments: second address: sede legale c/o Avvocato Michele Lai, Via G.La. Farina, 15, 50132 Firenze

Italian Centre of the Association du théâtre pour l'enfance et la jeunesse (ASSITEJ)
c/o Testoni Ragazzi – Centro Teatro ed Arte per L'Infanzia e la Gioventú, Via Matteotti 16, 40129 **Bologna**
Tel: 051-379 000 Fax: 051-377 851
E-Mail: testrag@iperbole.bologna.it
presidente Lucio D'Amelio; direttore artistico Valeria Frabetti
Role & Services: offers information and support to all those employed in the sphere of children's and young people's theatre

Italian Centre of the International Theatre Institute (ITI)
Istituto Internazionale del Teatro ITI Centro Italiano
via della Consulta 1, 00184 **Roma**
Tel: 06-4890 4651(from 10am-2pm)
Fax: 06-485 600
presidente Maurizio Giammusso; segretaria Silvia Signorelli; vice presidente Guiseppe Battista

Italian Centre of Union Internationale de la Marionnette (UNIMA)
c/o Cesare Felici, Largo Lucio Apuleio 5, 00136 **Roma**
Tel: 06-3972 7944 Fax: 06-3972 7944
Internet: unima-it.org
E-Mail: cfelici@freemail.it
presidente Otello Sarzi: via Adua 47, 42100 Reggio Emilia, tel: 522-511 826; vicepresidente Cesare Felici; segretario nazionale Enrico Spinelli
Comments: founded 1980; they publish a magazine four times a year

Italian National Council for Dance
Consiglio Nazionale Italiano della Danza (CNID)
Corso Re Umberto 77, 10128 **Torino**
Tel: 011-568 3913 Fax: 011-502 238
presidente Susanna Egri; vicepresident Anna Maria Prina

Italian Section of Jeunesse Musicales
Gioventu'Musicale d'Italia
via Santa Croce 4, 20122 **Milano**
Tel: 02-8940 0840/8 Fax: 02-5810 3697
Internet: www.jeunesse.it
E-Mail: jeunesse@tin.it
presidente Lando Lanni della Quara; consigliere delegato Maria Luisa Vanin Tarantino
Role & Services: promote about 500 concerts annually (chamber music, recitals, jazz)

Italian State Theatre Board
Ente Teatrale Italiano (ETI)
Via in Arcione, 98, 00187 **Roma**
Tel: 06-699 511 Fax: 06-679 7493
Internet: www.enteteatrale.it
E-Mail: eti@enteteatrale.it
commissario straordinario Prof Lorenzo Tian; direttore generale Dr. ssa Giovanna Marinelli
Role & Services: promotion of theatre in Italy, managing the seasons of different venues (historical theatre in Rome, Florence, Bologna and in other towns); development of theatre in the whole country with special events dedicated to the new generation, theatre for young, international training courses; to increase the mutual theatre exchange with other countries realizing an international early theatre festival called Percorsi Internazionali in Italy and other special projects

National Association of Jazz Musicians (AMJ)
Associazione Nazionale Musicisti di Jazz (AMJ)
Fortezza Medicea, 53100 **Siena**
Tel: 0577-271 401 Fax: 0577-271 404
Internet: www.sienajazz.si.it
E-Mail: sj@comune.siena.it
presidente Nicola Pisani; vicepresidente Alessandro Fabbri; segretario Luca Losi
Role & Services: publishes a biannual bulletin with a wide range of information for jazz musicians and a catalogue of Italian jazz musicians; among their activities is the L.I.R.A. (Libera Iniziativa ricerca Artistica) which deals with the organization and the management of 36 festivals in Italy which are meant to promote the diffusion and research in the jazz music field in Italy; they have an orchestra named Goami Orchestra Nazionale Ami

National Association of Orchestral Concert Institutions
Associazione Nazionale Istituzioni Concertistiche Orchestrali (ICO)
Via di Villa Patrizi 10, 00161 **Roma**
Tel: 06-884 731 (switchboard)/73253 (secretary)
Fax: 06-440 4254
presidente Giovanni Ondertoller; vice presidente Vittorio Antonellini

National Association of Performing Arts' Venues
Associazione Nazionale Teatri di Arte Drammatica (ANTAD)
Via di Villa Patrizi 10, 00161 **Roma**
Tel: 06-884 731 (switchboard) Fax: 06-440 4254
presidente Ivo Chiesa; vice presidente Mauro Carbonoli, Agostino Re Rebaudengo
Role & Services: association of owners of arts venues and performing art companies (Dance, Theatre, Music)

National Association of Private Independent Theatres
Associazione Nazionale Teatro Privato Indipendente (ANTPI)
Via di Villa Patrizi 10, 00161 **Roma**
Tel: 06-884 731 Fax: 06-440 4254
presidente Fioravante Cozzaglio; vice presidenti Maurizio Panici, Paolo Cattin

National Association of Regional Theatre Activity
Associazione Nazionale Attivita' Regionali Teatrali (ANART)
Via di Villa Patrizi 10, 00161 **Roma**
Tel: 06-884 731 (switchboard)/73255 (secretary)
Fax: 06-440 4254
presidente Crescenzo Gentile; vice presidente vicario Mario del Bello; vice presidente Vincenzo D'Onofrio

Private Theatres Association
Associazione Teatri Stabili Privati (ANTS d'Interesse Pubblico)
Via di Villa Patrizi 10, 00161 **Roma**
Tel: 06-884 731 (switchboard)/73255 (secretary)
Fax: 06-440 4254
presidente Giuseppe Battista; vice presidente Elio de Capitani

Sindacato Lavoratori Comunicazione (SLC)
Piazza Sallustio, 24, 00187 **Roma**
Tel: 06-421 071 Fax: 06-482 4325
Internet: cgl.it/slc
E-Mail: slc@mail.cgl.it
segretario generale Fulvio Fammoni
Comments: the Trade Union represents all the workers of the various media fields from the technicians who build the telecommunication web to the cultural and artistic operations; they are part of the CGL

LATVIA (+371)

Contemporary Art Center of the Soros Foundtion – Riga, The
Latvijas Sorosa fonda Musdienu makslas centrs – Riga
11 Novembra krastmala 35-201, 1050 **Riga**
Tel: 7-228 478 Fax: 7-820 252
E-Mail: iboiko@sfl-paic.lv
director Janis Borgs

Culture Capital Foundation
Latvijas Kulturkapitala Fonds
Pils iela 20, 1050 **Riga**
Tel: 7-503 177 Fax: 7-503 176
E-Mail: kkf@parks.lv
director Maris Berzins
Role & Services: support and promote development of creative activity in all branches of cultura and arts, acquiring of education, and preserving of cultural heritage *Comments:* see also Promoters

E Melngailis Folk Art Centre
E Melngaila Tautas Makslas Centrs
4 Pils laukums, 1050 **Riga**
Tel: 7-228 985 Fax: 7-227 405
director Janis Kurpnieks
Comments: a state institution, implementing state cultural policy in the field of amateur art and traditional culture, coordinates amateur art activities and renders methodological help to amateur and folk art groups; centre organises festivals and other events; see also Festivals

Foundation for Creative Work
Jaunrades fonds, RLB, Merkela iela 13, 1050 **Riga**
Tel: 7-226 267 Fax: 7-226 267
president Dzemma Skulme

International Cinema Centre
Starptautiskais Kino centrs
Marstalu 14, 1050 **Riga**
Tel: 7-210 114 Fax: 7-820 445
E-Mail: arsenals@latnet.lv
director Augusts Sukuts

International New Music Centre
Starptautiskais Jaunas muzikas centrs
Jelgavas 25, 1004 **Riga**
Tel: 7-828 538 Fax: 7-828 538
director Egils Straume

Latvian Artists' Union
Latvijas Makslinieku Savieniba
11 Novembra Krastmala 35, 1050 **Riga**
Tel: 7-228 497 Fax: 7-226 066
E-Mail: lms@re-lab.net.
president Egils Rozenbergs

Latvian Association of Architects
Latvijas Arhitektu Savieniba
11 Tornu, 1855 **Riga**
Tel: 7-212 802 Fax: 7-223 902
chairman Juris Poga

Latvian Association of Brass Bands
Latvijas Puteju orkestru asociacija
Maza Smilsu iela 8, 1050 **Riga**
Tel: 7-210 504 Fax: 7-225 039
E-Mail: lulc@lanet.lv
president Janis Purins
Role & Services: membership consists of conductors and musicians of symphonic and wind ensembles,music teachers of music schools; organise seminars, lessons, courses and meetings for conductors

Latvian Centre of the International Theatre Institute (ITI)
Starptautiska Teatra instituta Latvijas centrs
RLB, 13 Merkela, 1050 **Riga**
Tel: 7-212 622/471 Fax: 7-212 471
E-Mail: guna_iti@latnet.lv
contact Guna Zeltina

Latvian Choir Association
Latvijas koru asociacija
Merkela 13, 1050 **Riga**
Tel: 7-226 924 Fax: 7-226 924
president Juris Klavins
Comments: independent organisation for amateur choirs, uniting 43 choirs from different regions, member of the International Choir Organisation EUROPACANTAT

Latvian Cinematographers' Union
Latvijas Kinematografistu savieniba
Elizabetes 49, 1010 **Riga**
Tel: 7-288 536 Fax: 7-240 545
chairman Valdis Eglitis

Latvian Culture Foundation
Latvijas Kulturas Fonds
12 Basteja, 1050 **Riga**
Tel: 7-227 230 Fax: 7-212 545
E-Mail: peteris@parks.lv
chairman Peteris Bankovskis

Latvian Designers' Society
Latvijas Dizaineru Savieniba
Gertrudes 5a, 1010 **Riga**
Tel: 7-313 314 Fax: 7-313 316
E-Mail: lia@index.apollo.lv
head of board Inguna Lauce

Latvian National Film Centre
Latvijas Nacionalais Kinemotografijas Centrs
Elizabetes 49, 1010 **Riga**
Tel: 7-505 074/075 Fax: 7-505 077
E-Mail: nfc@com.latnet.lv
director Bruno Ascuks

Latvian Photo Artists' Union
Latvijas Fotomakslinieku Savieniba
Marstalu 6, 1050 **Riga**
Tel: 7-210 327 Fax: 7-210 327
E-Mail: latv.photo@apollo.lv
director Aivars Akis

Latvian Professional Ballet Association
Latvijas Profesionala Baleta Asociacija
Dzirnavu 135, 1050 **Riga**
Tel: 7-287 895 Fax: 7-287 895
president Arturs Ekis

Latvian Theatre Workers Union
Latvijas Teatra darbinieku savieniba
Dzirnavu 135, 1050 **Riga**
Tel: 7-287 895 Fax: 7-287 895
chairman Arturs Ekis

Latvian Union of Composers
Latvijas Komponistu savieniba
11 Novembra krastmala 35, 1050 **Riga**
Tel: 7-214 353 Fax: 7-214 353
chairman Leons Amolins

Music Society of Latvia
Latvijas Muzikas Biedriba
85 Brivibas, 1001 **Riga**
Tel: 2-272 259 Fax: 2-278 060
president Gatis Ulmanis

New Theatre Institute of Latvia, The
Latvijas Jauna teatra instituts
RLB, 13-426 Merkela iela, 1050 **Riga**
Tel: 7-212 622/471 Fax: 7-212 471
E-Mail: baiba@re-lab.lv
contact, director Baiba Tjarve
Comments: alternative E-mail: jti@latnet.lv

Oriental Music Centre
Orientalas muzikas centrs
Brivibas 85, 1001 **Riga**
Tel: 2-275 575 Fax: 2-278 060
director Dr Boris Avramecs

Riga Early Music Centre
Rigas Senas muzikas centrs
85 Brivibas, 1001 **Riga**
Tel: 2-275 575 Fax: 2-278 060
director Boris Avramecs
Comments: maintains tradition of early music in Latvia, unites endeavours of professional and amateur musicians in popularising the music and manner of the performance characteristic to the Medieval, Renaissance and Baroque epochs

Soros Foundation – Latvia
Sorosa Fonds – Latvija
K.Barona iela 31, 1011 **Riga**
Tel: 7-280 641 Fax: 7-821 251
E-Mail: sfl@ssl.lv
executive director Vita Terauda

Writers' Union of Latvia
Latvijas Rakstnieku Savieniba
Kursu iela 24, 1426 **Riga**
Tel: 7-555 180 Fax: 7-554 034
chairman Valdis Rumnieks

LITHUANIA (+370)

Agency of Lithuanian Copyright Protection Association (LATGA)
Autoriu teisiu gynimo asociacijos agentura LATGA
Vilniaus 25, 2601 **Vilnius**
Tel: 2-618 462 (director)
Fax: 2-225 261
director Edmundas Vaitekunas

Cultural Foundation of Lithuania
Lietuvos kulturos fondas
A.Jaksto 9, 2001 **Vilnius**
Tel: 2-620 508 Fax: 2-620 508
chairman Jurgis Dvarionas

Institute of Culture and Art
Kultúros ir meno institutas
Tilto 6, 2001 **Vilnius**
Tel: 2-613 646/626 091 Fax: 2-610 989
director Stanislovas Juknevicius

Lithuanian Accordian Association
Lietuvos akordeonininku asociacija
Vilniaus 39, 2001 **Vilnius**
Tel: 2-670 273/778 447/618 140 Fax: 2-226 982
president Ricardas Sviackevicius

Lithuanian Association of Artists
Lietuvos meno kureju asociacija
K. Sirvydo 6, 2600 **Vilnius**
Tel: 2-223 939 Fax: 2-619 696
president Vytautas Martinkus

Lithuanian Centre of the International Theatre Institute (ITI)
Tarptautinio teatro instituto Lietuvos centras
Gedimino pr. 1, 2001 **Vilnius**
Tel: 2-623 586 (president) Fax: 2-610 814
president Jouzas Budraitis

Lithuanian Choirs' Union
Lietuvos choru sajunga
B. Radvilaites 8a, 2600 **Vilnius**
Tel: 2-612 530/610 996
Fax: 2-612 607/224 033
E-Mail: lscc@lscc.lt
president Vytautas Miskinis

Lithuanian Cinematographers' Union
Lietuvos kinematografininku sajunga
Birutes 18, 2004 **Vilnius**
Tel: 2-220 759 Fax: 2-220 759
chairman Gytis Luksas

Lithuanian Composers' Union
Lietuvos kompozitoriu sajunga
A. Mickeviciaus 29, 2600 **Vilnius**
Tel: 2-223 611/027 Fax: 2-220 939
Internet: www.mic.lt
E-Mail: center@mipc.vno.osf.lt
chairman Gintaras Sodeika

Lithuanian Concert Promoters' Association
Lietuvos koncertines veiklos menedzeriu asociacija
Zemaitijos 8/11-222, 2001 **Vilnius**
Tel: 2-628 503 Fax: 2-220 966
contact E Zalpys
Comments: see also Agents and Producers

Lithuanian Cultural Workers Training Centre
Lietuvos kulturos darbuotoju tobulinimosi centras
Saltoniskiu 58, 2034 **Vilnius**
Tel: 2-752 777 Fax: 2-790 304
director Lina Baniene

Lithuanian Dance Information Centre (LDIC)
Totoriu g. 15-2, 2001 **Vilnius**
Tel: 2-223 641/904 0945 Fax: 2-223 641/610 814
E-Mail: dancelt@takas.lt
director Audronis Imbrasas; manager Viktoras Karpusenkovas; public relations/press Vita Mozuraite
Role & Services: LDIC is a non-profit organisation whose goals are to collect and distribute information about dance, to promote and lobby new forms of dance and to function as an umbrella organisation for dance in Lithuania; from the beginning the emphasis has been on modern and contemporary work, this being a relatively new direction in Lithuanian dance; the LDIC divides its activities into workshops, new local dance productions, tours of foreign companies (ballet, modern/contemporary dance), the international contemporary dance festival New Baltic Dance and ongoing information; the centre is partner of some international dance programmes (Aerowaves, etc.)

Lithuanian Folk Artists' Union
Lietuvos tautodailininku sajunga
Stikliu 16/18, 2001 **Vilnius**
Tel: 2-220 564 Fax: 2-220 564
chairman Jonas Rudzinskas

Lithuanian Independent Theatres' Association
Lietuvos laisvuju teatru asociacija
Gedimino pr. 1, 2001 **Vilnius**
Tel: 2-227 464 Fax: 2-610 814
president Juozas Pocius

Lithuanian Institute of Culture and Art
Lietuvos kulturos ir meno institutas
Tilto 4, 2001 **Vilnius**
Tel: 2-626 091/613 646 Fax: 2-610 989
director Arvydas Virgilijus Matulionis

Lithuanian Music Information and Publishing Centre
A.Mickeviciaus 29, 2600 **Vilnius**
Tel: 2-726 986 Fax: 2-726 986
E-Mail: center@micp.vno.osf.lt

Lithuanian Musicians' Aid Foundation
Lietuvos muziku remimo fondas
Bernardinu 8/8, 2001 **Vilnius**
Tel: 2-613 127/171/146/221 284 Fax: 2-613 174/171
E-Mail: lmrf@pub.osf.lt
director Liucija Stulgiene

Lithuanian Society of Musicians
Lietuvos muziku draugija
Gedimino pr.32-2, 2001 **Vilnius**
Tel: 2-623 043/221 615 Fax: 2-220 302
president Rimvydas Zigaitis

Lithuanian Theatre Union
Lietuvos teatro sajunga
Gedimino 1, 2001 **Vilnius**
Tel: 2-623 586 Fax: 2-610 814
chairman Algis Matulionis

Lithuanian Writers' Union
Lietuvos rasytoju sajunga
K. Sirvydo 6, 2000 **Vilnius**
Tel: 2-223 919 Fax: 2-619 696
chairman Valentinas Sventickas

Nordic Information office in Vilnius
Siaures krastu informacijos biuras Vilniuje
Isganytojo 4, 2001 **Vilnius**
Tel: 2-222 211 Fax: 2-222 423
Internet: www.nmr.lt
E-Mail: info@nmr.lt
director Knut Hjorth-Johansen

Open Society Foundation Lithuania
Atviros Lietuvos Fondas
J. Jaksto 9, 2600 **Vilnius**
Tel: 2-221 687 Fax: 2-221 419
Internet: www.osf.lt
E-Mail: fondas@osf.lt
director Diana Vilyte
Role & Services: promotes open society, with branches throughout Lithuania *Comments:* see also Promoters

Open Society House
Atviros Lietuvos fondo namai
Sv. Jono 5, 2001 **Vilnius**
Tel: 2-223 698 Fax: 2-223 691
E-Mail: elona@svjono.osf.lt
performing arts programme coordinator Elona Bajoriene

Soros Contemporary Art Centre
Soroso siuolaikinio meno centras
Vilniaus 22/1, 2001 **Vilnius**
Tel: 2-222 997 Fax: 2-222 888
E-Mail: lolita@sccali.osf.lt
director Lolita Jablonskiene

The Art Agency Kitas krantas
Meno agentura Kitas krantas
Liauksmino 8/3, **Vilnius**
Tel: 2-610 814/904 1455 Fax: 2-610 814
director Aristidas Balcetis

Theatre and Cinema Support Foundation
Teatro ir kino remimo fondas
Bernardinu St. 10, 2600 **Vilnius**
Tel: 2-626 502 Fax: 2-610 814
E-Mail: audral@puni.osf.lt
director Aristidas Balcietis

Vytautas Landsbergis' Fund
Vytauto Landsbergio fondas
A.Mickeviciaus 29, 2600 **Vilnius**
Tel: 2-223 026 Fax: 2-790 505
director Grazina Rucyte-Landsbergiene

World's Fund of the Lithuanian Songs Festival
Pasaulio lietuviu dainu sventes fondas
B.Radvilaites 8, 2600 **Vilnius**
Tel: 2-614 467 (director) Fax: 2-224 033

LUXEMBOURG (+352)

Jeunesses Musicales du Luxembourg
129 Mühlenweg, 2155 **Luxembourg**
Tel: 492 924 Fax: 492 884
E-Mail: rfranck@pt.lu
président Jean Wenandy; secrétaire général Rémy Franck
Role & Services: organises concerts
Comments: see also Promoters

Luxembourg Society for Contemporary Music
Letzebuerger Gesellschaft fir Nei Musek
Boite postale 828, 2018 **Luxembourg**
Tel: 225 821 Fax: 225 823
Internet: www.lgnm.lu
E-Mail: lgnm@lgnm.lu
artistic director Marcel Wengler; président John Schadeck; vice-président René Hemmer; secrétaire général Luc Rollinger
Role & Services: the LGNM is organiser of concerts and publisher of the CD series Anthologie de Musique Luxembourgeoise (10 CDs with orchestra and chamber music, 5 portrait CDs) *Comments:* organiser of the ISCM World Music Days 2000, the festival has more than 25 events in all types of music and takes place in Luxembourg

MACEDONIA (+389)

Association of Macedonian Composers
Sojuz na kompozitorite ná Makedonija
Maksim Gorki 18, 91000 **Skopje**
Tel: 91-220 567/234 953 Fax: 91-235 854
president Vlastimir Nikolovski;
secretary Marko Kolovski
Comments: publication: Informer

Institute of Folklore Marko Cepenkov – Skopje
Institut za Folklor Marko Cepenkov – Skopje
Ruzveltova 3, p.f. 319, 91000 **Skopje**
Tel: 91-233 876/367
director Blagoj Stoicovski

Macedonian Centre of the International Theatre Institute (ITI)
c/o Ljubisha Nikodinovski-Bish, Kej. Dimitar Vlahov b.b., PO Box 690, 91000 **Skopje**
Tel: 91-115 225/239 152 Fax: 91-115 225/906
Internet: www.unet.com.mk/iti-macedonia
E-Mail: iti-mac@unet.com.mk
president Goran Stefanovski; secretary general Ljubisha Nikodinovski-Bish

Macedonian Section of Jeunesses Musicales
Muzicka mladina na Makedonija
Ilindenska bb., 91000 **Skopje**
Tel: 91-117 882 Fax: 91-116 545

Society of musical artists of Macedonia
Zdruzenie na muzicki umetnici na Makedonija
Maksim gorki 18, 91000 **Skopje**
Tel: 91-220 567/234 953 Fax: 91-235 854
president Milan Firfov

MOLDOVA (+373)

Cinematographers' Union of Moldova
Cosmonautilor str. 7, 2012 **Chisinau**
Tel: 2-237 768
chairman Anatol Codru

Composers' Union of Moldova
153, 31 August Str., 2012 **Chisinau**
Tel: 2-247 272
chairman Ghenadie Alexandru Ciobanu

French Alliance
Alianta Franceza
Sfatul Tarii str. 18, 2012 **Chisinau**
Tel: 2-237 234 Fax: 2-234 781
director Bernardo Barbero

Interarta – Republican Association of Artistic Impressariat
21 Puskin str., 2012 **Chisinau**
Tel: 2-238 258/257
director Victor Bublitchi
Comments: see also Promoters

Moldavian National Commission for UNESCO
24 A Coropceanu str, 2001 **Chisinau**
Tel: 2-248 438 Fax: 2-247 593
general secretary Constantin Rusnac

Moldova Theatre Union
Puskin str. 24, 2012 **Chisinau**
Tel: 2-224 138
chairman Petru Baracci

Soros Foundation of Moldova
32, Bulgara str, 2012 **Chisinau**
Tel: 2-260 031 Fax: 2-260 307
executive director Victor Ursu

Union of Musicians of Moldova
43 Puskin str, 2012 **Chisinau**
Tel: 2-243 443 Fax: 2-212 390
president Maria Biesu

MONACO (+377)

Monaco Centre of the International Theatre Institute (ITI)
Centre Monegasque de L'Institut International du Théâtre
c/o M Rocchi, 8 rue Louis Notari, 98000 **Monte Carlo**
Tel: 93-158 303 Fax: 93-506 694
directeur des affaires cultural Rainier Rocchi

NETHERLANDS (+31)

Association Cultural Marketing and Communication (ACMC)
Associatie Culturele Marketing en Communicatie
POB 9877, 1006 AN **Amsterdam**
Tel: 20-669 9777 Fax: 20-669 3738
E-Mail: gvr@euronet.nl
project manager H Schraag
Role & Services: to create a platform to bring cultural marketing and communication to a higher standard

Association of Dutch Dance Companies
Directie Overleg Dans (DOD)
Keizersgracht 462, 1016 GE **Amsterdam**
Tel: 20-620 3500 Fax: 20-620 3502
E-Mail: dod@dod.nl
contact Lineke Burghout
Role & Services: dance and ballet companies:
- confirming union agreements
- joint interests, lobbying
- joint promotion campaign for dance

Association of Dutch Orchestras
Contactorgaan van Nederlandse Orkesten (CNO)
Herengracht 62, 1015 BP **Amsterdam**
Tel: 20-620 9000 Fax: 20-638 5151
E-Mail: cno@xs4all.nl
chief executive Rudolf Wolfensberger; personal assistant Cornélie Kars
Role & Services: representative association of the 15 professional symphony orchestras; advocacy with central government; collective negotiating with broadcasting companies and unions; all general orchestral matters; member of Pearle* Performing Arts Employers Associations League Europe, and of IAOA International Alliance of Orchestra Associations

Association of Theatre and Concert Hall Managers in the Netherlands
Vereniging van Schouwburg- en Concertgebouwdirecties (VSCD)
Johannes Vermeerstraat 55, 1071 DM **Amsterdam**
Tel: 20-664 7211 Fax: 20-675 2691
E-Mail: vscd@euronet.nl
director Jan Knopper; assistant Erica Haffmans
Role & Services: furthers the interests of its 125 members and thus contributes to the cultural policies of state and local authorities; supplies information, organises courses, provides legal assistance; go-between over differences of opinion between theatres, impresarios, etc

Buerau of Art & Gender
Axis Bureau voor de Kunsten v/m
Oudezods Voorburgwal 72, 1012 GE **Amsterdam**
Tel: 20-427 4525 Fax: 20-427 1412
Internet: www.axisvm.nl
axis@axisvm.nl
managing director Carolien van der Schoot; programming Annet Oekker, Nio Harmes, Deanna Herst; publicity Marieke Istha
Role & Services: organises projects, performing arts and visual arts with central focus in gender

Centre for Choreography and Contemporary Dance
DWA DansWerkplaats Amsterdam
Arie Biemondstraat 107 B, 1054 PD **Amsterdam**
Tel: 20-689 1789 Fax: 20-612 4324
Internet: www.euronet.nl/users/~dwa
E-Mail: dwa@euronet.nl
artistic director Ger Jager; business manager Paul Dijkema
Role & Services: programmes to help young dancers and choreographers; rehearsal spaces, classes, workshops etc. with the emphasis on contemporary dance

Centre for New Choir Music
Centrum Nieuwe Koormuziek
Haarlemmer Houttuiten 47, 1013 GM **Amsterdam**
Tel: 20-625 9473/624 2372
Fax: 20-620 2864
E-Mail: cnk@euronet.nl
director René Nieuwint
Role & Services: a podium dedicated to contemporary choral music

Donemus Foundation (Netherlands Committee of the International Music Council)
Paulus Potterstraat 16, 1071 CZ **Amsterdam**
Tel: 20-676 4436 Fax: 20-673 3588
Internet: www.donemus.nl
E-Mail: donemus@wxs.nl
general manager B Deuss; promotion manager Michael Nieuwenhuizen
Role & Services: documentation centre and publishing house of Dutch contemporary music
Comments: own CD label: Composers' Voice

Dutch Centre of the Association du théâtre pour l'enfance et la jeunesse (ASSITEJ)
De Bundeling/ASSITEJ-NL, PO Box 66, 3500 AB **Utrecht**
Tel: 30-238 1255 Fax: 30-233 2096
E-Mail: svdree@worldonline.nl
contact for international affairs Kim van der Boon; secretary, policy making official Saskia van de Ree
Role & Services: information and advisory body to promote Dutch Youth Theatre; members fees entitle them to information on government rules and funding; organise international activities/festivals

Dutch Federation for the Entertainment Industry
Nederlandse Vereniging van Producenten en Importeurs van beeld-en geluidsdragers (NVPI)
Albertus Perkstraat 36, 1217 NT **Hilversum**
Tel: 35-625 4411 Fax: 35-625 4410
E-Mail: info@nvpi.nl
managing director Paul Solleveld
Comments: member of the International Federation of the Phonographic Industry (IFPI); member of International Video Federation (I.V.F.); member of Interactive Software Federation Europe (ISFE)

Dutch National Institute for Choral Singing (SNK), The
Samenwerkende Nederlandse Korenorganisaties
Plompetorengracht 3, 3512 CA **Utrecht**
Tel: 30-231 3174 Fax: 30-231 8137
E-Mail: snk@euronet.nl
director Drs Jeroen Schrÿner
Role & Services: a central, national and professional institute to support choral singing; the SNK organises training courses for conductors, publishes books and CDs, subsidizes choirs, organises The Dutch International Choir Festival in Arnhem 2001 (q.v.) and many other activities, one of which is The 1999 World Symposium on choral music in Rotterdam (q.v)

Dutch Section of Jeunesses Musicales
PO Box 424, 1000 AK **Amsterdam**
Tel: 20-626 5938 Fax: 20-420 8130
E-Mail: secr@jmnl.demon.nl
secretary general t.b.a.; board member Otto Van Tubergen
Role & Services: federation of organisations for national youth music projects; promotion of music education in schools; represents Youth Orchestras of Holland

FNV KIEM – Federation of Unions of Art, Information and Media
Postbox 9354, 1006 AJ **Amsterdam**
Tel: 20-355 3636 Fax: 20-355 3737
Internet: www.fnv-kiem.nl
E-Mail: fnvkiem@worldonline.nl
general secretary Herman Leisink
Role & Services: member of International Federation of Actors; International Federation of Musicians; Media and Entertainment International *Comments:* visiting address: Jan Touropstraat 1, 1062 BK Amsterdam

Foundation for the Collection of Neighbouring Rights (SENA)
Stichting ter Exploitatie van Naburige rechten
Vaartweg 51, 1211 JE **Hilversum**
Tel: 35-624 4653
Fax: 35-628 0971
Internet: www.sena.nl
E-Mail: sena@sena.nl
contact Marijke Remkes (performing arts department); international artistic relations Nathalie Loop
Role & Services: its main goals are the collection of fees paid for so-called secondary use of sound carriers and the distribution of the sums payable to those entitled, i.e. record producers and all the artists and musicians involved

Gaudeamus Foundation – Contemporary Music Center
Swammerdamstraat 38, 1091 RV **Amsterdam**
Tel: 20-694 7349 Fax: 20-694 7258
Internet: www.xs4all.nl/~gaud
E-Mail: gaud@xs4 all.nl
director Henk Heuvelmans
Role & Services: supports young composers, promoters, performers, International Gaudeamus Music Week, International Interpreters Competition, composers' workshops and contemporary music concerts in the Netherlands and abroad; Documentation/information centre; Secretariat for: Dutch section of the ISCM, the International Confederation for Electroacoustic Music, European Conference of Promoters of New Music, see also Festivals and Competitions

Institute of Sponsors for Culture
Genootschap voor Reclame – Sectie Sponsors Voor Kunst
POB 9877, 1006 AN **Amsterdam**
Tel: 20-669 9777 Fax: 20-669 3738
E-Mail: gvr@euronet.nl
managing director W F Falter
Comments: organisation is currently in transition and undergoing re-organisation

KNTV (Royal Netherlands Musicians Union)
Keizersgracht 480, 1017 EG **Amsterdam**
Tel: 20-522 1020 Fax: 20-620 0229
E-Mail: office@kntv.nl
director H H J Luif; legal advisor G Kortooms; consultant C Gyzen
Role & Services: provides help to professional/student musicians; publishes KNTV magazine (sent on request)
Comments: former name: Koninklijke Nederlandse Toonkunstenaars Vereniging

Muziek & Theater Netwerk
Keizergracht 462, 1016 GE **Amsterdam**
Tel: 20-624 1063 Fax: 20-627 6009
Internet: www.euronet.nl/~mtn
E-Mail: mtn@euronet.nl
directors Jan Schretzmeijer, Jeannette Smit; public relations Ariane van Pelt
Role & Services: intermediate (between companies, venues, audience and government), selective touring funding; marketing services, consultancy, training, meetings; optimise staging possibilities and public interest in contempory theatre, music, jazz and improvised music

Netherlands Federation of Concert Agents and Managers
Weteringschans 130, 1017 XV **Amsterdam**
Tel: 20-421 1611 Fax: 20-421 1747
E-Mail: concertdirectie@samama.nl
secretary Niels Veenhuijzen
Role & Services: national umbrella organisation for Dutch concert agents and member of the European Association of Concert Agents *Comments:* see also entry under Agents & Producers

Netherlands Music Centre
Centrum Nederlandse Muziek
PO Box 1634, 1200 BP **Hilversum**
Tel: 35-624 0957 Fax: 35-621 0570
Internet: www.cnm.nl
E-Mail: info@cnm.nl
managing director Drs J W ten Broeke
Role & Services: promotion of serious Dutch music in the Netherlands and abroad; organizes various concert series in the Netherlands; releases CDs on the NM Classics label, a joint venture with Radio Netherlands; CDs are dedicated exclusively to serious Dutch music; initiates and co-ordinates music broadcasting on Dutch radio and abroad

Statistics on culture, tourism and recreation
Statistics Netherlands
Prinses Beatrixlaan 428, 2273 XZ **Voorburg**
Tel: 70-337 5609 Fax: 70-337 5996
Internet: www.cbs.nl
E-Mail: fhve@cbs.nl
sectorial manager Frans Hoeve
Role & Services: statistical research and publications on culture, tourism and recreation of which performing arts form a substantial part; strives to be the independent provider of highly reputable, reliable, coherent public statistical information on in principle all areas of Dutch society

Stichting stemra
Buma/Stemra-huis, Prof E.M. Meijerslaan 3, 1183 AV **Amstelveen**
Tel: 20-347 0911
Fax: 20-347 0496
Internet: www.buma.nl
c.e.o & chair of the board of directors C P Vervoord
Role & Services: monitor the exploitation of mechanical reproduction rights
Comments: member of Groupement Européen des Sociétés d'Auteurs et Compositeurs (q.v.)

Theater Instituut Nederland
Herengracht 168, 1016 BP **Amsterdam**
Tel: 20-551 3300 Fax: 20-551 3303
E-Mail: info@tin.nl
director Dragan Klaic; international relations & research and development Rudy Engelander; library, collection, documentation Rob van Gaal; communication & production Edith Lindhout

Role & Services: supports and contributes to the development of the performing arts in the Netherlands and abroad; the institute maintains a broad focus which encompasses historical evolution in the performing arts as well as addressing present and future developments in these fields; the range of activities undertaken by the Institute further reflects its diversity: systematic collection of information and documentation on the contemporary performing arts; organization of debates, conferences and exhibitions for a broad and interested public; publication of books, CDs and periodicals, including Carnet (quarterly) in conjunction with Vlaams Theater Institut, Brussels (q.v. publications); stimulation of networking and collaboration on an international scale; ongoing research, both historical and contemporary in character; presentation and promotion of the Dutch theatre and dance abroad; and the initiation of workshops and discussions on a variety of subjects, designed to raise the expertise of those working in the performing arts; the institute defines its sphere of activity as broadly as possible: the word 'theatre' in the name embraces drama, dance, mime, puppetry, object and image theatre, opera and operetta, musical, cabaret and circus, and children's theatre
Comments: Theater Instituut Nederland; postal address: Postbus 19304, 1000 GH Amsterdam

Theatre Companies Association
Vereniging van Nederlandse Theatergezelschappen
Herengracht 174, 1016 BR **Amsterdam**
Tel: 20-620 0201
Fax: 20-421 6525
E-Mail: vnt@xs4all.nl
general manager Jaap Jong; office manager Ineke van den Berg; manager Monique ten Boske
Role & Services: employers association representing the interests of Dutch theatre in general but specifically those of its members; only represents subsidised companies

NORWAY (+47)

Association of Norwegian Theatres and Orchestras
Norsk Teater – Og Orkesterforening (NTO)
PO Box 1511, Uika, 0117 **Oslo**
Tel: 2241 9660
Fax: 2241 9661
Internet: www.nto.no
E-Mail: nto@nto.no
general director Morten Gjelten; legal advisor Kirsten Martinsen
Role & Services: a service organisation for theatres and orchestras in Norway; negotiate wages with state-financed theatres and orchestras *Comments:* visiting address: Kroriprinsenssemärthasplass 1, 0160 Oslo

Association of Recording Artists
Gramart Grammofonartistenes Forening
Arbeidersamfunnets Plass 1, 0181 **Oslo**
Tel: 2211 0551 Fax: 2211 0572
Internet: www.gramart.org
E-Mail: gramart@online.no
chairman Stein Groven; managing director Øevend Myrvoll
Role & Services: organisation for recording artists; assists with legal help, politics, etc.

Center for the Art of Dance, The
Senter for Dansekunst
Tollbugaten 19, 0152 **Oslo**
Tel: 2241 2700 Fax: 2241 2701
Internet: home.sol.no/~artdance/
E-Mail: sfd.kunst@online.no
director Randi Urdal; administrator Christine Sletsjøe; information & it consultant Carl Sindre Jacobsen
Role & Services: non-profit organisation; information office and proficiency center for dance, publishes bi-monthly newsletter with a dance calendar and Dance in Norway (updated every 2 or 3 years) and a library and videotheque are established in addition to an international network and a database of contemporary and historical documentation
Comments: alternative e-mail: randi@artofdance.no

Council for Music Organisations in Norway
Norsk Musikkrad
Tollbugata 28, 0157 **Oslo**
Tel: 2242 4550 Fax: 2242 4410
Internet: www.musikk.no/
E-Mail: mmr@musikk.no
director Øyvend Ståsett
Role & Services: council for music organisations in Norway, 30 member organisations, 2200 members

Dance and Theatre Forum
Danse Og Teatersentrum
Stranden 3, 0250 **Oslo**
Tel: 2201 4020 Fax: 2201 4021
Internet: www.dtsentrum.no
E-Mail: dts@dtsentrum.no
director Tove Bratten (9155 4291 mobile); artistic & managing director Inger Buresund
Role & Services: umbrella organisation representing professional dance and theatre companies; owner of Black Box theatre in Oslo (q.v.) with two stages

Gramo
Karl Johansgata 21, 0159 **Oslo**
Tel: 2200 7777 Fax: 2200 7778
Internet: www.gramo.no
E-Mail: firmapost@gramo.no
director Tom B Hovde
Role & Services: joint collecting society for musicians, performing artists and phonogram producers

Jeunesses Musicales
Musikk og Ungdom
Tollbugaten 28, 0157 **Oslo**
Tel: 2242 4550 Fax: 2242-4410
E-Mail: kristin.clementz@musikk.no
director Kristin Clementz
Role & Services: organises exchanges of young musicians with other countries

Kopinor
Stenersgt 1A, 0050 **Oslo**
Tel: 2217 9417 Fax: 2217 9422
Internet: www.kopinor.no/
E-Mail: kopinor.post@kopinor.no
director John-Willy Rudolph
Role & Services: reproduction rights organisation of Norway

Multi-Cultural Music Centre
Rikskonsertene – Norwegian Concert Institute, PO Box 2835 Solli, 0204 **Oslo**
Tel: 2283 8350 Fax: 2283 1610
Internet: www.rikskonsertene.no
E-Mail: anne.moberg@rikskonsertene.no
general manager Tom Gravlie (email: tom.gravlie@rikskonsertene.no); producer Anne Moberg; information officer Hanne Houen (email: hanne.houen@rikskonsertene.no); touring coordinator Gørild Skille (email: gorild.skille@rikskonsertene.no)
Role & Services: presents high-quality live music from non-european cultures; cultural exchange, organises festivals, seminars

NASOL – Norwegian Association for Symphonic Orchestras
NASOL – Norske Symfoniorkestres Landsforbund
Tollbugata 28, 0157 **Oslo**
Tel: 2242 1919 Fax: 2242 0292
director Jan Ola Amundsen

National Federation of Norwegian Musical Artists
Norsk Tonekunstnersamfund
c/o Ole Behn, Bogstadvn. 66, 0366 **Oslo**
Tel: 2260 3583 Fax: 2269 7513
E-Mail: olebehn@hotmail.com
director Ole Bøhn
Rol & Services: promotes the welfare of professional music soloists *Comments:* affiliated to Nordisk Solistråd

NCB Norge
PO Box 9171, Grønland, 0134 **Oslo**
Tel: 2205 7200 Fax: 2205 7250
Internet: www.tono.no/
E-Mail: tono@sn.no
managing director Emborg Thorkil
Role & Services: Norwegian office of the Nordisk Copyright Bureau (Copenhagen) for mechanical rights

Norwegian Actors' Equity Association
Norsk Skuespillerforbund
Wesselsgate 8, 0165 **Oslo**
Tel: 2241 1874
Fax: 2241 7044
E-Mail: norsk.skuespillerforbund@online.no
president Bernhard Ramstad; general secretary Kirsti Camerer
Role & Services: trade union activity, services to members (performers) and non-members (employers) art information and employment placement; member of International Federation of Actors and the Norwegian Centre of the ITI

Norwegian Artists' Council
Norges kunstnerråd
Skippergata 17, 0106 **Oslo**
Tel: 2247 8040 Fax: 2242 4040
Internet: www.filmenshus.no/kunstner
E-Mail: kunstner@raadet.filmenshus.no
executive director Fredrik Glans
Role & Services: to stengthen the position of professional Norwegian artists, to gain recognition of the importance of art in society and to lobby for mutual interests and general policies within the artistic community
Comments: publishes a bi-monthly newsletter and also surveys of funding resources

Norwegian Ballet Equity Organisation
Norsk Ballettforbund
Wesselsgate 8, 0165 **Oslo**
Tel: 2241 3304 Fax: 2236 0602
president Liv Bjørgum; secretary Bitten Arnø; executive officer Tone Øvrebø Johannessen
Role & Services: independent trade union for dancers and choreographers; member of International Federation of Actors

Norwegian Centre of International Federation of the Phonographic Industry (IFPI)
Sandakerveien 52, 0477 **Oslo**
Tel: 2222 1788 Fax: 2222 1768
E-Mail: ifpi.sekretariat@ifpi.no
chairman Rune Higbirg; director general & secretary Saemund Fiskvik
Role & Services: member of the International Federation of the Phonographic Industry

Norwegian Centre of the Association du théâtre pour l'enfance et la jeunesse (ASSITEJ)
Postboks 2838, Tøyen, 0608 **Oslo**
Tel: 2267 8606 Fax: 2268 9634
chairman Helge Andersen; secretary Ragnhild Sørvig (2267 1139)
Role & Services: organisation for supporting and increasing both in quantity and quality theatre for children and young people; also supporting people in all categories who work for the same *Comments:* host the 1999 World Congress in Tromsø

Norwegian Choir Association
Norges Korforbund
Tollbugata 28, 0157 **Oslo**
Tel: 2242 6720 Fax: 2241 5808
Internet: www.korforbundet.no
E-Mail: kaareha@notam.uio.no
president Pål Uisat; secretary general Kåre Hanken
Role & Services: publishes Korbladet six times a year; members of the association: 1070 choirs *Comments:* alternative e-mail: nk@korforbundet.no

Norwegian Directors Guild
Norsk sceneinstuktørforening
Kristian Augustvei 19, 0164 **Oslo**
Tel: 2220 4302 Fax: 2220 4303
E-Mail: nsfc@online.no
director Kai Johnsen
Role & Services: service organisation for professional theatre directors

Norwegian Impresarios' Association
Den Norske impresario forening (DENIF)
c/o Rainbow Booking, Postboks 365, 1701 **Sarpsborg**
Tel: 6915 6000 Fax: 6915 6052
Internet: home.sol.no/~denifno/
E-Mail: denif@online.no
chair person Per Langsholt
Role & Services: service organisation for Norwegian impresarios, currently 55 members

Norwegian Music Information Centre
Tollbugt 28, 0157 **Oslo**
Tel: 2242 9090 Fax: 2242 9091
Internet: www.notam.uio.no/nmi/
E-Mail: info@mic.no
director Jostein Simble
Role & Services: publishes three editions of the magazine Listen to Norway annually; other information material provided by the centre are composer biographies and Address Guide to Music in Norway; the Centre arranges exhibitions for festivals, concerts and fairs around the world, either alone or in cooperation with other music information centres; manuscript and reference library with orchestral rental materials, study and listening rooms available

Norwegian Music Publisher's Association
Norsk Musikkforleggerforening
c/o Musikk-Husets Fortag a/s, PO Box 822, Sentrum, 0104 **Oslo**
Tel: 2242 5090 Fax: 2242 5541
director Arne Damsgaard

Norwegian Musician's Union
Norsk Musikerforbund
Postbox 8806, Youngstorget, 0028 **Oslo**
Tel: 2306 2150 Fax: 2306 2151
E-Mail: musiker@online.no
chairman Tore Nordvik
Role & Services: 3300 members (musicians, opera singers, dancers, music teachers, prompters, stage managers); legal and insurance services; magazine

Norwegian Network for Technology, Acoustics and Music (NoTAM)
NoTAM-Norsk nettverk for teknologi, akustikk og musikk
P.O.Box 1137, Blindern, 0317 **Oslo**
Tel: 2285 7970/3 Fax: 2285 7974
Internet: www.notam.uio.no
E-Mail: notam@notam.uio.no
director Jøran Rudi (joranru@notam.uio.no)
Role & Services: NoTam aims to stimulate research and development of practical and theoretical knowledge about the use of technology in composition, production, educational activity and mediation of sound and music on a national level; it also aims to structure and distribute knowledge and information about development within this field nationally and internationally
Comments: the University of Oslo has assumed the responsibility of hosting NoTAM whose studios are available to composers, researchers, pedagogues, students and musicians; visiting address: Gydasvei, 0363 Oslo

Norwegian Opera Singers' Equity Association
Norsk Operasangerforbund
c/o Kristin Theisen, Sarbuvollvn. 8A, 1363 **Høvik**
Tel: 6759 0546 Fax: 6759 0546
director Kristin Theisen
Role & Services: association of opera singers
Comments: second address: Youngsgt 11, 0181 Oslo, Tel: 2306 1496, Fax: 2306 1498

Norwegian Performing Rights Society (TONO)
Norsk selskap for forvaltning av fremføringsrettigheter til musikkverk
Postbox 9171, Grønland, 0134 **Oslo**
Tel: 2205 7200 Fax: 2205 7250
Internet: www.tono.no
E-Mail: tono@sn.no
managing director Cato Strøm; assistant managing director Berit Kolstad; information & negotiation adviser t.b.a.; negotiation leader Geir Gaarder
Comments: visiting address: Galleriet, Tøyenbekken 21, 0134 Oslo; member of Groupement Européen des Sociétés d'Auteurs et Compositeurs (q.v.)

Norwegian Society of Composers
Norsk Komponistforening
Tollbugata. 28, 0157 **Oslo**
Tel: 2241 8240 Fax: 2241 8231
Internet: www.notam.uio.no/nkf/nkf.html
E-Mail: komponist@komponist.no
chairman Glenn Erik Haugland; director Tina Tangestuen
Role & Services: help to ensure favourable conditions for composers and to promote contemporary music
Comments: produce contemporary music CDs on 2 labels

Norwegian Theatre Union – Norwegian Centre of the International Theatre Institute (ITI)
c/o Norsk Teaterunion
Wesselsgt 8, 0160 **Oslo**
Tel: 2220 9092 Fax: 2220 9093
E-Mail: maaby@online.no
president Margrethe Aaby; secretary Elin Tinhot
Role & Services: ITI's objectives are: to promote international exchange in the domain of performing arts
Comments: Secretariat is open Thursdays and Fridays

Ny Musikk – Norwegian Section of the International Society for Contemporary Music (ISCM)
Tollbugate 28, 0157 **Oslo**
Tel: 2233 7090 Fax: 2233 7095
Internet: www.notam.uio.no/ny_musikk
E-Mail: ny-musikk-adm@notam.uio.no
executive director Janne Stang Dahl; president Peter Tornquist; Cikada manager Sten Cranner; producer Jon Halvor Bjornseth
Role & Services: arrange concerts; administer Cikada, group performing contemporary music, New Music's Composers Group, Albedo record label
Comments: see also Promoters

Rikskonserten Norwegian Concert Institute
PO Box 2835 Solli, 0204 **Oslo**
Tel: 2283 8350 Fax: 2283 1610
Internet: www.rikskonsertene.no
E-Mail: post@rikskonsertene.no
executive director Einar Solbu
Comments: Norway's largest producer and distributor of live music (approx. 10000 concerts annually); strives towards an overall artistic vision, public concerts, concerts for children, projects, multicultural music

Riksteatret National Touring Theatre Institute
Postboks 724 Sentrum, 0153 **Oslo**
Tel: 2220 6015 Fax: 2220 6052
Internet: www.riksteatret.no/
director Bente Erichsen; head of information Steinar Vestli
Role & Services: national agency for touring theatre, presents approx. 600 performances a year produced, co-produced and presented
Comments: visiting address: Kongensgate 1, Oslo; see also Drama

UNIMA – Norway
Hovinvn. 1, 0576 **Oslo**
Tel: 2267 7356 Fax: 2268 9634
secretary Frances Anderson; chairperson Camilla Tostrup
Role & Services: organisation for protecting the interests of puppet players both amateur and professional, aims to promote the exchange of information in professional circles and to the public

POLAND (+48)

Association of Audio-Video Producers (ZPAW)
Zwiazek Producentów Audio-Video (ZPAW)
Kruczkowskiego 12/2, 00-380 **Warszawa**
Tel: 22-625 6699 Fax: 22-625 1661

Association of Authors and Composers
Zwiazek Autorow i Kompozytorow (ZAiKS)
ul. Hipoteczna 2, 00-092 **Warszawa**
Tel: 22-827 6061 Fax: 22-635 1347

Association of Polish Artists of Theatre and Film (ZASP)
Zwiazek Artystow Scen Polskich
Al. Ujazdowskie 45, 00-536 **Warszawa**
Tel: 22-628 7808/629 3271 Fax: 22-621 4820
president Kazimierz Kaczor; documentation centre Dorota Buchwald (tel: 22-621 4556)
Comments: member of International Federation of Actors (FIA)

Associations of Polish Composers (ZKP)
Zwiazek Kompozytorow Polskich (ZKP)
ul. Rynek Starego Miasta 27, 00-272 **Warszawa**
Tel: 22-831 1634 Fax: 22-831 1741
E-Mail: festival@warsaw-autumn.waw.pl
president Krzysztof Knittel
Role & Services: library and sound library, centre of documentation of Polish contemporary music; organisation of concerts and festivals of contemporary music (Warsaw Autumn)

Baltic Sea Culture Centre, The
Nadbaltyckie Centrum Kultury
ul. Korzenna 33.35, 80-851 **Gdansk**
Tel: 58-301 1051 Fax: 58-301 1957
E-Mail: cultbalt@softel.gda.pl

Centre of Contemporary Art – Zamek Ujazdowski
Centrum Sztuki Wspolczesnej
al. Ujazdowskie 6, 00-461 **Warszawa**
Tel: 22-628 7683/1271 Fax: 22-628 9550
E-Mail: csw@ikp.atm.com.pl
director Wojciech Krukowski
Comments: see also Venues

Centre of Polish Scenography
Centrum Scenografii Polskiej
Oddzial Muzeum Slaskiego, pl.Sejmu Slaskiego 2, 40-032 **Katowice**
Tel: 32-251 5714

Cultural Promotion Centre
Centrum Animacji Kultury
ul. Krakowskie Przedmiescie 21/23, 00-071 **Warszawa**
Tel: 22-826 5982 Fax: 22-826 0662
Internet: kultura-polska.biz.pl
E-Mail: cak@kultura-polska.biz.pl
Role & Services: databases and addresses of cultural institutions and activities in Poland

Franziscans Culture Centre
Franciszkanskie Centrum Kultury
ul. Sw. Trojcy 4, 80-822 **Gdansk**
Tel: 58-305 5796/6026 28026 Fax: 58-301 0752
director Marek Wysoczynski

Fredric Chopin Academy of Music, The
ul. Okûlnik 2, 00-368 **Warszawa**
Tel: 22-827 7241
rector Ryszard Zimak
Role & Services: collections of specialists publications, scientific works, photocopies, microfilms, organisations of concerts and courses of classical music

Fryderyk Chopin Society
Towarzystwo im. Fryderyka Chopina
ul. Okolnik 1, 00-368 **Warszawa**
Tel: 22-827 9589/5471 Fax: 22-827 9599
general director Albert Grudzinski; president Prof. Tadeusz Chmielewski
Comments: see also Venues

Institute of Art of Polish Academy of Sciences (PAN)
Instytut Sztuki Polskiej Akademii Nauk (PAN)
PO Box 994, Dtuga 26/28, 00-950 **Warszawa**
Tel: 22-831 3271/3149 Fax: 22-831 3149
director Lech Sokol
Comments: collections recording Polish culture from 13th C. to the present

Institute of Culture Information and Documentation Branch
ul. Swietojerska 2, 00-288 **Warszawa**
Tel: 22-835 4564 Fax: 22-835 4564
Internet: www.institute-of-culture.pl
E-Mail: zinaj@warman.com.pl
Role & Services: databases of cultural research and cultural image of Polish communities, culture centres and institutions

Polish Centre of Art for Children and Young People
Ogolnopolski Osrodek Sztuki olla Dzieci i Mlodziezy
ul. Sw. Marcin 80/82, 61-809 **Poznan**
Tel: 61-853 6090 Fax: 61-852 8580

Polish Centre of International Organisation of Scenographers, Theatre Architects and Technicians (OISTAT)
c/o Teatr Wielki, Pl. Teatralny 5, 00-950 **Warszawa**
Tel: 22-692 0294 Fax: 22-826 0423

Polish Centre of the Association du Théâtre pour l'enfance et la jeunesse (ASSITEJ)
ul. Siekierkowska 28, 00-709 **Warszawa**
Tel: 22-841 7217
president Halina Machulska

Polish Centre of the International Theatre Institute (ITI)
Plac Pilsudskiego 9, 00-078 **Warszawa**
Tel: 22-826 1771/3027 Fax: 22-826 3027
secretary general Malgorzata Semil-Jakubowicz; director Malgorzata Majewska-Waraszkiewicz

Polish Centre of Union Internationale de la Marionette (UNIMA)
c/o Teatr Arlekin, Ul. 1 Maja 2, 90-718 **Lodz**
Tel: 42-632 7385 Fax: 42-633 7385
president Marek Waszkiel

Polish Early Music Society
Polskie Towarzystwo Muzyki Dawnej
ul. Westerplatte 10, 31-033 **Kraków**
Tel: 12-422 0064 (music department of Jagiellonian University) Fax: 12-422 0064
E-Mail: anmarko@kr.onet.pl
president Antoni Markowski; vice-presidents Jacek Urbaniak, Marta Czermy-Kaczmarska (tel: 12-229 062); president Warsaw branch Jacek Urbaniak (tel: 22-831 2482, email: jurbi@friko7.onet.pl)
Role & Services: aims to popularise the performance of early music; society organises concerts, festivals, courses, conferences and research as well as editing music sources and bibliographical data; publishes Bulletin quarterly *Comments:* Warsaw Office: ul. Zakroczymska 2/2, 00-225 Warszawa

Polish Musicians Association
Stowarzyszenie Polskich Artystow Muzykow (SPAM)
ul. Lwowska 15/12, 00-660 **Warszawa**
Tel: 22-621 8647 Fax: 22-621 8647
president Jerzy Kusiak

Polish Section of International Association of Theatre Critics (AICT)
ul. Glogowa 21, 81-589 **Gdynia**
Tel: 58-629 0762 Fax: 58-629 0762
president Andrzej Zurowski

Polish Section of International Society for Contemporary Music (ISCM)
Polskie Towarzystwo Muzyki Wspolczesnej
ul. Mazowiecka 11, 00-052 **Warszawa**
Tel: 22-827 6981 Fax: 22-827 7804
E-Mail: iscm_pl@ddg.art.pl
president Zygmunt Krauze; secretary Anna Dorota Wladyczka

Polish Section of Jeunesses Musicales
Hoza 50/51, 00-660 **Warszawa**
Tel: 2-625 1937 Fax: 2-625 5810
president Stanislaw Skoczynski; director Danuta Kaniewska

Polish Writers' Association (SPP) – Playwrights Section
Stowarzyszenie Pisarzy Polskich (SPP)
ul. Krakowskie Przedmiescie 87/89, 00-079 **Warszawa**
Tel: 22-826 0589 Fax: 22-826 0589

Polish Writers' Union (ZLP) – Playwrights Section
Zwiazek Literatow Polskich (ZLP)
ul. Krakowskie Przedmiescie 87/89, 00-079 **Warszawa**
Tel: 22-826 5785/826 0866

Theatre Museum
Muzeum Teatralne
Teatr Wielki, Pl.Teatralny 1, 00-950 **Warszawa**
Tel: 22-692 0211/0224 Fax: 22-826 0423
director Andrzej Kruczynski

Warsaw Music Society
Warszawskie Towarzystwo Muzyczne im. Stanislawa Moniuszki,
ul. Morskie oko 2, 02-511 **Warszawa**
Tel: 22-849 5651 Fax: 22-849 5651
director Andrzej Mrowiec; president Anna Malewicz-Madey
Role & Services: concerts, library, manuscripts of Moniuszko, Chopin, Paderewski, Karlowicz

PORTUGAL (+351)

Arts and Drama Trade Union
Sindicato das Artes e Espectáculo (SIARTE)
Parque Mayer, 1200 **Lisboa**
Tel: 1-346 4312 Fax: 1-346 4312
presidente António Rêdes Cruz; secretário Francisco Froes; tesoureiro Carlos Gualdino; 1º vogal Maria Tavares; 2º vogal José Carlos Oliveira
Role & Services: aims to defend the rights of its members – professionals in the sphere of the arts, audio-visual media and performance; offers legal advice and information

Calouste Gulbenkian Foundation
Fundação Calouste Gulbenkian
Avenida de Berna 45-A, 1067 **Lisboa** Codex
Tel: 1-793 5131 Fax: 1-793 5139
E-Mail: musica@gulbenkian.pt
chairman of the board of trustees Dr. Vitor de sa Machado; trustee of music department Dr. José Blanco; director, music department Dr. Luis Pereira Leal; assistant director, music department Dr. Carlos Pontes Leça;

director, department of animation, artistic creation and education through art (ACARTE) Prof. Doutora Yvette Centeno; director, United Kingdom Branch Paula Ridley OBE; director, France Branch Prof. Dr. António Coimbra Martins
Role & Services: supports culture extensively within Portugal and can also provide aid for Portugese culture in other countries; has a London office which provides aid to UK cultural activities; runs the Ballet Gulbenkian (q.v.), Orquestra Gulbenkian (q.v.), 1200 and 344 seat venues (q.v.), a choir, 2 major museums, and the largest network of libraries in Portugal; also organises concerts throughout Portugal and abroad; accounts for approx. 25% of arts funding in Portugal

Centro em Movimento (CEM)
Praça de Alegria 27, 2°, 1250 **Lisboa**
Tel: 1-342 5422 Fax: 1-342 5422
director Sofia Neuparph
Role & Services: promotes and encourages theatre projects, particularly experimental performing arts projects; has a studio which is regularly used by groups to put on experimental shows; encourages projects from all over Portugal
Comments: funded by the Ministry of Culture, The Gulbenkian Foundation and Lisbon's Regional Government; has carried out projects with the International Performance Network

Clube Português de Artes e Ideias
Rua do Sol ao Rato 73 – 1°, 1250-262 **Lisboa**
Tel: 1-387 8121/2 Fax: 1-387 6667
E-Mail: artes.ideias@mail.telepac.pt
presidente Jorge Barreto Xavier; directors Paulo Goweia, Marta Anjos, Anabela Rodriguez, Paula Castro Rosa, Rui Gonçalves
Role & Services: national non-profit arts association funded by the government; promotes young artists in all areas of the arts; organises national contests, prizes and exchanges; helps members to produce their art projects; provides information about young Portuguese artists; productions all over Portugal, annual arts festival; member of IETM and Network of Cultural Centres of the Council of Europe; venue: Fábrica de Pólvora. Bercarena

Dance Forum
Forum Dança – Associação Cultural
Rua de são Domingos à Lapa 8n, 1200-835 **Lisboa**
Tel: 1-396 9117/8 Fax: 1-396 9117
E-Mail: ip200676@ip.pt
directors Magdalena Victorino, Cristina Santos, Ezequiel Dos Santos
Role & Services: national cultural association founded in 1991 to promote dance through performance and education; publishes Forum Dança-Revista yearly
Comments: receives government funding for its promotion of new choreography and for the training of dance amateurs in the community

Discoveries Foundation
Fundação das Descobertas
Centro Cultural de Belém, Praça do Imperio, 1449-003 **Lisboa**
Tel: 1-361 2400 Fax: 1-361 2500
Internet: www.ccb.pt
E-Mail: ccb@ccb.pt
president Prof. Dr. Fraústo da Silva; director of cultural activities and member of the board Dr. Miguel Lobo Antunes; member of the board Dra. Adelaide Rocha; director of the performing arts centre Dr. Miguel Leal Coelho; exhibition centre director Margarida Veiga
Role & Services: cultural activities include exhibitions, theatre, dance, opera, music etc; services include conferences, congresses, workshops etc.; arts-related educational activities
Comments: see also Venues

Fundação Oriente
Rua do Salitre, 62-66, 1269-065 **Lisboa**
Tel: 1-352 7002 Fax: 1-352 7042
board of directors Carlos Augusto Pulido Valente Monjardino (Chairman), Mário Brandão, João de Deus Ramos; assistance to the board Luisa Ramuzat (head of department); culture department João Calvão (head); financial and administrative department Guilherme Vaz (head); president Carlos Augusto Pulido Valente
Role & Services: promotes cultural, educational, artistic, scientific and philantropic co-operation with Macau and the Far East
Comments: Portuguese private non-profit foundation with a head office in Lisbon and two delegations (in Macau and Goa, India)

International Society for Music Education
Associação Portuguesa de Educação Musical (APEM)
Rua Rosa Araújo 6, 3°, 1250 **Lisboa**
Tel: 1-355 7118 Fax: 1-355 7118
board: president Graziela Cintra, secretary João Chaves Santos, treasurer Ana Claudia de Sousa, members Graça Palheiros, Paulo Rodrigues
Role & Services: courses, seminars and conferences, youth concerts; quarterly musical bulletin in general music matters; representative of ISME in Portugal
Comments: see q.v. – Portuguese Music Council

Luso-American Development Foundation
Fundação Luso-Americana para o Desenvolvimento
Rua do Sacramento à Lapa, 21, 1200 **Lisboa**
Tel: 1-393 5800 Fax: 1-396 3358
E-Mail: fladport@flad.pt
president, exec council Rui Machete; director Bernardino Gomes; head of cultural department Luis Ferro
Role & Services: private organisation which aims to promote links between Portugal and the United States in all fields (business, science and culture)

Musicians Trade Union
Sindicato dos Músicos
Av D. Carlos 1, 72-D-2°, 1200 **Lisboa**
Tel: 1-396 6551 Fax: 1-395 0208
director Carlos Passos; vice-director Fernando Serafim
Role & Services: offers legal advice to its members and information services *Comments:* in the process of establishing a library

National Centre of Culture
Centro Nacional de Cultura
Rua Antonio Maria Cardoso 68, 1249-101 **Lisboa**
Tel: 1-346 6722 Fax: 1-342 8250
Internet: www.cnc.pt
E-Mail: info@cnc.pt
president Helena Vaz da Silva; cultural heritage Maria Calado; pr Teresa Tamen; data bank co-ordinator Teresa Gomes
Role & Services: private association promoting cultural cooperation world-wide, organises meetings, conferences, heritage courses, cultural trips, publishes a quarterly newsletter; has a library and a documentation centre about Lisbon history and cultural itineries

Portuguese Centre of l' Union Internationale de la Marionette (UNIMA)
União de Marionetistas Portugueses, Rua Guilherme Felgueiras, 85, 4450 **Matosinhos**
Tel: 2-937 0889 Fax: 2-937 0889
president Santos Queiroga; directors Isabel Alves Costa, José Ramalho, José Russo, José Jeronimo
Comments: address of the president: Tr. Maria Carmo Freire, 71 Praia do Cargo-Lavra, 4460 Matosinhos, Tel: 2-996 8241

Portuguese Centre of the Association du théâtre pour l'enfance et la jeunesse (ASSITEJ)
Rua de Santo António Estrela 60, 1350 **Lisboa**
Tel: 1-395 3289/90 Fax: 1-397 0626
president João Brites
Comments: see also Drama: 'O Bando'

Portuguese Music Council
Conselho Português da Música
Rua Rosa Araújo, 6 – 3°, 1250-195 **Lisboa**
Tel: 1-355 7118 Fax: 1-355 7118
president Alvaro Salazar; secretary t.b.a.; treasurer Graziela Cintra Gomes (APEM)
Role & Services: promotes music; organises concerts
Comments: see q.v. – International Society for Music Education (APEM)

Portuguese Phonographic Association
Associação Fonográfica Portuguesa
Rua Augusto dos Santos 2, 4th floor, 1050 **Lisboa**
Tel: 1-352 9189 Fax: 1-314 7325
executive director Dr. Eduardo Simoes; president Carlos Pinto
Role & Services: member of the International Federation of the Phonographic Industry; protect the rights of the associates

Portuguese Section of Jeunesses Musicales
Juventude Musical Portuguesa
Rua Rosa Araújo 6-3° andar, 1250-195 **Lisboa**
Tel: 1-357 3131
Fax: 1-354 3330
E-Mail: juv@telepac.pt
president Emanuel Frazão Pereira; secretary general Antonio Jorge Alpendre; director of international relations Sérgio Fontão
Comments: organise symphony concerts, chamber music concerts and recitals; see other National Organisations: International Society for Music Education and Portuguese Music Council, and see also Promoters

Portuguese Society of Contemporary Music – Portuguese Section of ISCM
Sociedade Portuguesa de Música Contemporânea c/o Conservatório Nacional,
Rua dos Caetanos 29-1° andar, 1200 **Lisboa**
Tel: 1-346 3801 Fax: 1-342 3605
contact Prof. José Machado, Dr. José Coutinho

Sociedade Portuguesa de Autores
Avenida Duque de Loulé, 31, CP, 1069 **Lisboa** Codex
Tel: 1-357 8320 Fax: 1-353 0257
E-Mail: geral@spantores.pt
presidente Dr. Luíz Francisco Rebelo
Role & Services: represent portuguese and foreign writers in Portugal, collaborate with groupement européen des sociétés d'auteurs et compositeurs (q.v.)

STE – Sindicato dos Trabalhadores de Espectáculos
Rua da Fé 23, 2°, 1150-149 **Lisboa**
Tel: 1-885 2728
Fax: 1-885 3787
president Estrela Novais; administration Daniel Garcia; international João Vidigal; public relations André Gago; women's issues Estrela Novais
Role & Services: includes and serves performing artists, technicians, administrators in theatre, dance, circus, variety; member of International Federation of Actors

ROMANIA (+40)

Institutul de Memorie Culturalá (CIMEC)
Pia-a Presei Libere 1, 33-90, 71341 **Bucharest**
Internet: www.cimec.ro
E-Mail: dan@cimec.ro
director Dan Matei
Role & Services: database and archives
Comments: funded by the Romanian Ministry of Culture

Jeunesses Musicales Romania
CP 13-53, **Bucharest** 13
Tel: 1-9238 3542 Fax: 1-323 6600
E-Mail: jmrluigi@dial.kappa.ro
president Luigi Marian Gageos; director programs Hortensia Orcula

Romanian Centre of the Association du théâtre pour l'enfance et la jeunesse (ASSITEJ)
OF P.T.T.R. 54-54-36, C.P. 22.61, 70160 **Bucharest**
Tel: 1-615 9720
contact Ion Lucian

Romanian Centre of the International Theatre Institute (ITI)
c/o UNITER, Str George Enescu 2-4, 70141 **Bucharest** 1
Tel: 1-315 3636 Fax: 1-312 0913/311 3214
E-Mail: uniter@buc.soros.ro
president Ion Caramitru; secretary Margareta Barbutza

Romanian Centre of Union Internationale de la Marionette (UNIMA)
Str. Compozitorilor 33, Bl. C 12 Ap. 98, 77351 **Bucharest**
contact Christian Pepino

Romanian Composers' and Musicologists' Union
Calea Victoriei 141, Sector 1, 71102 **Bucharest**
Tel: 1-650 2838 Fax: 1-210 7211
president Adrian Iorgulescu
Comments: member of CISAC

Romanian Theatre Union (UNITER)
Str. George Enescu 2-4, 70141 **Bucharest** 1
Tel: 1-311 3214/613 4278/315 3636
Fax: 1-312 0913
president Ion Caramitru; vice-president Cornel Todea

RUSSIA (+7)

All-Russian Cultural Fund
Miliutinsky per 19/4, 101000 **Moscow**
Tel: 095-925 3400 Fax: 095-923 8913
chairman Evgeny Stoletov

Cultural Fund
Kulturny Fond
Arts Center, 2 Pirogova str, 630090 **Novosibirsk**
Tel: 3832-397 818/343 Fax: 3832-302 237
Internet: www.nsu.ru/art_center
E-Mail: artcen@nsu.ru
director R H Deriglazova

International Ballet Association
ul Gertsena 14/2, 103009 **Moscow**
Tel: 095-229 5905 Fax: 095-229 9823
president Yuri Grigorovich; vice president Sergey Usanov
Role & Services: represents the interests of ballet dancers, choreographers and ballet masters. Arranges Russian ballet dancers' visits abroad and foreign dancers' visits to Russia. Organises music classes, festivals, national and international competitions

International Confederation of Theatre Unions
Leontyevsky per 21/1, 103009 **Moscow**
Tel: 095-229 3785 Fax: 095-742 0933
chairman Kirill Lavrov; executive secretary Valery Shadrin
Comments: organisers of Moscow International Chekhov Festival

International Union of Musicians
Bolshaya Nikitskaya 14/2, 103009 **Moscow**
Tel: 095-229 6029/201
Fax: 095-201 6956
chairman Irina Arkhipova
Role & Services: coordinates the work of various musical associations e.g. ballroom dancers', ballet dancers', piano makers' etc.
Comments: union holds music festivals, organizes international and national musicians competitions, commercial and non-commercial tours of Russia

Meyerhold Centre
Arbat 35, 121835 **Moscow**
Tel: 095-248 1280 Fax: 095-241 1285
general manager Valery Fokin; executive manager Oleg Lerner
Role & Services: aims to support all forms of new and innovative artistic projects in Russia and abroad; focus on helping young artists; organises tours at home and abroad, publications etc

Public Fund of Culture
Obshestvenny Fond Kultury
Nevsky pr 31, 191011 **St Petersburg**
Tel: 812-311 8371 Fax: 812-311 8349
chairman Iury Mudrov

RASSITEJ – Russian Centre of the Association du théâtre pour l'enfance et la jeunesse (ASSITEJ)
Strastnoj Bulvar 10, 103031 **Moscow**
Tel: 095-200 1546 Fax: 095-200 1546/230 2258
Internet: www.theatre.ru/rassitej
E-Mail: Rassitej@orc.ru
president Adolf Shapiro; secretary Marina Medkova

Russian Arts Foundation
c/o Baker McKenzie, Two Embarcadero Center, 24th Floor, San Francisco, **aa** CA 94111, United States of America
Tel: 1 415-984 3885 Fax: 1 415-576 3099
E-Mail: richard.walker@bakernet.com
contact Richard Walker
Role & Services: formed in 1992 the Foundation works to preserve and promote Russian arts by issuing grants and providing fund-raising assistance to independent performers and artists in Russia and by sponsoring exhibitions and educational programs. *Comments:* works mainly through a network of volunteers in Europe, Japan, Russia and the USA; major arts project support is Russian National Orchestra

Russian Authors' Society (RAO)
Bolshaya Bronnaya 6a, 103670 **Moscow**
Tel: 095-200 1210/203 3260 Fax: 095-200 1263
chairman Georgi Ter-Gazaryantz
Comments: formerly the state copyright agency GAASP, member of CISAC

Russian Centre of the International Theatre Institute (ITI)
c/o Theatre of Nations, Petrovski per. 3, 103031 **Moscow**
Tel: 095-229 5672 Fax: 095-229 6033/5672
secretary general Valery Khasanov; president Mikhail Oulianov
Comments: organiser of biannual International One Man Show Festival; services: helping foreign theatre production tours in Russia and Russian theatre production tours abroad, theatre information, contacts, launching theatre projects, international theatre expertise

Russian Centre of Union Internationale de la Marionette (UNIMA)
Strastnoj bulvar 10, 103031 **Moscow**
Tel: 095-229 9783 Fax: 095-230 2258
president Valery Volkhonsky;
secretary Irina Zharovtseva

Russian Composers' Union
Brjussov per. 8/10, kor 2, 108878 **Moscow**
Tel: 095-229 0867 Fax: 095-229 5218
chairman Kazenin I. Vladislav
Comments: Russian section of the International Music Council

Russian Cultural Fund
Gogolevsky bulvar 6, 121019 **Moscow**
Tel: 095-202 6984 Fax: 095-200 1238
chairman Nikita Mikhalkov

Russian Cultural Workers' Union
Zemlianoj Val 64, building 1, 109004 **Moscow**
Tel: 095-915 2625 Fax: 095-915 0943
chairman Genadij Poroshin; contact Valerij Kolotiuk
Role & Services: member of International Federation of Actors

Russian National Federation of International Festivals (ROSINTERFEST)
12 Sadovaya Triumfalnaya Ul 12/14, 103006 **Moscow**
Tel: 095-209 2261/200 6585 Fax: 095-209 9709
E-Mail: rosinterfest@glas.apc.org
president & director general Igor Gurevich

Russian State House of Folk Arts
Rossiiski Gosudarstvenny Dom Narodnogo Tvorchestva
Sverchkov per. 8, bldg 3, **Moscow**
Tel: 095-921 9284 Fax: 095-921 7917
director Elvira Kunina
Comments: nation-wide organisation working with folk music, dance and song groups, amateur theatre, amateur painting, embroidery and other handicraft artists; organises exhibitions, festivals and competitions, Russian professional and amateur folk groups tours abroad; see also Promoters

Russian Theatre Union (STD RF)
Strastnoj bulvar 10, 103031 **Moscow**
Tel: 095-209 2846 Fax: 095-230 2258
chairman Alexandr Kaliagin; executive secretary Valery Zakharov
Role & Services: 72 branches in different Russian cities

Russian Union of Concert Workers
Mokhovaya ul. 15, 191028 **St Petersburg**
Tel: 812-273 5735 Fax: 812-272 8368
president Iouri Tietirnatov; secretary co-ordinator Daskin M. Istrailevitch

St Petersburg Composers Union
45 Hertzen st., 190000 **St Petersburg**
Tel: 812-311 3548 Fax: 812-314 5818
E-Mail: Lobanov@ML1337.spb.edu

Union of Russian Circus Workers
Pushechnaya ul. 4, 101440 **Moscow**
Tel: 095-928 8790
chairman Emil Kio

SLOVAKIA (+421)

Many telephone and fax numbers in Slovakia are in the process of being changed. We have included all new numbers known at the time of going to print.

Association for Protection of Authors Rights (SOZA)
Slovensky ochranny zväz autorsky (SOZA)
Rastislavova 3, 813 27 **Bratislava**
Tel: 7-5556 1333/9362 Fax: 7-5556 9409
E-Mail: soza@gtinet.sk
director Dr. Peter Kliment
Role & Services: mechanical and performing right society

Association for the Protection of Slovak Performers
Ochranné zdruzenie interprétov Slovenska
Nevädzova 8, 821 01 **Bratislava**
Tel: 7-4329 5946/4333 5061/0905-259 806 (mobile)
Fax: 7-4333 5061
E-Mail: ozis@internet.sk
director Miroslav Smíd

Contemporary Dance Association, The
Asociácia súcasného tanca
PO Box 78, 810 00 **Bratislava**
Tel: 7-5273 3462/905-567 277 (mobile) Fax: 7-5273 3462
E-Mail: ast@contdance.sk
chairman Miroslava Kovárová

Contemporary Theatre Association, The
Asociácia súcasného divadla
Dunajská 36, 812 92 **Bratislava**
Tel: 7-5292 2107 Fax: 7-5292 6677
chairman René Parák

Music Fund
Hudobny fond
Medená 29, 811 02 **Bratislava**
Tel: 7-5443 1110 Fax: 7-5443 1110
director Milos Kocián
Role & Services: archive, lending service, music publisher, promoter

Music Information Centre of the Music Fund
Hudobné informacné stredisko hudobného fondu
Medená 29, 811 02 **Bratislava**
Tel: 7-5443 1380 Fax: 7-5443 3569
Internet: www.his.sk
E-Mail: his@his.sk
executive manager Alena Volná
Comments: the organisation was being re-named in Sept.-Oct. 1999, new name not known at time of going to print

National Music Centre
Národné hudobné centrum
Michalská 10, 815 36 **Bratislava**
Tel: 7-5443 4003/0379 Fax: 7-5443 0379/2652
Internet: www.slovkoncert.sk
E-Mail: slovkoncert@netlab.sk
general director Mgr. Olga Smetanová
Role & Services: Insitute established by the Ministry of Culture; departments include: Department of Methods, Musical Culture Research, Documentation, Publishing Department, Artists and Concert Management Activities Department/Agency Slovkoncert *Comments:* the organisation was being re-named in Sept.-Oct. 1999, new name not known at time of going to print

Slovak Association of Theatre Professionals
Zdruzenie divadelníkov na Slovensku
Dunajská 36, 812 92 **Bratislava**
Tel: 7-5292 2107 Fax: 7-5292 6677
chairman Adela Gáborová

Slovak Centre of the International Association du théâtre pour l'enfance et la jeunesse (ASSITEJ)
Slovenske centrum Medzinárodnej asociácie divadiel pre deti a mládez (ASSITEJ)
Bábkové Divadlo na Rázcestí, Kollárova 18, 975 90 **Banská Bystrica**
Tel: 88-412 5623/4193 Fax: 88-412 5623/4193
president Iveta Skripková

Slovak Centre of the International Association of Libraries and Museums of the Performing Arts (SIBMAS)
Slovenske centrum Medzinárodnej asociácie knizníc a múzeí divadelného umenia (SIBMAS)
The Theatre Institute, Jakubovo nám, 12, 813 57 **Bratislava**
Tel: 7-5293 1513/1535 Fax: 7-5293 1571
president Dr. Oleg Dlouhy

Slovak Centre of the International Association of Theatre Critics (AICT)
Slovenske centrum Medzinárodneho zväzu divadelnych kritikov (AICT)
Kabinet Divadla a filmu SAV (Theatre and Cinema Cabinet of the Slovak Academy of Science), Dúbravská cesta 9, 813 64 **Bratislava**
Tel: 7-5477 7193 Fax: 7-5477 3567
E-Mail: kadfmimi@savba.savba.sk
president Dr. Milos Mistrík

Slovak Centre of the International Organization of Scenographers, Theatre Architects and Technicians (OISTAT)
Slovenské centrum Medzinárodnej asociácie scénografov, divadelnych architektov a technickych pracovníkov (OISTAT)
The Theatre Institute, Jakubovo nám, 12, 813 57 **Bratislava**
Tel: 7-5293 1513/1535 Fax: 7-5293 1513
E-Mail: du@du.savba.sk
president Ján Zavarsky

Slovak Centre of the International Theatre Institute (ITI)
VSMU, Venturska 3, 813 01 **Bratislava**
Tel: 7-533 2306
Fax: 7-533 0125
president Martin Porubjak; vice-president Darina Karova; secretary general Dana Sliukova

Slovak Centre of the ITI
Jakubovo Namesta 12, 813 57 **Bratislava**
Tel: 7-5443 2306/5293 1535/1513/5296 3276
Fax: 7-5443 2579/5293 1513
E-Mail: dvvsmu@ba.sanet.sk
president Martin Porubjak
Comments: alternative E-mail: du@du.savba.sk

Slovak Centre of the Union Internationale de la Marionette (UNIMA)
Slovenské centrum Medzinárodnej bábkérskej organizácie (UNIMA)
Nadácia Art Film, Konventná 8, 811 03 **Bratislava**
Tel: 7-5441 1679 Fax: 7-5441 1679
president Ida Hledíková

Slovak Jazz Society
Slovenská jazzová spolocnost
Michalská 10, 815 36 **Bratislava**
Tel: 7-5443 1395 Fax: 7-5443 1395
president Peter Lipa

Slovak Music Council – IMC UNESCO
Slovenská hudobná rada – MHR UNESCO
Michalská 10, 815 36 **Bratislava**
Tel: 7-5443 4526
Fax: 7-5443 2652
executive vice-president Marián Lapsansky

Slovak Music Union
Slovenská hudobná únia
Michalská 10, 815 36 **Bratislava**
Tel: 7-5443 5291 Fax: 7-5443 0188
chairman Vladimír Bokes

Slovakian Centre of International Federation of the Phonographic Industry (IFPI)
Medzinárodná federácia fonografického priemyslu – Národná skupina Slovenskej republiky
Jakubovo nám 14, 813 48 **Bratislava**
Tel: 7-5292 3886 Fax: 7-5292 3886
director Dr. Miroslav Lindtner

Theatre Institute, The
Divadelny ústav
Jakubovo nám. 12, 813 57 **Bratislava**
Tel: 7-5293 1513/1535 Fax: 7-5293 1571
Internet: www.du.sk
E-Mail: du@du.savba.sk
general director Mgr. Silvia Hroncová

SLOVENIA (+386)

Association of Ballet Artists of Slovenia
Drustvo baletnih umetnikov Slovenije
Zupanciceva 1, 1000 **Ljubljana**
Tel: 61-159 0776
Fax: 61-159 0776
president Dr Henrik Neubauer; secretary Darinka Lavric
Role & Services: integration of creative interests in ballet art; national and international cooperation; popularisation of ballet art in Slovenia: organises seminars, lectures, video presentations, ballet concerts, ballet competitions, International Day of Dance, annual congresses; documentation centre

BUNKER
Zavod za organizacijo in izvedbo kulturnih prireditev
Rimska 2, 1000 **Ljubljana**
Tel: 61-224 563 Fax: 61-224 563
E-Mail: nevenka.koprivsek@guest.arnes.si
Role & Services: production centre (production, presentation, promoter, dance theatre, festival Mladi Levi) member of networks: Junge Hunde, IETM, DBM; see also Promoters

Copyright Agency of Slovenia
Avtorska agencija za Slovenijo
Slovenska 47, 1000 **Ljubljana**
Tel: 61-300 1560 Fax: 61-310 240
Role & Services: obtains the necessary licenses for Slovene theatres, radio, TV and other users of foreign copyright works; arranges payments of royalties or other fees abroad, and takes care of related tax issues; has own law offices; lawyers act both as counsels as well as trial lawyers, representing authors and rights holders (both foreign and domestic) before Slovene courts

Delak Center of Performance Research
Center za raziskave scenskih umetnosti Delak
Krakovska 27, 1000 **Ljubljana**
Tel: 61-125 5503 Fax: 61-125 5503
E-Mail: jana.pavlic@guest.arnes.si
director Jana Pavlic
Role & Services: research, development and information unit intended for the world of performing arts

Found for Amateur Cultural Activities of Republic of Slovenia
Sklad Republike Slovenije za ljubiteljske kulturne dejavnosti
Stefanova 5, 1000 **Ljubljana**
Tel: 61-126 2083/125 9355 Fax: 61-125 4421
director Vojko Stopar; counsellor for performing arts Jurij Rudolf
Role & Services: links associations; encourages culture and production of cultural projects; international cooperation of Slovenian non-professional artists, either through guest performances of cultural groups at international festivals or through exchange of experts in the field of cultural education; arranges about 40 educational seminars annually; organises about 20 performances per year, covering several cultural fields; a copious publication programme, the main pupose of which is to fill the blanks left by other publishers eg. printed music, editions on the conservation of the natural and cultural heritage of Slovenia

National Association of Drama Artists
Zdruzenje Dramskih Umetnikov Slovenije
Cankarjeva 11, 1000 **Ljubljana**
Tel: 61-125 8222 Fax: 61-217 044
president Marko Simcic; foreign secretary Majda Grbac

National Theatre Museum
Slovenski gledaliski muzej
Mestni trg 17, 1000 **Ljubljana**
Tel: 61-210 142/212 728 Fax: 61-210 142
director Ivo Svetina (email: sgm@guest.arnes.si); museum consultant Francka Slivnik (email: francka.slivnik@guest.arnes.si)
Role & Services: founded 1952; member of SIBMAS; collecting materials related to the history of Slovene theatre: books, periodicals, play texts, photographs, manuscripts, correspondence, programmes, clippings, sound recordings, videos, stage designs, costume designs, posters, portraits, offical documents
Comments: subjects: drama theatre, opera, operette, dance/ballet, puppetry, festivals publication yearbook, magazine Dokumenti, books on the history of Slovene theatre; also temporary exhibitions

Slovene Contemporary Dance Association
Drustvo za sodobni ples Slovenije
Metelkova 6, 1000 **Ljubljana**
Tel: 61-132 3390
E-Mail: dspslj@guest.arnes.si
president Ksenija Hribar; contact Nana Mravinec
Role & Services: to improve legal, cultural, political and social status of contemporary dance in Slovenia; information centre; issues a newsletter for members

Slovene Section of the IITM – Instituto Internazionale del Teatro del Meditarraneo
Slovenska sekcija IITM
Vilharjeva 11, 1000 **Ljubljana**
Tel: 61-310 610 Fax: 61-133 5025
E-Mail: tomaz.toporisic@guest.arnes.si
president Vito Taufer
Role & Services: the aim of the IITM network is to create and maintain international cultural contacts to promote the vidibility of performing arts in a large Mediterranean setting

Slovenian Centre of the International Theatre Institute (ITI)
Slovenski center Mednarodnega gledaliskega instituta c/o Drama SNG v. Ljubljani, Erjavceva 1, 1000 **Ljubljana**
Tel: 61-221 462/92 Fax: 61-223 885
president Dr. Henrik Neubauer; director Moja Kranjc

Slovenian Centre of Union Internationale de la Marionette (UNIMA)
Krekov Trg 2, 1000 **Ljubljana**
Tel: 61-314 422/966
Fax: 61-316 892
president Alenka Pirjevec
Comments: organiser of the international festival Puppet Arts and collaborates in the travelling festival Puppeteers Haven

Slovenian Section of Jeunesses Musicales
Kersnikova 4, 1000 **Ljubljana**
Tel: 61-131 7039 Fax: 61-322 570
Internet: www.gms.drustvo.si
president Silvester Mihelcic; secretary general Kaja Sivic
Role & Services: promotes young musicians, offers help to young musicians trying for scholarships, participating in master-courses, international music camps, organises its own International Summer Music Camp in Dolenjske Toplice, organises school concerts for young audiences, edits musical magazine *Comments:* GMS is also an active member of International Federation of Jeunesses Musicales/Federation International des Jeunesses Musicales/with its seat in Brussels; see also Promoters

University of Ljubljana – Academy of Theatre, Radio, Film and Television – Research Center for Theatre and Film
Univerza v Ljubljani – Akademija za gledalisce, radio, film in televizijo – Center za teatrologijo in filmologijo
Nazorjeva 3, 1000 **Ljubljana**
Tel: 61-210 412 Fax: 61-210 450/125 1424
head of research center Prof Dr Marko Marin
Role & Services: information, documentation and research centre; library, videotheque, iconotheque and other reference documenation on Slovene and European theatre

SPAIN (+34)

ADETCA – Associació d'empreses de teatre de Catalunya
c/ Hospital 51, 08005 **Barcelona**
Tel: 93-309 7900 Fax: 93-485 1512
president Daniel Martínez de Obregón; administracion Helena Jorge
Role & Services: professional body of producers and agents working in Catalonia *Comments:* publishes a quarterly guide on performing arts

Andalucian Dance Centre
Centro Andaluz de Danza
Calle Calatrava s/n, 41002 **Sevilla**
Tel: 95-490 1493 Fax: 95-490 7573
director José Antonio Ruiz
Role & Services: worldwide promotion of Andalucian dance; organises courses on contemporary dance

Andalucian Flamenco Center
Centro Andaluz de Flamenco
Palacio Pemartín nº1, Plaza de San Juan,
11403 **Jerez de la Frontera (Cádiz)**
Tel: 956-349 265/322 711
Fax: 956-321 127
Internet: caf.cica.es
E-Mail: caf@cica.es
consejero de cultura Carmen Calvo Poyato; director general de instituciones del patrimonio Reinaldo Fernandez Manzano; director Centro Andaluz de Flamenco Calixto Sanchez Marín
Role & Services: worldwide promotion of flamenco; organises exhibitions, runs a documentation centre with own library; dance and music studios
Comments: belongs to the Andalucian Regional Government (Junta de Andalucía)

Andalucian Musical Documentation Center
Centro de Documentación Musical de Andalucía
c/Carrerra del Darro 29, 18010 **Granada**
Tel: 958-223 500/1 (dirección)/825 (dept. documentación)/610 (dept. biblioteca)
Fax: 958-228 464
director Beatriz de Miguel Albarracín; librarian Alfonso Ramos; research and documentation Encarnación Vilchez Ruiz; administrator Leandro Herranz
Role & Services: regional music library and documentation centre; runs annual Music Research Funds
Comments: publishes books and CD on sacred music and Andalucian music & folk

Association of Dance Professionals
Asociación de Profesionales de la Danza
c/Atocha 105, 1ºA, 28012 **Madrid**
Tel: 91-420 3032 Fax: 91-420 3963
E-Mail: danza@line-pro.es
presidente Ana Victoria Cabo; vice-presidente Jorge Lopez
Role & Services: professional association; trade unions and mems union, centre de documentacíon, workshops, seminars, lectures; biggest union in Spain; legal assistance, job listings, professional contacts
Comments: in collaboration with Asociacion Cultural Por la Danza; organise auditions, courses and International Day of Dance; see also Publications

Association of Independent Venues
Coordinadora de Salas Alternativas
c/Desengaño 12, 5º Puerta 2, 28004 **Madrid**
Tel: 91-522 6940 Fax: 91-522 6940
gerente Encarna Piedrabuena; presidente coordinadora estatal Juan Muñoz; presidente coordinadora madrileña Alfonso Pindazo
Role & Services: coordinates the joint activities of its members (23 independent venues throughout Spain); organises festivals, annual congress; publishes newsletter UBÚ

Association of Performing Arts Producing Companies of Madrid (ARTEMAD)
Asociación de Empresas Productoras de Artes Escénicas de la Comunidad de Madrid
San Bernardo 97-99, 2-C (Ed. Colomina), 28015 **Madrid**
Tel: 91-593 0120/1422 Fax: 91-593 3934
presidente Mariano Llorente; vicepresidente Eladio Sánchez; secretario David Virosta; tesorería José Manuel Pérez Aguilar
Role & Services: defense of the interests of the performing arts, dance and theatre companies of Madrid region *Comments:* collective negotiation with national organistions, institutions and authorities; advisory; courses

Association of Playwrighters
Asociación de Autores de Teatro
c/ Sagasta 28, 5º, 28004 **Madrid**
Tel: 91-594 4798 Fax: 91-594 4798
presidente Jesus Campos García; vicepresidente Domingo Miras Molina; secretario general Santiago Martin Bermudez; presidente de honor Antonio Buero Vallejo
Role & Services: national organisation for professional authors focused on the defence of the rights of the Spanish playwrighters *Comments:* organises conferences and congresses; also publication of essays and texts

Association of Theatre Technicians (ARTE)
Asociación de Representantes Técnicos del Espectáculo (ARTE)
c/Rosario Pino 6, 6º B, 28020 **Madrid**
Tel: 91-572 2511/0391 Fax: 91-572 2614
Internet: www.la-red.com/arte
E-Mail: artte@arrakis.es
presidente Emilio Santamaría; vice presidente 1º Martin Gonzalez Fernandez; vice presidente 2º t.b.a.; secretario Francisco Carrillo Fernandez; director gerente Manuel Valcárcel Ruano
Role & Services: national, professional association; publish monthly magazine; receives no government subsidy; members include agents, promoters; negotiates with Ministerio de Trabajo; negotiates with Ministerio de Cultura and regional governments

Association Theatre, Music, Dance and Performance Arts Producers
Asociación de Productores de Teatro, Musica, Danza y Empresarios de Espacios Escenicos de la comunidad de Madrid – APTEMDE
c/Juan Bravo 20, Entreplanta izq., 28006 **Madrid**
Tel: 91-435 2068 Fax: 91-578 0691
presidente Enrique Cornejo; secretario general Jesús Cimarro; tesorero Fernando Rojas; vocal Juan José Seoane
Role & Services: Madrid community professional body of theatre producers; at present all members based in Madrid *Comments:* member of Federación Estatal de Empresas Productoras de Teatro y Danza de España

Basque Country Actors' Union
Union de Actores Vascos – Euskal Aktoreen Batasuna
Apartado de Correos 546,
20080 **San Sebastian – Donostia**
Tel: 943-455 267/2492 Fax: 943-452 492
Internet: www.paisuasco.com/eab
E-Mail: eab@nauta.es
secretario general Kike Diaz de Rada
Role & Services: the organisation acts a a professional syndicate aiming to promote, train and give legal and professional advice to actors
Comments: organises courses and publishes an actors' guide; publishes a news bulletin – Jokalaria, and 4 promotional video tapes

Catalalonian Section of Jeunesses Musicales
Joventuts Musicals de Catalunya
Apdo.70, 17257 **Torroella de Montgri (Girona)**
Tel: 972-760 605 Fax: 972-760 648
Internet: www.ddgi.es/tdm/fimtdm.html
E-Mail: jjmmttm@ddgi.es
presidente Esteve María Costajussa; secretario general Albert Bou
Role & Services: to help young musicians; works in schools; 250 concerts a year throughout Catalonia; concerts in schools; funding diverse cultural activities

Catalonia Association of Sound Technicians
Asociación Catalana de Técnicos de Sonido
Luis Antúnez 6, 2º, 08006 **Barcelona**
Tel: 93-218 6548 Fax: 93-218 6548
E-Mail: acts@hostiatnet.es
president Jose Mª Toledo; secretary Mapamusicx

Catalonian Association of Classical Music Performers
Asociación Catalana de Interpretes de Músic Clásica
Luís Antúnez 6, 2°, 08006 **Barcelona**
Tel: 93-218 6548 Fax: 93-218 6548
E-Mail: acts@hostiatnet.es
president Anna Ricci; secretary Mapamusicx

Catalonian Association of Dance Professionals
Asociació de Professionals de la Dansa de Catalunya
Via Laietana 52, Entr. 7, 08003 **Barcelona**
Tel: 93-268 2473 Fax: 93-268 0680
Internet: dancespain.com
E-Mail: dansa_catalunya@ols.es
president Gilberto Ruiz-Lang; general coordinator Sumsi Salvatella, Elisa Huertas, Xavier Bagä
Role & Services: association of professionals working in the dance industry; general, legal and professional advice for members of the association *Comments:* lobbying, organisation of festivals, publications

Catalonian Association of Professional Actors and Directors
Associació d'Actors i Directors professionals de Catalunya
Paseo de San Juan 10, Pral 2ª, 08010 **Barcelona**
Tel: 93-231 1484 Fax: 93-231 2448
Internet: www.bcn.es/tjussana/aadpc
E-Mail: aadpc@mail-cinet.es
president Hermann Bonnin; vice-president Vicky Peña; secretaria general Ferran Rañe; secretaria de finances Xavier Tur; secretaria sindical Carme Sansa; secretaria de direcció Lurdes Barba; secretaria de cultura Jordi Dauder
Role & Services: actors' Trade Union, aims to promote Catalonian culture and to create new openings for actors and directors; publishes an biennial guide for actors and the magazine Entreacte
Comments: see also Publications

Catalonian Composers Association
Associació Catalana de Compositors
Paseo de Colón N°6, Espacio 4°, 08002 **Barcelona**
Tel: 93-268 3719 Fax: 93-268 1259
Internet: www.accompositors.com
E-Mail: acc@accompositors.com
presidente Agustin Charles Soles; vicepresidente Oriol Graus Ribas; secretario Josep María Balanya
Role & Services: organises Avuimusica a season of concerts for contemporary music *Comments:* publishes the magazine Music D'ara; see also Publications

Choreographic Centre of Valencia Regional Government
Centro Coreográfio de la Comunidad Valenciana
c/o Teatres de la Generalitat Valenciana, Parc de la Granja s/n, 46100 **Burjassot (Valencia)**
Tel: 96-390 4774/5 Fax: 96-390 4772
E-Mail: tgvprog@redteatros.inaem.es
director artístico Juan Alfonso Gil Albors; coordinadora Immaculada Gil Lázaro
Role & Services: platform to stimulate contemporary dance at a regional, national and international level; runs an educational programme and a public programme of talks, conferences etc.; works as an intermediary between Valencian and international institutions *Comments:* alternative email: fmedina@cul.gva.es; organisers of Festival Dansa Valencia, see also Festivals

Documentation Centre for the Andalucian Peforming Arts
Centro de Documentación de las Artes Escénicas de Andalucía
c/ San Luis 37, 41003 **Sevilla**
Tel: 95-490 1493 Fax: 95-491 5710
Internet: cdaea.cica.es
E-Mail: cdaea@cica.es
directora Lola Vargas-Zúñiga; gabinete de comunicación Raquel Fuente
Role & Services: an autonomous body dependent from the Consejeria de Cultura de la Junta de Andalucía; it covers all performing arts and comprises the following sections: especialized library, audio-visual room, documentary archive, research and publishing
Comments: member of the European Network of Information Centres for the Performing Arts (ENCIPA) (q.v.)

Extremadura Region – Theatre and Music Centre
Centro Dramático y de Música de Extremadura
c/ Almendralejo 14, 06800 **Mérida**
Tel: 924-381 222 Fax: 924-381 313
Internet: www.festival-d-merida.com
E-Mail: gabicom@biz.servicom.es
director Carmelo Sayago Hernández
Role & Services: organise events in theatre, music and folk in different cities of the Extremadura region; give courses on theatre interpretation; give funding on music, theatre and dance *Comments:* part of Consejería de Cultura y Patrimonio de la Junta de Extremadura; manages Sala Trajano, see also Venues and Nat. Min.

Jeunesses Musicales – Barcelona Section
Joventuts Musicales de Barcelona
c/ Pau Claris 139, 4° 1ª, 08009 **Barcelona**
Tel: 93-215 3657/2918 Fax: 93-487 2970
Internet: www.teleline.es/personal/jmb.bcn
E-Mail: jmb.bcn@suport.org
presidente Juan Millá
Role & Services: organises concerts for young musicians; composition competition for young composers
Comments: see also Festivals and Competitions

Latin American Centre of Theatrical Creativity and Research – (CELCIT)
Centro Latinoamericano de Creación e Investigación Teatral – (CELCIT)
c/Infantas 19, 3° Dcha H, 28004 **Madrid**
Tel: 91-521 3296 Fax: 91-521 3273
E-Mail: celcit@seker.es
presidente María Teresa Castillo; director general Luis Molina López
Role & Services: research and training of Spanish-American theatre groups; publishes Teatro Celcit. Courses; meetings and seminars *Comments:* Latin-American address: Celcit Venezuela: Avenida Juan Germán Roscio N° 9 Quinta 'Marisela' – San Bernardino, Caracas, Venezuela. Tel: +58 92-511 675, fax: +58 92-513 540

Lleida Puppet Centre
Centre de Titelles de Lleida
Plaça de L'Hort de Sta Teresa 1, 25002 **Lleida**
Tel: 973-270 249 Fax: 973-264 515
director artístico Joan Andreu Vallvé; director pedagógico y gestión Julieta Agustí
Role & Services: documentation; artistic creation; education; annual Feria Internacional de Teatro de Títeres; has own puppet company and season; workshops, publications; member of International Federation of Centres for Puppetry Arts, see also Festivals
Comments: see also Puppets and Festivals

Madrid Actors' Union
Gran Via 50, 3° Dcha, 28013 **Madrid**
Tel: 91-541 5318 Fax: 91-541 6072
Internet: vbimagen.es-guiadeactores
E-Mail: uniondeactores@render.es
general secretary Jorge Bosso; organisation & finance secretary Alicia Agut; labour & institutional relations secretary Juan Matute
Role & Services: member of the Spanish Federation of Actors; member of FIA – International Federation of Actors *Comments:* this union only represents the region of Madrid – member of the National Federation of Actor's Unions; see also Publications

Municipal Centre of Puppetry Arts
Centro Municipal de las Artes del los Títeres
PO Box 5090, 48009 **Bilbao**
Tel: 94-424 5902/0437 Fax: 94-424 2550
dirección Concha de la Casa; secretaria Marian Sánchez; biblioteca y videoteca Luis Melendo
Role & Services: actors, perfromances, new productions, type puppets, venues, touring; library with 40-space reading room *Comments:* local funding; publishes Spanish puppet and marionette yearbook, Puck Magazine, books on history and theory of puppetry; organises puppet festival; see also Festivals and Publications; visiting address: Casa de Cultura, Barrainkua N°5, 48009 Bilbao

Music and Dance Documentation Centre
Centro de Documentación de Música y Danza
c/ Torregalindo 10, 28016 **Madrid**
Tel: 91-350 8600 Ext. 146 (secretaría)/110
Fax: 91-359 1579
E-Mail: cdmyd@sarenet.es
director Antonio Alvarez Cañibano
Role & Services: national musical and dance documentation centre, part of Instituto Nacional de las Artes Escénicas y de la Música (Ministry of Education and Culture), publish 'Recursos Musicales y de la Danza en España' (directory of musical and dance resources in Spain); directory of the Database of the same title
Comments: exhibitions and publications; see also Publications

Spanish Association of Symphonic Composers
Confederación Española de Compositores Sinfónicos
Escuela Sotomesa, San Felipe de Neri 4, 28013 **Madrid**
Tel: 91-448 2475/547 8583
E-Mail: sotomesa@arrakis.es
presidente Francisco Otero
Role & Services: aims to further the artistic and professional interests of its members; Advocates greater recognition and status of Spanish symphonic composers and better policies and funding; collaborates with the Ministry of Education and Culture

Spanish Association of Symphonic Orchestras
Asociación de Orquestas Sinfónicas Españolas
Via Laietana 41, 08003 **Barcelona**
Tel: 93-317 1096 Fax: 93-317 5439
Internet: www.obc.es
E-Mail: informacio@obc.es
presidente Francisco José Senra (tel: 95-456 1536)
Role & Services: aims to coordinate the activities of its 24 members on an artistic, technical and management level *Comments:* also acts as information centre on Spanish orchestras

Spanish Association of Theatre Directors
Asociación de Directores de Escena de España
Costanilla de los Ángeles 13, 28013 **Madrid**
Tel: 91-559 1246 Fax: 91-548 3012
secretario general Juan Antonio Hormigón
Role & Services: professional association uniting the majority of theatre directors in Spain; publishes magazine, books etc; cooperates with similar associations in Europe and South America; represented on Madrid's national and regional theatre councils; try to participate in all the political theatrical organisations as well as holding seminars, courses

Spanish Centre of ASSITEJ
Associación Española de Teatro para la Infancia y la Juventud (AETIJ)
Avda. Baviera 14, 28028 **Madrid**
Tel: 91-356 8475 Fax: 91-356 8475
secretaria general Doña Maria Luisa Barredo; presidente Manuel Gómez García
Role & Services: promote children's and youth theatre; run theatre festivals and 'Premio Nacional de Teatro' for outstanding service to children's theatre; library and video centre open to public; 'Premio Nacional de Autor A.E.T.I.J.' for new playwrights

Spanish Centre of the International Theatre Institute (ITI)
Centro Español del Instituto Internacional del Teatro de UNESCO
c/ Museo Nacional del Teatro, Villar, 4, 13270 **Almagro (Ciudad Real)**
Tel: 92-688 2244 Fax: 92-688 2533
Internet: www.mcu.es/museoteatro
E-Mail: museoteatro@insetel.es
secretario general Pedro Pardo Moreno; tesorera Julia García Verdugo; presidente Antonio Gala; vice-presidentes Enrique Cornejo, José Antonio Ruiz ; secretary Mª Antonia Ortega Cano
Role & Services: promotes international exchanges in theatre arts and education, organise 'Día Internacional de la Danza' annually; also organise Dia Mundial del Teatro & Dia Internacional de la Danza

Spanish Centre of Union Internationale de la Marionette (UNIMA)
Centro Español de la Unión Internacional de la Marioneta (UNIMA)
Plaça de l'Hort de Santa Teresa, 1, 25002 **Lleida**
Tel: 973-270 249 Fax: 973-264 515
president Joan-Andreu Valivé Cordomi; general secretary Juan Antonio Conde
Role & Services: promotes theatre of puppetry, provides members with information on all types of puppetry activities; courses, festivals and publications *Comments:* 12 members, one in each region with the presidency changing every four years (currently in Lleida); address general secretary: Juan Antonio Rodríguez, Urbanización Ciudad Verde, Casa 227, 41020 Sevilla, Tel: 95-440 5094

Spanish Committee of the International Dance Council of UNESCO
Comité Español del Consejo Internacional de la Danza en la UNESCO
Avda Reina Victoria 43, 5° A, 28003 **Madrid**
Tel: 91-553 3523 Fax: 91-553 3523
directora Mariemma
Role & Services: works with Centro Coreográfico Mariemma

Spanish Federation of Actors' Unions
Federación de la Unión de Actores del Estado Español
c/ Montera 34, 1° Dcha, 28013 **Madrid**
Tel: 91-522 2804 Fax: 91-522 6055
E-Mail: fedactors@mx2.redestb.es
secretario general Jorge Bosso; secretaria de organización María Amparo Soto
Role & Services: federation of all actors' unions in Spain; acts as a mediator between them and other organisations

Spanish Managing Society of Actors
Actores e Intérpretes Sociedad de Gestión de España (AISGE)
c/ Gran Via 22 Dpto. 5° Planta, 28013 **Madrid**
Tel: 91-521 0412 Fax: 91-521 7506
E-Mail: correo@aisge.es
presidente dto asistencial Juan Polanco; director general Julián Grimau; vicepresidente y tesorero Jaume Nadal; vicepresidente y secretario general Patxi Barco; presidente dto promocional Claudio Sierra
Role & Services: manages the intellectual property of actors; promote activities for the training and promotion of the actors

Spanish Phonographic and Videographic Association (AFYVE)
Asociación Fonográfica y Videográfica Española (AFYVE)
c/Pedro Muguruza 8 Entreplanta izq, 28036 **Madrid**
Tel: 91-345 4150 Fax: 91-345 6674
director & general secretary Carlos Grande; president Claudio Conde
Role & Services: member of the International Federation of the Phonographic Industry

Spanish Section of Jeunesses Musicales
Juventudes Musicales de España
Marina 164, Pral.3ª, 08013 **Barcelona**
Tel: 93-265 2371 Fax: 93-265 9080
Internet: www.clubjm.org
E-Mail: jmspain@opensl.es
presidente Jordi Roch; secretario general Joaquín Cardellach; dirección ejecutiva Esther Vorgas
Role & Services: 700 concerts throughout Europe; school concerts; international exchanges, courses, competitions, quarterly bulletin; organises concerts for young musicians *Comments:* see also Promoters and Competitions

Spanish Section of the International Society for Contemporary Music (ISCM)
Sociedad Internacional de Música Contemporánea: Sección Española
Avenida de América 58-5° dcha, 28028 **Madrid**
Tel: 91-356 3621/532 7427
presidente Luis de Pablo; general secretary José María Franco Gil; secretary Cristina Jiménez
Role & Services: promotes contemporary music, especially Spanish; concerts; recordings *Comments:* receives grant from Ministerio de Educación y Cultura

Spanish Society for Authors and Publishers
Sociedad General de Autores y Editores de España (SGAE)
Fernando VI, nº4, 28004 **Madrid**
Tel: 91-349 9550/580 Fax: 91-349 9555
Internet: www.sgae.es
director general Enrique Loras García; presidente Manuel Gutierrez Aragón; presidente del consejo de dirección Eduardo Bautista García
Role & Services: upholds the rights of authors (including composers) belonging to the society; support eg loans, for new authors/composers; authors' prizes; gives research grants, promotes the work of members of the association with tours *Comments:* has a cultural branch, Fundación Autor, that coordinates the promoting activities of the organisation; represents 49000 members, organises courses of new technologies for dance, music, theatre; see also Promoters

Theatre Documentation Centre
Centro de Documentación Teatral
c/ Torregalindo 1, 28006 **Madrid**
Tel: 91-350 8600 Fax: 91-359 9705
Internet: www.mcu.es/inaem/teatro01.htm
directora Cristina Santolaria Solano
Role & Services: national centre of documentation on Spanish theatre; belongs to the INAEM (National Institute of Performing Arts & Music) and to the Education and Culture Ministry *Comments:* the publication of Anuario Teatral (theatre yearbook) is currently being restructured; will also publish Guía Teatral '99 (biannual directory of Spanish Theatre); see also Publications

Theatre Institute of Barcelona Provincial Government
Institut del Teatre de la Diputació de Barcelona
Sant Pere més baix, 7, 08003 **Barcelona**
Tel: 93-268 2078 Fax: 93-268 1070
E-Mail: i.teatre@diba.es
contact Artur García Jiménez; director Pau Monterde; subdirector Agustí Humet; manager Francesc Colomer
Role & Services: principally a centre of theatre education; member of Réseau Européen des Centres d'Information du Spectacle (q.v.-Supranational); keeps a library and file open to public; produces own publications; has a research department: Centre d'Investigació, Documentació i Difusió (c/ Almogavers 177, 08018 Barcelona, tel 93-309 9158, fax 93-300 2153), jefa del centro Monse Álvarez); technical studies for the performing arts *Comments:* see also Festivals

Theatres of the Valencian Region
Teatres de la Generalitat Valenciana
c/ Barcas 15, 46002 **Valencia**
Tel: 96-351 0051 Fax: 96-394 2184
Internet: www.cult.gva.es/tgv
E-Mail: fmedina@cult.es
conseller Manuela Taracon; director Consuelo Ciscar Casaban; gerente German Marco Ponce; director artístico Juan Alfonso Gil-Albors; jefe de protocolo Mª José Muñoz Peirats; jefe de prensa Milagros Moya
Role & Services: centre of production, development and promotion of theatre productions; manages Teatro Rialto, Sala Moratín, Sala Arniches (Alicante), Teatro Talia and Teatro Principal; organises shows
Comments: see also Venues and Festivals

Women in Music Association
Asociación Mujeres en la Música
c/o Almagro 28, desp. 2-5, 28010 **Madrid**
Tel: 91-308 4588 Fax: 91-308 4588
E-Mail: yeyes@grn.es
secretaria María José Bayo; presidenta María Luisa Ozaita
Role & Services: promotes music composed by women; promotes classical music, also makes classical music more accessible to people through lectures, concerts, educational concerts and information
Comments: partly funded by Instituto de la Mujer, Ministerio de Asuntos Sociales

SWEDEN (+46)

Arts & Business
Föreningen Kultur och Näringsliv
Storgatan 10, Box 5403, 114 84 **Stockholm**
Tel: 8-666 6460/61 Fax: 8-660 7051
Internet: www.kultur-naringsliv.se
E-Mail: info@kultur-naringsliv.se
director Carin Adlen; assistent Anna Carin Möller
Role & Services: offers free advice to members on policy and general services on different aspects of business sponsorship of the arts, including research for members on sponsorship projects, seminars and regular meetings; Yearly award for arts sponsorship

Association of Swedish Theatres and Orchestras
Teatrarnas Riksförbund (TR)
PO Box 1778, 111 87 **Stockholm**
Tel: 8-440 8370 Fax: 8-440 8389
E-Mail: musik.teater@teatrarnsriks.se
chairman Sture Carlsson; executive director Thomas Nyh; directors Claes W Englund, Kajsa Herngren, Per Dejke
Role & Services: TR is the Swedish employers' and trade organisation for theatre, music and radio; it manages the working team for the cooperation of the Nordic professional symphony and opera orchestras; secretariat of International Alliance of Orchestra Association

Folkets Hus Riksorganisation (FHR)
PO Box 17194, 104 62 **Stockholm**
Tel: 8-702 6700/07 Fax: 8-640 7591
Internet: www.fhr.se
E-Mail: info@fhr.se
managing director John Brattmynr; cultural director Gunno Sandahl; information officer Peter Axelsson
Role & Services: a Folkets Hus is a Labour Movement Community Centre and there are now over 700 throughout Sweden; a hundred or so are municipal cultural centres with cinemas and theatres; a few rank as regional cultural centres with concert halls and large theatres; the National Federation is responsible for joint activities and is a trade and employer organisation

Folkparkerna
PO Box 17194, 104 62 **Stockholm**
Tel: 8-452 2500 Fax: 8-452 2505
Internet: www.folk.parkerna.se
E-Mail: info@folkparkerna.se
executive director John Brattmynr; cultural director Gunno Sandahl; information officer Peter Axelsson
Role & Services: unites 165 Folkparks whose activites are supported by non-governmental organisations and/or local authorities; it acts as an agency promoting dance, music, artists, theatre and other activities

Office of Swedish Music Festivals
Rödhakevägen 3, 906 51 **Umeå**
Tel: 90-142 580 Fax: 90-777 505
Internet: www.musikfestivaler.se
E-Mail: info@musikfestivaler.se
secretary general Bengt Lidström
Role & Services: deals with marketing, information, experience interchange and other matters of common interest to the large summer music festivals of Sweden; an annual program is published every year in January in English, French and German, including around 40 festivals *Comments:* information also: Erik Nordien, Secretary, PL 944, 880 37 Junsele, Sweden tel: 621-10715

Riksteatern – Swedish National Touring Theatre
Hallundavägen 30, 145 83 **Norsborg**
Tel: 8-5319 9100 Fax: 8-5318 3012
Internet: www.riksteatern.se
E-Mail: riks@riksteatern.se
general man. Thomas Lyrevik; press officer Anna Nystedt
Role & Services: to increase the interest in theatre; also arranges tours of companies including international ones; theatre organization, based on more than 240 theatre associations in Sweden; altogether it puts on about 50 different theatre programs: Riksteatern includes: the Cullberg Ballet, Tyst Teater (theatre for the Deaf), Unga Riks (Theatre for Children and Youth), Riks Drama and selected Riks guest performances; see also Drama

Royal Swedish Academy of Music
Kungl. Musikaliska Akademien
Blasieholmstorg 8, 111 48 **Stockholm**
Tel: 8-407 1800
Fax: 8-611 8718
chairman Daniel Boertz; secretary Bengt Holmstrand
Role & Services: promoting the arts and artistic development, publictions, scholarships, prizes

Swedish Artists' and Musicians' Interest Organisation (SAMI)
Döbelnsgatan 3, 111 40 **Stockholm**
Tel: 8-453 3400 Fax: 8-453 3440
Internet: www.sami.se
E-Mail: info@sami.se
managing director Hans Lindström
Role & Services: organisation for collective administration of performers' (statutory) rights according to the Swedish Copyright Act and corresponding foreign legislation *Comments:* SAMI is a member of AEPO and SCAPR (q.v.)

Swedish Arts Grant Committee
Konstnärsnämnden
PO Box 1610, 111 86 **Stockholm**
Tel: 8-402 3570 Fax: 8-402 3590
Internet: www.konstnarsnamnden.se
E-Mail: info@konstnarsnamnden.se
director Nils Johansson; chairman Lars Lönnroth; head of department of visual arts Lars Olof Gustafson; assistant Kate Ekblad
Role & Services: gives grants to professionals in the visual arts, music, the performing arts, film and video; a recipient must have his main artistic activity in Sweden *Comments:* visiting address: Fredsgatan 12, Stockholm

Swedish Centre of International Federation of the Phonographic Industry (IFPI)
PO Box 1008, 171 21 **Solna**
Tel: 8-730 9750 Fax: 8-273 745
Internet: www.ifpi.se
E-Mail: lgustavsson@ifpi.se
chairman Dag Häggqvist; director Lars Gustavsson; information officer Claes Olson

Swedish Centre of the Association du théâtre pour l'enfance et la jeunesse (ASSITEJ)
Box 6033, 121 06 **Johanneshov**
Tel: 8-659 8633 Fax: 8-659 8901
Internet: www.quicknet.se/assitej
E-Mail: svenska_assitej@hotmail.com
chairman Judit Benedex; vice-chairman Niclas Malmcrona

Swedish Centre of the International Theatre Institute (ITI)
Svensk Teaterunion – Svenska ITI
Mosebacke Torg 1, 116 46 **Stockholm**
Tel: 8-462 2530 Fax: 8-462 2535
E-Mail: swedish@iti.a.se
director Ann Mari Engel; chairman Lars Edström
Role & Services: Svenska ITI is a meeting place for all institutions and organisations that pursue artistic, pedagogic, scientific, or other professional activity within the theatrical field; it also represents Sweden in the Nordic Theatre Union and in the International Theatre Institute; its objective is to promote co-operation among and give information to different organizations and individuals in the Swedish theatre as well as to promote international exchange in the field of the theatre; the Centre publishes an annual magazine Swedish Theatre Suedois in English and French and, the Nordic Theatre Checklist with addresses to theatres, dance-groups, theatre schools, theatre periodicals in the Nordic countries; the members and subscribers are provided with monthly information
Comments: second address: PO Box 15035, 10465 Stockholm; promote the Swedish Theatre Biennale (next: May 2001)

Swedish Centre of Union Internationale de la Marionette (UNIMA)
Swedish Centre – UNIMA
Högdalens Dockteater, Box 121, 124 21 **Bandhagen**
Tel: 8-647 6148 Fax: 8-749 1122
contact Karl Erik Lindgren

Swedish Concert Institute
Svenska Rikskonserter
Nybrokajen 11, 111 48 **Stockholm**
Tel: 8-407 1600 Fax: 8-407 1650
Internet: www.srk.se
E-Mail: infosrk@srk.se
director Martin Martinsson; head of childrens productions Kerstin Fondberg; head of Caprice Records Kjell Söderqvist
Role & Services: organises and develops musical activity on a national level – organises concert tours of Swedish and international musicians, orchestras, choirs and ensembles of all types, including classical music, folk music, world music and jazz; using government funding coordinates music festivals, commissions new music and produces recordings on the Caprice Record label; is responsible for EMS (Electro-Acustic Music Centre), percussion Ensemble Camerata and Nybrokajen 11 (19th century Concert Hall)

Swedish Dance Committee
Svensk Danskommitté
Svensk Teaterunion/Svenska ITI, Box 15035, 104 65 **Stockholm**
Tel: 8-462 2536
Fax: 8-462 2535
E-Mail: lena.sundberg@iti.a.se
dance secretary Lena Sundberg
Role & Services: is a forum for the entire professional field of dance in Sweden – the artistic, educational, scientific etc. – and work for dance in a cultural-policy perspective; objective is to support and promote cooperation between the different branches of Swedish dance, to function as a coordinator for cultural political matters, to develop and facilitate international information and exchange; represented in the ITI Dance Committee within the International Theatre Institute; seminars; monthly information to members; general information service

Swedish Early Music Society
Föreningen för Tidig Musik (FFTM)
Nybrokajen 11, 111 48 **Stockholm**
Tel: 8-407 1723/24 Fax: 8-407 1727
Internet: www.mh.luth.se//fftm
E-Mail: tidig.musik@switnet.se
director Per-Erik Öhru; administrative director Hilleve Hogman
Role & Services: aims to expand interest in listening to and performing early music and dancing in education and the media *Comments:* publish a journal of early music quarterly and an annual catalogue of early music courses and a directory of early music artists

Swedish Insitute, The
Svenska Institutet
Stockholm
Comments: see entry under National & Regional Ministries of Culture

Swedish Music Council
c/o The Music Library of Sweden, PO Box 16326, 103 26 **Stockholm**
Tel: 8-5195 5418 Fax: 8-5195 5445
E-Mail: veslemoy.heintz@muslib.se
chairman Roland Sandberg; secretary t.b.a.; contact Veslemoy Heintz

Swedish Music Information Centre
Svensk Musik
PO Box 27327, Sandhamnsgatan 79, 102 54 **Stockholm**
Tel: 8-783 8800 Fax: 8-783 9510
Internet: www.mic.stim.se
E-Mail: swedmic@stim.se
director Roland Sandberg
Role & Services: provide information about serious Swedish art music and popular music; sell copies of serious Swedish music; Publish scores (Edition Suecia) and recordings (Phono Suecia), catalogues, booklets, etc

Swedish Music Publishers Association
Svenska Musikförläggereföreningen upd (SMFF)
PO Box 27327, Sandhamnsgatan 79, 102 54 **Stockholm**
Tel: 8-783 8800 Fax: 8-663 4962
Internet: www.smff.se
; managing director Carl Lindencrona (e-mail: carl.lindencrona@SMFF.se); legal adviser Ellinor Gyllenstierna (e-mail: ellinor.gyllenstierna@smff.se)
Role & Services: represent the economical and cultural interests of 69 music publishers

Swedish Musician's Union
Svenska Musikerförbundet
PO Box 43, 101 20 **Stockholm**
Tel: 8-5870 6000 Fax: 8-168 020
Internet: www.musikerforbundet.se
E-Mail: info@musikerforbundet.se
chairman Roland Almlén; secretary Göran Ivarson; legal adviser Håkan Hillerström

Swedish Performing Rights Society
Svenska Tonsettares Internationella Musikbyra (STIM)
Sandhamnsgatan 79, PO Box 27327, 111 40 **Stockholm**
Tel: 8-783 8800 Fax: 8-783 9595
Internet: www.stim.se
E-Mail: gunnar.petri@stim.se
directeur général Gunnar Petri; chairman Per Dermspen
Role & Services: member of Groupement Européen des Sociétés d'Auteurs et Compositeurs (q.v.); represents the rights of performers in Sweden

Swedish Section of Jeunesses Musicales
Musik för Ungdom
c/o Rikskonserter, Nybrokajen 11, 111 82 **Stockholm**
Tel: 8-407 1600 Fax: 8-407 1645
E-Mail: kersten.fondberg@srk.se
chairman Martin Martinsson; general secretary Kersten Fondberg
Comments: manages National Swedish Youth Music Festival, Musik Direkt (q.v.)

Swedish Section of the International Society for Contemporary Music
Nybrokajen 11, 111 48 **Stockholm**
Tel: 8-407 1638 Fax: 8-407 1649
E-Mail: christina.falk@srk.se
secretary Christina Falk; chairman of the board Ivo Nilsson
Role & Services: chiefly to mark selection of Swedish works to be presented at ISCM World Music Days, and to publish Nutida Musik (contemporary music) quarterly; also coordinate concerts arranged by 8 special presenters of contemporary music
Comments: contact: Christina Falk, Swedish Concert Institute, Tel: 8-407 1638, Fax: 8-407 1649

Swedish Union for Theatre, Artists and Media
Svenska Teaterförbundet
PO Box 12710, 112 94 **Stockholm**
Tel: 8-441 1300 Fax: 8-653 9507
E-Mail: info@teaterforbundet.se
chairman Tomas Bolme; vice chairman Anna Carlson; general secretary Jaan Kolk
Role & Services: trade union for theatrical employees – singers, dancers, actors, directors, film and theatre technicians, and theatre administrators; member of International Federation of Actors

SWITZERLAND (+41)

Association Faitiere Suisse des Professionnels de la Danse (ASD)/Schweizerischer Dachverband der Fachkräfte des Künstlerischen Tanzes (SDT)
Dufourstrasse 45, 3005 **Bern**
Tel: 31-351 6050 Fax: 31-352 1502
E-Mail: sdt-messerli@access.ch
president ASD/SDT Annemarie Pareich; vice president ASD/SDT Armin Wild; responsable ASD/SDT Hans Meister; responsable ASD/SDT Brigitte Mattenzzi; respondable ASD/SDT Oliver Dähler; respondable ASD/SDT Philippe Saire; Secretariat Theres Messerli
Comments: publishes: Magazine & poster Tanz – la danse suisse; works for better recognition of dance, to better the social position of dancers

Association of Swiss Concert Agents
Association des Agents et Organisateurs de Spectacles et de Concerts en Suisse/Verband der Künstler und Konzert-Agenten und Organisatoren in der Schweiz
Case postale 67, 1211 **Genève** 21
Tel: 22-741 4147 Fax: 22-741 4148
president Jack Yfar; vice-president (head classical branch) Rolf Hamberger; classical branch Heidi Widmer

Association of Swiss Professional Orchestras
Association Suisse des Orchestres Professionnels/Verband Schweizerischer Berufsorchester
Waisenhausplatz 14, Case postale 6509, 3001 **Bern**
Tel: 31-311 0779 Fax: 31-311 0982
managing director Thomas Hanke; president Jürg Keller
Role & Services: members are the 12 main Swiss orchestras

Federal Society of Orchestras
Société Fédérale des Orchestres/Eidgenössischer Orchesterverband
Postfach 428, 3000 **Bern** 7
Tel: 31-991 2270 Fax: 31-991 2270
E-Mail: kenplo@bluewin.ch
president Käthi Engel Pignolo
Role and Services: Swiss association of amateur orchestras

Schweizerischer Bühnenkünstlerverband
Leonhardsstr. 38, 4051 **Basel**
Tel: 61-274 1520 Fax: 61-274 1522
Internet: www.bkv.com
E-Mail: sbkv@sbkv.com
secretary Rolf Simmen
Role & Services: member of International Federation of Actors; 750 members

Swiss Association of Puppet Theatre
Schweizerische Vereinigung für Puppenspiel/Association Suisse pour le Théâtre de Marionnettes
Postfach, 8401 **Winterthur**
Tel: 52-213 6991 Fax: 52-213 6991
president Kurt Fröhlich; contact Irmgard Wehrle
Role & Services: publish Figura 4 times a year in German (and partly French) *Comments:* Redaktorin of the journal FIGURA: Elke Krafka, Johannisstr. 3, 89231 Neu-Ulm, Tel/Fax: +49 731-82259

Swiss Centre of International Federation of the Phonographic Industry (IFPI)
Toblerstrasse 76A, 8044 **Zürich**
Tel: 1-252 5866 Fax: 1-252 6167
secretary & legal adviser Dr Peter Vosseler
Role & Services: 30 sound recording companies are affilited to the IFPI Switzerland; its aim is to defen the interests and protect the rights of the sound recording sector

Swiss Centre of the Association du théâtre pour l'enfance et la jeunesse (ASSITEJ)
Gessnerallee 13, 8001 **Zürich**
Tel: 1-226 1919 Fax: 1-226 1918
E-Mail: astej@span.ch
president Roger Lille; contact Gunhild Hamer, Dieter Sinniger

Swiss Centre of the International Theatre Institute (ITI)
Gessnerallee 13, 8001 **Zürich**
Tel: 1-226 1910 Fax: 1-226 1911
E-Mail: iti-swiss@swissonline.ch
president Bert Schläpfer; secretariat Annelis Koeng
Role and Services: international network for the performing arts promoting cultural exchange

Swiss Centre of Union Internationale de la Marionette (UNIMA)
Zentralstelle, Postfach, 8401 **Winterthur**
Tel: 52-213 6991 Fax: 52-213 6991
contact Irmgard Wehrle
Role and Services: promotion of cultural exchange between puppeteers

Swiss Music Council
Schweizer Musikrat
Gönhardweg 32, 5000 **Aarau**
Tel: 62-822 9423 Fax: 62-822 9407
E-Mail: musikrat@aarauonline.ch
president Prof. Jakob Stämpfli; secretary general Ursula Bally-Fahr
Role & Services: umbrella organisation of all national organisations representing musical life
Comments: president's address: Haldenweg 24 C, 3626 Hünibach; since 1991The Swiss Council of Music hosts the European Music Council; The European Music Council is the European Regional Group within the International Music Council/UNESCO; Ursula Bally-Fahr is the Secretary General of the European Music Council; The European Music Council is a network for European collaboration in music and a platform for representatives of the National Music Councils and all organisations involved in the fields of music education, creation, performances, heritage etc. from all European countries

Swiss Music Information Centre
Fondation SUISA pour la Musique
Rue de l'Hôpital 22, 2001 **Neuchâtel**
Tel: 32-725 2536Fax: 32-724 0472
Internet: www.fondation-suissa.ch
E-Mail: info@fondation-suisa.ch
director Claude Delley; president Jean Balissat
Role & Services: encourages Swiss musical creations of all types; supports Swiss composers' projects and music publication companies which encourage Swiss music

Swiss Musicians' Association
Association Suisses des Musiciens
11 bis Av. du Grammont, Case Postale 177, 1000 **Lausanne** 13
Tel: 21-614 3290
Fax: 21-614 3299
executive secretary Jacques Lasserre; president Roman Brotbeck
Role & Services: members: composers, soloists, musicologists

Swiss Section of Jeunesses Musicales
Maison de la Radio, Case Postale 233, 1211 **Genève** 8
Tel: 22-328 7064 Fax: 22-796 8852
président Jean-Louis Juvet; secrétaire générale Christiane Buntschu
Role & Services: organise training courses (music) for all ages

Swiss Society for Contemporary Music – Swiss Section of the ISCM
Société Suisse pour la Musique Contemporaine/ Schweizer Gesellschaft für Neue Musik
c/o Association Suisse des Musiciens, Case Postale 177, 1000 **Lausanne** 13
Tel: 21-614 3290
Fax: 21-614 3299
executive secretary Jacques Lasserre

Swiss Society for the Rights of Authors of Musical Works
Société Suisse pour les droits des auteurs d'œuvres musicales (SUISA)
Bellariastrasse 82, Postfach 782, 8038 **Zürich**
Tel: 1-485 6666 Fax: 1-482 4333
Internet: www.suisa.ch
E-Mail: suisa@suisa.ch
directeur général Alfred Meyer
Role & Services: collective administration of performing, broadcasting and mechanical rights on musical works; legal advice in the related fields for members; membership: CISAC/BIEM/GESAC Groupement Européen des Sociétés d'Auteurs et Compositeurs

Swiss Theatre Society
Société Suisse du Théâtre/ Schweizerische Gesellschaft für Theaterkultur
Postfach 1940, 4001 **Basel**
Tel: 61-321 1060
Fax: 61-321 1075
Internet: www.theater.ch/sgtk.html
E-Mail: sgtk@theater.ch
Geschäftsführer Hansueli W. Moser-Ehinger
Role & Services: main aim is to support, document and develop Swiss theatre in all its forms; organises colloquiums and symposia, awards annual prize; publication of books and magazines (MIMOS) and directory of Swiss Theatre

Swiss Theatres' Federation
Schweizerischer Bühnenverband/ Union des Théâtres Suisses
Postfach 9, 8126 **Zumikon**
Tel: 1-918 1880
Fax: 1-918 1889
E-Mail: mbadilatti@access.ch
president Yvo Reichlin; secretary Marco Badilatti
Role & Services: umbrella organisation of professional Swiss theatres and opera; 28 members

Syndicat Suisse-Romand du Spectacle
Sécretariat Jeanne Ferreux, La Levratte 38, 1260 **Nyon**
Tel: 21-361 1765 Fax: 21-361 1765
E-Mail: jferreux@vtx.ch
président Michel Toman; secrétariat Jeanne Ferreux; administrateur financier Samy Benjamin
Role & Services: member of International Federation of Actors; to maintain work *Comments:* Michel Toman rue Tivali n°-20, 1007 Lausanne, tel: 21-320 9209; contact: Samy Benjamin, La Ruelle 3, 1302 Vufflens-la-ville; tel: 21-702 2702/701 4040; publication, Le Journal, quarterly; member of the International Theatre Institute

Vereinigung für Künstler/innen, Theater-Veranstalter/innen (KTV/ATP)
Obergasse 1, Postbox 3350, 2500 **Biel** 3
Tel: 32-323 5085 Fax: 32-323 5072
Internet: www.ktv.ch
E-Mail: ktv-atp@bluewin.ch
Direktor Denis Alber; Sekretariat Marianne Gschwind, Martin Clémence, Ursula Lehmann; Präsident Peter Bissegger
Role & Services: to promote theatre and performing arts, produce a quarterly bulletin, partly runs Pro Helvetia, runs Schweizer Kunstbörse (every last week in April)
Comments: see also atp artist & theatre promotion (KTV) (Promoters), ktv/atp – Künstlerbörse (artists exchange) (Festivals)

TURKEY (+90)

General Directorate of Turkish State Theatres
Mithatpasa Cad. 29/2, Kizilay, **Ankara**
Tel: 312-310 7225 Fax: 312-312 6507
director Bozkurt Kuruç

Music Producers' Society
Mü-Yap
Istiklal Cad. N° 348, Suriye pasaji, Kat 2 D-35, Galatasaray, **Istanbul**
Tel: 212-520 5020 Fax: 212-520 5018
president Sahin Özer
Comments: member of the International Federation of the Phonographic Industry

Opera and Ballet Foundation
Kennedy Cad. 28/47, Kavaklidere, **Ankara**
Tel: 312-467 1506/7 Fax: 312-467 1508
general director Unal Algin

Turkish Centre of the Association du théâtre pour l'enfance et la jeunesse (ASSITEJ)
Mihatpasa Cad 29/2, 206420 **Kizilay (Ankara)**
Tel: 312-432 4908 Fax: 312-433 7397
president Özcan Özer
Comments: collaborates with TOBAV (q.v.) organising Alagati International Children's Theatre Festival

Turkish Centre of the International Theatre Institute (ITI)
Yildiz Sarayi, Besiktas, **Istanbul**
Tel: 212-259 1636 Fax: 212-258 7700
general secretary Recep Bilginer; president Refik Erduran; centre director Ehsan Sham
Role & Services: helps coordinate theatrical activity in the public and private sectors; provides the Ministry of Culture with guidelines in its field; encourages new playwriting; further research, education and criticism in performing arts; assists actors' and directors' professional organisations; organizes give-and-take between Turkey's practitioners of the theatre and their counterparts in other countries

Turkish Centre of Union Internationale de la Marionette (UNIMA)
Mithatpasa Cad. No. 18 Kat: 5, Yenisehir, 06441 **Ankara**
Tel: 312-433 4527 Fax: 312-431 0297
manager Mevlüt Özhan; general secretary Mustafa Mutlu

Turkish Foundation of Opera and Ballet Workers – TOBAV
Tunali Hilmi Cad. 72/1, 06680 **Kavaklidere (Ankara)**
Tel: 312-427 8588 Fax: 312-427 8909
director Taner Levent (tel: 532-321 6009 mobile); general secretary Yavuz Sepetçi

UKRAINE (+380)

Association New Music – Ukranian Section of the ISCM
48 Bazarna str, apt. 1, 270011 **Odessa**
Tel: 482-225 283/261 689 Fax: 482-225 283/261 689
E-Mail: new_music@paco.net

Music Information Centre of Ukraine Composers
Kiev
Tel: 44-228 3304 Fax: 44-229 6940
president Mr V Simonenko

Ukrainian Centre of the International Theatre Institute (ITI)
c/o Union of Theatre Artists of Ukraine, PO Box 329, **Kiev** 34
Tel: 44-224 9107 Fax: 44-246 5829
president Larysa Kadyrova; secretary general Vera Bilyk
Comments: visiting address: Yaroslaviv val 14, Kiev 34

Ukranian Centre of the ITI
c/o Union of Theatre Artists of Ukraine, PO Box 329, 252034 **Kiev (Kyiv)** 34
Tel: 44-224 9107
Fax: 44-246 5829
president Larysa Kadyrova; secretary Vera Bilyk

Ukranian Composers Union
Tchaikovsky str. 7, 290000 **Lviv**
Tel: 322-742 349 Fax: 322-725 847
E-Mail: olia@lim.lviv.ua
contact Volodymyr Syvokhip

UNITED KINGDOM (+44)

ADiTi – National Organisation of South Asian Dance
3rd Floor, Oldebourne House, 46-47 Chancery Lane, **London** WC2A 1JB
Tel: 20-7831 5288/242 8088
Fax: 20-7831 5299
E-Mail: aditi@globalnet.co.uk
director Shanti Nagarajah; administrator Clare Holland-Martios
Role & Services: aims to raise the profile of South Asian dance in the UK by means of a comprehensive information service; a membership organisation – it also produces a quaterly magazine, National Directory, selected publications, education packs and holds conferences *Comments:* have an international membership with links to South Asian dancers and musicians

Agents' Association (Great Britain)
54 Keyes House, Dolphin Square, **London** SW1V 3NA
Tel: 20-7834 0515 Fax: 20-7821 0261
Internet: www.agents-uk.com
E-Mail: association@agents-uk.com
president Bob James; hon. secretary Ann Zahl; administrator Carol Richards
Role & Services: founded in 1927; Professional association for all types of theatrical entertainment agents in UK; Negotiates with unions, informs members, gives advice on legislation affecting employment agents

Alternative Arts
47 A Brushfield Street, Spitalfields, **London** E1 6AA
Tel: 20-7375 0441 Fax: 20-7375 0484
directors Maggie Pinhorn, Liz Weston
Role & Services: invest in new artists and new ideas and present a programme of open-air arts events throughout the year
Comments: see also Festivals, Promoters

Arts and Business
Nutmeg House, 60 Gainsford Street, Butler's Wharf, **London** SE1 2NY
Tel: 20-7378 8143 Fax: 20-7407 7527
Internet: www.AandB.org.uk
E-Mail: head.office@AandB.org.uk
chief executive Colin Tweedy; director of programmes Tim Stockil; development manager Anna Simson
Role & Services: promotes and encourages business support for the arts in all its forms; it has over 300 business members and offers advice and information in the form of publications, workshops and seminars; manages the Pairing Scheme, (The National Heritage Arts Sponsorship Scheme) on behalf of the Department of Culture, Media and Sport; it also runs 'The Placement Scheme', a programme offering business skills to arts managers
Comments: restructuring took place in1999; no further details known at time of going to print

Arts Marketing Association
Boltons Warehouse, 23 Tenison Road, **Cambridge** CB1 2DG
Tel: 1223-578 078
Fax: 1223-578 078/9
Internet: www.a-m-a.co.uk/ama
E-Mail: ama@pipex.dial.com
chairman Ted Baker; membership administrator Julie Aldridge
Role & Services: keep members up todate on new developments in marketing, especially arts marketing

Asian Music Circuit
Ground Floor, Unit E, West Point, 33/34 Warple Way, **London** W3 0RG
Tel: 20-8742 9911 Fax: 20-8749 3948
Internet: www.amc.org.uk/asianmusic
E-Mail: info@amc.org.uk
chairman Viram Jasani; programme coordinator Penny King; secretary Kuldeep Jalf; education coordinator Alistair Will
Role & Services: touring organisation; promotes music and culture from all parts of Asia concentrating on the Indian Sub-Contintent and the Far East; also involved in education work throughout the UK; contacts being made with European promoters to extend Asian music throughout Europe; mailing list members receive up to date information on all concerts and artistes performing throughout the UK; also provide master classes and lecture demonstrations and workshops
Comments: funded by the Arts Council of England (q.v.); is a registered charity

Association of Arts Fundraisers
38 Convent Road, **Broadstairs** CT10 3BE
Tel: 1843-600 586 Fax: 1843-600 586
E-Mail: artrais@aol.com
chair Jeff Fendall
Role & Services: to reflect the interests and concerns of all those in the Arts charged with raising funds or concerned with development; issues a newsletter and runs meetings, seminars and training courses for the benefits of members

Association of British Choral Directors (ABCD)
46 Albert Street, **Tring** HP23 6AU
Tel: 1442-891 633 Fax: 1442-891 633
Internet: www.abcd.org.uk
E-Mail: marie.louise.petit@abcd.org.uk
general secretary Marie-Louise Petit; chair Howard Layfield
Role & Services: promotes the education, training and development of choral directors in all sectors of choral music, provides a forum for choral conductors in the United Kingdom

Association of British Concert Promoters
12 Woodford Close, Radyr Way, Llandaff, **Cardiff (Wales)** CF5 2PH
Tel: 29-2056 4569 Fax: 29-2056 4569
chairman Aidan Plender; deputy chairman Andrew Jowett (121-200 2000); secretary Rosemary Jones (1604-626 222)
Role & Services: exists to represent the interests of concert halls throughout the United Kingdom; meetings and seminars with other organisations take place on a regular basis *Comments:* for full details please contact: Aidan Plender or Rosemary Jones at Derngate Theatre, Northampton (q.v.)

Association of British Orchestras
Pegasus House, 37-43 Sackville Street, **London** W1X 1DB
Tel: 20-7333 0371 Fax: 20-7287 9959
Internet: www.abo.org.uk
E-Mail: info@abo.org.uk
director Libby MacNamara; chairman Stephen Carpenter
Role & Services: supports the interests of all professional orchestras in the UK; provides services, events, activities, specialist training, publications and general advocacy

Association of British Theatre Technicians (ABTT) (British Centre of OISTAT)
47 Bermondsey Street, **London** SE1 3XT
Tel: 20-7403 3778 Fax: 20-7378 6170
Internet: www.abtt.org.uk
executive director Howard Bird; chairman Richard Brett; administrator Jenny Straker
Role & Services: a membership organisation, formed in 1961, providing information, advice and a forum for discussion on all aspects of technical theatre; through its committees, the ABTT aims to influence standards and regulations and provides an advisory service for those involved in the planning of theatre buildings
Comments: the Society of British Theatre Designers, Society of Theatre Consultants and the Theatres Advisory Council can be contacted at the above address

Association of Fundraising Consultants
The Grove, **Harpenden** AL5 1AH
Tel: 1582-762 446 Fax: 1582-461 489
E-Mail: ema@eaafundraising.demon.co.uk
chairman Mike Westerman; company secretary & treasurer David Morris; membership secretary Elizabeth Anderson; hon. secretary Andrew Thomas
Role & Services: the AFC is the professional association for qualifying members within the fundraising consultancy profession; the purpose is to agree, promote and protect standards of service

Association of Professional Theatre For Children and Young People (APT)
c/o Brian Bishop, Warwick Arts Centre, University of Warwick, **Coventry** CV4 7AL
Tel: 24-7652 4252 Fax: 24-7652 3883
Internet: www.apt.org.uk/index2.html
E-Mail: b.c.bishop@warwick.ac.uk
contact Brian Bishop
Role & Services: APT promotes and develops the work of professional theatre organisations and individuals working for and/or with children and young people; its membership consists of producing and presenting theatres, festival programmers, local authorities, freelance writers, directors, administrators, performers and designers; APT publishes Theatre First, Britain's only magazine dedicated to theatre for young people which also contains a directory of member activities; APT is the British Centre of ASSITEJ

Black Theatre Forum
c/o 74C Kings Cross Road, **London** WC1X 9QG
Tel: 20-7713 5732
co-ordinator Maria McConnell
Comments: currently undergoing major changes; at time of going to print information about future role and services was not available

British Academy of Composers and Song Writers
The Penthouse, 4 Brooke Street,
London W1Y 1AA
Tel: 20-7629 0992 Fax: 20-7629 0993
Internet: www.britishacademy.com
E-Mail: info@britishacademy.com
chief executive Chris Green
Role & Services: the Acadmy represents the interests of music writers across all genres and advices on professional and artistic matters; publishes quarterly magazine and other printed information
Comments: the Acadamy was formed by the merging of Composers Guild of Great Brtian, Association of Professional Composers and the British Academy of Song Writers, Composers and Authors

British Actors' Equity Association (incorporating the Variety Artistes Federation)
Guild House, Upper St. Martin's Lane,
London WC2H 9EG
Tel: 20-7379 6000 Fax: 20-7379 7001
Internet: www.equity.org.uk
E-Mail: info@equity.org.uk
president t.b.a.; general secretary Ian McGarry; general manager Fred Jostland; assistant secretary – film,tv and radio Andy Brodger; assistant secretary – theatre and variety Christine Payne; campaign, press & pr officer Martin Brown; research & parlimentary officer Adam Baxter; marketing & membership service Louise Grainger
Role & Services: trade union representing the interests of actors, club and circus performers, stage management, designers and directors, choreographers, dancers, singers and many others in the arts and entertainment industry; also operates student membership scheme

British Arts Festivals Association
3rd Floor, The Library, 77 Whitechapel High Street,
London E1 7QX
Tel: 20-7247 4667 Fax: 20-7247 5010
Internet: www.artsfestivals.co.uk
E-Mail: bafa@netcomuk.co.uk
president Sir John Manduell; vice presidents Sir John Drummond, Sir Ian Hunter, Gavin Henderson; chairman Tim Joss; deputy chairpeople Chris Barron; coordinator Gwyn Rhydderch
Role & Services: BAFA is the meeting point for arts festivals in the UK; it aims to represent a full range of arts festivals and to be the voice and focus for a festivals moment; all festival members appear in an arts festivals listing and the website has a map, A-Z directory and links to individual festival sites

British Association of Choreographers (BAC)
London
Comments: see under Dance UK, companies merged

British Centre of the Association du théâtre pour l'enfance et la jeunesse (ASSITEJ)
c/o APT, Warwick Arts Centre, University of Warwick,
Coventry CV4 7AL
Tel: 24-7652 4252
Fax: 24-7652 3883
Internet: www.apt.org.uk/index2.html
E-Mail: b.c.bishop@warwick.ac.uk
contact Brian Bishop
Role & Services: see Association of Professional Theatre for Children and Young People (APT); ASSITEJ is the International Association for Children and Young People with branches in over 60 countries worldwide

British Centre of the International Theatre Institute (ITI)
Goldsmith's College, University of London,
Lewisham Way, **London** SE14 6NW
Tel: 20-7919 7276 Fax: 20-7919 7277
E-Mail: iti@gold.ac.uk
chairman Neville Shulman OBE; administrator Lynne Kendrick
Role & Services: International organisation providing information on performing arts worldwide; created in 1948 under the auspices of UNESCO and has over 80 national centres worldwide

British Centre of Union Internationale de la Marionette (UNIMA)
c/o Cross Border Arts, Wysing Arts Centre, Fox Road,
Bourn CB3 7TX
Tel: 1954-718 181
Fax: 1954-718 333
E-Mail: lorraine@cba.eastern-arts.co.uk
general secretary Lorraine von Gehlen; chairman Ray DaSilva; treasurer & membership secretary Martin McGilp
Role & Services: British Centre of an international association dedicated to the pursuit of understanding between peoples through the art of puppetry; affiliated to UNESCO; membership association of people with a professionl or amateur interest in puppetry; organises puppetry events, often with an international focus; publishes the BrUNIMA Bulletin 3 times a year with international news, art and book reviews, also a members' newsletter; it has a panel of consultants with specialist skills; registered charity

British Choral Institute
6 Chailey Avenue, Rottingdean,
Brighton BN2 7GH
Tel: 1273-300 894 Fax: 1273-308 394
E-Mail: britchorinst@fastnet.co.uk
director Dr. Roy Wales; administrator Christine Wales
Role & Services: advisory, promotional, educational and training body for choral singers, conductors, choral administrators and organisers from all sectors of the choral community

British Federation of Young Choirs
Devonshire House, Devonshire Square,
Loughborough LE11 3DW
Tel: 1509-211 664 Fax: 1509-260 630
E-Mail: admin@bfyc.demon.co.uk
chief executive Susan Lansdale; hon secretary Andrew Fairbairn; administrator Ruth Grainger
Role & Services: to stimulate choral singing in the UK and to improve its quality through singing events and training courses; to encourage links between youth choirs in Britain and their counterparts overseas; member of the European Federation of Young Choirs; members receive advice, information and financial assistance towards overseas travel; also reduced participation fees at BFYC events, and a twice-yearly news letter and monthly information updates

British Film Institute (BFI)
21 Stephen Street, **London** W1P 2LN
Tel: 20-7255 1444 Fax: 20-7436 7950
Internet: www.bfi.org.uk
E-Mail: mail@bfi.org.uk
director t.b.a.; deputy director Jon Teckman; chairman Alan Parker
Role & Services: BFI is the UK national agency with responsibility for encouraging the arts of film and television and conserving them in the national interest
Comments: the work of the BFI includes The National Film and Television Archive, National Film Theatre, Museum of the Moving Image, BFI Production, BFI Films, BFI TV, Library and Information Services, Research and Edcuation and a number of film festivals including the London Film Festival

British Music Information Centre
10 Stratford Place, **London** W1N 9AE
Tel: 20-7499 8567 Fax: 20-7499 4795
Internet: www.bmic.co.uk
E-Mail: info@bmic.co.uk
director Matthew Greenall; information manager Simon Woolf
Role & Services: reference library and information centre of 20th century British classical music with concerts on Tuesday and Thursdays; Open 12-5pm each weekday
Comments: also has a database collection of 45 000 items available on the website

British Phonographic Industry Ltd
25 Savile Row, **London** W1X 1AA
Tel: 20-7287 4422 Fax: 20-7287 2252
Internet: www.bpi.co.uk
E-Mail: general@bpi.co.uk
director general John Deacon; legal adviser Emma Fanning; director of research and development Peter Scaping; consultant Fiona Haycock
Role & Services: trade association for major and small record companys in UK; organiser of Brit Awards

British Puppet and Model Theatre Guild
65 Kingsley Avenue, **London** W13 0EH
Tel: 20-8997 8236 Fax: 20-8997 8236
Internet:
ourworld.compuserve.com/homepages/ted.beresford-puppetman
chairman Peter Charlton
Role & Services: voluntary society established 1925; membership subscription; aims to advocate the use of puppetry and model theatre, to raise the state of puppetry in all its forms; regular meetings in London and the provinces; panel of consultants; library and archive; regional councillors available for contact; monthly newsletter, annual magazine, technical sheet at intervals; exhibitions, festivals, weekend schools; overseas members welcome

British Society for Practitioners of Jewish Music
c/o Membership Secretary, 38 Sherwood Road,
London NW4 0PU
Tel: 20-8203 9640 Fax: 20-8203 9640
chairman t.b.a.; membership secretary Joanna Fellerman; treasurer Barry Weinberg; secretary John Abranson
Role & Services: to promote, research and perform the wealth of Jewish musical tradition; a directory of performers and a calendar of Jewish musical events is planned; regular forum for the performance of Jewish music

Broadcasting Entertainment Cinematograph & Theatre Union (BECTU)
111 Wardour St., **London** W1V 4AY
Tel: 20-7437 8506 Fax: 20-7437 8268
Internet: www.bectu.org.uk
E-Mail: bectu@geo2.poptel.org.uk
general secretary Roger Bolton; assistant general secretary Gerry Morrissey, Marilyn Goodman; supervisory officials Martin Spence (freelance divisions), Luke Crawley (BBC), Sharon Elliott (Independent Broadcasting), Willy Donaghy (Arts & Entertainment); Stage Screen & Radio editor Janice Turner
Role & Services: trade union representing all technical, administration, ancillary and non-performance staff in the Arts, Broadcasting and Film industries; provides a journal Stage, Screen & Radio free to members ten times a year; free legal advice and representation to members on industrial and work related matters

Catalan Consortium for the Exteral Promotion of Culture
17 Fleet Street, 3rd Floor, **London** EC4Y 1AA
Tel: 20-7353 2253 Fax: 20-7353 1166
Comments: main branch in Barcelona, see entry under Spain

Centre for Creative Communities (formerly British American Arts Association)
118 Commercial Street, **London** E1 6NF
Tel: 20-7247 5385
Fax: 20-7247 5256
Internet: www.creativecommunities.org.uk
E-Mail: baaa@easynet.co.uk
director Jennifer Williams
Role & Services: serves performers and artists of all kinds by promoting the arts as a vital element of community-development work; the centre assists artists to make contacts with the voluntary and education sectors for the purpose of developing collaborative projects; it also maintains a library of materials in this field and acts as the sole UK distributor for books published by Americans for the Arts
Comments: CCC is not a grantgiving organisation

Chinese Cultural Centre
27 Old Gloucester Street, **London** WC1N 3XX
Tel: 20-7633 9878 Fax: 20-7405 1656
E-Mail: greenf5@ibm.net
administrator Susie Wong; artistic director Dai Ailian
Role & Services: national organisation for Chinese arts; promotes Chinese arts in the UK *Comments:* venue base for London Chinese Orchestra, Chinese Dance and Mime Theatre Companies

Commerical Radio Companies Association
77 Shaftesbury Avenue, **London** W1V 7AD
Tel: 20-7306 2603 Fax: 20-7470 0062
Internet: www.crca.co.uk
E-Mail: info@crca.co.uk
chairman & chief executive Paul Brown; research & communications manager Rachell Fox; public affairs manager Ms Nick Irvine; financial controller Bhaskaran Jeganathan
Role & Services: trade body for commercial radio; deals with copyright bodies; funded by its members, represents commercial radio to Government, the Radio Authority and others; owns network chart show sponsored by Pepsi, jointly with the BBC owns Rajar – industry audience measurement system
Comments: formerly known as the AIRC (the Association of Independent Radio Companies)

Concert Promoters Association
6 St. Mark's Road, **Henley-on-Thames** RG9 1LJ
Tel: 1491-575 060
Fax: 1491-414 082
chairman Harvey Goldsmith; secretary Carole Smith
Role & Services: matters concerned with all aspects of promotion of events, including rights, health, safety, insurance, touting; c. 28 members and 4 associate members

Dance 4 Ltd
@ Preset, 3-9 Hockley, **Nottingham** NG1 1FH
Tel: 115-941 0773
Fax: 115-941 0776
Internet: www.innotts.co.uk/~preset
E-Mail: dance4@innotts.co.uk
administrator Rachel Emmett; director Jane Greenfield
Role & Services: National Dance Agency for the East Midlands region; commission and promotions of new dance, training, advice and resources for dancers and choreographers; education and community work in the region; manage annual NOTT Dance Festival which promotes new, small-scale dance and performance

Dance City-National Dance Agency
Peel Lane, Off Waterloo Street,
Newcastle-upon-Tyne NE1 4DW
Tel: 191-261 0505 Fax: 191-230 0486
E-Mail: info@dancecity.enta.net
director Janet Archer; general manager Judith Cashman; head of finance Ian McKeown; marketing officer Sarah McPhail; dance deveopment officer Jane Marescaux, Christine Grimwood
Role & Services: provides a focal point for professional dance in the region; presents dance seasons and choreographic platforms; hosts a full-time Higher National Diploma in Dance, and offers over 50 weekly dance classes at all levels; organises and runs community project

Dance Collective (Agency) N.I., The
34 Station Road, Sydenham,
Belfast (Northern Ireland) BT4 1RF
Tel: 28-9065 3541
Fax: 28-9028 6025
coordinator Anthea McWilliams; administrator Carrie-Anne McAlonan; chair and board of directors Anna Cutler
Role and Services: promoting and supporting all forms of dance in Northern Ireland *Comments:* supported by Arts Council of Northern Ireland, Belfast City Council and the National Lottery; The Dance Collective is dedicated to implementing and developing a sustainable infrastructure for dance, in all it's forms, in Northern Ireland (primarily); membership is open to all practitioners, teachers, performers, choreographers and regular dancers (ie community groups/individuals who are active in dance and those interested in the development of Dance in NI); enquiries welcome

Dance UK
c/o Battersea Arts Centre, Lavander Hill,
London SW11 5TF
Tel: 20-7228 4990
Fax: 20-7223 0074
E-Mail: danceuk@easynet.co.uk
director Jane Attenborough; chairman Jane Mooney; general manager Suzie Leighton; healthier dancer programme manager Jessica Shenton
Role & Services: represents all professional dancers and dance companies; lobbies and offers help, advice and support services; manages healthier dancer programme

Dance Xchange
Birmingham Hippodrome, Hurst Street,
Birmingham B5 4TB
Tel: 121-622 3253
Fax: 121-622 3496
chair Jane Hawksley; artistic director David Massingham; assistant director Sally Francis
Role & Services: to establish a network for dance activities in the region in partnership with dance artists, companies, educators and venues, for participants of all ages, abilities and cultural backgrounds; funded by West Midlands Arts, Birmingham City Council and the Arts Council of England, Dance Xchange aims to nurture a dynamic regional, national and international dance culture; The Dance Xchange provides community classes for children and adults and professional dance classes, as well as hosting workshops, residencies, master classes and performances; Dance Xchange is able to advise and assist in marketing companies touring in the region, and has three fully equipped dance studios and a studio theatre; Dance Xchange also comission new work

Directors' Guild of Great Britain
15-19 Great Titchfield Street, **London** W1P 7FB
Tel: 20-7436 8626
Fax: 20-7436 8646
Internet: www.dggb.co.uk
E-Mail: guild@dggb.co.uk
chief executive Malcolm Moore; events & communications director t.b.a.; administrator Sarah Wain; chair Herbert Wise
Role & Services: union and craft guild representing directors in all media: film, tv, theatre, radio, commercials, etc; arrange major events, European conferences, workshops, screenings; annual directory of members *Comments:* publishes Direct magazine quarterly; organises Theatre Directors Forums in various European cities

Early Music Network
31 Abdale Road, **London** W12 7ER
Tel: 20-8743 0302
Fax: 20-8743 0996
Internet: www.earlymusic.org.uk
E-Mail: glyn@earlymusicnet.demon.co.uk
administrator Glyn Russ
Role & Services: to generate and service the development of early music through the promotion of live performances, education and the dissemination of information; publish a magazine called Early Music News; produces an annual directory for promoters; also a biennial competition for young musicians
Comments: see also Promoters

Eastern Orchestral Board
10 Stratford Place, **London** W1N 9AE
Tel: 20-7629 9601
Fax: 20-7495 4710
E-Mail: eob@compuserve.com
director David Richardson; education manager Stuart Bruce; marketing manager Jan Ford; administrator Nancy Buchanan
Role & Services: Eastern Orchestral Board is a development agency for professional orchestral music in the areas of the Eastern, East Midlands and part of Southern Arts Boards; working with its member local authorities, orchestras and other agencies, EOB supports concerts, community and education projects and audience development initiatives through financial assistance and advisory services to create a regional strategy of high quality orchestral residencies and tours

Incorporated Society of Musicians
10 Stratford Place, **London** W1N 9AE
Tel: 20-7629 4413 Fax: 20-7408 1538
Internet: www.ism.org
E-Mail: membership@ism.org
chief executive Neil Hoyle; head of professional policy Helenn Houghton; head of legal & general services Karen D'Rozario; head of finance & systems Ralph Seed; manager corporate affairs & publications Kim Davenport Gee; manager marketing & development Victoria Benbow; manager specialist section services Fiona McLeod; manager membership information Gradgle Bent; office assistant Elizabeth O'Dwyer
Role & Services: the U.K.'s professional body for all musicians, performers, composers, conductors, teachers and lecturers; aims to promote the art of music, protect the interests of all who work with music, raise standards within the profession and offer its members the best possible range and quality of services; professional advice, 24 hour legal, tax and councelling helplines, insurances (public liability to £10m, legal expenses), contracts and agreements, minimum fees, discounts on goods and services, information sheets, publications, branded merchandise
Comments: publishes Music Journal (editor: Neil Hoyle), Yearbook and three annual promotional registers of specialists

Independent Television Commission (ITC)
33 Foley Street, **London** W1P 7LB
Tel: 20-7255 3000 Fax: 20-7306 7800
Internet: www.itc.org.uk
E-Mail: publicaffairs@itc.org.uk
chief executive Peter Rogers; director of economic regulations Sheila Cassells; director of advertising & sponsorship Stephen Locke; director of regions & public affairs Paul Smee; head of press James Conway; head of publications & publicity Andy Bailey
Role & Services: the public body responsible for licensing and regulating commercially funded television services provided in and from the UK; these include Channel 3 (ITV), Channel 4, Channel 5, public teletext and a range of cable, local delivery and satellite services, also digital television services

Independent Theatre Council (ITC)
12, The Leather Market, Weston Street,
London SE1 3ER
Tel: 20-7403 1727 Fax: 20-7403 1745
Internet: www.itc-arts.org
E-Mail: itc@dircon.co.uk
director Nicola Thorold; deputy director Charlotte Jones; training officer William Forrest; finance officer Kevin Dunn
Role & Services: the managers association and representative body for all types of smaller performing arts companies and venues in UK; has comprehensive seminars and training programme for arts administrators; runs courses; also offers legal advice and help with company and charity registration; carries out lobbying for the sector

Jewish Music Heritage Trust
PO Box 232, **Harrow** HA1 2NN
Tel: 20-8909 2445 Fax: 20-8909 1030
E-Mail: jewishmusic@jmht.org
director Geraldine Auerbach
Role & Services: education, performance, information; dedicated to the celebration, preservation and development of the living heritage of Jewish music for the benefit of all *Comments:* also organises the London International Jewish Music Festival and the Joe Loss Lectureship in Jewish Music; recordings, performances and commissions with the School of Oriental and African Studies, University of London; see also Festivals

Laban Centre London
Laurie Grove, **London** SE14 6NH
Tel: 20-8692 4070 Fax: 20-8694 8749
Internet: www.laban.co.uk
E-Mail: info@laban.co.uk
director Dr Marion North PhD DArts; vice principals Anthony Bowne, Mirella Bartripp
Role & Services: as the leading centre for professional contemporary dance training in Europe, Laban Centre London has a teaching faculty with an unrivalled range of expertise; situated in London, the Centre is at the forefront of undergraduate and graduate study in dance, providing a creative environment to challenge the dancer, choreographer, therapist, community dance practitioner, designer and scholar; a great strength is the range of possible study, due to the diversity of specialised courses available; the Centre has a Library with an Archive facility, and is home to Dance Theatre Journal and Transitions Dance Company (Britain's professional training company for contemporary dancers) *Comments:* see also Publications and Dance

London Playwrights
61 Collier Street, **London** N1 9BE
Tel: 20-7713 7125 Fax: 20-7837 1850
administrator Greg Branson
Role & Services: promotes writers' work, monthly newsletters, masterclasses and regular workshops for members

MCPS (Mechanical Copyright Protection Society Ltd)
Copyright House, 29/33 Berners Street,
London W1P 4AA
Tel: 20-7580 5544 Fax: 20-7306 4455
Internet: www.mcps.co.uk
E-Mail: info@mcps.co.uk
chief executive John Hutchinson; director of business affairs Chris Martin; head of member services Dominic McGonigal; head of licensing services Sharon Dean
Role & Services: MCPS represents writers and publishers of music, licensing their works whenever they are recorded and collecting the mechanical royalties accrued on their behalf
Comments: Streatham Office: Elgar House, 41 Streatham High Street, London SW16 1ER, Tel: 181-664 4400, Fax: 181-769 8792, Website: www.mcps.co.uk

Music Performance Research Centre, The
The Barbican Library, The Barbican Centre, Silk Street,
London EC2Y 8DS
Internet: www.musicpreserved.org
E-Mail: mprc@dial.pipex.com
independent chairman Basil Tschaikov; administrator Margaret Gray (tel/fax: 1730-893 611)
Role & Services: archive and study centre that preserves our heritage of public performances; it makes and receives non-commerical archive recordings of public performances that would otherwise be lost to posterity; it houses a unique selection of over 1200 performances from the 1930s to the present that can not be heard, and in some cases also seen, elsewhere; these performances can be experienced by any of the general public, free of charge, at the MPRC Studio in the Barbican Library; the MPRC also records conversations with international performers: over 80 artists can be heard talking about music and their lives

Musicians' Union
60-62 Clapham Road, **London** SW9 0JJ
Tel: 20-7582 5566 Fax: 20-7582 9805
Internet: www.musiciansunion.org.uk
E-Mail: info@musiciansunion.org.uk
general secretary Dennis Scard; assistant general secretary, media John Smith; assistant general secretary, live engagements Bob Wearn; assistant general secretary, administration Andy Knight
Role & Services: the organisation for all those following the profession of music which negotiates with all the main media outlets: film, tv, video etc and gives contractual advice to members
Comments: 31,000 members in 80 branches nationwide

National Association of Youth Orchestras, The
Ainslie House, 11 St. Colme Street,
Edinburgh (Scotland) EH3 6AG
Tel: 131-539 1087 Fax: 131-539 1069
Internet: www.nayo.org.uk
E-Mail: admin@nayo.org.uk
director Carol Main; administrator Jenny Brockie
Role & Services: national association for youth orchestras throughout UK; activities include annual Festival of British Youth Orchestras in Edinburgh and Glasgow, Anglo-German Youth Music Week, British Reserve Insurance Conducting prize (biennial), British Reserve Insurance Youth Orchestra Awards (annual), newsletter (3 p.a.) free to members, Marion Semple Weir library of chamber music, no hire charges to members

National Association of Youth Theatres (NAYT)
The Arts Centre, Vane Terrace,
Darlington DL3 7AX
Tel: 1325-483 271 Fax: 1325-369 404
Internet: www.nayt.org.uk
E-Mail: nayt@ndirect.co.uk
director Stuart Hawkes; administration officer Liz Clapham
Role & Services: established in 1982; the aim of the organisation is to increase the range and quality of Youth Theatre in the UK through a programme of advocacy training, information services and participation; NAYT publishes a monthly bulletin and offers youth theatres the opportunity to network with other groups across the country; it has a database of approximately 700 Youth Theatres across Britain; NAYT holds its annual Big Youth Theatre Festival each July with the support of the Arts Council of England and in April 99 launched a 3 year regional development programme funded in partnership with the DFEE *Comments:* alternative e-mail: shawkes001@aol.com

National Campaign for the Arts
Francis House, Francis Street,
London SW1P 1DE
Tel: 20-7828 4448 Fax: 20-7931 9959
Internet: www.artscampaign.org
E-Mail: mail@artscampaign.org
director Victoria Todd; magazine editor Simon Tait
Role & Services: the independent lobby for the arts; committed to changing public and political attitudes to the arts; specialises in research, information services, parliamentary lobbying and public campaigning; publishes a quarterly magazine and occassional briefing papers

National Dance Agency Network – Yorkshire Dance
3 St Peter's Buildings, St Peter's Square,
Leeds LS9 8AH
Tel: 113-243 9867 Fax: 113-259 5700
Internet: www.yorkshiredance.org.uk
E-Mail: admin@yorkshiredance.org.uk
director Bush Hartshorn; admin director Alison Owen; marketing officer Cathy O'Neill; dance development officers Jan Burkhardt, Alex Sutherland; projects officer Mairead Turner; general manager Cathy Woodall
Role & Services: established in 1982, Yorkshire Dance works to promote the accessibility of dance to all sectors of the community; in addition to a huge range of community classes and workshops, Yorkshire Dance is at the forefront of choreographic development and a key producer of new work for touring

National Early Music Association NEMA
Southside Cottage, Brook Hill, Albury,
Guildford GU5 9DJ
Tel: 1483-202 159 Fax: 1483-203 088
E-Mail: lutesoc@aol.com
administrator Christopher Goodwin; chairman Dr Peter Holman; president John Mansfield Thomson
Role & Services: an umbrella organisation for those involved in early music; information centre; publishes register of early music annually and quarterly magazine

National Federation of Music Societies (NFMS)
Francis House, Francis Street, **London** SW1P 1DE
Tel: 20-7976 4930 Fax: 20-7828 5504
Internet: www.nfms.org.uk
E-Mail: nfms@nfms.org.uk
chief executive Robin Osterley; membership & operations manager Chris Wright; training & development officer Robin Simpson; pr to chief executive Harriette Sutcliffe
Role & Services: umbrella organisation providing financial, legal and music advice for 1700 affiliated choirs, orchestras, music clubs and other voluntary music groups, provides arts adminstration training for members. A key area of NFMS' activity is lobbying on behalf of its members

National Music Council
Francis House, Francis Street, **London** SW1P 1DE
Tel: 20-8347 8618 Fax: 20-8347 8618
administrator Jennifer Goodwin; chairman Russell Jones; vice-chairman Mark Isherwood
Role & Services: member of International Music Council, working to support the interests of music in the UK; dedicated to promoting and representing the interests of all those working within the field of music in the United Kingdom

National Resource Centre for Dance
University of Surrey, **Guildford** GU2 5XH
Tel: 1483-259 316 Fax: 1483-259 500
Internet: www.surrey.ac.uk/capitals/NRCD.html
E-Mail: h.roberts@surrey.ac.uk
administrator Helen Roberts; consultant Judith A Chapman
Role & Services: dance archive and reference collection – visitors by appointment; short courses; Dance Current Awareness Bulletin published 3 times a year; general information service, information on and provider of courses, conferences, new publications; directories; resource packs; videos
Comments: a number of special dance archive collections from specific dance organisations, contemporary and ballet dance companies, and dance individuals

Opera and Music Theatre Forum
Pegasus House, 37-43 Sackville Street,
London W1X 1DB
Tel: 20-7287 7018
Fax: 20-7287 9959
chair Andrew Bennett; manager Jean Nicholson
Role & Services: the representative body for small and middle-scale professional opera and music theatre in the UK; it advocates and informs on behalf of its members, dissemination of information to members, representation at conferences and meetings in the UK and abroad; organises seminars, workshops, conferences etc *Comments:* the OMTF is a member of the Association of British Orchestras (q.v.)

Performing Artists' Media Rights Association Ltd (P@MRA)
160 Borough High Street, **London** SE1 1HR
Tel: 20-7940 0400 Fax: 20-7407 2008
Internet: www.pamra.org.uk
E-Mail: members@pamra.org.uk
chief executive Anne Rawcliffe-King; general services administrator Christine Grey; directors Sheila Ferguson, Benny Gallagher, Robert King, Mike Berry, Mitch Dalton, Ashley Mason, Ian Partridge, John Patrick, Colin Sheen
Role & Services: non-profit making company run by and for performers; membership organisation administering performers rights; collecting and distributing monies to all UK perfomers irrespective of contractual status or role for all territories, including the UK; also collect free for all overseas performers who are members of the Association

Performing Right Society (PRS)
Copyright House, 29-33 Berners Street, **London** W1P 4AA
Tel: 20-7580 5544 Fax: 20-7306 4455
Internet: www.prs.co.uk
E-Mail: info@prs.co.uk
chief executive John Hutchinson; director of performance licensing John Axon; director of membership John Sweeney; director of planning & corporate communication Terri Anderson; director of copyright enforcement Graham Churchill; director of international Diana Derrick; director of new technology Mark Isherwood; director of legal affairs David Lester; director of business accounts Chris Martin; director of operations Mike Orchard; director of finance Steve Porter; director of information systems John Rathbone; director of corporate services John Rowe
Role & Services: PRS collects royalties on behalf of music creators and publishers for the public performance and broadcast of their copyright musical works
Comments: Streatham Office: Elgar House, 41 Streatham High Street, London SW16 1ER, Tel: 181-664 4400, Fax: 181-769 8792

Phonographic Performance Ltd (PPL)
1 Upper James Street, **London** W1R 3HG
Tel: 20-7534 1000 Fax: 20-7534 1111
managing director John Love; head of external affairs Colleen Hue; chief executive officer Charles Andrews
Role & Services: collecting society, licensing the broadcasting and public performance of sound recordings in the UK on behalf of record companies and performers

Portuguese Arts Trust, The
Palingswick House, 241 King Street, **London** W6 9LP
Tel: 20-8748 0884 Fax: 20-8748 4187
E-Mail: info@portugal600.demon.co.uk
executive director Michael Collins; admin. Miguel Santos
Role & Services: promotes Portuguese cultural interests and markets their image in the United Kingdom and the Republic of Ireland; its main aims are to promote Portuguese culture and to initiate colloboration between Portuguese and British/Irish artists and performers

Puppet Centre Trust
BAC, Lavender Hill, **London** SW11 5TN
Tel: 20-7228 5335 Fax: 20-7228 8863
E-Mail: pct@puppetcentre.demon.co.uk
director Lorretta Howells; general admin.Allyson Kirk
Role & Services: umbrella organisation for professional and amateur puppeters; offers information and advice on puppetry; reference library and archive; historical collection of puppets
Comments: produces bi-monthly publication Animations, education packs, directory of professional puppeteers; organises occassional courses, workshops and festivals; visitors centre open 2-6pm every weekday; touring exhibitions; see also Puppets

rescen – centre for research into creation in the performing arts
Trent Park, Bramley Road, **London** N14 4YZ
Tel: 20-8362-6288 Fax: 20-8362 6148
Internet: www.adpa.mdx.ac.uk
E-Mail: rescen@mdx.ac.uk
head of centre Prof Christopher Bannerman
Role & Services: promote research on creation in the performing arts

Royal Choral Society
Studio 9, 92 Lots Road, **London** SW10 0QD
Tel: 20-7376 3718 Fax: 20-7376 3719
Internet: go.ourworld.nu/royalchoralsociety
E-Mail: royalchoralsociety@compuserve.com
musical director Richard Cooke; administrator Graeme Tonge; choir secretary Helen Body
Comments: see also Promoter and Choirs

Scottish Arts Network, The
c/o Royal Lyceum, 30b Grindlay Street,
Edinburgh (Scotland) EH3 9AD
Tel: 131-228 3885 Fax: 131-228 3955
chairman John Gray; administrator Ruth Holloway
Role & Services: independant and non-political federation of arts organisations in Scotland; offers information, advice, support to members, organises conferences and seminars on cultural issues; aims to raise profile of the arts and press for better policies and funding

Scottish Mask and Puppet Theatre Centre
8-10 Balcarres Avenue, Kelvindale,
Glasgow (Scotland) G12 0QF
Tel: 141-339 6185 Fax: 141-357 4484
Internet: www.scot-art.org/smpc
E-Mail: sm010@post.almac.co.uk
contact Malcolm Knight (director); administrator Lisa Daifuku; special effects designer/ maker Grant Mason; development officer John Clarke
Role & Services: houses an 80-seat studio theatre, cafe, shop, production design workshops, and office complex with reference library; specialises in education, cultural animation projects, and service to professional puppeteers and film and television; creative puppet documentation centre; promotes puppet and mask companies, exhibitions, conferences, master courses, international residencies and work; full-time training courses (2 years) – HND-level offered in partnership with Anniesland College; permanent exhibition of puppets from around the world – The Magical World of Puppets and The Miles Lee Collection
Comments: setting up the Anima Project, an international visitors centre comprising of theatre, museum and documentation centre, due to have opened at the end of October 1999; see also Puppetry

Scottish Music Information Centre Ltd
1 Bowmont Gardens, **Glasgow (Scotland)** G12 9LR
Tel: 141-334 6393 Fax: 141-337 1161
Internet:
www.music.gla.ac.uk/HTMLFolder/Resources/SMIC/homepage.html
E-Mail: smic@glasgow.almac.co.uk
director Morag Brooksbank; information officer Alasdair Pettinger; administrator Caitie Faulds
Role & Services: SMIC exists to document and promote the works of Scottish and Scottish-based composers past and present; services include a resource centre containing thousands of scores, books, recordings and manuscripts; a hire library; the production of a newsletter, Music Current; high quality photocopying and binding service for composers; an up-to-date information database, published as the Scottish Music Handbook; SMIC is subsidised by the Scottish Arts Council; Open weekdays (except Wednesday) 9.30am - 5.30pm

Society for Dance Research
The Library, Laban Centre London, Laurie Grove,
London SE14 6NH
Tel: 20-8692 4070 (ext 120) Fax: 20-8694 8749
Internet: www.laban.co.uk
E-Mail: p.bassett@laban.co.uk
administrative secretary Peter Bassett FLA
Role & Services: promotes and fosters the quality and scope of scholarship and research relating to dance in all its forms and aspects and to enhance the role of dance in society; Activities include c. 3 meetings a year and the publication of Dance Research and a newsletter both twice a year *Comments:* second address: Appletrees, Brown's Lane, Storrington, RH20 4LQ, Tel: 1903-742 019

Society for Theatre Research
c/o The Theatre Museum, 1e Tavistock Street,
London WC2E 7PA
Internet: www.unl.ac.uk/str
E-Mail: E.Cottis@bt.internet.com
president Timothy West; joint honorary secretaries Eileen Cottis, Frances Dann; honorary treasurer Barry Sheppard; chairman Pieter van der Merwe
Role & Services: founded in 1948 to foster research into historical and current theatre practice; Issues its regular journal Theatre Notebook and annual publications; arranges lectures and other activities *Comments:* awards up to £4,000 annually in grants to aid research that is substantially concerned with the history and practice of the British theatre; also awards annual Theatre Book Prize (currently £400) for best book on British theatre research that year (written in English)

Society of London Theatre (SOLT)
32 Rose Street, **London** WC2E 9ET
Tel: 20-7557 6700 Fax: 20-7557 6799
Internet: www.OfficialLondonTheatre.co.uk
E-Mail: Emma@solttma.co.uk
chief executive Rupert Rhymes; development officer Emma de Souza; industrial officer Peter Morris; legal officer Louis Norman; commercial manager Paul James; editor Howard Watson; president Martin McCallum
Role & Services: SOLT is the trade association acting on behalf of theatre owners, managers and producers for Londons' 50 West End Theatres; SOLT publishes the London Theatre Guide, The Theatre List & Update, The Disabled Access Guide, administers the Laurence Olivier Awards, runs the nationwide Theatre Tokens scheme and manages the Half Price Ticket Booth in Leicester Square; also runs promotions such as Kids Week in the West End

Sound Sense
Riverside House, Rattlesden,
Bury St. Edmunds IP30 0SF
Tel: 1449-736 287 Fax: 1449-737 649
E-Mail: 100256.30@compuserve.com
administrator Clare Adams; director Kathryn Deane; projects officer Kate Murdoch; information officer Margaret Sloan; communications officer Anita Holford
Role & Services: the national development agency for participatory music-making in the community offers information exchange network, research and consultancy to arts, community and educational organisations; support, advice and training to community musicians and groups; lobbies on behalf of participatory music making *Comments:* also runs the NMDIS which is the National Music Dsability Information Service, which gives advice and information on all matters concerning music and disabilites – contact Sarah Bennett-Day Tel: 1449-736 287

Spnm – promoting new music
Francis House, Francis Street, **London** SW1P 1DE
Tel: 20-7828 9696 Fax: 20-7931 9928
Internet: www.spnm.org.uk/
E-Mail: spnm@spnm.org.uk
executive director Gill Graham; administrator Katy Bignold; education consultant Sarah Gibbon; publications officer Rachel Duncombe
Role & Services: from contemporary jazz, classical and popular music to that written for film, dance and other creative media, spnm is one of the main advocates of new music in Britain today; education work with young people and their teachers; publishes 'new notes' concert listings magazine and Beat Magazine for 16-19 year-olds

The Place Dance Services
Mary Ward House, 5 Tavistock Place, **London** WC1H 9SN
Tel: 20-7383 3524 Fax: 20-7388 5407
Internet: www.theplace.org.uk
E-Mail: danceservices@theplace.org.uk
director (The Place Dance Services) Theresa Beattie; administrator(The Place Dance Services) Catherine Willmore; manager (The Video Place) Steve Jackman; editor Juice magazine (the Place Dance Services) Carolyn Deby
Role & Services: The Place Dance Services (tel: 171-383 3524, fax: 171-388 5407) provides dance information at local, regional, national and international levels for Independent dance profession also on areas including, festival, promoters, venues, companies, funding criteria and guidelines, rehearsal spaces; auditions; The Video Place (tel:171-383 0516) aims to provide a comprehensive video service for the independent dance profession; the viewing facility is open (weekdays by appointment) to dance programmers, festival directors, producers, choreographers, teachers and students; editing and tape copying is also available; TPDS publishes Juice, a monthly magazine listing professional opportunities for independent dancers/choreographers; subscription membership of TPDS costs £15 upwards *Comments:* 3rd area covers prefessional development for dancers, choreographers, composers & dance film makers

Theatre's Trust, The
22 Charing Cross Road, **London** WC2H 0HR
Tel: 20-7836 8591 Fax: 20-7836 3302
E-Mail: ttt@theatrestrust.org.uk
director Peter Longman
Role & Services: established by an act of parliament to promote better protection of theatres for the benefit of the nation

Theatrical Management Association
32 Rose Street, **London** WC2E 9ET
Tel: 20-7557 6700 Fax: 20-7557 6799
chief executive Rupert Rhymes; industrial officer Peter Morris; legal officer Louise Norman; senior executive officer David Emerson
Role & Services: TMA is the trade association for theatre managers, theatre owners and producers, both grant-aided and commercial, in England, Scotland, Wales and Northern Ireland; it was founded in 1894 and now has a membership of nearly 400; activities include industrial relations, legal advice for members, lobbying, training, events such as the Barclays Theatre Awards, and publications including Prompt, a quarterly magazine

Total Theatre – UK umbrella organisation for mime and physical theatre and visual performance
At The Circus Space, Coronet Street, **London** N1 6NU
Tel: 20-7729 7944 Fax: 20-7729 7945
E-Mail: magtotaltheatre@easynet.co.uk
director & company secretary Annabel Arndt
Role & Services: Total Theatre was founded by practitioners in 1984 to advocate for greater recognition and status for Mime and Physical Theatre; aims to raise public profile of Mime and Physical Theatre and Visual Performance; provides information for the public and practitioners; work regionally and nationally; produces research and publications which currently include: Guide to Mime in Education, Moving into Performance Report, Blueprint for Regional Mime Development and UK Mime and Physical Theatre Training Directory; publishes a quarterly magazine Total Theatre Magazine sent free to members; organises conferences and seminars; organises annual Total Theatre Awards at the Edinburgh Fringe Festival
Comments: formerly Mime Action Group

Welsh Independent Dance
Chapter, Market Road, **Cardiff (Wales)** CF5 1QE
Tel: 29-2038 7314 Fax: 29-2038 7314
chair executive committee Janet Fieldsend; development director Belinda Neave; administration Carol Blade, Pebs Jones
Role & Services: umbrella organisation for dancers living and working in Wales; artist led initiative that: exists secifically to promote the work of Welsh based independent dancers, choreographers and companies; to create opportunities and platforms for the making, showing and promotion of this work; to promote a wide range of artistic quality and excellence *Comments:* organise development programme – Dance Bytes, training workshops and dance related activities; operate a membership scheme, data and information service and acts as a lobbying voice to raise the profile of dance in Wales; offer choreographic development programme

Writers' Guild of Great Britain
430 Edgware Road, **London** W2 1EH
Tel: 20-7723 8074 Fax: 20-7706 2413
Internet: www.writers.org.uk/guild
E-Mail: postre@wggb.demon.co.uk
general secretary Alison V Gray; president Ian Curteis; chair Alan Drury
Role & Services: trade union representing established writers in film, radio, television, theatre and publishing; the Guild advises on all aspects of writers' agreements and leads the way in campaigns for minimum terms for writers working in film, radio and theatre

Youth & Music Ltd – British Section of Jeunesses Musicales
28 Charing Cross Road, **London** WC2H 0DB
Tel: 20-7379 6722 Fax: 20-7497 0345
Internet: www.stagepass.yandm.org.uk
E-Mail: stagepass@yandm.org.uk
executive director Monica Ferguson; company secretary Kate Meadows; publications officer Kate Powell
Role & Services: market the arts to young people (16-29 years) including the nationwide Stage Pass ticket discount scheme; British representatives of Jeunesses Musicales Internationale including the World Orchestra and the World Choir

YUGOSLAVIA (+381)

Due to the war in Kosovo we have been unable to update the following entries for Yugoslavia

Association of Composers of Serbia
Misarska 12, 11000 **Belgrade**
Tel: 11-334 0894
Fax: 11-323 8637
contact Milan Mihajlovic

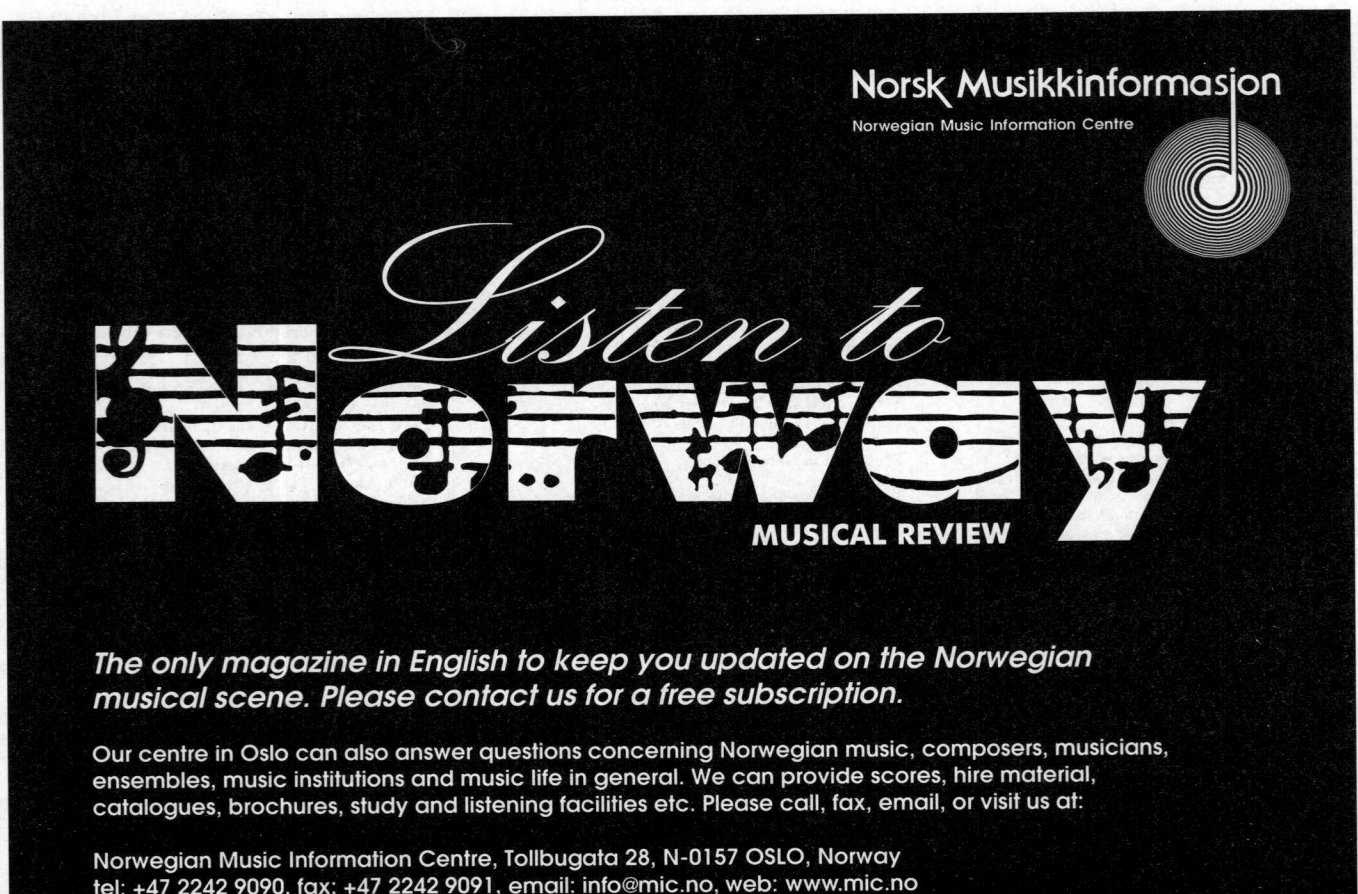

SOKOJ-MIC (Music Information Centre – ISCM Section – National Music Committee)
Trg Nikole Pasica 1/V, 1100 **Belgrade**
Tel: 11-324 5192 Fax: 11-323 6168
Internet: www.iamic.ie/yugoslavia/index.html
director Ana Kotevska; liaison officer Vesna Koric
Role & Services: to collect, produce and publish musical works and publications; to promote Yugoslav' composers' music and make them available to music professionals and the public at home and abroad

Opera

Opera
This list comprises companies which spend all or much of their life presenting opera and/or operetta or music theatre. The large number in Germany reflects the extraordinary infra-structure of that enlarged country. The companies are mainly building-based, but there are a significant number of touring companies. **Within country the companies are ordered by city, and alphabetically within city.**

Opéra
Cette rubrique englobe les compagnies qui présentent principalement de l'opéra/opérette ou du théâtre musical. Le grand nombre de compagnies allemandes reflète l'infrastructure extraordinaire de ce pays. Pour la plupart, les compagnies sont sédentaires mais un nombre significatif d'entre elles font des tournées.
Pour chacque pays, les compagnies sont classées dans l'ordre des villes et par ordre alphabétique.

Oper
In diesem Kapitel sind Opernensembles eingetragen, die sich vor allem mit Opern-, Operetten- oder Musiktheaterveranstaltungen befassen. Die große Zahl solcher Gruppen in Deutschland spiegelt die außergewöhnliche kulturelle Infrastruktur dieses Landes wider. Die Operngruppen haben hauptsächlich ein festes Haus, es gibt aber auch eine große Zahl von 'Tourneegruppen'. **Die Einträge der Kategorie 'Oper' sind für alle Staaten alphabetisch nach Stadt und innerhalb der Stadt alphabetisch nach Namen geordnet.**

Opera
Questo elenco include compagnie che lavorano esclusivamente o quasi esclusivamente presentando opere liriche, operette e musicals. Il grande numero di tali compagnie in Germania riflette le enormi infrastrutture di cui la Nazione dispone. Le compagnie sono per la maggior parte stabili e con una loro sede fissa, ma ce n'é anche un considerevole numero 'di giro'. **Le cittá sono ordinate alfabeticamente all'interno di ogni Paese e cosí anche le compagnie d'opera.**

Opera
Este listado se compone de compañías que dedican todo o gran parte de su tiempo a presentar opera y/o zarzuela. El gran número de tales compañías en Alemania refleja la infraestructura extraordinaria que existe en este vasto país. La mayoría de las compañías tienen su propia sala de espectáculo, pero hay un número significante de ellas que son compañías itinerantes. **Dentro del país, las compañías están ordenadas por ciudades, siguiendo un orden alfabético dentro de cada ciudad.**

Opera (오페라)

이 리스트는 오페라나 오페레타 혹은 뮤지컬 등의 공연을 전문으로 하는 단체들로 구성되었다. 독일에 특히 많은 단체들이 나열된 사실은 통일 독일의 훌륭한 예술 기반 시설을 반영한다. 대부분의 단체들은 한 곳에 주둔하고 있지만, 상당수는 순회 공연하는 단체들이다. **리스트는 국가별, 도시별, 그리고 다시 알파벳순으로 기재되었다.**

歌剧
这一名单包括了那些将它们全部的或者大部分的时间花在上演歌剧和/或轻歌剧或音乐戏剧的公司。在德国有许多这类公司，这反映出该版图增大的国家的非凡的基础结构。这些公司大多有固定的办公楼，但也有为数不少的巡演式公司。**在每个国家里公司是按城市的顺序来排列的，在每一城市里公司又是按字母顺序来排列的。**

オペラ

ここではオペラ、オペレッタ、ミュージックシアターでの公演を目的に存在している団体を掲載しました。ドイツは際だって団体数が多くなっていますが、これは統一ドイツによって拡大された同国の社会基盤構造を反映しています。団体の大半が劇場ベースですが、相当数の巡回オペラ団も含まれます。**リストは国、都市別で、都市内ではアルファベット順に記載されています。**

ALBANIA (+355)

Theatre of Opera and Ballet
Teatri i Operas dhe i Baletit
Skenderbej square, **Tirana**
Tel: 42-26747/27471/74127 Fax: 42-24753/24753
E-Mail: root@tob.tirana.al
general director Dr Vasil S. Tole
No of Prods: 10 *Touring:* international *Comments:* see also Dance, Orchestras and Venues

ARMENIA (+374)

Armenian State Song Theater
13a Khandjian Street, 375010 **Yerevan**
Tel: 2-567 044
artistic director Arthur Grigorian

National Opera and Ballet Theatre of Armenia, The
58 Tumanian Street, 375001 **Yerevan**
Tel: 2-586 311/527 992/565 803 Fax: 2-527 992
artistic director Gegham Grigorian
Comments: see also Dance

AUSTRIA (+43)

Stadttheater Baden bei Wien
Theaterplatz 7, 2500 **Baden bei Wien**
Tel: 2252-48338/48547 Fax: 2252-483 3850/40
Internet: www.baden-bei-wien.at-stadttheater
E-Mail: stadttheater@baden-bei-wien.at
Intendant Frau Kammersängerin Elisabeth Kales-Wallner; musikalische Leitung Franz Josef Breznik; Verwaltungsdirektor Regierungsrat Wilfried Frankmann; Dramaturgin/Öffentlichkeits – Arbeit Mag. Martina Malzer; Choreographie Bohdan Simova
Perfs: 150 *No of Prods:* 13 *Venues:* Stadttheater 702, Sommerarena 657 *Comments:* mainly operettas; see also Festivals

Theater für Vorarlberg
Seestrasse 2, 6900 **Bregenz**
Tel: 5574-42870 Fax: 5574-48366
Intendant Harald F Petermichel; Dramaturgie Andreas Hutter; Verwaltungsleiterin Barbara Haidlen
Perfs: 20 *No of Prods:* 11 *Venues:* Theater am Kornmarkt 556 *Comments:* see also Drama

Opernhaus Graz
c/o Vereinigte Bühnen Kaiser-Josef-Platz 10, 8010 **Graz**
Tel: 316-8008-0 Fax: 316-800 8585
Internet: www.buehnen-graz.com
E-Mail: info@buehnen-graz.com
Intendant Dr Gerhard Brunner; künstlerischer Betriebsdirektor Dr. Michael Lakner; Ballettdirektorin Linda Papworth; Leitender Operndramaturg Johannes Frankfurter; Operndramaturgie Bernd Krispin, Dr. Birgit Amlinger; Verwaltungsdirektor Dr. Peter Nebel; Technischer Direktor Dipl. Ing. Jörg Koßdorff
Perfs: 191 (inc. opera, operetta, musicals, ballet) *No of Prods:* 17 (10 new) *Venues:* Opernhaus 1424 (1224 seats + 200 standing), Studiobühne 300 *Comments:* see also Dance, Orchestras and Drama

Tiroler Landestheater
Rennweg 2, Postfach 134, 6010 **Innsbruck**
Tel: 512-52074-0 Fax: 512-52074-333
Internet: www.landestheater.at
E-Mail: tiroler@landestheater.at
Intendant Brigitte Fassbaender; Musikdirektor Georg Schmöhe; Schauspieldirektor Klaus Rohrmoser; Tanztheaterleitung Marie Luise Jaska; Betriebsdirektor Harald Mayr; künstlerisches Betriebsbüro & Disposition Dieter Senft; Dramaturgie Dr Doris Happl, Katharina Tarján (Musiktheater), Jörg Huwer (Schauspiel); Öffentlichkeitsarbeit Claudia Schwarz; 1. Kapellmeister Patrick Furrer; Chordirektor Claudio Büchler; technischer Direktor Werner Oberweger; Ausstattungsleitung Bettina Munzer
No of Prods: 13 (11 new: opera, operetta, musical) *Venues:* Grosses Haus 801, Kammerspiele up to 250, Werkraum 99 *Comments:* see also Dance and Drama

ARBOS – Gesellschaft für Musik und Theater
Box 130, 9010 **Klagenfurt**
Tel: 463-503 618 Fax: 463-503 6184
künstlerischer Leiter Herbert Gantschacher; Chefdramaturg Dzevad Karahasan; Produktionsmanagement Birgitta Fina
Perfs: 160 *No of Prods:* 27 *Touring:* Denmark, Greenland, Norway, Finland, Russia, Australia, South Africa, Argentina, Singapore *Comments:* contemporary new music theatre (incl productions for deaf people/Gehörlosentheater); own orchestra: ensemble kreativ; second address: Box 166, 5024 Salzburg; members of: musica reanimata, National and Worldwide Deaf Theatre Conference, International Conference of Contemporary Music-Theatre and Opera, European Chamber Opera Pool (ECOP); second address: Weiserhofstrasse 5, 5020 Salzburg

Stadttheater Klagenfurt
Theaterplatz 4, 9020 **Klagenfurt**
Tel: 463-55266 Fax: 463-516 949
Internet: www.stadttheater-klagenfurt.at
E-Mail: s.zoltan@stadttheater-klagenfurt.at
Intendant Dietmar Pflegerl; künstlerisches Betriebsbüro Erwin Zak; Dramaturgie Dr. Maja Haderlap (Hauptdramaturgin), Sylvia Brandl; Chordirektor Alexander Kowalsky; Besetzungsbüro für musik. Theater Heide Rabal; Chefdisponentin Emöke Szomraky
Perfs: 60 *No of Prods:* 4 *Venues:* Stadttheater Klagenfurt 757 *Comments:* theatre re-opened in Sept '98 after extensive refurbishment; alternative E-mail: m.haderlap@stadttheater-klagenfurt.at; see also Orchestras and Drama

Landestheater Linz
Promenade 39, 4020 **Linz**
Tel: 732-7611-0 Fax: 732-7611 308/333
E-Mail: landestheater@linz.info.at
Intendant Dr. Michael Klügl; Balletdirektor Robert Poole; Schauspieldirektoren Gerhard Willert, Dagmar Schlingmann
No of Prods: 10 (9 new) *Venues:* Grosses Haus 756, Kammerspiele 421, u/hof: Kinder-und Jugend-theater 100, Eisenhand 100 *Comments:* Dennis Russell Davies will be chief conductor of Landestheater Linz from 2002; see also Dance, Drama and Orchestras (Bruckner Orchester Linz)

Salzburger Landestheater
Schwarzstraße 22, 5020 **Salzburg**
Tel: 662-871 512 Fax: 662-8715 1213
Internet: www.theater.co.at
E-Mail: service@theater.co.at
Generalintendant Lutz Hochstraate; Künstlerischer Betriebsdirektor Diethmar Strasser; Dramaturgie Dr Christian Fuchs; Ballettdirektor Peter Breuer; Chordirektor Steffen Schubert; Generalmusikdirektor Hubert Soudant; Kaufmännische Direktion Anton Schmidjell
Perfs: 40 *No of Prods:* 4 *Venues:* Landestheater 711, Kammerspiele 137, Großes Festspielhaus 2179, Kleines Festspielhaus 1384 *Touring:* 2 guest appearances in Fürth, Germany (31 May & 1 June) *Comments:* see also Dance and Drama

Theater der Landeshaupstadt St Pölten Theater für Niederösterreich
Rathausplatz 11, 3100 **St Pölten**
Tel: 2742-352 026 Fax: 2742-3520 2652
Internet: www.theater-stpoelten.at
E-Mail: INTENDANZ@theater-stpoelten.at
Intendant Peter Wolsdorff; Intendant-Stellvertreter Pani Stamotopolos; Betriebsbüro Peter Offner; Ballettmeister Heinz Heidenreich; musikalischer Leiter/ Choreinstudierung Klaus-Dieter Jung; Öffentlichkeitsarbeit (PR) Pani Stamotopolos; technischer Leiter Ing. Edith Fellner; Leiterin des Kostümwesens Reinhilde Condin
Perfs: 132 *No of Prods:* 9 *Venues:* Theater der Landeshaupstadt 383 *Comments:* see also Drama

Jugendstiltheater – Kulturstandort Baumgartnerhöhe
Baumgartnerhöhe 1, 1145 **Wien**
Tel: 1-911 2492/0 Fax: 1-911 2492/15
Internet: www.jugendstiltheater.co.at/jt
E-Mail: info.an@jugendstiltheater.co.at
Geschäftsführer Alois Hofinger; PR Michaela Falkner
Perfs: 100 *No of Prods:* 10 *Venues:* Kleine Bühne 99, Kleiner Saal 140, Großer Saal 350, Hinterbühne 99
Comments: concerts, drama, musicals, opera, dance

Musikwerkstatt Wien
Speisingerstraße 149/1, 1230 **Wien**
Tel: 1-889 1996 Fax: 1-889 1996
E-Mail: MWWien@compuserve.com
Intendant Mag Anna-Maria Birnbauer; Künstlerischer Leiter Huw Rhys James
Perfs: 10-15 *No of Prods:* 2-3 *Comments:* 20th century chamber opera, baroque opera; see also Orchestras

Raimund Theater
Wallgasse 18-20, 1060 **Wien**
Tel: 1-599 77 Fax: 1-599 7777
Internet: www.musicalvienna.at
E-Mail: info@vbw.at
Intendant Rudi Klausnitzer; Kaufm. Direktor Franz Häußler; Künstl. Produktion Barbara Quiehl-Masmeier; Dramaturgie Peter Back-Vega; Presse Uli Stepan; Marketing Mag. Wolfgang Hülbig; Technische Leitung Peter Bouchier
Perfs: 320 *Venues:* Raimund Theater 1281 *Comments:* at present musicals only

Ronacher Etablissement
Seilerstätte 9, 1010 **Wien**
Tel: 1-514 11 Fax: 1-514 11511
Internet: www.musicalvienna.at
E-Mail: info@vbw.at
Kaufmännischer Direktor Franz Häußler; Intendant Rudi Klausnitzer; Verwaltung Dr. Franz Schlosser; Koordination Peter Back-Vega; KBB Beatrix Pecha
Perfs: guest perfs 250 *Comments:* venue is rented out to guest companies; see also Venues

Theater an der Wien
Linke Wienzeile 6, 1060 **Wien**
Tel: 1-588-30 Fax: 1-588 3033
Internet: www.musicalvienna.at
E-Mail: info@vbw.at
Intendant Rudi Klausnitzer; Kaufmännischer Direktor Franz Häußler; Künstlerische Produktion Barbara Quiehl-Masmeier; Dramaturgie Peter Back-Vega; Presse Uli Stepan; Marketing Mag. Wolfgang Hülbig; Technische Leitung Peter Bouchier
Perfs: 160 *No of Prods:* 1 musical (Mozart!) *Venues:* capacity 1177 *Comments:* musicals from September to April; from April to July the Theater an der Wien is a venue for Wiener Festwochen; musicals, opera and drama performed during the Festwochen; see also Vereinigte Bühnen Wien GmbH and Orchester der Vereinigten Bühnen Wien GmbH

Vereinigte Bühnen Wien GmbH
Linke Wienzeile 6, 1060 **Wien**
Tel: 1-588-30 Fax: 1-588 3033
Internet: www.musicalvienna.at
E-Mail: info@vbw.at
Kaufmännischer Direktor Franz Häußler; Intendant Rudi Klausnitzer; Künstlerische Produktion Barbara Quiehl-Masmeier; Dramaturgie Peter Back-Vega; Presse Uli Stepan; Marketing Mag. Wolfgang Hülbig; Technische Leitung Peter Bouchier
Perfs: 850 *Comments:* the organisation behind Theater an der Wien (q.v.), Raimund-Theater (q.v.), Ronacher (q.v.)

Volksoper Wien
Währingerstrasse 78, 1090 **Wien**
Tel: 1-514 44-0 Fax: 1-5144 43215
Direktor Dominique Mentha; kaufmänn Geschäftsführerin Dkfm Angelika Kopitsch; Stellvert. des Direktors, Öffentlichkeitsarbeit & Vertrieb Otto Hochreiter; Presse Mag. Julia Birner-Schuschu
Perfs: 300 *No of Prods:* 7 *Venues:* capacity 1313
Comments: see also Orchestras & Dance

Wiener Kammeroper
Fleischmarkt 24, 1010 **Wien**
Tel: 1-512 0100 Fax: 1-5120 10030
Internet: members.magnet.at/wienerkammeroper
E-Mail: wienerkammeroper@magnet.at
Intendant Josef Hussek; Dramaturgie, Presse- und Öffentlichkeitsarbeit Dr. Michael Macek; Marketing Holger Bleck
Perfs: 78 Theater am Fleischmarkt, 30 Theater of the Schönbrunn Palace *No of Prods:* 5 *Venues:* Theater am Fleischmarkt 312, Schloßtheater Schönbrunn 350
Comments: summer season in theatre of the Schönbrunn Palace; see also Wiener Staatsopernballet and Burgtheater

Wiener Operntheater
Myrthengasse 5/11, 1070 **Wien**
Tel: 1-526 2136 Fax: 1-526 2136
Intendant Dr Sven Hartberger; musikalischer Leiter Andreas Mitisek
Comments: modern, classical opera, contemporary opera; no performances in 2000

Wiener Staatsoper
Opernring 2, 1010 **Wien**
Tel: 1-514 44-0 Fax: 1-5144 42330
Internet: www.wiener-staatsoper.at
Staatsoperndirektor Ioan Holender; kaufmännischer Geschäftsführer Thomas W Platzer; Betriebsdirektorin Mag. Elisabeth Sobotka; Personl Referentin des Direktors Sabine Hödl; Ballettleitung Renato Zanella; Dramaturgie Mag. Christoph Wagner-Trenkwitz; Chordirektor Ernst Dunshirn; Presse Mag. Irina Kubadinow
Perfs: ca. 300 *No of Prods:* 67 (incl ballet) – 8 new *Venues:* capacity: seated 1709; standing 567 *Touring:* guest performances in Japan *Comments:* opera tent for children on the roof terrace of Staatsoper

AZERBAIDZHAN (+994)

Azerbaidzhan Folk Music Theatre 'Mugam'
Mendjinsky St. 9, 370004 **Baku**
Tel: 12-924 998
director Kasiyev Arif Rafi ogly; artistic director Rzayev Islam Taptyg ogly

Azerbaidzhan R Beybutov State Theatre of Song
R Beybutov St. 12, 370000 **Baku**
Tel: 12-939 415
director Aslanov Niyazi Ingilab ogly

Azerbaidzhan State Academic Opera and Ballet Theatre
Nizamy St. 95, 370000 **Baku**
Tel: 12-931 651
director Melikov Akif Turan oglu; chief conductor Jafarov Javanshir Khalil oglu
Comments: see also Dance

Azerbaidzhan State Musical Comedy Theatre
Azerbaijan Avenue 8, 370056 **Baku**
Tel: 12-932 411
director & artistic director Bagirov Gadjybaba Agarza oglu; chief conductor Gadjialibekov Nazim Enver oglu

BELARUS (+375)

National Academic Theatre of Opera
Nacionalnyj Akadjemichjeskij Opjernyj Tjeatr
Pl. Parizhskoj Kommuny 1, 220029 **Minsk**
Tel: 172-340 584 Fax: 172-340 584
director Sjergjej Kartes

State Musical Comedy Theatre of the Republic of Belarus
Gosudarstvjennyj Tjeatr Muzykalnoj Komjedii Rjespubliki Bjelaruss
ul. Mjasnikova 44, 220050 **Minsk**
Tel: 172-209 907 Fax: 172-208 055
director Rostislav Buzuk

BELGIUM (+32)

Antwerp Musical Theatre
Theatreplain 1, 2000 **Antwerp**
Tel: 3-231 7136 Fax: 3-231 1756
artistic director Anna Bossens; general manager Marie-Rose Vrijens (3-227 0306)
No of Prods: 1 (Phantom of the Opera) *Venues:* Stadsschouwburg 1600 *Comments:* musicals

Vlaamse Opera, De
Flanders Opera
Van Ertbornstraat 8, 2018 **Antwerp**
Tel: 3-233 6808 Fax: 3-232 2661/231 0785
Internet: www.vlaamseopera.be
general manager Marc Clémeur; administration and finance Jean Joris; music director Massimo Zanetti; permanent guest conductor Silvio Varviso; chorus master Peter Burian
Perfs: 100 *No of Prods:* 8 *Venues:* Frankryklai 3, Antwerp 1065, Schouwburgstraat 3, Gent 969 *Comments:* 80-piece orchestra; also organise symphonic and chamber music concerts and lunch concerts; Ghent: Tel. 9-223 0681, Fax 9-223 8726

Walpurgis, Ensemble for Contemporary Opera and Music Theatre
Sergeyselsstraat 20, 2140 **Borgerhout (Antwerp)**
Tel: 3-235 6662 Fax: 3-272 3382
Internet: www.walpurgis.informaat.nl
E-Mail: vindevogel@walpurgis.be
general direction Judith Vindevogel; coordinator Emmanuel Devriendt (email: manu.devriendt@walpurgis.be); press & communication Greet Duquesne (email: info@walpurgis.be)
Perfs: 100 *No of Prods:* 5 *Venues:* own working space used for small public performances of work-in-progress cap. 100 *Touring:* Belgium, Netherlands, France, Switzerland, Germany *Comments:* organises the annual FENIKS FESTIVAL: FENIKS FESTIVAL 2000 will take place from 30 March-2 April, presenting music theatre productions in progress; records most creations on the Walpurgis Records label

La Monnaie/De Munt (Théâtre Royal de la Monnaie/Koninklijke Muntschouwburg)
4, rue Leopold, 1000 **Brussels**
Tel: 2-229 1200 Fax: 2-229 1380/87 (press office)
Internet: www.demunt.be (Flemish-speaking)
E-Mail: press@lamonnaie.be
general director Bernard Foccroulle; music director Antonio Pappano; orchestra manager Ingrid De Backer; artistic director Bernd Loebe; director of the chorus Renato Balsadonna; financial director Bernard Coutant; head of administration Raf Cansse, Marco Bouteiller; head of press dpt Paul Lambrechts; technical director Josep Maria Folch; commercial director Stanislaw Bromelski
Perfs: 200 *No of Prods:* 2 revivals, 8 new *Venues:* La Monnaie/De Munt 1152, Lunatheater 600, Palais des Beaux-Arts, Halles De Schaerbeek, Cirque Royal 1300, deSingel (Antwerp) *Comments:* La Monnaie also programmes concerts, recitals, jazz and world music as well as dance performances; dance company in residence at the opera: Rosas (q.v.) (choreographer and artistic director Anne-Teresa De Keersmaeker), alternative website www.lamonnaie.be

Opéra Royal de Wallonie
1 Rue des Dominicains, 4000 **Liège**
Tel: 4-221 4720 Fax: 4-221 0201 (admin.)/221 3566 (theatre)
Internet: www.orw.be
E-Mail: direction@orw.be
general manager Jean-Louis Grinda; secretary general André Dewez; commercial director Arnold Picard; director of communications Maitine van Zuyler; scenery director Philipe Liemand; technical director Yvan Rosiuo; administrative and financial director Oscar Defrere; musical director Friedrich Pleyer
Perfs: 100 *No of Prods:* 4 *Venues:* Théâtre Royal de Liège 1033, Petit Théâtre 100 *Touring:* Luxembourg, France, Netherlands, Germany

BOSNIA & HERZEGOVINA (+387)

Opera of the National Theatre
Obala Kulina Bana 9, 71000 **Sarajevo**
Tel: 71-445 138/663 647 Fax: 71-445 138
director Tvrtko Kulenovic; director of opera and ballet Pasa Gackic
No of Prods: see also Drama, Dance

BULGARIA (+359)

Blagoevgrad Chamber Opera
2 Ivan Vazov Str., 2700 **Blagoevgrad**
Tel: 73-20703 Fax: 73-29329
director Anguel Anguelov
Venues: capacity 400, chamber hall 100

Opera and Philharmonic Society – Bourgas
2 Kliment Ohridski Str., 8000 **Bourgas**
Tel: 56-43057 Fax: 56-42698
director Rossen Grouev
Venues: capacity 799

Opera and Philharmonic Society – Plovdiv
19 Gourko Str., 4000 **Plovdiv**
Tel: 32-235 198 Fax: 32-263 064
director Borislav Ivanov
Venues: capacity 523

Opera and Philharmonic Society – Rousse
7 Sveta Troitza Sq, 7000 **Rousse**
Tel: 82-225 368 Fax: 82-270 012
director Mihail Anguelov
Venues: capacity 523

National Opera – Sofia
30 Dondoukov Str., 1000 **Sofia**
Tel: 2-988 5869 Fax: 2-987 7998
director Plamen Kartalov
Venues: capacity 1200

State Music Theatre Stefan Makedonski
3 Panaiot Volov Str., 1000 **Sofia**
Tel: 2-442 321/443 876 Fax: 2-441 342
director Svetozar Donev
Venues: capacity 1024

State Opera and Ballet – Stara Zagora
30 Metodi Kussev blvd. , 6000 **Stara Zagora**
Tel: 42-41015
director Alexander Maroulev
Venues: capacity 600

Opera and Philharmonic Society – Varna
1 Nezavisimost Square, 9000 **Varna**
Tel: 52-602 385 Fax: 52-602 088
director Hristo Ignatov
Perfs: 120 *No of Prods:* 3 to 5
Venues: capacity 620

Konstantin Kissimov Drama and Music Theatre
4 Vassil Levski Str., 5000 **Veliko Turnovo**
Tel: 62-25851
director Sava Dimitrov
Venues: capacity 644

CROATIA (+385)

Opera of the Croatian National Theatre Osijek
Opera Hrvatskog Narodnog Kazalista Osijek
Zupanijska 9, 31000 **Osijek**
Tel: 31-220 734/766
Fax: 31-220 700/734
general director Zeljko Cagalj; opera director Zoran Juranic

Opera of the Croatian National Theatre Ivan pl. Zajc
Opera Hrvatskog Narodnog Kazalista Ivan Pl. Zajca
Uljarska 1, 51000 **Rijeka**
Tel: 51-212 322 Fax: 51-212 600
general director Srecko Sestan; opera director Bojan Sober
Comments: venue address: Verdijeva bb, 51000 Rijeka

Opera of the Croatian National Theatre Split
Opera Hrvatskog Narodnog Kazalista Split
Trg Poljana Tina Ujevica bb, 21000 **Split**
Tel: 21-585 999 Fax: 21-583 643
general director Marija Gotovac; opera director Haris Bodre

Opera of the Croatian National Theatre Zagreb
Opera Hrvatskog Narodnog Kazalista Zagreb
Trg Marsala Tita 15, 10000 **Zagreb**
Tel: 1-482 8550 Fax: 1-482 8531
general director Georgij Paro; opera director Vladimir Kranjcevic

CYPRUS (+357)

Cyprus Operatic Stage
Lyrike Skene Lemessou – Kyprou
Thessalonikis 32A, 3025 **Limassol**
Tel: 5-361 725 Fax: 5-361 725
director Ioli Mousteri; president George Nicolaou
Perfs: 20 *No of Prods:* 2 (1new)
Venues: Municipal Theatre, Nicosia; Patticheon Theatre, Larnaca *Touring:* Cyprus, Greece, Israel, Egypt, UK, Switzerland

CZECH REPUBLIC (+420)

Milos Wasserbauer Chamber Opera – Opera studio of the Music Faculty JAMU Brno
Komorní opera Milose Wasserbauera – Operní studio hudební fakulty JAMU Brno
nám. Svatopluka Cecha 35a, 612 00 **Brno**
Tel: 5-4121 3206 Fax: 5-4121 3206
manager ing. Zdenka Vlachovská
Perfs: 30 *No of Prods:* 2
Venues: Theatre BARKA 150
Comments: school theatre

National Theatre Brno – Opera and Operetta
Národní divadlo v Brne – opera a opereta
Dvorákova 11, 657 70 **Brno**
Tel: 5-4232 1285/1300 Fax: 5-4221 7045
Internet: www.ndbrno.cz
E-Mail: ndb@netbrno.cz
director Mojmír Weimann; opera director Tomás Simerda; operetta director Frantisek Zacharnik
Perfs: 110 (opera), 200 (operetta) *No of Prods:* 5 (opera), 5 (operetta) *Venues:* Janáckovo divadlo 1270, Mahenovo divadlo 577 *Comments:* see also Drama and Dance

South Bohemian Theatre – Opera
Jihoceské divadlo – opera
Dr. Stejskala 23, 370 47 **Ceské Budejovice**
Tel: 38-671 1111 Fax: 38-55640
Internet: mojweb.cz/www/jihocdivadlo
E-Mail: jihoceskedivadlo@iol.cz
director ing. Jan Mrzena; opera director Milan Kanák
Perfs: 120 *No of Prods:* 5 *Venues:* capacity 240, Dum kultury Metropol 517 *Comments:* see also Drama and Dance

F X Salda Theatre – Opera
Divadlo F X Saldy – opera
Zhorelecká 344/5, 460 37 **Liberec**
Tel: 48-510 4288/4188 Fax: 48-510 4181
Internet: www.infolbc.cz/divadlo/uvodni.htm
E-Mail: mic@info.lbc.cz
director & opera director Frantisek Dána
Perfs: 110 *No of Prods:* 5 *Venues:* capacity 619
Comments: see also Drama and Dance

Moravian Theatre – Opera
Moravské divaldo – opera
Trída Svobody 33, 771 07 **Olomouc**
Tel: 68-522 3651 Fax: 68-522 5781
Internet: mdo.olomouc.cz
E-Mail: mdo@olomouc.com
director Václav Kozusník; opera director Václav Málek; manager Marcela Arelyová
Perfs: 180 *No of Prods:* 6 *Venues:* capacity 504
Comments: see also Drama and Dance

Silesian Theatre – Opera
Slezské divadlo – opera
Horní nám. 13, 746 69 **Opava**
Tel: 653-621 156 Fax: 653-623 656
director Jirí Merínsky; opera director Petr Sumník
Perfs: 120 *No of Prods:* 5 *Venues:* capacity 416
Comments: see also Drama

Moravian & Silesian National Theatre – Opera & Operetta
Národní divadlo moravskoslezké – opera a opereta
Cs. Legií 14, 701 04 **Ostrava**
Tel: 69-611 2821 Fax: 69-611 2881
Internet: www.ndm.cz
E-Mail: narodni_divadlo_ostrava@oasanet.cz
director & opera director Ludek Golat; operetta director Miroslav Urbánek
Perfs: 130 (opera), 180 (operetta) *No of Prods:* 4 (opera), 5 (operetta) *Venues:* Divadlo Jiriho Myrona 600, Divadlo Antonína Dvoráka 868
Comments: see also Drama and Dance

J K Tyl Theatre – Opera and Operetta
Divadlo J.K. Tyla – opera a opereta
Prokopova 14, 304 11 **Plzen**
Tel: 19-722 4256 (opera)/6743 (operetta)
Fax: 19-220 190
Internet: www.central.cz/djkt
E-Mail: reditelstvi@djkt.plzen.city.cz
director Jan Burian; opera director Petr Kofron; operetta director Jan Jezek
Perfs: 120 (opera), 150 (operetta) *No of Prods:* 4 (opera), 5 (operetta) *Venues:* Velké divadlo (Great Theatre) 446, Komorní divadlo (Chamber Theatre) 444
Comments: see also Drama and Dance

Milenium Theatre
Divadlo Milenium
PO Box 120, 170 04 **Praha** 7
Internet: www.rusalka.cz
E-Mail: rusalka@rusalka.cz
director Vlastimil Jezek
Venues: cap. 860
Comments: musical; visiting address: Bubenské nábr. 306, 170 04 Praha 7

Music Theatre Karlín
Hudební divadlo Karlín
Krizíkova 10, 186 17 **Praha** 8
Tel: 2-2421 2776 Fax: 2-2421 2132
Internet: hdkarlin.cz
E-Mail: hdkarlin@czn.cz
director Ladislav Zupanic
Perfs: 220 *No of Prods:* 4 *Venues:* capacity 1308
Comments: only operetta and musical

Opera Mozart – Opera Furore
Sevastopolská 14, 110 00 **Praha** 10
Tel: 2-7174 1403/2624 Fax: 2-7174 1733/2481 9327
Internet: www.mozart.cz
E-Mail: mozart@telecom.cz
director ing. Jiri Herold; manager ing. Martin Lokaj
Perfs: 180 *No of Prods:* 2 *Comments:* touring company

Opera studio of the Music Faculty AMU Prague
Operní studio hudební fakulty AMU Praha
AMU-Hudební fakulta, Malostranské nám 13,
110 00 **Praha** 1
Tel: 2-530 493 Fax: 2-536 229
Perfs: 20 *No of Prods:* 2 *Comments:* school theatre

Original Prague Music Theatre
Originální hudební divadlo Praha
Kartouzská 4, 150 00 **Praha**
Tel: 2-546 806 Fax: 2-546 806
director Tomás Hása; artistic director René Nachtigalová
Perfs: 150 *No of Prods:* 1 new *Comments:* touring company

Prague National Theatre – Opera
Národní divadlo – opera
PO Box 865, 112 30 **Praha** 1
Tel: 2-2491 0312/2673/2757 Fax: 2-2491 3528
Internet: www.anet.cz/nd
E-Mail: ntprague@ntprague.anet.cz
director Jiri Srstka; opera director Josef Prudek
Perfs: 300 *No of Prods:* 5 *Venues:* Národni divadlo (National Theatre) 998, Stavovské divadlo (Estates Theatre) 684 *Comments:* see also Drama and Dance

Spiral Theatre
Divadlo Spirála
LDS 1/15, Vystaviste, 170 00 **Praha** 7
Tel: 2-371 197 Fax: 2-371 141
Internet: www.evita.praha.cz
E-Mail: jaroslav.panenka@musical.sro.cz
director Stanislav Aubrecht; artistic director Petr Novotny
Venues: cap. 600 *Comments:* musical

State Opera Prague
Státní opera Praha
Legerova 75, 111 21 **Praha**
Tel: 2-2422 7696/9898 Fax: 2-2423 0410/2422 9437
director Daniel Dvorak
Perfs: 220 *No of Prods:* 5 *Venues:* capacity 1000

Ústí nad Labem City Theatre-Opera
Mestské divadlo- opera
PO Box 4, 400 01 **Ústí nad Labem**
Tel: 47-521 1748/1564 Fax: 47-520 9996
E-Mail: divadlo-usti@telecom.cz
director Petr Jonás; opera director Lubomír Havlák
Perfs: 150 *No of Prods:* 7 *Venues:* capacity 500
Comments: see also Dance

DENMARK (+45)

Danish National Opera
Den Jyske Opera
Musikhuset Aarhus, Thomas Jensens Allé, 8000 **Aarhus** C
Tel: 8931 8260 Fax: 8613 3710
Internet: www.jyske-opera.dk
E-Mail: post@jyske-opera.dk
general director Troels Kold; administration manager Tonny Borup Mortensen
Perfs: 100 *No of Prods:* 4 (all new) *Venues:* capacity 1500

Danish Royal Theatre, The
Det Kongelige Teater
Postbox 2185, 1017 **Copenhagen** K
Tel: 3369 6933 Fax: 3369 6519
Internet: www.kgl-teater.dk
E-Mail: admin@kgl-teater.dk
general manager Michael Christiansen; opera director Kasper Holten; ballet director Aage Thordal-Christensen; theatre director Klaus Hoffmeyer; pr Niels Michael Jacobsen; music director Michael Schønwandt
Perfs: 125 *No of Prods:* 13 (4 new) *Venues:* Kongelige Teater 1300 *Touring:* Denmark and international
Comments: see also Dance and Drama

Rimfaxe Teater
Holsteinsgade 31,4 tv, 2100 **Copenhagen**
Tel: 3538 1016 Fax: 3538 1016
director Andreas Kofed Bendtsen
Perfs: 30-100 *Touring:* Europe
Comments: tour schools and theatres

The Other Opera
Den Anden Opera
Kronprinsinsgade 7, 1114 **Copenhagen** K
Tel: 3332 3830/5556 (information) Fax: 3332 3836
E-Mail: denandenopera@get2net.dk
manager Jesper Lützhøft
Perfs: 150 *No of Prods:* 5 *Venues:* big hall 150, small hall 50 *Comments:* the opera company performs new music only; see also Venues

ESTONIA (+372)

Pärnu Opera
Kuninga 24, 80011 **Pärnu**
Tel: 44-44993
intendant Andrus Kallastu
Comments: producing one opera annually with international artists, also educational activities, see also Promoters

Estonian National Opera Estonia
Eesti Rahvusooper Estonia
Estonia pst. 4, 10148 **Tallinn**
Tel: 6-260 201 Fax: 6-260 299
Internet: www.ooper.ee/index1.htm
E-Mail: estonia@opera.teleport.ee
managing director Paul Himma; chief conductor Paul Mägi
Venues: capacity 682 *Touring:* Finland, Sweden
Comments: see also Dance, Orchestra

Opera, Ballet and Drama Company Vanemuine
Teater Vanemuine
Vanemuise 6, 51003 **Tartu**
Tel: 7-439 012 Fax: 7-441 065
Internet: www.halo.ee/vanemuine
E-Mail: vanem@uninet.ee
chief conductor Endel Nõgene; managing director Jaak Viller
Venues: main stage 682, concert hall 842, small house 440 *Touring:* Germany *Comments:* see also Dance, Orchestra and Drama

FINLAND (+358)

Finnish National Opera
Suomen Kansallisooppera
Helsinginkatu 58, POB 176, 00251 **Helsinki**
Tel: 9-403 021
Fax: 9-4030 2305 (marketing dept)/2295 (press dept)
Internet: www.operafin.fi
general director Juhani Raiskinen; administrative director John Eric Westö; principal conductor Okko Kamu; press & publicity Heidi Almi; marketing Tuula Grundström; ballet director Jorma Ustinen; casting director Heljä Angervo
Perfs: 300 *No of Prods:* 27 opera and ballet *Venues:* Main Stage 1365, Small Stage 250 to 400 *Comments:* see also Finnish National Ballet

Joensuu Opera
Joensuun Ooppera
c/o Raimo Paltakari, Kirkkokatu 10B 17, 80110 **Joensuu**
Tel: 13-251 2251 Fax: 13-251 4590
E-Mail: raimo.paltakari@jnor.joensuu.fi
director Raimo Paltakari
Perfs: 8 *No of Prods:* 1 *Venues:* Carelia Hall 600

Jyväskylä Opera
Jyväskylän Ooppera
c/o Christine Bengtsson-Lumio, Kilpisenkatu 12 B 18, 40100 **Jyväskylä**
Tel: 14-616 921 Fax: 14-211 803
director Christine Bengtsson-Lumio
Perfs: 12 *No of Prods:* 1 (Carmen)
Venues: Jyväskylä Theatre 547

Kotka Opera
Kotkan Ooppera
Kumarruspuuntie 1 A 3, 48400 **Kotka**
Tel: 5-228 3544 Fax: 5-228 3544
artistic director Kare Wilenius
Perfs: 10-20 *No of Prods:* 1 *Venues:* Kotka Theatre 500, Kunininsuu 200 (old movie theatre)

Kuopio Opera
Kuopion Ooppera
Vuorikatu 15, 70100 **Kuopio**
Tel: 17-261 8893 Fax: 17-261 8869
director Aino Tapaninen
Perfs: 1 *Venues:* Kuopio Music Keskus 1000

Lahti Opera
Lahden Ooppera
Kuhilaankatu 6, 15900 **Lahti**
Tel: 3-753 5236 Fax: 3-753 536
director Marja Tikka
Venues: Lahti Theatre 650

Mikkeli Opera
Mikkelin Ooppera
Vuorikatu 3 a, 50100 **Mikkeli**
Tel: 15-162 063 Fax: 15-191 2323
E-Mail: mikkeli.musicfestival@iwn.fi
manager Kyösti Kostiainen; producer Kimmon Suortamo
Perfs: 7-10 *No of Prods:* 1
Venues: Mikkeli Concert Hall 600

Oulu Opera
Oulun Ooppera
c/o Oulu City Theatre, Kaarlenvaylá 2, 90100 **Oulu**
Tel: 8-5584 7000 Fax: 8-5584 7099
Internet: www.ouka.fi/teatteri
E-Mail: teatteri@ouka.fi
director Leena Salonen; conductor Kari Veisterä
Perfs: 30-40 *No of Prods:* 1
Venues: Oulu City Theatre (q.v.) 581

Pori Opera
Porin Ooppera
Pietniementie 22, 28660 **Pori**
Tel: 2-637 8400/8125/50-591 3042 Fax: 2-637 8125
director Heikki Jylhäsaari
Perfs: 15 *No of Prods:* 1 *Venues:* Theatre Pori 320

Savonlinna Opera Festival
Savonlinnan Oopperajuhlat
Olavinkatu 27, 57130 **Savonlinna**
Tel: 15-476 750 Fax: 15-476 7540
Internet: www.operafestival.fi
E-Mail: info@operafestival.fi
general director Paavo Suokko; artistic director Jorma Hynninen; marketing manager Helena Kontiainen
Perfs: 22-25 *No of Prods:* 5 *Venues:* Olavinlinna Castle 2233 *Comments:* also series of concerts during the festival season: July 1 – 30, 2000; see also Festivals

Tampere Opera
Tampereen Ooppera
Vellamonkatu 2 C, 33100 **Tampere**
Tel: 3-212 7726 Fax: 3-222 0266
E-Mail: ooppera@tampere.fi
director Jussi Tapola
No of Prods: 2 annually mainly in cooperation with Tampere Philharmonic Orchestra and the Tampere Hall or one of the two big repertory theatres of Tampere

Turku Opera
Turun Oopperayhdistys ry.
Aninkaistenkatu 9, 20110 **Turku**
Tel: 2-231 4563/040-596 2337 Fax: 2-244 4104
director Markku Uotinen; executive manager Hilkka Urho
Perfs: 8 *No of Prods:* 1 *Venues:* Turun Kaupunginteatteri 650

Vaasan Ooppera – Opera Alueooppera
Koulukatu 10, 65100 **Vaasa**
Tel: 6-317 3135 Fax: 6-317 9971
general manager Prof. Irma Rewell
Perfs: 20 *No of Prods:* 2 (1 world premiere) *Venues:* capacity 400, outdoor events 2000 *Touring:* Sweden
Comments: opera founded in 1956

FRANCE (+33)

CREA – Centre Regional D'Eveil Artistique
85, rue Anatole France, 93600 **Aulnay-sous-Bois**
Tel: 1-4866 8753 Fax: 1-4866 8868
directeur Didier Grojsman
Perfs: 10 *No of Prods:* 2 new *Venues:* Espace Jacques Prévert 800 *Touring:* France *Comments:* for all ages

Opéra d'Avignon et des Pays de Vaucluse
BP 111, 84007 **Avignon** Cedex 1
Tel: 4-9082 4242 Fax: 4-9085 0423
directeur général Raymond Duffaut; service animation Suzy Bonet; directeur du chœur Michel Capperon; directeur du Ballet M. Eric Vu-An; directeur de la scène et des services techniques Patrick Richalet; directeur de production Philippe Turchi; directeur du personnel René Jouffre
Perfs: +40 (incl. operettas) *No of Prods:* 3 new *Venues:* Théâtre a l'italienne 1100 *Comments:* classical and contemporary; produce and co-produce; permanent choir (30 singers); see also Dance

Opéra Théâtre Besançon
Place du Théâtre, 25000 **Besançon**
Tel: 3-8182 0200 (administration)/8183 0333 (location)
Fax: 3-8182 3900
directeur Didier Brunel; chargée de communication Francette Gahier; assistante de direction Odile Gratsac; communication Francette Gahier; comptable Jocelyne Magnin; relations avec le public Valérie Charles, Pierre-François Evrard; régisseur général Betty André
Perfs: 7 opera, 1 operetta, 18 concerts + 3 pieces de théâtre, 5 concerts musiques du monde + 2 ballets *No of Prods:* 4 operas *Venues:* salle de l'Opéra Théâtre 1000

Opera de Bordeaux
BP 95, 33025 **Bordeaux** Cedex
Tel: 5-5600 8520 Fax: 5-5681 9366
directeur général Thierry Fouquet; directeur administratif et financier François Vienne; directeur artistique t.b.a.; directeur technique Giulio Aetilli; secrétaire gral t.b.a.
Perfs: 250 *No of Prods:* 7 *Venues:* Grand Théâtre 1114, Palais des Sports 1660, Theatre Femina 1100
Comments: see also Dance, Orchestras and Venues

Opéra de Clermont-Ferrand
Rue Abbé de l'Epée, 63000 **Clermont-Ferrand**
Tel: 4-7335 5010 (administration)/6411 (opera)
Fax: 4-7334 2078
directeur Jean-Pierre Jourdain; directeur technique Daniel Fauriat; administratrice Colette Dumas-Fariney; assistant directeur technique Daniel Fauriat
Perfs: 92 *No of Prods:* 32 (10 new)
Venues: Théatre á l'Italienne 850 *Comments:* venue address: Rue Nestor Perret, 63000 Clermont-Ferrand; see also Venues and Promoters

Atelier du Rhin – Centre Dramatique Règional d'Alsace
La Manufacture, 6, route d'Ingersheim, 68008 **Colmar** Cedex
Tel: 3-8941 7192 Fax: 3-8941 3326
directeur Matthew Jocelyn; directeur technique Jean-Claude Stephan; administrateur Frédéric de Beauvoir; directrice de la communication Michèle Gaujard
Perfs: 13 (for music theatre) *No of Prods:* 2 new *Venues:* capacity 100 and 340 *Touring:* national and international
Comments: see also Drama, Venues, Promoters

Théâtre Français de la Musique (TFM)
Théâtre Imperial, 3, rue Othenin, 60200 **Compiegne**
Tel: 3-4440 1710 Fax: 3-4440 4404
Internet: www.cci.oise.fr/théâtre
general/artistic director Pierre Jourdan; communication Catherine Gravot
Perfs: 34 *No of Prods:* 1 *Venues:* théâtre á l'italienne moderne 816 *Touring:* Europe *Comments:* commissioned in 1867 by Napoleon III; recently restored & very special theatre; freephone booking number from within France: 0800 031 346; see also Venues

Opéra de Lille
Maison de l'habitat, 2 rue Alexandre Desrousseaux, 59800 **Lille**
Tel: 3-2085 9537 (artistic direction) Fax: 3-2052 2258
directeur artistique Ricardo Szwazer
Comments: closed for two years for refurbishment; see also Venues and Promoters

Grand Théâtre Municipal de Limoges, Le
48, rue Jean Jaurès, 87000 **Limoges**
Tel: 5-5534 1212/5545 6173 Fax: 5-5532 2126
administrateur général et directeur musical Guy Condette; régisseur général Robert Mercier; maître de ballet Elizabeth Kerherve; attaché de presse Caroline Gambier; relations publiques Pascale Rousseaud
Perfs: 12 *No of Prods:* 3 operas, 3 operettas *Venues:* Grand Theatre 1500 *Comments:* also ballet, orchestra and choir for the Grand Théâtre

Opéra National de Lyon
Place de la Comédiè, BP 1219, 69203 **Lyon** Cedex 1
Tel: 4-7200 4545 Fax: 4-7200 4546
Internet: www.opera-lyon.org
E-Mail: republic@opera-lyon.org
directeur général Alain Durel; directeur de la communication Marie-Thérése Aulas; directeur administrative et financier Jean-Marc Peraldi; directeur musical Louis Langrée; délégué général atelier lyrique et maîtrise Francis Meunier; pr Hélène Guilbert
Perfs: 196 *No of Prods:* 5 + 7 new (including 1 world premiere and 1 musical) *Venues:* Grande Salle 1100, Amphithéâtre 200 *Touring:* France *Comments:* orchestre de l'opéra de Lyon – 58 musicians, 26 choir singers, 30 dancers, 15 singers; visiting address: 1 Place de la Comédie, 69001 Lyon; see also Dance

Opéra de Marseille
2, rue Molière, 13001 **Marseille**
Tel: 4-9155 2110/2107/11/9133 1050 (press/pr)
Fax: 4-9154 9415/9155 0178 (press/pr)
Internet: www.mairie-marseille.fr
directeur de l'opera M. Jean-Louis Pujol; administrateur général Jean-Jacques Chazalet; directeur administratif Guy Marquet; relations publiques Monique Cagnoli; attachée de presse Francine Jouve
Perfs: 30 & ballet and concerts *No of Prods:* 2 *Venues:* Ernest Reyer 1832 *Comments:* permanent orchestra and choir and permanent ballet company

Théâtre des Salins – Scéne Nationale de Martigues
BP 75, 13692 **Martigues** Cedex
Tel: 4-4244 3601 Fax: 4-4244 3636
directeur Laurent Ghilini; administratrice Michelle Hettiger
Perfs: 59 *No of Prods:* 3 (1 dance, 2 theatre)
Venues: Grande Salle 615, Salle au bout de la ruit 180
Comments: visiting address: 19 quai Paul Doumer, 13692 Martigues; see also Venues

Opéra de Massy
1 Place de France, BP 75, 91303 **Massy** Cedex
Tel: 1-6013 1414 (admin)/1313 (bookings)
Fax: 1-6013 1405
Internet: www.opera-massy.com
E-Mail: info@opera-massy.com
directeur général Jack-Henri Soumère; adminstrateur général Philippe Bellot; responsable de la communication Frédéric Louis; directeur technique Patrick de Vandeville
Perfs: 45 *No of Prods:* 10 *Venues:* Amphithéâtre 800, Auditorium 150 *Comments:* companies resident at the Opera: Compagnie Christine Bastin, Orchestre de Massy – these companies organise workshops and educational programmes

Opéra-Théâtre de Metz
4-5, Place de la Comédie, 57000 **Metz**
Tel: 3-8755 5171 Fax: 3-8731 3237
Internet: www.marie-metz.fr:8080
directeur administratif Marie Hélenè Mejzinger-Nicolay; directrice artistique Danielle Ory; relations publiques Agnès Jacques; chef des choeurs Jean-Pierre Aniorte
Perfs: 5 operas 4 operettas *No of Prods:* 3 opera 4 operettas *Venues:* capacity 750 *Comments:* see also Dance & Drama

Opéras de Montpellier
11, boulevard Victor Hugo, 34967 **Montpellier** Cédex 2
Tel: 4-6760 1980 (administration)/1999 (location)
Fax: 4-6760 1990
Internet: www.opera-montpellier.com
directeur général Henri Maier;
administratrice Renée Panabière
Perfs: 60 *No of Prods:* 12 *Venues:* Opéra-Comédie 1200, Opéra Berlioz/ Le Corum 2000 *Comments:* also chamber music, recitals, melodies, dance

Opéra de Nancy et de Lorraine
1, rue Sainte Catherine, 54000 **Nancy**
Tel: 3-8385 3320/3060 (bookings) Fax: 3-8385 3066
E-Mail: opera@mairie-nancy.fr
directeur général Jean-Marie Blanchard; directeur musical Sebastian Lang-Lessing; administrateur Christophe Bezzone; déléguée générale Liliane Martinez; directeur technique Serge Gachet
Perfs: 20 *No of Prods:* 10 *Venues:* Opera 950, Salle Poirel 980 *Comments:* see also Venues, Orchestras & Promoters

Opéra de Nantes
Théâtre Graslin, BP 10929, 44009 **Nantes** Cedex 1
Tel: 2-4041 9060 Fax: 2-4041 9077
E-Mail: opera@mairie-nantes.fr
administrateur général Serge Cochelin; directeur artistique Philippe Godefroid; responsable du service communication Sylvie Saint-Cyr; choir director Merion Powell
Perfs: 57 (32 home productions) *No of Prods:* 11+ 2 co-productions *Venues:* Théatre Graslin 986 *Touring:* Angers, Rennes, Berne *Comments:* 37-member choir; also presents 11 theatre productions and concerts; visiting address: 1, rue Moliére, 44000 Nantes

Opéra de Nice
Mairie de Nice, Théatre de L`Opéra,
06364 **Nice** Cedex 4
Tel: 4-9217 4044 (relations publiques)
Fax: 4-9380 3483/9362 6926 (relations publiques)
Internet: www.nice-coteazur.org
E-Mail: opera@nice-coteazur.org
directeur général Gian-Carlo del Monaco; adjoint au directeur général Paul Emile Fourny; directeur de la danse Marc Ribaud; directeur musical Marcello Panni; directeur services techniques Michel Henocq; directrice des relations publiques/attachée de presse Elisabeth Touraille; délégué général de l'Orchestre André Coussinet; administratrice Anne Marie Quillon; maitre de ballet Jean-Michel Bouvron; directeur de production Anne Stegant
Perfs: 100 *No of Prods:* 15 *Venues:* Opéra de Nice 1100, Acropolis-Salle Apollon 2500
Comments: see also Orchestra & Dance

Compagnie Alain Germain
29 rue de Paradis, 75010 **Paris**
Tel: 1-4246 3783 Fax: 1-4246 6785
Internet: agermain.citeweb.net
E-Mail: agermain@mail.dotcom.fr
directeur Alain Germain; administrateur Dominique Bataille; directeur technique Philippe Mermin; secrétariat général Véronique Duchamp-Jay; relations presse Sabine Arman
Perfs: 100 *No of Prods:* 2 *Touring:* France
Comments: see also Dance

Compagnie Cantus
21, rue de Cloÿs, 75018 **Paris**
Tel: 6-6222 3310 Fax: 1-4257 3310
Internet: perso.libertysurf.fr/hodie
E-Mail: compagnie.cantus@libertysurf.fr
honorary president Prof Serge Gut; chief executive Prof Katarzyna Le Fé; artistic & much director Dr Maximianno Cobra
Perfs: 35-50 *No of Prods:* 4 *Venues:* Conservatoire d'Art Dramatique de Paris and others *Touring:* Europe, USA, Japan *Comments:* repertoire: Mozart's complete opera in four seasons (1998-2002); offer musicology symposiums, master classes and workshops and an active search for young singers, instrumentalists and stage directors

Opéra National de Paris – Opéra Bastille
120, rue de Lyon, 75012 **Paris**
Tel: 1-4001 1399 Fax: 1-4473 1374
Internet: www.opera-de-paris.fr
director Hugues Gall; deputy director Philippe Agid; dance director Brigitte Lefèvre; musical advisor & permanent conductor James Conlon; chorus master Denis Dubois; cultural and educational services Martine Kahane; lyric centre Christine Bullin; dance administrator Bruno Hamard; general secretaries Christian d Pange; assistant directors Christian Schirm, Frédéric Chambert
Perfs: 389 *No of Prods:* 216 operas (7 new), 5 symphonic concerts, 7 chamber music concerts, 32 Beethoven sonates *Venues:* Opera Bastille 2703, Palais Garnier 1971 *Touring:* France & abroad *Comments:* see Opera Garnier, send mail to the general secretary Christian Schirm at the Opera Garnier; see also Dance

Opéra National de Paris – Palais Garnier
8, rue Scribe, 75009 **Paris**
Tel: 1-4001 1789 Fax: 1-4001 2274 (palais garnier)
Internet: www.opera-de-paris.fr
director Hugues Gall; deputy directors Philippe Agid, Bruno Schuster; dance director Brigitte Lefèvre; musical advisor & permanent conductor James Conlon; chorus master Denis Dubois; cultural and educational services Martine Kahane; lyric centre Christine Bullin; dance administrator Bruno Hamard; general secretaries Christian de Pange; assistant directors Christian Schirm, Frédéric Chambert
Perfs: 168 *No of Prods:* 16 (opera, dance, concerts)
Venues: Palais Garnier 1979 *Touring:* France & abroad
Comments: see Opera Bastille; see also Dance

Théâtre de l'Opéra Comique
5 rue Favart, 75002 **Paris**
Tel: 1-4244 4540
Fax: 1-4286 8578 (direction)/4926 0593 (pr)
Internet: www.operacomique.com
directeur Pierre Médecin; directeur administratif Dominique Seridj; directrice de la communication Nadia Dussol; directeur de productions François Bou; directeur musical Andreas Stoehr
Perfs: 24 *No of Prods:* 1 *Venues:* Salle Favart 1300
Comments: Jeune Théâtre Lyrique de France: 8 permanent singers

Théâtre des Champs-Elysees
15 avenue Montaigne, 75008 **Paris**
Tel: 1-4952 5050 Fax: 1-4952 0741
E-Mail: theatre.champs.elysees@wanadoo.fr
directeur Dominique Meyer; directeur adjoint Francis Lepigeon; secrétaire générale Catherine Lachaux
Perfs: 140 *No of Prods:* 7 *Venues:* capacity 1901
Comments: see also Venues

Théâtre du Châtelet
2 rue Edouard Colonne, 75001 **Paris**
Tel: 1-4028 2828 Fax: 1-4236 8975
directeur général Jean Pierre Brossmann; directeur administratif Jacques Hedouin; secrétaire général Jean-François Brigy; directeur technique Jurgen Hoser
Perfs: 210 *No of Prods:* 8 opera (4 ballets + concerts)
Venues: Grande Salle 2010 (Théâtre à l'italienne), Foyer 250 *Comments:* the Châtelet is the musical theatre in Paris and the Frankfurt Ballet's Paris home; see also Venues

Théâtre de Poissy
Hôtel de Ville, Place de la République,
78303 **Poissy** Cedex
Tel: 1-3979 0303/3922 5592 Fax: 1-3065 8018
directeur artistique Christian Chorier; administrative Miss Wiss
Perfs: 20 *Venues:* Theatre (Amphithéâtre) 980-1028
Comments: see also Venues

Grand Theatre de Reims
9 rue Chanzy, 51110 **Reims**
Tel: 3-2647 4443 (bookings)/2650 3100
Fax: 3-2684 9002
directeur Serge Gaymard; relations publiques Marie-Claire Legrand; directeur musical Gilles Nopre; directeur administratif Jilbert Henry; chorégraphe Eric Margouet; directeur de scéne Tony Amirati
Perfs: 4 *No of Prods:* 2 *Venues:* Comédie de Reims 259
Touring: France *Comments:* Le Grand Theatre is closed until October 2000; see also Venues

Opéra de Rennes
BP 3126, 35031 **Rennes** Cédex
Tel: 2-9978 4868 Fax: 2-9978 4865
direction Daniel Bizeray; administrateur Eric Lebihan; directeur technique Jerome Daix; regisseur general Michael Lacroix; relations publiques Rozenn Chambard
Perfs: 50 *No of Prods:* 9 *Venues:* capacity 630

Théâtre des Arts – Opéra de Normandie
route du docteur Rambert, 76000 **Rouen**
Tel: 2-3598 5098 Fax: 2-3515 3349
E-Mail: opera.2.rouen@wanadoo.fr
président François Tron; directeur général Laurent Langlois; relations publiques Olivier Lefebvre; assistante artistique Béatrice Lhommet; chef d'orchestre Oswald Sallaberger
Perfs: 100 *No of Prods:* 10 *Venues:* capacity 1352
Touring: regional *Comments:* choir, ballet and orchestra; see also Dance & Venues

Opéra Eclaté
18 Avenue du Docteur Roux, BP 59, 46400 **Saint-Céré**
Tel: 5-6538 2908/6372 5876 Fax: 5-6538 3594
Internet: www.opera-eclaté.org
E-Mail: opera.eclate@wanadoo.fr
administration director François Boudeau; artistic director Olivier Desbordes; head of singing Dominique Trottein
Perfs: 100 *No of Prods:* 4 *Venues:* le théâtre de castres 600 *Touring:* Europe *Comments:* created the lyrical productions for the Festival de Saint-Céré (q.v.)

L'esplanade St Etienne Opéra
BP 237, 42013 **St Etienne** Cédex 2
Tel: 4-7747 8340 (booking)/47 (admin.)/43 (press)
Fax: 4-7747 8369
directeur Jean-Louis Pichon; administrateur Michel Fabre; directeur musical Patrick Fournillier
Perfs: 21 lyrical, 12 musical *No of Prods:* 3 *Venues:* Théâtre Ephémère 1100 *Touring:* France, Eruope
Comments: due to a fire at Grand Théâtre they will be at Théâtre Ephémère and from February 2001 will be at Théâtre Massenay; see also Venues and Promoters

Opéra national du Rhin
Boîte Postale 320, 67008 **Strasbourg** Cedex
Tel: 3-8875 4800 Fax: 3-8824 0934/8825 5259
Internet: www.opera-du-rhin.com
E-Mail: direction@opera-du-rhin.com
directeur général Rudolf Berger; directeur administratif Lucien Collinet; adjoint du directeur général Daniel Dollé; directeur de la communication Anne-France Boissenin
Perfs: 150 *No of Prods:* 7 new *Venues:* Théâtre de Strasboug 1142, Palais des Congrès Strasbourg 1985, Théâtre de Mulhouse 822, Théâtre de Colmar 707, La Filature, Mulhouse 1200 *Touring:* Finland, UK, France *Comments:* visiting address: 19, Place Broglie

Opéra de Toulon
Boulevard de Strasbourg, 83000 **Toulon**
Tel: 4-9493 0376 Fax: 4-9409 3029
directeur général Guy Grinda; directeur administratif Serge Lopez; relations publiques Danièle Gossuin; directeur musical Christian Segarici; directrice de la danse Monique Andreoletti; directeur de la scène Henri Murgue; regisseur général Philippe Pellier
Perfs: 30 (operas, operettas, ballets) *No of Prods:* 2 *Venues:* Théâtre à l'italienne 1500
Comments: see also Venues

Théâtre du Capitole
Place du Capitole, BP 129, 31014 **Toulouse** Cedex 06
Tel: 5-6122 3131 Fax: 5-6272 2832
Internet: www.theatre-du-capitole.org
directeur administratif Robert Gouazé; directeur artistique Nicolas Joël; relations publiques Jean-Paul Laffont; presse Marie-Claire Rettig
Perfs: 9 opera and operetta *No of Prods:* 9 (3 new) *Venues:* Théâtre du Capitole 1100 *Comments:* see also Dance and Venues

Atelier Lyrique de Tourcoing – Région Nord-Pas de Calais
82 Bld. Gambetta, 59200 **Tourcoing**
Tel: 3-2026 6603 Fax: 3-2027 9119
directeur Jean-Claude Malgoire; administatrice générale Catherine Noël; déléguée générale artistique Renée Boyer; relations publiques Laurence Lecomte
Perfs: 20 *No of Prods:* 5 out of 5 (& 5 concerts) *Venues:* capacity 950 *Touring:* France *Comments:* 17th, 18th and 20th century works

Grand Théâtre de Tours
34, rue de la Scellerie, 37000 **Tours**
Tel: 2-4705 3347 Fax: 2-4766 1192
directeur Michel Jarry; responsable administratif Luc Cavalier; directeur technique Denis Baling; directeur musical Mr Talmont; communication Stéphane de Decker; choregraphe Nadine le Claire; chef des choeurs Claire-Marie Mille
Venues: capacity 1010
Comments: see also Choirs and Venues

Palais des Congrés Opéra de Vichy
5, rue du Casino, BP 2805, 03208 **Vichy** Cedex
Tel: 4-7030 1717/5050 Fax: 4-7030 5010
direction artistique Diane Polya; chargée de communication Dominique Lagrange
Perfs: 25 *No of Prods:* 20 *Venues:* Opera Palais des Congrés *Comments:* attached to La Mairie de Vichy, BP 2158, 03208 Vichy Cedex; see also Venues

GEORGIA (+995)

Batumi Opera Theatre
1 Rustaveli st., 381450 **Batumi**
Tel: 222-76240
artistic director Aleko Khomeriki; manager Avtandil Grekov
Perfs: 10 *Venues:* Batumi Opera Theatre
Comments: performs classical opera

Balanchivadze Kutaisi Opera and Ballet Theatre
19 St. Nine str., 384002 **Kutaisi**
Tel: 31-52432/52123 Fax: 31-51010
general manager Devis Akhvlediani; artistic director Medez Amiranashvili; assistant to general manager Vakhtang Asatiani
Perfs: 30-40 *Prods:* 9 *Venues:* Kutaisi Opera Theatre
Touring: Spain, Germany

Abashidze State Musical Theatre
182 Agmashenebeli ave., 380012 **Tbilisi**
Tel: 32-342 773/348 090/347 708
manager Nestor Chiladze; assistants Giga Lortkipanidze, Nugzar Kacharava

Tbilisi National Opera and Ballet Theatre
25 Rustaveli Ave, 380008 **Tbilisi**
Tel: 32-931 894/999 561/983 248 Fax: 32-383 250
general manager Zurab Lomidze; deputy manager Tamaz Laperashvili; artistic director Jansug Kakhidzde; assistant to artistic director Guram Meliva; technical director Vitali Nodia
Perfs: 70 *No of Prods:* 14 *Venues:* Tbilsi Opera & Ballet Theatre *Touring:* Poland, Germany, Italy, Malta
Comments: performs classical opera repertoire, contemporary Georgian operas

GERMANY (+49)

Theater Aachen
Theaterplatz, 52062 **Aachen**
Tel: 241-47841 Fax: 241-478 4200
Internet: www.theater-aachen.de
E-Mail: pressestelle@theater.aachen.de
Generalintendant Claus Schmitz (from August: Dr. Paul Esterhazy); GMD Elio Boncompagni; Chefdramaturg Lukas Popovic; Schauspieldirektor Michael Klette; Choreograph Peter Wissmann; Leiterin Presse/PR Renate Faßbender; Disposition Tessa Beecken; KBB Sigrid Nowowiejski; Orchesterbüro Jane Kowalski
Perfs: 60 *No of Prods:* 4 *Venues:* Theater: Grosses Haus 857, Kammerspiele 165, Studiobühne Mörgens 99
Comments: see also Drama and Orchestras

Eduard-Von-Winterstein-Theater Annaberg
Buchholzer Straße 67, 09456 **Annaberg-Buchholz**
Tel: 3733-1407-0 Fax: 3733-1407 180
Geschäftsführer Patrick Wasserbauer; Intendant & Oberspielleitung Prof. Hans Hermann Krug; Musikalische Oberleitung Richard Vardigans; Öffentlichkeitsarbeit Angelika Gläsemann; Chefdramaturg Michael Eccarius
Perfs: 30 *No of Prods:* 2 *Venues:* Freilichtbühne Greifenstein 1200, Stammhaus 300, Studiobühne 90
Comments: see also Drama

Theater Augsburg
Kasernstaße 4-6, 86152 **Augsburg**
Tel: 821-324 4912 Fax: 821-324 4544/4478
Internet: www.augsburg.de
Intendant Dr. Ulrich Peters; Generalmusikdirektor Peter Leonard; Künstlerischer Betriebsdirektor Axel Peppermüler; Chefdramaturg Helmar von Hanstein; Ballettdirektor Erich Payer; Leiter des Ausstattungsateliers Wolfgang Buchner; Kaufmännischer Direktor Dr. Klaus Engert; Technischer Direktor Erwin Hammer
No of Prods: 7 new *Venues:* Stadttheater 976, Kongresshalle 1395, Komödie 310, Freilichtbühne Am Roten Tor 2117
Comments: see also Drama, Dance and Orchestra

Stella Musical Management – Starlight Express Musical – Production GmbH
Stadionring 24, 44791 **Bachum**
Tel: 234-506 020 Fax: 234-506 0253
Theaterdirektor Burkard Koch; Künstlerische Leitung Garry Noakes; Choreographie Artlene Phillips; Music Supervisor Phil Edwards
Perfs: 500 *Venues:* capacity 1700 *Comments:* Starlight Express is the only production

Berliner Kammeroper
Kottbusser Damm 79, 10967 **Berlin**
Tel: 30-693 1054 Fax: 30-692 5201
E-Mail: berlinerkammeroper@t-online.de
künstlerische Gesamtleitung Brynmor Llewelyn Jones; Produktionsleitung Dirk Kiefer; Dramaturgie/Öffentlichkeitsarbeit Jens Schubbe
No of Prods: 3 *Venues:* Hebbel Theater 600 *Comments:* Baroque to contemporary music theatre

Deutsche Oper Berlin
Richard-Wagner Strasse 10, 10585 **Berlin**
Tel: 30-34384-01 Fax: 30-34384-232
Internet: www.deutsche-oper.berlin.de
E-Mail: DOBtickets@t-online.de
Generalintendant Prof Götz Friedrich; Generalmusikdirektor Christian Thielemann; Geschäftsführender Direktor André Schmitz; Operndirektor Dr Alard von Rohr; Künstlerischer Betriebsdirektor Jean-François Monnard; kommissarische Ballettdirektorin Sylviane Bayard; Chordirektor Helmut Sonne; Leitender Dramaturg Curt A Roesler; Pressestelle Barbara Hering
Perfs: 220 + 70 special attractions + 9 concerts *No of Prods:* opera: 33 (4 new); ballet 10 (2 new); for children: 12 opera, 9 ballet *Venues:* Deutsche Oper 1865, Parkett-Foyer 200 *Comments:* performances of opera and ballet for young people in the foyer; venue address: Bismarckstr. 35, 10627 Berlin; see also Dance

Komische Oper Berlin
Behrenstrasse 55-57, 10117 **Berlin**
Tel: 30-20260-0/4799 7400 (box-office) Fax: 30-202 60405
Internet: komische-oper-berlin.de
E-Mail: opera@berlin.snafu.de
Intendant Albert Kost; Operndirektor Prof. Harry Kupfer; GMD Yakov Kreizberg; 1. Koordinierter Kapellmeister Vladimir Jurowski; 2. Kapellmeister Tetsuro Ban; künstlerischer Betriebsdirektor Kai Luft; Chefchoreograph Richard Wherlock
Perfs: 285 *No of Prods:* operas: 31, dance: 3 *Venues:* capacity 1270 *Comments:* operas sung in German

Metropol-Theater
Friedrichstraße 101-102, 10117 **Berlin**
Tel: 30-202 46-0 Fax: 30-208 0116/4236
Comments: closed – maybe reopening in Autumn 2000

Neuköllner Oper
Karl-Marx-Straße 131-133, 12043 **Berlin**
Tel: 30-6889 0777 Fax: 30-6889 0789
Internet: members.aol.com/neukOper/
künstlerische Leitung/Geschäftsführung Peter Lund; künstlerische Leitung Winfried Radeke; Öffentlichkeitsarbeit, Dramaturgie Nils Steinkrauss; kaufmännische Leitung/Geschäftsführung Kerstin Iskra
Perfs: 250 *No of Prods:* 10 (5 new) *Venues:* capacity 225, studiobühne 60

Revuetheater Friedrichstadtpalast GmbH
Friedrichstraße 107, 10117 **Berlin**
Tel: 30-232 620/2326 2326 (tickets)
Fax: 30-282 4578/2326 2323 (tickets)
Internet: www.friedrichstadtpalast.de
E-Mail: friedrichstadtpalast@berlin.de
Intendant Alexander Iljinskij; Geschäftsführer Holger Markmann; Ballettdirektor Roland Gawlik; Chefdirigent Detlef Klemm; Spielleiter Jürgen Nass; Pressesprecher Günter Strohbach
Venues: Große Revue 1889

Staatsoper Unter den Linden Berlin
Unter den Linden 5-7, 10117 **Berlin**
Tel: 30-203 54-0 Fax: 30-2035 4206
Internet: www.staatsoper-berlin.org
E-Mail: contact@staatsoper-berlin.org
Intendant Georg Quander; Künstlerischer Leiter und Generalmusikdirektor Daniel Barenboirn; Geschäftsführender Direktor Georg Vierthaler; Künstlerischer Betriebsdirektor Achim Dobschall; Persönlicher Referent des Intendanten und Leiter der Pressearbeit Dr. Stephan Adam; Leiterin Marketing Sabine Turner; Chefdramaturgin Dr. Regula Rapp; Dramaturgie Dr. Ralf Waldschmidt, Ilka Seifert; Dramaturgie Ballett und Ballettbetriebsdirektorin Dr. Christiane Theobald; Chordirektor Eberhard Friedrich; Kostümdirektorin Hannelore Wedemeÿer; Technischer Direktor Klaus Wichmann
Perfs: 165 opera, 55 ballet, 23 symphony, 25 chamber, 5 recitals, 8 opera abroad *No of Prods:* 26 + 9 new *Venues:* Grosses Haus 1396, Apollo-Saal 249 *Touring:* Vienna, Madrid *Comments:* symphony and chamber concerts in the 2 halls and in the Konzerthaus Berlin; Box office: tel: 30-2035 4555, fax: 30-2035 4483; see also Dance

Theater des Westens
Kantstraße 12, 10623 **Berlin**
Tel: 30-319 030 Fax: 30-3190 3188
Internet: theater-des-westens.de
E-Mail: info@theater-des-westens.de
Intendant und künstlerischer Leiter Prof. Elmar Ottenthal; Stellvertretender künstlerischeleiter Jürg Burth
Perfs: 260 *No of Prods:* 3-4 *Venues:* Theater des Westens 1354 *Touring:* national *Comments:* guest performances; see also Drama and Dance

Theater Wilde Mischung Berlin
c/o Altermann, Sanderetr. 21, 12047 **Berlin**
Tel: 30-624 8763 Fax: 30-624 8763
Direktor Lilly Walden; Musikalische Oberleitung Birgitta Altermann
Perfs: 150 *No of Prods:* 1 new *Touring:* London
Comments: touring company; can also perform in English and Spanish

Theater Bielefeld
Brunnenstrasse 3-9, 33602 **Bielefeld**
Tel: 521-513 077/177 077 (box office)
Fax: 521-513 430/516 411 (box office)
Internet: www.bielefeld.de
Intendantin Regula Gerber; Generalmusikdirektor Peter Kuhn; künstlerischer Betriebsdirektor Sabine Schweitzer; Leiter der Öffentlichkeitsarbeit Petra Kicherer; Ballettdirektor Philip Lansdale; Chordirektor Angela Sleeman; technischer Direktor Detlef Plümecke
No of Prods: 8 (6 new) *Venues:* Großes Haus 775, Kleines Haus 304 *Comments:* see also Drama, Dance and Orchestra

Theater der Bundesstadt Bonn, Oper/Choreographisches Theater
Am Boeselagerhof 1, 53111 **Bonn**
Tel: 228-778 000 Fax: 228-778 371
Internet: www.uni-bonn.de/theaterbonn
E-Mail: oper@bonn.de
Intendant Dr Manfred Beilharz; Generalmusikdirektor Marc Soustrot; Direktor des Choreographischen Theaters Pavel Miskulastik; Chefdramaturg Dr Paul Esterhazy (until Aug 2000); Öffentlichkeitsarbeit Dr Marie Luise Maintz; Chordirektorin Sibylle Wagner; kaufmännischer Direktor Rolf Oltmanns
Perfs: 160 *No of Prods:* 11 (6 new) *Venues:* Opera House 1040, Werkstattbühne 150 *Comments:* Tickets: Opernkasse, Mülheimer Platz 1, 53111 Bonn, Tel: 228-773 6666

Brandenburger Theater
Grabenstraße 14, 14776 **Brandenburg**
Tel: 3381-511-0 Fax: 3381-511 160
Internet: www.fh-brandenburg.de/theater
Intendant t.b.a.; Generalmusikdirektor t.b.a.; Geschäftsführer Andreas Wansing; Chefdisponentin/Leiterin des KBB Sibylle Jentsch; Chefdramaturgie Bettina Bartz; Chordirektor t.b.a.
No of Prods: 6 (4 new) *Venues:* Große Bühne (due to open in 2000) 600, Studiobühne 200, Malsaal 60, Neue Probebühne 70 *Comments:* see also Drama, Orchestras and Puppetry

Staatstheater Braunschweig
Am Theater, 38100 **Braunschweig**
Tel: 531-1234-0 Fax: 531-1234-114
Internet: www.staatstheater.braunschweig.de
E-Mail: service@staatstheater-braunschweig.de
Generalintendant Wolfgang Gropper; Generalmusikdirektor Jonas Alber; Verwaltungsleiter Thomas Fehrle; Ballettdirektor Pierre Wyss; Oberspielleiter Musiktheater Uwe Schwarz; Leiter des Kinder- und Jugendtheaters Jörg Gade; Chefdramaturgin Ursula Werdenberg
Perfs: ca. 500 including all venues *No of Prods:* 29 *Venues:* Grosses Haus 906, Theaterspielplatz 99, Kleines Haus 330
Comments: also has children's and young people's theatre; see also Drama, Dance and Orchestras

Bremer Theater
Am Goetheplatz 1-3, 28203 **Bremen**
Tel: 421-36530 Fax: 421-365 3415
Internet: www.bremertheater.com
Geschäftsführer Dr. Klaus Pierwoß; Generalmusikdirektor Günter Neuholt; Chordirektor Theo Wiedebusch; Tanztheater Susanne Linke
No of Prods: 7 new *Venues:* Theater am Goetheplatz (depending on whether orchestra is in place) 907-894, Schauspielhaus 330, Concordia 99, Brauhauskeller 60
Comments: see also Drama and Dance

Stadttheater Bremerhaven
Postfach 120541, 27519 **Bremerhaven**
Tel: 471-482 060 Fax: 471-4820 6274
Internet: www.bremerhaven.de
Intendant Peter Grisebach; künstlerischer Betriebsdirektor Gunther Volz; Chefdramaturgin Petra Hofmann-Paczkowski; Generalmusikdirektor Prof Leo Plettner; Ballettdirektor Ricardo Fernando; Verwaltungsdirektor Jürgen Ahlf
No of Prods: 2 opera, 3 operettas, 1 musical, 1 music theatre *Venues:* Kleines Haus 122, children's, young people's theatre, Niederdeutsche Bühne, Theater im Fischereihafen 300, Musik- und Konzertsaal, Karl-Schwz-Kazerne 715, Cinema 330, Stadthalle 1000, Cityport 400 *Comments:* visiting address: Theodor-Heuss-Platz, 27568 Bremerhaven; see also Drama and Dance; see also Drama, Dance & Orchestras

Städtische Theater Chemnitz GmbH
Postfach 756, 09007 **Chemnitz**
Tel: 371-6969-5 Fax: 371-6969-8961/699
Internet: www.freiepresse.de/theater-chemnitz
E-Mail: theater-chemnitz@abo.freiepresse.de
Generalintendant Rolf Stiska; Generalmusikdirektor Oleg Caetani; Operndirektor Michael Heinicke
Perfs: 240 *No of Prods:* 24 *Venues:* Opernhaus 720, Opernhaus/Hinterbühne 100
Touring: New York, Tel Aviv *Comments:* visiting address: Käthe-Kollwitz-Str. 7, 09111 Chemnitz; see also Dance, Drama and Orchestras

Landestheater Coburg
Großes Haus, Schlossplatz 6, 96450 **Coburg**
Tel: 9561-8850 Fax: 9561-793 979
Intendant Norbert Kleine Borgmann; Ballettdirektor Neng Sheng Yu; Chordirektor Stefan Mlier; Leiter des Betriebsbüros Günter Hagemann; Chefdramaturg Peter Biermann
Perfs: 400 *No of Prods:* 24 *Venues:* Grosses Haus 557, Theater in der Reithalle 99 *Touring:* guest performances in Germany *Comments:* see also Drama and Dance; see also Orchestra

opera mobile basel
Karl-Liebknecht Straße 28A, 03046 **Cottbus**
Tel: 355-21567 Fax: 355-21567
Contact/Director Adrian Stern
Perfs: 12 *No of Prods:* 1 *Touring:* Germany, Switzerland, Austria *Comments:* touring company

Staatstheater Cottbus
Karl-Liebknecht-Straße 136, 03046 **Cottbus**
Tel: 355-78240 Fax: 355-791 333
Intendant Christoph Schroth; Geschäftsführender Direktor Steffen Rohr; Persönliche Referentin des Intendanten und Geschäftsführende Regisseurin Schauspiel Anu Saari; Technischer Direktor Matthias Günther; Direktor für Ausstattung Joachim Vogler; Musikalischer Oberspielleiter GMD Reinhard Petersen; Operndirektor Martin Schüler; Chordirektor Christian Möbius
Perfs: 420 (all genres) *No of Prods:* 21 *Venues:* Großes Haus am Schillerplatz 678, Kammerbühne up to 140, Theaterscheune Ströbitz up to 130, Marstallhof Schloß Branitz up to 136, Kreuzkirche Cottbus up to 250
Comments: see also Dance, Drama and Orchestra

Staatstheater Darmstadt
Marienplatz 2, 64283 **Darmstadt**
Tel: 6151-28111 Fax: 6151-281 1226
Intendant Gerd Theo Umberg; Generalmusikdirektor Marc Albrecht; Chefdramaturgie Davud Boucheri; Leiterin Tanztheater Birgitta Trommler; Chordirektor André Weiss; Pressereferentin Dr Juliane Kuhn; Leitende Musikdramaturgin Bettina Auer; Operndirektor Prof. Friedrich Meyer-Oertel
Perfs: 141 *No of Prods:* 14 (9 new) *Venues:* Grosses Haus 956, Kleines Haus 450, Werkstattbühne 99 *Comments:* see also Drama and Dance

Anhaltisches Theaters Dessau
Postfach 1203, 06812 **Dessau**
Tel: 340-2511-0 Fax: 340-251 1215
Internet: www.anhaltisches-theater.de
E-Mail: anhaltisches.theater.dram@topmail.de
Generalintendant u. Chefregisseur des Musiktheaters Johannes Felsenstein; Verwaltungsdirektor Joachim Landgraf; Schauspieldirektor Helmut Straßburger; Chefchoreograph Gonzalo Galguera; Disponent Peter Gogler; Chefdramaturg Wolfgang Lange; Generalmusikdirektor Carlos Kalmar
No of Prods: 39 (16 new) *Venues:* Großes Haus 1096, Studio 80, Foyer 130 *Touring:* nationally *Comments:* visiting address: Friedensplatz 1a, 06844 Dessau; see also Drama, Dance, Orchestra and Puppetry

Landestheater Detmold
Theaterplatz 1, 32756 **Detmold**
Tel: 5231-97460 Fax: 5231-974 701
Internet: www.landestheaterdetmold.de
E-Mail: 113217.3637@compuserve.com
Intendant Ulf Reiher; Dramaturgie Elisabeth Wirtz; Generalmusikdirektor Steffen Leißner; Ballettmeisterin Elsa Genova; Chordirektor Carsten Bowien; Leiter des Musiktheaters Rainer Worms; 1. Kapellmeister Matthias Forenhy
Perfs: 640 *No of Prods:* 7 (4 new) *Venues:* Großes Haus 650, Studiobühne 90 *Touring:* national & Benelux
Comments: see also Drama, Dance and Orchestra

Theater Dortmund
Kuhstraße 12, 44137 **Dortmund**
Tel: 231-502 5547 (switchboard) Fax: 231-502 2461
Internet: www.dortmund.de/theater/
E-Mail: theater@dortmund.de
Generalintendant John Dew; künstlerischer Leiter KJT Wolfgang Trautwein; Verwaltungsdirektor/ kaufmännischer Direktor Wilhelm Scheer; Generalmusikdirektor Anton Marik; Ballettdirektoren Jean Renshaw, Mei Hong Lin, Zoltan Ravasz; PR Rüdiger Beermann
Perfs: 84 *No of Prods:* 10 (8 new) *Venues:* Opernhaus 1170, Schauspielhaus 496, Studio 100, children and youth theatre 200 *Comments:* philharmonic orchestra with 93 musicians, see also Drama, Dance and Orchestra

Sächsische Staatsoper Dresden
Theaterplatz 2, 01067 **Dresden**
Tel: 351-4911-0 Fax: 351-491 1691
Internet: www.semperoper.de
E-Mail: bestellung@semperoper.de
Intendant Christoph Albrecht; Chefdirigent der Oper Semyon Bychkov; Chefdirigent der Sächsischen Staatskapalle Giuseppe Sinopoli; geschäftsführender Direktor Roland Beneke; Operndirektor Rolf Wollrad; künstlerischer Betriebsdirektor Hans-Joachim Frey; Chordirektor Matthias Brauer; Orchesterdirektor Jan Nast; Ballettdirektor Vladimir Derevianko; Technischer Direktor Volker Butzmann; Kostümdirektorin Frauke Schernau; Öffentlichkeitsarbeit Martina Miesler
Perfs: 310 *No of Prods:* 5
Venues: Semperoper 1323, kleine szene 99 *Touring:* South Korea, France, Spain, Italy, Japan, China
Comments: alternative E-mail: presse@semperoper.de; Opernfestspiele (6-24 April 2000)

Semperoper
Dresden
Comments: please see Sächsische Staatsoper Dresden

Staatsoperette Dresden
Pirnaer Landstrasse 131, 01257 **Dresden**
Tel: 351-20799-0 Fax: 351-20799-22
Intendant Fritz Wendrich; Verwaltungsdirektor u. stellv. Intendant Jürgen Eggert; Chefdirigent Volker M Plangg; Technischer Direktor Christfried Scharfenberg; Chefdramaturg Peter Gunold; Chordirektor Siegfried Fischer; Künstlerisches Betriebsbüro Erika Zimmermann; Ausstattungsleiterin Frau Sabine Pommerening
Perfs: 300 *No of Prods:* 4 *Venues:* Großer Saal 604, TheaterCasino 60 *Touring:* Germany *Comments:* operetta concerts in Dresdner Zwinger, Schloßpark Pillnitz, Großer Garten, Felsenbühne in Rathen; see also Dance

Landesbühnen Sachsen
Meißner Strasse 152, 01445 **Dresden-Radebeul**
Tel: 351-8954-0 Fax: 351-895 4201
Internet: www.dresden-theater.de
E-Mail: landesbuehnen.sachsen@dresden-theater.de
Intendant Christian Schmidt; Operndirektor Steffen Piontek; Verwaltungsdirektorin Barbara Kunz; Generalmusikdirektor Prof. Alexander von Brück; Direktor Management, Öffentlichkeitsarbeit Till Wanschura
Perfs: 146 *No of Prods:* 11 (6 new) (Madam Butterfly, Wiener Blut, Kron-prinz Friedrich, Der Wildschütz
Venues: various venues in Sachsen; main venue Landesbühne Sachsen
Touring: national guest performances
Comments: see also Dance, Orchestras and Drama

Deutsche Oper am Rhein – Düsseldorf-Duisburg
Heinrich-Heine-Allee 16a, 40213 **Düsseldorf**
Tel: 211-89080 Fax: 211-890 8289
Internet: www.deutsche-oper-am-rhein.de
E-Mail: Rheinoper@aol.com
Generalintendant Prof. Tobias Richter; Chefdirigent John Fiore; Chefdisponent Stephen Harrison; Chefdramaturg Michael Lainert; Ballettdirektor Youri Vàmos; Chordirektor Volkmar Olbrich; Geschäftsführender Direktor Dr Werner Hellfritzsch
Perfs: 42 + 5 guest *No of Prods:* 10 new *Venues:* Opernhaus Düsseldorf 1342, Theater der Stadt Duisburg 1118
Touring: Shanghai (China), Brasil
Comments: second address: Neckarstr. 1, 47051 Duisburg, tel: 203-30090, fax: 203-300 9210; see also Dance

Thüringer Landestheater Eisenach-Rudolstadt-Saalfeld GmbH Haus Eisenach
Theaterplatz 4-7, 99817 **Eisenach**
Tel: 3691-256-0
Fax: 3691-256 159
Intendant und künstlerischer Geschäftsführer Johannes Steurich; Geschäftsführerin Petra Mitdank; Chefdirigent d.Landeskapelle Eisenach GMD Wolfgang Wappler; Chefdirigent der Thüringer Symphoniker Saalfeld-Rudolstadt MD Oliver Weder; Operndirektor Dieter Reuscher; Chordirektor MD Manfred Jäckel
Perfs: 520 *No of Prods:* 29 (13 new)
Venues: Theater Eisenach 660, Studio Theater Eisenach 45, Theater Rudolstadt 270, Studio Theater Rudolstadt 50 *Comments:* address Haus Rudolstadt: Anger 1, 07407 Rudolstadt; see also Dance, Orchestras and Schauspiel Rudolstadt

Theater Erfurt
Postfach 244, 99084 **Erfurt**
Tel: 361-223 3100 Fax: 361-223 3120
Internet: www.theater-erfurt.de
E-Mail: alanger@theater-erfurt.de
Generalintendant Dietrich Taube; Ballettdirektor Juergen Heiss; Generalmusikdirektor Wolfgang Rögner; Chefdramaturg Dr Klaus Gronau; Leiter der Öffentlichkeitsarbeit Dr Arne Langer
Perfs: 120 *No of Prods:* 8
Venues: Kuppeltheater 685, Schauspielhaus 420, Domstufen 1000 *Comments:* visiting address: Walkmühlstrasse 13, 99084 Erfurt; see also Dance, Drama and Orchestras

Aalto Theater
Aalto-Theater, Opernplatz 10, 45128 **Essen**
Tel: 201-8122-0 Fax: 201-812 2112
Internet: www.theater-essen.de
E-Mail: infoaalto@theater-essen.de
Opernintendant und Generalmusikdirektor Stefan Soltesz; Geschäftsführer Theater & Philharmonie Essen Otmar Herren; Chefdisponentin Juliane Pschigode; Dramaturgie Dr Kerstin Schüssler, Ina Wragge; Ballettdirektor Prof Martin Puttke; Pressereferat Dr Anna Linoli (fax: 201-812 2211)
Perfs: 172 (opera & ballet) *No of Prods:* 16 (7 new)
Venues: Aalto Theater 1125 *Comments:* see also Dance (aalto ballett theater), Drama and Orchestras

Kammeroper Frankfurt e.V.
Sternstraße 31, 60318 **Frankfurt am Main**
Tel: 69-556 189 Fax: 69-556 189
Intendant Rainer Pudenz; Musikdirektor Roland Böer; Ausstattung Iz Maglov; Kostüme Margarete Berghoff
Perfs: 40 *No of Prods:* 4 (2 new) *Venues:* Loge zur Einigkeit 250, Palmengarten 500, Holzhausenschloesschen 120

Neuburger Kammeroper
Friedberger Landstr. 189, 60389 **Frankfurt am Main**
Tel: 69-553 781
Leitungsgremium Anton Sprenzel, Heinrich Wladarsch, Horst Vladar; künstlerischer Leiter Horst Vladar; musikalische Leitung Alois Rottenaicher; Dramaturgie Annette und Horst Vladar; PR and techn. Leiter Hans Buttmann
Perfs: 5 *No of Prods:* 1
Venues: Stadttheater Neuburg 300
Comments: venue address: Stadttheater Neuburg, 86633 Neuburg a.d. Donau

Städtische Bühnen Frankfurt am Main
OPER FRANKFURT, Untermainanlage 11, 60311 **Frankfurt am Main**
Tel: 69-212-02
Fax: 69-2123 7518
Internet: www.frankfurt-business.de/oper
E-Mail: pressereferat.oper@stadt-frankfurt.de
geschäftsführender Intendant Dr. Martin Steinhoff; Künstlerischer Berater des Intendanten Prof. Hans Peter Doll; Chefdirigent der Museumsorchesters Paolo Carigrani; Pers. Referent des Chefdirigenten Rüdiger Jacobsen; Operndirektor Udo Gefe; Chefdisponent Mark Schönwasser-Görke; Pressereferentin und Leiterin der Öffentlichkeitsarbeit Brigitta Mazanec; Chefdramaturg Dr Norbert Abels
Perfs: 150 *No of Prods:* 18 (7 new)
Venues: Opernhaus 1367
Comments: see also under Drama (Schauspiel Frankfurt) and Dance (Frankfurt Ballett)

Mittelsächsische Theater und Philharmonie gemeinnützige GmbH
Borngasse 1, 09599 **Freiberg**
Tel: 3731-35820 Fax: 3731-23406
Intendant Dr Ingolf Huhn; GMD Georg Christoph Sandmann; Chefdramaturg Dr Roland Dreßler; Chefdisponentin Dr Yvonne Grunke; Leiter Öffentlichkeitsarbeit Dr Christoph Nieder
Perfs: 130 (music theatre only) *No of Prods:* 11 *Venues:* Theater Freiberg 295, Bühne in der Borngasse 60, Theater Döbeln 308 *Comments:* see also Drama and Orchestras

Städtische Bühnen Freiburg
Bertoldstraße 46, 79098 **Freiburg**
Tel: 761-201 2807/2950 Fax: 761-201 2999
Internet: www.uni-freiburg.de/theater/
Intendant Hans J. Ammann; Musikalische Oberleitung GMD Kwamé Ryan; Künstlerische Direktion Ballett Amanda Miller; Künstlerische Betriebsdirektorin Elke Hoch; Öffentlichkeitsarbeit Heike Neumann
Perfs: 230 *No of Prods:* 9 (7 new) + 1 musical *Venues:* Großes Haus 850; Schauspielhaus Kurbel 350; Theater cafe 150; Kamera 99 *Comments:* see also Drama, Dance, Orchestras, Fesitvals and Venues

Schillertheater NRW – Musiktheater Gelsenkirchen
Kennedyplatz, 45881 **Gelsenkirchen**
Tel: 209-40970 Fax: 209-409 7250
Internet: www.schillertheater-nrw.de
Theaterleitung/Geschäftsführung Ludwig Baum, Holk Freytag, Peter Neubauer; Intendant Musiktheater und Ballett Ludwig Baum; Persönlicher Referent und Vertreter des Intendanten Jörg Maecker; Dramaturgie Norbert Klein, Martin Griesemer, ; Generalmusikdirektor der Stadt Wuppertal und musikalischer Leiter des Schillertheaters NRW George Hanson; Ballettdirektor Bernd Schindowski; Chordirektor Nandor Ronay; Künstlerischer Betriebsdirektor und Leiter des Künstlerischen Betriebsbüro Björn Peleikis; Öffentlichkeitsarbeit Oda Mahnke
Perfs: ca. 180 *No of Prods:* ca. 12 *Venues:* Grosses Haus 1008, Kleines Haus 350, Opernhaus Wuppertal 845 *Comments:* also has a youth theatre; concerts and musicals; see also Dance (Ballett Schindowski) and Drama; see also entry for Wuppertal

Altenburg Gera Theater GmbH
Küchengartenallee 2, 07548 **Gera**
Tel: 365-8279-0 Fax: 365-827 9135
Internet: www.theater.altenburg.gera.de
E-Mail: boehme_pock@t-online.de
Generalintendant Michael Grosse; Generalmusikdirektor Russel N. Harris; Operndirektor u. Stellvertreter d. Generalintendanten Hubert Kross jr; Ballettdirektor Siegfried Martin Wende; Direktorin für Dramaturgie und Öffentlichkeitsarbeit Dagmar Kunze; Chordirektor Günter Heinig; Verwaltungs- und Personaldirektorin Heidrun Neumann
Venues: Theatersaal Gera 670, Theatersaal Altenburg 544, Konzertsaal Gera 733, Kleines Theater im Zentrum Gera 176, Kammerspiele Gera 176, Heizhaus Altenburg 120, Theater unterm Dach Altenburg 60 *Comments:* address of Altenburg Theater: Theaterplatz 19, 04600 Altenburg; see also Drama, Dance and Orchestras

Stadttheater Gießen
Berliner Platz, 35390 **Gießen**
Tel: 641-79570 Fax: 641-795 780
Intendant Guy Montavon; Kommissarischer GMD Herbert Gietzeu
Perfs: 88 *No of Prods:* 12 + 2 *Venues:* Stadttheater 574, Theaterstudio 199 *Comments:* see also Drama, Dance, Orchestra and Venues

Theater Görlitz
Demianiplatz 2, 02826 **Görlitz**
Tel: 3581-474 721/22 Fax: 3581-474 736
Internet: www.via-regia.de
E-Mail: Theater-goerlitz@t-online.de
Intendant Dr Michael Wieler; Verwaltungsdirektor Günter Püschel; Chefdirigent GMD Christof Escher; Ballettmeister Franz Huyer; Künstlerischer Betriebsdirektor Klaus Arauner; Chefdramaturg Jürgen Hartmann; Chordirektor Milos Krejci
Perfs: ca. 220 *No of Prods:* 7 new *Venues:* Theater der Stadt Görlitz 604, Foyer 85, Appollo 99, Untermarkt (Freiluft), Scheune/Ludwigsdorf, Gehard-Hauptmann-Theater/Zittau, Deutsch-Sorbisches- Volkstheater/Bauzen, Lausitzhalle/Hoyerswerda, Lessing-Theater/Kamenz
Comments: alternative Internet: www.goerlitz.de

Theater Vorpommern
Greifswald
Internet: www.theater-vorpommern.de
Comments: Please see entry under Stralsund

Theater Hagen
Elberfelder Strasse 65, 58095 **Hagen**
Tel: 2331-207 3210 Fax: 2331-207 2446
Internet: www.hagen.de/THEATER/welcome.html
E-Mail: theater@stadt-hagen.de
Intendant Peter Pietzsch; Chefdisponentin Ingrid Hartmann; Dramaturgie Sabine Busch, Prof Dr Peter P. Pachl; Generalmusikdirektor Georg Fritzsch; Ballettmeister und Leiter des Balletts Gabor Tasfi; Chordirektor Konrad Haenisch
Perfs: c.a. 300 *No of Prods:* 15 (11 new) *Venues:* Großes Haus 800, Theater Cafe 110, Toz 300 *Touring:* guest performances *Comments:* see also Dance and Orchestras; the theatre also puts on one theatre production each year with guest actors

Nordharzer Städtebundtheater
Spiegelstrasse 20a, 38820 **Halberstadt**
Tel: 3941-6965-0 Fax: 3941-442 652
Internet: www.halberstadt.de/theater
E-Mail: theater@halberstadt.de
Intendant Kay Metzger; Chefdramaturg Peter Oppermann; Verwaltungsdirektor Roland Hinkel; Oberspielleiter Schauspiel Malte Kreutzfeldt; Oberspielleiter Musiktheater Horst Kupich; Musikalischer Oberleiter Christian Hammer
Perfs: 520 (in total) *No of Prods:* 30 (in total) *Venues:* Großes Haus Halberstadt 501, Kammerbühne Halberstadt 99, Großes Haus Quedlinburg 280, Neue Bühne Quedlinburg 70

OPERNHAUS HALLE
Universitätsring 24, 06018 **Halle (Saale)**
Tel: 345-5110-0 Fax: 345-511 0106/102
Internet: opernhaus.halle.de
E-Mail: opernhaus@halle.de
Intendant Klaus Froboese; Direktor Reinhard Popp; Generalmusikdirektor Roger Epple; Chefdisponent Ralf-Friedrich Voß; Chordirektor Dietrich Schlegel; Ballettdirektor Ralf Rossa
Perfs: 290 (incl. concerts) *No of Prods:* 34 (12 new) *Venues:* Großer Saal 660, Konzertfoyer 60, Opernrestaurant 100, Goethe-Theater Bad Lauchstädt 454, Georg-Friedrich-Händel-Halle 1253 *Comments:* Orchester des Opernhauses Halle, collegium instrumentale, Händelfestspielorchester

Hamburgische Staatsoper
Große Theaterstraße 34, 20354 **Hamburg**
Tel: 40-3568-0 Fax: 40-3568 456
Internet: www.hamburgische-staatsoper.de
E-Mail: pressestelle@hamburgische-staatsoper.de
Intendant Dr Albin Hänseroth; Sekretariat Sabine Rosenberg; Staatsoperndirektor Detlef Meierjohann; Sekretariat Kerstin Rodenwald; Generalmusikdirektor Ingo Metzmacher; Sekretariat Claudia Boldnan; Ballettintendant John Neumeier; Sekretariat Birgit Pfitzner; Presse und Öffentlichkeitsarbeit Christiane Rubien
Perfs: 300 *No of Perfs:* 17 (7 new) *Venues:* Staatsoper 1675, Opera Stabile 100 *Comments:* see also Dance

Operettenhaus Hamburg
Spielbudenplatz 1, 20359 **Hamburg**
Tel: 40-31117-0 Fax: 40-3111 7252
Vorstandsvorsitzender Stella Musical AG Hemjö Klein; musikalischer Leiter Linda Faith Roland; Produzent Rolf Deyhle
Perfs: 415 *Venues:* capacity 1125 *Comments:* only production 'Cats'; see also Venues

Niedersächsische Staatsoper Hannover
Opernplatz 1, 30159 **Hannover**
Tel: 511-1684 6727 Fax: 511-363 2536
Internet: www.staatstheater-hannover.com
Intendant Prof Hans-Peter Lehmann; Betriebsbüro Dieter Kreuzer; Chefdramaturg Dominica Volkert; Generalmusikdirektor Andreas Delfs; Verwaltungsdirektor Knut Lehmann
Perfs: 263 (opera + ballet) *No of Prods:* 30 (opera + ballet) *Venues:* Opernhaus 1207

Theater der Stadt Heidelberg – Oper
Friedrichstrasse 5, 69117 **Heidelberg**
Tel: 6221-583 508 Fax: 6221-583 599
Intendant Dr Volkmar Clauß; PR Bertram Hacke; Chordirektorin Heike Kiefner; Chefdisponentin Christa Oser; Generalmusikdirektor Thomas Kalb; Musikdramaturg Christoph Zimmermann
Perfs: 500-600 (including drama & dance) *No of Prods:* 6 *Venues:* Städtische Bühnen 619, Studiobühne 130 *Comments:* see also Dance (Heidelberg Ballett), Drama and Orchestras

Stadttheater Hildesheim
Theaterstr. 6, 31141 **Hildesheim**
Tel: 5121-1693-0 Fax: 5121-169 393
Intendant Dr Martin Kreutzberg; Musikalischer Oberleiter Werner Seitzer; Dramaturgie Dr. Sabine Jehner
No of Prods: 8 (5 new) *Venues:* Stadtheater Grosses Haus 607, Theo/Studiobühne 68, Foyer 65 *Comments:* see also Drama, Dance, Orchestras and Venues

Städtebundtheater Hof
Kulmbacher str.5, 95030 **Hof**
Tel: 9281-7070-0 Fax: 9281-707 0299
Internet: www.theater-hof.com
E-Mail: info@theater-hof.com
Intendant Uwe Drechsel; künstlerisches Betriebsbüro u. Disposition Petra Gorki; Generalmusikdirektor Daniel Kleiner; Marketing Leiter Petra Müller; Chefdramaturg Thomas Schindler; Musikdramaturg Michaela Peterseil; Ballettdirektor Jerzy Graczyk; Generalmusikdirektor Golo Berg; 1. Kapellmeister Phillipp Pointner
Perfs: 200 *No of Prods:* 3 Operas, 2 Operettas, 2 Musicals *Venues:* Stadttheater 567, Studio 99 *Touring:* Germany *Comments:* see also Drama and Dance

Pfalztheater
Willy-Brandt-Platz 4-5, 67657 **Kaiserslautern**
Tel: 631-3675-0 Fax: 631-307 5213
Intendant Wolfgang Quetes; Chefdisponent Peter Bachmaier; Chefdramaturg Stephan Kopf; GMD Lior Shambadal; Verwaltungsdirektor Günter Albert; Ballettdirektor Eva Reinthaller; Presse und Werbe-organisation Günther Fingerle
No of Prods: 10 *Venues:* Großes Haus 720, Werkstatt 200 *Comments:* see also Drama, Dance and Orchestra

Badisches Staatstheater Karlsruhe
76125 **Karlsruhe**
Tel: 721-3557-0 Fax: 721-373 223 (Verwaltung)/355 7155 (Int.)
Internet: www.karlsruhe.de/kultur/staatstheater
E-Mail: kartenverkauf@bstaatstheater.bul.de
Generalintendant Pavel Fieber; Verwaltungsdir. Wolfgang Sieber; Generalmusikdir. Kazushi Ono; Schauspieldir. Peter Schroth; Ballettdir. Olaf Schmidt; stellvertr. Operndir. Frank Gersthofer; Oberspielleiter des Schauspiels Klaus Kusenberg; künstlerische Betriebsdir. Gudrun Pappermann; Technischer Dir. Harald Faßlrinner; Leitender Dramaturg Joachim Putlitz; Leiterin des Künstlerischen Betriebsbüros Roswitha Roth; Chordir. Carl Robert Helg; Presse- und Öffentlichkeitsarbeit Anna-Renate Sörgel, Gabi Oetterer; Assistent des Generalintendanten Carl Philip vonMaldeghem
Perfs: 253 (musical, opera, ballet) *No of Prods:* 17 (11 new) *Venues:* Großes Haus 1002, Kleines Haus 385, and other venues with various capacities, ZKM Konzerthaus Karlsruhe *Touring:* München, Ludwigsburg, Wilhelmshaven (Expo 2000) *Comments:* venue address: Baumeisterstrasse 11, 76137 Karlsruhe; see also Drama, Dance, Orchestras and Festivals

Staatstheater Kassel
Friedrichsplatz 15, 34117 **Kassel**
Tel: 561-1094-0 Fax: 561-109 4204
Intendant Prof Dr Christoph Nix; künstlerische Betriebsdirektion Johannes Schwärsky; Chefdramaturg Ralf Fiedler; Generalmusikdirektor Roberto Paternostro; Operndirektor Wolfram Melwing; Oberspielleiter Sebastian Baumgarten; Schauspieldirektion Armin Petras
Perfs: 190 *No of Prods:* 12 (8 new) *Venues:* Opernhaus 953, Schauspielhaus 540, Casanova 99, Frizz 99
Comments: see also Drama, Dance and Orchestras

Bühnen der Landeshauptstadt Kiel – Opernhaus
Rathausplatz 4, 24103 **Kiel**
Tel: 431-901 2880 Fax: 431-9016 2889
Internet: www.kiel.de/duehnen
E-Mail: buehnen@lhstadt.kiel.de
Künstlerisches Leitungsteam Kirsten Harms, Raymund Richter; künstlerisches Betriebsbüro Heidrun Kuschel; Ballettdirektor Stephan Toss; Chordirektor Jaume Niranda; Dramaturgie Andreas K. W. Meyer, Katharina John; Öffentlichkeitsarbeit Karla Mäder
No of Prods: 10 (7 new) *Venues:* Opernhaus 822, Schauspielhaus 411, Kindertheater 120 *Comments:* see also Drama, Dance and Orchestra

Theater der Stadt Koblenz
Clemensstrasse 1, 56068 **Koblenz**
Tel: 261-129 2870 Fax: 261-129 2800
Internet: www.koblenz.de/~kultur/theater
Intendantin Annegret Ritzel; Generalmusikdirektor Shao-Chia Lü; Chordirektor Bernhard Steiner
Perfs: 120 *No of Prods:* 6 *Venues:* Großes Haus am Deinhardplatz 501,Kammerspiele am Florinsmarkt 151
Comments: see also Drama and Dance

Ars Vitalis
c/o Kulturbüro Köln, Engelbertstrasse 32, 50674 **Köln**
Tel: 221-240 3133 Fax: 221-240 3247
Internet: ourworld.compuserve.com/homepages/vitalis
E-Mail: kulturbk@aol.com
contact Klaus Huber, Buddy Sacher, Peter Wilmanns
Perfs: 100 *No of Prods:* 1 *Comments:* radio productions, composition of film-music, multi-media events

Bühnen der Stadt Köln – Oper
Offenbachplatz, 50667 **Köln**
Tel: 221-2212 8400 (ticket office)/2212 8282 (press office)
Fax: 221-2212 8210
Generalintendant Günter Krämer; Geschäftsführender Direktor und Stellvertreter des GI Bernd Fülle; Stellvertreter des GI in künstlerischen Fragen Dr. Ralf Hertling; Chefdirigent Graeme Jenkins; Operndirektorin Karen Stone; Referentin für Öffentlichkeit Claudia Nola
Perfs: 210 (Kinderoper 100) *No of Prods:* 12 (5 new)
Venues: Opernhaus 1319, Kinderoper in der Yacult Halle 130 *Comments:* see also Drama

Oper der Vereinigten Städtischen Bühnen Krefeld und Mönchengladbach
Theater Krefeld, Theaterplatz 3, 47798 **Krefeld**
Tel: 2151-8050 Fax: 2151-28295
Internet: members.aol.com/vsbühnen
Generalintendant Jens Pesel; Generalmusikdirektor Anthony Bramall; Geschäftsführer Reinhard Zeileis; Balletdirektorin Heidrun Schwaarz; Operndirektor Andreas Wendholz; Oberspielleiter Schauspiel Peter Hosthway
Perfs: 550 *No of Prods:* 15 (new) + 1 children's musical
Venues: Theater Krefeld 832, Theater Mönchengladbach 811 *Comments:* see also entry under Mönchengladbach; see also Dance, Drama and Orchestras

Oper Leipzig – Musikalische Komödie
Haus Dreilinden, Dreilindenstraße 30, 04177 **Leipzig**
Tel: 341-12610 Fax: 341-1261-150
Internet: www.leipzig-online.de/oper
E-Mail: oper@leipzig-online.de
Intendant Prof. Udo Zimmermann (Intendant Oper Leipzig); Direktorin Musikalische Komödie und Ballettmeisterin Monika Geppert; GMD und Chefdirigent Roland Seiffarth; Chefdisponent u. stellvertr Direktor Klaus Drescher; Chordirektor Wolfgang Horn; Leiterin des Büros der Direktion Frau Korn
Perfs: 137 *No of Prods:* 20 (2 new) *Venues:* Haus Dreilinden 529 *Touring:* Germany, Switzerland
Comments: see also Dance

Oper Leipzig – Opernhaus
Postfach 100346, 04003 **Leipzig**
Tel: 341-12610 Fax: 341-126 1385
Internet: www.leipzig-online.de/oper
E-Mail: oper@leipzig-online.de
Intendant Prof Udo Zimmermann; Verwaltungsdirektorin Bettina Pesch; Chefdirigent Michail Jurawski; Direktor für künstlerische Produktion Axel Joliet; Pressereferent Michael Ernst; Chefdramaturgin Brunhild Matthias; Chordirektor Anton Tremmel; Ballettdirektor und Chefchoreograph Prof Uwe Scholz
Perfs: ca. 180 *No of Prods:* 21 (4 new) *Venues:* Opernhaus 1426, Kellertheater 100, Drehscheibe Opernhaus 200, Munkalische Komodie, Haus Dreilinden 529
Comments: visiting address: Augustusplatz 12, 04109 Leipzig; see also Dance

Bühnen der Hansestadt Lübeck
Beckergrube 16, 23539 **Lübeck**
Tel: 451-708 8112 Fax: 451-708 8177
Generalintendant Dietrich von Oertzen; Generalmusikdirektor Erich Wächter; Leiter des künstlerischen Betriebsbüros Dr. Nargrit Lindner; Verwaltungsleiter Peter Skrock; Konzert-und Operndramaturg Karsten Bartels; Geschäftsführender Dramaturg Andreas Strähnz; Leitender Dramaturg für das Musiktheater Dieter Kroll
No of Prods: 7 *Venues:* Großes Haus 782, Kammerspiele 327, Studio 99 *Comments:* see also Drama and Orchestras

Theater Lüneburg GmbH
Postfach 2829, 21318 **Lüneburg**
Tel: 4131-7520 Fax: 4131-404 210
Internet: www.theater-lueneburg.de
E-Mail: dramaturgie@theater-lueneburg.de
Intendant Jan Aust; Musikdirektor Urs-Michael Theus; Ballettdirektorin Ingrid Burmeister; Verwaltungsdirektor Wolfgang Dannenefeld
Perfs: 30 *No of Prods:* ca. 10 *Venues:* Theater 553
Comments: visiting address: An den Reeperbahnen 3, 21335 Lüneburg; see also Drama, Dance and Orchestras

Theater der Landeshauptstadt Magdeburg
Postfach 12 40, 39002 **Magdeburg**
Tel: 391-540 6444/6555 (Besucherservice) Fax: 391-540 6599
Internet: www.theater-magdeburg.de
Generalintendant Max K Hoffmann; Verwaltungsdirektor Reinhard Odenstein; Generalmusikdirektor Christian Ehwald; Oberspielleiter Musiktheater R Christian Kube; Chefdramaturg Dietmar Goergen
Perfs: 20 *No of Prods:* 8 new (opera, operetta, musical)
Venues: Theater am Universitätsplatz 688, Podiumbühne ca. 40, kabaret Die Kuoelbitze 186
Comments: visiting address: Universitätsplatz 9, 39104 Magdeburg; see also Dance

Staatstheater Mainz
Gutenbergplatz 7, 55116 **Mainz**
Tel: 6131-2851-0 Fax: 6131-285 1333
Internet: www.staatstheater-mainz.de
E-Mail: theatmain@aol.com
Intendant Georges Delnon; kaufmännischer Geschäftsführer Lutz-Uwe Dünnwald; Generalmusikdirektor Stefan Sanderling; Chefdramaturg Martin Apelt; Ballettdirektor Martin Schläpfer; Chordirektor István Gyöngyösi; Künstlerischer Betriebsdirektor Hajo Fouquet
Perfs: Phönixhalle 137, Kleines Haus 178, TIC 110 *No of Prods:* 25 (24 new) *Venues:* Phönixhalle ca. 800, Kleines Haus ca. 400, TIC (Studiobühne) 99 *Comments:* Großes Haus is being refurbished during 99/2000 season; see also Drama, Dance and Orchestras

Nationaltheater Mannheim
Mozartstrasse 9, 68161 **Mannheim**
Tel: 621-1680-0 Fax: 621-168 0385
Internet: mannheim.nationaltheater.de
E-Mail: nationaltheater.kasse@mannheim.de
Generalintendant Ulrich Schwab; Künstlerlerischer Direktor und Chefdisponent Joel Revelle; Generalmusikdirektor Jun Märkl; Operndirektor Dietmar Schwarz; Chordirektor Wolfgang Balzer
Perfs: ca. 350 *No of Prods:* 11 new *Venues:* Opernhaus 1154 *Comments:* see also Drama, Dance and Orchestras

Meininger Theater – Südthüringisches Staatstheater, Das
Bernhardstr. 5, 98617 **Meiningen**
Tel: 3693-4510 Fax: 3693-502 285
Internet: www.das-meininger-theater.de
E-Mail: kasse@das-meininger-theater.de
Intendant Christine Mielitz; Verwaltungsdirektorin Regina Schwabe; Generalmusikdirektorin Marie-Jeanne Dufour; Schauspieldirektor Karl Georg Kayser; Chefdirektor Wolfgang Liesk; Ballettdirektorin Sabine Wake
No of Prods: ca. 5 *Venues:* Großes Haus 740, Georgie's Off (Studiobühne) 90 *Comments:* see also Drama, Dance and Orchestras

Theater Mönchengladbach
Vereinigten Städtischen Bühnen Krefeld und Mönchengladbach, Odenkirchener Str. 78, 41236 **Mönchengladbach (Rheydt)**
Tel: 2166-61510 Fax: 2166-420 110
Internet: members.aol.com/vsbuehnen
Generalintendant Jens Pesel; Geschäftsführer Reinhard Zeileis; Generalmusikdirektor Anthony Bramall; Operndirektor Andreas Wendholz; Schauspieloberspielleiter Peter Hathazy; Ballettdirektorin Heidrun Schwaarz
No of Prods: 15 (musiktheater) + 1 (operngala)
Venues: Opernhaus 811, Stadttheater Krefeld 832
Comments: second address: Stadttheater Krefeld, Theaterplatz 3, 47798 Krefeld, Tel: 2151-805-0, Fax: 2151-28295; see also Drama, Dance and Orchestras; see also entry under Krefeld

Bayerische Staatsoper
Bavarian State Opera
Postfach 100148, 80075 **München**
Tel: 89-218 501 Fax: 89-2185 1133
Internet: www.bayerische.staatsoper.de
E-Mail: presse@st-oper.bayern.de
Staatsintendant Peter Jonas; geschäftsführender Direktor Dr Roland Felber; Operndirektor Gerd Uecker; Generalmusikdirektor Zubin Metha; Ballettdirektor Ivan Liska; Dramaturgie Dr Hanspeter Krellmann; Pressesprecherin und Leiterin PR Dr Ulrike Hessler; Chordirektor Udo Mehrpohl
Perfs: 350 *No of Prods:* 39 (7 new)
Venues: Nationaltheater 2101, Cuvilliéstheater 523, Prinzregententheater 1100 *Comments:* visiting address: Max-Joseph-Platz 2, 80359 München; see also Dance, Drama, Orchestras and Festivals

Staatstheater am Gärtnerplatz
Postfach 140569, 80455 **München**
Tel: 89-202 411 Fax: 89-2024 1237
Internet:
www.staatstheater.bayern.de/gaertner/welcom.htm
E-Mail: tickets@st-gaertner.bayern.de
Intendant Klaus Schultz; Künstlerischer Betriebsdirektor Joachim R Lang; Dramaturgie & Pressesprecher Konrad Kuhn; Chefdirigent David Stahl; Ballettdirektor Philip Taylor; Chordirektor Hans-Joachim Willrich
Perfs: 224 *No of Prods:* 5 new *Venues:* Staatstheater am Gärtnerplatz 864, Studiobühne im Zerwirkgewölbe 98
Touring: national guest performances *Comments:* main house was due to re-open 10 December 1999; see also Dance and Orchestras

Städtische Bühnen Münster
Neubrückenstrasse 63, 48143 **Münster**
Tel: 251-5909-0 Fax: 251-590 9202
Internet: www.muenster.de/stb
E-Mail: Staedt-Buehnen@stadt-muenster.de
Generalintendant Thomas Bockelmann; Assistentin des Generalintendanten Anja-Brigitta Lucke; künstlerisches Betriebsbüro Burkhard Kolb; Chefdramaturgie Horst Busch; Generalmusikdirektor Will Humburg; Ballettdirektor Daniel Goldin; Chordirektor Peter Heinrich; Chefdisponentin Bettina Reith
Perfs: ca. 100 *No of Prods:* 10 (5 new) *Venues:* Grosses Haus 955, Kleines Haus 321 *Comments:* see also Drama, Dance and Orchestras

Landestheater Mecklenburg GmbH Neustrelitz
Friedrich-Ludwig-Jahn-Strasse 14, 17235 **Neustrelitz**
Tel: 3981-2770 Fax: 3981-205 435
Internet: www.landestheater-mecklenburg.de
E-Mail: info@landestheater-mecklenburg.de
Intendant Urs Leicht; Verwaltungsdirektor Petra Eichstädt; Chefdirigent Jürgen Weisser; Öffentlichkeitsarbeit Dr. Christoph Dammann; Chordirektor Gotthard Franke; Chefdramaturg Hans-Jörg Grell
Perfs: 400 *No of Prods:* 6 *Venues:* Großes Haus 397, Kleines Haus 60, Theater im Probenhaus 60, Theater im Foyer 60, Theater im Club 60 *Touring:* Germany
Comments: see also Drama

Theater Nordhausen/Loh-Orchester Sondershausen GmbH
Käthe-Kollwitz-Strasse 15, 99734 **Nordhausen**
Tel: 3631-6260-0 Fax: 3631-626 0147
Internet: www.theater.nordhausen.de
E-Mail: theater@nordhausen.de
Intendant Dr Monika Pirklbauer; Generalmusikdirektor Peter Stangel; Ballettdirektorin Birgitt Relitzki
Perfs: 425 *No of Prods:* 22 Großes Haus, 19 concerts, 8 small productions *Venues:* Großes Haus 488, Theater unterm Dach (TuD) 99, Foyer 50, hinterm Eisernen Vorhang 60, Haus der Kunst 381, Achteckhaus (Sonderhausen) 320 *Touring:* guest performances in Germany *Comments:* alternative Internet: www.theater.nordhausen.de

Pocket Opera Company
Gertrudstrasse 21, 90429 **Nürnberg**
Tel: 911-329 047
Fax: 911-314 606
Internet: www.pocket-opera.com
E-Mail: info@pocket-opera.com
künstlerischer Leiter Peter Beat Wyrsch; musikalischer Leiter David Seaman; Projektmanagement und Öffentlichkeitsarbeit Doris Groß; Verwaltung Anke Wolter; technischer Leiter Dieter Reeps; musikalischer Leiter für zeitgenössisches Musiktheater Andrea Molino
No of Prods: 27 (1 new) *Touring:* Italy, France, UK, Germany *Comments:* contemporary chamber opera and traditional operas; member of E.C.O.P. (European Chamber Opera Pool), touring company

Städtische Bühnen Opernhaus Nürnberg
Richard-Wagner-Platz 2-10,
90443 **Nürnberg**
Tel: 911-231 3523 Fax: 911-231 3522
Internet: oper.nuernberg.de
E-Mail: oper@stadt.nuernberg.de
Generalintendant Dr Wulf Konold; Leitung GMD Philippe Auguin; künstlerischer Direktor Wilfried Weisel; leitender Dramaturg Dr Klaus Angermann; Chordirektor Christoph Kurig; Geschäftsführender Direktor Dr Axel Baisch
Perfs: 204 *No of Prods:* 8
Venues: Opernhaus 1011
Comments: see also Drama and Dance

Oldenburgisches Staatstheater
Theaterwall 28, 26122 **Oldenburg**
Tel: 441-2225-0
Fax: 441-222 5222 (ticket service)
Internet: www.oldenburg.staatstheater.de
E-Mail: kasse@oldenburg.staatstheater.de
Generalintendant Stephan Mettin; Verwaltungsleiter Reinhard Knappert; künstlerisches Betriebsbüro Dr Rüdiger Zagolla; Dramaturgie Anke Hoffmann (Musiktheater), Matthias Schiffner; Generalmusikdirektor Reinhard Seifried; Chordirektor Thomas Bönisch; persönal Referent des GI Thomas Regensburger; Chefdramaturgin Georgia Eilert
Prods: 7 (5 new) *Venues:* Großes Haus 881, Kleines Haus 350 *Comments:* see also Drama, Dance and Orchestras

Städtische Bühnen Osnabrück
Domhof 10-11, 49074 **Osnabrück**
Tel: 541-323 4310 Fax: 541-323 3297
Internet: www.theater-osnabrueck.de
E-Mail: theateros@aol.com
Intendant Norbert Hilchenbach; Generalmusikdirektor Luther Königs; kaufmännischer Direktor Norbert Kronisch; Musikdramaturg Stefan Klawitter; Chefdisponent Matthias Otto; Chordirektor Ulrich Paetzholdt; Leitender Regisseur Musiktheater Thomas Münstermann; Leiter des Tanztheaters Gregor Zöllig
Perfs: 135 *No of Prods:* 8 (7 new) *Venues:* Großes Haus 639, emma-theater 99, Stadthalle Osnabrück (opera and symphony concerts) 1200 *Touring:* Germany
Comments: see also Drama, Dance (Tanztheater der Städtischen Bühnen) and Orchestras

Südostbayerisches Städtetheater
Musikalische Abteilung, Gottfried-Schäffer-Straße 2-4, 94032 **Passau**
Tel: 851-929 1910/1966 Fax: 851-929 1930
Internet: www.suedostbayerisches-staedtetheater.de/
E-Mail: Stadttheater.Passau@t-online.de
Intendant Johannes Reitmeier; Verwaltungsleiter Rudi Senff; Dramaturgie Schauspiel Brigitte Hermann, Kerstin Müller-Römer; Musikdirektor Roger Boggasch; Verwaltungsleiter Passau Ralf Schützenberger; Dramaturgie (Musikal. Abteilung/Passau) Andreas Frane
Perfs: 145 *No of Prods:* 6 *Venues:* Stadttheater Landshut 365, Fürstbischöfliches Opernhaus – Passau 350, Theater Am Hagen-Straubing 374
Comments: see also Drama

Stadttheater Pforzheim
Am Waisenhausplatz 5, 75172 **Pforzheim**
Tel: 7231-392 438 Fax: 7231-391 485
Internet: www.pforzheim.de/theater
E-Mail: theater@stadt-pforzheim.de
Intendant Ernö Weil; Dramaturg und Leiter des Schauspiels Frank Wilmes; Generalmusikdirektor Jari Hämäläinen; Dramaturgin und Leiterin des Musiktheaters Beate Bucher-Heller; Chordirektorin Gwendolyn Phear; Ballettdirektor Anthony Sterago
No of Prods: 20 (in total) *Venues:* Großes Haus 510, Podium 199 *Touring:* guest performances
Comments: see also Drama and Dance

Vogtland Theater Plauen
Theaterplatz 1-3, 08523 **Plauen**
Tel: 3741-291 2431 Fax: 3741-222 620
Intendant Dieter Roth; Generalmusikdirektor Dieter-Gerhardt Worm; Verwaltungsleitung Renate Wünsche; Direktor PR Christian Pöllmann
Perfs: 420 *No of Prods:* ca. 3 *Venues:* Großes Haus 467, Kleines Haus 99, Festhalle Plauen 456
Touring: Germany
Comments: see also Drama, Dance and Orchestras

Hans Otto Theater
Berliner Str. 27a, 14467 **Potsdam**
Tel: 331-9811-0/275 710 (boxoffice) Fax: 331-981 1180/275 7123
Intendant Ralf Günter Krolkiewicz; Geschäftsführender Direktor Volkmar Raback; Operndirektorin Dr Andrea Palent; Chefdisponentin Ilse Schmidt-Hänsel; Öffentlichkeitsarbeit Silvia Pickert, Georg Kehren
Perfs: 50 *No of Prods:* 4 + 20 (theatre, children & youth drama theatre) *Venues:* Theaterhaus Am Alten Markt 600, Scholßtheater im Neuen Palais Potsdam Sanssouci 220, Orangerie Sanssouci Openair 200
Comments: see also Drama

Theater Regensburg
Bismarckplatz 7, 93047 **Regensburg**
Tel: 941-507 1428/2424 Fax: 941-507 4429
Intendantin Marietheres List; Kaufmännischer Direktor Holger von Berg; Generalmusikdirektor Guido Johannes Rumstadt; Oberspielleiter Schauspiel Michael Bleiziffer; Disponent und Leiter des Künstlerischen Betriebsbüros Johannes Fiedler; Chefdramaturg (Musiktheater) Dr. Gerhard Heldt; Geschäftsführende Schauspiel-dramaturgin Dr. Christa-Renate Thutewohl; Referentin für Presse u. Öffentlichkeitsarbeit Kathrin Schäfer
Perfs: 140 *No of Prods:* 8 *Venues:* Stadttheater (closed until 2001), Theater am Haidplatz 138, Freilichttheater im Hof des Thon-Dittmer-Palais 382, Velodrom 600
Comments: see also Drama, Dance and Orchestras

Volkstheater Rostock
Patriotischer Weg 33, 18057 **Rostock**
Tel: 381-2440/211 (Intendanz)/251/325 017
Fax: 381-492 3410 (Dramat.)/251 017/244 213 (Intend.)
Intendant Dr Michael Winrich Schlicht; Operndirektor k.s. Frank Brandau; Generalmusikdirektor t.b.a.; Ballettdirektor Tomasz Kajdanski; Leitung Marketing und Öffentlichkeitsarbeit Jürgen Opel; Orchesterdirektor Bernd Windisch
Perfs: 140 *No of Prods:* 16 (7 new) *Venues:* Großes Haus 579, Barocksaal 167, Ateliertheater 40, Theater im Stadthafen 200 *Touring:* national, Switzerland
Comments: see also Drama, Dance and Orchestra

Thüringer Landestheater – Haus Rudolstadt Rudolstadt
Comments: please see entry for Eisenach

Saarländisches Staatstheater
Postfach 102735, 66027 **Saarbrücken**
Tel: 681-3092-0 Fax: 681-309 2325
Internet: www.saarland.de/staatstheater/
E-Mail: sst.01@t-online.de
Generalintendant u. Geschäftsführer Kurt-Josef Schildknecht; kaufmännischer Direktor u. Geschäftsführer Helmut Beckamp; Operndirektor Matthias Kaiser; Oberspielleiter Schauspiel t.b.a.; Leiterin des künstlerischen Betriebsbüros Claudia Reisinger; GMD Olaf Henzold; Oberspielleiter Musiktheater Philipp Himmelmann; Ballettleiter Bernd Roger Bienert; Chefdisponentin Sylvia Prantscheff
Perfs: 180 *No of Prods:* 31 (25 new) *Venues:* Staatstheater 875 *Touring:* Switzerland, Luxembourg, Austria, Germany *Comments:* visiting address:Schillerplatz 1, 66111 Saarbrücken; see also Drama, Dance, Orchestras and Venues

Schleswig-Holsteinisches Landestheater und Sinfonieorchester GmbH
Lollfuß 49-53, 24837 **Schleswig**
Tel: 46-219 6700 Fax: 46-2196 7083
Internet: www.landestheater.de
E-Mail: kontakt@landestheater.de
Generalintendant Dr Horst Mesalla (from August: Michael Grosse); Generalmusikdirektor Pierre Borin; Operndirektor Dr Harald Höferl; Chordirektor Raimund Heusch; Verwaltungsdirektor Reiner Schmeckthal; Öffentlichkeitsarbeit Angela Möller; Chefdramaturg Dietmar Buchholz (from August: Christian Marten-Molnár)
Venues: Landestheater Flensburg 459, Landestheater Rendsburg 510, Landestheater Schleswig 508
Comments: see also Orchestras, Dance and Drama

Bayerische Kammeroper
Wengertspfad 2, 97523 **Schwanfeld**
Tel: 9384-8772 Fax: 9384-8678
Intendant Dr Blagoy Apostolov; Generalmusikdirektor Prof Siegfried Köhler
No of Prods: 3 *Venues:* Mainfrankensäle 500 *Touring:* Belgium, Finland, North Italy, France, England, South Korea *Comments:* co-productions with other opera ensembles, see also Festivals (Internationale Kammermusikwoche)

Mecklenburgisches Staatstheater
Alter Garten, 19055 **Schwerin**
Tel: 385-5300-131 Fax: 385-5300-137
Internet: www.svz.de
E-Mail: presse@theater-schwerin.de
geschäftsführender Intendant Joachim Kümmritz; Generalmusikdirektor und Operndirektor Ivan Törzs; Balletdirektor Stefan Haufe
Perfs: 110 *No of Prods:* 5 new *Venues:* Großes Haus 670, E-Werk 99 *Touring:* Germany, Austria, Switzerland
Comments: see also Dance, Drama and Orchestras

Theater Vorpommern
Olof-Palme-Platz, 18439 **Stralsund**
Tel: 3831-2646-0 Fax: 3831-292 896
Internet: www.theater-vorpommern.de
E-Mail: theater@t-online.de
Intendant Rüdiger Blach; kaufmännischer Geschäftsführer Joachim von Trützschler; Generalmusikdirektor Darian Wilson; Operndirektor Arnold Schrem; Leiter für Presse und Öffentlichkeitsar-beit Marion Gerhardt; technischer Direktor Rainer Darr
Perfs: 135 *No of Prods:* 12
Venues: Theater Stralsund 520, Theater Greifswald 460
Comments: address for Theater Greifswald: Anklamer Str. 106, 17489 Greifswald, Tel: 3834-5722-0, Fax: 3834-502 779; see also Drama, Dance and Orchestras

Disney Musical Produktions GmbH
Plieninger Str. 109, 70567 **Stuttgart**
Tel: 711-900 660 Fax: 711-9006 6610
Internet: www.stella.de
Theatre Manager Renate Gritschke; Assistant Theatre Manager Thomas Eissler (teissler@mail.stella.de)
No of Prods: 1 (The Beauty and the Beast)
Venues: cap. 1800 *Comments:* The Beauty and the Beast is the only production

Staatstheater Stuttgart
Oberer Schloßgarten 6, 70173 **Stuttgart**
Tel: 711-2032-0 Fax: 711-203 2389
Internet: www.staatstheater.stuttgart.de
E-Mail: tkoch.presse@oper-stuttgart.s.shuttle.de
Geschäftsführender Direktor Hans Tränkle; Opernintendant u. Chefdramaturg Klaus Zehelein; Ballettintendant Reid Anderson; Chordirektor Prof Ulrich Eistert; Koordinierte, künstlerische Betriebsdirektion Pamela Rosenberg; Schauspielintendant Friedrich Schirmer; Geschäftsführende Dramaturgin Juliana Vottela
Perfs: 169 *No of Prods:* 31 (7 new) *Venues:* Großes Haus 1396, Kleines Haus 851 *Comments:* voted German Opera House of the Year in 1999; see also Drama, Dance and Orchestras

Freilichtspiele Tecklenburg
Postfach 1143, 49537 **Tecklenburg**
Tel: 5482-220 Fax: 5482-1269
Intendant Radouf Beuleke; künstler. Betriebsdirektor u. Dramaturg Fred Banse; Ballettdirektor Annette Fischer
Perfs: ca. 60 *No of Prods:* 4 *Venues:* Freilichttheater 2500
Comments: visiting address: Schloßstrasse 7, 49545 Tecklenburg; see also Dance and Festivals

Theater Trier
Am Augustinerhof, 54290 **Trier**
Tel: 651-718 3464 Fax: 651-718 1468
Intendant Heinz Lukas-Kindermann; Chefdisponentin Anke Bergemann; Chefdramaturg Alexander Etzel-Ragusa; Dramaturgie Anja Gewalt; Spielleiter des Schauspiels Klaus-Dieter Köhler; Ballettmeister Sergey B. Volobuyev; Generalmusikdirektor István Dénes; Öffentlichkeitsarbeit Philipp Förster; Verwaltungsdirektor Werner Reichert
Perfs: 87 *No of Prods:* 8 (7 new)
Venues: Stadttheater 622, Studio 65
Comments: see also Drama, Dance and Orchestras

Ulmer Theater
Olgastr. 73, 89073 **Ulm**
Tel: 731-161 4400 (Intendant)
Fax: 731-161 1619
Internet: www.theater.ulm.de
E-Mail: UlmerTheater@theater.ulm.de
Intendant Ansgar Haag; Leiter der Oper, Chefdisponent und pers. Referent des Intendanten Dr Klaus Rak (731-161 4416); Generalmusikdirektor James Allen Gähres (731-161 4418); Musikdramaturg Stephan Steinmetz (731-161 4424); Presse- und Öffentlichkeitsarbeit Frau Mayer (731-161 4410); Künstlerisches Betriebsbüros Frau Giathe (731-161 4434)
Perfs: 156 *No of Prods:* 9 + 1 Wiederaufnahme *Venues:* Ulmer Theater 815, Podium 200 *Comments:* see also Orchestras, Drama and Dance

Deutsches National Theater Weimar
Postfach 3&5, 99401 **Weimar**
Tel: 3643-755-0 Fax: 3643-755 218/307
Internet: www.deutsches-nationaltheater.weimar.de
E-Mail: dnt.service@weimar.net
Generalintendant Günther Beelitz; Generalmusikdirektor und Chefdirigent der Staatskapelle Weimar Prof. George Alexander Albrecht; Operndirektor Ehrhard Warneke; Presse-/ Öffentlichkeitsarbeit Sylvia Obst; Musikdramaturgin Brita Schmallowsky
No of Prods: 19
Venues: Werkstattbühne 176, Großes Haus 859
Touring: national and international guest performances
Comments: visiting address: Theaterplatz 2, 99423 Weimar; see also Dance, Drama and Orchestras

Hessisches Staatstheater Wiesbaden
Postfach 3247, 65022 **Wiesbaden**
Tel: 611-1321 Fax: 611-132 337
Internet: www.staatstheater-wiesbaden.de
Intendant Achim Thorwald; Betriebsdirektor Thomas Brux; Dramaturgie Margrit Poremba; Ballettdirektor Ben van Cauwenbergh; Chordirektor Thomas Lang; GMD Toshiyuki Kamioka; Operndirektor Dominik Neuner; Leiter der musik-theater-werkstatt Ernst-August Klötzke
No of Prods: 18 (6 new)
Venues: Staatstheater 1041, Kleines Haus 328, Studio Souterrain 89, Vesti-Bühne 69
Comments: visiting address: Christian-Zais-Strasse 1-3, 65189 Wiesbaden; see also Drama and Dance

Mitteldeutsches Landestheater
Thomas Müntzer Strasse 14-15, 06886 **Wittenberg**
Tel: 3491-47370 Fax: 3491-473 710
Internet: www.theater-wittenberg.de
E-Mail: theater-wb@t-online.de
Intendant Reinhold Stövesand; Verwaltunsleiterin u. Stellvertr. d. Intend. Siglinde Schluter; Musikalische Leitung GMD Jörg Iwer; Oberspielleiter Musiktheater Markus Schuliers; PR Hartmut Gorgs
Perfs: 100 *No of Prods:* 10 (8 new)
Venues: Großes Haus 380, Studio 100, Brett'l Keller 80
Touring: national
Comments: see also Drama and Orchestras

Schillertheater NRW – Opernhaus Wuppertal
Spinnstraße 4, 42283 **Wuppertal**
Tel: 202-563 4230 Fax: 202-563 8430
Internet: www.schillertheater-nrw.de
Theaterleitung/Geschäftsführung Ludwig Baum, Holk Freytag, Peter Neubauer; Intendant Musiktheater und Ballett Ludwig Baum; Persönlicher Referent und Vertreter des Intendanten Jörg Maecker; Dramaturgie Martin Griesemer; Generalmusikdirektor der Stadt Wuppertal und musikalischer Leiter des Schillertheaters NRW George Hanson; Chordirektor t.b.a.; Künstlerischer Betriebsdirektor und Leiter des Künstlerischen Betriebsbüros Bjoern Peleikis; Öffentlichkeitsarbeit Oda Mahnke
Perfs: 110 *No of Prods:* 12 *Venues:* Opernhaus 845
Comments: see also Drama and Dance (Tanztheater Wuppertal Pina Bausch); see also Gelsenkirchen

Stadttheater Würzburg
Theaterstrasse 21, 97070 **Würzburg**
Tel: 931-3908-0 Fax: 931-3909-102
Internet: www.theaterwuerzburg.de
E-Mail: info@theaterwuerzburg.de
Intendant Wolfgang Schaller; PR Jürgen Hartmann; Dramaturgie Jön Philipp von Linden; Generalmusikdirektor Jonathan Seers; Verwaltungsdirektorin Heidrun Glosauer
Perfs: 600 *No of Prods:* 27 (4 opera, 1 operetta, 1 musical) *Venues:* Stadttheater 744, Kammerspiele 92
Touring: Germany (Gastspiele, Schweinfurt, Fielda, Aschaffenburg u.a.)
Comments: see also Drama and Dance

theater zwickau GmbH
Postfach 201039, 08012 **Zwickau**
Tel: 375-834 600 Fax: 375-834 609
Internet: www.th-zwickau.de/zwickau/theater/th1.htm
E-Mail: theater.zwickau@abo.freiepresse.de
Operndirektor Rainer Wenke; Generalmusikdirektor Welisar Gentscheff; Intendant und amtierender Schauspieldirektor Wolfgang Hauswald; Verwaltungsdirektor Henry Klüglich
Perfs: 97 *No of Prods:* 9 *Venues:* Gewandhaus 399, Kleine Bühne 120 *Touring:* Germany
Comments: visiting address: Gewandhaustraße 7, 08056 Zwickau; see also Drama and Dance

GREECE (+30)

Ethniki Liriki Skini
National Opera of Greece
18A Charilaou Trikoupi Street, 10679 **Athens**
Tel: 1-361 4433/360 0180
Fax: 1-362 5604/364 8309
administration & financial manager t.b.a.; director Loukas Karitinos; president S Evagelatos; deputy directors t.b.a.; pr manager Marilena Karytinos
Perfs: ca. 100 (winter), 20 (summer) *No of Prods:* 13 (11 winter, 2 summer) *Venues:* Theatro Olympia (winter) 900, Odeon of Herodes Atticus (summer) 4700
Touring: Greece, Cyprus *Comments:* performs with orchestra of the National Opera; see also Orchestras

HUNGARY (+36)

Budapest Operetta Theatre
Budapesti Operett Színház
PO Box 7, 1387 **Budapest**
Tel: 1-269 3870 Fax: 1-332 2549/331 8924
general director Imre Halasi; music director László Makláry; artistic secretary András Aczél; conductor Katalin Várady
Perfs: 300 *No of Prods:* 10 *Venues:* capacity 970
Comments: 44 actors, 35 dancers, 96 musicians, 32 choir; visiting address: Nagymez u.17, 1065 Budapest; venue for Rock Theatre productions

Budapesti Kamaraopera – Budapest Chamber Opera
Belgrád rakpart 25, 1056 **Budapest**
Tel: 1-266 0107/317 7863 Fax: 1-266 0108/317 7863
artistic director Domokos Moldován

Hungarian State Opera
Magyar Állami Operaház
PO Box 503, 1373 **Budapest**
Tel: 1-331 2550 Fax: 1-331 9817
general director Miklós Szinetár; managing director Imre Kiss; general secretary Attila Fülöp; music director t.b.a.; international manager Márta Pölös (tel: 1-332 7372)
Perfs: 350 *No of Prods:* 7 *Venues:* capacity 1110, Erkel Szinház-Theatre 2250, Thália Szinház – Thália Theatre 510 *Comments:* Erkel Színház-Theatre address: Köztársaság tér 30, 1081 Budapest. Tel: 1-333 0108, fax: 1-313 7832; have 2 theatres, 2 orchestras, 2 choirs, under the same management sharing the same company of singers; visiting address: Andrássy út 22, 1061 Budapest

Csokonai Theatre Debrecen
Debreceni Csokonai Színház
PO Box 79, 4001 **Debrecen**
Tel: 52-417 811 Fax: 52-410 837
artistic and managing director György Lengyel; first associate director István Pinczés; music director Balázs Kocsár; artistic secretary Rozi Berényi
Perfs: 332 *No of Prods:* 14 new *Venues:* capacity 560 *Comments:* visiting address: Kossuth Lajos u. 10, 4024 Debrecen; 17 singers, 12 dancers; see also Drama

National Theatre Györ
Györ Nemzeti Színház
PO Box 401, 9002 **Györ**
Tel: 96-312 167 Fax: 96-313 276
general manager György Korcsmáros; art director Géza Tordy; principal conductor Benedek Csala
Perfs: 100 *Venues:* capacity 690 *Comments:* visiting address: Czuczor Gergely u. 7, 9022 Györ; see also Dance and Drama

National Theatre Miskolc
Miskolci Nemzeti Színház
PO Box 113, 3501 **Miskolc**
Tel: 46-344 711 Fax: 46-334 832
Internet: www.olh.hu/MiskolcNemetiSinhaz
E-Mail: mszinhaz@mail.olh.hu
administrative and artistic director Árpád Jutocsa Hegyi; music director Gergely Kesselyak
Perfs: 220 *No of Prods:* 10 + 1 opera + 1 operetta + 1 dance + 1 for children *Venues:* capacity 670 *Comments:* modern/classical/comedy/operetta; visiting address: Déryné u. 1, 3530 Miskolc; see also Drama

National Theatre Pécs
Pécsi Nemzeti Színház
PO Box 126, 7601 **Pécs**
Tel: 72-211 983 Fax: 72-211 986
director Tamás Baliko; music director Lajos Blázy; managing director István Simon
Perfs: 100 *No of Prods:* 2 *Venues:* capacity 530 *Comments:* visiting address: Perczel u. 17, 7621 Pécs; see also Dance, Drama and Puppet

Petöfi Theatre, Sopron
Soproni Petöfi Színház
PO Box 241, 9401 **Sopron**
Tel: 99-511 700 Fax: 99-511 716
director István Mikó (tel: 99-511 741)
Comments: regional theatre company which produces drama, musicals and operetta; visiting address: Petöfi Sándor tér 1, 9400, Sopron

National Theatre Szeged
Szegedi Nemzeti Színház
PO Box 79, 6700 **Szeged**
Tel: 62-479 279 Fax: 62-475 562
managing and artistic director Karoly Korognai; opera director Tamás Pál; general secretary Mária Hollandi
Perfs: 80 *No of Prods:* 3 *Venues:* capacity 700 *Comments:* visiting address: Deák Ferenc u.12, 6720 Szeged

Savaria Chamber Opera
Savaria Kamaraopera
Batsányi utca 20, 9700 **Szombathely**
Tel: 94-321 594/340 562 Fax: 94-321 594
E-Mail: pnemeth@mail.matav.hu
artistic director Pál Németh
Comments: regional company, tours the country

Petöfi Theatre, Veszprém
Veszprémi Petöfi Színház
PO Box 133, 8201 **Veszprém**
Tel: 88-424 064 Fax: 88-420 046
director László Vándorfi (tel: 88-420 444)
Comments: drama, musicals and operetta; visiting address: Óváry Ferenc utca 2, 8200, Veszprém

ICELAND (+354)

Islenska Operan
Icelandic Opera
PO Box 1416, Ingólfasstraeti, 101 **Reykjavík**
Tel: 552 7033 Fax: 552 7384
E-Mail: opera@opera.is
general manager Bjarni Danielsson; artistic director Gerrit Schuil
Perfs: 40 *No of Prods:* 2-3 *Venues:* capacity 473 *Comments:* works in collaboration with Symphony Orchestra; see also Venues

IRELAND Republic of (+353)

Opera Ireland
John Player House, 276-288 South Circular Road, **Dublin** 8
Tel: 1-453 5519/20 Fax: 1-453 5521
Internet: www.opera-ireland.ie
E-Mail: info@opera-ireland.ie
general manager David Collopy; artistic director Dieter Kaegi; administrator Kay Keilthy
Perfs: 19 *No of Prods:* 4 *Venues:* Gaiety Theatre, Dublin 1100 *Comments:* bi-annual season: early Dec, and Easter; company Co-Opera for regional touring and opera development, 2 tours a year, project manager: Marie Breen, director: Michael Hunt, performances: 25, no of productions: 2

Opera Theatre Company
The Music Centre, Curved Street, Temple Bar, **Dublin** 2
Tel: 1-679 4962 Fax: 1-679 4963
Internet: www.imn.ie/otc
E-Mail: otc@imn.ie
director James Conway; marketing and education Nick Costello; administrator Gemma Murray; technical director Paul Tucker; public relations officer Jan Duffy; administrative assistant Sadhbh O'Connor
Perfs: 42 around Ireland + 10 outside *No of Prods:* 4 (3 new) *Venues:* cap. 300 *Touring:* Ireland and abroad *Comments:* OTC is a national & international touring company; commision new works

Wexford Festival Opera
Theatre Royal, 27 High Street, **Wexford**
Tel: 53-22400 Fax: 53-24289
Internet: www.iol.ie/-wexopera
E-Mail: info@wexopera.ibl.ie
chief executive Jerome Hynes; artistic director Luigi Ferrari
Perfs: 18 *No of Prods:* 3 rare or neglected operas annually *Venues:* Theatre Royal 550 *Comments:* only performs during the festival; see also Festivals

ITALY (+39)

Banda Osiris
via Milazzo 5, 40121 **Bologna**
Tel: 051-252 898 Fax: 051-252 854
contact Terry Cheggia
Perfs: 70 *No of Prods:* 2 *Venues:* Teatro delle Moline (BO) 60 *Touring:* Italy, Egypt, Spain, Denmark

Teatro Comunale di Bologna
largo Respighi 1, 40126 **Bologna**
Tel: 051-529 901/957(press) Fax: 051-529 934/905/945(press)
Internet: nettuno.it/bo/teatro-comunale
E-Mail: teatro.comunale@bo.nettuno.it
sovrintendente Felicia Bottino; direttore artistico Gianni Tangucci; segretario artistico Aldo Sisillo; direttore musica Daniele Gatti; capo ufficio stampa e pubbliche relazioni Michele D'Agostino
Perfs: 90 *No of Prods:* 3 new + 5 revivals *Venues:* Teatro Comunale 'Sala del Bibiena' 960 *Touring:* Opera Festivals in Italy *Comments:* see also Venues and Orchestras

Teatro Lirico di Cagliari
Nuovo Teatro Comunale, via Santa Alenixedda, 09128 **Cagliari**
Tel: 070-40821/408 2216 (uff. stampa) Fax: 070-408 2245 (sovrintendenza)/51/40822 (uff. stampa)
sovrintendente Mauro Meli; presidente Mariano Delogu; segretario generale Salvatore Sanna; direttore artistico Massimo Biscardi; segretario artistico Giancarlo Liuzzi; maestro del coro Paolo Vero; direttore allestimenti scenici Massimo Teoldi; direttore di palcoscenico Cristian Venturini; ufficio stampa e relazioni esterne Arturo Clavuot
Perfs: 30 *No of Prods:* 6 (1 new) *Venues:* Nuovo Teatro Comunale 1640, Anfiteatro Romano 5000 (during Summer) *Touring:* Italy *Comments:* see also Orchestras

Teatro Massimo Bellini Ente Autonomo Regionale
Via Perrotta 12, 95131 **Catania**
Tel: 095-730 6111 (switchboard)/715 0200 (press office)
Fax: 095-321 830 (press office)
sovrintendente Alberto Bombace; direttore artistico Piero Rattalino; direttore amministrativo Antonio Ferro; responsabile comunicazione Nino Milazzo; direttore del coro Tiziana Carlini; direttore principale Yorah David
Perfs: 54 *No of Prods:* 9 *Venues:* Teatro Bellini 1250, Giardino Bellini (open-air) 3500 *Touring:* Italy *Comments:* see also Orchestras and Venues

Teatro del Maggio Musicale Fiorentino
via Solferino 15, 50123 **Firenze**
Tel: 055-27791/213 535/211 158 (box office)
Fax: 055-239 6954/277 9410 (box office)
Internet: www.maggiofiorentino.com
E-Mail: tickets@maggiofiorentino.com
sovrintendente t.b.a.; direttore artistico Cesare Mazzonis; direttore principale dell'orchestra Zubin Mehta; direttore ospite principale Semyon Bychkov; responsabile artistico balletto Davide Bombana; direttore del coro José Luis Basso; ufficio stampa Susanna Colombo
Perfs: ca. 98 *No of Prods:* ca. 26 *Venues:* capacity 2004, Teatro della Pergola 1000, Piccolo Teatro 520 *Touring:* Italy *Comments:* also concerts and festival, Maggio Musicale Fiorentino

CEL – Teatro di Livorno
Via Goldoni 83, 57125 **Livorno**
Tel: 0586-889 111 Fax: 0586-899 920
Internet: www.inlineanet.com.\cel
E-Mail: cel@mclink.it
presidente Marco Bertini; consulente artistico lirica Alberto Paloscia; amministrazione e produzioni Isabella Bartolini; affari generali e programmazione Paolo Demi; comunicazione-immagine e responsabile ufficio stampa Antonella Peruffo
Perfs: 18 *No of Prods:* 9 *Venues:* Teatro La Gran Guardia 1500, Teatro Quattro Mori 600, Teatro La Goldonetta 200, Nuovo Teatro delle Commedie 115, Teatro Mascagni di Villa Corridi 200 *Comments:* see also Drama

Teatro alla Scala di Milano, Fondazione di Diritto Privato
via Filodrammatici 2, 20121 **Milano**
Tel: 02-88791 (servizio infotel Scala 7200 3744)
Fax: 02-887 9331
Internet: www.lascala.milano.it
sovrintendente Carlo Fontana; direttore musicale Riccardo Muti; direttore artistico Paolo Arcà; relazioni esterne Donatella Brunazzi (887 9264); direttore di ballo t.b.a.; uff. stampa Luciana Fusi (887 9412)
Perfs: 100 *No of Prods:* 11 *Venues:* capacity 2000 *Touring:* Japan *Comments:* recitals, chamber and symphony concerts, ballet and opera; see also Dance, Orchestra and Venues

Teatro di San Carlo – Fondazione
via S Carlo 98 F, 80132 **Napoli**
Tel: 081-797 2111 Fax: 081-797 2306/09
Internet: www.teatrosancarlo.it
E-Mail: infoteatro@teatrosancarlo.it
sovrintendente Francesco Canessa; direttore artistico Carlo Mayer; segretario generale Mariano Apicella; capo ufficio stampa Filippo Arriva (tel: 797 2202, fax: 797 2306)
Perfs: 65 *No of Prods:* 9 *Venues:* Teatro di San Carlo 1400 *Comments:* see also Dance, Orchestras and Venues

Fondazione del Teatro Massimo di Palermo
via Riccardo Wagner 2, 90139 **Palermo**
Tel: 091-605 3111 Fax: 091-605 3325
Internet: teatromassimo.it
E-Mail: infotm@teatromassimo.it
presidente Leoluca Orlando; soprintendente Francesco Giambrone; direttore artistico Marco Betta; direttore operativo Antonio Cognata; altro maestro del coro Marcello Iozzin; press office Laura Oddo; direttore allestimento scenico Sergio De Giorgi; direttore della produzione Giovanni Mazzara
Perfs: 196 *No of Prods:* 20 *Venues:* Teatro Massimo 1300, Teatro Politeama Garibaldi 950 *Comments:* performs at: Teatro Di Verdura Di Villa Castelnuovo every summer for the summer season

Associazione Teatro di Pisa
via Palestro 40, 56127 **Pisa**
Tel: 050-941 111 Fax: 050-543 555 (press office)
Internet: www.teatrodipisa.pi.it
E-Mail: meucci@teatrodipisa.pi.it
direttore Riccardo Bozzi; presidente Ilario Luperini; direttore artistico Alberto Batisti; direttore attività formative sett. musica Claudio Proietti; uff. stampa Valeria Della Mea, Maria Beatrice Meucci (050-941 152/41)
Perfs: 15 *No of Prods:* 4 *Venues:* Teatro Giuseppe Verdi 800 *Touring:* Italy *Comments:* permanent collaboration with Cittá Lirica Orchestra and with Micha Van Hoecke Ensemble; hosts the European Drama School in San Miniato, June/July; see also Venues

Edipo Management SRL
Viale Piave 37, 42100 **Reggio Emilia**
Tel: 0522-452 518 Fax: 0522-452 277
administrative & technical director Francesco Pulvirenti; public relations Monica Conti
Perfs: 75 *No of Prods:* 5 + 1 new *Comments:* promotes and produces opera; see also Agents & Producers

INSCENA s.r.l (Compagnia Operette Corrado Abbati)
Via Galgana 6, 42100 **Reggio Emilia**
Tel: 0522-455 193 Fax: 0522-454 319
Internet: www.inscena.it
technical & administrative director Stefano Maccarini; presidente Salvatore Fangareggi; artistic director Corrado Abbati; press officer Constanza Lasagni
Perfs: 170 *No of Prods:* 4 *Venues:* Teatro Comunale Valliu (Reggio Emilia) 1100 *Touring:* Italy

Fondazione Teatro dell'Opera di Roma
Pza Beniamino Gigli 1, 00184 **Roma**
Tel: 06-481601 (switchboard)/4816 0210/0211 (sovrintendenza)/474 2595 (press office) Fax: 06-488 1253
Internet: www.themix.it
E-Mail: sovrintendenza@opera.rome.it
sovrintendente Francesco Ernani; presidente Francesco Rutelli; direttore artistica e musicale Giuseppe Sinopoli; maestro del coro Marcel Seminara
Perfs: 105 *No of Prods:* 16
Venues: Teatro Nazionale 700, Teatro delle Opera 1653 *Comments:* organise concerts at Teatro Opera; see also Dance, Orchestras, Festivals and Venues

TEATRO COMUNALE DI BOLOGNA

FONDAZIONE

>>>>>>>>>>>>>>>>>> STAGIONE 1999 - 2000 <<<<<<<<<<<<<<<<<<

27 NOVEMBRE
2,5,7,9,12,14,16,19,21 DICEMBRE 1999
Allestimento del Teatro Comunale di Bologna

TOSCA*

Musica di GIACOMO PUCCINI

Interpreti principali:
Daniela Dessì/Elmira Veda,Vincenzo La Scola/Alfredo Portilla, Ruggero Raimondi/Alan Titus, Enrico Turco/Marco Vinco, Mauro Utzeri/Alessandro Busi, Enrico Cossutta/Stefano Consolini

DANIELE GATTI maestro conc. e dir.
PAOLO ARRIVABENI(21/12) altro direttore
ALBERTO FASSINI regia
WILLIAM ORLANDI scene e costumi
PIERO MONTI maestro del coro

11,13,15,16,18,26,28,30 APRILE
2 MAGGIO 2000

LA VOIX HUMAINE

Musica di FRANCIS POULENC
(Société anonyme ed. RICORDI, Paris)

Interprete Raina Kabaivanska

CHRISTIAN BADEA maestro conc. e dir.
ROBERTO POLASTRI(18/04, 2/05) altro dir.

Coproduzione con «Ravenna Festival»

I PAGLIACCI

Parole e Musica di RUGGERO LEONCAVALLO
(Ed. CASA MUSICALE SONZOGNO, Milano)

Interpreti principali:
José Cura/Giorgio Merighi, Daniela Dessì/Simona Baldolini, Alberto Mastromarino/Marco Chingari, Dalibor Jenis/Massimiliano Gagliardo

CHRISTIAN BADEA maestro conc. e dir.
ROBERTO POLASTRI(18/04, 2/05) altro dir.
LILIANA CAVANI regia
DANTE FERRETTI scene
GABRIELLA PESCUCCI costumi
PIERO MONTI maestro del coro

4,6,8,10,13,15,17,19,20 FEBBRAIO 2000
Allestimento dell'Opéra di Lille

PELLÉAS ET MÉLISANDE

Musica di CLAUDE DEBUSSY
(Ed. Durand S.A - rappr. CASA MUSICALE SONZOGNO di Piero Ostali, Milano)

Interpreti principali:
William Joyner/Tracey Welborn, Lucio Gallo/Gaetan Laperrière, Nicolaj Ghiaurov/Eldar Aliev, Marina Domashenko/Cassandra Riddle, Debora Beronesi/Claudia Nicole Bandera

VLADIMIR JUROWSKI maestro conc. e dir.
ROBERTO POLASTRI (15/02) altro dir.
PIER'ALLI regia, scene e costumi
PIERO MONTI maestro del coro

L'opera si rappresenta in lingua originale con aopratitoli in italiano

30 MAGGIO, 1,3,4,8,11,13,14 GIUGNO 2000
Allestimento della «De Nederlandse Opera» di Amsterdam

WOZZECK

Musica di ALBAN BERG
*(Universal Edition, Wien
rappr. per l'Italia CASA RICORDI, Milano)*

Interpreti principali:
Jürgen Linne, Edward Cook, Benedikt Kobel, Sergio Bertocchi, Johann Werner Prein, Pierre Lefebvre, Maria Russo, Annette Elster

DANIELE GATTI maestro conc. e dir.
WILLY DECKER regia
WOLFGANG GUSSMANN scene e costumi
PIERO MONTI maestro del coro

L'opera si rappresenta, senza intervalli, in lingua originale con sopratitoli in italiano

15,16,18,19,21,22,24,26 MARZO 2000
Allestimento del Teatro «Romolo Valli» di Reggio Emilia

SALOME*

Musica di RICHARD STRAUSS
(Ed. Musicali Fürstner/ Schott - rappr. CASA MUSICALE SONZOGNO di Piero Ostali, Milano)

Interpreti principali:
Wolfgang Neumann, Chris Merritt, Julia Juon, Susan Anthony/Anna-Katrin Behnke, Jürgen Linne, Matthias Klink

DANIELE GATTI maestro conc. e dir.
PIER LUIGI PIZZI regia, scene e costumi
LUCA VEGGETTI coreografia

L'opera si rappresenta in lingua originale con sopratitoli in italiano

24,25,27,28,29,30 GIUGNO, 1,2 LUGLIO 2000
Allestimento del Teatro «A. Rendano» di Cosenza

LA NOTTE DI UN NEVRASTENICO

Musica di NINO ROTA
(Ed. CASA RICORDI, Milano)

Interpreti principali:
Simone Alberghini/Domenico Colaianni, Luca Canonici/Valter Borin,Alida Ferrarini, Mario Bolognesi

ZOLTÁN PESKÓ maestro conc. e dir.
ROBERTO POLASTRI (1,2/07) altro dir.
PIERA DEGLI ESPOSTI regia
PASQUALE GROSSI scene e costumi
PIERO MONTI maestro del coro

Nuovo allestimento

GIANNI SCHICCHI

Musica di GIACOMO PUCCINI
(Ed. CASA RICORDI, Milano)

Interpreti principali:
Bruno Praticò, Alida Ferrarini, Cinzia De Mola, Luca Canonici, Mario Bolognesi, Adelina Scarabelli, Massimiliano Gagliardo, Simone Alberghini, Alessandro Patalini, Tiziana Tramonti, Domenico Colaianni, Gastone Sarti

ZOLTÁN PESKÓ maestro conc.e dir.
ROBERTO POLASTRI (1,2/07) altro dir.
MARCO GANDINI regia
PASQUALE GROSSI scene e costumi

** L'allestimento sarà utilizzato nell'ambito della collaborazione fra il Teatro Comunale ed i Teatri di Tradizione dell'Emilia Romagna*

>>>>>>>>>>>> <<<<<<<<<<<<

STAGIONE D'OPERA

>>>>>>>>>>>> <<<<<<<<<<<<

ORCHESTRA E CORO DEL TEATRO COMUNALE DI BOLOGNA

Compagnia Lirica Internazionale
c/o AGS, Via Casalborgone 16, 10132 **Torino**
Tel: 011-918 7457/819 3529/5803 Fax: 011-819 3529
Internet: www.alfateatro.it
E-Mail: info@alfateatro.it
administrator/legal representative Nella Actis Perino; artistic director Renzo Rovedi; pr & press officer Claudio Bertoni
Perfs: 80 *No of Prods:* 15 *Venues:* Alfa Teatro 300, Le Serre 400 *Touring:* Europe *Comments:* also school of lyric singing, auditions and casting; legal address: Via Breus 5, 10020 San Sebastiano Da Po (To); see also Venues and Agents & Producers

Compagnia Stabile di Operette Alfa Folies
c/o AGS, Via Casalborgone 16, 10132 **Torino**
Tel: 011-819 3529/5803 Fax: 011-819 3529
Internet: www.alfateatro.it
E-Mail: grilli@alfateatro.it
administrator/legal representative Augusto Grilli; artistic director Cesare Goffi; pr & press officer Claudio Bertoni
Perfs: 90 *No of Prods:* 15 *Venues:* Alfa Teatro 300 *Touring:* Italy, France, Switzerland *Comments:* see also Venues and Agents & Producers

Teatro Regio Torino
piazza Castello 215, 10124 **Torino**
Tel: 011-88151 Fax: 011-881 5214
Internet: www.REGIO.TORINO.ORG
E-Mail: Regio@arpnet.it
direttore artistico Claudio Desderi; direttore stabile orchestra t.b.a.; direttore del coro Bruno Casoni; direttore tecnico e allestimento scenico Silvano Cova; vice direttore artistico Roberto Bosio; sovrintendente Valter Vergnano; ufficio stampa Ugo Sandroni (tel: 881 5236, fax: 881 5268)
Perfs: 87 *No of Prods:* 11 (2 new) *Venues:* Teatro Regio 1620, Piccolo Regio Puccini 386 *Comments:* see also Orchestras, Festivals and Venues

Fondazione Teatro Comunale Giuseppe Verdi
Riva 3 Novembre 1, 34121 **Trieste**
Tel: 040-672 2111 Fax: 040-672 2249
Internet: www.teatroverdi-trieste.com
E-Mail: info@teatroverdi-trieste.com
sovrintendente Dott Lorenzo Jorio; direttore dell'amministrazione Alessandra Delfin; direttore affari generali Antonio Quadrelli; segretario artistico Maestro Giovanni Pacor; direttore del corpo di ballo Tuccio Rigano; direttore di produzione Gianni Gori; responsabile ufficio stampa e relazioni esterne Nicoletta Cavalieri (tel: 40-672 2209); direttore artistico Giandomenico Vaccari
Perfs: 8 per production *No of Prods:* 6-7 *Venues:* Sala Tripcovich 934, Teatro Comunale G.Verdi 1370
Comments: international operetta festival every summer; see also Dance, Orchestras, Festival and Venues

Gran Teatro La Fenice – Palafenice
Isola Nuova del Tronchetto, 30135 **Venezia**
Tel: 041-786 511 Fax: 041-786 580
Internet: www.tin.it/fenice
E-Mail: fenice@interbusiness.it
sovrintendente Mario Messinis; direttore principale Maestro Isaac Karabtchevsky; direttore di produzione Dino Squizzato; direttore artistico Paolo Pinamonti; direttore generale Tito Menegazzo; capo ufficio stampa e relazioni esterne Cristiano Chiarot
Venues: Palafenice Al Tronchetto 1200 *Touring:* Germany, Japan, Spain *Comments:* theatre under refurbishment; see also Orchestras and Venues

Arena di Verona
piazza Bra 28, 37121 **Verona**
Tel: 045-805 1811 (switchboard)/1891 (press office)
Fax: 045-803 1443 (press office)
Internet: www.arena.it
secretario generale Angela Spocci; presidente Michela Sironi Mariotti; vice presidente Giordano Veronesi; sovrintendente Renzo Giacchieri; direttore corpo di ballo Maria Grazia Garofoli; maestro del coro Armando Tasso; principal guest conductor Giuliano Carella
Perfs: 200 *No of Prods:* 3 new *Venues:* Arena di Verona 16,000, Teatro Filarmonico 1100, Teatro Nuovo 600
Comments: Nov-May use Teatro Filarmonico; Jul-Aug: Arena; see also Dance, Orchestras and Venues

LATVIA (+371)

Latvian National Opera
Latvijas Nacionala Opera
3 Aspazijas Blvd., 1050 **Riga**
Tel: 7-225 747/223 927 Fax: 7-228 930
Internet: www.lmuza.lv/opera
E-Mail: admin@opera.lv
general manager Andrejs Zagars; musical directors Gintaras Rinkevicius, Andris Veismanis

LITHUANIA (+370)

Kaunas State Musical Theatre
Kauno valstybinis muzikinis teatras
Laisves al. 91, 3000 **Kaunas**
Tel: 7-200 633 (artistic director)/200 866/228 784
Fax: 7-227 787
artistic director Gintas Zilys

Klaipeda Musical Theatre
Klaipedos muzikinis teatras
Danes 19, 5800 **Klaipeda**
Tel: 6-215 526 Fax: 6-215 526
artistic director Stasys Domarkas

Lithuanian National Opera and Ballet Theatre
Lietuvos nacionalinis operos ir baleto teatras
A. Vienuolio 1, 2600 **Vilnius**
Tel: 2-620 093/618 197/314 065/620 515 Fax: 2-623 503
Internet: www.opera.lt
E-Mail: opera@lithill.lt
general director Julius Andrejevas; marketing director Arunas Simaska

MACEDONIA (+389)

Opera of the Macedonian Theatre
Makedonski Naroden Teatar – Opera
Kej Dimitar Vlahov, 91000 **Skopje**
Tel: 91-114 908/511 Fax: 91-114 060
general director Ilija Rajkovski
Comments: see also Dance

MOLDOVA (+373)

Opera Nationala Chisinau
National Opera Chisinau
152 Stefan cel Mare Bld, 2012 **Chisinau**
Tel: 2-245 088 Fax: 2-238 257
managing director Svetlana Bivol-Baltag

MONACO (+377)

Opéra de Monte-Carlo
Place du casino, BP 139, 98007 **Monaco** cedex
Tel: 92-162 318 Fax: 93-300 757
Internet: www.opera.mc
E-Mail: opera@sbm.mc
director John M Mordler (92-162 318); resident producer and production manager Patricia Panton (92-162 474); financial manager Marie-Christine Forestier (92-162 473); artistic co-ordinator Michel Arene (92-166 474); press Suzy Lefort (33 1-4757 4170); communication Olivier Lefebvre (92-166 473)
Perfs: 20 *No of Prods:* 6 *Venues:* Salle Garnier 520

NETHERLANDS (+31)

Hoofdstad Operette
Kloveniersburgwal 87-89, 1011 KA **Amsterdam**
Tel: 20-623 9531 Fax: 20-623 2587
managing director Marke Tulp; artistic director Jaap Montagne
Perfs: 140 *No of Prods:* 3 *Touring:* Netherlands, Belgium, Germany, Switzerland *Comments:* touring company

Nederlandse Opera, De
Waterlooplein 22, 1011 PG **Amsterdam**
Tel: 20-551 8922 Fax: 20-551 8311
E-Mail: info@nederlandse-opera.nl
artistic administrator Niels-Peter van Doorn; artistic director Pierre Audi; general administrator Truze Lodder; chief conductor Edo de Waart; dramaturg Klaus Bertisch; chorus master Winfried Maczewski; head of planning Jaap Mosterd; chorus manager Bridget Kievits
Perfs: 94 *No of Prods:* 11 (4 new)
Venues: Muziektheater 1600

Orkater
Postbus 57145, 1040 BA **Amsterdam**
Tel: 20-606 0600 (switchboard)/0601 (press office)
Fax: 20-606 0616
Internet: www.orkater.nl
E-Mail: info@orkater.nl
managing directors Marc van Warmerdam, Ton Schippers; publicity Wim Wentzel
Perfs: 120 *No of Prods:* 2 (1 new) *Venues:* capacity 500 to 1000 *Touring:* national *Comments:* the Orkater Foundation explores different combinations of music (Orkest) and theatre (theater); visiting address: Westergasfabriek, Haarlemmerweg 8-10, Amsterdam; see also Drama, Agents and Producers

Taller Amsterdam
Keizersgracht 607, 1017 DS **Amsterdam**
Tel: 20-624 6734 Fax: 20-627 1539
managing director Freek Van Kleij; artistic directors Armando Bergallo, Hector Vilche
Comments: contemporary opera & music theatre; new production for 2000: opera-tango; see also Drama

Nationale ReisOpera
Perikweg 97, PO Box 1321, 7500 BH **Enschede**
Tel: 53-487 8500 Fax: 53-432 1882
E-Mail: nationale@reisopera.nl
administrator Bert Eemink; artistic director Louwrens Langevoort
Perfs: 79 *No of Prods:* 10 (5 new) *Venues:* Twentse Schouwburg 700-2000, and surrounding area

Opera Zuid
PO Box 104, 6200 AC **Maastricht**
Tel: 43-321 0166 Fax: 43-325 7655
Internet: www.operazuid.nl
E-Mail: office@OperaZuid.nl
managing director Jan Nijsten; artistic director t.b.a.; press and marketing Marÿne Thomas
Perfs: 36 *No of Prods:* 3 *Venues:* Theater aan het Vrijthof
Touring: Netherlands *Comments:* visiting address Wilhelminasingel 97, 6221 BH Maastricht

Opera O.T.
Onafhankelijk Toneel
Sint Jobsweg 3, 3024 EH **Rotterdam**
Tel: 10-478 0281/476 9029 Fax: 10-425 7915
Internet: www.ot-rotterdam.nl
E-Mail: ot@ot-rotterdam.nl
directors Mirjam Koen, Gerrit Timmers, Ton Lutgerink; administration Corry Prinsen; publicity Gerda Roest
Perfs: 50 (incl dance and drama) *No of Prods:* 4-9 (incl dance and drama) *Venues:* O.T. Theater up to 100
Touring: national, international *Comments:* full score operas with Combattimento Consort Amsterdam and other orchestras; a collective of professionals from different backgrounds – visual arts, singing, modern dance, acting; see also Dance and Drama

NORWAY (+47)

Opera Bergen / West Norwegian Opera
Post box 763, 5807 **Bergen**
Tel: 5532 3856 Fax: 5532 2435
Internet: www.bgnett/operab
E-Mail: opera@bgnett.no
production manager Tone Kvam Thorsen; artistic director Anne Randine Øverby
Perfs: c.30 *No of Prods:* 5 *Venues:* Grieghall 1500, Logen 350, Bergen National Theatre 450 *Comments:* also church music, popular, musicals, chamber music concerts during season

Opera Vest
Edvard Griegs Plass 1, 5015 **Bergen**
Tel: 5521 6120 Fax: 5521 6121
Internet: www.operavest.nl
E-Mail: operavest@operavest.no
Administrative Director Stein Olav Henrichsen
Perfs: 15 *No of Prods:* 3 *Touring:* France, Norway

Kristiansund Opera
Operaen i Kristiansund Midtnorsk Musikkteater
PO Box 401, 6501 **Kristiansund**
Tel: 7167 7733 Fax: 7158 9961
E-Mail: oper@oik.no
administrative director Olav Grytnes; ballet directors Catherine Smirles Ingebrigtsen, Amy Timpson; music director Kjell Seim
Perfs: 25 *No of Prods:* 3 *Venues:* Festiveteten 420
Comments: orchestra varies from full symphonic orchestra to small ensemble; visiting address: King Olav V's Street 1, 6501 Kristiansund; regularly performs with Kristiansund Ballet School, see also Dance

Norwegian National Opera
Den Norske Opera
PO Box 8800 Youngstorget, 0028 **Oslo** 1
Tel: 2331 5000/5200 (marketing, sales, info)
Fax: 2331 5030 (admin)/5211 (marketing & sales)
Internet: www.wit.no/norskopera
E-Mail: info@norskopera.no
general manager and artistic director Bjoern Simensen; ballet director Dinna Bjørn; finance director Bernt E. Bauge; marketing director Terje Baskerud; information director Inger Schedell
Perfs: 90, 6 concerts, 1 recital *No of Prods:* 10 opera (3 new), 6 ballet (2 new) *Venues:* Den Norske Opera 1051, Musik Teatret 150 *Touring:* Norway, Denmark, Greece, England *Comments:* visiting address: Storgaten 23, 0184 Oslo; see also Dance and Orchestras

Opera Omnia
Enga 2, 0250 **Oslo**
Tel: 2283 5133 Fax: 2283 5134
E-Mail: zone5@zone5.org
contact Glenn Erik Haugland

Stavanger Cabaret Ensemble
Stavanger Revyteater Glaskaperne
Siriusgate 23, 4721 **Stavanger**
Tel: 5187 2938 Fax: 5187 2938
director Jon Arne Saegrov

Magna Vox Musikkteater
Teaterhuset Avantgarden, Olav Tryggvassonsgate 5, 7011 **Trondheim**
Tel: 7352 1039/9074 4495 (mobile) Fax: 7352 4732
Venues: Avantgarden Playhouse
Touring: Europe, USA

POLAND (+48)

Opera Nova
al. Gdanska 20, 85-006 **Bydgoszcz**
Tel: 52-224 985 Fax: 52-224 985
Internet: www.psi.com.pl/on/
E-Mail: on@psi.com.pl
general director Maciej Figas; ballet director Wladimir Glinskich; choir director Henryk Wierzchon
Perfs: 4 p.w. *Comments:* own building under construction

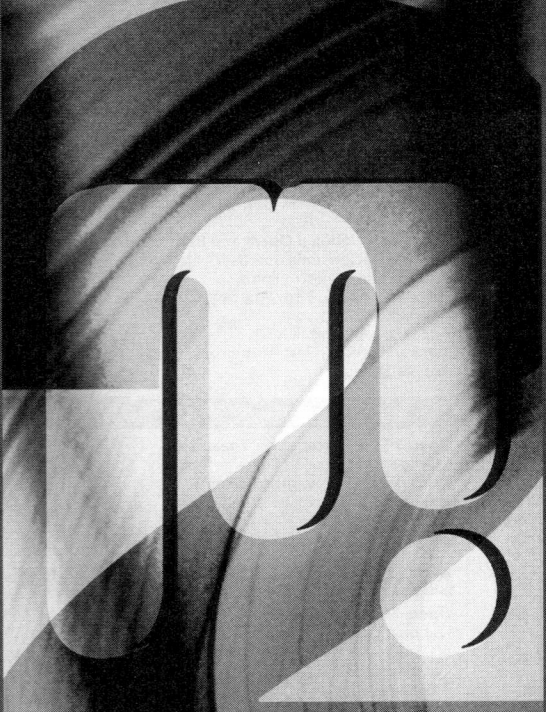

Silesian Opera
Opera Slaska
ul. Moniuszki 21, 41-900 **Bytom**
Tel: 32-281 3430 Fax: 32-281 4335
Internet: www.opera.silesia.top.pl
E-Mail: opera@opera.silesia.top.pl
general & artistic director Tadeusz Serafin; choreographer Henryk Konwinski; ballet director Olga Kozimala-Klis; choir director Jaroslaw Bagrowski
Perfs: 5 p.w. *Venues:* capacity 530 *Comments:* opera and ballet; 37 singers, 12 dancers and permanent choir

Entertainment Theatre
Teatr Rozrywki
Konopnickiej 1, 41-500 **Chorzow**
Tel: 32-241 3231 Fax: 32-241 4195
Internet: entropia.com.pl/teatrrozrywki
general and artistic director Dariusz Milkowski; ballet director Janusz Krzypkowski; choir director Grzegorrz Czaja
Venues: capacity 603

Baltic Opera
Opera Baltycka
al. Zwyciestwa 15, 80-219 **Gdansk**
Tel: 58-341 0134 Fax: 58-341 3827
Internet: operabal.itnet.com.pl
general director Wlodzimierz Nawotka; artistic director Andrzej Knap; ballet director Andrzej Stasiewicz; choir director Elzbieta Wiesztordt
Perfs: 6 p.w. *Venues:* State Opera 500 *Comments:* opera and ballet; 10 singers, 27 dancers and permanent choir

Danuta Baduszkowa Music Theatre
Teatr Muzyczny im. Danuty Baduszkowej
Plac Grunwaldzki 1, 81-372 **Gdynia**
Tel: 58-620 0105/9521 Fax: 58-620 3347
E-Mail: teatrmuz@trojmiasto.com.pl
general & artistic director Maciej Korwin; music director Rafal Jacek Delekta
Comments: musicals, 61 actors

Music Theatre
Teatr Muzyczny
ul. Nowy Swiat 55/57, 44-100 **Gliwice**
Tel: 32-232 2215 Fax: 32-232 1339
Internet: heros.juni.gliwice.pl/rozrywka/teatr/
E-Mail: tmw@ka.onet.pl
general director Pawel Gabara; artistic director Andrzej Zubek; choir director Henryk Wicherek; ballet director Jacek Nowosielski
Perfs: 15 per month, including 3 outside Gliwice *Venues:* capacity 509 *Comments:* gives guest performances in and outside Gliwice; Impresariat: Rynek 18, 44-100 Gliwice, Tel/Fax: 32-231 3729; musicals and operetta, 23 singers, 24 dancers and permanent choir

Opera and Operetta
Dietla 50, 31-039 **Krakow**
Tel: 12-422 6210 Fax: 12-422 0878
Internet: www.opera.krakow.top.pl
E-Mail: marketing@opera.krakow.top.pl
general director Jerzy Nowarol; ballet director Jacek Drozdowski; choir director Ewa Bator
Perfs: 2 opera & 4 operettas per week *Venues:* operetta stage 530 *Comments:* opera performs in Teatr im. Juliusza Slowackiego; operetta performs: ul. Lubicz 48; 27 singers, 25 dancers and permanent choir

Grand Theatre
Teatr Wielki
Plac Dabrowskiego, 90-249 **Lodz**
Tel: 42-633 9960/636 2272 Fax: 42-631 9552
Internet: www.teatr-wielki.lodz.pl/welcome.htm
E-Mail: teatr@mm.com.pl
general director Marcin Krzyzanowski; deputy director Stanislaw Dyzbardis; artistic director Tadeusz Kozlowski; choir director Marek Jaszczak; ballet director Kazimierz Wrzosek
Perfs: 6 p.w. *Venues:* Grand Theatre 1200
Comments: opera and ballet; 35 singers, 25 dancers and permanent choir

Music Theatre
Teatr Muzyczny
ul. Polnocna 47/51, 91-425 **Lodz**
Tel: 42-678 2612 Fax: 42-678 1901
Internet: tliapn@friko2.onet.pl
general director Wieslaw Ostojski; music director Dariusz Rozankiewicz; ballet director Marzena Marianska; choir director Roman Paniuta
Venues: capacity 1114
Comments: operetta and musicals; 24 singers, 20 dancers and permanent choir

Music Theatre
Teatr Muzyczny
ul. Sklodowskiej 5, 20-029 **Lublin**
Tel: 81-532 7613
Internet: www.teatrmuzyczny.safe.net.pl
general & artistic director Andrzej Chmielarczyk; music director Ryszard Komorowski; ballet director Beata Kaminska
Perfs: 160 per season *Venues:* capacity 400
Comments: operetta and musicals; 23 singers, 8 dancers

Music Theatre
Teatr Muzyczny
ul. Niezlomnych 1, 61-766 **Poznan**
Tel: 61-852 3267 Fax: 61-852 3267
Internet: www.info.poznan.pl/culture/theatres
general and artistic director Daniel Kustosik; ballet pedagogue Juliusz Standa
Comments: operetta and musicals; 12 singers, 17 dancers

Stanislaw Moniuszko Grand Theatre
Teatr Wielki im. Stanislawa Moniuszki
ul. Fredry 9, 60-967 **Poznan**
Tel: 61-852 4478 Fax: 61-852 7464
Internet: www.info.poznan.pl/culture/theatres/
general director Slawomir Pietras; artistic director Marek Weiss-Grzesinski; ballet director Liliana Kowalska; choir director Jolanta Dota-Komorowska
Perfs: 6 p.w. *Venues:* Grand Theatre 900
Comments: opera and ballet; 52 singers, 19 dancers and permanent choir

Opera & Operetta
ul. Korsarzy 34, 70-540 **Szczecin**
Tel: 91-489 0340 Fax: 91-434 5557
general & artistic director Warcislaw Kunc; music director Jan Jazownik; ballet director Miroslaw Rozalski; choir director Pawel Osuchowski
Perfs: 6 p.w. *Venues:* capacity 530
Comments: opera, operetta, ballet; 20 singers, 14 dancers and permanent choir

Grand Theatre – National Opera
Teatr Wielki – Opera Narodowa
Plac Teatralny 1, 00-950 **Warszawa**
Tel: 22-692 0200/0293/692 0500/01/826 3289
Fax: 22-826 0423/826 5012
Internet: www.teatrwielki.pl
E-Mail: office@teatrwielki.pl
general director Waldemar Dabrowski; artistic director Jacek Kaspszyk; deputy director Jerzy Bojar; ballet director Emil Wesolowski; choir director Bogdan Gola; technical director Janusz Chojecki
Perfs: 6 p.w. *Venues:* Stanislaw Moniuszko Hall 1837, Emil Mlynarski Hall 248, Theatre Museum *Comments:* Theatre Museum Tel: 22-692 0211/24; opera and ballet

Music Theatre ROMA
Teatr Muzyczny ROMA
ul. Nowogrodzka 49, 00-695 **Warszawa**
Tel: 22-628 7071/621 8037 Fax: 22-621 7233
Internet: venus.icu.eom.pl/teatry/roma
E-Mail: tmroma@box43.gnet.pl
general & artistic director Wojciech Kepczynski; music director Maciej Pawlowski; ballet director Danuta Petrow; choir director Ewa Marchwicka
Perfs: c.260 per season (together) *Venues:* capacity 1003
Comments: musical and operetta; 26 singers, 19 dancers, and permanent choir

Studio Theatre Buffo
Teatr Studio Buffo
ul. Konopnickiej 6, 00-491 **Warszawa**
Tel: 22-625 4706 Fax: 22-621 8452
Internet: www.studiobuffo.com.pl/buffo/teatr.htm
president Janusz Stoklosa; artistic director Janusz Jozefowicz
Comments: musical & cabaret, 33 actors (singers & dancers)

Warsaw Chamber Opera
Warszawska Opera Kameralna
ul. Nowogrodzka 49, 00-695 **Warszawa**
Tel: 22-628 3096 Fax: 22-629 3233
Internet: www.wok.pol.pl
E-Mail: j.mrozik@wok.pol.pl
artistic & general director Stefan Sutkowski
Perfs: 6 p.w. *Venues:* performs at Solidarnosci 76b, 00-145 Warszawa, cap. 150, tel: 22-831 2240, fax: 22-831 4764 *Comments:* 75 singers; group Mime Stage: 7

Music Theatre – Wroclaw Operetta
Teatr Muzyczny – Operetka Wroclawska
ul. Pilsudskiego 72, 50-020 **Wroclaw**
Tel: 71-343 8051/344 4916
Fax: 71-343 8726
general and artistic director Marek Rostecki; ballet director Waldemar Staszewski
Perfs: max. 150 per season *Venues:* Cinema Silesia 600
Comments: operetta and musical; 25 singers, 20 dancers

Wroclaw Opera
Opera Wroclawska
ul. Swidnicka 35, 50-066 **Wroclaw**
Tel: 71-343 8641/2753
Fax: 71-343 6742
general & artistic director/conductor Ewa Michnik; ballet director Maria Kijak; choir director Malgorzata Orawska
Perfs: 130 *Venues:* Opera 600 *Touring:* Benelux countries, UK *Comments:* 18 singers, 37 dancers, and permanent choir; contact in the UK: Artsfusion Ltd, E-mail: admin@artsfusion.demon.co.uk (see Promoters, Agents and Producers)

PORTUGAL (+351)

Royal Theatre Chamber Opera of Queluz
Opera de Câmara do Real Teatro de Queluz
Rua Dos Bombeiros Voluntarios 137 5° Esq,
2775 **Carcavelos**
Tel: 1-456 6139/354 5028 (secretary) Fax: 1-456 2310
president Dr Manuel Ivo Cruz; secretary Mário Monte Alverne; artistic direction Manuel Ivo Cruz, Elsa Saque, Armando Vidal
Perfs: 40 *No of Prods:* 4 *Touring:* national *Comments:* the Opera is funded by Ministerio de Cultura, INATEL, municipal governments, Banco Espirito Santo and other private organisations; promotes Portuguese singers

São Carlos National Opera Company
Teatro Nacional de São Carlos
Rua Serpa Pinto 9, 1200 **Lisboa**
Tel: 1-346 8408/5320/342 7722/346 5914 (box office)
Fax: 1-342 8957 (production)/347 1738 (administration)
E-Mail: saocarlos@mail.telepac.pt
artistic and TNSC director Dr. Paulo Ferreira de Castro
Perfs: 26 opera, 2 recitals, 6 concerts, 11 dance *No of Prods:* 6 (2 new) *Venues:* capacity 948 *Comments:* present opera, concerts and recitals; hire and own productions; see also Choirs and Orchestras

Oporto Opera Company, The
Circulo Portuense de Opera
Rua Nossa Senhora de Fátima, 231, r/c A, 4050-428 **Porto**
Tel: 2-606 5404 Fax: 2-609 2885
co-artistic directors Timothy Coleman, Jorge Vaz de Carvalho; general manager Maria-José Graf; technical director & chairman of the board Manuel Graf; chief designer Matthias Nitsche; head of costumes Manuela Bronze; chorus master Luis-Filipe de Sa; children's chorus mistress Palmira Troufa
Perfs: 12 *No of Prods:* 2-3 *Venues:* Coliseu do Porto 3200, Rivoli Theatre 800 *Touring:* national, touring productions for schools *Comments:* artistic director Timothy Coleman can be contacted in UK, Tel: +44 1273-625 557

ROMANIA (+40)

Brasov Musical Theatre, Brasov
Str Operei 51, 2200 **Brasov**
Tel: 68-419 380/417 271 Fax: 68-411 794
director Carmen Dobrescu
Venues: capacity 415

Musical Theatre Constantin Tanase – Bucharest
Calea Victoriei 33, **Bucharest**
Tel: 1-614 1979 Fax: 1-321 029
director Alexandru Arsinel
Venues: Sala Savoy 555

Operetta Theatre Ion Dacian – Bucharest
B-dul Nicolae Balcescu 2, 70121 **Bucharest**
Tel: 1-614 1187/410 6348 Fax: 1-312 6583
director t.b.a.
Venues: capacity 460

Romanian State Opera – Bucharest
Blvd. M. Kogalniceanu 70-72, 70609 **Bucharest**
Tel: 1-614 6980/410 1857 Fax: 1-615 7849
director general Ràzvan Cernat (tel:1-615 7939)
Venues: capacity 950

Cluj-Napoca Hungarian Opera, Cluj-Napoca
Str. Emil Isac 26-28, 3400 **Cluj-Napoca**
Tel: 64-193 463 Fax: 64-193 469
director Simon Gábor
Venues: capacity 857

Cluj-Napoca Romanian Opera, Cluj-Napoca
Piata Stefan cel Mare 24, 3400 **Cluj-Napoca**
Tel: 64-197 175 Fax: 64-197 129
director Petre Sbârcea
Venues: capacity 923

Fantasio Musical Theatre, Constanta
Blvd Republicii 11, 8700 **Constanta**
Tel: 41-616 036 Fax: 41-616 607
general director Mihai Sorin Vasilescu
Venues: capacity 500

Opera Constanta
St. Mircea cel Batran 97, 8700 **Constanta**
Tel: 41-615 268 Fax: 41-615 080
general director George Stanciu

Craiova Lyrical Theatre
Str. Mihail Viteazu 1, 1100 **Craiova**
Tel: 51-418 426 Fax: 51-415 570
director Emil Maxim

Teatrul de Estrada Deva
B-dul 1 Decembrie 1918 nr 15, 2700 **Deva**
Tel: 54-615 344
director Petru Marila

Galati Musical Theatre Nicolae Leonard – Galati
St. Mihai Bravu 50, 6200 **Galati**
Tel: 36-418 912 Fax: 36-418 096
director Florin Melinte

Iasi Romanian Opera
St. Agatha Barsescu 18, 6600 **Iasi**
Tel: 32-211 144 Fax: 32-211 146
directors Corneliu Calistru
Venues: capacity 846

Timisoara Romanian Opera
St. Marasesti 2, 1900 **Timisoara**
Tel: 56-133 020/134 530 Fax: 56-190 615
director Ion Iancu
Venues: capacity 711

RUSSIA (+7)

Ekaterinburg Academic Opera and Ballet Theatre
Lenin street 46a, 620151 **Ekaterinburg**
Tel: 3432-558 101 Fax: 3432-589 882
director Vladislav Viatkine

Tatarian National Academic Opera and Ballet Theatre M.Jalil
pl. Svobody 1, 420015 **Kazan (Tatarstan)**
Tel: 8432-324 762

Chamber Music Theatre
Nikolskaya st. 17, 103012 **Moscow**
Tel: 095-929 1320
director Boris Pokrovskogo

International Music Dramatic Theatre Arlekin
Boyarski per. 2/3, 107078 **Moscow**
Tel: 095-923 8180

Judith Music Dramatic Theatre Lekhaim
Taganskaya sq. 12/4, 109172 **Moscow**
Tel: 095-912 5651

Moscow Music Theatre New Opera
Moskovski muzykalny teatr Novaya Opera
Filipovski pereulok 11-2, 121019 **Moscow**
Tel: 095-272 2771/291 1100 Fax: 095-291 9313
artistic director Evgueni Kolobov

Moscow State Theatre Gelikon Opera
B. Nikistkaya ul. 19, 103009 **Moscow**
Tel: 095-290 0971

Music Academy Theatre named by K. Stanislavski and V. Nimerovich-Danchenko
B. Dmitrovka 17, 103009 **Moscow**
Tel: 095-229 2835

Music Theatre Amadey
B. Suharevskaya Sq. 3, 129010 **Moscow**
Tel: 095-921 8449

Music Theatre for Children Natalia Sats
Detski muzykalny teatr imeni Natalii Sats
prospekt Vernadskogo 5, 117296 **Moscow**
Tel: 095-930 5243 Fax: 095-930 5243
director Viktor Provorov

Music Theatre Helikon
Muzykalny teatr Gelikon
Bolshaya Nikitskaya street 19, 103009 **Moscow**
Tel: 095-291 1323 Fax: 095-291 3626
artistic director Dmitri Bertman; conductor Kirill Tikhonov
No of Prods: 20 (3 new) *Venues:* 3 stages: 300, 100, 100 (open air) *Touring:* Russia, Europe, Lebanon *Comments:* several CD recordings; contact in the UK: Ensemble Productions Ltd, 7 Roman Close, London W3 8HE, Tel: +44 20-8896 0461, Fax: +44 20-8896 0462, E-mail: balakleets@globalnet.co.uk, contact Olga Balakleets

Musical Comedy Theatre – Operetta Theater
Dmitrovka Bol. Ul.6, 103009 **Moscow**
Tel: 095-292 2345 Fax: 095-229 0851
director Vladimir Tartakovsky

Musical Theatre of Plastic Art
Novaya Basmannaya 25/2, build. 2, 107066 **Moscow**
Tel: 095-261 1198

New Opera
Karetny Ryad 3, 103006 **Moscow**
Tel: 095-200 2255

Stanislavsky and Nemirovich-Danchenko Musical Theatre
Dmitrovka Bol. ul. 17, 103031 **Moscow**
Tel: 095-229 8388/0649
artistic director Alexandre Titel

State Academic Bolshoi Theatre of Russia
Theatralnaya Pl. 1, 103009 **Moscow**
Tel: 095-292 9986/3108 Fax: 095-292 9032
artistic director & general manager Vladimir Vassiliev; executive manager Vladimir Kokonin; ballet director Yuri Bogatyrev

U Nikitskikh Vorot Theatre
23/9B. Nikitskaya Street 14/9, 121019 **Moscow**
Tel: 095-202 8919/6216 Fax: 095-291 9538
E-Mail: nikitsky@glasnet.ru
director Mark Rozovsky
Touring: Europe *Comments:* see also Drama

Novosibirsk State Academic Opera and Ballet Theatre
36, Krasny Prospect, 630099 **Novosibirsk**
Tel: 3832-226040 Fax: 3832 227400
E-Mail: opera@nstu.nsk.ru
theatre director Valery Egoudin; artistic director & chief conductor Alexei Lyudmilin; artistic ballet director Vladimir Vladimirov

Opera & Dance Theatre P Tchaikovsky
ul. Kommunistitcheskaya 25a, 614000 **Perm**
Tel: 342-232 4253 Fax: 342-232 5165
artistic director Vladimir Korochkine

Samara Academic Opera and Ballet Theatre
pl. Kuybysheva 1, 443010 **Samara**
Tel: 8462-320 827

Chamber Musical Theatre St Petersburg – Opera
4 Galernaya str., 190000 **St Petersburg**
Fax: 812-271 4022
artistic director Jury Alexandrov (tel: 812-314 0955); director Irina Artimovitch (tel: 812-315 6769)

St Petersburg State Academic Mussorgsky Opera and Ballet Theatre
1 Arts Square, 191011 **St Petersburg**
Tel: 812-219 1943/1989 Fax: 812-312 2774/314 3653
artistic and general director S Gaudassinsky; administrative director Viktor Kusch; deputy artisitic & general director Victoria Gordievskaya; chief conductor Andrey Anikhanov; artistic director of ballet Nikolay Bojartchikov

St Petersburg State Marinsky Theatre (Kirov)
Theatralnaya Pl. 1, 190000 **St Petersburg**
Tel: 812-114 4441/4154 Fax: 812-314 1444
general artistic director Valery Gergiev (812-114 4110); theatre director Yuri Schwartzkopf

St Petersburg State Musical Theatre Music Hall
4 Alexandrovsky park, 197198 **St Petersburg**
Tel: 812-232 9466 (director) Fax: 812-232 5329
artistic director Ilia Rakhlin (tel: 812-232 6165)

St Petersburg State Theatre of Musical Comedy
13 Italianskaya str., 191011 **St Petersburg**
Fax: 812-311 7651
artistic director Alexander Belinsky (tel: 812-110 5982); director Vladimir Pashkov (tel: 812-210 4689)

St Petersburg State Theatre Rock-Opera
36 Labutina str., 190008 **St Petersburg**
Tel: 812-114 8473 (director) Fax: 812-114 8473
artistic director Vladimir Podgorodinsky (tel: 812-114 0547)

Bashkirian National Opera and Ballet Theatre
Lenin street 5a, 450000 **Ufa (Bashkortostan)**
Tel: 3472-229 110

SLOVAKIA (+421)

Many telephone and fax numbers in Slovakia are in the process of being changed. We have included all new numbers known at the time of going to print.

State Opera in Banská Bystrica
Státna opera v Banskej Bystrici
Národná 11, 974 73 **Banská Bystrica**
Tel: 88-415 4544 Fax: 88-415 3457
Internet: www.pcb.sk
E-Mail: sobbs@pcb.sk
director of the opera Rudolf Ilromada
Perfs: 110 *No of Prods:* 4 *Venues:* capacity 380

Music Theatre Nová Scéna
Zivnostenská 1, 812 14 **Bratislava**
Tel: 7-5292 3230/5296 3584/5296 3573 Fax: 7-5296 1431
Internet: www.kultura.gratex.sk/nscena
E-Mail: riaditel-ns@ba.entry.sk
director of the Nová Scéna Marek Tapak; artistic director Karol Cálik
Venues: capacity 500 *Comments:* see also Drama

Opera of the Slovak National Theatre/Opera SND
Opera Slovenského národného divadla
Gorkého 4, 815 86 **Bratislava**
Tel: 7-5443 5085 Fax: 7-5443 5072
general director of the Slovak National Theatre Dusan Jamrich; director of the Opera of the SNT Juraj Hrubant
Perfs: 200 *No of Prods:* 5 *Venues:* capacity 600
Comments: see also Dance and Drama

Opera of the State Theatre Kosice
Opera Statneho divadla Kosice
Hlavná 58, 042 77 **Kosice**
Tel: 95-622 1231/2474 Fax: 95-622 8235
general director of the State Theatre
Kosice Jozef Fiffik; artistic director of the Opera Frantisek Balún
Comments: see also Dance and Drama

Jonás Záborsky Music Theatre in Presov
Spevohra Divadla Jonasa Zaborskeho v Presove
Nám Legionárov 6, 082 61 **Presov**
Tel: 91-723 888 Fax: 91-734 915
Venues: capacity 600 *Comments:* see also Drama

SLOVENIA (+386)

Slovene National Theatre Opera and Ballet Ljubljana
Slovensko narodno gledalisce Opera in balet Ljubljana
Zupanciceva 1, 1000 **Ljubljana**
Tel: 61-125 4680 Fax: 61-126 2249
managing director & artistic director Borut Smrekar; public relations manager Tea Majkic
Perfs: c.100 *No of Prods:* 4 *Venues:* capacity 550, Cankarjev Dom (q.v.) *Touring:* within Slovenia
Comments: see also Dance and Orchestras

Opera of the Slovene National Theatre Maribor
Slovensko Narodno Gledalisce
Slovenska Ulica 27, 2000 **Maribor**
Tel: 62-22840 Fax: 62-221 207/223 215/ 228 4050
Internet: www.sng-mb.si
E-Mail: sng.maribor@sng-mb.si
general manager Blaz Rafolt; artistic director Stane Jurgec
Comments: alternative E-mail: marketing.sng.maribor@sng-mb.si

SPAIN (+34)

Amigos de la Zarzuela
Av. de la Constitución s/n, 30550 **Abarán (Murcia)**
Tel: 968-450 171/770 222
presidente Pedro José Carrasco Goméz; vice-presidente Jesús de la Cruz Montiel Ruíz
Perfs: 25 *No of Prods:* 25 *Venues:* Capitol Cartagena 1500, Teatro Circo 2000 and open air venues cap. 800-3000
Touring: inside Spain

Acteon
c/ Girona 97 1° 1ª , 08009 **Barcelona**
Tel: 93-207 5773 Fax: 93-207 5773
Internet: www.cccbxaman.org/acteon
E-Mail: acteon@arrakis.es
director Claudio Zulián; production & communication Montse Herrera
Perfs: 20-30 *No of Prods:* 5 *Touring:* Spain, Europe
Comments: multimedia and contemporary opera; managed by Acteon Productions; see also Agents

Catalunya Producciones Zarzuela Rigual
c/Florida 125, Hospitalet de Llobregat, 08905 **Barcelona**
Tel: 93-449 8341/6897 56905 Fax: 93-449 2652
director Ferran Rigual; gerente Tony Rigual
Perfs: 100 *No of Prods:* 40 *Venues:* Teatre la Farandula de Sabadell 1200 *Touring:* Spain *Comments:* eldest Zarzuela company in the world

Asociación Bilbaína de Amigos de la Opera (ABAO)
c/ José María Olabarri nº 2/4, bajo, 48001 **Bilbao**
Tel: 94-435 5100 Fax: 94-435 5101
directora general Ana Esteban Arroyo; presidente Fco. de Larracoechea; secretario Juan Carlos Matellanes; vice presidente Otto Vargas Gold; director del coro Boris Dujin; coordinador artístico Luis López Tejedor
Perfs: 24 *No of Prods:* 8 *Venues:* Palacio de Congresos Euskalduna 2200 *Comments:* regional and provincial governments and private funding; see also Festivals

Teatro Villamarta
Plaza Romero Martínez s/n, 11402 **Jerez de la Frontera**
Tel: 956-329 313 Fax: 956-329 511
Internet: www.webjerez.com
E-Mail: teatrovillamarta@redteatros.inaem.es
director Francisco López; comunicacion José Angel Bermejo
Perfs: 10 *No of Prods:* 7 + lyric performances
Venues: Teatro Villamarta 1300 *Touring:* Spain
Comments: managed by Fundación Teatro Villamarta; see also Venues

Asociación de Amigos de la Opera de la Coruña
Cantón Grande, 16-18, 9° H, 15003 **La Coruña**
Tel: 981-211 443
presidente Cristino Alvarez; secretario Antonio Vasco
Perfs: 4 *No of Prods:* 4 *Venues:* Auditorio del Palacio de Congresos de la Coruña *Comments:* regional & municipal funding; also receives funding from private promoters; organises and produces concerts, opera, lectures and seminars

Asociación de Amigos Canarios de la Opera
Teatro Pérez Galdós, Plaza Stagno 1,
35002 **Las Palmas de Gran Canarias**
Tel: 928-370 125/364 389 Fax: 928-369 394
Internet: www.canarias-internet.com/wehf/opera/
E-Mail: amigoscanarios@lpa.servicom.es
presidente Juan de Leon Suarez; director artístico del festival Roger Rossel; gerente Miguel Alarcón
Perfs: 15 *Venues:* Teatro Pérez Galdós 1340, Auditorio Alfredo Krauss 1600 *Comments:* organize Festival de Opera de las Palmas; perform with Orquesta Filarmónica de Gran Canarias & Coral Lírica de Las Palmas; season Feb-May; see also Festivals

Antología de la Zarzuela
Marqués de Casa Riera 2 2°, 28014 **Madrid**
Tel: 91-522 3403 Fax: 91-522 1926
dirección y creación José Tamayo
No of Prods: 1 *Venues:* Teatro Bellas Artes 600 *Touring:* national, USA and South America

Asociación de Amigos de la Opera de Madrid
c/Mayor 6, 4° pta 2, 28013 **Madrid**
Tel: 91-521 5759 Fax: 91-521 2018
president Juan Cambreleng Roca
Comments: publish bulletin every three months

Compañía de Opera del Teatro Calderón
Atocha 18, 28012 **Madrid**
Tel: 91-369 1434 Fax: 91-420 2424
Comments: theatre is closed for refurbishment; reopening date t.b.a.

Compañía Lírica Amadeo Vives
c/o Teatro Bellas Artes, c/Marqués de Casa Riera 2, 28014 **Madrid**
Tel: 91-522 3403 Fax: 91-522 1926
director José Tamayo; director de producción Antonio Díaz Martínez; director musical José Antonio Torres
Venues: Teatro Bellas Artes 800 *Touring:* Spain, South America, USA *Comments:* 7 soloists, 14 dancers, 24 orchestra, 24 choir; see also Dance

Fundación del Teatro Lírico – Teatro Real
Plaza de Isabel Segunda s/n, 28013 **Madrid**
Tel: 91-516 0600 Fax: 91-516 0651
director Juan Cambreleng; director artístico y musical Luis Antonio García Navarro
Perfs: 128 *No of Prods:* 12 opera, 6 ballet, 6 concerts, 4 conciertos *Venues:* Teatro Real 1748 to 1854 *Comments:* non-permanent company; see also Venues

La Zarzuela S.L.
Marques de Casa Riera nº 2, 28014 **Madrid**
Tel: 91-522 3403 Fax: 91-522 1926
director José Tamayo; director ejecutivo Manuel Ganchegui
Perfs: 100 *No of Prods:* 1 *Touring:* Spain, South America, USA *Comments:* see also Dance and Agents & Producers

Opera Cómica de Madrid
Calle del Acuerdo, 17, 1° A, 28015 **Madrid**
Tel: 91-522 0583 Fax: 91-522 0583
presidente Francisco Matilla; jefe de producción Alicia García Alegre; director musical Luis Martínez
Perfs: 70 *No of Prods:* 20 (4 new) *Touring:* Spain, South America, Europe *Comments:* organise concerts with other orchestras; special attention to Spanish music with research work; revival of 19th century music

Asociación Asturiana de Amigos de la Ópera-Temporada de Opera de Oviedo
Melquíades Alvarez 20, 1°E, 33003 **Oviedo**
Tel: 985-211 705 Fax: 985-212 402
president Luis Alvarez Bartolomé
Perfs: 4-5 *No of Prods:* 4 *Venues:* Teatro Campamor 1552
Comments: office hours: 1700 to 2000 hours Mon to Fri; Season Sept-Jan (Temporada de Opera de Oviedo); see also Festivals

Compañía de Opera del Teatro Principal de Palma de Mallorca
c/ Sa Riera, 2A, 07003 **Palma de Mallorca**
Tel: 971-713 346/725 548 Fax: 971-725 542
Internet: www.teatreprincipal.com
E-Mail: teatreprincipal@cim.net
director en funciones y administrador Pedro Noguera; asesora artístico musical Sylvia Corbacho; coordinadora de las temporadas de opera y zarzuela Encarnita Grizon; director de los Coro Del Teatre Principal Francesco Bonnin; coordinadora de la escola de musica del Teatre Principal Guillem Grimalt
Perfs: 20 *No of Prods:* 4 + 1 concierto *Comments:* Coro del Teatre Principal 80-voice choir, funded by Consell Insular de Mallorca, negotiating coproductions with other theatres, also opera for schools; see also Venues

Associació d'Amics de l'Ópera de Sabadell
Plaça Sant Roc 22, 2° 1ª, 08201 **Sabadell**
Tel: 93-725 6734/726 5470 Fax: 93-727 5321
Internet: www.amics-opera-sabadell.es
E-Mail: ami@sumi.es
presidenta y directora artística Mirna Lacambra Domenéch; vicepresidente y prensa Xavier Gondolbeu; vicepresidente y asesor jurídico joaquim Gil Sallarés; secretario de la junta Antoni Quintana Petrus; tesorero y delegado del concurso nacional eugenio marco para cantantes de opera Jordi Torrents Ponce
Perfs: 25 *No of Prods:* 4 *Venues:* Teatro Fortuny de Reus 850, Centre Cultural Sant Cugat 788, Teatre Municipal de Girona 800, Teatro la Farandula (Sabadell) 800, Auditori Enric Granados, Lleida *Touring:* Cataluña
Comments: they have set up Escuela de Opera de Sabadell para Jovenes Cantantes (Sabadell's opera school for young singers); organise competition for young opera singers – Eugenio Marcos; see also Choirs, Competitions and Festivals

Asociación Tinerfeña de Amigos de la Opera
C/ del Castillo 17, 2°, 38002 **Santa Cruz de Tenerife**
Tel: 922-272 535 Fax: 922-277357
presidente Roberto Oliva Niebla; gestor Alberto Bello Alonso
Perfs: 5 (from Oct. to Dec.) *No of Prods:* 4 *Venues:* Teatro Guimerá 1004 *Comments:* perform with Orquesta Sinfóníca de Tenerife, Coral Universitaria

b quadro ópera
c/o Arte 4, T4 S.A., C/ Real 19, 28250 **Torredolones (Madrid)**
Tel: 91-859 3962/907-745 423 (mobile) Fax: 91-859 4637
Internet: www.greencom.net/arte4
E-Mail: arte4@greencom.net
director Germán Torrellas; artistic director Rafael Romero Marchent; production M. Fueyo, Macarena Torrellas, Antonia Sánchez
Perfs: 20 *No of Prods:* 4 + 1 new every 2 years *Comments:* chamber opera company, managed by Arte 4, T4 S.A.; see also Agents & Producers

Madrid Goyesco
c/o Arte 4, T4 S.A., C/ Real 19, 28250 **Torredolones (Madrid)**
Tel: 91-859 3962/607-745 423 (mobile) Fax: 91-859 4637
Internet: www.greencom.net/arte4
E-Mail: arte4@greencom.net
director Germán Torrellas; artistic director Rafael Romero Marchent; production M. Fueyo, Antonia Sánchez, Macarena Torrellas
Perfs: 50 *No of Prods:* 1 new every year *Touring:* South America (Venezuela, Santo Domingo, Puerto Rico)
Comments: lyric company (5 singers + 7 musicians) for international touring, performs with local orchestras; specialise in Spanish XVIII century music; managed by Arte 4, T4 S.A.; see also Agents & Producers

Taller de Opera
Palau de la Música – Paseo de la Alameda, 30, 46023 **Valencia**
Tel: 96-337 5020 Fax: 96-337 1521
Internet: www.palauvalencia.com
E-Mail: palaudelamusica@resone.es
director María Irene Beneyto
Perfs: 10 *No of Prods:* 1 *Venues:* Palau de la Musica *Touring:* Spain *Comments:* also has a workshop to prepare and perform an opera every year

Asociación Cultural Salzburgo
Apdo 3160, c/ Recoletas 4, 47006 **Valladolid**
Tel: 983-339 542 Fax: 983-222 469
representante José Antonio Nieto de Miguel; secretaria Marina Pilar Gutiérrez Lozano; vice presidente Antonio Medina Cabrerizo
No of Prods: 5-6 (opera, ballet, classical music) *Venues:* Teatro Calderon, Auditorio de la Feria Internacional de Muestras 625 *Comments:* see also Promoters

SWEDEN (+46)

GöteborgsOperan
Christina Nilssons Gata, 411 04 **Göteborg**
Tel: 31-108 000 Fax: 31-108 030
Internet: www.opera.se
E-Mail: info@opera.se
general manager Dag Hallberg; artistic director Kjell Ingebretsen; finance manager Mikael Milocco; marketing manager Pernilla Warberg Andersson; programme editor Astrid Pernille-Hartmann; ballet director Anders Hellström; personnel manager Else-Marie Ling; technical director Maths Nyström
Perfs: 220-230 perfs at main stage, 100-150 perfs at experimental stage
No of Prods: 20 opera, operetta and ballet *Venues:* main auditorium 1250, experimental stage 200

Värmlandsoperan – Musikteatern i Värmland
Älvgatan 49, 652 30 **Karlstad**
Tel: 54-140 840 Fax: 54-100 533
Internet: www.musikteaternivarmland.se
E-Mail: musikteatern@alfaskop.net
managing director Hans Hiort; opera producer Pernilla Eduard; orchestral manager Ole Wiggo Bang; marketing manager Kristina Bergh; financial director Christina Nilsson; freelance producer Lena Gynnemo
Perfs: 130 (opera and concerts) *No of Prods:* 1 opera, 1 musical *Venues:* Karlstad Theatre 380 *Touring:* Sweden
Comments: permanent opera company, 85 members, inc 3 singers; orchestra (29 players) is Värmlands Sinfonietta (q.v.); see also Promoters

Ystadoperan
Knut den Stores gata 7, 222 21 **Lund**
Tel: 46-129 689
E-Mail: roa.bark@ystadoperan.se
director Richard Bark

Malmö Musikteater
Box 175 20, 200 10 **Malmö**
Tel: 40-208 400 Fax: 40-208 423
general director, head of opera & music Philip Zanden; head of planning Jola Eriksson
No of Prods: 5 operas, 1 musical, 8 concerts
Venues: Storan 1460 *Comments:* traditional and modern opera, operetta, musicals, concerts

Musikteatergruppen Oktober
Box 254, 151 23 **Södertälje**
Tel: 8-5508 6160 Fax: 8-5508 6170
administrative director/producer Jan Karlén; artistic leader Ninne Olsson; public relations Åsa Olofsson
Perfs: 180 *No of Prods:* 2 (new) *Venues:* Castor 200
Comments: type: music theatre

Confidencen
Ulriksdals Slottsteater, 170 79 **Solna**
Tel: 8-857 016
Fax: 8-856 121
director Ture Rangström
Comments: no permanent company; performs for example with artists from Royal Opera, Royal Swedish Ballet and young artists; season from May – October; also chamber music, recitals, jazz, regular theatre and ballet; see also Dance

Drottningholms Slottsteater
PO Box 27050, 102 51 **Stockholm**
Tel: 8-660 8225(tickets)/665 1400(office)
Fax: 8-665 1473
Internet: www.drottningholmsteatern.dtm.se
E-Mail: dst@dtm.se
general manager Per Forsström; artistic director Per-Erik Öhrn; marketing manager Eva Lundgren (tel: 8-759 0406)
Perfs: May-Sept, annual
Venues: Drottningholms Slottsteater 454
Comments: administrative address: Drottningholms Teatermuseum, Box 27050, 10251 Stockholm; no permanent opera or ballet company; perform 18th century opera, ballet and concerts; the stage scenery and machinery is authentic 18th century, as is the theatre building itself which is listed under the World Heritage (UNESCO)

Folkoperan
Hornsgatan 72, 118 21 **Stockholm**
Tel: 8-616 0700
Fax: 8-844 146
Internet: www.folkoperan.se
E-Mail: ticket@folkoperan.se
general manager Magnus Aspegren; artistic director Claes Fellbom; music director Kerstin Nerbe
Perfs: 160 *No of Prods:* 3
Venues: Folkoperan 591
Comments: traditional opera and new works; independent company with permanent stage

Kungliga Operan
Royal Swedish Opera
Box 16094, 103 22 **Stockholm**
Tel: 8-791 4300
Fax: 8-791 4444
general director Bengt Hall; artistic opera director Clas Häkan Ahansgö; artistic ballet director Petter Jakobson; music director Leif Segerstam; marketing director t.b.a.; press officer Staffan Carlweitz (tel:8-791 4353, fax:8-411 6305)
Perfs: 280 annually
Venues: Kungliga Operan: Main stage 1100, Rotunda stage 150; Drottingholm Court Theatre, Confidencen and Vasateatern
Comments: regular vocal (voice and piano), chamber and orchestral concerts, ballet workshops etc.

Stockholms Operettensemble
Box 7123, 174 07 **Sundbyberg**
Tel: 8-628 6111 Fax: 8-628 6111
artistic director Anne-Lie Kinnunen
Touring: Sweden
Comments: the company has no permanent venue at present

Norrlandsoperan
PO Box 360, 901 08 **Umeå**
Tel: 90-154 300 Fax: 90-126 845
Internet: www.vbm.se
E-Mail: info@vbm.se
general & artistic director Lars Tibell; deputy general director & finance manager Helen Sundström-Hetta; assistant to director Thomas Kerslow; company manager Eva Lindh-Holmgren; marketing officer Camilla Fahlander; press officer Björn Björklund; technical administrator Anders Andersson; production manager t.b.a.
Perfs: 100 (Aug-June) *No of Prods:* 5-6
Venues: Norrlandoperan 300, The Sagatheatre 380, The Iduntheatre 580 *Touring:* national
Comments: see also Promoters

SWITZERLAND (+41)

Theater Basel
Elisabethenstrasse 16, 4010 **Basel**
Tel: 61-295 1100/1133 (bookings)
Fax: 61-295 1200/1410 (bookings)
Internet: www.theater-basel.ch
E-Mail: info@theater-basel.ch
general manager Michael Schindhelm; administrative director Ivo Reichlin; general music director Julia Jones; choir director Henryk Polus; opera director Albrecht Puhlmann; drama director Stefan Bachmann; dance director Joachim Schlöner; Chefdisponentin Barbara Masson
Perfs: 175 (Große Bühne), ca 200 (Komödie), ca 220 (Kleine Bühne)
No of Prods: 9 (Große Bühne), 8 (Komödie), 5 (Kleine Bühne), 4 (Foyer Große Bühne) *Venues:* Stadttheater Grosse Bühne 1015, Kleine Bühne 322, Komödie 579
Comments: see also Drama

Stadttheater Bern
Nägeligasse 1, 3000 **Bern** 7
Tel: 31-312 1711 Fax: 31-311 3947/312 3670
Internet: www.stub.unibe.ch/kultur/stth/index.html
Direktor Eike Gramss; Stellv. Direktor u. Chefdisponent Jochen Sostmann; Musikdramaturg Benedikt Holtbernd; Studienleiter Eckart Manke; Ballettdirektor Félix Duméril; Chordirektor Lech-Rudolf Gorywoda; Technischer Direktor Gino Fornasa; Personaldirektorin Lucia Sternthal, Solorepetitor Karin Diem, Assistentin Barbara Hauser
Perfs: 83 + 20 musicals *No of Prods:* 5 new, 2 revivals, 1 operetta, 1 musical *Venues:* Stadttheater 730, Kornhausbühne 130 *Comments:* see also Dance and Drama

ensemble Theater der Regionen/Théâtre des Régions Biel/Bienne – Solothurn
Burgasse 13, Postfach, 2500 **Biel** 3
Tel: 32-328 8969 Fax: 32-328 8967
Direktion Peter Theiler; Chefdisponent und persönlicher Referent des Direktors Mario Bettoli; musikalische Leitung Marc Tardue; künstlerische Leitung Oper Martin Markun, Marc Tardue, Peter Theiler; Betriebsbüro Oper und Sekretariat Anita Bruman, Claire Jacot; leitender Regisseur Oper/théâtre lyrique Martin Markun; Verwaltungsleiter Anton Stocker
Perfs: 154 *No of Prods:* 5 *Venues:* Stadttheater Biel 280, Stadttheater Solothurn 280, Théâtre Palace 550 *Touring:* Switzerland, France, Germany *Comments:* address Solothurn: Theatergasse 16-18, CH-4500 Solothurn; see also Orchestras, Drama and Promoters

Grand Théâtre de Genève
Geneva Opera House
11 bd du Théâtre, 1211 **Genève** 11
Tel: 22-418 3000 Fax: 22-418 3001
Internet: www.geneveopera.ch
E-Mail: dirgen@geneveopera.ch
director general Renée Auphan; secretary general François Duchêne; public relations/press director Marie-Claire Mermoud; technical director Jacques Ayrault; ballet administration François Passard; artistic co-ordination of the ballet Giorgio Mancini; choir master Guillaume Tourniaire
Perfs: 100 (20 ballet) *Prods:* 10 + 5 recitals *Venues:* Grand Théâtre 1488, Foyer (chamber concerts, recitals) 260, Bâtment des Forces Motices 985 *Touring:* Switzerland, Italy, France, Germany, China, Greece, Turkey
Comments: see also Dance and Drama

Opéra de Lausanne
Théâtre Municipal de Lausanne, Case postale 3972, 1002 **Lausanne**
Tel: 21-310 1616 (admin) Fax: 21-310 1690
director Françis Xavier Hauville; director of administration Paul Durussel; executive secretaries Marie-Laure Chabloz; press attachée & pr Laurence Authier
Perfs: 6 (opera). 8 (ballet), 8 (concerts) *No of Prods:* 2 *Venues:* Théâtre Municipal de Lausanne 993, Théâtre de Jorat à Mézières 1040, Salle Metropole *Comments:* live and recorded music; see also Drama

Luzerner Theater
Theaterstrasse 2, 6002 **Luzern**
Tel: 41-210 3363 Fax: 41-210 3367
Internet:
www.centralnet.ch/kultur/luzernertheater/index.html
E-Mail: luzernertheater@centralnet.ch
Direktor Barbara Mundel; Chefdramaturgin Ann-Marie Arioli; Chefdisponent Jürgen Heene; Administrator Adrian Balmer; Musikdirektor Jonathan Nott; Chordirektor Wolfgang Müller-Salow; Ballettdirektor Walter Heun; Dramaturgin/Pressebeauftragte Ruth Schürmann
Perfs: 110 *No of Prods:* 25
Venues: Luzerner Theater 558 *Touring:* Switzerland
Comments: see also Dance and Drama

Stadttheater St.Gallen
Museumstrasse 24, 9004 **St Gallen**
Tel: 71-242 0606 Fax: 71-242 0506/7
Internet: www.stadttheaterstgallen.ch
E-Mail: theater.stgallen@bluewin.ch
geschäftsführender Direktor Werner Signer; Schauspieldirektor Peter Schweiger; Operndirektor Laurent Wagner
Perfs: 228 *No of Prods:* 7 operas, 1 ballet, 6 dramas, 2 children's theatre, 1 operetta, 2 musicals *Venues:* Stadttheater 741, Studiobühne 120 *Touring:* Switzerland
Comments: see also Drama and Dance

Opernhaus Zürich
Falkenstrasse 1, 8008 **Zürich**
Tel: 1-268 6400 Fax: 1-268 6401
Intendant Alexander Pereira; kaufmännischer Direktor Otto Grosskopf; Marketing and PR Mathias von Bausznern; Ballettdirektor Heinz Spoerli; Chordirektor Jörg Hämmerli; Chefdirigent Franz Welser-Möst; künstlerischer Betriebsdirektor Grischa Asagaroff; leitende Dramaturgin Ronny Dietrich; Pressereferent Paul Martin Padrut
Perfs: 280 *No of Prods:* 17 new productions, 23 revivals + concerts, recitals, lectures *Venues:* Opernhaus 1200, Studiobühne 200, Tonhalle Zürich, also Winterthur and surroundings *Touring:* Austria
Comments: see also Orchestra and Dance

TURKEY (+90)

Ankara State Opera and Ballet
Ankara Devlet Opera ve Balesi
Atatürk Bulvari N° 50, Ulus, 06050 **Ankara**
Tel: 312-311 2430 Fax: 312-311 9731
director Hasan Hüseyin Akbulut
Venues: Opera Stage 718, Operetta stage 426

Istanbul State Opera and Ballet
Istanbul Devlet Opera ve Balesi
Atatürk Kültür Merkezi, Taksim, 80124 **Istanbul**
Tel: 212-243 2011 Fax: 212-245 3916
administrative and artistic director Yekta Kara; general music director Michael Chasson; head choreographer Özkan Aslan; chief director Yekta Kara
Perfs: 225 (including ballet, concerts etc.) *No of Prods:* 10 *Venues:* Grand Hall 1300, Concert Hall 502

Izmir State Opera and Ballet
Izmir Devlet Opera ve Balesi
Konak, **Izmir**
Tel: 232-484 6450 Fax: 232-441 0173
director Aytül Büyüksarag
Perfs: 4 opera, 2 operetta
Venues: Opera Stage 410

Mersin State Opera and Ballet
Mersin Devlet Opera ve Balesi
Cumhuriyet Alani, Eski Halkevi Bínasi, **Mersin**
Tel: 324 238 0493/2371904
Fax: 324-237 4719
director Erdogan Sanal
Perfs: 8-9 (opera) 2-3 (operetta)
Venues: Opera Stage 588

UKRAINE (+380)

Dnipropetrovsk State Opera
Dnipropetrovskyj derzhavny teatr opery ta baletu
Karl Marx Prospect 32a, 320000 **Dnipropetrovsk**
Tel: 562-445 975
director Yurij Chayka

Donetsk State Opera
Donetskyj derzhavnyj akademichnyj teatr opery ta baletu
Artema St. 82, 340055 **Donetsk**
Tel: 622 930 969

Kharkiv State Opera
Kharkivskyj derzhavnyj akademichnyj teatr operj ta baletu
Sumska St. 25, 310000 **Kharkiv**
Tel: 572 477 216

Kiev Childrens' Music Theatre
Derzhavnyj Muzychnyj Dytiachyj Teatr
Velyka Zhytomyrska St. 2, 252134 **Kiev (Kyiv)**
Tel: 44-228 1166

Kiev State Operetta
Kyyivkyj Derzhavnyj Teatr Operety
Chervonoarmiyska St. 51a, 252005 **Kiev (Kyiv)**
Tel: 44-227 4457

National Opera of Ukraine
Shevchenko boulevard, 252003 **Kiev (Kyiv)**
Tel: 44-224 0424 Fax: 44-229 3819
director Anatolij Mokrenko

Lviv State Opera
Lvivskyj Derzhavnyj Akademichnyj Teatr Opery ta Baletu im I Franka
Kulisha St. 6a, 290058 **Lviv**
Tel: 322 728 562

Odessa Musical Comedy Theatre
Odeskyj Teatr Muzychnoji Komediji
Czyzhova St. 3, 270012 **Odessa**
Tel: 482-249 410

Odessa State Opera
Odeskyj Derzhavnyj Akademichnyj Teatr opery ta baletu
Tchaikovsky Provulok 1, 270026 **Odessa**
Tel: 482 291 310

Crimea Ukrainian Musical Theatre
Krymskyj Ukrainskyj Muzychnyj Tetr
Kirova 17, 333000 **Simferopol**

UNITED KINGDOM (+44)

City of Birmingham Touring Opera
205 The Argent Centre, 60 Frederick Street, **Birmingham** B1 3HS
Tel: 121-246 6644 Fax: 121-246 6633
administrator Andrew Bennett; artistic director Graham Vick; principal conductor Simon Halsey
Perfs: 20-30 *No of Prods:* 3
Touring: national, international *Comments:* productions include Pelleas and Melisande in 2000 and Wozzeck in 2001; core promoters in England in Aldeburgh, Burton upon Trent, Dudley, Cambridge, Middlesbrough, Salisbury and Shropshire

Buxton Festival
1 Crescent View, Hall Bank, **Buxton** SK17 6EN
Tel: 1298-70395 Fax: 1298-72289
Internet: www.buxtonfestival.freeserve.co.uk
E-Mail: info@buxtonfestival.freeserve.co.uk
general manager Glyn Foley; chairman Sir Roy Hattersley; artistic director Aidan Lang; head of communications Lee Barnes; develpment co-ordinator Jean Ball
Perfs: 10 opera; 30 classical music/talks/drama/recitals (all in July) *No of Prods:* 2 *Venues:* Opera House 943; St John's 400; Palace Hotel 400; Octagon up to 800; Old Clubhouse 100 *Comments:* annual; specialize in rarely heard operas; also young artists, jazz, concerts and recitals; the company will be moving at the end of '99 for new address please contact them at the above phone no.; see also Festivals

Music Theatre Wales
5 Llandaff Road, Canton, **Cardiff (Wales)** CF11 9NF
Tel: 29-2023 0833 Fax: 29-2034 2046
administrator Elizabeth Cowling; artistic directors Michael Rafferty, Michael McCarthy
Perfs: up to 14 *No of Prods:* 1 *Venues:* medium and small scale *Touring:* national, international *Comments:* provide educational workshops in connection with each production; also do signed and audio describe performances

Welsh National Opera
John Street, **Cardiff (Wales)** CF10 5SP
Tel: 29-2046 4666 Fax: 29-2048 3050
general director Anthony Freud; musical director Carlo Rizzi; director of administration Geoffrey Rowe; director of development Lucy Stout; director of marketing Peter Bellingham
Perfs: 105-120 *No of Prods:* 9 (3 new) The Turn of the Screw, The Carmelites, Cosi Fan Tutte
Venues: major large-scale venues in Britain *Touring:* Wales, England *Comments:* orchestra also performs for concerts and recording

Clonter Opera (Clonter Farm Music Trust/Clonter Opera For All)
Clonter Opera Theatre, Swettenham Heath, **Congleton** CW12 2LR
Tel: 1260-224 638 Fax: 1260-224 742
general manager & artistic director Jeffery Lockett; musical director t.b.a.; administrator Leanna Issac
Perfs: 20-30 (touring & residential) *No of Prods:* 2
Venues: Clonter Opera Theatre 285 *Touring:* UK – Festivals *Comments:* Clonter Farm Music Trust is a registered charity which aims to provide the best possible training and performance opportunities for young singers embarking on professional careers; Clonter Opera For All extends this work to the wider community; educational workshops in primary and secondary schools undertaken

Scottish Opera
39, Elmbank Crescent, **Glasgow (Scotland)** G2 4PT
Tel: 141-248 4567 Fax: 141-221 8812
Internet: www.scottishopera.org.uk
E-Mail: s005@post.aramc.co.uk
general director Adrian Trickie; music director Richard Armstrong; director of planning Jenny Slack; head of press and marketing Roberta Doyle; head of fundraising & sponsorship Catrinona Reynolds
Perfs: 69 *No of Prods:* 8(3 new) *Venues:* Theatre Royal, Glasgow; Edinburgh Festival Theatre; His Majesty's Theatre, Aberdeen, Sunderland Empire Theatre *Touring:* national *Comments:* small-scale opera productions & concerts; educational outreach programmes

Opera North
Grand Theatre, 46 New Briggate, **Leeds** LS1 6NU
Tel: 113-243 9999/244 5326 (info line)
Fax: 113-243 5745(technical)/ 244 0418 (publicity)
Internet: www.operanorth.co.uk/operanorth/
general director Richard Mantle; music director Steven Sloane; head of music James Holmes; controller of planning Christine Jane Chibnall; acting chorus master Philip Sunderland; orchestra & concerts manager Malcom Wane-Holland; press officer Shona Galletly; technical director Rick Green
Perfs: 110 (opera) 25 (orchestral) 50 (community & education projects) *No of Prods:* 9 (2 new) *Venues:* Grand Theatre 1461; Palace Theatre, Manchester 1942; Theatre Royal Nottingham 1104; Theatre Royal, Newcastle 1190; York Theatre Royal *Touring:* England

Modern Music Theatre Troupe
10 Lime Grove, Blady, **Leicester** LE8 4GS
Tel: 116-278 8326 Fax: 116-278 8326
Internet: www.mmtt.co.uk
E-Mail: caro@mmtt.co.uk
artistic directors Caroline Sharman, Christopher Newell; composer in association Paul Barker
Perfs: 20 *No of Prods:* 3 (including 1 digital opera and 1 touring opera) *Venues:* arts centre, concert halls, theatres and leisure centres capacity 300 to 500
Touring: national, international
Comments: MMTT creates & produces new music theatre with an integrated artistic credo: including at various times dance, theatre, circus, music, instrumental, vocal & fine arts and multi-media

Glyndebourne Festival Opera
Glyndebourne, **Lewes** BN8 5UU
Tel: 1273-812 321/815 000 (information line)
Fax: 1273-812 783
Internet: www.glyndbourne.com
general director Nicholas Snowman; music director Sir Andrew Davis CBE; director of productions Graham Vick
Perfs: 70-80 *No of Prods:* 6 (incl 2 new per year)
Venues: Glyndebourne Opera House 1200

Glyndebourne Touring Opera
Glyndebourne, **Lewes** BN8 5UU
Tel: 1273-812 321/815 000 (information line)
Fax: 1273-812 783
Internet: www.glyndbourne.com
administrator Helen McCarthy; music director Louis Langrée
Perfs: 45 *No of Prods:* 3 *Touring:* Glyndebourne, UK

First Act Musical Company
18 Ballymacash Road,
Lisburn (Northern Ireland) BT28 3BR
Tel: 1846-662 183 Fax: 1846-662 183
director Peter Kennedy
Perfs: 2 *No of Prods:* 2 *Venues:* Ulster Hall 1800
Touring: Ireland

Broomhill Opera
Wilton's Music Hall, Graces Alley, Wellclose Square,
London E1 8JB
Tel: 20-7702 9555 Fax: 20-7702 9555
E-Mail: opera@broomhill.demon.co.uk
artistic director Mark Dornford-May; music director Charles Hazlewood; producer Flora Smith
Venues: Horsham 500; Wilton's Music Hall 300
Comments: concentrating on new opera productions; 2-month season (July-August) and Autumn/Winter season at Wiltons; see also Venues (Wilton's Music Hall)

D'Oyly Carte Opera Company
Powerhouse, 6 Sancroft Street, **London** SE11 5UD
Tel: 20-7793 7100 Fax: 20-7793 7300
Internet: www.doylycarte.org.uk
E-Mail: mail@doylycarte.org.uk
administration manager Ian Martin; technical manager Jon Sherwood
Perfs: 100 *No of Prods:* 2 new *Venues:* all major UK theatres capacity 2000 *Touring:* UK tour annually
Comments: orchestra size 24-30; orchestral and operatic concerts; education work

English Bach Festival Trust
15 South Eaton Place, **London** SW1W 9ER
Tel: 20-7730 5925 Fax: 20-7730 1456
E-Mail: english.bachfestival@which.net
director Lina Lalandi OBE
Venues: small-large scale from opera houses – ancient buildings *Touring:* national and abroad at international festivals; Baroque opera productions in London and abroad *Comments:* see also Early Music and Festivals

English National Opera
London Coliseum, St Martin's Lane, **London** WC2N 4ES
Tel: 20-7836 0111/7632 8300 (box office) Fax: 20-8736 8379/497 9052 (PR)
Internet: www.eno.org
general director Nicholas Payne; music director Paul Daniel; executive director Russell Willis Taylor; head of press Jane Livingston; director public relations Maggie Sedwards; production controller Terri-Jayne Griffin; casting director John Barry
Perfs: 180 *No of Prods:* 10 new, 11 revivals *Venues:* Coliseum 2356 *Comments:* The Studio is dedicated to the development and performance of new opera and music theatre; the only venture of its kind in the country, the Studio supports, commissions and performs new work for the operatic stage, providing an environment for composers and artists to collaborate at every stage in the creative process and to develop their skills, also run the Baylis Programme which is the Education, Community and Outreach team at English National Opera, dedicated to making opera and theatre accessible for people of all ages and cultural and economic backgrounds

English Touring Opera
250A Kennington Lane, **London** SE11 5RD
Tel: 20-7820 1131/7820 1141 Fax: 20-7735 7008
director of productions Robert Chevara; music director Andrew Greenwood; chief executive Katharine Herbert; marketing manager John Haywood; production manager t.b.a.; education manager Paul Reeve; development director t.b.a.
Perfs: 100-110 *No of Prods:* 4 (2 new)
Venues: capacity up to 1000 *Touring:* England
Comments: 26-30 member orchestra

European Chamber Opera
60c Kyverdale Road, Stoke Newington, **London** N16 7AJ
Tel: 20-8806 4231/1949/9996 Fax: 20-8806 4465
Internet: www.echo-opera.com
artistic director Stefan Sanchez; administrator Tamsin Stanley; orchestral director Lara Taylor; echoreverb director Darren Royston; rpr Jane Read
Perfs: 100 *No of Prods:* 5 (4 new) *Venues:* stately homes capacity 400 up to 1500, theatres, parks, schools, opera houses *Touring:* Far East, France, Italy, England (stately homes + theatre venues), Wales *Comments:* no theatre company attached, but there is the European Chamber Ensemble; Opera Galas performed; Opera performed with chorus, also do own sound and lighting on large scale events

Music Theatre London
Chertsey Chambers, 12 Mercer Street,
London WC2H 9QD
Tel: 20-7240 0919 Fax: 20-7240 0805
administrator Andrew Taylor; artistic director Tony Britten
Venues: Lyric Theatre 550 *Touring:* UK and abroad
Comments: standard operatic repertoire; casting policy of actors who sing rather than opera singers; all works performed in contemporary English translation; chamber ensemble accompaniment of 6-9 players, no performances during 2000 as they are working on future productions

Opera Circus Ltd
1 Aberdeen House, 22 Highbury Grove, **London** N5 2EA
Tel: 20-7288 1222 Fax: 20-7228 1220
E-Mail: operacircu@aol.com
artistic director Tina Ellen Lee ; associate director David Pearl; general manager Tracey T. McAteer
Perfs: 85 *No of Prods:* 3 (2 new) *Venues:* indoor and outdoor venues to live accompaniment; capacity 100-800 *Touring:* national and international *Comments:* classically trained opera singers who have also studied physical theatre – mime, commedia dell'arte, acrobatics & improvisation

Opera Holland Park
Central Library, Phillimore Walk, **London** W8 7RX
Tel: 20-7361 3364 Fax: 20-3761 2317
E-Mail: ohp@dial.pipex.com
director of libraries & arts Chris Koster; head of public services John McEachen; principal arts office Gabriel West; theatre manager Mick Goggin; marketing & publicity Michael Volpe; administrator Ray Bingle
Perfs: 20 *No of Prods:* 4 (3 new) *Venues:* Holland Park Theatre 826 *Comments:* also art galleries in the park: the Icehouse and the Orangery

Opera Rara
134-146 Curtain Road, **London** EC2A 3AR
Tel: 20-7613 2858 Fax: 20-7613 2261
Internet: www.opera-rara.com/
E-Mail: operarara@amity.co.uk
musicologist Robert Roberts; artistic director Patric Schmid; managing director Stephen Revell
Venues: Henry Wood Hall/All Saints, London
Comments: see also Recorded Media

Opera Restor'd
54 Astonville Street, **London** SW18 5AJ
Tel: 20-8870 7649 Fax: 20-8516 6313
musical director Peter Holman; artistic directors Peter Holman, Jack Edwards; administrator Caroline Anderson
Perfs: 10 *No of Prods:* 4 [incl. 1 new: double bill – La Cantarina (Haydn) & La Dirindina (Scarlatti)]
Venues: small-mid scale ranging from theatres to stately homes *Touring:* UK and Europe *Comments:* touring company; 1 education project; 1 recording; orchestra also performs for concerts; 3 recordings on Hyperion

Royal Opera, The
Covent Garden, **London** WC2E 9DD
Tel: 20-7240 1200 Fax: 20-7240 2954
Internet: www.royaloperahouse.com
executive director Michael Kaiser; director Elaine Padmore; music director Bernard Haitink (from 2002 Antonio Pappano); artistic director Richard Jarman; head of press Amanda Jones; director of marketing, press and publications Richard Shaw; director of casting Peter Mario Katona
Comments: the Royal Opera House reopens in Dec 99; the opening season's productions will include Falstaff, Le Grand Macabre, Gawain, The Nutcracker and Coppelia, for more information of the full season please contact the box office on 20-7304 4000, the house will also offer a wide range of free events and will be open for visitors from 10am-3pm (Mon-Sat)

Selfmade Music Theatre
Basement Flat, 16D Hampstead Hill Gardens,
London NW3 2PL
Tel: 20-7794 3610 Fax: 20-7794 3610
artistic administrator Michael Christie; artistic director Susannah Self
Perfs: 3 – 6 *No of Prods:* 1-3
Venues: range from pub theatres and large private studio spaces to arts centres, small halls and theatres capacity 70 to 300 *Touring:* nationally, internationally
Comments: raises part of its operating funds from the proceeds of exhibitions of artwork; aims to present new works of music theatre; productions are small, portable and flexible as to space and length of programme, and are designed to appeal to a wide variety of audiences, vocal workshops available

VOCEM electric voice theatre
39 Birnam Road, **London** N4 3LJ
Tel: 20-7281 0672 Fax: 20-7281 0672
E-Mail: frances@birnam39freeserve.co.uk
aritistic director Frances M Lynch; sound design engineers Alan Burgess, Paul Bull; lighting design engineer Charlotte McClelland; marketing director Herbie Clarke
Perfs: 25 *No of Prods:* 2 new *Venues:* schools to small-scale theatres and concert halls capacity 50 to 1000
Comments: no instruments used (except when collaborating with another company) only voices with live and pre-recorded electronics; Vocem Evt is interested in performing new works for voice (plus instruments where relevant) as part of outside productions where the vocal demands are unusual or difficult

First Act Opera International Ltd.
The Thatched House, West Farleigh,
Maidstone ME15 0NJ
Tel: 1622-747 762 Fax: 1622-745 276
Internet: members.tripod.com/~operavox/
E-Mail: figaro@globalnet.co.uk
managing director Elaine Holden; musical director Kenneth Roberts; producer John von Nuding
Perfs: 130 *No of Prods:* 5 (L'elisir d'amore, Cosi fan tutte, Tosca, Carmen, Eugene Onegin (in Russian), Mister Butterfly *Venues:* all types, for example stately homes, country houses, halls, theatres (including open-air)
Touring: East Asia, Europe, North America, Japan
Comments: non-profit distributing company limited by guarantee; determined to ensure opera reaches a wider audience; recordings available

Opera Europe
European Opera Centre, 68 Grosvenor Street,
Manchester M1 7EW
Tel: 161-273 8111 Fax: 161-273 8222
chairman Sir John Manduell CBE; managing director Kenneth Baird; artistic consultant Helga Schmidt; head of music staff Bryan Evans; artistic administrator Nicholas Winter
Perfs: average 40/year *No of Prods:* 1-2/year + associated concert and recording activity *Touring:* selected EU member States *Comments:* funded by the European Union and in partnership with major European opera companies, the organisation aims above all to provide a secure route from advanced training to professional employment

Mayfield Chamber Opera
Wilton's Music Hall, Grace's Alley, **Mayfield** TN20 6AL
Tel: 1435-872 187 Fax: 1435-872 187
Internet: www.landini.org/mayfield
E-Mail: m.fields@cwcom.net
musical and artistic director Michael Fields
Perfs: 10-15 *No of Prods:* 3 *Venues:* capacity up to 600
Comments: formed to present perfs of music-dramas from Baroque period and earlier

Longborough Festival Opera
New Banks Fee, Longborough,
Moreton-in-Marsh GL56 0QF
Tel: 1451-830 292 Fax: 1451-830 605
E-Mail: longboroughfestivalopera@btinternet.com
directors Martin Graham, Lizzie Graham; pr & marketing Tei Williams (tel: 1865-883 139/884 240, fax: 1865-884 011, email: tei@artsmarketing.demon.co.uk); sponsorship manager Susan Foster (tel: 1865-735 201)
Venues: converted barn cap 470 (stalls 370, boxes 100)
Touring: national
Comments: company formed annually for the Longborough Festival; see also Venues and Festivals

London Opera Players
Broadmeade Copse, Westwood Lane,
Wanborough GU3 2JN
Tel: 1483-811 004 Fax: 1483-811 721
managing director Elisabeth Parry; music director Peter Gellhorn; promotion Peter Andrews; marketing Jean Taylor; secretarial & accounts Jane McKinnon; stage Derek Chappel, Jennie Chappel
Perfs: 30 per annum *No of Prods:* 6 *Venues:* touring venues, UK (theatres, festivals, schools, charity performances, stately homes etc) up to 1000 *Touring:* UK
Comments: tour with orchestra 10-14 players depending on Opera; also operatic concerts, workshops and interactive performances for schools

YUGOSLAVIA (+381)

Due to the war in Kosovo we have been unable to update the following entries for Yugoslavia

Opera of the National Theatre
Narodno Pozoriste – Opera
Francuska 3, 11000 **Belgrade**
Tel: 11-624 565 Fax: 11-622 560
director Dejan Miladinovic

Opera of the Serbian National Theatre
Srpsko Narodno Pozoriste – Opera
Pozorisni Trg 1, 21000 **Novi Sad**
Tel: 21-22455 Fax: 21-623 391
director Branislav Jatic

Customer Service Page

Dear colleague

All the staff here at Arts Publishing International are continually working to ensure that the PAYE is the most valuable and easy-to-use reference book for the European performing arts market. With your individual requirements you are in the best position to tell us if the PAYE meets your needs. We would therefore be most grateful if you could send us your suggestions and comments on the book.

As well as your suggestions we would appreciate your help in keeping our records as accurate as possible. Please use this page to request information, amend your editorial entry for the next edition or send us new editorial entries. Please direct your mail to: **Editorial Department, Arts Publishing International Ltd., Lime Wharf, Vyner Street, London E2 9DJ, England** or contact us by telephone **(+44) 20 8709 9050**, by fax **(+44) 20 8709 9080** or by e-mail on **paye@api.co.uk**

Amendments

1 Amendments to existing entries in the Performing Arts Yearbook for Europe 2000

Please note: You will receive our formal entry correction letter to update your entry for the PAYE 2001 in May 2000. This space should be used if your information changes after you have returned our request for correct information next May.

Section (eg opera, dance, services and suppliers)

Original company name

New company name (if applicable)

New address

New telephone numbers

New fax numbers

New e-mail address/web site

Changes to personnel

Comments

New Entries

2 New entries for Performing Arts Yearbook for Europe 2001

Please note: All entries are free of charge, but are included at the Editor's discretion

Section

Company name

Address

Telephone numbers

Fax numbers

E-mail address/web site

Personnel

Comments

Mailing

3 Please complete the following section if you want information on our other publications, conferences or special events*

Organisation

Name

Job Title

Address

Tel Fax

E-mail

- The information you have provided may be stored and used under the provisions of the Data Protection Act. If you prefer not to receive mail from third parties please tick this box ☐

Dance

Dance
The companies listed here represent a broad range of type and size. The only common feature is that virtually all are in receipt of subsidy. Some of the German and Austrian ballet companies listed perform in theatres which present opera and drama and do not have an existence outside that theatre. **Within country the companies are ordered by city and alphabetically within city.**

Danse
Les compagnies de danse sont très variées en genre et en importance. Elles ont en commun le fait d'être presque toutes subventionnées. Quelques compagnies de ballet autrichiennes et allemandes sont liées à des théâtres qui accueillent aussi de l'opéra et du théâtre, et n'existent pas à l'exterieur de ce théâtre. **Pour chacque pays, les compagnies sont classées dans l'ordre des villes et par l'ordre alphabétique.**

Tanz
In diesem Kapitel werden verschiedenartige Tanzgruppen aufgeführt. Nahezu alle dieser Tanzgruppen sind subventioniert. Einige der aufgeführten deutschen und österreichischen Ballettensembles arbeiten in Mehrspartentheatern und sind nicht außerhalb des Theaters tätig. **Die Einträge für alle Staaten sind alphabetisch nach Stadtnamen und innerhalb der Stadt alphabetisch nach Namen geordnet.**

Compagnie di Danza e Balletto
Le compagnie di danza da noi elencate sono di diverso tipo e grandezza. L'unico fattore che ne accomuna alcune é che ricevono un sussidio statale. Alcune compagnie di balletto Tedesche ed Austriache enumerate in questa sezione tengono i propri spettacoli soltanto in teatri d'opera e prosa e non hanno alcuna attivitá al di fuori di queste sedi. **L'ordine alfabetico all'interno di ogni Paese segue i nomi delle cittá e a sua volta i nomi delle varie compagnie.**

Danza

Las compañías que están listadas aquí representan una amplia gama en cuanto a tipo y tamaño. El único factor común es que casi todas reciben subvención estatal. Algunas de las compáñías de ballet alemanas y austriacas actuan unicamente en las salas en las que representan ópera o teatro. **Dentro de cada país las compañías están ordenadas por ciudades siguiendo un orden alfabético dentro de cada ciudad.**

Dance (무용)
종류 및 크기가 다른 광범위한 단체들이 기재되었다. 이들 단체들이 가진 단 한 가지 공통점은 거의 모두가 보조금을 받는 다는 사실이다. 여기 나온 몇몇 독일 및 오스트리아 발레단들은 오페라나 연극 극장에서 공연하는 단체들로서 그 극장 밖에서는 존재하지 않는다. **리스트는 국가별, 도시별, 그리고 다시 알파벳순으로 기재되었다.**

舞蹈
这里列出的公司展示了一系列各种的公司类型和规模。这些公司唯一的共同特征就是实际上它们都有津贴。一些列出的德国和奥地利芭蕾舞公司只在戏剧院上演歌剧和戏剧，而不外出演出。**在每个国家里公司是按城市的顺序来排列的，在每一城市里公司又是按字母顺序来排列的。**

舞踏
ここでは様々なタイプ、規模の舞踏団体を掲載しました。唯一の共通点は、ほとんどすべての団体が助成を受けているということです。ここに記載されたドイツ、オーストリアのバレエ団のいくつかは、オペラと演劇を公演する劇場でのみ活動し、劇場外では存在しないものも含まれます。**リストは国、都市別で、都市内ではアルファベット順に記載されています。**

ALBANIA (+355)

Albanian State Ballet
Trupat e baletit / Balley
Sheshi Skenderbej, **Tirana**
Tel: 42-26747
artistic director Kozeta Bakiu

Folk State Ensemble, The
Sheshi Skynderbej, **Tirana**
Tel: 42-25848
artistic director Arian Avrazi

Theatre of Opera and Ballet
Skenderbej square, **Tirana**
Tel: 42-26747 Fax: 42-24753
general director Vasil S. Tole (tel: 42-27471/74127, fax: 42-24753)
Dancers: 40 *Type:* ballet
Comments: see also Opera and Orchestras

ARMENIA (+374)

Armenian State Dance Ensemble
54 Toumanian Street, 375001 **Yerevan**
Tel: 2-581 752/426/260 888
artistic director Souren Chanchurian

Choreographic State Ensemble Friendship
Aram Khachaturian Concert Hall, 46 Mashtots Avenue, 375019 **Yerevan**
Tel: 2-565 307 Fax: 2-151 055/581 142
artistic director & chief ballet master Norair Mehrabian

National Opera and Ballet Theatre of Armenia
58 Tumanian Street, 375001 **Yerevan**
Tel: 2-586 311/527 992/565 803 Fax: 2-527 992
chief choreograph Villen Galstian; artistic director Gegham Grigorian
Comments: see also Opera

AUSTRIA (+43)

Ballett des Stadttheaters Baden bei Wien
Theaterplatz 7, 2500 **Baden bei Wien**
Tel: 2252-48338 Fax: 2252-483 3850
Internet: www.baden-bei-wien.at/stadtheater
E-Mail: stadtheater@baden-bei-wien.at
Intendant Kammersängerin Kales-Wallner; Ballettmeisterin Bohdan Simova; Verwaltungs Direktor Reg. Rat. Wilfried Frankmann (Regierungsrat); musikalische Leitung Franz Josef Breznik
Dancers: 10 *Perfs:* 147 (inc. musicals) *No of Prods:* 8 (own) + 4 guest *Venues:* Stadttheater 702, Sommerarena 657
Comments: see also Opera and Drama

Vereinigte Bühnen Graz – Ballett
Kaiser Josef-Platz 10, 8010 **Graz**
Tel: 316-8008/1928 Fax: 316-800 8586
Internet: www.buehnen-graz.com
E-Mail: info@buehnen-graz.com
Intendant Dr Gerhard Brunner; Ballettdirektorin Linda Papworth
Dancers: 24 *Perfs:* 10 (ballet) *No of Prods:* 1 *Type:* classic, modern ballet, musicals, operetta *Accomp:* orchestra and recorded *Venues:* Opernhaus 1424 (1224 seated & 200 standing), Schauspielhaus 564, Next Liberty 350
Comments: see also Opera, Orchestras and Drama

Tiroler Landestheater – (Tanztheater)
Rennweg 2, Postfach 134, 6020 **Innsbruck**
Tel: 512-52074 Fax: 512-52074-333
Internet: www.landestheater.at
E-Mail: tiroler@landestheater.at
Leiter des Tanztheaters Maria Luise Jaska; Musikdirektor Georg Schmöhe; Intendant Brigitte Fassbaender
Dancers: 12 *Perfs:* 40-50 *No of Prods:* 3 *Type:* modern *Accomp:* live/recorded *Venues:* Großes Haus 801, Kammerspiele 250
Comments: see also Opera and Drama

Ballett des Landestheaters Linz
Promenade 39, 4020 **Linz**
Tel: 732-7611-0 Fax: 732-7611 308
Internet: linz.info.at/landestheater
E-Mail: landestheater@linz.info.at
Intendant Dr Michael Klügl; Balletdirektor Robert Poole; kaufmänn. Direktor Dr Gerbert Schwaighofer
Dancers: 14 *No of Prods:* 4 *Type:* ballet *Accomp:* recorded *Venues:* Grosses Haus 756, Kammerspiele 421, Eisenhand 100 *Comments:* see also Opera, Drama and Orchestras (Bruckner Orchester Linz)

Erika Gangl Tanzkompagnie
c/o Tanzstudio Erika Gangl, Bockgasse 2, 4020 **Linz**
Tel: 732-658 6460 Fax: 732-600 103
künstlerische Leitung & Choreographie Erika Gangl, Marina Koraiman; musikalische Leitung Prof. Mag. Dr Alfred Peschek; Öffentlischkeitsarbeit Mag. Oliver Kojan
Dancers: 5 *No of Prods:* 6-7 (all new)
Type: modern, classical *Accomp:* live, recorded
Venues: Bergtheater im Tanzstudio Erika Gangl 120
Touring: national, international
Comments: cooperation with Neues Ensemble Linz

Ballett des Salzburger Landestheaters
Schwarzstrasse 22, 5020 **Salzburg**
Tel: 662-871 512/43 Fax: 662-8715 1213
Internet: www.peterbreuer.com
E-Mail: info@peterbreuer.com
Intendant Lutz Hochstraate; Ballettdirektor Peter Breuer; Ballettmeister Eric Assandri
Dancers: 12 for small productions, 24 for large productions Perfs: 50-90 No of Prods: 3-5 Type: from classical to modern Accomp: live, tape *Venues:* Landestheater 724 *Touring:* Germany, Italy, Brazil, Austria
Comments: see also Opera and Drama

Ballet der Volksoper Wien
Währingerstrasse 78, 1090 **Wien**
Tel: 1-51444-3244 Fax: 1-51444-3215
Internet: www.volksoper.at
E-Mail: tickets@volksoper.at
Direktor Dominique Mentha; Leiterin Liz King; Dramaturg Manfred Biskup; Balletkoordination Elisabeth Bolius; Training Judy Reyn, Bettina Wagner, Liz King
Dancers: 28 *Perfs:* 10 (ballet) + 170 (including opera, operetta & musical) *No of Prods:* 2 *Type:* classical, jazz, modern *Accomp:* live, recorded *Venues:* Volksoper 1313
Touring: national, international
Comments: see also Opera, Dance and Orchestras

Compagnie Smafu
Lenaugasse 19/11, 1080 **Wien**
Tel: 1-405 1732 Fax: 1-405 1732
E-Mail: kunstgriff@xpoint.at
manager Rainer Warrings; artistic director Elisabeth Orlowsky
Dancers: 1-6 *No of Prods:* 5-6 *Type:* contemporary *Accomp:* live, recorded *Touring:* Europe

Lux Flux
Schleifmühlgasse 13/24, 1040 **Wien**
Tel: 1-581 5866 Fax: 1-581 5866
E-Mail: Luxflux@to.or.at
organisation & performance Inge Kaindlstorfer, Jack Hauser, Annette Pfefferkorn
Dancers: 1-6 *No of Prods:* 6 *Type:* performance *Accomp:* live, recorded *Touring:* Europe, Russia, Africa

Tanz Atelier Wien
Neustiftgasse 38/7, 1070 **Wien**
Tel: 1-522 6044 Fax: 1-523 3994
E-Mail: danzatelierwien@aon.at
coordination Bettina Kogler, Gertraud Morocutti; artistic director Sebastian Prantl; music director Cicilia Li
Dancers: 1-10 or 12 *No of Prods:* 1-2 *Type:* choreographic and inter-arts projects *Accomp:* mainly live *Venues:* Tanz Atelier Wien 48 *Touring:* Europe, America, Far East
Comments: non-profit organisation in search of new frontiers regarding contemporary dance

Tanztheater Homunculus
Pfeilgasse 21112, 1080 **Wien**
Tel: 1-409 3774 Fax: 1-409 3774
Künstlerischer Leiter Manfred Aichinger; Leitung und PR Nikolaus Selimov; Technische Leiterin Silvia Auer; Komponist Martin Kratochwil
Dancers: 10 *Perfs:* 40 *No of Prods:* 4 *Type:* contemporary

Wiener Staatsopernballett
Opernring 2, 1010 **Wien**
Tel: 1-5144 42501 Fax: 1-5144 42518
Staatsoperndirektor Ioan Holender; Ballettdirektor und Chefchoreograph Renato Zanella; Stellvertreterin des Ballettdirektors Admininstration Traude Klöckl; Ballettmeister Carlos Gacio; Leiterin des Ballettbetriebsbüros Brigitte Zehetgruber; Ballettdramaturgie und Presse Alfred Oberzaucher
Dancers: 80 *Perfs:* 53 *No of Prods:* 10 (2 new) *Type:* classical and modern ballets *Accomp:* live *Venues:* Staatsoper 1709, Odeon 300 *Touring:* Spain
Comments: see also Burgtheater, Wiener Kammeroper; see also Opera

AZERBAIDZHAN (+994)

Baku Choreography School
Byul-Byul Avenue 56, 370014 **Baku**
Tel: 12-957 807
director t.b.a.

Ballet of the Azerbaidzhan State Academic Opera and Ballet
Nizamy St. 95, 370000 **Baku**
Tel: 12-931 651
ballet master Akhundova Rafiga Hadji kizi
Comments: see also Opera

F Amirov State Song and Dance Ensemble of Azerbaidzhan
Istiglaliyat St. 2, 370001 **Baku**
Tel: 12-931 651
artistic director Gurbanov Garkhmaz Agababa oglu

State Dance Ensemble of Azerbaidzhan
Istiglaliyat St. 2, 370001 **Baku**
Tel: 12-957 520
artistic director Melikova Afak Suleyman kizi

State Song and Dance Ensemble 'Gek-Gel'
Atayevs St. 135, 374700 **Giandja**
Tel: 12-89522/85289
director Bayramov Adil Museib ogly

State Song and Dance Ensemble of the Nakchivan Autonomous Republic
Nakchivan
Tel: 12-8236 56898

BELARUS (+375)

Belarussian State Choreography Group Khoroshki
Belaruskij Gosudarstvennyj Chorjeografychjeskij Ansambl Khoroshki
pr. Franciska Skoryny 50, 220005 **Minsk**
Tel: 172-316 557 Fax: 172-316 052
director Nikolaj Dudchjenko

Minsk Classical Ballet Company
Objedinjenije Minskij Klassichjeskij Baljet
ul. Mjasnikova 44, 220050 **Minsk**
Tel: 172-209 907 Fax: 172-208 055
dirctor Rostislav Buzuk; head ballet mistress Nina Dyachjenko

National Academic Ballet Theatre of the Republic of Belarus
Nacionalnyj Akadjemicheskij Tjeatr Baljeta Rjespubliki Belarus
Pl. Parizhskoj Kommuny 1, 220029 **Minsk**
Tel: 172-340 036 Fax: 172-340 036
director Valjentin Elizarjev

State Dance Group of the Republic of Belarus
Gosudarstvjennyj Ansambl Tanca Rjespubliki Bjelaruss
pr. Franciska Skoryny 50, 220005 **Minsk**
Tel: 172-313 405 Fax: 172-847 184
director Valentin Dudkjevich

BELGIUM (+32)

Compagnie Aimé de Lignière
Desguinlie 90, B9l, 2018 **Antwerp**
Tel: 3-489 3948 Fax: 3-489 0833
E-Mail: a.deligniere@wordonline.be
administrative director Martine Tack; artistic director Aimé de Lignière; dance master Wini Jacobs
Dancers: 7-8 *Perfs:* 30-50 *No of Prods:* 3-4 *Type:* contemporary *Accomp:* live, recorded *Touring:* Europe, Asia, Japan, China

Royal Ballet of Flanders
Koninklijk Ballet van Vlaanderen
Kattendykdok-Westkaai 16, 2000 **Antwerp**
Tel: 3-234 3438 Fax: 3-233 5892
Internet: www.koninklijkballetvanvlaanderen.be
E-Mail: gi32423@online.be
general director Jan Vanderschoot; artistic director Robert Denvers; public relations & tour manager Nora Van Dessel; artistic director musicals Linda Lepomme; chief executive Roger Claeys; chairman John Cordier
Dancers: ballet: 50; musical: depends on production
Perfs: ballet: 100; musical 180 *No of Prods:* 5 *Type:* classical, modern ballet/musical *Accomp:* ballet: live, recorded; musical: live *Venues:* Theater 't Eilandje, Antwerp 302, Opera, Ghent 900

Troubleyn/Jan Fabre
Italielei 56, 2000 **Antwerp**
Tel: 3-201 1300 Fax: 3-233 1501
E-Mail: maai.meukens@troubleyn.be
managing director Barbara De Coninck; artistic director Jan Fabre; financial manager Maai Meukens
Dancers: varies *Perfs:* 50 *No of Prods:* 5 *Type:* dance, theatre *Accomp:* live & recorded *Venues:* Resident at deSingel (3 studios), Antwerp *Touring:* Belgium, Germany, France, Portugal, Spain, USA, Italy, Poland
Comments: alternative E-mail: barbara.deconinck@troubleyn.be; see also Drama

Un Oeuf is Un Oeuf / Biters Productions
c/o Gilles Monnart, Lammekensstraat 651, 2140 **Antwerp**
Tel: 3-272 3826 Fax: 3-272 3826
artistic director Gilles Monnart
Perfs: 30 *No of Prods:* 3 *Type:* contemporary dance theatre *Touring:* Belgium, France, Switzerland, Germany

Compagnie de Ballet Théâtre de l'Aube – Alix Riga
rue des Communes , 1475 **Baisy-Thy**
Tel: 67-780 585 Fax: 67-780 585
E-Mail: aden@skynet.be
administrator Antoine Panier; artistic director Alix Riga
Dancers: 5 *Perfs:* 15 *No of Prods:* 1 *Type:* contemporary *Accomp:* recorded *Venues:* Résidence Palace 500
Touring: Switzerland, Belgium

ALPHA
Av. Coghen 35, 1180 **Brussels**
Tel: 2-345 2693 Fax: 2-345 2693
choreographer & artistic director Avi Kaiser; administrator Carmen Mayo
Dancers: 1-5 *Perfs:* 8 *No of Prods:* 1
Type: modern dance-theatre *Accomp:* recorded
Touring: Germany, Israel, France, Netherlands

Compagnie Félicette Chazerand
Rue Vanderkindere 449, 1180 **Brussels**
Tel: 2-347 4949 Fax: 2-347 4949
directrice artistique Félicette Chazerand
Dancers: 3 *Perfs:* 20-30 *No of Prods:* 2
Type: contemporary, dance theatre *Accomp:* live, recorded *Venues:* Centre Culturel J Franck 400
Touring: national, international
Comments: organise training

Compagnie Michèle Anne De Mey
49 rue St. Josse, 1210 **Brussels**
Tel: 2-217 4127 Fax: 2-217 5167
Internet: www.uniscene.org/demey
E-Mail: cie.m/ma.demey@skynet.be
administrator t.b.a.; artistic director Michèle Anne De Mey
Dancers: up to 6 *Perfs:* 30-50 *No of Prods:* 2
Type: contemporary *Accomp:* recorded
Touring: national, international

Compagnie Mossoux-Bonté
3 rue Berckmans, 1060 **Brussels**
Tel: 2-538 9077 Fax: 2-538 5730
Internet: users.skynet.be/aden/dance/MossouxBonte.htm
E-Mail: cie.mossoux.Bonte@skynet.be
administrators Yves Degen, Martine Dara; artistic directors Nicole Mossoux, Patrick Bonté; public relations Martine Godat
Dancers: 1-7 *Perfs:* 30-40 *No of Prods:* 4
Type: dance-theatre *Accomp:* recorded
Touring: France, Belgium, Germany, Spain, Czech Republic, Egypt, Canada, England, Italy
Comments: the company is in residence at Charleri/Danses (Centre Chorégraphique de la Communauté Françoise de Belgique); films and video programme available

Compagnie Nadine Ganase
c/o Opening Night Productions a.s.b.l,
Rue Vandeweyer 63-65, 1030 **Brussels**
Tel: 2-245 2083 Fax: 2-245 2562
Internet: www.axel-danses.be/ganase.htm
E-Mail: n/ganase@hotmail.com
chorégraphe Nadine Ganase; administrator Philippe Franck
Dancers: 5 *Perfs:* 30 *No of Prods:* 3
Type: contemporary dance
Accomp: live, recorded
Touring: Belgium, France, Germany, UK, India

Compagnie Onnagata Rea
Quai à la Haille 7b7, 1000 **Brussels**
Tel: 2-511 7512/7514/7576/7532/7518/7524
Fax: 2-344 7360/7362/7319/7313/7318
Internet: www.uniscene.org/Pezzella/
E-Mail: bs743458@skynet.be
artistic director/choreograph Enzo Pezzella
Dancers: 6 *No of Prods:* 1 (for 2001)
Type: contemporary dance theatre
Accomp: recorded (always original music)
Touring: Belgium, France, Italy

Compagnie Pierre Droulers
19 rue des Ateliers, 1080 **Brussels**
Tel: 2-411 6629 Fax: 2-410 3051
E-Mail: pierre.droulers@pophst.unit.be
art director Pierre Droulers; production manager Christoph Slagmuylder
Dancers: per production *Perfs:* 20-50
No of Prods: 3 *Type:* contemporary
Accomp: recorded, live
Touring: France, Belgium, Switzerland, USA

Compagnie Thor
143 rue Philippe Baucq, 1040 **Brussels**
Tel: 2-223 2600 Fax: 2-646 5767
E-Mail: thor@skynet.be
administrator Laurent Henri; president Antoine Pickels; artistic director Thierry Smits
Dancers: 4 *Perfs:* 14+ *No of Prods:* 1
Type: contemporary, also theatre productions
Accomp: recorded
Touring: Belgium, Scotland, Netherlands

Company Karin Vyncke
Fortstraat 35, 1060 **Brussels**
Tel: 2-538 9426 Fax: 2-538 9426
E-Mail: karin.vyncke@ping.be
artistic director Karin Vyncke
Dancers: varies *Type:* contemporary
Accomp: recorded, live (original music)

Damaged Goods / Meg Stuart
OLV Van Vaakstraat 83, 1000 **Brussels**
Tel: 2-513 2540 Fax: 2-513 2248
Internet: www.damagedgoods.be
E-Mail: damagedgoods@village.uunet.be
artistic director Meg Stuart; company manager John Zwaenepoel; pr Ayco Duyster; technical director Ralf Nonn
Dancers: 7 *Perfs:* 60 *No of Prods:* 3
Type: contemporary dance *Accomp:* recorded
Touring: Europe, Eastern Europe

Idea – Compagnie José Besprosvany
Rue Félix Delhasse, 29, 1060 **Brussels**
Tel: 2-538 0535 Fax: 2-538 0535
Internet: users.skynet.be/idea
E-Mail: idea@skynet.be
artistic director José Besprosvany; pr Bénédicte Duhaut
Dancers: varies *Perfs:* 40+ *Type:* contemporary (combination of texts, dance, music), musical theatre *Accomp:* live, composition and interpretation *Touring:* international

Michèle Noiret – Compagnie Tandem
58, rue de la Lys, 1080 **Brussels**
Tel: 2-425 8937 Fax: 2-425 8939
E-Mail: MiNo@skynet.be
administrator Cathy Zarté; artistic directors Michèle Noiret, Bud Blumenthal; promotion Alexandra de Laminne
Dancers: 6-7 *Perfs:* 30-60 *No of Prods:* 4 (incl 1 new)
Type: contemporary *Accomp:* recorded, live *Venues:* Theatre les Tanneurs 400 *Touring:* Norway, Finland, Germany, Spain, Belgium, France, Israel *Comments:* also production of Bud Blumenthal work

Needcompany/Grace Ellen Barkey
Hooikaai 35, 1000 **Brussels**
Tel: 2-218 4075 Fax: 2-218 2317
Internet: needcompany.vgc.be
E-Mail: needcompany@skynet.be
artistic director Jan Lauwers; managing director Christel Simons; production manager Carl Gydé; administrator Christel Simons; assistant administrator An Van der Donckt
Dancers: 3 + 1 actor *Perfs:* 20 *No of Prods:* 1 *Type:* dance-theatre *Accomp:* recorded *Touring:* Europe, America
Comments: see also Drama

Rosas
Van Volxemlaan 164, 1190 **Brussels**
Tel: 2-344 5598 Fax: 2-343 5352
Internet: www.rosas.be
E-Mail: rosas@rosas.be
general director Kees Eyrond; artistic director Anne Teresa De Keersmaeker; administrator Guy Gypens; technical director Luc Galle
Dancers: 14 *Perfs:* 110 *No of Prods:* 8 *Type:* contemporary *Accomp:* live *Touring:* USA, Austria, Switzerland, Germany, France, Belgium, Finland, Netherlands, Portugal *Comments:* PARTS (Performing Arts Research and Training Studios)

Théâtre de la Balsamine
Ave. Félix Marchal 1, 1030 **Brussels**
Tel: 2-732 9618 (admin)/735 6468 (bookings)
Fax: 2-733 2302
E-Mail: balsamine@skynet.be
director Christian Machiels; administrator Michel van Slijpe
Perfs: 90 *No of Prods:* 6-7 *Accomp:* recorded *Venues:* currently building new theatre (opens); in 2000 performances will take place in various venues *Touring:* France *Comments:* only co-produce; see also Drama

Ultima Vez
Werfstraat 2, 1000 **Brussels**
Tel: 2-219 5528 Fax: 2-219 6802
Internet: www.ultimavez.com
E-Mail: ultim@ibm.net
manager Bart Van Langendonck; artistic director Wim Vandekeybus; tour administration Kristien de Coster
Dancers: 10 *Perfs:* 70 *No of Prods:* 1 *Type:* movement theatre, contemporary dance *Accomp:* live, recorded *Venues:* Luna Theatre 750 *Touring:* Europe, Asia, North America, South America

Ballet Novart
74 Avenue de L'Europe, 6000 **Charleroi**
Tel: 71-323 991 Fax: 71-302 742
Internet: www.uniscene.org/novart
general director Ohara Yuka
Dancers: 12-15 *Type:* neo-classical, contemporary
Accomp: live, recorded *Touring:* Belgium, France, Brazil

Compagnie Charleroi – Plan K/Danses Centre Choréographique de la Communauté Française de Belgique
45 rue du fort, 6000 **Charleroi**
Tel: 71-205 640 Fax: 71-205 649
Internet: www.charleroi-danses.be
E-Mail: contacts@charleroi-danses.be
director general Guy Rassel; artistic director Frédéric Flamand; coordinator Bernard Degroote
Dancers: 15 *No of Prods:* 1 every two years *Type:* contemporary *Accomp:* live, recorded *Venues:* Les Écuries (Charleroi) *Touring:* Belgium, Europe, Brazil, Mexico

Ballets C. de la B., Les
Citadellaan 40, 9000 **Gent**
Tel: 9-221 7501 Fax: 9-221 8172
E-Mail: info@lesballetsodela.be
manager Lieven Thyrion; artistic director Alain Platel; administrative director Herwi Onghena; tour managing & production directors Linda Suy, Ilse Joliet; assistant production manager Iris Raspoet; technical director Gerd Van Looy; administration Erna Van Akoleyen; choreographers Koan Augustijnen, Christine De Smedt, Alain Platel, Hans Van Den Broeck
Dancers: 19 *Perfs:* 150 *No of Prods:* 4 *Type:* dance-theatre
Accomp: live *Touring:* Europe, America, Australia, Latin America *Comments:* contact Frans Brood Production
Tel: 9-234 1212, Fax: 9-265 9650

Hush Hush Hush, The Hip Hop Collective
Frans Brood Productions, Muinklaan, 10, 9000 **Gent**
Tel: 9-234 1212 Fax: 9-265 9650
Internet: www.fransbrood.com
E-Mail: info@fransbrood.com
director Pascal Nicolas
Dancers: 8 *Perfs:* 80 *No of Prods:* 1 *Type:* street dance, hip hop & contemporary *Accomp:* live/recorded
Touring: Europe *Comments:* managed by Frans Brood Productions

As Palavras – Compagnie Claudio Bernando
c/o Centre Culturel de La Région De Mons,
8 rue des Arbalestriers, 7000 **Mons**
Tel: 65-355 664 Fax: 65-355 743
administration Klaus Ludwig
Dancers: varies *No of Prods:* 2 *Type:* dance theatre, contemporary *Accomp:* live, recorded *Touring:* Europe, Brazil, Mexico, USA

BOSNIA & HERZEGOVINA (+387)

National Theatre Sarajevo
Obala Kulina Bana 9, 71000 **Sarajevo**
Tel: 71-445 138/665 960/663 647 Fax: 71-445 138
director Tvrtko Kulenovic; director of opera & ballet Pasa Gackic; manager of ballet ensemble Tefeda Abazovic
Comments: see also Drama, Opera

BULGARIA (+359)

State Ensemble for Folk Songs and Dance Pirin
1 Georgi Izmirliev Square, 2700 **Blagoevgrad**
Tel: 73-23893/22236/24188 Fax: 73-23893
director Prof Kiril Stefanov
Dancers: choir 26, orchestra 15, dancers 43 *Perfs:* 120
Type: folk music, songs and dances from West Bulgaria, and other Folk regions in the country
Touring: national, international

Opera & Philharmonic Society
2 Kliment Orhidski Str., 8000 **Bourgas**
Tel: 56-43057 Fax: 56-42698
director Rossen Grouev
Dancers: 27 *Perfs:* 80 *Type:* contemporary and classical ballets *Accomp:* tape

State Ensemble for Folk Songs and Dances Dobroudja
etno.-kv. Staria Dobritch, 9300 **Dobritch**
Tel: 58-22402 Fax: 58-42024
artistic director Kostadin Buradjiev
Dancers: 28 *Perfs:* 80 *No of Prods:* 1 *Type:* folk music, songs and dances from North-East Bulgaria and other folk regions in the country

Opera & Philharmonic Society
19 Gurko Str., 4000 **Plovdiv**
Tel: 32-235 198 Fax: 32-263 064
director Borislav Ivanov
Dancers: 25 *Perfs:* 20 *Type:* contemporary ballet
Accomp: tape

State Folk Ensemble Trakia
1 Dame Gruev Str., 4000 **Plovdiv**
Tel: 32-773 876/260 161 Fax: 32-767 127
artistic director Daniela Djeneva
Dancers: 30 *Perfs:* 100 *No of Prods:* 1 *Type:* folk music, songs and dances from South Bulgaria and other regions in the country

Kapanski Ensemble for Folk Songs and Dances
40 Cherna Str, 7200 **Razgrad**
Tel: 84-33081 Fax: 84-28458
artistic director Alexander Hristov
Dancers: 28 *Perfs:* 65 *No of Prods:* 2 *Type:* folk music, songs and dances from North-East Bulgaria and other folk regions in the country

Opera & Philharmonic Society
11 Dragan Tzankov Str., 7000 **Rousse**
Tel: 82-227 902
director Michael Anguelov
Dancers: 25 *Perfs:* 14 *No of Prods:* 1
Type: classical and modern ballet

Ballet Arabesque
3 Panaiot Volov Str., 1000 **Sofia**
Tel: 2-437 754 Fax: 2-620 578
director Kalina Bogoeva
Dancers: 20 *Perfs:* 60 *No of Prods:* 2 *Type:* contemporary and modern ballet *Accomp:* tape *Venues:* State Music Theatre 1000 *Touring:* national and international

National Folklore Ensemble Philip Koutev
3 Slaveikov Square, 1000 **Sofia**
Tel: 2-879 720/882 180 Fax: 2-879 965
director Elena Kouteva
Dancers: 18 + 18 women's choir + 15 orchestra *Perfs:* 100
No of Prods: 1 *Type:* Folk music and dances

National Opera Sofia
30 Doundoukov Str., 1000 **Sofia**
Tel: 2-877 011 Fax: 2-877 998
director Plamen Kartalov
Dancers: 111 *Perfs:* 42 *Type:* ballet, classical repertoire, but emphasis on modern dance *Accomp:* live

State Music Theatre Stefan Makedonski
3 Panaiot Volov Str., 1000 **Sofia**
Tel: 2-442 321/443 876 Fax: 2-441 342
director Svetozar Donev

State Opera and Ballet
30 Metodi Kusev Blvd., 6000 **Stara Zagora**
Tel: 42-41015
director Alexander Maroulev
Dancers: soloists/choir/orchestra/dancers: 230 *Perfs:* 30 *No of Prods:* 1 *Type:* contemporary ballet

Opera & Philhamonic Society
1 Nezavisimost Square, 9000 **Varna**
Tel: 52-602 086 Fax: 52-602 088
director Hristo Ignatov
Dancers: 30 *Perfs:* 32 *No of Prods:* 1 *Type:* classical and contemporary ballets

CROATIA (+385)

Ballet studio Zorin Dom
Gradsko kazaliste Zorin Dom
Domobranska 1, 47000 **Karlovac**
Tel: 47-614 950/951 Fax: 47-614 951
director Prof Ljerka Lackovic

Ballet of the Croatian National Theatre Ivan pl. Zajc
Balet Hrvatskog Narodnog Kazalista Ivana Pl. Zajca
Uljarska 1, 51000 **Rijeka**
Tel: 51-216 003 Fax: 51-212 600
ballet director Leo Stipanicic
Comments: venue address: Verdijeva bb, 51000 Rijeka

Ballet of the Croatian National Theatre Split
Balet Hrvatskog Narodnog Kazalista Split
Trg Gaja Bulata 1, 21000 **Split**
Tel: 21-585 999 Fax: 21-583 643
ballet director Boris Tonin

Ballet of the Croatian National Theatre Zagreb
Balet Hrvatskog Narodnog Kazalista Zagreb
Trg Marsala Tita 15, 10000 **Zagreb**
Tel: 1-482 8537/8550 Fax: 1-482 8537
ballet director Almira Osmanovic

Lado – Folk Dance Ensemble
Folklorni ansambl Lado
Trg Marsala Tita 6a, 10000 **Zagreb**
Tel: 1-482 8474 Fax: 1-482 8474
Internet: www.tel.hr/ador/lado
manager Davor Kovac
Dancers: 44 (includes dancer-singers and orchestra)

CZECH REPUBLIC (+420)

Brno National Theatre – Ballet
Národní divadlo v Brne – balet
Dvoráková 11, 657 70 **Brno**
Tel: 5-4221 5188/4232 11285 Fax: 5-4221 7045
Internet: www.ndbrno.cz
E-Mail: ndb@netbrno.cz
director Mojmír Weimann; ballet director Zdenek Prokes
Dancers: 74 *Perfs:* 70 *No of Prods:* 2 *Type:* classical and neo-classical ballet *Accomp:* live, recorded *Venues:* Janáckovo divadlo 1270, Mahenovo divadlo 577 *Comments:* see also Opera and Drama

MIMI FORTUNAE
Merhautova 51, 613 00 **Brno**
Tel: 5-4524 5221/2
E-Mail: fortunae@email.cz
director Hana Smrcková
Type: historical dance

South Bohemian Theatre – Ballet
Jihoceské divadlo – balet
dr. Stejskala 23, 370 46 **Ceské Budejovice**
Tel: 38-671 1111 Fax: 38-55640
Internet: www.mojweb.cz/jihocdivadlo
E-Mail: jihoceskedivadlo@iol.cz
director ing. Jan Mrzena; ballet director Libuse Králová
Perfs: 20 *No of Prods:* 2 *Type:* classical and neo-classical ballet *Accomp:* live, recorded *Venues:* capacity 249 *Comments:* see also Opera and Drama

F.X. Salda Theatre – Ballet
Divadlo F.X. Saldy – balet
Zhorelecká 344/5, 460 37 **Liberec**
Tel: 48-510 4288 Fax: 48-510 4181
Internet: www.info.lbc.cz/divadlo/uvodni.htm
E-Mail: mic@info.lbc.cz
director Frantisek Dána; ballet director Ljubov Dancenko
Dancers: 12 *Perfs:* 20 *No of Prods:* 2 *Type:* dance-theatre, expressionist dance *Accomp:* live, recorded *Venues:* capacity 637 *Comments:* see also Opera and Drama

Moravian Theatre – Ballet
Moravské divadlo – balet
Trida Svobody 33, 771 07 **Olomouc**
Tel: 68-522 3651 Fax: 68-522 5727
Internet: mdo.olomouc.cz
E-Mail: mdo@olomouc.com
director Václav Kozusník; director ballet Jirí Sekanina
Dancers: 25 *Perfs:* 30 *No of Prods:* 2 *Type:* classical and neo-classical ballet *Accomp:* live, recorded *Venues:* capacity 504 *Comments:* see also Opera and Drama

Moravian and Silesian National Theatre – Ballet
Národní divadlo moravskoslezské – balet
Cs. legií 14, 701 04 **Ostrava** 1
Tel: 69-611 2821 Fax: 69-611 2881
Internet: www.ndm.cz
E-Mail: narodni_divadlo_ostrava@oasanet.cz
director Ludek Golat; ballet director Igor Vejsada
Dancers: 54 *Perfs:* 50 *No of Prods:* 2 *Type:* classical ballet, dance theatre *Accomp:* live, recorded *Venues:* Divadlo Antonína Dvoráka 800, Divadlo Jirího Myrona 600 *Comments:* see also Opera and Drama

J.K. Tyl Theatre – Ballet
Divadlo J. K. Tyla – balet
Prokopova 14, 304 11 **Plzen**
Tel: 19-722 6743 Fax: 19-220 190
Internet: www.central.cz/djkt
E-Mail: reditelstvi@djkt.plzen.city.cz
director Jan Burian; ballet director Pavel Dumbala
Perfs: 25 *No of Prods:* 2 *Type:* classical and neo-classical ballet, dance theatre *Accomp:* live, recorded *Venues:* Velké divadlo 446, Komorní divadlo 444 *Comments:* see also Opera and Drama

Ballet Prague
Balet Praha
Legerova 75, 110 00 **Praha** 1
Tel: 2-2423 2401 Fax: 2-2423 2401
director ing. Antonín Schneider; artistic director Libor Vaculík
Dancers: 16 *Perfs:* 120 *No of Prods:* 3 *Type:* neo-classical *Accomp:* recorded *Comments:* touring company

Dance Theatre
Tanecní divadlo
U Vetrníku 3, 162 00 **Praha** 2
Tel: 2-2061 1980 Fax: 2-2061 0306
director Vlasta Schneiderová; manager Antonín Schneider
Type: classical & neo-classical ballet, dance-theatre *Comments:* school theatre (Dance Centre Prague)

Déja Donné Production
Nad Klikovkou 20, 150 00 **Praha** 5
Tel: 2-9004 3018 Fax: 2-9004 3018
artistic directors Lenka Flory (Czech Republic), Simone Sandroni (Italy); pr Heather McGadie; technical direction Jan Benes
Dancers: 4-6 *Type:* contemporary dance theatre *Touring:* national and international *Comments:* first international professional dance theatre company in the Czech Republic, offer workshops in performance locations

DOMINO dance company
Nechvilova 1843/5, 148 00 **Praha** 4
Tel: 2-792 6984 Fax: 2-793 5986
E-Mail: dancep@pha.inect.cz
director Lenka Ottová
Type: modern *Comments:* touring company

Duncan Centre
Branická 41/147, 140 00 **Praha** 4
Tel: 2-4446 1810 Fax: 2-4446 2354
Internet: www.osf.cz/dc
E-Mail: duncanct@mbox.vol.cz
director Eva Blazícková
Type: modern dance *Comments:* school theatre

Jiri Srnec's Black Theatre
Cerné divadlo Jirího Srnce
U. lékárny 597, 156 00 **Praha** 5
Tel: 2-5792 1835 Fax: 2-5792 1835
director Jirí Srnec
Perfs: 200 *No of Prods:* 1 *Type:* black theatre *Accomp:* recorded *Comments:* touring company

Laterna magika
Národni 4, 110 00 **Praha** 1
Tel: 2-2108 0111 Fax: 2-2222 2039
Internet: www.laterna.cz
E-Mail: info@laterna.cz
director Ing. Peter Tosovsky
Dancers: 42 *Perfs:* 300 *No of Prods:* 1 *Type:* combination of dance-theatre and dance movie *Accomp:* recorded *Venues:* capacity 395

Mime Theatre Alfred in courtyard
Divadlo mimu Alfred ve dvore
Fr. Krízka 36, 170 00 **Praha** 7
Tel: 2-2057 1584 Fax: 2-2057 1584
E-Mail: alfred@login.cz
artistic director Ctibor Turba; manager & technical producer Václav Mottl (603-468 489)
Dancers: varies *Perfs:* 150 *No of Prods:* 4 new *Type:* mime, movement theatre *Accomp:* recorded

Monika Rebcová Dance Company
Novy lesík 9, 162 00 **Praha** 6
Tel: 2-312 3569
artistic director Monika Rebcová
Type: modern

Movement Theatre 22
Pohybové divadlo 22
Fr. Kadlece 8, 180 00 **Praha** 8
Tel: 2-652 4655 Fax: 2-8384 2173
E-Mail: ztomes@seznam.cz
artistic chief Zdenek Tomes
Perfs: 150 *No of Prods:* 1 *Type:* movement theatre, pantomime *Accomp:* recorded

Petr Tyc – Contemporary Dance
Petr Tyc – Soudoby tanec
Na Smukyrce 12, 150 00 **Praha** 5
Tel: 2-5721 0402 Fax: 2-643 1169
Internet: web.iol.cz/tanectyc
E-Mail: TEC@iol.cz
director Petr Tyc
Dancers: varies *No of Prods:* 1 new *Type:* dance theatre *Accomp:* recorded *Comments:* touring company

PONEC
Tanec Praha, Jirsíkova 4, 186 00 **Praha** 8
Tel: 2-2421 9842 Fax: 2-231 9576
Internet: www.tanecpha.cz
E-Mail: ponec@tanec.pha.cz
director Karel Saffin
Type: modern

Prague Chamber Ballet
Prazsky komorní balet
Legerova 75, 111 21 **Praha** 1
Tel: 2-6731 1486 Fax: 2-6731 1034
directors Jirí Opela, Pavel Smok; artistic director Idbor Vaculík; manager Vladimír Cabalka
Dancers: 16 *Perfs:* 120 *No of Prods:* 1 *Type:* neo-classical *Accomp:* recorded *Comments:* touring company

Prague Festival Ballet
Prazsky Festivalovy Ballet, **Praha**
Comments: see entry under London address

Prague National Theatre – Ballet
Národní divaldo – balet
PO Box 865, 112 30 **Praha** 1
Tel: 2-2108 0111/2491 4204 Fax: 5-2422 6262
Internet: www.anet.cz/nd
E-Mail: ntprague@ntprague.anet.cz
director Jirí Srstka; ballet director Vlastimil Harapes
Dancers: 24 (soloists) 62 (corps) *Perfs:* 105 *No of Prods:* 2 *Type:* classical and neo-classical ballet *Venues:* Národni divadlo 639, Státní opera Praha 1046, Stavovské divadlo 639 *Comments:* visiting address: Ostrovní 1, 112 30 Praha 1; see also Opera and Drama

Teatr novoG.O. fronta
Korenského 13, 150 00 **Praha** 5
Tel: 2-5732 7169 Fax: 2-5732 7169
director Petr Bergmann; artistic director Ales Janák
Dancers: 2 *No of Prods:* 1 new *Type:* mime, performance *Comments:* touring company

This Fantastic Theatre
Divadlo Ta Fantastika
Karlova 8, 110 00 **Praha** 1
Tel: 2-2222 1369 Fax: 2-2222 0386
director Julius Hirsch; manager Michaela Hirschová
Perfs: 200 *No of Prods:* 1 *Type:* movement and black theatre *Accomp:* recorded *Venues:* capacity 220

UNO
c/o Pragokoncert, Pecková 13, **Praha** 8
Tel: 2-2481 7272/8277 Fax: 2-2481 8272
artistic director Richard Hess
Dancers: 15 *No of Prods:* 1 *Type:* modern *Accomp:* recorded *Comments:* touring company; see also Agents

Usti nad Labem City Theatre – Ballet
Mestské divadlo – balet
PO Box 4, 400 01 **Ustí nad Labem**
Tel: 47-521 1748 Fax: 47-520 9996
E-Mail: divadlo-usti@telecom.cz
director Petr Jonás; ballet director Josef Starosta
Perfs: 18 *No of Prods:* 2 *Type:* classical and neo-classical ballet *Accomp:* live, recorded *Venues:* capacity 500 *Comments:* see also Opera

DENMARK (+45)

Dancetheater Terpsichore, The
Frederiks Allé 20 B, 8000 **Aarhus** C
Tel: 8619 8331 Fax: 8620 1093
Internet: www.djembe.dk/bands/terp
E-Mail: terpsichore@worldcafe.dk
director Sacha World; dancer, choreographer & artistic director Pernille Overø; composers & musicians Max Bering, Cengiz Cevik, Rikke Rohde, Mads Bischoff
Dancers: 1 *Perfs:* 20 *No of Prods:* 1 per season + small performances *Type:* dance-theatre inspired by ritual dances and mythology; created through improvisations with both dance and music *Accomp:* live

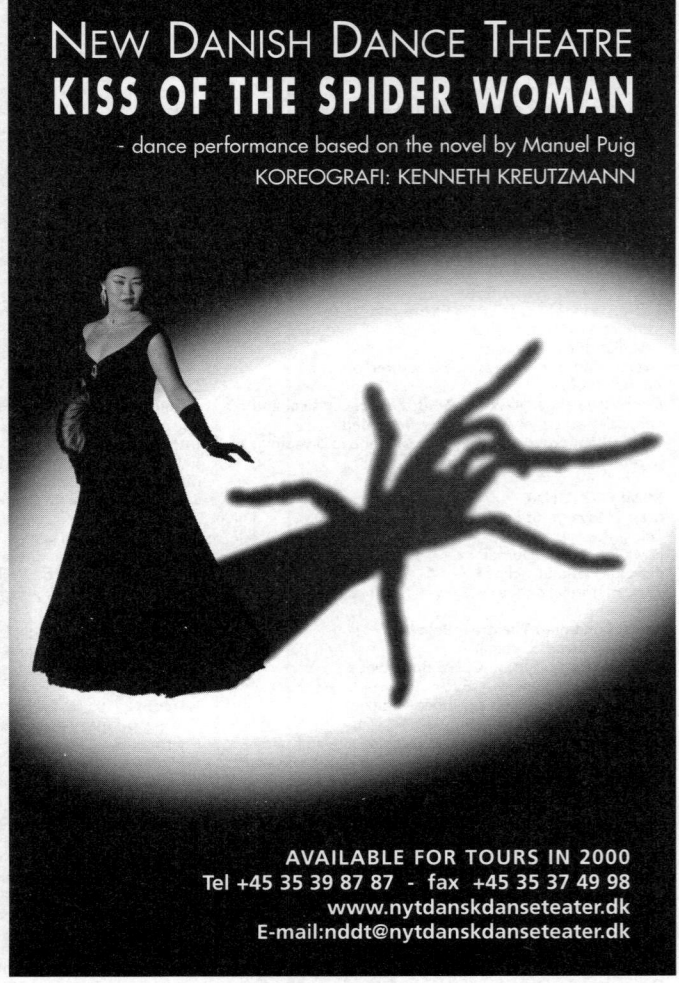

MBT Danseteater
Frederiks Alle 20, 8000 **Aarhus** C
Tel: 8613 7067 Fax: 8619 0811
E-Mail: mbtdans@post6.tele.dk
technical leader/administrator Hans-Olof Tani; artistic director Marie Brolin-Tani
Dancers: 7 *Perfs:* 40 *No of Prods:* 2-3
Type: modern *Accomp:* live, recorded
Venues: MBT-Dance Theatre/MBT-Danseteater 180
Touring: Denmark, Sweden, Hungary
Comments: offers workshops for children and young people; also educational programme

Åben Dans Productions
Hørsholmsgade 20,3, 2200 **Copenhagen** N
Tel: 3582 0610 Fax: 3582 0610
managing director Pernille Møller Taasinge; artistic director Lisbeth Klixbüll; choreographer Thomas Eisenhardt
Dancers: 5 *Perfs:* 24 *No of Prods:* 2
Type: new dance theatre and improvisation
Accomp: live, recorded *Venues:* Dansescenen (Copenhagen), empty warehouses in Copenhagen (open spaces), museums *Touring:* Denmark, USA

De Quincey/Lynch Productions
Sønder Boulevard 18, 5th,
1720 **Copenhagen** V
Tel: 3331 1532 Fax: 3331 1532
Internet: www.bodyweather.net
dancer/choreographer Tess de Quincey; performer/director Stuart Lynch
Dancers: 2-30 *Perfs:* 200 *No of Prods:* 8
Type: dance, performance, events
Accomp: recorded, live *Venues:* standard black box to site specific and landscape work *Touring:* national, international *Comments:* choreograph and direct dance/performance groups in Europe and Australia; production of solo, duo and group works; teach & research the dance and body training system BODY WEATHER; Australian Address: 8 Joly Parade, Hunters Hill, NSW 2110, Australia, Telephone: +61 2-9817 4542, Fax: +61 2-9817 1440, E-mail: dql@ozemail.com.au

Kreutzmann Dance
Nansensgade 10, 1366 **Copenhagen** K
Tel: 3316 1550 Fax: 3316 1560
artistic director Kenneth Kreutzmann; administration Eva Hein
Dancers: 9 *Perfs:* 20 *No of Prods:* 2
Type: modern dance *Accomp:* recorded
Venues: Dansescenen (Copenhagen) *Touring:* Europe
Comments: a new cooperation with Tim Feldmann/WILDA Dance Producitons and Micado Danse Ensemble will enhance touring

Micado Danse Ensemble
Nansensgade 10, 1366 **Copenhagen** K
Tel: 3312 1262 Fax: 3316 1560
E-Mail: produktionskontoet@get2net.dk
artistic director Charlotte Rindom; administration Jesper Kunuk Egede
Dancers: 6 *Perfs:* 12 *No of Prods:* 1
Type: modern dance *Accomp:* recorded *Venues:* Dansescenen (Copenhagen) *Comments:* cooperate with Kreutzmann Dance and Time Feldmann/ WILDA Dance Productions to enhance touring

New Danish Dance Theatre
Nyt Dansk Danseteater
Guldbergsgade 29 A, I, 2200 **Copenhagen** N
Tel: 3539 8787 Fax: 3537 4998
Internet: www.nytdanskdanseteater.dk
E-Mail: nddt@nytdanskdanseteater.dk
manager Poul Richard Pedersen; artistic supervisor Sorella Englund; administrator Ellen Jacobsen
Dancers: 8-11 *Perfs:* 60+ *No of Prods:* 3 *Type:* modern dance *Accomp:* recorded, live orchestra *Venues:* Dansescenen 260, Sceneriet/Det Ny Teater 220
Touring: Denmark

Royal Danish Ballet, The
Den Kongelige Ballet
Det Kongelige Teater, PO Box 2185,
1017 **Copenhagen** K
Tel: 3369 6933 Fax: 3369 6575
Internet: www.kgl-teater.dk
E-Mail: admin@kgl.teater.dk
general manager Michael Christiansen; artistic director Aage Thordal Christensen; deputy director Johnny Eliasen; ballet administrator Tine Winther Nissen; 1st ballet mistress Colleen Neary
Dancers: 93 *Perfs:* approx 120 *No of Prods:* 17
Type: modern and classical *Accomp:* live, recorded
Venues: capacity 1250 *Touring:* China, Japan

Teatret Dance Lab
Kigkurren 1, 2300 **Copenhagen** S
Tel: 3296 9030 Fax: 3296 1290
administrator Anny Dirchsen; artistic director Anita Saij; accountant Winnie Skødt Jørgenson; press coordinator Pernille Møller Taasinge
No of Prods: 1 *Type:* expressionistic, minimalistic, use of light and sound *Accomp:* live, recorded
Touring: Denmark

Tim Feldmann/WILDA Dance Productions
Nansensgade 10, 1366 **Copenhagen** K
Tel: 3316 1570 Fax: 3316 1560
artistic directors Tim Feldmann, Jesper Kunuk Egede
Dancers: 6 *Perfs:* 40 *No of Prods:* 3 *Type:* release based contemporary dance *Accomp:* recorded
Venues: Dansescenen (Copenhagen)
Touring: South and North America, Europe
Comments: a new cooperation with Kreutzmann Dance and Micado Danse Ensemble will enhance touring

Body Brains Unlimited
Flintholm Alle 26K-1, 2000 **Frederiksberg**
Tel: 3888 9100 Fax: 3888 6561
Internet: www.bodybrainsunlimited.com
E-Mail: dance@bodybrainsunlimited.dk
administrative director Lis Freundt Pol; artistic directors Nanna Nilson, John Bruun
Dancers: 6 *Perfs:* 20+ *No of Prods:* 1 per season + repertory *Type:* postmodern dance theatre *Accomp:* recorded, live *Venues:* New Now Dancing Space 50
Touring: Denmark, Sweden, Norway, Germany, England, Finland, Netherlands *Comments:* new production: Fate; one summer workshop per year (week long) for semi-professional and professional dancers; also one day workshops and seminars for non-professional and semi-professional dancers

Corona Danseteater
Sct. Annagaede 77, 3000 **Helsingoer**
Tel: 4921 0740 Fax: 4921 1741
E-Mail: wittrock@image.dk
administrator Carsten Wittrock; artistic director Jørgen Carlslund
Dancers: varies *Perfs:* 150 *No of Prods:* 3 (2 new)
Type: dance theatre for children and young people
Accomp: mostly live
Touring: mostly Denmark, but also international (incl Austria) *Comments:* touring company

Peter Schaufuss Ballet
Musikteatret Holstebro, Ved Hallen 4,
7500 **Holstebro**
Tel: 9740 5122/7382 Fax: 9740 7860
E-Mail: schaufussballet@post.tel.dk
artistic director Peter Schaufuss; administration Lisette Stobbe; company manager Yianni Papoutsis; company assisant Lydia Sørensen
Dancers: 22 *Perfs:* 80 *No of Prods:* 4 (incl 2 new)
Type: classical, neo-classical and modern
Accomp: recorded & live
Venues: Edinburgh Festival Theatre 1800, Saint Quentin Enyvelines (Paris) 1100, Atatürk Grand Hall (Istanbul) 1400, Musikhuset (Århus) 1700
Touring: Denmark, UK, France, Spain, Germany, Turkey

ESTONIA (+372)

Dance Company BOX RM
c/o 2.tants, Rataskaevu 10, 10123 **Tallinn**
Tel: 6-269 090 Fax: 6-269 099
artistic director Merle Saarva
Dancers: 6 *No of Prods:* 6 *Type:* contemporary *Touring:* Russia, Poland, Sweden, Lithuania, Ukraine

Estonia Theatre Ballet Company
Estonia pst. 4, 10148 **Tallinn**
Tel: 6-260 201/242 Fax: 6-260 299
Internet: www.ooper.ee/index1.htm
E-Mail: estonia@opera.teleport.ee
managing director Paul Himma; artistic director Mai Murdmaa; chief conductor Paul Mägi
Dancers: 45 *No of Prods:* 3 *Type:* classical, modern
Accomp: live, some recorded
Venues: Opera House 682 *Touring:* Finland, Sweden
Comments: state repertory theatre

Estonian Summer Dance Company
c/o 2.tants, Rataskaevu 10, 10123 **Tallinn**
Tel: 6-269 090 Fax: 6-269 099
producer Pritt Raud
Dancers: 6-12 *No of Prods:* 1-2 *Type:* contemporary
Accomp: tape *Comments:* aim is to promote contemporary dance by inviting young emerging foreign choreographers to work with Estonian dancers; working period spring-summer

Fine 5 Dance Theatre
Tantsuteater Fine 5
Tööstuse 47, 10416 **Tallinn**
Tel: 6-120 628 Fax: 6-120 628
manager Tiina Ollesk; artistic director Renee Nõmmik
Dancers: 5 *No of Prods:* 3 *Type:* modern, jazz
Accomp: tape *Touring:* Finland, Italy

Vanemuine Theatre Ballet Company
Vanemuise 6, 51003 **Tartu**
Tel: 7-439 012 Fax: 7-441 065
Internet: www.halo.ee/vanemuine
E-Mail: vanem@uninet.ee
managing director Jaak Viller; chief conductor Endel Nõgene; artistic director Mare Tomingas
No of Prods: 3 *Type:* classical, modern *Accomp:* live, some recorded *Venues:* main stage 682 *Touring:* Germany *Comments:* state repertory theatre

FINLAND (+358)

Company Toothpick
Kristianinkatu 7 C 39, 00170 **Helsinki**
artistic director Tero Saarinen
Dancers: 6 *Perfs:* 48 *No of Prods:* 2 p.a. *Type:* contemporary dance *Accomp:* recorded, live *Touring:* Austria, Belgium, Denmark, France, Finland, Germany, Hungary, Israel, Italy, Luxembourg, Poland, Switzerland, UK, USA *Comments:* International management: Pablo Guzman 16, Avenue Galliéni, 77590 Bois le Roi, France, Tel/Fax: +33 1-6481 1070

Dance Theatre Hurjaruuth
Tanssiteatteri Hurjaruuth
Tallberginkatu 1/117, 00180 **Helsinki**
Tel: 9-693 1227 Fax: 9-693 1299
Internet: www.hurjaruuth.fi
E-Mail: hurjaruuth@kaapeli.fi
chief choreographer Arja Petterson
Dancers: 4 core dancers *Perfs:* 150 *No of Prods:* 4
Type: modern *Venues:* Kaapelitehdas
Touring: national, international *Comments:* telephone and fax numbers were due to change, details not available at time of going to print

Dance Theatre Jazz Point
Tallberginkatu 1B, PL 57, 00180 **Helsinki**
Tel: 9-694 1619 Fax: 9-6227 8860
Internet: www.tanssi.com
E-Mail: vivi@tanssi.com
contact Nina Lindholm (tel: 9-694 9090); artistic director Vivianne Bodsko-Lommi
Perfs: 23 *No of Prods:* 2 *Type:* modern (not only jazz techniques), performances also directed at children and young people

Dance Theatre Rollo
Tanssiteatteri Rollo
Vääksyntie 4C, 00510 **Helsinki**
Tel: 9-726 1121 Fax: 9-726 1121
director Sanna Monto
Perfs: 95 *No of Prods:* 4 *Type:* modern dance, mime, dance theatre *Accomp:* recorded, live *Venues:* Studio Rollo *Touring:* Finland, France, Sweden
Comments: also productions for children

Finnish National Ballet
Suomen Kansallisbaletti
Po Box 176, 00251 **Helsinki**
Tel: 9-4030 2211 Fax: 9-4030 2295
Internet: www.operafin.fi
general manager Juhani Raiskinen; ballet director Jorma Uotinen
Dancers: 74 *Perfs:* 5 *Type:* classical, modern *Venues:* capacity 1365, Alminsali 487 *Touring:* national, international *Comments:* visiting address: Helsinginkatu 58, 00250 Helsinki

Helsinki City Theatre Dance Company
Helsingin Kaupunginteatterin Tanssiryhmä
Ensi linja 2, 00530 **Helsinki**
Tel: 9-39401 Fax: 9-394 0244
Internet: www.hel.fi/citytheatre/tanssia.html
E-Mail: firstname.lastname@hkt.fi
production coordinator Jyri Pulkkinen
Dancers: 12 *Perfs:* 150 *No of Prods:* 4 *Venues:* mainstage 947, small stage 340, Studio Elsa 150 *Touring:* national, international *Comments:* independent within the organisation of the theatre

Katrilli
Bulevardi 23-27, 00180 **Helsinki**
Tel: 9-608 989 Fax: 9-612 1824
Internet: personal.inet.fi/taide/katrilli
E-Mail: katrilli@co.inet.fi
artistic director Anu Haapoja; music director Pekka Pentikäinen; general manager Helena Valtonen
Dancers: 26 dancers, musicians, singers *Perfs:* 100
No of Prods: 4 *Type:* Finnish folk art Finno-Ugrian Folk Arts *Touring:* Finland, Europe

Nomadi Productions
Nomadi-tuotanto
Pursimiehenkatu 9 B 30, 00150 **Helsinki**
Tel: 9-630 984 Fax: 9-630 984
Internet: www.kaapeli.fi/~aaltokos/index.htm
E-Mail: nomadi@artic.net
dancers/choreographers Alpo Aaltokoski, Jyrki Karttunen, Arja Raatikainen, Katri Soini
Type: modern and contemporary dance *Touring:* national, international *Comments:* full-evening danceworks, shorter creations by various choreographers; other emails: aaltokos@kaapeli.fi and karttu@kaapeli.fi

Physical Art Theatre PAT
Tallberginkatu 1E/64, 00180 **Helsinki**
Tel: 9-694 1201 Fax: 9-694 1201
Internet: www.valo.uta.fi/projektif/koko
E-Mail: physartt@kaapeli.fi
artistic director Sanna Kekäläinen; producer Sari Väänänen
Dancers: 3 *Perfs:* 40 *No of Prods:* 2
Type: dance theatre
Touring: Finland, Europe

Reijo Kela
Tanssigalleria, Uudenmaankatu 33 E, 00120 **Helsinki**
Tel: 9-651 131
Dancers: solo *Perfs:* 50-70 *Type:* modern, 'environmental' dance, improvisation *Accomp:* live *Venues:* uses 'intimate' venues, especially museums, art galleries; outdoor venues *Touring:* Finland, Europe

Zodiak Center for New Dance
Tallberginkatu 1/154, 00180 **Helsinki**
Tel: 9-694 4948 Fax: 9-562 5805
Internet: zodiak.kaapeli.fi
E-Mail: zodiak@kaapeli.fi
Perfs: 110 *No of Prods:* 20 *Type:* modern dance using visual artists, new music, theatre *Venues:* the old cable factory 110 *Comments:* an association for freelance choreographers, dancers and groups; Zodiak's aim is to produce new dance performances and offer venues, courses and other activities to the contemporary dance field

Dance Theatre Kaie
c/o Anne Jouhtinen, Jousikatu 3A 3, 04230 **Kerava**
Tel: 9-294 1221/50-360 9167

Dance-Theatre Minimi
Sotku, Suokatu 42/2, 70110 **Kuopio**
Tel: 17-580 0583/262 2544 Fax: 17-580 0583
E-Mail: minimi@iwn.fi
marketing Hanna Mari Kokkonen; dancers and choreographers Anja Lappi, Kirsi Saastamoinen, Liisa Ruuskanen, Sonja Ryhänen; light and sound designer Sam Siltavuori; costume designer Jaana Kurttila
Dancers: 4 *Perfs:* 144 *No of Prods:* 2 *Type:* modern dance-theatre *Accomp:* recorded, live *Comments:* also organises dance courses

Jojo – Oulun Tanssin Keskus
Nuku – Keskus, Hallituskatu 7, 90100 **Oulu**
Tel: 8-5584 7560 Fax: 8-5584 7589
Internet: wnet.suomi.net/kotisivu/dance.info
E-Mail: dance.info@jojo.suomi.net
producer Merja Aakko; artistic director Pirjo Yli-Maunula

Rimpparemmi
Lapin Kävijäntie 3, 96100 **Rovaniemi**
Tel: 16-315 605 Fax: 16-315 008
E-Mail: Rimpparemmi@co.inet.fi
artistic director Petri Kauppinen
Type: folk dance

Dance Theatre Mobita/Dansco
Tanssiteatteri Mobita/Dansco
Tanssi – Frenckell, Puutarhakatu 2 G, 33100 **Tampere**
Tel: 3-222 1111 Fax: 3-213 0113
Internet: www.mobitadansco.com
contact Johanna Tirronen
Dancers: 7 *Perfs:* 170 *No of Prods:* 7 *Type:* modern dance *Venues:* Tanssi-Frenckell (studio theatre) *Touring:* national, international

Aurinkobaletti
Manilla, Itäinen Rantakatu 64, 20810 **Turku**
Tel: 2-234 1222 Fax: 2-234 2404
Internet: www.kolumbus.fi/aurinkobaletti
E-Mail: aurinkobaletti@kolumbus.fi
artistic director Raija Lehmussaari
Dancers: 6 *Perfs:* 100-120 *No of Prods:* 8 *Type:* contemporary dance *Accomp:* recorded, live *Venues:* Manilla 90 *Touring:* national, international

Tanssiteatteri Eri
Yliopistonkatu 7, 20110 **Turku**
Tel: 2-250 1032 Fax: 2-250 1041
contact Tiina Lindfors
Dancers: 5 *Perfs:* 90 *No of Prods:* 4 *Type:* contemporary/dance-theatre *Accomp:* live, recorded *Touring:* all major cities in Finland, Bonn, Bielefeld, Malmö, Stockholm, Rome

Raatikko Dance Theatre
Tanssiteatteri Raatikko
Viertolankuja 4, 01300 **Vantaa**
Tel: 9-873 1184/2306 Fax: 9-873 3294
Internet: www.raatikko.fi
E-Mail: raatikko@raatikko.fi
administration director Ulla Jarla; artistic director Marja Korhola
Dancers: 4 *Perfs:* 176 *No of Prods:* 4 *Type:* modern

FRANCE (+33)

Ballet Preljocaj, Centre Choréogaphique National de la Région Provence-Alpes-Côte d'Azur, de la Ville d'Aix-en-Provence et du Département des Bouches du Rhône
Cité du Livre, 8, 10 rue des Allumettes,
13098 **Aix-en-Provence** Cedex 02
Tel: 4-4293 4800 Fax: 4-4293 4801
Internet: www.preljocaj.org/
E-Mail: preljocaj@dial.oleane.com
directeur Nicole Said; directeur artistique Angelin Preljocaj; notatrice Dany Levêque; directeur technique Claude Marmillod; administrateur Jean-Philippe Guet; assistante de communication Isabelle Ricard; assistante de production Didier Debles
Dancers: 24 *Perfs:* 100 *No of Prods:* 1 *Type:* contemporary *Accomp:* recorded, also with orchestra *Venues:* Cité du Livre (studio) *Touring:* worldwide incl: Japan, Europe, USA, Mexico, Australia, Russia

Compagnie la Place Blanche/Groupe Grenade
37 Boulevard Aristide Briand, 13100 **Aix-en-Provence**
Tel: 4-4296 3756 Fax: 4-4296 0915
directrice Josette Baïz; administration Léonard Ballani; relations publiques/diffusion Babette Camus-Sendyk (tel: 4-9007 5223)
Dancers: 5 in the Compagnie *Perfs:* 30 *No of Prods:* 4 (2 new) *Type:* contemporary, hip-hop *Accomp:* recorded *Touring:* France *Comments:* Groupe Grenade: adolescents & young non-professional dancers (modern dance, hip-hop)

Centre National de Danse Contemporaine d'Angers L'Esquisse
42, bd Henri Arnauld, BP 2137, 49021 **Angers** Cedex 02
Tel: 2-4124 1212 Fax: 2-4124 1200
E-Mail: CNDC.l.Esquisse@wanadoo.fr
administrateur Patrick Pernin; direction artistique Joëlle Bouvier, Régis Obadia; direction des Etudes Marie-France Delieuvin; production et diffusion Sylvie Demaizière; comptabilité Colette Veau; secrétariat Sandrine Rod; communication, sensibilisation et formation Dominique Orvoine
Dancers: 2-10 *Perfs:* 6 *No of Prods:* 1 *Type:* contemporary *Accomp:* recorded *Venues:* Grand Théâtre d'Angers 650, Salle NTA Beaurepaire 450 *Touring:* worldwide *Comments:* the centre has several objectives: productions by the company L'esquisse; accommodates other companies; high school of contemporary dance

MA to MA
Abbaye de Royaumont, 95270 **Asnieres s/Oise**
Tel: 1-3035 5990 Fax: 1-3035 3945
artistic director (dance) Susan Buirge; adminstrateur Jacques Segueilla
Dancers: varies *Perfs:* 9 *No of Prods:* 4 (1 new) *Type:* contemporary dance *Accomp:* contemporary music created on computer *Touring:* France *Comments:* a unique concept of mixing the Japanese classical culture and the western culture; choregraphy by Susan Buirge

Les Laboratoires d'Aubervilliers
72, rue Henri Barbusse, 93300 **Aubervillers**
Tel: 1-5356 1590 Fax: 1-5356 1599
directeur Mr Verret; administrateur Christine Manchet
Dancers: varies *Type:* contemporary *Accomp:* live, recorded *Venues:* up to 250

Ballet de l'Opéra d'Avignon
BP 111, Cedex 1, 84007 **Avignon** Cedex 1
Tel: 4-9082 4242 Fax: 4-9085 0423
directeur général et administrateur Raymond Duffaut; directeur artistique du ballet Eric Vu-An; relations publiques Charlyne Blaise
Dancers: 13-18 *Perfs:* 6 *No of Prods:* 6 (incl 3 new) *Type:* classical, modern *Accomp:* orchestra – Orchestre Lyrique de Région Avignon Provence (q.v.) *Touring:* national *Comments:* see also Opera

Compagnie Jean Ribault
4, rue du Rampart St Lazanne, 84000 **Avignon**
Tel: 4-9085 0366/9027 1300 Fax: 4-9027 1300
choregraphe Jean Ribault; chargé de production Virna Cirignano
Dancers: varies *No of Prods:* 1 *Type:* contemporary, theatrical dance *Accomp:* live, recorded with compositions *Touring:* Brussels

Compagnie Contre-Jour
Centre Chorégraphique National de Franche-Comté à Belfort Sochaux, 3 avenue de l'Espérance,
90000 **Belfort**
Tel: 3-8458 4488 Fax: 3-8458 4489
administratrice Thierry Bore; directrice artistique Odile Duboc; conseillère artistique et technique Françoise Michel; diffusion George Baldacchino
Dancers: varies *Type:* contemporary *Accomp:* recorded *Venues:* Lieu de Création 120 *Touring:* France, Eastern Europe *Comments:* touring abroad supported by the 'Association Française D'action Artistique'

Schmid Pernette
3 Bis Rue du Chapitre, 2500 **Besançon**
Tel: 3-8161 9644 Fax: 3-8161 9644
E-Mail: cie.schmid.pernette@wanadoo.fr
artistic directors Natalie Pernette, Andreas Schmid; administrator Luc Pallegoix
Dancers: varies *Perfs:* 30 *No of Prods:* 1-2 *Type:* contemporary *Accomp:* live, recorded *Touring:* international

Roc in Lichen
154 rue Maurice Berteaux, 95870 **Bezons**
Tel: 1-3998 7492 Fax: 1-3998 7493
directors Bruno Dizien, Laura de Nercy; administrator/producer K Desrues
Dancers: varies *Perfs:* 25 *No of Prods:* 4 *Type:* contemporary *Accomp:* recorded *Venues:* Theatre Paul Eluard de Bezons *Touring:* France *Comments:* independent company, subsidised by the Ministry of Culture

Ballet Biarritz (formerly La Compagnie Temps Présent)
Centre Choréographique National, 26 Avenue Foch, 64200 **Biarritz**
Tel: 5-5924 6719 Fax: 5-5924 7540
Internet: perso.wanadoo.fr/ballet/biarritz
E-Mail: ballet.biarritz@wanadoo.fr
artistic director Thierry Malandain; admin. Yves Kordian
Dancers: 12 *Perfs:* 45 *No of Prods:* 2 *Type:* nouveau classique (new classical) *Accomp:* live, recorded *Venues:* Gare du Midi-Biarritz 1400 *Touring:* Europe, North Africa, Asia, USA, South America *Comments:* agent: DLB Spectacles, 8 Cité du Midi, 75018 Paris, Tel: 1-4251 7363, Fax: 1-4223 7776

Ballet de l'Opera de Bordeaux
Grand Théâtre de Bordeaux, BP 95, 33025 **Bordeaux** Cedex
Tel: 5-5600 8520 Fax: 5-5681 9366
directeur général Thierry Fouquet; secrétaire général Jean-Luc Maeso; directeur de la compagnie Charles Judes; directeur administratif et financier François Vienne; directeur technique Giulio Achilli
Dancers: 36 *Perfs:* 40 *No of Prods:* 8 *Type:* classic, modern *Accomp:* live (Orchestre National Bordeaux Aquitaine) *Venues:* Grand Théâtre de Bordeaux 1114, Palais des Sports 1660 *Comments:* see also Opera, Orchestras and Venues

Compagnie Paul Les Oiseaux
49, rue Paul Courteault, 33000 **Bordeaux**
Tel: 5-5690 0589 Fax: 5-5696 8332
E-Mail: paul.les.oiseaux@wanadoo.fr
administratrice Catherine Cossa; direction artistique Valerie Riviere
Dancers: varies *Perfs:* 15 *No of Prods:* 1 new *Type:* contemporary *Accomp:* live *Touring:* France

Compagnie Claudio Basilio
64 Boulevard de la Republique Bat 6, 92100 **Boulogne**
Tel: 1-4608 0308 Fax: 1-4608 0308
Internet: members.aol.com/CieBasilio/
E-Mail: CieBasilio@aol.com
directeur artistique, chorégraphe, danceur Claudio Basilio; manager Chantal Feusier
Dancers: 1-16 *Perfs:* 70 *No of Prods:* 4 *Type:* modern dance *Accomp:* live, recorded *Touring:* France, Brasil, USA *Comments:* Brasilian shows, Capoeira

Compagnie de Danse Christine Burgos
2, rue Beaumarchais, 01000 **Bourg-en-Bresse**
Tel: 4-7435 5704 Fax: 4-7435 5704
direction Olivier Gelpe; présidente Jeanine Burgos; administration Henri Burgos
Dancers: varies *Perfs:* 20 *No of Prods:* 1 *Type:* contemporary *Accomp:* recorded, live *Venues:* Studio des 4 vents 40 *Touring:* France, Netherlands, Japan

Centre Chorégraphique National de Caen/Basse-Normandie
10, rue Pasteur, B P 128, 14009 **Caen** Cedex
Tel: 2-3185 7316 Fax: 2-3123 4899
Internet: www.saporta-danse.com
E-Mail: ccncaen@mail.cpod.fr
directrice Karine Saporta; administrateur Phillippe Girerd; secretaire générale Sophie Renaud; régisseur général Jean-Philippe Nedellec
Dancers: 10-12 *Perfs:* 100 *No of Prods:* 3 *Type:* contemporary *Accomp:* recorded (original music), live *Venues:* Théâtre de Caen 1000, Théâtre d' Herouville 600 *Touring:* worldwide *Comments:* regularly offers lectures, workshops and training for beginners to professionals

Centre Chorégraphique National de Créteil Montalvo-Hervieu
Maison des Arts, 1 place Salvador Allende, 82400 **Creteil**
Tel: 1-5671 1320 Fax: 1-5671 1322
E-Mail: montalvo@club-internet.fr
directeur artistique José Montalvo, Dominique Hervieu; directeur admministrative Anne Saurage
Dancers: 20 *No of Prods:* 4 (1 new) *Type:* contemporary *Accomp:* recorded *Venues:* Maison d'Art de Créteil *Touring:* international *Comments:* multi-media productions, dance video

Association CA – Compagnie Hervé Diasnas
9 rue Victor Lespargne, 94120 **Fontenay-sous-Bois**
Tel: 1-4875 2399 Fax: 1-4876 8772
administration & production/diffusion Florine Dauny-Ordonnaud; directeur artistique Hervé Diasnas
Dancers: 7 *Perfs:* 24 *No of Prods:* 1 per year *Type:* contemporary *Accomp:* recorded, musicians *Touring:* South America *Comments:* sponsored by the Ministry of Culture – délégation à la danse; tours supported by AFAA

Castafiore
Espace CHIRIS, Espace chorégraphique,
Avenue de Provence, 06130 **Grasse**
Tel: 4-9336 8060 Fax: 4-9336 4099
E-Mail: biscuit@francenet.fr
co. directrice chorégraphe Marcia Barcellos; co. directeur compositeur Karl Biscuit; diffusion Perés Barbanel
Dancers: 5 + 1 actor *Perfs:* 32 *No of Prods:* 3 (1 new) *Type:* contemporary *Accomp:* recorded live *Touring:* France, Hong Kong
Comments: contact: Perés Barbanel, Artservice International, tel. 1-4893 6654; fax 1-4239 1402

GALLOTTA/Groupe Emile Dubois
Centre Chorégraphique National de Grenoble, Le Cargo – BP 2448, 4, rue Paul Claudel, 38034 **Grenoble** Cedex 2
Tel: 4-7625 7056 Fax: 4-7625 7383
directeur général Jean-Yves Langlais; directeur artistique Jean-Claude Gallotta; directeur technique Pierre Escande; chargé de la communication Caroline Jejou; administration des tournées Jean Ripahette
Dancers: 10 *Perfs:* 30 *No of Prods:* 3 (1 new) *Type:* contemporary *Accomp:* recorded *Venues:* Le Cargo/Grenoble *Touring:* Europe *Comments:* films and video programme available with or without the company's venue; see also Venues and Drama

Ballet Atlantique – Régine Chopinot
Ballet National Contemporain de Création et de répertoire, 4 rue Saint-Jean du Pérot,
17025 **La Rochelle** Cedex 01
Tel: 5-4641 1775 Fax: 5-4641 0728
Internet: www.artotal.com/comp/barc.htm
E-Mail: regine.chopinot@wanadoo.fr
directeur artistique Régine Chopinot; assistant de production Patrick Barbanneau; directeur technique Yanick Ros
Dancers: 14 *No of Prods:* 3 *Type:* contemporary *Accomp:* recorded, live *Touring:* Europe, Asia, Latin America, Africa

Centre Chorégraphique National du Havre Haute-Normandie
30, rue des Briquetiers, 76600 **Le Havre**
Tel: 2-3526 2300 Fax: 2-3526 2309
chorégraphe Hervé Robbe; directrice adjointe Carole Rambaud
Dancers: 8 *Perfs:* 30 *No of Prods:* 5 (3 new) *Type:* contemporary *Accomp:* recorded *Touring:* Europe, Japan, America

Compagnie Pierre Doussaint
La Médiathèque, av Paul Raoult, 78130 **Les Mureaux**
Tel: 1-3091 9930 Fax: 1-3091 4496
directeur Pierre Doussaint; administratif Gustave Galeote
Dancers: 6 *Perfs:* 20-30 *No of Prods:* 3 (1 new) *Type:* contemporary + circus *Accomp:* live, recorded *Touring:* France *Comments:* organises dance courses for children in deprived inner city areas

Ballet de L'Opéra Nationale de Lyon
Opéra Nationale de Lyon, 1 Place de la comédie, 69001 **Lyon**
Tel: 4-7200 4581 Fax: 4-7200 4585
Internet: www.operalyon.org
E-Mail: ballet@opera-lyon.com
directeur Yorgos Loukos; délégué général Thierry Leonardi; régisseur général Vincent Payen
Dancers: 30 *No of Prods:* 4 new *Type:* contemporary, classical, neo-classical *Accomp:* recorded
Venues: Grande salle 1100 *Touring:* USA, Greece
Comments: see also Opera

Compagnie de Danse Hallet-Eghayan
51, quai Paul Sédaillan, 69009 **Lyon**
Tel: 4-7864 8498 Fax: 4-7864 8760
E-Mail: Hallet_Eghayan@aol.com
directeur artistique Michel Hallet Eghayan; administration Anna Alexandre; diffusion/production Thierry Rollet
Dancers: 6 *No of Prods:* 1 new *Type:* contemporary *Accomp:* recorded *Touring:* Lebanon *Comments:* professional dance training, University exchange programs

Ballet National de Marseille
20 Boulevard de Gabes, 13417 **Marseille** Cedex 08
Tel: 4-9171 0303 Fax: 4-9171 5112
administrator & artistic director Marie Claude Pietragalla; responsable de relations publique Christophe Mely
Dancers: 45 *Perfs:* 70 *Type:* classical and neo-classical ballet *Accomp:* recorded, live *Touring:* Italy, France, Switzerland, Germany, Spain, Denmark, USA, Japan, Greece *Comments:* based at Ecole Nationale Supérieure de Danse de Marseille

Compagnie Kelemenis
5 place du général de Gaulle, 13001 **Marseille**
Tel: 4-9611 1120 Fax: 4-9611 1129
E-Mail: compagnie.kelemenis@wanadoo.fr
administrateur Patrice Poyet; directeur artistique Michel Kelemenis; coordination Nathalie Ducoin; information presse Nathalie Guillebert
Dancers: 6-10 *Perfs:* 35-40 *No of Prods:* 2 *Type:* contemporary *Accomp:* recorded *Venues:* theatres, festivals *Touring:* international *Comments:* provide a selection of performances on video for promotion and distribution

Compagnie la Liseuse
91, rue D'Endoume, 13007 **Marseille**
Tel: 4-9159 3460 Fax: 4-9159 3461
administration Denise le Guidec; directeur artistique Georges Appaix; diffusion-production Cristiano Carpanini (tel: 4-9155 6806, mobile: 608-228 840); relations avec le public Claire Gaborel
Dancers: 10 *Perfs:* 30 *No of Prods:* 4 *Type:* contemporary with vocals *Accomp:* recorded, live (vocal) *Venues:* Théâtre de la Ville (Paris) *Touring:* France, Europe *Comments:* production/diffusion: l'Officina, 29 rue Neuve St Catherine, 13007 Marseille, Tel: 4-9155 6806/608-328 840 (mobile), Fax: 4-9155 6713

Opéra-Théâtre de Metz
4-5, Place de la Comédie, 57000 **Metz**
Tel: 3-8755 5171 Fax: 3-8731 3237
Internet: www.mairie-metz.fr.8080
directeur administratif Marie-Hélène Metzinger-Nicolay; directrice artistique Danièlle Ory; relations publiques Agnès Jacques; maître de ballet Patrick Salliot
Dancers: 14 *Perfs:* 10 *No of Prods:* 4 *Type:* classical
Accomp: orchestra *Venues:* capacity 750
Comments: see also Opera

Red Notes – Compagnie Chorégraphique associée à la Ville de Montauban
Ancien College, 2, rue du College, 82000 **Montauban**
Tel: 5-6391 5132 Fax: 5-6391 0909
E-Mail: red.notes-cie.andy.degroat@wanadoo.fr
administration Anne Berthelier; directeur artistique Andy Degroat; chargée de production- diffusion Dominique Martin; assistante de production Samira Elouaracq; coordinatrice Wah Loo Tin Tin
Dancers: 10 *Perfs:* 35-40 *No of Prods:* 3 (1 new) *Type:* contemporary *Accomp:* recorded *Venues:* Theatre de Montauban *Touring:* Europe *Comments:* sponsored by the Ministère de la Culture et de la Communication, the Région Midi-Pyrénées, la DRAC Midi-Pyrénées, the Ville de Montauban, Conseil Général Tarn et Garonne and Direction Départementale de la Jeunesse et des Sports; also has a dance company for children: Walloo-Tintin

ARTEFACT
20 rue Frédéric Peysson, 34000 **Montpellier**
Tel: 4-6764 0502 Fax: 4-6764 0502
directeurs artistiques Jeannette Dumeix, Marc Vincent
Dancers: 6 *Perfs:* 10 *No of Prods:* 3 (1 new) *Type:* contemporary dance (from mediterranean traditional to modern) *Accomp:* live *Venues:* Théâtre Jean Vilar *Touring:* France

Camionetta, la
25 rue de la loge, 34000 **Montpellier**
Tel: 4-9155 6806 Fax: 4-9155 6713
directeurs artistiques Hélène Cathala, Fabrice Ramalingom
Perfs: 10-15 *No of Prods:* 6 (3 new) *Type:* contemporary dance *Venues:* Théâtre de Nîmes, Dieppe Scène Nationale, l'Equinoxe de Châteauroux, Biennale du Val de Marne *Touring:* France *Comments:* c/o L'Officina, 2, rue Neuve St Catherine, 13007 Marseille

Centre Chorégraphique National de Montpellier – Languedoc Roussillon
Les Ursulines, boulevard Louis Blanc, 34000 **Montpellier**
Tel: 4-6760 0670 Fax: 4-6766 4479
Internet: www.imaginet.fr/~dehexe
E-Mail: dehexe@imaginet.fr
directrice artistique Mathilde Monnier; directeur délégué Jean Marc Urrea; directeur technique Thierry Cabrera; production/ diffusion Michel Chialvo
Dancers: 3 *Perfs:* 52 *No of Prods:* 4 (1 new) *Type:* contemporary *Accomp:* recorded, live *Venues:* 3 studios; size of one venue: 140 *Touring:* Europe, Canada, Australia *Comments:* Centre de Création Résidence pour la Danse; offeres courses for professionals, teaching and for young public, courses to develop young audiences; see also Venues

Compagnie Didier Théron
MpT Léo Lagrange, Mas de la Paillade, BP 7269, 34184 **Montpellier** Cedex 4
Tel: 4-6703 3822 Fax: 4-6703 3837
choregraphe/directeur Didier Théron; co-directeur Michèle Murray; secrétaire générale Guilaine Beau-Clair
Dancers: 6 *Perfs:* 15 *No of Prods:* 3 (1 new) *Type:* contemporary *Accomp:* recorded *Venues:* Théâtre Jean Villar *Touring:* Germany, Italy, France

Compagnie Taffanel
7 boulevard Sarrail, 34000 **Montpellier**
Tel: 4-6760 4230 Fax: 4-6760 4185
chorégraphe Jackie Taffanel; diffusion & production Thierry Gourmelen; assistant of director Nathalie Carcenac; administration Patrick Camoin; médiatrice culturelle Fanny Virelizier
Dancers: 9 *Perfs:* 40 *No of Prods:* 4 (1 new)
Type: contemporary *Accomp:* live *Touring:* France

Compagnie K Danse
12 rue Saint-Just, 93100 **Montreuil**
Tel: 1-4851 0730/6-1177 5456 Fax: 1-4851 0730
Internet: www.metafort.com/kdanse/
E-Mail: kdmatos@worldnet.fr
directeur artistique Jean-Marc Matos; directeur technique José Cloquell, Anne-Laure Hautran; attachée de production Catherine Kettler; assistantes Aude Jeanroy, Anne Holst
Dancers: varies *Perfs:* 20 *No of Prods:* 4 *Type:* modern, contemporary and butho dance, multimedia performance, on-line projects *Accomp:* recorded + live music, film, slides, video (live, pre-recorded, interactive), computer graphics, original compositions
Venues: Scènes nationales, Arts & Technology Festivals, Cultural Centers *Touring:* France, Europe
Comments: information centre, courses for professional dancers; research on dance and computer technology, dance on-line projects

Ballet de l'Opera National Du Rhin
38, passage du Théâtre, 68100 **Mulhouse**
Tel: 389-459 410 Fax: 389-664 017
Internet: www.opera-national-du-rhin.com
E-Mail: ballet@opera-national-du-rhin.com
directeur général Rudolf Berger; directeur artistique Bertrand d'At; administrateur Philippe Durand; relations publiques Claude Kientz
Dancers: 33 *Perfs:* 60 *No of Prods:* 12 *Type:* classical, contemporary and crossovers, neo-classical *Accomp:* recorded, orchestra *Venues:* Opera de Strasbourg 1142, de Mulhouse 822, Théâtre de Colmar 707, La Filature Mulhouse 1200 *Touring:* France, Eastern Europe, Asia, USA, South America

Ballet National de Nancy et de Lorraine
3, rue Henri Bazin, BP 645, 54010 **Nancy** Cedex
Tel: 3-8336 7807/7220 (public relations) Fax: 3-8330 3444
directeur administratif Jean-Jacques Robin; directeur artistique Françoise Achet; chargé des relations publiques Vanessa Mestre; regisseur général et scène Thiery Louis
Dancers: 45 *Perfs:* 80 *Type:* classical, contemporary
Accomp: orchestra, recorded (some original music)
Venues: Opéra de Nancy et de Lorraine 1000 *Touring:* national and international

Centre Chorégraphique National de Nantes / Brumachon – Lamarche
Studio Jacques Garnier, 23, rue Noire, 44000 **Nantes**
Tel: 2-4093 3097 Fax: 2-4093 3011
directeur Claude Brumachon; directeur adjoint Benjamin Lamarche; chargée de production et diffusion Francesca Poloniato; administratrice Denise Maggio; régisseur général Jean-Jacques Brumachon; chargée de communication & logistique Véronique Guiho
Dancers: 14 *Perfs:* 142 *No of Prods:* 4-5 *Type:* contemporary *Accomp:* recorded but original music (Christopher Zurfluh, Bruno Billaudeau) *Venues:* Studio Garnier 210 *Touring:* Asia *Comments:* organises Les Connivences de Juin: shows by other choreographers & by Brumachon, annually in June, venue: Studio Garnier 210

Ballet de l'Opéra de Nice
4-6, rue Saint-François de Paule, 06300 **Nice**
Tel: 4-9217 4000 (opera)/9229 3270 (ballet)
Fax: 4-9229 3271
Internet: www.nice-coteazur.org
E-Mail: opera@nice-coteazur.org
directeur général Gian Carlo del Monaco; directeur de la danse Marc Ribaud; directrice relation publiques Elisabeth Touraille
Dancers: 30 *Perfs:* 40 *No of Prods:* 1 *Type:* classic & contemporary *Accomp:* live, recorded *Venues:* Opéra de Nice 1100 *Touring:* Europe *Comments:* see also Orchestras and Opera

Centre National de Creations et de Diffusions Culturelles
BP 118, 83192 **Ollioules** Cedex
Tel: 4-9422 7400 Fax: 4-9422 7419
régisseur général Philippe Billoret; administratrice Nicole Jarrié; information Nataley Bernard
Dancers: varies *Type:* contemporary, oriental, classical, hip-hop *Accomp:* live, recorded *Venues:* Amphithéâtre 1200, Théâtre couvert 500, Cinéma 100 *Comments:* see also Venues, Promoters and Festivals

Centre Chorégraphique National d'Orléans
Carré Saint Vincent, 45000 **Orléans**
Tel: 2-3862 4100 Fax: 2-3877 0855
E-Mail: ccnorleans@xernet.com
directeur Josef Nadj; diffusion/production Martine Dionisio (tel: 1-4289 6102, fax: 1-4289 4466)
Dancers: 15 *Perfs:* 80-110 *No of Prods:* 1 new *Type:* dance theatre, contemporary *Accomp:* recorded, musicians
Venues: Carré Saint-Vincent 1000 *Touring:* international
Comments: see also Venues, Drama and Promoters

Ballet de L'Opéra National de Paris
120, rue de Lyon, 75012 **Paris**
Tel: 1-4001 1790/1399 Fax: 1-40473 1374
Internet: www.opera-de-paris.fr
director Hugues Gall; deputy director Phillipe Agid; dance director Brigitte Lefèvre; lyric centre Christine Bullin; director of the ballet school Claude Bessy; dance administrator Bruno Hamard; general secretary Christian de Pange; assistant directors Christian Schirm, Frédéric Chambert
Dancers: 154 *Perfs:* 389 (incl Dance school) *No of Prods:* 15 (incl Dance school) *Type:* classical and contemporary *Accomp:* live *Venues:* Palais Garnier 1970, Opéra Bastille 2703 *Touring:* France and abroad *Comments:* merged with Opéra National de Paris-Palais Garnier; send mail to General Secretary, Palais Garnier

Blanca Li Dance Company
7 rue des Petites Ecuries, 75010 **Paris**
Tel: 1-5334 0405 Fax: 1-5334 0012
Internet: www.artotal.com/comp/blancali.htm
E-Mail: blanca.li@wanadoo.fr
director Etienne Li; artistic director Blanca Li; administrator Annick Peauger
Dancers: 8 *Perfs:* 26 *No of Prods:* 2 *Type:* contemporary, modern *Accomp:* recorded, live *Touring:* Europe
Comments: dance school and studio space

Cie. Larsen/Stephanie Aubin
129 Avenue Philippe Auguste, 75011 **Paris**
Tel: 1-4356 7397 Fax: 1-4356 7366
E-Mail: compagnie.larsen@wanadoo.fr
directeur administratif Soraya Rebbouh; directrice artistique Stephanie Aubin
Dancers: varies *Perfs:* 40 *No of Prods:* 5 (2 new) *Type:* contemporary *Accomp:* recorded, live *Touring:* France
Comments: Cie Larsen: Créations et Actions Chorégraphiques organise L'Art en scéne at the Théâtre de la Cité Internationale à Paris

Compagnie Alain Germain – Ballet Théâtre Musical de France
29, rue de Paradis, 75010 **Paris**
Tel: 1-4246 3783 Fax: 1-4246 6785
Internet: agermain.citeweb.net
E-Mail: agermain@mail.com.fr
directeur Alain Germain; administrateur Dominique Bataille; directeur technique Philippe Mermin; secrétariat général Véronique Duchamp-Jay; relations presse Sabine Arman
Type: contemporary, dance theatre, opera *Accomp:* live
Comments: see also Opera

Compagnie Anonyme
302, rue de Charenton, 75012 **Paris**
Tel: 1-4424 2293/6-8255 1729
directrice Sidonie Rochon; responsable de diffusion t.b.a.
Dancers: varies *Perfs:* 15 *No of Prods:* 1 *Type:* contemporary, dance theatre *Accomp:* recorded

Compagnie Cre-Ange
14, rue Crefpin du Gast, 75011 **Paris**
Tel: 1-4021 7990 Fax: 1-4338 2007
E-Mail: cre.ange@wanadoo.fr
choregraphers Charles Cre-Ange, Christie Lehuede; administration Sophie le Jeune; diffusion Marie Royer
Dancers: varies *Perfs:* 18+ *No of Prods:* 1 *Type:* contemporary *Accomp:* recorded, live *Touring:* France

Compagnie Jean Gaudin
174, rue du Temple, 75003 **Paris**
Tel: 1-4804 9774 Fax: 1-4461 0033
administratrice Marie-Anne Rosset; directeur artistique Jean Gaudin
Dancers: 15 *Perfs:* 30 *No of Prods:* 7 *Type:* contemporary *Accomp:* recorded, live *Touring:* National, Europe, Korea, Switzerland

Compagnie Jean-François Duroure
144, rue du Faubourg Saint-Antoine, 75012 **Paris**
Tel: 1-4307 0808 Fax: 1-4307 0809/0516
E-Mail: duroure@easynet.fr
directeur Jean-Francois Duroure; administratrice Marie-Laure Jordan; assistànte de production Corinne Duguest
Dancers: varies *Perfs:* 40 *No of Prods:* 1 *Type:* contemporary, street dance *Accomp:* live, recorded
Comments: videos available

Compagnie Philippe Genty
40, rue Sedaine, 75011 **Paris**
Tel: 1-4700 7261 Fax: 1-4357 7443
administratrice Mireille Abeille; directeur artistique, metteur en scène Philippe Genty; management Marie-Pierre Paillard (MPM International 1-4923 8360); choréographe Mary Underwood
Dancers: 8 (actors) *Perfs:* 100-110 *No of Prods:* 2 (1 new) *Type:* combine dance, drama and marionettes
Accomp: recorded, live *Venues:* Théâtre de la Ville de Paris 1100 *Touring:* worldwide
Comments: see also Drama and Puppets

International Dreems Associated – I.D.A.
Amelia Serrano, 2 Ter, Passage de Clichy, 75018 **Paris**
Tel: 1-4387 7407 Fax: 1-4387 7407
administratrice Amelia Serrano; directeur artistique Mark Tompkins
Dancers: 1-10 *Perfs:* 30 *No of Prods:* 5 + 2 new
Type: contemporary *Accomp:* live, recorded
Touring: Europe *Comments:* from Oct. 98 to 2000 the company will be in residence in Strasbourg, but will keep address, tel & fax in Paris

Junior Ballet du Conservatoire de Paris
département des études chorégraphiques, 209 avenue Jean Jaurès, 75019 **Paris**
Tel: 1-4040 4631 Fax: 1-4040 4602
E-Mail: danse@cnsmdp.fr
maître de ballet Martine Clary, Muriel Belmondo; directeur des études chorégraphiques Quentin Rouillier; chargé de production Frédéric Moreau; administrateur danse Yannick Marzin
Dancers: 15 (per ballet) *Perfs:* 20 *No of Prods:* 2 junior ballets (1 classical, 1 contemporary) *Type:* classical, neo-classical, contemporary *Touring:* France, Europe, Asia, America *Comments:* the Ballet du Conservatoire de Paris is made up of fifth year students, aged 17-20; the repertoire changes annually and is composed of works by major choreographers

Opéra National de Paris – Palais Garnier
Paris
Comments: merged with Ballet de L'Opéra National de Paris (q.v.)

Post Retroguardia – Compagnie Paco Dècina
43 Avenue de la République, 75011 **Paris**
Tel: 1-4806 0214 Fax: 1-4806 0718
E-Mail: cie.decina@wanadoo.fr
manager Jean Christophe Boissonnade; artistic director Paco Décina
Dancers: 6-7 *Perfs:* 35 *No of Prods:* 7 *Type:* contemporary *Accomp:* recorded, live *Touring:* France, Europe, South-East Asia *Comments:* see also Compagnie Faggianelli (Drama & Dance)

Santiago Sempere Chorégraphie
4, rue Androuët, 75018 **Paris**
Tel: 1-4255 3230 Fax: 1-4255 3230
directeur artistique chorégraphe Santiago Sempere; conseillére de production Sophie Gelinier
Dancers: 7 *Perfs:* 25-30 *No of Prods:* 2 *Type:* contemporary *Accomp:* live, recorded *Touring:* Europe, Japan

Centre Chorégraphique National de Rennes et de Bretagne
38 rue Sainte Melaine, BP 6023, 35060 **Rennes** Cedex 3
Tel: 2-9963-8822 Fax: 2-9936 4859
E-Mail: ccnrb@wanadoo.fr
administratrice Andrée Hilbert; directeur artistiques Catherine Diverrès; regisseur general Pascal Abhervé; sécretaire Estelle Hervouin
Dancers: 4-10 *No of Prods:* 3 (1 new) *Type:* contemporary *Accomp:* recorded *Venues:* Théâtre National de Bretagne 1300 *Touring:* international

Compagnie Maguy Marin
Centre Chorégraphique National de Rillieux-la-Pape, 10, boulevard de Lattre de Tassiny, BP 106, 69143 **Rillieux-la-Pape** Cedex
Tel: 4-7201 1230 Fax: 4-7201 1231
Internet: www.compagnie-maguy-marin.fr
E-Mail: info@compagnie-maguy-marin.fr
directrice artistique Maguy Marin; administrateur et directeur de producteur Antoine Manologlou; directeur technique Alexandre Bénétaud; chargée de communication Gwenaële Magnet
Dancers: 13 *Perfs:* 60 *No of Prods:* 3 (2 new) *Type:* contemporary *Accomp:* live, recorded *Venues:* Maison de la Culture 1000 *Touring:* international

Ballet du Nord
33, rue de l'Epeule, 59100 **Roubaix**
Tel: 3-2024 6666 Fax: 3-2036 0747
E-Mail: ballet.du.nord@wanadoo.fr
directeur Maryse Delente; administrateur Christiane Gauthier-Lafaye; relations publiques Caroline Jamelin
Dancers: 28 *Perfs:* 6 *No of Prods:* 1 new *Type:* live (accompanied by piano) *Venues:* Le Colisée, Roubaix
Touring: Europe

Théâtre de Rouen
route du docteur Rambert, 76000 **Rouen**
Tel: 2-3598 5098 Fax: 2-3515 3349
E-Mail: opera.2.rouen@wanadoo.fr
directeur général Laurent Langlois; administrateur t.b.a.; assistant relations publiques Beatrice Lhommet; chef d' orchestre Oswald Sallaberger; relations publiques Olivier Lefebvre
Dancers: no permanent ensemble *Type:* contemporary
Venues: capacity 1350 : see also Opera and Venues

Compagnie DCA
La Chaufferie Fabien, 10 bis, Avenue Maurice Thorez, 93200 **Saint-Denis**
Tel: 1-4813 0506 Fax: 1-4813 0912
E-Mail: dca@imaginet.fr
directeur artistique Philippe Decouflé; administratrice Pascale Henrot; communication & production Michel Quéré
Dancers: 18 *No of Prods:* 2 *Type:* contemporary *Accomp:* recorded, live *Touring:* international

Ballet du Capitole
Place du Capitole, BP 129, 31014 **Toulouse** Cedex 06
Tel: 5-6113 8747 Fax: 5-6272 2832
directeur administratif Robert Gouazé; directeur artistique Nicolas Joël; directrice du ballet Nanette Glushak; relations publiques Jean-Paul Laffont; presse Marie-Claire Rettig; diffusion & promotion du ballet, responsable des tournées Carole Teulet
Dancers: 35 *Perfs:* 50 *No of Prods:* 45 *Type:* classical, contemporary, neo-classical *Accomp:* live (l'orchestre national), recorded *Venues:* La Halle aux Grains 1800, Théatre du Capitole 1100 *Touring:* USA, Europe, China, Ukraine *Comments:* see also Opera and Venues

Centre Chorégraphique National de Tours – Daniel Larrieu
47, rue du Sergent Leclerc, 37000 **Tours**
Tel: 2-4736 4600 Fax: 2-4736 4601
Internet: www.ccnt-larrieu.com
E-Mail: info@ccnt-larrieu.com
directeur artistique Daniel Larrieu; directrice communication, relations publiques Victoire Dubruel; administrateur Danièle Burckel
Dancers: 20 (non-permanent) *Perfs:* 40-50 *No of Prods:* 3 (1 new) *Type:* contemporary *Accomp:* recorded, electronic music *Touring:* Europe, Georgia, Armenia
Comments: organises: 'Chore-graphique' (see Festivals)

Compagnie Stanislaw Wisnieski
Centre Culturel Charlie Chaplin, Place de la Nation, 69120 **Vaulx-en-Velin**
Tel: 4-7204 8118 Fax: 4-7204 3703
chorégraphe Stanislaw Wisnieski
Dancers: 7 *Perfs:* 8 (in the theatre) *No of Prods:* 1 *Type:* contemporary *Accomp:* live *Touring:* France, Europe
Comments: see also Dance, Festivals and Venues

Compagnie Anne Dreyfus
3, passage du Moutier, 94800 **Villejuif**
Tel: 1-4521 8937/6-1078 7516
Fax: 1-4521 9102
directrice-chorégraphe Anne Dreyfus
Dancers: 3-7 *Perfs:* 30 *No of Prods:* 1 *Type:* modern
Accomp: live, recorded (original music by Jean-François Pauvros) *Venues:* Théâtre Romain Rolland 800, and other venues in Villejuif *Touring:* France

GEORGIA (+995)

Balanchivadze Kutaisi Opera and Ballet Theatre
19 St. Nino st., 384002 **Kutaisi**
Tel: 31-52432/52123 Fax: 31-01010
general manager Devis Akhvlediani; artistic director Medea Amiranashvili; assistant to general manager Vakhtang Asatiani
Venues: Kutaisi Opera Theatre
Touring: Spain, Germany

Georgian National Ballet
123 Agmashenebeli av., 380002 **Tbilisi**
Tel: 32-950 611/955 183 Fax: 32-942 199
artistic director Tengiz Sukhishvili
Dancers: 80 *Perfs:* 30-40 *Accomp:* live, tape *Venues:* Tbilisi Central Concert Hall *Touring:* USA, Japan, Australia, South America, Europe

Georgian National Dance Company Rustavi
103 Agmeshenebeli av., 380002 **Tbilisi**
Tel: 32-959 473/952 652
Fax: 32-958 996
artistic director Anzor Erkomaishvili; chief choreographer Fridon Sulaberidze
Dancers: 50 *Perfs:* 20-30 *Type:* national dance
Accomp: live *Venues:* Tbilisi Central Concert Hall
Touring: USA, Japan, South America, Europe

Tbilisi National Opera Ballet Theatre
25 Rustaveli Ave., 380008 **Tbilisi**
Tel: 32-931 894/983 248
Fax: 32-983 250
general manager Zurab Lomidze; artistic director Jansug Kakhidzde; deputy manager Tamaz Laperashvili; assistant to artistic director Guram Meliva; technical director Vitali Nodia
Venues: Tbilisi Opera and Ballet Theatre

GERMANY (+49)

Ballet Theater Augsburg
Kasernstaße 4-6, 86152 **Augsburg**
Tel: 821-324 4912
Fax: 821-324 4544/4478
Internet: www.augsburg.de
Intendant Dr Ulrich Peters; Generalmusikdirektor Peter Leonard; Künstlerischer Betriebsdirektor Axel Peppermüller; Chefdramaturg Helmar von Hanstein; Balletdirektor Jochen Heckmann; Kaufmännischer Direktor Dr Klaus Engert
Dancers: 12 *No of Prods:* 3
Type: modern *Accomp:* recorded
Venues: Stadtheather 976, Kongresshalle 1395, Komödie 310, Freilichtbühne Am Roten Tor 2117
Comments: see also Drama, Opera and Orchestras

Ballett des Sorbischen National-Ensembles GmbH
Äußere Lauenstr. 2, 02625 **Bautzen**
Tel: 35-91358-0 Fax: 35-914 3096
Ballettmeister Konrad Naumann; Chefdirigent Dieter Kempe; Gechäftsführer Meto Benad
Dancers: 31 *Perfs:* 250 *No of Prods:* 10
Type: ballet, folklore, dancetheatre, children's performances *Accomp:* live, recorded
Touring: national, Spain, Oman
Comments: see also Choirs and Puppetry

Ballett der Deutschen Oper Berlin
Richard-Wagner Strasse 10, 10585 **Berlin**
Tel: 30-3438 4265 Fax: 30-3438 4429
Internet: www.deutsche-oper.berlin.de
E-Mail: DOBtickets@t-online.de
Generalintendant Prof. Götz Friedrich; Ballettdirektorin Sylviane Bayard; Ballettdramaturg Adolphe Binder; Generalmusikdirektor Christian Thielemann; Künstlerischer Betriebsdirektor Jean-François Monnard
Dancers: 50 *Perfs:* 220 + 70 special + 9 concerts
No of Prods: 10 (2 new)
Type: classical, modern *Accomp:* live, recorded
Venues: Deutsche Oper Berlin 1869 Plätze, Parkett-Foyer 200 Plätze, Max-Beckmann Saal, apprx 500
Touring: Austria
Comments: venue address: Opernhaus, Bismarckstraße 35, 10627 Berlin, address for Max-Beckmann Saal, Luxembourgstr. 29, 13353

BerlinBallett Komische Oper
Behrenstrasse 55-57, 10117 **Berlin**
Tel: 30-2026 0290 Fax: 30-2026 0356
Internet: www.icf.de/ko
E-Mail: opera@berlin.snafu.de
Intendant Albert Kost; Künstlerischer Leiter und Chefchoreograph Richard Wherlock; Operndirektor und Chefregisseur Harry Kupfer; GMD Yakov Kreizberg
Dancers: 30 *Perfs:* 37 *No of Prods:* 3 *Type:* contemporary dance, neo-classical, modern *Accomp:* live, recorded *Venues:* Komische Oper Berlin 1270 *Touring:* national and international

Choreographisches Theater/Volksbühne am Rosa-Luxemburg-Platz
Linienstr. 227, 10178 **Berlin**
Tel: 30-2406 5622 Fax: 30-2406 5622
Intendant F Castorf; Ltr. u. Choreograph Johann Kresnik; stellv. Ltr. u. Assistent Maciej Miedzinski; Trainingsltr Beatrice Cordua; organisation Tomke Doren
Dancers: 20 *Perfs:* 84 *No of Prods:* 8 (4 new) *Type:* classical, modern *Accomp:* live *Venues:* Volksbühne, Prater 3, Stock *Touring:* Denmark, Czech Republic

Dance Theatre Raydiation
Savignyplatz 9, 10623 **Berlin**
Tel: 30-313 9727
Choreograph Herbie Hack
Dancers: varies *Type:* dance-theatre, modern jazz, modern dance *Accomp:* live, recorded *Comments:* both professional and amateur dancers

Fountainhead Tanz Theatre
Tempelhofer Damm 52, 12101 **Berlin**
Tel: 30-782 1621/751 8438 Fax: 30-786 3466
Internet: members.aol.com/bicdance
E-Mail: bicdance@aol.com
Künstlerische Direktoren/Choreographen Gayle McKinney Griffith, Donald M. Griffith; Programme Co-ordinator Angela Kramer; Public Relations Marion Kramer, Anthony Phillips, Nancy Kruse, V. Hale (USA, fax: +1 212-491 2555); seminar co-ordinator Dr Themba Kalalie-Bealin
Dancers: 8 *Type:* contemporary ballet, jazz, modern dance theatre *Accomp:* live, recorded *Comments:* also organises XV Black International Cinema Film-Video Festival 2000 New York/Berlin, Cottbus Potsdam

Ingo Reulecke & Company
c/o Kultur und Theater Management Dietrich Brocke, Blücherstr. 15, 10961 **Berlin**
Tel: 30-693 2695 Fax: 30-694 9939
Choreograph Ingo Reulecke
Dancers: varies *Perfs:* 10-20 *No of Prods:* 3 *Type:* modern dance theatre *Accomp:* live & recorded

Philippe RIVES – BewegungsKünstler
Weisetrasse 46, 12049 **Berlin**
Tel: 30-6270 5136 Fax: 30-6270 5136
E-Mail: bkcic@hotmail.com
contact Philippe Rives
No of Prods: 3 *Type:* dance improvisation, physical, art of movement *Comments:* also workshops

Regina Baumgart Tanzensemble RBT
c/o Kultur und Theater Management Dietrich Brocke, Blücherstr. 15, 10961 **Berlin**
Tel: 30-693 2695 Fax: 30-694 9939
choreography Regina Baumgart
Comments: performances are planned for the year 2000

Rubato
Karl Kunger Str. 13, 12435 **Berlin**
Tel: 30-5321 9930 Fax: 30-5321 9930
E-Mail: rubato@berlin.snafu.de
Künstlerische Leitung Dieter Baumann, Jutta Hell
Dancers: 3-7 *Perfs:* 40 *No of Prods:* 2 *Type:* mixture of expressive dance theatrical elements, voice and mime *Accomp:* live, recorded composed music *Touring:* Germany, Italy, France, USA, Canada, Cyprus, China, Estonia, Lithuania, Columbia, singapore, Turkey *Comments:* artist in residence at: Theater am Halleschen Ufer, Hallesches Ufer 32, 10963 Berlin (q.v. Venues)

Staatsoper Unter den Linden: Staatsopernballett
Unter den Linden 5-7, 10117 **Berlin**
Tel: 30-20354-0 Fax: 30-2035 4206
Internet: www.staatsoper-berlin.org
E-Mail: contact@staatsoper-berling.org
Intendant Georg Quander; Künstlerischer Leiter und Generalmusikdirektor Daniel Barenboim; Geschäftsführender Direktor Georg Vierthaler; Künstlerischer Betriebsdirektor Achim Debschall; Persönlicher Referent des Intendanten und Leiter der Pressearbeit Dr. Stephan Adam; Leiterin Marketing Sabine Turner; Chefdramaturgin Dr. Regula Rapp; Dramaturgie Dr. Ralf Waldschmidt, Ilka Seifert, Dr. Christiane Theobald (Ballet); Ballettbetriebsdirektorin Dr. Christiane Theobald
Dancers: 67 *Perfs:* 55 *No of Prods:* 10 (3 new) *Type:* classical and modern ballet *Accomp:* live *Venues:* Staatsoper Unter den Linden (Großes Haus) 1396, Staatsoper Unter den Linden (Apollo-Saal) 249, Parochialkirche 67 *Comments:* see also Opera

Tanzfabrik/Dance Factory Berlin
Möckernstrasse 68, 10965 **Berlin**
Tel: 30-786 6103 Fax: 30-786 1586
E-Mail: tanzfabrik@p-soft.de
Verwaltungsleiterin Eva-Maria Hoerster; Künstlerische Leiterin Claudia Feest
Venues: own studio 99 *Comments:* due to lack of funding there are no productions planned for next season, but they will be acting as a receiving venue for other companies

Tanzlabor
Lilienthalstr. 18, 10965 **Berlin**
Tel: 30-692 3590 Fax: 30-692 3590
Direktor Norbert Servos; Choreographen Norbert Servos, Tatjana Orlob
Dancers: varies *Perfs:* 10 *No of Prods:* 3 *Type:* modern, dance theatre *Accomp:* recorded *Venues:* Akademie der Künste 450 *Touring:* Europe

tatoeba – Théâtre Danse Grotesque
Grossgörschenstr. 6, 10827 **Berlin**
Tel: 171-494 7333 (mobile) Fax: 171-1349 47333
E-Mail: tatoeba@gmx.de
managing artistic director Delta Ra'i; choreographers/artistic director Yumiko Yoshioka
Dancers: 1-3 *Perfs:* 1-5 *Type:* experimental, expressionist, dance theatre, Butoh related *Accomp:* recorded, live *Venues:* Schloß Bröllin studio stage 100 *Touring:* Europe, USA, worldwide *Comments:* workshop performance projects for professionals and amateurs

Theater des Westens
Kantstraße 12, 10623 **Berlin**
Tel: 30-319 03-0 Fax: 30-3190 3188
Internet: theater-des-westens.de
E-Mail: info@theater-des-westens.de
Intendant und Künstlerischer Leiter Prof. Elmar Ottential; Stellvertredender Intendant und Künstlerischer Leiter Jürg Burth
Dancers: varies *Perfs:* 260 *No of Prods:* 3-4 *Type:* musicals *Accomp:* orchestra *Venues:* Theater des Westens 1354 *Touring:* national *Comments:* guest performances; see also Drama and Opera

Thomas Guggi Tanz / Theaterproduktionen
Danziger Str. 57, 10435 **Berlin**
Tel: 30-442 6353 Fax: 30-441 2556
Direktor Thomas Guggi
Dancers: 10 *Perfs:* 30 *No of Prods:* 6 *Type:* modern, contemporary dance, circus, mime *Accomp:* recorded, live *Venues:* guest performances (municipal halls, open-air, European stages, railway stations) *Touring:* France, Deutschland, Itay *Comments:* touring company; main emphasis: international co productions

Toladá Dance Company
c/o Tmim, Mommsenstr. 23, 10629 **Berlin**
Tel: 30-3270 6008 Fax: 30-3270 6008
artistic director Joseph Tmim
Dancers: 6-8 *Perfs:* 60 *No of Prods:* 2-4 *Type:* modern dance *Accomp:* live, recorded *Venues:* Theater am Halleschen Ufer 250

Ballett des Theaters Bielefeld
Postfach 10 03 53, 33503 **Bielefeld**
Tel: 521-512 502 Fax: 521-513 430
Intendantin Regula Gerber; Musikdramaturgie Dr. Astrid Schweimler; technischer Direktor Detlef Plümecke; Ballettdirektor Philip Lansdale; Ballettdramaturgie Carsten Thuesen; Trainingsleiterin Sabine Lütz
Dancers: 11 *Perfs:* 22 *No of Prods:* 2 *Type:* neo-classical, modern *Accomp:* live, playback/tape *Venues:* Bühnen der Stadt Bielefeld (Großes Haus 775, Kleines Haus 304) *Comments:* visiting address: Brunnenstr. 3-9, 33602 Bielefeld; see also Opera, Drama and Orchestra

Choreographisches Theater Bonn
Am Boeselagerhof 1, 53111 **Bonn**
Tel: 228-778 000 Fax: 228-728 371
Internet: www.uni-bonn.de/theaterbonn
E-Mail: oper@bonn.de
Generalintendant Dr Manfred Beilharz; Direktor des Choreographischen Theaters Pavel Miskulastik; Chefdramatury Dr Paul Esterhazy; Öffentlichkeitsarbeit Dr Marie Luise Maintz; Kaufmämmischer Direktor Rolf Oltmanns
Dancers: 12 + guests *Perfs:* 30 *No of Prods:* 4 (3 new) *Type:* choreographic theatre *Accomp:* live, recorded *Venues:* Grosses Haus 1040, Werkstattbühne 150 *Comments:* see also Opera

Ballett Braunschweig – Staatstheater Braunschweig
Postfach 45 39, 38035 **Braunschweig**
Tel: 531-123 4152 Fax: 531-123 4153
Internet: www.staatstheater-braunschweig.de
E-Mail: service@staatstheater-braunchschweig.de
Generalintendant Wolfgang Gropper; Ballettdirektor u. Chefchoreograph Pierre Wyss; 1.Ballettmeister & Trainingsleiter Claudio Schellino; Ballettmeister und Trainingsleiter Piero Rocchetti; Organisation Delia Schorhtschabel
Dancers: 16 *Perfs:* 60-70 *No of Prods:* 6 *Type:* neo-classical, modern *Accomp:* recorded, live *Venues:* Grosses Haus 900, Neues Kleines Haus 283 *Touring:* guest performances in China, Croatia, Germany *Comments:* visiting address: Am Theater, 38100 Braunschweig; see also Opera

Sylvia Heyden Solo – Sylvia Heyden & Company
Hamburger Straße 273b, 38114 **Braunschweig**
Tel: 531-332 271 Fax: 531-790 431
Künstlerische Leitung, Choreographie und Management Sylvia Heyden
Dancers: 8 *Perfs:* 30 *No of Prods:* 6 *Type:* modern dance, dance theatre, experimental *Accomp:* recorded, live *Venues:* T.A.N.Z. 99, Staatstheater Braunschweig and others *Comments:* own dance school called T.A.N.Z.

Bremer Tanztheater
Postfach 10 10 46, 28010 **Bremen**
Tel: 421-365 3374 Fax: 421-365 3234
Internet: www.bremertheater.com
E-Mail: info@bremertheater.com
Generalintendant Dr. Klaus Pierwoß; Tanztheater Susanne Linke, Urs Dietrich; GMD Günter Neuhold; Verwaltungsleiter Jens Walter
Dancers: 13 *Perfs:* 49 *No of Prods:* 4-5 *Type:* dance-theatre *Accomp:* recorded, live *Venues:* Schauspielhaus 320 *Touring:* Spain, France, Europe *Comments:* visiting address: Am Goetheplatz 1-3, 28203 Bremen; see also Drama and Opera

Ballett des Stadttheaters Bremerhaven
Postfach 12 05 41, 27519 **Bremerhaven**
Tel: 471-482 060 Fax: 471-4820 6274
Internet: www.brem.de-info-bremerhaven-theater-index.htm
Intendant Peter Grisebach; Ballettdirektor Ricardo Fernando
Dancers: 10 *Perfs:* 30 *No of Prods:* 4 *Type:* classical, modern *Accomp:* live, recorded *Venues:* Kleines Haus 122, Kinder- u. Jugendtheater, Niederdeutsche Bühne, Theater im Fischereihafen 300, Musik-und Konzertsaal Karl-Schwz-Kaserne 715, Cinema 330, Stadthalle 1000, Cityport 1400 *Comments:* visiting address: Theodor-Heuss-Platz, 27568 Bremerhaven; see also Opera, Drama and Orchestras.

Ballett Company der Städtischen Theater Chemnitz
Käthe-Kollwitz-Straße 7, 09111 **Chemnitz**
Tel: 371-696 9860 (Ballettdir.) Fax: 371-696 9860 (Ballettdir.)
Internet: www.freiepresse.de/theater-chemnitz
E-Mail: theater-chemnitz@abo.freiepresse.de
Generalintendant Rolf Stiska; Ballettbetriebsdirektor Gottfried Messenbrink; Generalmusikdirektor Oleg Caetani; Ballettdirektor und Chefchoreograph Ricardo Fernando; Trainingsmeister/Choreograph Vladimir Fedianine
Dancers: 28 *No of Prods:* 10 (5 new) *Type:* classical, dance-theatre *Accomp:* recorded, live *Venues:* Opernhaus Chemnitz 713 *Comments:* see also Drama, Opera and Orchestras

Ballett des Landestheaters Coburg
Großes Haus, Schlossplatz 6, 96450 **Coburg**
Tel: 9561-8850 Fax: 9561-793 979
Intendant Norbert Kleine-Borgmann; Ballettdirektor Neng-Sheng Yu
Dancers: 13 *Perfs:* 35 (ballet only) *No of Prods:* 3 + 1 workshop *Type:* modern, classic, theater *Accomp:* live, recorded *Venues:* Theater in der Reithalle, Grosses Haus 557 *Comments:* see also Drama, Opera and Orchestras

Staatstheater Cottbus, Musiktheater/Ballett
Karl-Liebknecht-Straße 136, 03046 **Cottbus**
Tel: 355-78240 Fax: 355-791 333
Geschäftsführ. Direktor Steffen Rohr; Chefchoreograph & künstlerischer Leiter des Ballets David Sutherland; Trainingsleiter/Assistent Mark Loomis; Ballettmeisterin Sigrid Kreßmann-Brück; Chordirektor Christian Mobius; technischer Direktor Matthias Günther
Dancers: 8 *Perfs:* 420 (in total) *No of Prods:* 7 *Type:* contemporary, modern ballet & dance *Accomp:* recorded *Venues:* Großes Haus 678, Kammerbühne 140 *Comments:* see also Opera, Drama and Orchestras

Tanz/Theater Darmstadt
Marienplatz 2, 64283 **Darmstadt**
Tel: 6151-281 1204 Fax: 6151-281 1226
Intendant Gerd-Theo Umberg; Leiterin des Tanztheaters Birgitta Trommler
Dancers: 9 + guests *Perfs:* 16 + 9 guest performances *No of Prods:* 2 *Type:* dance theatre *Accomp:* live, recorded *Venues:* Staatstheater Großes Haus 956, Kleines Haus 482, Werkstatt Bühne 99 *Touring:* Europe *Comments:* see also Drama and Opera

Ballett des Anhaltischen Theaters Dessau
Postfach 1203, 06812 **Dessau**
Tel: 340-2511-0 Fax: 340-251 1215
Internet: www.anhaltisches~theater.de
E-Mail: anhaltisches.theater.dram@topmail.de
Generalintendant Johannes Felsenstein; Choreograph Gonzalo Galguera; Verwaltungsdirektor Joachim Landgraf; Chefdramaturg Wolfgang Lange
Dancers: 20-25 *Perfs:* 9 (+ 11) *No of Prods:* ca. 2 *Accomp:* live, recorded *Venues:* Großes Haus 1096, Bühne 200 *Touring:* national *Comments:* see also Opera, Drama, Orchestra and Puppets

Ballet Director
Ivan Liška
National Theatre
Munich

Principals/
Soloists
Lisa-Maree Cullum
Maria Eichwald
Elena Pankova
Judith Turos
Anna Villadolid
Kusha Alexi
Natalja Trokaj
Beate Vollack
Alen Bottaini
Kirill Melnikov
Oliver Wehe
Norbert Graf
Udo Kersten
Luca Masala
Dirk Segers
Patrick Teschner

Guests
Darcey Bussell
Evelyn Hart
Susan Jaffe
Uljana Lopatkina
Elisabeth Platel
Ethan Stiefel
Vladimir Derevianko
Adam Cooper

Repertory
99/2000
Apollo
Artifact II
La Bayadère
Chaconne
A Cinderella Story
Concerto Barocco
Don Quijote
Emma B.
Giselle
Giselle- Mats Ek
Die Kameliendame
Onegin
Sarkasmen
the second detail
Terpsichore Gala 1
The Unsung
Die vier
Temperamente
Zakouski

Creations
Petruschka
Le Sacre du Printemps

Choreographers
George Balanchine
Patrice Bart
Ray Barra
Lucinda Childs
John Cranko
Mats Ek
William Forsythe
Jean Grand-Maître
Amir Hosseinpour
Leonid Jakobson
Jiři Kylián
José Limòn
Hans van Manen
Peter Martins
John Neumeier
Marius Petipa
Saburo Teshigawara
Sir Peter Wright

Bayerisches
Staatsorchester
Conductors:
André Presser
Gabriel Feltz
Markus Lehtinen

Information:
Telephone
089/2185-1711
Telefax
089/2185-1703

Ballett des Landestheaters Detmold
Theaterplatz 1, 32756 **Detmold**
Tel: 5231-97460 Fax: 5231-974 701
Internet: www.landestheaterdetmold.de
E-Mail: 113217.3637@compuserve.com
Intendant Ulf Reiher; Ballettdirektorin Elisa Genova; Leiter des Musiktheaters Raines Worms
Dancers: 11 *Perfs:* 640 (in total) *No of Prods:* 7 (4 new) (in total) *Type:* dance-theatre *Accomp:* live, recorded *Venues:* Großes Haus 676, Studiobühne 90 *Comments:* see also Drama, Opera and Orchestras

Ballett der Städtischen Bühnen Dortmund
Kuhstraße 12, 44137 **Dortmund**
Tel: 231-502 5547/6079
Fax: 231-502 2479/22461
Internet: www.dortmund.de/theater
E-Mail: theater@dortmund.de
Generalintendant John Dew; Ballettmeister Zoltán Ravasz; GMD Anton Marik; Choreographin Mei Hong Lin, Jean Renshaw
Dancers: 22 *Perfs:* 85 *No of Prods:* 6 *Type:* modern, classical *Accomp:* live, recorded *Venues:* Opernhaus 1160, Schauspielhaus 496 *Touring:* Netherlands *Comments:* see also Opera, Orchestras and Drama

Ballett der Staatsoperette Dresden
Pirnaer Landstr. 131, 01257 **Dresden**
Tel: 351-207 990 Fax: 351-207 9922
Intendant Fritz Wendrich; Ballettdirektorin Michael Apel; Musikdirektor Volker M Blangg; Ausstattungsleiterin Sabine Pommerening; Stellvertretende Ballettdirektorin Brigitte Richter
Dancers: 19 *Perfs:* 300 *No of Prods:* 4 *Type:* musicals *Accomp:* live *Venues:* Großes Saal 604, Theater Casino 60 *Touring:* Germany *Comments:* see also Opera

Coogan Dancers
Behrischstr. 17, 01277 **Dresden**
Tel: 351-311 8248 Fax: 351-311 8248
E-Mail: cooganbrandt@t-online.de
Choreograph u. Künstlerische Leiterin Jenny Coogan; Komponist Jörg Seibold; Licht Rainer Ludwig
Dancers: 4-8 *No of Prods:* 1 *Type:* contemporary *Accomp:* recorded *Touring:* Europe

Sächsische Staatsoper Dresden – Ballett Dresden
Theaterplatz 2, 01067 **Dresden**
Tel: 351-491 1469 Fax: 351-491 1669
Internet: www.semperoper.de
Intendant Christoph Albrecht; Ballettdirektor Vladimir Derevianko; Ballettbetriebsdirektor Dieter Lösche
Dancers: 56 *Perfs:* 68 *No of Prods:* 1 *Type:* classical, neoclassical, modern *Accomp:* live (Staatskapelle Dresden) *Venues:* Zuschauerplatze 1320, Kleine Szene 99 *Touring:* Italy, Germany, Switzerland *Comments:* see also Opera

Ballett der Deutschen Oper am Rhein Düsseldorf-Duisburg
Opernhaus, Niederkasseler Kirchweg 36, 40547 **Düsseldorf**
Tel: 211-890 8340 Fax: 211-890 8343
Ballettdirektor Youri Vàmos; künstl. Assistent und Leiter Ballettschule Leon Kjellsson; Betriebsleitung und Management Oliver Königsfeld
Dancers: 50 *Perfs:* 90 *No of Prods:* 5 *Type:* classical ballet, modern *Accomp:* live, recorded *Venues:* Opernhaus, Düsseldorf 1342, Theater der Stadt Duisburg 1118 *Touring:* Italy, Switzerland *Comments:* see also Opera

Neuer Tanz
Marstall Schloß Benrath, 40593 **Düsseldorf**
Tel: 211-718 7777 Fax: 211-710 3291
künstlerische Leitung, Autor VA Wölfl; Referentin Barbara Sydow
Dancers: 7-10 *Perfs:* 40 *No of Prods:* 1 *Type:* new dance *Accomp:* live, recorded *Venues:* Marstall 80 *Touring:* Europe

Theater der Klänge
Winkelsfelderstr. 21, 40477 **Düsseldorf**
Tel: 211-462 746 Fax: 211-467 722
Internet: www.folkwang.uni-essen.de/TdK/
E-Mail: THEATER-DER-KLAENGE@t-online.de
Direktor/künstlerische Leitung Jörg U. Lensing; musikalische Leitung Thomas Neuhaus; Balletdirektoren Jacqueline Fischer, Kerstin Hörner
Dancers: 4 permanent + guest artists *Perfs:* 40 *No of Prods:* 2 *Type:* modern dance theatre *Accomp:* recorded, live *Touring:* Europe *Comments:* acting, dance and music fusion; see also Drama

Ballett des Thüringer Landestheaters Eisenach-Rudolstadt-Saalfeld
Theaterplatz 4-7, 99817 **Eisenach**
Tel: 3691-2560 Fax: 3691-256 159
Intendant u. künstlerischer Geschäftsführer Johannes Steurich; Balletmeisterin Sabine Pecheul; Generalmusikdirektor Wolfgang Wappler
Dancers: 10 *Perfs:* 40 *No of Prods:* 2 *Type:* modern, classical *Accomp:* live, recorded *Venues:* Theater 630, Theater Rudolstadt 300 *Comments:* see also Drama, Orchestra and Opera

Ballett des Theaters Erfurt
Postfach 244, 99084 **Erfurt**
Tel: 361-223 3100 Fax: 361-223 3120
Internet: www.theater-erfurt.de
E-Mail: alanger@theater-erfurt.de
Intendant Dietrich Taube; Musikdirektor Wolfgang Rögner; Ballettdirektor Jürgen Heiss; Chefdramturg Dr Klaus Gronau
Dancers: 18 (16 group dancers, 2 soloists) *Perfs:* 40-50 *No of Prods:* 3 *Type:* ballet, modern *Accomp:* live, recorded *Venues:* Schauspielhaus 420, Kleine Bühne 73, Kuppeltheater 685 *Comments:* Visiting address: Walkmühlstr. 13, 99084 Erfurt; see also Opera, Drama and Orchestras

Ensemble Tako
Forstmannstr. 27, 45239 **Essen**
Tel: 201-409 362 Fax: 201-409 362
E-Mail: sdscarde@aol.com
artistic directors Stefan Hilterhaus, Olimpia Scardi
Dancers: 4 *Perfs:* 15-20 *No of Prods:* 1 *Type:* modern dance-theatre *Accomp:* recorded, live (specially composed and performed music) *Venues:* various theatres in North Rhine-Westphalia *Touring:* Germany *Comments:* working mostly for theatre and opera

Essener Ballett im Aalto Theater
Opernplatz 10, 45128 **Essen**
Tel: 201-8122-0 Fax: 201-812 2242
Internet: www.theater-essen.de
E-Mail: infoaalto@theater-essen.de
Geschäftsführer Otmar Herren; Ballettdirektor Prof. Martin Puttke
Dancers: 30 *Perfs:* 46 *No of Prods:* 5 *Type:* classical ballet, modern *Accomp:* live, recorded *Venues:* Aalto Theater 1125 *Comments:* see also Opera, Drama and Orchestras

Folkwang Tanzstudio
Klemensborn 39, 45239 **Essen**
Tel: 201-490 3109/189 Fax: 201-490 3110/110
Leitung Henrietta Hom; Künstlerische Leitung Pina Bausch; Organisation/PR Claudia Lüttringhaus
Dancers: 11 *Perfs:* 20-30 *No of Prods:* 2 *Type:* modern, dance theatre *Accomp:* recorded *Venues:* Folkwang Hochschule 377 *Touring:* international

Tanztheater Christine Brunel
Brunostr. 23, 45130 **Essen**
Tel: 201-770 183 Fax: 201-770 183
Organisation Claudia Lüttinghaus; Choreographin u. Kontakt Christine Brunel
Dancers: 3-5 *Perfs:* 20-30 *No of Prods:* 2 *Type:* dance theatre, contemporary *Accomp:* recorded, live *Venues:* Tanztheater 60 *Touring:* international

Malaika Kusumi Ballet Theatre Frankfurt
Mörfelder Landstr. 68HH, 60598 **Frankfurt**
Tel: 69-6199 5263 Fax: 69-6199 5265
artistic director Malaika Kusumi; management Daphna Baum; assitant manager Karin Femers; office manager Aizen Kusumi; production assistant Serkan Gül
Dancers: 10-15 *No of Prods:* 7 *Type:* ballet theatre, neo-classical, contemporary, modern *Accomp:* CD, live *Venues:* Schauspielhaus Frankfurt 663, Theater Hameln 688, Friedrich Wolf Theater in Eisenhüttenstadt 720, Staatstheater Kassel – Schauspielhaus 400 *Touring:* Germany, North America, Sweden, Netherlands

Company Vivienne Newport
Elbestr. 17, 60329 **Frankfurt am Main**
Tel: 69-252 974 Fax: 69-252 974
E-Mail: vivnewcomp@aol.com
artistic director Vivienne Newport
Dancers: 7 (actors/dancers) *Perfs:* 30 *No of Prods:* 1 *Type:* dance theatre *Accomp:* recorded, live

Dansa Dansa
Schneckenhofstr. 20, 60596 **Frankfurt am Main**
Tel: 69-623 117/616 058 Fax: 69-616 058
Choreographin und Leiterin Chananjah Plößer
Dancers: 5 (+2 musicians) *Perfs:* 20 *No of Prods:* 3-4 *Type:* dance theatre, expressionist, new dance *Accomp:* live, recorded *Touring:* Germany *Comments:* some fixed/set pieces/choreographies, but also live improvised performances with jazz musicians

Frankfurt Ballet
Untermainanlage 11, 60311 **Frankfurt am Main**
Tel: 69-2123 7319 Fax: 69-2123 7177
Internet: frankfurt-ballett.de
E-Mail: ballett.frankfurt@stadt-frankfurt.de
Intendant u. künstlerischer Direktor William Forsythe; künstlerisches Betriebsbüro Urs Frey; Werbung Christine Wetzel; Presse Mechtild Rühl
Dancers: 34 *Perfs:* 100 *No of Prods:* 5 *Type:* modern ballet *Accomp:* recorded, live *Venues:* Opernhaus 1300, Schauspielhaus 800, TAT up to 450 *Touring:* Spain, Portugal, Sicilly, Belgium, Germany, France, Austria, Czech Republic *Comments:* see also Drama (TAT and Städlische Bulineu) and Venues (TAT)

Freies Tanztheater Frankfurt
Wilhelm-Leuschnerstr. 13, 60329 **Frankfurt am Main**
Tel: 69-252 393 Fax: 69-232 485
Inhaberin u. Choreographin Marie-Luise Thiele
Dancers: 1-10 *Perfs:* 25-30 *No of Prods:* 2 *Type:* dance-theatre, modern dance, performance *Accomp:* live, recorded *Venues:* various venues in Frankfurt *Touring:* Europe

Helena Waldmann
Eckenheimer Landstr. 56, 60318 **Frankfurt am Main**
Tel: 69-597 3719/ 171 832 0017 (mobile) Fax: 69-597 5643
Internet: www.arc.de/22
E-Mail: helenaw@compuserve.com
Regisseurin Helena Waldmann
Dancers: varies *Perfs:* 100 *No of Prods:* 7 *Type:* performance arts, cross-over dance, video, light, music, voice, space *Accomp:* live, singing, recorded, video, dj *Venues:* Künstlerhaus Mousonturm, Frankfurt am Main *Touring:* national, international *Comments:* agency: Ecotopia, Tel: 7141-903 384, Fax: 7141-903 385

Leibliches Theater Köln
Triftweg 35, 50226 **Frechen**
Tel: 2234-691 860 Fax: 2234-691 860
contact Eva Schmale
Dancers: varies *Perfs:* 20 *No of Prods:* 1 *Type:* developed own dance form = Leibliches theater *Accomp:* mostly recorded, sometimes live *Venues:* various venues *Touring:* Germany, international

Ballett Freiburg Pretty Ugly
Bertoldstr. 46, 79098 **Freiburg**
Tel: 761-201 2970 Fax: 761-202 4614
Internet: www.pudg.org
E-Mail: ballet@uni-freiburg.de
artistic director Amanda Miller; managing director Daniel Nicolai
Dancers: 11 *Perfs:* 55 *No of Prods:* 4 *Type:* contemporary *Accomp:* recorded, live *Comments:* alternative E-mail: ballet@pudg.org; see also Drama, Opera, Orchestras and Festivals (for Städtische Bühnen)

Choreographisches Theater der Städtischen Bühnen Freiburg
Comments: please see Ballet Freiburg Pretty Ugly

Freiburger Tanztheater Oberlinden
Oberlinden 4, 79098 **Freiburg**
Tel: 761-30479/763-38671 Fax: 763-38671
artistic director Eva Weismann
Dancers: 10 *Perfs:* 5-20 *No of Prods:* 2 *Types:* modern, dance theatre *Accomp:* live *Touring:* national

moving art company
c/o bewegungs-art, Guntramstr 52, 79106 **Freiburg**
Tel: 761-276 167
contact Bernd Ka
Comments: organise annual festival New Dance Tage in October; during 1999 the company suspended activities, it might restart in 2000, at time of going to print no more information was available

Tanztheater Renate Killmann
Högestr. 15, 79108 **Freiburg**
Tel: 7665-912 877 Fax: 7665-912 892
Choreographin und Leiterin Renate Killmann
Dancers: 6-7 *Perfs:* 8-10 *No of Prods:* 1 *Type:* modern dance, dance-theatre *Accomp:* live, recorded *Venues:* E.Werk Freiburg 280, Morathalle 150

Ballett Schindowski
Schillertheater NRW, Kennedyplatz, 45881 **Gelsenkirchen**
Tel: 209-409 7138 Fax: 209-409 7262
Internet: www.schillertheater-nrw.de
E-Mail: b.schindowski@cityweb.de
Intendant Ludwig Baum; Ballettdirektor Bernd Schindowski; Ballett-Manager Alberto Salvagnini
Dancers: 20 *Perfs:* 70 *No of Prods:* 6-7 *Type:* contemporary ballet *Accomp:* live, recorded *Venues:* Grosses Haus 1008, Kleines Haus 350, Oper Wuppertal 845, Schauspielhaus Wuppertal 750

Ballet der Altenburg Gera Theater GmbH
Bühnen der Stadt Gera
Küchengartenallee 2, 07548 **Gera**
Tel: 365-82790 Fax: 365-827 9135
Internet: www.theater.altenburg.gera.de
E-Mail: boehme-pock@t-online.de
Generalintendant Michael Grosse; Ballettdirektor Siegfried Martin Wende; Choreograph Peter Werner; Ballett- und Trainingsmeisterin Anait Gregorian
Dancers: 34 *No of Prods:* 4 (2 new) *Type:* classical ballet, modern *Accomp:* live, recorded *Venues:* Theatersaal Gera 670, Theatersaal Altenburg 544 *Touring:* national, international *Comments:* address of Theater Altenburg: Theaterplatz 19, 04600 Altenburg, Tel: 3447-5850, Fax: 3447-585/86; see also Opera, Drama and Orchestras

Tanzcompagnie Gießen
Berliner Platz, 35390 **Gießen**
Tel: 641-79570 Fax: 641-795 780
Intendant Guy Montovan; Kommisarischer GMD Herbert Gietzen
Dancers: 9 *Perfs:* 40 *No of Prods:* 4 (3 new) *Type:* modern dance *Accomp:* recorded, live *Venues:* Stadttheater 574, Theaterstudio 199 *Comments:* see also Drama, Opera, Orchestra and Venues

Ballett des Theater Görlitz
Demianiplatz 2, 02809 **Görlitz**
Tel: 3581-474 721/22 Fax: 3581-474 736
Internet: www.via-regia.de
E-Mail: Theater-Goerlitz@t-online.de
Intendant Dr. Michael Wieler; Chefdirigent Christof Escher; Ballettdirektor Franz Huyer
Dancers: 16 + 3 guests *Perfs:* 3 *No of Prods:* 1 *Type:* classical, modern *Accomp:* live, recorded *Venues:* Theater Görlitz 604, Foyer 85, Appollo 99, Untermarkt (Freiluft), Scheunel Ludrsigsdorf, Gerhard-Hauptmann-Theater (Zittau), Deutsch-Sorbisches-Volkstheater (Bauzen), Lausitzhalle (Hoyerswerda) Lessing-Theater (Kamenz) *Touring:* Poland, Czech Republic, Germany *Comments:* alternative Internet: www.goerlitz.de; see also Opera

Theater Vorpommern (Ballet)
Postfach 179, 17461 **Greifswald**
Tel: 3834-57220/572 255 (box office)
Fax: 3834-502 779
Internet: www.theatervorpommern.de/
E-Mail: theater@t-online.de
Intendant/Geschäftsführer Rüdiger Bloch; Verwaltung/Geschäftsführer Joachim von Trützschler; künstlerischer Leiter d. Ballets Ralf Dörnen
Dancers: 13 + guests *Perfs:* 75 *No of Prods:* 4 *Type:* classical, modern *Accomp:* live (orchestra) *Venues:* Großes Haus (Greifswald) 460, Großes Haus (Stralsund) 520 *Touring:* Hannover – Expo 2000 *Comments:* see also Opera and Drama

Ballett Theater Hagen
Elberfelder Strasse 65, 58095 **Hagen**
Tel: 2331-207 3210 Fax: 2331-207 2446
Internet: www.hagen.de/THEATER/welcome.html
E-Mail: theater@stadt-hagen.de
Intendant Peter Pietzsch; Ballettmeister und Leiter des Balletts Gabor Tarfs
Dancers: 16 *No of Prods:* 4 *Venues:* Großes Haus 800, Theater Cafe 110, Tor2 300 *Touring:* regional *Comments:* see also Opera & Orchestras

Ballett des Nordharzer Städtebundtheaters
Spiegelstrasse 20A, 38820 **Halberstadt**
Tel: 3941-6965-0/3946-96220
Fax: 3941-442 652/3946-962 220
Internet: www.halberstadt.de/theater
E-Mail: theater@halberstadt.de
Intendant Gero Hammer; Musikdirektor Christian Hammer; Oberspielleiter Musiktheater Horst Kupich; Ballettmeister Tarek Azzam; 1. Kapellmeister/Studienleiter John Lawson Webber; Oberspielleiter Schauspiel Klaus-Udo Klix; Chefdramaturg Dieter Braun; Ausstattungsleiter Frank Borisch
Dancers: 15 *Perfs:* 520 (in total) *No of Prods:* 30 (in total) *Type:* classical, modern

Ballett des Opernhauses Halle
Universitätsring 24, 06108 **Halle (Saale)**
Tel: 345-51100 Fax: 345-511 0333
Internet: www.opernhaus.halle.de
E-Mail: opernhaus@halle.de
Intendant Klaus Froboese; Ballettdirektor und Chefchoreograph Ralf Rossa
Dancers: 24 *Perfs:* 31 *No of Prods:* 5 (2) *Type:* modern dance-theatre, classical ballet *Accomp:* live, recorded *Venues:* Großer Saal 672, Kammertheater 120 *Comments:* see also Opera & Orchestras

Hamburg Ballett
Ballettzentrum Hamburg John Neumeier, Caspar-Voght-Strasse 54, 20535 **Hamburg**
Tel: 40-211 1880 Fax: 40-2111 8888
Internet: www.hamburgballett.de
E-Mail: presse@hamburgballett.de
Ballettintendant & Chefchoreograph John Neumeier; Ballettbetriebsdirektorin Ulrike Schmidt; Presse und Öffentlichkeitsarbeit Sascha Merlin; Tourneeleitung Katharina Benthaak; Produktionsdramaturgie Angela Dauber
Dancers: 56 *Perfs:* 100 *No of Prods:* 10 *Type:* ballet which is influenced and based on the choreography of John Neumeier & guest choreographers *Accomp:* live, recorded *Venues:* Hamburgische Staatsoper 1672 *Touring:* France, South America *Comments:* box office: Hamburgische Staatsoper, Große Theater Str. 34/35, 20354 Hamburg, tel. 40-351 721 ; see also Opera

Triknia Kábhelioz Danza Contemporánea
c/o Carlos Jaramillo, Langenhorner Chaussee 50, 22335 **Hamburg**
Tel: 40-532 1291/531 3606/171-471 8177 (mobile)
Fax: 40-533 9011
Internet: www.triknia.de
E-Mail: TrikniaKabhelioz@compuserve.com
general director Sonya Rima; administrative director León Jairo Mora; artistic director & choreographer Carlos Jaramillo; secretary Hellena Stemm
Dancers: 4 *No of Prods:* 6 (1 new)
Type: contemporary (with Colombian, AfroCaribbean & Latin American elements) *Accomp:* recorded, live *Touring:* national, international

YANCI
c/o Kaleidoscope Presentations, Kleiberweg 144a, 22547 **Hamburg**
Tel: 40-8407 9397 Fax: 40-8407 9397
Internet: www.yanci.com
E-Mail: yanci@yanci.com
contact Julia Plückebaum
Dancers: 4 *Type:* pantomime, visual theater, mask theater, magic *Comments:* touring company

Ballett der Niedersächsischen Staatstheater Hannover GmbH
Opernhaus, Opernplatz 1, 30159 **Hannover**
Tel: 511-1684 6110 Fax: 511-363 2536
Internet: www.staatstheater-hannover.com
Intendant Hans-Peter Lehmann; Ballettdirektor Mehmet Balkan; Betriebsbüro Dieter Kreuzer; Generalmusikdirektor Herr Delft; Öffentlichkeitsarbeit Barbara Krüger (tel: 511-1684 6124, fax: 511-363 2536)
Dancers: 38 *Perfs:* 42 *No of Prods:* 6 *Type:* classical and modern ballet *Accomp:* live *Venues:* Opernhaus 1207 *Comments:* see also Opera, Orchestras and Drama

Commedia Futura
Eisfabrik, Seilerstr 15-17, 30171 **Hannover**
Tel: 511-816 353 Fax: 511-816 353
Regisseure Wolfgang A. Piontek; Künstlerischer Leiter Wolfgang Piontek; Öffentlichkeitsarbeit u. Dramaturgie Peter Piontek
Dancers: 5-10 *Perfs:* 80 *No of Prods:* 2-3 *Type:* multimedia dance theater *Accomp:* live, recorded *Venues:* Schwarzer Saal, Zentralhalle 99 *Touring:* Europe *Comments:* see also Drama and Venues (Eisfabrik, Hannover)

Heidelberg Ballett
Tanztheater Heidelberg, Friedrichstraße 5, 69117 **Heidelberg**
Tel: 622-583 508 Fax: 622-583 599
Intendant Dr. Volkmar Clauß; Generalmusikdirektor Thomas Kalb; Chefdisponentin Christa Oser
Dancers: 12 *Perfs:* 500-600 (incl drama & opera) *No of Prods:* 3 *Type:* modern ballet with a strong theatrical content *Accomp:* recorded & live *Venues:* Städtische Bühnen 619, Studio 130 *Comments:* see also Opera, Drama and Orchestras

Tanzkompanie des Stadttheaters Hildesheim
Theaterstraße 6, 31141 **Hildesheim**
Tel: 5121-169 359 Fax: 5121-169 393
Intendant Dr. Martin Kreutzberg; Ballettdirektor Ralf Jaroschinski; Referentin Simone David
Dancers: 11 *Perfs:* 110 *No of Prods:* 10 (6 dance & 4 music theatre) *Type:* contemporary *Accomp:* live, recorded *Venues:* Stadttheater Grosses Haus 600+ *Touring:* national, France

Ballett des Städtebundtheaters Hof
Kulmbacherstr. 5, 95030 **Hof**
Tel: 9281-70700 Fax: 9281-707 0299
Internet: www.theater-hof.com
E-Mail: info@theater-hof.com
Intendant Uwe Drechsel; Generalmusikdirektor Golo Berg; stellv. GMD Philipp Pointner; künstlerisches Betriebsbüro u. Disposition Petra Gorki; Chefdramaturg Thomas Schindler; Musikdramaturgin Michaela Peterseil; Ltrin. Marketing Petra Müller; Ballettdirektor Jerzy Graczyk; Choreographieassistent/Ballettassistentin Barbara Buser; Spielleiterin/Schauspiel Helga Fleig
Dancers: 13 *Perfs:* 20 (in total with music theatre 120) *No of Prods:* 2 *Type:* classical, modern *Accomp:* live, recorded *Venues:* Stadttheater 567, Studio 99 *Touring:* Germany *Comments:* see also Drama and Opera

Doris Schaefer Tanztheater Regenbogen Koblenz
Brunnenstr. 12b, 56829 **Kail**
Tel: 2672-910 777 Fax: 2672-910 778
Verwaltung Csongor Kölcze; Choreograph Doris Schaefer
Dancers: 8 *Perfs:* 30 *No of Prods:* 1 *Type:* modern and classical ballet *Accomp:* live, recorded *Touring:* Germany *Comments:* touring company

Ballett des Pfalztheaters Kaiserslautern
Willy-Brandt-Platz, 67655 **Kaiserslautern**
Tel: 631-3675-0 Fax: 631-307 5213
Intendant Wolfgang Quetes; Ballettdirektor Eva Reinthaller; GMD Lior Shambadal; Künstl. Betriebsdirektor Peter Bachmaier
Dancers: 16 *No of Prods:* 1 *Accomp:* live, recorded *Venues:* Großes Haus 720 *Comments:* see also Opera, Orchestras and Drama

Ballett des Badischen Staatstheaters – Danza Vista
Badisches Staatstheater Karlsruhe, 76125 **Karlsruhe**
Tel: 721-35570
Fax: 721-373 223 (Verwaltung)/355 7155 (Intendanz)
Internet: www.karlsruhe.de/kultur/staatstheater
E-Mail: kartenverkauf@bstaatstheater.bwl.de
Generalintendant Pavel Fieber; künstlerische Betriebsdirektorin Gudrun Pappermann; Verwaltungsdirektor Wolfgang Sieber; Ballettdirektor Olaf Schmidt; Presse-und Öffentlichkeitsarbeit Anna-Renate Sörgel
Dancers: 34 *Perfs:* 253 (ballet, opera, musical) *No of Prods:* 4 *Type:* classical and modern *Accomp:* recorded *Venues:* Großes Haus 1002, Kleines Haus 385 *Comments:* venue address: Baumeisterstr.11, 76137 Karlsruhe, see also Opera, Drama, Orchestra and Festivals

Ballett des Staatstheaters Kassel
Friedrichsplatz 15, 34117 **Kassel**
Tel: 561-10940 Fax: 561-109 4204
Intendant Prof. Dr. Christoph Nix; Ballettdirektor Henning Paar; Ballettrepetitor Maciej Janaszkiewicz
Dancers: 16 *Perfs:* 140 *No of Prods:* 3 *Type:* classical, modern, jazz *Accomp:* live, recorded *Venues:* Opernhaus 953, Schauspielhaus 540, Frizz 99, Casanova 99 *Comments:* see also Drama, Orchestras and Opera

Ballett der Bühnen der Landeshauptstadt Kiel
Theater Kiel, Rathausplatz 4, 24103 **Kiel**
Tel: 431-901 2858 Fax: 431-9016 2858
Internet: www.kiel.de
E-Mail: buehnen@lhstadt.kiel.de
Künstlerisches Leitungsteam Kirsten Harms, Raymund Richter; Ballettdirektor Stephan Thoß; Balletdramaturg t.b.a.
Dancers: 17 *Perfs:* 30-40 *No of Prods:* 5-6 *Type:* contemporary ballet and dance *Accomp:* live, recorded *Venues:* Opernhaus 822, Schauspielhaus 411 *Comments:* see also Drama, Opera and Orchestra

Theater der Stadt Koblenz
Clemensstrasse 1, 56068 **Koblenz**
Tel: 261-129 2870 Fax: 261-129 2800
Internet: www.koblenz.de/~kultur/theater
Intendant Annegret Ritzel; Ballettmeister und Choreograph Anthony Taylor
Dancers: 16 *Perfs:* 35 *No of Prods:* 2 *Type:* classical ballet *Accomp:* live, recorded *Venues:* Große Haus am Deinhardplatz 501 *Comments:* see also Drama and Opera

Arrazzo Tanztheater
Theresienstr. 94, 50931 **Köln**
Tel: 221-279 0668 Fax: 221-279 0668
E-Mail: arrazzo@uni-bonn.de
artistic direction and choreographer Gabrielle Staiger
Dancers: varies *Perfs:* 50 *No of Prods:* 9 *Type:* physical theatre, contemporary dance *Accomp:* recorded *Touring:* Germany, Japan *Comments:* also site-specific and video dance productions; touring company

Britta Lieberknecht & Technicians
Piccoloministr. 316, 51067 **Köln**
Tel: 221-631 571 Fax: 221-631 571
artistic director/choreogrpher Britta Lieberknecht
Dancers: 2-6 *Perfs:* 20 *No of Prods:* 8 *Type:* contemporary with media art forms *Accomp:* recorded, live *Touring:* Europe *Comments:* films, art-installations, outdoor performances

Katharine Sehnert
Volksgartenstr. 10, 50677 **Köln**
Tel: 221-329 648 Fax: 221-932 2232
Künstlerische Leiterin & Choreographin Katharine Sehnert
Dancers: 1-3 *Perfs:* 10 *No of Prods:* 2 *Type:* expressionist dance, butoh-dance *Accomp:* live, recorded *Venues:* Tanzraum 60 *Touring:* Germany, Mexico, Ecuador *Comments:* series 'MultiArt -guest artists in TANZRAUM' 3x a year

Knupp Tanzt
c/o Rainer Knupp, Geisselstr. 15, 50823 **Köln**
Tel: 221-952 5349 Fax: 221-510 3016
E-Mail: rainerknupp@hotmail.com
choreographer Rainer Knupp
Dancers: 5 *Perfs:* 15 *Type:* contemporary, movement and performance *Accomp:* live, tape *Venues:* Buergerhaus Stollwerk (Köln), Tanzhaus NRW (Dusseldorf), The Place (London) *Touring:* Germany, UK *Comments:* UK address: 46 Elmbourne Rd., Tooting Bec., London SW17 8JJ, Tel: +44 20-8767 2106

Lina Do Carmo
c/o Theatertransfer, Volksgartenstr. 20, 50677 **Köln**
Tel: 221-312 088 Fax: 221-328 097
Internet: www.theatertransfer.de
E-Mail: hilleckenbach@NetCologne.de
contact agent Michael Hilleckenbach
Dancers: varies *Perfs:* 40 *No of Prods:* 4 *Type:* contemporary expressionist dance *Accomp:* live, recorded

Mind The Gap Tanztheater
c/o Kölner Tanzagentur, Industriestr. 170, 50999 **Köln**
Tel: 2236-963 589/590 Fax: 2236-963 590
Leitung – Kölner Tanzagentur Kim von Kothen; Choreographin/ künstlerische Leitung Kristine Sommerlade
Dancers: 6 *Perfs:* 40 *Type:* dance theatre *Accomp:* live, recorded *Touring:* international

Monteure
Geisselstr. 15, 50823 **Köln**
Tel: 221-510 3016 Fax: 221-510 3016
künstlerische Leitung Joachim von der Heiden, Andi Lucas
Dancers: number of dancers, musicians and actors varies depending on production *Perfs:* 120 *No of Prods:* 5 *Type:* musical dance-theatre/new dance *Accomp:* live/recorded music (especially composed for each production) *Touring:* international, national *Comments:* own productions only; see also Drama

SusaHee Performance
Bismarckstr. 44, 50672 **Köln**
Tel: 221-510 1359
Internet: theaterszene-koeln.de//susannehelmes/
E-Mail: SusaHee@hotmail.com
Leiterin und Choreographin Susanne Helmes
Dancers: varies (basically solos) *Perfs:* 25-50 *No of Prods:* 2-5 per year *Type:* performance arts, contemporary dance, modern *Accomp:* live, occasionally recorded, DJ *Venues:* theatres, galleries, open air (50-200) *Touring:* national, international *Comments:* co-productions with other artists; productions for museums; cooperation with Time and Space Limited, Hudson, NY, USA; see also entry in Spain (Palma de Mallorca)

Tanzensemble Maja Lex
c/o Kölner Tanzagentur, Industriestr. 170, 50999 **Köln**
Tel: 2236-963 589/590 Fax: 2236-963 590
Leitung – Kölner Tanzagentur Kim von Kothen; Künstlerische Leiterin & Choreographin Koni Hanft
Dancers: 7 *Perfs:* 40 *Type:* contemporary dance with expressionist elements *Accomp:* recorded, live *Touring:* international

TanzEnsemble Rahel Weißmann
Taubengasse 19, 50676 **Köln**
Tel: 221-213 999
artistic director Rahel Weißmann
Dancers: 7 *Perfs:* 20 *No of Prods:* 8 *Type:* modern dance *Accomp:* live, recorded *Touring:* Germany, Europe *Comments:* themes concerning politics, society and the relationship between mankind and nature

Off-Off Theater in der Tanzwerkstatt
Kreuzlinger Strasse 54, 78462 **Konstanz**
Tel: 7531-26838 Fax: 7531-25716
Leitung Inge Missmahl
Dancers: 6-10 *Perfs:* 24 *No of Prods:* c. 3 *Type:* dance-theatre *Accomp:* live *Venues:* Off-Off Theatre 80

Ballet der Vereinigten Städtischen Bühnen Krefeld und Mönchengladbach
Stadttheater Krefeld, Theaterplatz 3, 47798 **Krefeld**
Tel: 2151-8050 Fax: 2151-28295
Comments: see also Opera, Drama and Orchestras; see entry under Mönchengladbach

Ballett der Musikalischen Komödie Oper Leipzig
Dreilindenstraße 30, 04177 **Leipzig**
Tel: 341-12610 Fax: 341-126 1150
Intendant Prof. Udo Zimmermann; Direktorin u. Ballettmeisterin Monika Geppert
Dancers: 16 *Perfs:* 120-150 *No of Prods:* 3 *Accomp:* live *Venues:* Musikalische Komödie 529 *Touring:* national and international *Comments:* see also Opera

Leipziger Ballett (Oper Leipzig)
Augustusplatz 12, 04109 **Leipzig**
Tel: 341-126 1251/303 Fax: 341-126 1376
Internet: www.leipzig-online.de/ballett
E-Mail: ballett@leipzig-online.de
Intendant Prof. Udo Zimmermann; Ballettdirektor u. Chefchoreograph Prof. Uwe Scholz; Assistent Christoph Markert; Organisation und Probendisposition Angela Luksch; Ballettmeister Ivaylo Iliev, Jocelyn Alizart
Dancers: 52 *Perfs:* 40 *No of Prods:* 8 (2 new) *Type:* classical, neoclassical, contemporary *Accomp:* live (Gewandhausorchester Leipzig) *Venues:* Opernhaus 1426 *Touring:* Germany, France, Austria, Denmark *Comments:* see also Opera

Tanz Companie Lübeck
Eschenburgstr. 35a, 23568 **Lübeck**
Tel: 451-384 185 Fax: 451-384 185
künstlerische Direktorin Juliane Rössler; manager t.b.a.
Dancers: 6 *Perfs:* 80 *No of Prods:* 3 *Type:* dance-theatre, contemporary *Accomp:* live, recorded *Venues:* Theater Lübeck/Kammerspiele *Touring:* national, international *Comments:* cooperation with Theater Lübeck (q.v.); co-productions with opera

Rui Horta Stage Works
c/o Ecotopia Dance Productions, Bunzstr. 3, 71638 **Ludwigsburg**
Tel: 7141-903 383 Fax: 7141-903 385
contact Claudia Bauer, Meinrad Huber; artistic director Rui Horta
Dancers: 6 *Perfs:* 60-70 *No of Prods:* 2 *Type:* contemporary dance *Accomp:* recorded *Venues:* Muffathalle/München 500 *Touring:* worldwide

Ballett der Theater Lüneburg GmbH
Postfach 2829, 21318 **Lüneburg**
Tel: 4131-7520 Fax: 4131-404 210
Internet: www.theater-members.de
E-Mail: dramaturgie@theater-lueneburg.de
Generalintendant Jan Aust; Ballettdirektorin Ingrid Burmeister
Dancers: 9 *Perfs:* 20 *No of Prods:* 2
Type: classical ballet *Accomp:* live
Venues: Theater 553
Comments: visiting address: An den Reeperbahnen 3, 21335 Lüneburg, see also Opera, Drama and Orchestra

Theater der Landeshauptstadt Magdeburg
Postfach 12 40, 39002 **Magdeburg**
Tel: 391-540 6500 Fax: 391-540 6599
Internet: www.theater-magdeburg.de
Generalintendant Max K. Hoffmann; Verwaltungsdirektor Reinhard Odenstein; Ballettdirektorin u. Choreographin Irene Schneider; Generalmusikdirektor Christian Ehwald; Chefdramaturg Dietmar Goergen
Dancers: 19 *Perfs:* 30 *No of Prods:* 2 new *Type:* dance-theatre, classical *Accomp:* live, recorded *Venues:* Theater am Universitätsplatz 688 *Comments:* visiting address: Universitätsplatz 9, 39104 Magdeburg; see also Opera

Ballett des Staatstheaters Mainz
Gutenbergplatz 7, 55116 **Mainz**
Tel: 6131-2851-0 Fax: 6131-285 1109
Internet: www.staatstheater-mainz.de
E-Mail: theatmainz@aol.com
Intendant Georges Delnon; Kaufm. Geschäftsführer Lutz-Uwe Dünnwald; Presse Eva Freund; Ballettdirektor Martin Schläpfer; Referentin des Ballettdirektors Karin Bovisi; Ballettmeister Leslie Hughes, Didier Chape; Generalmusikdirektor Stefan Sanderling; Chefdramaturg Martin Apelt
Dancers: 18 *Perfs:* 38 (ballet) + 25 (musical) *No of Prods:* 3 (ballet) + 1 (musical) *Type:* neo-classical, contemporary *Accomp:* live, recorded *Venues:* Phönixhalle 742, Kleines Haus 415, TIC 200 *Comments:* see also Drama and Opera

Desperate Figures Dance
c/o Mainzer Kammerspiele, Rheinstr. 4, 55116 **Mainz**
Tel: 6131-225 002 Fax: 6131-225 004
E-Mail: kammersp@mainz-online.de
director/choreographer Nancy Seitz-McIntyre; press Egbert Rühl (tel: 69-9441 9564)
Dancers: 6 *Perfs:* 40 *No of Prods:* 2 *Type:* contemporary dance, dance theatre *Accomp:* mainly recorded (original music) *Venues:* Mainzer Kammerspiele 400 *Touring:* Germany, Europe *Comments:* 2nd address: Hofäckerstr. 25, 65207 Wiesbaden, email: seitz-mcintyre@t-online.de

Ballett des Nationaltheaters Mannheim
Mozartstrasse 9, 68161 **Mannheim**
Tel: 621-1680-0 Fax: 621-168 0448
Internet: www.mannheim.nationaltheater.de
E-Mail: nationaltheater.kasse@mannheim.de
Generalintendant Ulrich Schwab; Ballettdirektor Philippe Talard; Dramaturgie Erik Raskopf
Dancers: 16 *Perfs:* 80 *No of Prods:* 3 *Type:* classical, modern *Accomp:* live, recorded *Venues:* Opernhaus 1154, Schauspielhaus 639, Studiobühne 99 *Comments:* see also Opera, Orchestras, Drama

Nostos Tanztheater
Landsknechtweg 17, 68163 **Mannheim**
Tel: 621-407 407 Fax: 621-407 407
Internet: www.nostos.regio-info.de
E-Mail: nostos@regio-info.de
contact Werner Traschütz
Dancers: 3+ *No of Prods:* 1-2 *Type:* modern dance *Accomp:* mostly recorded, sometimes live

Ballett des Meininger Theaters
Bernhardstrasse 5, 98617 **Meiningen**
Tel: 3693-4510 Fax: 3693-502 285
Internet: das_meininger_theater.de
Intendantin Christine Mielitz; Musikdirektor J.M. Dufour; Ballettdirektorin Sabine Wake
Dancers: 15 *Perfs:* 115 *No of Prods:* 6 (3 new) *Type:* classical, modern *Accomp:* live, recorded *Venues:* Meininger Theater, Grosse Bühne 733, Studiobühne 90 *Touring:* Switzerland, Romania

Ballett der Vereinigten Städtischen Bühnen Krefeld und Mönchengladbach
Opernhaus, Odenkirchener Str. 78, 41236 **Mönchengladbach**
Tel: 2166-61510 Fax: 2166-420 110
Generalintendant Jens Pesel; Generalmusikdirektor Anthony Bramall; Geschäftsführer Reinhard Zeileis; Ballettdirektorin Heidrun Schwaarz; Schauspieloberspielleiter Peter Hathazy
Dancers: 18 *No of Prods:* 6 *Type:* classical ballet and modern dance *Accomp:* live, recorded *Venues:* Stadttheater 832 *Comments:* venue address: Stadttheater Krefeld, Theaterplatz 3, 47798 Krefeld, Tel: 2151-805-0, Fax: 2151-28295; see also Opera, Dance and Orchestra; see also under Krefeld

Artgenossen
c/o Tanztendenz München, Lindwurmstr. 88/k, 80337 **München**
Tel: 89-721 1015 Fax: 89-721 2249
E-Mail: tanzmuc.aol.com
Künstlerische Leiterin Angelika Meindl
Dancers: 5 *No of Prods:* 2 *Type:* contemporary dance theatre, music-performance *Accomp:* live
Venues: various *Touring:* Germany, Europe

Awar-Dance
Bereiter Anger 15, 81541 **München**
Tel: 89-651 9636 Fax: 89-658 641
Management Heike Ratfisch; Choreographin Marta Binetti
Dancers: 8 *No of Prods:* 8 *Type:* dance-theatre *Accomp:* live, recorded *Touring:* guest performances in Germany and Spain *Comments:* Address in Spain: Apartado de Correos N° 20, 17488 Cadaqués (Girona), Spain, tel/fax: +34 972-259 022

Ballett des Staatstheaters am Gärtnerplatz
Postfach 140569, 80455 **München**
Tel: 89-202 411 Fax: 89-2024 1237
Internet: www.staatstheater.bayern.de/gaertner/welcome.htm
E-Mail: jan.adamiak@st-gaertner.bayern.de
Intendant Klaus Schultz; Ballettdirektor Philip Taylor; Verwaltungsdirektor Eugen Friedl
Dancers: 25 *Perfs:* 35 *No of Prods:* 9 (1 new)
Type: classical, contemporary *Accomp:* live, recorded
Venues: Staatstheater am Gärtnerplatz 864
Comments: see also Opera and Orchestras

Bavarian National Ballet
Bayerisches Staatsballett München
Platzl 7, 80331 **München**
Tel: 89-2185 1711 Fax: 89-2185 1703
Internet: www.bayerisches.staatsballett.de
E-Mail: tickets@st-oper.bayern.de
Ballettdirektor Ivan Liska
Dancers: 65 *Perfs:* 90 *No of Prods:* 14 *Type:* classical, modern ballet *Accomp:* live, recorded *Venues:* Nationaltheater 2101, Cuvilliés-Theater 523, Prinzregenten Theater 1100 *Comments:* see also Opera, Orchestras, Drama and Festivals

C & K Show Produktion
Trappentreu Str. 29, 80339 **München**
Tel: 89-5407 1671 Fax: 89-5407 1672
Internet: www.chris-crazy.com
E-Mail: ck-showproduktion@t-online.de
Manager Yehonatan Carmi; Direktor Christian Kolonko
Dancers: varies *Perfs:* 200-350 *No of Prods:* 2-4 *Type:* jazz, step variete *Accomp:* live (own musicians)

Chris Crazy Show
Trappentrau. Str. 29, 80339 **München**
Tel: 89-5407 1671 Fax: 89-5407 1672
Internet: www.chris-crazy.com
E-Mail: ck-showproduktion@t-online.de
Geschäftsführer Yehonatan Carmi; Direktor, Texter und Chorégraphie Christian Kolonko; Musikalische Leitung Bastian Pusch
No of Prods: 3 *Type:* jazz, step *Accomp:* live (own band)

Dance Energy
c/o Joint Adventures, Emil-Geis-Str. 21, 81379 **München**
Tel: 89-724 2515 Fax: 89-723 7782
E-Mail: JOINTADVENTURES@t-online.de
Manager Walter Heun; Choreograph Micha Purucker
Dancers: 1-6 *Perfs:* 20 *No of Prods:* 1-2 *Type:* contemporary *Accomp:* live, recorded *Venues:* up to 600 *Touring:* national, international *Comments:* video-dance installations, installations with live dance, site specific performances

Iwanson Dance Company
Adi-Maislinger Str. 12, 81373 **München**
Tel: 89-760 6085 Fax: 89-760 5999
Internet: www.iwanson.de
Choreographin Jessica Iwanson; Schulleiter Stefan Sixt
Dancers: 10 *Perfs:* 10-20 *No of Prods:* 1 *Type:* contemporary *Venues:* various *Touring:* Europe

Move Art
Heigelhofstr 37, 81377 **München**
Tel: 89-711 814
Choreographin Susanne Stortz
Dancers: 3-8 *Perfs:* 8 *No of Prods:* 1 *Type:* contemporary *Accomp:* live, recorded *Venues:* various in München

Tanz-Tanz-Theater München
Weltistr. 9a, 81477 **München**
Tel: 89-795 699 Fax: 89-791 8244
Choreographin E. M. Lerchenberg-Thöny
Dancers: 3-12 *No of Prods:* 1 *Type:* modern dance-theatre *Accomp:* recorded *Touring:* Germany, Tunisia, Egypt, Brazil

Rebel Dance Company
Berliner Platz 23, 48143 **Münster**
Tel: 251-47849 Fax: 251-47841
E-Mail: Rebel@muenster.net
Inhaber David Rebel; Choreograph, Tanzlehrer, Tänzer Günther Rebel
Dancers: 15-25 *No of Prods:* 2+ *Type:* dance-theatre *Accomp:* recorded *Venues:* Kulturschiene, Münster 100 *Touring:* national, international

Tanztheater der Städtischen Bühnen Münster
Neubrückenstrasse 63, 48143 **Münster**
Tel: 251-590 9193 Fax: 215-590 9202
Internet: www.muenster.de/stb
E-Mail: TanzTh@stadt-muenster.de
Intendant Thomas Bockelmann; Leiter des Tanztheaters Daniel Goldin; Generalmusikdirektor Will Humburg; Chefdisposition Bettina Reith; company manager Sabine Dollink; PR Tanja Gellermann
Dancers: 10 *Perfs:* 50 *No of Prods:* 4 *Accomp:* recorded & live *Venues:* Grosses Haus 955, Kleines Haus 321 *Comments:* see also Opera, Drama and Orchestra

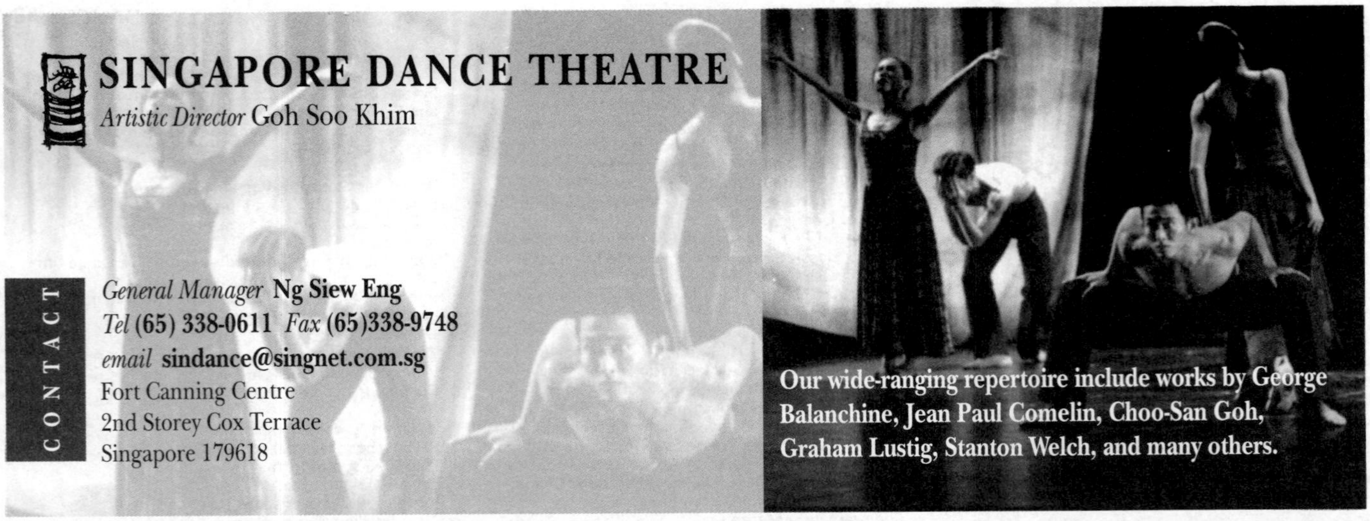
SINGAPORE DANCE THEATRE
Artistic Director Goh Soo Khim
CONTACT
General Manager Ng Siew Eng
Tel (65) 338-0611 Fax (65)338-9748
email sindance@singnet.com.sg
Fort Canning Centre
2nd Storey Cox Terrace
Singapore 179618
Our wide-ranging repertoire include works by George Balanchine, Jean Paul Comelin, Choo-San Goh, Graham Lustig, Stanton Welch, and many others.

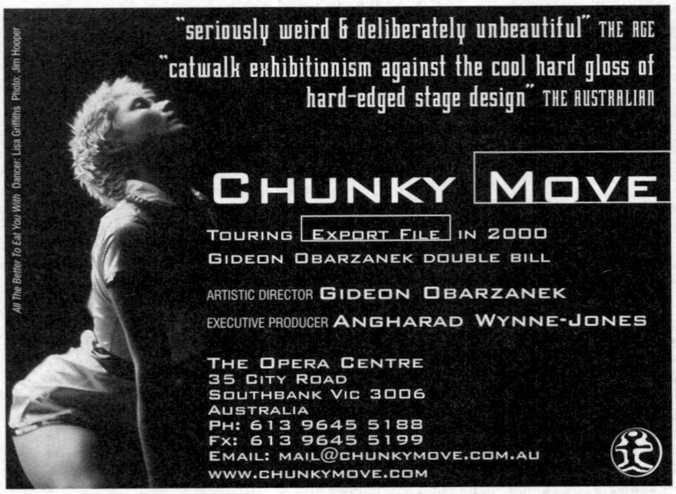
"seriously weird & deliberately unbeautiful" THE AGE
"catwalk exhibitionism against the cool hard gloss of hard-edged stage design" THE AUSTRALIAN
All The Better To Eat You With Dancer: Lisa Griffiths Photo: Jim Hooper
CHUNKY MOVE
TOURING EXPORT FILE IN 2000
GIDEON OBARZANEK DOUBLE BILL
ARTISTIC DIRECTOR GIDEON OBARZANEK
EXECUTIVE PRODUCER ANGHARAD WYNNE-JONES
THE OPERA CENTRE
35 CITY ROAD
SOUTHBANK VIC 3006
AUSTRALIA
PH: 613 9645 5188
FX: 613 9645 5199
EMAIL: MAIL@CHUNKYMOVE.COM.AU
WWW.CHUNKYMOVE.COM

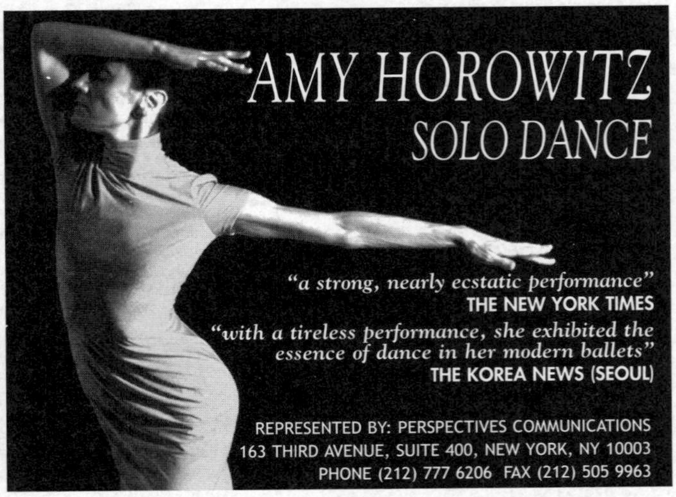
AMY HOROWITZ
SOLO DANCE
"a strong, nearly ecstatic performance"
THE NEW YORK TIMES
"with a tireless performance, she exhibited the essence of dance in her modern ballets"
THE KOREA NEWS (SEOUL)
REPRESENTED BY: PERSPECTIVES COMMUNICATIONS
163 THIRD AVENUE, SUITE 400, NEW YORK, NY 10003
PHONE (212) 777 6206 FAX (212) 505 9963

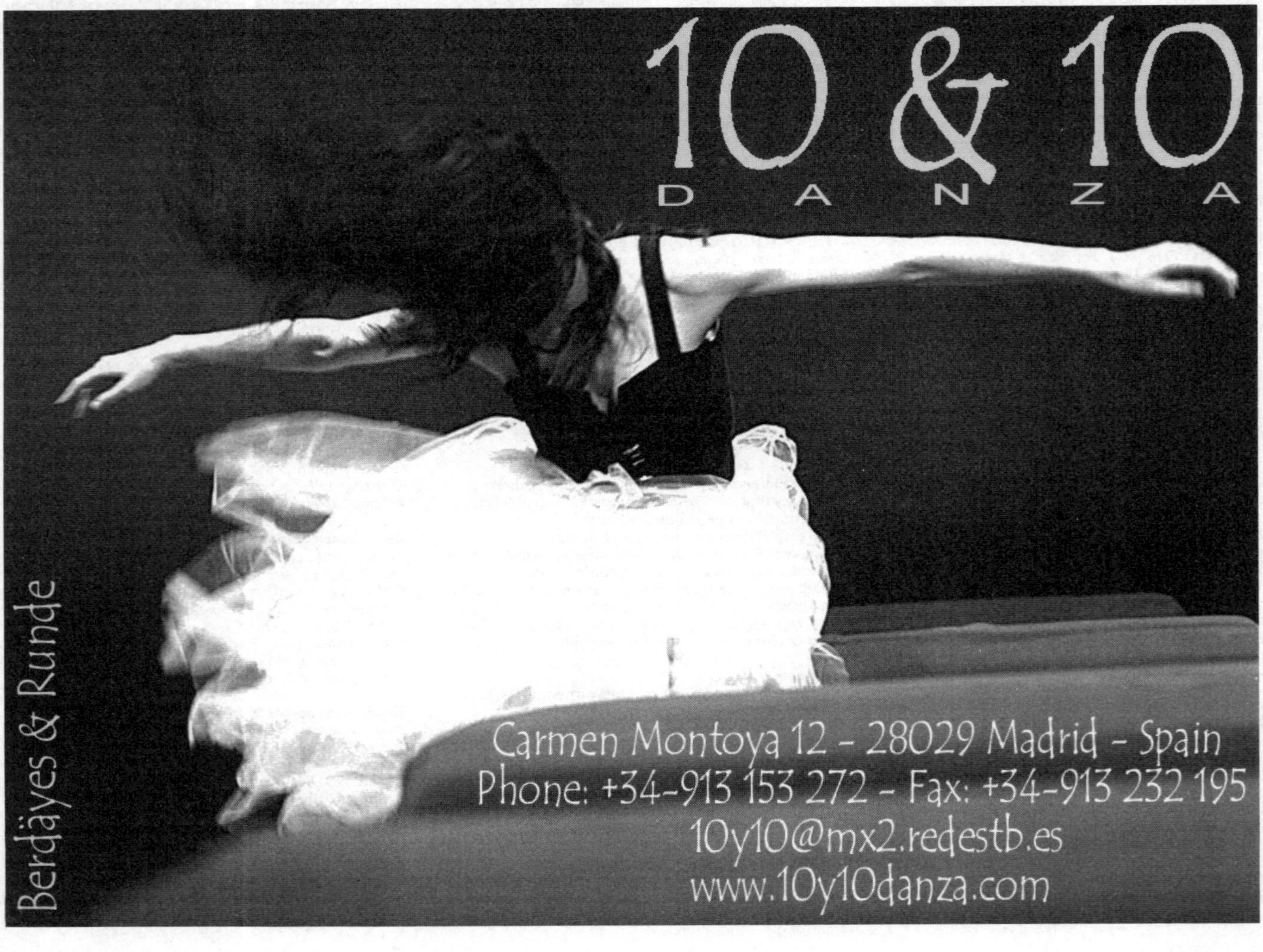
10 & 10
DANZA
Berdäyes & Runde
Carmen Montoya 12 - 28029 Madrid - Spain
Phone: +34-913 153 272 - Fax: +34-913 232 195
10y10@mx2.redestb.es
www.10y10danza.com

Deutsche Tanzkompanie – Stiftung für traditionellen Tanz im Land Mecklenburg-Vorpommern
Wilhelm-Riefstahl-Platz 7, 17235 **Neustrelitz**
Tel: 3981-203 334 Fax: 3981-203 327
Künstlerischer Direktor/Vorstandsvorsitzender Jürgen Goewe; Kaufmännischer Direktor Willi Denne; Leitende Choreographin Eva Brehme-Solacoln
Dancers: 24 *Perfs:* 100-120 *No of Prods:* 8 (1 new)
Type: dance theatre, medieval to modern; also folk dance performances for children *Accomp:* recorded
Venues: various in the region *Comments:* try to combine tradition and innovation

Theaters Nordhausen / Loh-Orchester Sondershausen GmbH
Käthe-Kollwitz-Strasse 15, 99734 **Nordhausen**
Tel: 3631-62600 Fax: 3631-626 0147
Internet: www.theater.nordhausen.de
E-Mail: theater@nordhausen.de
Intendantin Dr. Monika Pirklbauer; GMD Peter Stangel; Ballettdirektorin Birgitt Relitzki
Dancers: 12 *No of Prods:* 2 new *Type:* classic and modern ballet/dance *Accomp:* live, recorded *Venues:* Großes Haus 488, Studio 'TuD' 99, Foyer 50, hinterm Eisernen Vorhang 60 *Touring:* Germany *Comments:* the ballet also does opera and operetta performances

Abstract Dance Company
Wielandstr. 7, 90419 **Nürnberg**
Tel: 911-393 8888
E-Mail: dvclemen@ewf.uni-erlangen.de
artistic directors Romana Ondra, Detlev Clemens
Dancers: 5 *Perfs:* 10 *Type:* contemporary dance
Accomp: recorded, live *Venues:* Tafelhalle 300
Touring: national, international

Ballett Nürnberg
Richard-Wagner-Platz 2-10, 90443 **Nürnberg**
Tel: 911-231 5472 Fax: 911-231 8238
Internet: www.oper.nuernberg.de
E-Mail: inga-harenborg@th.stadt.nuernberg.de
Produktionsleitung Inga Harenborg; Ballettdirektorin Daniela Kurz
Dancers: 16 *Perfs:* 50 *No of Prods:* 5 (3 new)
Type: modern, contemporary
Venues: Opernhaus 1061, Schauspielhaus 539
Touring: guest performances in Germany
Comments: see also Opera, Orchestras and Drama

Palindrome Inter-Media Performance Group
Johannistrasse 42, 90419 **Nürnberg**
Tel: 911-397 472 Fax: 911-397 472
Internet: www.palindrome.de
E-Mail: info@palindrome.de
Künstlerischer Leiter u. Choreograph Robert Wechsler; Computer systems designer Frieder Weiß; Komponisten Erling Wold, Butch Rowan
Dancers: varies *Perfs:* 50 *No of Prods:* 3 *Type:* interactive *Accomp:* interactive *Venues:* Tafelhalle, Nürnberg 350 *Touring:* Germany, Europe, USA, Austria, Czech Republic, Denmark *Comments:* work exclusively with computer controlled interactive systems

Tanz Theater Irina Pauls / Oldenburgischen Staatstheaters
Theaterwall 28, 26122 **Oldenburg**
Tel: 441-222 5230 (Tanz Theater)
Fax: 441-222 5221 (ticket servide)
Internet: www.oldenburg.staatstheater.de
E-Mail: drama@.oldenburg.staatstheater.de
Generalintendant Stephan Mettin; Direktorin des Tanztheater und Choreographin Irina Pauls; Referentin der Direktorin/Dramaturgie u. Organisation Brigitte Knöß
Dancers: 4-11 *Perfs:* 57 *No of Prods:* 5
Type: dance theatre *Accomp:* live (Oldenburgisches Staatsorchester), recorded
Venues: Großes Haus 881, Kleines Haus 350
Comments: 5th International Ballett-Tage 2001

Tanztheater der Städtischen Bühnen Osnabrück
Domhof 10-11, 49074 **Osnabrück**
Tel: 541-323 4310/3347 Fax: 541-323 3297
Internet: www.theater-osnabrueck.de
E-Mail: theateros@aol.com
Intendant Norbert Hilchenbach; Generalmusikdirektor Lothar Königs; Kaufmännischer Direktor Norbert Kronisch; Leiter des Tanztheaters Gregor Zöllig; Chefdisponent Matthias Otto
Dancers: 12 *Perfs:* 50 *No of Prods:* 3
Type: modern *Accomp:* live, recorded
Venues: Emma Theater 99, Stadtheater 639
Comments: see also Drama and Opera

Ballett des Stadttheaters Pforzheim
Am Waisenhausplatz 5, 75172 **Pforzheim**
Tel: 7231-392 438 Fax: 7231-391 485
Internet: www.pforzheim.de/theater
E-Mail: theater@stadt-pforzheim.de
Intendant Ernö Weil; Ballettmeister Anthony Sterago
Dancers: 10 *Perfs:* 20 (in total) *No of Prods:* 2 *Type:* modern, dance-theatre, classical ballet
Accomp: live, recorded *Venues:* Großes Haus 510, Podium 150 *Touring:* Germany
Comments: see also Drama and Opera

Ballett des Vogtland Theaters Plauen
Theaterplatz 1-3, 08523 **Plauen**
Tel: 3741-291 2463 Fax: 3741-222 620
Intendant Dieter Roth; Verwaltungsleitung Renate Wünsche; Chefdramaturgin Christa Stöß; künstlerische Leitung Gundula Peuthert; GMD Dieter-Gerhardt Worm; kaufmännische Leitung Mandy Kringel
Dancers: 8 *No of Prods:* 3 *Type:* modern *Accomp:* recorded *Venues:* Großes Haus 450, Kleines Haus 100, Festhalle Plauen 1000 *Comments:* see also Drama, Opera and Orchestra

Ballett der Landesbühnen Sachsen
Meißner Str. 152, 01445 **Radebeul**
Tel: 351-8954-0 Fax: 351-895 4201
Internet: www.dresden-theater.de
E-Mail: landesbuehnensachsen@dresden-theater.de
Intendant Christian Schmidt; Generalmusikdirektor Prof. Alexander von Brück; Verwaltungsdirektorin Barbara Kunz; Chordirektor Sebastian Matthias Fischer; Operndirektor Steffen Piontek; Ballettdirektor Reiner Feistel
Dancers: 13 *Perfs:* 20 (ballet only) *No of Prods:* 4 (2 new) *type:* classical, modern *Accomp:* live (orchestra of the Landesbühnensachsen) *Venues:* Landesbühnensaal 402, P100 (Kleine Bühne) 80 *Comments:* ballet also performed in conjunction with music theatre; see also Opera, Orchestras and Drama

Theater Regensburg – Ballett
Bismarckplatz 7, 93047 **Regensburg**
Tel: 941-507 1428 Fax: 941-507 4429
Intendantin Marietheres List; Choreographie Dieter Gößler; Kaufmännischer Direktor Holger von Berg; Disponent und Leiter des künstlerischen Betriebsbüros Johannes Fiedler
Dancers: 10 *Perfs:* 22 *No of Prods:* 2 *Type:* classical, modern *Accomp:* recorded *Venues:* Stadttheater 538 (closed until 2001) alternative venue: Velodrom 600, Theater am Haidplatz 138 *Comments:* see also Opera, Drama and Orchestra

Volkstheater Rostock Ballett
Postfach 102215, 18003 **Rostock**
Tel: 381-244-0 Fax: 381-244 213
Internet: www.ssi.de/vrb
Generalintendant Dr Michael Winrich Schlicht; Generalmusikdirektor t.b.a.; Ballettdirektor u. Chefchoreograph Thomasz Kajdanski; Marketing & Öffentlichkeitsarbeit Jürgen Opel
Dancers: 16 *No of Prods:* 3 *Type:* classical, contemporary *Accomp:* live, recorded *Venues:* Großes Haus 579, Barocksaal 167, Theater im Stadthafen 203 *Comments:* visiting address: Patriotischer Weg 33, 18057 Rostock; see also Opera, Orchestras and Drama

Ballett des Saarländischen Staatstheaters Saarbrücken
Schillerplatz 1, Postfach 102735, 66111 **Saarbrücken**
Tel: 681-3092-0/317 Fax: 681-309 2325
Internet: www.saarland.de/staatstheater/
E-Mail: sst02@t-online.de
Generalintendant Kurt Josef Schildknecht; Leiter des Balletts Bernd Roger Bienert
Dancers: 19 *Perfs:* 82 *No of Prods:* 4 *Type:* mixed (classical & modern) *Accomp:* live, recorded *Venues:* Grosses Haus 879 *Touring:* Europe *Comments:* see also Drama, Opera, Orchestras and Venues

Schleswig-Holsteinisches Landestheater – Ballett
Lollfuß 49-53, 24837 **Schleswig**
Tel: 4621-9670-0 Fax: 4621-967 083
Internet: www.landestheater.de
E-Mail: kontakt@landestheater.de
Generalintendant Dr Horst Mesalla (from August 2000: Michael Grosse); Verwaltungsdirektor Reiner Schmeckthal; Offentlichkeitsarbeit Angela Möller; Generalmusikdirektor Pierre Borin; Ballettmeister u. Choreographie Fijbrand de Lange
Dancers: 10 *Type:* classical, modern *Accomp:* live, recorded *Venues:* Landestheater Schleswig 508, Landestheater Flensburg 459, Landestheater Rendsburg 510 *Touring:* Germany
Comments: performs regularly in 25 different venues; see also Opera, Orchestras and Drama

Ballett Company Vieru
Sekretariat und Verwaltung, Roßbrunnstraße 9, 97421 **Schweinfurt**
Tel: 9721-16800 Fax: 9721-188 001
E-Mail: Vieru.Ballett@t-online.de
Managerin/Geschäftsführerin Mihaela Schumacher-Vieru; Ballettmeister und Choreograph Nicolai Vieru
Dancers: 14 *No of Prods:* 2 *Type:* neoclassical, modern, classical *Accomp:* recorded, live *Touring:* Italy, Spain, Bulgaria, Germany *Comments:* independent company with international dancers

Ballett des Mecklenburgischen Staatstheaters Schwerin
Alter Garten, 19055 **Schwerin**
Tel: 385-530 0157 Fax: 385-530 0200
Internet: www.hansenet.de
geschäftsführender Intendant Joachim Kümmritz; Ballettdirektor Stefan Haufe; Ballettmeister u. Trainingsleiter Jasmina Wergowa, Ralf Schloßer; Gasttraining Stéphane Flecher, Jana Lück, Dirk Lienig, Carlos Matos, James Sutherland
Dancers: 18 *Perfs:* 60 (ballet) + 40 (opera + operetta) *No of Prods:* 6 (ballet), 5 (opera + operetta) *Type:* neo-classical, modern *Accomp:* live, recorded *Venues:* Großes Haus 670, E-Werk 100 *Comments:* see also Drama and Opera

Stuttgarter Ballett
Oberer Schlossgarten 6, 70173 **Stuttgart**
Tel: 711-203 2235 Fax: 711-203 2236/2491
Geschäftsführender Direktor Hans Tränkle; Ballettdirektor Reid Anderson; Ballettadministration Ingrid Bruy; Musikdirektor James Tuggle
Dancers: 64 *Perfs:* 78 *No of Prods:* 18
Type: mainly classical and modern ballet *Accomp:* mainly live, recorded *Venues:* Großes Haus 1440, Kleines Haus 851, Kammertheater 225 *Touring:* Europe, South America, North America
Comments: see also Opera, Drama and Orchestras

TELOS Dance Company
TELOS-Tanzkompanie
Florianstr. 20, 70188 **Stuttgart**
Tel: 711-282 872 Fax: 711-281 824
Leiterin Ursula Bischoff-Mußhake
Dancers: 7-8 *Perfs:* 30-40 *No of Prods:* 10 *Type:* modern dance, youth dance-theatre *Accomp:* recorded *Venues:* capacity 100 *Touring:* national

Ballett der Freilichtspiele Tecklenburg
Postfach 1143, 49537 **Tecklenburg**
Tel: 5482-220/227 Fax: 5482-1269
Intendant Radulf Beuleke; Ballettleiterin Anette Fischer; Geschäftsführung Fred Banse
Dancers: 6-10 *Perfs:* 60 *No of Prods:* 4 *Type:* classical
Accomp: live *Venues:* Freilichtbühne 2500 *Comments:* visiting address: Schloßstrasse 7, 49545 Tecklenburg; see also Opera and Festivals

Theater Trier
Am Augustinerhof, 54290 **Trier**
Tel: 651-718 3464 Fax: 651-718 1468
Intendant Heinz Lukas-Kindermann; Ballettmeister Sergey Volobuyev
Dancers: 12 *Perfs:* 31 *No of Prods:* 2 *Type:* classical, modern *Accomp:* live *Venues:* Stadttheater 622, Studio 65 *Comments:* see also Drama, Opera and Orchestra

Ulmer Ballett
Postfach 89070, 89073 **Ulm**
Tel: 731-161 4500/4432 Fax: 731-161 1619
Internet: www.theater.ulm.de
E-Mail: UlmerTheater@theater.ulm.de
Intendant Ansgar Haag (731-161 4400); Leiter des Balletts Andris Plucis (731-161 4432); Presse- und Öffentlichkeitsarbeit Frau Mayer (731-161 4410); Künstlerisches Betriebsbüro Frau Glathe (731-161 4434)
Dancers: 10 *Perfs:* 54 *No of Prods:* 3 + 1
Type: modern *Accomp:* live, recorded
Venues: Ulmer Theatre 815, Podium 200
Comments: visiting address: Olgastr. 73, 89073 Ulm; guest performances in different venues; see also Opera, Orchestras and Drama

Ricardo Viviani/mammut Tanzproduktion
Marktstr 4, 99423 **Weimar**
Tel: 177-281 4587 Fax: 3643-853 041
Internet: www.bigfoot.com/~rviviani
E-Mail: rviviani@bigfoot.com
contact Ricardo Viviani
Dancers: 2-4 *Perfs:* 20 *Type:* contemporary *Accomp:* recorded, live *Touring:* Italy, New York City, Germany

Tanztheater des Deutschen Nationaltheaters Weimar
Postfach 3-4, 99401 **Weimar**
Tel: 3643-755-0
Fax: 3643-755 218/307
Internet: www.deutsches-nationaltheater-weimar.de
E-Mail: dnt.service@weimar.net
Generalintendant Günther Beelitz; Leiter d. Tanztheaters u. Chefchoreograph Ismael Ivo; Generalmusikdirektor und Chefdirigent der Staatskapelle Weimar George Alexander Albrecht; Presse/Öffentlichkeitsarbeit Sylvia Obst
Dancers: 12 *No of Prods:* 8 *Type:* modern *Accomp:* live, recorded *Venues:* Werkstattbühne 176, Grosses Haus 859 *Touring:* worldwide *Comments:* visiting address: Theaterplatz 2, 99423 Weimar; see also Opera, Drama and Orchestras

Ballett des Hessischen Staatstheaters Wiesbaden
Postfach 3247, 65189 **Wiesbaden**
Tel: 611-132 278/325 Fax: 611-132 337
Internet: www.staatstheater.wiesbaden.de
Intendant Achim Thorwald; Ballettdirektor u. Chefchoreograph Ben van Cauwenbergh; Generalmusikdirektor Toshiyuki Kamioka; Stellvertreter des Ballettdirektors Tom van Cauwenbergh; Ballettmeisterinnen Vivien Loebar; Persönlicher Mitarbeiter des Ballettdirektors Gabriel Sala (tel/fax: 611-378 439)
Dancers: 30 *Perfs:* 95 (incl. opera, operettas etc.)
No of Prods: 2 *Type:* classical, modern
Venues: Opernhaus 1041 *Touring:* international
Comments: see also Opera, Orchestras and Dance

Tanztheater Wuppertal Pina Bausch
Spinnstraße 4, 42283 **Wuppertal**
Tel: 202-563 4253 Fax: 202-563 8171
Internet: www.pina-bausch.de
E-Mail: 100031.204@compuserve.com
Direktorin u. Choreographin Pina Bausch; Geschäftsführer Matthias Schmiegelt
Dancers: 32 (+ guests) *Perfs:* 70 *No of Prods:* 13 *Type:* dance-theatre *Accomp:* recorded, live *Venues:* Opernhaus 845, Schauspielhaus 792
Touring: Berlin, USA, Rome, Seoul, Budapest, Istanbul, Hamburg, Paris, Avignon
Comments: see also Schillertheater NRW, Kartenvorverkauf: Tel: 202-569 4444 (Opera and Drama)

Ballett des Stadttheaters Würzburg
Theaterstr. 21, 97070 **Würzburg**
Tel: 931-3908-0 Fax: 931-390 8102
Internet: www.theaterwuerzburg.de
E-Mail: info@theaterwuerzburg.de
Intendant Wolfgang Schaller; Ballettdirektor Mario Schröder; PR Jürgen Hartmann; Dramaturgie Jön Philipp von Linden; Generalmusikdirektor Jonathan Seers; Verwaltungsdirektorin Heidrun Glosauer
Dancers: 12 *No of Prods:* 3 *Type:* modern ballet *Accomp:* live, recorded *Venues:* Stadttheater 744, Kammerspiele 92 *Comments:* see also Opera, Drama and Orchestras

Ballett der theater Zwickau GmbH
Postfach 201039, 08012 **Zwickau**
Tel: 375-834 600 Fax: 375-834 609
Internet: www.fh-zwickau.de/zwickau/theater/th1.htm
E-Mail: theaterzwickau@abo.freiepresse.de
Intendant und amtierender Schauspieldirektor Wolfgang Hauswald; Ballettdirektor Bronislav Roznos; Operndirektor Rainer Wenke; Generalmusikdirektor Welisar Gentscheff
Dancers: 10 *Perfs:* 32 *No of Prods:* 4 *Type:* modern *Accomp:* live, recorded *Venues:* Gewandhaus 399, experimental venues *Touring:* Germany, Czech Republic *Comments:* visiting address: Gewandhausstr. 7, 08056 Zwickau; see also Drama and Opera

GREECE (+30)

Centre of Multiple Expression
Kentro Pollaplis Ekfrasis
Angelikara 4, 11742 **Athens**
Tel: 1-651 4815 Fax: 1-362 4439
artistic director/choreographer Marilena Kareta; musical director Michalis Klepakis
Dancers: 5 + 4 musicians *No of Prods:* 1-2 annually *Type:* dance-theatre *Accomp:* percussion (live) *Touring:* Greece *Comments:* introducing elements of Greek myths and tradition using Mediterranean and World music

Choreftes, Orchestral Art Company
Asklipiou 9, 10679 **Athens**
Tel: 1-361 4221/653 7049 Fax: 1-361 4221/653 7049
E-Mail: mary@mail.otenet.gr
contact Maria Anthimidou, Aliki Kazouri
Dancers: 6-8 *Perfs:* 15 *No of Prods:* 3-4 *Type:* contemporary & experimental *Venues:* Athens Month of Dance, Ergostasio Theatre, Kipou Theatre Thessaloniki, Aschyle a Festival *Touring:* Rome, Amsterdam *Comments:* has cooperated on productions with England and Netherlands

Contemporary Movement Ensemble EO
Omada Syghronis Kinisis EO
Polymnias 29, Cholargos, 15561 **Athens**
Tel: 1-652 7331
director/choreographer Maria Gaitani
Dancers: 6 *Perfs:* 6-8 *No of Prods:* 1 *Type:* contemporary *Accomp:* recorded, live *Venues:* Knossos Theatre, Agsostis Municipal Theatre and others

Dance Studio Proskaire Synthesis
Aegeou 58, Nea Smirni, 17123 **Athens**
Tel: 1-933 8991/895 9546 Fax: 1-933 8991
choreographer/artistic director Dorina Kalethrianou
Dancers: 7 *Perfs:* 20 *No of Prods:* 1-2 *Type:* contemporary *Accomp:* live, recorded *Venues:* Knossos Theatre, Ergostasio Theatre, Open Theatre, College of Athens Theatre *Touring:* various festivals in Greece *Comments:* winners (twice) of the 'Rallou Manou" competition

Dora Stratou Greek Dances Theater Company
8 Scholiou Str, Plaka, 10558 **Athens**
Tel: 1-324 4395/324 6188 Fax: 1-324 6921
Internet: users.hol.gr/~grdance
E-Mail: grdance@hol.gr
president Prof Alkis Raftis
Dancers: 65 + 15 musicians *Perfs:* 80 *Type:* Greek folk dances *Accomp:* live *Venues:* open-air theatre 1000
Touring: Europe *Comments:* also have publications: books, CDs, CD-Roms etc. and organise workshops on dance, costumes etc.

Edafous Dance Theatre
Parnassou 2, 10561 **Athens**
Tel: 1-321 5465 Fax: 1-321 5465
artistic director Demetris Papaioannou; core members A. Stellatou, N. Dragonas, G. Lagós, A. Papanikolaou; contact Mrs Kavatha
Dancers: 20 *Perfs:* 40-50 *No of Prods:* 1-3 annually *Type:* dance-theatre, visual-kinetic theatre *Accomp:* recorded, live *Venues:* Rex-Kotopouli Theatre, Fine Arts School-University of Athens, Old DEI Factory, Moschato
Touring: USA, Italy, Israel

Enniamorfo
Mitropoulou 19, Neo Heraklio, 14121 **Athens**
Tel: 1-748 5382/271 3879/ 93-237 6259 (mobile)
Fax: 1-271 8034
contact T. Nikolopoulou, Mrs. Moscholidaki
Dancers: 9 *Perfs:* 8-10 *No of Prods:* 2-3 *Type:* modern
Accomp: recorded, live instruments
Touring: Greece, Europe

HELIX – Dance Ensemble
Eressou 16, 10680 **Athens**
Tel: 1-363 3691 Fax: 1-360 5964
E-Mail: helix@compulink.gr
director, choreographer Christina Klissiouni
Dancers: 4 *Perfs:* 5-10 *No of Prods:* 1 *Type:* contemporary, dance theatre, contact improvisation *Accomp:* recorded, live *Venues:* Ergostasio, Megaro Mousikis, Fournos Theatre *Comments:* interested in co-productions and contacts with dancers and choreographers who can use voice and contact improvisation

Kinitiras Theater
4, Dimokratias Str , Voula, 16673 **Athens**
Tel: 1-899 4185/944-263 697 (mobile) Fax: 1-342 3516
choreographer Antigone Gyra; artistic directors Amalia Bennett, Vicky Adamou
Dancers: 10 *Perfs:* 20-30 *No of Prods:* 1 *Type:* movement theatre *Accomp:* recorded *Venues:* Simio Theatre, Mousouri Theatre, Factory Theatre, Creta International Dance Festival, Hania Firka Theatre, International Dance Festival of Thessaloniki, Month of Dance (Athens) *Touring:* Italy

OKTANA – Dance-Theatre
Pyrgou 5, Ilioupolis, 16345 **Athens**
Tel: 1-995 2064/881 4360/94-427 1884 (mobile)
Fax: 1-823 8117
artistic director, choreographer Rigos Konstantinos; managing director Natsoulis Nikos, 33 Troias Str., 11257 Athens
Dancers: 10 *Perfs:* 30-40 *No of Prods:* 2 *Type:* dance-theatre, modern dance *Accomp:* live, recorded *Venues:* Italian stage, open air theatres, industrial areas, amphitheatres *Touring:* Greece, Portugal, Russia, France, Sweden, Georgia, Italy, England, Israel

Omada Klassikou & Synghronou Chorou, Nikis Kontaxaki
Ialemou 24, 11142 **Athens**
Tel: 1-293 2894 Fax: 1-293 2894
contact/artistic director Niki Kontaxaki
Dancers: 30 *Perfs:* 20 *No of Prods:* 5 *Type:* classical, neo-classical, modern *Accomp:* recorded *Venues:* Rex Theatre, Palace Theatre, College of Athens Theatre, Knossos Theatre *Touring:* Greece

Proschema Dance Company
5, Lefkosias Str, Ag Paraskevi, 15341 **Athens**
Tel: 1-651 1324 Fax: 1-653 6686
Dancers: 6 *Perfs:* 3-6 *No of Prods:* 2 new *Type:* contemporary dance *Touring:* Greece, UK *Comments:* all 7 members are also choreographers; collaboration with visual artists and musicians from Greece

Septdora
Studio for Experimental Practice in Theatre, Dance and Other Related Arts)
Vas. Sophias 33, 10675 **Athens**
Tel: 1-722 3985/808 8966 Fax: 1-623 0535
director Angela Lyra
Dancers: varies + actors *Perfs:* 10-20
No of Prods: 3-4 *Type:* performance art based on improvisation, theme and texts *Accomp:* live, vocal
Touring: England, Poland, Russia *Comments:* emphasis on Hellenic mythology, Byzantine culture, Ancient Greek drama and epic literature

Seresta – Dance Company
2 Fedias St., Thisseo, 11851 **Athens**
Tel: 1-345 5456/342 1268/ Fax: 1-522 9871
director Christine Beskou; manager Gunnar Wensell
Dancers: 6-9 *Perfs:* 20+ *No of Prods:* 2 new *Type:* modern ballet *Accomp:* recorded, live *Venues:* Open Theatre of Lycabettus during the Athens Festival, Athens College, Ergostasio, Knossos Theatre *Touring:* national and international *Comments:* Greek 'rebetiko' and opera themes; influences: jazz and South American dance; Bar Sur Tango production to tour Greek Islands and Europe

Stamatopoulou's Modern Dance Ensemble
Omada Synchronou Chorou Persas Stamatopoulou
Spirou Merkouri 56, Pagrati, 11634 **Athens**
Tel: 1-721 4492
artistic director/choreographer Persa Stamatopoulou
Dancers: 2-5 *Perfs:* 15 *No of Prods:* 1-2
Type: choro-drama, contemporary dance theatre
Accomp: recorded *Venues:* Ergostasio Theatre, Theatre Chororoes, Athens Municipal Theatre, Athens Open Theatre *Touring:* Festivals in Mykonos, Crete, Thessaloniki, Cyprus, Stockholm

State School of Dance Company
57 Omirou Street, 10672 **Athens**
Tel: 1-361 2263/362 4249
Fax: 1-362 4357
E-Mail: Ksot1@internet.gr
president Pavlos Petridis; director Deni Efthimiou-Tsekoura
Dancers: 60 *Perfs:* 10-15 *No of Prods:* 10
Type: classical, ballet, modern, contemporary
Accomp: recorded, live (piano, percussion)
Venues: Theatre Rex, Athens; Municipal Theatre of Piraeus, Theatre Chora (Athens)
Touring: Greece, Cyprus

Theatrokinesis
Laskareos 2, 11471 **Athens**
Tel: 1-646 9634 Fax: 1-645 8947
artistic director/choreographer Isidoros Sideris; music director Dimitris Ziakis
Dancers: 7 + 3 actors + 4 musicians *Perfs:* 12-20
No of Prods: 1-2 *Type:* contemporary dance-theatre
Accomp: recorded
Venues: Meyaron, National Theatre
Touring: Greece

ROES Dance-Theatre
14/16 Iakhou Street, 11854 **Gazi**
Tel: 1-347 9426/2664
Fax: 1-347 9426
artistic director/choreographer Sophia Spyratou
Dancers: 6-10 *Perfs:* 170 *No of Prods:* 3
Type: contemporary with theatre techniques
Accomp: live (Greek folk and ethnic music), recorded
Venues: Theatre Roes
Touring: Monaco, Luxembourg, New York, Paris, Brussels, Cyprus, USA, Turkey
Comments: emphasis on themes from classical and modern Greek literature; also offers seminars, specialising in: acting, dance, vocal performance, percussion, lighting design and video

Maladie d'Amour Theatre of Arts
PO Box 1040, 41221 **Larissa**
Tel: 41-285 684 Fax: 41-285 684
E-Mail: maladie@otenet.gr
artistic director/composer Jannos Eoulu; administrative director Aspasia Dassios
Dancers: 2-6 (dancers and singers) *Perfs:* 20 per year *No of Prods:* 1 new every 2 years *Type:* multi-media; dance theatre – a fusion of cinema, contemporary dance, neo-romantic symphonic music, poetry and operatic singing *Accomp:* live (local orchestra/choir/opera singers), recorded *Venues:* capacities 300 + *Touring:* productions & specially designed to tour worldwide *Comments:* create stage works based on a fusion of cinema, contemporary dance, neo-romantic symphonic music, poetry and operatic singing; presentations in 6 languages; CDs available

Contemporary Dance Company of Harris Mantafounis
Eras 8, 15452 **Psychico**
Tel: 1-934 1756/674 7383 Fax: 1-935 3018
stage manager Zachos Kalogeropoulos; choreographer & artistic director Harris Mantafounis
Dancers: 8 *Perfs:* 15 *No of Prods:* 1-2
Type: modern-classical dance *Accomp:* recorded
Venues: Open Theatre at Mt. Lycabetus and Irodion (during Athens Festival); College of Athens Theatre, Palace Theatre, Atticon Theatre, Rex Theatre (during winter) *Touring:* Greece, France, Spain, Germany, Italy, Switzerland *Comments:* the company has won many prizes and distinctions in European festivals and competitions; Harris Mantafounis gives seminars in Athens and Europe

Emmeleia Modern Dance Company
78, M Botsari & 30, Mantinias street, 5644 **Thessaloniki**
Tel: 31-822 200/308 282 Fax: 31-886 2827
artistic director Dimitra Koroneou; contact Poly Voikou
Dancers: 15 *Perfs:* 25 *No of Prods:* 3
Type: modern dance *Accomp:* recorded
Venues: Centre for the Art of Dance of the City of Thessaloniki, Avlea Theatre, Forest Theatre
Touring: Greece, Cyprus, Italy, Russia

HUNGARY (+36)

ARTUS
Kökörcsin u. 9, 1113 **Budapest**
Tel: 1-466 7505/209 0330
Fax: 1-209 0330
Internet: www.c3.hu/artus
E-Mail: artus@freemail.c3.hu
artistic director Gábor Goda; choreographers/directors Gábor Goda, Ildikó Mándy; coordinator/international management Ernst Süss (tel/fax: 26-350 214)
Dancers: 3-12 *Perfs:* 30-60
No of Prods: 1-2 in a year
Type: dance theatre, crossover (dance, theatre, video, live music, choir)
Touring: Europe, Israel, New Zealand, Egypt, Tunisia
Comments: coproduction with the Human Garden Dance Company (New Zealand '93) and the Israelian Dance Company VERTIGO ('95); see also Drama

Bartók Dance Ensemble
Bartók Táncegyüttes
Budapest Müvelödési Központ (BMK), PO Box 145, 1518 **Budapest**
Tel: 1-203 4646 Fax: 1-203 4632
Internet: www.datanet.hu/~nagyzj/bartok.htm
E-Mail: bmk@mail.matav.hu
artistic director Zoltán J Nagy (tel/fax: 1-312 2085, email: nagyzj@mail.datanet.hu)
Type: folk dance *Comments:* established in 1958, its members are committed to preserving and protecting those folk traditions which, whilst still alive in remote villages, are nonetheless in imminent danger of extinction; has own orchestra; visiting address: Budapest Müvelödési Kuozpont (BMK), Etele út 55, 1119 Budapest XI; alternative E-mail: muvhazak@c3.hu

Bekecs Ensemble, Budapest
Bekecs Együttes, Budapest
Alsóteleki út 2/a III/7, 1201 **Budapest** XX
Tel: 1-284 3657/201 3766 Fax: 1-201 5164
Internet: www.datanet.hu/tanchaz/bekecs.htm
E-Mail: tanchaz@mail.datanet.hu
director András Vavrinecz
Type: folk dance and music
Comments: founded in 1992 by András Vavrinecz and Attila Csávás; undertakes regular research into the folkloric traditions of Somogy and Szatmár, Slovakia and Transylvania; has made several recordings; makes regular appearances at overseas festivals

Central Europe Dance Theatre
Közép Európa Táncszínház
Bethlen Gábor ter 3, 1071 **Budapest**
Tel: 1-342 7163 Fax: 1-342 7163
managing and artistic director Csaba Szögi; assistant manager István Tanács
Dancers: 22 *Perfs:* 90 *No of Prods:* 3
Type: dance-theatre (contemporary)

Compagnie Yvette Bozsik
Bozsik Yvette Társulat
Bocskai út 43-45, X/223, 1113 **Budapest**
Tel: 1-385 4978 Fax: 1-385 4978
director & artistic secretary Yvette Bozsik; manager Henrietta Ámon
Dancers: 6 *Perfs:* 100 *No of Prods:* 2
Type: contemporary, experimental dance performance *Accomp:* recorded *Touring:* Europe, America, Asia, Australia *Comments:* touring company

Dance Ensemble Budapest – Chamber Group of the Hungarian State Folk Ensemble
Budapest Táncegyüttes
PO Box 4, 1251 **Budapest**
Tel: 1-201 5407 Fax: 1-201 5407
Internet: www.c3.hu/-dancebp
E-Mail: dancebp@c3.hu
managing & artistic director Zoltán Zsuráfszki; manager Gusztáv Takách
Dancers: 20 *Perfs:* 80 *Type:* traditional folk dance and dance theatre based on authentic folklore
Accomp: traditional folk music ensemble (5 members)
Venues: Folklore Theatre (FMH) 430
Touring: France, Belgium, Austria; in 2000: 3 month tour in USA, Canada
Comments: visiting address: Szentháromság tér 6, 1014 Budapest; venue address: Fehérvári út 47, 1119 Budapest; tour in 2000 managed by Columbia Artist Management, New York

Duna Folkdance Ensemble
Duna Müvészegyüttes
Nemetvölgyi 41-45, 1124 **Budapest**
Tel: 1-201 6613 Fax: 1-311 3026
Internet: www.b-m.hu/duna-palota
artistic director Janos Mucsi; artistic secretary Zoltan Safrany
Dancers: 33 *Perfs:* 100
Type: folk dance, dance theatre
Venues: own venue 300
Touring: national, international

Experidance Company
Szigligeti Tánct´rsulat
Magyar Táncmüvészeti Média Központ, PO Box 160, 1734 **Budapest**
Tel: 1-217 0795 Fax: 1-217 0795
artistic director Sándor Román; manager Miklós Kékesi
Type: special kind of contemporary dance based on Hungarian folk dancing but drawing on western techniques *Comments:* visiting address: Magyar Táncmüvészeti Média Központ, Ráday utca 37, 1092 Budaspest IX

Honvéd Dance Theatre
Honvéd együttes – Táncszínház
Kerepesi út 29/B, 1087 **Budapest**
Tel: 1-210 0000 Fax: 1-334 3772
general director Károly Aranyos; artistic director Ferenc Novák
Dancers: 34 *Perfs:* 100 *No of Prods:* 3
Type: dance-theatre, folklore *Accomp:* own orchestra
Venues: Magyar Honvédség Müvelödési Háza (Culture Centre of the Hungarian Army)

Hungarian Festival Ballet
Magyar Fesztivál Balett
Budapesti XII Kerületi Müvelödési Központ, Csörsz utca 18, 1124 **Budapest** XII
Tel: 1-319 9855/6 Fax: 1-319 9855
artistic director Iván Markó
Type: contemporary ballet *Touring:* national, international *Comments:* established in 1996 by former Maurice Béjart star Iván Markó and based at Budapest XIIth District Cultural Centre; performs regularly throughout the country

Hungarian State Folk Ensemble
Magyar Állami Népiegyüttes
Corvin tér 8, 1011 **Budapest**
Tel: 1-201 5773 Fax: 1-201 5017
general manager Sándor Serfözö; artistic director Ferenc Sebö; financial director Gizella Horváth; manager Mária Ferencz
Dancers: 36, 14 gypsy musician, 6 folk musicians *Perfs:* 150 *No of Prods:* 1 *Type:* folk dance *Accomp:* live music – own orchestra *Venues:* capacity 290 *Touring:* Europe, Far East, USA

Hungarian State Opera Ballet Company
Magyar Állami Operaház Balettegyüttese, Magyar Nemzeti Balett
PO Box 503, 1373 **Budapest**
Tel: 1-331 2550/110/332 0923 Fax: 1-332 0923
ballet director Gyula Harangozó; international manager Márta Pölös; general director Miklós Szinetár; managing director Imre Kiss; secretary general Attila Fülöp; chief conductor Géza Oberfrank
Dancers: 108 + 226 musicians (2 orchestras playing in 2 venues) *Perfs:* 100 *No of Prods:* 4 *Type:* classical ballet, modern dance *Accomp:* live music (own orchestra), recorded music *Venues:* Hungarian State Opera House 1260, Erkel Theatre 2300 *Comments:* visiting address: Andrássy út 22, 1061 Budapest

Kompmánia Contemporary Dance Theatre
Kompmánia Kortárs Táncszínház
Magyar Táncmüvészeti Média Központ, PO Box 160, 1734 **Budapest**
Tel: 1-217 0795 Fax: 1-217 0795
artistic director Attila Csabai; manager Miklós Kékesi
Type: contemporary dance *Comments:* established in 1997; based at Szkéne Theatre, Budapest; visiting address: Magyar Táncmüvészeti Média Központ, Ráday utca 37, 1092 Budapest IX

Rajkó Folk Ensemble
Rajko Népiegyüttes
Rottenbiller u.16-22, 1074 **Budapest**
Tel: 1-321 4825/322 4841 Fax: 1-341 5700
E-Mail: talentum.kult.fórum@iskola.alba.hu
general manager István Gerendási
Dancers: 20 + 40 musicians *Perfs:* 200 *No of Prods:* 1 *Type:* folk dance, gypsy dance *Accomp:* live (own orchestra) *Venues:* Pesti Vigadó (Redoute) 1051, Budapest Convention Centre 1750 *Touring:* Europe
Comments: alternative E-mail: talentum.kult.forum@mail.alba.hu

Györ Ballet
Györi Balett
PO Box 401, 9002 **Györ**
Tel: 96-312 044 Fax: 96-326 999
Internet: www.different.hu/kultura/gybalett/mgybalett.html
E-Mail: gyori.balett@mail.datanet.hu
director, artistic director János Kiss; economic manager Ilona Bész; art. secr., marketing manager Péter Stangl; technical director Tibor Vidos
Dancers: 26 *Perfs:* 60 (20 on tour) *No of Prods:* 3
Accomp: recorded music *Venues:* capacity 690 *Touring:* Europe *Comments:* visiting address: Györi Nemzeti Szinház, Czuczor Gergely u.7, 9022 Györ

Jászság (Jaszygian) Folk Dance Ensemble
Jászság Népiegyüttes
Jászság Népiegyüttes Ház, PO Box 116, 5100 **Jászberény**
Tel: 57-411 294 Fax: 57-411 294
Internet: www.interj.datanet.hu/jneszh/jne.html
E-Mail: jneszh@mail.datanet.hu
artistic director Gábor Szücs
Type: folk dance *Comments:* established in 1971; undertakes research into the traditional music and dance of the Hungarian peasantry of the Carpathian Basin and stages performances of this music and dance in traditional costume; organises the annual Csángó Folk Festival of European Minorities and the International Folk Music and Folk Dance Camp; has recorded several videos and cassettes; visiting address: Jászság Népiegyüttes Ház, Viz utca 1, 5100 Jászberény

Pécs Ballet – Ballet Sopianae
Pécsi Ballet – Balett Sopianae
PO Box 126, 7601 **Pécs**
Tel: 72-512 660/667 Fax: 72-211 986
ballet director István Herczog; managing director Tamás Balikó
Dancers: 34 *Perfs:* 30 *Type:* modern dance *Accomp:* live, recorded *Venues:* capacity 530 *Comments:* visiting address: Pécsi Nemzeti Szinház, Perczel u.17, 7621 Pécs

Pécs Mecsek Dance Ensemble
Pécsi Mecsek Táncegyüttes
Pécsi Kulturális Központ, Szinház tér 2, 7621 **Pécs**
Tel: 72-310 783 Fax: 72-310 783
Internet: www.pserve.hu/kultur/mmecstnc.htm
E-Mail: pkkinfo@c3.hu
Type: folk dance

Tanac Folk Dance Ensemble
Tanac Néptáncegyüttes
Nagyvárad utca 13, 7623 **Pécs**
Tel: 72-330 211
Internet: www.datanet.hu/tanchaz/thclub.htm
artistic director József Szávai (mobile: 30-939 1620)
Type: folk dance *Comments:* established in 1988; its repertoire and the ethnic provenance of its members make it the most important representative of Croatian folk culture in Hungary; has its own Dance House in Pécs; organises dance camps and festivals and has recorded several videos and music cassettes; visiting address: c/o Tanac Táncház, Ifjúsági Ház, Nagy Lajos király utca 13, 7622 Pécs; alternative Internet: www.4.pgh.net/~jdv/tamb/tanac1.htm#assoc

Szeged Contemporary Ballet
Szegedi Kortars Balett
Szegedi Nemzeti Szinház, Deàk Ferenc u. 12, 6720 **Szeged**
Tel: 62-476 080 Fax: 62-476 080
E-Mail: szkb@mail.tiszanet.hu
artistic director Tamás Juronics; ballet director András Pataki
Dancers: 14 *Perfs:* 50 *No of Prods:* 2 annually
Type: contemporary dance/modern dance with acrobatic elements *Accomp:* recorded *Venues:* capacity 700 *Touring:* Hungary, Switzerland, Austria, Germany, Mexico, Italy, Denmark, Luxembourg, Poland, Slovakia, United Kingdom *Comments:* work regularly with international guest choreographers

Alba Regia Folk Dance Group
Alba Regia Táncesgyüttes
Malom utca 6, 8000 **Székesfehérvár**
Tel: 22-312 795/501 700/701 Fax: 22-312 795
Internet: www.datatrans.hu/~artefolk/folkarteng.htm
E-Mail: artefolk@mail.matav.hu
leader József Botos
Type: folk dance
Comments: established in 1949

Szigligeti Dance Ensemble
Szigligeti Tánc Társulat
Tizsapark 1, 5000 **Szolnok**
Tel: 56-342 633 Fax: 56-342 633
artistic/managing director Sandor Roman
Dancers: 20
Type: mixes elements of modern and folkdance

ICELAND (+354)

Icelandic Ballet / Iceland Dance Company, The
Íslenski dansflokkurin
Borgarleikhúsio, Box 3067, 123 **Reykjavík**
Tel: 588 0900 Fax: 588 0910
Internet: www.id.is
E-Mail: id@id.is
general director Valgeir Valdimarsson; artistic director Katrin Hall; ballet master Lauren Hauser
Dancers: 11 *Perfs:* 40 *No of Prods:* 4-5 *Type:* modern dance based on classical and modern techniques
Accomp: live, recorded *Venues:* City Theatre and National Theatre, resident at the Reykjavik City Theatre 526 *Touring:* Bergen, Belgium, Avignon, Prague

IRELAND Republic of (+353)

CoisCéim Dance Theatre
Top Floor, 7 South Great Georges Street, **Dublin** 2
Tel: 1-670 4134 Fax: 1-670 4076
Internet: www.homepages.iol.ie/~coisceim
E-Mail: coisceim@iol.ie
company manager Bridget Webster; artistic director David Bolger
Dancers: 3-8 *Perfs:* 20-30 *No of Prods:* 2-3
Type: contemporary dance theatre with new music composition *Accomp:* combination of live and recorded sound *Venues:* cap. 200-300
Touring: Ireland, UK, Europe

John Scotts Irish Modern Dance Theatre
SFX Centre, Upper Sherrard Street, **Dublin** 1
Tel: 1-874 9616 Fax: 1-878 7784
Internet: www.imdt.iol.ie
E-Mail: ScottDance@internet-eireann.ie
administrator Marinna Rafter; artistic director John Scott; ballet master varies according to production
Dancers: varies *Perfs:* 30 *No of Prods:* 3 (2 new)
Type: contemporary dance-theatre *Accomp:* recorded, live, always new music commissioned by the company
Venues: Project Arts Centre 200, Samuel Beckett Theatre 400, Tivoli Theatre 400; Abbey Theatre, Peacock Stage 120, SFX Centre 300, RHA Gallery 250
Touring: Scandinavia, France, UK, USA
Comments: project basis-funded by Arts Council and Dublin Corporation

New Balance Dance Company
23 Goatstown Road, **Dublin** 14
Tel: 1-298 4167/284 1784
artistic director Adrienne Brown
Dancers: 1-12 (project-based company) *Perfs:* 5 (twice a year) *Type:* contemporary *Accomp:* live, recorded *Venues:* Samuel Beckett Theatre 250 *Touring:* national *Comments:* classes & workshops being held – both for the able-bodied and disabled; Adrienne Brown also teaches choreography & improvisation

Riverdance
Abhann Productions, 133 Capel Street, **Dublin** 1
Tel: 1-662 7200 Fax: 1-662 7218
Internet: www.riverdance.com
E-Mail: info@riverdance.ie
executive producer Julian Eorkane; director of operations Ronan Smith
Dancers: 50 per company (3 companies) *Perfs:* 360 per company *No of Prods:* 1 *Type:* Irish traditional dance/flamenco, tap dance, ballet, folk *Accomp:* live *Touring:* worldwide *Comments:* 3 companies: The LIFFEY, The LEE, The Lagein

Rubato Ballet Company
19 Stamer Street, **Dublin** 8
Tel: 1-453 8657 Fax: 1-478 4353
Internet: www.iol.ie/~rubato
E-Mail: rubato@iol.ie
administrator Zelda Francesca; artistic director Fiona Quilligan; production Hector Heathwood
Dancers: 6 dancers, 3/4 musicians *Perfs:* 60 + dance in education performance projects *No of Prods:* 2 + ongoing Dance in-Ed workshops *Type:* neo-classical *Accomp:* live *Venues:* RHA Gallagher Gallery 1000, Project Arts Centre 200, Colaiste Mhuire 400, Samuel Beckett Theatre 300, National Gallery of Ireland 300, Backstage Theatre, Longford 300, Garage Theatre, Monaghan 250 *Touring:* Ireland *Comments:* multi-media company working with dancers, musicians, artists, using newly-commissioned scores by Irish composers. Winner of the AIB Better Ireland Award, 4 sponsors: FÁS, Peace & Reconciliation Programme, Dublin Corporation, Arts Council, Co-operation North, Southern Education Library Board and Nijinsky Medal

Dance Theatre of Ireland
13 Clarinda Park No., **Dun Laoghaire (Co. Dublin)**
Tel: 1-280 3455 Fax: 1-280 3466
E-Mail: danceire@iol.ie
artistic directors Robert Connor, Loretta Yurick; administrator Orla O'Doherty
Dancers: 7-9 *Perfs:* 35 *No of Prods:* 3 *Type:* contemporary, dance-theatre *Accomp:* live, recorded, original music by Irish composers *Venues:* Tivoli Theatre 400, The Samuel Beckett Theatre 200 *Touring:* Ireland, Northern Ireland, Europe, France *Comments:* Dance Pop (Dance Performance Outreach Programme) – extensive outreach programme, including workshops and classes for professionals as well as youth and community groups, masterclasses

Daghdha Dance Company
University of Limerick, **Limerick**
Tel: 61-202 804 Fax: 61-202 943/330 316
Internet: www.ul.ie/~ddc
E-Mail: daghdha@ul.ie
company manager Bridget Cleary; artistic director t.b.a.
Dancers: 3-7 (one musician) *Perfs:* 60 *No of Prods:* 2 *Type:* modern *Accomp:* commissioned original works – live, recorded, text *Venues:* varies *Touring:* Ireland, England, Germany, France, Spain, Sweden, Mexico *Comments:* 2 productions annually – one created specifically for schools, one created specifically for young audiences

ITALY (+39)

Balletto della Fondazione Concerti N Piccinni
Via Beltrami, 2, 70124 **Bari**
Tel: 080-558 6906 Fax: 080-558 6906
segretario generale Saverio Catacchio; presidente avv. Gianvito Pugliese
Dancers: 20 *No of Prods:* 1 *Type:* classical *Accomp:* recorded *Venues:* Teatro Royal 500, Teatro Barium 150 *Comments:* work in collaboration with the province and the region

Materiali Resistenti
Via Codussi 40, 24124 **Bergamo**
Tel: 035-236 724 Fax: 035-236 724
Type: experimental, contemporary

Saraswati Dance Association
Via Bassini 17, 24100 **Bergamo**
Tel: 035-257 505 Fax: 035-257 505
Internet: www.kalinga.net/ileana
E-Mail: ileana5@hotmail.com
artistic director Ileana Citaristi
Dancers: 6-12 *Perfs:* 15 *No of Prods:* 6 *Type:* Indian dance (Odissi and Mayurbhan ji Chhau style) *Accomp:* live (4 musicians) *Touring:* Italy (May-Oct), India (Nov-April) *Comments:* second address: Miss Ileana Citaristi, director ART VISION, 294, Mahatab Road, 751002 Bhubaneswar, India, Tel: +91 6744 33779; Fax: +91 674 433 779

Chorea Contemporary Dance Company
Via Pirandello 14, 40127 **Bologna**
Tel: 051-633 1186 Fax: 051-330 931
E-Mail: chorea@tin.it
director & choreographer Nicoletta Sacco; administrator Piero Fazzini; organization Belinda Diamanti, Francesca Franzoso, Martina Marini
Dancers: 3-8 *Perfs:* 20-30 *No of Prods:* 5 *Type:* contemporary dance – physical-theatre *Accomp:* live, recorded *Touring:* Europe *Comments:* dance company for the young: educational program provides regular courses in the centre; workshop, stages, conferences; also runs the dance school 'Chorea Centro Studi Danza Moderno-Creativa' at the Centre Atelier Pilastro Danza Musica Teatro

Associazione Sarda Musica e Danza (ASMED)
Via Machiavelli 110, 09131 **Cagliari**
Tel: 070-494 281/492 645/0335-813 6666
Fax: 070-492 645
E-Mail: asmed@tiscalinet.it
direttore organizzativo Massimo Leoni; direttore artistico Paola Leoni; promozione Rosaria Tarantini; ufficio stampa Christiana Lamba
Dancers: 7+ *Perfs:* 50 *No of Prods:* 18 *Type:* contemporary *Accomp:* recorded, live *Touring:* Sardinia, Italy, UK, France, Germany *Comments:* stage courses, seminars, Festival Internazionale Nuova Danza Citta di Cagliari; see also Festivals

Associazione Sosta Palmizi – Raffaella Giordano, Giorgio Rossi
Viale Regina Elena 81/83,
52042 **Camucia di Cortona (Arezzo)**
Tel: 0575-630 678/0347-364 7717 (mobile)
Fax: 0575-630 989
E-Mail: spalmizi@technet.it
segretaria organizzativa Laura Stanganini; choreographers & artistic directors Raffaella Giordano, Giorgio Rossi; projett speciali & press agent Flavia Marini; director tecnico Marco Cassini; administrator Milena Colasimole
Dancers: 8 *Perfs:* approx 60 *No of Prods:* Giordano: 6 (1 new), Rossi: 6 (1 new) *Type:* dance-theatre, experimental *Accomp:* recorded, live *Touring:* France, Switzerland, Italy, Germany, Portugal
Comments: professional training workshops

Compagnia di Danza Efesto
Via Montegrappa 5,
00010 **Colleverde di Guidonia (Roma)**
Tel: 0774-363 296/0335-562 8585
Fax: 0774-363 296
E-Mail: mparisi@priminet.com
direttori artistici Donatella Capraro, Marcello Parisi
Dancers: 6 *Perfs:* 20 *No of Prods:* 2 *Type:* contemporary *Accomp:* live, recorded *Touring:* Italy

ARTEMIS
Via XXV Aprile n.30, 44100 **Ferrara**
Tel: 0521-200 750 Fax: 0521-231 232
direttore artistico Monica Casadei; disegno luci Claudio Coloretti; suono Andrea Romanin
Dancers: 6 *Perfs:* 50 *No of Prods:* 2 *Type:* dance theatre *Accomp:* recorded, live *Venues:* Teatro Stabile di Parma *Touring:* Italy, France *Comments:* resident at Teatro Stabice di Parma

Balletto di Toscana
Via Claudio Monteverdi 3/A, 50144 **Firenze**
Tel: 055-351 530 Fax: 055-353 856
Internet: www.programmifuturi.it/balletoditoscana
E-Mail: bdt@programmifuturi.it
direttore amministrativo Riccardo Donnini; direttore artistico Cristina Bozzolini; organizzatrice Bruna Umbro; ufficio promozione e marketing Lorena Cipriani
Dancers: 16 *Perfs:* approx 80 *No of Prods:* 11 *Type:* contemporary dance *Accomp:* live, recorded *Touring:* Europe, USA

KinKaleri
Piazza Puliti 1/r, 50121 **Firenze**
Tel: 055-676 853/0335-523 8751 (mobile)
Fax: 055-676 853
Internet: www.mega.it/KinKaleri
E-Mail: KinKaleri@mega.it
contact Luca Camilletti, Matteo Bambi
Dancers: 6 *Perfs:* 25 *No of Prods:* 2 *Type:* research *Accomp:* live *Comments:* see also Festivals (Camera di Espansione)

MaggioDanza di Firenze
c/o Teatro del Maggio Musicale Fiorentino, via Solferino 15, 50123 **Firenze**
Tel: 055-27791/211 258(Box Office)
Fax: 055-239 6954
Internet: www.maggiofiorentino.com
E-Mail: tickets@maggiofiorentino.com
sovrintendente t.b.a.; direttore di MaggioDanza di Firenze Davido Bombana; uff.stampa Susanna Colombo
Dancers: 45 *Perfs:* 28 *No of Prods:* 6 *Type:* classical and modern ballet *Accomp:* live, recorded *Venues:* Teatro Comunale 2004, Teatro della Pergola 1000 *Comments:* see also Opera, Orchestras, Festivals and Venues

Compagnia Italiana Balletto
Via Orti, 31, 20122 **Milano**
Tel: 02-5501 1485 Fax: 02-5501 1485
direttore artistico e legale rappresentante Beppe Menegatti
Dancers: 30 *Perfs:* 30
No of Prods: 5 *Type:* classical
Accomp: live, recorded *Touring:* Italy

Corte Sconta
Via Nino Bixio N.45, 20129 **Milano**
Tel: 02-2951 7962/89
Fax: 02-2951 79896
E-Mail: corte.sconta@agora.it
organizzazione Enrica Abbate; direzione artistica e coreografia Laura Balis, Cinzia Romiti
Dancers: 8-10 *Perfs:* 20
Type: contemporary *Accomp:* recorded
Touring: Italy, Germany, Switzerland

Franco Parenti Danza
c/o S. Bettrami, Via L. Pasteur 2,
20128 **Milano**
Tel: 02-261 5807 Fax: 02-256 5149
direttore artistico Susanna Beltrami, Luciana Savignano; direttore generale Michele Casula; amministratore Daniele Luppino
Dancers: 6-10 *Perfs:* 150 *No of Prods:* 2
Type: contemporary *Accomp:* live, recorded
Venues: Teatro Carcano, Teatro Franco Parenti Milano
Touring: USA, England, Italy, France, Germany
Comments: 2 auditions a year: December and April; venue address: Teatro Franco Parenti (Via Pierlombardo Milano, Tel: 02-5518 4075)

Teatro alla Scala Fondazione di Diritto Privato
Via Filodrammatici 2, 20121 **Milano**
Tel: 02-88791 Fax: 02-887 9411
Internet: www.lascala.milano.it
sovrintendente Carlo Fontana; direttore artistico Paolo Arcá; direttore del ballo t.b.a.; relazioni esterne Donatella Brunazzi (887 9264); uff. stampa Luciana Fusi (887 9412)
Dancers: 97 *Perfs:* 88 *No of Prods:* 10
Type: classical, modern *Accomp:* live (orchestra)
Venues: Teatro alla Scala 2000
Touring: Japan *Comments:* see also Opera, Orchestras and Venues

Compagnia Abbondanza-Bertoni
Loc. Dosse 6, 38060 **Nago (TN)**
Tel: 0464-506 258/051-270 518
Fax: 0464-506 258
E-Mail: mas2297@iperbole.bologna.it
direttori artistici Michele Abbondanza, Antonella Bertoni; organizzazione Elena Cervellati
Dancers: 7 *Perfs:* 50 *No of Prods:* 2 *Type:* dance theatre *Accomp:* live, recorded *Touring:* Italy, France, Germany

Balletto di Napoli – Compagnia Regionale di Danza
Via Ligorio Pirro 20, 80129 **Napoli**
Tel: 081-556 4029/556 6745/556 7935
Fax: 081-556 7935
direttore amministrativo e organizzativo Marcello di Vincenzo; presidente e direttore artistico Mara Fusco
Dancers: 12 *Perfs:* 60
No of Prods: 2 *Type:* classical, contemporary
Accomp: recorded *Touring:* USA, Greece

Compagnia di Balletto del Teatro di San Carlo
Via S Carlo 98 F, 80132 **Napoli**
Tel: 081-797 2111 Fax: 081-797 2306
Internet: www.teatrosancarlo.it
E-Mail: infoteatro@teatrodisancarlo.it
sovrintendente Francesco Canessa; direttore corpo di ballo Luciano Cannito; direttore artistico Carlo Mayer; directtore scuola di ballo Anna Razzi
Dancers: 64 *Perfs:* 30 *No of Prods:* 3
Type: classical, modern
Accomp: live, recorded
Venues: Teatro San Carlo 1400
Comments: see also Opera, Orchestras and Venues

Movimento Danza
Via Bonito 19/a, 80129 **Napoli**
Tel: 081-578 0542
Fax: 081-556 8466
director & choreographer Gabriella Stazio; manager Gigi Castaldo; press office Roberta Albano; secretariat Rossana Scepi; production secretary Barbara Lattes
Dancers: 8-12 *Perfs:* 40 *Type:* contemporary
Accomp: recorded, live
Touring: Ireland, Australia, Jordan, Guatemala, Malta, Russia, Switzerland, Uganda

ALEF danzateatro
Via Malabranca 15, 05018 **Orvieto (TR)**
Tel: 0763-341 479
Fax: 0763-340 669
direttore artistico e legale rappresentante Rossella Fiumi; amministratore Maurizio Silvio; pubbliche relazioni Roberto Buffa
Dancers: 5 *Perfs:* 20-30 *No of Prods:* 1
Type: contemporary, theatre dance
Accomp: live, recorded

Corpo di Ballo del Teatro Massimo di Palermo
Via Riccardo Wagner 2, 90139 **Palermo**
Tel: 091-605 3111 (switchboard)
Fax: 091-605 3325
Internet: www.teatromassimo.it
E-Mail: infotm@teatromassimo.it
presidente Leoluca Orlando; sovrintendente Francesco Giambrone; direttore operativo Antonio Cognata; direttore artistico Marco Betta; coordinatore artistico Micha van Hoecke; etoille principale ospite Alessandra Ferri; press office Laura Oddo; responsabile e coreografo Piccoli Danzatori Alexandre Skepkine; direttore allestimento scenico Sergio De Giorgi; direttore della produzione Giovanni Mazzara
Dancers: 26 (Corpo di Ballo Teatro Massimo) + 62 (Piccoli Danzatori) *Perfs:* 60 (Corpo di Ballo Teatro Massimo) + 30 (Piccoli Danzatori) *No of Prods:* 3 (Corpo di Ballo Teatro Massimo) + 3 (Piccoli Danzatori) *Type:* classical, contemporary *Accomp:* live, recorded *Venues:* Teatro Massimo 1300, Teatro Politeama Garibaldi 950, Teatro di Verdura 2238 (estivo) *Comments:* see also Venues, Opera and Orchestras; Piccoli Danzatori is a dance company of 10-18 year olds

L'Ensemble Association
c/o Teatro Verdi, via Palestro 40, 56127 **Pisa**
Tel: 050-941 144 Fax: 050-941 158
direttore artistico Micha Van Hoecke; presidente Marina Van Hoecke; organizzazione Claudia Zippi
Dancers: 13 *Perfs:* 6 *No of Prods:* 4 *Type:* dance-theatre *Accomp:* recorded, live *Venues:* Teatro Verdi 993 *Touring:* Italy, Europe

Aterballetto
c/o Centro Regionale della Danza, Via Giglioli Valle, 25, 42100 **Reggio Emilia**
Tel: 0522-273 011 Fax: 0522-273 050/60
Internet: www.crd-aterballetto.it
E-Mail: centrodanza@crd-aterballetto.it
presidente Federico Grilli; direttore artistico Mauro Bigonzetti
Dancers: 16 *Perfs:* 100 *No of Prods:* 11 new *Type:* classical, contemporary, neoclassical *Accomp:* live, recorded *Venues:* Theatro Municipale Valli 1100 (seats) *Touring:* worldwide *Comments:* Aterballetto is the official company of the Centro Regionale della Danza and can be contacted through Centro Regionale della Danza, Tel: 0522-273 011, Fax: 0522-273 060

Compagnia Balletto Classico Liliana Cosi – Marinel Stefanescu – Reggio Emilia
Via Bernini 17, 42100 **Reggio Emilia**
Tel: 0522-517 234 Fax: 0522-516 486
E-Mail: lilcosi@tin.it
direttore artistico Liliana Cosi, Marinel Stefanescu
Dancers: 12 *Perfs:* 70-80 *No of Prods:* 10
Type: classical, neo-classical *Accomp:* recorded, live
Touring: Italy, Europe

Aire
Roma
Comments: merged with MDA Produzioni Danza (q.v.)

Associazione Culturale Teatrokoros – Compagnia di Danza Massimo Moricone
Via degli Orti Gianicolensi u.5, 00152 **Roma**
Tel: 06-583 6769 Fax: 06-583 6769
E-Mail: koros.ac@flashnet.it
direzione artistica Massimo Moricone; direzione organizzativa Danila Ciavatti
Dancers: 7 *Perfs:* 30-40 *No of Prods:* 1-2 *Type:* contemporary *Accomp:* live, recorded *Touring:* India, Mexico

Associazione Vera Stasi
Via Orti Gianicolensi N. 5, 00152 **Roma**
Tel: 06-588 5967 Fax: 06-588 5967
direzione artistica Silvana Barbarini, Ian Sutton
Dancers: varies per production *Perfs:* 30 *No of Prods:* 2 each year *Type:* dance theatre *Accomp:* recorded *Venues:* Teatro Vascello 400 (Roma), Tuscania Supercinema 100 (Tuscania) *Touring:* Czech Republic, Spain, Senegal, Egypt, USA *Comments:* Vera Stasi is an association of two choreographers, it is part of a three year project of acting in residence for music, dance and theatre; the association is based in Tuscania, c/o Tuscania Teatro, Via delle Logge 11, 01017 Tuscania (VT), Tel: 0761-443 728, Fax: 0761-444 170

Balletto 90
Via Andronico 26, 00136 **Roma**
Tel: 06-3972 8950 Fax: 06-3972 8950
responsabile organizzativo Simona Di Luise (tel/fax: 06-8724 7977); direttore artistico e legale rappresentante Anita Bucchi
Dancers: 8-15 *Perfs:* 30-40 *No of Prods:* 3
Type: contemporary *Accomp:* live, recorded

Balletto di Roma
Via Aurelia 477, 00165 **Roma**
Tel: 06-662 2813 Fax: 06-662 2813
presidente Franca Bartolomei; direzione artistica Amadeo Amodio; direzione generale Walter Zappolini
Dancers: 12 *Perfs:* approx 50 *No of Prods:* 5 (incl 2 new) *Type:* classical, neo-classical, contemporary, jazz *Accomp:* recorded, live *Touring:* Italy, China

Compagnia di Danza Enzo Cosimi
Via Degli Orti Giani Colensi, 5, 00152 **Roma**
Tel: 06-581 0041 Fax: 06-581 0041
E-Mail: cosimi.danza@spqr.ats.it
artistic director Enzo Cosimi; organisation/administration Diletta Gorgolo
Dancers: 8 *Perfs:* 30 *Type:* contemporary *Accomp:* recorded *Touring:* Germany, France, Denmark, Netherlands

Compagnia di Danza Kybalion
Via Antonio Serra 82, 00191 **Roma**
Tel: 06-334 0198 Fax: 06-334 1098
artistic director Gisella Johnson
Dancers: 8 + 5 musicians *No of Prods:* 7
Type: contemporary *Accomp:* live, occassionally recorded *Comments:* dance company funded by the Ministry of Culture; see also Promoters and Competitions

Corpo di Ballo del Teatro dell' Opera di Roma
P.za Beniamino gigli N.1, 00184 **Roma**
Tel: 06-481 601/8392 Fax: 06-488 1253
Internet: www.themix.it
E-Mail: sovrintendenza@opera.roma.it
sovrintendente Francesco Ernani; direttore artistico e musicale Giuseppe Sinopoli; direttore del ballo Amedeo Amodio; uff. stampa Renato Bossa
Dancers: 70 *Perfs:* 70 *No of Prods:* 5 (2 new) *Type:* classical, contemporary *Accomp:* live, recorded *Venues:* Teatro dell' Opera 1604, Teatro Nazionale *Comments:* see also Opera, Orchestra, Festival and Venues

Danzacompagnia Anna Catalano – Associazione Culturale Metropolis Europa
c/o Centro Petra Lata, Via di Pietralata 159A, 00158 **Roma**
Tel: 06-451 5756/347-713 2220 (mobile)
Fax: 06-451 5756
Internet: www.geocities.com/vienna/strasse/7392
E-Mail: petra01@global-italianet.it
rapresentante legale Antonino Catalano; procuratore speciale Francesca Mandará; direzione artistica e coreografia Anna Catalano, Anthony Basile; coreografa Anna Catalano e altri; maitre de ballet Anthony Basile
Dancers: 10-12 *Perfs:* 100 *No of Prods:* 6 *Type:* contemporary dance theatre *Accomp:* live, recorded *Venues:* Centro Petralata up to 500 *Touring:* Europe *Comments:* the company is one of the few examples in Italy of permanent contemporary dance theatre companies; it is the resident dance company of the Centro Petralata Dance; see also Venues

Gruppo Danza Oggi
Via G. Luporini 19, 00124 **Roma**
Tel: 06-509 0147/418 2146 (studio)
Fax: 06-509 0147
direttore artistico Patrizia Salvatori; presidente e responsable pubbliche relazioni Gabriella Gasparini
Dancers: 5-9 *Perfs:* 20-24 *No of Prods:* 1 *Type:* classical, modern, contemporary, mime, classical spanish
Accomp: recorded

MDA Produzioni Danza
Via Salaria 72, 00198 **Roma**
Tel: 06-841 6174/6224 Fax: 06-841 6174
E-Mail: mda@mclink.it
presidente e dir. artistico Aurelio Gatti; consiglio artistico Roberta Escamilla Garrison, Sandra Fuciarelli, Fabrizio Monteverde, Nicoletta Giavotto, Marianna Troise; manager Antonello Gatti
Dancers: 16 *Perfs:* 90 *No of Prods:* 5 + 5 repertory *Type:* neo-classical, dance theatre, contemporary ballet *Accomp:* live, recorded *Comments:* the company is active for 11 months of the year; merged with Aire

Patrizia Cerroni e I Danzatori Scalzi
vicolo del Babuccio 37, Fontana di Trevi, 00187 **Roma**
Tel: 06-678 1963 Fax: 06-679 2657
E-Mail: ids97@flashnet.it
presidente e direttore artistico Patrizia Cerroni
Dancers: 6-10 *Perfs:* 50-60 *No of Prods:* 5 *Type:* modern, contemporary *Accomp:* live, recorded *Touring:* Italy, Greece, Australia, Singapore, Thailand, Brazil, USA

Renato Greco Ballet
Via Ruggero Leoncavallo 16, 00199 **Roma**
Tel: 06-860 8010 Fax: 06-860 7740
artistic director Maria Teresa dal Medico; promotion officer Palma Marzilli
Dancers: 12 *Perfs:* 100 *No of Prods:* 6
Type: jazz ballet, classical, modern
Accomp: recorded *Venues:* Teatro Greco 392
Touring: Italy *Comments:* the theatre is supported by Ministero dei Beni Culturali; see also Venues

Company Blu
Via Cadorna 18, 50019 **Sesto Fiorentino (FI)**
Tel: 055-440 265 Fax: 055-440 265
choreographers Charlotte Zerbey, Alessandro Certini
Dancers: 5 *Perfs:* 28 *No of Prods:* 2 *Type:* contemporary *Accomp:* live, recorded *Venues:* studio *Touring:* Europe *Comments:* organises the festival Estate a Villa di San Lorenzo, 2 weeks in July, annual, Artistic Directors C. Zerbey, A. Certini, arts types: modern & contemporary

Compagnia Virgilio Sieni Danza
Via di San Romano 13, 50135 **Settignano-Firenze**
Tel: 055-655 7435/863 Fax: 055-697 646
Internet: www.sienidanza.it
E-Mail: sienidanza@ats.it
direttore organizzativo Lucilla Bigi; direttore artistico Virgilio Sieni
Dancers: 8 *Perfs:* 45 *No of Prods:* 7 *Type:* contemporary *Accomp:* recorded; live (sometimes)
Touring: worldwide

Accademia Regionale di Danza
c/o Fondazione Teatro Nuovo, Corso Massimo d'Azeglio 17, 10126 **Torino**
Tel: 011-650 0211 Fax: 011-650 0265
Internet: www.tnt.nuovo
E-Mail: nuovotnt@mail.tin.it
direttrice attivitá formative Germana Erba
Dancers: approx 40 *Type:* classical *Accomp:* recorded *Comments:* the Fondazione Teatro Nuovo runs 3 college course, legally recognised: Liceo Artistico, Liceo Artistico Coreutico, Liceo per l'Arte e lo Spettacolo, all 5 years long; see also Agents & Producers, Venues and Festivals

Compagnia di Danza Teatro di Torino
Via Principessa Clotilde 3, 10144 **Torino**
Tel: 011-473 0189 Fax: 011-473 2996
Internet: www.Teatro-danza.it
E-Mail: furno@teatro-danza.it
legale rappresentante Loredana Furno; direttore artistico Loredana Furno; ufficio stampa Donatella Antonellini
Dancers: 25 *Perfs:* approx 60 *No of Prods:* 5
Type: classical, neo-classical, contemporary, jazz dance *Accomp:* live, recorded *Venues:* Teatro di Torino 950 *Touring:* Turkey, Tunisia

Compagnia di Danza Teatro Nuovo
corso Massimo d'Azeglio 17, 10126 **Torino**
Tel: 011-650 0211 Fax: 011-650 0265
Internet: www.tnt.nuovo.it
E-Mail: nuovotnt@mail.tin.it
direttore artistico Gian Mesturino; legale rappresentante Lino Bongiovanni; ufficio promozione Roberto Angi
Dancers: 12 *Perfs:* 100 *No of Prods:* 4
Type: neo-classical, contemporary dance
Accomp: live, tape *Venues:* Teatro Nuovo: Sala Grande 1000 *Touring:* Italy *Comments:* the Fondazione Teatro Nuovo has opened a new college course, legally recognised, called Liceo Artistico Coreutico, Liceo per l'Arte e lo Spettacolo, all 5 years; see also Venues, Festivals and Agents & Producers

Compagnia Jazz Ballet
Largo Francia 113, 10138 **Torino**
Tel: 011-433 5522 Fax: 011-650 0265
direttore artistico e legale rappresentante Adriana Cava
Dancers: 10 + 2 guests *Perfs:* 20 *No of Prods:* 1
Type: modern jazz *Accomp:* recorded, live
Venues: Teatro Alfieri 1500, Teatro Nuovo 980
Touring: Italy
Comments: also organize annual jazz dance workshops with international jazz dancers and choreographers

Sutki
Via Amedeo Avogadro n.4, 10121 **Torino**
Tel: 011-530 614 Fax: 011-546 076
direttore amministrativo Dr. Gennaro Labanca; direttore artistico Anna Sagna; assistente alle coreografie Philip Kilner; direttore luci e suono Francesco Comazzi
Dancers: 9-12 *Perfs:* 82-84 *No of Prods:* 2
Type: dance-theatre *Accomp:* recorded, live
Touring: Italy *Comments:* a small auditorium (capacity 30-40) which is sometimes used for public performances

Balletto di Sicilia Roberto Zappalà
Piazza Tivoli 1, 95030 **Tremestieri Etneo (Catania)**
Tel: 095-712 6561 Fax: 095-712 7018
Internet: www.tau.it/bds
E-Mail: zappala@tau.it
artistic director & main choreographer Roberto Zappalà; public relations Maria Inguscio
Dancers: 7 *Perfs:* 25-35 *No of Prods:* 5
Type: contemporary *Accomp:* live, recorded
Touring: Europe

Corpo di ballo Stabile del Teatro Lirico Giuseppe Verdi
Riva 3 Novembre 1, 34121 **Trieste**
Tel: 040-672 2111 Fax: 040-672 2249
Internet: www.teatroverdi-trieste.com
E-Mail: info@teatroverdi-trieste.com
sovrintendente Dott. Lorenzo Jorio; segretario artistico Maestro Giovanni Pacor; direttore del ballo Tuccio Rigano; responsabile ufficio stampa e relazioni esterne Nicoletta Cavalieri (tel: 040-672 2209); direttore artistico Giandorenico Vaccari
Dancers: 12 *Perfs:* 10 *No of Prods:* 3
Type: classical and modern ballet
Accomp: live, recorded *Venues:* Teatro Comunale G. Verdi 1370, Sala Tripcovich 934 *Comments:* see also Opera, Orchestras, Festivals and Venues

SHAKTI in swan lake

AVAILABLE FOR TOUR

SHAKTI challenges: Perception of Erotica; The Nature of Dance; The Meaning of Culture; Borders of Art; Philosophy of Life.

"She has no boundaries, no fear of leaping beyond our perception of normality." **(Jakki Phillips –The Argus)**

"Unlike any Swan Lake you have ever seen!" **(Tokyo Press)**

"A wild dance experience not to be missed!" **(What's On)**

"A Dance Genius." **(New York Times)**

KATSUSHIKA-KU HORIKIRI 3-8-13-209
TOKYO 124-0006 JAPAN
TEL: **+81-3-3697-6899** FAX: **+81-3-3695-0483**
E-MAIL: **shakti@tka.att.ne.jp**
WEB SITE: **http://home.att.ne.jp/gold/shakti/**

at the **Adelaide Fringe Festival**: Feb.25–Mar.4 2000

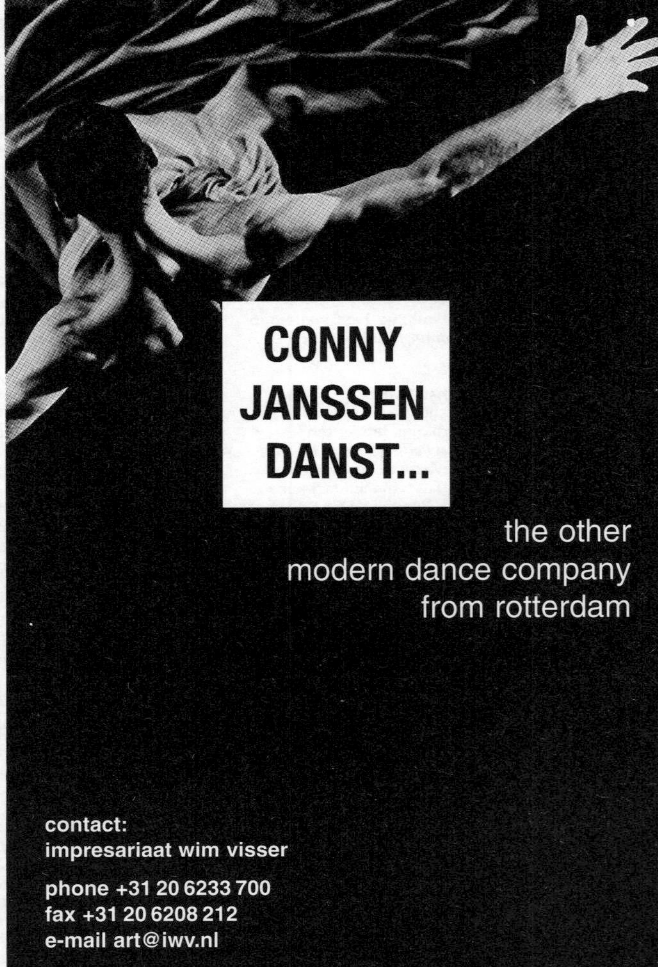

Terra Nuova, La
Via Romeggio 566, 06019 **Umbertide (PG)**
Tel: 075-925 5857/338-935 7468 (mobile) Fax: 075-941 3688
Internet: www.netemedia.net/laterranuova
E-Mail: ltn@krenet.it
direttore artistico & legale rappresentante Luca Bruni; vice presidente Yoko Wakabayashi; co-direttore artistico Marco Ferrari
Dancers: 8-15 *Perfs:* 30-40 *No of Prods:* 3 *Type:* contemporary, street dance *Accomp:* recorded, live *Touring:* Canada, USA, Brazil, Netherlands *Comments:* represented abroad by: La Gala – Internationale Kulturprojekte, Postfach 300808, 50778 Köln, Tel: +49 221-550 4315, Fax: +49 221-955 3508, E-mail: lagalaint@aol.com

Corpo di Ballo dell'Arena di Verona
piazza Bra 28, 37121 **Verona**
Tel: 045-805 1811 (switchboard)/1891/1832 (press office)
Fax: 045-803 1443 (press office)
Internet: www.arena.it
presidente Michela Sironi Mariotti; sovrintendente Renzo Giacchieri; direttore del corpo di ballo Maria Grazia Garofoli
Dancers: 30 (winter); 60 (summer) *Type:* classical, modern, opera, operetta *Accomp:* live, recorded (on tour) *Venues:* Teatro Filarmonico 1100, Arena 1600, Teatro Romano 3000, Teatro Nuovo 600 *Comments:* see also Opera, Orchestras and Venues

LATVIA (+371)

Latvian National Opera Ballet Company
Latvijas Nacionalas Operas balets
3 Aspazijas Blvd, 1050 **Riga**
Tel: 7-225 747 Fax: 7-228 930
E-Mail: admin@opera.lv
artistic director Aivars Leimanis

Olga Zitluhina Contemporary Dance group
Olgas Zitluhinas deju trupa
Kurzemes pr. 66-43, 1067 **Riga**
Tel: 2-428 078 Fax: 2-463 844
E-Mail: zitluhina@iname.com
artistic director Olga Zitluhina

LITHUANIA (+370)

Aura Dance Company
Sokiu teatras Aura
Leliju 6, 3000 **Kaunas**
Tel: 7-221 561/748 897 Fax: 7-203 858
director Nirute Letukaite; administrator Arnas Zdanevicius
Type: modern *Accomp:* recorded

Dance Group Fluidus
Sokiu grupe Fluidus
V.Kreves av. 24-50, 2330 **Kaunas**
Tel: 7-790 078
artistic director Aira Nagineviciute
Type: modern, contemporary *Accomp:* recorded

Dance Company Polekis
Sokiu kolektyvas Polekis
Vilniaus m. kulturos rumai, Vytenio 6, 2009 **Vilnius**
Tel: 2-730 672 (Elena Juodisiene)/239 214
artistic director Elena Juodisiene
Type: contemporary and classic *Accomp:* recorded
Comments: contact address Mrs E. Juodisiene: Mickeviciaus 16-1, 2004 Vilnius

Lithuanian State Opera and Ballet Theatre
Lietuvos valstybinis operos ir baleto teatras
A. Vienuolio 1, 2600 **Vilnius**
Tel: 2-620 636/193 Fax: 2-623 503
E-Mail: opera@lithill.lt
director Kestutis Minderis; artistic director Julius Andrejevas

MACEDONIA (+389)

Ballet of the Macedonian National Theatre
Makedonski Naroden Teatar – Balet
Kej Dimitar Vlahov , 91000 **Skopje**
Tel: 91-114 908/114 511 Fax: 91-114 060
general director Llija Rajkovski; ballet director Snezana Filipovska

MOLDOVA (+373)

Ensemble of sportive Dance – CODREANCA
20, Petru Mevila str, 2012 **Chisinau**
Tel: 2-248 761 Fax: 2-242 036
artistic director Petru Guzun

Folk Music and Dance Ensemble FLUIERAS
21 Puskin str, 2012 **Chisinau**
Tel: 2-238 258/257 Fax: 2-223 442
artistic director Constantin Seremet

National Ensemble of Folk Dance and Music JOC
Mesager str. 2, 2000 **Chisinau**
Tel: 2-238 258/257 Fax: 2-223 442
artistic director Vladimir Cozma Curbet

MONACO (+377)

Ballets de Monaco
Casino de Monte-Carlo, 98000 **Monaco**
Tel: 92-162 420 Fax: 93-254 303
E-Mail: bmc@mcn.mc
directeur et chorégraphe Jean-Christophe Maillot; administrateur général Jean-Marc Genestie; communication Sophie Verdure, François Thiolat; chargée de promotion et de publicite Muriel Provenzani; responsable technique Bertrand Grandguillot; diffusion Jean Baptiste Bello-Portu
Dancers: 50 *Perfs:* 100
Type: neo-classical/contemporary
Accomp: live, recorded *Venues:* Salle Garnier 520
Touring: international
Comments: performances in summer on Terrasses du Casino and winter-spring: Salle Garnier Casino of Monte-Carlo

NETHERLANDS (+31)

Unieke Zaken
Terborchlaan 301, 1816 MH **Alkmaar**
Tel: 72-511 1442 Fax: 72-511 1442
administration & pr Paula Dekker; artistic directors Peter Bolten, Mirjam Morsch
Dancers: 8 + 3 musicians *Perfs:* 170
No of Prods: 2 *Type:* movement theatre/mime (for children) *Accomp:* recorded, live
Venues: diverse venues throughout Netherlands and Belgium, capacity 250 *Touring:* Netherlands, Belgium, Austria, Lithuania, Germany

Danstheater DEE
c/o Kleine Spui Produkties, Kleine Spui 26, 3811 BE **Amersfoort**
Tel: 33-465 2660 Fax: 33-465 2618
Internet: www.kleinespui.demon.nl
E-Mail: ksp@kleinespui.demon.nl
managing directors Kleine Spui Carla Kogelman, Prisca Maas; artistic director Marieke Joosten
Dancers: 3 *Perfs:* 100 *No of Prods:* 2 (1 new)
Venues: schools, theatres up to 200
Touring: Netherlands, Germany, Belgium
Comments: modern dance for children

Angelika Oei
c/o Van Baasbank & Baggerman, Keizersgracht 258, 1016 EV **Amsterdam**
Tel: 20-624 2631/627 6818 Fax: 20-622 7850
E-Mail: baasbank.baggerman@wxs.nl
artistic director Angelika Oei
Perfs: 30 *No of Prods:* 2+ *Type:* contemporary *Accomp:* recorded original music *Venues:* De Rotterdam Schouwburg *Touring:* worldwide

Ballo Cantabile
Van Woustraat 235-2, 1074 AR **Amsterdam**
Tel: 20-664 6819 Fax: 20-664 6819
E-Mail: mcrevser@xs4all.nl
director Joaquim Sabaté
Dancers: 2-4 *Perfs:* 50 *No of Prods:* 1 per year
Type: dance-opera *Accomp:* live
Touring: Europe

Beppie Blankert
c/o Dansers Studio, Entrepotdok 4, 1018 AD **Amsterdam**
Tel: 20-638 9398 Fax: 20-638 2265
artistic director Beppie Blankert
Type: modern dance
Accomp: live (modern composers), recorded
Venues: Municipal Theatre Amsterdam 850, Bellevue Theatre, Amsterdam 75-100, Nesjtheater Frascati Amsterdam 30-150, Stadtschouwburg (Amsterdam)
Touring: UK, USA

Blok & Steel
c/o Narante Productions, Vendelstratt 1012, 1016 EV **Amsterdam**
Tel: 20-638 4505 Fax: 20-421 6853
E-Mail: narante@narante.nl
artistic directors Suzy Blok, Christopher Steel
Dancers: 6 dancers, 6 musicians
Perfs: 50 *No of Prods:* 1 *Type:* physical dance theatre
Accomp: live music *Touring:* Europe

Conny Janssen Danst...
Impresariaat Wim Visser, Kloveniersburgwal 47, 1011 JX **Amsterdam**
Tel: 20-623 3700 Fax: 20-620 8212
E-Mail: iwv@xs4all.nl
producer Wim Visser; choreographer Conny Janssen
Dancers: 8 *Perfs:* 40 *No of Prods:* 1 *Type:* modern
Accomp: recorded *Touring:* Netherlands

Dance Company Leine & Roebana
Bureau Berber, Culturele Affaires, Karte Leidsedwarsstraat 12, 1017 RC **Amsterdam**
Tel: 20-627 0455 Fax: 20-625 0616
choreographers Andrea Leine, Harijono Roebana
Dancers: varies *Type:* modern dance
Venues: capacity 100-600 *Touring:* national, international *Comments:* see also Promoters

Dansgroep Krisztina de Châtel
Luchtvaartstraat 2, 1059 CA **Amsterdam**
Tel: 20-669 5755 Fax: 20-669 6864
Internet: www.dechatel.nl
E-Mail: chatel@xs4all.nl
general manager Cees de Graaff; artistic director Krisztina de Châtel; publicity Marthijn Stam; production Han van Poucke; administration Bart van Sambeek
Dancers: 8 *Perfs:* 80 *No of Prods:* 4 *Type:* contemporary
Accomp: live, recorded *Venues:* theatres and outdoor location *Touring:* Netherlands, Switzerland

Desirée Delauney
Stichting Bilski Algemeen, 1078 DC **Amsterdam**
Tel: 20-676 4472 Fax: 20-676 4472
E-Mail: borisg@xs4all.nl
artistic directors Désirée Delauney, Boris Gerrets
Dancers: 1 *No of Prods:* 1 *Type:* modern, movement theatre *Accomp:* recorded
Venues: Brakke Grond 170 *Touring:* national
Comments: managed by Noranti Productions (tel: 20-638 4505) see also Agents & Producers

Dutch National Ballet
Het Nationale Ballet
Postbus 16486, 1001 RN **Amsterdam**
Tel: 20-551 8225 Fax: 20-551 8070
Internet: www.het-nationale-ballet.nl
E-Mail: info@het-nationale-ballet.nl
administrative director Jaap Mulders; artistic director Wayne Eagling; resident choreographer Toer van Schayk
Dancers: approx. 80 *Perfs:* 100 *No of Prods:* 8 *Type:* classical and contemporary ballet *Accomp:* live, recorded *Venues:* Het Muziektheater 1600
Touring: Netherlands *Comments:* second address: Waterlooplein 22, 1011 PG, Amsterdam

Eishout / Händeler
Bureau Barber, Culturele Affaires, Karte Leidsedwarsstraat 12, 1017 RC **Amsterdam**
Tel: 20-627 0455 Fax: 20-625 0616
choreographers Diane Eishout, Frank Händeler
Dancers: varies *Type:* modern dance *Venues:* capacity 100-600 *Touring:* national, international
Comments: see also Promoters

Gevogeld Verlangen, Het
PO Box 11087, 1001 GB **Amsterdam**
Tel: 20-625 5572 Fax: 20-624 0470
E-Mail: stoa.ilja@inter.nl.net
managing director Chris De Jong; artistic director Barbara Duyfjes; administrator & manager Ilja Frie
Dancers: 1 (solo) *Perfs:* 20 *No of Prods:* 1 *Type:* experimental movement theatre *Accomp:* live, recorded
Touring: Netherlands

Internationaal Danstheater, Het
Postbus 16885, 1001 RJ **Amsterdam**
Tel: 20-623 9112 Fax: 20-627 1163
E-Mail: info@intdanstheater.nl
business manager Dick van de Vooren; artistic director Maurits van Geel; musical director Floor Minnaert; chef de bureau Willie Rückert; pr/marketing Sietske de Haan; ballet masters Thérese Laurant, Andre Verdoner
Dancers: 26 + 7 musicians *Perfs:* 120 *No of Prods:* 3
Type: international folklore *Accomp:* live *Venues:* Stadsschouwburg 800, Doelenzaal 175 *Touring:* Germany, Belgium, USA, Netherlands, Taiwan, Japan, UK *Comments:* only professional international folklore group in Western Europe

OPUS ONE
Gigard Brandt Straat 26-28, 1054 JK **Amsterdam**
Tel: 20-612 5034 Fax: 20-489 7205
Internet: www.opusone.digiface.nl
producer Maarten Voogel; public relations Michel Bypost
Dancers: 15 *Perfs:* 130 *No of Prods:* 2 (1 new)
Type: classical, tap, modern *Accomp:* recorded
Venues: Stadschouwburg Amsterdam 900, Meervaart 100 (Amsterdam) *Touring:* Netherlands, Belgium
Comments: business management: Impresariaat Frans Van Bronkhorst, Postbus 1024, 1200 BA Hilversum, tel: 35-621 7248, fax: 35-623 1768

Paco Peña Flamenco Dance Company
c/o Impresariaat Wim Visser, Kloveniersbrugwal 47, 1011 JX **Amsterdam**
Tel: 20-623 3700 Fax: 20-620 8212
E-Mail: iwv@xs4all.nl
artistic leader Paco Peña; producer Wim Visser
Dancers: 2-10 (depending on production) *Perfs:* 100 *No of Prods:* 3 *Type:* flamenco *Accomp:* live (singers: 1-4, guitarists: 1-4 + percussionist) *Venues:* capacity up to 5000 *Touring:* worldwide *Comments:* managed by: Impresariaat Wim Visser

Pauline De Groot & Co
1e Leliedwarsstraat 19/1, 1015 SZ **Amsterdam**
Tel: 20-622 6859
E-Mail: pdgdans@xs4all.nl
artistic director Pauline de Groot
Dancers: varies *Perfs:* 20 *No of Prods:* 2-3
Type: contemporary *Accomp:* live *Venues:* Theatre Frascati 200 *Touring:* international

Matthew Rushing in "Bad Blood". Photo Barbara Bordnick.

Shusaku – Bodytorium
Quellijnstraat 60, HS, 1072 XV **Amsterdam**
Tel: 20-662 4692 Fax: 20-662 4692
artistic director Shusaku Takeuchi (20-662 4692); business director Francan Jageneau (20-623 3988)
Dancers: 2-16 *No of Prods:* 4+ *Type:* dance theatre, movement theatre *Accomp:* live, recorded

Stamina
Vendelstraat 2, 1012 XX **Amsterdam**
Tel: 20-427 3343 Fax: 20-676 6747
E-Mail: bianca.van.dillen@stamina.nl
artistic director Bianca Van Dillen
Dancers: 16-20 *Perfs:* 20 *No of Prods:* 3 *Type:* modern concrete dance using multi-media *Accomp:* live, recorded *Venues:* Theatre Frascati 200 *Touring:* Netherlands

Truus Bronkhorst
Stoa, Postbus 93044, 1090 BA **Amsterdam**
Tel: 20-625 5572 Fax: 20-624 0470
business manager Betty Kaan
Dancers: 1-8 (solo + group performances) *Perfs:* 70 *No of Prods:* 2 *Type:* modern *Accomp:* recorded *Venues:* Brakke Grond 200 *Touring:* national, international

Introdans
Vijfzinnenstraat 80-82, 6811 LN **Arnhem**
Tel: 26-351 2111 Fax: 26-351 5647
managing director Hans Focking (until Jan 2001); artistic directors Ton Wiggers, Roel Voorintholt; chef de bureau Elly van der Sluis, Koottae Krüse; manager public relations en marketing Jeannette Eygenraam; director introdans ensemble for Youth Roel Voorintholt; chef de technique t.b.a.
Dancers: 18 *Perfs:* 80 (abroad not included) *No of Prods:* 3 new *Type:* modern ballet *Accomp:* recorded, live *Venues:* Introdans Studiotheater 86, Schouwburg, Arnhem 760, Stadsschouwburg Nijmegen 875 *Touring:* national, international *Comments:* also runs Introdans ensemble for Youth, with 14 dancers, 45 theatre productions, 55 school performances, and 75 workshops

Montazstroj
Nieuwe Huizen 41, 4811 TL **Breda**
Tel: 76-522 8575 Fax: 76-541 5440
E-Mail: mstrog@inn.nl
artistic directors Borut Siparovic, Tamara Huilmand
Dancers: varies *Type:* modern dance theatre, performance *Accomp:* specially composed music, recorded *Touring:* national, international *Comments:* see also Agents (Stichting Nieuwe Huizen)

Stichting Zuil van Volta
Postbus 2221, **Breda**
Tel: 76-522 8575 Fax: 76-541 5440
E-Mail: mstrog@inn.nl
artistic director Tamara Huilmand
Dancers: varies *Type:* modern + theatre *Accomp:* special composed (recorded) music *Touring:* national, international *Comments:* visiting address: Nieuwe Huizen 41, 4811 TL Breda; works together with dance company Montazstroj; see also Agents (Stichting Nieuwe Huizen)

NDT 2
Den Haag
Comments: see 'Nederlands Dans Theater 2'.

NDT 3
Den Haag
Comments: see 'Nederlands Dans Theater 3'.

Nederlands Dans Theater I
Postbus 333, 2501 CH **Den Haag**
Tel: 70-360 9931 Fax: 70-361 7156
Internet: www.ndt.nl
managing director Jaap Hülsmann; general artistic director, Nederlands Dans Theater Marian Sarstädt; executive artistic director, NDTI Glenn Edgerton; company manager Johan Taal; resident choreographers Jiri Kylian, Hans van Manen
Dancers: 32 *Perfs:* 150 *No of Prods:* 6 new + 9 revivals in 6 programmes *Type:* modern ballet based on classical techniques *Accomp:* live & recorded *Venues:* Lucent Danstheater 1001 *Touring:* France, Germany, USA, South Africa, UK, Mexico, Australia *Comments:* 3 companies have been operating within Nederlands Dans Theater: Nederlands Dans Theater 1 (main company), Nederlands Dans Theater 2 (junior company for age 17-22), Nederlands Dans Theater 3 (established for older dancers); visiting address: Schedeldoekshaven 60, 2511 EN Den Haag

Nederlands Dans Theater II
Postbus 333, 2501 CH **Den Haag**
Tel: 70-360 9931 Fax: 70-361 7156
Internet: www.ndt.nl
executive artistic director Gerald Tibbs; company manager Carmen Thomas
Dancers: 14 *Perfs:* 100 *No of Prods:* 2 programmes containing 3 new works & 1 house production with NDT I *Type:* contemporary ballet based on classical techniques *Accomp:* recorded, live
Venues: Lucent Danstheater 1001
Touring: Germany, UK, Belgium, France, Czech Republic, USA, South America, Italy *Comments:* visiting address: Schedeldoekshaven 60, 2511 EN Den Haag

Nederlands Dans Theater III
Postbus 333, 2501 CH **Den Haag**
Tel: 70-360 9931 Fax: 70-361 7156
Internet: www.ndt.nl
executive directors Egon Madsen, Ulf Esser; assistant executive director Gérard Lemaitre; organisation Carina de Goederen
Dancers: 5 *Perfs:* 80 *No of Prods:* 2 new *Type:* modern ballet based on classical techniques *Accomp:* recorded, live *Venues:* Lucent Danstheater 1001 *Touring:* Germany, France, Italy, Czech Republic, India, Japan, Switzerland *Comments:* visiting address: Schedeldoekshaven 60, 2511 EN Den Haag

Euregio Dans Forum
c/o Stadsschouwburg Heerlen, Postbus 300, 6400 AH **Heerlen**
Tel: 45-571 4870 Fax: 45-571 4878
administrative director J Polomski; artistic director t.b.a.
Perfs: 30 *No of Prods:* 3 a year *Comments:* founded by the Stadsschouwburg Heerlen (Netherlands), Stadttheater Aachen (Germany) and L'Opéra Royal de Wallonie in Liège (Belgium); co-operation in musicals in Aachen (Adam and Eve, 42x) and opera's in Liège (La Traviata)

Nederlands Historisch Dans en Theaterensemble (NHDT)
Het Ven 1, 6997 AX **Hoog Keppel**
Tel: 314-381 254 Fax: 314-381 254
E-Mail: h.angadgaur@hccnet.nl
artistic director Maria Angad Gaur; stage manager Juan Carlos Tajos; collaborators Alwthe van Nié, Mary Haidi Sayre (music), Yumiko Kunimori (music)
Dancers: 6 + flexible number of actors & musicians
Perfs: 20 *No of Prods:* 3 *Type:* historical music (renaissance and baroque), theatre and dance *Accomp:* live (baroque ensemble) *Touring:* Netherlands, Germany, Czech Republic, Japan, Belgium *Comments:* the NHDT is part of the Stichting voor Oude Muziek en Dans, Het Susato Collectief; also perform for special occasions and commemorations; see also Early Music

DRD – Rotterdamse Dansgroep, De
s-Gravendijkwal 58a, 3014 EE **Rotterdam**
Tel: 10-436 4511 Fax: 10-436 4147
Internet: www.drd.org
E-Mail: info@drd.org
managing director Monica van Steen; artistic director Käthy Gosschalk; p.r. Ilja van Heynungen
Dancers: 10 *Perfs:* 75 *No of Prods:* 8
Type: contemporary *Accomp:* recorded
Venues: Schouwburg Premiering Theatre, Rotterdam
Touring: Netherlands, Germany, Belgium

Independent Theatre
Onafhankelijk Toneel
Sint Jobsweg 3, 3024 EH **Rotterdam**
Tel: 10-478 028/476 9029 Fax: 10-425 7915
Internet: www.ot-rotterdam.nl
E-Mail: ot@ot-rotterdam.nl
directors Mirjam Koen, Gerrit Timmers, Ton Lutgerink; administration Corry Prinsen; publicity Gerda Roest; choreographers Amy Gale, Ton Lutgerink; light design Paul van Laak
Dancers: varies *Perfs:* 50 *No of Prods:* 4-9
Type: modern dance combined with other disciplines
Venues: O. T. Theatre up to 100
Touring: national, international *Comments:* a collective of theatre makers with various backgrounds – visual arts, modern dance, acting – all of which are combined in productions; see also Drama and Opera

Meekers, De
Cool Haven 100A, 3024 AH **Rotterdam**
Tel: 10-244 9893 Fax: 10-244 9894
E-Mail: meekers@hetnet.nl
artistic director Arthur Rosenfeld
Dancers: 4 *Perfs:* 75-100 *No of Prods:* 2 + 1 new
Type: dance theatre, dance for children *Touring:* national, Germany, Switzerland

Scapino Ballet Rotterdam
Boomgaardsstraat 69, 3012 XA **Rotterdam**
Tel: 10-414 2414 Fax: 10-413 2250
Internet: www.Luna-nl/~Scapino
business manager Harald Moes; artistic director & choreographer Ed Wubbe; publicity manager Maureen Hol; production manager Ruben Stern; ballet masters Jay Augen, Valerie Lecoq, Keith-Derrick Randolph; technical manager Benno Veen
Dancers: 30 + 5 students *Perfs:* 100 *No of Prods:* 3
Type: modern dance based on classical and modern techniques *Accomp:* live, tape
Venues: Rotterdamse Schouwburg, Rotterdam 800
Touring: regularly worldwide

Raz / Hans Tuerlings
Spoorlaan 181, 5038 CB **Tilburg**
Tel: 13-583 5929 Fax: 13-583 5920
E-Mail: raz@raz.nl
business manager Evert Burggrave; artistic director Hans Tuerlings; office Louisa Henderson; publicity & production Manon Berendse
Dancers: up to 10 *Perfs:* 85 *No of Prods:* 3 *Type:* contemporary *Accomp:* live, recorded *Venues:* Schouwburg Tilburg hall A 870, hall B 175 *Touring:* Belgium, Germany, Netherlands, UK, Switzerland, Italy
Comments: choreographer Hans Tuerlings mixes dance, text and music; he evokes images, attempts to create an atmosphere with an effect which approaches that of a film; within the coming years Raz will be working on – casa del sogno – a series of sixteen performances

Dansend Hart
PO Box 12019, 3501 AA **Utrecht**
Tel: 30-232 8385 Fax: 30-232 8385
artistic directors Wies Merax, Charles Cornealle
Dancers: 5+ *Perfs:* 80 *No of Prods:* 8 *Type:* contemporary dance *Accomp:* recorded/live *Touring:* Europe
Comments: also have workshops and performances for children

NORWAY (+47)

Grouppe AB
Gruppi AB
Georgernes Verft 3, 5011 **Bergen**
Tel: 5523 8641
artistic directors Liv Basberg, Benedicte Meyer Amundsen
Dancers: 2 *No of Prods:* 2 *Type:* out-door performances, mixed media performance *Accomp:* live, recorded (often original music) *Touring:* Netherlands, Norway

Jo Strømgren Kompani
Rosenbergaten 18, 5015 **Bergen**
Tel: 5523 1639 Fax: 5590 2147
E-Mail: js.kompani@bergen.online.no
director Jo Strømgren; administrative director Agnes Kroepelien
Type: contemporary dance

New Carte Blanche (NCB)
Danseteater, Sigurdsgt. 6, 5015 **Bergen**
Tel: 5530 8680 Fax: 5530 8681
Internet: www.ncb.no
E-Mail: ncb@ncb.no
artistic director Karen Foss
Dancers: 13 *Perfs:* 60-70 *No of Prods:* 10 (4 new)
Type: modern *Accomp:* live, recorded *Venues:* Danseteateret 300 *Touring:* Czech Republik, Belgium, Italy, France, Finland *Comments:* special youth programmes for schools

Stellaris Danseteater
Mylingen 6, 9600 **Hammerfest**
Tel: 7841 0007 Fax: 7841 0041
E-Mail: cstellar@alpha.barentsnett.no
choreographer/artistic director Solveig Leinan Hermo
Dancers: 5 permanent + guest dancers
No of Prods: 3 *Type:* mainly modern dance, tapestry, film, slides, actors and musicians occasionally used
Accomp: live, recorded *Touring:* Norway, Europe

Oslo Danseensemble
Torstadskogen 60C, 0134 **Hvlastad**
Tel: 6677 3584/9091 8358
E-Mail: o.d.e@online.no
artistic director Merete Lingjaerde
Dancers: 12-15 *Type:* jazz and modern dance

Midtnorsk Ballett – Og Dansesenter
PO Box 401, 6501 **Kristiansund**
Tel: 7158 9960 Fax: 7158 9961
E-Mail: opera@oik.no
admin. director Olav Grytnes; ballet directors Catherine Smirles Ingebrigtsen, Amy Timpson, Marit G Dullaert; music director Kjell Seim; production manager Rune Svendsen; finance Anne Naess
Perfs: 20 *No of Prods:* 7 *Type:* ballet (classical and modern), jazz, tap *Accomp:* Kristiansund Symphony Orchestra, the Opera Sinfonietta, some recorded
Venues: Festivitaten 423 *Touring:* Norway
Comments: company regularly performs with Kristiansund Opera; see also Opera

Un-Magritt Nordseth danseproduksjon
Brønnøyveien 53, 1315 **Nesøya**
Tel: 6698 0882 Fax: 6698 0882
E-Mail: unmnord@online.no
artistic director Un-Magritt Nordseth
Type: contemporary dance

Hexadin
Odinsgate 25, 0266 **Olso**
Tel: 2255 0089 Fax: 2255 0089
choreographer Lise Faerner
Dancers: varies *Type:* contemporary dance

Bresée Dance Company
Ole Bullsgate 45, 0475 **Oslo**
Tel: 2215 1839
E-Mail: rklakegg@online.no
choreographer/artistic director Kathryn Bresée; management Tone Westad
Dancers: 5-6 *Perfs:* varies *No of Prods:* 2
Type: modern, contemporary
Accomp: live, recorded *Touring:* Norway
Comments: also dance video, and working with a storyteller on a project for audiences of all ages (not specifically child orientated)

Dans Design
Reichweinsgate 1, 0254 **Oslo**
Tel: 2255 1945 Fax: 2244 6525
choreographers Leif Hernes, Anne Grete Eriksen
Dancers: 8 *No of Prods:* 1 *Type:* post-modern choreography for stage, film, TV *Accomp:* live, recorded; texts by actors' voices *Touring:* national, international

Dans og toner
Jacob Aalsgate 5A, 0368 **Oslo**
Tel: 2243 0875 Fax: 2243 0125
E-Mail: danstone@online.no
artistic director Peter John Lodwick; managing director Marit Krogeide
Type: contemporary dance for children and youth audiences *Comments:* touring company

IBP – Ingun Bjørnsgaard Prosjekt
Ebbelsgate 1, 0183 **Oslo**
Tel: 2220 6605
artistic director Ingun Bjørnsgaard
Type: contemporary dance *Touring:* national, international

Imago Danseteater
Frognerveien 1B, 0257 **Oslo**
Tel: 2244 8170/9153 8106 (mobile) Fax: 2244 8170
artistic director Lise Eger
Dancers: 4 *Perfs:* 20-40 *No of Prods:* 1 *Type:* modern *Touring:* Scandinavia, Italy, France

Impro Project, The
Ragnhild Schibbyesvei 54, 0968 **Oslo**
Tel: 2210 8415 Fax: 2210 8415
directors Katrine Kirsebom, Hilde Rustad, Bibbi Winberg, Camilla Grønneberg
Dancers: 4 *Type:* contemporary, performance, site-specific works

Jane Hveding Danceproductions
Kirkevn 50, 0368 **Oslo**
Tel: 2246 3728 Fax: 2259 2653
choreographer Jane Hveding
Dancers: 1-8 *No of Prods:* 3-4 *Type:* modern, dance-theatre, contemporary *Accomp:* live, recorded *Touring:* Europe

Karsten Solli Produksjoner
Kongensgate 16, Indre gard, 2 etg, 0153 **Oslo**
Tel: 2241 4282 Fax: 2241 4283
artistic director Karsten Solli
: cross disciplinary work (dance, performance, fine art, voice, movement)

Norwegian National Ballet, The
Norske National Ballett
Den Norske Opera, Box 8800 Youngstorget, 0028 **Oslo**
Tel: 2331 5037/5039 Fax: 2242 0573
Internet: wit.no/norskopera/
E-Mail: info@norskopera.no
ballet director Dinna Bjørn; ballet administrator Paul Podolski
Dancers: 46 *Perfs:* 50 *No of Prods:* 15 *Type:* classical, modern *Accomp:* live *Venues:* Opera House 1051 *Touring:* national, international
Comments: alternative email: salg@norskopera.no; see also Opera and Orchestras

Passage Nord
Stensgaten 32c, 0358 **Oslo**
Tel: 2269 4428 Fax: 2269 4428
artistic director Kjetil Sköien
Dancers: 8 *Perfs:* 100 *No of Prods:* 2
Type: visual theatre, performance art, modern dance *Venues:* Passage Nord Theatre 80 *Touring:* Norway, Italy, UK, Denmark, Sweden *Comments:* organise workshops for dance and theatre professionals; also invite guest performances to their own venue; company involved in international co-productions

Stiftelsen Ø J produksjoner
Majorstueveien 35B, 0367 **Oslo**
Tel: 2269 0354 Fax: 2269 0354
artistic director Øyvind Jørgensen
Type: dance and movement inspired by butoh dance
Comments: production management services also available

Tromsø Danseteater
Skippergate 21, 9008 **Tromsø**
Tel: 7768 6619 Fax: 7768 6619
leaders Sally Eilertsen, Marianne Nordnes
Dancers: 2-7 *Perfs:* 12 *No of Prods:* 2 new *Type:* modern ballet *Accomp:* commissioned recorded music, live *Venues:* Rådstuateater and Kulturhuset, Tromsø 200 *Touring:* Norway

POLAND (+48)

Ballet of the Bydgoszcz Opera Nova
al. Gdanska 20, 85-006 **Bydgoszcz**
Tel: 52-224 985 Fax: 52-224 985
Internet: www.psi.com.pl/on/
E-Mail: on@psi.com.pl
general director Maciej Figas; ballet director Wladimir Glinskich
Dancers: 45 *Type:* classical *Venues:* Polski Teatr 600

Ballet of the Silesian Opera
ul Moniuszki 21, 41-900 **Bytom**
Tel: 32-281 3430 Fax: 32-281 4335
Internet: www.opera.silesia.top.pl
E-Mail: opera@opera.silesia.top.pl
general & artistic director Tadeusz Serafin; choreogapher Henryk Konwinski; ballet director Olga Kozimala-Klis
Dancers: 12 *Type:* classical *Venues:* capacity 530

Silesian Dance Theatre
Slaski Teatr Tanca
ul. Zeromskiego 27, 41-902 **Bytom**
Tel: 32-281 8253/55 Fax: 32-281 8252
Internet: www.stt.art.pl
E-Mail: theatre@polbox.com
director Jacek Luminski
Dancers: 8 *Type:* contemporary dance *Touring:* worldwide

Ballet of the Baltic Opera
ul. Zwyciestwa 15, 80-219 **Gdansk**
Tel: 58-341 0134 Fax: 58-341 3827
Internet: operabal.itnet.com.pl
general director Wlodzimierz Nawotka; artistic director Andrzej Knap; ballet director Andrzej Stasiewicz
Dancers: 27 *Type:* classical, contemporary
Venues: State Opera 500

State Folk Song and Dance Ensemble Slask
Panstwowy Zespól Ludowy Piesni i Tanca Slask
ul. Zamkowa 3, 42-286 **Koszecin-Zamek**
Tel: 32-516 221
artistic director Stanislaw Hadyna
Dancers: 40 *Type:* folk

Ballet of the Krakow Opera & Operetta
ul Dietha 50, 31-039 **Krakow**
Tel: 12-422 6210 Fax: 12-422 0879
Internet: www.opera.krakow.top.pl
E-Mail: marketing@opera.krakow.top.pl
general dir. Jerzy Noworol; ballet dir. Jacek Drozdowski
Dancer: 25 *Type:* classical

Ballet of the Grand Theatre of Lodz
Plac. Dabrowskiego, 90-249 **Lodz**
Tel: 42-633 9960/636 2272 Fax: 42-631 9552
Internet: www.teatr-wielki.lodz.pl/welcome.htm
E-Mail: teatr@mm.com.pl
general director Marcin Krzyzanowski; deputy director Stanislaw Dyzbardis; ballet director Kazimierz Wrzosek
Dancers: 25 *Type:* classical, contemporary *Venues:* Grand Theatre 1200

State Folk Song and Dance Ensemble Mazowsze
Panstwowy Zespol Ludowy Piesni i Tanca Mazowsze
Karolin, 05-805 **Otrebusy**
Tel: 22-758 5001 Fax: 22-758 5790
general director Brygida Linartas; deputy director Ireneusz Narowski; choreographer & head of ballet Michal Jarczyk
Dancers: dancers + orchestra 90 *Type:* folk

Ballet of the Stanislaw Moniuszko Grand Theatre of Poznan
ul. Fredry 9, 60-967 **Poznan**
Tel: 61-852 4478 Fax: 61-852 7464
Internet: www.info.poznan.pl/culture/theatres/
general director Slawomir Pietras; ballet director Liliana Kowalska
Dancers: 19 *Type:* classical, contemporary
Venues: Grand Theatre 900

Polish Dance Theatre – Ballet of Poznan
Polski Teatr Tanca – Balet Poznanski
ul. Kozia 4, 61-835 **Poznan**
Tel: 61-852 4241/2 Fax: 61-852 4242
general & artistic director Ewa Wycichowska; ballet director Mariola Hendrykowska
Dancers: 21 *Type:* contemporary
Venues: Grand Theatre, Poznan

Theatre of Expression
Teatr Ekspresji
ul. Chrobrego 3, 81-756 **Sopot**
Tel: 58-551 7568 Fax: 58-551 7568
E-Mail: ekspresja@usa.net
director Wojciech Misiuro
Dancers: 14 *Type:* contemporary

Ballet of the Szczecin Opera & Operetta
ul Korsarzy 34, 70-540 **Szczecin**
Tel: 91-489 0340 Fax: 91-434 5557
general and artistic director Warcislaw Kunc; ballet director Miroslaw Rozalski
Dancers: 14 *Type:* classical *Venues:* capacity 530

Artistic Ensemble of the Polish Army
Reprezentacyjny Zespól Wojska Polskiego
Kredytowa 5/7, 00-056 **Warszawa**
Tel: 22-826 9594 Fax: 22-826 7034
ballet director Bogdan Jedrzejak

Ballet of the Grand Theatre – National Opera
Balet Teatru Wielkiego – Opery Narodowej
Plac Teatralny 1, 00-950 **Warszawa**
Tel: 22-692 0273/826 5019 Fax: 22-826 0423/5012
Internet: www.teatrwielki.pl
E-Mail: office@teatrwielki.pl
general director Waldemar Dabrowski; artistic director Jacek Kaspszyk; ballet director Emil Wesolowski
Dancers: 90 *Perfs:* 50 full ballet evenings *Type:* classical and modern *Accomp:* live *Venues:* Moniuszko Hall 1837, Mlynarski Hall 248 *Comments:* see also Opera

Warsaw Pantomime Theatre
Warszawski Teatr Pantonimy
Teatr Zydowski, Plac Grzybowski 12/16, 00-115 **Warszawa**
Tel: 22-620 6281/4954 Fax: 22-624 3233
director Stafan Niedzialkowski
Type: mime

Ballet of the Wroclaw Opera
ul. Swidnicka 35, 50-066 **Wroclaw**
Tel: 71-343 8641/2753 Fax: 71-343 6742
general director Ewa Michnik; ballet director Maria Kijak
Dancers: 37 *Type:* classical *Venues:* Opera 600

Wroclaw Pantomime Theatre
Wroclawski Teatr Pantomimy
Debowa 16, 53-121 **Wroclaw**
Tel: 71-675 280 Fax: 71-675 280
general director Kazimierz Doniec; artistic director Henryk Tomaszewski
Dancers: 20 *Type:* movement mime *Venues:* Teatr Polski Wroclaw *Comments:* touring company

PORTUGAL (+351)

Companhia de Dança de Almada
Pt. Francisco Vierra de Almeida N°1 r/c, 2800-406 **Almada**
Tel: 1-258 3175 Fax: 1-250 0524
artistic director Maria Franco; production director Nasciolinda Silva
Dancers: 7 *Perfs:* 30-40 *No of Prods:* 5 *Type:* contemporary *Accomp:* live, recorded *Venues:* Forum Municipal Romeu Correia (Almada) 300 *Touring:* national, Europe *Comments:* also special performances for children

Companhia de Dança de Aveiro
Centro cultural é de Congressos de Aveiro, 3810-200 **Aveiro**
Tel: 34-312 801/383 602 Fax: 34-523 327/384 382
E-Mail: cia.danca.aveiro@mail.telepac.pt
director José Luis Martins Pereira; artistic director Maria do Carmo Costa; technical director Octaviano Costa
Dancers: 18 *Perfs:* 20-30 *No of Prods:* 3-4 *Type:* contemporary, modern, avant-guarde, traditional dance turned into modern dance *Accomp:* live, recorded
Touring: France, Spain, China, Brazil, Portugal

Ballet Gulbenkian
Fundação Calouste Gulbenkian (Serviço de Música), Avenida de Berna 45-A, 1067-001 **Lisboa** Codex
Tel: 1-793 5131 (music department) Fax: 1-793 7296
Internet: www.ip.pt/musica-fcg
E-Mail: musica@gulbenkian.pt
artistic director Iracity Cardoso; production director Isabel Ayres; administrative assistant and tour contacts Mário Esteves; press contact João Costa
Dancers: 28 (4 apprentices) *Perfs:* 45 *No of Prods:* 12 (8 new) *Type:* contemporary and modern ballet
Accomp: tape and live music *Venues:* Grande Auditório Gulbenkian 1200 *Touring:* Portugal, Macau
Comments: see also Ministries, Orchestras, Choirs, Festivals (2), Venues, Promoters

Companhia Nacional de Bailado
Rua Vitor Cordon 20, 1200-484 **Lisboa**
Tel: 1-347 4048/346 5970 Fax: 1-342 5790
Internet: www.cnb.pt/
E-Mail: ip215255@ip.pt
director Jorge Salavisa; artistic director Luisa Taveira; subdirector Carlos Vargas
Dancers: 58 *Perfs:* 100 *No of Prods:* 9 *Type:* classical ballet, modern, contemporary *Accomp:* live, recorded *Venues:* capacity 1500 *Touring:* Portugal, Europe

Lisbon Dance Company
Companhia de Dança de Lisboa
Rua Costa do Castelo 23, 1100 **Lisboa**
Tel: 1-887 8261 Fax: 1-886 4687
Internet: www.cidadevirtual.pt/cdl
E-Mail: cdlisbondanceco@mail.telepac.pt
director José Manuel Oliveira; principal choreographer Célia Gouvêa; ballet master Irina Stupina
Dancers: 10 *Perfs:* 20 *Type:* modern and contemporary *Accomp:* live, recorded *Touring:* Portugal, Portuguese Language Countries, Spain, Brazil, Italy, Israel, Macau, Japan, Canada, South Africa, Australia, Belgium, Luxembourg, Netherlands

O Rumo Do Fumo
Avenida da Liberdade, N° 177, 4° Esq., 1250-141 **Lisboa**
Tel: 1-354 3545 Fax: 1-354 3545
Internet: www.rumo-fumo.pt
E-Mail: rumofumo@mail.telepac.pt
director Vera Mantero
Dancers: varies *Perfs:* 45 *No of Prods:* 1-2 *Type:* contemporary *Accomp:* recorded *Touring:* national, international

Ballet Teatro – Companhia
Praça 9 de Abril 76, 4200 **Porto**
Tel: 2-550 8918/9 Fax: 2-550 8919
directors Isabel Barros; producer Olga Carneiro
Dancers: 12 *Perfs:* 30 *No of Prods:* 3 *Type:* dance-theatre *Accomp:* live, recorded *Venues:* capacity 200
Comments: see also Promoters, Venues

CeDeCe – Companhia de Dança Contemporânea
Largo José Afonso (Pavilhão Municipal), 2900 **Setúbal**
Tel: 65-527 146 Fax: 65-234 248
directors Maria Bessa, António Rodrigues; publicity Ana Duarte, Amorim Carvalho; assistant to producer & director Elsa Chagas
Dancers: 12 *Perfs:* 50 *No of Prods:* 6 *Type:* contemporary, jazz *Accomp:* live, recorded *Venues:* Forum Municipal Luisa Todi 1200 *Touring:* national, international
Comments: sponsored by Setubal's town hall and the Ministry of Culture

Companhia Paulo Ribeiro
Teatro Viriato, Largo Muozinho de Albuquerque, Apartado 1057, 3511-901 **Viseu**
Tel: 32-480 112 Fax: 32-480 112
Internet: www.cidadevirtual.pt/pauloribeiro
E-Mail: pauloribeiro.co@mail.telepac.pt
director/choreographer Paulo Ribeiro; management Albino Mourna
Dancers: 7 *Perfs:* 30 *No of Prods:* 1 new *Type:* modern, dance-theatre *Accomp:* recorded *Venues:* Pequeno Auditório of Centro Cultural de Belém, Lisbon 300; Teatro Viriato, Visen 280, Teatro Rivoli, Purto 600 *Touring:* Germany, Portugal *Comments:* winner of several prestigious awards in recent years; second address: Rua S. Vicente de Paulo, 8, 1070 Lisboa, Tel: 1-385 6624

ROMANIA (+40)

Ballet of Brasov Musical Theatre
Str Operei 51, 2200 **Brasov**
Tel: 68-419 380/417 271 Fax: 68-411 794
director Carmen Dobrescu
Venues: capacity 415

Ballet of Musical Theatre Constantin Tanase – Bucharest
Calea Victoriei 33, **Bucharest**
Tel: 1-614 1979 Fax: 1-312 1029
director Alexandru Arsinel
Venues: Sala Savoy 555

Ballet of Operetta Theatre Ion Dacian
B-dul Nicolae Balcescu 2, 70121 **Bucharest**
Tel: 1-614 1187/410 6348 Fax: 1-312 6583
director t.b.a.
Venues: capacity 460

Ballet of Romanian State Opera
Blvd. M. Kogalniceanu 70-72, Sector 1, 70609 **Bucharest**
Tel: 1-614 6980/410 1857 Fax: 1-615 7849
director general Razvan Cernat (tel: 1-615 7939)
Venues: capacity 950

Centrul de Cultura (Ansamblul Artistic) 'Tinerimea Romana' – Bucuresti
Str. Gutenberg 16, **Bucharest**
Tel: 1-312 1962/615 4326/4976 Fax: 1-312 1962
director Voicu Enachescu

Ballet of Cluj-Napoca Hungarian Opera
Str. Emil Isac 26-28, **Cluj-Napoca**
Tel: 64-193 463 Fax: 64-193 469
director Simon Gabor
Venues: capacity 857

Ballet of Cluj-Napoca Romanian Opera
Piata Stefan cel Mare 24, 3400 **Cluj-Napoca**
Tel: 64-197 175 Fax: 64-197 129
director Petre Sbârcea
Venues: capacity 927

Ballet of Fantasio Musical Theatre
Blvd Republicii 11, **Constanta**
Tel: 41-616 036 Fax: 41-616 607
general director Mihai Sorin Vasilescu
Venues: capacity 500

Ballet of Opera Constanta
St. Mircea cel Batran 97, 8700 **Constanta**
Tel: 41-615 268 Fax: 41-615 080
general director George Stanliu

Constanta Classical Contemporary Ballet Theatre
Str. Rascoalei 1907 nr.1, 8700 **Constanta**
Tel: 41-665 219 Fax: 41-638 398
director t.b.a.

Ballet of Craiova Lyrical Theatre
Str. Mihail Viteazu 1, 1100 **Craiova**
Tel: 51-418 426 Fax: 51-415 570
director Emil Maxim

Ballet of Teatrul de Estrada Deva
B-dul 1 Decembrie 1918 nr 15, 2700 **Deva**
Tel: 54-615 344
director Petru Marilla

Ballet of Galati Musical Theatre Nicolae Leonard
St. Mihai Bravu 50, 6200 **Galati**
Tel: 36-418 912/096 Fax: 36-418 096
director Florin Melinte
Venues: capacity 460

Ballet of Iasi Romanian Opera
St. Agatha Barsescu 18, 6600 **Iasi**
Tel: 32-211 144 Fax: 32-211 146
director Corneliu Calistru
Venues: capacity 846

Ballet of Timisoara Romanian Opera
St. Marasesti 2, **Timisoara**
Tel: 56-133 020/134 530 Fax: 56-190 615
director Ion Iancu
Venues: capacity 711

RUSSIA (+7)

Contemporary Dance Theatre
DK. Dgelezodorodgnikov, 54 tscviling Str., 454001 **Chelyabinsk**
Tel: 3512-370 428 (work)/528 624 (home) Fax: 3512-653 602
E-Mail: sergesh@chel.surnet.ru
contact Olga and Vladimir Pona
Type: contemporary

Dance Theatre of Chelyabinsk Culture Institute
Ul. Ordgenikidze 36a, 454000 **Chelyabinsk**
Tel: 3512-338 967 (chair)
contact Elena Krasilnikova
Type: contemporary

Dance Company Kipling
Ul. smazchikov 8 kv.31, 620070 **Ekaterinburg**
contact Levchenko Natalia (tel: 3432-326 671), Martemianov Evgeny (tel: 3432-652 386)
Type: contemporary

Provincial Dance
Ul Festivalnaya 12, of. 405, 620088 **Ekaterinburg**
Tel: 3432-510 160/329 027 (11am – 3pm)
Fax: 3432-510 160/329 027 (11am – 3pm)
artistic director Renat Hazbatov
Dancers: 8 *No of Prods:* 3 *Type:* modern *Accomp:* recorded

Dance Theatre Way out of City
3-71 Kulakhmetov str., 420033 **Kazan (Tatarstan)**
Tel: 8432-425 040
contact Lilia and Arat Bagautdinovy
Type: contemporary

Ballet of the State Academic Bolshoi Theatre of Russia (Bolshoi Ballet)
Teatralnaya Pl. 1, 103009 **Moscow**
Tel: 095-292 0050/9986/3108 Fax: 095-292 9032
artistic director & general manager Vladimir Vassiliev; executive manager Vladimir Kokonin; ballet director Yuri Bogatyrev

Ballet Theatre of State Kremlin Palace
Kremlin, 103073 **Moscow**
Tel: 095-929 7726
artistic director Andrei Petrov; executive manager Yuri Tokarev

Chamber Ballet Moscow
Novoriazanskaya ul. 16 of. 46, 107078 **Moscow**
Tel: 095-267 2388 Fax: 095-267 2388
contact Elena Bogdanovich
Type: contemporary

Classic Ballet Theatre
Starokoniushennyi per. 18, 121002 **Moscow**
Tel: 095-241 4240 Fax: 095-291 5137
Internet: dialspace.dial.pipex.com/town/place/xcp46/MCB-home.html
E-Mail: smirnov@dial.pipex.com
director Victor Smirnov-Golovanov; management Eilina Tikhomirova

Moscow Ballet Theatre
Skakovaya Ul.3, 125040 **Moscow**
Tel: 095-251 3221 Fax: 095-251 2691

Moscow State Russian Ballet Theatre
Volgogradsky prosp 121, 109443 **Moscow**
Tel: 095-379 4324
artistic director Vyatcheslav Gordeev

Natalya Kasatkina and Vladimir Vasiliev Classical Ballet Theatre
Pushechnaya Ul. 2/6, 103012 **Moscow**
Tel: 095-251 2691/921 3127 Fax: 095-921 3127
artistic director & general manager Vladimir Vasiliov; artistic director & chief choreographer Natalya Kasatkina

Russian National Ballet Company Moscow
Internet: www.aha.ru/~vladmo/b_com_rad.html
artistic director Sergei Radchenko; choreographer Elena Radchenko; director Alexander Sochinsky

Saira Blansh Theater
Dekabristov 28, 1, App. 230, 127273 **Moscow**
Tel: 095-907 8644/116 9121 Fax: 095-144 6221
E-Mail: saira@andrianov.msk.ru
artistic director Saira Blansh
Type: performance and dance *Comments:* theatrical and dance experiments; free improvisation on stage

Sasha Pepelyaev's Kinetic Theatre
23-1-24, 1st Novokuzminskaya str, 109377 **Moscow**
Tel: 095-335 0951 Fax: 095-335 0951
Internet: www.redline.ru/~kinetic
E-Mail: kinetic@redline.ru
artistic director Sasha Pepelyaev
Dancers: 6 *No of Prods:* 3 *Type:* modern, contemporary *Accomp:* recorded *Touring:* Slovenia, Netherlands, UK
Comments: management: Priit Raud, c/o TIKE, Rataskaevu 10, 0001 Tallinn, Estonia, Tel: +372 6421 1501, Fax: +372 631 3237, E-mail: jffice@esp.ee

Smirnov-Golovanov Classical Ballet Theatre
Starokonushenny per. 18, 121002 **Moscow**
Tel: 095-241 4240
Type: classical ballet

Contemporary Dance Studio
Arts Center, 2 Pirogova str., 630090 **Novosibirsk**
Tel: 3832-397 818/343 Fax: 3832-355 237/397 101

Natalia Fixel Dance Theatre
Arts Center, 2 Pirogova str, 630090 **Novosibirsk**
Tel: 3832-397 818/343 Fax: 3832-355 237/397 101
Internet: www.nsu.ru/art_center
E-Mail: artcen@nsu.ru
artistic director Natalia Fixel
Type: classical, contemporary, jazz

Novosibirsk State Academic Opera and Ballet Theatre
36, Krasny Prospect, 630099 **Novosibirsk**
Tel: 3832-226 040 Fax: 3832 227 400
Internet: www.nstu.nsk.ru/opera/main.en.html
E-Mail: opera@nstu.nsk.ru
theatre director Valery Egoudin; artistic director & chief conductor Alexei Lyudmilin; artistic ballet director Vladimir Vladimirov
Perfs: 100 (incl opera) *No of Prods:* 15
Venues: auditorium 2000 *Touring:* national, international *Comments:* see also Opera

Opera and Ballet Theatre P Tchaikovsky
ul Kommunistitheskaya 25 a, 614000 **Perm**
Tel: 342-232 4253 Fax: 342-232 5165
artistic director Vladimir Korochkine

Iguana Dance Theater
Kanonersky ostrov 8a, 198184 **St Petersburg**
Tel: 812-328 1230 Fax: 812-311 8463
Internet: www.ips.net/serge/iguana
E-Mail: iguana@yahoo.com
director Nina Gasteva
Type: contemporary

Kirov Ballet
Theatralnaya pl. 1, 190000 **St Petersburg**
Tel: 812-114 5924 Fax: 812-314 1744
theatre director Yuri Schwartzkopf; artistic director and principal conductor Valery Gergeyev

Sasha Kukin Dance Company
Chudnovskogo 9, kv 88, 193318 **St Petersburg**
Tel: 812-580 0036
artistic director Sasha Kukin
Dancers: 4 *No of Prods:* 2 *Type:* modern, contemporary *Accomp:* recorded

St Petersburg Ballet on Ice
St Petersburg
Tel: 812-315 2075 (director) Fax: 812-315 4128

St Petersburg State Academical Ballet Theatre
St Petersburg
Tel: 812-273 1997 (artistic director) Fax: 812-273 0589
artistic director Askold Makarov

St Petersburg State Ballet Theatre
Lizy Chaikinoi 2, 197198 **St Petersburg**
Tel: 812-232 1862 Fax: 812-232 1862
artistic director Boris Eifman

St Petersburg State Mussorgsky Opera and Ballet Theatre
1 Arts Square, 191011 **St Petersburg**
Tel: 812-219 1988/85/89/43 Fax: 812-314 7284/3653/2774
artistic director ballet Nikolay Bojartehikov; artistic general director Stanislav Gaudassinsky; deputy artistic director Victoria Gordievskaya; administrative director Victor Kusch
Comments: see also Opera and Choirs

Ensemble Balalaika
c/oYuri Ivanov, 22-68 Plekhanovskaya Street, 394030 **Voronezh**
Tel: 0732-521 248 Fax: 50-2200 2101
E-Mail: guest1@comch.ru
Dancers: 10 *Type:* folk music and dance

SLOVAKIA (+421)

Many telephone and fax numbers in Slovakia are in the process of being changed. We have included all new numbers known at the time of going to print.

Dance Studio Banská Bystrica, The
Stúdio tanca Banská Bystrica
Námestie Slobody 3, 974 00 **Banská Bystrica**
Tel: 88-414 5154 Fax: 88-414 6540
Internet: www.pcb.sk/present/studio_tanca
E-Mail: bbdance@pcb.sk
director Zuzana Hájková

Ballet of the Music Theatre Nová scéna Bratislava
Balet Novej scény v Bratislave
Zivnostenská 1, 812 14 **Bratislava** 1
Tel: 7-5292 3230/3341 Fax: 7-5296 1431
Internet: kultura.gratex.sk/nscena
E-Mail: riaditel-ns@ba.entry.sk
director of the Nová scéna Bratislava Marek Tapák; artistic director of the ballet Miroslav Stauder

Ballet of the Slovak National Theatre
Balet SND
Gorkého 4, 815 86 **Bratislava** 1
Tel: 7-5443 0444/3890 Fax: 7-5443 0444
general director Dusan Jamrich; artiststic director of ballet Jozef Sabovcík; director of ballet Emil T Bartko
Dancers: 60, soloists 10 *Perfs:* 80 + 80 opera performances *No of Prods:* 2-3 *Venues:* Slovak National Theatre 600 *Comments:* see also Opera and Drama

Dance Theatre of Bratislava – BDT
Bratislavské divadlo tanca
Karloveská 64, 842 58 **Bratislava** 4
Tel: 7-6542 3274 Fax: 7-6542 3274
E-Mail: bdt@mail.eurotel.sk
director Robert Mesko

Lúcnica
Slovak Folk Ensemble
Stúrova 6, 811 02 **Bratislava** 1
Tel: 7-5296 2432 Fax: 7-5296 3341
director Pavol Corej; artistic director Stefan Nosál
Dancers: 35-40, choir: 25, folk group: 6 *Type:* folk dance, music and singing

Slovak Folk Artistic Ensemble
Slovensky l'udovy umelecky kolektív
Balkánska 31, 853 08 **Bratislava-Rusovce**
Tel: 7-6285 9125/9134 Fax: 7-6285 9291
director Ing Peter Litomericky; artistic director Jaroslav Moravcik
Dancers: 30, choirs 25, folk group 6 *Type:* folk dance, music and singing *Touring:* international (60 countries)

Ballet of the State Theatre Kosice
Balet Státneho divadla Kosice
Hlavná 58, 042 77 **Kosice**
Tel: 95-622 1231/1232 Fax: 95-622 8235
general director Ing Jozef Fiffíki; director of the ballet Marta Zecová
Dancers: 25 *Perfs:* 100 *No of Prods:* 1 *Venues:* State Theatre 600, Studio 200

PULS – Folk Arts Ensemble of A Duchnovic Theatre
PULS – Poddukliansky ludovy umelecky súbor Divadla A Duchnovica
Jarkova 77, 080 01 **Presov**
Tel: 91-732 700 Fax: 91-734 422
director t.b.a.; artistic director Juraj Svantner

SLOVENIA (+386)

Ballet of the Slovene National Theatre Ljubljana
Slovensko Narodno Gledalisce Opera n Balet Ljubljana
Zupanciceva 1, 1000 **Ljubljana**
Tel: 61-125 8330/4680/126 2170
Fax: 61-126 2249
managing director Dr Borut Smrekar; public relations Tea Majkic; artistic director of ballet Tomaz Rode
Touring: within Slovenia

Betontanc
Rimska 2, 1000 **Ljubljana**
Tel: 61-224 563 Fax: 61-224 563
artistic director & choreographer Matjaz Pograjc
Dancers: 7 *Perfs:* 15 *No of Prods:* 1 *Type:* dance theatre *Touring:* Europe, America

Dance Theatre Ljubljana
Plesni Teater Ljubljana
Kersnikova 4, 1000 **Ljubljana**
Tel: 61-329 184/132 3092
Fax: 61-329 184/218 756 (studio)
E-Mail: ptl@mail.ljudmila.org
director Ziva Brecelj; artistic direction Ksenija Hribar, Sinja Ozbolt
Dancers: 8-10 *Perfs:* 50-80 *No of Prods:* 3-5
}*Type:* dance-theatre, contemporary dance
Accomp: live, recorded *Touring:* Europe
Comments: venue address: Prijateljeva 2, 1000 Ljubljana; independant production house, professional company, education

En-Knap
Metelkova 6, 1000 **Ljubljana**
Tel: 61-130 6770 Fax: 61-130 6775
Internet: www2.arnes.si/ljenknap1/
E-Mail: en.knap@guest.arnes.si
manager Valter Kobal; artistic director Iztok Kovac; international contact Nico Okkerse (nico.okkerse@ipr.nl)
Dancers: 5-6 *Perfs:* 50 *No of Prods:* 3 *Type:* contemporary dance, dance film, education *Touring:* Europe, America

Flota
c/o Cankarjev dom, presernova 10, 1000 **Ljubljana**
Tel: 61-125 8121 Fax: 61-125 8121
E-Mail: matjaz.faric@guest.arnes.si
artistic director & choreographer Matjaz Faric; contact Uros Korencan
Dancers: 6 *Perfs:* 15 *No of Prods:* 1 *Type:* contemporary dance *Touring:* Europe

Fourklor
Zelena pot 21, 1000 **Ljubljana**
Tel: 61-331 724
choreographer Branko Potocan
Dancers: 5-6 *Perfs:* 10 *No of Prods:* 1 *Type:* contemporary dance theatre *Touring:* Europe

Koreodrama Ljubljana
Prazakova 12, 1000 **Ljubljana**
Tel: 61-133 6334/312 045 Fax: 61-312 045
Internet: www.koreodrama.si
E-Mail: koreodrama@guest.arnes.si
artistic director Damir Zlatar Frey; organisation & production Ksenija Kaucic
Dancers: varies *No of Prods:* 3 *Type:* contemporary dance-theatre *Comments:* see also Drama

Ballet of the Slovene National Theatre Maribor
Slovensko Narodno Gledalisce
Slovenska Ulica 27, 2000 **Maribor**
Tel: 62-22840 Fax: 62-221 207/228 4050
Internet: www.sng-mb.si
E-Mail: sng.maribor@sng-mb.si
artistic director Stane Jurgec; general manager Blaz Rafolt
Venues: Old Hall 380, New Big Hall 864, Small Scene 150, Kazinska Hall 200 *Comments:* 2nd E-mail: marketing.sng.maribor@sng-mb.si

Plesna izba Maribor
Partizanska 5, 2000 **Maribor**
Tel: 62-214 657/41-757 393 Fax: 62-226 374
E-Mail: pcm.maribor@siol.net
artistic director Minka Veselic Kolosa
Dancers: 12 *Perfs:* 40 *No of Prods:* 2 *Type:* contemporary dance *Accomp:* recorded *Comments:* production and education centre

SPAIN (+34)

La Ribot – compañía de danza
Comments: see entry under United Kingdom

Ballet Español de Murcia
Apdo. de Correos nº 132, 30157 **Algezares (Murcia)**
Tel: 96-884 7609
dirección Carmen Rubio, Matile Rubio; escenografo Francisco Martinez Almagro; diseño de luces Paco Azorin; asesor Antonio Morales; regidor Maria Dolores Rubio
Dancers: 18 *No of Prods:* 1 *Type:* classic Spanish dance, flamenco, bolero, dance-theatre *Accomp:* live, recorded *Touring:* Spain

Ballet Español Raquel Peña
Plaza Florida Nº35, Campo Verde, Pilar de la Horadada, 03191 **Alicante**
Tel: 96-676 2507 Fax: 96-676 2683
E-Mail: raquelpenya@jnc.es
directora artística Raquel Peña; director musical Gustavo Sánchez
Dancers: 7 + 3 musicians *Perfs:* 30-50 *No of Prods:* 3 *Type:* Spanish dance and flamenco *Accomp:* live (guitarist, singer & percussion), recorded *Touring:* Spain, Europe, USA *Comments:* Co. has a resident conductor and can also perform as guest artists with symphony orchestras; master classes and choreograpy for other companies

Nadia Marquez y Su Quadro Flamenco
Plaza Florida Nº35, Campo Verde, Pilar de la Horadada, 03191 **Alicante**
Tel: 96-676 2507 Fax: 96-676 2683
E-Mail: raquelpenya@jne.es
directore artística Raquel Peña; director musical Gustavo Sánchez
Dancers: 1 + 6 musicians *Type:* flamenco *Accomp:* live *Touring:* national, Europe, USA

Andrés Corchero
c/ Manzanares 16 esc. 3 3º 1ª, 08014 **Barcelona**
Tel: 93-296 8073 Fax: 93-296 8073
E-Mail: acorchero@correo.datanet.es
director y bailarin Andrés Corchero; asistente y bailarina Rosa Muñoz; bailarinas Carme Torrent, Constanza Brncic; musico colaborador Agustí Fernandez; director técnico Luces-Edvard Inglés
Dancers: 4 *Perfs:* 35-45 *No of Prods:* 4 *Type:* butoh, contemporary dance *Accomp:* recorded, live *Venues:* up to 400 *Touring:* Europe (cultural capitals)

Arsis Ballet de Cambra
c/ Ciutat de Balaguer nº 60, 08022 **Barcelona**
Tel: 93-211 9722 Fax: 93-211 9722
direccion Berta Vallribera; maestros de baile Enric Castan, Xavier Bagà; coreografes José de Udaeta, Berta Vallribera, Xavier Bagà
Dancers: 10 *Perfs:* 40 *Type:* classical Spanish 'castañuela viva' and 'españa-ña' and 'glass' *Accomp:* recorded *Touring:* Spain, Italy, Germany

Avelina Argüelles Compañía de Danza Contemporánea
C/Llagostera 8, 08026 **Barcelona**
Tel: 93-203 2187/455 1952 Fax: 93-311 0210
director Avelina Argüelles; gerente Jose Luis Miranda
Dancers: 4-8 *Perfs:* c. 25 *No of Prods:* 1
Type: contemporary *Accomp:* recorded, live
Venues: El Arca (own venue) 200 *Touring:* Spain, Europe
Comments: second address: Trinquet, 16 Atic, 08034 Barcelona; see Venues (El Arca)

Búbulus Dance Company
Compañía de Danza Búbulus
c/ Petrarca 51, 1º 2ª, 08031 **Barcelona**
Tel: 93-358 7721 Fax: 93-358 7721
Internet: www.bubulus.com
E-Mail: bubulus@ols.es
director and choreograph Carles Salas Monforte; management Silvia Folch
Dancers: 3 *Perfs:* 25 *No of Prods:* 2 *Type:* contemporary, dance-theatre *Accomp:* recorded, live *Touring:* Spain, Europe *Comments:* regional funding

cuerpo transitorio cía de danza-teatro
c/ Tamarit, 82 2º 2ª, 08004 **Barcelona**
Tel: 93-211 8248/619-707 006/
Fax: 93-211 8248
E-Mail: cuerpotransitorio@usa.net
artistic management Rosana Barra, Fedora Fonseca; technical management & coordination Miguel Muñoz
Dancers: 2-4 *Perfs:* 35-50 *No of Prods:* 4 *Type:* dance theatre, butoh dance, contemporary dance *Touring:* national, France, Portugal, South America

Danat
Apartado de Correos 9388, 08080 **Barcelona**
Tel: 93-306 4128/909-985 375
Fax: 93-306 4106
E-Mail: Danat@CCCB.org
artistic direction Sabine Dahrendorf, Alfonson Ordónez; administration Marta Pons; communication & press Teresa Roig
Dancers: 8 + 1 actor *Perfs:* 50 *No of Prods:* 5 (1 new) *Type:* contemporary dance *Accomp:* live, recorded *Touring:* Spain, Mexico, Cuba, Germany, Austria, Brussels
Comments: associate company: Centre de Cultura Contemporánea de Barcelona (CCCB); visiting address: c/ Montalegre 5, 08001 Barcelona, Spain

erre que erre
Tamrit 175, 4º 2ª, 08015 **Barcelona**
Tel: 93-425 5119 Fax: 93-425 5119
E-Mail: errequeerre@hotmail.com
promoters Monica Silla, Mario G. Saez; art direction erre que erre
Dancers: 6 *No of Perf:* 20 *No of Prods:* 6 (1 new) *Type:* contemporary dance, dance-theatre *Accomp:* tape

Gelabert/Azzopardi Companyia de Dansa
Domènech 9 4º 1ª, 08012 **Barcelona**
Tel: 93-416 0068 Fax: 93-416 0193
E-Mail: gelabertazzopardi@compuserve.com
gestión Montse Garcia Otzet; manager Maria Rosas
Dancers: 7 *Perfs:* 50-60 *No of Prods:* 2 (1 new) *Type:* contemporary *Touring:* Germany, Italy, France, Spain, Portugal *Comments:* resident company at Teatre Lliure, Barcelona, and co-resident to Hebbel Theatre Berlin (see Venues)

General Eléctrica
La Rambla 48, 08002 **Barcelona**
Tel: 93-317 8753 Fax: 93-317 8753
E-Mail: agee@jet.es
dirección Tomás Aragay (dance); artístíca Roger Bernat (theatre); produccion y gestión Mónica Arùs
Dancers: 10 *Perfs:* 35 *No of Prods:* 4 *Type:* contemporary dance, theatre *Accomp:* live, recorded *Touring:* national, France, Belgium *Comments:* centre of creation where performers/choreographers can develope their projects

Iliacán S.C.C.L
c/ Aragón 312 4º3ª, 08009 **Barcelona**
Tel: 93-487 0214/0424 Fax: 93-487 0424
E-Mail: ILIACAN@iquadrat.com
director artistico Alvaro de la Peña; managers Susana Roca, Marianna Roige
Dancers: 6 *Perfs:* 40 *No of Prods:* 1 *Type:* contemporary, dance theatre *Accomp:* CD *Venues:* La Caldera (rehearsal & small scale productions) *Touring:* Spain, Europe, South America *Comments:* runs courses and workshops; regional and national funding

Increpación Danza
Paseo Juan de Borbon 27, 6, 08003 **Barcelona**
Tel: 93-225 9729 Fax: 93-225 9730
E-Mail: increpacion@ordenatas.es
director artistico/coreografo Ramón Baeza, Montse Sanchez; manager Eulalia Rodrigo
Dancers: 6 *Perfs:* 45 *No of Prods:* 4 *Type:* Spanish contemporary dance *Accomp:* recorded, live *Venues:* Sala Becket 80 *Touring:* Spain, Europe *Comments:* also runs flamenco workshops and courses

Lanònima Imperial
C/. Morales 21-27, 1K, 08029 **Barcelona**
Tel: 93-439 1191 Fax: 93-405 0556
E-Mail: lanonima@correo.interlink.es
director gerente Dietrich Grosse; director artístico Juan Carlos García
Dancers: 7-10 *Perfs:* 50 *No of Prods:* 3 *Type:* contemporary *Accomp:* recorded, live *Venues:* Teatre Nacional de Catalunya, Mercat de les Flors *Touring:* international *Comments:* national and regional funding

Magnet & Burch Dance Company
Magnet i Burch Compañia de Dansa
La Granada del Penedés, 27 bxs., 08006 **Barcelona**
Tel: 93-217 2648/7850 Fax: 93-217 2648
E-Mail: evandellos@cinet.for.es
directora Cristina Magnet i Burch; ayudante de dirección Norma Axenfeld; manager Edvard Vandellós
Dancers: 4 *Perfs:* 30 *No of Prods:* 1 *Accomp:* recorded, live *Venues:* capacity 700 *Touring:* Spain, Mexico

Mal Pelo
Aribau 45, ático 1°, 08011 **Barcelona**
Tel: 93-454 9089/2727 Fax: 93-454 9089
E-Mail: malpelo@arrakis.es
manager Pepa Pasamón Lara; directores artisticos María Muñoz, Pep Ramis
Dancers: 2 *Perfs:* 30 *No of Prods:* 2 *Type:* dance-theatre *Accomp:* recorded *Touring:* Europe, America, Asia

Mudances
c/ Morales 21-27, 08029 **Barcelona**
Tel: 93-430 8763 Fax: 93-405 0556
E-Mail: mudances@arrakis.es
gerente de produccion Teresa Carranza; director artístico Angels Margarit
Dancer: 15 *Perfs:* 35-40 *No of Prods:* 2 *Type:* contemporary *Accomp:* recorded, live *Venues:* Mercat de las Flors 600, Teatro Nacional de Cataluña 340 *Touring:* Europe, Spain *Comments:* regional and national funding

Projecte Gallina
c/ Gutemberg 6, 2° 1ª, 08035 **Barcelona**
Tel: 93-212 5292/418 1448 Fax: 93-212 5292
E-Mail: gallina@eic.ictnet.es
director Emili Gutièrrez; producer Rosa Pìno
Dancers: 6-8 *Perfs:* 15 *No of Prods:* 2 (+1 new) *Type:* contemporary dance *Accomp:* recorded *Touring:* national, Europe

Ramón Oller-Metros companyia de dansa
Consell de Cent 264, 1er. 2ª, 08011 **Barcelona**
Tel: 93-453 7573 Fax: 93-451 8318
E-Mail: ramonoller@abaforum.es
direcció Ramon Oller; asistent direcció Alícia Pérez-Cabrero; iluminación y dirección Gloria Montesinos; maquinaria y attrezo Natalia Barot; promoción y distribución Rosa Peris
Dancers: 12 *Perfs:* 60 *No of Prods:* 5 *Type:* contemporary dance, flamenco-contemporary *Accomp:* live, recorded

Roseland Musical
c/ L'Avenir 58, 08021 **Barcelona**
Tel: 93-201 1924 Fax: 93-414 4460
E-Mail: roseland@mx3.redestb.es
dirección artística y coreógrafa Marta Almirall
Dancers: 6 *Perfs:* 90 *No of Prods:* 2 *Type:* musical comedy (jazz, tap-dancing etc.), dance & theatre for all audiences *Accomp:* recorded *Touring:* Spain *Comments:* regional and national funding

Senzatempo
c/ Del Bisbe 2 bis, 08002 **Barcelona**
Tel: 93-319 2755 Fax: 93-319 2755
E-Mail: senzatemp@mx3.redestb.es
contact Carles Mallol, Ines Boza
Dancers: 5 *Perfs:* 40 *No of Prods:* 1 *Type:* dance-theatre *Accomp:* recorded *Touring:* Europe, Spain *Comments:* runs dance-theatre courses

Sol Picó
Provenza 14, Bajo, 08029 **Barcelona**
Tel: 93-430 0616/649-884 638 (mobile) Fax: 93-430 0616
E-Mail: 106554.1140@compuserve.com
directora artistica Sol Picó; producción/manager Pia Mazuela (tel:93-442 0578)
Dancers: varies *Perfs:* 40 *No of Prods:* 5 *Type:* contemporary, outdoor dance *Accomp:* live, recorded *Venues:* La Caldera (rehearsal only) *Touring:* Spain, Europe

Tragant Dansa
Font del Coll. 6 Atic A3, 08023 **Barcelona**
Tel: 93-213 7013 Fax: 93-685 0272
directora Olga Tragant; contacts Maria Roca, Karola Egaña
Dancers: 3 *Perfs:* 15 *No of Prods:* 3 *Type:* contemporary *Accomp:* live, recorded *Touring:* national

Awar-Dance
Apartado de Correos N° 20, 17488 **Cadaqués (Girona)**
Tel: 972-259 022 Fax: 972-259 022
choreograper Marta Binetti
Dancers: 8 *Perfs:* 25 *No of Prods:* 1 *Type:* dance-theatre *Accomp:* live, recorded *Touring:* guest performances in Germany, Spain, Russia, Italy *Comments:* see also entry in Germany

Color Cia. de Danza
San Josep 13, 08211 **Castellar del Valles (Barcelona)**
Tel: 93-715 9048/60-939 2961 (mobile)
Fax: 93-714 3915
director Mª Rosa Grau; produccion Assumpta Taulé; maangement Silvia Calvo
Dancers: 8 *Perfs:* 20 *No of Prods:* 3 *Type:* Spanish contemporary dance/contemporary flamenco *Accomp:* recorded *Venues:* Auditori del Centre Cultural, Sant Cugat del Vallés 900 *Touring:* national *Comments:* funded by regional governments

Paco Peña Flamenco Dance Company
Cordóba
Comments: managed by: Impresariaat Wim Visser; see entry under Amsterdam

Compañía Ferroviaria Paco Macía
Partida Peña de las Águilas, Polígono 3 # 36, 03296 **Elche (Alicante)**
Tel: 93-268 4841/965-444 333
Fax: 965-444 333
E-Mail: ferro@lobocom.es
contact Francesc Macía Vicent
Dancers: varies *No of Prods:* 5 *Type:* contemporary, dance theatre, drama *Accomp:* live, recorded *Venues:* Teatro Romea 1000 *Touring:* Spain, mediterranean *Comments:* formerly Robadura Dansa

Manuel Morao y Gitanos de Jerez
Aptdo 592, 11480 **Jerez**
Tel: 956-345 657/338 312
Fax: 956-345 657/338 312/325 224
Internet: www.gitanosdejerez.com
E-Mail: morao@gitanosdejerez.com
director artistico y musical Manuel Morao; productor ejecutivo Luis Pérez; producción Gitanos de Jerez S.L.
Dancers: 43 *No of Prods:* 5 *Type:* flamenco-theatre *Accomp:* live (guitar) *Touring:* Spain, Europe, USA, Spain *Comments:* own recording label 'En Compas de Origen', specialise in flamenco music

Ananda Dansa
Barranco de Serra, 6, Apdo. 81, 46182 **La Cañada (Valencia)**
Tel: 96-132 2699 Fax: 96-132 5680
Internet: www.infoescena.es/barbotegi
E-Mail: ananda.dansa@teleline.es
director general Rosangeles Valls; director artístico Edison Valls; gestor Mercedes Guzmán; distributión Concha Busto
Dancers: 8 *Perfs:* 50 *No of Prods:* 2 *Type:* contemporary dance *Accomp:* recorded *Venues:* Red Nacional de Teatros Publicos y Auditorios *Touring:* Europe *Comments:* receives funding from the Ministry of Culture and the Generalitat Valenciana

Ballet Galego Rey de Viana
Complejo Polideportivo de Elviña, El Birloque s/n, 15008 **La Coruña**
Tel: 981-134 946 Fax: 981-134 946
directora y coreógrafa Victoria Eugenia Canedo
Dancers: 50, 10 musicians *No of Prods:* 4 *Type:* regional/traditional style ballet *Accomp:* live, recorded *Comments:* subsidised by Xunta de Galicia and IGAEM, Pabellón de Galicia – San Lázaro s/n, 15703 Santiago de Compostela, Tel: 981-577 126; see also National and Regional Ministries

10 & 10 Danza
Centro Coreográfico la Ventilla,
Calle Carmen Montoya 12, 28029 **Madrid**
Tel: 91-315 3272 Fax: 91-323 2195
E-Mail: 10y10@mx2.redestb.es
artistic directors Pedro Berdäyes, Monica Runde; manager Ondine Perret (mobile: 619-482 499, e-mail: ondina66@redestb.es)
Dancers: 8 *Perfs:* 50-60 *No of Prods:* 2-3 (1 new) *Type:* contemporary dance, movement theatre *Accomp:* recorded *Touring:* Spain, France, UK, Italy, Germany, Switzerland, USA, Brazil, Cuba, Israel, Holland, Venezuela, Indonesia
Comments: regional and national funding

Aracaladanza
c/ Santa Brígida 31, 3° izq, 28004 **Madrid**
Tel: 91-521 1824 Fax: 91-521 1824
E-Mail: aracalad.teleline.es
artistic director Enrique Cabrera; executive producer Gracy Hunter; choreographer Ourique Cabrera
Dancers: 6 *Perfs:* 80 *No of Prods:* 1 *Type:* contemporary, specialise in performances for children and families *Comments:* telephone number may change during 1999

Arrieritos
San Graciano 7, 6°A Escalera Derecha, 28026 **Madrid**
Tel: 91-476 0858
choreographers & dancers Teresa Nieto, Florencio Campo, Patricia Torrero, Elena Santonja, Tacha Gonzalez
Dancers: 7 *Perfs:* 40 *No of Prods:* 2 *Type:* mix of flamenco and contemporary dance *Accomp:* live, recorded *Touring:* Spain, Scotland

Ballet de la Comunidad de Madrid/Victor Ullate
Doctor Castelo, 7, 28009 **Madrid**
Tel: 91-575 0385/577 9142
Fax: 91-578 0918
E-Mail: victorullate@hardwaresystem.es
director artístico Victor Ullate
Dancers: 55 *Perfs:* 100 *No of Prods:* 3 *Type:* classical and neo-classical *Venues:* Teatro Albeniz (Madrid) 1000, Teatro Real 1400 *Touring:* Spain, England, Italy, France, Germany, USA *Comments:* funded by the Comunidad Autonoma de Madrid

Ballet Español de María Rosa
Ayala 43, 28001 **Madrid**
Tel: 91-576 7238 Fax: 91-575 0079
director Maria Rosa; gerente Javier Garcia Avila
Dancers: 20 *Perfs:* 80-100 *No of Prods:* 1 *Type:* Spanish classical dance, flamenco *Accomp:* recorded, live *Venues:* Centro Cultural de la Villa 781, Teatro de Madrid 1000 *Touring:* Spain, South America, Italy, Portugal

Ballet Flamenco Antonio Canales
c/ Don Ramón de la Cruz, 109, 1°, B, 28006 **Madrid**
Tel: 91-402 4468/600-535 033 (mobile)
Fax: 91-402 4092
director artístico Antonio Canales; manager Lucho Ferruzzo
Dancers: 20 *Perfs:* 200 *No of Prods:* 2 *Type:* flamenco dance *Accomp:* 10 flamenco musicians *Venues:* Teatro Albeniz (Madrid) 1200, Teatro Apolo (Madrid) 1500 *Touring:* worldwide *Comments:* organise courses of flamenco dance every summer in their own rehearsal space; public and private funding

Ballet Flamenco Blanca del Rey
San Nicolas 5, bajo, 28013 **Madrid**
Tel: 91-542 1655 Fax: 91-542 1655
Internet: www.blancadelrey.com
E-Mail: correo@blancadelrey.com
director Angel Martín de Fuentes
Dancers: 9 *Perfs:* 45 *No of Prods:* 2 *Type:* flamenco *Accomp:* 6 musicians *Touring:* Europe, Asia, Spain

Ballet Nacional de España
Paseo de la Chopera, 4, 28045 **Madrid**
Tel: 91-517 4686/4510 Fax: 91-517 5594
Internet: www.mcu.es/bne/index.html
E-Mail: prensa.e@bne.inaem.es
director Hans Tino; dirección artistica Aida Gomez; jefe de prensa Eduardo López; director técnico Florencio Sanchez
Dancers: 50 *Perfs:* 100 *No of Prods:* 12 *Type:* Spanish dance *Accomp:* live guitarrists and 'cantaores'
Venues: Teatro de la Zarzuela
Touring: Japan, Europe, USA, Spain

Ballet Ricardo Cue
c/ Ayala 64, 4°, 28001 **Madrid**
Tel: 91-435 2750 Fax: 91-431 8182
director Ricardo Cue
Dancers: 3 *Perfs:* 40 *No of Prods:* 3 *Type:* classical, flamenco *Accomp:* live, recorded *Venues:* Teatro de la Zarzuela, Madrid 1100 *Touring:* Spain

Blanca Calvo Dance Company
Blanca Calvo – Compañía de Danza
Julio Danvila, n° 12, 28033 **Madrid**
Tel: 91-302 0615 Fax: 91-302 0615
E-Mail: blancalvo@compuserve.com
directora y coreógrafa Blanca Calvo; choreographer Ion Munduate
Dancers: 2 *Perfs:* 15 *No of Prods:* 1 *Type:* contemporary dance *Accomp:* recorded *Venues:* Sala Cuarta Pared (Madrid) 200 *Touring:* Spain, Portugal, Belgium, Italy

Campanas Flamencas
c/o Francisco Sánchez, Carretas 14-4°E, 28012 **Madrid**
Tel: 91-532 4320/521 3847 Fax: 91-532 4797
E-Mail: saumatum@teleline.es
artistic director & executive producer Francisco Sánchez; general manager Saúl Rodríguez
Dancers: 6 dancers, 4 singers, 4 guitarists *No of Prods:* 1 *Type:* flamenco *Accomp:* live *Comments:* managed by Sauma & Tumbao; see also Agents & Producers

Compañía Antonia Andréu
Marquez de Pontejos 1, 28012 **Madrid**
Tel: 91-521 9183 Fax: 91-521 9183
E-Mail: aandreur@nexo.es
directora y coreógrafa Antonia Andréu; ayudante dirección Willy Sánchez Verdoux; producción ejecutiva Sonia Suárez
Dancers: 4-6 *Type:* modern, contemporary
Accomp: live, recorded

Compañía Antonio Márquez
Contrata Artistica Pepa Mediavilla, c/ Lope de Hoyo 142, 3, 36, 28002 **Madrid**
Tel: 91-415 7846 Fax: 91-413 8564
director artístico Antonio Márquez
Dancers: 11 *Perfs:* 70-80 *No of Prods:* 10 *Type:* classical, Spanish dance, flamenco *Accomp:* 5 flamenco musicians *Venues:* Teatro Real (Madrid) 1800 *Touring:* Spain, Italy, Austria, USA *Comments:* one of the few companies left which work with pure classic Spanish dance; company gives classes of Spanish classical dance and flamenco; agent & distributor: Pepa Mediavilla, Tel: 91-415 7846, see also Agents & Producers

Compañía de Danza Flamenca Carmen Cortes (Art-Danza S.L.)
c/ Sta. Isabel nº 12, 1º dcha, 28012 **Madrid**
Tel: 91-528 7397 Fax: 91-528 7397
director ejecutivo Lola Cortés; director artístico Carmen Cortés
Dancers: 12 *Perfs:* 50-60 *No of Prods:* 2 *Type:* flamenco *Accomp:* live *Venues:* Teatro de Madrid 870 *Touring:* Spain, Greece, South America, Italy *Comments:* resident company at Teatro de Madrid

Compañía Elvira Andrés
c/ Oriente nº 3 3º izq, 28005 **Madrid**
Tel: 91-366 9309 Fax: 91-366 9309
E-Mail: lurof@redestb.es
directora artística Elvira Andrés; manager & production Luis Romero
Dancers: 10 + 4 flamenco musicians *Perfs:* 15 *Type:* Spanish classical dance and flamenco *Accomp:* live *Venues:* Teatro Albeniz (Madrid) 1200 *Touring:* national, France *Comments:* the essence of classical Spanish dance with contemporary forms

Compañía Flamenco Contemporáneo
Monteleón 31, Cuarto Derecho, 28010 **Madrid**
Tel: 91-445 2333/610-825 212 Fax: 91-445 2333
Internet: www.cempresarial.com/nelsonmusicspain
E-Mail: nelsonmusic@cempresarial.com
director Angeles Arranz del Barrio; management Nelson Hernan Muñoz
Dancers: 5 *Type:* flamenco, contemporary, traditional *Accomp:* own troupe of singers and guitarrists, occasionally use recorded sound *Venues:* theatres, cultural centres, etc. *Touring:* Spain *Comments:* also do conferences and workshops in flamenco

Compañía Impulsos Flamencos
Beneficio 30 1º 1, 28260 **Madrid**
Tel: 91-858 6802 Fax: 91-858 4715
Internet: www.cempresarial.com/nelsonmusicspain
E-Mail: nelsonmusic@cempresarial.com
directors Jose Luis Monton, Belen Maya
Dancers: 3 *Type:* flamenco *Accomp:* live *Venues:* theatres, open-air *Comments:* managed by: Nelson Music Spain

Compañía Lírica Amadeo Vives S.A.
c/o Teatro Bellas Artes, c/Marqués de Casa Riera 2, 28014 **Madrid**
Tel: 91-522 3403 Fax: 91-522 1926
director José Tamayo; director de producción Antonio Díaz Martínez; director musical José Antonio Torres
Dancers: 14 (+ 24 choir, 24 orchestra, 7 soloist) *Perfs:* 80-100 *Type:* Zarzuela, Spanish dance *Accomp:* orchestra 30-36 or recorded *Venues:* Teatro Bellas Artes 800 *Touring:* Spain, Turkey, USA, South America *Comments:* see also Opera

Compañía Nacional de Danza de España
Paseo de la Chopera, 4, 28045 **Madrid**
Tel: 91-517 2072 Fax: 91-473 4291
Internet: www.mcu.es/cnd
E-Mail: prensa@cnd.inaem.es
jefe de producción Isabel Sanchez Barreno; director artistico Nacho Duato; jefe de difusión Maite Villanueva; encargada administración Carmen Arranz
Dancers: 30-35 *Perfs:* 100 *No of Prods:* 5 *Type:* contemporary *Accomp:* recorded, live *Touring:* Europe, USA, South America, Japan, Israel, Australia, New Zealand

Contratiempo Flamenco Con-Fusión
c/ Marcelino Álvarez 18, 4º D, 28017 **Madrid**
Tel: 91-404 9428/730 7054 Fax: 91-882 2373
general manager Auberto Muyo
Dancers: 4 + contracted musicians *Perfs:* 80 *No of Prods:* 5 (2 new) *Type:* flamenco combined with drama and comedy *Accomp:* live, recorded *Touring:* Spain, Europe, South America *Comments:* regional funding; runs courses for pupils of Conservatorio de Danza

Cumbre Flamenca
c/o SAUMA & TUMBAO, c/ Carretas 14-4º E, 28012 **Madrid**
Tel: 91-532 4320/521 3847 Fax: 91-532 4797
Internet: www.absystem.com/sauma&tumbao
E-Mail: saumatum@telelines.es
artistic director & executive producer Francisco Sanchez; general manager Saúl Rodriguez
Dancers: 5 dancers, 4 singers, 4 guitarists *Perfs:* 500 *No of Prods:* 1 *Type:* flamenco *Accomp:* live *Touring:* USA, Canada, Japan, Taiwan, Hong Kong, Australia, Europe, mainly Spain *Comments:* managed by: Sauma & Tumbao (see Agents & Producers)

Denis Perdikidis
Fernandez de los Rios 22, 6º Puerta 6, 28015 **Madrid**
Tel: 91-448 9897
director Denise Perdikidis
Dancers: 8 *Perfs:* 100 *No of Prods:* 1 *Type:* contemporary video dance, multi-media *Touring:* Spain, USA

El Bailadero
tesoro 13, 3ºD, 28004 **Madrid**
Tel: 91-521 5616 Fax: 91-521 5616
contact Monica Valenciano
Dancers: 1+ *Perfs:* 30 *No of Prods:* 3 *Type:* contemporary, experimental *Touring:* Spain
Comments: member of La Inesperada (q.v.)

La Corrala de la Danza de Lucía Real y El Camborio
c/Doctor Piga, 5 bis, Lavapiés, 28012 **Madrid**
Tel: 91-539 5845 Fax: 91-468 6823
director El Camborio
Dancers: 9 + 6 musicians *Type:* Flamenco, Spanish dance *Accomp:* live (guitarists, singers), recorded *Venues:* La Corrala de la Danza
Touring: national, international

La Inesperada
c/ Nuñez de Arce, 11 local 3, 28012 **Madrid**
Tel: 91-532 2701 Fax: 91-532 2701
E-Mail: anabui@hotmail.com
choreographers Ana Buitrago, Blanca Calvo, Olga Mesa, La Ribot, Monica Valenciano
Dancers: 1 *Perfs:* 10 *No of Prods:* 2 *Touring:* Spain
Comments: collective formed by 5 choreographers; organises workshops, improvisation sessions and programming (DESVIACIONS Ciclo Nueva Danza)

Larumbe Danza
c/ Antonio de Leyva 11, 4ºE, 28019 **Madrid**
Tel: 91-469 0398 Fax: 91-569 9265
E-Mail: larumbe@ctv.es
director y coreógrafo Juan de Torres; co-directora Daniela Merlo
Dancers: 7 *Perfs:* 70 *No of Prods:* 5 *Type:* contemporary *Accomp:* live (mondo sextet) *Touring:* Spain, Central Europe *Comments:* funded by Comunidad de Madrid and INAEM

Los Ballets de Madrid
c/ Ribera de Curtidores 2, 28005 **Madrid**
Tel: 91-366 7213 Fax: 91-366 7213
Internet: www.redestb/es/personal/bladerun
E-Mail: bladerun@mx2.redestb.es
gerente Odilo Dominguez; director artistico Adolfo León
Dancers: 35 *Perfs:* 75 *No of Prods:* 4
Type: neoclassical, Spanish expressionist (Falla) *Accomp:* recorded, live *Venues:* Centro Cultural de la Villa *Touring:* Egypt, France, Spain
Comments: owns dance school Escuela Mayor de Danza del Ayuntamiento de Madrid

Losdedae
c/ Carretas, 14 8º D, Ofic. 2-2, 28012 **Madrid**
Tel: 91-523 4622 Fax: 91-532 9201
director/coreographer Chevi Muraday; pr Gachi Pisani
Dancers: 6 *No of Prods:* 2 *Type:* contemporary dance *Accomp:* recorded *Touring:* national, Europe
Comments: represented by: Gachi Pisani

Monica Valenciano & Co
c/ Zurita 27, 3º 2º, 28012 **Madrid**
Tel: 91-530 4027 Fax: 91-521 5616
contact Monica Valenciano
Dancers: 1 + extras *Perfs:* 10 *No of Prods:* 2
Touring: national
Comments: member of La Inesperada and El Bailadero

Nuevo Ballet Español
c/ Carretas 14, 8º D Oficina 2ª, 2º, 28012 **Madrid**
Tel: 91-523 4622 Fax: 91-532 9201
E-Mail: gpf00000@teleline.es
directors artísticos Angel Rojas, Carlos Rodriguez
Dancers: 8 + 7 musicians *Perfs:* 100 *No of Prods:* 4
Type: flamenco and Spanish dance *Accomp:* live
Touring: France, Finland, Venezuela, Peru, Netherlands, Germany

Olga Mesa – Compañía de Danza
Sta. Isabel 18, 1 ext Derecha, 28012 **Madrid**
Tel: 91-527 8847 Fax: 91-527 8847
contact Olga Mesa
Dancers: 4 *Perfs:* 30 *No of Prods:* 4 *Type:* contemporary, experimental *Accomp:* recorded *Touring:* Spain, Portugal
Comments: member of La Inesperada (q.v.); has produced 2 video-creations

Pasion Gitana S.L
Quintana 2 7º 9ª, 28008 **Madrid**
Tel: 91-547 5283 Fax: 91-542 8698
productor ejecutivo Pino Sagliocco;
productor artistico Joaquín Cortés; tour manager Jose María García Biosca
Dancers: 25 dancers, 11 musicians, 6 singers *Perfs:* 150
Type: contemporary flamenco *Accomp:* live *Touring:* Europe, USA, South America, Australia, Japan, Canada

Provisional Danza
c/ Luis Feito, 24, 28047 **Madrid**
Tel: 91-525 6276 Fax: 91-525 6276
Internet: personal5.iddea.es/provisionaldanza
E-Mail: provisionaldanza@zetemail.es
director artistico Carmen Werner; gerente Alejandro Morata
Dancers: 10 *Perfs:* 60 *No of Prods:* 7 (4 contemporary, 3 street dance) + 4 video-dances *Type:* contemporary, street dance, video-dance, opera dance *Accomp:* recorded, live *Touring:* Germany, Colombia, Italy, France, England, Scotland *Comments:* funded by Ministerio Educacion y Cultura, Ministerio de Relaciones Exteriores, and Comunidad de Madrid (regional Government), FUNDACION AUTOR-S.G.A.E.

Rayo Malayo Danza
c/ Barbieri 9 2b, 28004 **Madrid**
Tel: 91-521 9555 Fax: 91-521 9775/9555
director Francesc Bravo
Dancers: 7 *Perfs:* 20 *No of Prods:* 2 *Type:* contemporary
Touring: Philippines, festivals in Spain

Sara Baras y Compañía
Don Ramón de la Cruz 109, 28006 **Madrid**
Tel: 91-402 4468/600-535 033 (mobile) Fax: 91-402 4092
director Sara Baras; producer Lucho Ferrucho
Dancers: 10 *Perfs:* 160 *No of Prods:* 2 *Type:* flamenco, dramaturgies *Accomp:* live *Venues:* Teatro Apolo Tivoli
Touring: worldwide

Teatro de Danza Española
c/ Felipe III 4, 1º izq, 28012 **Madrid**
Tel: 91-365 8404/05 Fax: 91-364 0018
director artistico Luis Davila Luisillo
Dancers: 28 *Perfs:* 70-80 *No of Prods:* 3 *Type:* flamenco and Spanish dance *Accomp:* live, recorded *Touring:* Italy, Spain, China, Japan, Germany *Comments:* managed by Euroarte Management, administrador Luis P Vivó; see also Agents

Teresa Nieto en Compañía
Calle Puebla 8-4º, 28004 **Madrid**
Tel: 91-531 4036 Fax: 93-442 9763
E-Mail: lastrado@teleline.es
directora/coreogi Teresa Nieto; manager David Garcia (tel: 93-442 9763)
Dancers: 6 *Perfs:* 60 *No of Prods:* 3 *Type:* contemporary *Accomp:* recorded *Touring:* Spain

Zarzuela s.l, La
Marques de Casa Riera Nº2, 28014 **Madrid**
Tel: 91-522 3403 Fax: 91-522 1926
director Jose Tamayo; director ejecutivo Manuel Ganchegui
Dancers: 16 *Perfs:* 100 *No of Prods:* 1 *Type:* classical Spanish *Accomp:* live *Venues:* Teatro Nuevo Apolo 1200
Touring: Istanbul, South America, Spain *Comments:* see also Agents & Producers, and Opera

Compañía Murciana de Danza
c/ Ricardo Gil 4, 4 A, 30004 **Murcia**
Tel: 968-343 721/218 8925
directoras Purificacion Lopez-Gomez, Olivia Bella Hernandez
Dancers: 28 *Perfs:* 15-20 *No of Prods:* 4 (1 new) *Type:* Spanish dance *Accomp:* recorded, live *Venues:* Conservatorio de Danza de Murcia (rehearsal venue)
Comments: collaboration with theatre company Antaviana, managed by Lateral; see also Agents and Producers

AU MENTS dansa
calle Jesus 8a, 2º B, 07003 **Palma de Mallorca**
Tel: 97-129 9700 Fax: 97-129 9700
E-Mail: gomila@arrakis.es
directores e intérpretes Tomeu Gomila, Andrea Cruz
Dancers: 3 *Perfs:* 32 *No of Prods:* 2 *Type:* dance, visual theatre *Accomp:* live *Touring:* Spain, Chile

SusaHee Performance
Sa Torre 42, Alqueria Blanca, 07691 **Palma de Mallorca**
Fax: 971-164 202
Internet: theaterszene-koeln.de/susannehelmes
E-Mail: SusaHee@hotmail.com
manager & choreographer Susanne Helmes
Dancers: varies *Perfs:* 25-50 *No of Prods:* 2-5 per year
Type: performance arts, contemporary dance, modern *Accomp:* live, occassionally recorded, DJ *Venues:* various, theatres, galleries, open-air (up to 200)
Touring: national, international *Comments:* co-productions with other artists; productions for museums; cooperation with Time and Space Limited, Hudson, NY, USA; see also entry in Germany (Köln)

Nats Nus Dansa
Calle Martorell 20, 22 bajo, 08190 **San Cugat del Valles**
Tel: 93-589 6260 Fax: 93-589 6260
E-Mail: natsnus@webhouse.es
production Silvia Lorente; management Sonia Lorente; artistic direction & choreography Toni Mira Martínez
Dancers: 6 *Perfs:* 70 *No of Prods:* 4 (1 new)
Type: dance-theatre, contemporary, dance-theatre for children *Accomp:* recorded
Touring: Georgia, Spain, Germany, Italy, Israel, Wales, South America, Israel *Comments:* member of the multi-media centre La Caldera, Barcelona

Urbeltzen Euskal Baleta
984 posta-kutxa, 20080 **San Sebastián – Donosti**
Tel: 943-291 747 Fax: 943-291 345
director artístico Juan Antonio Urbeltz
Dancers: up to 150 depending on production *Perfs:* 20 *No of Prods:* 1 *Type:* traditional basque dances and re-interpretations, dances about traditional tales *Accomp:* live *Venues:* Teatro Victoria Eugenia (San Sebastián), Teatro Arriaga (Bilbao), Palacio de Festivales de Biarritz *Comments:* regional funding

Lazzard Danza Circo
Pasaje Marañuelas N° 24, 38001 **Santa Cruz de Tenerife**
Tel: 922-618 863/607-705 876 (mobile) Fax: 922-618 863
directors & choreographers Esteban Berenguer, Txell Janot
Dancers: varies according to production *No of Prods:* 4 *Type:* acrobatic dance, improvisation *Accomp:* live, recorded *Venues:* La Nave Va (rehearsal venue) *Touring:* national *Comments:* rehearsal venue to open as alternative venue

DANTEA Spanish Dance Theatre Company
Compañia de Danza Teatro Española DANTEA
c/ San Luis N° 36, 2° dcha, 39010 **Santander**
Tel: 942-376 921 Fax: 942-371 635
Internet: www.dantea.camerdata.es
E-Mail: danteasl@camerdata.es
directores artísticos Miriam González-Gay, Gonzalo San Miguel; jefe de producción Belén González-Gay
Dancers: 14 + 3 musicians *Perfs:* 80 *No of Prods:* 1 *Type:* flamenco, Spanish classical dance, dance-theatre *Accomp:* live, recorded *Touring:* Italy, Germany *Comments:* see also Drama

Antonio el Pípa y Compañía
Macande, Av. República Argentina 24 2° A Modulo 3, Torre Los Remedios, 41011 **Sevilla**
Tel: 95-427 1700/631 1152 Fax: 95-427 8508
Internet: www.macande.zoom.es
E-Mail: macande@zoom.es
director, choreographer, dancer Antonio el Pípa
Dancers: 5 *Perfs:* 60-70 *No of Prods:* 1 *Type:* flamenco *Accomp:* live *Touring:* national, Europe, Japan *Comments:* managed by: Macande; see also Agents & Producers

Ballet Cristina Hoyos
c/ Betis 14 ACC, 41010 **Sevilla**
Tel: 95-434 0311 Fax: 95-434 0364
Internet: www.trajana.com
E-Mail: trajana@arrakis.es
general manager Tina Panadero; administrator Rafael Diaz; dirección artistica y coreografia Cristina Hoyos
Dancers: 10 + 6 musicians *Type:* flamenco *Accomp:* live *Touring:* worldwide *Comments:* performances, master-classes and choreographies; managed by Trajana Producciones; see also Agents

Compañía Andaluza de Danza (CAD)
c/ San Luis N°37, 41002 **Sevilla**
Tel: 95-490 1493/4729 Fax: 95-490 0707/7573
Internet: www.cica.es/cat/cat.html
E-Mail: ivargas@cica.es
director José Antonio Ruiz; jefa de prensa Raquel Fuentes; jefa de producción Mercedes Guillamón
Dancers: 14 *Perfs:* 80 *No of Prods:* 2 *Type:* flamenco *Accomp:* live, recorded *Venues:* Teatro Central 470 *Touring:* worldwide *Comments:* part of the Centro Andaluz de la Danza (q.v.); other email: yamuza@cica.es

Compañia Maria Pages Flamenco
Ximenez de Enciso 17, 41004 **Sevilla**
Tel: 639-602 727 Fax: 954-224 853
E-Mail: miguel@eclipse.net
directora artistica Maria Pages; productor ejecutivo Miguel Marin
Dancers: 15 + 8 musician *Type:* flamenco

Israel Galván y Compañía
Av. República Argentina 24 2° A Modulo 3, Torre Los Remedios, 41011 **Sevilla**
Tel: 95-427 1700 Fax: 95-427 8508
Internet: www.macande.zoom.es
E-Mail: macande@zoom.es
director, choreographer, dancer Israel Galvan
Dancers: varies *Perfs:* 60-70 *No of Prods:* 1 *Type:* flamenco *Accomp:* live *Venues:* Teatro Lope de Vega (Sevilla) 2000 *Touring:* national, Europe, Japan *Comments:* managed by: Macande; see also Agents & Producers

Jaleo Flamenco Dance Company
c/ Archeros 5, 41004 **Sevilla**
Tel: 95-441 1285 Fax: 95-441 1285
contact Carmen Campos, Peter Holloway
Dancers: 3 *Perfs:* 90 *No of Prods:* 1 *Type:* flamenco *Accomp:* live (2 guitarists, 2 singers) *Touring:* worldwide *Comments:* larger company also available; contact in UK: Peter Holloway, 45 Franklands, Longton, Preston PR4 5PD, Tel: +44 1772-614 235 (q.v.)

Juan Martin's Flamenco Dance Co.
Sevilla
Comments: see entry under United Kingdom (London)

Ballet Contemporani de Barcelona
c/ Bisbe Catalá 7, 08391 **Tiana (Barcelona)**
Tel: 93-465 2138 Fax: 93-465 2138
E-Mail: musicavista@mx3.redestb.es
produccion Maria Rosas; directora artistica Amelia Boluda
Dancers: 6 *Perfs:* 45 *No of Prods:* 2 *Type:* contemporary *Accomp:* recorded, live *Touring:* Spain, Europe *Comments:* published book – 20 Años Ballet Contemporaneo de Barcelona

Compañía Vicente Saez
c/ Bonaire, 12-3°, 46003 **Valencia**
Tel: 96-394 4196 Fax: 96-394 2513
administrador Jean-Marc Liverato; choreógrafo Vicente Saez
Dancers: 10 *Perfs:* 50 *No of Prods:* 2 *Type:* contemporary *Accomp:* recorded (original music) *Touring:* Europe, USA *Comments:* federal and regional funding; associated to Centro Coreográfico de la Comunidad de Valencia

Sonrisa de Caín, La
Pza. Santa Margarita 1 – 8, 46003 **Valencia**
Tel: 96-392 4402 Fax: 96-392 4402
Internet: www.danza.net
E-Mail: cain@danza.net
directora Cristina Andreu; gerente Vicenta Chaparro
Type: contemporary dance

Grupo de Danza Castilla Joven
C/ Recoletas 4, 3° C, 47006 **Valladolid**
Tel: 983-339 471 Fax: 983-357 999/397 373
director Javier Sanz Robles; musical director Alejandro Berdote Paz
Dancers: 50 *Perfs:* 60-70 *No of Prods:* 1 *Type:* traditional, folklore *Accomp:* live *Touring:* Portugal, France, Spain

Ballet de Zaragoza
Centro Cultural Palafox, c/ Domingo Miral, n° 3, 50009 **Zaragoza**
Tel: 976-566 411 Fax: 976-569 077
director gerente y persona de contacto Víctor Fernández; director artístico de funciones Patsy Kuppe-Matt
Dancers: 30 *Perfs:* 60-80 *No of Prods:* 3 *Type:* classical, neo-classical, contemporary *Accomp:* recorded, live *Venues:* Teatro Principal Zaragoza 1100 *Touring:* Spain, France, Italy, Cuba, Mexica and South America

SWEDEN (+46)

Atalante
Övre Husargatan 1, 411 22 **Göteborg**
Tel: 31-711 8200 Fax: 31-136 317
Internet: www.atalante.org
E-Mail: atalante@atalante.org
artistic direction, dance production & choreography Eva Ingernarsson; artistic direction & poetry choreography Gunilla Witt; artistic direction & music Niklas Rydén
Dancers: varies *Perfs:* 60 *No of Prods:* 1 + 1 *Type:* contemporary *Accomp:* live, recorded *Venues:* Atalante 100 *Touring:* Europe, Scandinavia

Göteborgs Operans Balett
Christina Nilssons Gata, 411 04 **Göteborg**
Tel: 31-108 000/064 Fax: 31-108 060
Internet: www.opera.se
E-Mail: susann.lorenius@opera.se
managing director Dag Hallberg; ballet director Anders Mellström; opera director Kjell Ingebreksten; finance manager Mikael Milocco; ballet project manager Ivor Howard; ballet administration Susann Lorenius; marketing manager Pernila Warberg-Andersson
Dancers: 40 *Perfs:* 80 *No of Prods:* 6 *Type:* modern ballet, classical *Accomp:* live, recorded *Venues:* Göteborgs Operan 1250, annexe 250

Swedish Ballet Production
Bergsätravägen 2, 181 61 **Lidingö**
Tel: 8-767 6597 (admin)/715 0254/70-456 6038 (mobile)
Fax: 8-767 6597
E-Mail: SUSANNE_VALENTIN@alfa.telenordia.se
administrator Barbro Skarström; artistic director Susanne Valentin; producer Wiveca Dedering
Dancers: 3-15 *Perfs:* 20 *No of Prods:* 4 *Type:* choreographic theatre, modern and sacred dance, dance performance for children *Accomp:* live *Venues:* Rotunda (Royal Opera), Cathedral Parish in Stockholm *Touring:* Sweden *Comments:* millennium project, City Hall Stockholm, for Swedish Television (SVT)

Skånes Dansteater
Box 175 20, 200 10 **Malmö**
Tel: 40-208 471 Fax: 40-208 474
Internet: www.skanesdansteater.se
E-Mail: info@skanesdansteater.se
director Lena Josefsson; producer Elisabeth Secher Svenstedt; public relations Annica Widmark, Christine Thoulouis; technical manager Johan Söderberg; stage manager Anders Myhrman; lighting manager Imre Zsibrik; stage coordinator Claes Nilsson
Dancers: 14 *Perfs:* 100 *No of Prods:* 2-3 *Type:* modern *Accomp:* live *Venues:* Storan, Malmö 1450 *Touring:* national, international *Comments:* school programme

Cullberg Ballet
The National Swedish Touring Theatre, 145 83 **Norsborg**
Tel: 8-5319 9157 Fax: 8-5319 9159
Internet: www.riksteatern.se/culbergballet
E-Mail: cullbergballet@riksteatern.se
managing director Mikael Jönsson; artistic directors Margareta Lidström, Lena Wennergren-Juras
Dancers: 20 *Perfs:* 60-70 *No of Prods:* 10 (3 new) *Type:* modern based on classical *Accomp:* recorded *Venues:* rehearsal studios at Riksteatern *Touring:* Germany, France, Spain, Italy, Norway, Sweden, Estonia, Finland

Susanne Jaresand Dansproduktion
Bergvägen 2, 131 50 **Saltsjö-Duvnäs**
Tel: 8-716 0798
choreographer Susanne Jaresand
Dancers: 5-10 *No of Prods:* 2 *Type:* modern *Accomp:* live *Touring:* national, international

Confidencen
Ulriksdals Slottstheater, 170 79 **Solna**
Tel: 8-857 016 Fax: 8-856 121
director Ture Rangström
Type: ballet and opera *Comments:* no permanent company; performs for example with artists from Royal Opera and Royal Swedish Ballet; season from May to Oct.; regluar theatre; see also Opera

Birgitta Egerbladh Production
c/o Kario – Kultur, Brännkyrkagatan 41, ög, 118 22 **Stockholm**
Tel: 8-462 0280 Fax: 8-462 0280
E-Mail: kario@bahnof.se
producer Irma Kario-Elgstrand; choreographer, dancer, composer, musician Birgitta Egerbladh
No of Prods: 1 new *Type:* contemporary, dance-theatre *Accomp:* live, recorded *Comments:* free lance company, employs dancers/performers depending on productions; emphasis on interpretation of poetry and spoken word

Björn Elisson
DPS, Wallingatan 21, 111 24 **Stockholm**
Tel: 8-676 9620 Fax: 8-676 9624/30
Internet: www.dansklotet.se
E-Mail: dps@dansklotet.se
Dancers: 1-10 *Perfs:* 25 *No of Prods:* 2 *Type:* contemporary *Accomp:* recorded

Claire Parsons Co
Nybrog. 76, 114 47 **Stockholm**
Tel: 708-274 180 (mobile) Fax: 8-304 034
Internet: claireparsons.com
E-Mail: info@claireparsons.com
choreographer & artistic director Claire Parsons; technical director Fia Juréen; chairman Marie Liljedahl
Dancers: varies per production *Perfs:* approx. 40 *No of Prods:* 2 *Type:* contemporary, dance-theatre *Accomp:* live, recorded *Venues:* large and small scale *Touring:* Scandanavia, Latin America, Baltic countries, Europe, USA *Comments:* also Dance film production, theatre and opera choreography; also video and installations

Cristina Caprioli Artificial Project, CCAP
DPS, Wallingatan 21, 111 24 **Stockholm**
Tel: 8-676 9620 Fax: 8-676 9624
Internet: www.dansklotet.se
E-Mail: caprioli@dansklotet.se
artistic director Cristina Caprioli
Dancers: varies *Perfs:* 40 *No of Prods:* 2-3 *Type:* contemporary *Accomp:* live, recorded *Venues:* varies from small studios 100 to big houses 1000 *Touring:* national, international

Dansgruppen Pyramiderna
Moderna Dansteatern, Hus 103, Skeppsholmen, 111 49 **Stockholm**
Tel: 8-611 1456/3233 Fax: 8-611 9087
Internet: www.mdt.a.se
E-Mail: office@mdt.a.se
artistic director and choreographer Margaratha Åsberg; director Niklas Brunius; manager Ann Larsson
Type: post modern dance and choreographical theatre *Accomp:* live, recorded *Venues:* Dansteatern 130

E.L.D. Mälardalens dansensemble
Norrtullsgatan 7, 113 29 **Stockholm**
Tel: 8-346 760 Fax: 8-309 450
Internet: www.pi.se/eld-p/
E-Mail: efva.lilja@eld-p.se
administration Urban Skoglund; artistic director Efva Lilja; international coordinator Maria Morberg (maria.morberg@eld-p.se
Dancers: 4-8 *Perfs:* 90 *No of Prods:* 9 (2 new) *Type:* contemporary *Accomp:* recorded, live *Touring:* Sweden, Denmark, Germany, England, Iceland *Comments:* festivals, TV/video-productions

Greta Lindholm Dance Company
Bjurholmsgatan 9A, 116 38 **Stockholm**
Tel: 8-642 1964 Fax: 8-642 1964
E-Mail: gretalind@hotmail.com
artistic director Greta Lindholm
Dancers: 3-7 *No of Prods:* 1 *Type:* contemporary *Accomp:* live, recorded *Comments:* international festivals, dance concerts including body-percussion, bare foot tap dancing

Jens Östberg
DPS, Wallingatan 21, 111 24 **Stockholm**
Tel: 8-676 9620 Fax: 8-676 9624
E-Mail: jensostberg@hotmail.com
Dancers: 5-10 *Perfs:* 60 *Type:* contemporary, dance theatre *Accomp:* live, recorded *Touring:* Sweden, Israel, Norway, Netherlands, Germany *Comments:* temporary ensemble on a project basis

K. Kvarnström & Co
c/o DPS, Wallingatan 21, 111 24 **Stockholm**
Tel: 8-676 9620 Fax: 8-676 9624
Internet: www.dansklotet.se
E-Mail: dps@dansklotet.se
contact Kenneth Kvarnström
Dancers: varies per production *Perfs:* 25 *No of Prods:* 1 *Type:* contemporary dance
Touring: national, international

KORDA moving Arts
Gästrikegatan 17, 2tr, 113 62 **Stockholm**
Tel: 8-308 378 Fax: 8-315 884
E-Mail: korda@algonet.se
choreographer Linda Forsman; composer/light & set designer Lou Lundqvist
Dancers: 1 *No of Prods:* 1 stage production *Type:* new dance *Accomp:* recorded, live (specially composed electro-acoustic pieces) *Touring:* Sweden

Örjan Andersson Dance Co.
Box 15089, 104 65 **Stockholm**
Tel: 8-676 9620 Fax: 8-676 9624
E-Mail: ads@dansklotet.se
producer Mia Larsson; artistic leader Örjan Andersson
Dancers: 6 *Perfs:* 20 *No of Prods:* 3 *Type:* contemporary
Touring: Sweden, Europe

Örjan Andersson Dance Company
Box 15089, 104 65 **Stockholm**
Tel: 8-676 9620 (DPS) Fax: 8-676 9624 (DPS)
Internet: www.dansklotet.se
E-Mail: adc@dansklotet.se
artistic director Örjan Andersson; producer Mia Larsson
Dancers: 3-6 *Perfs:* 30 *No of Prods:* 3 *Type:* contemporary
Touring: national, international

Per Jonsson Dance Company
Folkkulturcentrum, Skeppsholmen, 111 49 **Stockholm**
Tel: 8-611 9801
choreographer & artistic director Per Jonsson
Type: contemporary *Accomp:* recorded, live
Touring: Sweden, UK

Philippe Blanchard
c/o 5th Art Productions, Götgatan 23, 4th floor, 116 46 **Stockholm**
Tel: 8-5560 0181 Fax: 8-462 0662
Internet: www.dansklotet.se
E-Mail: philippe.blanchard@stockholm.mail.telia.com
choreographer Philippe Blanchard; rehearsal director Anna Diehl; producer/administrator Åsa Edgren
Dancers: 5-7 *Perfs:* 45 *No of Prods:* 1 *Type:* modern, physical theatre *Accomp:* live *Venues:* the House of Dance, Stockholm *Touring:* Sweden, France, Scandinavia, Germany, Netherlands *Comments:* performance Transes Formations in collaboration with l'Orchestre de Contrebasses

Reich & Szyber
Östgötagatan 14, 116 25 **Stockholm**
Tel: 8-644 5244 Fax: 8-644 9798
Internet: www.reich-szyber.com
E-Mail: information@reich-szyber.com
choreographers, set & costume designers, directors Carina Reich, Bogdan Szyber; producer Mia Larsson
Dancers: 9 *Perfs:* 4026 *No of Prods:* 11 site specific project *Type:* performance
Accomp: live, recorded *Venues:* site specific projects, filmwork, festivals *Touring:* Sweden
Comments: for information on the Millenium Project: www.millenniumprojektet.org

Royal Swedish Ballet
Kungliga Baletten
Box 160 94, 103 22 **Stockholm**
Tel: 8-791 4300/248 8240 Fax: 8-791 4326
Internet: www.kunglingaoperan.se
general director Bengt Hall; artistic ballet director Petter Jacobsson; press officer Staffan Carlweitz (tel: 8-791 4353, fax: 8-411 6305)
Dancers: 75 *Perfs:* 100 *No of Prods:* 6 *Type:* classical, modern *Accomp:* live *Venues:* main stage 1100, Rotunda stage 150, Drottningholm Court theatre, Confidencen Teatern *Comments:* see also Opera and Orchestras (Kungliga Hovkapellet)

Tiger Dance Company
c/o Signe Eliasson, Pick & Pack Production, Karlbergsvägen 36B, 113 27 **Stockholm**
Tel: 8-341 910 Fax: 8-341 910
administrator Signe Eliasson; choreographer Anne Külper
Dancers: 2-7 *Perfs:* 90 *No of Prods:* 5
Type: contemporary *Accomp:* live, recorded

Virpi Pahkinen
DPS, Wallingatan 21, 111 24 **Stockholm**
Tel: 8-676 9620 Fax: 8-676 9624
Internet: www.dansklotet.se
E-Mail: pahkinen@dansklotet.se
producer Birgitta Ström; coordinator & tour manager Ulrika Nilsson
Dancers: 1-5 *Perfs:* 45 *No of Prods:* 4 *Type:* contemporary *Accomp:* live, recorded *Touring:* Mexico, USA, Lebanon, Germany, France, Austria, Denmark, Finland, Sweden

SWITZERLAND (+41)

Overall Bewegungstheater
Schönbuchstr. 14, 4055 **Basel**
Tel: 61-273 4300 Fax: 61-273 4301
E-Mail: hpjundt@datacom.ch
contact H P Jundt
Dancers: 5 *Perfs:* 10 *No of Prods:* 1 *Type:* modern *Accomp:* live, recorded *Touring:* Switzerland, Southern Germany

Tanztheater Basel
Postfach, 4010 **Basel**
Tel: 61-295 1100/1448 Fax: 61-295 1595
Internet: www.theater-basel.ch
E-Mail: tanztheater@theater-basel.ch
administrative director Dirk Elwert; ballet director/choreographer Joachim Schlömer
Dancers: 19 *Perfs:* 60 *No of Prods:* 5 *Type:* modern *Accomp:* live *Venues:* Stadttheater 1015, Komödie 579, kleine Bühne 300 *Touring:* Europe

BabaJaga
Könizstr. 27, 3008 **Bern**
Tel: 31-382 2044 Fax: 31-382 2044
contact Barbara Winzenried
Dancers: 3 *Perfs:* 10-20 *Type:* dance-theatre, modern dance *Accomp:* recorded, live *Venues:* Dancezentale 1000 *Touring:* national

Ballett des Stadttheaters Bern
Nägeligasse 1, 3000 **Bern** 7
Tel: 31-312 1711 Fax: 31-312 3670
Internet: www.euroflash.com/berne-ballet
Direktor Eike Gramss; stellv. Direktor und Chiefdisponent Jochen Sostmann; Presse Katrin Diem; Ballettdirektor Félix Duméril; Ballettmeister Oliver Dähler; Leitung Schauspiel Nicola May, Urs Schaub
Dancers: 14 *Perfs:* 23 ballet + 20 musicals *No of Prods:* 3 + musical production *Type:* neoclassical, contemporary *Accomp:* live, recorded *Venues:* Stadttheater 730 *Touring:* Switzerland *Comments:* see also Opera and Drama

Dance Company L.E.S
Gutenbergstr. 52, 3011 **Bern**
Tel: 31-372 1903 Fax: 31-372 8415
E-Mail: nivo@bluewin.ch
künstlerische Leitung Nicole Voyat
Dancers: 5-10 *Perfs:* 20 *No of Prods:* 7 *Type:* modern jazz *Accomp:* recorded *Touring:* Switzerland

LYNX
Worblentalstr. 8, 3063 **Bern-Ittingen**
Tel: 31-921 8485 Fax: 31-921 8485
contact Monique Schnyder, Christian Mattis
Dancers: 5 *Perfs:* 20 *No of Prods:* 5 *Type:* movement theatre *Accomp:* live, recorded *Touring:* worldwide

Schweizer Kammerballet/Ballet de Chambre Suisse
c/o Promenade 24, 5200 **Brugg**
Tel: 56-4410 0261 Fax: 56-411 1626
ballet director Jean Deroc; choreographer Enrico Musmeci; ballet master t.b.a.; pr Büro Georg Weber
Dancers: varies *Perfs:* 10-15 *No of Prods:* 3 *Type:* classical, jazz, modern dance *Accomp:* live, recorded *Venues:* Colombo Dance Factory, Zürich *Touring:* national, international *Comments:* PR Büro: Stamfenbach str. 69, 8001 Zürich, Tel: 1-350 2828, Fax: 1-350 2825, E-mail: BGW@suisseonline.ch

Alias Compagnie
14 Av. de Sécheron, 1202 **Genève**
Tel: 22-731 2361 Fax: 22-731 2460
director Guilherme Botelho; administration Samia Ben Hamida
Dancers: 5 *Perfs:* 30-35 *No of Prods:* 7 *Type:* contemporary *Accomp:* recorded *Touring:* Switzerland, Europe, Canada

Ballet du Grand Théâtre de Genève
11 bd du Théâtre, 1211 **Genève**
Tel: 22-418 3000 (admin)/3130 (booking) Fax: 22-418 3001
Internet: www.geneveopera.ch
E-Mail: ballet.sec@geneveopera.ch
general director Renée Auphan; direction of the ballet François Passard, Giorgio Mancini
Dancers: 22 *Perfs:* 70-80 *No of Prods:* 6 *Type:* contemporary, neo-classical *Accomp:* live, recorded *Venues:* Bâtiment des Forces Motrices (Geneva) 980 *Touring:* Germany, France, Switzerland, Italy, China, Japan, Egypt *Commenst:* see also Opera and Drama

Compagnie Laura Tanner
Rue Verte 11, 1205 **Genève**
Tel: 22-320 9390/312 2036 Fax: 22-312 2036
artistic director Laura Tanner; administrator Diane Baud
Dancers: 5-7 *Perfs:* 20 *No of Prods:* 3 *Type:* contemporary dance *Accomp:* tape (own composer) *Touring:* national, France, Netherlands *Comments:* independent dance company works with visual artist

METAL-COMPAGNIE Fabienne Abramovich
40 rue de la Servette, 1202 **Genève**
Tel: 22-733 0719 Fax: 22-733 0719
artistic director Fabienne Abramovich
Dancers: 5-7/solo *Perfs:* 10-30 *No of Prods:* 1 *Type:* contemporary *Accomp:* recorded *Touring:* France
Comments: currently planning the building of a new venue for contemporary dance with the ADC (Association of Contemporary Dance)

Vertical Danse – Compagnie Noemi Lapzeson
8, rue de la Coulouvrenière, 1204 **Genève**
Tel: 22-329 4200 Fax: 22-329 6868
administration Patrick Pioggia; artistic director Noemi Lapzeson
Dancers: 2-7 *Perfs:* 10-60 *No of Prods:* 10 *Type:* contemporary *Accomp:* live, recorded *Touring:* Switzerland, Europe, South America

Tanzprojekt Elfi Schäfer-Schafroth
Sekretariat Ursula Schmid, Postfach, 8522 **Häuslenen**
Tel: 52-721 6980 Fax: 52-721 7630
Internet: www.tanznetz.ch/elfi
secretary Ursula Schmid; artistic director Elfi Schäfer-Schafroth
Dancers: 1-5 *Perfs:* 20 *No of Prods:* 1 large + several small productions *Type:* modern dance *Accomp:* recorded, live *Touring:* Switzerland, USA, Germany, Austria
Comments: second address: Dolderstr. 32, 8032 Zürich, Tel: 1-262 1090, Fax: 1-262 1090

Compagnie Drift Jaccard/Schelling/Bertinelli
Bergstr. 12a, 8700 **Küsnacht**
Tel: 1-910 4570 Fax: 1-910 4570
Internet: www.tanznetz.ch
E-Mail: drift@access.ch
music Ernst Thoma, Massimo Bertinelli, François Gendre; agent (Germany) Claudia Bauer (tel: +49 7141-903 383, fax: +49 7141-903 380)
Dancers: 3-5 *Perfs:* 50 *No of Prods:* 5 (1 new) *Type:* contemporary dance theatre *Accomp:* recorded *Touring:* Switzerland, Germany, France, Russia *Comments:* co-productions with Rote Fabrik Zürich, Theaterhaus, Gessnerallee

OBJET-FAX
10 rue de la Côte, 2300 **La Chaux-de-Fonds**
Tel: 32-968 2846 Fax: 32-968 2846
E-Mail: objfax@bluwin.ch
administration & artistic direction Ricardo Rozo, Jean-Claude Pellaton
Dancers: 5 *Perfs:* 50-60 *No of Prods:* 3 *Type:* contemporary dance *Accomp:* recorded (original music) *Touring:* Europe, Colombia, Venezuela, Mexico, Brasil
Comments: work with company in Bogota: EL Contragolpe, Carrera calle o n° 2-73, Santafé de Bogota, Colómbia, Tel/Fax: +57 1-286 5320

Sinopia Ensemble de Dance
Case postale 1354, 2301 **La Chaux-de-Fonds**
Tel: 32-913 9983 Fax: 32-913 9982
general manager/choreographer Etienne Frey; secretary Glorianne Gazareth
Dancers: 2-12 *Type:* contemporary *Accomp:* recorded
Touring: Switzerland, worldwide

Béjart Ballet Lausanne
Chemin du Presbytère, CP 25, 1000 **Lausanne** 22
Tel: 21-641 6464 Fax: 21-641 6466
Internet: www.bejart.ch
E-Mail: admin@bejart.ch
director Maurice Béjart; administrator Emmanuel de Bourgknecht
Dancers: 32 *Perfs:* 100 *No of Prods:* 3 *Type:* contemporary *Accomp:* live, recorded *Touring:* worldwide

Compagnie Fabienne Berger
Ch. de la Motte 6, 1018 **Lausanne**
Tel: 21-351 3063 Fax: 21-351 3064
E-Mail: anton.production@span.ch
administration Fabienne Rossier; artistic director Fabienne Berger; production Xavier Munger; music composer Jean-Philippe Héritier
Dancers: 2-6 *Perfs:* 31+ *No of Prods:* 2 (1 new) *Type:* contemporary *Accomp:* recorded, live *Venues:* Octogone (Lausanne) 400 *Touring:* Europe, USA, Moscow, Eastern Europe

Compagnie Philippe Saire
Case Postale 110, 1000 **Lausanne** 20
Tel: 21-626 3812 Fax: 21-626 3814
Internet: www.philippesaire.ch
E-Mail: cie.saire@bluewin.ch
directeur artistique Philippe Saire; administratrice Claudine Geneletti, Murielle Perritaz; promotion North America Natacha Noverraz
Dancers: 10 *Perfs:* 60-80 *No of Prods:* 4 (from a repertoire of 16) *Type:* contemporary *Accomp:* recorded, live *Venues:* Théâtre Sévelin 36, Lausanne 180 *Touring:* USA, Switzerland, Europe, South America
Comments: professional independent dance company

ZÜRCHER BALLETT

Artistic Director **Heinz Spoerli**

Contact **Zürcher Ballett**
Falkenstrasse 1
8008 Zürich
Phone +41 1 268 64 62
Fax +41 1 268 65 84

Teatro Sunil
Viale Cassarate 4, 6900 **Lugano**
Tel: 91-923 2850 Fax: 91-922 6285
E-Mail: sunil@ticino.com
artistic directors Maria Bonzanigo, Daniele Finzi-Pasca
Dancers: 2 *Perfs:* 150 *No of Prods:* 8 (6 theatre, 2 dance) *Type:* contemporary *Accomp:* live, recorded *Touring:* worldwide *Comments:* all the shows are represented in different languages – Italian, French, German, Spanish, English and Portuguese; see also Drama

luzerntanz – Choreographisches Zentrum im Luzerner Theater
Luzerner Theater, Theaterstr. 2, 6002 **Luzern**
Tel: 41-210 3363 Fax: 41-210 3367
Internet: www.luzerner-theater.ch
Directrisse Barbara Mundel; administrative director Adrian Balmer; artistic director Walter Heun; production manager Beatrice Rossi; dramaturgy Brigitte Knöss
Perfs: 65 *Type:* contemporary *Venues:* Theater 558, UG, La Forumi, Boa-Halle, KKL *Comments:* produce, co-produce, hosts international and national groups

Compagnie 100% Acrylique
CP 126, 1213 **Onex-Genève**
Tel: 22-300 2363 Fax: 22-300 2363/328 8504
directrice Evelyne Castellino (tel: +33 4-5039 7891, fax: +33 4-5039 7897); administration Philippe Clerc (tel: 22-328 8504, 87 Bd. Carl Vogt, 1205 Genève)
Dancers: 6-12 *Perfs:* 40 *No of Prods:* 1-2 *Type:* dance theatre video *Venues:* Théâtre de la Parfumerie *Touring:* Switzerland, France *Comments:* venue shared with 3 other companies; venue address: Théâtre de la Parfumerie, 7 ch. de la Gravière, 1227 Acacias-Geneve

Linga Danse Projet Katarzyna Gdaniec, Marco Cantalupo
c/o L'Octogone theatre, 41 ave. de Lavaux, 1009 **Pully/Lausanne**
Tel: 21-721 3603 Fax: 31-721 3616
directors Katarzyna Gdaniec, Marco Cantalupo; administration Marianne Hausmann
Dancers: 7 *Perfs:* 30-40 *Type:* contemporary *Accomp:* recorded, live *Venues:* L'Octogone 455 *Touring:* Europe, Middle East, USA, Canada

3 X 1 Tanzkompanie
Kamorstr. 8, 9400 **Rorschach**
Tel: 71-841 1133 Fax: 71-841 1123
Direktion, künstlerische Leitung Ruth Ackermann, John Brooks
Dancers: 4-10 *Perfs:* 10 *No of Prods:* 1 *Type:* contemporary *Accomp:* recorded *Venues:* Dance Loft Studio Theatre 80, Tanzhaus Wasserwerk Zürich *Touring:* national

Compagnie Bruno Verdi
CP 284, 1950 **Sion** 2
Tel: 27-934 3858/79-417 0931 (mobile) Fax: 27-934 3858
Internet: www.regard.ch/bruno-verdi
E-Mail: cie.brunoverdi@bluewin.ch
artistic director Bruno Verdi
Dancers: 4+ *Perfs:* 30 *No of Prods:* 1 *Type:* new dance, multimedia dance *Accomp:* live *Touring:* Europe, worldwide *Comments:* offers professional training (3 years); competition every 3 years all types of techniques

Teatrodanza Tiziana Arnaboldi
Via Arbibecchio 3, 6600 **Solduno**
Tel: 91-751 8724 Fax: 91-751 0393
contact Tiziana Arnaboldi
Dancers: 5-6 *Perfs:* 30 *No of Prods:* 1 every 2 years *Type:* drama-based contemporary dance *Accomp:* recorded (original composition) *Touring:* Switzerland, France, Italy, Germany, Spain

Ballettensemble des Stadttheaters St. Gallen
Museumstrasse 24, 9004 **St. Gallen**
Tel: 71-242 0505 Fax: 71-242 0507
Internet: www.stadttheaterstgallen.ch
Geschäftsführender Direktor Werner Signer; Ballettmeister Jens-Peter Urbich
Dancers: 14 *Perfs:* 25 (excluding studio performances) *No of Prods:* 3 music theatre, 1 ballet, 2 studio production *Type:* classical *Accomp:* live, recorded *Venues:* Stadttheater 741, Studiobühne 120 *Touring:* national *Comments:* see also Opera and Drama

labor G.RAS
c/o Susanne Braun, Schiffmühleweg 24, 5417 **Untersiggenthal**
Tel: 56-288 0748 Fax: 56-288 0748
E-Mail: labor888@aol.com
contacts Susanne Braun (booking: Switzerland, Europe), Renate Graziadei (booking: Germany, Europe)
Dancers: 3 *Perfs:* 20-30 *No of Prods:* 3 *Type:* dance theatre, contemporary *Accomp:* recorded, composed *Touring:* Europe *Comments:* second address: labor G.RAS, Annenstrasse 3, 20359 Hamburg, Germany, Tel/Fax: 49 40-316 057

Compagnie Nomades le Loft Vevey
Chaussée de la Guinguette, 1800 **Vevey**
Tel: 21-922 8069 Fax: 21-922 2002
E-Mail: nomades@span.ch
administration Alain Vuignier; artistic direction Florence Faure, Serge Campardon
Dancers: 6 *Perfs:* 200 *No of Prods:* 29 *Type:* contemporary *Accomp:* live, recorded *Venues:* Théâtre de Vevey 750 *Touring:* national, international *Comments:* regularly offers lectures, workshops and training

aka! tanat
Kirchweg 28, 8404 **Winterthur**
Tel: 52-242 1961 Fax: 52-242 1961
contact Ana Tajouiti
Dancers: varies *Perfs:* 10 *No of Prods:* 7 *Type:* contemporary dance *Accomp:* recorded, live *Venues:* Theater am Gleis 100

Carambole Dance & Theatre
Hägelerweg 7, 8055 **Zürich**
Tel: 1-461 6707 Fax: 1-461 6707
E-Mail: carambole@befoee.ch
artistic directors/choreographers Silvano Mozzini, Christiane Loch
Dancers: 2-3 *Perfs:* 25-30 *No of Prods:* 5 *Type:* movement theatre, dance theatre *Touring:* Europe, Egypt *Comments:* Intern. management, Beatrice Rossi/ 4 ARTS, Eröd u. 20, H-1027 Budapest, Tel/Fax: +36 1-201 6430

Compagnie n'est-ce pas
Seefeldstrasse 192, 8008 **Zürich**
Tel: 1-422 1881 Fax: 1-422 2075
Internet: www.tanznetz.ch
E-Mail: bettinah@access.ch
Choreografin Bettina Holzhausen
Dancers: 2-4 *Type:* contemporary dance *Touring:* national, Europe

Denise Lampart Companie
Kalkbreitestr. 131, 8003 **Zürich**
Tel: 1-451 5072 Fax: 1-451 5126
E-Mail: stratos@span.ch
choreographer, artistic director Denise Lampart; managing director Stratos Hatzipanagiotidis
Dancers: 1-11 *Perfs:* 70-80 *No of Prods:* 4-5 (incl 1 with Berner Ballet) *Type:* contemporary dance theatre *Accomp:* live *Touring:* Europe, USA

LENAS
Forchstr. 148, 8032 **Zürich**
Tel: 1-381 0542 Fax: 1-422 6878
Internet: www.lenas.ch
E-Mail: lenas@lenas.ch
contact Dinah & Heinz Geiger
Perfs: 30 *No of Prods:* 4 *Type:* contemporary dance-theatre, interdisciplinary *Accomp:* live *Touring:* Switzerland, Germany, France, USA

Ventura Dance Company
Zeltweg 87, 8032 **Zürich**
Tel: 1-252 5437 Fax: 1-252 5437
Internet: www.home.ch/~spaw1167/
E-Mail: ventura@span.ch
artistic director Pablo Ventura; assistant director Arlette Kunz
Dancers: 4 *Perfs:* 1 *No of Prods:* 1 *Type:* contemporary, modern *Accomp:* recorded *Touring:* Switzerland, Spain *Comments:* funded by city of Zürich

zet Tanztheater (zornige elfen träumen)
Ottikerstr. 23, 8006 **Zürich**
Tel: 1-362 0103 Fax: 1-362 0103
director/choreographer Elvi Leu; administrator Linda Moser
Dancers: 1-5 *Perfs:* 10-15 *No of Prods:* 4 *Type:* dance-theatre *Accomp:* recorded, live *Touring:* Switzerland, Germany, Eastern Europe *Comments:* didactic programs and work with children (age 8-15)

Zürcher Ballett
Falkenstrasse 1, 8008 **Zürich**
Tel: 1-268 6462 Fax: 1-268 6584
Ballettdirektor und Chefchoreograph Heinz Spoerli
Dancers: 37 *Perfs:* 55 + 40 touring *No of Prods:* 7 *Type:* classical, modern *Accomp:* live *Venues:* Opernhaus 1200 *Touring:* Germany, Spain, South Africa
Comments: see also Opera and Orchestras

TURKEY (+90)

Ankara State Ballet
Ankara Devlet Balesi
Atatürk Bulvari N° 50, Ulus, 06050 **Ankara**
Tel: 312-311 2430 Fax: 312-311 9731
general intendant Hasan Hüseyin Akbulut; music director Antonio Pirolli; ballet director Fahrratten Güvan
Dancers: 70 *Venues:* Opera stage 718, Operetta stage 426 *Comments:* includes a 'Modern Dance Company' (15/16 dancers)

General Directorate of State Opera and Ballet
Devlet Opera ve Balesi Genel Müdürlügü
Atatürk Bulvari N° 50, Ulus, 06050 **Ankara**
Tel: 312-311 2430 Fax: 312-311 9731
general intendant Hasan Hüseyin Akbulut

State Folk Dance Group
Devlet Halk Danslari Toplulugu
Atatürk Kültür Merkezi, Hipodrom, **Ankara**
Tel: 312-341 0775 Fax: 312-341 1926
president Mustafa Turan

Contemporary Lovers of Mevlana
Inonu Mahallesi Uftade Sokak, No. 3/5, Elmadal, **Istanbul**
Tel: 212-261 3092 Fax: 212-249 5708
contact Carole Douglas

Istanbul State Ballet
Istanbul Devlet Balesi
Atatürk Kültür Merkezi, Taksim, 80124 **Istanbul**
Tel: 212-243 2011 Fax: 212-245 3916
director Yekta Kara
Venues: Grand Hall 1300, Concert Hall 500

Izmir State Ballet
Izmir Devlet Balesi
Konak, **Izmir**
Tel: 232-484 6450 Fax: 232-441 0173
director Nükhet Sevger
Venues: Opera stage 410

Mersin State Ballet
Mersin Devlet Balesi
Cumhuriyet Alani, Eski Halkevi Binasi, **Mersin**
Tel: 324-238 0493 Fax: 324-237 7119
director Erdogan Sanal
Venues: Opera stage 588

UKRAINE (+380)

Bukovyna Folk Song & Dance Ensemble
Philharmonia Plaza 10, 274000 **Czernivtsi**
Tel: 372-35846/24930
artistic director Andriy Kushnironko

Dnipropetrovsk Opera Ballet
K. Marx Prospect 72, 320000 **Dnipropetrovsk**
Tel: 562-445 667
director Yuriy Chayka

Slavutych Folk Song and Dance Ensemble
Pr. Kalinina 47, 320008 **Dnipropetrovsk**
Tel: 562-422 513/423 326 Fax: 562-422 613
artistic director Heorhiy Klovok

Donetsk Opera Ballet
Artema St. 82, 340055 **Donetsk**
Tel: 622-556 915
director Valeriy Slasevych

Khaytarma Folk Song & Dance Ensemble of the Crimean Tatars
Theater Plaza, Pushkin Theater, 334320 **Evpatoria**
Tel: 6569-32406/62350
artistic director Sevzy Belanov

Hutsul Folk Song & Dance Ensemble
Les Kurbas St. 3, 284000 **Ivano-Frankivsk**
Tel: 342-23156/64285
artistic director Petro Kniazevych

Kharkiv Opera Ballet
Sumska St. 25, 310057 **Kharkiv**
Tel: 572-477 216
director Volodymyr Pantiushev

Kaiyna Ukrainian Folklore Ensemble
Richna St. 4, 252135 **Kiev (Kyiv)**
Tel: 44-244 4945/227 7069
artistic director Valeriy Debelyi

Kiev Theatre of Classical Ballet
Richna St. 4, 252135 **Kiev (Kyiv)**
Tel: 44-216 4871/229 6146 Fax: 44-216 4871
artistic director Valeriy Kovtun

National Opera of Ukraine Ballet
Volodymyrska St. 50, 252003 **Kiev (Kyiv)**
Tel: 44-225 5134
director Viktor Lytvnov

Virsky Ukrainian State Dance Company
Shevlchenko Blvd. 50/52, 252032 **Kiev (Kyiv)**
Tel: 44-274 8123/228 5812 Fax: 44-216 8316
artistic director Myroslav Vantukh

Zoryano Folklore Ensemble
Ordzhonikidze St. 8, 318050 **Kirovohrad**
Tel: 522-241 200/248 143
Fax: 522-241 200
artistic director Anatoliy Kryokhyzha

Lviv Opera Ballet
Kulisha St. 6A, 290058 **Lviv**
Tel: 322-728 362/561
director Herman Yusupov

Odessa Opera Ballet
Tchaikovsky Provulck 1, 270026 **Odessa**
Tel: 482-224 904 Fax: 482-246 762
director Valentin Semenov

Poltava Folk Song and Dance Ensemble
Komsomolska St. 37/19, 314011 **Poltava**
Tel: 53-273 127/229 507
artistic director Pavlo Baklanov

Ternopil Folk Dance Ensemble Nadzbruchanka
Ostrovsky St. 9, 282000 **Ternopil**
Tel: 3522-26109
artistic director Yuriy Pats

UNITED KINGDOM (+44)

Adonais Ballet Company
183 Aston Clinton Road, Weston Turville, **Aylesbury** HP22 5AD
Tel: 1296-630 390/1252-543 838
Fax: 1296-630 390/1252-543 838
Internet: www.zynet.co.uk/pebbles/adonais
artistic director Jan Kitteridge; administrative director Graham Mitchell; technical manager Brian O'Carroll
Dancers: 10-12 *Perfs:* 100 per year *No of Prods:* 1 per season (new) *Venues:* UK, Ireland, international *Touring:* educational outreach programmes

In Transit Dance Company
20 Belmont Church Road, **Belfast (Northern Ireland)** BT4 3FF
Tel: 28-9045 1846/9028 2129
director Sandi Cutberth
Type: contemporary

Birmingham Royal Ballet
Thorp Street, **Birmingham** B5 4AU
Tel: 121-622 2555
Fax: 121-689 3070 (admin)/3071 (press & marketing)
Internet: www.brb.org.uk
E-Mail: info@brb.org.uk
administrative director Derek Purnell; artistic director David Bintley
Dancers: 60 *Perfs:* varies *No of Prods:* 10+ *Type:* classical *Accomp:* live *Venues:* Birmingham Hippodrome 1857 *Touring:* national, international *Comments:* regular seasons throughout England; established education programme; now independent of the Royal Opera House; principal sponsor Powergen

Kokuma Dance Theatre
418-419 The Custard Factory, Gibbs Street, Digbeth, **Birmingham** B9 4AA
Tel: 121-608 7744 Fax: 121-608 7755
E-Mail: kokum@dial.pipex.com
artistic director Patrick Acogny; executive producer Wanjiku Nyachae; production manager t.b.a.; outreach development oficer Pam Johnson; programme administrator Rachel Harrision; administrative assistant Anita Clarke
Dancers: 6, 3 musicians *Perfs:* 40 *No of Prods:* 3 *Type:* African Caribbean & contemporary fusion *Accomp:* live *Venues:* small-mid scale 400 *Touring:* national *Comments:* also provides workshops for schools & colleges

Divas
20 Montpelier Street, **Brighton** BN1 3DJ
Tel: 1273-327 894/235 532 Fax: 1273-327 894/235 533
E-Mail: divas.com@virgin.net
administrator/contact Emma Haughton; artistic directors Liz Aggiss, Billy Cowie
Dancers: 1 (+ 2 live music) *No of Prods:* 2 *Type:* cabaret style dance with text, songs, humour: programme can be supported by dance on screen films by Divas *Accomp:* live (specially composed), vocals *Venues:* small scale touring venues and festivals *Touring:* Europe *Comments:* supported by the British Council, South East Arts

High Spin Dance Company
Carousel, Community Base, 113/117 Queens Road, **Brighton** BN1 3XG
Tel: 1273-234 734 Fax: 1273-234 735
administrators Liz Hall, Katie Symes; combined arts workers Mark Richardson, Ingrid Ashberry, Alice Fox; marketing/development Esther Gill
Dancers: 10 *Perfs:* 6-10 *No of Prods:* 1 *Type:* dance-theatre *Accomp:* live, recorded *Venues:* capacity up to 500 *Touring:* UK

Belinda Neave
67 Richards Terrace, Roath, **Cardiff (Wales)** CF2 1RW
Tel: 29-2048 2772 Fax: 29-2048 2772
artistic director Belinda Neave; technical director John Thorne
Type: contemporary, mixed-media *Comments:* please contact for further information; Belinda Neave currently working as development director for the Welsh Independent Dance (q.v.)

Diversions Dance Company
Ebenezer Studio, Charles Street, **Cardiff (Wales)** CF10 2GA
Tel: 29-2022 8855 Fax: 29-2022 7176
E-Mail: diversions@diversionsdance.co.uk
administration manager Jocelyn Elmer; director Roy Campbell-Moore; publicity officer Louise Piper; marketing Karen Pimbley; associate director Ann Sholem; technical manager Grant Barden
Dancers: 8 *Perfs:* 55 *No of Prods:* 3 *Type:* contemporary dance *Accomp:* live, recorded *Venues:* mid-large scale up to 1500 *Touring:* worldwide *Comments:* national dance company of Wales; also have educational/outreach programme

Earthfall
Chapter Arts Centre, Market Road, **Cardiff (Wales)** CF5 1QE
Tel: 29-2022 1314/7930-402 820 (mobile)
Fax: 29-2034 2259
Internet: www.dspace.dial.pipex.com/earthfall
E-Mail: earthfall@dial.pipex.com
artistic directors Jessica Cohen, James Ennis; administrative director Ruth Leary
Dancers: 4-10 *Perfs:* 55 *No of Prods:* 2 *Type:* physical dance/theatre *Accomp:* live *Venues:* all scales (100-1200) *Touring:* worldwide *Comments:* agents for Europe: H.D.V. Productions, Arnhem, Netherlands, Tel: +31 48-142 5709; agents for UK: UK Arts International, Tel: 1905-26424, E-mail: janryan@amendmnt.demon.co.uk, Internet: www.ukarts.com

Jenny Barbieri & Dancers
c/o Welsh Independent Dance, Chapter, Market Road, Canton, **Cardiff (Wales)** CF5 1QE
Tel: 29-2038 7314 Fax: 29-2038 7314
choreographer & aritstic director Jenny Barbieri
Type: contemporary dance; often incorporates other dance disciplines such as Brazilian dance and tango Argentino *Comments:* sometimes collaborates with theatre artists and musicians; during 99/00 season Jenny Barbieri is teaching and studying in Buenos Aires and the company will not be producing work in Europe

Striking Attitudes
116 Kimberley Road, Penylan, **Cardiff (Wales)** CF2 5DN
Tel: 29-2049 5079
artistic director Caroline Lamb
Dancers: 6-8 *Perfs:* varies *No of Prods:* varies *Type:* dance theatre (contemporary/physical theatre) *Accomp:* recorded *Venues:* small-mid scale *Touring:* national, Europe *Comments:* works with dancers who can act and actors who can move; Use dance/movement, text, video and a wide variety of music; project funded company

Scottish Dance Theatre
Dundee Rep Theatre, Tay Square, **Dundee (Scotland)** DD1 1PB
Tel: 1382-342 600 Fax: 1382-228 609
Internet: www.sdt.co.uk
E-Mail: sdt@dircon.co.uk
artistic director Janet Smith; senior administrator Amanda Chinn; administrator Amanda Roberts
Dancers: 8 *Perfs:* 32-33 *No of Prods:* 4 *Type:* contemporary *Accomp:* recorded, live *Venues:* Dundee Rep Theatre 450 *Touring:* national, international *Comments:* see also Drama and Venues

Scottish Ballet
261 West Princes Street, **Glasgow (Scotland)** G4 9EE
Tel: 141-331 2931/333 1092
Fax: 141-331 2629/353 0084
Internet: www.scottishballet.co.uk
E-Mail: promo@scottishballet.co.uk
general manager (Scottish Ballet/Scottish Opera) Norman Quirk; artistic director Robert North; assistant artistic director Kenn Burke; music director Alan Barker; director of marketing & development Roberta Doyle
Dancers: 36 *Perfs:* 145 *No of Prods:* 3 full lenth, several mixed programmes *Type:* classical and modern ballet *Accomp:* live (orchestral accompaniment), recorded *Venues:* Theatre Royal, Glasgow 1547, Edinburgh Festival Theatre 1769, Hull New Theatre 1087, Theatre Royal, Newcastle 1208, His Majesty's, Aberdeen 1339, Theatre Royal, Norwich, MacRoberte Centre, Sterling *Touring:* national (also medium & small scale venues), international *Comments:* various educational activities: creative dance workshops, theatre insights, lecture demonstrations and evening classes for all abilities; affiliated with the Dance School of Scotland; freelance orchestra, 40-70 musicians

Timbala Music and Dance, La
13 Small Lees Road, Ripponden, **Halifax** HX6 4DZ
Tel: 1422-825 273 Fax: 1422-824 939
E-Mail: admin@latimbala.demon.co.uk
director Christian Weaver
Dancers: 4 (contracted per performance) *Perfs:* varies *No of Prods:* 4 *Type:* Afro Cuban based work, rumba, congo, orisa dances, carnival with other contemporary, experimental choreographic elements *Accomp:* live (6 percussionists/vocalists) *Touring:* England, Germay, European Festival tour *Comments:* Cuban address: Perez 465, entre Melones y Guasabacoa, Lugano, 10 de Octubre, Habana, Cuba; see also MOD

Akshaya Dance Theatre
20 Brisbane Road, **Ilford** IG1 4SR
Tel: 20-8554 4054 Fax: 20-8554 4054
E-Mail: pushkala@iname.com
artistic director Pushkala Gopal
Dancers: varies from 2-6 *No of Prods:* 2-6 *Type:* classical South-Indian dance-theatre *Accomp:* live and/or recorded *Touring:* national, international *Comments:* workshops and residencies available

Ludus Dance Agency & Company
Assembly Rooms, King Street, **Lancaster** LA1 1RE
Tel: 1524-35936/389 901 Fax: 1524-847 744
E-Mail: ludus@ecna.org
director Deborah Barnard; head of dance development Hannah Curr; head of touring Jacqueline Greaves; head of finance Joan Dowthwaite
Dancers: 4 + 1 stage manager *Perfs:* 120 *No of Prods:* 1 *Type:* dance-theatre aimed at young people & first-time dance audiences *Accomp:* specially commissioned music on tape *Comments:* Britain's longest established company providing dance performances, educational workshops and community performances for young people; Ludus as a dance agency provides dance development services for Lancashire and is also a partner in Dance North West – the national dance agency

Charnock Company, The
Spa Arts Services, 40 Clarendon Square, **Leamington Spa** CV32 5QZ
Tel: 1926-339 640 Fax: 1926-330 747
E-Mail: gvs@spa-arts.demon.co.uk
artistic director Nigel Charnock; producer Gwen Van Spijk; executive producer Anthony Peppiatt
Dancers: 1-5 *Perfs:* 50 *No of Prods:* 2 *Type:* multi-skilled physical theatre *Accomp:* recorded, live *Venues:* small-mid scale *Comments:* workshops available

Claire Russ Ensemble
SPA Arts Services, GFF, 40 Clarendon Square, **Leamington Spa** CV32 5QZ
Tel: 1926-339 640 Fax: 1926-330 747
E-Mail: gvs@spa-arts.demon.co.uk
producer Gwen Van Spijk; artistic director Claire Russ
Dancers: 5 *Perfs:* 14 *No of Prods:* 1 *Type:* contemporary dance performance incorporating fashion *Accomp:* recorded, live *Touring:* international particularly Europe *Comments:* funded by National Dance Agencies, West Midlands Art, Birmingham City Council, North Arts and Arts Council of England, residencies and schools work offered internationally; community dance projects

Motionhouse
13 Spencer Street, **Leamington Spa** CV31 3NE
Tel: 1926-887 052 Fax: 1926-316 734
E-Mail: admin@motionhouse.demon.co.uk
artistic directors Louise Richards, Kevin Finnan
Dancers: 3-5 *Perfs:* 30+ *No of Prods:* 2 *Type:* contemporary dance theatre *Accomp:* recorded *Venues:* capacity 50-900 *Touring:* national, international *Comments:* has educational workshops and community programmes

Northern Ballet Theatre
West Park Centre, Spen Lane, **Leeds** LS16 5BE
Tel: 113-274 5355 Fax: 113-274 5381
Internet: www.nbt.co.uk
E-Mail: press@nbtdance.demon.co.uk
executive director Mark Skipper; artistic director Stefano Giannetti; financial controller Julia Grime; music director John Pryce-Jones; head of press & pr Anna M D Izza; head of marketing Katherine Scott; head of development Andrew Whitlaw; head of education Greta Dawson
Dancers: 34 *Perfs:* 162 *No of Prods:* 5 (1 new) *Type:* classical dance drama/modern new ballets *Accomp:* live orchestral accompaniment – The Northern Ballet Theatre Orchestra *Venues:* mid-large scale *Touring:* mainly UK and international

Phoenix Dance Company
3 St Peter's Buildings, St Peter's Square, **Leeds** LS9 8AH
Tel: 113-242 3486 Fax: 113-244 4736
E-Mail: phoenix@dircon.co.uk
general manager t.b.a.; artistic director Thea Nerissa Barnes
Dancers: 10 *Perfs:* 40-50 *No of Prods:* 3-4 *Type:* contemporary dance *Accomp:* recorded, live *Venues:* capacity up to 1000 *Touring:* international *Comments:* repertory company; provides educational workshops to schools and the community and out-reach programmes

Company Kumar Saswat
132 Uppingham Road, **Leicester** LE5 0QF
Tel: 116-266 2342 (SAMPA)/276 7765 Fax: 116-276 5148
artistic directors Kumari Saswati, Kumar Saswat
Dancers: up to 10 *Perfs:* 20-24 *No of Prods:* 2 *Type:* Kathak dance & music *Accomp:* live vocals and instruments *Venues:* small to medium scale and studio spaces *Touring:* national, international *Comments:* classes in dance, music and vocals are given at SAMPA: Belper Street (off Catherine Street), Leicester, by highly-skilled, international resident teachers; SAMPA also undertake commissioned work

Glasshouses Projects
The Church House, 1 Springfield Road, Clarendon Park, **Leicester** LE2 3BB
Tel: 116-270 8636 Fax: 116-257 7825
E-Mail: jbreslin@dmu.ac.uk
artistic director Jo Breslin; administrator J Katodrytis
Dancers: 2-4 *Perfs:* 4-12 *No of Prods:* 1-3 *Type:* new dance *Accomp:* recorded, live *Venues:* small to medium scale and studio spaces, site-specific *Touring:* UK *Comments:* continuing research and development education/performance programmes

Common Ground Sign Dance Theatre
4th Floor, Hanover House, Hanover Street,
Liverpool L1 3DY
Tel: 151-707 8033/8380(minicom)/0800-515 152 (typetalk) Fax: 151-707 8033
Internet: dspace.dial.pipex.com/common.sign/
E-Mail: common.sign@dial.pipex.com
administration Barry Avison; workshop leader/performer Denise Armstrong (fax or minicom); artistic co-ordinator Isolte Avla
Dancers: 3-4 performers *Perfs:* 70+ *No of Prods:* 4 *Type:* sign dance theatre: a collaborative performance style of expressive dance, theatre, live music, sign language theatre *Accomp:* live, original *Venues:* small-mid scale *Touring:* regional throughout the year; international *Comments:* an innovative cross arts fusion taking the everyday language of the deaf and translating it into poetry of the body; devised and performed by deaf and hearing artists from different cultural and artistic backgrounds; working with the deaf, disabled, and non-disabled; also organise creative workshops and residency work

Adventures in Motion Pictures
Suite 3, 140A Gloucester Mansion, Cambridge Circus,
London WC2H 8HD
Tel: 20-7836 8716 Fax: 20-7836 8717
Internet: www.amp.uk.com
E-Mail: simon@ampltd.demon.co.uk
artistic director Matthew Bourne; producer Katharine Doré; general manager Simon Lacey; assistant artistic directors Scott Ambler, Etta Murfitt; assistant to directors Philip Belfield; company administrator Richard McDermott; managing director Robert Noble; production administrator Jonathan Stott
Dancers: 25+ *Perfs:* 400-600 *No of Prods:* 3 *Type:* dance theatre *Accomp:* live *Venues:* large scale venues *Touring:* worldwide (2000: USA, Europe, Japan) *Comments:* have educational workshops and outreach programmes; also run mailing list and friends scheme

Adzido Pan African Dance Ensemble
Canonbury Business Centre, 202 New North Road,
London N1 7BL
Tel: 20-7359 7453 Fax: 20-7704 0300
Internet: www.adzido.co.uk
E-Mail: info@adzido.co.uk
artistic director George Dzikunu; touring & marketing director Amanda Davis; executive director Zagha Oyortey; marketing manager Marian Grag; ecucation manager t.b.a.
Dancers: 24 *Perfs:* 90 *No of Prods:* 2 *Type:* traditional African *Accomp:* live onstage drummers *Venues:* capacity up to 1500 *Touring:* France, UK, Italy, North America, Spain, Austria, Canada, Republic of Ireland

Aletta Collins Dance Company
c/o independance, The Ground Floor, 130 Brixton Hill,
London SW2 1RS
Tel: 20-8678 6664 Fax: 20-8678 6641
E-Mail: farooq.independance@virgin.net
artistic director Aletta Collins; manager Farooq Chaudhry
Dancers: 4-5 (varies per project)
Type: contemporary dance with strong theatrical elements *Touring:* UK

Alexander Roy London Ballet Theatre
North House, 69 Eton Avenue, **London** NW3 3EU
Tel: 20-7586 2498 Fax: 20-7722 9942
director Alexander Roy; associate director Christina Gallea
Dancers: 12-16 *Perfs:* 50 *No of Prods:* 2 *Type:* classical/modern ballet-theatre *Accomp:* recorded, live *Venues:* capacity 500-2000 *Touring:* UK, France, Germany, Greece, USA, Canada, South East Asia, Israel, Turkey

Arc Dance Company
Chertsey Chambers, 12 Mercer Street,
London WC2H 9QD
Tel: 20-7497 0688 Fax: 20-7240 0805
E-Mail: kim.brandstrup@virgin.net
general manager Mark Ashman; artistic director Kim Brandstrup
Dancers: 10-16 *Perfs:* 20-25 *No of Prods:* 2 *Type:* dance theatre *Accomp:* live, recorded *Venues:* capacity 800-1200 *Touring:* UK *Comments:* touring only company based in London; education programme based on current productions

Badejo Arts
1 Forge Place, Ferdinand Street, **London** NW1 8DQ
Tel: 20-7482 4292 Fax: 20-7482 4292
Internet: www.badejo.demon.co.uk
E-Mail: badejoarts@badejo.demon.co.uk
general manager Chantelle Michaux; artistic director Peter Badejo
Dancers: 6 *Perfs:* 20 *No of Prods:* 2 *Type:* traditional and contemporary African dance, music, story telling *Accomp:* live (drummers) *Venues:* small to mid scale *Touring:* international *Comments:* runs annual African dance and music course called Bami Jo for professionals and beginners; available for choreography, consultancy, workshops etc

bi ma Dance Company
Marylebone Dance Studio, 12 Lisson Grove,
London NW1 6TS
Tel: 20-7258 0767 Fax: 20-7258 1868
E-Mail: bimadance@btinternet.com
artistic director Pit Fong Loh; co-director Ming Low; general manager Tim Tubbs
Dancers: up to 6 *Perfs:* 25-30 *No of Prods:* 2 *Type:* contemporary *Accomp:* recorded *Venues:* The Place 300 *Touring:* national, international *Comments:* a unique style bridging the dance idiom of east & west in an original way

Carl Campbell Dance Company 7
Thomas Calton Centre, Alpha Street,
London SE15 4NX
Tel: 20-7639 4875 (admin)/7703 2388
Fax: 20-7639 4875 (minicom)
E-Mail: ccdc7@easynet.co.uk
administrator Lynne Salter; artistic director Carl Campbell; youth development worker Karen Foster; workship leader/principal dancer Deborah Biddulph
Dancers: 4-8 *Perfs:* 20 *No of Prods:* 1-2 *Type:* contemporary Caribbean dance theatre *Accomp:* live, recorded *Venues:* small-mid scale *Comments:* specialises in dance theatre in education and as a performing art, geared towards young people; workshop residency and in service training for teachers

Cholmondeleys, The
Unit 1.1, Lafone House, The Leathermarket,
11-13 Leathermarket Street, **London** SE1 3HN
Tel: 20-7378 8800 Fax: 20-7378 8810
E-Mail: admin@cholmondeleys.freeserve.co.uk
manager Sue Wyatt; artistic director Lea Anderson; administrator Jane Corry
Dancers: 10 *Perfs:* 20 *No of Prods:* 1 *Type:* contemporary *Accomp:* live, recorded (specially commissioned) *Venues:* mid scale *Touring:* UK, Europe, USA, Africa *Comments:* funded by the Arts Council of England

City Ballet of London
3rd Floor, Lloyds Bank, 113 Leadenhall Street,
London EC3A 4AX
Tel: 20-7623 4737 Fax: 20-7623 4738
Internet: freespace.virgin.net/david.browne/cbl.htm
general manager June Gamble; artistic director Harold King; head of marketing/deputy general manager Sara Winnington; development director Judith Pleasance; management assitant/education officer Sheila Ghelani
Dancers: 22+ *No of Prods:* 2
Type: classical, neo-classical
Accomp: recorded, live *Venues:* small-mid scale *Touring:* national, international *Comments:* educational outreach programmes, including corporate training ballet banquest-corporate initiative, CBL productions (production company) and CBL Preview Club

Clerkinworks
Greenwich Dance Agency, Borough Hall, Royal Hill,
London SE10 8RE
Tel: 20-8858 6356 Fax: 20-8858 6356
E-Mail: clerkinworks@diplodocus.demon.co.uk
artistic director Máire Clerkin; general manager Donna Philips
Dancers: 8 *Perfs:* 50 *No of Prods:* 3 *Type:* contemporary & Irish dance theatre *Accomp:* recorded *Touring:* UK, Ireland *Comments:* funded by the Arts Council

DV8 Physical Theatre
c/o Arts Admin, Toynbee Studios,
28 Commercial Street, **London** E1 6LS
Tel: 20-7247 5102 Fax: 20-7247 5103
Internet: www.dv8.co.uk
administration Leonie Gombrich; artistic director Lloyd Newson; administrator Katie Judge
Dancers: 5-12 *Perfs:* 34 *No of Prods:* 1 *Type:* physical theatre *Accomp:* recorded *Venues:* 250-1000 *Touring:* international

English National Ballet
Markova House, 39 Jay Mews, **London** SW7 2ES
Tel: 20-7581 1245 Fax: 20-7225 0827
Internet: www.ballet.org.uk
E-Mail: info@ballet.org.uk
executive director Carole McPhee; artistic director Derek Deane
Dancers: 64 *Perfs:* 196 *No of Prods:* 6-8 productions in repertoire per year *Type:* classical, some modern works *Accomp:* live, some recorded music for new work *Venues:* capacity up to 11000 *Touring:* London, regional, and abroad *Comments:* also splits company into two and tours to small venues through the UK each year

European Ballet, London
18 Lynton Gardens, **London** N11 2NN
Tel: 20-8888 3675 Fax: 20-8888 3675
director Stanislav Tchassov; administrative director Inessa Tchassov; technial manager t.b.a.; press manager t.b.a.
Dancers: 15 *Perfs:* 110 per year *No of Prods:* 1
Type: classical ballet (full-length) *Accomp:* recorded, chamber orchestra *Venues:* medium-large scale theatres *Touring:* UK, Ireland *Comments:* every production involves children from the local dance schools

Featherstonehaughs, The
LF1.1, Lafone House, The Leathermarket,
11-13 Leathermarket Street, **London** SE1 3HN
Tel: 20-7378 8800 Fax: 20-7378 8810
E-Mail: admin@cholmondeleys.freeserve.co.uk
manager Sue Wyatt; artistic direction/choreographer Lea Anderson; administrator Jane Corry
Dancers: 10 *Perfs:* 20 *No of Prods:* 1 *Type:* contemporary *Accomp:* live, recorded (specially commissioned) *Venues:* mid scale *Touring:* UK, Europe, USA, Africa *Comments:* funded by the Arts Council of England; one of Britain's few all male dance companies

Gaby Agis
c/o Bolton & Quinn Ltd., 8 Pottery Lane, Holland Park,
London W11 4LZ
Tel: 20-7221 5000 Fax: 20-7221 8100
contact Erica Bolton

Green Candle Dance Company
224 Aberdeen House, 22 Highbury Grove, **London** N5 2DQ
Tel: 20-7359 8776 Fax: 20-7359 5840
E-Mail: GreenCandle@compuserve.com
general manager Jayne Andrew; artistic director Fergus Early; education and music director Sally Davies; touring and publicity officer Charmaine Bickley; education officer Rachel Elliott
Dancers: 3-8 *Perfs:* 40 *No of Prods:* 1 *Type:* fusion of contemporary/folk/classical dance theatre *Accomp:* specially commissioned live music and/or text *Venues:* small-mid scale *Touring:* UK and overseas *Comments:* work with people of all ages and varying physical and mental abilities; education and community work

Heightened Reality
90 Fordwych Road, **London** NW2 3TJ
Tel: 20-8450 8634 Fax: 20-8450 8634
E-Mail: heightened@heightened.demon.co.uk
contacts Sordi Cortés Molina, Eva Eklös, Ferran Audi, Andrew Trice
Perfs: 50-60 *No of Prods:* 1 *Type:* contemporary dance theatre *Accomp:* recorded *Venues:* Theatre de la cité Internationale TCI 180 *Touring:* Europe, South America, New Zealand *Comments:* second address: Ferran Audi, 102 Rue Saint-Maur, 75011 Paris, France, Tel: +33 1-5336 7756, Fax: +33 1-5336 7756

IRIE! Dance Theatre
Albany Centre, Douglas Way, **London** SE8 4AG
Tel: 20-8691 6099 Fax: 20-8694 8464
Internet: www.irie.inuk.com
E-Mail: dance@irie.inuk.com
general manager t.b.a.; artistic director Beverley Glean; diploma course coordinator Jackie Guy (Mr)
Dancers: 5 *Perfs:* 20 *No of Prods:* 1 (comprising 4 pieces) *Type:* fusion of African, Caribbean and contemporary dance, music and theatre *Accomp:* live, recorded *Venues:* capacity 800 *Touring:* national *Comments:* established England's first diploma course in African & Caribbean dance; for the next 3-5 years will be nurturing the profile of new black female choreographers, creating opportunities to showcase their work in major venues

Isadora Duncan Dance Group
4a Oswyth Road, **London** SE5 8NH
Tel: 20-7701 6379 Fax: 20-7277 1184
artistic director Barbara Kane
Dancers: 6 *No of Prods:* 8 *Type:* early contemporary *Accomp:* recorded, live *Touring:* Europe, USA *Comments:* second address: 16 Rue Pierre Leroux, 75007 Paris, France, Tel: +33 1-4273 3483; workshops and residencies; work with young people as well as with the frail/elderly

Jane Gingell and Timedance
10 Westside, 68, Fortis Green, **London** N2 9ES
Tel: 20-8444 0707 Fax: 20-8444 0707
E-Mail: anna.lejfelt-sahlen@dha.slu.se
director Jane Gingell
Dancers: 2-20 *Type:* historical dance *Accomp:* live, recorded *Touring:* national, international *Comments:* also available for courses and workshops

Javier de Frutos & Co
10 Tregothnan Road, **London** SW9 9JX
Tel: 20-7274 0785/7970-859 272 (mobile)
Fax: 20-7274 0785
choreographer/co-director Javier de Frutos; co-director Terry Warner
Dancers: 7 *Perfs:* 20 *No of Prods:* 1 *Type:* contemporary dance *Accomp:* recorded *Venues:* Queen Elizabeth Hall *Touring:* Europe, Australia *Comments:* co-produce with Royal Festival Hall, dietheater (Wien), T-Junction, Gegenwartstanz (Wien); funded by the Arts Council

JazzXchange Music and Dance Company
ADL Management, 183 Southfield Road, **London** W4 5LD
Tel: 20-8723 0771/0973 320 747 (mobile) Fax: 20-8723 0771
E-Mail: ADLMgnt@aol.com
manager Angela Dreyer-Larsen; artistic dir. Sheron Wray
Dancers: 6-12 *Perfs:* varies *No of Prods:* up to 3 *Type:* music & dance *Accomp:* live, recorded *Venues:* capacity 300-500 *touring:* national & international *Comments:* corporate work undertaken; also offer educational workshops and residencies

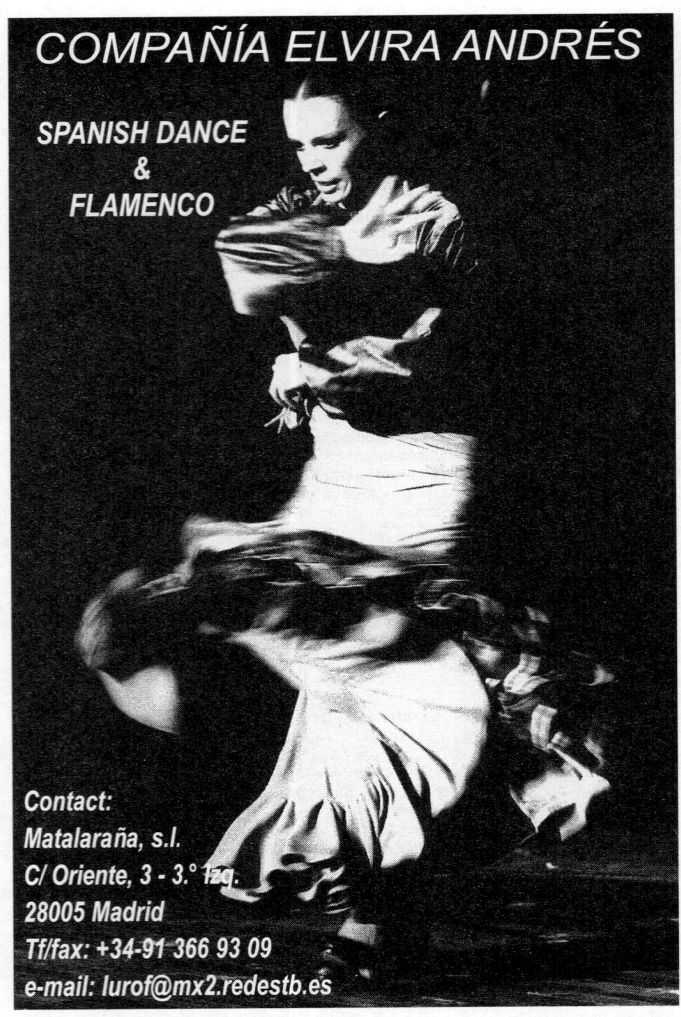

COMPAÑÍA ELVIRA ANDRÉS
SPANISH DANCE
&
FLAMENCO
Contact:
Matalaraña, s.l.
C/ Oriente, 3 - 3.° Izq.
28005 Madrid
Tf/fax: +34-91 366 93 09
e-mail: lurof@mx2.redestb.es

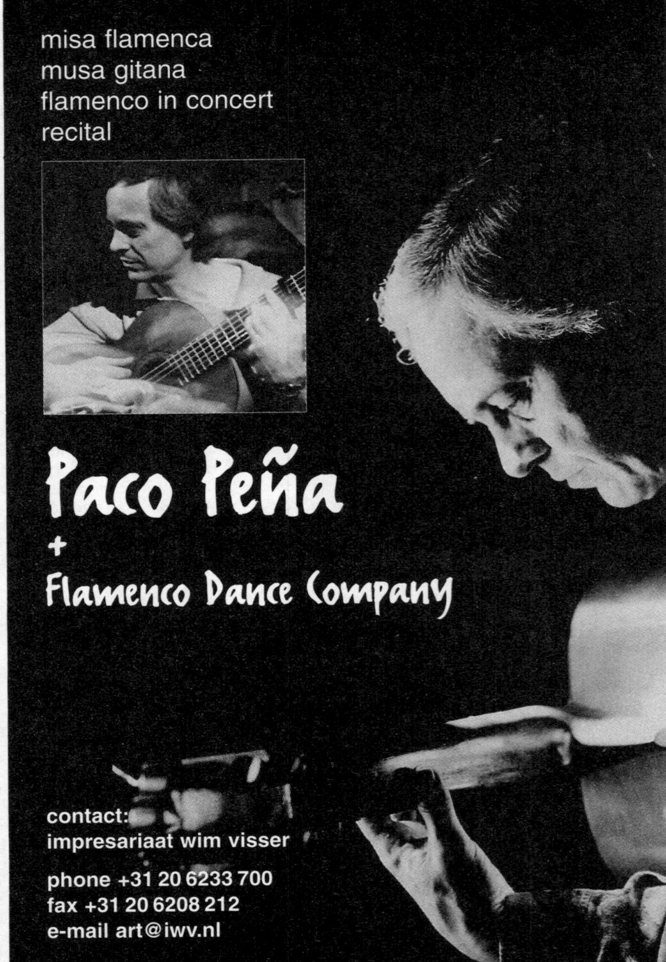

misa flamenca
musa gitana
flamenco in concert
recital
Paco Peña
+
Flamenco Dance Company
contact:
impresariaat wim visser
phone +31 20 6233 700
fax +31 20 6208 212
e-mail art@iwv.nl

Cloud Gate
Dance Theatre
of Taiwan
雲門舞集
Artistic Director Lin Hwai-min
"Asia's leading contemporary dance theatre." The Times, London
"Lin Hwai-min has succeeded brilliantly in fusing dance techniques and theatrical concepts from the East and West." The New York Times
Contact: Ms. Wenwen YEH, General Manager Tel+886-2-2712-2102 Fax+886-2-2712-2106 E-mail wenwen@cloudgate.org.tw http://www.cloudgate.org.tw

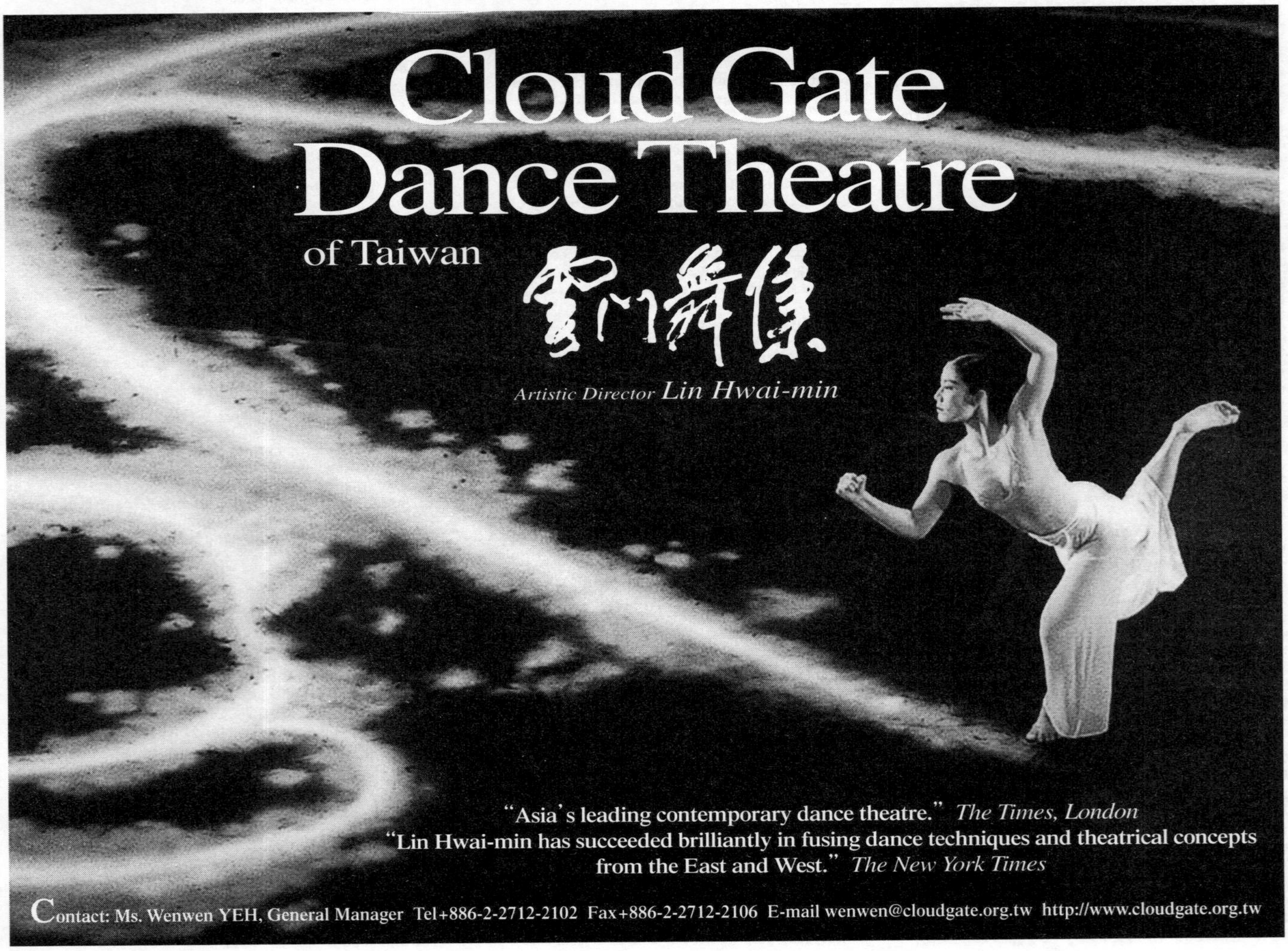

Jiving Lindy Hoppers
35 Newton Avenue, Acton, **London** W3 8AR
Tel: 20-8992 8128 Fax: 20-8752 0683
Internet: www.lindyhoppers.org.uk
E-Mail: jivinglindyhoppers@yahoo.com
artistic director Carolene Hinds; dance & education director Warren Heyes; research and development director Terry Monaghan; administrator Russell Sargeant
Dancers: 10-14 *Perfs:* 200 annually *No of Prods:* 3 *Type:* Lindy Hop, authentic American jazz dance, tap *Accomp:* live jazz bands, swing orchestras, recorded music *Venues:* small-large scale, indoor & outdoor *Touring:* USA, UK *Comments:* also offer workshops, teachers INSET, and choreography

Jonathan Burrows Group, The
c/o Simon Jackson, 3 St. Saviour's Wharf, 23 Mill Street, **London** SE1 2BH
Tel: 20-7334 7790 Fax: 20-7334 7790
E-Mail: juliac@callnetuk.com
manager Julia Carruthers; artistic director Jonathan Burrows; press/marketing Guy Chapman Associates (tel: 171-379 7474, fax: 379 8484)
Dancers: varies *Perfs:* 20-30 *No of Prods:* evening of short works *Type:* contemporary *Accomp:* recorded/live *Venues:* small-mid scale *Touring:* international (incl. Australia)

Juan Martín's Flamenco Dance Co.
c/o Flamenco Vision, 54 Windsor Road, **London** N3 3SS
Tel: 20-8346 4500 Fax: 20-8346 2488
Internet: www.flamencovision.com
E-Mail: hvmartin@dircon.co.uk
managing director Helen Martín; artistic director Juan Martín
Dancers: 9-26 *Perfs:* varies *No of Prods:* varies *Type:* flamenco *Accomp:* live *Venues:* capacity 2000 *Touring:* UK, USA, Turkey *Comments:* occassional workshops

K Ballet Company
c/o Louise Shand-Brown, 18, Cloudesley Street, **London** N1 0HX
Tel: 20-7278 3695 Fax: 20-278 3547
artistic director Tetsuya Kumakawa; contact (London) Louise Shand-Brown
Comments: contact in Japan: Toshiko Yajima Office Co, Ltd, Tel: +81 3-3423 6959, Fax: +81 3-3423 6426

La Ribot – compañía de danza
c/o Artsadmin, Toynbee Studio, 28 Commercial Street, **London** E1 6LS
Tel: 20-7247 5102 Fax: 20-7247 5103
Internet: www.artsadmin.co.uk
E-Mail: eduardo@artsadmin.co.uk
contact Eduardo Bonito
Type: contemporary, experimental
Accomp: recorded *Touring:* UK, Europe
Comments: member of UVI – La Inesperada (q.v.)

MacLennan Dance and Company
52 Hazelbourne Road, **London** SW12 9NS
Tel: 20-8673 4522
artistic director Sue MacLennan
Dancers: 2-6 *Perfs:* 10 *No of Prods:* 1+ *Type:* new, collaborating with composers, visual and new technology
Accomp: live, recorded *Venues:* small-mid scale
Comments: currently only performing occassionally, please contact above for further information

Mark Baldwin Dance Company
c/o Guy Chapman Associates, 1-2 Henrietta Street, **London** WC2E 8PS
Tel: 20-7379 7474 Fax: 20-7379 8484
E-Mail: matthew@g-c-a.co.uk
artistic director Mark Baldwin; contact Matthew Bartlett
Dancers: 2-10 *Perfs:* 25 *No of Prods:* 1 new *Type:* contemporary/classical *Accomp:* live, recorded *Venues:* mid scales *Touring:* national, international *Comments:* through his work with his own company, the Royal Ballet and other companies around the world, Mark Baldwin has proven his reputation as one of the most musically gifted choreographers working today; outreach programme available

Prague Festival Ballet
Prazsky Festivalovy Ballet
c/o GAMMA, 1 Carriage Hall, 29 Floral Street, **London** WC2E 9DP
Tel: 20-7483 3383/1 800-747 0409 (USA)
Fax: 20-7483 3353
Internet:
www.dialspace.dial.pipex.com/gamma.london/
E-Mail: gamma.london@dial.pipex.com
ballet choreographer, director David Slobaspyckyj
Dancers: 8-10 *Perfs:* 20-30 *No of Prods:* 6 *Type:* modern ballet, all types of ballet *Accomp:* recorded, live music *Venues:* small-large scale *Touring:* USA, UK, Czech Republic, Egypt, Far East, Europe *Comments:* see also Promoters and Agents & Producers

Rambert Dance Company
94 Chiswick High Road, **London** W4 1SH
Tel: 20-8995 4246 Fax: 20-8747 8323
Internet: www.london-dance.net
E-Mail: rambert@globalnet.co.uk
artistic director Christopher Bruce; executive director Christopher Nourse
Dancers: 24 *Perfs:* 90 *No of Prods:* 13 (4 new) *Type:* contemporary dance *Accomp:* live, recorded *Venues:* capacity 1000 up to 2000 *Touring:* national & international *Comments:* education department providing workshops for schools; international summer school; also masterclasses

Random Dance Company
The Jerwood Space, 171 Union Street, **London** SE1 0LN
Tel: 20-7928 3145 Fax: 20-7928 3374
Internet: www.cyberiacafe.net/random
E-Mail: randomdance@btinternet.com
development director Sophie Hansen; general manager Louise Wilson; education officer Jasmine Fitter
Perfs: 30-50 per year *Type:* contemporary dance with digital media, graphic film, animation, intelligent lighting *Touring:* UK, Europe *Comments:* October 2000 live site specific interactive performance in London linked real-time to Australian collaborators

Richard Alston Dance Company
Cecil Sharp House, 2 Regent's Park Road, **London** NW1 7AY
Tel: 20-7387 0324 Fax: 20-7482 5785
E-Mail: radc@theplace.org.uk
administrative director Chris May; artistic director Richard Alston; press & marketing manager Sue Lancashire; adminstrative assistant Katie Neill; technical manager Charles Balfour
Dancers: 10 *Perfs:* 35-40 *No of Prods:* 6 *Type:* contemporary *Accomp:* live, recorded *Venues:* capacity up to 1700 *Touring:* national and international
Comments: until July 2000 the above address is correct; then the company moves back to The Place, 17 Duke's Road, London WC1H 9AB

Ricochet Dance Company
84 Englefield Road, **London** N1 3LG
Tel: 20-8293 4260/7226 7433
Fax: 20-8298 4260/7226 7433
E-Mail: ricochetdanceco@btconnect.com
manager Frank Ottersbach; artistic directors Kate Gowar, Karin Potisk
Dancers: 5 *Perfs:* 30-40 *No of Prods:* 1 per year (2 part programme) *Type:* modern dance *Accomp:* recorded *Venues:* mid scale *Touring:* UK, Taiwan, Hong Kong, Moscow, Europe *Comments:* administration address: c/o Greenwich Dance Agency, Borough Hall, Royal Hill, London SE10 8RE, manager: Frank Ottersbach

Rosemary Lee
29 Harcourt Road, **London** N22 7XW
Tel: 20-8889 7221 Fax: 20-8374 7256
artistic director Rosemary Lee; project administrator Nicky Childs (artsadmin)
Dancers: varies *Perfs:* 10 *No of Prods:* 1 large production per year *Type:* contemporary/new dance *Accomp:* live, recorded *Venues:* small scale to site-specific e.g. disused factories, cathedrals, outdoor sites *Touring:* UK, Europe *Comments:* project based, often site-specific work, sometimes involving professional and non-professional of all ages; presently making dance films for broadcast; future plans include new site specific work and stage work for large cross-generational cast

Royal Ballet Company, The
Covent Garden, **London** WC2E 9DD
Tel: 20-7212 9165/9241 Fax: 20-7379 7059
Internet: www.royalopera.org
chief executive Michael Kaiser; director of The Royal Ballet Sir Anthony Dowell; administrative director Anthony Russell-Roberts; ballet company manager t.b.a.; assistant director Monica Mason; artistic administrator Jeanette Laurence; head of press Amanda Jones
Dancers: 85 *Perfs:* 150 *No of Prods:* 41 *Type:* classical *Accomp:* live *Venues:* Royal Opera House (due to have re-opened December 1999) *Touring:* London, regionally and abroad *Comments:* the Royal Opera House reopened December 1999

Russell Maliphant Company
c/o independance, The Ground Floor, 130 Brixton Hill, **London** SW2 1RS
Tel: 20-8678 6664 Fax: 20-8678 6641
E-Mail: juliac@callnetuk.com
artistic director Russell Maliphant; administrator Julia Carruthers
Dancers: 2-4 *Type:* contemporary dance *Touring:* April to October 2000: UK, France, Belgium, Germany

Sakoba Dance Theatre
Marylebone Dance Studio, 12 Lisson Grove, **London** NW1 6TS
Tel: 20-7258 0767 Fax: 20-7258 1868
Internet: www.london-dance.net
E-Mail: ukfd@globalnet.co.uk
company secretary Tim Fosberry; artistic director Bode Lawal; manager Tim Tubbs
Dancers: 6 *Perfs:* 40 *No of Prods:* 2 *Type:* modern African *Accomp:* live (3 musicians), recorded *Venues:* capacity 200-800 *Touring:* UK *Comments:* Sakoba is a flexible touring company creating genuinely contemporary African inspired dance with music; excellent teaching & residency work offered

Shobana Jeyasingh Dance Company
Jerwood Place, 171 Union Street, **London** SE1 0LN
Tel: 20-7928 6294 Fax: 20-7928 3603
E-Mail: admin@shobana.u-net.com
general manager Anu Giri; artistic director Shobana Jeyasingh; education development officer Elizabeth Hill; marketing co-ordinator Katy Manuel (tel: 171-323 2355)
Dancers: 5-6 *Perfs:* 25 *No of Prods:* 2 (1 new) *Type:* British-Indian contemporary dance *Accomp:* especially commisssioned contemporary music; live (musicians 4-5), electronic *Venues:* arts centres and middle scale repertory theatres, The Place Theatre 300, Queen Elizabeth Hall 1000 *Touring:* national, international
Comments: creates work which is Asian in technique, British in context and personal and contemporary in vision; the work contributes to the development of contemporary dance in Britain by introducing a vocabulary which takes as its starting point the technique of Bharatha Natyam and forges it into an inventive and personal dance language; also workshops and outreach programmes

Siobhan Davies Dance Company
31 Waterside, 44-48 Wharf Road, **London** N1 7UX
Tel: 20-7250 3030 Fax: 20-7250 1221
Internet: www.sddc.org.uk
E-Mail: admin@sddc.org.uk
executive director Sian Alexander; artistic director Siobhan Davies; associate director David Buckland; administrator Kirsty Lloyd; production manager Ollie Brown; press liaison Sophie Cohen; marketing manager Simon Gough; administrative assistant Sarah Richardson
Dancers: 8 dancers, 4 musicians *Perfs:* 20 *No of Prods:* 1-3 (including revivals) *Type:* contemporary dance
Accomp: live *Venues:* mid scale *Touring:* UK and abroad
Comments: educational work available

Suraya Hilal and Company
Flat 2, 76 Priory Road, **London** NW6 3NT
Tel: 20-7624 2549 Fax: 20-7624 2549
artistic director Suraya Hilal
Dancers: 1-6 + 6-10 musicians *Perfs:* 30 (UK), 30 (Europe) *No of Prods:* 2 *Type:* Raqs Sharqi, Egyptian dance, traditional innovative *Accomp:* live (7-10 Egyptian musicians) *Venues:* mid scale 500-1200 *Touring:* Europe, UK *Comments:* Swiss address: HILAL ART: Freihofstr. 3, 8280 Kreuzlingen, Switzerland, Tel/Fax: +41 71-672 9251, E-mail: HilalArt@compuserve.com

The Kosh
59 Stapleton Hall Road, **London** N4 3QF
Tel: 20-8374 0407 Fax: 20-8374 5661
E-Mail: the-kosh@dircon.co.uk
artistic director Michael Merwitzer; choreographer Sian Williams
Dancers: 2-20 *Perfs:* 85 *No of Prods:* 3 (1 new)
Type: dance theatre, film *Accomp:* live, recorded
Venues: capacity 800 *Touring:* UK, Europe, Far East, USA, South America

Tobias Tak
Flat 2, 10 Holmdale Road, **London** NW6 1BS
Tel: 20-7794 9867 Fax: 20-7794 9867
artistic director Tobias Tak; musical director Marc Forde; main dancers Donna Berlin, Tobias Tak
Dancers: 3 *Perfs:* 50+ *No of Prods:* 1 *Type:* rhythm tap, lindy-jazz *Accomp:* live *Venues:* artcentres 250, mid scale theatres 500-600 *Touring:* national, international
Comments: celebration of American rhythm tap varying from early styles, amoungst other 1940's swing to new interpretations of funk tap, samba and hip-hop

Transitions Dance Company
Laban Centre London, Laurie Grove, New Cross, **London** SE14 6NH
Tel: 20-8692 4070 Fax: 20-8694 8749
Internet: www.laban.co.uk
E-Mail: anthonyb@laban.co.uk
executive director Anthony Bowne; company director Lorn McDougal; administrator Ellie Beedham
Dancers: 10 *Perfs:* 35 *No of Prods:* 6 (incl. 4 new per year) *Type:* contemporary *Accomp:* recorded *Venues:* small-mid scale *Touring:* national & international *Comments:* professional training company; each year four new works are commissioned by talented choreographers from the UK, USA and Europe, and two pieces of dance theatre are revived from the Companys' repertoire; substancial education programmes; touring period: March-July

Union Dance Company
Marylebone Dance Studio, 12 Lisson Grove, **London** NW1 6TS
Tel: 20-7724 5765 Fax: 20-7224 8911
Internet: www.detek.org
E-Mail: danceunion@aol.com
artistic director Corrine Bougaard; administrative director Penelope Easton; education officer Rachel Attfield
Dancers: 5-7 *Perfs:* 60 *No of Prods:* 2 *Type:* culturally diverse contemporary dance *Accomp:* recorded, occasionally live *Venues:* capacity 700
Touring: national and international
Comments: offers workshops and residencies

V-TOL Dance Company
92-94 Judd Street, **London** WC1H 9NT
Tel: 20-7278 2432 Fax: 20-7278 0883
E-Mail: info@vtol.demon.co.uk
general manager Suzanne Walker; artistic director Mark Murphy; administrator Jo Holding; marketing manager Tiffany Evans
Dancers: 5-6 *Perfs:* 35 *No of Prods:* 1-2 *Type:* physical dance theatre *Accomp:* recorded and filmed dance footage, live *Venues:* mid scale *Touring:* UK, Europe *Comments:* educational workshops and residency available; touring company

Viva Flamenco
122B Wood Vale, **London** SE23 3EB
Tel: 07000-352 636 Fax: 20-8299 6602
Internet: www.vivaflamenco.com
E-Mail: juan@vivaflamenco.com
artistic director Juan Ramirez
Dancers: varies *Type:* flamenco *Accomp:* live *Touring:* UK, Europe, Far East, Middle East *Comments:* from solo guitarist to full company of 20 artistes

Walker Dance
c/o BAC, Lavender Hill, **London** SW11 5TF
Tel: 20-7978 4200 Fax: 20-7978 5200
E-Mail: nsweeting@dial.pipex.com
artistic director/choreographer Fin Walker; manager/administrator Nick Sweeting; composer Ben Park (Park Music)
No of Prods: 4 + 6 touring *Type:* contemporary dance *Touring:* national, international *Comments:* develope collaborations with artists from different disciplines and particular music

Yolande Snaith Theatredance
Arts Admin, Toynbee Studios, 28 Commercial Street, **London** E1 6LS
Tel: 20-7247 5102 Fax: 20-7247 5103
Internet: www.artsadmin.co.uk
E-Mail: ystd@artsadmin.co.uk
administration Nicky Molloy; artistic director/choreographer Yolande Snaith
Dancers: 6-10 *Perfs:* 25-35 *No of Prods:* 2 (1 new) *Type:* contemporary dance theatre, highly visual *Accomp:* live, recorded *Venues:* small-mid scale venues and range of festivals in the UK and abroad *Touring:* national and international *Comments:* also offer performance related workshops and residencies in England and abroad; funded by the Arts Council

Cwnmi Ballet Gwent
30 Glasllwch Cres, **Newport (Wales)** NP9 3SE
Tel: 1633-253 985/0374-947 582 (mobile)
Fax: 1633-221 690
Internet: www.welshballet.co.uk
E-Mail: cwmniballet@dial.pipex.com
artistic director Darius James; administrative director Yvonne Williams
Dancers: 8 *No of Prods:* 2 *Type:* ballet theatre *Touring:* UK, Ireland and selected overseas *Comments:* Wales own ballet company

Jaleo Flamenco Dance Company
45 Franklands, Longton, **Preston** PR4 5PD
Tel: 1772-614 235 Fax: 1772-615 944
contact Peter Holloway; contact (Spain) Carmen Campos
Dancers: 3 *Perfs:* 90 *No of Prods:* 1 each year *Type:* flamenco *Accomp:* live – 2 guitarists, 2 singers *Venues:* mid to large-scale *Touring:* worldwide *Comments:* larger company also available; contact Spain: Carmen Campos, c/ Archeros 5, 41004 Sevilla, Spain, Tel/Fax: +34 95-441 1285, (q.v.)

Irek Mukhamedov & Company
35 Yorke Road, Croxley Green, **Rickmansworth** WD3 3DW
Tel: 1923-772 691 Fax: 1923-897 952
E-Mail: 101320.1746@compuserve.com
director/company manager Julia Matheson; artistic director Irek Mukhamedov
Type: classical ballet
Accomp: live piano, recorded
Venues: mid-large scale venues, including Sadlers Wells *Comments:* small classical ballet company assembled only by invitation by Irek Mukhamedov for short seasons in UK and abroad

Chitraleka and Company
6 Merca Close, Coton Green, **Tamworth** B79 8LZ
Tel: 1827-52076 Fax: 1827-52076
E-Mail: sharad.bolar@virgin.net
artistic director & choreographer Chitraleka Bolar; marketing Sharad Bolar
Dancers: up to 12 *Perfs:* 12-14 *No of Prods:* 1
Type: main style is Bharathanatyam; innovative use of classical dance vocabulary
Accomp: live, recorded *Venues:* small, middle and large scale theatres *Touring:* national, international *Comments:* funded by Arts Council of England, West Midlands Arts, Birmingham City Council; established Bharathanatyam teacher, training the second generations and preparing the third generations from this country to professional standard; widely known for residency and schools work; education work; choreographs for other companies interested in classical Indian dance; also has a youth group called The Chitraleka and Company Youth Group

YUGOSLAVIA (+381)

Due to the war in Kosovo we have been unable to update the following entries for Yugoslavia

Ballet of the National Theatre
Narodno Pozoriste – Balet
Francuska 3, 11000 **Belgrade**
Tel: 11-622 153 Fax: 11-622 560
director Dusan Simic

City Ballet
c/o Adriana Aja Pavic, Francuska 30, 11000 **Belgrade**
Tel: 11-324 7494 Fax: 11-324 7494
director Adriana Aja Pavic
Type: modern ballet

Folk dance ensemble Kolo
Ansambl narodnih igara i pesama Kolo
Mitropolita Petra 8, 11000 **Belgrade**
Tel: 11-762 361
Fax: 11-763 144
director Bogdanka Djuric

Mimart Theatre of Movement
Mimart Teater pokreta
c/o Nela Antonovic, Gandijeva 11/31, 11070 **Novi Beograd**
Tel: 11-177 6188/659 277
Fax: 11-657 361
director Nela Antonovic
Type: avant garde ballet

Ballet of Serbian National Theatre
Srpsko Narodno Pozoriste – Ballet
Pozorisni Trg 1, 21000 **Novi Sad**
Tel: 21-621 411/52655 Fax: 21-623 391
director Erika Marijas
Perfs: 40 *No of Prods:* 2

Orchestras

Orchestras
In the main, only subsidised symphony or chamber orchestras, or those contracted to do regular recording work, are included in this list. **Within country the orchestras are ordered by city, and alphabetically within city.**

Orchestres
Dans son ensemble cette rubrique ne contient que des orchestres symphoniques ou de chambre qui sont subventionnés, ou qui sont régulièrement contactés pour faire des enregistrements. **Pour chaque pays les orchestres sont classés dans l'ordre des villes et par ordre alphabétique.**

Orchester
Hauptsächlich sind subventionierte Symphonie- oder Kammerorchester eingetragen, sowie Orchester, die regelmäßig Aufnahmen einspielen. Einige der aufgeführten deutschen und österreichischen Orchester arbeiten in Mehrspartentheatern und sind nicht außerhalb des Theaters tätig. **Die Einträge sind innerhalb aller Staaten alphabetisch nach Stadt und innerhalb der Stadt alphabetisch nach Namen geordnet.**

Orchestre
Sono incluse tutte quelle orchestre, sia sinfoniche che da camera, che ricevono un contributo statale oppure che hanno un contratto discografico. Le orchestre dei teatri dell'opera sono state incluse in questa sezione. **All'interno di ogni Paese, le cittá vengono elencate in ordine alfabetico e cosí anche le orchestre.**

Orquestas
Por lo general, sólo están incluidas orquestas sinfónicas o de cámara o orquestas que reciben con regularidad contratos de grabación. Generalmente no se han incluido las orquestas de ópera, pero para información sobre ellas remitimos al lector a la sección de ópera. **Dento de cada país, las orquestas están ordenadas por ciudades siguiendo un orden alfabético dentro de cada ciudad.**

Orchestras (오케스트라)
주로, 보조금을 받는 심포니, 실내악단 아니면 레코드사와 정식 계약을 맺고 있는 오케스트라단들만 이 리스트에 포함되었다. 오페라 하우스의 오케스트라는 포함되지 않았으므로, 이에 대한 정보가 필요할 경우는 오페라 부문을 참조하시오. **리스트는 국가별, 도시별 그리고 알파벳순으로 기재되었다.**

管弦乐队
大体来说，只是有津贴的交响乐或室内管弦乐队，或那些签有合同作经常性的录音工作的管弦乐队才包括在这一名单上。歌剧院的管弦乐队一般不列在名单上，建议读者阅歌剧一章节以获取他们所要求的信息。**在每个国家里公司是按城市的顺序来排列的，在每一城市里公司又是按字母顺序来排列的。**

オーケストラ
このリストには主に、助成を受けている、あるいは定期的な録音契約を有するオーケストラを掲載しました。オペラ劇場専属のオーケストラは原則としては掲載されておらず、詳しい情報の入手希望者はオペラの章をご覧下さい。**リストは国、都市別で、都市内ではアルファベット順に記載されています。**

ALBANIA (+355)

Jan Kukuzeli
Rr. Andon Naci, nr. 66, **Durres**
Tel: 52-25473 Fax: 52-25473
conductor Petrika Afezolli
Type/spec: string orchestra

Academy of Arts String Orchestra
Akademia e Arteve, Sheski Nene Tereza, **Tirana**
Tel: 42-46941
contact Isak Shehu

June Emerson Bass Quartet
Rr. Lidhja e Prizrenit, P. 11, shkalla 1/5, **Tirana**
Tel: 42-24920
concert master Fatos Jaho
Type/spec: bass quartet

Madre Tereza
Rr. Thanas Ziko, p. 98, Shkalla 11, ap. 1, **Tirana**
Tel: 42-22502 Fax: 42-22502
conductor Ylli Leka
Type/spec: string quartet

String Orchestra of Young Albanians, The
Rr. Ali Demi, P. 159/1, ap. 11, **Tirana**
Tel: 42-72198
artistic director Pjeter Guralumi

Symphonic Orchestra of Albanian Radio-Television (RTVSH)
Tirana
Tel: 42-28310/27745/28310 (general director RTSH)/24308
Fax: 42-27745/28310 (general director RTSH)
general director Albert Minga; assistant to general director Sefedin Cela; RTSH orchestra leader Dhimiter Gjoka; artistic director Zhani Ciko
Comments: also address of Youth String Orchestra of Tirana; see also Radio & Television

Symphonic Orchestra of Music Faculty, The
Academy of Arts, Music Faculty, **Tirana**

Symphony Orchestra of Opera Theatre
Skenderbej square, **Tirana**
Tel: 42-27471/24753/74127 Fax: 42-27471/24753
E-Mail: root@tob.tirana.al
general director Dr Vasil S. Tole
Size: 55 musicians + collaborators, 48 singers, 20 soloists *Type/Spec:* symphonic, opera *Comments:* see also Opera and Dance

Tirana String Quartet
Tirana
Tel: 42-33714
concert master Anton Berovski

Virtuous of Tirana, The
Tirana
Tel: 42-24340
conductor Zhani Ciko
Type/spec: string orchestra

ANDORRA (+376)

Orquestra Nacional de Cambra D'Andorra
Dept. Cultura Govern D'Andorra, **Ordino**
Tel: 8-75700
Internet: www.onca.ad
E-Mail: onca@andorra.ad
concertino – director Gerard Claret; secretaria Mercé Alegre
Size: 15 *Perfs:* 30-40 *Type/spec:* from baroque to contemporary classical music, focus on catalan contemporary repertoire *Venues:* Auditori Nacional D'Andorra, Ordino, 500 *Touring:* Spain, France, Italy *Comments:* recordings with Nimbus; funded by Govern D'Andorra, sponsored by Fundació Credit Andorra; administrative address: c/ Mariné 28A, 08190 San Cugat del Vallés, Spain, Tel/Fax: +34 93-674 1613/317 7774

ARMENIA (+374)

Aram Khachaturian String Quartet
Aram Khachaturian House – Museum, 3 Plekhanov Street, 375001 **Yerevan**
Tel: 2-580 178/220 927 Fax: 2-151 431
E-Mail: nbart@arminco.com
director David Movsesian

Armenian Philharmonic Orchestra
46 Mashtots Avenue, 375019 **Yerevan**
Tel: 2-580 701/567 438/560 645/1-407 176
Fax: 2-151 055/581 142
artistic director & principal conductor Loris Tjeknavorian

Komitas Quartet
4-4 Azatoutian Street, 375037 **Yerevan**
Tel: 2-254 493/525 840 Fax: 2-151 431/525 840
Internet: www.arminco.com/homepages/nab
E-Mail: nbart@arminco.com
manager Nika Babaian
Size: 4 *Type/spec:* classical and contemporary *Touring:* international *Comments:* recordings available; the oldest performing quartet in the world (founded in 1924 with 3rd generation of players at present)

National Chamber Orchestra of Armenia
Yerevan Chamber Music Hall, 1 Isahakian Street, 375025 **Yerevan**
Tel: 2-589 514/526 718 Fax: 2-526 718
artistic director & conductor Aram Gharabekian

Quintet of Yerevan State Conservatory
Yerevan Chamber Music Hall, 1 Isahakian Street, 375025 **Yerevan**
Tel: 2-526 718/633 569
artistic director Alla Berberian; manager Hovhanes Oganian

Serenade – Chamber Orchestra
4-4 Azatoutian Street, 375037 **Yerevan**
Tel: 2-254 493/525 840
Fax: 2-151 431 (AT & T)/525 840
Internet: www.arminco.com/homepages/nab
E-Mail: nbart@arminco.com
artistic director & conductor Edouard Toptchian
Size: 24-27 *Type/spec:* symphony and chamber music for strings, classical and contemporary

Symphony Orchestra of Radio Company of Armenia
5 Alek Manookian Street, 375000 **Yerevan**
Tel: 2-553 714/561 852 (Governmental tel. 71-92)
Fax: 2-506 442/151 947
artistic director & conductor Ogan Durian

Trio Akhnazarian
4-4 Azatoutian Street, 375037 **Yerevan**
Tel: 2-254 493/525 840 Fax: 2-151 431 (AT & T)/525 840
Internet: www.arminco.com/homepages/nab
E-Mail: nbart@arminco.com
manager Nika Babaian

Yerevan City Council Chamber Orchestra
1/3 Pavstos Byuzand Street, 375010 **Yerevan**
Tel: 2-267 122/529 863
prinicpal conductor Merujan Simonian

Yerevan International Festival Symphonic Orchestra
4-4 Azatoutian Street, 375037 **Yerevan**
Tel: 2-254 493/525 840 Fax: 2-151 431 (AT & T)/525 840
Internet: www.arminco.com/homepages/nab
E-Mail: nbart@arminco.com
artistic director & principal conductor Emin Khachaturian

Yerevan Symphonic Orchestra
46 Mashtots Avenue, 375019 **Yerevan**
Tel: 2-580 701/567 438/560 645/1-407 176
Fax: 2-151 055/581 142
artistic director & principal conductor Loris Tjeknavorian

AUSTRIA (+43)

Badener Städtisches Orchester
Theaterplatz 7, 2500 **Baden bei Wien**
Tel: 2252-48338/39 Fax: 2252-483 3850/40
Verwaltungsleiter Regierungsrat Wilfried Frankmann; Kapellmeister Franz Josef Breznik; Konzertmeister Gheorge Ille; PR Mag. Martina Malzer
Size: 25 *Perfs:* 150 *Type/spec:* operettas *Venues:* Stadttheater 702, Sommerarena 657 *Comments:* see also Opera, Dance, Drama and Festivals

Wiener Concert-Verein
c/o Christian Roscheck, Vogelsanggasse 35, 2102 **Bisamberg**
Tel: 2262-63424 Fax: 2262-63298
manager Christian Roscheck
Size: 15-50 *Perfs:* 30 *Type/spec:* chamber orchestra, music of 18th, 19th & 20th century *Venues:* 5 concerts in Vienna Musikverein under the title: Composer In Residence – every year, and other concerts in Austria (Bregenzer Festspiele) *Touring:* South America, France *Comments:* chamber orchestra of the Wiener Symphoniker

Städtisches Orchester Bludenz
Postfach 120, 6700 **Bludenz**
Tel: 5552-32414 Fax: 5552-324 142
E-Mail: ghutter@bludenz.at
Chefdirigent u Orchesterdirektor Herbert Baumgartner; Konzertmeister Klaus Pfefferkorn
Size: 50 *Perfs:* 2 *Type/spec:* symphony: baroque, classical, romantic *Venues:* Stadtsaal 600 *Comments:* orchestra is made up of amateurs and professionals

Symphonieorchester Vorarlberg / Camerata Bregenz
Römerstraße 15, 6900 **Bregenz**
Tel: 5574-43447 Fax: 5574-43448
Geschäftsführer Michael Löbl; Chefdirigent Christoph Eberle; Präsident Dr Bertram Grass
Size: 90 *Perfs:* 30 *Venues:* Festspielhaus Bregenz 1200, Montforthaus Feldkirch 900 *Touring:* national *Comments:* Camerata Bregenz is the core orchestra (size 35, chamber orchestra with wind instruments) of the Symphonieorchester

Jugendsinfonieorchester
Rosenstraße 6, 6850 **Dornbirn**
Tel: 5572-306 4851 Fax: 5572-306 4858
Verwaltungsdirektor Christina Rigger; Chefdirigent Guntram Simma; Konzertmeister Thomas Furrer
Size: 80-100 *Perfs:* 20 *Type/spec:* classical *Venues:* Kulturhaus 730 *Touring:* Austria, Spain

Grazer Philharmonisches Orchester
Vereinigte Bühnen Graz, Kaiser Josef-Platz 10, 8010 **Graz**
Tel: 316-8008 1904 Fax: 316-800 8598
Internet: www.buehnen.graz.com
E-Mail: info@buehnen-graz.com
Intendant Dr Gerhard Brunner; 1. Kapellmeister Wolfgang Bozic
Size: 94 *Perfs:* 191 *Type/spec:* baroque to modern, opera recitals *Venues:* Stefaniensaal 1100, Opernhaus 1424 (1224 seats, 200 standing), Kasematten 500-600
Comments: see also Opera, Dance and Drama

Grazer Symphonisches Orchester
Albrechtgasse 1, 8010 **Graz**
Tel: 316-822 184 Fax: 316-837 418
Internet: www.sime.com/musikfreunde-stmk
E-Mail: musikfreunde.stmk@sime.com
Geschäftsführung Dr Günther Ziesel; Chefdirigent Milan Horvat; künstlerische Leiterin Ulrike Danhofer
Size: 70+ *Perfs:* 11 *Type/spec:* mainly classical music and operetta *Venues:* Stefaniensaal 1100
Comments: see also Promoters

Grieskirchner Kammerorchester
Postfach 49, 4710 **Grieskirchen**
Tel: 7249-48219
Chefdirigent Prof Gunter Waldek; Präsident Dr Eduard Puffer
Size: 30 *Perfs:* 20 *Type/spec:* chamber music – baroque to modern *Venues:* Veranstaltungs Zentrum Manglburg 250 to 600

Tonkuenstler Kammerorchester
Tonkuenstler Chamber Orchestra Vienna
Wienerstraße 2, 3580 **Horn**
Tel: 2982-4319 Fax: 2982-43194
Internet: www.allegro.vivo.music.at
E-Mail: tko@music.at
Leitung Bijan Khadem-Missagh; Sekretariat Robert Berger
Size: 17 *Perfs:* 20-25 *Type/spec:* baroque, classical, romantic, modern *Touring:* Australia, Japan in 2001
Comments: orchestra in residence at the International Chamber Music Festival Austria Allegro Vivo

Tiroler Symphonieorchester-Innsbruck
Universitätsstraße 1, 6020 **Innsbruck**
Tel: 512-583 117 Fax: 512-5864 5226
Orchestermanagement Werner Leithmayer; Musikdirektor Georg Schmöhe
Size: 68 *Perfs:* 160 *Type/spec:* classical, opera, musical, operetta *Venues:* Kongresshaus 1500, Tiroler Landestheater 800 *Touring:* guest performances in Austria and abroad

Orchester des Stadttheaters Klagenfurt / Kärntner Symphonieorchester
Theaterplatz 4, 9020 **Klagenfurt**
Tel: 463-55266 Fax: 463-5526 6724
Internet: www.stadttheater-klagenfurt.at
E-Mail: s.zoltan@stadttheater-klagenfurt.at
Geschäftsführer Dr Günther Fliedl
Size: 49 *Perfs:* 8
Type/spec: theatre orchestra for opera, musicals, theatre *Venues:* Stadttheater 757
Comments: see also Opera and Drama

Wiener Jeunesse Orchester
Vivenotweg 12, 3411 **Klosterneuburg**
Tel: 2243-26626 Fax: 2243-33886
E-Mail: wjo@gmx.at
chief conductor Herbert Böck; chairman of board Martin Bramböck; general manager Dr Renate Böck
Size: 80-100 *Perfs:* 10-15
Type/spec: youth symphony orchestra, repertoire ranging from classic and romantic era to contemporary music *Venues:* major venues and festivals in Austria
Touring: Italy, France, Netherlands, Germany, Turkey
Comments: Austrian youth orchestra operating on a national level; annual auditions, age 18-26; member of the EFNYO (European Federation of National Youth Orchestras) (q.v.)

Bruckner Orchester Linz
Promenade 39, 4020 **Linz**
Tel: 732-761 1194 Fax: 732-761 1315
Internet: www.linz.info.at/landestheater
E-Mail: landestheater@linz.info.at
Kaufmännischer Direktor DDr Gerbert Schwaighofer; Generalsekretär Dipl Ing Carl F Steiner; Chefdirigent Martin Sieghart (from 2002: Dennis Russell Davies)
Size: 110 *Perfs:* 50 *Type/spec:* especially Bruckner, Mozart, Haydn and Brahms
Venues: Brucknerhaus 1400, Landestheater 750
Touring: Switzerland, Germany (Expo 2000, Hannover)
Comments: see also Drama, Opera and Dance

Linzer Konzertverein
Hörzingerstraße 40, 4020 **Linz**
Tel: 732-384 407 Fax: 732-384 407
Präsident, Verwaltung Konsulent Prok Wolfram Ziegler; Konzertmeister Prof Eduard Arzt
Size: 80 *Perfs:* 2-4 *Type/spec:* classical, contemporary, operetta *Venues:* Brucknerhaus 1400

Collegium Viennenses
Quellenstr. 10, 2340 **Moedling**
Tel: 2236-864 271 Fax: 2236-864 271
E-Mail: a8371034@unit.univie.ac.at
contact Peter Schreiber, Kurt Franz Schmid, Gottfried Pokorni
Size: 9 *Perfs:* 8-10 *Type/spec:* wind music, classical *Touring:* national, Czech Republic
Comments: CD available

Camerata Academica Salzburg
Bergstraße 22, 5020 **Salzburg**
Tel: 662-873 104 Fax: 662-873 1045
Internet: www.camerata.at
E-Mail: camerata@net4you.co.at
Generalsekretär Benedikt Fohr; chief conductor Sir Roger Norrington
Size: 26-45 *Perfs:* 80 *Type/spec:* classical, romantic, contemporary – chamber music *Venues:* Mozarteum Salzburg 800, Konzerthaus Wien 1800
Touring: Europe, USA, Japan

Juvavum Brass – Salzburg
Gruberfeldsiedlung 219, 5023 **Salzburg**
Tel: 662-650 237 Fax: 662-650 237
Internet: www.juvavum.at
E-Mail: juvavum.brass@aon.at
contact Horst Hofer
Size: 5-12 *Type/spec:* brass ensemble, renaissance to jazz/classical to modern *Touring:* worldwide
Comments: see also Festivals

Mozarteum Orchester Salzburg
Erzbischof-Gebhard Str. 10, 5020 **Salzburg**
Tel: 662-843 571 Fax: 662-8435 7123
Direktor Prof. Mag. Erwin Niese; Chefdirigent Hubert Soudant
Size: 91 *Perfs:* 31 *Type/spec:* all types, mainly symphony, also opera *Venues:* Großes Festspielhaus 2500, Kleines Festspielhaus 2000, Stiftung Mozarteum, 700 Landestheater 450 *Touring:* Germany, Netherlands
Comments: orchestra of Salzburger Landestheater; participant at Salzburger Festspiele

Salzburger Kammerorchester
Lieferinger Hauptstr. 136, 5013 **Salzburg**
Tel: 662-436 870 Fax: 662-436 970
E-Mail: mozart@salzburg.co.at
künstlerischer Leiter Harald Nerat
Size: 15-30 *Perfs:* 30 *Type/spec:* classical to modern (emphasis on Mozart) *Touring:* Austria, Japan, Germany, Italy

Salzburger Residenz-Solisten
Lieferinger Haupstr. 136, 5013 **Salzburg**
Tel: 662-436 870 Fax: 662-436 970
E-Mail: mozart@salzburg.co.at
künstlerischer Leiter Harald Nerat
Size: 5 *Perfs:* 40 *Type/spec:* baroque, chamber, classical
Touring: Germany, Austria, Japan

Wiener Kammermusiker
Anton Brucknergasse 23, 2231 **Strasshof bei Wien**
Tel: 2287-4170 Fax: 2287-4170
Leitung Prof Wolfgang Kühn
Size: 10 *Perfs:* 10 *Type/spec:* classical to modern
Venues: Musikverein, Vienna *Touring:* China

1.Frauen-Kammerorchester von Österreich
1.Women's Chamber Orchestra of Austria
Maria-Theresien-Straße 11, 1090 **Wien**
Tel: 1-31316 83880 Fax: 1-3131 67984
Präsidentin Brigitte Ratz
Size: 40 *Perfs:* 20 *Type/spec:* classical and contemporary repertoire, works of female composers
Venues: Wiener Konzerthaus, Minoritenkirche, Odeon
Touring: Europe, Israel
Comments: also smaller ensembles

Bühnenorchester der Wiener Staatsoper
Opernring 2, 1010 **Wien**
Tel: 1-5144 42717 Fax: 1-5144 42625
Internet: www.oebthv.gv.at
E-Mail: postmaster@oebthv.gv.at
managing director Prof Erich Kitir
Size: 45 *Perfs:* 304 *Venues:* Staats-, Volksoper, Burg – Akademietheater, Theater a. d. Wien (during Festwochen) *Touring:* Festspiele

Collegium Musicum Wien
Sonnenuhrgasse 1/11, 1060 **Wien**
Tel: 1-596 4426(home number)
Fax: 1-596 4426
E-Mail: mitisek@aol.com
Musikalischer Leiter Andreas Mitisek
Size: up to 25 *Type/spec:* baroque, classical
Comments: see also Early Music

Concentus Musicus Wien
Grillparzerstr. 75, Perchtoldsdorf, 2380 **Wien**
Tel: 1-8659 7624 Fax: 1-8659 7624
contact Helmut Mitter; Musikalische Leitung Prof Nikolaus Harnoncourt
Size: 35-40 *Perfs:* 22 *Type/spec:* mainly Baroque, Mozart, Haydn, Viennese classics *Venues:* Wiener Konzerthaus , Wiener Musikverein *Touring:* throughout Europe, Styriarte Graz, Salzburger Mozartwoche
Comments: CD recording

die reihe
Seidlgasse 28/6, 1030 **Wien**
Tel: 1-710 3206 Fax: 1-710 3296
Internet: homepages.netway.at/diereihe/
E-Mail: diereihe@netway.at
Geschäftsführer Rudolf Illavsky; Künstlerischer Leiter HK Gruber; Ehrenpräsident Friedrich Cerha; stage manager Johann Regner
Size: 17 *Perfs:* 15 *Type/spec:* new music, 20th C.
Venues: Großer Sendesaal des Österreichischen Rundfunks, Wiener Konzerthaus *Touring:* Austria, England, Romania, Germany *Comments:* Cycle '40 years die reihe' in ORF

Ensemble Wien-Paris
Franz Josefs Kai 49/15, 1010 **Wien**
Tel: 1-533 3837 Fax: 1-533 3886
E-Mail: ewc@blackbox.ping.at
contact René Staar
Size: 5 *Type/spec:* chamber music

Ensemble Wiener Collage
Franzensbrückengasse 6/8/15, 1020 **Wien**
Tel: 1-218 5560/533 3837
Fax: 1-218 5560
Internet: www.spinnst.co.at/ewc
E-Mail: ewc@blackbox.ping.at
administrative manager Erik Freitag; artistic director René Staar; member of board Eugene Hartzell
Size: 10-15 *Perfs:* 50 *Type/spec:* chamber, 20th century classics and new works *Touring:* Europe
Comments: festivals, concerts, concert series

Gustav Mahler Jugendorchester
Goethegasse 1, 1010 **Wien**
Tel: 1-512 9833 Fax: 1-512 9835
Internet: www.gmjo.at
E-Mail: office@gmjo.at
Musikdirektor Claudio Abbado; Assistent des Musikdirektors Stefan Anton Reck; Generalsekretär Alexander Meraviglia-Crivelli; Künstlerisches Betriebsbüro Christa Redik; Orchestermanagement Florian Scheiber; Büroleitung Atle Vestersjoe
Size: 130-150 *Perfs:* 15-20 *Type/spec:* classical, romantic and contemporary symphonic music *Touring:* Europe, North and South America
Comments: age limit: 26 years; auditioned annually throughout 20 European countries

Haydn Sinfonietta Wien
Bossigasse 76, 1130 **Wien**
Tel: 1-877 5208 Fax: 1-876 4623-17
E-Mail: haydn_sinfonietta@netway.at
Musikalischer Direktor Manfred Huss; Management Mag. Karl Gerhard Strassl; Marketing Mag. Odilo Strutzenberger
Size: 6-45 *Perfs:* 40 *Type/spec:* orchestral and chamber music of the late 18th and early 19th century on period instruments *Venues:* historic venues *Touring:* Europe
Comments: recording exclusively with Koch-Schwann; see also Festivals (Festival Wiener Klassik)

Johann Strauss Ensemble
c/o Künstlersekretariat Buchmann GmbH, Schachnerstr. 27, 1220 **Wien**
Tel: 1-203 6357 Fax: 1-203 7483
E-Mail: buchmann@xpoint.at
artistic director Alfred Pfleger
Size: 20-32 *Perfs:* 15
Type/spec: Strauss, Schubert, Lanner, Mozart
Touring: Europe

Klangforum Wien
Kirchengasse 1a, 1070 **Wien**
Tel: 1-521 6710 Fax: 1-521 6730/1
Internet: www.klangforum.at
E-Mail: info@klangforum.at
Chefdirigent Sylvain Cambreling; Präsident der Gesellschaft Friedrich Cerha; Produktion Mag. Monika Kalitzke-Bergmann
Size: 21 *Perfs:* 80 *Type/spec:* contemporary, new music, experimental *Venues:* Konzerthaus Wien, Mozartsaal 750, Schleswig-Holstein Festival, Salzburger & Regensburger Festspiele *Touring:* Japan, USA, France, Germany, Italy, LA, Portugal, Spain *Comments:* CD on Durian Records available

Melos Ensemble Wien
Postfach 71, 1037 **Wien**
Tel: 1-714 9196 Fax: 1-714 9191
Chefdirigent Christian May
Size: 19-25 *Perfs:* 38
Type/spec: chamber orchestra
Touring: Germany, UK, France, Italy, Belgium

Musikwerkstatt Wien
Speisingerstraße 149/1, 1230 **Wien**
Tel: 1-889 1996 Fax: 1-889 1996
E-Mail: MWWien@compuserve.com
Künstlerische Leitung/Chefdirigent Huw Rhys James; Geschäftsführung Mag. Anna-Maria Birnbauer
Size: 15-20 *Perfs:* 15-20 *Type/spec:* baroque and 20th C., chamber concerts and opera *Comments:* see also Opera

Niederösterreichisches Tonkünstlerorchester – NTO
Elisabethstraße 22/9, 1010 **Wien**
Tel: 1-586 8383 Fax: 1-587 6492
E-Mail: nto@nto.at
Direktor Peter Roczek; Chefdirigent Fabio Luisi; Orchesterinspektor Peter Grubinger
Size: 100 *Perfs:* 130 *Type/spec:* symphony *Venues:* Grosser Musikvereinsaal 2044

Orchester der Vereinigten Bühnen Wien GmbH
Linke Wienzeile 6, 1060 **Wien**
Tel: 1-5883 0266 Fax: 1-588 3034
Internet: www.musicalvienna.at
E-Mail: info@vbw.telecom.at
Musikdirektor & Dirigent Caspar Richter; Dirigenten Adrian Manz, Adrian Werum, Wolfgang Hattinger
Size: 85 *Perfs:* 600 *Type/spec:* musical theatre orchestra
Venues: Theater an der Wien 1177, Raimund Theater 1233 *Comments:* see also Opera, Dance and Drama

Orchester der Volksoper Wien
Währingerstraße 78, 1090 **Wien**
Tel: 1-5144 43240 Fax: 1-5144 43215
Direktor Dominique Metitha; Chefdirigent Asher Fisch; Konzertmeister Udo Zwölfer, Bettina Gradinger, Sebastian Gürtler; Orchesterinspektor Wilfried Karlinger; Presse Julie Birner-Schuschu; Disposition Burghard Hattendorff; Dramaturgie Dr Birgid Meyer; Chorleitung Michael Tomaschek; Ballettleiterin Liz King
Size: 95 *Perfs:* 300 *Type/spec:* operas, operettas, musicals
Venues: Volksoper Wien 1313 *Comments:* see also Opera

Orchester Pro Musica International
Praterstraße 76/8, 1020 **Wien**
Tel: 1-216 7333 Fax: 1-212 1555
Chefdirigent u Orchesterdirektor Prof Gerhard Track; Konzertmeister Joanna Lewis
Size: 52 *Perfs:* 3-4 *Type/spec:* symphony, Viennese music
Venues: Grosser Musikvereinssaal 1480

Österreichische Kammersymphoniker
Goldschmiedgasse 10/3/3, 1010 **Wien**
Tel: 1-534 6287 Fax: 1-534 6267
E-Mail: proart@magnet.at
Leitung Mag. Ernst Theis; Büro Heidemarie Dobner
Size: 40 *Perfs:* 15 *Type/spec:* classical, 20thC *Touring:* Japan, major Austrian festivals, Turkey, USA, Ukraine, Germany *Comments:* biannual CD productions of 20th century composers; label: CANTATE – musicaphon

Quadri Musical
Salesianergasse 8/56, 1030 **Wien**
Tel: 1-712 1673 Fax: 1-712 1673
Leitung Sofia Taliani,
Size: varies *Perfs:* 30 p.a. *Type/spec:* lieder, ensemble, piano music *Venues:* Klangbogen Wien, dietheater Künstlerhaus, Jenesse Festival-Wien, Concerti in Ville (Italy – Veneto, Emilia Romagna, Lazio) *Touring:* Austria, Italy, UK *Comments:* also musicaL/literary performances

Radio Symphonieorchester Wien
Argentinierstraße 30a, 1041 **Wien**
Tel: 1-50101 18747 Fax: 1-50101 18358
Internet: www.rso-wien.orf.at
E-Mail: rso-wien@orf.at
Leiter des Orchesterbüros Christian Edlinger; Chefdirigent Dennis Russell Davies; Künstlerische Leitung und Management Dr Andrea Seebohm
Size: 98 *Perfs:* 35 different performances *Type/spec:* symphony; emphasis on 20th century *Venues:* Wiener Musikverein 1744, Konzerthaus 1900 *Touring:* USA (March 2000), Europe (May-June 2000) *Comments:* also perform for radio productions; recordings available

Strauss Festival Orchester Wien
c/o Künstlersekretariat Buchmann GmbH, Schachnerstr. 27, 1220 **Wien**
Tel: 1-203 6357 Fax: 1-203 7483
E-Mail: buchmann@xpoint.at
dirigent Peter Guth
Size: 30 *Perfs:* 30-50 *Touring:* Hong Kong, Japan, Europe, South America, USA

Symphonieorchester der Wiener Volksoper
Währingerstraße 78, 1090 **Wien**
Tel: 1-317 6124 Fax: 1-310 7688
Internet: www.cso.net/vienna-volksoper-s-o.at
E-Mail: guenter.schoenig@highway.co.at
Orchesterdirektor Dr Günter Schönig (Tel & Fax: 1-405 8185); Verwaltungsdirektor Johann Spitzer
Size: 80-85 *Perfs:* 40-50 *Type/spec:* symphonic: baroque to modern, music of Vienna *Venues:* Musikverein, Konzerthaus, Suntory Hall (Tokyo) *Touring:* Japan, Spain, Germany, Vietnam, Hong Kong, Brunei, Malaysia, Indonesia Thailand, Taiwan
Comments: see also Opera, Dance, Choirs

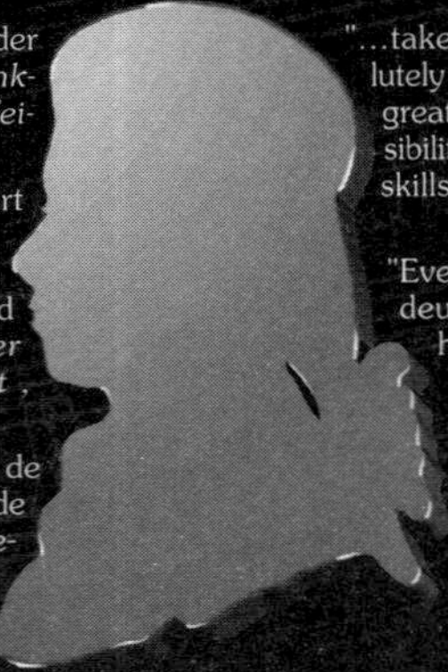

Twentieth Century Ensemble, The
Ensemble 20 Jahrhundert
c/o Dr. Peter Burwik, Hügelgasse 12, 1130 **Wien**
Tel: 1-512 9134 Fax: 1-512 9134
E-Mail: e20j@aon.at
künstlerischer Leiter Dr. Peter Burwik
Size: 25-30 *Perfs:* 10-15 *Type/spec:* contemporary *Venues:* Großer Sendesaal des ORF 275, Wiener Konzerthaus 300 to 800, Arnold Schönberg Center, Wien 120 *Comments:* promoters: William. M. Colleran, London (Tel: +44 171-372 7210); Patricia Dantois, Paris (Tel: +33 1-4234 5346)

Wiener Akademie
Reisnerstrasse 32, 1030 **Wien**
Tel: 1-713 6082 Fax: 1-718 2913
E-Mail: wienak@eunet.at
Musikalische Leitung Martin Haselböck
Size: varies *Perfs:* 30-40 *Type/spec:* baroque, classical, romantic *Venues:* Musikverein Wien 2000 *Touring:* South America, England *Comments:* perform on period instruments; 30 CDs recorded; see also Early Music

Wiener Hofburg-Orchester
Margaretenstraße 3, 1040 **Wien**
Tel: 1-587 2552 Fax: 1-587 4397
Internet: www.wr-hofburg-orchester.at/konzerte/
E-Mail: konzerte@wr-hofburg-orchester.at
Musikalischer Leiter/Dirigent Gert Hofbauer
Size: 40 *Perfs:* 90 *Type/spec:* Mozart, Strauss, operetta *Venues:* Hofburg 1300, Wiener Konzerthaus/Grosser Saal 1800, Musikverein 1600 *Comments:* from May-October perform every Tuesday, Thursday and Saturday

Wiener Instrumentalsolisten (Vienna Virtuosi)
Coulombgasse 5/90/3, 1210 **Wien**
Tel: 1-272 3388/4852-71508
Fax: 1-272 3388
Generalsekretär Prof. Helmut Ascherl
Size: minimum 5 chamber ensemble to chamber orchestra (strings: 5/4/3/2/1 plus windes) *Perfs:* 30-50 *Type/spec:* renaissance, baroque, classical, 20th century, including jazz *Touring:* Germany, Italy, Turkey, Far East *Comments:* 4 CDs available

Wiener Johann Strauß-Orchester
Lothringerstrasse 20, 1030 **Wien**
Tel: 1-713 9260 Fax: 1-713 6071
Internet: www.members.magnet.at/strauss/
E-Mail: strauss@magnet.at
Verwaltung Mag. Johannes Holik; Ständiger Dirigent Alfred Eschwe, Franz Bauer-Theussl
Size: 43 *Perfs:* 50 *Type/spec:* music of the Strauss family *Touring:* Japan, China, Korea, etc. *Comments:* address due to have changed at end of 1999, no further details known at time of going to print

Wiener Kammerorchester
Schachnerstraße 27, 1220 **Wien**
Tel: 1-203 6357 Fax: 1-203 7483/204 3750
Internet: www.user.xpoint.at/buchmann
E-Mail: buchmann@xpoint.at
Geschäftsführer Christian Buchmann
Size: 25-40 *Perfs:* 90 *Type/spec:* Wiener Klassik, 20th century *Venues:* Konzerthaus 2000, 650 *Touring:* USA, Japan, Italy, France, Spain, Germany, South America *Comments:* different music cycles throughout the season incl. Zyklus-Internationale Preisträger where international prize winners are presented to the public

Wiener Kammerphilharmonie
Schlösselgasse 24/18, 1080 **Wien**
Tel: 1-402 1960 Fax: 1-402 1960
Chefdirigent Claudius Traunfellner
Size: 24-32 *Perfs:* 30-40 *Type/spec:* Viennese classics and modern *Venues:* Musikverein Wien 1400 *Touring:* Italy, Spain, Germany, France, Brazil, Scandinavia *Comments:* participates in Schubertiade (q.v.)

Wiener Mozart Orchester
Brucknerstr. 4, 1040 **Wien**
Tel: 1-5057 7660 Fax: 1-505 9720
Internet: www.mozart.co.at
E-Mail: concerts@mozart.co.at
Orchesterdirektor Gerald Grünbacher; Chefdirigenten Konrad Leitner, Manuel Hernandez-Silva; Konzertmeister Esther Haffner, Bettina Gradinger
Size: 30 *Perfs:* 130 *Type/spec:* chamber *Venues:* Konzerthaus 1800 & 700, Musikverein 1700, Hofburg 1300 *Touring:* Japan, Asia, Germany, Canada and USA

Wiener Philharmoniker
The Vienna Philharmonic
Bösendorferstraße 12, 1010 **Wien**
Tel: 1-505 6525
Internet: www.vienna.at/philharmoniker
Geschäftsführer Peter Pecha; Präsident Dr Clemens Hellsberg
Size: 142 *Type/Spec:* symphonic, subscription series & special performances *Venues:* Musikvereinssaal, Wien *Touring:* worldwide *Comments:* performances include: Salzburger Mozartwoche, Salzburger Festspiele, subscription, special concerts at Wiener Festwochen, Vienna Philharmonic Week in Japan and Vienna Philharmonic Week in Carnegie Hall, New York

Wiener Sinfonietta
Vienna Sinfonietta
Girzenberggasse 3a, 1130 **Wien**
Tel: 1-877 6138/1215 Fax: 1-877 1215
Orchesterdirektor Prof Leopold Brandstetter; Chefdirigent Prof Kurt Rapf; Orchesterdirektor Peter Mayrhofer
Size: 15-28 *Perfs:* 15-20
Type/spec: baroque to modern (including performances of works of living composers) *Venues:* Brahmssaal, Musikverein 550; Schubertsaal, Konzerthaus 336
Touring: Spain, Korea, China
Comments: records available on various labels including Calig label

Wiener Symphoniker
Lehárgasse 11/Stg 2, 1060 **Wien**
Tel: 1-589 790 Fax: 1-589 7954
Internet: www.wiener-symphoniker.at
E-Mail: office@wienersymphoniker.at
Generalsekretär Dr Rainer Bischof; Chefdirigent Vladamir Fedosejev
Size: 127 *Perfs:* 152 *Type/spec:* mainly classical, some opera *Venues:* Musikverein Konzerthaus, Bregenz Festival, Wiener Musiksommer – Klangbogen
Touring: national, Germany, Japan, Slovenia, Poland, Finland, USA

AZERBAIDZHAN (+994)

Azerbaidzhan Niyazi State Symphony Orchestra of Television and Radio
M. Guseyn St. 1, 370001 **Baku**
Tel: 12-931 900
artistic director Hadjiyev Ismail Djevdet ogly

Azerbaidzhan State Variety Orchestra 'Gaya'
X Rzayeva St. 5, 370004 **Baku**
Tel: 12-384 315
artistic director Mirzoyev Teymur Ibrahim ogly

Azerbaidzhan Uzeyir Hadjibekov State Symphony Orchestra
Istiglaliyat St. 2, 370001 **Baku**
Tel: 12-931 651
artistic director & chief conductor Abdullayev Rauf Janbakhish ogly

Jabbar Karyagdy Mugam Ensemble
c/o Jahangir Selimkhanov, Yeni Musiqi, Haqverdiev Kuchesi, 3A-32, 370141 **Baku**
Tel: 12-973 398 Fax: 12-387 601
E-Mail: jselimkhanov@arts.osi-az.baku
artistic leader Mohlet Muslimov

K. Karayev Azerbaidzhan State Chamber Orchestra
Istiglaliyat St. 2, 370001 **Baku**
Tel: 12-931 651
artistic director Gekchayev Teymur Anvar oglu

Seid Rustamov Folk Orchestra of the Azerbaidzhan Television and Radio Company
M. Guseyn St. 1, 370011 **Baku**
Tel: 12-931 900
artistic director Azimov Nariman Gulam oglu

Symphony Orchestra of the Azerbaidzhan State Academic Opera and Ballet Theatre
Nizamy St. 95, 370000 **Baku**
Tel: 12-931 651
chief conductor Jafarov Javanshir Khalil ogly

Variety Orchestra of the Azerbaidzhan State Television and Radio Company
M. Guseyn St. 1, 370011 **Baku**
Tel: 12-931 900
artistic director Sudjaddinov Faik Miri ogly

Folk Orchestra of Giandja Philarmony
Atayevs St. 135, 374400 **Giandja**
artistic director Mirzayev Elman Srafil ogly

State Chamber Orchestra of the Gandja Philharmony
Atayevs St. 135, 374400 **Giandja**
director Bayramov Rafael Ali ogly

State Chamber Orchestra of the Nakchivan Philharmony
Azadlyg Avenue 1, 363730 **Nakchivan**
artistic director Akhundov Chinciz Mammed ogly

BELARUS (+375)

Kapella of Grodno
c/o City Council of Grodno, Department of Culture, Tizengauz square 4, apt.20, 230023 **Grodno**
Tel: 152-443 478 Fax: 152-967 322
artistic director & manager Aleksei Solodukhin; conductor chamber orchestra Vladimir Bormotov; conductor chamber choir Larisa Ikonnikova
Size: chamber orchestra: 19, chamber choir: 35
Perfs: 100 *Type/spec:* old and modern Belarussian composers, Russian and West European classics of 17th – 20th Centuries, church music
Touring: Europe

State Academic Symphony Orchestra of the Republic of Belarus
Gosudarstvjennyj Acadjemichjeskij Simfonichjeskij Orkjestr Rjespubliki Bjelaruss
pr. Franciska Skoryny 50, 220005 **Minsk**
Tel: 172-315 547 Fax: 172-319 050
director Natalija Kuznjecova
Touring: Italy, Spain, Germany, Moscow

State Chamber Orchestra of the Republic of Belarus
Gosudarstvennyj Kamjernyi Orkjestr Rjespubliki Bjelaruss
pr. Franciska Skoryny 50, 220005 **Minsk**
Tel: 172-314 831 Fax: 172-314 831
director Aljexandr S Gusjev

State Symphony and Estrade Music Orchestra of the Republic of Belarus
Gosudarstvjennyj Orkjestr Simfonicheskoj i Estradnoj Muzyki Rjespubliki Belaruss
mail box N 1, 220002 **Minsk**
Tel: 172-334 252 Fax: 172-391 409
director Mihail Finbjerg

Zhinovich State Academic Folk Orchestra of the Republic of Belarus
Gosudarstvjennyj Acadjemichjeskij Narodnyj Orkjestr Rjespubliki Bjelaruss imjeni Zhinovicha
pr. Franciska Skoryny 50, 220005 **Minsk**
Tel: 172-312 686 Fax: 171-319 050
director Gjennadij V Abibok

BELGIUM (+32)

Beethoven Academie
Desguinlei 25, 2018 **Antwerp**
Tel: 3-226 3511 Fax: 3-226 5609
E-Mail: info@beethoven.be
intendant Job Maarse; artistic director Jan Caeyers; planning Els T'seyen
Size: 35 *Perfs:* 60 *Type/spec:* chamber; late18th-early19thC, 20th C and contemporary music *Venues:* International Arts Centre Desingel 800, Antwerp; Cultureel Centrum Hasselt 800; Palais des Beaux-Arts, Brussels 2000

Champ d'Action
Londonstraat 17, 2000 **Antwerp**
Tel: 3-231 5753 Fax: 3-231 5753
E-Mail: champ.d.action@skynet.be
artistic director Luk Vaes; general director Bait de Sier
Size: 1-25 *Perfs:* 10-30 *Type/spec:* contemporary *Touring:* Belgium, Netherlands, Germany, Brazil, Portugal, Spain, Canada, France

Nuove Musiche
Magdalenastraat 6, 2018 **Antwerp**
Tel: 3-272 5544 Fax: 3-272 5544
intendant Guido Spruyt; music director Eric Lederhandler
Size: 12-40 *Perfs:* 50 *Type/spec:* classical, romantic, 20th century *Touring:* concerts in Europe and touring in Spain and France

Royal Philharmonic Orchestra – Cultural Ambassador for Flanders
Koninklijk Filharmonisch Orkest van Vlaanderen
Brazilieestraat 15, 2000 **Antwerp**
Tel: 3-231 3737 Fax: 3-213 5400
E-Mail: admin@kfovv.be
manager Luc Vanackere; president Bob Ridder Stouthuysen; conductors Philippe Herreweghe, Peter Rundel, Michael Schønwandt; artistic planning Margarethe Grolig
Size: 97 *Perfs:* 90 *Type/spec:* symphony (classical, romantic & 20th century)
Venues: de Singel-Blauwe Zaal 900, Queen Elizabeth Hall 2000, Bourla Theatre 1000, Palais des Beaux Arts (Brussels) 2300 *Touring:* Japan, Holland, France, Germany, Austria, Spain

Symfonisch Orkest van de Vlaamse Opera
Flanders Opera Orchestra
Van Ertbornstraat 8, 2018 **Antwerp**
Tel: 3-233 6808 Fax: 3-232 2661
Internet: www.vlaamseopera.be
E-Mail: info@vlaamseopera.be
general manager Marc Clémeur; musical director Massimo Zanetti; permanent guest conductor Silvio Varviso
Size: 78 musicians, 50 chorus members *Perfs:* 80
Type/spec: symphony/opera *Venues:* Antwerp Opera House 1060, Ghent Opera House 960
Comments: 2nd address: Schouwburgstraat 3, 9000 Ghent tel: 9-223 0681, fax: 9-223 8726; resident orchestra for Flanders Opera

Collegium Instrumentale Brugense
Vijversdreef 9b, 8310 **Bruges**
Tel: 50-353 717 Fax: 50-362 717
administrateur Lieve Geerolf; musical director Patrick Peire
Size: 16-30 + 18-30 vocal ensemble
Perfs: 50 *Type/spec:* chamber: baroque to 20thC *Touring:* Great Britain, France, Spain, Germany, Netherlands

Anima Eterna Symphony Orchestra
Akenkaai 2, 1000 **Brussels**
Tel: 2-201 0874 Fax: 2-201 5418
E-Mail: anima.eterna@euronet.be
conductor & artistic director Jos van Immerseel; production & office director Sandra Fol; pr & sales coordinator Patrick Suttels; technical director Frank Van Elsen
Size: 40-55 *Perfs:* 40-50 *Type/spec:* 18th & 19th century, specific repertoires are studied in depth, using the newest musicological research and playing period instruments *Touring:* Europe, Japan *Comments:* recording with Channel Classics, Sony Classical; see also Early Music

Brussels Chamber Orchestra
rue du Prévôt 121, 1050 **Brussels**
Tel: 2-345 1079 Fax: 2-345 1079
director Maurice Bonnaerens
Comments: no performances in 1999

Chamber Orchestra Charlemagne
Avenue E. Van Becelaere 26A/90, 1170 **Brussels**
Tel: 495-532 110 (mobile) Fax: 2-675 0571
Internet: www.geocities.com/Vienna/Strasse/9192/
E-Mail: ch.orch.ch@skynet.be
artistic director/conductor B H Van de Velde; concert master Marek Kowalski; artists management Agnes de Hooghe (tel: 2-375 7821, fax: 2-375 8073, email: agnes.de.hooghe@skynet.be)
Size: 25 *Perfs:* 12 concerts *Type/spec:* baroque, classical, modern *Touring:* USA, Brazil

I Musici Brucellensis
16 Rue Major Petillon, 1040 **Brussels**
Tel: 2-733 0974/735 9312 Fax: 2-735 9312
manager Claude Vial; musical director & conductor Zofia Wislocka
Size: 12-20 *Type/spec:* string orchestra, baroque, romantic, contemporary + less well-known work, Belgian composers *Touring:* France, Egypt, Spain
Comments: CDs available

ICTUS Contemporary Music Ensemble
Van Volxemlaan 164, 1190 **Brussels**
Tel: 2-340 0383 Fax: 2-344 4463
Internet: www.ictus-ensemble.org
E-Mail: lukas.pairon@skynet.be
director Lukas Pairon; away coordinator Tom Bruwier; artistic coordinator Jean-Luc Plouvier; home coordinator Kathleen Deboutte
Size: 20 *Perfs:* 60-80 *Type/spec:* contemporary

Jonge Filharmonie/Jeune Philharmonie
Wolstraat/Rue Aux Laines 20, 1000 **Brussels**
Tel: 2-512 0725 Fax: 2-511 4764
E-Mail: joply@ping.be
general manager Magda van den Bosch
Size: 100 *Type/Spec:* symphonic orchestra: symphonic repertoire, chamber music, contemporary music
Touring: 2000 Festival of EFNYO (Utrecht, Berlin)
Comments: 1999 and 2000 conductor's summer projects: member of EFNYO (q.v); collaboration with the Queen Elizabeth Competition (q.v.); the orchestra's size varies because it is formed on a yearly basis

Nationaal Orkest van België/ Orchestre National de Belgique
3 Galerie Ravenstein bte 10, 1000 **Brussels**
Tel: 2-552 0464/60 Fax: 2-552 0468
general manager Albert Wastiaux; production Gilles Ledure; music director Yuri Simonov
Size: 90 *Perfs:* 82 *Type/spec:* 18th-20th century, symphonic, oratorio, new compositions *Venues:* La Monnaie/De Munt, Théâtre Royal de Namur, Opéra Royal de Wallonie, Palais des Beaux Arts de Charleroi, De Bijloke Gent *Touring:* UK, Austria, Germany, Spain, France *Comments:* privileged partner of the Société Philharmonique de Bruxelles; regular guest of Festival van Vlaanderen, Festival de Wallonie, Festival de Bruxelles; orchestra of Queen Elizabeth Music Competition 1999 (q.v.)

Orchestre Symphonique du Théâtre Royal de la Monnaie
Rue Lèopold 4, 1000 **Brussels**
Tel: 2-229 1227 Fax: 2-229 1386
Internet: www.demunt.be
general director Bernard Foccroulle; orchestra manager Ingrid De Backer; music director Antonio Pappano; artistic administrator Bernd Loebe
Size: 95 *Perfs:* 100 (opera/concerts) *Type/spec:* symphony orchestra *Venues:* La Monnaie de Munt 1150
Touring: Europe *Comments:* alternative Internet: www.lamonnaie.be; see also Opera

Oxalys Ensemble
Regentschapsstraat 30, 1000 **Brussels**
Tel: 2-503 1602 Fax: 2-503 3824
Internet: digitaalbrussel.vgl.be/users/oxalys
E-Mail: info@oxalys.be
artistic coordinator Toon Fret; general manager Helmut Schmitz; press/public relations Kathleen van Schel
Size: 8 *Perfs:* 60-70 *Type/spec:* impressionist, romantic and contemporary chamber music *Touring:* Russia, Italy, Germany, Spain, USA, Japan

Quatuor Danel
10 rue Mommaerts, 1080 **Brussels**
Tel: 2-411 5237 Fax: 2-414 0369
Internet: www.quatuordanel.com
E-Mail: info@quatuordanel.com
contact Catherine Lemeunier
Size: 4 *Perfs:* 80 *Type/spec:* chamber music, classic and contemporary *Touring:* Europe *Comments:* UK agent: Neil Chaffey, 9 Munts Meadow, Weston, SG4 7AE, United Kingdom, Tel: +44 1462-790 910, Fax: +44 1462-790 929

Solisti del Vento
Bleidenhoek 1, 2570 **Duffel**
Tel: 15-310 596 Fax: 15-310 596
musical directors Francis Pollet, Joris Van den Hauwe
Size: 10 *Perfs:* 25 *Type/spec:* classical, romantic, 20th century *Touring:* Belgium, Netherlands, Germany, Spain

SPECTRA Ensemble, Het
Spitaalpoortstr. 88, 9000 **Gent**
Tel: 9-228 6953 Fax: 9-228 6905
E-Mail: hetspectraens@hotmail.com
artistic director/conductor Filip Rathé; coordinator Alvaro Guimaraes
Size: 8-15 *Type/spec:* new and 20thC chamber music
Touring: Brazil, France, Germany, Netherlands, Denmark

Flemish Radio Orchestra & Choir
Vlaams Radio Orkest – VRO
Pleinstraat 135, 3001 **Leuven**
Tel: 16-294 191 Fax: 16-294 441
Internet: vlaams-radio-orkest-koor.be
E-Mail: music@vro-vrk.be
intendant Dries Sel; artistic director Gunther Broucke; chief-conductor Frank Shipway
Size: orchestra: 90, choir: 25
Perfs: orchestra: 60, choir: 40 *Type/spec:* classical, romantic, contemporary *Touring:* national, Germany, Switzerland, Spain, Netherlands

Petite Bande, La
rue Vital Decoster 72, 3000 **Leuven**
Tel: 16-230 830 Fax: 16-227 610
Internet: www.ping.be/lapetitebande
E-Mail: geert.robberechts@ping.be
manager Geert Robberechts; conductor Sigiswald Kuijken
Size: 30-50 *Perfs:* 40 *Type/spec:* baroque, classical
Touring: Belgium, France, Spain, Portugal, Hungary, Switzerland, Holland, Germany, Italy, Poland, USA, Japan, South America, Australia
Comments: see also Early Music

Prima la Musica Chamber Orchestra of Flanders
Interleuvenlaan 62A, Zone 2, 3001 **Leuven**
Tel: 16-406 000 Fax: 16-408 000
E-Mail: primalamusica@bcleuven.be
manager Koen Vandyck; conductor Dirk Vermeulen; artistic advisor Jan Dewilde
Size: 17-30 *Perfs:* 60 *Type/spec:* ranges from baroque to contemporary, specialising in late 18th/early 19th C music, particularly Joseph Haydn's early symphonies
Touring: Belgium, Portugal, Morocco, Netherlands, Austria, Spain, Israel, USA

Orchestre Philharmonique de Liège et de la Communauté Française
Rue Forgeur 11, 4000 **Liège**
Tel: 4-223 6360/6774 (bookings)
Fax: 4-223 7065
Internet: www.skynet.be/opl
E-Mail: opl@skynet.be
directeur/coordinateur Paul-Emile Mottard; directeur financier Georges Viatour
Size: 93 *Perfs:* 85-90 *Type/spec:* classical *Venues:* Conservatoire Royal de Musique de Liège 974 (being renovated for 2 years), during this time: Basilique St Martin Liège 800 *Touring:* France, Netherlands, Luxembourg, South America

Ex Tempore (Chamber Orchestra)
Koninginlaan 22, 9820 **Merelbeke (Gent)**
Tel: 9-231 9712 Fax: 9-231 9712
E-Mail: yves.rosseel@skynet.be
manager Yves Rosseel; music director/conductor Florian Heyerick
Size: 12-24 *Perfs:* 40 *Type/spec:* 16th-20thC chamber music, oratorio, cantatas, chamber operas *Touring:* Netherlands, Russia, France, Belgium, Germany
Comments: see also Choirs (Ex Tempore); managers' address: Brusselsesteenweg 324, 9050 Ledeberg, Belgium, Tel: 9-232 1926/32-7579 8561 (mobile), Fax: 9-232 0999

Ensemble Musiques Nouvelles
106, Rue de Nimy, 7000 **Mons**
Tel: 65-847 044 Fax: 65-321 158
director Jean-Paul Dessy; conductor Patrick Davin
Size: varies *Perfs:* 10-15
Type/spec: chamber, contemporary
Touring: Belgium

Orchestre Royal de Chambre de Wallonie
Rue de Nimy 106, 7000 **Mons**
Tel: 65-847 044 Fax: 65-321 158
directeur musical Jean Paul Dessy; administrateur Robert Leleu
Size: 14 (strings) *Perfs:* 60 *Type/spec:* romantic, classical, 20thC *Touring:* France, Germany, Switzerland, Belgium, Italy, England

Het Symfonieorkest van Vlaanderen
Albrecht Rodenbachstraat 44, 8020 **Oostkamp**
Tel: 50-840 587 Fax: 50-840 687
president Roland Coryn; manager Dirk Coutigny; chief conductor Davis Angus; press, promotion & communication officer Filipp Decruynaere; accountant Katrijn De Meyer; production leader Geert Stubbe
Size: 58-65 *Perfs:* 50 *Type/spec:* from classic to contemporary *Touring:* Italy

Thalia Trio (formerly Mozart StringTrio)
c/o Square Music, Persoonstraat 29, 3454 **Rummen**
Tel: 11-583 030 Fax: 11-583 033
E-Mail: squaremusic@ibm.net
Size: 3 *Type/spec:* classical, contemporary and lesser-known scores

Vega Trio and Ensemble
c/o Square-Music, Persoonstraat 29, 3454 **Rummen**
Tel: 11-583 030 Fax: 11-583 033
manager Geert Lavrysen
Size: 3-5 *Type/spec:* piano & strings

I Fiamminghi
Buizenbergstraat 1C, 9830 **St Martens-Latem**
Tel: 9-282 7134 Fax: 9-282 7831
E-Mail: i.fiamminghi@ping.be
artistic director/conductor Rudolf Werthen
Size: 16-75 *Perfs:* 90 *Type/spec:* from baroque to contemporary, crossover & multimedia project, music theatre, opera *Venues:* Amsterdam, Concertgebouw 2000; Tilburg, Concertzaal 850, Brussels; Lunatheater 550; Gent-Bÿloke 1100 *Touring:* Europe, USA, Japan, South America *Comments:* see also Early Music

Arioso VZW
Dageraadstraat 32, 2300 **Turnhout**
Tel: 14-413 730 Fax: 14-413 730
music director Werner Van Mechelen; co-ordinator Lydie Marien
Size: 2-5 *Perfs:* 150 *Type/spec:* all vocal productions (lied, oratorio, opera), baroque to contemporary *Touring:* Spain, Italy, Switzerland, Germany, Netherlands, Canada, France, England

Kempische Oratorium Vereniging VZW
Dageraadstraat 32, 2300 **Turnhout**
Tel: 14-413 730 Fax: 14-413 730
admin. Lydie Marien; music dir. Werner Van Mechelen
Size: 20 musicians, 50-55 singers *Perfs:* 10 *Type/spec:* chamber orchestra and instrumental/vocal productions
Venues: CC Warande *Touring:* Switzerland, France

Belle Epoque Orchestra, The
Pastoor de Conincklaan 18, 2610 **Wilrijk (Antwerpen)**
Tel: 3-828 6762 Fax: 3-828 2439
Internet: www.pws.be
E-Mail: info@pws.be
director/conductor Wim Brabants; manager Jean Alleyn; public relations Lutgard Heyvaerts
Size: 35 musicians + conductor *Perfs:* 25 *Type/spec:* symphonic orchestra: classical music second half 19th century (belle epoque period), Strauss, Stolz and many other contemporary composers *Venues:* concert halls capacity 1000 *Touring:* full concert tour mainly in Belgium, the Netherlands and Eruope

BOSNIA & HERZEGOVINA (+387)

Chamber Orchestra of the Music Academy
Josip Stadler Str 1, 71000 **Sarajevo**
Tel: 71-200 299/444 896 Fax: 71-444 896
Type/spec: chamber

Percussion Orchestra
Secondary Music School, Josipa Stadlera 1, 71000 **Sarajevo**
Tel: 71-207 951 Fax: 71-441 951
conductor Desanka Jovanovic

Sarajevo Philharmonic Orchestra
Sarajevska filharmonia
Obala Kulina Bana 9, 71000 **Sarajevo**
Tel: 71-666 520/21/23 Fax: 71-213 853
director Emir Nuhanovic

Sarajevo String Quartet
c/o Music Academy, Jospi Stadler Str 1, 71000 **Sarajevo**
Tel: 71-200 299/444 896 Fax: 71-444 896
contact Dzevad Sabanagic
Type/spec: string quartet

Accordion Orchestra of the Secondary Music School
c/o Secondary Music School, Ludvika Kube 1, 75000 **Tuzla**
Tel: 75-222 551 Fax: 75-222 551
conductor Midhat Zulic

Chamber Symphonic Orchestra Zenica
Zeniske brigade Str 11, 72000 **Zenica**
Tel: 72-415 089 Fax: 72-419 323
artistic director Senad Kazic

BULGARIA (+359)

Opera & Philharmonic Society
1 Vola Str., 8000 **Bourgas**
Tel: 56-840 516 Fax: 56-840 516
director Rossen Grouev
Perfs: 80 *Venues:* capacity 300

Bulgarian New Chamber Orchestra
25 September Str., 9300 **Dobritch**
Tel: 58-27349/24063
director Temenoujka Konstantinova

Pleven State Philharmonic Orchestra with Open Opera Stage
122 Vassil Levski Str., 5800 **Pleven**
Tel: 64-22692 Fax: 64-23886
director Ivailo Atanassov
Perfs: 85

Opera & Philharmonic Society
1 Central Square, 4000 **Plovdiv**
Tel: 32-236 525 Fax: 32-236 525
director Borislav Ivanov
Perfs: 98 *Venues:* capacity 750

Opera & Philharmonic Society
1 Aleia Vazrajdane Str. , 7000 **Rousse**
Tel: 82-225 680 Fax: 82-225 327
director Michael Anguelov
Perfs: 92 *Venues:* capacity 600

Shoumen State Philharmonic Orchestra
10 Dimitar Blagoev Str., 9700 **Shoumen**
Tel: 54-55105
artistic director/conductor Stanislav Ushev
Perfs: 73 *Venues:* capacity 320

Big Band of the Bulgarian National Radio, The
4 Dragan Tzankov Blvd., 1000 **Sofia**
Tel: 2-8541 Fax: 2-661 812
conductor Janko Milandinov
Size: 20

Sofia Philharmonic Orchestra
1 Benkovski Str., 1000 **Sofia**
Tel: 2-883 197/195 Fax: 2-874 072
principal concuctor & artistic director Emil Tabakov; director Bedros Papazian
Perfs: 108 *Venues:* capacity 1134

Sofiiski Solisti Chamber Orchestra
Kulturen dom Krasno selo, 1000 **Sofia**
Tel: 2-870 824/544 660
director/conductor Plamen Djourov

Symphonic Orchestra of the Bulgarian National Radio
4 Dragan Tzankov Blvd., 1000 **Sofia**
Tel: 2-8541 Fax: 2-662 388
conductor Milen Nachev

Opera & Philharmonic Society
20 Atanas Gueorguiev Str., 9000 **Varna**
Tel: 52-234 145 Fax: 52-234 145
artistic director Hristo Ignatov
Perfs: 97 *Venues:* capacity 1000

Vidin State Philharmonic Orchestra
4 Gradinska Str., 3700 **Vidin**
Tel: 94-24675 Fax: 94-24675
director Miroslav Krastev
Perfs: 70 *Venues:* capacity 700

Vratza State Philharmonic Orchestra
1 Christo Botev Square, 3000 **Vratza**
Tel: 92-23434 Fax: 92-60053
director Dimitar Panov
Perfs: 57 *Venues:* capacity 380

Chamber Orchestra
Community Centre Saglassie, 20 Rakovski Str., 8600 **Yambol**
Tel: 46-28811
conductor Nikolay Soultanov

CROATIA (+385)

Dubrovnik Symphony Orchestra
Dubrovacki Simfonijski Orkestar
Put Dr. Ante Starcevica 29, 20000 **Dubrovnik**
Tel: 20-417 101/110
Fax: 20-417 734
director Piero Cavaliero

Orchestra of the Croatian National Theatre
Orkestar Hrvatskog Narodnog Kazalista
Zùpanijska 9, 31000 **Osijek**
Tel: 31-220 700 Fax: 31-220 734
theatre director Zeljko Cagalj

Orchestra of the People's Theatre 'I. Pl. Zajca
Orkestar Narodnog Kazalista I. Pl. Zajca
Uljarska 1, 51000 **Rijeka**
Tel: 51-212 322/318 Fax: 51-212 600
theatre director Srecko Sestan

Orchestra of the Croatian National Theatre
Orkestar Hrvatskog Narodnog Kazalista
Trg Gaja Bulata 1, 21000 **Split**
Tel: 21-585 999 Fax: 21-583 643
theatre director Marija Gotovac

Zadar Chamber Orchestra
Zadarski Komorni Orkestar
Obala Kneza Branimira 10, 23000 **Zadar**
artistic director Drago Novak (tel: 23-312 786)

Zadar town orchestra
Gradska glazba Zadar
Zagrebacka bb, 23000 **Zadar**
Tel: 23-430 439
dirigent Marin Kovic

Lado Folk Ensemble
Folklorni ansambl Lado
Trg Marsala Tita 6a, 10000 **Zagreb**
Tel: 1-482 8473 Fax: 1-482 8474
director Josip Guberina

Orchestra of the Croatian National Theatre
Orkestar Hrvatskog Narodnog Kazalista
Trg Marsala Tita 15, 10000 **Zagreb**
Tel: 1-482 8533 Fax: 1-446 488
general director Georgij Paro
Comments: see also Dance, Drama and Opera

Symphony Orchestra of Croatian RTV
Simfonijski orkestar HRT
Dezmanova 10/3, 10000 **Zagreb**
Tel: 1-480 7111/7344/7218 Fax: 1-480 7191
chief conductor Niksa Bareza; director Stanislav Mlinar

Tamburaski orkestar HRT
Dezmanova 10/3, 10000 **Zagreb**
Tel: 1-480 7111 Fax: 1-480 7191
director Stanislav Mlinar; chief conductor Leopold Sinisa

Zagreb Philharmonic Orchestra
Zagrebacka Filharmonija
Trg. Stjepana Radica 4, 10000 **Zagreb**
Tel: 1-611 1561/1547 Fax: 1-611 1577
director Andelko Ramuscak

Zagreb Soloists
Zagrebacki Solosti
Trg. Svetog Marka 9, 10000 **Zagreb**
Tel: 1-425 551/420 017 Fax: 1-423 667/425 551
artistic director Andelko Krpan

CYPRUS (+357)

Cyprus State Chamber Orchestra
Cultural Services – Ministry of Education and Culture, 20 Byron Avenue, 1437 **Nicosia**
Tel: 2-303 337/302 442 Fax: 2-673 565
artistic director & resident conductor Roland Melia
Size: 40 *Perfs:* 50 *Type/spec:* opera & operetta, contemporary, symphonic, oratorio *Venues:* Municipal Theatre (Nicosia) 1200; Pattichieon Municipal Theatre (Limassol)750; Markideion Theatre (Paphos) 380; Kasteliotissa (Nicosia) 250; Falcon School Ampitheatre (Strovolos) 900; Muncipal Theatre (Larnaka) 400; Rialto Theatre (Limassol) 560 *Touring:* Greece, Bulgaria

Cyprus Youth Orchestra
Cultural Services – Ministry of Education and Culture, 20 Byron Avenue, 1437 **Nicosia**
Tel: 2-303 337/302 442 Fax: 2-673 565
orchestra director Michael Stavrides; artistic director & resident conductor Roland Melia
Size: 65 *Perfs:* 12-15 *Type/spec:* symphony, chamber, contemporary *Venues:* Municipal Theatre (Nicosia) 1200; Pattichelon Municipal Theatre (Limassol) 750; Falcon School Amphitheatre (Strovolos) 900; Rialto Theatre (Limassol) 560 *Touring:* Greece

CZECH REPUBLIC (+420)

Jan Cikker Symphony Orchestra
Symfonicky Orchester Jana Cikkera
Narodna 11, 974 73 **Banska Bystrica**
Tel: 88-412 4418/5021 Fax: 88-415 3457
director Rudolf Hromada; chief conductor Pavol Tuzinsky

Brno Brass Band
Solnicní 6, 602 00 **Brno**
Tel: 5-4221 0852
conductor Evzen Zámecník
Size: 10 brass insturments and percussion

Brno State Philharmonic
Státní filharmonie Brno
Komenského nám. 8, 602 00 **Brno**
Tel: 5-4221 2300/4255 Fax: 5-4221 2300/8284
Internet: www.musica.cz/bpo/
E-Mail: filharmoniebrn@mbox.vol.cz
director Mgr. Bohus Zoubek; conductor Aldo Ceccato

Middle Europe Percussion Ensemble Dama Dama
Berkova 35, 612 00 **Brno**
Tel: 5-745 965/4124 7180 Fax: 5-4323 3358
artistic chief Ing. Mgr. Dan Dlouhy

South Bohemian Chamber Philharmonic
Jihoceská komorní filharmonie
Knezská 6, 370 21 **Ceské Budejovice**
Tel: 38-63561-2 Fax: 38-731 1554
director Ing. Milena Andrlová; conductor Stanislav Vavrínek

Hradec Králové Philarmonic
Filharmonie Hradec Králové
Eliscino nábr 777, 500 10 **Hradec Králové**
Tel: 49-611 491/375/563 5058 Fax: 49-619 672
director Martin Strejc; conductor Frantisek Vajnar

Symphonic Orchestra Karlovy Vary
Karlovarsky symfonicky orchestr
I. P. Pavlova 14, 360 01 **Karlovy Vary**
Tel: 17-28707 (switchboard)/322 3310 (director)
Fax: 17-322 3753
director Alois Jezek
Comments: without a permanet conductor

West Bohemian Symphonic Orchestra
Západocesky symfonicky orchestr
Ruská 155, POB 274, 353 21 **Mariánské Lázne**
Tel: 165-622 567 (manager) Fax: 165-5641
manager Karolina Hromádková; conductors Radomil Eliska, Frantisek Drs

Czech Trio
Ceské trio
Sportovní 653, 251 64 **Mnichovice**
Tel: 204-641 184/2-499 031/603-583 310 (mobile)
Fax: 204-641 184
contact Dana Vlachová, Mrioslav Petrá, Milan Langer

Moravian Philharmonic Orchestra
Moravská filharmonie
Horní nám. 23, 772 00 **Olomouc**
Tel: 68-522 8971/522 4922 Fax: 68-522 8511
director Vladislav Kvapil (tel: 68-522 5302); conductor Jin Wang

Janácek Philharmonic
Janáckova filharmonie Ostrava
Michálkovická 181, 710 08 **Ostrava**
Tel: 69-621 4800/624 1270-71/222 886 Fax: 69-222 886
director Jan Haliska; conductor Christian Arming

Pardubice Chamber Philharmonic
Komorní filharmonie Pardubice
KD Dubina, J. Zajíce 983, 530 12 **Pardubice**
Tel: 40-626 2775/5461 Fax: 40-626 5462
director Gabriela Gutwirthová; conductor Karel Smeták

Pilsen Philharmonic
Plzenská Filharmonie
nám. Míru 10, 320 70 **Plzen**
Tel: 19-272 254 Fax: 19-272 254
director Jan Motlík; conductor Jan Chalupecky
Size: 48

Symphonic Orchestra Bohemia Podebrady
Symfonicky orchestr Bohemia Podebrady
Za nádrazím 56, 290 01 **Podebrady**
Tel: 324-3537/8 Fax: 324-5345
conductor Jirí Mikula
Size: 55 *Perfs:* 120 *Type/spec:* symphony, opera *Venues:* capacity 400 *Touring:* France, Italy, Germany

Afflatus Quintet
Krakovská 12, 110 00 **Praha** 1
Tel: 2-2221 0324/603-470 570 (mobile) Fax: 2-2221 0324
manager Roman Novotny
Size: 5 *Type/spec:* wind quintet

Agon Orchestra
Terronská 64, 160 00 **Praha** 6
Tel: 2-311 6913/312 0324 Fax: 2-311 6913/312 0324
director Ivan Bierhanzl
Type/spec: contemporary music

Czech Nonetto
Ceské noneto
Strojnická 9, 170 00 **Praha** 7
Tel: 2-807 634 Fax: 2-807 634
manager Vladimíra Klánská

Czech Philharmonic Orchestra
Ceská filharmonie
Alsovo nábr 12, 110 01 **Praha** 1
Tel: 2-2489 3111/3203/231 9051 Fax: 2-2489 3228/26/231 9051
Internet: www.czechphilharmonic.cz
E-Mail: cforch@mbox.vol.cz
director Jirí Kolár; artistic director Vladimir Ashkenazy; conductors Vladimír Válek, Sir Charles Mackerras, Ken-Ichiro Kobayashi
Comments: alternative E-mail: cfmark@mbox.vol.cz

Due Boemi di Praga
Bubenská 9, 170 00 **Praha** 7
Tel: 2-801 889
bass-clarinet Josef Horák; piano Emma Kovárnová
Type/spec: contemporary music

Prague Brass Quintet
Prazské zest'ové kvinteto
Kovárova 11, 155 00 **Praha** 5
Tel: 2-625 1957 Fax: 2-625 1957
artistic chief Josef Svejkovsky

Prague Chamber Orchestra
Prazsky komorní orchestr
Cernokostelecká 6, 100 00 **Praha** 10
Tel: 2-772 697 Fax: 2-772 703
Internet: www.pko.cz
E-Mail: pkoagent@login.cz

Prague Chamber Philharmonic
Prazská komorní filharmonie
Krocinova 1, 110 00 **Praha** 1
Tel: 2-2423 2488/447 086
Fax: 2-2423 5118
Internet: www.pkf.cz
E-Mail: pkf@bohem-net.cz
conductor Jirí Belohlávek; director Ilja Smíd; manager Daniela Pokorna; foreign contacts Dan Vorísek

Prague Madrigalists
Prazstí Madrigalisté sro
Pocernická 61, 108 00 **Praha** 10
Tel: 0602-272 974 (mobile)
Fax: 2-776 969
Internet: www.paretc.copin.it/turboprint/madriga.htm/
manager Luca Gualco; artistic chief Damiano Binetti
Type/spec: chamber ensemble: early music, renaissance, baroque and contemporary
Comments: see also Early Music

Prague Radio Symphony Orchestra
Symfonicky orchestr Ceského rozhlasu
Vinohradská 12, 120 99 **Praha** 2
Tel: 2-2409 4111 (switchboard)/2421 8275
Fax: 2-2424 2043/2421 8290
Internet: www.cro.cz
E-Mail: socr@cro.cz
conductors Vladimír Válek, Ondrej Kukal

Prague Symphony Orchestra
Symfonicky orchestr hlavního mesta Prahy
nám. Republiky 5, 110 00 **Praha** 1
Tel: 2-231 1900/5981/2048/2200 2425
Fax: 2-231 0784
Internet: www.fok.cz
E-Mail: fok@login.cz
manager Ing. Roman Belor
Comments: without a permanet conductor

Stamic Quartet
Stamicovo kvarteto
Zalovská 11, 180 00 **Praha** 8
Tel: 2-855 6380/603-277 995 (mobile)
Fax: 2-855 6380
contact Vladimír Leixner

Talich Quartet
Talichovo kvarteto
Vodièkova 17, 110 00 **Praha** 1
Tel: 2-2494 9143 Fax: 2-581 2410
artistic chief Jan Talich

Virtuosi di Praga
Ag. Lupulus Korunní 60, 120 00 **Praha** 2
Tel: 2-2251 1752/3782 Fax: 2-2251 1752/3782
artistic director Oldrich Vlcek
Type/spec: chamber

North Bohemian Philharmonic
Severoceská filharmonie
U zámku 1, 415 28 **Teplice**
Tel: 417-29463/26471 Fax: 417-26471
director Tomás Ondrásek; conductor Charles Olivieri-Munroe

Bohuslav Martinu Philharmonic Zlín
Filharmonie Bohuslava Martinu Zlín
Dum umení, nám T.G. Masaryka 2570, 760 27 **Zlín**
Tel: 67-721 0623/0207/0479
Fax: 67-721 0169
E-Mail: bmpzlin@mbox.vol.cz
intendant Marek Obdrzálek; conductor Tomáú Koutník

DENMARK (+45)

Aalborg Symfoniorkester Symfonien
Kjellerupsgade 14, 9000 **Aalborg**
Tel: 9813 1955 Fax: 9813 0378
Internet: www.aalborgsymfoniorkester.dk
E-Mail: symfoni@pip.dknet.dk
music director Finn Schumacker; chief conductor Moshe Atzmon
Size: 65 *Perfs:* 100 *Type/spec:* symphonic repertoire
Venues: Aalborg Hall 1104

Aarhus Symfoniorkester
Musikhuset Aarhus, Thomas Jensens Allé, 8000 **Aarhus** C
Tel: 8931 8280 Fax: 8612 7466
E-Mail: aso@post3.tele.dk
chief conductor James Loughran; concerts and personnel manager Anne Herskind; publicity director Mariann Sejer Nielsen; general & artistic manager Jorn Bærentzen (from Feb 2000: Leif Balthzersen)
Size: 72 *Perfs:* 60 (30 at the Musikhuset) *Venues:* Musikhuset 1500 *Comments:* funded by the Municipality of Aarhus; CD recordings; performs with Danish National Opera in Aarhus

Collegium Musicum
c/o Nils Dittmer, Hyskenstrade 14#, 1207 **Copenhagen** K
Tel: 3316 0533 Fax: 3316 0533
chairman Toke Lund Christiansen; principal conductor/artistic director Michael Schønwandt
Size: 40 *Perfs:* 5-10 *Type/spec:* chamber music, symphony *Venues:* Tivoli Concert Hall 2300
Touring: Europe *Comments:* recordings available on Da Capo and Kontrapunkt

Kongelige Kapel, Det
Royal Danish Orchestra
Tordenskjoldsgade 8, Postboks 2185, 1017 **Copenhagen** K
Tel: 3369 6933 Fax: 3369 6967
Internet: www.kgl-teater.dk
E-Mail: admin@kgl-teater.dk
artistic director (opera and orchestra) Elaine Padmore; assistant t.b.a.; chief conductor Paavo Berglund
Size: 104 *Perfs:* 130 opera, 140 ballet, + 10 concerts
Venues: Old Stage, Royal Danish Theatre (Kongelige Teater, Det) resident company *Touring:* national and international *Comments:* resident orchestra of the Royal Danish Ballet and Royal Danish Opera

Sjællands Symfoniorkester/Copenhagen Philharmonic Orchestra
Ny Kongensgade 13, 1472 **Copenhagen** K
Tel: 3391 1199 Fax: 3314 9034
E-Mail: cph.phil@get2net.dk
chief conductor Heinrich Schiff; administration Maria Sørensen
Size: 74 *Perfs:* 112 *Type/spec:* symphony orchestra, opera
Venues: Tivoli Concert Hall *Touring:* Japan 2001
Comments: performs as 'Tivoli Symphony Orchestra' May-September

Esbjerg Ensemble
Islandsgade 50, 6700 **Esbjerg**
Tel: 7513 9399 Fax: 7513 3242
Internet: www.esbjerg-ensemble.suite.dk
E-Mail: ee@esbjerg-ensemble.dk
administrative director Leif Pedersen; artistic director Michel Camille
Size: 12 *Perfs:* 50 *Type/spec:* classical, new music
Venues: capacity 1200 *Touring:* Scandinavia, UK, Germany, France, USA

Vestjysk Symfoniorkester
Symphony Orchestra of Western Jutland
Islandsgade 50, 6700 **Esbjerg**
Tel: 7513 9399 Fax: 7513 3242
Internet: www.esbjerg-ensemble.suite.dk
E-Mail: vso@esbjerg-ensemble.dk
administrative director Leif Pedersen; orchestra chairman Kaj Tagmose
Size: 60-70 *Perfs:* 5-6 concerts per season
Type/spec: symphonic repertoire
Touring: national

Danish National Radio Symphony Orchestra
Radiohuset, 1999 **Frederiksberg** C
Tel: 3520 3040 Fax: 3520 6121
Internet: www.dr.dk/rso
E-Mail: pev@dr.dk
artistic director and general manager Per Erik Veng; executive producers Katharina Ronnefeld (RSO) & Gordon Alsing (Choir); principal conductor Gerd Albrecht; principal guest conductors Yuri Temirkanov, Michael Schønwandt; principal conductor (choir) Stefan Parkman; principal guest conductor (choir) Stephen Layton
Size: 99 *Perfs:* 60 *Venues:* Danish Radio Concert Hall 1050 *Touring:* national, USA, Iceland, Germany, Salzburg Festival, Proms (London), Edinburgh Festival
Comments: more than 65 CD's for Chandos; see also Choirs

Danish Radio Concert Orchestra
Radiounderholdningsorkestret
Radiohuset, 1999 **Frederiksberg** C
Tel: 3520 6329 Fax: 3520 6122
artistic & administrative director Kim Bohr-Christensen; chief conductor Adam Fisher
Size: 42-65 *Perfs:* 65
Type/spec: small symphony, 18th century to 20th century popular music
Venues: Radio Concert Hall 1100, concert halls, theatres
Touring: Denmark, Hungary *Comments:* also perform under the name Danish Radio Sinfonietta

Aarhus Sinfonietta
c/o Kasper Hanmer Pihl, Lille Elstedvej 271, Elsted, 8520 **Lystrup** C
Tel: 8674 1350/2620 5350 (mobile) Fax: 8674 1341
Internet: www.sinfonietta.dk
E-Mail: sinfonietta@bip.cybercity.dk
artistic director Niels Marthinsen; conductor Søren K.Hansen
Size: 18-20 *Perfs:* 9 *Type/spec:* new music *Venues:* Århus Musikhus – small hall 300 *Comments:* CDs available on Dacapo, BIS and Kontrapunkt

Odense Symfoniorkester
Claus Bergs Gade 9, 5000 **Odense** C
Tel: 6612 0057/9357 Fax: 6591 0047
E-Mail: orchestra@odensesymfoni.dk
general manager Per Holst; chief conductor Jan Wagner
Size: 73 *Perfs:* 100 *Type/spec:* symphony orchestra, classical, modern, popular *Venues:* Odense Koncerthus 1300 *Touring:* USA, Spain, Japan

Randers Chamber Orchestra
Randers Byorkester
Værket, Mariagervej 6, 8900 **Randers**
Tel: 8641 2833 Fax: 8641 2414
Internet: home3.inet.tele.dk/rbo/
E-Mail: rbo@post3.tele.dk
chief conductor and manager David Riddell; publicity Bjarne Mørch Jensen
Size: 10 (permanent)-30 *Perfs:* 50 including opera
Type/spec: chamber, classical *Touring:* Scandinavia, Greenland *Comments:* CDs available

Danish Philharmonic Orchestra, South Jutland, The
South Jutland Muiskhuset, Skovvej 16, 6400 **Sønderborg**
Tel: 7442 6161 Fax: 7442 6106
E-Mail: lvsb@sonderjyllands-symfoniorkester.dk
general manager Leif V.S. Balthzersen
Size: 64 *Perfs:* 90 *Type/spec:* symphony orchestra – whole repertoire *Venues:* capacity 250-1500
Touring: southern Jutland, north Germany *Comments:* touring orchestra

ESTONIA (+372)

Haapsalu City Orchestra
Haapsalu Linnaorkester
Posti 34, 90502 **Haapsalu**
Tel: 4-744 755
conductor Jüri Ruut-Kangur

Pärnu City Orchestra
Pärnu Linnaorkester
Nikolai tn. 8, 80011 **Pärnu**
Tel: 4-445 634 Fax: 4-444 167
Internet: styx.parnu.ee/orkester
E-Mail: tarmo@parnu.ee
director Tõiv Tiits

Estonia Theatre Opera Orchestra
Estonia Teatri Orkester
Estonia pst. 4, 10148 **Tallinn**
Tel: 6-260 201 Fax: 6-260 299
Internet: www.ooper.ee/index1.htm
E-Mail: estonia@opera.teleport.ee
chief conductor Paul Mägi; managing director Paul Himma
Size: 84 *Type/spec:* symphony *Venues:* Estonia Theatre, Estonia Concert Hall

Estonian National Symphony Orchestra
Eesti Riiklik Sümfooniaorkester
Estonia pst. 4, 10148 **Tallinn**
Tel: 6-446 597 Fax: 6-314 055
E-Mail: erso@estpak.ee
chief conductor Arvo Volmer; managing director Ville-Markus Kell
Size: 100 *Type/spec:* symphony
Venues: Estonia Concert Hall

NYYD Ensemble
Peeter Süda 3-5, 10118 **Tallinn**
Tel: 6-463 238 Fax: 6-463 238
E-Mail: nyydens@online.ee
conductor Olari Elts
Type/spec: 20th century music

Symphony Orchestra of the Estonian Music Academy
Eesti Muusikaakadeemia Sümfooniaorkester
Vabaduse pst. 130, 10920 **Tallinn**
Tel: 6-314 643 Fax: 6-706 809
administrator Krista Karu; conductor Jüri Alperten
Size: 70 *Type/spec:* symphony

Tallinn Baroque Orchestra
Tallinna Barokkorkester
Rävala pst. 12, 10143 **Tallinn**
Tel: 6-466 655 Fax: 6-466 656
director Egmont Välja

Tallinn Chamber Orchestra
Tallinna Kammerorkester
Toompuiestee 18c, 10149 **Tallinn**
Tel: 2-452 453 Fax: 2-453 421
chief conductor Tõnu Kaljuste
Size: 16 *Type/spec:* chamber music

Vanemuine Symphony Orchestra
Vanemuine Sümfooniaorkester
Vanemuise 6, 51003 **Tartu**
Tel: 7-439 012 Fax: 7-441 065
Internet: www.halo.ee/vanemuine
E-Mail: vanem@uninet.ee
conductor Endel Nõgene
Type/spec: symphony

FAROE ISLANDS (+298)

Faroe Symphony Orchestra
Føroya Symfoniorkestur
Undir Brúnni 5, 700 **Klaksvík**
Tel: 456 502 Fax: 456 502
E-Mail: fso@pose.olivan.fo
manager Bogi Lützen; conductor Martin Mouritsen
Size: 50 *Perfs:* 5 *Type/spec:* symphony
Venues: Nordic House (base) 360 *Touring:* Faroe Islands *Comments:* commission composers from the Faroe Islands

Aldubáran
PO Box 1074, 110 **Torshavn**
Tel: 314 815/312 611 Fax: 314 825/312 611
E-Mail: tutl@olivant.fo
artistic director Jóhannes Andreasen; composer Kristian Blak; administrative director Olavur Jakobsen
Size: 9 *Type/spec:* classical and contemporary (specialising in contemporary compositions from the Faroe Islands) *Touring:* national, Denmark, Sweden, Iceland

FINLAND (+358)

Espoo City Orchestra – Tapiola Sinfonietta
Espoon Kaupunginorkesteri – Tapiola Sinfonietta
Espoon Kulttuurikeskus, Kulttuuriaukio, 02100 **Espoo**
Tel: 9-8165 7251 Fax: 9-8165 7259
Internet: www.tapiolasinfonietta.fi
E-Mail: tapiola.sinfonietta@espoo.fi
managers Satu Angervo, Outi Mattila; conductors Jean-Jacques Kantorow, Tuomas Ollila; publicity manager Raija Palomäki
Size: 37 *Perfs:* 45-60 *Type/spec:* symphony, chamber
Venues: Tapiola Hall 789
Touring: national, Europe, Japan

Hämeelinna City Orchestra
Hämeenlinnan Kaupunginorkesteri
Keinusaarentie 13, 13200 **Hämeenlinna**
Tel: 3-675 6877 Fax: 3-621 2811
manager Arla Jokinen (tel: 3-675 6877); conductor Tuomas Pirilä; chairman Maire Rissanen
Size: 20-36 *Venues:* Kirkko 700, Raatihuone 200, Janne-Sali 220

Avanti! Chamber Orchestra
Avanti! Kamariorkesteri
Tallberginkatu 1, B 80, 00180 **Helsinki**
Tel: 9-694 0091 Fax: 9-694 2208
Internet: www.avantimusic.fi
E-Mail: avanti@kaapeli.fi
managing director Aila Manninen; president Ilkka Oramo; artistic director Kari Kriikku; administrator Riikka Noreila
Size: 20-50 *Perfs:* 30 *Type/spec:* baroque to contemporary but focus on 20th century, especially Finnish contemporary music *Touring:* France, Portugal, Italy, Estonia *Comments:* music festival in Porvoo (2000: June 28-July 2, 2001: June 27-July 1); several recordings

Finnish National Opera Orchestra
Suomen Kansallisoopperan orkesteri
Helsinginkatu 58, 00260 **Helsinki**
Tel: 9-4030 2220 Fax: 9-4030 2402
orchestra manager Heikki Riikonene; chief conductor Okkó Kamu
Size: 112 *Perfs:* 200 *Type/spec:* mainly opera, some symphony and chamber *Venues:* Opera House 1365

Helsinki Philharmonic Orchestra
Helsingin kaupunginorkesteri
Finlandia Hall, Karamzininkatu 4, 00100 **Helsinki**
Tel: 9-4024-1/264 (general manager)
Fax: 9-406 484
Internet: www.hel.fi/filharmonia
E-Mail: helsinki.philharmonic@fin.hel.fi
chief conductor Leif Segerstam; general manager Helena Ahonen; publicity manager Marianna Kankare-Loikkanen (9-402 4265)
Size: 98 *Perfs:* 70-80 *Type/spec:* classical *Venues:* Finlandia Hall 1700 *Touring:* Europe, Canary Islands, Japan, USA *Comments:* recording for Ondine (Finnish) Sibelius, Rautavaara, Schedrin

Sibelius Academy Symphony Orchestra, The
PO Box 86, 00251 **Helsinki**
Tel: 9-405 4582/4710 Fax: 9-405 4707
E-Mail: juhanipoutanen@siba.fi
orchestra manager Juhani Poutanen; assistant manager Sari Lilja
Size: 90-100 *Perfs:* 7-8 *Type/spec:* classical & contemporary, mainly Finnish *Venues:* capacity 500-1000 *Touring:* Europe *Comments:* member of EFNYO (q.v)

Hyvinkään Orkesteri
Ivars, Vantaankatu 65, 05800 **Hyvinkää**
Tel: 19-431 927/417 564 Fax: 19-417 564
manager Milko Vesalainen
Size: 43 *Perfs:* 15 *Type/spec:* contemporary *Venues:* Hyvinkää Hall 457 *Comments:* open to young musicians

Joensuu City Orchestra
Joensuun Kaupunginorkesteri
Torikatu 21C, 80100 **Joensuu**
Tel: 13-267 5321 Fax: 13-267 5320
Internet:
www.jns.fi/palvelut/kultturi/okester/orkesteri.htm
E-Mail: pirkko.ahola@jns.fi
manager Pirkko Ahola; conductor & artistic director Atso Almila
Size: 32 *Perfs:* 50 *Type/spec:* symphony, chamber, opera *Venues:* Carelia Hall 600, Joensuu Church 1000, Art Museum 70 *Comments:* alternative internet: www.jns.fi/palvelut/kulttuuri/orkester/orkesteri.htm

Jyväskylä Symphony Orchestra
Jyväskylä Sinfoniaorkesteri
Puistokatu 2A, 40100 **Jyväskylä**
Tel: 14-626 680 Fax: 14-626 685
Internet: personal.inet.fi/musiikki/jkl.sinfonia/
E-Mail: mari.ltaranta@jkl.fi
managing dircetor Lasse Allonen; music director t.b.a.
Size: 33 *Perfs:* 45 *Type/spec:* symphony, chamber, opera
Venues: Jyväskylä City Theatre 551 *Touring:* Japan

Kajaanin Orkesteri
Voudintíe 3D-30, 87200 **Kajaani**
Tel: 8-613 1130 Fax: 8-613 1130
chairman Tarmo Lehtinen; secretary Anne Maksníemí (tel: 8-622 577)
Size: 20 *Perfs:* 10 *Venues:* Kaukametsä Hall 486

Kemi City Orchestra
Kemin kaupunginorkesteri
Meripuistokatu 19, 94100 **Kemi**
Tel: 16-259 462 (conductor)/458 (manager)/463 (box office) Fax: 16-259 461
Internet: www.kemi.fi/musiikki
E-Mail: pertti.hynninen@kemi.fi
conductor Pertti Hynninen; economic manager Riitta Hyvönen (tel: 16-259 458); adinistration Anne Hänninen (tel: 16-259 463)
Size: 4-55 *Perfs:* 15 *Type/spec:* symphony, chamber
Venues: Kemi Concert Hall 496

Ostrobothnian Chamber Orchestra – Kokkola Orchestra
Mannerheiminaukio 4, 67100 **Kokkola**
Tel: 6-822 0146 Fax: 6-831 0079
Internet: www.orkesteri.kokkola.fi
E-Mail: orch@kpko.kpnet.fi
general manager Gun-Maj Peltoniemi ; conductor Juha Kangas (6-831 4261)
Size: 20 (OCO), 64 (KO) *Perfs:* 60 *Type/spec:* string orchestra *Venues:* Snellman Hall 600, Conservatoire Hall 196 *Touring:* Netherlands, Lithuania, France

Kymi Sinfonietta
Keskuskatu 33, 48100 **Kotka**
Tel: 5-234 4709/08 Fax: 5-234 4708
E-Mail: joukokoivukoski@kotka.fi
conductor Juha Nikkola; general manager Jouni Maunula
Size: 29 *Perfs:* 50 *Type/spec:* symphony, chamber, opera, musicals *Venues:* Concert Hall 456, City Hall 400
Comments: formed in 1999 from the recently disbanded Kotka and Kouvola City Orchestras

Kuopio Symphony Orchestra
Kuopion kaupunginorkesteri
Kuopionlahdenkatu 23D, 70100 **Kuopio**
Tel: 17-182 361/2/7 Fax: 17-182 373
Internet: www.kuopio.fi/kut/muk/index.htm
E-Mail: musiikkikeskus@kuopio.fi
general manager Michael Claussen; conductor Atso Almila
Size: 46 *Perfs:* 60 *Type/spec:* symphony, opera, chamber
Venues: Music Centre 1064 *Touring:* Finland *Comments:* resident orchestra at Kuopio Music Centre (see Venues)

Lahti Symphony Orchestra (Sinfonia Lahti)
Sibeliuksenk. 8, 15110 **Lahti**
Tel: 3-814 4452/781 8700 (box office) Fax: 3-814 4451
Internet: www.lahti.fi/symphony
E-Mail: hilka.liinavirta@lahti.fi
general manager Tuomas Kinberg; music director Osmo Vänskä; principal guest conductor Joseph Swensen; economic manager Ritva Frisk (tel: 3-814 4453); publicity manager Taina Räty (tel: 3-814 4459)
Size: 59 *Perfs:* 40 + 70 in small groups during street music events etc. *Type/spec:* symphony, 18th century and 20th century (Finnish music especially in recordings) *Venues:* Lahti Concert Hall 581, Church of the Cross 1050 *Touring:* Europe, Far East *Comments:* composer in residence: Kalevi Aho

Lappeenranta City Orchestra
Lappeenrannan kaupunginorkesteri
Kaivokatu 7B, 53100 **Lappeenranta**
Tel: 5-616 2361/2362 (general manager) Fax: 5-616 2363
general manager Tuulikki Närhinsalo;
conductor Hannu Norjanen
Size: 20 permanent (35-40 occassionaly) *Perfs:* 20-40
Type/spec: symphony, chamber, opera *Venues:* Lappeenranta Hall 750, Lappeenranta Music Institute Hall 220 *Touring:* regional

Lohja City Orchestra
Lohjan Kaupunginorkesteri
PL 71, 08101 **Lohja**
Tel: 19-369 1462 Fax: 19-369 1201
Internet: www.lumo.lohja.fi/orkester.htm
E-Mail: tuula.welling@lohja.fi
manager & conductor Petri Sakari; general manager Felix von Willebrand
Size: 59 (10 permanent) *Perfs:* 36 *Type/spec:* symphony, chamber *Venues:* Laurentius Hall 474

Mikkeli City Orchestra
Mikkelin kaupunginorkesteri
Sointukatu 1, 50100 **Mikkeli**
Tel: 15-212 956 Fax: 15-212 930
manager Helina Tepponen; conductor Ari Angerro
Size: 12 *Perfs:* 23-25 *Type/spec:* string orchestra, mainly chamber repertoire *Venues:* Concert Hall 694, Chamber Music Hall 170

Oulu Symphony Orchestra
Oulun kaupunginorkesteri
PL 4, 90015 **Oulu**
Tel: 8-5584 7210 Fax: 8-5587 2299
Internet: www.ouka.fi/musiikki
E-Mail: riitta.pulliainen@ouka.fi
manager Riitta Pulliainen; conductor Arno Volmer (until end July 1999)
Size: 53 *Perfs:* 60 *Type/spec:* symphony, chamber, opera
Venues: Oulu City Theatre: Madetoga Hall 816, Tulingberg Hall 220 *Touring:* national *Comments:* the orchestra is responsible for the musical direction of the Oulu Opera; see also Opera and Venues

Pori City Orchestra
Porin Kaupunginorkesteri
Itsenäisyydenkatu 47, 28100 **Pori**
Tel: 2-621 1097 Fax: 2-621 1099
E-Mail: ritva.ulmas@pori.fi
manager Ritva Ulmas; conductor Juhani Lamminmäki
Size: 28-35 *Perfs:* 75 *Type/spec:* symphony, chamber, opera *Venues:* Palmgren Hall 255, Pripoli Hall 392
Touring: Scandinavia

Symphony Orchestra VIVO
Sinfoniaorkesteri VIVO
Arjavirrankatu 17, 11100 **Riihimäki**
Tel: 19-722 722 Fax: 19-732 875
Internet: www.mtv3.fi/vivo
E-Mail: vivo.ruponen@kolumbus.fi
managing director Riitta Nisonen; conductor Mikko Frank; general manager Sauli Ruponen (tel: 19-722 722)
Size: 95 *Perfs:* 5 *Type/spec:* symphony *Venues:* Finnish National Opera *Touring:* Finland, Europe

Chamber Orchestra of Lapland – Rovaniemi City Orchestra, The
Lapin Kamariorkesteri – Rovaniemen kaupunginorkesteri
Hallituskatu 7, 96100 **Rovaniemi**
Tel: 16-322 2669 Fax: 16-322 3035
Internet: www.rovaniemi.fi/taide/orkka/orkka
E-Mail: ulla-maija.kanerva@rovaniemi.fi
manager Ulla-Maija Kanerva; conductor John Storgårds
Size: 21 (13 permanent) *Perfs:* 50 *Type/spec:* symphony, chamber *Venues:* Rovaniemi Church 800, Rovaniemi Art-Museum 150, Lappia-House 560

Savonlinnan Orkesteri
Sotilaspojank 1, 57100 **Savonlinna**
Tel: 15-273 745 Fax: 15-515 182
general manager Miikka Vuo
Size: 4-15 *Perfs:* 30 *Type/spec:* wide repertoire
Venues: Music Institute 250 *Touring:* national

Seinäjoki Orchestra
Seinäjoen Orkesteri
Keskuskatu 32 A, 60100 **Seinäjoki**
Tel: 6-420 2924 Fax: 6-420 2940
E-Mail: epn.musiikkiopisto@co.inet.fi
conductor/general manager Antti Vainio (tel: 6-420 2920); economic manager Raija Väliharju (tel: 6-420 2922)
Size: 48 (10 permanent) *Perfs:* 40 *Type/spec:* symphony, chamber *Venues:* Seinäjoki Hall 360, Town Hall 300

Tampere Philharmonic Orchestra
Tampereen kaupunginorkesteri
Yliopistonkatu 55, PL 16, 33101 **Tampere**
Tel: 3-243 4411 Fax: 3-243 4400
Internet: www.tampere.fi/or
E-Mail: Maritta.Hirvonen@tt.tampere.fi
general manager Maritta Hirvonen; assistant manager Sirkka-Liisa Joki; artistic director Eri Klas; publicity manager Katri Maasalo
Size: 83 *Perfs:* 50 *Type/spec:* symphony, chamber, opera
Venues: Tampere Hall 1806
Touring: Netherlands
Comments: regular recordings; alternative E-mail: orchestra@tampere.fi

Turku Philharmonic Orchestra
Turun kaupunginorkesteri
Sibeliuksenkatu 2A, 20100 **Turku**
Tel: 2-231 4577 Fax: 2-232 8231
Internet: www.turku.fi/kaupunginorkesteri
E-Mail: orchestra@turku.fi
manager Elina Siltanen; assistant manager Tuulikki Lehtinen; principal guest conductor Ralf Gothóni; chief conductor Hannu Lintu
Size: 73 *Perfs:* 90-100 *Type/spec:* mainly symphony, chamber, opera *Venues:* Concert Hall 1002 *Touring:* China

Vaasa City Orchestra
Vaasan kaupunginorkesteri
Sanatenkatu PL 3, 65101 **Vaasa**
Tel: 6-325 3766 Fax: 6-325 3761
manager Merja Tyynelä; conductor Hannu Norjanan
Size: 31 *Perfs:* 80 *Type/spec:* symphony, chamber, opera *Venues:* City Hall 400

Vantaa Pops Orchestra
Vantaan Viihdeorkesteri
Martinlaaksontie 36, 01620 **Vantaa**
Tel: 9-890 346 Fax: 9-5045 5954
E-Mail: iiris.lehtonen@vo.inet.fi
organiser Tuomas Kolehmainen; general manager Iiris Lehtonen; conductor Markku Johansson
Size: 65 *Type/spec:* light *Venues:* Martinus-Sali 406 *Touring:* national

Finnish Radio Symphony Orchestra
Radion Sinfoniaorkesteri
PL14, 00024 **Yleisradio**
Tel: 9-1480 4366 Fax: 9-1480 3551
Internet: www.yle.fi/rso
E-Mail: helena.hiilivirta@yle.fi
manager Helena Hiilivirta (9-1480 4367); chief conductor Jukka-Pekka Saraste; co-principal conductor Sakari Oramo
Size: 98 *Perfs:* 46 + broadcasts *Venues:* Finlandia Hall 1718, House of Culture 1400 *Touring:* national

FRANCE (+33)

Orchestre Bernard Thomas
148 Rue Paul Vaillant Couturier, 94140 **Alfortville**
Tel: 1-4378 0300 Fax: 1-4376 3124
Internet: www.ffi.oise.fr-classicnews
président Jacques Jenvrin; directeur musical Bernard Thomas
Size: 15-50 *Type/spec:* classical, romantic, contemporary, Mozart, chamber music *Touring:* international

Orchestre National d'Île de France
19 rue des Écoles, 94140 **Alfortville**
Tel: 1-4179 0340 Fax: 1-4179 0350
E-Mail: orchestrenationalidf@compuserve.com
président Guy Dumélie; directeur artistique – chef d'orchestre Jacques Mercier; administrateur général Philippe Fanjas; administrateur adjoint Catherine Delcroix; chargée de la communication Anne Rubinstein
Size: 76 *Perfs:* 90-100 *Type/spec:* symphony: classical, contemporary, film music, jazz *Venues:* Salle Pleyel 2300 *Touring:* mainly Île de France but also national, international *Comments:* vast rehearsal hall, available for rent

Orchestre de Picardie
45 rue Pointin, 80040 **Amiens** Cedex 1
Tel: 3-2292 1584 Fax: 3-2292 8308
administrateur général Rose Lowry; directeur musical Edmon Colomer; président t.b.a.
Size: 35 permanent *Perfs:* 85 *Type/spec:* symphonic *Venues:* Maison de la Culture d'Amiens 1000

Orchestre National des Pays de la Loire
BP 5246, 49052 **Angers** Cedex
Tel: 2-4124 1124 Fax: 2-4187 8052
administrateur général Michel Ayroles; président Patrice Chéreau; directeur musical Hubert Soudant; secrétariat artistique Juliette de Marigny; directeur de la communication Arnaud Hie
Size: 102 *Perfs:* 180-200 (incl. opera, concerts for young people) *Type/spec:* baroque, classical, romantic, 20thC and for Opéra de Nantes, Théâtre Musical d'Angers *Venues:* Cité des Congrès de Nantes 2000, Auditorium du centre des congrès d'Angers 1200 *Touring:* France, Germany, Austria *Comments:* visiting address: Maison des Arts, 26 Av Montaigne, BP 5246, 4905 Angers Cedex 2; other address: 7 rue de Valmy, BP 71229, 44012 Nantes Cedex 1, Tel: 2-5125 2929, Fax: 2-5125 2920

Ensemble Orchestral d'Aquitaine
Polifonia-Eliane Lavail, Château Feydeau, 33370 **Artigues-près-Bordeaux**
Tel: 5-5632 6956 Fax: 5-5632 6956
E-Mail: polifoniae@aol.com
directrice Eliane Lavail; présidente Odette Drupin (députée de la Gironde); vice-président Daniel Chrétien; trésorier-secrétaire général François Tabanous; secrétaire Françoise Rouquié
Size: 10-60 *Perfs:* 6 *Type/spec:* purely for accompanying choirs of the region at performances *Touring:* France *Comments:* see also Choirs (Madrigal de Bordeaux)

Orchestre Lyrique de Région Avignon Provence
250 route des Rémouleurs, BP 967, 84 093 **Avignon** Cedex
Tel: 4-9085 2239 Fax: 4-9085 1512
E-Mail: orch.avi@avignon.pacwan.net
administrateur Jany Audigier; directeur musical François-Xavier Bilger; secrétaire administrative Catherine Balestri; président délégue Thierry Mariani (vice-président du conseil général du Vaucluse); secrétaire artistique Joelle Stroelb; adjoint de l'ad Mr Loustaunau
Size: 45 *Perfs:* 8 symphonic, 8 operas, 8 operettas, 30 outdoor concerts *Type/spec:* symphony, opera, operetta, ballet *Venues:* Opéra d'Avignon 1000 and other venues in Provence *Touring:* France

Orchestre Régional, Bayonne – Côte Basque
29 Cours du Comte de Cabarrus, 64100 **Bayonne**
Tel: 5-5931 2172 Fax: 5-5931 2171
administrateur Danielle Chambon; directeur musical Xavier Delette; président Jean-Michel Barate
Size: 20 permanent *Perfs:* 25 orchestra, 15 chamber music *Type/spec:* symphony & chamber all periods *Venues:* Gare du Midi, Biarritz 1200, Théâtre de Bayonne 800, Casino Municipal de Biarritz 1000 *Touring:* Europe

Orchestre National Bordeaux Aquitaine
Place de la Comedie, BP 95, 33025 **Bordeaux** Cedex
Tel: 5-5600 8520 Fax: 5-5681 9366
directeur général Thierry Fouquet; directeur musical Hans Grass; dèlègué général Pierre Choffé; directeur administratif François Vienne
Size: 120 *Perfs:* 160 *Type/spec:* opera, symphony, chamber music *Venues:* Grand Théâtre de Bordeaux 1114, Palais des Sports 1400, Théâtre Fénina 1100 *Touring:* national, international *Comments:* see also Opera, Dance and Venues

Orchestre de Chambre et Chorale Paul Kuentz
44 rue Guillaume Apollinaire, 91220 **Bretigny-sur-Orge**
Tel: 1-6988 9351 Fax: 1-6988 9351
directeur musical Paul Kuentz; responsable des tournées Charles et Camille Kiesgen
Size: 13-60 *Perfs:* 50-80 *Type/spec:* chamber, all repertoire, lyric, sacred *Venues:* Salle Pleyel 2300, Eglise Saint Séverin 700, Salle Groveau 1000 *Touring:* worldwide

L'Ensemble – Orchestre Regional de Basse-Normandie
Abbaye aux Dames, Place Reine Mathilde, BP 331, 14016 **Caen** Cedex
Tel: 2-3106 9886 Fax: 2-3193 2036
Internet: www.net-music.com/lensemble
E-Mail: Orbn@net-music.com
administrateur Philippe Dolfus; président Pierre Aguiton; directeur musical Dominique Debart; régisseur général Annick Aleon-Leguéné; déléguée général Véronique Daufresne; régisseur Didier Lelièvre; secrétaire Nathalie Peschard; secrétaire Corinne Kerhoas
Size: 19 permanent *Perfs:* 100 *Type/spec:* chamber and orchestra *Venues:* Abbaye aux Dames 160 *Touring:* international *Comments:* collabration with opera and ballet productions

Orchestre Régional de Cannes Provence Alpes Côte d'Azur
104 Avenue Francis Tonner, BP 46, 06156 **Cannes-la-Bocca** Cedex
Tel: 4-9348 6110 Fax: 4-9348 6374
administratrice Catherine Morschel; directeur musical Philippe Bender; président Pierre Simonet
Size: 40 permanent *Type/spec:* baroque, classical, romantic, contemporary *Venues:* Théâtre Debussy in Palais des Festivals et des Congrès 1000, Théâtre Noga in Hotel Noga Hilton 850

Orchestre des Pays de Savoie
6 rue Métropole, 73000 **Chambéry**
Tel: 4-7933 4271 Fax: 4-7933 4300
E-Mail: orchestrepaysavoie@wanadoo.fr
administratrice Odile Ollagnon; directeur musical Mark Foster; président Claude Bosser
Size: 19 *Perfs:* 65 *Type/spec:* chamber *Venues:* Espace Malraux 940, Théâtre Bonlieu 1000, Victoria Hall Relais culturel Annemasse *Touring:* France

Ensemble 2e2m
4 rue Proudhon, 94500 **Champigny-sur-Marne**
Tel: 1-4706 1776 Fax: 1-4882 2645
Internet: www.multimusic.com/2e2m
E-Mail: ens2e2m@imaginet.fr
administratrice Christine Nollier; directeur artistique Paul Méfano; régisseur de scéne Christian Loret
Size: 5-25 *Perfs:* 40 *Type/spec:* contemporary music, electro-acoustic music, musical theatre and opera *Venues:* Radio France 600, Le Trianon 900, Auditorium St Germain des Prés 450 *Touring:* national, international

Orchestre d'Auvergne
Centre Delille, 2, rue Urbain II, 63000 **Clermont Ferrand**
Tel: 4-7314 4747 Fax: 4-7314 4776
administrateur Alain Riviére; directeur musical Arie van Beek; assistante de direction Valérie Audebert; président Valéry Giscard d'Estaing; comptable Evelyne Delpeuch; régisseur adjoint Olivier Hebrard; coordinateur des actions musicales Jean-Paul Boithiaf
Size: 22 *Perfs:* 80 *Type/spec:* chamber, all periods *Venues:* Maison des Congrès 1400, Conservatorie, Faculté de Droit (amphithéatre) *Touring:* national and international

Octuor de France
8 rue Léonard Euler, 94000 **Creteil**
Tel: 1-4339 8907/607 311718 (mobile)
Fax: 1-4980 9171
Internet: www.octuordefrance.com
président Daniel Naftalski; directeur musical Jean-Louis Sajot; communication Ariane Fournier
Size: 9 *Perfs:* 60-70 *Type/spec:* contemporary and classical, music for silent film *Touring:* France, USA, Canada, Japan *Comments:* from Mozart to present day + Samuel Colridge, Charles Villiers-Standford, Howard Fergusson; see also Festival – Musique de chambre à l'orangerie de Bagatelle, Paris

Orchestre Symphonique de Douai
Symphonic Orchestra of Douai
87, Rue de la Fonderie, 59500 **Douai**
Tel: 3-2771 7777 Fax: 3-2771 7778
Internet: perso.wanadoo.fr/orchestre.douai/
E-Mail: orchestre.symphonique.de.douai@wanadoo.fr
director Henri Vachey; public relations Emmanuelle Raes; régie Herve Fremery
Size: 80 *Perfs:* 50 annually *Venues:* auditorium 600 *Comments:* also organise an international competition; see also Competitions

L'Orchestre de Chambre de Grenoble – Les Musiciens du Louvre
1 rue du Vieux Temple, BP 3046, 38816 **Grenoble** Cedex 1
Tel: 4-7642 4309 Fax: 4-7651 5530
directeur administratif Jean-Denis Culié; directeur musical Marc Minkowski; président Jean-Louis Schwartzbrod
Size: 8 *Perfs:* 50 *Type/spec:* classical, baroque, contemporary *Venues:* Le Cargo 1000 & 500, Eglise Saint Jean, La Rampe 800 (Echirolles) *Touring:* Europe *Comments:* experimentation using ancient and modern techniques; see also Early Music

Orchestre Philharmonique de Versailles
21, rue de Buc, 78350 **Les Loges-en-Josas**
Tel: 1-3956 2625
conductor Trajan Popesco
Size: 40 *Perfs:* 2 *Type/spec:* classical music *Venues:* Versailles *Comments:* see also Choirs (Association Pro Musica de Paris)

Orchestre de Sénart
100 rue de Paris, 77567 **Lieusaint** Cedex
Tel: 1-6413 5370 Fax: 1-6413 5389
Internet: www.sen.senart.fr
directeur général Jean-Pascal Quilès; directeur musical Michael Dian
Size: 20-30 *Perfs:* 20 *Type/spec:* chamber orchestra; mainly 20th century classics *Venues:* Scène Nationale de Sérart Aréne 400 to 700, Thèâtre 370, Rotonde 370, Auditorium Gabriel Fauré 300, Auditorium Yves Montaud 210 *Touring:* France

Orchestre National de Lille Région Nord Pas de Calais
30 Place Mendès France, BP 119, 59027 **Lille** Cedex
Tel: 3-2012 8240 Fax: 3-2078 2910
Internet: www.onlille.com
E-Mail: jbrochen@onlille.com
directeur Jean-Claude Casadesus; président Ivan Renar; déléguée générale Jacqueline Brochen; conséiller artistique & directeur délégué à la programmation Michel Riviere des Borderies
Size: 100 *Perfs:* 137 *Type/spec:* symphony, opera, chamber *Venues:* Auditorium du Nouveau Siècle 1950 *Touring:* Belgium, Netherlands, France, UK

Conservatoire National de Région de Musique et Danse
4 montée Cardinal Decourtray, 69321 **Lyon** Cedex 5
Tel: 4-7825 9139 Fax: 4-7238 7708
Internet: www.cnrlyon.fr
directeur du conservatoire René Clément; chargé des relations exterieures (artistic manager) Xavier Jacquelin
Size: 80-100 (big orchestra) + 6 other orchestras (60 musicians) *Perfs:* 20 (big orchestra) *Tyep/spec:* strings, winds, or symphonic, big band *Venues:* Lyon and Rhône-Alpes region *Touring:* England, Romania, Italy, Spain, Germany, Argentina, Malta, Austria, Czech Republic *Comments:* there are 3000 permanent students, so there are many possibilities for new orchestras to be formed

Orchestre National de Lyon
82 rue de Bonnel, 69431 **Lyon** Cedex 3
Tel: 4-7895 9500 Fax: 4-7860 1308
E-Mail: onl@l.asi.fr
directeur géneral Patrice Armengau; directeur musical Emmanuel Krivine (until Oct 2000), David Robertson (from Oct 2000); conseiller artistique Alain Surrans
Size: 100 *Perfs:* 120 *Type/spec:* symphony, classical music *Venues:* Auditorium de Lyon 2043 *Touring:* national, international *Comments:* see also Venues (Auditorium de Lyon)

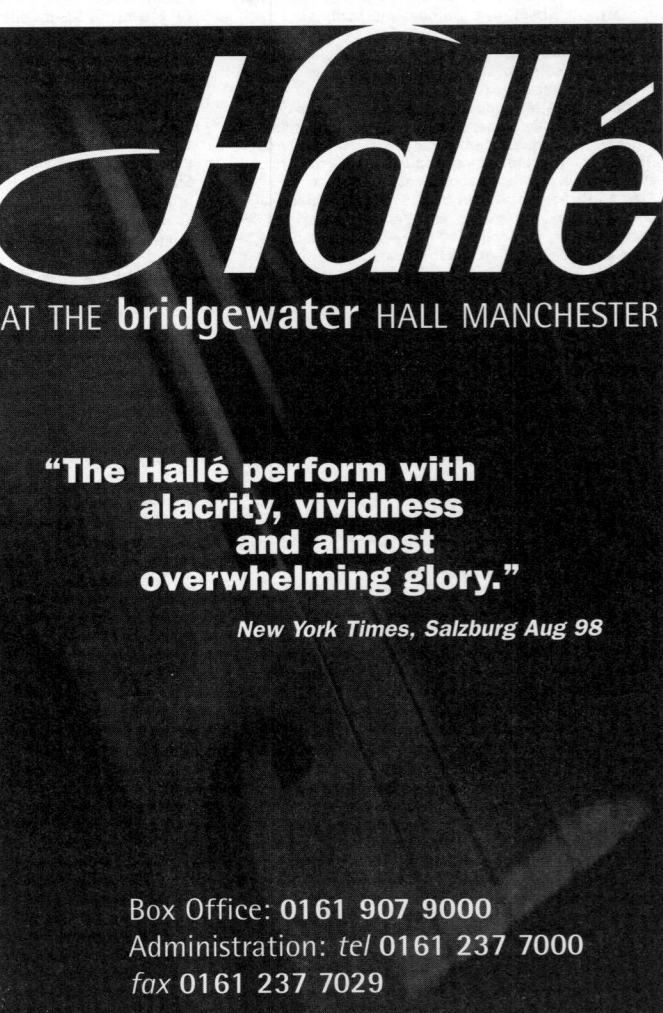

Musicatreize
53 Rue Grignan, 13006 **Marseille**
Tel: 4-9155 0277 Fax: 4-9155 0393
Internet: www.musicatreize.com
E-Mail: musicatreize@musicatreize.com
conductor Roland Hayrabedian; administrator Thierry Boblet; business relations manager Marthe Lemut
Size: 12-80 *Perfs:* 30-40 *Type/spec:* concerts for voices a capella or accompanied by instrumental formations, concerts with orchestra and soloists, musical theater, opera *Touring:* Italy, Spain, Germany, Belgium, Russia, Czech Republic, Indonesia, Denmark, Singapore
Comments: Musicatreize is particularly involved in contemporary music and creation; winners of the most imporatant prizes in France (Victories de la Musique, Prix Olivier Messiaen, Prix Bettencourt de l'Institut de France); see also Choirs

Orchestre des Jeunes de la Méditerranée
23, rue François Simon, 13003 **Marseille**
Tel: 4-9108 2222 Fax: 4-9108 2223
E-Mail: spiquemal@aix.pacwan.net
directeur général Philippe Bachman
Size: 50 *Perfs:* 36 *Type/spec:* classical symphonic orchestra *Venues:* Salle Diocásaine, Théâtre de l'Archevêché 1600 (Aix-en-Provence) *Touring:* international *Comments:* reunited for only 5 weeks in July/August

Philharmonie de Lorraine, La
25 Av Robert Schuman, BP 30451, 57008 **Metz** Cedex 1
Tel: 3-8755 1202 Fax: 3-8765 6936
Internet: www.mairie-metz.fr:8080
E-Mail: PascalSchwan@wanadoo.fr
administrateur général Pascal Schwan; présidente Christine Raffin; directeur musical Jacques Lacombe; chargée de communication Brigitte Bertelle
Size: 75 *Perfs:* 80-85 *Type/spec:* classical, contemporary, lyric *Venues:* Salle de l'Arsenal 1200 *Touring:* national, Europe, Canada

Orchestre Philharmonique de Montpellier – Languedoc Roussillon
Le Corum, BP 9056, 34041 **Montpellier** Cedex 1
Tel: 4-6761 6721 Fax: 4-6761 6720
Internet: www.intel-media.fr/opm
E-Mail: opm@www.intel-media.fr
directeur général René Koening; président Georges Freche; directeur musical Friedemann Layer; directeur administratif Jany Macaby; délégué général Jean-Luc Granier; chargé de communication Pascal Dufour
Size: 91 *Perfs:* 45 symphony – 44 chamber *Type/spec:* classic, contemporary, symphonic, opera *Venues:* Opéra Berlioz, Le Corum 2000; Salle Pasteur 800 *Touring:* Italy, Spain, France, Lebanon, Germany
Comments: see also Venues

Orchestre Symphonique de Mulhouse – La Filature
20, allée Nathan Katz, 68090 **Mulhouse** Cedex
Tel: 3-8936 2826 Fax: 3-8936 2827
E-Mail: osm@lafilature.asso.fr
administrateur Nicole Moehlin; président Jean-Marie Bockel; directeur musical Cyril Diederich; relations publiques Charlotte Ponton
Size: 56 *Perfs:* 18 *Type/spec:* symphony, opera: baroque to 20thC *Venues:* La Filature 1217

Orchestre Symphonique et Lyrique de Nancy
1, rue Sainte-Catherine, 54000 **Nancy**
Tel: 3-8385 3320/3065 (bookings) Fax: 3-8385 3066
E-Mail: opera@mairie-nancy.fr
administrateur Christophe Bezzone; directeur général Jean-Marie Blanchard; déléguée générale Liliane Martinez
Size: 58 *Type/spec:* mainly classical, contemporary
Venues: Salle Poirel 1000, Opéra de Nancy 1000
Comments: see also Opera, Venues and Promoters

Orchestre Philharmonique de Nice
4/6 rue Saint François de Paule, 06300 **Nice**
Tel: 4-9217 4000 Fax: 4-9380 3483
Internet: www.nice-coteazur.org
directeur général Gian Carlo del Monaco; directeur musical Marcello Panni; délégué général André Coussinet; directeur du chœur Giulio Magnanini; directrice des relations pubiques Elisabeth Touraille; administratrice Anne-Marie Guillem-Quillon
Size: 98 *Perfs:* 14 symphonic + 50 other concerts
Type/spec: opera, chamber, symphony *Venues:* Acropolis 2500, Opéra de Nice 1100, Mama 250 *Comments:* see also Opera and Dance

Arts Florissants, Les
2 rue de Saint Petersbourg, 75008 **Paris**
Tel: 1-4387 9888 Fax: 1-4387 3731
Internet: www.arts-florissants.com
E-Mail: info@arts-florissants.com
présidente Catherine Massip; directeur musical William Christie; general administrator Christopher Bayton; chargé de production Dermot Agnew; chargé du personnel artistique Pascal Duc; chargé de communication Arianne Groos
Size: 10-100 *Perfs:* 80 *Type/spec:* orchestra and vocal ensemble, especially baroque and operatic repertoire
Touring: USA, Europe, international

Ensemble de Chambre de Paris
APJA musique en scéne, Salle Pleyel Studio, 507, 252 rue du fbg St-Honoré, 75008 **Paris**
Tel: 1-5375 2067/6-0751 9548/4293 9112/612-173 221 (mobile) Fax: 1-5375 2067
administrateur Emmanuel Phillipe; direction musicale Brigitte Bladou
Size: 8-15 *Perfs:* 15+ *Type/spec:* classical, French music and 20th C *Touring:* France, USA *Comments:* see also Drama (Musique et Parole)

Ensemble Intercontemporain
223 avenue Jean-Jaurès, 75019 **Paris**
Tel: 1-4484 4450 Fax: 1-4484 4451/61
Internet: ensembleinter.com
directeur administratif Sophie Quéré; président d'honneur Pierre Boulez; président Stéphane Martin; directeur musical Jonathan Nott (only until August 2000); administrateur général Hervé Boutry; assistante artistique Marice Linden; relations publiques Monique Bondoux; attaché de presse Marie Hélène Arbour; régisseur général Jean Redel; responsable production Monique Jarrier
Size: 31 *Perfs:* 70-75 *Type/spec:* 20th Century music, contemporary *Venues:* Théâtre du Châtelet 2000, Centre Pompidou 400, IRCAM 300, Cité de la Musique 900, Museé d'orsay 350 *Touring:* worldwide *Comments:* resident orchestra at Cité de la Musique, musical education, masterclasses

Ensemble Orchestral de Paris
Salle Pleyel, 252 rue du Fbg St Honoré, 75008 **Paris**
Tel: 1-4562 1152 Fax: 1-4563 4615
directeur général George Schneider; président Bruno Racine; directeur musical John Nelson; délégué artistique/communication Didier Grzes
Size: 43 *Perfs:* 70 *Type/spec:* Mannheim orchestra: baroque to contemporary *Venues:* Salle Pleyel 2300, Théâtre de Champs Elysées 2000, Opéra Comique 1800, Salle Ecortot *Touring:* national, Eastern Europe

GRM Multiphonies
Maison Radio France, 116 Av. du Président Kennedy, 75016 **Paris**
Tel: 1-4230 2988 Fax: 1-4230 4988
E-Mail: grm@ina.fr
responsable du GRM et artistique Danielle Teruggi; administrateur Bourges Renard
Type/spec: electroacoustique music *Comments:* concerts are broadcast on Radio France Musique

Orchestre Colonne
2 rue Edouard Colonne, 75001 **Paris**
Tel: 1-4233 7289 Fax: 1-4233 1391
secrétaire général Gilles Kasic
Size: 80 *Perfs:* 10 *Type/spec:* symphony, classical and contemporary *Venues:* Salle Pleyel 2300, various churches in Paris

Orchestre de Paris – Société des Concerts du Conservatoire
Salle Pleyel, 252 rue du Fbg St Honoré, 75008 **Paris**
Tel: 1-4561 6565 Fax: 1-4289 2449
Internet: www.orchestredeparis.com
président Michel Prada; directeur général Georges-François Hirsch; chef de chœur Arthur Oldham; directeur musical Christoph Eschenbach; sécretaire général Hervé Burckel de Tell; programmation Didier Alluard; production Benoit Braescu; directeur technique Pierre Druart, communication Jean-Marie Amartin; comptabilité Chantal Lefèvre
Size: 113 *Perfs:* 25 *Type/spec:* symphony & opera, chamber, oratorio (with choir) *Venues:* Salle Pleyel 2300
Touring: national and international: Italy, Japan
Comments: LOI 1901: supported by the State and the City of Paris

Orchestre des Champs-Elysées
La Chapelle Royale, 10 rue Coquilliere, 75001 **Paris**
Tel: 1-4026 5800 Fax: 1-4026 3837
Internet: www.lachapelleroyale.com
E-Mail: info@lachapelleroyale.com
administration Nicolas Droin; musical director Philippe Herreweghe; artistic director Stephan Maciejewski; sales & orchestra fixer Rachel Dale; technical manager Pierre Etienne Nageotte
Size: orchestra: 45-70 + choir: 25-35 *Perfs:* 30-35
Type/spec: classical and romantic on period instruments
Venues: Theatre des Champs Elysées, Paris 2000, Palais des Beaux Arts, Brussels 1900 *Touring:* Europe, Japan, Australia *Comments:* see also Early Music and Choirs (La Chapelle Royale)

Orchestre des Concerts Lamoureux
252 rue du Faubourg Saint Honoré, 75008 **Paris**
Tel: 1-4563 4434/6062 Fax: 1-4562 0541
secrétaire général Frédéric Aladjem; président Lionel Evans; administratrice Annie Foultier; chef principal Yutaka Sado; communication Jean-Luc Caradec (tel: 6-6028 7436); déléguée artistique Bernadette Gardey
Size: 96 *Perfs:* 13 *Type/spec:* symphony, 18th, 19th, 20th century *Venues:* Salle Pleyel 2300
Touring: national *Comments:* plan to have concerts for the celebrations of the millenium of Jerusalem; also a few concerts for young audiences

Orchestre Français des Jeunes
Pièce 8502, Maison de Radio France, 116, Ave. du Président Kennedy, 75220 **Paris** Cedex 16
Tel: 1-4230 4945 Fax: 1-4230 4990
E-Mail: ofjeunes@aol.com
directeur administratif Pierre Barrois; chef d'orchestre Jesús López Cobos; conseiller musical Marek Janowski; assistante du directeur Séverine Denoël
Size: 100 *Perfs:* 10 *Type/spec:* symphonic repertoire
Touring: Europe, France
Comments: member of EFNYO (q.v)

Orchestre National de France
116 Av du Président Kennedy, 75220 **Paris** Cedex 16
Tel: 1-4230 2603 Fax: 1-4230 4333
directeur musical Charles Dutoit; presse et relations extérieures Hélène Montussac (tel: 1-4230 1373); délégué artistique Patrice d'Ollone
Size: 120 *Perfs:* 70 *Type/spec:* symphony and chamber
Venues: Théâtre des Champs-Elysées 1900, Salle Pleyel 2300, Radio France 1000 *Touring:* worldwide

Orchestre Pasdeloup
252 Faubourg St Honoré, 75008 **Paris**
Tel: 1-4563 4626 Fax: 1-4563 4623
administrateur Claude Burguière; président Jean Gagnon; abonnements/collectivités Jocelyne Cau
Size: 95 *Perfs:* 15 *Type/spec:* symphony: classical, popular classics *Venues:* Salle Pleyel 2300, Opera Comique 1800
Touring: Réunion

Orchestre Philharmonique de Radio-France
116 Av du Président Kennedy, 75220 **Paris** Cedex 16
Tel: 1-4230 3630 Fax: 1-4230 4748
E-Mail: dominguez@radiofrance.francenet.fr
directeur musical Marek Janowski; délégué artistique Eric Montalbetti; administrateur delegué José Blazquez; attachée de presse Cécile Kauffmann; régisseur principal Stéphane Spada
Size: 138 *Perfs:* 70 *Venues:* Salle Olivier Messiaen 900, Salle Pleyel 2300 *Touring:* Spain, Pays-Baltes, St Petersburg, Latin America
Comments: participates in French festivals (Montpellier, Colmar and Orange in July)

Orchestre Poitou Charente
3 place Prosper Merimée, BP 422, 86011 **Poitiers** Cedex
Tel: 5-4955 9110 Fax: 5-4960 1221
administrateur Claudine Gilardi; directeur musical Charles Frey; président David Cameo
Size: 40-45 *Perfs:* 25-30 *Type/spec:* classical, contemporary *Touring:* France

Orchestre de Bretagne
BP 5018, 35059 **Rennes** Cedex 3
Tel: 2-9927 5275 Fax: 2-9927 5276
Internet: www.orchestre-de-bretagne.com
E-Mail: orchestre@orchestre-de-bretagne.com
directeur délégués Jean-Marc Bador, Gérard Riou; président Claude Champaud; directeur musical Stefan Sanderling
Size: 45 permanent *Perfs:* 70-100 *Type/spec:* symphony
Venues: Théâtre National de Bretagne – TNB 1000
Touring: national, Germany, Italy, USA, UK

Groupe AKSAK
BP 07, 84400 **Rustrel**
Tel: 4-9004 9634 Fax: 4-9004 9634
Internet:
www.geocities.com/yosemite/forest/2380/AKSAK/index.htm
pr Isabelle Courroy
Size: 5 *Perfs:* 35 *Type/spec:* classical
Touring: national, Italy

Ensemble Musical Futurs Musiques
Université Paris VIII, 2, rue de la Liberté, 93526 **Saint Denis** Cedex
Tel: 1-4940 6528 Fax: 1-4821 0446
E-Mail: aca@univ-paris8.fr
administrateur Jean-Philippe Dequin; directeur artistique Denis Gautheyrie; chargé de production Marc Valero
Size: 5-70 *Perfs:* 20 concerts (30 creations) *Type/spec:* contemporary 20th C *Touring:* Brazil, Italy, France, Germany, Spain, Corsica, USA, Czech Republic
Comments: work for the Festival d'Automne (Paris) and the Vocal Ensemble Soli-Tutti; see also Choirs

Art Zoyd
15 allée Massenet, 93270 **Sevran**
Tel: 1-4383 4953 Fax: 1-4936 0439
Internet: www.cicv.fr/epidemic
E-Mail: epidemic@compuserve.com
directeurs Richard Castelli, Gérard Hourbette; directeur technique Philippe Colpin; secrétariat général Florence Berthaud
Size: 4-5 *Type/spec:* acoustic and electronic music, concerts, music for drama, ballet, silent films with new music *Venues:* Théâtre du Manège, Maubeuge: Luna 1500, Scène Nationale Créteil 1100 *Touring:* Europe, international *Comments:* has its own digital recording studio; organises residencies of composers for symphonic orchestras and new technologies; see also Agents: Epidemic

Orchestre Philharmonique de Strasbourg – Orchestre National
Palais de la Musique et des Congrès, Place de Bordeaux, 67070 **Strasbourg** Cedex
Tel: 3-8815 0900 Fax: 3-8815 0901
directeur administratif Albert Moritz; directeur musical Jan Latham-Koenig
Size: 112 *Perfs:* 51 *Type/spec:* classical, romantic, 20thC *Venues:* Palais de la Musique, Salle Erasme 2000 *Touring:* Europe

Orchestre de Chambre National de Toulouse
4 rue Clemence Isaure, 31000 **Toulouse**
Tel: 5-6230 3440 Fax: 5-6230 3441
E-Mail: bboissard@europost.org
président Horst Hombourg; directeur administratif t.b.a.; directeur artistique Alain Moglia; responsable de la communication Bertrand Boissard
Size: 11 *Perfs:* 80 *Type/spec:* classical, contemporary *Venues:* Halle aux Grains 2500, Théâtre du Capitole 1200 *Touring:* USA, Japan
Comments: 4 new records per year

Orchestre National du Capitole de Toulouse
Halle aux Grains, Place Dupuy, 31000 **Toulouse**
Tel: 5-6199 7800 Fax: 5-6162 1048/7077
Internet: www.onct.mairie-toulouse.fr
administrateur général Robert Gouaze; directeur artistique Michel Plasson; délégué général t.b.a.; administrateur déléguée de l'orchestre Régine Jonquière; chef associé Stéphane Cardon
Size: 102 *Perfs:* 30 + tours: 15 regional, 3 abroad *Type/spec:* symphony: classical, contemporary *Venues:* Halle aux Grains 2546 *Touring:* Europe

Orchestre Symphonique Français
49 bd. du Lycée, 92170 **Vanves**
Tel: 1-4648 0303 Fax: 1-4648 0159
E-Mail: patrick.charmetant@wanadoo.fr
directeur, chef permanent Laurent Petitgirard; administrateur Patrick Charmetant
Size: no permanent musicians *Type/spec:* symphonic
Comments: CDs, film music, adverts

Atelier de Musique de Ville D'Avray
Jean Louis Petit, Chateau de Ville D'Avray, 10 Rue de Marnes, 92410 **Ville D'Avray**
Tel: 1-4750 4428 Fax: 1-4750 5390
conductor Jean Louis Petit
Comments: see also Promoters

Orchestre de Chambre de Jean-Louis Petit, l'
34 rue Corot, 92410 **Ville D'Avray**
Tel: 1-4709 2282 Fax: 1-4750 5390
Internet: perso.club-internet.fr/jlpetit/
directeur musical Jean-Louis Petit; administrateur Marie-Blanche Colonne
Size: 13-25 *Perfs:* 30 *Type/spec:* chamber, classic, contemporary *Touring:* worldwide

GEORGIA (+995)

Georgia State String Quartet
37 Rustaveli av., 380008 **Tbilisi**
Tel: 32-931 488/932 255 Fax: 32-999 037
artistic director Konstantin Vardeli
Size: 4 *Type/spec:* classical and contemporary music *Touring:* Germany, France, Italy, Spain

Georgia State String Trio
37 Rustaveli av., 380008 **Tbilisi**
Tel: 32-931 488/932 255 Fax: 32-999 037
artistic director Zurab Khutsishvili
Size: 3 *Type/spec:* classical and contemporary music *Touring:* Italy, Netherlands, Germany

Georgian Radio Orchestra
68 Kostava st., 380015 **Tbilisi**
Tel: 32-368 963
artistic director/chief conductor Givi Azmaiparashvili; general manager Nunu Gabunia
Size: 80 *Perfs:* 20 *Type/spec:* classical, contemporary and light symphonic music *Touring:* Turkey, Spain, Italy

Georgian State Chamber Orchestra
136 Agmashenebeli Ave., 380002 **Tbilisi**

Georgian State Music Society Orchestra
123 Agmashenebeli Ave., 380002 **Tbilisi**

Georgian State Symphony Orchestra
125 Agmashenebeli ave., 380002 **Tbilisi**
Tel: 32-959 727
artistic director/chief conductor Vakhtang Machavariani; general manager Kote Loladze
Size: 103 *Perfs:* 50 *Type/spec:* classical and contemporary symphonic music *Venues:* Symphony Hall of Tbilisi Centre for Music & Culture
Touring: Poland, Germany, UK

Tbilisi Symphony Orchestra
125 Agmashenebeli ave., 380002 **Tbilisi**
Tel: 32-960 620/950 119 Fax: 32-958 996
artistic director/chief conductor Jansug Kakhidze; manager Nazaret Muradov
Size: 100 *Perfs:* 20-25 *Type/spec:* classical and contemporary symphonic music *Venues:* Symphony Hall of Tbilisi Centre for Music & Culture *Touring:* France, Switzerland, Luxembourg, Turkey

Tbilsi National Opera and Ballet Theatre Orchestra
25 Rustaveli ave., 380008 **Tbilisi**
Tel: 32-990 456/642 Fax: 32-983 250/933 250
artistic director Jansug Kakhidzde; manager David Djikia
Size: 120 *Perfs:* 70 *Type/spec:* opera and ballet performances *Venues:* Tbilisi Opera & Ballet Theatre *Touring:* Italy, Germany, Malta

GERMANY (+49)

Sinfonie Orchester Aachen
Stadttheater und Musikdirektion Aachen, Hubertusstr. 3-8, 52064 **Aachen**
Tel: 241-47841 Fax: 241-4784 200/201
Internet: www.theater-aachen.de
E-Mail: pressetelle@theater-aachen.de
Generalmusikdirektor Elio Boncompagni; Sekretariat und Orchesterbüro Jane Kowalski; Konzertmeister Alexis Vincent
Size: 68 *Perfs:* 200 *Type/spec:* classic and popular concerts, opera, musical *Venues:* Eurogress 1537, special concert series in the Grosse Haus 700 to 880
Comments: see also Opera and Drama

Erzgebirgisches Sinfonieorchester Aue
Bambergstraße 9, 09456 **Annaberg-Buchholz**
Tel: 3733-130 1212 Fax: 3733-130 1226
Geschäftsführer Patrick Wasserbauer; Musikalischer Leiter Richard Vardigans
Size: 46 *Perfs:* 100 *Type/spec:* symphony, chamber, opera, operetta *Venues:* Kulturhaus Aue 784, Eduard-von-Winterstein-Theater 290 *Touring:* Germany, Czech Republic

Philharmonisches Orchester der Stadt Augsburg
c/o Theater Augsburg, Kasernstraße 4-6, 86152 **Augsburg**
Tel: 821-324 4912 Fax: 821-324 4544/4478
Internet: www.augsburg.de
Intendant Dr Ulrich Peters; Generalmusikdirektor Peter Leonard; Künstlerischer Betriebsdirektor Axel Peppermüller; Chefdramaturg Helmar von Hanstein; Leiter des Ausstattungsateliers Wolfgang Buchner; Kaufmännischer Direktor Dr Klaus Engert
Size: 72 *Perfs:* 180 *Type/spec:* symphonic, opera, operetta, ballet, musical *Venues:* Stadttheater 976, Kongreßhalle 1395, Freilichtbühne am Roten Tor 2117
Comments: see also Opera, Drama and Dance

Philharmonisches Orchester Bad Reichenhall
Postfach 2123, 83423 **Bad Reichenhall**
Tel: 8651-8661 Fax: 8651-710 551
Geschäftsführer Jochen Rösch; Musikdirektor u. Chefdirigent Klaus-Dieter Demmler
Size: 40 *Perfs:* 450 *Type/spec:* symphony, chamber *Venues:* Theater im Kurgastzentrum, Bad Reichenhall 600; Wandelhalle, Bad Reichenhall 600
Touring: Germany, Austria

Baden-Badener Philharmonie
Schloß Solms, Solmsstr. 1, 76530 **Baden-Baden**
Tel: 7221-932 791 Fax: 7221-932 794
Generalmusikdirektor Werner Stiefel; Orchestermanager Cornelius Grube; Sekretariat Monika Wüst; Konzertmeister Yasushi Ideue
Size: 34-70 *Perfs:* 340 – chamber, symphony, recitals, opera *Venues:* Kurhaus 500, Weinbrennersaal *Touring:* France, Switzerland, Spain

Bamberger Symphoniker e.V.
Mußstraße 1, 96047 **Bamberg**
Tel: 951-964 7100 Fax: 951-964 7123
Intendant Mathias Weigmann; Ehrendirigent Horst Stein; Konzertmeister Peter Rosenberg, Ya'kov Rubinstein
Size: 113 *Perfs:* 80 *Type/spec:* emphasis on 'deutsche Romantik' + classics of the 20th century *Venues:* Sinfonie an Der Regnitz 1400 *Touring:* national, international *Comments:* see also Choirs

Akademie für alte Musik Berlin
Management, Zossener Str. 50, 10961 **Berlin**
Tel: 30-694 1415 Fax: 30-694 1413
E-Mail: akamus@t-online.de
manager Folkert Uhde
Size: 16 *Perfs:* 90 *Type/spec:* solo, chamber and orchestral music, specialising in music composed at the Berlin court in the 18th C, opera productions *Venues:* Berlin: Konzerthaus, Staatsoper, Philharmonie *Touring:* Germany, Italy, France, Belgium, Austria, Japan, Switzerland, Netherlands, Norway, Denmark
Comments: since 1994 CDs exclusively on Harmonia Mundi France; see also Early Music

AVA Ensemble für die Musik der 21 Jahrhunderts
Lenbachstr. 22, 10245 **Berlin**
Tel: 30-294 0686/177-649 9030 Fax: 30-294 0686
contact Peter Köszeghy
Size: 5 + guests *Type/spec:* contemporary music
Comments: touring ensemble

Berliner Oktett
Konzerthaus Berlin-Schauspielhaus am Gendarmenmarkt 2, 10117 **Berlin**
Tel: 30-203 090 Fax: 30-2030 92209
Internet: www.konzerthaus.de
contact Christian Mencke, Heluth Löchel, Rainer Luft
Size: 8 *Type/spec:* wide repertoire *Venues:* Konzerthaus (Grosser Saal 1500, Kleiner Saal 400, Musikclub 80)
Touring: worldwide

Berliner Philharmonisches Orchester
Herbert-von-Karajan-Strasse 1, 10785 **Berlin**
Tel: 30-254 880
Fax: 30-2548 8105 (Intendanz)/261 4887 (Presse)
Internet: www.berlin-philharmonic.com
E-Mail: presseinfo@philharmonic.sireco.de
Intendant Dr. Elmar Weingarten; Künstlerischer Leiter Claudio Abbado; Konzertmeister Daniel Stabrawa, Toru Yasunaga; Presse-und Öffentlichkeitsarbeit Dr Helge Grünewald; Künstlerisches Betriebsbüro Angela Eichhorst, Gabriele Behrsing
Size: 122 *Perfs:* ca. 100 *Type/spec:* symphony 18th-20th century *Venues:* Philharmonie (Großer Saal) 2440, Kammermusiksaal (Kleiner Saal) 1180
Touring: Austria, France, Italy, UK, USA, Japan
Comments: alternative email: presse@philharmonic.sireco.de

Berliner Sinfonie-Orchester
Im Konzerthaus Berlin, Schauspielhaus an Gendarmenmarkt, Gendarmenmarkt 2, 10117 **Berlin**
Tel: 30-20309-0(switchboard)/2330(Intendant)
Fax: 30-20309-2209
Internet: www.konzerthaus.de
E-Mail: intendanz@konzerthaus.de
Intendant Prof Dr Frank Schneider; Ehrendirigent Kurt Sanderling; Erster Gastdirigent Michael Gielen; chief conductor Eliahu Inbal
Perfs: 100 *Venues:* Konzerthaus; Großer Saal 1700, Kleiner Saal 392

Berliner Symphoniker
Christstraße 30, 14059 **Berlin**
Tel: 30-321 1017 Fax: 30-325 5326
Internet: www.berliner-symphoniker.de
E-Mail: kontakt@berliner-symphoniker.de
Intendant Jochen Thärichen; Chefdirigent Lior Shambadal; Konzertmeister Götz Bernau; Orchesterbüro Marlis Andersch
Size: 65 *Perfs:* 75 *Type/spec:* mainly classical *Venues:* Philharmonie 2200, Schauspielhaus (Konzerthaus am Gendarmenmarkt) 1400 *Touring:* Italy, Germany, Switzerland *Comments:* performs schools and family concerts

Deutsches Kammerorchester
Suarezstrasse 15-17, 14057 **Berlin**
Tel: 30-322 1923 Fax: 30-3260 8610
Internet: www.dko-berlin.de
E-Mail: office@dko-berlin.de
Dirigenten Burkhard Glaetzner; management Julia Miehe
Size: 20 *Perfs:* 60 *Type/spec:* chamber *Venues:* Konzerthaus: Kammermusiksaal 385, Philharmonie: Kammermusiksaal 1100 *Touring:* Japan, Italy

Deutsches Symphonie-Orchester Berlin
Charlottenstr. 56, 10117 **Berlin**
Tel: 30-2030 92014 Fax: 30-204 1518
Internet: www.dso-berlin.de
E-Mail: info@dso-berlin.de
Intendant Dr Dieter Rexroth; Chefdirigent Kent Nagano (until Sept 2000); Geschäftsführer Wolfgang Ogrisek; Sekretariat Frau Koser; Künstlerisches Betriebsbüro Regine Bassalig; Ehrendirigent Günter Wand; Pressestelle Jutta Obrowski; Orchesterbetriebüro Konstanze Klopsch
Size: 113 *Perfs:* 90 *Type/spec:* new & contemporary music, classical repertoire *Venues:* Philharmonie 2205, Schauspielhaus 1623 *Comments:* formerly RIAS-Symphonie-Orchester followed by Radio Symphonie-Orchester *Comments:* formerly Radio-Symphonie-Orchester Berlin; member of Rundfunk-Orchester-und Chöre GmbH

Ensemble Oriol Berlin
Hardenbergplatz 2, 10623 **Berlin**
Tel: 30-2655 5415 Fax: 30-2655 5417
Internet: www.ensemble-oriol.de
E-Mail: ensemble-oriol@snafu.de
managing director Frauke Roth
Size: 21 *Perfs:* 50 *Type/spec:* baroque, classical, romantic, contemporary *Venues:* Kammermusiksaal der Philharmonie Berlin 1100 *Touring:* Europe, USA, Mexico, India

Jeunesses Musicales World Orchestra
Schloss-Str. 48, 12165 **Berlin**
Tel: 30-791 4196 Fax: 30-791 4198
E-Mail: jm.worldorchestra@t-online.de
managing director Michael Jenne; artistic advisor Yakov Kreizberg; orchestra manager Jochen Schäfsmeier
Size: 105 *Perfs:* 10-20 *Type/spec:* symphony orchestra, mainly 19/20th century *Touring:* Germany, USA, Canada, Switzerland, Poland, Austria

Kammerensemble Neue Musik Berlin
Zionskirchstr. 34, 10119 **Berlin**
Tel: 30-4435 9777 Fax: 30-4435 9773
Internet: www.kammerensemble.de
E-Mail: production@kammerensemble.de
director Thomas Brons
Size: 8 *Perfs:* 20 *Type/spec:* contemporary *Touring:* international *Comments:* interdisciplinary projects, new media

Kammerorchester Berlin / Berlin Chamber Orchestra
Mindener Str 11, 10589 **Berlin**
Tel: 30-3490 2032 Fax: 30-3490 2033
Internet: www.KOBerlin.de
E-Mail: info@KOBerlin.de
künstlerische Leitung Katrin Scholz; manager Thomas Voigt
Size: 15-35 *Perfs:* 25 *Type/spec:* baroque to contemporary *Venues:* Konzerthaus Berlin 1400, Philharmonie Berlin 1000 *Touring:* USA, Germany

Kammerorchester Carl Philipp Emanuel Bach, Berlin
Landsberger Allee 144, 10369 **Berlin**
Tel: 30-972 6717 Fax: 30-9760 9900
Internet: www.kammerorchester-berlin.de
E-Mail: Krueger.Konzertmanagement@t-online.de
personal manager Gisela Krüger; artistic director Prof Hartmut Haenchen
Size: 17-25 *Perfs:* 8-10 *Type/spec:* chamber, baroque, classical *Venues:* Konzerthaus Berlin 1400, Kammermusiksaal der Philharmonie 1100 *Touring:* Germany, Switzerland, Italy, international music festivals

Mahler Chamber Orchestra
Heinrich-Roller-Str. 16-17, 10405 **Berlin**
Tel: 30-4434 0833 Fax: 30-4434 0847
Internet: mahler-chamber.de
E-Mail: mahler-chamber@snafu.de
general manager Andrea Zietzschmann; founder Claudio Abbado; principal guest conductor Daniel Harding
Size: 48 *Perfs:* 50-60 *Type/spec:* chamber, sinfonietta, opera *Venues:* Festival International d'Art Lyrique d'Aix-en-Provence, Ferrara Musica *Touring:* Festival Aix-en Provence, Europe *Comments:* pan-european ensemble

Orchester der Berliner Bach-Akademie
c/o Hedwig Breuer, Str zum Löwen 2A, 14109 **Berlin**
Tel: 30-805 1073 Fax: 30-805 1073
contact Hedwig Breuer
Size: varies *Perfs:* 12 *Type/spec:* classical, modern *Venues:* St Matthäuskirche an der Philharmonie 700, Kammermusiksaal der Philharmonie 1000 *Touring:* Spain, Athens

Orchester der Deutschen Oper Berlin
Richard-Wagner-Strasse 10, 10585 **Berlin**
Tel: 30-34384-01 Fax: 30-3438 4232
Internet: www.deutsche-oper.berlin.de
E-Mail: dobtickets@t-online.de
Generalintendant Prof Götz Friedrich; Generalmusikdirektor Christian Thielemann
Size: 131 *Perfs:* 220 *Type/spec:* symphony, chamber, opera, all repertoire *Venues:* Deutsche Oper Berlin *Comments:* see also Opera and Dance

RIAS-Jugendorchester
Hans-Rosenthal-Platz, 10825 **Berlin**
Tel: 30-8503 5655 Fax: 30-8503 5659
E-Mail: karin.drescher@dradio.de
Geschäftsführerin Karin Drescher
Size: 80-95 *Perfs:* 3 *Type/spec:* classical to contemporary *Venues:* Philharmonie Berlin, Konzerthaus Berlin *Touring:* national, Paris, Bologna *Comments:* member of EFNYO (q.v), and of Jeunesses Musicales

Rundfunk-Sinfonieorchester Berlin (RSB)
Charlottenstr. 56, 10117 **Berlin**
Tel: 30-2030 92215 Fax: 30-2030 92489
Internet: www.rsb-online.de
E-Mail: info@rsb-online.de
Direktor Bernd Runge; Chefdirigent Rafael Frühbeck de Burgos
Size: 114 *Perfs:* 60 *Type/spec:* symphonic music from the 19th/20th centuries *Venues:* Schauspielhaus 1400, Philharmonie 2200, Gr. Sendesaal, Sender Freies Berlin 1000 *Touring:* Germany, Switzerland *Comments:* member of Rundfunk-Orchester-und Chöre GmbH

Soharoun Ensemble / Ensemble der Berliner Philharmonisches Orchester
Herbert von Karajan Strasse 1, 10785 **Berlin**
Tel: 30-2548 8178/254 880 Fax: 30-2548 8105/261 4887
contact Mr Riegelbaum
Size: 8+ *Type/spec:* wide repertoire *Touring:* worldwide

Philharmonisches Orchester der Stadt Bielefeld
Brunnenstr. 3-9, 33602 **Bielefeld**
Tel: 521-512 494 Fax: 521-516 408
Intendantin Regula Gerber; Generalmusikdirektor Peter Kuhn; Chordirektor Angela Sleeman; Technischer Direktor Detlef Plümecke
Size: 68 *Type/spec:* classical, opera, music theatre *Venues:* Bühnen der Stadt Bielefeld (Großes Haus 775, Kleines Haus 304), Oetkerhalle (Konzerthalle) *Comments:* see also Drama, Opera and Dance

Bochumer Symphoniker
Prinz-Regent-Strasse 50-60, 44795 **Bochum**
Tel: 234-910 8622 Fax: 234-910 8616/11
Internet: www.bochum.de
E-Mail: 41BS@bochum.de
Orchesterdirektor Heribert Schröder; Chefdirigent Steven Sloane; Sekretariat des Chefdirigenten Simone Brieskorn; Konzertmeister Gerhard Griep; pers. Referent d. GMD Dr. Joel Ethan Fried
Size: 85 *Type/spec:* symphonic: classic, modern, baroque *Venues:* Schauspielhaus 830, Audimax Ruhr-Universität Bochum 1315, Thürmer Saal 450 *Touring:* Germany

Rundfunkblasorchester Sachsen
Kulturraumorchester Leipziger Raum GmbH, Kulturhaus Böhlen Leipziger Str. 40, 04564 **Böhlen**
Tel: 34206-54080 Fax: 34206-54083
Internet: www.rbo-leipzig.de
E-Mail: rbo.leipzig-symphonie@regionett.de
Geschäftsführer Ralf Zimmermann; Dirigent Jochen Wehner
Size: 35 *Perfs:* 100 *Type/spec:* classical, modern

Westsächsisches Symphonieorchester
Kulturraumorchester Leipziger GmbH, Kulturhaus Böhlen Leipziger Str. 40, 04564 **Böhlen**
Tel: 34206-54080 Fax: 34206-54083
Internet: www.rbo-leipzig.de
E-Mail: rbo.leipzig-symphonie@regionett.de
Geschäftsführer Ralf Zimmermann; Dirigent Ruben Gazarian
Size: 35 *Perfs:* 145 *Type/spec:* classical and modern, 18th-20th century *Venues:* Goldener Stern Borna 200, Kulturhaus Böhlen 900, Gewandhaus Leipzig (Kleiner Saal)

Deutsche Bachsolisten
Goddard Str. 28, 53125 **Bonn**
Tel: 228-257 476 Fax: 228-257 476
Musikalischer Leiter Prof Helmut Winschermann
Size: 30-40 *Perfs:* 30-40 *Type/spec:* chamber orchestra, mainly baroque, specialise in Bach (orchestra & choir) *Venues:* Beethovenhalle Bonn *Touring:* Germany, Japan, Paris (UNESCO), Spain *Comments:* management: Konzertdirektion Dietrich Frankfurt/Main and Kajimoto Concerts Tokyo

Klassische Philharmonie Bonn, gefördert durch die Deutsche Telekom
Theaterstraße 10, 53111 **Bonn**
Tel: 228-654 965 Fax: 228-634 850
Geschäftsführung Jürgen-Peter Freudenberg; Musikalischer Leiter Heribert Beissel
Size: 40-60 *Type/spec:* classic symphony *Venues:* Musikhalle, Hamburg; Glocke, Bremen; Landesfunkhaus Niedersachsen, Hannover; Beethovenhalle, Bonn; Kurhaus, Wiesbaden; Meistersingerhalle, Nürnberg, Liederhalle Stuttgart, Kuppelsaal Hanover *Touring:* Germany, Spain

Orchester der Beethovenhalle Bonn
Wachsbleiche 2, 53111 **Bonn**
Tel: 228-774 533/508/630 031 Fax: 228-630 376
Internet: www.uni-bonn.de/beethoven/info
Generalmusikdirektor Marc Soustrot; Orchesterdirektor Laurentius Bonitz; Persönliche Referentin des GMD Brigitte Rudolph; Orchestergeschäftsführer Luis Wüst; Orchesterverwaltung Harald Henseler, Helga Eimermacher; Sekretariat Helga Mebus, Margot Siebert; Presse- und Öffentlichkeitsarbeit Claudia Jost; Konzertmeister Rudolf Gähler, Liviu Casieanu, Olga Littmann-Skalar, Radu Iancovici, Kosta Kirkov
Size: 121 *Perfs:* 60 *Type/spec:* symphonic: classical and contemporary *Venues:* Beethovenhalle 1500, Beethovenhaus 200, La Redoute 300, Kunst-und Ausstellungshalle der Bundesrepublik Deutschland 500, Schumannhaus 120, Villa Prieger 100

Brandenburger Symphoniker
Brandenburger Theater, Grabenstr. 14, 14776 **Brandenburg**
Tel: 3381-511-0 Fax: 3381-511-120
Internet: www.fh-brandenburg.de/theater
Intendant t.b.a.; Generalmusikdirektor t.b.a.
Size: 46 *Type/spec:* symphony, 18th-20th century *Venues:* Studio 250 *Comments:* see also Opera, Drama and Puppets

Staatsorchester Braunschweig
Staatstheater Braunschweig, Am Theater, 38100 **Braunschweig**
Tel: 531-1234-130 Fax: 531-1234-123
Generalintendant Wolfgang Gropper; Generalmusikdirektor Jonas Alber; Verwaltungdirektor Thomas Fehrle; Orchestermanager Martin Weller; Orchesterinspektor Hans-Ulrich Kolf; Orchesterbüro Beate Lange
Size: 85 *Perfs:* 40 concerts, 130 operas *Venues:* theatre 963, Stadthalle 2300

Deutsche Kammerphilharmonie
Erste Schlachtpforte 1, 28195 **Bremen**
Tel: 421-328 262 Fax: 421-328 268
Internet: www.bia-bremen.de/dkph/
E-Mail: deutschekammerphilharmonie@t-online.de
Geschäftsführer Albert Schmitt; Intendant Günther Breest
Size: 34 *Perfs:* 80-100 *Type/spec:* from baroque to contemporary music *Venues:* subscription series in Bremen: Glocke 1400; in Hamburg: Musikhalle 2000 *Touring:* Germany, Europe, USA, Japan

Philharmonisches Staatsorchester der Freien Hansestadt Bremen
Wüstestätte 11, 28195 **Bremen**
Tel: 421-361 4178/94 Fax: 421-361 6026
Geschäftsführer Axel Ketzer; Konzertmeister Anette Behr-König; GMD Günter Neuhold
Size: 87 *Perfs:* at least 24 concerts + various with opera *Type/spec:* classical *Venues:* Konzerthaus Die Glocke 1380, Theater am Goetheplatz 980

Städtisches Orchester Bremerhaven
Postfach 120541, 27519 **Bremerhaven**
Tel: 471-482 060 Fax: 471-4820 6274
Internet: www.bremerhaven.de
Intendant Peter Griesebach; Chefdirigent Prof Leo Plettner; Verwaltungsdirektor Jürgen Ahlf; Konzertmeister Dan Ungureanu
Size: 52 *Perfs:* 15 + for theatre *Type/spec:* classical, opera, symphony *Venues:* Großes Haus 722, Morgensternmuseum 120 *Comments:* visiting address: Theodor-Heuss-Platz, 27568 Bremerhaven; see also Opera, Dance and Drama

Kölner Kammerorchester
Schloßstraße 2, 50321 **Brühl**
Tel: 2232-944 220 Fax: 2232-944 229
Artistic Director Helmut Müller-Brühl; Public Relations Isabel Götte; Secretary's office Beate Brenig
Size: 35 *Perfs:* 50 *Type/spec:* classical, baroque (18th C) *Venues:* Kölner Philharmonie 2196, Schloss Augustusburg Brühl 471, Prinzregententheater München 1070, Théâtre des Champs Elysees Paris 1850, Palais des Beaux-Arts, Brüssels 1950 *Touring:* European Festivals *Comments:* recordings available, Koch-Schwann, Naxos

Neues Rheinisches Kammerorchester Köln
Lövenicher Strasse 17, 50321 **Brühl**
Tel: 2232-23259 Fax: 2232-23259
E-Mail: nrko-htl@t-online.de
Geschäftsführer Gerhard Anders; künstlerische Leitung Peter Matzka, Inge Scheerer
Size: 15 (strings) *Perfs:* 45 *Type/spec:* baroque to 20th century *Venues:* Kölner Philharmonie 2171, Schnütgen-Museum, Köln 300 *Comments:* used to be Rheinisches Kammerorchester (founded in 1957)

Robert Schumann Philharmonie
Postfach 756, 09007 **Chemnitz**
Tel: 371-696 9807 Fax: 371-696 9897
Internet: www.freiepresse.de/theater-chemnitz
E-Mail: theater-chemnitz@abo.freiepresse.de
Generalintendant Rolf Stiska; Chefdirigent GMD Oleg Caetani; Orchesterdirektor Matthias Winkler; Orchesterbüro Eva Scheffler
Size: 108 *Perfs:* 270 *Type/spec:* chamber, classical, opera *Venues:* Opernhaus Chemnitz 720, Stadthalle Chemnitz 1780, Opernhaus/Hinterbühne 100, Opernhausfoyer 100, Schloßbergmuseum 135 *Comments:* visiting address: Käthe-Kollwitz-Str. 7, 09111 Chemnitz

Orchester des Landestheater Coburg
Coburger Landestheater, Schloßplatz 6, 96450 **Coburg**
Tel: 9561-8850 Fax: 9561-793 979
Internet: www.coburg.bynet.de/veranstl/theater.htm
Intendant Nobert Kleine Borgmann; Chefdirigent Hiroshi Kodama; Orchesterinspektor Klaus Rohleder; Orchestervorstand Herbert Graf; Konzertmeister Wolf Dieter Vollmann
Size: 54 *Perfs:* 260 *Type/spec:* symphony and opera, musical, operetta, ballet
Venues: Landestheater, Großes Haus 557; Theater in der Reithalle 100 *Touring:* national
Comments: see also Opera, Dance and Drama

Brandenburgisches Kammerorchester
Schwalbenweg 28, 03044 **Cottbus**
Tel: 355-862 8111 Fax: 355-862 8111
management & künstlerische Leitung Heike Kube; Vereinsvorsitzende Rainer Kube, Thomas Korneck
Size: 9 *Perfs:* 8-9 *Type/spec:* chamber, mainly 17th and 18th century, also contemporary

Philharmonisches Orchester Cottbus
The Cottbus Philharmonic
Karl-Liebknecht-Straße 136, 03046 **Cottbus**
Tel: 355-78240 Fax: 355-791 333
Intendant Christoph Schroth; Geschäftsführender Direktor Steffen Rohr; Musikalischer Oberleiter/Chefdirigent Reinhard Petersen; Operndirektor Martin Schüler; Chordirektor Christian Möbius; Public Relations und Marketing Anne Heym; technischer Direktor Matthias Günther
Size: 76 (+ 35 choir) *Perfs:* 26
Type/spec: orchestral, opera, musical repertoire *Venues:* Großes Haus am Schillerplatz 678
Comments: see also Drama, Dance and Opera

Kammerphilharmonie Merck
Frankfurter Str. 250, 64293 **Darmstadt**
Tel: 6151-727 198/424 523 Fax: 6151-729 0198
Internet:
www.merck.de/german/corporate/culture/ukphil.de.html
E-Mail: kammerphilharmonie@merck.de
Orchestermanager Stefan Reinhardt; Dirigent Christian Rudolf Riedel
Size: 25-45 *Perfs:* 15-20 *Type/spec:* classical, modern
Venues: Orangerie Darmstadt 468, Landesmuseum 280, Staatstheater Darmstadt 956 *Touring:* national, international *Comments:* see also Festivals

Orchester des Staatstheaters Darmstadt
Marienplatz 2, 64283 **Darmstadt**
Tel: 6151-28111 Fax: 6151-281 1226
Orchestermanagement t.b.a.; Generalmusikdirektor Marc Albrecht; Intendant Gerd Theo Umberg
Size: 78 *Perfs:* 10 + opera, theatre, etc. *Type/spec:* classical and modern *Venues:* Staatstheater 956

Anhaltische Philharmonie Dessau
Friedensplatz 1a, Postfach 1703, 06812 **Dessau**
Tel: 340-2511-0 Fax: 340-2511 213
Internet: www.anhaltisches~theater.de
E-Mail: anhaltisches.theater.dram@topmail.de
Generalintendant Johannes Felsenstein; Verwaltungsdirektor Joachim Landgraf; Generalmusikdirektor Carlos Kalmar; Chefdramaturg Wolfgang Lange
Size: 84 *Perfs:* 21 + 120 opera *Type/spec:* 18th to 20th century *Venues:* Großes Haus 1096, Foyer 150, Schloß Georgium 80 *Comments:* see also Opera, Dance, Drama and Puppets

Orchester des Landestheater Detmold
Landestheater Detmold, Theaterplatz 1, 32756 **Detmold**
Tel: 5231-97460 Fax: 5231-974 701
Internet: www.landestheaterdetmold.de
E-Mail: 113217.3637@compuserve.com
Orchestergeschäftsführer Michael Bank; Generalmusikdirektor Steffen Leißner; 1. Kapellmeister Matthias Foremny
Size: 52 *Perfs:* 600 *Type/spec:* symphony, chamber
Venues: Großes Haus 650 *Touring:* national and Benelux
Comments: see also Drama, Opera and Dance

Philharmonisches Orchester Dortmund
Kuhstrasse 12, 44137 **Dortmund**
Tel: 231-502 2477/28 Fax: 231-501 5116
Internet: www.dortmund.de/theater/
E-Mail: theater@dortmund.de
Orchesterverwaltung Horst-Dieter Roggenbach; Generalmusikdirektor Anton Marik; Verwaltungsdirektor Wilhelm Scheer
Size: 94 *Perfs:* 40 + performances for music theatre/opera *Type/spec:* symphonic and operatic repertoire *Venues:* Opernhaus 1170 *Comments:* see also Opera, Dance and Drama

Dresdner Philharmonie
Dresden Philharmonic
Postfach 120424, Kulturpalast Am Altmarkt, 01005 **Dresden**
Tel: 351-486 6282 Fax: 351-486 6283
Internet: www.dresdnerphilharmonie.de
E-Mail: contact@dresdnerphilharmonie/de
Intendant Dr. Olivier von Winterstein (486 6282); designierter Chefdirigent und Künstlerischer Leiter Marek Janowski (from 2001); Ehrendirigent Prof. Kurt Masur; Öffentlichkeitsarbeit Sabine Grosse (486 6202); Orchesterinspektor Matthias Albert (486 6321)
Size: 119 *Perfs:* 80 in Dresden, 20 on tour *Type/spec:* symphony *Venues:* Festsaal des Kulturpalastes 2400
Touring: Germany, Japan, Spain

Landesjugendorchester Sachsen
c/o Sächsischer Musikrat, Bautzner Str. 130, 01099 **Dresden**
Tel: 351-802 4280 Fax: 351-802 3023
Internet: www.Deutscher-Musikrat.de/SMR
E-Mail: Saechsischer-Musikrat@t-online.de
Geschäftsführer Matthias Pagenkopf; Dirigent Reinhard Seehafer
Size: 75 *Perfs:* 10 *Type/spec:* symphony
Touring: Germany, Hungary, USA, Cyprus

Leipziger Bachkollegium
Weltestr. 16, 01157 **Dresden**
Tel: 351-421 2030 Fax: 351-421 0401
Internet: www.guettler.com
E-Mail: 03514212030@t-online.de
Geschäftsführer Martin Steude
Size: 7 *Perfs:* 40 *Type/spec:* works by J.S.Bach, W.A.Mozart, J.Haydn, + some modern *Venues:* Dresdner Semperoper 2500, Krippla d. Frauenkirche 350 *Touring:* Europe

Leipziger Blechbläser Ensemble Ludwig Güttler
Weltestr. 16, 01157 **Dresden**
Tel: 351-421 2030 Fax: 351-421 0401
E-Mail: 03514212030@t-online.de
Geschäftsführer Martin Steude
Size: 11 *Perfs:* 40 *Type/spec:* early baroque, classical, modern *Venues:* Dresdner Seperoper 2500, Krypta d. Frauenkirche 350 *Touring:* Italy, Germany, Poland

musica-viva – ensemble dresden
c/o Dresdner Zentrum für zeitgenössische Musik, Schevenstrasse 17, 01326 **Dresden**
Tel: 351-26462-0 Fax: 351-26462-23
Internet: www.zeitmusik.de
E-Mail: wirrmann@zeitmusik.de
Leitung Prof. Udo Zimmermann; Musikdirektor Jürgen Wirrmann; Sekretariat Brigitte Uhlmann
Size: 16-20 *Perfs:* 10+ *Type/spec:* contemporary
Venues: Dresdner Zentrum für Zeitgenössische Musik 100 *Touring:* Spain *Comments:* see also National Organisation and Festivals

Sächsische Staatskapelle Dresden
Theaterplatz 2, 01067 **Dresden**
Tel: 351-4911-340/440 Fax: 351-491 1633
Internet: www.semperoper.de
E-Mail: presse@semperoper.de
Orchesterdirektor Jan Nast; Chefdirigent Giuseppe Sinopoli; Ehrendirigent Sir Colin Davies
Size: 159 *Type/spec:* classical to 20th century
Venues: Sächsische Staatsoper (Semperoper)1323
Touring: international
Comments: see also Dance, Opera and Drama

Virtuosi Saxoniae
Weltestr. 16, 01157 **Dresden**
Tel: 351-421 2030 Fax: 351-421 0401
E-Mail: 03514212030@t-online.de
Geschäftsführer Martin Steude
Size: 25 *Perfs:* 70 *Type/spec:* early baroque, classical, modern *Venues:* Crypta of Frauenkirche 350, Dresdner Semperoper 2500
Touring: Germany, Western Europe

Duisburger Sinfoniker
Neckarstrasse 1, 47051 **Duisburg**
Tel: 203-3009-0 Fax: 203-3009-220
Internet: www.duisburg.de
Generalmusikdirektor/Chefdirigent Bruno Weil; Sekretariat Sandra Kokke; Intendant Rolf Rüdiger Arnold; Öffentlichkeitsarbeit Gerd Rataj; Orchestergeschäftsführer Wilfried Gehse
Size: 93 *Perfs:* 50 + 140 opera *Type/spec:* old and new symphonic works *Venues:* Mercator-Halle 1700, Theater der Stadt Duisburg 1079
Touring: international *Comments:* orchestra of the Deutsche Oper am Rhein (Theatergemeinschaft Düsseldorf/Duisburg)

Düsseldorfer Symphoniker
Ehrenhof 1, Tonhalle, 40479 **Düsseldorf**
Tel: 211-899 3606 Fax: 211-892 9049/9143
Internet: www.duesseldorf.de/tonhalle
E-Mail: tonhalle@compuserve.com
Intendantin Vera van Hazebrouck; Orchesterverwaltung Thomas Stührk; Dramaturgin Elisabeth von Leliwa; PR Udo Flaskamp (tel: 211-899 2884); designierter GMD Joh Fiore
Size: 130 *Perfs:* 42 concerts + 200 opera/ballet performances *type/spec:* symphony and opera *Venues:* Tonhalle 1933, Deutsche Oper am Rhein 1342
Comments: the Düsseldorfer Symphoniker is the only professional orchestra of Düsseldorf and the orchestra of the Deutsche Oper am Rhein; see also Venues

MusikFabrik
Orangerie Schloß Benrath, Urdenbacher Allee 6, 40593 **Düsseldorf**
Tel: 211-996 0560 Fax: 211-9960 5646
E-Mail: musikfabrik@bigfoot.de
Geschäftsführer Mona Fossen
Size: 18 *Perfs:* 50-60 *Type/spec:* chamber ensemble and chamber orchestra; 20th century, contemporary music
Venues: Tonhalle Düsseldorf, Orangerie Schloss Benrath, Musikwissenschaftliches Institut der Universität zu Köln *Touring:* international *Comments:* music-theatrical projects

Thüringer Landestheater Eisenach-Rudolstadtsaalfeld
Theaterplatz 4-7, 99817 **Eisenach**
Tel: 3691-256-0 Fax: 3691-256 159
Intendant und Künstlerischer Geschaftsführer Johannes Steurich; Geschäftsführerin Petra Mitdank; Chefdirigent GMD Wolfgang Wappler
Size: 51 *Type/spec:* opera, symphony concerts
Venues: Großes Haus 660, Studiobühne 45
Comments: see also Opera, Drama and Dance

Sinfonietta Köln
Auf der Kuhle 11, 51766 **Engelskirchen**
Tel: 2263-60082 Fax: 2263-952 959
E-Mail: sinfonietta.koeln@t-online.de
Künstlerische Leitung Cornelius Frowein
Size: 13 permanent (up to classical symphony orchestra) *Perfs:* up to 40 *Type/spec:* chamber and symphonic; baroque (early music) to contemporary
Touring: Italy, Spain, Belgium, Germany, Mozartfest Würzburg, Flandern Festival and Mozart Sommer Augsburg *Comments:* touring orchestra

Philharmonisches Orchester Erfurt
Dalbergsweg 2, 99084 **Erfurt**
Tel: 361-223 3170/1/2 Fax: 361-223 3173
Internet: www.theater-erfurt.de
E-Mail: theater@bs2000.ef.eunet.de
Orchesterdirektor Horst Gröninger; Generalmusikdirektor Wolfgang Rögner; Konzertmeister Barbara Bätzel-Chong
Size: 59 *Type/spec:* operas, musicals, symphonies
Venues: Schauspielhaus Erfurt 420, Kuppeltheater Erfurt 720
Comments: q.v. Theater Erfurt; see also Opera

Folkwang Kammerorchester Essen
Hollestrasse 1 g, 45127 **Essen**
Tel: 201-230 034/5 Fax: 201-200 696
Geschäftsführerin Tanja Plath; Chefdirigent Karl Heinz Bloemeke
Size: 16 *Perfs:* 50 *Venues:* Villa Hügel Essen

Philharmonie Orchester Essen
Opernplatz 10, 45128 **Essen**
Tel: 201-81220 Fax: 201-812 2280
Internet: www.theater-essen.de
E-Mail: infoaalto@theater-essen.de
Geschäftsführer Otmar Herren; Generalmusikdirektor u. Chefdirigent Stefan Soltesz; Orchesterdisponentin Andrea Linden
Size: 100 *Perfs:* 224 *Type/spec:* symphony, opera, ballet, musical *Venues:* Saalbau 1485, Aalto-Theater 1125
Touring: guest performances in Germany *Comments:* see also Opera, Dance and Drama

Schleswig-Holsteinisches Sinfonieorchester
Rathausstrasse 22, 24937 **Flensburg**
Tel: 461-141 000 Fax: 461-141 0083
Internet: www.landestheater.de
E-Mail: kontakt@landestheater.de
General Intendant Dr Horst Mesalla; Generalmusikdirektor Pierre Borin (from August 2000: Generalintendant Michael Grosse); Operndirektor Dr Harald Höferl; Verwaltungsdirektor Reiner Schmeckthal; Chordirektor Raimund Heusch
Size: 62 *Type/spec:* classical and new music *Venues:* Landestheater Flensburg 459, Landestheater Rendsburg 510, Landestheater Schleswig 508 *Comments:* see also Opera, Dance and Drama

Ensemble Modern
Schwedlerstr. 2-4, 60314 **Frankfurt am Main**
Tel: 69-943 430-20 Fax: 69-943 430-30
Internet: www.ensemble-modern.com
E-Mail: ensmodern@aol.com
Geschäftsführer André Hebbelinck
Size: 22 *Perfs:* 80-100 *Touring:* international
Comments: renowned for 20thC music interpretation; seminars and workshops; opera and film projects

Frankfurter Museumsorchester
Untermainanlage 11, 60311 **Frankfurt am Main**
Tel: 69-2123 7382 Fax: 69-2123 7203
E-Mail: ruediger.jacobsen.amt46@stadt-frankfurt.de
Geschäftsführender Intendant Dr. Martin Steinhoff; Künstlerischer Berater des Intendanten Prof Hans Peter Doll; Chefdirigent des Museumsorchesters Paolo Carignani; Pers. Referent des Chefdirigenten Rüdiger Jacobsen; Operndirektor Udo Gefe
Size: 115 *Perfs:* 200
Type/spec: classic to modern
Venues: Opernhaus 1351, Alte Oper 2300

Junge Deutsche Philharmonie
Schwedlerstrasse 2-4, 60314 **Frankfurt am Main**
Tel: 69-943 430-50 Fax: 69-943 430-30
Internet: www.jdph.de
E-Mail: junge.deutsche.philharmonie@t-online.de
Geschäftsführer Hans-Peter Wirth; Organisation & Fundraising Matthias Ilkenhans; Erster Gastdirigent & Künstlerischer Berater Lothar Zagrosek; Öffentlichkeitsarbeit Birgit Achatz
Size: 115 *Perfs:* 35 *Type/spec:* from classical-romantic to contemporary *Comments:* member of EFNYO (q.v)

Radio-Sinfonie-Orchester Frankfurt
Hessischer Rundfunk, 60320 **Frankfurt am Main**
Tel: 69-155 2071 Fax: 69-155 2720
Internet: www.rso-frankfurt.de
E-Mail: rso-frankfurt@hr-online.de
Orchestermanager Medi Gasteiner-Girth; Chefdirigent Hugh Wolff; Programmbereichsleitung Musik Karsten Dufner; Pressestelle Michael Dartsch
Size: 121 *Perfs:* 70
Type/spec: mainly classical, modern, contemporary
Venues: Alte Oper 2300, hr-Sendesaal 800
Touring: Germany, Poland, France, Austria, Italy, USA, Japan *Comments:* Visiting address: Bertramstraße 8, 60320 Frankfurt am Main (symphony orchestra of the Hessischer Rundfunk)

Staatsorchester Frankfurt/Oder
Collegienstrasse 8, 15230 **Frankfurt an der Oder**
Tel: 335-680 2726 Fax: 335-680 2748
Geschäftsführendermanager Peter Wolfshöfer; GMD Nikos Athinäos; Orchesterdirektor Wolfgang Seibt; Dramaturgie/Marketing Franz Groborz
Size: 86 *Perfs:* 80+ *Type/spec:* symphony
Venues: Konzerthalle Carl Philipp Emanuel Bach 600, Universität 400 *Touring:* Europe (including Poland)
Comments: 1-2 CD productions per year

Mittelsächsische Theater und Philharmonie gemeinnützige GmbH
Borngasse 1, 09599 **Freiberg**
Tel: 3731-35820 Fax: 3731-23406
Intendant Dr. Ingolf Huhn; GMD Georg Christoph Sandmann
Size: 54 *Perfs:* 45 concerts + 126 musicals *Type/spec:* classical/symphony, modern/baroque *Venues:* Theater Freiberg 295, Theater Döbeln 308 *Comments:* see also Opera and Drama

Balthasar-Neumann-Ensemble
c/o Büro für Internationale Kulturprojekte GmbH, Schwarzaldstr. 298a, 79117 **Freiburg**
Tel: 761-612 238 Fax: 761-62229
E-Mail: Bik@fmf.notes-net.de
Musikalische Leitung Thomas Hengelbrock
Type/spec: chamber orchestra, mainly 17th-18th C., also symphonic repertoire, romantic to contemporary, stage music *Comments:* see also Choirs and Agents & Producers

Ensemble Aventure
Eschbachweg 5, 79117 **Freiburg**
Tel: 761-60526 Fax: 761-60546
Künstlerische Leitung Dr Wolfgang Rüdiger, Christian Hommel, Johannes Nied; Kontakt Klaus Stoy
Size: 1-15 *Perfs:* 35-50 *Type/spec:* tradition of modern music (Schönberg-school, Varèse, American Modern Music etc), nazi-persecuted composers, avantgarde after 1950, compositons from Latin America, intercultural activities *Venues:* Elisabeth-Schneider-Stiftung 120 *Touring:* Germany, Europe *Comments:* see also Agents & Producers (Künstleragentur Stoy)

Ferruccio Busoni Orchester
Schwarzwaldstraße 6, 79102 **Freiburg**
Tel: 761-700 201 Fax: 761-701 712
E-Mail: bnastasi@xs4all.nl
artistic director & principal conductor Massimiliano Matesic; management Basil Nastasi
Comments: international German-Italian orchestra for music students, concerts every summer and winter all over Europe; applications from musician to above mentioned address; Netherlands address: Nova Zemblastraat 521, 1013 RJ Amsterdam, Tel: +31 651-142 915, Fax: +31 20-686 5084

Freiburger Barockorchester
Konradstr. 7, 79100 **Freiburg**
Tel: 761-706 555 Fax: 761-706 557
Internet: www.barockorchester.de
E-Mail: f.b.o.@t-online.de
general manager Hans-Georg Kaiser; artistic director Gottfried von der Goltz; project manager Wolfram Lamparter; press manager Dr. Rüdiger Nolte
Size: 6-40 *Perfs:* 70-90 *Type/spec:* chamber orchestra, mainly 17th-18th century; also chamber music as FBO Consort *Venues:* capacity 70-90; own series in the Konzerthaus Freiburg 1800, Liederhalle Stuttgout 800, Kammermusiksaal Philharmonie Berlin 1200 *Touring:* Europe, USA, Asia, South America *Comments:* recordings on Harmonia Mundi (Germany and USA), BMG Classics, EMI, Erato, Carus; see also Early Music

Philharmonisches Orchester der Stadt Freiburg
Bertoldstrasse 46, 79098 **Freiburg**
Tel: 761-201 2821/2911 Fax: 761-201 2999
Internet: www.uni-freiburg.de/theater/
Intendant Hans J Ammann; Verwaltungsdirektor Henrik Huyskens; Künstlerisches Betriebsdirektorin Elke Hoch; GMD und Chefdirigent Kwamé Ryan; Konzertmeister Ildiko Moog-Ban
Size: 70 *Perfs:* 25 *Type/spec:* classical/modern *Venues:* Konzerthaus Freiburg: Großer Saal 1600, Kleiner Saal 300 *Comments:* see also Opera, Dance, Drama and Festivals

SWR Sinfonieorchester Baden-Baden und Freiburg
Konzerthaus, Konrad Adenauer Platz 1, 79098 **Freiburg**
Tel: 761-388 1205 Fax: 621-388 1213
Orchestermanager Reinhard Oechsler; Sekretariat des Orchestermanagements Eva Wüst; Chefdirigent Sylvain Cambreling; Sekretariat des Chefdirigenten Jutta Esger; Orchesterbüro Olaf Seesemann; Konzertmeister Christian Ostertag, Diego Pagin
Size: 99 *Perfs:* 48 *Venues:* Konzerthaus Freiburg *Touring:* Europe (including leading festivals)

Altenburg Gera Theater GmbH
Küchengartenallee 2, 07548 **Gera**
Tel: 365-82790 Fax: 365-827 9135
Internet: www.theater.altenburg.gera.de
E-Mail: boehme-pock@t-online.de
Generalintendant Michael Grosse; GMD Russel Harris; Chordirektor Günter Heinig
Size: 90 *Perfs:* 120 (2 orchestras, 10 philharmonic concerts) *Type/spec:* concerts, opera, operetta, musical *Venues:* Bühnen Gera: Theatersaal 670, Konzertsaal 820, Kammerspiele 169
Comments: address of Altenburg Theater: Theaterplatz 19, 04600 Altenburg, Tel: 3447-5850, Fax: 3447-585 186; see also Opera, Drama and Dance

Kieler Kammerorchester
c/o Klaus Jürgen Spoerel, Steenredder 16, 24214 **Gettorf**
Tel: 4346-7459 Fax: 4346-7459
contact Klaus Jürgen Spoerel; Chefdirigent Imry Salley; Verwaltungsdirektor Erhard Meisner; Konzertmeister Uwe Funck
Size: 37 *Perfs:* 4 *Type/spec:* symphonies, solo concerts, vocal pieces *Venues:* Petruskirche Kiel 900

Städtische Philharmonie Gießen
Berliner Platz, 35390 **Gießen**
Tel: 641-79570 Fax: 641-795 780
Intendant Guy Montavon; Kommissarischer Generalmusikdirektor Herbert Gietzen
Size: 40 *Perfs:* 104 *Type/spec:* symphony, classical, opera and chamber orchestra *Venues:* Stadttheater 662, Studiobühne 99 *Comments:* see also Drama, Opera, Dance and Venues

Neue Lausitzer Philharmonie
Postfach 300463, 02809 **Görlitz**
Tel: 3581-4783-0 Fax: 3581-4783-15
Internet: www.via-regia.de
E-Mail: theater-goerlitz@t-online.de
Geschäftsführer Dr. Michael Wieler; Generalmusikdirektor Christof Escher; Marketing & Media Bettina Langsch; Management t.b.a.; Dramaturgie Julia Cloot, Ulrike Schröder
Size: 57 *Perfs:* 300 *Type/spec:* 18th to 20th century *Venues:* Theater Görlitz 600, Stadthalle Görlitz 1500, Theater Bautzen 400, Theater Zittau 400, Lausitzhalle, Hoyerswerda 800 *Comments:* visiting address: Promenadenstrasse 60, 02827 Görlitz

Thüringen-Philharmonie Gotha/Suhl
Reinhardbrunner Straße 23, 99867 **Gotha**
Tel: 3621-751 776 Fax: 3621-751 775
Internet: www.thueringen-philharmonie.de
E-Mail: info@thueringen-philharmonie.de
Chefdirigent GMD Terje Mikkelsen; künstlerischer Direktor Hermann Breuer
Size: 84 *Perfs:* 90 *Type/spec:* symphony: baroque to 20th century *Venues:* Kulturhaus Gotha 795, Ekhoftheater 191, Kongresszentrum, Suhl 800

Göttinger Symphonie-Orchester
Godehardstrasse 19-21, 37081 **Göttingen**
Tel: 551-631 111 Fax: 551-62715
Internet: www.dabakus.de/gso
E-Mail: gso@dabakus.de
Orchesterdirektor Manfred Grabig; Chefdirigent Christian Simonis; Sekretariat des Chefdirigenten Angelika Gremmes, Carola Kasten
Size: 54 *Perfs:* 110 *Type/spec:* baroque to contemporary *Venues:* Stadthalle *Touring:* Germany *Comments:* known as the 'Reiseorchester Niedersachsens'

Philharmonisches Orchester Vorpommern
Theater Vorpommern, Anklamer Str. 106, 17489 **Greifswald**
Tel: 3834-57220 Fax: 3834-502 779
Internet: www.theater.vorpommern.de/
E-Mail: theater@t-online.de
Geschäftsführer Joachim von Trützschler; Generalmusikdirektor Dorian Wilson; Orchesterbüro Michael Struwe; Intendant Rüdiger Bloch
Size: 80 *Perfs:* 70 concerts (+ 135 Musiktheater) *Type/spec:* symphonic *Venues:* Theater Stralsund 519, Theater Greifswald 460 *Touring:* national, Japan, South-East Asia *Comments:* see also Opera, Drama and Dance

Vogtland Philharmonie Greiz/Reichenbach
Stavenhagenstraße 3-4, 07973 **Greiz**
Tel: 3661-3225 Fax: 3661-3225
Internet: www.vogtland-philharmonie.com
E-Mail: vogtland-philharmonie@t-online.de
Intendant und Geschäftsführer MD Stefan Fraas; Chefdirigent Doron Salomon; Orchesterdirektor Wolfgang Franz; Dramaturgie Andrea Buder
Size: 65 *Perfs:* 150 *Type/spec:* classical, symphony *Venues:* Theater der Stadt Greiz 500, Neuberinhaus Reichenbach 600 *Touring:* national, international *Comments:* address of main office in Reichenbach: Weinholdstraße 7 (Neuberinhaus), 08468 Reichenbach, tel: 3765-13470; see also Vogtland Philharmonic, Reichenbach/Greiz (under Reichenbach)

Philharmonisches Orchester Südwestfalen, Landesorchester Nordrheinwestfalen
Elberfelder Strasse 65, 58095 **Hagen**
Tel: 2331-207 3210 Fax: 2331-207 2446
Internet: www.hagen.de/theater/welcome.html
E-Mail: theater@stadt-hagen.de
Intendant Hermann Baumann; Generalmusikdirektor Georg Fritzsch; Sekretariat Heide Marie Wauters, Doreen Kamenik-Kirschner; Orchesterinspektor Peter Dahlhoff; Konzertmeister Sohei Takahata, Bernhard Ratajczak; Geschäftsführer Diethelm Hoffmann
Size: 118 *Perfs:* 250 *Type/spec:* repertoire from baroque to 20th century *Venues:* Leonhard-Gläser-Saal Siegen 800, Siegerlandhalle 1500, Stadthalle Hagen 1500, Theater Hagen, Aalto-Theater Essen, Deutsche Oper am Rhein, Düsseldorf *Comments:* result of merger between Philharmonisches Orchester Hagen and Südwestfälische Philharmonie Landesorchester Nordrhein-Westfalen; see also entry in Hilchenbach

Orchester des OPERNHAUSES HALLE
Universitätsring 24, 06108 **Halle (Saale)**
Tel: 345-51100 Fax: 345-511 0303
Internet: www.opernhaus.halle.de
E-Mail: opernhaus@halle.de
Generalmusikdirektor Roger Epple; Orchestergeschäftsführer Bruo Scharnberg
Size: 104 *Perfs:* 42 (incl. Kammermusiken) *Type/spec:* opera & ballet of all styles/epoches, operetta, musical, concerts *Venues:* Großer Saal d. Oper 660, Georg-Friedrich-Händel-Halle 1253, Freylinghausen-Saal 400 *Comments:* also home of 22-member Baroque orchestra, Collegium Instrumentale (Musikalischer Leiter: Arkadi Marasch), Hallisches Consort, Händelfestspielorchester, Teichmanntrio, 10 Cellisten und Bläsersolisten des Opernhauses Halle; visiting address: Universitätsring 24, 06108 Halle; see also Dance, Drama and Opera

Philharmonisches Staatsorchester Halle
Kleine Brauhausstr. 26, 06108 **Halle (Saale)**
Tel: 345-221 3001/3000 Fax: 345-221 3010
Internet: www.halle-leipzig.de/philhar.htm
E-Mail: ad.philharmonie@halle.de
Chefdirigent GMD Bernhard Klee; Leiter der Öffentlichkeitsarbeit Matthias Dahlmann; Leiter des Künstlerischen Betriebsbüros Bärbel Schreiber; Chefdramaturg und persönlicher Referent des GMD Ulfert Woydt; Leiter Neue Musik Thomas Müller
Size: 92 *Perfs:* 140 *Type/spec:* early to modern *Venues:* Georg-Friedrich-Händel-Halle 1300, Freylinghausen-Saal (Fränckischen Stiftungen) 400

Detmolder Kammerorchester
c/o Künstlersekretariat Rolf Sudbrack, Barkhausenweg 12, 22339 **Hamburg**
Tel: 5231-31603 Fax: 5231-31606
E-Mail: dtdko@t-online.de
Leiter Eckhard Fischer; Geschäftsführung Barbara Colell
Size: 21 *Type/spec:* classical, romantic, 20th century *Venues:* Hochschule für Musik, Detmold 600 *Touring:* Germany, Belgium, Spain, Namibia

Hamburger Symphoniker
Dammtorwall 46, 20355 **Hamburg**
Tel: 40-344 851 Fax: 40-353 788
Intendant Peter Dannenberg; Chefdirigent Miguel Gomez-Martinez; Konzertmeister Stefan Czermak; 1. Vorsitzender Professor Dr Hermann Rauhe
Size: 67 *Perfs:* 160 *Type/spec:* classical, romantic and modern *Venues:* Hamburg Musikhalle 2000 *Touring:* Germany, Spain

NDR-Sinfonieorchester
Norddeutscher Rundfunk Hamburg, Rothenbaumchaussee 132, 20149 **Hamburg**
Tel: 40-4156 2401/03/2708
Fax: 40-4156 3446
Internet: www.ndr.de
E-Mail: sinfonie@ndr.de
Redakteur des Sinfonieorchesters Paul Müller; Chefdirigent Christoph Eschenbach; Ehrendirigent Prof Günter Wand; Konzertmeister Roland Greutter und Stefan Wagner; Leiter Bereich Orchester und Chor Rolf Beck
Size: 113 *Perfs:* 85-90 *Type/spec:* early to modern *Venues:* Musikhalle, Hamburg 2018, Musik- und Kongreßhalle, Lübeck 2010, Kieler Schloss 1350, Glocke, Bremen *Touring:* Germany, Austria, Poland, Greece, Scotland, Japan

Philharmonie der Nationen
c/o Förderverein der Philharmonie der Nationen e.V., Wendenstrasse 195, 20537 **Hamburg**
Tel: 40-4135 1942 Fax: 40-4149 8903
music director Justus Frantz
Size: 70 *Perfs:* 150 *Type/spec:* classical symphony concerts *Touring:* worldwide *Comments:* the orchestra unites young musicians from over 40 countries; CDs available; touring orchestra; own TV show: Achtung Klassik

Philharmonisches Staatsorchester Hamburg
Große Theaterstrasse 34, 20354 **Hamburg**
Tel: 40-356 8360 Fax: 40-356 8464
Internet: philharmonisches-staatsorchester-hamburg.de
Intendant Dr Albin Hänseroth; Generalmusikdirektor Ingo Metzmacher; Assistentin des Intendanten Nina Sinz; Assistent des GMD Frank Beermann; Presse Christiane Rubien
Size: 127 *Perfs:* 29 concerts + 6 chamber concerts + operas *Type/spec:* operas and concerts *Venues:* Musikhalle 2025, Staatsoper 1675 *Touring:* Germany, Wien

Kammerorchester 'fonte di musica'
Neue Marktstrasse 29a, 31785 **Hameln**
Tel: 5151-25274 Fax: 5151-45471
Internet: www.kulturserver.de/home/fontedimusica
E-Mail: tkohlhaussen@metronet.de
Chefdirigent Wolfgang Kohlhaußen; Sekretariat des Chefdirigenten Inge Meßmann
Size: 11 (10 strings + 1 cembalo) *Perfs:* 70 *Type/spec:* chamber music for strings *Touring:* Italy, Austria, Benelux, Germany *Comments:* touring orchestra

Niedersächsisches Staatsorchester
Opernplatz 1, 30159 **Hannover**
Tel: 511-1684 6720/6161/62
Fax: 511-368 1768
Internet: www.staatstheater.hannover.com
Intendant Hans-Peter Lehmann; GMD u. Chefdirigent Andreas Delff; Orchesterdirektor Willhelm Plank; Konzertmeister Krisztof Wegrzyn, Ion Tanase
Size: 111 *Perfs:* 18 concerts + 5 chamber concerts + 4 opera *Type/spec:* symphony and opera orchestra (18th/19th C) *Venues:* Staatsoper 1207 *Comments:* see also Opera, Dance, Drama

Radio-Philharmonie Hannover des NDR
Rudolf-von-Bennigsen-Ufer 22, Postfach 4560, 30045 **Hannover**
Tel: 511-988-0/2340/2341 Fax: 511-988 2349
Internet: www.ndr.de/philharmonie/index.html
Abteilungsleitung Hansjoachim Reiser; Orchesterbüro Richard Wackeldehne; Konzertmeister Kathrin Rabus, Volker Worlitzsch
Size: 87 *Perfs:* 60-70 *Type/spec:* classical symphonies, light music, musicals, etc.
Venues: Großer Sendesaal des NDR 1200
Comments: concerts at Expo 2000 Hannover and various festivals; CD co-productions; available through Koch Records International and CPO; also accompany pop and rock acts as Hannover Pop Orchester

Philharmonisches Orchester der Stadt Heidelberg
Friedrichstrasse 5, 69117 **Heidelberg**
Tel: 6221-583 590/1/2/3 Fax: 6221-583 599
Internet: www.heidelberg.de
Orchesterbüro & Konzertdramaturgie Sigrid Brümmer; Sekretariat Brigitte Kappus; Konzertmeister Thierry Stöckel; GMD Thomas Kalb; Orchestergeschäftsführer Thorsten Schmidt
Size: 61 *Perfs:* 31 (8 symphony, 5 special concerts, 9 family, 4 choral, 5 serenades) *Type/spec:* symphonic, opera, operetta, musicals *Venues:* Kongresshalle 1263, Heidelberger Schloß, Thater der Stadt Heidelberg
Touring: Japan *Comments:* see also Opera, Drama and Dance

Württembergisches Kammerorchester Heilbronn
Postfach 3830, 74028 **Heilbronn**
Tel: 7131-87272/1 Fax: 7131-627 439
Chefdirigent and Geschäftsführer Prof Jörg Faerber; Orchestermanager Karl Nagel; Konzertmeister Yumino Toyoda
Size: 20 *Perfs:* 80-90 *Type/spec:* baroque to modern
Venues: Harmonie 1800 *Touring:* Germany, Europe
Comments: recordings and radio concerts

Nordwestdeutsche Philharmonie e.V
Stiftbergstrasse 2, 32049 **Herford**
Tel: 5221-98380 Fax: 5221-983 821
Internet: www.nwd-philharmonie.owl-online.de
E-Mail: nwd.philharmonie@owl-online.de
Geschäftsführer Christian Becker; Chefdirigent Toshiyuki Kamioka
Size: 78 *Perfs:* 100 *Type/spec:* symphony concerts, chamber music *Venues:* various halls primarily in North Rhine Westphalia, Nordwestdeutsche Philharmonie
Comments: also productions for TV, Radio, CD

Philharmonisches Orchester Südwestfalen, Landesorchester Nordrhein-Westfalen
Postfach 1320, 57271 **Hilchenbach**
Tel: 2733-4497 Fax: 2733-3726
Intendant Hermann Baumann; Generalmusikdirektor Georg Fritzsch; Sekretariat Heide Marie Wauters, Doreen Kamenik-Kirschner; Orchesterinspektor Peter Dahlhoff; Konzertmeister Sohei Takahata, Bernhard Ratajczak; Geschäftsführer Diethelm Hoffmann
Size: 118 *Perfs:* 250 *Type/spec:* repertoire from baroque to 20thC *Venues:* Leonhard-Gläser-Saal Siegen 800, Siegerlandhalle 1500, Stadthalle Hagen 1500, Theater Hagen, Aalto-Theater Essen, Deutsche Oper am Rhein, Düsseldorf *Touring:* mainly Germany *Comments:* visiting address: Im Langen Feld 2, Philchenbach; result of merger between Hilharmonisches Orchester Hagen and Südwestfälische Philharmonie Landesorchester Nordrhein-Westfalen; see also entry in Hagen

Orchester des Stadttheaters Hildesheim
Theaterstr. 6, 31141 **Hildesheim**
Tel: 5121-16930 Fax: 5121-169 393
Intendant Dr Martin Kreutzberg; Musikalischer Oberleiter Werner Seitzer; Verwaltungsdirektor Wolfgang Rothe; Konzertmeister Mariusz Januszkiewicz; Studienleiter/Kapellmeister Achim Falkenhausen
Size: 30 + 16 Orchestererweiterung
Type/spec: baroque, classical, modern, opera, operetta, musical
Venues: Stadttheater 607, Theo/Studiobühne 68
Comments: see also Opera, Dance and Drama

Hofer Symphoniker
Klosterstrasse 9-11, 95028 **Hof**
Tel: 9281-7200-0 Fax: 9281-720 072
Internet: www.hof.baynet.de/~hofer.symphoniker
E-Mail: hofer.symphoniker@hof.baynet.de
Intendant Wilfried Anton; Chefdirigent und GMD Golo Berg; Referentin des Intendanten Ingrid Schrader; Leiterin des künstlerischen Betriebsbüros Gabriele Hegner
Size: 60 *Perfs:* 54 + 154 for music theatre *Type/spec:* classical *Venues:* Festsaal der Freiheitshalle Hof 800
Touring: Germany

Jenaer Philharmonie
Volkshaus, Carl-Zeiß-Platz 15, 07743 **Jena**
Tel: 3641-590 010 Fax: 3641-590 026
Internet: www.jena.de/kultur/phil/philh.htm
E-Mail: Jenaer.Philharmonie@t-online.de
Intendantin Claudia Luthardt; Chefdirigent Andrey Boreyko; Chordirektor Hermann Kruse
Size: 85 *Perfs:* 65 *Type/spec:* classical *Venues:* Volkshaus Jena 749 *Touring:* Germany, Poland

Orchester des Pfalztheaters Kaiserslautern
Willi-Brandt Platz 4-5, 67655 **Kaiserslautern**
Tel: 631-3675-0 Fax: 631-3675-213
Orchesterverwaltung Markus Alsfasser; GMD Lior Shambadal; Verwaltungsdirektor Günter Albert; Konzertmeister Tiberiu Kisauer
Size: 63 *Perfs:* 4 (+ operas, operettas, theatre performances) *Type/spec:* classical *Venues:* Pfalztheater 730
Comments: see also Opera, Dance and Drama

SWR Rundfunkorchester Kaiserslautern
Fliegerstraße 36, 67657 **Kaiserslautern**
Tel: 631-362 2840 Fax: 631-362 2829
Orchestergeschäftsführer Werner Meyers; Chefdirigent Prof. Peter Falk; Sekretariat Anne-Rose Jacob-Darek; Orchesterdisponent Georg Emme; Konzertmeister Wilfried Gödde, Jiri Darek
Size: 45 *Perfs:* 40 *Touring:* Germany, Netherlands, Switzerland

Badische Staatskapelle Karlsruhe
c/o Badisches Staatstheater, 76125 **Karlsruhe**
Tel: 721-3557-0
Fax: 721-373 223 (Verwaltung) 355 7155 (Intendanz)
Internet: www.karlsruhe.de/kultur/staatstheater
E-Mail: kartenverkauf@bstaatstheater.bwl.de
Generalintendant Pavel Fieber; GMD Kazushi Ono; künstlerische Betriebsdirektorin Gudrun Pappermann; Verwaltungsdirektor Wolfgang Sieber; Presse-und Öffentlichkeitsarbeit Anna-Renate Sörgel
Size: 99 *Perfs:* 32 + opera and music theatre *Type/spec:* symphony, modern, classical, opera and music theatre
Venues: Großes Haus 1002, Kleines Haus 385, and other venues with various capacities *Comments:* venue address: Baumeisterstr. 11, 76137 Karlsruhe; see also Opera, Dance, Drama and Festivals

Deutsche Händel-Solisten e.V.
Baumeisterstr. 11, 76137 **Karlsruhe**
Tel: 721-3557-0 Fax: 721-373 223
Internet: www.karlsruhe.de/kultur/staatstheater
E-Mail: kartenverkauf@bstaatstheater.bwl.de
1. Vorsitzender Pavel Fieber; 2. Vorsitzender Wolfgang Sieber; Koordinator Prof Helmut Hofmann
Size: 40 *Perfs:* 8 *Type/spec:* early music on period instruments, mainly baroque; mainly works by G F Händel
Venues: Großes Haus 1002, Kleines Haus 385 and other venues *Touring:* among other festivals Händel-Festspiele Karlsruhe

Orchester des Staatstheaters Kassel
Friedrichsplatz 15, 34117 **Kassel**
Tel: 561-1094-0 Fax: 561-109 4204
Orchesterwart Bernd Schluckwerder; GMD Roberto Paternostro; Verwaltungsdirektor Dr. Frank Depenheuer
Size: 83 *Perfs:* 40 *Type/spec:* opera, classical *Venues:* Opernhaus 953, Schauspielhaus 540 *Comments:* see also Opera, Drama and Dance

Philharmonisches Orchester der Landeshauptstadt Kiel
Bühnen der Landeshauptstadt Kiel, Rathausplatz 4, 24103 **Kiel**
Tel: 431-901 2856
Fax: 431-9016 2838/2889
Internet: www.kiel.de/buehnen
E-Mail: buehnen@lhstadt.kiel.de
Orchestergeschäftsführerin Gabriele Koschnitzke; Chefdirigent u. GMD Ulrich Windfuhr; Konzertmeister Gabór Csapó
Size: 76 *Perfs:* 10 + opera *Type/spec:* classical to contemporary *Venues:* Konzertsaal im Schloß 1200, Opernhaus 866 *Comments:* see also Opera, Dance, Drama and Early Music

Staatsorchester Rheinische Philharmonie
Eltzerhofstrasse 6 a, 56068 **Koblenz**
Tel: 261-301 2272 Fax: 261-301 2277
Intendant Rainer Neumann; Chefdirigent u. GMD Shao-Chia Lü; Verwaltungsdirektor Udo Werner; Konzertmeister Ernst Triner, Kristian Schwertner
Size: 85 *Perfs:* 190 *Type/spec:* classic (symphonic concerts), opera *Venues:* Rhein-Mosel-Halle 1400, Opernhaus 550

Clara Schumann Orchester Köln
Brabanter Str 6, 50674 **Köln**
Tel: 221-251 533 Fax: 221-251 533
artistic director/conductor Elke Mascha Blankenburg
Size: 20-46 *Perfs:* 3 *Type/spec:* from chamber to symphony, specialises in works by female composers of past and present *Touring:* national, Italy *Comments:* professional women's orchestra; CD's available; see also Choirs (Köln Kurrende)

Concerto Köln
Am Grauen Stein, 51105 **Köln**
Tel: 221-983 4190 Fax: 221-983 419-99
Manager Olaf Lichke; Artistic Director & Leader Werner Ehrhardt; Administration S. Ehrhardt, C. Vieira, B. Uedelhoven
Size: 11-40 *Perfs:* 40 *Type/spec:* specialises in 18th century music (late baroque, classical and early romantic) *Touring:* Europe, USA *Comments:* orchestra plays without a conductor; exclusive contract with TELDEC Clasics Intern.; regular performances in baroque opera productions; see also Early Music

Das Orchester Damals und Heute
Franz-Marc-Str. 6, 50939 **Köln**
Tel: 221-430 1600 Fax: 221-430 1600
Internet: www.damalsundheute.com
E-Mail: contact@damalsundheute.com
conductor Michael Willens; director of operations Volker Gelhardt
Size: 17-50 depending on repertoire
Perfs: 30 *Type/spec:* 17th – 20th century music on both period and modern instruments
Touring: Festivals in Austria, Belgium, England, France, Germany, Netherlands, Spain, Ireland, Denmark
Comments: international orchestra whose members are also members of or have performed with prestigious Early Music and Contemporary Music Ensembles throughout the world

Gürzenich-Orchester Kölner Philharmoniker
Bischofsgartenstrasse 1, 50667 **Köln**
Tel: 221-2212 2437 Fax: 221-2212 3800
Direktor t.b.a.; Generalmusikdirektor James Conlon; Press Office/PR Birgit Heinemann
Size: 130 *Type/spec:* symphony and chamber *Venues:* Kölner Philharmonie 2171

Kölner Rundfunk-Sinfonie-Orchester
Westdeutscher Rundfunk, 50600 **Köln**
Tel: 221-2201/220 2146 Fax: 221-220 2945
Internet: www.wdr.de
Orchestermanagement Hans Martin Höpner; Chefdirigent Semyon Bychkov; Leitung Programmbereich Musik Gabriele Faust; Konzertmeister Kyoko Shikata; Promotion/Marketing Carola Anhalt
Size: 118 *Perfs:* 40 *Type/spec:* classical, new music, chamber *Venues:* Philarmonie 2171
Touring: national, international

Musica Antiqua Köln
Hochstadenstr 10, 50674 **Köln**
Tel: 221-923 2030/35 Fax: 221-923 2031
E-Mail: hansotto.mak@t-online.de
Leiter Reinhard Goebel; musikalische Leitung Hans Otto
Size: 5-30 *Perfs:* 120 *Type/spec:* baroque to classical
Venues: Kölner Philharmonie Deutschlandfunk *Touring:* USA, Italy, Europe (with Katia and Mirielle Labeque)
Comments: see also Early Music

Südwestdeutsche Philharmonie Konstanz
Spanierstrasse 3, 78467 **Konstanz**
Tel: 7531-5946-0 Fax: 7531-5946-22
Internet: www.konstanz.de/philharmonie
E-Mail: philharmonie@stadt.konstanz.de
Leiterin des Orchesterbüros Eva-Maria Seefelder; Chefdirigent Petr Altrichter; Verwaltungschef Peter Conzelmann; Konzertmeister Gottfried Müller-Ackermann
Size: 56 *Perfs:* 100
Type/spec: classical & contemporary *Venues:* Konzilgebäude 805 *Touring:* national, international
Comments: mainly touring orchestra

Niederrheinische Symphoniker-Orchester der Städte Krefeld und Mönchengladbach
Theater Mönchengladbach, Theaterplatz 3, 47798 **Krefeld**
Tel: 2151-8050 Fax: 2151-28295
Comments: see entry under Mönchengladbach; see also Opera, Dance and Drama

Leipziger Gewandhausorchester
Gewandhaus zu Leipzig, Augustusplatz 8, 04109 **Leipzig**
Tel: 341-1270-0 Fax: 341-127 0200
Internet: www.gewandhaus.de
E-Mail: publicrelations@gewandh.de
Verwaltungsdirektor Volker Stiehler; Chefdirigent Gewandhauskapellmeister Herbert Blomstedt; 1.Konzertmeister Prof. Karl Suske Prof. Christian Funke, Frank Michael Erben; Orchesterdirektor Dr. Siegfried Raschke
Size: 185 *Perfs:* 65 *Type/spec:* symphony orchestra, opera
Venues: Gewandhaus 1900, Oper 1600, Thomaskirche 1685 *Touring:* national, Austria, Spain, Italy, UK, Japan
Comments: see also Venues

MDR-Sinfonieorchester
Springerstrasse 22-24, 04105 **Leipzig**
Tel: 341-300 5705 Fax: 341-300 5701
Internet: www.mdr.de/klangkoerper
Chefdirigent Fabio Luigi; Management Holger Kruppe, Mario Plath, Helga Kuschmitz
Size: orchestra 168, choir 73 *Perfs:* 150 *Venues:* Neues Gewandhaus Leipzig, Altes Rathaus, Thomaskirche, MDR-Studio *Touring:* Italy, Switzerland, Austria, USA, China *Comments:* also the organisation for the MDR-Kammerphilharmonie

Orchester der Musikalischen Komödie Leipzig
Dreilindenstraße 30, 04177 **Leipzig**
Tel: 341-126 1114 Fax: 341-126 1150
GMD und Chefdirigent Roland Seiffarth; Chefdisponent Klaus Drescher
Size: 47 *Perfs:* 180 *Type/spec:* opera, operetta, but also symphonic and chamber *Venues:* Haus Dreilinden 529, Musikalische Komödie *Touring:* German speaking countries *Comments:* see also Opera

Westdeutsche Sinfonia
c/o Artists International, Humboldtstraße 17, 51379 **Leverkusen**
Tel: 2171-42663 Fax: 2171-43981
Künstlerischer Leitung Dirk Joeres; Management Linda Abberton
Size: 40 *Perfs:* 70 *Type/spec:* Viennese classics to contemporary *Venues:* Forum Leverkusen 1000 *Touring:* national, Spain, Austria, Hungary *Comments:* own series in Forum; recordings for BIS and Hallmark; see also Promoters and Agents & Producers

Orchesterakademie des Schleswig-Holstein Musik Festivals
Jerusalemsberg 7, 23568 **Lübeck**
Tel: 451-389 5718/19 Fax: 451-389 5716
Internet: www.shmf.de
E-Mail: shmf-oa@t-online.de
Head of the Orchestral Academy Christian Lorenz; conductors for 2000 Christoph Eschenbach (künstlerischer Leiter) and others
Size: 110 *Perfs:* 19 (13 symphonic, 6 chamber concerts) *Type/spec:* 19th and 20th C *Venues:* capacity from 100 to over 2000 *Comments:* summer address: Kulturzentrum Schloßsalzan, 24256 Fargau, Tel:4303-1846, Fax: 4303-1841; international youth orchestra, worldwide auditions in January/February, rehearsals and concerts in July/August; see also Festivals

Philharmonisches Orchester der Hansestadt Lübeck
Beckengrube 16, 23539 **Lübeck**
Tel: 451-708 8112/53 Fax: 451-708 8177
Generalintendant Dietrich von Oertzen; GMD und Chefdirigent Erich Wächter
Size: 66 *Type/spec:* classical, modern and music for opera performances, symphony *Venues:* Großes Haus 782, Kammerspiele 327, Studio 99, Musik-und Kongresshalle 1600, Audienzsaal 99 *Comments:* see also Opera and Drama

Staatsphilharmonie Rheinland-Pfalz
Heinigstrasse 40, 67059 **Ludwigshafen**
Tel: 621-599 090 Fax: 621-599 0940/50
Internet: www.staatsphilharmonie.de
E-Mail: Philharmonie-Ludwigshafen@t-online.de
Intendant Christoph Caesar; Verwaltung Werner Lenhart; Künstlerische Leitung, Chefdirigent Theodor Guschlbauer
Size: 96 *Perfs:* 95 *Type/spec:* symphony, opera, ballet *Touring:* Germany, UK, Austria, South America, China *Comments:* touring orchestra with concert series at Pfalzbau, Ludwigshafen and Kultur u. Kongresszentrum Rosengarten, Mannheim; see also Venues (BASF Feierabendhaus Ludwigshafen)

Orchester des Theaters Lüneburg
An den Reeperbahnen 3, Postfach 2829, 21318 **Lüneburg**
Tel: 4131-7520 Fax: 4131-404 210
Internet: www.theater-lueneburg.de
E-Mail: dramaturgie@theater-lueneburg.de
Verwaltung Wolfgang Dannenfeld; Musikdirektor Urs-Michael Theus; Konzertmeister Nick Birchby
Size: 29 *Perfs:* 80 *Type/spec:* opera, operetta, symphony, musical *Venues:* Theater 553 *Comments:* see also Opera, Dance and Drama

Mainzer Kammerorchester e. V.
Friedrich-Naumann Str. 9, 55131 **Mainz**
Tel: 6131-839 198 Fax: 6131-834 128
Verwaltung Monika Pruppacher; Musikalischer Leiter Volker Müller
Size: 8-30 *Perfs:* 65 *Type/spec:* baroque, classical, 20th C *Touring:* Europe *Comments:* touring orchestra

Philharmonisches Orchester des Staatstheaters Mainz
Gutenbergplatz 7, 55116 **Mainz**
Tel: 6131-285 1160 Fax: 6131-285 1161
Chefdirigent Stefan Sanderling
Size: 78 *Perfs:* 26 concerts + performances with music theatre *Type/spec:* symphonic and operatic repertoire *Venues:* Staatstheater (closed for refurbishment until autumn 2000) 860, now: Phoenixhalle 800
Comments: venue address: Hauptstr. 17-19, 55120 Mainz; see also Opera, Drama and Dance

Kurpfälzisches Kammerorchester Mannheim-Ludwigshafen
D6,2, 68159 **Mannheim**
Tel: 621-14554 Fax: 621-156 1288
Internet: www.kko.de
E-Mail: orchester@kko.de
Geschäftsführer Thomas Stricker; Künstlerischer Leiter Jiri Malát
Size: 14 *Perfs:* 80 *Type/spec:* chamber orchestra: Mannheim school, baroque, classical, modern *Venues:* Rittersaal des Schlosses 300, St. Sebastian church 300, Church Schloß Mannheim 300, Christus Church Mannheim 1200, Stadtpark Mannheim – Seebühne 1200 (open-air), Nationaltheater Mannheim 1000, Rosengarten Mannheim 800, Gesellschaftshaus der BASF Ludwigshafen 300 *Touring:* Germany, Switzerland, Austria, Czech Republic, Slovakia, Italy, Poland, Brazil, Croatia, Spain, China
Comments: several premieres; recordings available

Nationaltheater-Orchester Mannheim
Mozartstrasse 9, 68161 **Mannheim**
Tel: 621-168 0480 Fax: 621-168 0371
E-Mail: nationaltheater.kasse@mannheim.de
Chefdirigent Jun Märkl; Erster Konzertmeister Robert Frank; Leiterin des Orchesterbüros Laura Bettag
Size: 102 *Perfs:* 250
Type/spec: opera, operetta, musicals, symphony – classical and modern – 18th-20th century
Venues: Schauspielhaus, Opernhaus and Werkstattbühne, Konzertsaal Rosengarten
Comments: see also Opera, Dance and Drama

Philharmonia Hungarica in der Bundesrepublik Deutschland e.V.
Lord-Menuhin-Haus, Hochstr. 34, 45768 **Marl**
Tel: 2365-14007/13031
Fax: 2365-15877

Orchester des Meininger Theaters
Bernhardstr. 5, 98617 **Meiningen**
Tel: 3693-451 266 Fax: 3693-502 285
Internet: www.das_meininger_theater.de
Intendantin Christine Mielitz; Musikdirektorin Marie-Jeanne Dupur
Size: 60 *Type/spec:* classical and modern
Venues: Meininger Theater 742, Studiobühne 100
Touring: Switzerland, Romania
Comments: see also Opera, Drama and Dance

Niederrheinische Symphoniker – Orchester der Städte Krefeld und Mönchengladbach
Theater Mönchengladbach, Odenkirchener Strasse 78, 41236 **Mönchengladbach**
Tel: 2166-61510 Fax: 2166-420 110
Internet: members.aol.corr/vsbuehnen
Jens Pesel; Generalmusikdirektor Anthony Bramall; Geschäftsführer Reinhard Zeileis; Operndirektor Andreas Wendholz; Schauspieloberspielleiter Peter Hathazy; Ballettdirektorin Heidrun Schwaarz
Size: 83 *Perfs:* 7 symphonic concerts (28 perfs), 5 children's concerts (10 perfs) + various special concerts *Type/spec:* classic to modern symphonic, opera, operetta, musicals
Venues: Kaiser-Friedrich-Halle Mönchengladbach 850, Stadthalle Rheydt 830, Opernhaus 816
Comments: see also Opera, Dance and Drama; see also entry under Krefeld

Bayerisches Staatsorchester
Max-Joseph-Platz 2, 80359 **München**
Tel: 89-218 501 Fax: 89-2185 1133
Internet: www.bayerische.staatsoper.de
E-Mail: press@st-oper.bayern.de
Staatsintendant Peter Jonas; Generalmusikdirektor Zubin Mehta; Pressesprecherin und Leiterin PR Dr Ulrike Hessler; Chordirektor Udo Mehrpohl; Konzertmeister Luis Michal, Markus Wolf
Size: 144 *Perfs:* 350
Type/spec: symphony, modern, classical
Venues: Nationaltheater 2101, Cuvilliés Theater 523, Prinz-Regenten Theater 1100, Gasteig, Carl-Orff-Saal
Touring: national, international *Comments:* second address: Postfach 100148, 80075 München; see also Opera, Dance, Drama and Festivals

Junge Münchner Philharmonie e.V.
Offenbach Strasse 1, 81241 **München**
Tel: 89-836 606 Fax: 89-820 4232
E-Mail: J.M.Ph@T-online.de
conductor & artistic director Mark Mast; administrator Diane Clayton; administrative & financial assistant Dunja Weiss; orchestra manager Michael Schöne
Size: varies from chamber to symphony (400 members) *Perfs:* 50 p.a. *Touring:* Finland
Comments: the Junge Münchner Philharmonie e.V. is the umbrella organisation for three youth orchestras: the Münchner Jugendorchester (15-25 year olds), the Junge Münchner Philharmonie (20-30 year olds) and a smaller, purely educational orchestra for beginners (10-15 years); it also give institutional support to approximately 40 young chamber ensembles; each orchestra has it own artistic identity and programmes; ideas for exchanges/joint projects with other youth orchestras are always welcome

L'Orient Imaginaire
Zieblandstr. 9, 80799 **München**
Tel: 89-272 4243 Fax: 89-272 4243
E-Mail: dr_vladimir_ivanoff@compuserve.com
Musikalische Leitung Dr Vladimir Ivanoff
Size: 2-8 instrumentalists, 2-4 singers *Perfs:* 60
Type/spec: music of the 18th-20th C.
Touring: Europe, USA *Comments:* 4 CDs with TCI; see also Ensemble Sarband

Münchener Kammerorchester
Wittelsbacherplatz 2, 80333 **München**
Tel: 89-283 732/280 9309 Fax: 89-280 171
E-Mail: lenamaria@compuserve.com
Geschäftsführer Maria Grätze; Sekretariat Andrea Rings; Konzertmeister Muriel Cantoreggi, Daniel Giglberger; Künstlerischer Leiter Christoph Poppen; Künstlerischer Beirat Hans-Jürgen von Bose, Heinz Holliger, Mario Venzago
Size: 21 *Perfs:* 70 *Type/spec:* baroque to modern *Venues:* Herkules-Saal 1270, Max-Joseph – Saal 350, Brunnenhof (open air) 500 *Touring:* USA, Japan, Germany, Spain, South America, Scandinavia, Italy *Comments:* recordings (CD) available; radio performances

Münchner Philharmoniker – Orchester der Landeshauptstadt München
Gasteig-Kulturzentrum, Kellerstrasse 4/III, 81667 **München**
Tel: 89-4809 8509 Fax: 89-4809 8525
Internet: www.MuenchnerPhilharmoniker.de
E-Mail: MPhilhar@compuserve.com
Intendant Bernd Gellermann; Chefdirigent James Levine; Verwaltungsleiter Dieter Girstenbrei; künstlerisches Betriebsbüro Roswitha Wetz; Presse und Öffentlichkeitsarbeit Peter Meisel
Size: 130 *Perfs:* 90 *Type/spec:* mainly classical, some modern *Venues:* Philharmonie am Gasteig 2364
Touring: national

Münchner Rundfunkorchester
Rundfunkplatz 1, 80300 **München**
Tel: 89-5900 2355 Fax: 89-5900 3279
E-Mail: rundfunkorchester@br-mail.de
Disposition Jaroslav Opela; Chefdirigent Marcello Viotti
Size: 71 *Perfs:* 40 *Type/spec:* from classical to contemporary (no symphonic works) *Venues:* Studio 1 (400) (Bayerischer Rundfunk), Herkulessaal der Residenz 1270, Philharmonie im Gasteig 2400, Prinzregententheater 1025
Touring: national, international
Comments: recordings and radio concerts

Münchner Symphoniker e.V.
Drächslstr. 14, 81541 **München**
Tel: 89-448 6657 Fax: 89-487 568
Konzertmeister William Bouton; 1. Vereinsvorsitzander Prof. Cornelius Eberhardt; Intendant Karlheinz Zierold; Orchesterbüro Eva Ramft; Finanz- und Rechnungswesen Ingrid Abraham; Assistent d. Intendanten Sabine Hatz; Chefdirigent Heiko Mathias Förster
Size: 60 *Perfs:* 120 *Type/spec:* symphonic repertoire *Venues:* Herkules-Saal der Residenz 1270, Kulturzentrum Gasteig 2000, Prinz-Regenten Theater 1100 *Touring:* Germany, Spain, Greenland

Orchester des Staatstheaters am Gärtnerplatz
Postfach 140569, 80455 **München**
Tel: 89-202 411 Fax: 89-2024 1237
Internet: www.staatstheater.bayern.de/
E-Mail: gaertner/welcome.htm
Intendant Klaus Schultz; Chefdirigent David Stahl
Size: 77 *Perfs:* 224 *Type/spec:* operatic *Venues:* Staatstheater 893 *Touring:* Germany *Comments:* visiting address: Gärtnerplatz 3, 80469 München; see also Opera and Dance

Symphonieorchester des Bayerischen Rundfunks
Symphony Orchestra of Bavarian Broadcasting
Arnulfstrasse 42, 80333 **München**
Tel: 89-5900 2130/2230/2911
Fax: 89-5900 3377
Internet: www.br-online.de/kultur/klangkoerper
E-Mail: symphonieorchester@br-mail.de
Chefdirigent Lorin Maazel; Hauptabteilung Klangkörper Kurt Meister; Management Symphonieorchester Nine Herdner; Marketing Klangkörper Jörg Zizelmann
Size: 115 *Perfs:* 93 *Type/spec:* symphony
Venues: Herkulessaal der Residenz 1270, Philharmonie im Gasteig 2450 *Touring:* worldwide
Comments: CDs available

Symphonieorchester der Stadt Münster
Neubrückenstrasse 63, 48143 **Münster**
Tel: 251-590 9109/112 Fax: 251-590 9208
Internet: www.muenster.de/stb
E-Mail: staedt-buehnen@stadt-muenster.de
Orchestergeschäftsführer Gernot Wojnarowicz; Generalmusikdirektor Will Humburg; Konzertmeister Midori Goto
Size: 66 *Perfs:* 160
Type/spec: opera, operetta, classical, chamber
Venues: Städtische Bühnen: Großes Haus 955, Kleines Haus 321 *Comments:* see also Opera, Dance and Drama

Neubrandenburger Philharmonie
Ziegelbergstr. 5a, 17033 **Neubrandenburg**
Tel: 395-581 9511 Fax: 395-544 2099
Internet: www.nb-net.de/philharmonie
E-Mail: philharmonie.nb@t-online.de
Geschäftsführender Direktor Horst Beitz; GMD und Chefdirigent Prof Nicolas Pasquét; Dramaturgie Anke Völker-Zabka; Leiterin Öffentlichkeitsarbeit Gabriele Behr
Size: 76 *Perfs:* 300 *Type/spec:* early music, baroque, classical, contemporary (orchestral & chamber music) *Venues:* Haus der Kultur und Bildung Neubrandenburg 592, Schauspielhaus Neubrandenburg 200, Ernst-Barlach-Theater Güstrow 350, Landestheater Mecklenburg Neustrelitz 400 *Touring:* national, international *Comments:* have 25 chamber music groups (musicians from the orchestra) performing; see also Early Music

Deutsche Kammerakademie Neuss am Rhein
Oberstr. 17, 41460 **Neuss**
Tel: 2131-904 116 Fax: 2131-904 127
Manager Christian Kötter;
Chefdirigent Johannes Goritzki
Size: 21 permanent, up to 44 *Perfs:* 60 *Type/spec:* from Bach to Avantgarde *Venues:* Zeughaus Neuss 550, Stadthalle Neuss 1100 *Touring:* national and international

Nordhausen/Loh-Orchester Sondershausen GmbH
Käthe-Kollwitz-Straße 15, 99734 **Nordhausen**
Tel: 3631-6260-0 Fax: 3631-626 0147
Internet: www.loh-orchester.sondershausen.de
E-Mail: theater@nordhausen.de
Intendant Dr. Monika Pirklbauer; Geschäftsführer t.b.a.; Künstlerischer Betriebsdirektor Dr. Klaus Engert; GMD Peter Stangel; Oberspielleiter Wolfgang Barth (music), Armin Petras (theatre), Henning Paar (ballet); PR Harald Blaschke
Size: 60 *Perfs:* 21 + opera, ballet, music theatre, children's and youth theatre *Type/spec:* classical, opera, musical *Venues:* Nordhausen: Großes Haus 495, Theater unterm Dach 60, Foyer 50, hinterm Eisernen Vorhang 60; Sondershausen: Haus der Kunst 381, Ackteckhaus 320 *Touring:* Germany *Comments:* see also Opera, Dance and Drama

Nürnberger Symphoniker
Bayernstrasse 100, 90471 **Nürnberg**
Tel: 911-474 0140 Fax: 911-474 0150
Intendant Günter Einhaus; Konzertmeister Klaus Lieb; Intendanzbüro Sabine Randow; Verwaltungsleitung Karl Herbig; Chefdirigent Jac van Steen
Size: 56 *Perfs:* 108 *Type/spec:* all types for symphonic orchestra *Venues:* Meistersingerhalle 2121
Touring: Germany

Philharmonisches Orchester der Stadt Nürnberg
Richard-Wagner-Platz 2-10, 90443 **Nürnberg**
Tel: 911-231 3524 Fax: 911-231 3561
Internet: oper.nuernberg.de
E-Mail: oper@stadt.nuernberg.de
Leiter des Orchesterbüros Dr Axel Emmerling; Generalmusikdirektor Philippe Auguin; Konzertmeister Michael Sigler, Bernd Buß, Ferenc Babari
Size: 86 *Perfs:* 270 *Type/spec:* classical, opera, operette, modern, concerts *Venues:* Opernhaus 1011, Meistersingerhalle 2121 *Comments:* see also Opera, Dance and Drama

Collegium Cartusianum
Oberborsbacher Str. 6, 51519 **Odenthal**
Tel: 2202-70293 Fax: 2202-70294
manager Gianna Nicoletti; conductor Peter Neumann
Size: 20-35 *Perfs:* 15-20 *Type/spec:* chamber, symphony *Touring:* Germany, Italy, France, Netherlands *Comments:* recordings on EMI Classics, CPO, MDG; management address: Vicolo Monviso 1, 20010 Canegrate, Italy, Tel: +39 0331-411 142, Fax: +39 0331-401 515; see also Choirs (Kölner Kammerchor)

Oldenburgisches Staatsorchester
Theaterwall 28, 26122 **Oldenburg**
Tel: 441-22250 Fax: 441-222 5222
Internet: www.oldenburg.staatstheater.de
E-Mail: kasse@oldenburg.staatstheater.de
Generalintendant Stephan Mettin; GMD Reinhard Seifried; Konzertmeister Lev Guelbard; Orchesterinspektor Peter Morbitzer
Size: 68 *Perfs:* 8 symphony + 6 chamber + various special concerts *Venues:* Großes Haus 881, Weser-Ems-Halle 1400, Kleines Haus 350 *Comments:* see also Drama and Opera

Osnabrücker Symphonieorchester
Städt. Bühnen Osnabrück, Domhof 10/11, 49074 **Osnabrück**
Tel: 541-323 3355 Fax: 541-323 2751
Internet: www.theater-osnabrueck.de
E-Mail: theateros@aol.com
Intendant Norbert Hilchenbach; Generalmusikdirektor Lothar Königs; Kaufmännischer Direktor Norbert Kronisch; Musikdramaturg Stefan Klawitter; Leiterin d. Musikbüros und Referentin d. GMD Gabriele Eikermann; Sekretärin d. GMD und Musikbüros t.b.a.; Konzertmeister Horst Hegel
Size: 59 *Perfs:* 40 concerts + 150 music theatre/dance theatre *Type/spec:* opera, operetta, musical, dance theatre, classical to 20thC *Venues:* Städtische Bühnen Osnabrück: Großes Haus 642 (concert) 588 (theatre), emma-theater 100, Foyer/Orchesterstudio 100, Europasaal der Stadthalle Osnabrück 1400 *Comments:* see also Opera, Dance and Drama

Orchester des Südostbayerischen Städtetheaters
Musikalische Abteilung, Gottfried-Schäffer-Straße 2-4, 94032 **Passau**
Tel: 851-929 1930 Fax: 851-929 1933
E-Mail: stadttheater.passau@t-online.de
Verwaltung Ralf Schützenberger; Musikdirektor Roger Boggasch; Intendant Johannes Reitmeier
Size: 37 *Perfs:* 134 oper/operette, 7 concerts *Type/spec:* symphonic and operatic repertoire *Venues:* Stadttheater Landshut, Stadttheater Straubing, Stadttheater Passau *Comments:* alternative E-mail: theater@inet-nb.de

Städtisches Orchester Pforzheim
c/o Stadttheater, Am Waisenhausplatz 5, 75172 **Pforzheim**
Tel: 7231-392 873/719 Fax: 7231-392 566
Internet: www.pforzheim.de/theater
E-Mail: theater@stadt-pforzheim.de
Verwaltung Gustl Weber; Chefdirigent GMD Jari Hämäläinen; Dramaturgie Beate Bucher-Heller; künstlerisches Betriebsbüro Helene von Orlowsky; koord. Konzertmeister Borivoje Pejcic; Konzertmeister Attila Barta
Size: 40 *Perfs:* 6 symphony concerts, 3 chamber concerts, 180 music theatre, also children's concerts *Type/spec:* classical, contemporary, opera, operetta and musical repertoire and ballet *Venues:* Große Bühne Stadthalle 1800, Theater Pforzheim 510 *Touring:* guest performances in Baden-Württemberg *Comments:* see also Opera, Dance and Drama

Südwestdeutsches Kammerorchester
Westliche 257 a, 75172 **Pforzheim**
Tel: 7231-464 644 Fax: 7231-464 643
E-Mail: SWDKO-Pforzheim@t-online.de
Geschäftsführer Stephan Popp; Chefdirigent Vladislav Czarnecki; Sekretariat Elisabeth Rogge, Gabriele Rothfuß
Size: 15 *Perfs:* 90 *Type/spec:* chamber *Venues:* Stadthalle 1600 *Touring:* worldwide

Sinfonieorchester Pirna
Bergstraße 2, 01796 **Pirna**
Tel: 3501-445 190 Fax: 3501-578 932
Internet: www.novum-gmbh.de
E-Mail: novum_sp@t-online.de
Öffentlichkeitsarbeit Helene Paillelte; Chefdirigent Andreas Grohmann; Orchesterbüro Rolf Bäns; Geschäftsführer (NOVUM GmbH) Günter Müller-Rogalla
Size: 35 *Perfs:* 100 *Type/spec:* baroque to modern *Venues:* Tannen-Säle Pirna 500 and others throughout Saxony *Touring:* national, international *Comments:* Trustees: Neue Orchester Verwaltungs- und Marketing GmbH (NOVUM); see also Elbland-Philharmonie Sachsen

Philharmonisches Orchester des Vogtland Theaters
Vogtland Theater Plauen, Theaterplatz 1-3, 08523 **Plauen**
Tel: 3741-291 2435 Fax: 3741-222 620
Intendant Dieter Roth; 1. Kapellmeister Frank Zacher; GMD Dieter-Gerhardt Worm
Size: 58 *Perfs:* 150 *Type/spec:* opera, operetta, symphony, musicals *Venues:* Großes Haus 467, Kleines Haus 99, Festhalle Plauen *Touring:* Germany *Comments:* see also Opera, Drama and Dance

Brandenburgische Philharmonie Potsdam GmbH
Wilhelm-Staab-Str. 10, 14467 **Potsdam**
Tel: 331-270 9177 Fax: 331-270 9179
Internet: www.philharmonie.potsdam.com
E-Mail: philharmonie@potsdam.com
Intendant Jörg Potratz; GMD Victor Puhl; Dramaturgie Cornelia Fischer; Öffentlichkeitsarbeit Antje Horn-Conrad; Prokuristin Monika Gottweiss
Size: 67 *Perfs:* 80 *Type/spec:* baroque to modern *Venues:* Theaterhaus Am Alten Markt 600, Schloßtheater im Neuen Palais 200 *Comments:* due to close-down on 31 July 2000

Preußisches Kammerorchester
Uckerpromenade 41, 17291 **Prenzlau**
Tel: 3984-2255 Fax: 3984-2873
Intendant Jürgen Bischof; Chefdirigent Hans Rotman
Size: 23 *Perfs:* 80 *Type/spec:* baroque to 20thC *Venues:* Konzert-u. Plenarsaal Prenzlau 250, Uckermerkische Bühnen Schwedt 600, Multi-Kulturelles Zentrum Teplin 150 *Touring:* Germany, Europe

Orchester der Landesbühnen Sachsen
152 Meißner Str., 01445 **Radebeul**
Tel: 351-8954-0 Fax: 351-8954-201
Internet: www.dresden-theater
E-Mail: landesbuehnensachsen@dresden-theater.de
Generalmusikdirektor Prof. Alexander von Brück; 1. Kapellmeister Matthias Mücksch; 2. Kapellmeister Hans-Peter Preu
Size: 68 *Perfs:* 139 *Type/spec:* opera, operetta, symphony, musicals, classical to modern *Venues:* Stammhaus, Radebeul 436, Felsenbühne (Sommer), Rathen 2000, Schloß Pillnitz 200, Dresden 200, Burghof Meißen 200 *Comments:* see also Opera, Dance and Drama

Neue Philharmonie Westfalen
Castroper Str. 12c, 45665 **Recklinghausen**
Tel: 2361-48860 Fax: 2361-488 666
Geschäftsführender Intendant Norbert Thomas; Chefdirigent, GMD Dr Johannes Wildner
Size: 128 *Perfs:* 300 *Type/spec:* symphony, also opera, operettas, musicals *Venues:* Festspielhaus 1049, Saalbau 890, Großes Haus (Gelsenkirchen) 1008 *Touring:* Germany, Italy *Comments:* film concerts, open-air concerts; the Neue Philharmonie Westfalen was formed when the Westfälisches Sinfonieorchester and the Philharmonisches Orchester der Stadt Gelsenkirchen merged in 1996

Philharmonisches Orchester Regensburg
Bismarckplatz 7, 93047 **Regensburg**
Tel: 941-507 1422 Fax: 941-507 4429
Generalmusikdirektor und Leiter der Sinfoniekonzerte Guido Johannes Rumstadt; 1. Kapellmeister und Stellv. des GMD Kazuyuki Okamoto; Chordirektor und Kapellmeister Karl Andreas Mehling
Size: 56 *Perfs:* 15 Concerts + 4 youth concerts + opera, operetta and musical performances *Type/spec:* symphonic, musicals, opera, operetta and chamber music *Venues:* Stadttheater 538 (closed until 2001) instead: Velodrom 600, Audi Max Regensburg University 1500 *Comments:* see also Opera, Dance and Drama

Vogtland Philharmonie Greiz/Reichenbach
Weinholdstrasse 7 (Neuberinhaus), 08468 **Reichenbach**
Tel: 3765-13470 Fax: 3765-21170
Internet: www.vogtland-philharmonie.com
E-Mail: vogtland-philharmonie@t-online.de
Intendant/Geschäftsführer Stefan Fraas; Chefdirigent Doron Salomon; Orchesterdirektor Wolfgang Franz; Dramaturgie Andrea Buder
Size: 65 *Perfs:* 150 *Type/spec:* symphony *Venues:* Theater der Stadt Greiz 500, Neuberinhaus 600 *Touring:* national, international *Comments:* see also Vogtland Philharmonie Greiz/Reichenbach (under Greiz)

Kammerorchester Arcata Stuttgart
Elsterweg 5, 71686 **Remseck**
Tel: 7146-810 085/6 Fax: 7146-810 087
E-Mail: PatStrub@t-online.de
Organisation Elisabeth Asche; Dirigent Patrik Strub
Size: 19 strings *Perfs:* 25 *Type/spec:* baroque to contemporary *Touring:* Germany, Spain, France

Stiftung Württembergische Philharmonie Reutlingen
Marie-Curie-Str. 8, 72760 **Reutlingen**
Tel: 7121-963 220/221 Fax: 7121-963 225
Intendant t.b.a.; Orchesterbüro Ingo Wietersheim; GMD u. Chefdirigent Roberto Paternostro; Konzertmeister Georgios Mandylas, Krzysztof Baranowski
Size: 67 *Perfs:* 80 *Type/spec:* classical, modern, operatic *Venues:* Friedrich-List-Halle 1000 *Touring:* Netherlands, Switzerland, Belgium, Spain

Elbland-Philharmonie Sachsen
c/o NOVUM GmbH, Postfach 400102, 01579 **Riesa**
Tel: 3525-7226-0 Fax: 3525-7226-49
Internet: www.novum-gmbh.de
E-Mail: novum eps@t-online.de
Geschäftsführer Günter Müller-Rogalla; Generalmusikdirekor Peter Fanger
Size: 49 *Perfs:* 100 *Type/spec:* symphony, film concerts, chamber *Venues:* Stadthalle STERN *Touring:* national, international *Comments:* visiting address: Kirchstraße 3, 01591 Riesa; Trustees: Neue Orchester Verwaltungs- und Marketing GmbH (NOVUM); see also Sinfonieorchester Pirna

Norddeutsche Philharmonie Rostock
PF 102215, 18003 **Rostock**
Tel: 381-244 246 Fax: 381-244 239
Intendant Dr Michael Winrich Schlicht; Chefdirigent, GMD t.b.a.; Orchesterdirektor Bernd Windisch
Size: 90 *Perfs:* 100-150 *Type/spec:* symphony, musicals, opera, operetta and chamber music *Venues:* Großes Haus 579, Barocksaal 200, Theater im Stadthafen 203 *Touring:* national
Comments: see also Opera, Dance and Drama

Thüringer Symphoniker Saalfeld-Rudolstadt
Thüringer Landestheater GmbH – Eisenach, Rudolstadt -Saalfeld, Postfach 110, 07392 **Rudolstadt**
Tel: 3672-450-0 Fax: 3672-450 114
Internet: www.thuringerlandestheater.de
Intendant und künstlerischer Geschäftsführer Johannes Steurich; Geschäftsführer Petra Mitdank; Künstlerischer Betriebsdirektor Gerhard Hentschel; MD Oliver Weder; Kapellmeister Toni Steidl; Ausstattung Heinz-Dieter Ruhland; Chefdramaturg Bernhard Rohwedder
Size: 39 *Perfs:* 53 *Type/spec:* opera, symphony concerts, modern *Venues:* Großes Haus 271, Studiobühne 50 *Comments:* second address: Anger 1, 07407 Rudolstadt; see also Drama, Dance and Opera

PanArte
Spichererbergstr. 82, 66119 **Saarbrücken**
Tel: 681-589 6009/309 2244 Fax: 681-309 2273
E-Mail: panarte@t-online.de
Künstlerische Leitung Errico Fresis; Geschäftsführerin Caroline Armand; PR/Marketing Norbert Dirscherl, Astrid Hensler
Size: 1-32 *Perfs:* 4-20 *Type/spec:* interdisciplinary and multimedia events, contemporary music *Comments:* also workshops, masterclasses and multimedia projects

Rundfunk-Sinfonieorchester Saarbrücken
Funkhaus Halberg, 66100 **Saarbrücken**
Tel: 681-602 2250/51 Fax: 681-602 2249
Internet: www.sr-online.de/rso
Programmbereich Musik, Musikchefin Dr Sabine Tomek; Produktionsleiter Matthias Gawriloff; Konzertmeister Dora Bratschkova, Götz Rüstig; Chefdirigent Michael Stern
Size: 84 *Perfs:* 40 *Type/spec:* symphony orchestra, 18th-19th C + focus on 20th C works *Venues:* Kongreßhalle 1200, Großer Sendesaal 400 *Comments:* festival 'Musik im 20 Jahrhundert'

Saarländisches Staatsorchester Saarbrücken
Postfach 102735, 66027 **Saarbrücken**
Tel: 681-3092-0 Fax: 681-309 2360
Internet: www.staatstheater.saarland.de
Orchesterverwaltung Wera Bunge; GMD u. Chefdirigent Olaf Henzold; Konzertmeister Avram Popov, Wolfgang Mertes; 1. Kappellmeister Hiroaki Masuda
Size: 80 *Perfs:* 2 + 8 symphony concerts + opera *Type/spec:* classical, musical, opera, symphony *Venues:* Staatstheater 875, Kongresshalle 1095 *Comments:* see also Opera, Dance, Drama and Venues

Kammerphilharmonie Schönebeck GmbH
Tischlerstr. 13a, 39218 **Schönebeck (Elbe)**
Tel: 3928-400 429/597 Fax: 3928-400 429
Internet: www.landkreis-schoenebeck.de
Chefdirigent und Künstlerischer Leiter Stefanos Tsialis; Veranstaltungsorganisation Monika Neitzel; Manager Hans-Jörg Simon
Size: 28 *Perfs:* 150 *Type/spec:* symphony, chamber, opera, operetta, mainly classical *Venues:* Konzertsaal 250 *Touring:* Europe

Mecklenburgische Staatskapelle Schwerin
Alter Garten 2, 19055 **Schwerin**
Tel: 385-530 0152 Fax: 385-530 0200
Internet: www.theater-schwerin.de
E-Mail: presse@theater-schwerin.de
Orchesterdirektion Gebhard Kern; Musikdramaturgie Dieter Klett; GMD Ivan Törzs
Size: 86 *Type/spec:* classical, contemporary (symphonic and chamber), opera, operetta, musical, ballet *Venues:* Mecklenburgisches Staatstheater: Großes Haus 666, E-Werk 99, Thronsaal 80 *Touring:* guest performances in Germany *Comments:* see also Opera, Dance and Drama

Bergische Symphoniker – Orchester der Städte Remscheid und Solingen
Konrad-Adenauer-Strasse 72-74, 42651 **Solingen**
Tel: 212-280 183 Fax: 212-280 182
Internet: www.BergischeSymphoniker.de
E-Mail: Berg.Symph@aol.com
Generalmusikdirektorin Romely Pfund; Geschäftsführer Anselm Rose
Size: 84 *Perfs:* 113 *Type/spec:* symphony orchestra, music theatre, chamber music *Venues:* Theater und Konzerthaus Solingen 813 & 1050, Stadttheater Remscheid 620 *Touring:* national

Salonorchester Schwanen
Orchesterbüro Eberhard Wurst, PO Box 1407, 76293 **Stutensee**
Tel: 7249-7119- Fax: 7249-953 232
Internet: www.salonorchester-schwanen.de
E-Mail: ebimusix@aol.com
contact Eberhard Wurst
Size: 10 + 1 actor *Type/spec:* salon music in different programmes with conference

Staatsorchester Stuttgart
Oberer Schloßgarten 6, 70173 **Stuttgart**
Tel: 711-203 2466 Fax: 711-203 2445
Generalmusikdirektor Lothar Zakrosek; Orchestergeschäftsführer Rudolf Brückner; Konzertmeister Joachim Schall, Wolf-Dieter Streicher, Jewgeni Schuck
Size: 131 *Perfs:* 2 + 7 *Type/spec:* symphonic and music theatre *Venues:* Liederhalle, Beethovensaal 2016, Staatsoper 1399 *Touring:* Scotland (Edinburgh) *Comments:* see also Opera, Drama and Dance

Stuttgarter Kammerorchester
Johann-Sebastian-Bach-Platz, 70178 **Stuttgart**
Tel: 711-619 2121 Fax: 711-619 2122
E-Mail: SKammerorc@aol.com
geschäftsführender Direktor Andreas Kuntze; Orchesterverwaltung Angelika Fischer, Gerlinde Rettenberger; Chefdirigent Dennis Russell Davies
Size: 17 *Perfs:* 70 *Type/spec:* from baroque to avant-garde *Venues:* Hegelsaal 1970, Mozartsaal 752 (Liederhalle Stuttgart) *Touring:* Europe, Asia, North America

Stuttgarter Philharmoniker
Leonhardsplatz 28, 70182 **Stuttgart**
Tel: 711-216 7110/7843
Fax: 711-216 3640
Intendant Hannes Schmidt; Chefdirigent Jörg-Peter Weigle; 1.Konzertmeister Matthias Wächter
Size: 86 + 12 volunteers *Perfs:* 90 *Type/spec:* classical, romantic, modern, operetta *Venues:* Liederhalle 2016, Gustav-Siegle Haus 500 *Touring:* Germany *Comments:* concerts for children; public rehearsals

SWR Radiosinfonieorchester Stuttgart
Neckarstrasse 230, 70190 **Stuttgart**
Tel: 711-929 2590 Fax: 711-929 4053
Internet: www.swr-online.de/faszination-musik
E-Mail: monika.krueger@swr-online.de
Orchestermanager Felix Fischer; Chefdirigent Sir Roger Norrington; Konzertmeister Hans Kalafusz
Size: 107 *Perfs:* 70-90 *Type/spec:* classical to modern

Städtisches Orchester Trier
Am Augustinerhof, 54290 **Trier**
Tel: 651-718 3464 Fax: 651-718 1468
Intendant Heinz Lukas-Kindermann; Verwaltungsdirektor Werner Reichert; Generalmusikdirektor István Dénes; Orchesterverwaltung Anne Karmeier; Konzertdramaturgin Anja Gewalt; Konzertmeister Gil Shivek
Size: 48 *Perfs:* 10 + opera, musicals, operettas *Type/spec:* modern, classical, symphony *Venues:* Stadttheater 622 *Touring:* national & Luxembourg *Comments:* see also Opera, Dance and Drama

Kleines Europa
c/o Musikforum Kleines Europa e.V., Merksteiner Straße 24, 52531 **Übach-Palenberg**
Tel: 2451-43926 Fax: 2451-43926
President K Josten-Rühl; Künstlerischer Leiter/Dirigent Friedhelm Rühl
Size: 21 *Type/spec:* chamber, 17th-20th century *Comments:* international ensemble; see also Promoters

Philharmonisches Orchester der Stadt Ulm
Ulmer Theater, Olgastr. 73, 89073 **Ulm**
Tel: 731-161 4400 (Intendant) Fax: 731-161 1619
Internet: www.theater.ulm.de
E-Mail: UlmerTheater@theater.ulm.de
Intendant Ansgar Haag; Generalmusikdirektor James Allen Gähres (731-616 4418); Konzertdramaturg Stephan Steinmetz (731-616 4424); Presse- und Öffentlichkeitsarbeit Frau Mayer (731-161 4410); Künstlerisches Betriebsbüro Frau Glathe (731-161 4434)
Size: 56 *Perfs:* 5 symphony concerts, 9 chamber concerts, 9 popular concerts *Type/spec:* early music, classical, opera, music theatre *Venues:* Congress Centrum Ulm 1372 *Comments:* see also Opera, Dance and Drama

Staatskapelle Weimar
Postfach 3 und 5, 99401 **Weimar**
Tel: 3643-755-0 Fax: 3643-755 307
Internet: www.deutsches-nationaltheater-weimar.de
E-Mail: dnt.service@weimar.net
Generalintendant Günther Beelitz; Generalmusikdirektor u. Chefdirigent Prof. George Alexander Albrecht; Orchesterdirigent Alexandra Kalaidjie
Size: 94 *Perfs:* 10 symphony concerts + operas, operettas *Type/spec:* symphony, opera *Venues:* Werkstattbühne 176, Große Haus 859 *Touring:* national and international *Comments:* visiting address: Deutsches National Theater, Theaterplatz 2, 99423 Weimar; see also Dance, Opera and Drama

Kammerorchester Schloß Werneck e.V.
Balthasar-Neumann-Platz 8, 97440 **Werneck**
Tel: 9722-91610 Fax: 9722-916 161
Internet: www.kammerorchester.de
E-Mail: kammerorchester@swin.de
Intendant Ulf Klausenitzer; Geschäftsführer Luts Köller
Size: 60 *Perfs:* 40-70 *Type/spec:* classical, new music *Touring:* Europe *Comments:* promotes Wernecker Schlosskonzerte (q.v.)

Philharmonisches Kammerorchester Wernigerode GmbH
Bahnhofstr. 16, 38855 **Wernigerode**
Tel: 3943-9495-0 Fax: 3943-9495-29
Künstlerischer Leiter & Geschäftsführer Christian Fitzner; Prokurist Ansgar Waschbusch; Sekretariat Roswitha Hoppe
Size: 25 *Perfs:* 120 *Type/spec:* symphonic orchestra *Venues:* Kulturzentrum 700, Rathaussaal 200, Sylvestrikirche 400, Johanniskirche 250

Deutsches Kammerorchester Frankfurt am Main
Haus-Bredow-Str. 42B, 65189 **Wiesbaden**
Tel: 611-464 619/461 941 Fax: 611-464 755
Geschäftsführer Rista Savic
Size: 18-32 *Perfs:* 20-30
Type/spec: baroque, classic, romantic, modern *Venues:* Konzertsaal Palmgarten 1200 *Touring:* Italy, Holland, Belgium, Czech Republic, Slovenia, Japan *Comments:* konzert management: Classik 2000

Orchester des Hessischen Staatstheaters Wiesbaden
Christian-Zais-Strasse 3, 65189 **Wiesbaden**
Tel: 611-132-1 Fax: 611-132 337/368
Internet: www.staatstheater-wiesbaden.de
Intendant Achim Thorwald; Direktor Peter Janowsky; GMD Toshiyuki Kamioka
Size: 78 *Type/spec:* classical to modern, also music for opera, music theatre, ballet
Venues: Staatstheater, Friedrich-von-Thiersch-Saal im Kurhaus, Wiesbaden *Comments:* see also Opera, Dance and Drama

Orchester des Mitteldeutschen Landestheaters Wittenberg
Thomas-Müntzer-Str. 14/15, 06886 **Wittenberg**
Tel: 3491-47370 Fax: 3491-473 710
Internet: www.theater-wittenberg.de
E-Mail: theater-wb@t-online.de
Intendant Reinhold Stövesand; Musikdirektor Jörg Iwer; 1. Kapellmeister Klaus Hofmann
Size: 38 *Perfs:* 4 symphony concerts + opera, musicals, operetta (600) *Type/spec:* symphonic, opera, operetta, musicals *Venues:* Landestheater Wittenberg (Großes Haus 380) *Touring:* Germany
Comments: see also Opera and Drama

Philharmonisches Orchester Würzburg
Theaterstrasse 21, 97070 **Würzburg**
Tel: 931-3908-0 (theatre)/3908117 (orchestra direct)
Fax: 931-390 8100
Orchesterverwaltung Joachim Esser; Chefdirigent Jonathan Seers; Verwaltungsdirektorin Heidrun Glosauer; Konzertmeister Franz-Peter Fischer; Orchestervorstand Peter Herleux, Janos Török, Marion Basting
Size: 56 *Perfs:* 11 + for music theatre/opera
Type/spec: classical to modern symphonic repertoire and operatic *Venues:* Hochschule für Musik, Würzburg; Kaisersaal 700

Philharmonisches Orchester Zwickau
Postfach 201039, 08012 **Zwickau**
Tel: 375-834 613 Fax: 375-834 609
Orchesterleiter Welisar Gentscheff; Intendant Wolfgang Hauswald; Verwaltungsdirektor Henry Klüglich
Size: 61 *Perfs:* 116 (35 concerts)
Type/spec: symphony + special concerts, opera, operetta, musical *Venues:* Konzert- und Ballhaus Neue Welt 900, Gewandhaus 400 *Touring:* Germany
Comments: Robert-Schumann-Preisträger

GREECE (+30)

Athens State Orchestra
King George II Street 17-19, **Athens**
Tel: 1-725 7601/3 Fax: 1-725 7600
director Aris Garoufalis
Size: 140 *Perfs:* 50-60 *Type/spec:* classical symphonic
Venues: Megaro-Mousikis; Herod-Atticus Odeon (summer) 1950 *Touring:* Greece

Athens Symphony Orchestra
Municipality of Athens, 50 Akademias ave, 10679 **Athens**
Tel: 1-364 2067/360 7867/363 9521
Fax: 1-360 2102
Internet: www.athens-culture.ids.gr
music director Elevtherios Kalkanis; general administration Mrs Kalogeropoulou
Size: 70 *Type/spec:* classical, Greek & American composers *Venues:* Municipal Theatre of Athens; Theatre of Irodou Attikou *Touring:* USA *Comments:* varied season of symphony concerts, recording, touring & education programme

Camerata – Orchestra of the Friends of Music, La
Vass. Sofias & Kokkali, 11521 **Athens**
Tel: 1-728 2341/2 Fax: 1-725 0136
E-Mail: kamerata@admin.megaron.gr
artistic director Alexandros Myrat; administrative director Manolis Hadjiandreou
Size: 24 *Perfs:* up to 50
Type/spec: 17th C to contemporary and opera *Venues:* Athens Concert Hall and others
Touring: Stockholm, Montpellier, Florence *Comments:* orchestra in residence at Athens Concert Hall

National Orchestra of Light Music
Athens Broadcasting Musical Ensembles Directorate, 432 Messioghion Avenue, Aghia Paraskevi, 15342 **Athens**
Tel: 1-606 6094 Fax: 1-606 6099
director of Athens Broadcasting Musical Ensembles Alkis Baltas; musical director t.b.a; deputy director Vassilis Tenides
Size: 65 *Perfs:* 10-12 annually
Type/spec: modern Greek music, operetta, musical, jazz (classical and modern) *Venues:* Megaro Mousikis; Ethniki Lyriki Skini (National Opera); Palace Theatre, Athens; College Theatre (Physico Campus)
Touring: Greece, Cyprus
Comments: performs concerts for TV and radio broadcasting; studio recording of light, contemporary and jazz works (big band section), musicals; co-produces operettas with National Opera

National Symphony Orchestra
Athens Broadcasting Musical Ensembles Directorate , 432 Mesoghion Avenue, Aghia Paraskevi, 15342 **Athens**
Tel: 1-606 6094 Fax: 1-606 6099
director Alkis Baltas; musical director Vassilis Tenidis
Size: 102 *Type/spec:* pre-classical, classical, opera, contemporary, symphonic *Venues:* Palace Theatre, College Theatre (Psihiko), Athens Concert Hall, Herodes Atticus Theatre *Touring:* Greece, Cyprus, Switzerland, France *Comments:* N.S.O records concerts for TV, radio broadcasting; a major part of its activity is studio recording, mainly of symphonic or chamber works of classical and contemporary Greek composers

Orchestra of Colours
18, Alexandrou Soutsou, 10671 **Athens**
Tel: 1-362 8819/8589 Fax: 1-362 1477
artistic director George Kouroupos; principal conductor Miltos Logiades
Size: 100 *Perfs:* 20 *Type/spec:* classical, contemporary Greek music, music from cinema and theatre

Orchestra of the National Opera of Greece
18A Charilaou Trikoupi Street, 10679 **Athens**
Tel: 1-360 0180/363 3105/361 4433
Fax: 1-360 0224/364 8309
president Spyros Evagelatos; artistic director Lukas Karytinos; PR manager Marilena Karytinos
Size: 70 *Perfs:* 120 *Type/spec:* opera, classical, ballet, operettas, music-theatre *Venues:* Theatre Olympia 900, Odeon of Herodes Atticus (summer/Athens festival) 4700 *Touring:* various cities in Greece and Cyprus *Comments:* see also Opera

City of Thessaloniki Symphony Orchestra
17, Kountouriotou Str, 54621 **Thessaloniki**
Tel: 31-538 440/491/541 666
Fax: 31-541 666
conductor/artistic director Kosmas Galilea; administration Varvara Torounidu
Size: 55 *Perfs:* 40 *Type/spec:* classical, symphonic, opera *Venues:* State Theatre of Northern Greece 1500, Ceremony Hall of Aristotlean University 1200 *Touring:* Athens Festival and other festivals in Greece & Cyprus

Thessaloniki State Symphony Orchestra
Moni Lazariston, Kolokotroni 21, 56430 **Thessaloniki**
Tel: 31-602 970/606 524 Fax: 31-604 854
director Leonidas Kavakos
Size: 120 *Perfs:* 30-50 *Type/spec:* pre-classical, classical, contemporary, opera *Venues:* State theatre of North Greece 1500, Ceremony Hall of Aristotelian University of Thessaloniki 1200, Lazaristes Hall *Touring:* national: Athens festival, Dimitria festival (Thessaloniki), Rhodes festival (Rhodes Island), Olympus festival, Filippi-Thassos festival

HUNGARY (+36)

Bartók String Quartet
c/o Gergely Művészeti Kft (Gergely Arts Ltd.), Hollán Erno utca 25 I/1, 1136 **Budapest**
Tel: 1-329 4064/350 0846
Fax: 1-350 0846
director Mária Gergely

Budapest Festival Orchestra
Budapesti Fesztiválzenekar
Vörösmarty tér 1, 1051 **Budapest**
Tel: 1-266 2312 Fax: 1-338 4337
Internet: www.bmc.hu/bfz/index2_en.htm
E-Mail: 100324.3314@compuserve.com
managing director Eszter Lovas; principal conductor & music director Iván Fischer; manager Tamás Körner
Size: 96 *Perfs:* 20 *Type/spec:* symphony, 18th – 20th century *Venues:* Liszt Academy Grand Hall 1200, Budapest Convention Centre1750 *Touring:* national, international *Comments:* postal address: POB 101, 1364 Budapest

Budapest MÁV Concert Orchestra
Budapesti MÁV Szimfonikus Zenekar
Muzeum u 11, 1088 **Budapest**
Tel: 1-338 4085/2664 Fax: 1-338 4085
Internet: www.bmc.hu/mav/index1.htm
managing director Gábor Fenyo; principal conductor Tamás Gál
Size: 95 *Perfs:* 60-80 *Type/spec:* symphony, 18th – 20th century *Venues:* Liszt Academy Grand Hall 1200, Pesti Vigado (Redoute) Grand Hall 700 *Touring:* Europe

Budapest Philharmonic Orchestra
Budapesti Filharmóniai Társaság Zenekara
Hajós u 8-10, 1065 **Budapest**
Tel: 1-331 9478 Fax: 1-331 9478
president Béla Melis; principal conductor Rico Saccani; administrator Julianna Wirthmann
Size: 152 *Perfs:* 18-20 *Type/spec:* symphony, 18th – 20th century *Venues:* Hungarian State Opera 1150, Liszt Academy Grand Hall 1200, Budapest Convention Centre 1750 *Touring:* Europe, USA, Asia *Comments:* orchestra musicians also play in the orchestras of the Hungarian State Opera (2 venues)

Budapest Strauss Orchestra
Budapesti Strauss Zenekar
c/o Margit Jasper, Csorna 3, 1121 **Budapest**
Tel: 1-395 5219 Fax: 1-395 5219
principal conductor & artistic director István Bogár; secretary Margit Jasper
Size: 42 *Perfs:* 90 *Type/spec:* music composed by Strauss family *Venues:* Liszt Academy Grand Hall 1200, Pesti Vigado (Redoute) Grand Hall 700
Touring: Europe, USA, Asia

Budapest Strings
Budapesti Vonósok
Kiskorona utca 7, 1124 **Budapest**
Tel: 1-250 0288 Fax: 1-250 0288
manager Dr Zsuzsa Kanizsai; artistic director Karoly Botvay; concert master Béla Bánfalvi
Size: 17 *Perfs:* 25 *Type/spec:* strings, chamber orchestra repertoire *Venues:* Liszt Academy Grand Hall 1200, Pesti Vigadó (Redoute) Grand Hall 700 *Touring:* Europe *Comments:* postal address: POB 329, 1369 Budapest; UK representative: Sue Lubbock Concert Management, 25 Courthope Road, London NW3 2LE, tel: (+44 20) 7485 5932, fax: (+44 20) 7267 0179

Budapest Wind Ensemble
Postafiók 503, 1373 **Budapest**
Tel: 1-331 2550 Fax: 1-331 9817/332 7331
leader Kálmán Berkes
Type/spec: repertoire: classical, both old and new rarely played works *Comments:* visiting address: Magyar Állami Operaház, Andrássy út 22, 1061 Budapest

City Center Symphony Orchestra
Belvárosi Szimfonikus Zenekar
Kerepesi 43, 1101 **Budapest**
Tel: 1-317 5858 Fax: 1-317 5858
managing director Ferenc Szklenar; principal conductor Andras Deak
Size: 46 *Perfs:* 40 *Type/spec:* small symphony 18th-20th century *Venues:* BM Culture Centre (address above) 600

Concerto Armonico
c/o Clemens Concerts, József Attila út 61, 1013 **Budapest**
Tel: 1-212 2045 Fax: 1-212 2045/375 8162
E-Mail: ClemensConcerts@compuserve.com
director Pál Kelemen; artistic directors Péter Szüts, Miklós Spányi
Size: 12 *Perfs:* 50 *Type/spec:* strings: period instruments, baroque *Venues:* Liszt Academy Grand Hall 1200 *Touring:* Europe *Comments:* postal address: POB 437, 1371 Budapest; see also Early Music

Concertus Hungaricus Chamber Orchestra
Concertus Hungaricus Kamarazenekar
c/o Budapest Artists Management, Somloi 39, 1118 **Budapest**
Tel: 1-395 3004 Fax: 1-395 3004
director Péter Popa; artistic director Ildikó Hegyi; manager Péter Popa
Size: 16 *Perfs:* 30 *Type/spec:* strings *Venues:* Liszt Academy Grand Hall 1200, Pesti Vigadó (Redoute) Grand Hall 700 *Touring:* Europe

Danube Symphony Orchestra
BM Duna Szimfonikus Zenekar
Németvölgy út. 41, 1124 **Budapest**
Tel: 1-355 8330 Fax: 1-355 8330
Internet: www.b-m.hu/duna_palota
E-Mail: szklenar_ferenc@f24.kibernet.hu
chief conductor András Deák; artistic director Ferenc Szklenár
Size: 53 *Venues:* Duna Palace

Danubia Youth Symphony Orchestra
Eröd utca 10, 1027 **Budapest**
Tel: 1-201 7116 Fax: 1-201 7116
artistic director & principal conductor Domonkos Héja
Comments: management: Budapest Artists Management, Somloi 39, 1118 Budapest, Tel/Fax: 1-386 6790

Dohnányi Ernõ Symphony Orchestra Budafok
Budafolki Dohnányi Ernö Szimfonikus Zenekar
Anna u. 15b, 1221 **Budapest**
Tel: 1-322 1488/227 4021 Fax: 1-322 1488/227 4021
director László Nemes; conductor Gábor Hollerung
Size: 80

Failoni Chamber Orchestra
Failoni Kamarazenekar
c/o Roland Bokor, Andrassy út. 22, 1061 **Budapest**
Tel: 1-332 7372 Fax: 1-331 9817
E-Mail: failoni.orch@usa.net
director Roland Bokor; contact Béla Nagy
Size: 18 *Type/spec:* strings *Venues:* Magyar Állami Operaház – Budapest Opera 1260 *Touring:* Europe *Comments:* postal address: POB 503, 1373 Budapest

Ferenc Liszt Chamber Orchestra
Liszt Ferenc Kamarazenekar
Hollan 25 I/2, 1136 **Budapest**
Tel: 1-325 7312/250 4938 Fax: 1-270 0846/250 4938
general manager and administrator Eva Ronai; musical director and concertmaster János Rolla
Size: 18 *Perfs:* 100 *Type/spec:* strings, chamber orchestra *Venues:* Liszt Academy Grand Hall 1200 *Touring:* worldwide *Comments:* alternative address: Kiskorona ut. 7, 1036 Budapest

Hungarian National Philharmonic Orchestra
Magyar Nemzeti Filharmonikus Zenekar
POB 49, 1364 **Budapest**
Tel: 1-429 1090 Fax: 1-429 1099
Internet: www.bmc.hu/bfz/index2_en.htm
E-Mail: natphilharm@mail.matav.hu
music director Zoltan Kocsis; Laureate conductor Ken-Ichiro Kobayashi; managing director Geza Kovacs; resident conductor Zsolt Hamar; contemporary music advisor & guest conductor Peter Eötvös
Size: 105 *Perfs:* 40-50 *Type/spec:* symphony, 18th century through contemporary *Venues:* Liszt Academy Grand Hall 1200, Budapest Convention Centre 1750 *Touring:* Europe, USA, South America, Japan *Comments:* visiting address: Vörösmarty tér 1, 1051 Budapest

Hungarian Radio and TV Symphony Orchestra
Magyar Rádió és Televízió Szimfonikus Zenekara
Bródy Sándor u 5-7, 1080 **Budapest**
Tel: 1-328 7161 Fax: 1-328 7161
E-Mail: kovacsga@bartok.radio.hu
managing director Apor Héthy; principal conductor Tamás Vásáry
Size: 110 *Perfs:* 50 *Type/spec:* whole classical repertoire, 18th century through contemporary *Venues:* Liszt Academy Grand Hall 1200, Budapest Convention Centre 1750 *Touring:* Europe, USA, Far East, Australia *Comments:* other music ensembles incorporated in the Hungarian Radio are the Hungarian Radio's Mixed Choir, Hungarian Radio's Children's Choir

Hungarian Virtuosi Chamber Orchestra
Magyar Virtuózok Kamarazenekar
c/o IAG Europe, Becsi kapu ter 8, 1014 **Budapest**
Tel: 1-356 1866 Fax: 1-356 1866
manager András Mikle; artistic director Miklós Szenthelyi
Size: 21 *Perfs:* 50-60 *Type/spec:* strings, chamber *Venues:* Liszt Academy Grand Hall 1200, Pesti Vigadó (Redoute) Grand Hall 700 *Touring:* South America, Europe, USA, Canada *Comments:* postal address: POB 55, 1241 Budapest

MATÁV Hungarian Symphony Orchestra
MATÁV Szimfonikus Zenekara
Pava 10/12, 1094 **Budapest**
Tel: 1-215 5770 Fax: 1-215 5462
Internet: www.orchestra.matav.hu
E-Mail: orchestra@mail.matav.hu
managing director Gergely Laczko-Tóth; artistic director András Ligeti
Size: 86 *Perfs:* 50-60 *Type/spec:* symphony, 18th – 20th century *Venues:* Liszt Academy Grand Hall 1200, Pesti Vigado (Redoute) Grand Hall 700 *Touring:* Europe

New Budapest Quartet
Új Budapest Vonósnégyes
Mártonfa utca 6, 1121 **Budapest**
Tel: 1-393 1822/660-344 655 (mobile) Fax: 1-203 8932/3
director András Kiss
Type/spec: string quartet

Debrecen Symphony Orchestra
Debreceni MAV Szimfonikus Zenekar
Simonffy u I/c, 4025 **Debrecen**
Tel: 52-412 395 Fax: 52-412 395
director Laszlo Kovats; music director Imre Kollar; principal guest conductor Hans Richter
Size: 70 *Perfs:* 80 *Type/spec:* symphony, 18th – 20th century *Venues:* Bartók Hall, Culture Centre (home) 600 *Touring:* Europe

Györ Philharmonic Orchestra
Györi Filharmónikus Zenekar
Liszt Ferenc ut. 13, 9022 **Györ**
Tel: 96-312 452 Fax: 96-312 452
Internet: www.port.hu/owa/kultura
director Gabor Baross; music director Adam Medveczky
Size: 72 *Perfs:* 110 *Type/spec:* symphony, 18th – 20th C. *Venues:* Béla Bartók Culture Centre (home) 700

Musica Antiqua Ensemble, Hévíz
Musica Antiqua Együttes, Hévíz
Postafiók 8, 8380 **Hévíz**
Tel: 83-318 538 Fax: 83-318 538
artistic director Endre Varga
Size: 20 *Type/spec:* chamber ensemble; repertoire: renaissance, baroque, classical; authentic costume with authentic instruments *Touring:* Hungary, overseas *Comments:* visiting address: Kossuth Lajos utca 2, 8380 Hévíz

Miskolc Symphony Orchestra
Miskolci Szimfonikus Zenekar
Fábián u. 6, 3525 **Miskolc**
Tel: 46-323 488
director László Sír; principal conductor László Kovács
Size: 85 *Perfs:* 80 *Type/spec:* symphony, 18th – 20th century *Venues:* National Theatre Miskolc 670 *Touring:* Europe

North Hungarian Symphony Orchestra
Miskolc Miskolci Szimfonikus Zenekar
Postafiók 49, 3525 **Miskolc**
Tel: 46-323 488/494 Fax: 46-351 497
principal conductor László Kovács; director László Sír
Size: 84 *Perfs:* 90 *Type/spec:* repertoire: from baroque to contemporary *Comments:* visiting address: Fábián utca 6/a, 3525 Miskolc

Pécs Symphony Orchestra
Pécsi Szimfonikus Zenekar
Király ut. 19, 7621 **Pécs**
Tel: 72-242 793/324 350 Fax: 72-242 793/324 814
general manager Péter Szkladányi; principal conductor Howard Williams
Size: 80 *Perfs:* 100 *Type/spec:* symphony, 18th – 20th century *Venues:* Ferenc Liszt Hall (home) 500, POTE Aula Pécs 1000

Szeged Symphony Orchestra
Szegedi Szimfonikus Zenekar
Festó u 6, 6721 **Szeged**
Tel: 62-316 927/317 002/323 256
Fax: 62-316 927/317 002/323 256
secretary István Szelezsán; artistic director & conductor Gyüdi Sándor
Size: 72 *Perfs:* 35-40 *Type/spec:* symphony, 18th – 20th century *Venues:* National Theatre Szeged (home) 700 *Touring:* Europe

Savaria Symphony Orchestra
Szombathelyi Szimfonikus Zenekar
Thököly u 14b, 9700 **Szombathely**
Tel: 94-314 472/313 747 Fax: 94-316 808
E-Mail: savaria.symphony@mail.datanet.hu
managing director Laszlo Horvath; principal guest conductor Balazs Kocsar; principal conductor Masahiro Izaki
Size: 80 *Perfs:* 100 *Type/spec:* symphony, 18th – 20th century *Venues:* Béla Bartók Hall (home) 400

ICELAND (+354)

North Iceland Symphony Orchestra
Sinfóníuhljómsveit Nordulands
PO Box 29, 602 **Akureyri**
Tel: 462 1788 Fax: 461 1280
managing director Sigurbjörg Krestenardótter; conductor and musical director Gudmundur Oli Gunnarsson
Size: 30-50 *Perfs:* 4-6 *Type/spec:* chamber and symphony *Venues:* 2 churches: 500/600; Sportshall 700 *Comments:* Visiting address: Hafnarstrœti 81, 600 Akureyri

Caput – Contemporary Music Ensemble
PO Box 648, 129 **Reykjavík**
Tel: 551 3888 Fax: 551 3888
Internet: www.caput.net
E-Mail: gf@ismennt.is
manager Gudni Franzson
Size: 20 *Perfs:* 10-15 *Type/spec:* classically-based contemporary music *Touring:* Chile, USA, Europe

Iceland Symphony Orchestra
Sinfóníuhljómsveit Islands
PO Box 7052, 127 **Reykjavík**
Tel: 562 2255 Fax: 562 4475
Internet: www.sinfonia.is
E-Mail: sinfonia@sinfonia.is
general manager Thröstur Olafsson; chief conductor and music director Rico Saccani; concert manager Helga Hauksdóttir
Size: 70 *Perfs:* 65 *Type/spec:* symphony, contemporary *Venues:* University Concert Hall 976 *Comments:* Visiting Address: Háskólabíó/Hagatorg

Reykjavik Chamber Orchestra
Kammersveit Reykjavíkur
Háahlíd 14, 105 **Reykjavík**
Tel: 551 2261 Fax: 562 3124
manager, leader & administrator Rut Ingólfsdóttir
Type/spec: from baroque to contemporary *Touring:* Germany *Comments:* annual concert series (Oct-May)

Reykjavik Wind Quintet
Blásarakvintett Reykjavíkur
c/o Einar Jóhannesson, Thorsgata 22 A, 101 **Reykjavík**
Tel: 551 7672/7198 Fax: 552 0850
E-Mail: joseph@ismennt.is
contact Einar Jóhannesson

IRELAND Republic of (+353)

National Youth Orchestra of Ireland
37 Molesworth Street, **Dublin** 2
Tel: 1-661 3642 Fax: 1-661 3642
E-Mail: joanna@iol.ie
general manager Joanna Crooks; administrative officer Gillian Mohan
Size: 100-110 *Perfs:* 10-12 *Type/spec:* symphonic *Venues:* National Concert Hall 1100 Dublin, Cork City Hall 1000, University Concert Hall, Limerick 1100, Waterford WIT, Symphony Hall Birmingham, Royal Liverpool Philharmonic Hall, Concert Home, Berlin *Touring:* USA *Comments:* member of EFNYO (q.v); Junior Training Youth Orchestra – 102 members, under 18 years

RTE Concert Orchestra
RTE, Donnybrook, **Dublin** 4
Tel: 1-208 2142 Fax: 1-208 3340
Internet: www.rte.ie/
director of music Niall Doyle; executive prodcuer Gareth Hudson; principal conductor Proínnsías O'Duinn; orchestra manager Sam Ellis; concerts manager Claire Meehan (tel: 1-208 2765)
Size: 44+ *Perfs:* 70 + international tours *Type/spec:* from pop to classical *Venues:* National Concert Hall and major regional venues *Touring:* worldwide *Comments:* DGOS – Opera Ireland commercial recordings and numerous radio and tv broadcasts

RTE – National Symphony Orchestra of Ireland
RTE, The Music Department, Office Block, Donnybrook, **Dublin** 4
Tel: 1-208 2530 Fax: 1-208 2160
Internet: www.rte.ie/
E-Mail: meehan@admin.rte.ie
director of music Niall Doyle; general manager Martyn Westerman; principal conductor Alexander Anissimov; management assistant Szaboles Vedres; concerts manager Claire Meehan (tel: 1-208 2765)
Size: 88 *Perfs:* 70 + international tours *Type/spec:* classical *Venues:* National Concert Hall 1257 *Touring:* worldwide *Comments:* Wexford Festival Opera; recordings for Naxos and Marco Polo

RTÊ Vanbrugh String Quartet
The Music Department, Office Block, Dannybrook, **Dublin** 4
Tel: 1-208 4518 Fax: 1-208 2511
Internet: www.rte.ie/
director of music Niall Doyle; concerts manager Claire Meehan
Perfs: 12 *Touring:* Ireland

Concorde (New Music Ensemble)
1 Avondale Road, Highfield Park, **Galway**
Tel: 91-582 153 Fax: 91-582 153
E-Mail: patrick.m.oleary@ucg.ie
manager Jane O'Leary
Size: 10 *Perfs:* 80 *Type/spec:* contemporary and commisioned *Touring:* Ireland

Chandos Baroque Players
St Canice's Cottage, St Canice's Cathedral, **Kilkenny**
Tel: 56-61497 Fax: 56-61497
E-Mail: maya@tinet.ie
administrator Susan Proud
Size: 5-12 *Perfs:* 7 *Type/spec:* baroque instrumental ensemble, early music 17th and 18th century, specialising in repertoire of J.S.Bach *Venues:* churches and cathedrals *Touring:* Canada/USA, Ireland, Europe *Comments:* recordings available; see also Early Music

Irish Chamber Orchestra
Foundation Building, University of Limerick, **Limerick** 2
Tel: 61-202 620/659/583 Fax: 61-202 617
E-Mail: ico@ul.ie
chief executive John Kelly; artistic director Fionnuala Hunt
Size: 16-25 *Perfs:* 60 *Type/spec:* chamber *Venues:* National Concert Hall 1257, University Concert Hall of Limerick 1100 and other regional venues *Touring:* national, international *Comments:* International Music Festival, Killaloe Co. Clare (20-25 July)

ITALY (+39)

Società Filarmonica Marchigiana
via degli Aranci 2, 60121 **Ancona**
Tel: 071-206 168 Fax: 071-206 730
presidente Giuliano Gasparini; direttore artistico Gustav Kuhn; responsabile uffico stampa e pr Margherita Rinaldi
Size: varies *Perfs:* 100 *Type/spec:* classical, contemporary, symphonic, lyric and chamber *Touring:* France

Orchestra Sinfonica di Bari
via Emanuele Mola 34, 70121 **Bari**
Tel: 080-558 8583/87 Fax: 080-558 8511
conductor & artistic director Michele Marvulli
Size: 60 *Perfs:* 100 *Type/spec:* classical, symphony, opera *Comments:* CD available

Orchestra e coro del Teatro Comunale
Largo Respighi 1, 40126 **Bologna**
Tel: 051-529 011 Fax: 051-529 934/905/945
Internet: www.nettuno.it/bo/teatro-comunale
E-Mail: teatro.comunale@bo.nettuno.it
direttore stabile Daniele Gatti; sovrintendente Felicia Bottino; ufficio stampa e pubbliche relazioni Michele d'Agostino; vice presidente Federico Stame; direttore artistico Gianni Tangucci; segretario artistico Aldo Sisillo; direttore allestimenti scenici Italo Grassi
Size: 105 orchestra/ 80 choir *Perfs:* 80-100 *Type/spec:* lyric, symphonic, chamber *Venues:* Teatro Comunale di Bologna 1060 *Touring:* Japan
Comments: see also Venues and Opera

Orchestra Sinfonica Haydn di Bolzano e Trento
Via Dalmazia 30, 39100 **Bolzano**
Tel: 0471-200 395 Fax: 0471-930 209
Internet: www.haydn-orchestra.com
E-Mail: haydn@dnet.it
segretario generale Rosalia de Concini; presidente Giovanni Ondertoller; direttore artistico Hubert Stuppner
Size: 46 *Perfs:* 140 *Type/spec:* classical
Venues: Auditorium Bolzano 734 *Touring:* Italy
Comments: have recorded several CDs

Cameristi Lombardi
Via Elia Capriolo 48, 25122 **Brescia**
Tel: 030-280 188 Fax: 030-375 0602
manager/conductor Mario Conter
Size: 15 *Type/spec:* Italian, English & German Baroque music, contemporary, oratorios
Touring: national, France, Croatia, Turkey
Comments: players from La Scala, RAI Torino, La Fenice, I Solisti Veneti orchestras; Associated with Fondazione Romano Romanini; CDs available; see also Competitions

Gruppo da Camera Caronte
Via Rovigo, 28, 25125 **Brescia**
Tel: 030-353 2453 Fax: 030-354 7932
Internet: www.users.iol.it/gruppocaronte
E-Mail: gruppocaronte@iol.it
contact Ricky Perlotti
Size: 60 *Perfs:* 110 *Type/spec:* from medieval to jazz
Touring: Portugal, Spain, France, Switzerland, Austria, Germany, Denmark, Norway, Sweden
Comments: CD's available; co-organise the festival Girovagando in Musica – Itinera ri Turistici e Musicali; second address: Via Giovane Italia, 6, Brescia; see also Festivals

Orchestra del Festival Internazionale Arturo Benedetti Michelangeli di Brescia e Bergamo
c/o Teatro Grande via Paganora, 19/a, 25121 **Brescia**
Tel: 030-293 022 Fax: 030-240 0771
direttore e presidente Agostino Orizio; segretario Simona Salvi; ufficio stampa Dott.ssa Anna Bergonzelli
Size: 25-30 *Perfs:* 30 *Type/spec:* chamber *Venues:* Teatro Grande di Brescia *Touring:* Italy, Korea, Japan, Czech Republic, USA, Greece, France

Orchestra E Coro del Teatro Lirico di Cagliari
c/o Nuovo Teatro Comunale, Via Santa Alenixedda, 09128 **Cagliari**
Tel: 070-40821
Fax: 070-408 2251/45 (sovrintendenza)
direttore generale amministrativo Errico Zuddas; maestro del coro Paolo Vero; sovrintendente Mauro Meli; presidente Mariano Delogu; direttore artistico Massimo Biscardi; segretario artistico Giancaro Liuzzi; ufficio stampa Annamaria Clavuot
Size: 77 *Type/spec:* opera, operetta, symphony, contemporary, chamber
Venues: Nuovo Teatro Comunale 1600, Anfiteatro Romano 5000 *Touring:* Sardinia
Comments: see also Opera

Orchestra e Coro Stabile Del Teatro Massimo Bellini
Via Perrotta 12, 95131 **Catania**
Tel: 095-730 6111 (switchboard)/715 0200 (press office)
Fax: 095-321 830 (press office)
sovrintendente Alberto Bombace; direttore artistico Piero Rattalino; responsabile della produzione Mauro Trombetta; direttore amministrativo Dr Antonio Ferro; direttore del coro Tiziana Carlini; direttore principale Yoram David; responsabile comunicazione Nino Milazzo
Size: 160 *Perfs:* 90 (15 sinfonici, 15 camera, 60 opera)
Type/spec: lyric, chamber, symphonic, jazz
Venues: Teatro Bellini 1250, Giardino Bellini 3500 (open-air) *Comments:* see also Opera and Venues

I Fiati Italiani
Via L.Colazilli 5, 66100 **Chieti**
Tel: 0871-401 373/898 191/0360-618 035
Fax: 0871-401 373
Internet: www.alicom.com/fiati-italiani
E-Mail: sint@ch.alicom.com
president Antonello Pellegrini (mobile: 360-618 035); artistic director Maurizio Colasanti (Tel: 338-492 5463); press officer Stanislao Liberatore (mobile: 338-612 6507)
Size: 3-25 *Perfs:* 120 *Type/spec:* winds and piano
Touring: South America *Comments:* agent: Emilia Tonolla, Switzerland

Collegium Symphonium Veneto
Via Maragne 58, 35013 **Cittadella (PD)**
Tel: 049-597 5960/809 6225
Fax: 049-597 5960/809 6225
E-Mail: iullucgia@iol.it
presidente, legale rappresentante e direttore artistico Prof. Giulio Svegliado; coordinamento Carla Marchiori
Size: 65 orchestra, 40 choir *Perfs:* 40 *Type/spec:* symphony, lyrical, baroque
Venues: Teatro Sociale di Cittadella 220

Florence Symphonietta
Via Santa Reparata 40, 50129 **Firenze**
Tel: 055-477 805 Fax: 055-477 805
presidente Dott. Pierluigi Cecioni; direttore artistico Marco Fornaciari, Grazia Rossi
Size: 20-45 *Perfs:* 50 *Type/spec:* chamber music *Venues:* Chiesa di Dante, Palazzo Pitti (estate), Chiesa di Orsanmichele (museum) *Touring:* Spain, national

Orchestra della Toscana
Via Ghibellina 101, 50122 **Firenze**
Tel: 055-281 792/280 670
Fax: 055-281 640
Internet: www.dada.it/ort
E-Mail: ort@dada.it
direttore generale Marco Parri; direttore artistico Giorgio Battistelli; presidente Giorgio van Straten
Size: 45 *Perfs:* 110 *Type/spec:* symphony, chamber: Bach to contemporary *Venues:* Teatro Verdi 1538 *Touring:* Germany, France, Netherlands

Orchestra e Coro del Maggio Musicale Fiorentino
Teatro del Maggio Musicale Fiorentino, Via Solferino 15, 50123 **Firenze**
Tel: 055-27791 Fax: 055-239 6954
Internet: www.maggiofiorentino.com
E-Mail: tickets@maggiofiorentino.com
sovrintendente t.b.a.; direttore principale Zubin Mehta; direttore ospite principale Semyon Bichkov; direttore artistico Cesare Mazzonis; direttore del coro Josè Luis Basso; direttore onorario Giuseppe Sinopoci
Size: 120 *Perfs:* 39 *Type/spec:* symphony, chamber *Venues:* Teatro Comunale 2004, Teatro della Pergola 1000, Teatro Piccolo 520 *Comments:* see also Opera, Dance, Festivals and Venues

Associazione i Solisti Dauni
Piazza Marconi 11, 71100 **Foggia**
Tel: 0881-772 914/774 640
Fax: 0881-773 883
direttore e direttore artistico Domenico Losavio; consulente musicale Giulio D'Angelo; direttore organizzativo Lilly Carfagno
Size: 15 *Perfs:* 20 *Type/spec:* classical, contemporary *Venues:* Teatri in Puglia *Touring:* Italy *Comments:* non-profit organisation; see also Promoters and Festivals

Orchestra e Coro del Teatro Comunale dell'Opera Carlo Felice
Passo Eugenio Montale 4, 16121 **Genova**
Tel: 010-53811 (switchboard)/538 1223 (press office)/1254 Fax: 010-538 1222/33
Internet: www.carlofelice.it
E-Mail: cf.stampa@tin.it (press office)
sovrintendente Nicola Costa; maestro del coro Massimiliano Carraro; assistente del sovrintendente Luigi Molari; direttore artistico Alessio Vlad
Size: 108 orchestra/65 choir *Perfs:* 84 opera + ballet, 61 concerts, 255 educational exhibitions, 21 jazz *Type/spec:* lyric and symphony, jazz, ballet *Venues:* Sala Carlo Felice 2000 *Comments:* theatre E-mail: staff@carlofelice.it; see also Venues, Promoters and Festivals

Orchestra Sinfonica Abruzzese
Istituzione Sinfonica Abruzzese
via Fortebraccio 71, 67100 **L'Aquila**
Tel: 0862-411 103 Fax: 0862-62157
segretario generale Dr Giorgio Paravano; direttore artistico Vittorio Antonellini; presidente Dr Ludovico Nardecchia; assistente alla direzione artistico Marco Zuccarini; addetto ufficio stampa Dr. Antonietta Centofanti
Size: 30 + 6 *Perfs:* 130 *Type/spec:* mainly symphony *Touring:* Italy, Europe

I.C.O – Istituzione Concertistica Orchestrale dell'Amministrazione Provinciale di Lecce
Via Umberto I 13, 73100 **Lecce**
Tel: 0832-683 245/242/241 576 Fax: 0832-683 245
Internet: www.clio.it/provincialecce
E-Mail: urp.prov.le@mail.clio.it
segretario generale Dott. Gianni Lo Savio; presidente Avv. Lorenzo Ria; direttore artistico Giovanni Oliva
Size: 70 *Perfs:* 90 *Type/spec:* classical, symphony, opera *Venues:* Politeama Greco di Lecce 1000 *Comments:* CDs available; youth orchestra

Associazione Orchestra Sinfonica dell'Universita' Cattolica
Largo P. Agostino Gemelli 1, 20123 **Milano**
Tel: 02-7234 2311 Fax: 02-7234 2311
direttore artistico e musicale Simone Fermani; amministratore delegato Andrea Lavorato; presidente Alessandro Penati; vice-presidente Carlo Ghidelli
Size: 50 *Perfs:* 20 *Type/spec:* symphonic, lyric, classic and modern, opera *Venues:* main hall of Universita' Cattolica 700 *Touring:* USA, Spain *Comments:* professional orchestra sponsored by Universita' Cattolica

Divertimento Ensemble
Via Poggi 7, 20131 **Milano**
Tel: 02-7060 2800 Fax: 02-7063 2083
E-Mail: DIVERTIMENTO@iol.it
artistic director Sandro Gorli
Size: 8-25 *Perfs:* 20 *Type/spec:* contemporary

Filarmonica della Scala
Piazza Diaz N. 6, 20123 **Milano**
Tel: 02-7200 3383/7202 3671 Fax: 02-7202 3660
presidente Fedele Confalonieri; vice presidente Ernesto Schiavi; direttore principale Riccardo Muti
Size: 120 *Perfs:* 50 *Type/spec:* classical symphony *Venues:* Teatro Alla Scala 2000 *Touring:* worldwide *Comments:* have recorded several CDs; see also Opera, Dance and Venues

Orchestra da Camera di Milano Giorgio Federico Ghedini
Via Passione 1, 20122 **Milano**
Tel: 02-781 256/7600 3152 (Barbieri) Fax: 02-781 256
E-Mail: ambart@tiscalinet.it
direttore stabile ed artistico Adriano Barbieri
Size: 20-40 *Perfs:* 10 *Type/spec:* repertoire ranges from baroque to 20th century music

Orchestra del Teatro alla Scala
Via Filodrammatici 2, 20121 **Milano**
Tel: 02-8879-1 Fax: 02-887 9424
Internet: www.lascala.milano.it
sovrintendente Carlo Fontana; direttore musicale Riccardo Muti; direttore artistico Paolo Arcà; direttore del coro Roberto Gabbiani; reazioni esterne Donatella Brunazzi (02-887 9264); uff. stampa Luciana Fusi (02-887 9412)
Size: 140 (orchestra) + 80 (choir) *Perfs:* 86 *Type/spec:* from classical to contemporary *Venues:* Teatro alla Scala 2000 *Touring:* national, Japan *Comments:* see also Opera, Dance and Venues

Orchestra Guido Cantelli
Fondazione Orchestra Guido Cantelli, via Della Moscova 40/2, 20121 **Milano**
Tel: 02-655 391/2585 Fax: 02-655 3934
Internet: www.cantelli.com
E-Mail: info@cantelli.com
director Alberto Veronesi; vice director Raffaella Quadri
Size: 40 *Perfs:* +100 *Type/spec:* early to 1900 *Venues:* Conservatorio Giusseppe Verdi (Milano) *Touring:* Italy, America, Europe

Orchestra I Pomeriggi Musicali
via Francesco Guicciardini 5, 20129 **Milano**
Tel: 02-7600 1900 Fax: 02-7600 4562
Internet: www.ipomeriggi.org
E-Mail: stefipom@tiscalinet.it
music director Aldo Ciccato; consigliere delegato Giuseppe Manzoni; press office: Crew Italia Ezio Grillo
Size: 40 *Perfs:* 120 *Type/spec:* symphony – 18th and 20th century *Venues:* Conservatorio Milano – Sala Verdi 1600 *Touring:* France, Switzerland

Orchestra Sinfonica di Milano Giuseppe Verdi
Corso San Gottardo, angolo Via Torricelli, 20136 **Milano**
Tel: 02-8901 3121 Fax: 02-7209 9819
Internet: www.orchestrasinfonica.milano.it
E-Mail: info@orchestrasinfonica.milano.it
general manager Luigi Corbani; artistic secretary Luca Pozzoni; music director Riccardo Chailly; press office Gianni Testa; emeritus director Carlo Maria Giulini
Size: 115 *Perfs:* 130 *Type/spec:* from classical to contemporary, symphony and chamber *Venues:* Auditorium di Milano 1400 *Comments:* see also Choirs

Orchestra e Coro Stabile del Teatro di San Carlo
Via San Carlo 98/F, 80132 **Napoli**
Tel: 081-797 2111 Fax: 081-797 2306
Internet: www.teatrosancarlo.it
E-Mail: infoteatro@teatrosancarlo.it
sovrintendente Francesco Canessa; direttore stabile del coro Andrea Giorgi; coordinatore orchestra M. Bruno Imparato; capo ufficio stampa Filippo Arriva (tel: 081-797 2202, fax: 081-797 2306)
Size: 120 (musicians) 100 (choir) *Perfs:* 140 *Type/spec:* chamber, symphony, opera *Venues:* San Carlo 1400 and various regional theatres *Touring:* Austria

I Solisti Filarmonici Italiani
via Benvenuto Cellini 1, 35027 **Noventa Padovana (PD)**
Tel: 049-893 2793 Fax: 049-893 2793
Internet: members.easyspace.com/solfilita
E-Mail: solfilita@easypost.com
director Federico Guglielmo; secretary Giovanni Guglielmo
Size: 5-25 *Perfs:* 40 *Venues:* chamber to symphony *Touring:* worldwide *Comments:* several CDs available; contract with Denon

Complesso di Strumenti a Fiato di Padova
via A. Marangon 34, 35129 **Padova**
Tel: 049-628 326 Fax: 049-628 326
E-Mail: pad146k1@pd.nettuno.it
direttore Pierluigi Destro
Size: 13 *Perfs:* 20 *Type/spec:* chamber (classical, romantic, contemporary) *Touring:* Italy, Bulgaria, Republic of Moldova, Romania, Russia, Ukraine, Cuba, Brazil, Paraguay *Comments:* monographic CD on Wolfgango Dalla Vecchia available

I Solisti Veneti
Piazzale Pontecorvo, 4a, 35121 **Padova**
Tel: 049-666 128 Fax: 049-875 2598
Internet: www.promart.it/SolistiVeneti
segretario generale & tour manager Mirella Gualandi; presidente Maestro Giuliano Carella; direttore artistico Maestro Claudio Scimone
Size: 22-30 *Perfs:* 130/140 *Type/spec:* chamber to symphony *Touring:* international
Comments: see also Festivals

Interensemble
via San Marco 302, 35129 **Padova**
Tel: 049-893 0608 Fax: 049-629 113
Internet: www2.pavovanet.it/interens
E-Mail: pad456@padovanet.it
director Bernardino Beggio
Size: 12 permanent + 4 *Perfs:* 35 *Type/spec:* 20th C. music chamber group *Venues:* Teatro Maddalene *Touring:* Portugal, UK, Ireland, Poland, USA

Orchestra di Padova e del Veneto
via Marsilio da Padova 19, 35139 **Padova**
Tel: 049-656 848/875 3166 (press office)
Fax: 049-657 130
Internet: www.orchestrapadovaeveneto.it
E-Mail: info@orchestrapadonvaeveneto.it
segretario generale Matteo Mazzeo; direttore principale Peter Maag; programmazione artistica Filippo Juvarra; presidente Francesco Raimondo Donà
Size: 15-40 *Perfs:* 160 *Type/spec:* symphony, chamber *Venues:* Auditorium Pollini 548, Teatro Verdi 700 *Touring:* Europe, South America

Ente Autonomo Orchestra Sinfonica Siciliana
via La Farina 29, 90141 **Palermo**
Tel: 091-300 609/345 917 Fax: 091-300 155
Internet: www.gestelnet.it/eaoss
E-Mail: eaoss@gestelnet.it
segretario generale Vincenzo Rossitto; direttore artistico Giuseppe Cataldo; presidente Alberto Alessi; direttore d'orchestra stabile t.b.a.
Size: 92 *Perfs:* 120 + 30 *Type/spec:* symphony, classical and contemporary *Venues:* Teatro Golden 1080 *Touring:* Italy *Comments:* see also Venues

Orchestra e Coro Stabile Del Teatro Massimo
via R. Wagner 2, 90139 **Palermo**
Tel: 091-605 3111 (switchboard)/3253/3224 (press office) Fax: 091-605 3325/4/3330 (press office)
Internet: www.teatromassimo.it
E-Mail: stampatm@teatromassimo.it (press office)
sovrintendentes Attilio Orlando, Francesco Giambrone; direttore artistico Marco Betta; direttore operativo Dott. Antonio Cognata; direttore produzione Giovanni Mazzara; consulenza Micha van Hoecke; maestro coro Marcello Iozzia; presidente Leoluca Orlando; press office Laura Oddo
Size: 100 (and 80 choir) *Perfs:* 144 (30, 88 opera, 24 ballet) *Type/spec:* lyric, symphony, jazz, contemporary, opera, dance, concerts *Venues:* Teatro Politeama Garibaldi 950, Teatro di Verdura di Villa Castelnuovo (for the summer season), Teatro Massimo 1320 *Comments:* see also Opera, Dance and Venues

Ensemble Edgard Varese
Strada Degli Ospizi Civili 3, 43100 **Parma**
Tel: 0521-236 605 Fax: 0521-235 971
Internet: www.symbolic.pr.it/ensemble.html
E-Mail: prometeo@symbolic.it
direttore artistico e ricerche Martino Traversa; presidente onorario Claudio Abbado
Size: 20-25 *Perfs:* 8 *Type/spec:* contemporary, modern music *Venues:* Teatro Regio di Parma 1380, Teatro Farnese 200 *Comments:* the group created the 'Prometeo Project', a research group in electro-acoustics; also organises the festival 'Traiettorie', modern and contemporary music, Sept-Oct annual

Fondazione Arturo Toscanini – Orchestra Sinfonica dell'Emilia Romagna Arturo Toscanini e Rimini Chamber Orchestra
Via G. Tartini 13, 43100 **Parma**
Tel: 0521-2741 (switchboard)/274 417/27 (press, pr & marketing) Fax: 0521-272 134/785 257
Internet: www.fondazione-toscanini.it
E-Mail: fondazione@toscanini.dsnet.it
president Piero Manganoni; general manager Prof Gianni Baratta; music director Patric Fournillier; press office Nadia Frezza
Size: 100 *Perfs:* 120 *Type/spec:* symphony, chamber, classical to comtemporary, lyric *Touring:* Europe *Comments:* the Foundation organizes seven annual music Festivals and manages also the Academy of Music of Emilia-Romagna (advanced training courses for singers, percussionists, instrumentalists, composers), the Academy for Advanced Orchestral Training (AFOS) and the Arturo Toscanini Musical Archives and Documentations Center; CDs available

Paolo Giaro Ensemble
Via Ciro Menotti 147, 61100 **Pesaro**
Tel: 0721-414 341 Fax: 0721-414 341
Internet: www.ejn.it.mus/giazo.htm
E-Mail: musicalibera@abanet.it
artistic director Paolo Giaro; general manager Antonio Cioffi
Size: 1-7 *Type/spec:* mediterranean; the ensemble plays music by composer Paolo Giaro

Cittàlirica Orchestra Associazione
via Palestro 40, 56127 **Pisa**
Tel: 050-941 142/43 Fax: 050-941 158
presidente Giuliano Rossi
Size: 45-95 *Type/spec:* lyric, symphony, chamber music *Venues:* Teatro Verdi 800 (Pisa), Teatro del Giclio 750 (Lucca), Teatro Goldoni (Livorno) *Comments:* registered address: via Santa Cecilia 16, 56127 Pisa

Complesso Cameristico Musicando Insieme/ Ensemble Fiati
via Eleonora d'Arborea 34, 07046 **Porto Torres (SS)**
Tel: 079-514 324/515 012 Fax: 079-515 012
presidente Tina Parodi
Size: 18-20 *Perfs:* 30 *Type/spec:* chamber orchestra (mainly string), fiati for ensemble *Venues:* Basilica di San Gavino 800, Porto Torres; Teatro Olimpia 800, Porto Torres *Touring:* Italy (for the ensemble) *Comments:* offer masterclasses, workshops; see also Promoters

Accademia Bizantina
via Renato Serra 78, 48100 **Ravenna**
Tel: 0544-61199/0335-609 1160/0335-704 1155 (mobiles)
Fax: 0544-62125
E-Mail: accademiabizantina@ntt.it
president & general manager Romano Valentini; honorary president Luciano Berio; musical director Ottavio Dantone
Size: 15 *Perfs:* 50 *Type/spec:* chamber; baroque *Touring:* USA, South America, Japan
Comments: see also Early Music

Ensemble Seicentonovecento
c/o musicaimmagine Records (MR), Via del Corso 494, Basilica di San Giacomo, 00186 **Roma**
Tel: 06-3608 6838/3600 4667 Fax: 06-3600 4667
E-Mail: musicaimmagine@iol.it
direttore principale Flavio Colusso; consulenza artistica Andrea Coen; responsabile produzione Silvia De Palma; responsabile orchestra Gianfranco Russo
Size: 12-30 (18 permanent, 12-40 mixed choir + white voices choir and soloists) *Type/spec:* concert music, opera and oratory from 15th to 20th C., on period instruments *Venues:* Basilica di San Giacomo (Roma) *Touring:* France, Austria
Comments: see also Recorded Media

I Musici
c/o Massimo Paris, via delle Mantellate 24, 00165 **Roma**
Tel: 06-689 6115 Fax: 06-689 2724
presidente Massimo Paris
Size: 12 *Type/spec:* chamber *Venues:* diverse locations in Rome *Touring:* worldwide

Orchestra Clara Schumann Roma
c/o Gabriella Pallenberg, Via Novara 41, 00198 **Roma**
Tel: 06-8535 2683 Fax: 06-8535 2683
conductor Elke Mascha Blankenburg
Size: 45 *Type/spec:* classical, contemporary, especially works of female composers *Comments:* women musicians only; see also Orchestras (Clara Schumann Orchester Köln, Germany) and Choirs (Köln Kurrende)

Orchestra e Coro dell'Accademia Nazionale di Santa Cecilia
via Vittoria 6, 00187 **Roma**
Tel: 06-328 171 Fax: 06-361 1402/210
Internet: www.santacecilia.it
E-Mail: biglietteria@santacecilia.it
presidente e direttore artistico Prof. Bruno Cagli; direttore pincipale Myung-Whun Chung; maestro del coro Norbert Balatsch; coordinatore artistico Gaston Fournier-Facio, Mauro Bucarelli (06-3281 7308)
Size: 110 orchestra, 86 choir *Perfs:* 200 *Type/spec:* symphonic *Venues:* Auditorium di Via Della Conciliazione *Touring:* South America, Korea : alternativel Internet: www.santacecilia.it/italiano/email/index.htm; alternative E-mail: direzion_didattiche@santacecilia.it

Orchestra e Coro Stabile Dell'Opera di Roma
P.za Beniamino Gigli 1, 00184 **Roma**
Tel: 06-481 601/474 2595 (press office)
Fax: 06-488 1253/481 8847 (press office)
Internet: themix.it
E-Mail: sovrintendenza@opera.roma.it
sovrintendente Francesco Ernani; direttore artistico e musicale Giuseppe Sinopoli; uff. stampa Renato Rossa
Size: 117 *Type/spec:* symphony, chamber, opera, ballet *Venues:* Teatro Argentina, Teatro dell' Opera 1604, Basiliche di Roma, Teatro Nationale 700 *Comments:* see also Opera, Dance, Festivals and Venues

Orchestra Giovanile Italiana
Scuola di Musica di Fiesole, Via delle Fontanelle 24, 50016 **San Domenico di Fiesole (FI)**
Tel: 055-597 851 Fax: 055-599 686
Internet: www.scuolamusica.fiesole.fi.it
E-Mail: info@scuolamusica.fiesole.fi.it
general manager Adriana Verchiani; secretary Teresa di Felice
Size: 100 *Type/spec:* symphonic *Touring:* national
Comments: member of EFNYO (q.v)

Orchestra Sinfonica di San Remo
Corso Cavallotti 51, 18038 **San Remo (IM)**
Tel: 0184-505 764/532 009 (theatre) Fax: 0184-505 850
direttore artistico e principale Maestro Fabiano Monica
Size: 54 *Perfs:* 150 *Type/spec:* Symphony *Venues:* Teatro Centrale 1000, Teatro del Casino 800, Auditorium Franco Alfano 500

Orchestra Jazz della Sardegna
P. Box 505, 07100 **Sassari**
Tel: 079-239 465 Fax: 079-239 465
Internet: www.abno.com
E-Mail: abno@ssnet.it
direttore musicale Giovanni Agostino Frassetto; presidente Gavino Mele
Size: 20 *Perfs:* 30 *Type/spec:* jazz *Touring:* Sardinia, Italy
Comments: see also Promoters and Competitions

Orchestra Sinfonia Di Savona
via Manzoni 2-1, 17100 **Savona**
Tel: 019-824 663 Fax: 019-824 663
E-Mail: svmusica@tin.it
artistic director Claudio Gilio; president assoc. Giorgio Monacciani
Size: varies

Silver Symphony Orchestra
via G.Pascoli 11/b, 35030 **Selvazzano (Padova)**
Tel: 049-635 587 Fax: 049-630 786
Internet: www.silver.symp.com
E-Mail: castania@iol.it
principal conductor Fabrizio Castanìa; guest conductor Luciano Piovan; artistic director & general manager Maria Cristina Gelsomino
Size: 90-100 *Perfs:* 25-30 *Type/spec:* light classical and contemporary music, popular favourites
Venues: S.Maria dei Servi, Padova
Touring: national, international

L'Orfeo Ensemble – Gruppo musicale di Spoleto
via Beato Leopoldo 113, 06049 **Spoleto (PG)**
Tel: 0743-260 337 Fax: 0743-260 337
Internet: orfeo.ejb.net
E-Mail: orfeo.ensemble@altavista.net
responsabile artistico Mffl Fabrizio Ammetto; musicologa e pubbliche relazioni Dr Gioia Filocamo
Size: 2-15 *Perfs:* 25 *Type/spec:* instrumental, chamber: baroque to contemporary
Comments: CD's available; co-organise music seminars and courses, musicology conferences, publication of critical editions; see also Early Music

Orchestra e Coro del Teatro Regio di Torino
Piazza Castello 215, 10124 **Torino**
Tel: 011-88151 Fax: 011-881 5214
Internet: www.edibit.it/regio
E-Mail: dirarptr@inrete.it
sovrintendente Walter Verniano; direttore artistico Claudio Desderi
Size: 77 + 15 (orchestra), 65 + 15 (coro) *Perfs:* 92 in operas, 10 concerts *Type/spec:* opera, symphony, ballet, choral *Venues:* Teatro Regio 1600, Piccolo Regio G. Puccini 386 *Comments:* resident company of Teatro Regio di Torino; see also Venues, Festivals and Opera

Orchestra Sinfonica Nazionale della RAI
piazza Rossaro, 10124 **Torino**
Tel: 011-810 4961 (switchboard)/817 3872 (press)
Fax: 011-888 300/817 7410(Dott. Ercolini)
E-Mail: robotti@rai.it
general manager Dott. Cesare Dapino; direttore artistico Daniele Spini; responsabile struttura orchestra Dott. Alessandro Ercolini; uff. stampa Savina Neirotti
Size: 117 *Perfs:* 130 *Type/spec:* symphonic *Venues:* Auditorium G. Agnelli, Lingotto 2000 *Touring:* England, Spain, Switzerland, Italy, Austria, France, Japan
Comments: participates in several national and international festivals; the symphonic orchestra has some chamber groups which perform mainly in Piedmont; every concert of the symphonic orchestra is taped and broadcast live on radio/recorded on TV

Orchestra e Coro Stabile del Teatro Lirico Giuseppe Verdi
Riva 3 Novembre 1, 34121 **Trieste**
Tel: 040-672 2111 Fax: 040-672 2249
Internet: www.teatroverdi-trieste.com
E-Mail: info@teatroverdi-trieste.com
direttore coro Luigi Petrozziello; responsabile ufficio stampa e relazioni esterne Nicoletta Cavalieri (040-672 2209); sovrintendente Lorenzo Jorio; direttore artistico Giandomenico Vaccari; direttore di produzione Gianni Gori
Size: 98 orch + 75 choir *Perfs:* 80 *Type/spec:* ballet, symphony, operetta *Venues:* Sala Tripcovich 934, Teatro G. Verdi 1370 *Comments:* lyric, symphonic and dance seasons, international festival of Operetta; see also Venues, Festivals, Dance and Opera

Orchestra e Coro del Teatro La Fenice – Palafenice
Isola Nuova del Tronchetto, 30135 **Venezia**
Tel: 041-786 511 Fax: 041-786 580
Internet: www.tin.it/fenice
E-Mail: fenice@interbusiness.it
sovrintendente Mario Messinis; direttore principale Maestro Isaac Karabtchevsky; responsabile artistico Paolo Pinamonti; directtore del coro Giovanni Andreoli
Size: 100 orch + 80 choir *Type/spec:* symphony, chamber, opera, ballet *Venues:* Palafenice Al Tronchetto 1200 *Touring:* Italy, Europe *Comments:* The Gran Teatro La Fenice will probably be rebuilt after a fire

Orchestra e Coro della Fondazione Arena di Verona
Piazza Bra 28, 37121 **Verona**
Tel: 045-805 1811 Fax: 045-803 1443 (press office)
Internet: www.arena.it
E-Mail: ticket@arena.it
sovrintendente t.b.a.; direttore artistico t.b.a.; responsabile servizio marketing Corrado Ferraro
Size: 82-150 (orchestra), 160 (choir – during summer season) *Venues:* Teatro Filarmonico 1100, Arena Verona 15000 *Touring:* UK

LATVIA (+371)

Liepaja Symphony Orchestra
Liepajas simfoniskais Orkestris
50 Graudu, 3401 **Liepaja**
Tel: 34-25538 Fax: 34-81478
E-Mail: LSOvija@anet.lv
director Vija Feldmane; chief conductor Imants Resnis
Size: 62 *Perfs:* 60 *Type/spec:* symphonic orchestra
Touring: Spain, Sweden, Germany

Brass Band Riga (Wind Orchestra Riga)
Profesionalais puteju orkestris Riga
Maza Smilsu iela 8, 1050 **Riga**
Tel: 7-210 504/923 1172 (GSM) Fax: 7-225 039
E-Mail: lulc@lanet.lv
artistic director & principal conductor Janis Purins; manager Astrida Kenina
Size: 50 *Perfs:* 100 *Type/spec:* symphony orchestra

Chamber Orchestra of the Latvian Philharmonic Society
Latvijas Filharmonijas kamerorkestris
Kalku iela 11a, 1664 **Riga**
Tel: 7-223 618 Fax: 7-213 497
artistic director Dzintars Josts
Size: 20 *Perfs:* 50 *Venues:* Wagner Chamber Music Hall 260 *Touring:* Germany, Denmark

Latvian Chamber Orchestra, The
Latvijas Kamerorkestris
R. Vagnera 4, 1664 **Riga**
Tel: 9-476 333 Fax: 7-216 887
manager and conductor Andris Veismanis

Latvian National Symphonic Orchestra
Latvijas Nacionalais simfoniskais orkestris
Amatu 6, 1664 **Riga**
Tel: 7-229 537 Fax: 7-224 850
E-Mail: lnso@mail.bkc.lv
managing director Ilona Brege
Size: 102 *Perfs:* 50 *Venues:* The Big Gild Concert Hall 650
Touring: Europe

Riga Chamber Players
Rigas Kamermuziki
40/42 Masakavas iela, 1018 **Riga**
Tel: 7-211 273 Fax: 7-215 283
artistic director Normunds Sne
Size: 16-55 *Perfs:* 20 *Type/spec:* chamber symphony; repertoire: baroque, classical, 20th C *Touring:* Estonia, Norway, Finland, Switzerland, Russia, Lithuania
Comments: period style on modern instruments

Youth Symphony Orchestra of Riga Latvian Society
Rigas Latviesu Biedribas Jauniesu simfoniskais orkestris
RLB Merkela 13, 1050 **Riga**
Tel: 7-222 932 Fax: 7-226 924
artistic director and principal conductor Martins Bergs

LITHUANIA (+370)

Kauno kamerinis orkestras
Kaunas Chamber Orchestra
L. Sapiegos 5, 3000 **Kaunas**
Tel: 7-204 589 (director) Fax: 7-200 443
artistic/director/senior conductor Pavel Berman; director Jonas Beleckas

Chamber Ensemble Atrium Musicum
Kamerinis ansamblis Atrium Musicum
P. Vileisio 26-95, 2040 **Vilnius**
Tel: 2-340 503
E-Mail: atrium@takas.li
artistic director Tomas Bakucionis

Chamber Ensemble of Early Music Musica Humana
Senosios Muzikos Ansamblis Musica Humana
Ausros Vartu 5, 2001 **Vilnius**
Tel: 2-626 802 Fax: 2-622 859
artistic director Algirdas Vizgirda
Type/spec: early music *Comments:* see also Early Music

Contemporary Music Ensemble Ex Tempore
Siuolaikines muzikos ansamblis Ex Tempore
Svencioniu 4, 2014 **Vilnius**
Tel: 2-622 153
contact Gintare Skeryte

Ensemble of Ancient Music and Dance Banchetto Musicale
Senosios Muzikos ir Sokiu Ansamblis
Banchetto Musicale
Gedimino pr. 9, 2600 **Vilnius**
Tel: 2-756 332/233 795 Fax: 2-226 412
artistic director Jūrate Mikiskaite
Type/spec: early music *Comments:* see also Early Music

Light Music Orchestra of the Lithuanian Radio and TV
Lietuvos radijo ir televizijos lengvosios muzikos orkestras
S. Konarskio 49, 2674 **Vilnius**
Tel: 2-661 499 (conductor) Fax: 2-263 282
artistic director/senior conductor Jaroslavas Cechanovicius

Lithuanian Chamber Orchestra
Lietuvos kamerinis orkestras
Lithuanian National Philharmonic Society,
Ausros Vartu 5, 2001 **Vilnius**
Tel: 2-615 804/626 802
Fax: 2-627 062/622 859
artistic director Saulius Sondeckis
Size: 35 *Touring:* national, international

Lithuanian National Symphony Orchestra
Lietuvos nacionalinis simfoninis orkestras
Lithuanian National Philharmonic Society,
Ausros Vartu 5, 2001 **Vilnius**
Tel: 2-626 802/617 786 Fax: 2-622 859/617 786
artistic director Juozas Domarkas; director Eugenijus Janutenas
Size: 110

Lithuanian State Symphony Orchestra
Lietuvos valstybinis simfoninis orkestras
Zygimantu 6, 2600 **Vilnius**
Tel: 2-628 127 (director)/628 825 (artistic director and senior conductor) Fax: 2-220 966 (director)
E-Mail: lvso@iti.lt
director Jurgis Banevicius; artistic director Gintaras Rinkevicius

M.K. Ciurlionis String Quartet
M.K. Ciurlionio styginiu kvartetas
c/o Lithuanian National Philharmonic Society,
Ausros vartu 5, 2001 **Vilnius**
Tel: 2-626 802/726 411 Fax: 2-622 859
E-Mail: lipcius@takas.lt
artistic diretor Saulius Lipcius
Comments: alternative E-mail: lipcius@yahoo.com

Ruta and Zbignevas Ibelhauptai Piano Duet
Rutos ir Zbignevo Ibelhauptu fortepijonu duetas
Antakalnio 83-40, 2040 **Vilnius**
Tel: 2-342 379
Size: 2

St. Christopher' Chamber Orchestra
Sv. Kristoforo Kamerinis Orkestras
Sv. Ignoto St. 6, 2600 **Vilnius**
Tel: 2-721 808 Fax: 2-721 808
manager Sarunas Maciulevicius; artistic director & conductor Donatus Katkus

State Wind Instruments Orchestra – Trimitas
Valstybinis puciamuju instrumentu orkestras – Trimitas
T. Sevcenkos 19A, 2009 **Vilnius**
Tel: 2-238 368/263 586/233 804
Fax: 2-238 368/263 586/233 804
artistic director Algirdas Budrys

Vilnius Ensemble of New Music
Vilniaus Naujosios muzikos ansamblis
Vileisio 15-14, 2005 **Vilnius**
Tel: 2-749 766 (head) Fax: 2-221 485
artistic director/conductor Sarunas Nakas

Vilnius Municipality St. Kristophorus Chamber Orchestra
Vilniaus miesto savivaldybes Sv. Kristoforo kamerinis orkestras
Sv. Ignoto 6, 2001 **Vilnius**
Tel: 2-623 114/721 808 Fax: 2-623 114/721 808
E-Mail: cactus@post.omnitel.net
artistic director Donatas Katkus; director Sarunas Miculevicius

Vilnius State Quartet
Vilniaus valstybinis kvartetas
c/o Lithuanian National Philharmonic Society,
Ausros vartu 5, 2001 **Vilnius**
Tel: 2-619 086/626 802/615 715
Fax: 2-619 086/622 859/615 715
artistic director Audrone Vainiunaite
Size: 4

LUXEMBOURG (+352)

Ensemble for Contemporary Music
L.G.N.M., B.P. 828, 2018 **Luxembourg**
Tel: 225 821 Fax: 225 823
E-Mail: lgnm@lgnm.lu
Size: 10 *Type/spec:* contemporary, new compositions

Orchestre Philharmonique du Luxembourg
Villa Louvigny, BP 2243, 1022 **Luxembourg**
Tel: 229 901-1 Fax: 229 998
management Jacques Mauroy, Olivier Frank; chief conductor David Shallon
Size: 86 *Perfs:* 75 *Type/spec:* symphony *Venues:* Conservatoire de Luxembourg 680 *Touring:* France, UK

Solistes Européens Luxembourg
PO Box 74, 2010 **Luxembourg**
Tel: 462 765 Fax: 229 814
E-Mail: selprim@vo.lu
chairman and CEO Eugène Prim; general manager Jean Wenandy; musical director Jack Martin Handler; administration Anne Pierron
Size: 20-50 *Perfs:* 15-20 *Type/spec:* chamber orchestra, symphonic *Venues:* Conservatoire *Touring:* Spain *Comments:* address administration: 8, Rue J. P. Koenig, Luxembourg: office hours: Mon-Fri 9.00-17.00

MACEDONIA (+389)

Macedonian Philharmonia
Makedonska Filharmonija
Dom na ARM bb, 91000 **Skopje**
Tel: 91-235 753 Fax: 91-235 753
director Vasil Atanasov

Orchestra of the Macedonian National Theatre
Orkestar na Makedonski Naroden Teater
Kej Dimitar Vlahov, 91000 **Skopje**
Tel: 91-114 908/511 Fax: 91-114 060

Skopje Radio and Television Symphony Orchestra
Simfonijski Orkestar RTV Skopje
GOCE Delcev bb, 91000 **Skopje**
Tel: 91-112 200 Fax: 91-112 156

MOLDOVA (+373)

Chamber Orchestra of Moldova
Orchestra de camera din Moldova
Stefan cel Mare Bld 81, 2012 **Chisinau**
Tel: 2-238 258 Fax: 2-238 257
artistic director Christian Florea

Ensemble Feminine of Jazz
87 Alexei Mateevici str, 2012 **Chisinau**
Tel: 2-224 344 Fax: 2-241 036
artistic director Alexandr Rudenko

Folk Music Orchestra Folclor
1 Miorita str, 2072 **Chisinau**
Tel: 2-721 755
artistic director Pentru Neamtu

Folk Music Orchestra Lautarii
R. Puskin str 21, 2012 **Chisinau**
Tel: 2-238 258
artistic director Nicolae Dumitru Botgros

Folk Music Orchestra Mugurel
R. Puskin str 21, 2012 **Chisinau**
Tel: 2-238 258 Fax: 2-238 257
artistic director Ion Dascal

National Symphonic Orchestra for Radio and Television
Orchestra Nationala a Companiei de Stat Teleradio Moldova
Miorita str. 1, 2012 **Chisinau**
Tel: 2-721 088/497 921 Fax: 2-723 358/723 358
artistic director & principal conductor Gheorghe Ion Mustea; manager Gheorghe Mustea
Size: 97 *Type/spec:* symphonic works from classic, romantic contemporary repertoire, opera from national property *Touring:* international *Comments:* annual subscription series, master-class for young conductors

Symphony Orchestra of the National Philharmonic of Moldova
78 Mitropolit Vaarlam str., 2012 **Chisinau**
Tel: 2-238 258 Fax: 2-238 257
artistic director Valentin Doni

Symphony Orchestra of Theatre-Studio of Academy of Music
87 Alexie Mateevici , 2012 **Chisinau**
Tel: 2-224 344 Fax: 2-242 036
artistic director Mihail Secikin

Violonistele Moldovei – Feminine Orchestra of Popular Classical Music
21 Puskin str, 2012 **Chisinau**
Tel: 2-238 258 Fax: 2-238 257
manager Victor Bublitchi; artistic director Boris Dubossarschi

MONACO (+377)

Orchestre Philharmonique de Monte-Carlo
BP 139, 98007 **Monte Carlo**
Tel: 9216 2317 Fax: 9315 0871
administrateur René Croési; directeur musical Marek Janowski; délégué artistique Chandler Cudlipp
Size: 86 *Perfs:* 34 *Type/spec:* symphony, opera, ballet *Venues:* Centre de Congrès-Auditorium 1097, Cour d' Honneur du Palais Princier 1000, Salle des Princes, Salle Garnier (Opéra de Monte-Carlo) 500, Grimaldi Forum 1900 *Comments:* also plays for opera, ballet

NETHERLANDS (+31)

Amsterdam Percussion Group
PO Box 3897, 1001 AR **Amsterdam**
Tel: 20-686 6486 Fax: 20-686 9664
manager H Van den Abbeelen; artistic director Josep Vicent
Size: 5-8 *Type/spec:* contemporary percussion

Amsterdamse Bach Solisten
Korte Leidsedwarsstraat 12, 1017 RC **Amsterdam**
Tel: 20-623 8189 Fax: 20-420 4542
Internet: www.bloomline.net/amsbach
E-Mail: amsbach@wxs.nl
general manager Maartien Delprat
Size: 6-32 *Perfs:* 35-40 *Type/spec:* late 17th to early 19th C repertoire *Venues:* Concertgebouw, Vredenburg, Waalfikerk Amsterdam, Geeartekerk, Utrecht *Touring:* national, Germany *Comments:* some musicians are from the Royal Concertgebouw Orchestra

Asko Ensemble
Keizersgracht 261, 1016 EC **Amsterdam**
Tel: 20-622 3476 Fax: 20-622 9081
Internet: www.asko-ensemble.nl
E-Mail: asko@xs4all.nl
general director/music director Willem Hering; financial director Rosita Wouda
Size: 20-50 *Perfs:* 56 *Type/spec:* chamber orchestra, contemporary *Venues:* Amsterdam Concertgebouw *Touring:* USA, UK, Germany
Comments: the Asko Ensemble often plays together with the Schönberg Ensemble (q.v.)

Calefax reed quintet
Nassaukade 5, 1052 CE **Amsterdam**
Tel: 20-684 4322 Fax: 20-682 8799
E-Mail: hmoens@dds.nl
manager Joh Adriaan Moens
Perfs: 25 *Type/spec:* arrangements from 12th century to new compositions of the 20th *Touring:* 2001: USA
Comments: winner of the Philip Morris Finest Selection Prize 1997; exclusive CD-recording production

Dutch Contemporary Wind Orchestra
Orkest De Volharding
Weesperzijde 23, 1091 EC **Amsterdam**
Tel: 20-694 8187 Fax: 20-694 6607
Internet: www.volharding.com
E-Mail: volharding.ODV@inter.nl.net
manager Frans Vreede; conductor Jurjen Hempel; production Marianne Berenschot
Size: 13 *Perfs:* 40 *Type/spec:* contemporary chamber music from the Netherlands, new music on the borders of contemporary chamber music, jazz and rock *Venues:* capacity 200-1500 including De Ijsbreker, Amsterdam; Vredenburg, Utrecht; De Oosterport, Groningen; Korzo, The Hague; and others *Touring:* UK, Japan
Comments: music specially composed for the orchestra; CDs available

Hague Percussion Group
Slagwerkgroep Den Haag
Keizersgracht 264, 1016 EV **Amsterdam**
Tel: 20-622 6979/428 0064
Fax: 20-622 9081/428 0139
Internet:
www.xs4all.nl/~narcz/groups/slwgroepDenHaag.html
E-Mail: sdh@hglo.demon.nl
general manager Titia Daniels; artistic director Peter Adriaansz
Size: 6 *Perfs:* 25 *Type/spec:* contemporary percussion music *Venues:* Paradiso, Concertgebouw, Korzo Theater Den Haag, Anton Philipszaal, Vredenburg + larger venues (stage wise) *Touring:* Europe *Comments:* co-operates with other ensembles for performing larger works; see also Agents and Festivals

Maarten Altena Ensemble
Prinsengracht 754 achter, 1017 LD **Amsterdam**
Tel: 20-423 2451 Fax: 20-423 2452
E-Mail: altena1@xs4all.nl
general manager Roos Goossens; artistic director Maarten Altena
Size: 9 *Perfs:* 20 *Type/spec:* new music (composed and improvised) *Venues:* De IJsbreker and BIMhuis (Amsterdam); Oosterport (Groningen), Vredenburg (Utrecht) *Touring:* national, USA, Czech Republic, Japan

National Jeugd Orkest
Van Limburg Stirumstraat 20A, 1051 BB **Amsterdam**
Tel: 20-688 5700 Fax: 20-688 5545
Internet: www.njo.nl
E-Mail: njo@njo.nl
general manager Arthur van Dijk; orchestra manager Else van Ommen; staff assistant Arie Hordÿk
Size: 100 *Perfs:* 25 *Type/spec:* great symphonic, romantic music *Venues:* Concertgebouw (Amsterdam) + major cities *Touring:* Germany, Italy
Comments: member of EFNYO (q.v)

LEONID KUZMIN

Pianist

"Leonid Kuzmin – Remember the name and hold your breath!"
LOS ANGELES TIMES

E, A, G Sharp, Co.

www.eagsharp.com
eagsharp@eagsharp.com

235 West 102 Street - Suite 16 J
New York, N.Y. 10025

Phone (212) 864 6020
Fax (212) 864 6934

Netherlands Ballet Orchestra
Nederlands Balletorkest
Waterlooplein 22, 1011 PG **Amsterdam**
Tel: 20-551 8823 Fax: 20-620 8019
Internet: www.balletorkest.nl
E-Mail: info@balletorkest.nl
general manager Rob Tijsen; assistant manager Maurits Haenen; planning, special projects and education Julia Bastiaanse; chief conductor Thierry Fischer; artistic coordinator Jan Pieter Koch
Size: 90 *Perfs:* 140 *Venues:* Muziektheater Amsterdam; Lucent Danstheater Den Haag *Comments:* orchestra for The National Ballet and Nederlands DansTheater

Netherlands Philharmonic Orchestra and Netherlands Chamber Orchestra
Beurs van Berlage, Damrak 213, 1012 ZH **Amsterdam**
Tel: 20-627 1161 Fax: 20-622 9939/625 4739
E-Mail: roboverman@nedpho.nl
general manager Rob Overman; musical director Hartmut Haenchen; manager planning & touring Angela Garland; artistic director Herbert Slegers; assistant to managing director Michiko Lodder
Size: 132 *Perfs:* 100 + 40 opera *Venues:* Beurs van Berlage, Concertgebouw, Muziektheater, Amsterdam; Vredenburg, Utrecht *Touring:* 99: Spain; 2000: Japan *Comments:* see also Venues; see also Netherlands Chamber Orchestra

Netherlands Wind Ensemble
Nederlands Blazers Ensemble
Korte Leidsedwarsstraat 12, 1017 RC **Amsterdam**
Tel: 20-623 7806 Fax: 20-623 4948
Internet: www.nederlandsblazersensemble.nl
E-Mail: nbe@euronet.nl
managing & programming Johan Dorrestein, Bart Schneemann; production manager Floor Ziegler; pr Janine Jansen; librarian Erik Hense
Size: 8-40 *Type/spec:* chamber ensemble repertoire (18th C to contemporary)

Nieuw Ensemble
Keizersgracht 261, 1016 EC **Amsterdam**
Tel: 20-620 2331 Fax: 20-622 9081
Internet: www.nieuw-ensemble.nl
E-Mail: info@nieuw-ensemble.nl
musical director Ed Spanjaard; artistic director Joël Bons; production Caroline Bakker; business manager Babette Greiner
Size: 12-20 *Perfs:* 40 *Type/spec:* chamber orchestra/contemporary *Venues:* Paradiso, Concertgebouw Amsterdam *Touring:* Scotland, Sweden, Norway, Italy, Austria, Germany, France *Comments:* contemporary music often composed specifically for the ensemble; performs only contemporary music; typical for the ensemble is the use of plucked instruments (mandolin, guitar, harp) together with wind and string instruments, piano and percussion

Nieuw Sinfonietta Amsterdam
Paulus Potterstraat 12, 1071 CZ **Amsterdam**
Tel: 20-672 1022 Fax: 20-675 2607
general manager Frans Brouwer; music director Peter Oundjian
Size: 25-35 *Perfs:* 50-60 *Type/spec:* string, chamber, 20th century, Russian *Venues:* Concertgebouw (Amsterdam, Doelen, Rotterdam, Vredenburg, Utrecht)
Touring: Germany, Asia

Orchestra of the Eighteenth Century
Orkest van de Achttiende Eeuw
Borneokade 301, 1019 XG **Amsterdam**
Tel: 20-626 8236 Fax: 20-620 5932
Internet: www.orchestra18C.com
E-Mail: info@orchestra18C.com
general director Sieuwert Verster; music director Frans Brüggen; assistant to general director Ineke Huÿing
Size: 55 *Perfs:* 40-50 *Type/spec:* classical: specialising in 18th and early 19thC *Touring:* Europe, Japan, USA, South America, Australia *Comments:* touring orchestra performing 4 seasons per year

Ricciotti ensemble
Korte Leidsedwarsstraat 12, 1017 RC **Amsterdam**
Tel: 20-624 6115 Fax: 20-638 8355
E-Mail: ricciott@euronet.nl
managing director Geert Boogaard
Size: 40 *Type/spec:* classical, jazz, popular and ethnical music *Comments:* youth orchestra, mostly conservatory students, which plays at venues and for people who normally can't or won't hear any live symphonic music, such as prisons, (mental) hospitals and children

Royal Concertgebouw Orchestra
Koninklijk Concertgebouworkest
Jacob Obrechtstraat 51, 1071 KJ **Amsterdam**
Tel: 20-679 2211 Fax: 20-676 3331
Internet: concertgebouworkest.nl
E-Mail: info@concertgebouworkest.nl
executive director Jan Willem Loot; artistic manager Joel Fried; chief conductor Riccardo Chailly; director, public relations Sjoerd van den Berg
Size: 115 *Perfs:* 125 *Type/spec:* symphony
Venues: Concertgebouw Hall 2037
Touring: Europe, USA, Canada, Japan

Schönberg Ensemble
Keizersgracht 261, 1016 EC **Amsterdam**
Tel: 20-622 3476 Fax: 20-622 9081
Internet: www.schoenberg-ensemble.nl
E-Mail: schoenberg@xs4all.nl
general director Willem Hering; music director Reinbert de Leeuw; financial director Rosita Wouda
Size: 20-50 *Perfs:* 66 *Type/spec:* chamber orchestra, contemporary music *Venues:* Concertgebouw Amsterdam *Touring:* Switzerland, UK, Germany, Belgium, USA *Comments:* the Schoenberg Ensemble often performs with the Asko Ensemble

Willem Breuker Kollektief
Prinseneiland 99, 1013 LN **Amsterdam**
Tel: 20-623 9799 Fax: 20-624 3534
Internet: www.xs4all.nl/~wbk/
E-Mail: wbk@xs4all.nl
manager Susanna von Canon; artistic dir. Willem Breuker
Size: 11 *Perfs:* 100 *Type/spec:* jazz, wind, brass, rhythm
Touring: world-wide *Comments:* see also Festivals

Arnhem Philharmonic Orchestra
Het Gelders Orkest
Postbus 1180, 6801 BD **Arnhem**
Tel: 26-442 2632 Fax: 26-443 9966
general manager Jan Taat; principal conductor Lawrence Renes; public relations Agnes Bolwiender; deputy manager Dolf Hofs
Size: 96 *Perfs:* 110 *Type/spec:* symphony orchestra *Venues:* Arnhem Music Sacrum 1000, De Vereeniging, Nijmegen 1500 *Comments:* visiting address: Velperbuitensingel 12, 6825 CV Arnhem

Amsterdam Baroque Orchestra and Choir
PO Box 1163, 1400 BD **Bussum**
Tel: 35-692 6000 Fax: 35-692 6001
Internet: www.tonkoopman.nl
E-Mail: cdeklerk@abo.rem.nl
managing director Franco Panozzo; office manager Cecilia de Klerk; conductor Ton Koopman
Size: 30 + 30 singers *Perfs:* 40-50 *Type/spec:* classical, baroque (especially Bach) *Touring:* worldwide *Comments:* approx. 10 CDs; touring company; Franco Panozzo (artists management company), Via Valverde 32, 37122 Verona, Italy, Tel: +39 045-801 4041, Fax: +39 045-801 4980; see also Choirs and Early Music

Residentie Bachorkest
Leuvensestraat 44, 2587 GH **Den Haag**
Tel: 70-354 3746 Fax: 70-350 9395
manager Michiel de Ligt; conductor Jos Vermunt
Size: 17-35 *Type/spec:* chamber orchestra, mainly baroque and classical *Comments:* CD on Prisma label

Residentie Orkest (The Hague Philharmonic)
Spuiplein 150, Postbus 11543, 2502 AM **Den Haag**
Tel: 70-360 7925 Fax: 70-365 1907
Internet: www.residentieorkest.nl
E-Mail: info1@residentieorkst.nl
general manager Bert van den Akker; chief conductor Evgeni Svetlanov; concert art director Leo Samama
Size: 109 *Perfs:* 110 *Type/spec:* late romantic, contemporary, Dutch *Venues:* Dr Anton Philipszaal, The Hague 1890 *Touring:* Japan

Brabant Philharmonic Orchestra
Het Brabants Orkest
J. Van Lieshoutstraat 5, 5611 EE **Eindhoven**
Tel: 40-265 5699 Fax: 40-246 3459
E-Mail: hbo@brabantsorkest.nl
managing director Detlev Weers; chief conductor Marc Soustrot; principal guest conductor Jaap Van Zweden; pr/publicist Danielle Hermeler
Size: 80 *Perfs:* 110 *Type/spec:* symphony *Venues:* Muziekcentrum Frits Philips Eindhoven (home) 1249, Theater aan de Parade ('s-Hertogenbosch),Concertzaal (Tilburg), Chassé Theater (Breda) *Touring:* Germany, Austria, England *Comments:* postal address: PO Box 230, 5600 AE Eindhoven

Orkest van het Oosten
Stationsplein 3, 7511 JD **Enschede**
Tel: 53-487 8700 Fax: 53-434 2339
E-Mail: info@orkestvanhetoosten.nl
general manager Pieter Prick; chief conductor Jaap van Zweden; pr & marketing manager Menno van Duuren
Size: 79 *Perfs:* 70 concerts + 30 opera performances *Venues:* major concert halls in the eastern part of the Netherlands + main Dutch Opera theatres *Touring:* UK

Haydn Youth String Orchestra
GA Feithstraat 6, 9725 EP **Groningen**
Tel: 50-526 8340 Fax: 50-526 8345
Internet: www.welcome/hgso
E-Mail: yka@xs4all.nl
manager Yke Topoel; conductor Ben de Ligt
Size: 30 *Type/spec:* baroque, classical, contemporary *Venues:* Oostarpoort 1200 *Touring:* Italy *Comments:* 9 CDs with Haydn Unlimited (own record label)

Noord Nederlands Orkest
Palmslag 20, 9724 CS **Groningen**
Tel: 50-369 5800 Fax: 50-369 5815
E-Mail: nno@tref.nl
chief conductor Viktor Liberman; general manager H. B. van der Meer; associated manager drs P. M. Adema
Size: 89 *Perfs:* 100 p.a. *Type/spec:* symponic orchestra *Venues:* Oosterpoort *Comments:* visiting address: Palmslac 20, 9724 CS Groningen

Noordhollands Philharmonisch Orkest
Klokhuisplein 2A, 2011 HK **Haarlem**
Tel: 23-531 9248 Fax: 23-532 8533
general manager Stan Paardekooper; artistic manager Peter-Jan Wagemans; deputy manager Jan Treffers
Size: 60 *Perfs:* 70+ 20 ballet and 20 choral *Type/spec:* symphony *Venues:* Concertgebouw 1200
Touring: mostly Holland

Concertgebouw Chamber Orchestra
Concertgebouw Kamerorkest
Zwinglilaan 61, 1216 MB **Hilversum**
Tel: 35-621 6127 Fax: 35-621 6127
E-Mail: cko@gironet.nl
general manager Paul Peter Spiering; principal conductors Marco Boni, Roland Kieft
Size: 20 *Perfs:* 20 *Type/spec:* chamber, baroque, romantic *Venues:* throughout the Netherlands
Touring: international

Metropole Orchestra
Metropole Orkest
Heuvellaan 33, PO Box 125, 1200 AC **Hilversum**
Tel: 35-671 4160 Fax: 35-671 4171
E-Mail: f.dekker@mco.nl
manager Fred Dekker; assistant manager Bob Krikke; musical director Dick Bakker
Size: 50 *Perfs:* 12 + 60 studio recordings
Type/spec: light music *Venues:* MCO-studio, Hilversum; Vredenburg, Utrecht

Netherlands Radio Chamber Orchestra
Radio Kamerorkest
Heuvellaan 33 , PO Box 125, 1200 AC **Hilversum**
Tel: 35-671 4150 Fax: 35-671 4171
E-Mail: s.riedstra@mco.nl
manager Siebe Riedstra; conductors Peter Eötvös and Ton Koopman
Size: 39 *Perfs:* 40 *Type/spec:* classical/new

Netherlands Radio Philharmonic Orchestra
Radio Filharmonisch Orkest
Heuvellaan 33, PO Box 125, 1200 AC **Hilversum**
Tel: 35-671 4130 Fax: 35-671 4171
E-Mail: s.rosu@mco.nl
manager Stefan Rosu; music director Edo de Waart
Size: 98 *Perfs:* 40 symphony
Venues: Concertgebouw, Amsterdam; Vredenburg, Utrecht; De Doelen, Rotterdam

Netherlands Radio Symphony Orchestra
Radio Symfonie Orkest
Heuvellaan 33, PO Box 125, 1200 AC **Hilversum**
Tel: 35-671 4140 Fax: 35-671 4171
E-Mail: h.smit@mco.nl
manager Henk Smit; chief conductor Eri Klas; assistant manager Jacques de Graaf
Size: 93 *Perfs:* 40 *Venues:* Concertgebouw, Amsterdam; Vredenburg, Utrecht

Limburgs Symphony Orchestra
Limburgs Symphonie Orkest
Statenstraat 5, Postbus 482, 6200 AL **Maastricht**
Tel: 43-350 7000 Fax: 43-350 7025
Internet: www.lso.nl
E-Mail: info@lso.nl
managing director John Floore; chief conductor Junichi Hirokami; manager public relations & marketing Gert Geluk
Size: 66 *Perfs:* 110 *Type/spec:* symphony, opera *Venues:* Theatre aan het Vrijthof, Maastricht 900; De Maaspoort Venlo 700; Stadsschouburg Heerlen 750 *Touring:* Spain *Comments:* in July every year perform an open air concert: Brand Midsummer Concert

Combattimento Consort Amsterdam
Nooit Gedacht 118, 1398 EG **Muiden**
Tel: 294-262 341 Fax: 294-263 651
Internet: www.combattimento-consort.amsterdam.nl
E-Mail: office@cca-music.nl
assistant general manager Marcel Mandos; artistic director Jan Willem de Vriend; producer Diana Bohnenberger; press & pr officer Marco van Es; general manager Albert Adams; assistant artistic director Taco Stronks
Size: 12 *Perfs:* 70 *Type/spec:* baroque *Venues:* Concertgebouw, Amsterdam; Vredenburg, Utrecht; Dr. Anton Philipszaal Den Haag, De Doelen Rotterdam
Touring: Italy, Japan *Comments:* see also Early Music

Rotterdam Philharmonic Orchestra
Rotterdams Philharmonisch Orkest
de Doelen, Kruisstraat 2, 3012 CT **Rotterdam**
Tel: 10-217 1760 Fax: 10-411 6215
E-Mail: art.dir@rpho.nl
general manager t.b.a.; artistic leader Kees Hillen; principal conductor Valery Gergiev
Size: 114 *Perfs:* 105 *Type/spec:* symphonic
Venues: de Doelen 2200

Netherlands Bach Society
De Nederlandse Bachvereniging
Koningslaan 112, Postbus 12017, 3501 AA **Utrecht**
Tel: 30-251 3413 (box office)/252 4010
Fax: 30-251 1639
E-Mail: bachvereniging@wxs.nl
managing director Maria Hansen; musical director Jos van Veldhoven; production manager Chris van de Ven
Size: 20 orchestra + 20 member choir and 5-15 Cappella Figuralis singers and players *Perfs:* 40-45
Type/spec: baroque choir, orchestra and solo ensemble
Touring: Netherlands
Comments: CD recordings with Gustav Leonhardt, Ton Koopman and Jos van Veldhoven

Tell-Brass Koperensemble
Oudenoord 463, 3513 EP **Utrecht**
Tel: 30-234 1638 Fax: 30-223 2619
Internet: www.tell-brass.nl
E-Mail: mark.vondenhoff@tell-brass.nl
artistic director & manager Mark Vondenhoff
Size: 4-12 *Perfs:* 40 *Type/spec:* brass ensemble in various combinations (main ones are quintet and tentet), accompanies choirs *Venues:* Vredenburg (Utrecht)
Comments: 1999: Celebration of 10 years existence, concert series in Vredenburg with, among others, London Brass

NORWAY (+47)

Bergen Philharmonic Orchestra
Edvard Griegs pl. 1, 5015 **Bergen**
Tel: 5521 6100 Fax: 5531 8534
artistic manager Lorentz Reitan; orchestra manager Tarjei Flotve
Size: 97 *Perfs:* 90-100 *Type/spec:* classical and contemporary philharmonic repertoire *Venues:* Grieghallen 1500 *Touring:* Switzerland

BIT 20 / Bergen Ensemble for Contemporary Music
Grieghallen Edvard Griegs Plass 1, 5015 **Bergen**
Tel: 55-216 120 Fax: 55-216 121
E-Mail: bit20ens@bgnet.no
artistic director Stein Olav Henrichsen; projects coordinator Astrid Rodsand
Size: 18-20 (sinfonietta) *Perfs:* 30 *Type/spec:* 20th C.
Touring: worldwide

Young Norwegian Festival Strings
Unge Norske Festivalstrykere
c/o Pro Arte, John Lunds Plass 1, 5007 **Bergen**
Tel: 55-319 435 Fax: 55-960 765
Internet: home.sol.no/~prinmana
E-Mail: proarte@online.no
artistic director Olle Richard Kraggerud
Size: 10-20 *Touring:* national

Kristiansand Symfoniorkester
PO Box 777, 4601 **Kristiansand**
Tel: 3802 2440 Fax: 3802 2991
Internet: www.kso.no
E-Mail: post@kso.no
manager Öystein Eidsaa; chairman of the board Stein Erikstad; artistic leader Jan Stigmer
Size: 37 *Perfs:* 70 *Venues:* Agder Teater, Kristiansand Frikirke, Kristiansand Domkirke

Kristiansund Sinfonietta
c/o Operaen i Kristiansund, PO Box 401, 6501 **Kristiansund**
Tel: 71-678 524/589 960
Fax: 71-676 657
contact Od Williamson

MiNensemblet
Postboks 703, 8501 **Narvik**
Tel: 7694 4370 Fax: 7694 6670
managing director Karin Holdar; producers Trond Jonassen, Elisabeth Storjord
Type/spec: wind quintet, string quintet and piano

Borealis Ensemble
c/o Karl Ravnan, Holmenveien 83, 0376 **Oslo**
Tel: 2249 0413/92-822 839 (mobile)
Fax: 2249 0413/92-973 893
Size: 10 *Type/spec:* wind quartet, string quartet and piano

CIKADA
c/o Ny Musikk, Tollbugata 28, 0157 **Oslo**
Tel: 2233 7090 Fax: 2233 7095
Internet: www.nymusikk.no
E-Mail: sten@nymusikk.no
managing director Sten Cranner
Size: 10 *Perfs:* 17 *Type/spec:* contemporary
Venues: Cosmopolite, Oslo 600
Touring: 99/00: Norway, Sweden, Denmark, Belgium, UK *Comments:* commission works by Norwegian and international composers

Norske Blásere
c/o Gerard Oskamp, Trondheimsun 42, 0560 **Oslo**
Tel: 2271 7997 Fax: 2271 7997
Type/spec: wind orchestra

Norske Operas Orkester, Den
PO Box 8800, Youngstorget, 0028 **Oslo**
Tel: 2331 5000/2242 9475
Fax: 2233 4027/2231 5030
orchestra manager Knut Brotnow; orchestra director Sigmund Jaang
Size: 77 *Perfs:* 140 *Type/spec:* opera, ballet, concerts
Venues: Den Norske Opera 1060 *Comments:* annual symphony concert performance; visiting address: Storgaten 23, 0184 Oslo; see also Dance and Opera

Norwegian Chamber Orchestra
Det Norske Kammerorkester
Stockholmsgata 12, 0566 **Oslo**
Tel: 2204 6270 Fax: 2204 6290
E-Mail: kammerorkesteret@telepost.no
managing director Bernt Lauritz Larsen; artistic director Iona Brown
Size: 20-30 *Perfs:* 15 *Type/spec:* classical (early to contemporary) *Venues:* Universitetets Aula (University Festival Hall) 750
Comments: recordings for Chandos Music

Norwegian Radio Orchestra
NRK – Kringkastingsorkestret
Bjornstjerne Bjornsons pl. 1, 0340 **Oslo**
Tel: 2304 9590 Fax: 2304 8340
managing and artistic director Reidun Berg; chief conductor Ari Rasilainen
Size: 50 *Perfs:* 35 + tv and radio work *Type/spec:* classical, light music, contemporary
Venues: Radio Studio 300 *Comments:* recording CD for Finlandia (subsidiary of Warner)

Norwegian Youth Orchestra, The
Ungdomssymfonikerne
Norwegian State Academy of Music, PO Box 5190, 0302 **Oslo**
Tel: 2336 7010 Fax: 2336 7001
E-Mail: ab@nmh.no
general manager Idar Karevold; artistic director Astrid Bertelsen
Size: 110 *Perfs:* 4-5 *Type/spec:* mainly classical, but some contemporary *Venues:* mid-scale
Comments: member of EFNYO (q.v)

Oslo Philharmonic Orchestra
Oslo Filharmoniske Orkester
Haakon VII gate 2, 0250 **Oslo**
Tel: 2201 4900 Fax: 2201 4901
Internet: wit.no/ofo/
E-Mail: ofo@eunet.no
managing director Trond Okkelmo; music director Mariss Jansons; administration director Marit Gaasland; orchestra director Per E Kise Larsen; office manager Wigdis S Hoel
Size: 107 *Perfs:* 68 at home, 22 on tour *Type/spec:* symphony – wide repertoire *Venues:* Oslo Concert Hall 1400 *Touring:* national, international *Comments:* postal address: PO Box 1607 vika, 0119 Oslo

Oslo Sinfonietta
Tollbugata 28, 0157 **Oslo**
Tel: 2220 0709 Fax: 2220 7272
manager John Persen

Stavanger Symfoniorkester
Bjergsted, 4007 **Stavanger**
Tel: 5150 8830 Fax: 5150 8839
Internet: home.sol.no/~sso
E-Mail: symfonio@online.no
orchestra manager Erik Landmark; artistic leader and chief conductor t.b.a.; concerthouse director Anna-Marie Antonius; orchestra director Morten Moelster
Size: 70 *Perfs:* 75 *Type/spec:* symphonic; early music played on contemporary instruments *Venues:* Stavanger Konserthus 1178 *Touring:* Norway, Ireland, Denmark, Poland, Northern Europe *Comments:* orchestra is a pioneer in the field of music education and, in cooperation with Stavanger city council, performs concert programmes designed specifically for the various school age groups

Tromsø Symfoniorkester
PO Box 741, 9001 **Tromsø**
Tel: 7765 8554 Fax: 7768 5137

Oslo Camerata
Strindveien 38, 7052 **Trondheim**
Tel: 7394 5269 Fax: 7394 2788
E-Mail: blh.artists.management@hf.ntnu.no
general manager Bea Levine-Humm
Type/spec: from baroque to contemporary music
Touring: international

Trondheim Soloists Chamber Orchestra
Postbox 157, 7401 **Trondheim**
Tel: 7353 5433/908-34686 (mobile) Fax: 7353 5499
E-Mail: trondheimsoloists@c2i.net
managing director Trine Knutsen; artistic director Bjarne Fiskum (7352 8388)
Size: 18-30 *Perfs:* 30 *Type/spec:* chamber repertoire, contemporary *Touring:* Scandinavia, Germany
Comments: commision works by new composers; recordings available

Trondheim Symfoniorkester
Post Box 774 Sentrum, 7408 **Trondheim**
Tel: 7353 9800 Fax: 7353 9801
Internet: www.tso.no
E-Mail: post@tso.no
managing director Siri Fristad Mathisen; chief conductor Daniel Harding; manager Erland Braean
Size: 72 *Perfs:* 40 *Type/spec:* symphony orchestra, classical & contemporary *Venues:* Olavshallen 1200

Nord-Nordsk kammerorkester
Fylkeshuset, Postboks 443, 9801 **Vadsø**
Tel: 7895 1050 Fax: 7895 1970
producer Anders Eriksson
Size: 24-35 *Type/spec:* chamber orchestra, specialised in Viennese classics, romantic and contemporary music

POLAND (+48)

Bialystok Philharmonic
Filharmonia w Biatostochne
ul Podlesna 2, 15-227 **Bialystok**
Tel: 85-321 786/322 331/741 6709/732 7343
Fax: 85-741 6709/732 7343
artistic director Marcin Nalecz-Niesiokowski
Size: 70 *Perfs:* 40 *Venues:* capacity 300

Pomeranian Philharmonic
Filharmonia Pomorska
ul Libelta 16, 85-080 **Bydgoszcz**
Tel: 52-210 469 Fax: 52-210 752
artistic director Eleonora Harendarska; principal guest conductor Marek Pijarowski
Size: 80 *Perfs:* 40 *Venues:* Concert Hall 925, Chamber Hall 180

Czestochowa Philharmonic
Filharmonia w Czestochohie
Wilsona 16, 42-200 **Czestochowa**
Tel: 34-324 4230 Fax: 34-324 3437
general director Leszek Hadrian; artistic director Jerzy Swoboda
Size: 60 *Perfs:* 50 *Venues:* Concert Hall 900, Chamber Hall 200

Baltic Philharmonic
Panstwowa Filharmonia Baltycka
ul. Olowianka 1, 80-751 **Gdansk**
Tel: 58-305 2040/2041/3960
Fax: 58-305 2040/2041/3960
managing director Roman Perucki; artistic director Zygmunt Rychert
Size: 80 *Perfs:* 40 *Venues:* Opera House 550

Jelenia Gòra Philharmonic
Panstwowa Filharmonia w Jeleniej Gòrze im Ludomira Rózyckiego
J. Pilsudskiego 60, 58-500 **Jelenia Gòra**
Tel: 75-752 5284 Fax: 75-752 6075
director Zuzanna Dziedzic

Polish Radio Symphony Orchestra
Wielka Orkiestra Symfoniczna Polskiego Radia
Pl Sejmu Slaskiego 2, 40-032 **Katowice**
Tel: 32-518 903 Fax: 32-571 384
managing director Dr Irena Siodmok; artistic director Antoni Wit
Size: 100 and principal conductor *Perfs:* 20 *Venues:* Centrum Kultury im Grzegorza Fitelberga 800

Silesian Philharmonic
Panstwowa Filharmonia Slaska
ul. Sokolska 2, Skr. Poczt. 534, 40-084 **Katowice**
Tel: 32-586 261/589 885
Fax: 32-589 885
artistic director and principal conductor Mirostaw Blaszczyk; choir master Jan Wojtacha
Size: 100 + 70 choir *Perfs:* 70 *Type/spec:* chamber
Venues: Concert Hall 500

Silesian String Quartet (Slaski)
Katowice
Tel: 32-818 866
contact Marek Mos
Type/spec: modern, contemporary, chamber
Touring: national, international *Comments:* recordings for Polish radio and television

Kielce Philharmonic
Filharmonia w Kielcach im Oskara Kolberga
Pl. Moniuszki 2, 25-334 **Kielce**
Tel: 41-368 0501 Fax: 41-681 191
artistic director and principal conductor Szymon Kawalla; deputy director Leonard Skrobacz
Size: 70 *Perfs:* 40 *Venues:* Concert Hall 350

Koszalin Philharmonic Stanislaw Moniuszko
Panstwowa Filharmonia w Koszalinie im Stanislawa Moniuszki
Zwyciestwa 105, 75-001 **Koszalin**
Tel: 94-342 3696 Fax: 94-342 6220
artistic director and principal conductor Franciszek Stanczyk
Size: 50 *Perfs:* 40
Venues: Concert Hall, House of Culture 320

Cappella Cracoviensis
Ul. Zwierzyniecka 1, 31-103 **Kraków**
Tel: 12-421 4566/4219 151 Fax: 12-421 9660
conductor Stanislaw Galonski

Filharmonia Krakowska im Karola Szymanowskiego
Krakow Philharmonic Karol Szymanowski
ul Zwierzyniecka 1, 31-103 **Kraków**
Tel: 12-422 4312/9477 Fax: 12-422 4312
general director Anne Oberc; artistic director Tomasz Bugoj; principal guest conductor Jerzy Maksymiuk
Size: 110 + 95 choir *Perfs:* 60 *Venues:* Concert Hall 900

Rubinstein Philharmonic
Panstwowa Filharmonia im Artura Rubinsteina
Piotrkowska 243, 90-135 **Lódz**
Tel: 42-637 2652 Fax: 42-636 8232
managing director Katarzyna Nowicka; artistic director Piotr Redet
Size: 80 *Perfs:* 120
Venues: Concert Hall, Piotrkowska Street 350

Lublin Philharmonic
Panstwowa Filharmonia w Lublinie im Henryka Wieniawskiego
ul Marii Sklodowskiej Curie, 20-029 **Lublin**
Tel: 81-743 7821 Fax: 81-532 4421
artistic and managing director Teresa Ksieska Folger
Size: 70 *Perfs:* 40 *Venues:* Concert Hall 250

Olsztyn Philharmonic
Panstwowa Filharmonia w Olsztynie im Feliks Nowowiejskiego
ul Kosciuszki 39, 10-503 **Olsztyn**
Tel: 89-527 5175 Fax: 89-527 5175 ext 22
artistic director Leszek Skarzynski
Size: 60 *Perfs:* 40 *Venues:* Concert Hall 400

Opole Philharmonic
Panstwowa Filharmonia w Opolu im Józefa Elsnera
ul Krakowska 24, 45-075 **Opole**
Tel: 77-454 3371 Fax: 77-454 3736
general director Wieslaw Sierpinski
Size: 70 *Perfs:* 40 *Venues:* Concert Hall 380

Amadeus Chamber Orchestra
Orkiestra Kameralna Polskiego Radia 'Amadeus'
Al. Marcinkowskiego 3, 61-745 **Poznan**
Tel: 61-851 6686 Fax: 61-851 6687
artistic director and conductor Agnieszka Duczmal
Size: 20 *Perfs:* 15 *Venues:* Poznan University Hall 800

Poznan Philharmonic
Panstwowa Filharmonia w Poznaniu
ul Sw Marcina 81, 61-808 **Poznan**
Tel: 61-852 4708/09 Fax: 61-852 3451
general and artistic director Jose Maria Floréncio Júnior; deputy director Robert Szczepanski
Venues: Poznan University Hall 800 *Comments:* boys and mens choir, choirmaster Stefan Stuligrosz

Rzeszow Philharmonic
Panstwowa Filharmonia w Rzeszowie im Artura Malawskiego
ul Chopina 30, 35-055 **Rzeszow**
Tel: 17-622 333/628 408 Fax: 17-622 333/628 408
general director Wergiliusz Golabeck; artistic director Tadeusz Wojciechowski
Size: 70 *Perfs:* 40 *Venues:* Concert Hall 800, Chamber Hall 200

Slupsk Chamber Orchestra
Panstwowa Orkiestra Kameralna w Slupsku
Watowa 3, 76-200 **Slupsk**
Tel: 59-842 8434 Fax: 59-842 6338
director Bohdan Jarmolowicz

Szczecin Philharmonic
Panstwowa Filharmonia w Szczecinie im Mieczyslawa Karlowicza
Pl Armii Krajowej 1, 70-455 **Szczecin**
Tel: 91-220 589 Fax: 91-220 079
managing director Jadwiga Igiel; music director Jerzy Salwarowski
Size: 70 *Perfs:* 40 *Type/spec:* church music (oratories)
Venues: Concert Hall 500

Sudettic Philharmonic
Filharmonia Sudecka
ul Slowackiego 4, 58-300 **Walbrzych**
Tel: 74-24180 Fax: 74-22893
artistic director and principal conductor Jozef Wilkomirski
Size: 70 *Perfs:* 40 *Venues:* Concert Hall 500

National Philharmonic Warsaw
Filharmonia Narodowa Warszawa
ul Jasna 5, 00-950 **Warszawa**
Tel: 22-826 8311/7281 Fax: 22-826 5617
Internet: www.phil.pol.pl
E-Mail: phil@pol.pl
managing director Wojciech Nowak; artistic director and conductor Kazimierz Kord; choir master Henryk Wojnarowski
Size: 120 + 100 choir *Perfs:* 80
Venues: Concert Hall 1100, Chamber Hall 430

Polish Radio Orchestra Warsaw
Polska Orkiestra Radiowa w Warszawie
Studio S-1, ul. Woronicza 17, 00-999 **Warszawa**
Tel: 22-645 5051
Fax: 22-434 462
artistic director Wojciech Rajski
Size: 50 *Perfs:* 20 *Venues:* Studio S-1 450

Sinfonia Varsovia
Centrum Sztuki Studio, Palac Kultury, I Nauki, 00-901 **Warszawa**
Tel: 22-620 4369 Fax: 22-620 0138
managing director Franciszek Wybranczyk; music director Krzysztof Penderecki
Size: up to 40 *Perfs:* up to 20 in Poland
Type/spec: chamber

Warsaw Soloists Concerto Avenna
Concerto Avenna – Warszawscy Solisci
ul. Anieli Krzywon 2 m.165, 01-391 **Warszawa**
Tel: 22-664 3944
artistic director Andrzej Mysinski
Size: up to 24 *Perfs:* up to 20 concerts in Poland
Type/spec: chamber

Wroclaw Chamber Orchestra Leopoldinum
Wroclawska Orkiestra Kameralna Leopoldinum
Centrum Sztuki 'Impart', ul. Mazowiecka 17, 50-412 **Wroclaw**
Tel: 71-343 8154 Fax: 71-343 2962
manager Barbara Migurska
Size: 15 string players and extra woodwind *Perfs:* 20
Type/spec: chamber

Wroclaw Philharmonic
Panstwowa Filharmonia we Wroclawiu im. Witolda Lutoslawskiego
J. Pilsudskiego 19, 50-044 **Wroclaw**
Tel: 71-342 2001-3
Fax: 71-342 8980
artistic director and principal conductor Marek Pijarowski; deputy director Tadeusz Nesterowicz
Size: 80 *Perfs:* 40 *Venues:* Concert Hall 500

Zielona Góra Philharmonic Tadeusz Baird
Panstwowa Filharmonia w Zielonej Górze im Tadeusza Bairda
Plac Powstanców Wielkoposkich 10, 65-075 **Zielona Góra**
Tel: 68-325 6514/5/6 Fax: 68-325 6513
general and artistic director Czeslaw Grabowski
Size: 60 *Perfs:* 40 *Venues:* Concert Hall 240

PORTUGAL (+351)

Gulbenkian Orchestra
Fundação Calouste Gulbenkian (Music Department), Av de Berna 45-A, 1067 **Lisboa** Codex
Tel: 1-793 5131 Fax: 1-793 7296
Internet: www.telepac.pt/earte/gulbenkian
E-Mail: musica@gulbenkian.pt
music department director Dr. Luis Pereira Leal; principal conductor Muhai Tang; honorary conductor Claudio Scimone; principal guest conductor Michael Zilm
Size: 60 *Perfs:* 103 *Type/spec:* classical, baroque, contemporary music, avant-garde *Venues:* Auditorium 1200, Auditorio Dois 344 *Touring:* Europe, China
Comments: see also Ministries, Dance, Choirs, Festivals (2), Venues and Promoters

Orquestra Metropolitana de Lisboa
Lisbon Metropolitan Orchestra
Edificio Standart Electrica, Travessa da Galé 36, 1349-028 **Lisboa**
Tel: 1-362 3830 Fax: 1-362 3833
E-Mail: oml@oml.pt
executive director Cristina Ribeiro; artistic director Miguel Graca Moura; assistant director Paulo Gaio Lima; assistant maestro Jean-Marc Burfin; international relations Ana Lacerda
Size: 40 *Perfs:* 100 orchestra + 200 chamber music + recitals 300 *Type/spec:* chamber, 18th, 19th and 20th century *Venues:* capacity 150
Touring: Portugal, France

Orquestra Sinfónica Portuguesa
Portuguese Symphony Orchestra
Teatro São Carlos, Rua Serpa Pinto N°9, 1200 **Lisboa**
Tel: 1-343 1734 Fax: 1-343 1735
artistic director of Teatro de São Carlos Dr Paulo Ferreira de Castro; artistic director & principal conductor Ramon Ençinar
Size: 111 *Perfs:* 30-40 *Type/spec:* Symphony
Venues: National Theatre of São Carlos, Centro Cultural de Belém *Touring:* Germany, Spain
Comments: see also Opera & Choirs

Orquestra Nacional do Norte
Mosteiro de Paço de Sousa, 4560 **Penasiel**
Tel: 55-755 591 Fax: 55-755 591
conductor Ferreira Lobo
Size: 40 *Perfs:* 100 *Type/spec:* classical *Touring:* national
Comments: belongs to Regional Agency of Secretary of State for Culture – North

Orquestra Nacional do Porto
Oporto National Orchestra
Mosteiro de S Bento da Vitória, Rua São Bento da Vitória, 4050 **Porto**
Tel: 2-205 2132 Fax: 2-205 2111
artistic director Filipe Pires
Size: 52 *Perfs:* 100 *Type/spec:* 18th-20th century chamber music, chamber opera *Touring:* national *Comments:* government funded; recordings available

ROMANIA (+40)

Arad State Philharmonic – Arad
Piata George Enescu 1, 2900 **Arad**
Tel: 57-281 554 Fax: 57-280 519
director Dorin Frandes
Venues: capacity 520

Bacau State Philharmonic Mihail Jora – Bacau
St. Razboieni 22, 5500 **Bacau**
Tel: 34-113 545 Fax: 34-113 545
director Ovidiu Balan
Venues: capacity 400

Botosani State Philharmonic – Botosani
Blvd. Mihai Eminescu 72, 6800 **Botosani**
Tel: 31-516 510 Fax: 31-516 925
director Marieta Baciu
Venues: capacity 500

Brasov State Philharmonic George Dima – Brasov
str. Apollonia Hirscher 10, 2200 **Brasov**
Tel: 68-143 113 Fax: 68-150 960
Venues: capacity 412

Ensemble ARCHAEUS
c/o Romanian Composers and Musicologists Union, Calea Victoriei 141, Sector 1, 70149 **Bucharest**
Tel: 1-650 2838
Size: 7 *Type/spec:* contemporary

George Enescu State Philharmonic – Bucuresti
St Franklin 1-3, Sector 1, 79741 **Bucharest**
Tel: 1-614 4183 Fax: 1-312 2983
director Cristian Mandeal
Venues: capacity 814

Philarmonia
c/o Centrul de Cultura Tinerimea Româna, Str. Gutemberg 16, **Bucharest**
Fax: 1-312 1962
conductor Nicolae Iliescu
Type/spec: chamber string orchestra

Voces String Quartet
c/o Romanian Broadcasting Corporation, Str. General Berthelot 60-62, Sectorul 1, **Bucharest**
Tel: 1-222 5647 Fax: 1-312 1057
contact Bujor Prelipceanu

ARS NOVA Ensemble
c/o Academy of Music Gheorghe Dima, Str. I. C. Bratianu 25, 3400 **Cluj-Napoca**
Tel: 64-193 879
conductor Cornel Taranu
Type/spec: contemporary

Cluj-Napoca State Philharmonic 'Transilvania' – Cluj-Napoca
St Emanuel de Martonne 1, 3400 **Cluj-Napoca**
Tel: 64-430 063 Fax: 64-430 060
director Emil Simon
Venues: capacity 998

Constanta State Philharmonic – Constanta
Str. Mircea cel Batran 97, 8700 **Constanta**
Tel: 41-617 522 Fax: 41-619 906
director Radu Ciorei
Venues: capacity 504

Oltenia State Philharmonic – Craiova
Calea Unirii 22, 1100 **Craiova**
Tel: 51-412 334 Fax: 51-418 112
director Mihai Ungureanu
Venues: capacity 360

Iasi Philharmonic
Cuza Voda 29, 6600 **Iasi**
Tel: 32-212 620/114 601/112 100
Fax: 32-214 160
conductor Doru Morariu
Size: 70 *Type/spec:* religious and carols, vocal/symphonic

Moldova State Philharmonic – IASI
St Cuza Voda 29, 6600 **Iasi**
Tel: 32-114 601/112 100 Fax: 32-214 160
director Viorel Bujor Prelipceanu
Venues: capacity 220

Oradea State Philharmonic – Oradea
str. Romana 3, 3700 **Oradea**
Tel: 59-130 853 Fax: 59-431 740
director Romica Rîmbu
Venues: capacity 670

Ploiesti State Philharmonic Paul Constantinescu – Ploiesti
St Anton Pann 5, 2000 **Ploiesti**
Tel: 44-142 812 Fax: 44-115 841
director Virgil Manolache
Venues: capacity 361

Râmnicu Vâlcea State Philharmonic – Râmnicu Vâlcea
Str. Tudor Vladimirescu 72, **Râmnicu Vâlcea**
Tel: 50-732 956 Fax: 50-732 957
director Mihail Stefanescu

Satu Mare State Philharmonic Dinu Lipatti – Satu Mare
Piata Libertatii 8, 3900 **Satu Mare**
Tel: 61-712 666/739 404 Fax: 61-712 666
director Rudolf Fatyol
Venues: capacity 450

Sibiu State Philharmonic – Sibiu
St Filarmonicii 2, 2400 **Sibiu**
Tel: 69-433 506 Fax: 69-433 506
director Marian Didu
Venues: capacity 387

Banatul State Philharmonic – Timisoara
Bdul. C.D. Loga 2, 1900 **Timisoara**
Tel: 56-192 521 Fax: 56-192 521
director Remus Georgescu
Venues: capacity 1079

Tirgu-Mures State Philharmonic – Targu Mures
St George Enescu 2, 4300 **Tirgu Mures**
Tel: 65-162 548 Fax: 65-162 548
director Vasile Cazan
Venues: capacity 776

RUSSIA (+7)

Trio Clarte
Sonia Krivaya Str. 67, apt. 36, 454080 **Cheliabinsk**
Tel: 3512-349 034
Fax: 3512-335 322/331 766
E-Mail: clarte@unilib.chel.su
manager Olga Morozova
Size: 3 (permanent) *Type/spec:* chamber music of 20th C. *Venues:* Cheliabinsk Concert Hallall of Organ and Chamber Music 300, Concert Hall of Cheliabinsk Pictures Gallery 60, Chelibinsk State Academic Opera and Ballet Theatre 1000, Miass City Concert Hall 600, Cheliabinsk Institute of Culture and Arts: small concert hall 150, Shuvalov Concert Hall (Moscow) 150 *Touring:* national, Netherlands

Chamber Orchestra Archetto
57, Lomonosova Str, 620042 **Ekaterinburg**
E-Mail: stas@ese.mplik
director Roman Nikolaev; contact Julian Dan (tel: +1 212-740 2112 USA)

Chamber Orchestra B-A-C-H
13-A Lenin Street, 620219 **Ekaterinburg**
Tel: 3432-513 914 Fax: 3432-556 017
consultant manager Tatiana Kovaleva; general manager Elena Matveychuk
Size: 21 *Perfs:* 60-80 *Type/spec:* 18th-20th century classical music and commissions *Touring:* Russia, Ukraine, Italy, Switzerland, Austria

Symphony Academic Orchestra
Ul. Karla Libknechta 38-A, 620151 **Ekaterinburg**
Tel: 3432-515 683 Fax: 3432-544 468
conductor Dmitry Liss; director Koloturskу

Academic Bolshoi Concert Orchestra of Russian State Musical Centre of TV and Radio
M. Nikitskaya 24, 121810 **Moscow**
Tel: 095-222 0033

Chamber Orchestra Kremlin
Khoroshevskoe Shosse 56, kv 108, 123007 **Moscow**
Tel: 095-941 1617 Fax: 095-941 1617
Internet: www.ChamberOrchKremlin.com
E-Mail: music@glasnet.ru
music director Misha Rachlevsky
Type/spec: chamber *Touring:* USA, Europe, Far East
Comments: postal address: 30710 Red Maple Lane, Suite 17, Southfield, MI 48076, USA, Tel: +1 248-647 5355, Fax: +1 248-647 5718; recordings: Claves Records (Switzerland)

Ensemble XII Moscow
Ostochenka 12 K, **Moscow**
Tel: 095-205 6239 Fax: 095-205 6239
director Pia Siirala; musical director and conductor Lygia O'Riordan
Size: 18-24 *Perfs:* 60-65 *Type/spec:* String orchestra, repertoire spanning 4 Centuries *Touring:* Finland, UK, Germany, Austria, Hungary *Comments:* Postal address: PO BOX 289, Weybridge KT1 3WJ, UK – Ref account no ESB 194 (courier service Britain-Russia)

Moscow Philharmonic Symphony Orchestra
Tverskaya st. 31, 103050 **Moscow**
Tel: 095-229 4254
chief conductor Juri Simonow; general manager Anton Shershnew

Musica VIVA Academic Chamber Orchestra
Zhivopisnaya 4-3-27, 123103 **Moscow**
Tel: 095-197 3128

National Academic Orchestra of Folk Instruments of Russia
Tverskaya 31, 103050 **Moscow**
Tel: 095-299 4300

Russain State Symphony Orchestra of Culture Ministry of the Russian Federation
B. Zlatoustinski per. 8/7, 101000 **Moscow**
Tel: 095-925 8594

Russian National Orchestra
Bakhrushina 28, kv. 55, 113054 **Moscow**
Tel: 095-235 7745 Fax: 095-292 6511
conductor laureate Mikhail Pletnev; general manager Sergej Markov; music director & principal conductor Vladimir Spivakov; associate conductors Andrey Boreyko, Dmitri Liss, Robert Bachmann
Size: 105 *Touring:* Europe, USA
Comments: exclusive contract with Deutsche Grammophon; for further information also contact Russian Arts Foundation (q.v.)

Russian Philharmonia Symphony Orchestra
Sinfonitchesky Orkestr 'Russkaya Filarmonia'
Malaya Nikitskaya 22/24, 121812 **Moscow**
Tel: 095-290 1205 Fax: 095-290 1205
E-Mail: Fond@glasnet.ru
artistic director & chief conductor Alexandr Vedernikov; general director Sergei Smirnov
Size: 90 *Perfs:* 30-35 *Type/spec:* symphony, contemporary, film music *Venues:* Great Hall of the Conservatory 1600, Tchaikovsky Concert Hall 2200
Touring: Benelux, Italy, Greece

Russian Philharmonic Orchestra (TV-6 Moscow)
Malaya Nikitskaya st. 22/24, 121812 **Moscow**
Tel: 095-222 0788/0726
Fax: 095-290 1205
chief conductor Alexandr Vedernikov

Russian State Academic Chamber Vivaldi Orchestra
Kitaygorodsky pr 7, 4th floor, 103693 **Moscow**
Tel: 095-220 4568/972 3536 (home)
artistic director Svetlana Bezrodnaya

Russian State Symphony Orchestra of Cinema
Sretenka 4/1, 103045 **Moscow**
Tel: 095-924 5171

State Academic Orchestra of the Bolshoi Theatre
Theatralnaya pl. 1, 103009 **Moscow**
Tel: 095-292 0579
Fax: 095-292 9032
Bolshoi Theatre artistic director & general manager Vladimir Vassilyev; Bolshoi Theatre executive manager Vladimir Kokonin; Bolshoi Theatre orchestra's artistic director Petar Seranets; Bolshoi Theatre orchestra's deputy artistic director Mark Ermler
Size: 130 *Type/spec:* classical concerts, opera

State Academic Russian Concert Orchestra Boyan
Novoryazanskaya 38, Building 2, 107066 **Moscow**
Tel: 095-261 9258

State Academic Russian Orchestra im. N P Osipova
Tverskaya Ul. 31, 103050 **Moscow**
Tel: 095-299 4800 Fax: 095-200 5822
artistic director & chief conductor Nikolai Kalinin

State Academic Symphony Kapella of Russia
Pitanitskaya ul. 2, 113035 **Moscow**
Tel: 095-953 5194 Fax: 095-953 8996
chief conductor Valery Poljansky; general manager Alexander Shanin
Comments: recordings for Chandos label; managed by Sovinart (q.v.)

State Academic Symphony Orchestra
Spartakovskaya Square 1/2, 107082 **Moscow**
Tel: 095-261 9021
director Paul Kogan

State Academic Symphony Orchestra (GASO) of the Russian Federation
Bolshaya Nikitskaya ul. 13, 108871 **Moscow**
Tel: 095-229 7410/7469
chief conductor Yevgeni Svetlanov; manager Rumyantsev; inspector Vsevolod Chernysh
Comments: recordings for Japanese 'Canyon' label

State Brassband of Culture Ministry of the Russian Federation
Kasatkina 15, 129301 **Moscow**
Tel: 095-283 3674

State Chamber Orchestra
Tverskaya ul. 31, 103050 **Moscow**
Tel: 095-156 6075
chief conductor Konstantin Orbelian; general manager Evgeny Nepalo
Type/spec: chamber

State Chamber Orchestra of Jazz
Nizhnayaya Krasnselskaya 35, 107066 **Moscow**
Tel: 095-264 3674
director O. Lungstrem

State Symphony Kapella of Russia
Ul. Piatnitskaya 2, 113035 **Moscow**
Tel: 095-953 5194 Fax: 095-953 5194
artistic director & chief conductor Valery Polansky

State Tchaikovsky Bolshoi Symphony Orchestra
Malaya Nikitskaya Street 24, 121069 **Moscow**
Tel: 095-222 0024 Fax: 096-291 8243
artistic director & principal conductor Vladimir Fedoseev; manager Mikhail Katznelson
Comments: managed by Sovinart; see also Agents & Producers

Symphony Orchestra of Russia under Direction of Veronika Dudarova
Nezhdanova ul. 8/10, Building 2, 103009 **Moscow**
Tel: 095-299 6233 Fax: 095-299 6233
chief conductor Veronica Dudarova; general manager Alexander Mashkovich
Size: 120 *Venues:* Tchaikovsky Hall and Conservatoire
Touring: Germany, Sweden, Greece, North America
Comments: set up in 1991 with private sponsorship and support of Russian Composers Union; regular series of concerts at Tchaikovsky Hall and Conservatoire and has been participant in Tchaikovsky Competition; recordings for Olympia and Russian Disc label, notably first modern recording of Myaskovsky 6th Symphony

Folk Ensemble Krasota
Arts Center, 2 Pirogova ul., 630090 **Novosibirsk**
Tel: 3832-397 818/343 (3pm-9pm) Fax: 3832-302 237
Internet: www.nsu.ru/art_center
E-Mail: artcen@nsu.ru

Novosibirsk Philharmonic Orchestra
Spartak ul. 11, 630007 **Novosibirsk**
Tel: 3832-224 910/223 484 Fax: 3832-225 659
artistic director & principal conductor Arnold Katz
Touring: Spain ('99-2000) *Comments:* recordings on Sony label

State Symphony Orchestra of the Ministry of Culture – Republic of Karelia, The
Kirov ul. 12, 185035 **Petrozavodsk**
Tel: 814-74353/78103
artistic director & principal conductor Oleg Soldatov

Academic Simphony Orchestra of the Philharmonic St Petersburg
im. Dm. Shostakovich, Mikhaylovskaya ul. 2, 191011 **St Petersburg**
Tel: 812-311 7331 Fax: 812-311 2126
artistic director Alexandr Dmitriev

Ensemble of Winds Music and Chamber Choir
Naberezhnaya river Fontanka 41, 191011 **St Petersburg**
Tel: 812-110 4043 Fax: 812-311 2066
director Alexandre Stupnev
Comments: see also Choirs

Hermitage – St. Petersburg Philharmonic Orchestra
Nevsky pr. 31, 191011 **St Petersburg**
Tel: 812-311 8349 Fax: 812-311 8349
artistic director & principal conductor Yury Aliev

Orchestra of the Mariinsky Theatre St Petersburg
Teatralnaia pl. 1, 190000 **St Petersburg**
Tel: 812-114 4441/4424 Fax: 812-314 1744
artistic director and principal conductor Valery Gergeyev

St Petersburg Academic State Capella Orchestra
Moika nab 24, **St Petersburg**
Tel: 812-314 1073 Fax: 812-110 6913
chief conductor Alexander Chernishenko; manager Viatchaslav Glazunov
Size: 110 *Venues:* Capella Hall *Touring:* France, Switzerland
Comments: formerly Court Orchestra and re-established in 1991 with assistance of Mayor and Russian Government; recorded for several labels; regular series of concerts at Capella Hall and acted as orchestra for several competitions in Russia; notable recordings of contemporary music of W.European composers

St Petersburg Chamber Orchestra
Ul. Mikhailovskaya 2, 191011 **St Petersburg**
Tel: 812-311 7331 Fax: 812-311 2126
conductor Eduard Serov

St. Petersburg Military District Band
Liteiny pr. 26, 191028 **St Petersburg**
Tel: 812-272 8137 Fax: 812-529 8512
artistic director & principal conductor Col. Nilkolai Uschapovsky

St. Petersburg Mozarteum Choir and Chamber Orchestra
Liteiny pr. 20, 191028 **St Petersburg**
Tel: 812-110 4022/278 8661 Fax: 812-279 7486
artistic director & principal conductor Arkady Shteinlukht

St Petersburg Philharmonic Orchestra
Ul. Mikhailovskaya 2, 191011 **St Petersburg**
Tel: 812-311 7331 Fax: 812-311 2126
orchestra director Anton Getman; music director and principal conductor Yuri Temirkanov; associate principal conductor Mariss Jansons; orchestra manager Sergei Cherniadiev
Size: 105 *Type/spec:* Russian orchestral *Venues:* Philharmonic Hall: Big Hall 1300; Chamber Hall 400

St. Petersburg State Symphony Orchestra
Palace of Princes's Belosselsky Belozersky, Nevsky pr. 141, 191025 **St Petersburg**
Tel: 812-310 7080 Fax: 812-315 5010
artistic director & principal conductor Ravil' Martynov

State Symphony Orchestra of St. Petersburg
13th line V.O. 18, 199178 **St Petersburg**
Tel: 812-213 4103 Fax: 812-213 4704
artistic director & principal conductor Andrei Anikhanov

Symphony Orchestra of the Rimsky-Korsakov Musical College
Matveev per. 1a, 190121 **St Petersburg**
Tel: 812-114 1753 Fax: 812-552 4846
artistic director & principal conductor Algidras Paulavichius

Tchaikovsky Youth Orchestra
Nevsky pr. 86, 191025 **St Petersburg**
Tel: 812-275 1305 Fax: 812-275 1598
principal conductor Andrey Shevchuk
Comments: managed by STARLET Stage Business Agency

Young Virtuosos from St Petersburg
Basseynaya Street 77-2, 196211 **St Petersburg**
Fax: 812-352 3317
E-Mail: polina@irus.pmnet.spb.ru
director & conductor Olga Golota
Type/spec: chamber ensemble

National Symphony Orchestra of Bashkortostan
Sovetskaya st. 18 – 402, 450008 **Ufa**
Tel: 3472-510 039 Fax: 3472-510 095
artistic director & chief conductor Taghir Kamalov
Size: 180 *Perfs:* 60 *Type/spec:* symphony

Volgograd Philharmonic Orchestra
Chuikova ul., Central Concert Hall, **Volgograd**
Tel: 8442-632 424 Fax: 8442-366 487
principal conductor Edward Serov

Ensemble Balalaika
22-68 , Plekhanovskaya, 394030 **Voronezh**
Tel: 732-521 248 Fax: 502-200 2101
Internet: www.comch.ru/~bal/index.htm
director Yuriy Ivanov
Type/spec: from russian folk songs to classical music

SAN MARINO (+378)

Orchestra Sinfonica della Repubblica di San Marino
via Oddone Scarito n.33, **Borgo Maggiore** 47031
Tel: 903 002/902 002 Fax: 907 089
E-Mail: ims@omniway.sm
responsabile orchestra Prof. Italo Capicchioni
Size: 60 *Perfs:* 6 *Type/spec:* symphonic *Venues:* Teatri di San Marino 500 to 900

Musica Festival Orchestra
Via Elisabetta da Montefeltro 18, **Serravalle** 47899
Tel: 909 158/905 676 Fax: 909 158
direttore amministrativo Nadia Gatti; direttore musicale Orio Lucchi; president Leandro Maiani
Size: 35 + 10 *Type/spec:* Italian songs of the 50's
Touring: locally, Italy

SLOVAKIA (+421)

Many telephone and fax numbers in Slovakia are in the process of being changed. We have included all new numbers known at the time of going to print.

Cappella Istropolitana – Chamber Orchestra of Bratislava
Cappella Istropolitana – Komorny orchester mesta Bratislavy
Zidovska 17, 811 01 **Bratislava** 1
Tel: 7-5441 8506 Fax: 7-5441 8506
manager Karol Kopernicky

Slovak Chamber Orchestra
Slovensky komorny orchester
Medená 3, 816 01 **Bratislava** 1
Tel: 7-5443 3351/3353 Fax: 7-5443 3351/5956
artistic director Bohdan Warchal

Slovak Philharmonic Orchestra
Slovenská filharmónia
Medená 3, 816 01 **Bratislava** 1
Tel: 7-5443 3351/3353 Fax: 7-5443 5956
E-Mail: filharm@filharm.sk
director Ing. Jozef Tkácik; music director Ondrej Lenárd
Comments: includes: Slovak Chamber Orchestra, Slovak Philharmonic Choir, Musica Aeterna (early music ensemble), Moyzes Quartet

Slovak Radio Symphony Orchestra
Symfonicky orchester Slovenského rozhlasu
Mytná 1, PO Box 55, 811 05 **Bratislava** 1
Tel: 7-5727 3475 Fax: 7-5727 3386
Internet: www.slovakradio.sk/kultura.html
E-Mail: milos_jurkovic@slovakradio.sk
chief conductor Robert Stankovsky

State Philharmonic Kosice
Státna filharmónia Kosice
Dom umenia, Moyesova 66, 041 23 **Kosice**
Tel: 95-622 4514/4509
Fax: 95-622 4509/7216
Internet: www.sfk.sk
director Julius Klein; chief conductor Tomas Koutnik

Armonia Slovacca
Dolny Val 47, 011 28 **Zilina**
Tel: 89-48252 Fax: 89-626 972
E-Mail: ssz@isternet.sk
artistic director Ján Figura
Type/spec: Wind Nonet of Slovak Sinfonieta

Barock Quartet Zilina
Dolny Val 47, 011 28 **Zilina**
Tel: 89-48252 Fax: 89-626 972
E-Mail: ssz@isternet.sk

Slovak Sinfonietta of Zilina / State Chamber Orchestra of Zilina
Statny komornyorchester Zilina
Dolny Val 47, 011 28 **Zilina**
Tel: 89-620 256/007/979 Fax: 89-626 972
E-Mail: ssz@isternet.sk
chief conductor Leos Svárovsky; manager Vladimir Salaga; director Jozef Búda; music dramaturgist Elena Fillipi

Suchon Wind Quintet
Dolny Val 47, 011 28 **Zilina**
Tel: 89-48252 Fax: 89-626 972
E-Mail: ssz@isternet.sk
artistic director Ján Figura
Type/spec: Chamber Ensemble of Slovak Sinfonieta

SLOVENIA (+386)

Orchestra of the Slovene National Theatre Opera and Ballet Ljubljana
Orkester SNG Opera in Balet Ljubljana
Zupanciceva 1, 1000 **Ljubljana**
Tel: 61-125 4680/126 2178
Fax: 61-126 2249
managing director Dr Borut Smrekar
Comments: see also Dance, Drama and Opera

Slovenian Philharmonic
Slovenska Filharmonija
Kongresni trg 10, PO Box 156, 1000 **Ljubljana**
Tel: 61-213 554 Fax: 61-213 640
artistic director Marko Letonja; managing director Mojca Menart; artistic director of the choir Dr Mirko Cuderman
Size: 100 permanent *Perfs:* 70 (15 on tour) *Type/spec:* symphony *Venues:* Cankarjev dom, Slovenian Philharmonia *Touring:* national, international
Comments: concert subscription series with Cankarjev dom; recording for radio, tv and records; the orchestras also performs and records with its own professional choir: The Slovenian Chamber Choir; see also Choirs

Symphony Orchestra Radiotelevision Slovenia
Simfonicni Orkester RTV Slovenija
Tavcarjeva 17, 1550 **Ljubljana**
Tel: 61-175 2472 Fax: 61-175 2471

Orchestra of the Slovene National Theatre Maribor
Orkester Slovenskega Narodnega Gledalisca Maribor
Slovenska Ulica 27, 2000 **Maribor**
Tel: 62-22840 Fax: 62-228 4050
Internet: www.sng-mb.si
E-Mail: sng.maribor@sng-mb.si
general manager Blaz Rafolt
Comments: alternative E-mail: marketing.sng.maribor@sng-mb.si; see also Dance, Drama and Opera

SPAIN (+34)

Banda Sinfónica Municipal de Alicante
Padre Mariana 72 bajo, 03004 **Alicante**
Tel: 96-521 0154 Fax: 96-521 1010
director Bernabé Sanchis Sanz; sub-director Francisco Amat
Size: 53 *Perfs:* 90 *Type/spec:* band music *Venues:* Auditorio de la Esplanada (open air), Teatro Principal 800 *Touring:* regional

Jove Orquestra Sinfónica de Catalunya
Calabria 120, 08015 **Barcelona**
Tel: 97-353 2811 Fax: 97-353 2768
comision artística Jaume Cortadellas, Carles Riera; pr Carme Pollina; director orquesta Manuel Valdivieso
Size: 120 *Perfs:* 6-9 *Type/spec:* wide repertoire *Venues:* Auditorio Nacional de Catalunya *Touring:* Europe

Le Concert des Nations
Travesera de Gracia 18-20, 2°, 08021 **Barcelona**
Tel: 93-594 4760
Fax: 93-580 5606
E-Mail: 101617.3236@compuserve.com
director Jordi Savall; administrator Iréne Bloc
Size: 20-30 *Perfs:* 10
Type/spec: chamber orchestra; repertoire 17th, 18th, 19thC *Touring:* Germany, France, Portugal, Austria
Comments: recordings with Auvidis and Alia Vox

Orquesta de Cámara Teatre Lliure
Lliure Theatre Chamber Orchestra
Montseny 47, 08012 **Barcelona**
Tel: 93-218 9251 Fax: 93-237 1243
director musical Josep Pons; directors artístico Luis Vidal, Josep Pons, Jaume Cortadellas; relaciones públicas y prensa Marc Gall; manager Oriol Roch
Size: 20-30 *Perfs:* 30-40
Type/spec: 20th century, classical, contemporary
Venues: Teatre Lliure 300
Touring: national, Europe
Comments: recordings with Alia Vox and Harmonia Mundi, 11 records; see also Drama and Venues

Orquesta Sinfónica del Gran Teatre del Liceu
Gran Teatre del Liceu Symphony Orchestra
La Ramble 51-59, 08002 **Barcelona**
Tel: 93-485 9900 Fax: 93-485 9919
Internet: www.liceubarcelona.com
E-Mail: info@liceubarcelona.com
gerente Oriol Ponsa; director titular t.b.a.; director general Josep Caminal i Badia; director Bertrand de Villy
Size: 98 *Perfs:* 50
Type/spec: opera, ballet, concerts
Venues: Gran Teatre del Liceu
Touring: national
Comments: Titular orchestra of the Gran Teatre del Liceu; see also Venues

Orquestra de Cadaqués
Carrer dels Arcs 8, 1er 2°, 08002 **Barcelona**
Tel: 93-301 9555 Fax: 93-302 2670
Internet: www.trito.es
E-Mail: trito@bcn.servicom.es
director artístico Llorenç Caballero i Pàmies; manager María Pau Roca; director principal Gianandrea Noseda; directors principales invitados Sir Neville Marriner, G Rozhdestreusky
Size: 45 *Perfs:* 25
Type/spec: classical and opera
Touring: national, international
Comments: see also Festivals and Competitions

Orquestra de Cámbra Catalana (Orquesta de Cámara Catalana)
Gran de Sant Andreu 111, 08030 **Barcelona**
Tel: 93-212 4531/345 4392
Fax: 93-474 4903
director general y artístico Joan Pàmies; gerente Josep Pastor
Size: 15 strings plus wind and percussion according to programme *Perfs:* 25 *Type/spec:* all periods *Venues:* Casa de la Caritat, Barcelona (home venue) *Touring:* Spain, Europe *Comments:* season: Oct-May; funded by Ayuntamiento de Barcelona

Orquestra Simfònica de Barcelona i Nacional de Catalunya
Lepant 150, 08013 **Barcelona**
Tel: 93-247 9300 Fax: 93-247 9301
Internet: www.obc.es
E-Mail: informacio@obc.es
director administrativo Andreu Puig; director de recursos Victor Blanes; director técnico Abili Fort; director titular Lawrence Foster; principal director invitado Franz Paul Decker; prensa Marta Muntada
Size: 100 *Perfs:* 78 *Type/spec:* symphony, classical, chamber *Venues:* l'Auditori 1800, others 2300
Touring: Germany

Bilbo Orkestra Sinfonikoa
Bilbao Symphony Orchestra
Palacio Euskalouna, Obos, Av. Abandoibarra 4, 48011 **Bilbao**
Tel: 94-403 5205 Fax: 94-403 5115
director general Gorka Robles Alegría; director artístico Juan José Mena; pr Iñigo Zubizarreta
Size: 94 *Perfs:* 80 *Type/spec:* symphonic concerts, opera, zarzuela and educational concerts
Venues: Teatro Ayala 950, Teatro Arriaga 1327, Coliseo Albia 2000, Palacio Euskalduna 2250
Touring: Spain, Europe
Comments: resident orchestra in Palacio Euskalduna (q.v.), Tel: 94-403 5000

Orquesta de Córdoba
Avenida Gran Capitán 4, 2ª planta, 14008 **Córdoba**
Tel: 957-491 767/826 Fax: 957-491 837
gerente Alfonso Osuna; conductor Leo Brouwer
Size: 50 *Perfs:* 60 *Type/spec:* classical Spanish and contemporary music latin and opera/soundtracks
Venues: Gran Teatro de Córdoba 900
Touring: Spain, Europe, USA

Orquesta de Cámara de l'Empordà
c/ Sant Pau 6, 1°, 17600 **Figueres (Gerona)**
Tel: 972-670 790 Fax: 972-670 790
secretaria de dirección y jefe de programación Carmen Ramírez; director artístico Carles Coll i Costa; press officer Merce Cuartiella
Size: 13 *Perfs:* 120 *Type/spec:* chamber baroque to contemporary, pays special attention to Catalan composers *Venues:* Teatro El Jardí, Figueras 1065 (rehearsal venue)
Touring: Europe, Russia, Canary Islands, Philippines, Guam, China, Japan
Comments: regional & national funding

Moscow Virtuosi
Virtuosos de Moscú
Quinta del Principe 4, 33204 **Gijon**
Tel: 985-134 279 Fax: 985-134 279
Internet: www.moscowvirtuosi.com
E-Mail: orchestra@moscowvirtuosi.com
conductor Vladimir Spivakov; general manager Beatriz Montes
Size: 24 *Perfs:* 40-50 *Type/spec:* classical, romantic, modern *Venues:* Carnagie Hall, Concertgebauw, Teatro Colon, Palau de la Musica, Bolshoi Hall, Champs Elysee Teatre *Touring:* France, Russia, Spain, Germany, USA, Romania *Comments:* 25 CDs with BMG Classics

Orquesta Ciudad de Granada
Centro Cultural Manuel de Falla,
Paseo de los Mártires s/n, Alhambra, 18009 **Granada**
Tel: 958-220 022 Fax: 958-222 322
Internet: www.orquestaciudadgranada.es
E-Mail: ocg@orquestaciudadgranada.es
director artístico Josep Pons; jefe de prensa Pedro Consuegra; directora técnica Sara Terrés; jefe de producción Juan Carlos Cantudo; coordinadora de programación Pilar García
Size: 49 *Perfs:* 85 *Type/spec:* symphony, 18th-20th century, Spanish music, contemporary music *Venues:* Centro Cultural Manuel de Falla 1300 *Touring:* Spain, France *Comments:* resident orchestra of Centro Cultural Manuel de Falla; see also Venues

Orquesta Sinfónica de Galicia
Teatro de la Opera, Glorieta de América n° 3, 15004 **La Coruña**
Tel: 981-252 021 Fax: 981-277 499
E-Mail: osg@lcg.servicom.es
manager Enrique Rojas Guillén; musical adviser Victor Pablo Pérez
Size: 85 *Perfs:* 133 *Type/spec:* symphony – all repertoire, opera, ballet *Venues:* Teatro de la Opera 1750, Auditorio de Galicia (Santiago de Compostela)1000, Palacio de Congresos, Centro Cultural Caixa Vigo (Vigo) 1100, Centros Musicales y Salas de Conciertos (Lugo, Orense, Pontevedra, Ferrol), Teatro Rosalía de Castro 700
Touring: Spain, Germany
Comments: organise 'Festival de Musica de la Coruña', 'Ciclo de Grandes Conciertos de Palacio', 'Festival Mozart de la Coruña' (June) and 'Musica en el Rosalia' (Oct-May); management: Consorcio para la Promocion de la Musica; see also Festivals

Banda Municipal de La Laguna
Organismo Autónomo Musical,
Ayuntamiento de La Laguna, c/ Obispo Rey Redondo 1, 38201 **La Laguna (Tenerife)**
Tel: 922-601 173/257 333/601 124
Fax: 922-601 119
presidenta Carmen Rosa Marrero del Castillo; director musical José Antonio Díaz León
Size: 64 *Perfs:* 70 *Type/spec:* Zarzuela, Spanish music, classical, soundtracks for films *Venues:* Paraninfo Universidad La Laguna 800 *Touring:* Spain

Orquesta Clásica de La Laguna
Organismo Autónomo Musical,
Ayuntamiento de La Laguna (Cultura),
c/ Obispo Rey Redondo 1, 38201 **La Laguna (Tenerife)**
Tel: 922-601 173/257 333/601 124
Fax: 922-601 119
presidenta Carmen Rosa Marrero del Castello; directores Juan José Olives, Mark Peters
Size: 35 *Perfs:* 30 *Type/spec:* classical, early romantic, zarzuela, baroque, modern *Venues:* Paraninfo de la Universidad de la Laguna 800

Orquesta de Pulso y Púa
Organismo Autónomo Musical,
Ayuntamiento de La Laguna, c/ Obispo Rey Redondo 1, 38201 **La Laguna (Tenerife)**
Tel: 922-601 173/257 333/601 124
Fax: 922-601 119
director Silvestre Álvarez Alemán; presidenta Carmen Rosa Marrero del Castillo
Size: 26 *Perfs:* 50 *Type/spec:* popular and classical music, musica de plectro
Venues: Paraninfo Universidad La Laguna 800

Orquestra de Cambra de Lleida
c/ Valencia 35, 1°, 08430 **La Roca del Valles (Barcelona)**
Tel: 93-879 5097
conductor Josep Maria Sauret; administration Sole Ruiz
Size: 15-35 *Perfs:* 20 *Touring:* national

Orquesta Filarmónica de Gran Canaria
Bravo Murillo 21-23,
35003 **Las Palmas de Gran Canaria**
Tel: 928-321 747 Fax: 928-314 747
Internet: www.orfigc.com
E-Mail: orfigc@orfigc.com
gerente Juan Antonio González Ojellón; secretaria técnica Marta Padilla Postigo; asesor musical y director principal Adrian Leaper; coordinador artístico Manuel Benitez González
Size: 90 *Perfs:* 40 *Type/spec:* symphony *Venues:* Auditorio Alfredo Kraus de Las Palmas de Gran Canarias 1700 *Touring:* Spain, Lisbon *Comments:* forms part of Fundación Orquesta Filarmónica de Gran Canaria; organises Ciclo de Conciertos Escolares para Niños y Jovenes; see Promoters

Orquesta Clásica de Madrid
c/ de las Cruces 6, bajo G, 28230 **Las Rozas (Madrid)**
Tel: 91-636 1562/1493 Fax: 91-637 6504
E-Mail: j.c.arderius@jet.es
director Ignacio Yepes; gerente Juan Carlos Arderius; coordinación Vicente Espinoza, Salvador Tudela
Size: 44 *Perfs:* 20-30 *Type/spec:* classical baroque, contemporary for classical orchestra *Venues:* Auditorio Nacional 2292 *Touring:* national *Comments:* dependent on Orquesta Nacional de España

Orquesta de Cámara de León 'Odón Alonso'
Avenida de San Mamés 3, Portal I 7° C,
24007 **León**
Tel: 987-227 742
secretario general directivo y presidente José Rodriguez Montero; director musical Dorel Murgu
Size: 68 *Perfs:* 22 *Type/spec:* classical *Venues:* Teatro Emperador, Hostal San Marcos & Cathedral (León)
Touring: national *Comments:* provincial, regional and municipal funding

Arsis Camera y Cuarteto 'Manuel de Falla'
c/ Suecia 53, 1° Derecha, 28022 **Madrid**
Tel: 91-775 6609/609-733 542
Fax: 91-775 6609
artistic director Adolfo Garcés
Size: varies *Perfs:* 50 *Type/spec:* string quartet, wind quintet, quartet 'Manuel de Falla' (clarinet quartet), playing classical and contemporary music
Venues: Auditorio Nacional 2193
Touring: South America, Europe

Banda Sinfónica Municipal de Madrid
Avda. de Portugal s/n, Pabellón 12, 28011 **Madrid**
Tel: 91-479 0462/526 0699 Fax: 91-526 1219
director Juan Foriscot Rìba; secretary administration Consuelo Sanchez; secretary direction Aurora San Miguel

Joven Orquesta Nacional de España (JONDE)
Auditorio Nacional, c/ Príncipe de Vergara 146, 28002 **Madrid**
Tel: 91-337 0270/1 Fax: 91-337 0246
E-Mail: jonde@sarenet.es
director artístico Llorenç Caballero; gerente Emilio Sáenz de Ormijana
Size: ranging from chamber to full orchestra (max.115)
Perfs: 30-40 *Type/spec:* classical and contemporary
Venues: Auditorio Nacional de Música 2280 *Touring:* Spain, Europe *Comments:* supported by INAEM (Instituto Nacional de las Artes Escenicas y de la Musica Ministerio de Educación y Cultura); recordings available; see also Venues (Auditorio Nacional)

Orquesta Sinfónica de Madrid
c/ Alcalá 21, 11 Izda, 28014 **Madrid**
Tel: 91-532 1503 Fax: 91-532 5364
presidente Pedro González Hernández; tesorero Rafael Angel Navarro; secretario Enrique de Cabo
Size: 99 *Perfs:* 100 *Type/spec:* opera, ballet zarzuela, concerts, recording *Venues:* Auditorio Nacional de Musica 2293, Teatro Real 1800
Comments: accompanying orchestra at the Teatro Real; funded by Fundacion Teatro Lirico

Orquesta Sinfónica y Coro de la Radiotelevisión Española
Joaquín Costa 43, 28002 **Madrid**
Tel: 91-581 7211 Fax: 91-581 7219
Internet: www.rtve.es
E-Mail: orquesta.ep@rtve.es
director titular de la orquesta Enrique García Asensio; director del coro Laszlo Heltay
Size: 110 *Perfs:* 44 + 15 special concerts & festivals
Type/spec: classical to contemporary, especially lesser-known works *Venues:* Teatro Monumental 1800 (managed by the orchestra)
Comments: includes choir (Coro de la Radiotelevision Española); venue address: Atocha, 65, Tel: 91-429 1281; see also TV, Radio and Choirs

Orquesta y Coro de la Comunidad de Madrid
Paseo de la Castellana 101, 28046 **Madrid**
Tel: 91-556 2361/2594 Fax: 91-556 2905
E-Mail: orq-coro-madrid@mad.servicom.es
director general Jorge Culla; director titular Miguel Groba Groba; coordinadora Carmen Lope
Size: 73 (42 strings) *Type/spec:* symphony, baroque to 20th century including new works and commissions from regional government, Zarzuela *Venues:* Auditorio Nacional 2193/698, Teatro de la Zarzuela 1200, Teatro Real 1600 *Comments:* receives funding from Comunidad de Madrid (regional government); moving premises in 2000; new address: c/ Mar Caspio s/n, Jardin Isabel Clara Eugenia, Madrid 28003, Tel: 91-381 6813/7278

Orquesta y Coro Nacionales de España
National Orchestra and Chorus of Spain
Auditorio Nacional de Música, Principe de Vergara 146, 28002 **Madrid**
Tel: 91-337 0264/59 (orchestra)/26/27 (choir)
Fax: 91-563 2907
Internet: www.orquestanacional.mcu.es
E-Mail: ocne@indem.mcu.es
managing director Alvaro León Ara; director coro Rainer Steubing-Negenborn; emeritus director Rafael Frühbeck de Burgos
Size: orch: 124; chorus: 112 *Perfs:* 100 *Type/spec:* symphony orchestra *Venues:* Auditorio Nacional de Música 2280 *Touring:* Spain, Europe, South America
Comments: Ciclo de Cámara y Polifonía (chamber music series): Oct to June, incl recitals, vocal and instrumental music; alternative Internet: www.coronacional.mcu.es; see also Festivals and Venues

Plural Ensemble
Plaza Gabriel Miró 1, 4° C, 28005 **Madrid**
E-Mail: veramoore@mixmail.com
contact Vera Moreno, Fabián Panisello
Type/spec: from soloists to chamber ensemble, 20th C. music, emphasis on Spanish contemporary composers

Orquesta Ciudad de Málaga
San Juan de Letrán 4 y 6, 2°C, 29012 **Málaga**
Tel: 952-229 562/222 805 Fax: 952-222 9599
gerente Juan Carlos Ramírez Aguilar
Size: 90 *Perfs:* 100 *Type/spec:* symphony, classical to contemporary, especially Spanish *Venues:* Teatro Municipal Miguel de Cervantes 1057

Orquesta de Jóvenes Región de Murcia
Auditorio y Centro de Congresos,
Av Primero de Mayo s/n, 30006 **Murcia**
Tel: 968-341 060 Fax: 968-342 477
Internet: www.auditoriomurcia.org
E-Mail: ojrm@auditoriomurcia.org
director Cesar J. Álvarez; coordinador Juan José Carmona López
Size: 87 *Perfs:* 20-25 *Type/spec:* chamber, 18th-20th century, baroque, symphony *Venues:* Sala A: Narciso Jepes 1800, Sala B: Sala de Camara 469 *Touring:* Auditorio Centro de Congresos Ciudad de Murcia 1838
Comments: funded by regional government: Region de Murcia Consejería de Cultura y Educación, Dirección General de Cultura

Orquesta Sinfónica del Principado de Asturias
Plaza Corrada del Obispo s/n, 33003 **Oviedo**
Tel: 98-521 0201 Fax: 98-522 9370
Internet: www.orfesed.com/ospa/ospa.htm
E-Mail: ospa@edecnet.com
gerente Immaculada Quintanal; director artístico Maximiano Valdés
Size: 69 *Perfs:* 100 *Type/spec:* symphony, opera

Orquesta Sinfónica de Baleares Ciutat de Palma
City of Palma Symphony Orchestra, Baleares
C/ Vicente Juan Rosselló 22B, 07013 **Palma de Mallorca**
Tel: 971-287 565 Fax: 971-287 758
director Salvador Brotons; administrador Mariano Isasi; gerente Sebastián Roig
Size: 67 *Perfs:* 60 *Type/spec:* symphonic orchestra, baroque, classical, symphony, contemporary *Venues:* Auditorium de Palma 1800, Teatro Principal de Palma 1100, Teatro Principal de Mahón 1000 *Touring:* Spain
Comments: organise festival of classical music 'Castell de Bellver'; see also Festivals

Orquesta Pablo Sarasate
Sandoval 6, 1° izq, 31002 **Pamplona**
Tel: 948-229 217 Fax: 948-211 948
E-Mail: pablosarasate@mx3.redestb.es
administración Ricardo Salcedo Bienzobas; presidenta María Jesús Artaiz; producción José Montes; director titular Ernest Martínez-Izquierdo; gerente Joan Oller
Size: 36 *Perfs:* 64 *Type/spec:* classical *Venues:* Teatro Gayarre 1060 *Touring:* national

Orquesta Sinfónica del Vallés
Valles Symphonic Orchestra
c/ Narcis Giralt 40, 08202 **Sabadell (Barcelona)**
Tel: 93-727 0300 Fax: 93-727 2228
Internet: www.osv.sumi.es
E-Mail: osv@sumi.es
presidente Albert Bardolet; director comercial Teresa Serra; direcor artístico Salvador Brotons
Size: 60 *Perfs:* 95 (80 symphony concerts + 15 opera)
Type/spec: symphony, 19th C and popular symphonic innovations *Venues:* Teatro Municipal la Farándula de Sabadell 1103 *Touring:* Catalonia, South of France
Comments: 80% self-financed

Orquesta Sinfónica de Euskadi
Basque National Orchestra
Paseo de Miramón 124, 20014 **San Sebastian**
Tel: 943-308 332/372 Fax: 943-308 324
Internet: www.orquestadeeuskadi.es
E-Mail: artistas@orquestadeeuskadi.es
director general Germán Ormazabal Artolazabal; intendente Jesús Aguirre Lazcano; administrador José Antonio Bueno Macho; press office Miren Elósegui Larrañeta; dirección musical Gilbert Varga, Mario Venzago
Size: 85 *Perfs:* 100 *Type/spec:* all types symphonic repertoire *Venues:* Auditorio Kursaal 1850, Teatro Gayarre (Pamplona) 1050, Palacio Euskalduna 2250, Teatro Principal (Vitoria) 1050 *Touring:* national, South America *Comments:* have new CDs

Orquesta Sinfónica de Tenerife
Tenerife Symphony Orchestra
Plaza de España 1, 38001 **Santa Cruz de Tenerife**
Tel: 922-239 801 Fax: 922-239 617
Internet: www.cabtfe.es/ost
E-Mail: ost@cabtfe.es
gerente Carmen Kemper; director titular Victor Pablo Perez; presidenta Dulce Xerach Perez
Size: 83 *Perfs:* 60 *Type/spec:* symphony *Venues:* Teatro Guimerá 900, Sala Teobaldo Power 1100, Paraninfo Universitario 580, Auditorio de El Sauzal 400 *Touring:* Spain *Comments:* CDs available

Real Filarmonia de Galica
Auditorio de Galicia, Avda Burgo das Nacions s/n, 15705 **Santiago de Compostela (La Coruna)**
Tel: 981-573 855 Fax: 981-572 292
Internet: www.audigal.es
E-Mail: info@audigal.es
director titular Helmut Rilling; director segundo Maximino Zumalave
Size: 39 *Perfs:* 75 *Type/spec:* chamber music, classical *Venues:* Auditorio de Galicia: Sala Brage 1000, Sala Mozart 320 *Touring:* Germany, Austria, Spain *Comments:* funded by regional government; resident orchestra at Auditorio de Galicia; CD recordings with Hanssler Classic

Orquesta Joven de Andalucía
San Luis 37, 41033 **Sevilla**
Tel: 95-490 1493/1296 Fax: 95-490 3600
Internet: www.arrakis.es/~rafaa
E-Mail: rafaa@arrakis.es
gerencia May Silva; director artístico Juan de Udaeta; coordinación Begoña Madruga; secretaria Esther Duque; producción Rafaél Villareal
Size: 112 *Perfs:* 9-15 *Type/spec:* symphonic orchestra 19th-20th C. *Touring:* national

Real Orquesta Sinfónica de Sevilla
Imagen 9, 2° dcha., 41003 **Sevilla**
Tel: 95-456 1536 Fax: 95-456 1888
Internet: www.rossevilla.com
E-Mail: info@rossevilla.com
director gerente Francisco José Senra Lazo; director artístico y títular Klaus Weise; director técnico José Manuel Delgado Rodríguez
Size: 103 *Perfs:* 100 *Type/spec:* symphony, opera, ballet, lyric *Venues:* Sala Apolo 807, Teatro de la Maestranza 1800, Paseo de Cristobal Colón, Sevilla *Touring:* Germany, South America *Comments:* organises fortnightly chamber concerts with soloists from the orchestra and with the new chamber orchestra of The Royal Seville Symphony Orchestra

Concento Musical Capella Bydgostiensis
c/o Arte 4, T4 S.A., c/ Real 19,
28250 **Torrelodones (Madrid)**
Tel: 91-859 3962/607-745 423 (mobile) Fax: 91-859 4637
Internet: www.greencom.net/arte4
E-Mail: arte4@greencom.net
producción M Fueyo, M Torrellas, A Sánchez; director Germán Torrellas
Size: 30 + 4-6 soloists + 24 choir *Perfs:* 10 *Type/spec:* classical orchestra with soloists and choir; repertoire Spanish XVIII century music and XVIII century oratoria *Comments:* managed by: Arte 4, T4 S.A. (q.v.)

Collegium Instrumentale
Palau de la Música de Valencia,
Paseo de la Alameda 30, 46023 **Valencia**
Tel: 96-337 5020 Fax: 96-337 1521
Internet: www.palauvalencia.com
E-Mail: palaudelamusica@resone.es
direction Franco Parejo, Vicente Balaguer; conductor Felix Ayo
Type/spec: chamber *Venues:* Palau de la Musica de Valencia *Touring:* national, Europe

Orquesta de Valencia
Palau de la Música, Paseo de la Alameda 30, 46023 **Valencia**
Tel: 96-337 5020
Fax: 96-337 1521 (prensa)/0988 (direccion)
Internet: www.palauvalencia.com
E-Mail: palaudelamusica@resone.es
presidenta Irene Beneyto; director Miguel Ángel Gómez Martínez; subdirector Alfred Pascual; secretario técnico Francisco Lorenzo
Size: 97-100 *Perfs:* 50 *Type/spec:* symphony, chamber, opera in concert *Venues:* Palau de la Música 1793 *Touring:* Germany, Spain *Comments:* home orchestra of Palau de la Música; see also Venues & Promoters

Orquesta Sinfónica de Castilla y León
Symphony Orchestra of Castille and Leon
c/ Santiago 19, 2°A, 47001 **Valladolid**
Tel: 983-370 076 Fax: 983-373 275
gerente Carlos Rubio; director Max Bragado Darman
Size: 74 *Perfs:* 70-75 *Venues:* Teatro Carrión 1000

Grupo Enigma Orquesta de Cámara del Auditorio de Zaragoza
Auditorio-Palacio de Congresos, c/ Eduardo Ibarra 3, 50009 **Zaragoza**
Tel: 976-721 300 ext 62
Fax: 976-350 514
E-Mail: a.dumall@teleline.es
director titular Juan José Olives; delegado orquesta Alejandro Dumall; director del auditorio de Zaragoza Miguel Ángel Tapia
Size: 15-37 *Perfs:* 15 *Type/spec:* mainly 20th century music and also other centuries
Venues: Sala Luis Galve del Auditorio de Zaragoza 400, Sala Mozart del Auditorio de Zaragoza 1900
Touring: Spain *Comments:* resident orchestra of the Auditorio; specially for touring; see also Venues

SWEDEN (+46)

Stockholm Sinfonietta
Belevägen 10, 182 64 **Djursholm**
Tel: 8-755 5520/708 493 312 (mobile)
Fax: 8-755 5562
Internet: www.sinfonietta.a.se
E-Mail: kimby@sinfonietta.a.se
managing director Anders Kimby; manager Carl-Gohan Norden
Size: 35-40 *Perfs:* 40 *Type/spec:* from baroque to contemporary *Touring:* Europe *Comments:* Stockholm Sinfonietta Festival: 15 concerts at the house of Nobility (Riddarhuset); see also Festivals

DalaSinfoniettan
Box 275, 791 26 **Falun**
Tel: 23-18250 Fax: 23-13540
E-Mail: dalasinfoniettan@musikedalarna.se
general manager Håkan Ivarson
Size: 20 *Perfs:* 50-60 *Type/spec:* classical
Venues: Kristinehallen 520, also various other in the area
Comments: visiting address: Nybrogatan 12, 79126 Falun

Gävle Symfoniorkester
Box 1071, 801 34 **Gävle**
Tel: 26-172 930 Fax: 26-172 935
Internet: www.gavle.se/symfoniorkester
E-Mail: gavle.symfoniorkester@gavle.se
general manager Haukur F. Hannesson; chief conductor Carlos Spierer
Size: 52 musicians *Perfs:* 90 *Type/spec:* symphony
Venues: Gävle Konserthus 820 *Touring:* Holland, South America

Bohuslän Big Band
c/o Stiftelsen Musik i Väst , PO Box 3066, 400 10 **Göteborg**
Tel: 31-102 100 Fax: 31-102 101
Internet: www.miv.se
E-Mail: bbb@miv.se
manager Göran Levin
Size: 16 *Perfs:* 100 *Type/spec:* big band jazz *Touring:* mainly Scandinavia *Comments:* CDs available; see also Promoters (Stiftelsen Musik i Väst)

Göteborgs Symfoniker
Göteborg Symphony Orchestra
Götaplatsen, 412 56 **Göteborg**
Tel: 31-615 300
Fax: 31-203 502/204 065
Internet: www.goteborgssymfoniker.com
E-Mail: info@goteborgs-konsert.se
general manager Sture Carlsson; chief conductor Neeme Järvi; recordings Lennart Dehn; orchestra manager Josef Rhedin; artistic manager Karin Tufvresson Hjörne; assistant planning manager Katarina Danielsson; administrative manager Maj Ahlqvist; tours & projects Lars Nyström; marketing manager Ulf Olsson
Size: 108 *Perfs:* 60 (35 different programmes)
Type/spec: symphonic repertoire, especially Nordic
Venues: Stora Salen 1286, Stenhammarsalen 402
Touring: Switzerland, Austria, Italy, Germany, USA
Comments: recording for DG; alternative Internet: www.goteborgs-konsert.se

Stockholm Baroque Orchestra
c/o Double Agent artist management, Aprikosgatan 29, 165 60 **Hässelby**
Tel: 8-471 9604 Fax: 8-471 9604
E-Mail: ann-charlotte.hell@swipnet.se
contact Ann-Charlotte Hell
Size: 6-30 *Perfs:* 15 *Type/spec:* chamber orchestra: baroque-Viennese classics

Helsingborgs Symfoniorkester
Helsingborg Symphony Orchestra
Konserthuset, 252 21 **Helsingborg**
Tel: 42-176 500 Fax: 42-123 197
Internet: www.helsingborg.se/hbg-symfoni
E-Mail: symfoniorkestern@helsingborg.se
manager Stefan Sköld; chief conductor t.b.a.; information, press & pr officer Inger Munck; orchestral manager Hans Bodin
Size: 52 *Perfs:* 60-70 *Type/spec:* symphonic music
Venues: Konserthuset 900, Halmstad Teater 950, Växjo Konserthus 800 *Touring:* Salzburg, Germany

Värmlands Sinfonietta
Alvgatan 49, 652 30 **Karlstad**
Tel: 54-140 840 Fax: 54-100 533
Internet: www.musikteaternsvarmland.se
E-Mail: musikteatern@altaskop.net
gral manager Hans Hiort; music dir. Ole Wiggo Bang
Size: 30 *Perfs:* 50 opera + 30 concerts *Type/spec:* classical, opera *Venues:* Karlstad Teater 381 *Touring:* Sweden, Norway, Denmark

Östgöta Winds Symphony
Box 140, 581 02 **Linköping**
Tel: 13-312 950 Fax: 13-122 640
E-Mail: www.ostgotamusiken.se
manager Perolow Pell
Size: 21 *Type/spec:* wind chamber repertoire, wind symphonic repertoire, new music *Venues:* Linköping Concert Hall 1200 *Comments:* see also Promoters (Stiftelsen Östgötamusikern)

Malmö Symfoni Orkester AB
205 80 **Malmö**
Tel: 40-343 510 Fax: 40-611 7505
orchestra manager Jim Lindeborg; program manager Anders Franzén
Size: 86 *Type/spec:* symphonic repertoire
Venues: Concert Hall 1280

Norrköpings Symfoniorkester
Box 2144, 600 02 **Norrköping**
Tel: 11-155 150/100 (tickets)
Fax: 11-184 721/155 155/074 (tickets)
Internet: www.symfonikerna.com
E-Mail: symfoniorkester@son.norrkoping.se
director Saga Broström; chief conductor Ole Kristian Ruud; information manager Agneta Lundgren; programming director Stig Jacobsson; artistic administrator Carina Eklöf
Size: 87 *Perfs:* 50 + school concerts *Venues:* Louis de Geer 1300 *Touring:* Scandinavia, Germany

Svenska Kammarorkestern
Swedish Chamber Orchestra
Box 335, 701 46 **Örebro**
Tel: 19-766 6211 Fax: 19-766 6213
Internet: www.srk.se/oreboro/
E-Mail: info@orebromusik.t.se
general manager Benny Marcel; orchestral manager & aritistic director Gregor Zubicky
Size: 40 *Perfs:* 100 *Type/spec:* chamber orchestra repertoire *Venues:* Örebro Konserthus 724
Touring: Europe, Asia, USA

Camerata Roman
Box 14, 572 21 **Oskarshamn**
Tel: 491-10667 Fax: 491-77915
Internet: www13.calypso.net/lansmusiken
E-Mail: camerata@lansmusiken.h.se
director Kjell Lindstroem; manager Per-Göran Olsson
Size: 15 *Perfs:* 80 *Type/spec:* string, orchestra, chamber
Venues: Konserthallen 350 *Touring:* England, Spain, Nordic countries

Kammarensemblen Stockholm
Kindstugatan 18 N.B., 111 33 **Stockholm**
Tel: 8-202 449 Fax: 8-202 449
executive director Ivo Nilsson; admin. Daniel Nelson
Size: 18 *Perfs:* 27 *Type/spec:* 20th century chamber music, mostly Nordic *Touring:* Scandanavia, Huddersfield Festival – UK
Comments: recordings available

Kroumata
St Eriksgatan 82, 113 62 **Stockholm**
Tel: 8-5454 1580 Fax: 8-5454 1595
Internet: srk.se/kroumata/
E-Mail: gunilla.teikmans@kroumata.srk.se
contact Leif Karlsson
Size: 6 *Perfs:* 6 *Type/spec:* percussion ensemble, chamber music with percussion *Touring:* worldwide

Kungliga Hovkapellet
Royal Swedish Opera Orchestra
Box 16094, 103 22 **Stockholm**
Tel: 8-791 4300 Fax: 8-791 4403
general director Bengt Hall; chief conductor Leif Segerstam; marketing director t.b.a.; press officer Staffan Carlweitz; orchestra manager Anders Johansson
Size: 112 *Perfs:* 250 *Type/spec:* 16-20thC chamber music
Venues: Kungliga Operan: main stage 1100
Touring: Sweden, Berlin, Japan, USA
Comments: also perform Symphony concerts

Opening doors 2

In the Nouvel-House of Lucerne, the Luzerner Sinfonieorchester is presenting a wide range of concerts with contemporary as well as classical music.

Chief Conductor: Jonathan Nott

For information please contact:

http://www.sinfonieorchester.ch
E-mail. info@sinfonieorchester.ch
Tel. ++41 (0)41 210 34 87

kammerorchesterbasel

Saison 1999/2000 und 2000/2001

Dirigenten:	Christopher Hogwood Umberto Benedetti Michelangeli Giovanni Antonini Philippe Jordan Ton Koopman
Solisten:	Thomas Demenga Robert Levin Giuliano Carmignola Raphael Oleg Pieter Wispelwey Christophe Coin u.a.

"Sprühend vor Energie" Neue Zürcher Zeitung

Repertoire: Barock, Klassik und (klassische) Moderne

Management: Christoph Müller, Byfangweg 22, CH-4051 Basel,
Tel. 0041 61 273 52 52, Fax 0041 61 273 52 53,
mail@kammerorchesterbasel.ch, www.kammerorchesterbasel.ch

Ticket-Service:
Musik Wyler, Schneidergassse 26, 4051 Basel, Tel. 0041 61 261 90 25

Sinfonietta de Lausanne

Artistic and music director
Jean Marc Grob

The leading "Young professional"
Swiss symphony orchestra.

Performs repertoire from 18th to the 21st century with conductors and soloists: Ferdinand Leitner, Jean Claude Casadesus, Heinz Holliger, Michel Corboz, Emmanuel Krivinc, Louis Langrée, Pierre Amoyal, Maxence Larrieu, Ghena Dimitrova, Julia Miguenes, Barbara Hendricks, Simon Estes, José van Dam.

Accompanies: Ballet, Jazz, Opera and Film.

Over 50 concerts a year at leading Swiss festivals and venues.

Own series of concerts promoted at the Métropole concert hall and Paderewski concert hall in Lausanne.

Regular guest orchestra at the Lausanne Opera House and Festival of Avenches (CH).

Touring: Milan, Florence, Besançon, Brussels, London and Izmir.

Discography: more than 20 recordings

Rehearsal of *Nabuco*

Information and enquiries about concert and touring availability:

Sinfonietta de Lausanne
Avenue du Grammont 11 bis
CH 1007 LAUSANNE
Tel: 41 21 616 71 35
Fax: 41 21 616 71 36

http://www.regart.ch/sinfonietta

Philharmonic Big Band
Box 7083, 103 87 **Stockholm**
Tel: 8-786 0200 Fax: 8-791 7330
contact Lars Hammarteg
Size: 20 *Type/spec:* modern big band music
Touring: national and international

Royal Stockholm Philharmonic Orchestra
Stockholm Concert Hall Foundation, PO Box 7083, 103 87 **Stockholm**
Tel: 8-786 0200 Fax: 8-791 7330
Internet: www.konserthuset.se
executive and artistic director Åse Hedström; planning director Mats Engström; orchestra manager Jan-Olav Wedin; finance director Rolf Österholm; marketing director Peter Schéle
Size: 106 *Perfs:* 90
Type/spec: symphony *Venues:* Concert Main Hall 1800, Grünewald Saalen 460 *Touring:* Europe
Comments: concert series; annual composer festival; also recording with Andrew Davis for Finlandia Records (subsidiary of Warner); recording with EMI Virgin Classics; plays annually (Dec) at the Nobel Prize Ceremony

Sveriges Radios Symfoniorkester
Swedish Radio Symphony Orchestra
Swedish Broadcasting Corporation, 105 10 **Stockholm**
Tel: 8-784 5000 Fax: 8-667 3283
Internet: www.sr.se/berwaldhallen
E-Mail: orkestern@bwh.sr.se
general manager Michael Tydén; artist & programme manager Lennart Stenkvist; principal conductor Evgeny Svetlanov (from autumn 2000: Manfred Honeck); touring manager Eva Bjurenhed; marketing manager Karen Adolfsson
Size: 103 *Perfs:* 80 *Type/spec:* symphony orchestra playing mainly classical *Venues:* Berwald Hall 1300
Touring: national & international
Comments: Recording with Sony Classical, Hyperion BIS and Caprice

Sundsvall Chamber Orchestra
Box 105, 851 03 **Sundsvall**
Tel: 60-184 881 Fax: 60-122 075
general manager Jan Wolf-Watz
Size: 35 *Type/spec:* chamber *Comments:* apart from regular concerts, emphasis has always been on active education and community work as well as promotion of new music

Umeå Symphony Orchestra
Umeå Symfoniorkester
PO Box 360, 901 08 **Umeå**
Tel: 90-154 300 Fax: 90-126 845
Internet: www.vbm.se
E-Mail: info@vbm.se
leader Jan Bjøranger; principal conductor Roy Goodman; personal manager Stefan Thysk
Size: 50 *Perfs:* 100 *Type/spec:* opera, chamber & symphony *Venues:* Norrlandsoperan 250-300
Touring: mostly regional/national
Comments: recordings available

Philharmonic Light Orchestra
Klockvägen 5, 194 39 **Uppl. Väsby**
Tel: 8-5903 1883
founder & conductor Lars Almgren
Size: 10-25 *Perfs:* 20 *Type/spec:* classical, light music
Comments: 4 recordings available on Bluebell

Uppsala Kammarorkester
Uppsala Chamber Orchestra
PO Box 3106, 750 03 **Uppsala**
Tel: 18-171 920 Fax: 18-171 930
Internet: www.miu.se
E-Mail: nos@miu.se
manager Nils Olof Sondell; artistic director Göran Kåver
Size: 40 *Perfs:* 20 *Type/spec:* classical
Venues: Uppsala University 1800

Västras Sinfonietta
c/o Västmanlandsmusiken, Hässlö Park, 721 31 **Västras**
Tel: 21-800 800 Fax: 21-800 801
manager Håkan Wikström
Size: 30 *Perfs:* 25
Type/spec: classical and modern
Venues: Västeras Konsertsal 913

Musica Vitae Chamber Orchestra
Villan-Kungsgatan 29, 352 33 **Växjö**
Tel: 470-18413/14/16
Fax: 470-39379
Internet: www.srk.se/musicavitae
E-Mail: musicavitae@mailbox.calypso.net
orchestra manager Thomas Liljeholm; producer Staffan Langemark; artistic director Peter Csaba
Size: 15 string musicians *Perfs:* 75-80
Type/spec: from renaissance to contemporary and new works *Touring:* mainly Sweden
Comments: recordings available on Swedish labels Caprice, Chamber Sound, Bis; organizing chamber music festival for youth aged 15-25 in May /June 2000

SWITZERLAND (+41)

Aargauer Symphonie-Orchester
Hans der Musik, Gönhardweg 32, 5000 **Aarau**
Tel: 62-822 4868 Fax: 62-822 4869
Geschäftsführung Monika Jürgbarth; Musikalische Leitung Räto Tschupp; President Dr. Stephan Bieri
Size: 60 *Perfs:* 22 *Type/spec:* symphonic *Venues:* Saalbau, Aarau 400 *Touring:* Switzerland

basel sinfonietta
Postfach 2224, 4002 **Basel**
Tel: 61-335 5415 Fax: 61-335 5535
Internet: www.baselsinfonietta.ch
E-Mail: mail@baselsinfonietta.ch
Geschäftsleitung Thomas Nidecker (61-692 0669); Sekretariat Caroline Fahrni, Claudia Waldmann
Size: 85-110 *Perfs:* 35 *Type/spec:* mainly contemporary, also classical *Venues:* Stadt Casino 1600
Touring: Europe

Kammerorchester Basel
Basel Chamber Orchestra
Byfangweg 22, 4051 **Basel**
Tel: 61-273 5252 Fax: 61-273 5253
Internet: www.kammerorchester/basel.ch
E-Mail: mail@kammerorchester.basel.ch
Geschäftsführer Christoph Müller; Konzertmeisterin Claudia Dora
Size: 35 *Perfs:* 15 *Type/spec:* chamber-focus on classical, 20th C. *Touring:* national

Sinfonieorchester Basel
Barfüsser Platz 8, Casino Basel, 4051 **Basel**
Tel: 61-205 0095 Fax: 61-205 0099
E-Mail: fe-sinfoniebasel@data
Direktor Jürgen Fabritius
Size: 110 *Perfs:* 170 including concerts + operas
Type/spec: baroque to modern *Venues:* Stadtcasino Basel, Volkshaus, Theater Basel and other venues throughout Switzerland *Comments:* recordings, broadcasts and TV productions

Kammersolisten Zürich
Cholibuck 13, 8121 **Benglen**
Tel: 1-825 3938
Konzertmeister Ernst Langmeier; Chefdirigent Arthur Heinz Lilienthal
Size: 12 *Perfs:* 5 *Type/spec:* baroque to modern
Touring: national

Berner Symphonie Orchester
Münzgraben 2, Postfach, 3000 **Bern** 7
Tel: 31-328 2424 Fax: 31-328 2425
Internet: www.stub.unibe.ch/kultur/bimg.index.html
Geschäftsführerin t.b.a.; Chefdirigent Dmitrij Kitajenko
Size: 105 *Perfs:* 21 *Venues:* Konzerthaus Casino 1300
Touring: Netherlands *Comments:* see also Promoters (Stiftung Berner Symphonieorchester)

Camerata Bern
Mayweg 4, 3007 **Bern**
Tel: 31-371 8688 Fax: 31-371 3835
Chef-Leitung Ana Chumachenko, Thomas Zehetmair (guest); Vereinspräsident Hans Kellerhals; Geschäftsführung Andreas Erismann
Size: 15 *Perfs:* 30-40 *Type/spec:* early baroque to 20thC
Touring: Spain, Argentina, Switzerland, Italy
Comments: CDs available

Orchestergesellschaft Biel-Bieler Symphonieorchester
Burggasse 13, 2500 **Biel** 3
Tel: 32-328 8979 Fax: 32-328 8977
Geschäftsführerin Jeannine Botteron; Musikalischer Oberleiter Marc Tardue; Präsident Dr Gerhard Thomke
Size: 46 *Perfs:* 130
Type/spec: symphonic repertoire *Venues:* Kongresshaus 1200, Stadttheater Biel 280, Stadttheater Solothurn 280, Théâtre Palace 550 *Touring:* Switzerland, Germany, France *Comments:* 9 subscription concerts and performances for Stadtheater

Geneva Chamber Orchestra, The
L'Orchestre de Chambre de Geneve
1 rue Gourgas, 1205 **Genève**

Orchestre de la Suisse Romande
2 rue Bovy-Lysberg, 1204 **Genève**
Tel: 22-807 0017 Fax: 22-807 0018
Internet: www.osr.ch
directeur artistique Fabio Luisi; président Georges Schürch
Size: 112 *Perfs:* 40-50 (24 general + 10 Lausanne + others) *Type/spec:* symphony *Venues:* Victoria Hall 1800, Palais de Beaulieu 1500 *Touring:* Greece, Turkey, Germany, China, Japan, Austria

Camerata Lysy Gstaad
Postfach 430, 3780 **Gstaad**
Tel: 31-951 8621 Fax: 31-951 8622
Musikalischer Leiter Alberto Lysy; Präsident Hans-Rudolf Brunner; Sekretariat Christa Renz
Size: 18 strings *Perfs:* 40 *Type/spec:* chamberside string orchestra *Touring:* worldwide *Comments:* perform at Menuhin Musikfestspiele in Gstaad

Kammermusiker Zürich, Die
Geduldweg 3, 8810 **Horgen**
Tel: 1-725 5024/363 1818(Direktor)
Fax: 1-725 1575/363 1818
Direktor Jürg Dähler; Sekretariat Ruth Bauman
Size: 6 (2/2/2) *Perfs:* 30 *Type/spec:* string sextet *Venues:* Tonhalle Zürich *Touring:* Switzerland, Germany, England, Australia, South America, USA, Italy
Comments: TonART, annual concert series in Zürich Tonhalle since founding in 1961

Orchestre de Chambre de Lausanne
Rue St. Laurent 19, 1003 **Lausanne**
Tel: 21-312 2707 Fax: 21-312 2863
Internet: www.regart.ch/ocl
E-Mail: ocl@vtxnet.ch
secrétaire général Patrick Peikert; directeur artistique Christian Zacharias; relations publiques Giovanna Panese
Size: 43 *Perfs:* 90 *Type/spec:* chamber repertoire: symphonic, baroque, contemporary *Venues:* Metropole Hall *Touring:* Europe

Sinfonietta de Lausanne (formerly Orchestre des Rencontres Musicales)
11 bis Av. du Grammont, 1007 **Lausanne**
Tel: 21-616 7135 Fax: 21-616 7136
regisseur général Catherine Bézieau; directeur musical Jean-Marc Grob; administrateur Jos Iambo
Size: up to 100, principally young professionals *Perfs:* 40
Touring: France, Italy, Germany, Belgium

Fondazione per l'Orchestra della Svizzera Italiana
Casella Postale 162, 6903 **Lugano**
Tel: 91-803 9191 (direct)/5111
Fax: 91-968 2773 (direct)/803 5355
E-Mail: carlascheffler@rtsi.ch
artistic and administrative director Pietro Antonini; maestro stabile Alain Lombard; primo direttore ospite Serge Bando
Size: 41-80 *Perfs:* 45 *Type/spec:* symphony, opera *Venues:* Auditorio Radio Tv Svizzera di Lingua Italiana 500, Palazzo dei Congressi (Lugano) 1150 *Touring:* Switzerland, Italy, France, Czech Republic *Comments:* alternative E-mail: fosi@rtsi.ch; see also Early Music, Radio and TV

Festival Strings Lucerne
Dreilindenstr. 93, 6006 **Luzern**
Tel: 41-420 6263 Fax: 41-420 6273
Chefdirigent Achim Fiedler; Konzertmeister Stanley Dodds, Gunars Larsens; Verwaltung Rita Dahinden
Size: 15 *Perfs:* 40-50 *Type/spec:* chamber, baroque to modern *Touring:* Switzerland, Germany, Austria, Italy, France, Japan, South America

Luzerner Sinfonieorchester
c/o Trägerverein Luzerner Sinfonieorchester, Zentralstrasse 44, 6003 **Luzern**
Tel: 41-210 5050/3487
Fax: 41-210 2693/3060
Internet: www.sinfonieorchester.ch
E-Mail: info@sinfonieorchester.ch
Geschäftsführer Peter Keller; Präsident Walter Studer; Chefdirigent Jonathan Nott
Size: 51 *Type/spec:* classical *Venues:* Kultur-und Kongresshaus Luzern 1800

Orchestre de Chambre de Neuchâtel
case postale 1840, 2002 **Neuchâtel** 2
Tel: 32-731 4916
administrateur Hans Tschumper; directeur musical Jan Schultsz
Size: 19-36 *Perfs:* 25 per year in Switzerland and abroad
Type/spec: chamber, show & classical *Venues:* Salle de Musique, Temple du Bas Neuchâtel 762 *Touring:* Switzerland and abroad

Collegium Musicum Zug (CMZ)
Stolzengrabenstr. 37, 6317 **Oberwil (Zug)**
Tel: 41-711 1087 Fax: 41-711 1094
Künstlerische Leitung Albor Rosenfeld; Administration Robert Herzog
Size: 20 *Perfs:* 6
Type/spec: chamber orchestra, from baroque to contemporary music

Orchestre Philharmonique Suisse
c/o Roland Müllener, Au-Wila, 8493 **Saland**
Tel: 52-386 1146 Fax: 52-386 1350
administrative director Roland Müllener
Size: 100 *Perfs:* 5-10
Type/spec: symphony *Venues:* Tonhalle, Zürich 1800; Stravinski Saal, Montreux 2500
Touring: Switzerland, Germany

Musica Nostalgica
Postfach 504, 4500 **Solothurn**
Tel: 32-621 1005 Fax: 32-621 1005
Internet: www.musica-nostalgica.ch
E-Mail: steiner@musica-nostalgica.ch
contact Matthias Steiner
Size: 2-13 *Perfs:* 180 *Type/spec:* 2 centuries of music from Vivaldi to South American composers
Touring: Canada, USA, Switzerland

Collegium Musicum St Gallen
c/o Mario Schwarz, Rohrschacher Str 107,
9006 **St Gallen**
Tel: 71-245 1158 Fax: 71-245 1168
E-Mail: collmus@dial.eunet.ch
Leitung Mario Schwarz
Size: 20 *Type/spec:* chamber
Comments: CDs available; several concerts at the Bodensee-Festival; see also Collegium Cantorum and Kammerchor Oberthurgan (Choirs)

Sinfonieorchester St Gallen
Museumstrasse 1, 9004 **St Gallen**
Tel: 71-242 0707 Fax: 71-242 0708
E-Mail: konzertverein.sg@bluewin.ch
Geschäftsführer Marc Walter Haefelin; Chefdirigent Jiri Kout
Size: 60 *Perfs:* 166
Type/spec: symphony, opera, operettas, ballet
Venues: Tonhalle 950, Stadttheater 750

Camerata Zürich
Bergstrasse 50G, 8712 **Stäfa**
Tel: 1-926 5270 Fax: 1-251 1993
Konzertsekretariat Rosemarie Kleinert; Musikalischer Leiter Räto Tschupp
Size: 17 *Perfs:* 10 subscriptions + 4/5 others *Type/spec:* classical to modern *Venues:* Tonhalle Zürich 636, Radio Studio Zürich 300

AURA Ensemble
Fichtenrain 11, 4106 **Therwil**
Tel: 61-721 8347 Fax: 61-721 8347
contact Conrad Wyss
Size: 5 *Type/spec:* chamber (piano quintet/quartet and strings trio/quartet), baroque to 20th century *Touring:* Germany, Switzerland, France

Strings of Zürich – Susanna Wipf
Bahnhofstr. 99, 9240 **Uzwil**
Tel: 71-951 9201 Fax: 71-951 9202
E-Mail: ahagentur@bluewien.ch
Orchesterdirektor Susanna Wipf; Dirigent Howard Griffiths
Size: 13-25 *Perfs:* 20-25 *Type/spec:* chamber
Venues: various places in Zürich
Touring: Germany, Italy, France
Comments: special programmes with visualized music; see also Agents (Agentur Susanna Wipf)

Orchestre des Concerts Europeens – E.C.O.
European Concerts Orchestra
13 chemin sur Rang, Case postale 22,
1234 **Vessy/Genève**
Tel: 22-731 7952/343 9597
Fax: 22-731 7592/342 2309
E-Mail: gest@span.ch
musical director, principal conductor Patrick Crispini; administrator Frank H Richard
Size: 60-80 *Perfs:* 15 *Type/spec:* symphony, opera, oratorio, film music, masterclass vocals and conductors, collaboration with 'Les Etoiles de la Voix – Stars of the Voice – Stelle-Della Voce' *Touring:* mainly Switzerland, Italy, France *Comments:* artistic director: Patrick Crispini, 6 rue des Buis, 1202 Genève

Camerata Vitodurum
Loorstrasse 22, 8400 **Winterthur**
Tel: 52-213 0566 Fax: 52-213 0566
founder & chief conductor Christoph Reimann
Size: 15-25 *Perfs:* 10-15
Type/spec: chamber including premieres, Swiss composers, contemporary music
Touring: international *Comments:* the ensemble consists of young, talented soloists

Musikkollegium Winterthur
Rychenbergstrasse 94, 8400 **Winterthur**
Tel: 52-268 1560 Fax: 52-268 1570
E-Mail: musikkollegium@musikkollegium.ch
Direktor Karl Bossert; Chefdirigent Heinrich Schiff; Orchesterdisponentin Monica Fröhlich
Size: 44 *Perfs:* 40-50 (full orchestra); 15-20 chamber, 2 operas *Type/spec:* chamber music, recitals, symphony, vocal *Venues:* Stadthaussaal 800
Touring: Switzerland, Germany
Comments: see also Promoters

Ripieno Kammerorchester
Mötteli Str. 34, 8400 **Winterthur**
Tel: 52-233 5288 Fax: 52-233 5288
Orchesterdirektor Urs Walker
Size: 5-20 *Perfs:* 20
Type/spec: string orchestra; repertoire ranges from baroque to modern
Venues: mainly Museum Oskar Reinhart 200

Ensemble für Neue Musik Zürich
Hegibachstr. 58, 8032 **Zürich**
Tel: 1-383 8181 Fax: 1-383 8181
Internet: www.ensemble.ch
E-Mail: ensemble@access.ch
manager Lisbeth Müller; conductor Jürg Henneberger
Size: 6 *Perfs:* 15 *Type/spec:* contemporary
Touring: Europe

Orchester der Oper Zürich
Falkenstrasse 1, 8008 **Zürich**
Tel: 1-268 6400 Fax: 1-268 6401
Intendant Alexander Pereira; Chefdirigent Franz Welser-Möst; kaufmännischer Direktor Otto Grosskopf; Orchesterdisponent Michael Bühler
Size: 101 *Perfs:* 270-280 *Type/spec:* opera, symphony, ballet *Venues:* Opernhaus *Touring:* Austria, Germany
Comments: see also Opera

Schweizer Jugend- Sinfonie- Orchester
Schaffhauserstr. 35, Postfach 367, 8042 **Zürich**
Tel: 1-360 3920 Fax: 1-360 3921
Internet: www.sjso.ch
E-Mail: info@sjso.ch
managing directors Dr. Martin Ungerer, Jonas Erni; Konzertmeister Herbert Cottrell
Size: 90-95 *Perfs:* 12 *Type/spec:* symphonic
Touring: Switzerland

Symphonisches Orchester Zürich
Postfach 1923, 8021 **Zürich**
Tel: 1-715 2045 Fax: 1-715 2058
Internet: www.swissworld.com/soz
general manager Paul Trachsel; Chefdirigent Daniel Schweizer (1-700 2695)
Size: 67 (varies) *Perfs:* 36 including guest performances
Type/spec: baroque, classical, romantic and contemporary *Venues:* Tonhalle 1458

Tonhalle-Orchester Zürich
Gotthardstrasse 5, 8002 **Zürich**
Tel: 1-206 3440 (admin)/3434 (box office)
Fax: 1-206 3436 (admin)/3469 (box office)
Executive Director Trygve Nordwall; Chief conductor & music director David Zinman; Artistic administrator Etienne Reymond
Size: 100 *Perfs:* 140 *Type/spec:* symphony, classical
Venues: Grosser Saal 1455, Kleiner Saal 636 *Touring:* France, Geneva, Italy, national

Zürcher Kammerorchester
Mühlebachstrasse 86, Postfach 1011, 8032 **Zürich**
Tel: 1-388 3600 Fax: 1-388 3610
E-Mail: zko@bluewin.ch
Geschäftsleitung Thomas Pfiffner; Direktor u. Dirigent Howard Griffiths
Size: 24 *Perfs:* 80-100 *Type/spec:* strings with additional wind and brass depending on repertoire *Venues:* Tonhalle 1548, Fraumunster 898 *Touring:* Brazil, Sweden, Germany, Austria, Czech Republic

TURKEY (+90)

Ankara Devlet Opera Ve Balesi Orkestrasi
Orchestra of the Ankara State Opera and Ballet
Atatürk Bulvari No 50, Ulus, 06050 **Ankara**
Tel: 312-311 2430/324 1476 Fax: 312-311 9731
general music director Rauf Abdullayev; artistic director Hasan Huseyin Akbulut
Size: 107 *Type/spec:* opera orchestra *Venues:* opera house 718, operetta stage 426

Cumhurbaskanligi Senfoni Orkestrasi
Presidential Symphony Orchestra
Talatpasa Bulvari 38, **Ankara**
Tel: 312-309 1343/311 0991/310 7290 Fax: 312-311 7548
director Nedim Tanrikulu
Size: 110 *Perfs:* 70 *Type/spec:* symphonic orchestra repertoire from all centuries *Venues:* Cumhurbaskanligi Senfoni concert hall 850
Touring: Istanbul, Izmir, Korea, Japan, Poland

Antalya State Symphony Orchestra
Antalya Devlet Senfoni Orkestrasi
Antalya
Tel: 242-243 2603 Fax: 242-244 0328
artistic director & conductor Inci Özdil

Bursa Symphony Orchestra
Bursa Senfoni Orkestrasi
Bursa Foundation for Culture and Arts, Açikhava Tiyatrosu, Kültür Park, **Bursa**
Tel: 224-234 4911 Fax: 224-234 4911
director Ahmet Erdönmez

Borusan Chamber Orchestra
Borusan Oda Orkestrasi
Istanbul
Tel: 212-252 7846 Fax: 212-249 1944
conductor Gürer Aykal; general manager Sami Caner

Cemal Resit Rey Symphony Orchestra
CRR, Konser Salonu, Harbiye, 80200 **Istanbul**
Tel: 212-246 0695 Fax: 212-248 5451
programme coordinator Murat Gürol; general artistic director Arda Aydogan

Istanbul Devlet Opera Ve Balesi Orkestrasi
Orchestra of the Istanbul State Opera and Ballet
Atatürk Kültür Merkezi, Taksim, **Istanbul**
Tel: 212-243 2011 Fax: 212-245 3916
director Mehmet Pervez
Size: 87 *Type/spec:* opera orchestra
Venues: opera house grand hall 1300, concert hall 502

Istanbul Devlet Senfoni Orkestrasi
Istanbul State Symphony Orchestra
Atatürk Kültür Merkezi, Taksim, 80090 **Istanbul**
Tel: 212-251 0507/243 1068
Fax: 212-251 0507
director Türkmen Güner; music director Erol Erdinç
Size: 106 *Perfs:* 75 *Type/spec:* symphonic, modern Turkish composers *Venues:* Ataturk Cultural Centre 1300 *Touring:* national, international

Milli Reasurans Chamber Orchestra
Milli Reasurans Tesrikiye Caddesi 43-57, Tesrikiye, **Istanbul**
Tel: 212-231 4730 Fax: 212-230 8608
music director Hakan Sensoy

Izmir Devlet Opera Ve Balesi Orkestrasi
Orchestra of the Izmir State Opera and Ballet
Konak, **Izmir**
Tel: 232-484 6450 Fax: 232-441 0173
director Aytül Büyüksaraç
Size: 63 *Type/spec:* opera house orchestra
Venues: opera house 410

Izmir Devlet Senfoni Orkestrasi
Izmir State Symphony Orchestra
Büro SSK Ishani C Blok 4, Kat Konak,
35260 **Izmir**
Tel: 232-484 8343 Fax: 232-484 5172
director Kenan Gökkaya
Size: 105 *Perfs:* 70 *Venues:* concert hall 350

Mersin Devlet Opera Ve Balesi Orkestrasi
Orchestra of the Mersin State Opera and Ballet
Cumhuriyet Alam, Eski Halkevi Binasi, **Mersin**
Tel: 324-238 0493 Fax: 324-274 719
director Erdogan Sanal

UKRAINE (+380)

Chernivtsi Chamber Orchestra
Philharmonia Place 10, 274000 **Chernivtsi**
Tel: 3722-22247 Fax: 3722-22148
artistic director Juri Gyna

Chernivtsi Ensemble of Soloists 'Consonance'
Philharmonia Place 10, 274000 **Chernivtsi**
Tel: 3722-22247 Fax: 3722-22148
conductor Pavel Chobotov

Dnipropetrovsk Symphony Orchestra
Kalinin St. 47, 320009 **Dnipropatrovsk**
Tel: 562-526 096 Fax: 562-423 326
conductor Viacheslav Blinov

Ivano-Frankivsk Chamber Orchestra
Les Kurbas St. 3, 248000 **Ivano Frankivsk**
Tel: 3422-23151 Fax: 3422-25151
conductor Oleg Geretta

Kharkiv Philarmonic Symphony Orchestra
Rymarskaja St.21 St. 1, 310057 **Kharkiv**
Tel: 572-432 749 Fax: 572-470 527
music director & chief conductor Victoria Zhadko

Kherson Chamber Orchestra
Horkoko St. 117, 325000 **Kherson**
Tel: 5522-41454 Fax: 5522-43270
conductor Georgy Vazin
Comments: Telex: 273 281 – rojal

Ensemble of soloists Kyivska Camerata
Pushkinskaja St.32, 252004 **Kiev (Kyiv)**
Tel: 44-228 0330 Fax: 44-225 1314
conductor Ivan Karabitz

Kiev Chamber Orchestra
Volodymyrskyj Uzviz 2, 252001 **Kiev (Kyiv)**
Tel: 44-229 1421 Fax: 44-220 7276
conductor Roman Kofman

National Opera of Ukraine Symphony Orchestra
Lysenko St. 5, 252034 **Kiev (Kyiv)**
Tel: 44-224 0424 Fax: 44-229 3819
conductor Volodymyr Kozhukhar

National Symphony Orchestra of Ukraine
Volodymyrskyj Uzviz 2, 252001 **Kiev (Kyiv)**
Tel: 44-229 8184 Fax: 44-229 6842
conductor Theodore Kuchar

Ridni Naspivy Ensemble of Folk Instruments
Volodymyrskyj Uzviz 2, 252001 **Kiev (Kyiv)**
Tel: 44-228 0330 Fax: 44-530 3721
conductor Anatoly Mamalyga

State Orchestra of Folk Instruments of Ukraine
Shevtchenko Blvd. 50/52, 252032 **Kiev (Kyiv)**
Tel: 44-224 3531 Fax: 44-224 3998
artistic director Viktor Hutsal

TV and Radio Orchestra of Ukraine
Khreshchatyk 26, 252001 **Kiev (Kyiv)**
Tel: 44-229 3322
conductor Volodymyr Sirenko

Kirovohrad Chamber Orchestra 'Concertino'
Ordzonikidze St. 8, 316050 **Kirovohrad**
Tel: 522-224 796 Fax: 522-221 317

Luhansk Symphony Orchestra
Lenin St. 23, 348000 **Luhansk**
Tel: 642-522 578

Lviv Symphony Orchestra
Tchaikovsky St. 7, 290001 **Lviv**
Tel: 322-725 864 Fax: 322-741 022
conductor Ivan Yuziuk

Mykolaiyiv Chamber Orchestra 'Capriccio'
wul. Marshala Vasylevskoho 55,
327008 **Mykolaiyiv**
Tel: 512-247 184

Ensemble of Contemporary Chamber Music 'Harmonium Mundi'
Pushkinskaja St. 13, kv.5, 270001 **Odessa**
Tel: 482-249 163 Fax: 482-224 101

Odessa Philharmonic Orchestra
Pushkinskaja St. 13, kv.5, 270001 **Odessa**
Tel: 482-249 163 Fax: 482-224 101
artistc director Victor Mytnyk; conductor Hobart Earle

Sumy Chamber Orchestra
Pietropavlivska St. 63, 244000 **Sumy**
Tel: 5422-20683
conductor Volodymyr Serebrjakov

Zakarpattia Chamber Orchestra
Teatralna pl. 10, 294000 **Uzhorod**
Tel: 3122-32322 Fax: 3122-33238
artistic director Vladislav Jurosh

Crimea Symphony Orchestra
Yekaterynynska St. 13, 334200 **Yalta**
Tel: 654-325 070 Fax: 654-323 726
conductor Oleksiy Hulanytsky

Zaporizzhia Symphony Orchestra
Lenin St. 183, 330006 **Zaporizzhia**
Tel: 612-226 471 Fax: 612-225 690
conductor Vjacheslav Redia

UNITED KINGDOM (+44)

Britten-Pears Orchestra and Baroque Orchestra
The Britten-Pears School for Advanced Musical Studies, High Street, **Aldeburgh** IP15 5AX
Tel: 1728-688 671 (general)/687 109 (orchestra)
Fax: 1728-688 171
Internet: www.aldeburgh.co.uk
E-Mail: bpo@aldeburghfestivals.org
director of Britten-Pears Orchestra Tadaaki Otaka; hon. president of Britten-Pears Baroque Orchestra Ton Koopmann; director of school Elizabeth Webb; administrator (orchestras) Ann Rawdon Smith
Size: 20-50 *Perfs:* 5-10
Type/spec: chamber, range of classical to contemporary works covering orchestral & operatic repertoire
Venues: mid-large scale, including Snape Maltings Concert Hall, London and South East
Touring: national *Comments:* a unique training orchestra for post-graduate musicians and young professionals; due to be moving to Snape in November 1999, new address not known at time of going to print, contact above telephone number for further information; see also Early Music

Corydon Orchestra
24 Kirdford Road, **Arundel** BN18 9EE
Tel: 1903-885 465 Fax: 1903-885 466
Internet: www.orchestranet.co.uk/corydon.html
E-Mail: corydon.office@BTinternet.com
general manager Linda Osborne; artistic director Matthew Best
Size: 30-90 *Perfs:* 10
Type/spec: chamber, symphony
Touring: international *Comments:* see also Choirs; extensive discography with Hyperion

Northern Ireland Chamber Orchestra
62 Ulsterville Av.,
Belfast (Northern Ireland) BT9 7AQ
Tel: 28-9043 4862/9031 6839
Fax: 28-9043 4862/9031 6839
contact Peter Scott
Type/spec: wide repertoire

Ulster Orchestra Society Limited
Elmwood Hall at Queens, 89 University Rd,
Belfast (Northern Ireland) BT7 1NF
Tel: 28-9066 4535 Fax: 28-9066 2761
chief executive David Fisk; principal conductor and artistic advisor Dmitry Sitkovetsky; chairman Jim Stewart; financial administrator Colm Crummey; marketing manager Norma Sinte; orchestral manager Lara Stokes; press officer Elish Martin
Size: 63 *Perfs:* 54 *Type/spec:* mixed repertoire
Venues: Ulster Hall, Belfast 1330, Waterfront Hall, Belfast 2400 *Touring:* national, international

Critical Band
Bancroft, Recory Lane, Fringford,
Bicester OX6 9DX
Tel: 1869-278 392 Fax: 1869-278 392
Internet: www.brailsford.demon.co.uk
E-Mail: cb@brailsford.demon.co.uk
director James Wood; administrator Matthew Brailsford
Size: 5-20 (flexible) *Type/spec:* chamber group, 20th century repertoire *Comments:* Critical Band has close performing links with New London Chamber Choir, and is affiliated to the Centre for Microtonal Music, London

Birmingham Contemporary Music Group
CBSO Centre, Berkley Street, **Birmingham** B1 2LF
Tel: 121-616 2616 Fax: 121-616 2622
Internet: www.cbso.co.uk/cbso/
E-Mail: bcmg@bcmg.org.uk
general manager Jackie Newbould; artistic director Simon Clugston; artistic advisor Sir Simon Rattle CBE; development manager Stephen Newbould; music director Thomas Adès
Size: 10-20 (flexible) *Perfs:* 30 *Type/spec:* chamber group/20th century repertoire
Venues: CBSO Centre 300

City of Birmingham Symphony Orchestra
CBSO Centre, Berkley Street, **Birmingham** B1 2LF
Tel: 121-616 6500/212 3333 (box-office)
Fax: 121-616 6518
Internet: www.cbso.co.uk
E-Mail: information@cbso.co.uk
chief executive Stephen Maddock; music director Sakari Oramo; orchestra manager Judy Dolman; director of marketing & development Sarah Gee; general manager Michael Buckley; concerts administrator Natalie Cruse; finance executive Cheryl Gentry; deputy chief executive Richard York; education manager Ann Tennant; librarian Alison Morrell
Size: 101 *Perfs:* 120 *Venues:* Symphony Hall 2200
Touring: Austria, France, Germany, Belgium

Kokoro Contemporary Music Ensemble
27 Wheaton Road, Pokesdown,
Bournemouth BH7 6LH
Tel: 1202-258 146 Fax: 1202-776 710
music director Kevin Field; manager Geraldine McDonnell; artistic advisor Cathy Nelson
Size: 6-25 freelance musicians *Perfs:* 5 (concerts at home venue), 10 (concerts touring) *Type/spec:* contemporary music ensemble performing and commissioning music of our time *Venues:* Poole Arts Centre, Poole, Dorset 2300 *Touring:* England

Welsh Chamber Orchestra
100 Ystrad Fawr, **Bridgend** CF31 4HW
Tel: 1656-658 891 Fax: 1656-658 891
administrator Barbara Parish; artistic director Anthony Hose; chairman Paul Loveluck CBE, JP
Size: 32 *Perfs:* 35 *Venues:* Brangwyn Hall, Swansea, New Pavilion, Llandudno, Reardon Smith Hall, Cardiff
Touring: France, Germany, Belgium, Netherlands

Academy of Ancient Music, The
10 Brookside, **Cambridge** CB2 1JE
Tel: 1223-301 509 Fax: 1223-327 377
Internet: www.aam.co.uk
E-Mail: administrator@aam.co.uk
director Christopher Hogwood CBE; associate conductor Paul Goodwin; associate director & concert master Andrew Manze; general manager Christopher Lawrence; concerts & tour manager Fiona Seers; administrator Madeleine Holmes
Size: 3-180 (including choir) *Perfs:* 100
Type/spec: baroque, classical
Venues: small-large scale *Touring:* Europe, USA
Comments: see also Early Music

Britten Sinfonia
12d Kings Parade, **Cambridge** CB2 1SJ
Tel: 1223-300 795 Fax: 1223-302 092
E-Mail: info@brittensinfonia.demon.co.uk
general manager David Butcher; artistic director Nicholas Cleobury; education director Glyn Evans; development manager Jackie Inverdale; orchestral manager Helen Busbridge; concerts & marketing manager Helen Thompson; education officer Anna Martin; composer-in-association David Matthews
Size: 20-60 *Perfs:* 70 *Type/spec:* chamber, symphonic, 20th century *Venues:* small-large scale *Touring:* USA, Europe *Comments:* recordings available through BMG Conifer, EMI and ASV

Britten Sinfonia Soloists
12d Kings Parade, **Cambridge** CB2 1SJ
Tel: 1223-300 795 Fax: 1223-302 092
E-Mail: info@brittensinfonia.demon.co.uk
general manager David Butcher; artistic director Nicholas Cleobury; education director Glyn Evans; development director Jackie Inverdale; orchestral manager Helen Busbridge; concerts & marketing manager Helen Thompson; education officer Anna Martin; composer-in-association David Matthews
Size: 3-15 *Perfs:* 15
Type/spec: chamber – main repertoire 20th century
Venues: small-mid scale *Touring:* UK, Europe

Duke Quartet
c/o Hazard Chase Ltd, Richmond House,
16-20 Regent Street, **Cambridge** CB2 1DB
Tel: 1223-312 400 Fax: 1223-460 827
Internet: www.hazardchase.co.uk
E-Mail: hilary.perrott@hazardchase.co.uk
Size: 4 *Type/spec:* string quartet

Eroica Quartet
c/o Hazard Chase Ltd, Richmond House,
16-20 Regent Street, **Cambridge** CB2 1DB
Tel: 1223-312 400 Fax: 1223-460 827
Internet: www.hazardchase.co.uk
E-Mail: hilary.perrott@hazardchase.co.uk
Size: 4 *Type/spec:* special repertoire: period instrument string quartet playing classical and romantic repertoire
Comments: see also Early Music

Pamela Thorby & Friends
c/o Hazard Chase Limited, Richmond House,
16-20 Regent Street, **Cambridge** CB2 1DB
Tel: 1223-312 400 Fax: 1223-460 827
E-Mail: info@hazardchase.co.uk
Size: 2-10 *Type/spec:* Celtic arrangements and own compositions for recorder, keyboard, percussion et alia

BBC National Orchestra and Chorus of Wales
BBC Broadcasting House, **Cardiff (Wales)** CF5 2YQ
Tel: 29-2032 2686 Fax: 29-2032 2575
E-Mail: now@bbc.co.uk
director Huw Tregelles Williams OBE; music director Mark Wigglesworth (from Sept 2000: Richard Hickox); conductor laureate Tadaaki Otaka CBE; conductor-in-residence Grant Llewellyn; senior producer Tim Thorne; press & marketing manager Joanna Sigsworth; educational community officer Andrew Burke; artistic administrator Kim Sargeant
Size: 88 *Perfs:* 80-90 *Type/spec:* symphony repertoire, new works by Welsh composers *Venues:* St David's Hall, Cardiff 1956; Brangusyn Hall, Swansea 1198; other venues throughout Wales and England *Touring:* Wales, UK, international *Comments:* extensive educational and community programme for all ages through out Wales

Charlie Barber and Band
62 Arran Street, Roath, **Cardiff (Wales)** CF24 3HT
Tel: 29-2049 7157 Fax: 29-2049 7157
E-Mail: sound.affairs@tesco.net
artistic director Charlie Barber; admin. Alex Lemmon
Size: 12 *Type/spec:* saxophones, brass, percussion, piano and string; specialise in specially commissioned works *Venues:* small-large scale venues *Touring:* national, international *Comments:* smaller ensemble also available e.g Entr'acte – string quartet & saxophone

PM Music Ensemble
46 Richmond Road, Roath, **Cardiff (Wales)** CF24 3AT
Tel: 29-2048 2183 Fax: 29-2048 2183
director Peter Reynolds
Size: 5-7 *Perfs:* 15 *Type/spec:* new music *Venues:* Norwegian Church Arts Centre, Cardiff 120 *Touring:* Wales, England *Comments:* specialise in Welsh composers; educational workshops

National Symphony Orchestra of London
Jumps Road, **Churt** GU10 2JY
Tel: 1252-792 315 Fax: 1252-795 120
Internet: www.nso.co.uk
E-Mail: enquiries@nso.co.uk
managing director Anne Collis; principal conductor Martin Yates; artistic director Perry Montague-Mason; consultant orchestral advisor Justin Pearson
Size: 40-70 *Perfs:* 10 (live) *Type/spec:* popular classics
Venues: mid-large scale *Touring:* International
Comments: spending increasingly more time in the studio; over the last 4 years recorded more than 40 complete classic musicals for TER; recordings being released gradually on CD

European Union Chamber Orchestra
Fermain House, Dolphin Street, **Colyton** EX24 6LU
Tel: 1297-552 272 Fax: 1297-553 744
E-Mail: euco@compuserve.com
director general Ambrose Miller
Size: 16-24 *Perfs:* 70 *Type/spec:* chamber *Venues:* small-large scale including Vienna Musik Verein 1800, Amsterdam Concertgebouw 1800 *Touring:* worldwide
Comments: CDs available on Hyperion, ASV, Carlton

London Mozart Players
92 Chatsworth Rd, **Croydon** CR0 1HB
Tel: 20-8686 1996 Fax: 20-8686 2187
Internet: www.lmp.org
E-Mail: info@lmp.org
managing director Ian Lush; music director Matthias Bamert; principal guest conductor James Galway; administrator Fiona Emmerson; marketing & development manager Alice Walton; music director designate Andrew Parrott
Size: 19-45 *Perfs:* 120 *Type/spec:* chamber *Venues:* Barbican Centre 2000, Fairfield Hall 1700, Queen Elizabeth Hall 900, St John's Smith Square 700
Touring: Switzerland, Austria, Japan, Netherlands, Germany, USA, Spain *Comments:* spec: Mozart, Haydn, 20thC British living composers

THE KING'S CONSORT

◆ ◆ ◆ ◆ ◆

Baroque & Classical Orchestra (20-45 players)
Choir of The King's Consort (18-26 voices)
Chamber Ensemble (4-15 performers)
Fully staged Opera and Dance projects

CONCERT TOURS 2000-2001

Austria • Australia • Belgium • Britain • Canada
Czech Republic • France • Germany • Italy
Japan • Malaysia • Mexico • Netherlands
New Zealand • Portugal • Spain • Singapore
Sweden • Switzerland • Taiwan • USA

MAJOR PROJECTS 2000-2001

- Mendelssohn *Violin Concerto* (with Thomas Zehetmair)
- Mozart *Requiem, C Minor Mass*
- Haydn *The Creation*
- Purcell *The Fairy-Queen* (fully-staged, Europe & Far East)
- *Lo Sposalizio* (massive Venetian reconstruction)
- Handel *L'Allegro, La Resurrezione, Judas Maccabaeus*
- *The Romantic Tragedy of Philip the Fair*
- Bach and his Contemporaries (year-long festival)
- Vivaldi *La Senna Festiggiante*
- Monteverdi *Vespers*
- Bach *Mass in B Minor* (European tour)
- Handel *Water Music* and *Fireworks Music*

GRAMOPHONE RECORDINGS

for Hyperion (75 recordings) including

- Handel *Joshua, Deborah, Judas Maccabaeus, Ottone Alexander Balus, Acis and Galatea, The Occasional Oratorio*
- Purcell *Complete Odes, Church Music, Secular Songs*
- Vivaldi *Complete Sacred Music*
- Telemann • Mozart • Bach • Schütz • Gabrieli
- Albinoni • Couperin • Pergolesi • *Lo Sposalizio*

...and much more

THE KING'S CONSORT

34 St Mary's Grove, London W4 3LN
telephone: +44 208-995 9994 fax: +44 208-995 2115
Email: info@the-kings-consort.org.uk

also represented by:
Austria: *MAM, Vienna* **France**: *Ian Malkin, Paris*
Italy: *Lorenzo Baldrighi, Mezzago* **Spain**: *Carmen Prieto, Madrid*
Switzerland: *Agence de Concerts Caecilia, Geneva*

Non-exclusive representation:
Harrison Parrott, London
IMG Artists (London & Asia offices)

THE SCHUBERT ENSEMBLE *of* LONDON

Photo: Clive Barda

SIMON BLENDIS – *violin*
DOUGLAS PATERSON – *viola*
JANE SALMON – *cello*
WILLIAM HOWARD – *piano*
with
PETER BUCKOKE – *double bass*

Britain's leading chamber group specialising in repertoire for piano and strings.

Recent winner of the Royal Philharmonic Society Award for Best Chamber Ensemble.

Management: Ann Senior, 32 Wolverton Gardens, London W6 7DY
Tel: +44(0) 208 563 0618 Fax: +44 (0) 208 741 5233 E-mail senior.mgt@dial.pipex.com
VISIT OUR WEBSITE: www.schubertensemble.com

ORCHESTRA

COLLEGIUM SYMPHONIUM VENETO

- Musical and Artistic Director GIULIO SVEGLIADO
- Administrative Secretary CIEMME STUDIO CARLA MARCHIORI

REPERTOIRE

- Symphony
- Choral & Solo
- Church music for solos, chorus & orchestra
- Specialised in opera: "Jocose Performances for Music" from the noble Venetian period of the mid '700s

- For further information please contact:
Collegium Symphonium Veneto
Via Maragne, 52 – 35013 Cittadella (PD) – Italy
Tel/Fax: +39 49 8096225 r.a.
Tel/Fax: +39 49 5975960

London Pro Arte Baroque Orchestra
17B St Augustine Avenue, **Croydon** CR2 6JN
Tel: 20-8688 2890/802-429 235 Fax: 20-8688 2901
Internet: ds.dial.pipix.com/proarte
E-Mail: proarte@dial.pipex.com
orchestra manager Richard Thomas; artistic director & principal conductor Murray Stewart
Size: 14+ *Perfs:* 12 *Type/spec:* baroque, classical (authentic instruments) *Venues:* South Bank Centre; Barbican; St John's, Smith Square; Colston Hall, Bristol *Touring:* France *Comments:* see also Early Music

London Pro Arte Orchestra
17B St Augustine Avenue, **Croydon** CR2 6JN
Tel: 20-8688 2890/802-429 235
Fax: 20-8688 2901
Internet: ds.dial.pipex.com/proarte
E-Mail: proarte@dial.pipex.com
orchestral manager John Cobb; artistic director and principal conductor Murray Stewart
Size: 14-60 *Perfs:* 16 *Type/spec:* chamber, symphony, 18th-20th century *Venues:* South Bank Centre, Barbican, St John's Smith Square, Blackheath Concert Halls, Blackheath; Walthamstow Town Hall; Colston Hall, Bristol; Fairfield Hall, Croydon; resident at Queen Mary and Westfield College, University of London
Comments: associated group are London Pro Arte Brass Ensemble (4-10 players), London Pro Arte Percussion Ensemble (q.v.)

Scottish Chamber Orchestra
4 Royal Terrace, **Edinburgh (Scotland)** EH7 5AB
Tel: 131-557 6800 Fax: 131-557 6933
Internet: www.sco.org.uk
E-Mail: info@sco.org.uk
managing director Roy McEwan; composer laureate Sir Peter Maxwell Davies; concerts director Judith Colman; conductor laureate Sir Charles Mackerras; affiliate composer James MacMillan; principal conductor Joseph Swensen
Size: 37 *Perfs:* 80 *Type/spec:* chamber *Venues:* Queen's Hall 850, Edinburgh; Glasgow City Hall 1200; Glasgow Royal Concert Hall 2300; Music Hall Aberdeen 1200
Touring: international

BBC Scottish Symphony Orchestra
BBC Broadcasting House, Queen Margaret Drive, **Glasgow (Scotland)** G12 8DG
Tel: 141-338 2606 Fax: 141-307 4312
E-Mail: bbcsso@bbc.co.uk
director Hugh Macdonald; manager Alan Davis; chief conductor Osmo Vänskä; conductor laureate Jerzy Maksymiuk; associate principal conductor Martyn Brabbins; composer/conductor Tan Dun; composer in association Stuart MacRae; senior producer Simon Lord
Size: 69+ *Perfs:* 60 *Type/spec:* the BBC's orchestra in Scotland, contemporary music occupies an important place in the orchestra's repertoire *Venues:* Studio One, BBC Scotland, Glasgow; City Hall, Glasgow 1200; Music Hall Aberdeen 1200; Town Hall, Ayr 700; Eden Court Theatre, Inverness 790; MacRobert Arts Centre, Stirling 500 *Touring:* Scotland, USA, Scandinavia *Comments:* Recording CDs for Hyperion, BIS, NMC, Koch, Naxos/Marco Polo, Wergo, Cala, Largo

BT Scottish Ensemble
5 Newton Terrace Lane, **Glasgow (Scotland)** G3 7PB
Tel: 141-221 2222 Fax: 141-221 4444
E-Mail: scottishensemble@yahoo.com
general manager Heather Duncan; artistic director Clio Gould; administration Martin Ritchie, Nicola Mutton
Size: 11 regular + guest soloists *Perfs:* 100+ *Type/spec:* ensemble, baroque through to present day *Venues:* Queen's Hall, Edinburgh 900; Strathclyde Suite, Glasgow 500; Hellenic Centre, London 200; Wigmore Hall, London; Mitchell Hall, Aberdeen 600; Eden Court Theatre, Inverness *Touring:* Scotland and the Islands, England, international *Comments:* extensive commissioning of new pieces

Mugenkyo – Taiko Drum Performance
PO Box 5124, **Glasgow (Scotland)** G76 9YA
Tel: 141-644 4971 Fax: 141-644 4971
Internet: mugenkyo-taiko.co.uk
E-Mail: mail@mugenkyo-taiko.co.uk
information Neil Mackie, Miyuki Williams, Masaaki Kurumaya
Size: 5 *Perfs:* 100+ *Type/spec:* Taiko drumming *Venues:* capacity up to 1000 *Touring:* UK, Europe, Japan
Comments: Taiko drumming is a traditional Japanese performing art; Mugenkyo are Europe's foremost touring group; also undertake lectures/demonstrations for schools, special events and festivals

National Youth Orchestra of Scotland
13 Somerset Place, **Glasgow (Scotland)** G3 7JT
Tel: 141-332 8311 Fax: 141-332 3915
Internet: users.colloquium.co.uk/~NYOS/
E-Mail: nyos@cqm.co.uk
director Richard Chester
Size: 120 *Perfs:* 5-8 *Type/spec:* standard classical – contemporary 20th C. *Venues:* Glasgow Royal Concert Hall 2500, Symphony Hall Birmingham, Philharmonic Hall Liverpool *Touring:* national, Europe
Comments: member of EFNYO (q.v)

Paragon Ensemble Scotland
20 Renfrew Street, **Glasgow (Scotland)** G2 3BW
Tel: 141-332 9903 Fax: 141-332 9904
Internet: www.scot-art.org/paragon
E-Mail: admin@paragon.sol.co.uk
artistic director David Davies; general manager Andrew Logan; administrator Karyn Mackie
Size: varies *Perfs:* 20-40 *Type/spec:* contemporary

Royal Scottish National Orchestra
73 Claremont Street, **Glasgow (Scotland)** G3 7JB
Tel: 141-225 3550 Fax: 141-221 4317
Internet: rsno.org.uk
E-Mail: admin@rsno.org.uk
chief executive Simon Crookall; music director & principal conductor Alexander Lazarev; conductor laureate Neeme Järvi; associate composer Michael Torke; principal guest conductor Marin Alsop; conductor emeritus Walter Weller
Size: 90 *Perfs:* 150 *Type/spec:* symphony *Venues:* Glasgow Royal Concert Hall, Edinburgh Festival Theatre; Music Hall, Aberdeen; Caird Hall, Dundee
Touring: regular overseas touring

Guildford Philharmonic Orchestra
Millmead House, Millmead, **Guildford** GU2 5BB
Tel: 1483-444 666 Fax: 1483-444 732
E-Mail: guildfordphil@guildford.gov.uk
general manager Nicola Goold; principal conductor En Shao
Size: 70-75 *Perfs:* 24 *Venues:* Civic Hall 1050, Guildford Cathedral 1000, Holy Trinity 480, Electric Theatre 200
Comments: varied season of symphony concerts and educational outreach

Orchestra of London, The
2 Meadow Walk, **Harpenden** AL5 5TG
Tel: 1582-461 657 Fax: 1582-461 657
directors Mike Fuller, Allan Wilson; principal conductor & music director Benedict Gunner
Size: 45-90 *Type/spec:* standard symphonic *Venues:* all major London venues *Touring:* Europe *Comments:* many of the musicians were principals of other London orchestras (i.e. LSO and LPO)

Philharmonic at U.H. (formerly The Hatfield Philharmonic Orchestra), The
c/o The Music Centre, University of Hertfordshire, College Lane, **Hatfield** AL10 9AB
Tel: 1707-284 441 Fax: 1707-285 098
Internet: www.herts.ac.uk
E-Mail: A.1.spence@hert.ac.uk
administrator Ron de Brito (tel: 1442-230 296); music director Howard Burrell; chairman Jonathan Brill; orchestra manager Adrian Smith
Size: 60-90 *Perfs:* 8 *Type/spec:* 19th/20thC plus new works *Venues:* University of Hertfordshire (Prince Edward Hall), Abbey of St. Albans
Touring: Czech Republic

Hanover Band, The
The Old Market, Upper Market Street, **Hove** BN3 1AS
Tel: 1273-206 978 Fax: 1273-329 636
Internet: www.hanoverband.com
E-Mail: mailbox@hanoverband.co.uk
artistic director Caroline Brown; chief executive Stephen Neiman; marketing & communication manager David Orams; pa to artistic director Jane Saunders; promotions manager Kathy Avdiev
Size: 15-60 *Perfs:* 35-40 *Type/spec:* baroque, classical, romantic, played on period instruments *Venues:* Wigmore Hall 500, St John Smith Square 800, The Old Market 300 *Touring:* Germany *Comments:* patron H.R.H. The Duke of Kent, K.G.; see also Early Music

Symphony of Harmony and Invention, The
Enslow House, Station Road, Enslow, **Kidlington** OX5 3AX
Tel: 1869-331 544 Fax: 1869-331 011
Internet: www.the-sixteen.org.uk
E-Mail: info@thesixteen.org.uk
general manager Gijs Elsen; general administrator Alison Stillman; development manager Peter Burrows; conductor Harry Christophers
Size: 10-40 *Type/spec:* renaissance, baroque, classical and 20th century *Touring:* Italy, Spain, Portugal, USA, Austria, Germany, France, Belgium, Netherlands, Australia, Far East
Comments: agents: Lorenzo Baldrighi (Italy), Carmen Prieto (Spain); see also Choirs (The Sixteen)

English Northern Philharmonia
Opera North, Grand Theatre, **Leeds** LS1 6NU
Tel: 113-243 9999 Fax: 113-244 0418
general director Richard Mantle; orchestra and concerts manager t.b.a.; principal conductor Steven Sloane
Size: 54 on contract, augments according to repertoire
Perfs: 30 concerts + 100 opera *Type/spec:* symphonic
Venues: Leeds Townhall, Huddersfield Townhall, Dewsbury Townhall + various others *Touring:* national
Comments: offer extensive community and educational outreach programmes; student training scheme; various recordings on Naxos, Chandos, Hyperion, Deutsche Grammophon

Royal Liverpool Philharmonic Orchestra
Philharmonic Hall, Hope Street, **Liverpool** L1 9BP
Tel: 151-210 2895/709 3789 (box-office)
Fax: 151-210 2902
Internet: www.rlps.co.uk
E-Mail: RLPSociety@aol.com
chief executive Antony Lewis-Crosby; principal conductor Petr Altrichter; orchestra manager Marian McGrath; director of orchestra department Sandra Parr; director of marketing Ian Archer
Size: 80-100 *Perfs:* 150 *Type/spec:* symphonic repertoire
Venues: Philharmonic Hall 1800
Comments: founded 1840; recently made a number of award-winning records including Michael Nymans Piano Concerto; see also Venues

Academy of St Martin in the Fields
Raine House, Raine Street, **London** E1 9RG
Tel: 20-7702 1377 Fax: 20-7481 0228
Internet: www.academysmif.co.uk
E-Mail: info@academysmif.co.uk
general manager George Brown (Mrs); music & artistic director Sir Neville Marriner; artistic director Kenneth Sillito; head of development & marketing Julia Seddon; administrator Dawn Day
Size: up to 95 *Perfs:* 150
Type/spec: chamber, symphony, 17th to 20th century
Venues: South Bank, Barbican and touring venues
Touring: worldwide
Comments: see also Choirs

BBC Concert Orchestra
The Hippodrome, North End Road, Golders Green, **London** NW11 7RP
Tel: 20-7765 4010
Fax: 20-7765 4929
E-Mail: concert.orch@bbc.co.uk
principal conductor Barry Wordsworth; principal guest conductor Vernon Handley; general manager Ian Maclay; orchestra manager Adrian Evett; assistant orchestra manager Jan Parr; promotions and marketing manager Sarah Biggs; librarian Martin Ward
Size: 56 *Perfs:* 150
Type/spec: light music orchestra – from classical works and grand opera to light music and popular song
Venues: Hippodrome 600 and various others throughout UK and abroad

BBC Symphony Orchestra
BBC SO, Room 14, BBC Studios, Delaware Road, **London** W9 2LG
Tel: 20-7765 2954 Fax: 20-7286 3251
Internet: www.bbc.co.uk/orchestras/so
E-Mail: BBCSO@bbc.co.uk
chief conductor Sir Andrew Davis CBE; general manager Paul Hughes; chief producer Ann McKay; marketing manager Christine Bisatt; orchestral manager Richard Smith
Size: 101 *Perfs:* 100
Type/spec: romantic, modern, particularly 20th century and contemporary *Venues:* BBC Studios, Royal Festival Hall, Barbican Centre, Royal Albert Hall
Touring: USA, Spain, Germany

Brodsky Quartet
c/o Brodsky Management, Delfina Studios, 50 Bermondsey Street, **London** SE1 3UD
Tel: 20-7378 8033 Fax: 20-7378 8034
Internet: www.brodskyquartet.co.uk
E-Mail: BrodskyQuartet@compuserve.com
manager Marjon Koenekoop
Size: 4 *Perfs:* 100
Type/spec: string quartet, classical/contemporary repertoire *Touring:* worldwide
Comments: collaborations with other musicians/artists; exclusive recording contract Vanguard Classics

Camerata Santa Dorotea
216 Amesbury Avenue, **London** SW2 3BL
Tel: 20-8674 4907
Fax: 20-8674 4477
E-Mail: rg-p@rocketmail.com
orchestra manager Robin Gordon-Powell; music director Robert Masarachi
Size: 15-80 *Type/spec:* wide repertoire, strings only or full symphonic and pops (to suit requirements)

Chamber Orchestra of Europe, The
8 Southampton Place, **London** WC1A 2EA
Tel: 20-7831 2326 Fax: 20-7831 8248
Internet: www.coeurope.org
E-Mail: redbird@coeurope.org
general manager June Megennis; artistic adviser Claudio Abbado; chairman Peter Readman; planning & personnel manager Simon Fletcher; tour manager Christopher Smith-Gillard; travel and office manager Julie Pickles; publicity Mollie Pearson
Size: 50 *Perfs:* approx. 60
Type/spec: chamber, sinfonietta
Venues: Kammermusiksaal of the Philharmonie, Berlin; Barbican Arts Centre, London; Stefaniensaal Graz; Alte Oper, Frankfurt, Philharmonie Köln; Cite de la Musique, Paris *Touring:* France, Germany, UK, Italy, Austria, Belgium, Switzerland, Netherlands, USA, Japan

City of London Sinfonia
11 Drum Street, **London** E1 1LH
Tel: 20-7480 7743 Fax: 20-7488 2700
Internet: www.cls.co.uk
E-Mail: info@cls.co.uk
music director Richard Hickox; composer-in-association Alasdair Nicolson; general manager Stephen Carpenter; administrator Elaine Baines; development director t.b.a.; orchestra manager Jane Lomas; marketing manager Catharine Pitt; education manager Sarah Guest; office manager & librarian Samantha Lodge; development officer Elizabeth Knock
Size: 37 *Perfs:* 100 *Type/spec:* chamber, baroque to 20th century *Venues:* Barbican 2026, South Bank Centre, Queen Elizabeth Hall, City Church venues
Touring: Germany *Comments:* resident orchestra of Ipswich and King's Lynn; thriving education and community programme

English Baroque Soloists
Monteverdi Choir & Orchestra Ltd,
61 Wandsworth High Street, **London** SW18 2PT
Tel: 20-8871 4750 Fax: 20-8871 4751
Internet: www.monteverdi.co.uk
E-Mail: info@monteverdi.org.uk
artistic director Sir John Eliot Gardiner; acting general manager Howard Gough; orchestra fixer David Adams; administrator Jan Normanton; project coordinator Andrew Hammond
Size: 20-45 *Type/spec:* period instrument orchestra specialising in baroque and early classical *Venues:* small-large scale *Touring:* UK, USA, Europe *Comments:* recordings available from DG Archives, Phillips Classics, Erato; see also Early Music

English Chamber Orchestra Ltd
2 Coningsby Road, **London** W5 4HR
Tel: 20-8840 6565 Fax: 20-8567 7198
E-Mail: mail@e-c-orch.demon.co.uk
directors Quintin Ballardie OBE FRAM, Pauline Gilbertson
Size: 35 *Perfs:* 100 *Type/spec:* chamber *Venues:* Barbican Hall, London, Royal Festival Hall, Queen Elizabeth Hall, London *Touring:* Europe, Far East, USA

English Concert, The
8 St George's Terrace, **London** NW1 8XJ
Tel: 20-7911 0905 Fax: 20-7911 0904
E-Mail: ec@englishconcert.co.uk
general manager Felix Warnock; artistic director Trevor Pinnock; orchestral manager Sarah Fenn; administrator Victoria Atkinson
Size: 10-50 *Perfs:* up to 50 *Type/spec:* 17th-18th century, chamber music *Venues:* St John's Smith Square, Queen Elizabeth Hall, Wigmore Hall, Barbican *Touring:* Europe, South America, USA, Japan *Comments:* all recordings on DG Archiv; see also Early Music

Ensemble X
37 Coltman House, Welland Street,
London SE10 9DW
Tel: 20-8853 0818 Fax: 20-8853 0818
composer/director Errollyn Wallen
Size: 4-15 *Perfs:* 12-20 *Type/spec:* original contemporary classical music, and jazz/popular *Venues:* South Bank, ICA, Union Chapel, London Jazz Festival, Queen Elizabeth Hall, Pizza on the Park, the Barbican *Touring:* national, international *Comments:* solo and small ensembles performances; won Peter Whittingham Award in 1996 which has sponsored recording

European Union Youth Orchestra
65 Sloane Street, **London** SW1X 9SH
Tel: 20-7235 7671 Fax: 20-7235 7370
Internet: www.euyo.oracle.com
E-Mail: info@euyo.org.uk
general manager Helen Shabetai; co-founder & secretary general Joy Bryer; music director Bernard Haitink
Size: 140 musicians under the age of 23, auditioned annually throughout the countries of the EU *Perfs:* 15-20
Type/spec: symphonic with repertoire mainly romantic and 20th century *Touring:* Scandinavia, Europe

Forest Philharmonic
c/o Jo Paton, 17 Ducie Street, **London** SW4 7RP
Tel: 20-7771 8037 Fax: 20-7377 1972
artistic director Mark Shanahan; orchestral manager Virginia Burdon Cooper (1442-877 486);
contact Jo Paton
Perfs: 6 *Venues:* Walthamstow Assembly Hall *Comments:* other contact name: Karen McDonald, 4 Levendale Road, Forest Hill, SE23 2TW, Tel: 20-8291 0390

Gabrieli Consort and Players
Room 13, The Annexe, Shoreditch Town Hall,
380 Old Street, **London** EC1V 9LT
Tel: 20-7613 4404 Fax: 20-7613 4414
Internet: www.gabrieli.com
E-Mail: gabrieliconsort@compuserve.com
general manager Anita Crowe; artistic director Paul McCreesh; administrator Lucy Miller; director of development Dawn Rotheram
Size: 12-60 *Perfs:* 40-60 *Type/spec:* 16th-18th century
Touring: Europe, South America, USA, Far East
Comments: authentic instruments, see also Early Music

Grand Union Orchestra
Shoreditch Town Hall, 380 Old Street,
London EC1V 9LT
Tel: 20-7729 8729 Fax: 20-7729 8789
E-Mail: grandunion@btconnect.com
general manager Catherine Mummery; artistic director Tony Haynes
Size: 16-20 (orchestra), 8-10 (band) *Perfs:* 20 (Grand Union Band:10) *Type/spec:* jazz, world music
Venues: Orchestra – Queen Elizabeth Hall, London; Birmingham Symphony Hall, Sadler's Wells, Poole Arts Centre *Touring:* UK, Lisbon, Paris
Comments: education work; large scale community projects

Guildhall Strings
4 Addison Bridge Place, **London** W14 8XP
Tel: 20-7371 3755 Fax: 20-7371 3756
director Robert Salter; general manager Jeremy Woods
Size: 11 (plus harpsichord for baroque music) *Perfs:* 70
Type/spec: string ensemble repertoire for strings inc. baroque, classical, romantic, contemporary, plus works with soloists *Venues:* Barbican, Wigmore Hall, St. Johns Smith Square, South Bank Centre
Touring: South East Asia, UK, USA, Germany, Austria, Italy, France, Belgium
Comments: professional string ensemble consisting of 6 violins, 2 violas, 2 cellos, 1 bass

Icebreaker
26 Stadium Street, **London** SW10 0PT
Tel: 20-7351 6519/1306-889 057
Fax: 20-7351 6519/1306-889 057
Internet: www.icebreaker.org.uk
E-Mail: admin@icebreaker.org.uk
administrator Lewis Mitchell; artistic director James Poke
Size: 11 *Perfs:* 10-15 *Type/spec:* amplified contemporary music ensemble *Venues:* capcities of 200 up to 1000 (including Queen Elizabeth Hall)
Touring: Slovenia, Lithuania, Poland, Austria, Italy
Comments: CDs out on Argo & Newtone Records

King's Consort, The
34 St Mary's Grove, **London** W4 3LN
Tel: 20-8995 9994 Fax: 20-8995 2115
Internet: www.the-kings-consort.org.uk
E-Mail: info@the-kings-consort.org.uk
artistic manager Edward Hossack; artistic director Robert King; development director Nicky Oppenheimer; touring manager Eugenia Pino; administrator Elizabeth Baines
Size: 15-50 + 16-30 choir *Perfs:* 75
Type/spec: baroque and early classical on period instruments with/without choir/soloists; also chamber ensemble
Venues: Queen Elizabeth Hall, Wigmore Hall, London
Touring: Austria, Australia, Belgium, Brazil, Canada, Czech Republic, France, Germany, Hong Kong, Italy, Mexico, Netherlands, New Zealand, Norway, Poland, Portugal, Spain, Sweden, Switzerland, USA
Comments: coming seasons include fully-staged operas by Handel, Purcell, Rameau and Mozart in various European centres

London Chamber Players, The
PO Box 84, **London** NW11 8AL
Tel: 20-8455 9200 Fax: 20-8455 9200
administrator Sheila Genden; music director Adrian Sunshine
Size: 15-34 (also chamber ensembles) *Perfs:* 16-30
Type/spec: 17th C works to contemporary commissions/chamber operas
Touring: France, Spain, Thailand, Malaysia, Taiwan, Middle East, South America, Caribbean, South Africa
Comments: ensemble-in-residence, Middlesex University, London

London Festival Orchestra
The Warehouse, 13 Theed Street,
London SE1 8ST
Tel: 20-7928 9251
Fax: 20-7928 9252
Internet: www.lfo.co.uk
E-Mail: orchestra@lfo.co.uk
general manager Ian Pressland; artistic director Ross Pople; education & outreach officer Sarah Roseblade; executive manager, The Warehouse Elizabeth Szücs
Size: 15-55 *Perfs:* 75
Type/spec: chamber/symphonic, baroque to 20th century *Venues:* The Warehouse 200
Touring: South America, Turkey, Israel, Germany, France *Comments:* the only orchestra in Britain with own rehearsal and performance space and recording studio, these are available for hire

London Harpsichord Ensemble
10 Avenue Road, Highgate, **London** N6 5DW
Tel: 20-8340 5461 Fax: 20-8347 5907
Internet: www.cdj.co.uk/impulse/lhe.htm
director Sarah Francis
Size: 5-8 *Type/spec:* 18th & 20th century
Venues: Oct and Feb Purcell Room, music clubs, festivals, etc. *Touring:* Japan *Comments:* CDs on Unicorn label Unicorn-Kanchana

London Musici
C134, Learning Resource Centre, Thames Valley University, St. Mary's Road, **London** W5 5RF
Tel: 20-8231 2319 Fax: 20-8231 2316
E-Mail: london.musici@tvu.ac.uk
artistic director Mark Stephenson; administrator Trea Hubbard; orchestral manager Wendy Hacker; marketing & development manager Oasim Kazmi
Size: up to 45 *Perfs:* 150 (including tour with Rambert Dance Company) *Type/spec:* chamber orchestra pioneering interactive, cross arts programmes, incorporating dance, film and art *Venues:* established UK concert halls, theatres and corporate buildings *Touring:* UK *Comments:* resident orchestra at the Thames Valley University, a creative multi-media centre for the commissioning of new work for young audiences

London Philharmonic Orchestra, The
County Hall, Riverside Building,
Westminster Bridge Road, **London** SE1 7PB
Tel: 20-7546 1600/1666 (ticket bookings)
Fax: 20-7546 1601
Internet: www.lpo.org.uk
chief executive/artistic director Serge Dorny; president Bernard Haitink KBE; composer in focus Henri Dutilleux; general manager Andrew Gambrell; artistic administrator Ruth Sansom; director of marketing & developement Dominique Savelkoul; principal conductor Kurt Masur
Size: 90 *Perfs:* 160 (live) *Type/spec:* symphony
Venues: resident at Royal Festival Hall, London 2900, Glyndebourne Festival Opera 1200
Touring: international

London Sinfonietta
Dominion House, 101 Southwark Street,
London SE1 0JF
Tel: 20-7928 0828 Fax: 20-7928 8557
Internet: www.londonsinfonietta.org.uk
E-Mail: londonsinfonietta@atlas.co.uk
music director Oliver Knussen CBE; artistic director Gillian Moore MBE; managing director Cathy Graham; artistic administrator Jane Williams; press & marketing Vicky Pope
Size: varies *Type/spec:* contemporary *Venues:* Queen Elizabeth Hall 900 *Touring:* international *Comments:* associate of the Royal Festival Hall plus touring, recording & education programme

London Symphony Orchestra
Barbican Centre, **London** EC2Y 8DS
Tel: 20-7588 1116 Fax: 20-7374 0127
Internet: www.lso.co.uk
E-Mail: admin@lso.co.uk
managing director Clive Gillinson; administrator Sue Mallet; head of marketing Karen Cardy; head of education Karen Irwin; Shell LSO scholarship administrator & LSO systems manager Helen Smith; head of development Alison Dunnell; head of finance Kay Ford; principal conductor Sir Colin Davis CBE; principal guest conductor Michael Tilson Thomas; conductor laureate André Previn KBE; associate guest conductor Richard Hickox; assistant conductor Paul Mann; associate composer Colin Matthews; music animateur Richard McNicol; friends administrator Harriet Cross
Size: 110 *Perfs:* 85 (London) *Venues:* Barbican Hall 2000
Touring: national, international *Comments:* resident orchestra at the Barbican; also has a large educational programme: Discovery Programme

Lontano
Toynbee Studios, 28 Commercial St.,
London E1 6LS
Tel: 20-7247 2950 Fax: 20-7247 2956
administrator Jan Hart; musical director Odaline de la Martinez
Size: 3-15 *Perfs:* 10+ *Type/spec:* contemporary
Venues: Purcell Room, South Bank Centre, and various mid-scale venues *Touring:* national, international
Comments: 12 CDs on Lorelt (own record label)

Matrix Ensemble
77 Thrale Road, **London** SW16 1NU
Tel: 20-8769 7002 Fax: 20-8696 7293
E-Mail: nicky@nickywebbassoc.demon.co.uk
general manager Nicky Webb; musical director and principal conductor Robert Ziegler
Size: 7-35 *Type/spec:* mainly 20th century including new commissions, live scores for silent films *Comments:* collaborations with theatre, puppetry, film and concerts

maximum legroom
Flat 1, Manor Court, 390 Seven Sisters Road,
London N4 2PQ
Tel: 20-8809 1120 Fax: 20-8387 6660
E-Mail: michal.puchir@virgin.net
directors Joanna Dudley, Natasha Anderson
Size: 3 *Perfs:* 2-6
Type/spec: from early music to contemporary; commissioned works; innovative collaborations between musicians, composers, artists and sound designers
Venues: from small site-specific to concert halls
Comments: contact address in Australia: 149, Stanley Street, North Adelaide, 5006 SA, Australia,
tel & fax: +61 8-267 5618

Music Collection, The
38 Fairhazel Gardens, **London** NW6 3SJ
Tel: 20-7328 9347 Fax: 20-7328 4689
E-Mail: max@musicol.demon.co.uk
director Susan Alexander-Max; manager Jessica Max
Size: core of the group is Fortepiano trio (violin and cello) *Perfs:* 40+ *Type/spec:* instrumental – fortepiano based adding strings and wind as required: classical (late 18th and early 19th century, on occasion brand new commissions for historic instruments
Touring: festivals throughout the UK, Europe, N. Ireland, USA, Japan *Comments:* musicians-in-residence in various galleries and museums nationwide; recordings on Meridian, ASV

Music Projects/London
11 Elmwood Road, **London** W4 3DY
Tel: 20-8994 9528 Fax: 20-8994 9595
artistic directors Richard Bernas, Roger Williams; concert manager Nancy Ruffer
Size: 10-50 *Perfs:* 20 *Type/spec:* 20th century
Venues: all types *Touring:* UK

Nash Ensemble of London, The
14 Cedars Close, **London** NW4 1TR
Tel: 20-8203 3025 Fax: 20-8203 9540
administration co-ordinator Alison Rae; artistic director Amelia Freedman MBE, FRAM
Size: 3-20 *Perfs:* 60-75
Type/spec: chamber 18th, 19th, 20th century, contemporary including commissions
Venues: Wigmore Hall, South Bank Centre, Barbican, Bath Mozart festival *Touring:* international (including: Germany, Israel) *Comments:* recordings on Hyperion, Virgin Classics, CRD, NMC, Tel Dec

New London Consort
12 Vathouse, Regents Bridge Gardens,
London SW8 1HD
Tel: 20-7735 8154 Fax: 20-7820 0801
E-Mail: Philip.Pickett@btinternet.com
director Philip Pickett
Size: 4-40 *Perfs:* 70 *Type/spec:* medieval, renaissance and baroque vocal and instrumental *Venues:* resident at the South Bank Centre *Touring:* worldwide *Comments:* recordings on Decca L'oiseau-Lyre; associate of the South Bank Centre; see also Early Music

New Mozart Ensemble, The
5 Kensington Park Gardens, **London** W11 3HB
Tel: 20-7792 8027 Fax: 20-7243 8305
E-Mail: boutan@msn.com
director Paul Boucher; director/soloist Melvyn Tan; leaders Andrew Manze, Marieke Blankestijn
Size: 5-25 *Perfs:* 25
Type/spec: period and modern instruments; classical repertoire; chamber ensemble and chamber orchestra repertoire includes Hadyn, Gluck, Mozart & contemporary commissions
Venues: small-medium or large concert halls
Touring: UK, Netherlands, Germany, France
Comments: founder ensemble of the Festival de Saint-Agreve, France; CDs available

New Queen's Hall Orchestra
13 Cotswold Mews, 30 Battersea Square,
London SW11 3RA
Tel: 20-7223 7265 Fax: 20-7585 2830
E-Mail: manygate@easynet.co.uk
administrative director James Thomson; artistic director John Boyden
Size: 70-100 *Perfs:* 20-30
Type/spec: romantic *Venues:* several venues, UK and overseas, including residencies at Cliffs Pavillion, Southend, Malvern Festival
Comments: performances on instruments in common use in London at the turn of this century, with the expressive style of the period

Opera-In-Concert Orchestra
15 Mount Pleasant, **London** WC1X 0AA
Tel: 20-7833 0884 Fax: 20-7833 9883
E-Mail: weintz@aol.com
general manager Gary Brown; personnel manager Trevor Ford
Size: 40-70 *Perfs:* 30 *Type/spec:* opera orchestra
Venues: mid-large scale, major UK halls
Touring: national *Comments:* perform at opera galas, international celebrity concerts

Orchestra of St John's Smith Square
The White House, Eltham College, Grove Park Road,
London SE9 4QF
Tel: 20-7378 1358/8857 8579
Fax: 20-7403 5620/8857 9340
general manager Nicky Goulder; artistic director John Lubbock; education & audience development manager Anna Hall; concerts co-ordinator Alison Atkinson; associate composers Deirdre Gribbin, John Woolrich; press & publicity officer Helen Willis
Size: 12-80 *Perfs:* 20 at home, 60 on tour
Type/spec: chamber, all repertoire
Venues: St John's Smith Square, London 780, Oxford Town Hall 620 *Touring:* international
Comments: see also Choirs

Orchestra of the Age of Enlightenment
5th Floor, Westcomb House, 56-58 Whitcomb Street,
London WC2H 7DN
Tel: 20-7930 0646 Fax: 20-7930 0626
E-Mail: oae@premier.co.uk
general manager David Pickard; artistic administrator James Ellis
Size: 20-60 *Perfs:* 40 *Type/spec:* baroque, classical
Touring: Austria, Spain, Italy, France, Germany, Switzerland *Comments:* operas at Glyndebourne; associate orchestra at South Bank Centre, London; see also Early Music

Orchestre Révolutionnaire et Romantique
61 Wandsworth High Street, **London** SW18 2PT
Tel: 20-8871 4750 Fax: 20-8871 4751
Internet: www.monteverdi.co.uk
E-Mail: info@monteverdi.org.uk
artistic director Sir John Eliot Gardiner; administrator Jan Normanton; orchestra manager David Adams; acting general manager Howard Gough
Size: 45-100 *Perfs:* 10-20 *Type/spec:* late classical and romantic *Venues:* mid to large scale
Touring: Europe, USA

Philharmonia Orchestra
First Floor, 125 High Holborn, **London** WC1V 6QA
Tel: 20-7242 5001 Fax: 20-7242 4840
Internet: www.philharmonia.co.uk
E-Mail: info@philharmonia.co.uk
managing director David Whelton; deputy managing director Fiona Martin; development director Olga Geroulandos; marketing manager Jill Pridmore; finance director Michael Elliston; personnel manager Mansel Bebb
Size: 90 *Type/spec:* large-scale romantic symphony orchestra with a broad repertoire of music, ranging from the classical period to the present day *Venues:* Bedford Corn Exchange 718, De Montfort Hall 1451, Royal Festival Hall 2900, also resident at the Châtelet Theatre, Paris & Megaron Athens *Touring:* worldwide
Comments: resident at Royal Festival Hall (40 perfs. annually), Bedford (Corn Exchange), Leicester (De Montfort Hall);9 concerts per season at each of the regional venues

Piano Circus
20 Mentmore Terrace, **London** E8 3MP
Tel: 20-8533 4027 Fax: 20-8533 4027
Internet: www.pianocircus.co.uk
E-Mail: studio@pianocircus.demon.co.uk
co-director Kate Heath
Size: 6 *Type/spec:* contemporary music for six pianos/keyboards *Venues:* arts centres, community halls, concert halls, outside events *Touring:* UK, Indonesia, Italy *Comments:* wide experience of educational projects; the group has a fully portable studio

Quartz Saxophone Quartet
c/o Christian Forshaw, 66 Dangan Road,
London E11 2RF
Tel: 20-8989 6567 Fax: 20-8926 0065
E-Mail: lewis_mitchell@excite.com
manager Lewis Mitchell
Size: 4 *Type/spec:* saxophone quartet: repertoire comprising specially composed and arranged material as well as standard quartet repertoire *Venues:* Purcell Room, St John's Smith Square, Space Arts Centre
Touring: UK, Ireland *Comments:* performances and education workshops for festivals, BBC Radio 3, Young Artist's Forum, Live Music Now

QuintEssential Sackbut and Cornet Ensemble
10 King's Highway, Plumstead Common,
London SE18 2NL
Tel: 20-8855 8584 Fax: 20-8855 8584
Internet: www.landini.org/quint
E-Mail: quintessential@gtemail.net
director Richard Thomas
Type/spec: 16th C. vocal-instrumental and early English
Touring: Finland, UK

Raphael Ensemble, The
c/o Tennant Artists, Unit 2, 39 Tadema Road,
London SW10 0PY
Tel: 20-7376 3758 Fax: 20-7351 0679
E-Mail: info@tennantartists.demon.co.uk
manager Angela Sullivan
Size: 6 *Type/spec:* string sextet/quintet, standard repertoire *Touring:* South America, Europe, USA

Royal Philharmonic Orchestra
16 Clerkenwell Green, **London** EC1R 0DP
Tel: 20-7608 2381 Fax: 20-7608 1226
Internet: www.rpo.co.uk
managing director John Manger; music director Daniele Gatti; conductor laureate Yuri Temirkanov; associate conductor/composer Sir Peter Maxwell Davies; chairman Andy Sippings; vice chairman Julian Coward; head of development Sara Lom; head of education Judith Webster
Size: 85 *Perfs:* 175-200 *Type/spec:* classical, modern
Venues: resident orchestra at Royal Albert Hall
Touring: Europe, USA *Comments:* also resident at Royal Concert Hall in Nottingham

San Felice Contempoensemble
2 Pepys Rd, **London** SE14 5SB
Tel: 20-7358 0686
Fax: 20-7358 0686
Internet:
soalinux.comune.firenze.it/sanfelice/default.htm
E-Mail: ensemble@sanfelice.demon.co.uk
artistic director Andrea Cavallari; manager Veronica Del Signore; project development Rachel Tambini
Size: 4-12 *Perfs:* 25
Type/spec: ensemble for contemporary music, repertoire: 20th C. music from Italian composers
Venues: Chiesa di San Felice 400
Touring: Poland, UK, USA
Comments: second address:Piazza San Firenze 5, 50125, Firenze, Italy, Tel: +39 055-223 476, Fax: +39 055-229 699,

Schubert Ensemble of London, The
32 Wolverton Gardens, **London** W6 7DY
Tel: 20-8563 0618
Fax: 20-8741 5233
Internet: www.schubertensemble.com
E-Mail: senior.mgt@dial.pipex.com
manager Ann Senior
Size: 3-6 *Perfs:* 60-80
Type/spec: 18th, 19th and 20th century chamber music for piano and strings including contemporary commissions *Venues:* Wigmore Hall, South Bank Centre, major UK festivals and chamber venues, BBC venues *Touring:* Canada, USA, Europe, South America
Comments: main recordings for ASV, also for Hyperion; also have the Chamber Music 2000 project, set in motion by members of the Schubert Ensemble of London, to commission a large number of chamber works for piano and strings, from leading composers suitable to be played by young and amateur musicians

Sinfonia 21
14 Prince's Gardens, **London** SW7 1NA
Tel: 20-7584 2759
Fax: 20-7581 0970
Internet: www.orchestranet.co.uk/sinf21.html
E-Mail: info@sinfonia21.co.uk
chairman Sir Dennis Stevenson CBE; principal conductor Martyn Brabbins; chief executive Sue Bottomley; concerts manager Claire Wright; development manager (education) Katy Dent; community programme co-ordinator Valerie Thorncroft
Size: 3-40 *Perfs:* 20 *Type/spec:* chamber ensemble/orchestra *Venues:* resident at Imperial College, London and De La Warr Pavilion, Bexhill-on-Sea *Touring:* plans for Scandinavia, Russia, USA, China
Comments: dynamic young chamber ensemble with a commitment to contemporary music and experience in touring; particular emphasis on education and science/technology

Smith Quartet, The
6 Elfindale Road, **London** SE24 9NW
Tel: 20-7564 5676 Fax: 20-7564 5676
E-Mail: njm@musicon.demon.co.uk
manager Nick Morrison
Size: 4 *Perfs:* 30-40 *Type/spec:* string quartet with an almost exclusively contemporary repertoire including many commissions and often involving electronically produced sound *Touring:* UK, Europe, Far East
Comments: collaborations with musicians from other genres, particularly jazz

Symphonic Wind Orchestra of North London (SWON)
8 Elm Gardens, East Finchley, **London** N2 0TF
Tel: 20-8883 3365
E-Mail: stephen.kersley@virgin.net
musical director Stuart Allen; administrator Stephen Kersley
Size: 45 *Perfs:* 3
Type/spec: classical to modern
Comments: weekly rehearsal Tuesday evenings during term time at Brooklands Junior School, Hill Top, Hampstead Garden Suburb, London NW11; new players always welcome (minimum requirement: Grade 5 Associated Board)

Taverner Choir, Consort & Players
Ibex House, 42-46 Minories, **London** EC3N 1DY
Tel: 20-7481 2103/7480 6426
Fax: 20-7481 2865
artistic director Andrew Parrott; associate director Malcolm Bruno; administrator Victoria Newbert
Size: 5-50 *Perfs:* 15-20
Type/spec: 14th – 20th century repertoire *Touring:* Germany, Switzerland, France, Scandinavia

Temps contre Temps
55 Marmora Road, **London** SE22 0RY
Tel: 20-8299 1914 Fax: 20-8299 1914
E-Mail: Hirstpr@aol.com
administrator Diana Hirst
Size: 2 *Type/spec:* vocal and keyboard music of the 18th, 19th and 20th centuries
Touring: national
Comments: 2000/2001: Anglo-American programme and Central European programme

Apollo Saxophone Quartet
27 Birkdale Close, Tytherington,
Macclesfield SK10 2UA
Tel: 1625-425 840 Fax: 1625-425 840
E-Mail: apollo4tet@aol.com
contact Rob Buckland
Size: 4 *Perfs:* 40 *Type/spec:* contemporary chamber group, original contemporary music for saxophone ensemble with jazz, folk and world music influences *Venues:* small-large scale *Touring:* Japan, UK (50th anniversary tour) *Comments:* innovative young ensemble committed to performing and commissioning new works; extensive education and community work; recordings on Argo & own label; new project: original music written by members of the group, accompanied by black and white silent films and live poetry respectively

English String/Symphony Orchestra
Rockliffe House, 40 Church Street,
Malvern WR14 2AZ
Tel: 1684-560 696 Fax: 1684-560 656
Internet: www.eso.co.uk
E-Mail: info@eso.co.uk
artistic/music director William Boughton; head of administration & finance Alison King; administration Kate Hodson
Size: 49 (symphony), 18-23 (string) *Perfs:* 130 *Type/spec:* symphony orchestra & string orchestra specialising in contemporary & 20th century English repertoire *Venues:* throughout UK, capacity 400 to 2120, including Symphony Hall, Birmingham; Oxford Sheldonian Theatre, Coventry Cathedral; New Space, Malvern theatres, Gloucester Cathedral, Worcester Cathedral, Hereford Cathedral, Concert Hall of the Nimbus Foundation, Telford Oakengates Theatre *Touring:* Switzerland, Italy, Norway, Lithuania, Germany, Spain, Greece *Comments:* over 50 recordings with Nimbus Records; charity no – 293345

BBC Philharmonic
New Broadcasting House, Oxford Road,
Manchester M60 1SJ
Tel: 161-244 4001 Fax: 161-244 4211
E-Mail: amanda.dorr@bbc.co.uk
orchestra manager Fiona Mcintosh; principal conductor Yan Pascal Tortelier; composer/conductor Sir Peter Maxwell-Davies (from 2001: James MacMillan); principal guest conductor Vassily Siaisky; conductor emeritus Sir Edward Downes; general manager Brian Pidgeon; marketing manager Amanda Dorr; projects manager Martin Maris
Size: 89 *Perfs:* 60 public (180 hrs for Radio 3) *Type/spec:* major pioneer of 20th century British music *Venues:* Studio 7, New Broadcasting House; Bridgewater Hall *Touring:* international *Comments:* 180 hours of broadcasting for Radio 3; exclusive recording contract with Chandos Records Ltd

Halle Orchestra
The Bridgewater Hall, **Manchester** M2 3WS
Tel: 161-237 7000 Fax: 161-237 7029
chief executive John Summers; music director and principal conductor Kent Nagano (from June 2000: Mark Elder); concerts & artistic planning director t.b.a.; sponsorship enquiries Lauren Gamsu; education director Richard Wigley; director of marketing & pr Andy Ryans; finance director Lesley Thomlinson
Size: 80 *Perfs:* 140 *Type/spec:* symphony
Venues: The Bridgewater Hall
Touring: national, international *Comments:* wide range of education and community work

Manchester Camerata
Zion Arts Centre, Stretford Road,
Manchester M15 5ZA
Tel: 161-226 8696 Fax: 161-226 8600
Internet: www.manchestercamerata.org.uk
E-Mail: mancam@compuserve.com
general manager Lucy Potter; principal conductor Sachio Fujioka
Size: 15-60 *Perfs:* 100 *Type/spec:* classical chamber repertoire *Venues:* The Bridgewater Hall, Manchester; Queen Elizabeth Hall, Oldham; Municipal Hall, Colne; Lyceum Theatre, Crewe; Civic Hall, Nantwich; Royal Northern College of Music, Manchester

Milton Keynes City Orchestra
3 Theatre Walk, **Milton Keynes** MK9 3PX
Tel: 1908-692 777 Fax: 1908-230 099
Internet: www.orchestranet.co.uk/miltonco.html
E-Mail: rodbirtles@cityorch.freeserve.co.uk
general manager Rod Birtles; artistic director Hilary Davan Wetton
Perfs: 8 *Venues:* Milton Keynes Theatre 1400

Romantic Chamber Group of London, The
Brick Kiln Cottage, Hollington, **Newbury** RG20 9XX
Tel: 1635-254 331 Fax: 1635-253 629
E-Mail: C.Medlam@BTINTERNET.COM
contact Charles Medlam
Size: 3+ *Perfs:* 20+ concerts *Type/spec:* from the romantic era to the present day with special emphasis on little known work *Touring:* Europe, USA
Comments: see also Early Music (London Baroque)

Northern Sinfonia
The Sinfonia Centre, 41 Jesmond Vale,
Newcastle-upon-Tyne NE2 1PG
Tel: 191-240 1812 Fax: 191-240 2668
E-Mail: nsinfonia@ndirect.co.uk
chief executive t.b.a.; artistic director t.b.a.; development & marketing director Lucy Bird; head of planning Christine Lee; finance director George Fox; marketing manager Emily Till
Size: 30 *Perfs:* up to 100 *Type/spec:* chamber *Venues:* mid-scale, including City Hall 2133 *Touring:* national, international *Comments:* CDs available; offer wide range of educational and outreach programmes

City of Oxford Orchestra
Bury Knowle House, North Place, Headington,
Oxford OX3 9HY
Tel: 1865-744 457 Fax: 1865-744 481/739 539
E-Mail: cityofoxford.orchestra@which.net
artistic director Roger Payne; chairperson Lindsay Sandison; associate conductor Duncan Hinnells
Size: up to 65 *Perfs:* 24 *Type/spec:* flexible repertoire, particular emphasis on baroque *Venues:* Sheldonian Theatre 850 *Touring:* international *Comments:* CDs with Carlton; all year round concerts; celebrating 35th anniversary in 2000

English Performing Arts Ensemble
7 Essluv Road, Lower House, **Oxford** OX4 1EA
Tel: 956-352 429 (mobile)
E-Mail: gleacox@hotmail.com
conductor and artistic director Graham Lea-Cox
Perfs: 5-20 *Type/spec:* instrumental/chamber orchestra inc. chorus and vocal soloists; late 18th/early 19th C, contemporary 20th C *Venues:* period venues, major concert halls (e.g. South Bank) *Touring:* international *Comments:* project-based ensemble conceived for recordings and specific programme work (inc. video/film); all programmes constructed and researched especially from original sources; performers drawn from leading London modern/period orchestras; agents contact: English Performing Arts

Bournemouth Sinfonietta
Bournemouth Orchestras, 2 Seldown Lane,
Poole BH15 1UF
Tel: 1202-670 611 Fax: 1202-687 235
managing director Michael Henson; director and associate conductor Richard Studt; concerts director Michael Marx; principal conductor Alexander Polianichko
Size: 30 *Perfs:* 130 *Type/spec:* chamber *Venues:* Wessex Hall, Poole Arts Centre 1593 *Touring:* UK, and continuous touring in South & West England *Comments:* community and education programmes; see also Bournemouth Symphony Orchestra

Bournemouth Symphony Orchestra
Bournemouth Orchestras, 2 Seldown Lane,
Poole BH15 1UF
Tel: 1202-670 611 Fax: 1202-687 235
managing director Michael Henson; general manager Cristina Rocca; principal conductor Yakov Kreizberg (until May 2000); conductor laureate Andrew Litton; chief guest conductor Kees Bakels; conductor emeritus Paavo Berglund; composer emeritus Henri Dutilleux
Size: 80 *Perfs:* 130 *Type/spec:* 19thC, contemporary *Venues:* Wessex Hall, Poole Arts Centre 1593, and 8 subscription venues *Touring:* UK, Europe; continuous touring in South & West England *Comments:* community and education programmes; see also Bournemouth Sinfonietta

Vivaldi Concertante
35 Laurel Avenue, **Potters Bar** EN6 2AB
Tel: 1707-650 735/643 366 Fax: 1707-650 735
conductor Joseph Pilbery; administrator Audrey Banker; chairman Maurice Powell
Size: 12-40 *Type/spec:* light classical *Venues:* St John's Smith Square, also various concert halls and stately homes *Comments:* specialise in helping young musicians; CDs available on own label

Northern Chamber Orchestra
2 Lodge Court, Preston Road, Inskip, **Preston** PR4 0TT
Tel: 1772-690 493 Fax: 1772-690 493
general manager Brian Leighton; musical director Nicholas Ward
Size: 24 players + extras as required *Perfs:* 40 *Type/spec:* chamber orchestra (chamber ensemble as NCO Soloists) *Venues:* Heritage Centre, Macclesfield 300; Blackburn Cathedral 400; Chorley Town Hall 300, Todmorden Town Hall 300, Preston Charter Theatre 780, Tatton Park 400 *Comments:* its reputation extends worldwide through its recordings on the Naxos label

English Sinfonia
1 Wedgwood Court, **Stevenage** SG1 4QR
Tel: 1438-350 990 Fax: 1438-350 930
Internet: www.Stevenage.gov.uk/EnglishSinfonia
E-Mail: EnglishSinfonia@tesco.net
chief executive Graham Pfaff; principal conductor Nicolae Moldoveanu; manager Karen Foster; composer in association David Bedford; leader Janice Graham
Size: 35 *Perfs:* 50 *Type/spec:* chamber, English music, classical period *Touring:* worldwide *Comments:* recording available; outreach work undertaken

English Classical Players
25b Epsom Lane South, **Tadworth** KT20 5TA
Tel: 1737-813 273 Fax: 1737-215 676
executive director Lyn Mumford; artistic director Jonathan Brett
Size: 20-60 players *Perfs:* 20 *Type/spec:* chamber, classical 18th & 19th century repertoire
Venues: theatres, concert halls 400 up to 1500
Touring: national, international
Comments: member of the Association of British Orchestras, approved by the Eastern Orchestral Board and supported by South East Arts; CD available

Allegri String Quartet
c/o Sarah Moyse, 5 The Barons, St Margarets,
Twickenham TW1 2AN
Tel: 20-8892 3848 Fax: 20-8892 3848
Internet: www.cdj.co.uk/impulse/allegri.htm
E-Mail: Allegri@moyse.demon.co.uk
Size: 4 *Type/spec:* string quartet

Haffner Wind Ensemble of London, The
c/o Upbeat Management, Sutton Business Centre, Restmor Way, **Wallington** SM6 7AH
Tel: 20-8773 1223 Fax: 20-8669 6752
E-Mail: classic@upbeat.co.uk
director Nicolas Daniel; contact Maureen Phillips
Size: 5

Academy of London
Studio 26, Building 56, Magnet Road, G.E.C. Estate, East Lane, **Wembley** HA9 7RG
Tel: 20-8908 4348 Fax: 20-8908 4713
artistic director Richard Stamp; general manage Joanne Lyoo
Size: 15-40 *Perfs:* 20
Type/spec: chamber

European Union Baroque Orchestra
Hordley, Wootton, **Woodstock** OX20 1EP
Tel: 1993-812 111 Fax: 1993-812 911
Internet: www.eubo.org.uk
E-Mail: info@eubo.org.uk
general administrator Paul James; orchestral manager Emma Wilkinson; development director Nick Berry; music director Roy Goodman
Size: 24 (100% annual renewal) *Perfs:* 40
Type/spec: baroque chamber orchestra (on authentic instruments) – main repertoire 17th and 18th century music *Touring:* worldwide *Comments:* pre-professional training orchestra funded by European Commission and Matsushita Electric Europe (Headquarters); see also Early Music

YUGOSLAVIA (+381)

Due to the war in Kosovo we have been unable to update the following entries for Yugoslavia

Belgrade Philharmonia
Beogradska Filharmonija
Akademski Trg 11, 11000 **Belgrade**
Tel: 11-635 518/630 744 Fax: 11-187 533
director Branka Cvejic

Belgrade Radio and Television Symphony Orchestra
Simfonijski Orkestar RTV Beograd
Hilendarska 2, 11000 **Belgrade**
Tel: 11-324 8888 Fax: 11-322 6768
director Stanko Marusic

Choir and Symphony Orchestra of the Yugoslav Army
Brace Jugovica 19, 11000 **Belgrade**
Tel: 11-323 4771

Jazz Orchestra of Belgrade Radio and TV
Jazz Orkestar RTV Beograd
Hilendarska 2, 11000 **Belgrade**
Tel: 11-324 8888 Fax: 11-322 6768
director Franjo Jenc

St. George String Orchestra
Kamerni orkestar gudaci Sv. jordja
Akademski trg 10, 11000 **Belgrade**
Tel: 11-637 573
conductor Petar Ivanovic

Nis Symphony Orchestra
Niski Simfonijski Orkestar
Stanka Paunovica 16, 18000 **Nis**
Tel: 18-23047 Fax: 18-23047
director Nenad Katanic

Belgrade Strings Orchestra 'Dusan Skovran'
Beogradski Gudacki Orkestar 'Dusan Skovran'
c/o Sava Centar, Milentija Popovica 9,
11070 **Novi Beograd**
Tel: 11-143 450/3/4322 x771 Fax: 11-311 1156
director & conductor Aleksandar Pavlovic

Montenegro Radio and Television Symphony Orchestra
Simfonijski orkestar RTV Crne Gore
Cetinjski pur bb, 81000 **Podgorica**
Tel: 81-25999
conductor Radovan Papovic

Early Music

Early Music
Information of groups in this section has been based on information received about engagements. We do not intend to pass judgement on quality. If you wish to be considered for inclusion, please send information regarding performances and touring engagements to the editor.
Within country the Early Music groups are ordered alphabetically by ensemble name.

Musique Ancienne
Les ensembles inclus dans cette rubrique ont été selectionnés selon les informations reçuees quant à leurs engagements. Nous ne faisons ainsi aucun jugement qualitatif. Si vous désirez être inclus, veuillez nous envoyer des informations de vos répresentations et vos tournées au redacteur.
Dans chacque section nationale les ensembles sont par ordre alphabétique selon le nom d'ensemble.

Alte Musik
Die in dieser Rubrik aufgeführten Gruppen wurden aufgrund Ihrer Angaben über Engagements ausgewählt. Es liegt uns fern, mit dieser Auswahl eine qualitative Beurteilung auszusprechen. Falls Sie Interesse daran haben, ebenfalls in dieser Rubrik aufgeführt zu werden, senden Sie bitte Informationen betr. Auftritte und Engagements an die Redaktion.
Die Einträge sind innerhalb aller Staaten alphabetisch nach Namen geordnet.

Musica Antica
La scelta dei gruppi di musica antica in questa sezione é avvenuta dopo aver considerato il numero degli spettacoli al cui il gruppo ha partecipato. L'inclusione non puó, perció, essere considerato in giudizo sulla qualitá del gruppo. Se siete interessati ad essere inclusi vi preghiamo di inviare delle informazioni riguardo il numero di spettacoli e/o di tournee al redattore del PAYE.
I gruppi di musica antica sono ordinati alfabeticamente all' interno dei paesi.

Música Antigua
Hemos incluido estos grupos de Música Antigua según información que investigamos sobre sus representaciones y calendarios, es decir si actuan a menudo o no/van de giras nacionales o internacionales o no/etc. No pretendemos asegurar de la calidad de los grupos. Si qualquier persona quiere que salgan datos de su grupo el la próxima edición, pongase en contacto con el redactor.
Dentro del país, se han ordenado los grupos de Música Antigua alfabéticamente por nombre del grupo.

Early Music (초기 음악)
이 부문에 기재된 그룹 정보는 입수된 공연 정보에 기초한다. 그룹 수준에 대한 평가는 하지 않는다. 이 리스트에 포함되기를 원하면, 공연 및 순회 공연에 대한 정보를 편집자에게 보내시오.**리스트는 국가별로 단체명에 따라 알파벳순으로 기재되었다.**

早期音乐
这一章节中的音乐团体情报是根据已收到的有关演出节目的情报而列出的。我们无意对演出的质量作出评判。如果您想让我们将贵公司考虑在内的话，请将有关演出和巡回演出节目的情报寄给编辑，**在每个国家里早期音乐团体是按剧团名字的字母顺序来排列的。**

古代音楽
この章には公演に関して提供された情報を基にグループが掲載されています。各グループの水準を判断するものではありません。リストへの掲載を希望するグループは公演に関する情報を編集者までお送り下さい。**リストは国別で、一国内ではアルファベット順に記載されています。**

ARMENIA (+374)

KEM – Early Music Quartet
Yerevan Chamber Music Hall, 1 Isahakian Street, 375025 **Yerevan**
Tel: 2-526 780/536 990
artistic director Armen Ghukasian
Size: 4

Sharakan Early Music Ensemble of Radio Company of Armenia
5 Alek Manookian Street, 375000 **Yerevan**
Tel: 2-722 496 Fax: 2-151 947
artistic director Grigor Danielian

Tagharan Early Music State Ensemble
Yerevan Chamber Music Hall, 1 Isahakian Street, 375025 **Yerevan**
Tel: 2-565 087/526 780/342 860/525 840 Fax: 2-525 840
artistic director Sedrak Yerkanian

AUSTRIA (+43)

Barocktrio Wien
c/o Mag. Eugen Lukaschek, Zanaschkagasse 14/43/39, 1120 **Wien**
Tel: 1-667 1913 Fax: 1-667 1913
Leitung Prof. Mag. Helmut Schaller; Sekretariat Mag. Eugen Lukaschek
Size: 3 *Type/Spec:* instrumental (recorder, harpsichord, viola da gamba) *Repertoire:* early and late baroque, pre-classic *Perfs:* 4-5 *Touring:* Argentina, South-Korea *Comments:* see also Kammertrio Linz-Wien

Clemencic Consort
Reisnerstrasse 26/7, 1030 **Wien**
Tel: 1-712 5341
Fax: 1-712 5020
Organisation Johanna Trabitsch; Leitung Prof. Dr. Rene Clemencic
Size: 3-45 *Type/Spec:* instrumental, vocal/instrumental *Repertoire:* medieval, renaissance, baroque & new compositions *Perfs:* 40 *Touring:* Austria, Italy, Spain, Switzerland, Germany

Collegium Musicum Wien
Sonnenuhrgasse 1/11, 1060 **Wien**
Tel: 1-596 4426 (home no.) Fax: 1-596 4426
E-Mail: mitisek@aol.com
music director Andreas Mitisek
Size: up to 25 *Repertoire:* baroque, classical *Comments:* see also Orchestra

Consortium Margaritari Ensemble für Alte Musik
c/o Margaretha Novak, Wiengasse 6/5/12, 1140 **Wien**
Tel: 1-979 2963 Fax: 1-586 1571
contact Prof. Margaretha Novak
Size: 8-15 *Type/Spec:* instrumental, vocal, dancers *Repertoire:* medieval, renaissance, early baroque *Perfs:* 10 *Touring:* Greece, Germany, Japan, Austria, Turkey, Tunisia, Czech Republic

Ensemble Accentus
Arnolz 10, 3834 **Pfaffenschlag**
Tel: 2848-6442 Fax: 2848-5058
artistic director Thomas Wimmer
Size: 4-12 *Type/Spec:* vocal/instrumental *Repertoire:* Spanish renaissance, Sephardic music, Austrian renaissance *Perfs:* 30 *Touring:* Spain, Portugal, Germany, Italy, Belgium, Switzerland *Comments:* CDs available; former recording with Naxos, also 1 CD produced by Innsbruck Festival of Early Music; new CD-series with GLOSSA: Austria and the East

Ensemble Unicorn
c/o Michael Posch, Hietzinger Kai 63/1, 1130 **Wien**
Tel: 1-876 6287 Fax: 1-876 6510
E-Mail: M.Posch@xpoint.at
artistic director Michael Posch
Size: 5-9 *Type/Spec:* instrumental and vocal *Repertoire:* 13th – 15th century *Perfs:* 25 *Touring:* worldwide *Comments:* 8 CDs available

Kammertrio Linz-Wien (KTLW)
Weiglgasse 21/18, 1150 **Wien**
Tel: 1-892 9332 Fax: 1-892 9332
Internet: www.pcnews.at/kknf/kknf.htm
Leitung Prof. Mag. Helmut Schaller;
Sekretariat Mag. Eugen Lukaschek
Size: 3 *Type/Spec:* recorder, baroque violin, Austrian guitar chamber music *Repertoire:* renaissance, early and late baroque, classical, 20th C, based on contemporary Austrian composers *Perfs:* approx. 20 *Touring:* Austria, Germany, France, Italy, South Korea, Indonesia, Tunisia *Comments:* 3 CDs and ensemble prospectus available; see also Barocktrio Wien (q.v.)

La Follia Salzburg
Moos Str. 41 G, 5020 **Salzburg**
Tel: 662-833 994
Fax: 662-833 994
artistic director Clemens Nußbaumer
Size: varies *Type/Spec:* small baroque ensemble (6) up to orchestra, instrumental, vocal *Repertoire:* baroque from 1600-1750

Orpheon Consort
Praterstraße 13/1/3, 1020 **Wien**
Tel: 1-214 3021 Fax: 1-214 3021
Internet: www.orpheon.org
E-Mail: orpheon@orpheon.org
Leitung Prof. José Vázquez
Type/Spec: vocal, instrumental and orchestral *Repertoire:* renaissance, baroque, classical music *Comments:* also Orpheon museum of historical string instruments from 16th, 17th and 18th centuries; instruments restored to baroque and renaissance measurements and used in concert, or loaned out to musicians for concerts, recordings, etc.

Piccolo Concerto – Wein
Knöllgasse 53/8, 1100 **Wien**
Tel: 1-606 5698 Fax: 1-606 5698
contact Johanna Sensi-Gamerith; Leitung Roberto Sensi
Size: 3-10 *Type/Spec:* instrumental, vocal *Repertoire:* classical, romantic chamber music on period instruments *Perfs:* 15 *Touring:* Italy *Comments:* successor of Gamerith Consort ensemble

Salzburger Barocksolisten
Ganshofstraße 31, 5020 **Salzburg**
Tel: 662-831 177 Fax: 662-831 1774
E-Mail: dacapo@eunet.at
Leitung Reinhold Malzer
Size: 5-8 *Type/Spec:* instrumental and vocal *Repertoire:* mainly baroque, some classical *Perfs:* 10 *Touring:* Europe

Wiener Akademie
Reisnerstrasse 32, 1030 **Wien**
Tel: 1-713 6082 Fax: 1-718 2913
E-Mail: wienak@eunet.at
Musikalische Leitung Martin Haselböck
Size: varies *Type/Spec:* instrumental, vocal *Repertoire:* baroque, classical, romantic on period instruments *Perfs:* 30-40 *Touring:* Europe, USA, Japan, South America

BELGIUM (+32)

Anima Eterna Baroque Ensemble
Akenkaai 2, 1000 **Brussels**
Tel: 2-201 0874 Fax: 2-201 5418
E-Mail: anima.eterna@euronet.be
conductor & artistic director Jos van Immerseel; production & office director Sandra Fol; pr & sales coordinator Patrick Suttels; technical director Frank Van Elsen
Size: 15-25 *Type/Spec:* specific repertoires are studied in depth using newest musicological research and playing period instruments *Repertoire:* 17th-18th century *Perfs:* 20-30 *Touring:* Europe, Japan, USA *Comments:* recordings with Channel Classics, Sony Classical; funded by the Government of Flanders; see also Orchestras and Instrumental Ensembles

Capilla Flamenca
Hambosstraat 31, 3150 **Tildonk**
Tel: 16-602 836 Fax: 16-602 836
E-Mail: capilla.flamenca@club.innet.be
artistic director & contact Dirk Snellings; programmation Eugeen Schreurs
Size: 4-10 *Repertoire:* medieval and early renaissance, 15th-16th C, polyphony of the low countries, Spain, Portugal *Perfs:* 25 *Touring:* Belgium, Netherlands, France, Poland, Austria, Spain, Portugal *Comments:* research on songs of the Franco-Flemish period; music of the court of the Dukes of Bourgondy; several CDs

Cetra d'Orfeo, La
Avenue de la Pinède 39, 1180 **Brussels**
Tel: 2-375 6292 Fax: 2-375 6292
Internet: www.cci-oise.fr/classic-news/cetra.htm
E-Mail: cetra.keustermans@skynet.be
contact Jacques Keustermans; artistic director Michel Keustermans
Size: 6-9 *Type/Spec:* 17th/18th C Italian, 18th C German and French composers, Belgium and Dutch baroque composers *Repertoire:* baroque *Perfs:* 25 *Touring:* France, Italy

Collegium Vocale Gent
Drongenhof 42, 9000 **Gent**
Tel: 9-265 9050 Fax: 9-265 9051
Internet: www.collegiumvocale.com
E-Mail: stephane.leys@collegiumvocale.com
manager Stephane Leys; conductor Philippe Herreweghe
Size: 18-42 *Repertoire:* baroque, rennaissance to romantic *Perfs:* 40-50 *Touring:* Europe, Japan, Australia, USA *Comments:* see also Choirs

Currende
Sint Albaansberg 57, 1020 **Brussels**
Tel: 2-479 0881 Fax: 2-479 8534
manager Gertie Lindemans; secretary Willem Ceuleers; artistic manager Erik ven Nevel
Size: Currende Consort (5-6 soloists); Concerto Currende (baroque orchestra 12 strings, 2-3 woodwinds); Capella Currende (choir 12-20) *Repertoire:* renaissance to classical, Flemish polyphony *Perfs:* 40 *Touring:* Germany, Israel, Spain, Italy, Netherlands *Comments:* recording 2 CDs each year, TV broadcast each year

Ensemble Contrepoint
c/o Isabelle Lamfalussy, Rue de Faux 61c, 1490 **Court-St-Etienne**
Tel: 10-616 144 Fax: 10-616 144
E-Mail: faux@infonie.be
contacts Isabelle Lamfalussy, Michel Igisch
Size: 3-8 *Type/Spec:* period instruments, thematic concerts *Repertoire:* baroque *Perfs:* 15 *Touring:* Belgium, Luxembourg, France

Ensemble Daedalus
Vital Decosterstraat 72, 3000 **Leuven**
Tel: 16-230 830 Fax: 16-227 610
E-Mail: geert.robberechts@ping.be
administrators Geert Robberechts, Marijke Van Campenhout; musical director Roberto Festa
Size: 6-20 singers and instrumentalists *Repertoire:* renaissance & baroque *Touring:* Switzerland, France, Belgium

Flanders Recorder Quartet Vier op 'n Rij
Vital Decosterstraat 72, 3000 **Leuven**
Tel: 16-230 830 Fax: 16-227 610
E-Mail: geert.robberechts@ping.be
administrator Marijke Van Campenhout
Size: 4 (programs with additional singers, b.c. or gamba consort are possible) *Repertoire:* mainly early music, also cross-over and contemporary *Perfs:* 50 *Touring:* USA, Japan, Slovenia, France, Germany, Mexico, Austria, Belgium, UK

Huelgas Ensemble
c/o Heiken 86, 2920 **Kalmthout**
Tel: 3-666 6651 Fax: 3-666 6651
music director/conductor Paul van Nevel
Size: 12-50 *Type/Spec:* vocal and instrumental *Repertoire:* medieval, renaissance *Perfs:* 35-40 *Touring:* Europe *Comments:* perform on period instruments; 24 recordings available; Paul van Nevel address: Diestsevest 115, PO 3000, Leuven tel:16-294 442 fax:16-236 533

I Fiamminghi
Buizenbergstraat 1c, 9830 **St-Martens-Latem**
Tel: 9-282 7134 Fax: 9-282 7831
E-Mail: i.fiamminghi@ping.be
artistic director/conductor Rudolf Werthen; pr, projects & music publishing manager Peter Gistelinck
Size: 15-50 *Type/Spec:* chamber, string, wind *Repertoire:* 19th/20th century, from baroque to contemporary music *Perfs:* 80 *Touring:* South America, USA, Europe, Japan *Comments:* see also Orchestras

Le Plaisir des Dames/Quartetto Giordani
Hollekelderstraat 12, 2920 **Kalmthout**
Tel: 3-666 2641 Fax: 3-666 5987
E-Mail: Wim.Brabants@village.uunet.be
director/conductor Wim Brabants
Size: Le Plaisir des Dames 4; Quartetto Giordani 4 *Repertoire:* Le Plaisir des Dames: baroque; Quartetto Giordani: classical *Perfs:* 20 *Touring:* Belgium

les ennemis confus
Arisdonk 18, 9950 **Waarschoot**
Tel: 9-378 4828 Fax: 9-233 6293
artistic director Marcel Ketels
Size: 4 *Type/Spec:* chamber music with 2 recorders, 1 harpsichord, 1 theorbo, 1 viola (when French repertoire) *Repertoire:* baroque 17-18th century *Perfs:* 15 *Touring:* Belgium, France *Comments:* 2 CDs available; last CD has won 4 Diapason awards

Petite Bande, La
rue Vital Decoster 72, 3000 **Leuven**
Tel: 16-230 830 Fax: 16-227 610
Internet: www.ping.be/lapetitebande
E-Mail: geert.robberechts@ping.be
manager Geert Robberechts; conductor Sigiswald Kuijken
Size: 30-50 *Type/Spec:* instrumental, occasionally vocal *Repertoire:* baroque, classical *Perfs:* 50 *Touring:* Belgium, France, Italy, Spain, Poland, Hungary, Japan, South America, Australia *Comments:* see also Orchestras

Terpsychore
Route de Jemeppe 7, 6950 **Harsin**
Tel: 84-344 492
director Xavier Haag
Size: 22-24 *Type/Spec:* instrumental and vocal, continuo, chamber orchestra *Repertoire:* baroque (Bach + others), 17th C, 20th C *Perfs:* 12-15 *Comments:* work in collaboration with the Terpsychore Choir (q.v.)

Trio Solstice
rue de Faux 61C, 1490 **Court-St-Etienne**
Tel: 10-616 144 Fax: 10-616 144
E-Mail: faux@infonie.be
contact Isabelle Lamfalussy
Size: 3 *Type/Spec:* classical & romantic (1760 – 1830); chamber music played on period instruments *Perfs:* 10

BOSNIA & HERZEGOVINA (+387)

Baroque Trio
c/o Music Academy, Josip Tadler Str 1, **Sarajevo**
Tel: 71-200 299/444 896 Fax: 71-444 896
contact Dzevad Sabanagic
Type/Spec: violin, flute, piano

BULGARIA (+359)

Aqua
National Academy of Theater, Rakovski Str., 1000 **Sofia**
Tel: 2-365 600
director Deljana Mitcheva
Type/Spec: vocal (percussions) *Repertoire:* Bulgarian folklore; medieval *Perfs:* 10 *Touring:* Europe

Te Deum Adoramus
Bl. 239 -4, ap. 19, Mladost, **Sofia**
Tel: 2-754 515
Internet: www.cblink.net/clients/tedeum
E-Mail: tedi@cblink.net
conductor Teodora Dimitrova
Repertoire: medieval, renaissance, classical, contemporary *Perfs:* 20 *Touring:* Europe

CZECH REPUBLIC (+420)

Ars Cameralis
Vápencová 10, 147 00 **Praha** 4
Tel: 2-428 7134 Fax: 2-428 7134
E-Mail: cameralis@email.cz
artistic director Lukás Matousek
Comments: also play contemporary music

Musica Antiqua Praha
Hroznová 2, 118 00 **Praha** 1
Tel: 2-533 506 Fax: 2-533 506
artistic director Pavel Klikar
Type/Spec: vocal and instrumental

Musica Florea
c/o Impresario, Celetná 19, 116 22 **Praha** 1
Tel: 2-231 8695 Fax: 2-2481 9135
Internet: www.musica.cz/mflorea
artistic director Marek Stryncl
Type/Spec: baroque music, vocal and instrumental

Musica Fresca
K brusce 4, 160 00 **Praha** 6
Tel: 2-3332 3592
E-Mail: cizner@mbox.vol.cz
director Kveta Cíznerová
Size: 5 vocalists + 3 instrumentalists *Type/spec:* vocal-instrumental *Repertoire:* specialise in authentic interpretation of renaissance and early baroque music *Comments:* the ensemble regularly cooperates with the Czech TV and radio; 2 CD's available on Bonton Music

Prazstí Madrigalisté
Pocernická 61, POB 69, 160 00 **Praha** 8
Tel: 2-8194 0467/602-272 974(mobile) Fax: 2-625 1957
Internet:
www.pareto.copin.it/turboprint/madridga.html
artistic director Damiano Binetti
Type/Spec: vocal and instrumental *Repertoire:* renaissance, early baroque, also play contemporary music

DENMARK (+45)

Concerto Copenhagen
c/o Greiff Musik, Gammeltofesgade 16, 1355 **Copenhagen** K
Tel: 3313 5570/5580 Fax: 3313 5540
Internet: www.coco.dk
E-Mail: info@coco.dk
production manager Anja Reiff; administrative manager Nicolai Gjessing
Size: 8-38 *Type/Spec:* baroque and classical on period instruments *Repertoire:* from Monteverdi to Mozart & Haydn *Perfs:* 20-30 *Comments:* opera productions at The Royal Opera, Copenhagen; historical marionette opera; radio productions; first recordings of Scandinavian composers

Oliver Hirsh
Råmosevej 7A, 4672 **Klippinge**
Tel: 5657 8254 Fax: 5657 8254
E-Mail: oliver@email.dk
contact Oliver Hirsh
Size: 5-6 *Type/Spec:* viol consort, consort song, chamber organ *Repertoire:* English music mid-16th/mid-17th C, especially William Byrd, Italian music from Cavazzoni to Frescobaldi *Touring:* Germany, Denmark

Opus 4
Svenstrupvej 10, 2700 **Brønshøj**
Tel: 3874 1042 Fax: 3874 1042
E-Mail: vick.dag@vip.cybercity.dk
contact Vicki Boeckman
Size: 4 *Type/Spec:* recorders, viol, lute and organ *Repertoire:* 17th and 18th century Trio sonatas, trios and quartets *Perfs:* 20-25 *Touring:* Denmark

Violon Banden
Herthavej 1B, 2920 **Charlottenlund**
Tel: 3990 1016 Fax: 3990 1218
E-Mail: trsv@get2net.dk
conductor Troels Svendsen
Size: 6 *Type/Spec:* string players and trombone *Repertoire:* baroque chamber music 17th and 18th century *Perfs:* 20 *Comments:* the conductor is also a member of the 18th century orchestra; 2 CDs available

ESTONIA (+372)

Cantores Vagantes
Pikk 26, 10133 **Tallinn**
Tel: 2-443 877 Fax: 6-313 199
artistic director Taavi-Mats Utt
Size: 5 *Type/Spec:* instrumental *Repertoire:* renaissance and baroque *Touring:* national, international

Estonian Baroque Soloists, The
Pallasti 28, PO Box 33, EE0910 **Tallinn**
Tel: 50-94166 Fax: 2-214 673
artistic director Grigori Maltizov
Size: 3-6 *Type/Spec:* instrumental *Repertoire:* baroque 17-18th C, period instruments *Perfs:* 60 *Touring:* Finland, Sweden, Russia, Denmark, Estonia *Comments:* 2nd address: Lasnamäe 34-5, 10014 Tallinn; 4 CDs available

Hortus Musicus
Lühike jalg 9, 10130 **Tallinn**
Tel: 6-440 719
artistic director Andres Mustonen
Size: 5 + 11 *Type/Spec:* instrumental *Repertoire:* renaissance, baroque, medieval *Touring:* national and international *Comments:* recording for numerous broadcasting companies; 14 albums released

Linnamuusikud
Vene 12-6a, 10123 **Tallinn**
Tel: 6-411 518 Fax: 6-411 519
artistic director Taivo Niitvägi

Rondellus
Uus-Tatari 16-12, 10134 **Tallinn**
Tel: 6-462 444 Fax: 6-462 444
Internet: www.rondellus.ee
contact Robert Staak, Maria Staak

Tallinn Baroque Orchestra
Tallinna Barokkorkester
Rävala pst. 12, 10143 **Tallinn**
Tel: 6-466 655 Fax: 6-466 656
director Egmont Välja

FINLAND (+358)

Battalia
Viinenkuja 3 A 9, 00370 **Helsinki**
Tel: 9-565 3184 Fax: 9-631 413
E-Mail: annamari.polho@siba.fi
contact Mika Suihkonen, Annamari Pölhö
Size: 5 permanent *Type/Spec:* instrumental *Repertoire:* early baroque, occasionally high baroque *Comments:* involved in work with singers and foreign groups

Les Goûts – Réünis
Johanneksentie 8 C, 00120 **Helsinki**
Tel: 9-626 997 Fax: 9-626 997
contact Kati Hämäläinen
Size: 3 *Type/Spec:* instrumental *Repertoire:* baroque

Sibelius – Academy Baroque Ensemble
Johanneksentie 8 C, 00120 **Helsinki**
Tel: 9-626 997 Fax: 9-629 997
contact Kati Hämäläinen
Size: 2-8 *Type/Spec:* instrumental – chamber ensemble, flutes/recorders, strings, continuo *Repertoire:* baroque

Sixth Floor Orchestra/Ensemble, The
Soukankaari 1B 33, 02360 **Espoo**
Tel: 9-809 1702 Fax: 9-809 1702
Internet: www.siba.fi/~amattila/kuudeskerros.html
E-Mail: anssi.mattila@siba.fi
artistic director Anssi Mattila; secretary Laura Kajander; treasurer Tuula Riisalo; members of direction Mika Suihkonen, Jari S. Puhakka
Size: 4-30 *Type/Spec:* in maximum a full baroque orchestra – brass, wind, strings, continuo *Repertoire:* baroque *Perfs:* 30 *Touring:* Europe, festivals in Finland

Tuulen Viemää
Gone with the Wind
Runeberginkatu 21 C 62, 00100 **Helsinki**
Tel: 9-454 4921 Fax: 9-826 842
Internet: www.siba.fi/~amattila/tuulenviemaa.html
E-Mail: tuulenviemaa@hotmail.com
contact Pekka Silén
Size: 3-4 *Type/Spec:* recorder trio/quartet *Repertoire:* medieval, renaissance, baroque, modern *Perfs:* 5-10 *Touring:* national, Germany

FRANCE (+33)

Arcane
9 rue Charles Gounot, 82000 **Montauban**
Tel: 5-6366 1906 Fax: 5-6366 1906
E-Mail: Agence.Villeminot@wanadoo.fr
directrice musical Fabienne Azéma
Size: 6 *Type/Spec:* instrumental (harpsichord, viola de gamba, lute/theorbo, baroque flute, violin), vocals *Repertoire:* French and German baroque music, 17th/18th C *Perfs:* 4 *Comments:* second address: Philippe Villeminot 'Lamourio', 46230 Montdoumerc, Tel: 5-6524 7027, Fax: 5-6531 6548; see also Agents & Producers

Arts Florissants, Les
2 rue de Saint-Pétersbourg, 75008 **Paris**
Tel: 1-4387 9888 Fax: 1-4387 3731
Internet: www.arts-florissants.com
E-Mail: info@arts-florissants.com
president Catherine Massip; chargé de production Dermot Agnew; general administrator Christopher Bayton; musical director William Christie
Size: 4-100 *Type/Spec:* instrumental, vocal, baroque *Repertoire:* 16th -18th century French, Italian, English, German, opera *Perfs:* 80 *Touring:* international

Capriccio Stravagante
4 rue Frédéric Sauton, 75005 **Paris**
Tel: 1-4051 0332 Fax: 1-4051 0390
E-Mail: witmenic@euronet.hl
artistic director/harpsichordist Skip Sempé
Size: 4-40 *Type/Spec:* instrumental and vocal, from chamber music to staged opera *Repertoire:* 1520-1750 *Perfs:* 60 *Touring:* France, Europe *Comments:* also Capriccio Stravagante Renaissance Orchestra (15-25) & Capriccio Stravagante Opera & Capriccio Stravagante (chamber music) (3-20); stage production, sound track; Skip Sempé is also soloist; recordings for Auvidis-Astrée and Deutsche Harmonia Mundi

Chapelle Royale, La
aa
Comments: see Orchestre des Champs Elysées

Concert de l'Hostel Dieu, Le
4 rue Bellievre, 69005 **Lyon**
Tel: 4-7842 2776
direction Franck-Emmanuel Comte; communication Stèphane Marvy; administrateur Claire Borel
Size: varies *Type/Spec:* baroque music (Monteverdi, Charpentier, Purcell, Delalende, Haendel) *Repertoire:* Italian, French, 17th C *Perfs:* 5 (Lyon) + festivals *Touring:* France *Comments:* 2 CD's available

Concert Spirituel, Le
42, rue du Louvre, 75001 **Paris**
Tel: 1-4026 1131 Fax: 1-4013 9135
directeur artistique Hervé Niquet; administratrice Chantal De Corbiac
Size: 10-80 *Type/Spec:* instrumental, vocal *Repertoire:* 17th/18th C baroque music *Perfs:* 45-50 *Touring:* France, Europe, Canada

Ensemble 415
c/o Florence Brunel, Athole Still International Management, 76 rue Lamarck, 75018 **Paris**
Tel: 1-4223 0522 Fax: 1-4259 5398
E-Mail: florencebrunel@infonie.fr
manager Florence Brunel; director Chiara Banchini
Size: 3 up to 40 orchestra *Type/Spec:* instrumental early music ensemble *Repertoire:* Italian baroque music, Bach, Haydn *Perfs:* 30 (10 on tour) *Touring:* Singapore, Australia, UK, France, Italy, Belgium *Comments:* recordings with Harmonia Mundi France

Ensemble Baroque de Limoges
La Borie, 87110 **Solignac**
Tel: 5-5531 8484 Fax: 5-5531 8485
Internet: www.ebl.laborie.com
E-Mail: info@ebl-laborie.com
directeur Christophe Coiru; adminIsabelle Depret-Bixio
Size: 4-30 *Type/Spec:* baroque *Repertoire:* 17th/18th C *Perfs:* 40 *Touring:* France, Europe

Ensemble Clement Janequin
118 rue Haxo, 75019 **Paris**
Tel: 1-4208 6814 Fax: 1-4003 8770
Internet: www.satirino.fr
E-Mail: satirino@compuserve.com
general manager Ian Malkin; artistic director Dominique Visse; agents Agence Satirino (director Ian Malkin)
Size: 6 *Type/Spec:* 16th C French chanson, vocal music *Repertoire:* renaissance *Touring:* international

Ensemble Fitzwilliam, L'
13, rue des Fraisiers, 91120 **Palaiseau**
Tel: 1-6010 1627 Fax: 1-6931 8670
administration Patrick Chauffournier; direction artistique Michèle Dévérité, Jean-Pierre Nicolas
Size: 4-5 *Type/Spec:* instrumental and vocal *Repertoire:* 17th-18th century, with emphasis on unknown works and Italian repertoire *Perfs:* 20 *Touring:* France *Comments:* recordings with Astrée-Auvidis

Ensemble Instrumental de Montpellier
401, rue des vignes blanches, 34980 **Saint-Gély-du-Fesc**
Tel: 4-6784 8017 Fax: 4-6784 8017
président Hervé Desmons
Type/Spec: chamber ensemble *Repertoire:* romantic, classical *Comments:* activities suspended temporarily

Ensemble Instrumental et Choeurs Monteverdi
44 Rés. le Corrot, N°37 rue Bottolier, 27000 **Evreux**
Tel: 2-3238 6767 Fax: 2-3238 6767/51
Maître de Chapelle Michel Dubois
Size: 5-25 *Type/Spec:* vocal and orchestral *Repertoire:* baroque, sacred (mainly sacred music by C. Monteverdi) *Touring:* France

Ensemble Organum
Fondation Royaumont, 95270 **Asnieres-sur-Oise**
Tel: 1-3035 5981 Fax: 1-3035 3945
E-Mail: organum@royaumont.com
director Marcel Peres; administrateur t.b.a
Size: 50 *Repertoire:* medieval 6th/17th C. *Perfs:* 50
Touring: international

Ensemble Philidor
2 ter rue des Ursulines, 37000 **Tours**
Tel: 2-4747 0636 Fax: 2-4747 0057
Internet: www.pro.wanadoo.fr/philidor/
E-Mail: philidor@wanadoo.fr
direction musicale Eric Baude-Delhommais; directeur de relations publiques Alexandra Vallat; directeur Bertrand Labarre
Size: 12 *Type/Spec:* wind ensemble, chamber music on period instruments *Repertoire:* French, German and Czech music 17th, 18th C + court music (Lully, Philidor, Mozart, Haydn, Telemann) *Perfs:* 50-60 *Touring:* France, international *Comments:* sponsored by Foreign Affairs Ministry, UNESCO, the region centre and by the regional authority

Grande Ecurie et la Chambre du Roy, La
Département du Nord, 82 boulevard Gambetta, 59200 **Tourcoing**
Tel: 1-6022 9845 (artist)/3-2026 6603 (admin.) Fax: 1-6022 0313 (artist)/3-2027 9119 (admin.)
directeur Jean-Claude Malgoire; déléguée générale artistique Renée Boyer-Vieilfault; administrateur général Catherine Noël
Size: 25-35 *Type/Spec:* recreation of rarely performed baroque works on period instruments, Mozart *Perfs:* 50 concerts, opera *Touring:* worldwide

Il Seminario Musicale
Fondation Royaumont, 95270 **Asnieres-sur-Oise**
Tel: 1-3035 5980 Fax: 1-3035 3945
Internet: www.ilseminariomusicale.com
E-Mail: lesnehl@royaumont.com
contact concerts etranger Hedwige de Limé (1-3035 5989); contact concerts France Yves Lecoq; direction Gérard Lesne
Size: 4-20; 1-5 soloist singers *Type/Spec:* rich continuo with cello, theorobo, harpsichord, organ + solo singers, (can be expanded by adding a string quartet or a small orchestra) *Repertoire:* 17th/18th C Italian and French music *Perfs:* 50 *Touring:* international *Comments:* 19 CDs available

La Fenice
c/o Jean Tubéry, Petit Chaubourg, 89150 **Saint Valérien**
Tel: 3-8688 8538 Fax: 3-8688 8473
music director Jean Tubéry; administrateur Annick Magniez
Size: min. 4 *Type/Spec:* mainly instrumental and vocal *Repertoire:* early baroque, 16th & 17th C, especially Italian repertoire *Perfs:* 25 *Touring:* France *Comments:* second address: Administration, A Magniez, Instant Pluriel, 51 rue de Chabrol, 75018 Paris, Tel: 1-4800 8100, Fax: 1-4800 8111

La Turbulente
c/o Frédérique Thouvenot, Apt. 8219, 170 Galerie de l'Arlequin, 38100 **Grenoble**
Tel: 4-7609 3994
E-Mail: rodifner@aol.com
administration contact Frédérique Thouvenot
Size: 4 *Type/Spec:* 17th/18th/20th C music, baroque ensemble: 2 recorders, 1 harpsichord, 1 cello *Perfs:* 2 *Comments:* CDs available

Musica Antiqua
Les Restanques – Résidence La Royale, 83190 **Ollioules**
Tel: 4-9463 1303 Fax: 4-9463 4059
music director Christian Mendoze
Size: 10-20 + 6 singers *Type/Spec:* baroque *Repertoire:* 17th/18th C Italian and German cantateo, sacred music and French baroque music, concerti and ouvertures, sonatas, cantates, etc. *Perfs:* 40 *Touring:* national, international *Comments:* recordings available

Musiciens du Louvre – Orchestre de Chambre de Grenoble
BP 3046, 38816 **Grenoble** Cedex 01
Tel: 4-7642 4309 Fax: 4-7651 5530
direction artistique Marc Minkowski; direction administrative Jean-Denis Culié
Size: 8 permanent + 5-60 variable *Type/Spec:* opera, oratorio; 17th, 18th century music of France, England and Italy *Repertoire:* Gluck, Haendel, Rameau, Pergolese, Mondonville *Perfs:* 70-80 *Touring:* Asia, Europe, France *Comments:* visiting address:1 rue du Vieux Temple, 38000 Grenoble; see also Orchestra (Orchestre de Chambre de Grenoble – Les Musiciens du Louvre)

Orchestre Baroque de Montauban
Grand Rue Sapiac, 82000 **Montauban**
Tel: 5-6322 1268 Fax: 5-6322 1268
Internet: www.Art6.com/obm.htm
E-Mail: jmandrieu@wanadoo.fr
directeur artistique Jean-Marc Andrieu; administrateur Philippe Villeminot
Type/Spec: string instruments *Repertoire:* baroque: 17th & 18th centuries *Perfs:* 25 *Touring:* France, Hungary *Comments:* Agent: Philippe Villeminot, Lamourio, 46230 Montdoumerc, Tel: 5-6524 7027, Fax: 5-6524 7485, E-mail: Agence.Villeminot@wanadoo.fr; funded by: Ville de Montauban, Conseil général Tarn et Garonne, Ministry of Culture

Orchestre des Champs Elysees
10 rue Coquillière, 75001 **Paris**
Tel: 1-4026 5800 Fax: 1-4026 3837
Internet: www.lachapelleroyale.com
E-Mail: info@lachapelleroyale.com
directeur musical Philippe Herreweghe; conseiller artistique Stephan Maciejewski; délégué général Nicolas Droin; chargée de diffusion Rachel Dale
Size: 50-70 *Type/Spec:* romantic orchestra *Repertoire:* romantic, classical *Perfs:* 50 *Touring:* Europe *Comments:* see also Orchestras and La Chapelle Royale

Parlement de Musique, Le
33 Route du Rhin, 67100 **Strasbourg**
Tel: 3-8844 4382 Fax: 3-8884 8696
E-Mail: parlement.musique@wanadoo.fr
administration Claire Guillemain; artistic director Martin Gester
Size: 2-40 *Type/Spec:* instrumental, vocal *Repertoire:* mainly baroque, classical

Petite Ménestrandise, La
249 rue Jules Ferry, 95360 **Montmagny**
Tel: 1-3021 7201 Fax: 1-4379 3207
directrice Isabelle Ramona; president Valerie Millancourt
Size: 3-10 *Type/Spec:* chamber, vocal *Repertoire:* baroque *Perfs:* 20 *Touring:* France *Comments:* second address: 64 rue des Chantiers, 78000 Versailles

Quai des Muses
La Perriere, 72190 **Coulaines**
Tel: 2-4382 4036 Fax: 2-4382 4036
contact Catherine Samouel
Size: 1-6 *Repertoire:* baroque, sacred music for instruments (harpsichord) and voice *Perfs:* 10 *Touring:* France

Simphonie du Marais, La
1 impasse Damesme, 75013 **Paris**
Tel: 1-4589 6964 Fax: 1-4589 6964
directeur artistique Hugo Reyne; administratrice Stella Ziegler
Size: 3-30 *Repertoire:* 17th/18th C, mainly French baroque *Perfs:* 20 *Touring:* France, Europe

Talens Lyriques, Les
11, passage de la Boule Blanche, 75012 **Paris**
Tel: 1-5346 6464 Fax: 1-5346 6469
Internet: www.lestalenslyriques.com
administrateur Lorraine Villermaux; directeur Christophe Rousset; chargé de production Anne-Judith Wiener
Type/Spec: vocal and instrumental, mainly opera
Repertoire: 17th/18th C motets, cantates, oratorios (French, Italian) *Perfs:* 60 *Touring:* international
Comments: mostly work with international baroque singers; recording exclusively with DECCA/L'Oiseau – Lyre; supported by Fondation d'entreprise France-Telecom

Tanagra – Quartuor de Guitare
c/o Agence Villeminot Lamourio, 46230 **Montdoumerc**
Tel: 5-6524 7027 Fax: 5-6524 7485
Internet: www.Art6.com
E-Mail: Agence.Villeminot@wanadoo.fr
Type/Spec: classical guitar *Touring:* France, Belgium, Netherlands *Comments:* see also Agents & Producers

Trio Orion
c/o Agence Villeminot Lamourio, 46230 **Montdoumerc**
Tel: 5-6524 7027 Fax: 5-6524 7485
Internet: www.Art6.com
E-Mail: Agence.Villeminot@wanadoo.fr
Size: 3 *Type/Spec:* Glass Harmonica *Touring:* France

Turner Quartet
La Chapelle Royale, 10 rue Coquillière, 75001 **Paris**
Tel: 1-4026 5800 Fax: 1-4026 3837
Internet: www.lachapelleroyale.com
E-Mail: rdale@lachapelleroyale.com
contact Rachel Dale
Size: 4 *Type/Spec:* strings *Repertoire:* classical and romantic on period instruments *Perfs:* 20 *Touring:* Europe, South America

GERMANY (+49)

Akademie für alte Musik Berlin
Management, Zossener Str. 50, 10961 **Berlin**
Tel: 30-694 1415 Fax: 30-694 1413
E-Mail: akamus@t-online.de
manager Foikert Ubde
Size: 16 *Repertoire:* solo, chamber and orchestral music; specialising in music composed at the Berlin court in the 18th C.; opera producations *Perfs:* 90 *Touring:* Germany, Italy, France, Belgium, Austria, Japan, Switerland, Netherland, Norway Denmark *Comments:* since 1994 CDs exclusively on Harmonia Mundi France; see also Orchestras

Arcadia Ensemble
Schöneckstr. 10, 79104 **Freiburg**
Tel: 761-32696
Fax: 761-32696
contact Janette Flöel;
artistic director Christian Zimmermann
Size: 4 *Type/Spec:* vocal and instrumental (singer, recorder, viola da gamba, flute)
Repertoire: renaissance, early baroque, German, Italian, French high baroque *Perfs:* 10-12 *Touring:* Germany

Balletto Terzo
c/o Dr. Eckhard Weber, Waisenhausgasse 47, 50676 **Köln**
Tel: 221-932 7435 Fax: 221-932 7435
Internet: www.balletto-terzo.de
E-Mail: e.weber@balletto-terzo.de
manager Dr. Eckhard Weber
Size: 3 permanent players; +1 percussion and 1 violin
Type/Spec: vocal and instrumental *Repertoire:* 16th-18th C. and contemporary works especially composed for Balletto Terzo *Perfs:* approx. 18 *Comments:* 2 CDs available, for further information www.aurel.de

Barockorchester Stuttgart
c/o Stuttgarter Musik Podium e.V., Christophstr. 5, 70178 **Stuttgart**
Tel: 711-239 1390 Fax: 711-2390 1399
E-Mail: smp@n.zgs.de
Geschäftsführer Gregory Johns;
Künstlerischer Leiter Frieder Bernius
Size: 25 *Type/Spec:* chamber orchestra
Repertoire: baroque, classic and romantic *Perfs:* 15
Touring: Estonia, Germany, Israel, France, Poland

Bochumer Gamben-Ensemble
c/o Gisela Block, Gerschermannweg 36, 45357 **Essen**
Tel: 201-606 305 Fax: 201-606 305
Leitung Wolfgang Eggers; contact Gisela Block
Size: 5 *Type/Spec:* instrumental, vocal *Repertoire:* from renaissance to baroque *Perfs:* 30 *Touring:* Germany
Comments: CD available

Camerata Köln
Siedlungsstraße 9, 76646 **Bruchsal**
Tel: 7257-931 185 Fax: 7257-931 188
Internet: www.camerata-koeln.de
E-Mail: CAMERATA.KOELN@t-online.de
Geschäftsführer Heinz R. Huber
Type/Spec: instrumental (woodwind and strings)
Repertoire: baroque, early classical *Perfs:* 30 *Touring:* Europe, Asia, USA, Near East *Comments:* CDs available

Cappella Coloniensis
WDR Alte Musik, 50600 **Köln**
Tel: 221-220 6410/2149
Fax: 221-220 6412/4245
Internet: www.wdr.de/radio/alte_musik
E-Mail: richard.lorber@wdr.de
artistic director Dr. Richard Lorber
Size: 22 strings *Type/Spec:* strings, wind instruments as needed, harpsichord, pianoforte
Repertoire: baroque, early classical, early romantic *Perfs:* 4 concerts + 4 radio productions *Comments:* modelled on the 18th century Dresdner Hofkapelle as directed by Johann Adolf Hasse

Cappella Sagittariana
Eisenstuckstr. 42, 01069 **Dresden**
Tel: 351-471 1002 Fax: 351-471 1002
Musikalische Leitung Wolfram Just
Size: 7+ *Type/Spec:* instrumental and vocal *Repertoire:* 17th and 18th century, especially music of the Court of Dresden *Perfs:* 15 *Touring:* Germany
Comments: CDs available

Chursächsische Philharmonie Bad Elster
Postfach 108, König Albert Theater, 08641 **Bad Elster**
Tel: 37437-71417
Fax: 37437-71233
Intendant/Geschäftsführung MD Florian Merz; Vorsitzender Christoph Flämig, Burgermeister der Stadt Bad Elster; Orchestersekretariat Konstanze Schmied
Size: 36 *Type/Spec:* instrumental, modelled on the Chursächsische Hofkapelle, period orchestra with baroque, classical and romantic instruments *Repertoire:* 18th and 19th century, symphony and opera
Perfs: 600 (including chamber concerts) *Touring:* Austria, Czech Republic, Spain, Italy, England, Belgium
Comments: second address:
Orsoyer Straße, 404704 Düsseldorf

concert royal Köln
c/o Konzertdirektion Heide Stock, Ferdinand-Wallbrecht-Str. 13, 30163 **Hannover**
Tel: 511-394 3114
Fax: 511-394 3115
E-Mail: heide.stock@gmt.de
manager Heide Stock;
artistic director Karla Schröter
Size: 4-18 *Type/Spec:* instrumental (strings, wind instruments, harpsichord)
Repertoire: 17th- 18th century *Perfs:* 40-60

Concerto Köln
Am Grauen Stein, 51105 **Köln**
Tel: 221-983 419-0 Fax: 221-983 419-99
manager Olfa Lischke; artistic director & leader Werner Ehrdhardt; administration S. Erhardt, C.Viera, B. Uedelhoven
Size: 11-40 *Type/Spec:* chamber orchestra *Repertoire:* specialises in 18th century music, baroque, classical and early romantic *Perfs:* 80 *Touring:* international *Comments:* orchestra plays without a conductor; exclusive contract with TELDEC Classics Intern; regular performances in baroque opera productions; see also Orchestras

Conventus Tandaradey
Auf der Adt 14, 66130 **Saarbrücken**
Tel: 6893-5312 Fax: 6893-986 095
Internet: members.aol.com/conventus
E-Mail: conventus@aol.com
künstlerischer Leiter Friedhelm Schneidewind
Size: 3-6 *Type/Spec:* music and dance of the middle ages and renaissance *Perfs:* 30 *Touring:* Germany

Corelli-Ensemble
Kasselerstr. 18, 63571 **Gellnhausen/Höchst**
Tel: 6051-979 125
Musikalische Leitung Uwe Sommerfeld
Size: 6-25 *Type/Spec:* instrumental *Repertoire:* chamber music from 1600-1760 *Perfs:* 20 *Touring:* Germany *Comments:* CD with Fono GmbH

Deutsche Händel-Solisten e.V.
Baumeisterstr. 11, 76137 **Karlsruhe**
Tel: 721-3557-0 Fax: 721-373 223
1. Vorsitzender Pavel Fieber; 2. Vorsitzender Wolfgang Sieber; Koordinator Prof. Helmut Hofmann; Geschäftsstelle Klaus Eßig
Size: 40 *Type/Spec:* early music on period instruments *Repertoire:* works of G.F. Handel *Touring:* national, international, a. o. Händel-Festspiele Karlsruhe

Ensemble für alte Musik§, Das
Domplatz 5, 38100 **Braunschweig**
Tel: 531-46473 Fax: 531-125 065
musikalische u. künstlerische Leitung Gerd-Peter Münden
Size: 15 *Type/Spec:* instrumental (cornets, gamba, horns) *Repertoire:* 14th – 17th century *Perfs:* 10 *Comments:* play on copies of original instruments

Ensemble für Frühe Musik Augsburg
Kemptener Str. 31, 86163 **Augsburg**
Tel: 821-664 639 Fax: 821-667 369
contact Claudia Schwamm
Size: 4 *Repertoire:* medieval, early renaissance *Perfs:* 30

Ensemble Sarband
Zieblandstr. 9, 80799 **München**
Tel: 89-272 4243 Fax: 89-272 4243
E-Mail: dr_vladimir_ivanoff@compuserve.com
Musikalische Leitung Dr. Vladimir Ivanoff
Size: 2-8 instrumentalists, 2-4 singers *Type/Spec:* instrumental and vocal *Repertoire:* music of the middle ages, early music of the orient and occident *Perfs:* 60 *Touring:* Europe, USA *Comments:* 6 CDs with Jaro, 1 with BMG/Deutsche Harmonia Mundi; see also L'Orient Imaginaire

Estampie- Münchner Ensemble für Frühe Musik
Lochhamer Str. 79, 82166 **Gräfelfing**
Tel: 89-8989 2848/171-384 1710 Fax: 89-707 145
Internet: www.Estampie.de
E-Mail: Info@Estampie.de
management Cornelia Bruckbauer
Size: 3-9 *Type/Spec:* vocal and instrumental *Repertoire:* monodic music and polyphonic of the middle ages; early music for theatre and film with modern elementals *Perfs:* 20-30 *Touring:* Germany, Spain, UK *Comments:* 5 recordings with Christopherus/MusiContact

Fiori musicali – Barockorchester Bremen eV
Obernstr 62-66, 28195 **Bremen**
Tel: 421-170 427 Fax: 421-18098/165 5436
musikalische Leitung Prof Thomas Albert; Geschäftsführung Frau Genth
Type/Spec: instrumental & vocal *Repertoire:* baroque chamber and orchestra, opera, oratorio *Touring:* national, international

Freiburger Barockorchester
Freiburg Baroque Orchestra
Konradstr. 7, 79100 **Freiburg**
Tel: 761-706 555 Fax: 761-706 557
Internet: www.barockorchester.de
E-Mail: f.b.o.@t-online.de
general manager Hans-Georg Kaiser; artistic director Gottfried von der Goltz; project manager Wolfram Lamparter; press manager Dr. Rüdiger Nolte
Size: 6-40 *Type/Spec:* chamber orchestra; also chamber music as FBO Consort *Repertoire:* mainly 17th and 18th century *Perfs:* 70-90; own series in Freiburg, Stuttgart and Berlin *Touring:* Europe, USA, Asia, South America *Comments:* recordings on Harmonia Mundi (Germany and USA), BMG Classics, EMI, Erato Carus; see also Orchestra

Kölner Violen-Consort
Herrenweg 21, 41541 **Dormagen-Zons**
Tel: 2133-42256 Fax: 2133-42256
Leitung Prof. Heiner Spicker
Size: 4 *Type/Spec:* instrumental (4 viole da gamba) *Repertoire:* renaissance, baroque, modern, specially commissioned works *Touring:* Italy, Poland, France

L'Orfeo Barockorchester
c/o Accento, Kiesseestr. 57a, 37083 **Göttingen**
Tel: 551-77930 Fax: 551-77932
E-Mail: accento-loepthien@t-online.de
Manager Wolfgang Loepthien; Konzertmeisterin Michi Gaigg
Size: 15-25 *Type/Spec:* chamber orchestra *Repertoire:* 17th/18th C, mainly French baroque and Vienna classic *Perfs:* 20-30 *Touring:* Europe *Comments:* several recordings

La Gamba
Wälderstr. 25, 79341 **Bombach**
Tel: 7644-913 133/171-542 1464 Fax: 7644-913 135
Internet: www.home.t-online.de/home/lagamba
E-Mail: e.weber@t-online.de
musical director Ekkehard Weber
Size: 3-7 *Type/Spec:* instrumental (viol-consort); sometimes vocal is added *Repertoire:* renaissance to late baroque, 20th C *Perfs:* 30-40 *Touring:* national, international *Comments:* radio and TV appearances, recordings; Ekkehard Weber teaches at Freiburg Hochschule für Musik; alternative internet: home.t-online.de/home/e.weber

La Stagione Frankfurt
c/o Dr. Thomas Weinsberg, Webergasse 43, 65183 **Wiesbaden**
Tel: 611-157 6826/7 Fax: 611-157 6828
E-Mail: La_Stagione_Frankfurt@t-online.de
general manager Dr. Thomas Weinsberg; artistic director and conductor Michael Schneider
Size: 40 *Type/Spec:* instrumental *Repertoire:* symphony, oratorio and opera of the 17th and 18th century *Perfs:* 40 *Touring:* UK, Belgium, Netherlands, Austria, Poland, France, Italy, Spain, Ukraine *Comments:* 25 CDs on BMG/Harmonia Mundi, Delta Music/Capriccio,CPO; motto- The unheard-of heard again

La Stravaganza Köln
c/o Christoph Lehmann, Ludwigshafener str. 35 C, 40229 **Düsseldorf**
Tel: 211-218 826 Fax: 211-218 852
Internet: www.home.pages.de/~lsk
E-Mail: ch.leh@t-online.de
administration Christoph Lehmann
Size: 15-25 *Type/Spec:* baroque chamber orchestra *Repertoire:* orchestra and ensemble music from 1680-1800; particular emphasis on extravagant programs integrating the conventional repertoire with little known, often newly unearthed concertos and orchestral works *Perfs:* 15-20 *Touring:* Germany, Holland, Austria, Spain *Comments:* Ca. 10 CDs primarily on the Denon label

Musica Alta Ripa
c/o Konzertagentur Heide Stock, Ferdinand Wallbrecht-Strasse 13, 30163 **Hannover**
Tel: 511-394 3144 Fax: 511-394 3115
E-Mail: heidestock@gmx.de
manager Heide Stock; artistic director Bernward Lohr
Size: 5-14 *Type/Spec:* instrumental (strings, wind, harpsichord) *Perfs:* 20-30

Musica Antiqua Köln
Hochstadenstr 10, 50674 **Köln**
Tel: 221-923 2030/2035 Fax: 221-923 2031
E-Mail: hansotto.mak@t-online.de
Manager Hans Otto; Musikalische Leitung Reinhard Goebel
Size: 5-30 *Type/Spec:* instrumental *Repertoire:* baroque to classical *Perfs:* 120 concerts – 2 additional recording for DG *Touring:* USA, Italy, Europe *Comments:* also available: courses for baroque instruments; see also Orchestras

Musica Fiata Köln
Emilstr. 35, 50827 **Köln**
Tel: 221-530 3180 Fax: 221-530 3191
Musikalische Leitung Roland Wilson
Size: 8-20 *Repertoire:* 1550-1700 *Perfs:* 25 *Touring:* Germany, Netherlands, Belgium, Denmark, Italy, Austria, France *Comments:* associated vocal consort La Capella Ducale (8-16 singers); records for Sony Classical, Deutsche Harmonia Mundi

Neubrandenburger Philharmonie
Ziegelbergstr. 5a, 17033 **Neubrandenburg**
Tel: 395-581 9511 Fax: 395-544 2099
Internet: www.nb-net.de/philharmonie
E-Mail: philharmonie.nb@t-online.de
Geschäftsführer Direktor Horst Beitz; GMD und Chefdirigent Prof. Nicolas Pasquét; Öffentlichkeitsarbeit Gabriele Behr; Konzertdramaturgin Anke Völker-Zapka
Size: 76 comprising 25 chamber groups varying in size *Type/Spec:* chamber and orchestral *Repertoire:* early music, baroque, classical, contemporary (orchestral & chamber music) *Perfs:* 300 *Touring:* national and international *Comments:* see also Orchestras

Nova Stravaganza
Leppestraße 171, 51709 **Marienheide**
Tel: 2263-952 454 Fax: 2263-70007
artistic director Siegbert Rampe
Size: 10-25 *Type/Spec:* baroque orchestra *Repertoire:* baroque to romantic *Perfs:* 35 *Touring:* Hungary, France, Belgium, Netherlands, Luxemburg, Canada, USA

Odhecaton
c/o Dr Berthold Neumann, Ottostr. 46, 50823 **Köln**
Tel: 221-552 770 Fax: 221-552 770
E-Mail: berthold.neumann@uni-koeln.de
contact Dr. Berthold Neumann
Size: 6-7 *Type/Spec:* instrumental, additional vocal when required *Repertoire:* medieval, renaissance- up to 1650 *Perfs:* 30 *Touring:* national, international *Comments:* CDs distributed by FSM, television and broadcast recordings; alternative E-mail: berthold.neumann@t-online.de

Orchester Damals und Heute, Das
Franz-Marc-Str. 6, 50939 **Köln**
Tel: 221-430 1600 Fax: 221-430 1600
Internet: www.damalsundheute.com
E-Mail: contact@damalsundheute.com
conductor Michael Willens; director of operations Volker Gelhardt
Size: 17-50 depending on repertoire *Type/Spec:* 17th-20th C. music on both period and modern instruments *Perfs:* 30 *Touring:* festivals in Austria, Belgium, England, France, Germany, Spain, Ireland, Denmark, Netherlands *Comments:* see also Orchestras

Pegasus Ensemble des Scola Cantorum Basilensis
Am Bahnhof 8, 79650 **Schopfheim-Raithbach**
Tel: 7622-65103 Fax: 7622-65103
E-Mail: J.fiedler@01019.freenet.de
contact Ulricke Küper, Jörg Fiedler, Oskar Peter
Size: 3 *Type/Spec:* instrumental *Repertoire:* classical, early romantic, renaissance *Perfs:* 5-8 *Touring:* Belgium, Switzerland, Germany

RIAS-Kammerchor
Charlottenstraße 56, 10117 **Berlin**
Tel: 30-2029 8730 Fax: 30-2029 8740
Internet: www.rias-kammerchor.de
E-Mail: info@rias-kammerchor.de
managing director Frank Druschel; chief conductor Marcus Creed; guest conductors René Jacobs, Philippe Herreweghe; public relations Ralf Schott; secretaries Rosmarie Arndt, Ingrid-Kann Waliat
Size: 35 *Type/Spec:* chamber choir, full-time professional *Repertoire:* early and contemporary music, a cappella and with chamber orchestra *Perfs:* 30-40, own series in the Philharmonie Berlin *Touring:* Germany, France, Belgium, Austria, Switzerland, Spain *Comments:* recordings on Harmonia Mundi France, Berlin Classics, Capriccio, EMI Classics and Deutsche Grammophon; 28 international recording awards; see also Choirs

Scala Köln
PO Box 50 18 33, 50978 **Köln**
Tel: 221-354 305
Fax: 221-354 335
Künstlerischer Leiter Christoph Mayer
Size: 5-11 *Type/Spec:* early chamber music *Perfs:* 20-30

Sequentia
Moltkestr. 8, 50674 **Köln**
Tel: 221-239 189 Fax: 221-219 827
E-Mail: sequentia@compuserve.com
artistic directors Benjamin Bagby
Size: 3-15 *Type/Spec:* vocal and instrumental (medieval harp, fiddle, flute) *Repertoire:* music of the middle ages *Perfs:* 40 *Touring:* worldwide *Comments:* CDs with German Harmonia Mundi, distributed worldwide through BMG Classics

Sonatori-Ensemble
c/o Berthold Fritz, Friedrichstrasse 36, 76229 **Karlsruhe**
Tel: 721-948 3154
Fax: 721-948 3155
conductor Berthold Fritz
Size: 4 *Type/Spec:* chamber ensemble *Repertoire:* baroque, classical, romantic (focus on Bohemian composers) *Perfs:* 30-40 *Touring:* Germany, Czech Republic, Japan, South America, USA *Comments:* 6 CDs available; at present recording Johann Nep Hummel's chamber music versions of all Beethoven's symphonies (world premiere)

Tölzer Knabenchor
Kaminskistrasse 13, 83671 **Benediktbeuern**
Tel: 8857-9061 Fax: 8857-1470
Internet: www.knabenchor.de
E-Mail: info@knabenchor.de
Leiter Prof. Gerhard Schmidt-Gaden; organisation/management Helga Schmidt-Gaden, May-Britt Andresen, Tilo Pitz; p.r. Jürgen Bierbaum
Size: 2 concert choirs (30) *Type/Spec:* boys choir, boy soloists *Repertoire:* standard choral repertoire; specialising in authentic performance of early music (authentic small size); also symphonic repertoire *Perfs:* 200-250 *Touring:* worldwide *Comments:* more than 100 CD recordings (Dt, Schallplattenpreis); see also choirs

un'anima cantava
c/o Konzertagentur Heide Stock, Ferdinand-Wallbrecht-Str. 13, 30163 **Hannover**
Tel: 511-394 3114 Fax: 511-394 3115
E-Mail: heide.stock@gmx.de
manager Heide Stock; artistic director Stephan Schrader
Size: 3-4 *Type/Spec:* instrumental & vocal *Repertoire:* 1550-1650 *Perfs:* 20-40 *Touring:* Europe

Weser-Renaissance
Mittelstrasse 12, 28203 **Bremen**
Tel: 421-327 454 Fax: 421-201 9225
Leiter Manfred Cordes
Size: 5-30 *Type/Spec:* vocal and instrumental (woodwind and strings), period instruments *Repertoire:* 16th-17th century *Perfs:* 20-30 *Touring:* Finland, Sweden, Spain, Belgium, Netherlands

HUNGARY (+36)

Benkõ Consort
c/o Daniel Benkõ, Vérhalom u. 20, 1025 **Budapest**
Tel: 1-316 5891
Fax: 1-316 5891
contact Daniel Benkõ
Size: 4-6 *Repertoire:* Hungarian and West European early music and dance music. Special emphasis on the works by early Hungarian master Balint Bakfark (1507-1576) *Touring:* national and international *Comments:* instruments include the guitar, orpharion, vihuela, psalter, baroque guitar, baroque lute, chitarrone, ud, zither, lyre, kobsa, baroque recorder, bagpipe, panpipe, reed pipe, crumhorn, rebec and viola da gamba; recordings on Hungaroton label

Camerata Hungarcia
c/o László Czidra, Zólyomi lépcsö 17, 1124 **Budapest**
Tel: 1-319 2473
artistic director László Czidra
Size: 15 *Type/Spec:* instrumental and vocal *Repertoire:* Baroque chamber music and chamber cantatas, music of the Middle Ages and the Renaissance *Touring:* national and international *Comments:* recordings on Hungaroton label

Capella Savaria
Batsányi u. 20, 9700 **Szombathely**
Tel: 94-321 594 Fax: 94-321 594
artistic director Pál Németh
Repertoire: 17th and 18th century *Touring:* national and international *Comments:* 2nd address: c/o Arts and Artists, Pajtas 22, 1131 Budapest, Tel/Fax: 1-340 0081, contact Katalin Kiricsi; Extensive recording history on the Hungaroton and Hungaroton Antiqua labels

Concerto Armonico
c/o Clemens Concerts, József Attila ut. 61, 1013 **Budapest**
Tel: 1-212 2045 Fax: 1-212 2045/375 8162
E-Mail: ClemensConcerts@compuserve.com
director Pál Kelemen;
artistic directors Péter Szüts, Miklós Spányi
Size: 12 *Type/Spec:* period string instruments, baroque *Perfs:* 50 *Touring:* Europe *Comments:* postal address: POB 239, 1360 Budapest; see also Orchestras

Corvina Consort
Podmaniczky utca 18, 1065 **Budapest**
Tel: 1-311 5914/302 0505
Internet: www.bmc.hu/corvina/index2_en.htm
artistic director Zoltán Kálmánovits

Festetich Quartet
c/o Arts and Artists, Pajtas 22, 1131 **Budapest**
Tel: 1-340 0081
Fax: 1-340 0081
director Katalin Kiricsi
Type/Spec: instrumental *Comments:* recordings on Hungaroton label

Mandel Quartet
Fodros 7B, 2040 **Budaörs**
Tel: 23-417 938
Fax: 23-417 007
Internet: www.mandel.hu
E-Mail: mandel@mail.datanet.hu
contact Robert Mandel
Type/Spec: instrumental and vocal – hurdy-gurdy, cello, percussion, recorder, harpsichord and strings *Repertoire:* medieval and renaissance dances, baroque concerti, sonatas and suites *Touring:* national and international *Comments:* recordings on the Hungaroton label and Thorofon Alternum, Unisono and GB-Records; see also Festivals (World Music Festival Budapest)

Orfeo
Pasareti 114,
1026 **Budapest**
Tel: 1-274 2678
Fax: 1-274 2678
artistic/managing director György Vashegyi
Comments: with choir

ICELAND (+354)

Musica Antiqua Island
c/o Snorri Örn Snorrason, Mjóstraeti 10, 101 **Reykjavík**
Tel: 551 0033 Fax: 551 0033
direction Snorri Örn Snorrason
Size: 3 (+ guests) *Type/Spec:* instrumental – lute, recorder *Repertoire:* pre-baroque, baroque and renaissance *Perfs:* 2 *Touring:* Iceland *Comments:* the group has an organisation called Musica Antiqua which organises concerts with other Icelandic musicians (q.v.); see also Promoters, Festivals

Skálholt Bach Consort
c/o Helga Ingólfsdóttir, Strönd, 225 **Bessastaðahreppur**
Tel: 565 0859 Fax: 565 2985
E-Mail: stsk@islandia.is
contact Helga Ingólfsdóttir
Size: 10-12 *Type/Spec:* instrumental *Repertoire:* baroque and pre-baroque

IRELAND Republic of (+353)

Chandos Baroque Players
St. Canice's Cottage, St. Canice's Cathedral, **Kilkenny**
Tel: 56-61497 Fax: 56-61497
E-Mail: maya@tinet.ie
administrator Susan Proud
Size: 6+ *Type/Spec:* instrumental (violins, oboe, flute, cellos, bassoon, harpsichord) *Repertoire:* baroque *Perfs:* 25 *Touring:* Ireland, Europe, USA

Douglas Gunn Ensemble, The
Ballaghmore Castle, County Laois, **Borris-in-Ossory**
Tel: 505-23093
Internet: www.iol.ie/~dgunn/dge.htm
E-Mail: dgunn@iol.ie
contact Douglas Gunn
Size: 4-5 *Type/Spec:* baroque *Repertoire:* baroque (incl Irish composers) *Perfs:* 120 *Touring:* national

ITALY (+39)

Accademia Bizantina
via Emanuele Filiberto 4, 20052 **Monza**
Tel: 039-744 703 Fax: 039-744 797
Internet: www.askesis.it/ricmus
E-Mail: gc.ricercar@askesis.it
general manager Gabriella Castelli; artistic director Ottavio Dantone; honorary president Luciano Berio
Size: 7-40 *Type/spec:* instrumental and vocal *Repertoire:* Italian baroque *Perfs:* 30 *Touring:* Europe, South America, USA *Comments:* CDs available; see also Orchestras

Affetti Musicali, Gli
Via Cavour 72, 12048 **Sommariva Bosco (CN)**
Tel: 0172-493 875/54974 Fax: 0172-54974
Internet: www.geocities.com/vienna/strasse/6450
E-Mail: gchiavazza@areacom.it
director Claudio Chiavazza
Size: 5-15 *Type/Spec:* vocal, instrumental *Repertoire:* baroque, sacred music *Perfs:* 10-15 *Touring:* Italy *Comments:* works closely with the 'Corale Polifonica di Sommariva Bosco' (q.v.)

Almagesto Vocale
Via Kennedy 5, 20060 **Ornago (MI)**
Tel: 039-601 0150 Fax: 039-601 0121
direttore artistico Bruno Raffaele Foti
Size: 10-18 *Type/Spec:* vocal and instrumental *Repertoire:* late renaissance to early baroque, sacred & secular *Perfs:* 30 *Comments:* see also Choirs

Armonia Antiqua
Via Francesco Ferrara 24, 00191 **Roma**
Tel: 06-329 6750/829 3196 Fax: 02-329 6750
E-Mail: aivessiehhost@sogei.it
artistic director Claudio Caponi
Size: 4 musicians +1 vocalists *Type/Spec:* instrumental and vocal *Repertoire:* medieval, renaissance *Perfs:* 25 *Touring:* Italy *Comments:* perform on copies of original instruments; CD's available

Camerata Di Cremona, La
Via Aselli 63, 26100 **Cremona**
Tel: 0372-413 078 Fax: 0372-21256
direttore artistico Marco Fracassi; presidente Gianfranco Carutti
Size: 60 choir + 30 orchestra *Type/Spec:* instrumental, vocal *Repertoire:* from Monteverdi to Schubert *Perfs:* 20 *Touring:* UK, Germany, Austria *Comments:* second address: Via Aselli 63, 26100 Cremona; see also Choirs and I Solisti di Cremona

Capella Ducale Venetia
via Emanuele Filiberto 4, 20052 **Monza**
Tel: 039-744 703 Fax: 039-744 797
Internet: www.askesis.it/ricmus
E-Mail: gc.ricercar@askesis.it
general manager Gabriella Castelli;
artistic director Livio Picotti
Size: 7-40 *Type/Spec:* vocal *Repertoire:* renaissance and baroque repertoire performed in St. Mark Venice for the Doge *Perfs:* 30 *Touring:* Europe, Israel *Comments:* see also Choirs

Cappella Artemisia
via Cavaroncello 4, 40010 **Sala Bolognese (BO)**
Tel: 051-681 4101 Fax: 051-681 4844
Internet: www.intr.net/~bleissa/lists/
E-Mail: dif6462@iperbole.bologna.it
contact Candace Smith
Size: 8-16 *Type/Spec:* music of Italian convents; 6-10 voices, basso continuo, occassionally cornetts and trombones, all women *Touring:* Italy, Switzerland, Belgium, Netherlands, Spain *Comments:* 3 CDs available on Tactus (Italian label)

Centro di Musica Antica La Pietà Dei Turchini, La
Centro di Musica Antica, Via S.Caterina da Siena N. 38, 80132 **Napoli**
Tel: 081-402 395
Fax: 081-402 395
Internet: www.turchini.it
E-Mail: turchini@tin.it
president and artistic director Antonio Florio;
director Federica Castaldo;
secretary and administration Marco Rossi
Size: 25 + 30 choir + 20 children choir voci bianche *Type/Spec:* instrumental, vocal *Repertoire:* Napolitan baroque + opera *Perfs:* 18 *Touring:* Austria, Spain, Germany, Israel, UK, France *Comments:* agent general: tel: +33 1-4343 5380 fax: +33 1-4343 5721; Italian agent: Mario Ingrassia tel:055-730 9131 fax:055-730 9131

Complesso di Strumenti a Fiato di Padova
Via A.Marangon 34, 35129 **Padova**
Tel: 049-628 326 Fax: 049-628 326
E-Mail: p.destro@pd.nettuno.it
direttore Pierluigi Destro
Size: 12 *Type/spec:* instrumental *Repertoire:* baroque to contemporary *Perfs:* 5-15 *Touring:* Cuba, Brasil, Paraguay, Ukraine *Comments:* CD available

Concerto Italiano
via Laura Mantegazza 8, 00152 **Roma**
Tel: 06-305 1508/534 4754 Fax: 06-305 1508/534 4754
E-Mail: digioale@tin.it
conductor Rinaldo Alessandrini (E-mail: rinaldo-ci@iol.it)
Size: 8-40 *Type/Spec:* vocal and instrumental *Repertoire:* madrigal, baroque, opera with emphasis on Italian works *Perfs:* 50-60 *Touring:* Holland, Belgium, France, Spain, Italy, Japan, UK, South America

Consort Veneto
via Anconetta 58, 35034 **Lozzo Atestino (PD)**
Tel: 0429-697 105
Fax: 0429-697 108
Internet: www.isnt.it/consortveneto
E-Mail: g.toffano@job.pd.it
director Giovanni Toffano
Size: 7 (singer and 6 instruments) + dancers *Type/Spec:* vocal and instrumental (recorders, crumhorn, dulcian, percussion) *Repertoire:* medieval, renaissance *Perfs:* 25 *Comments:* 5 CDs available;
concerts in period costumes

Coro Da Camera Italiano
c/o Lucilla Rodinó, via A. Serranti N. 75
00136 **Roma**
Tel: 06-3549 8882
Fax: 06-3549 8882
E-Mail: arizzet@iol.it
Size: 16 *Type/Spec:* vocal *Repertoire:* renaissance, baroque *Perfs:* 3 *Comments:* guest conductors

Dramsam
Loggia dei Mercanti – Calle dei Macellai, 2, 34072 **Gradisca d'Isonzo (GO)**
Tel: 0481-531 326 Fax: 0481-531 326
Internet: www.accademia.it
E-Mail: dramsam@mail.seta.it
director Guiseppe Paolo Cecere
Size: 3-15 *Type/Spec:* instrumental, vocal *Repertoire:* medieval to reinassance *Perfs:* 40 *Touring:* Austria, Germany *Comments:* see also Choirs and Promoters

Ensemble Barocco Italiano
Via Alessandria 4, 20144 **Milano**
Tel: 02-839 5855/2940 6732
Fax: 02-2940 6732
E-Mail: gentili@icil64.cilea.it
director Barbara Petrucci
Size: 4-6 *Type/Spec:* instrumental + vocal *Repertoire:* baroque, reinassance *Perfs:* 10 *Touring:* Yemen *Comments:* several CDs available (French music of the 17th century); the instruments used are copies of original instruments

Ensemble Cantilena Antiqua
via Silvagni 12, 40137 **Bologna**
Tel: 051-623 0017
Fax: 051-623 0017
Internet: www2.comune.bologna.it/bologna/enscanan
E-Mail: enscanan@iperbole.bologna.it
artistic director Stefano Albarello
Size: 4-9 *Type/Spec:* vocal and instrumental music *Repertoire:* medieval and pre-renaissance *Comments:* world premiere recordings with Symphonia Digital

Ensemble Concerto
Via Castello, 20, 27010 **Bascapé (PV)**
Tel: 0382-66153 Fax: 0382-66153
E-Mail: rgini@tin.it
artistic director Roberto Gini
Size: 8-30 *Type/Spec:* instrumental, vocal *Repertoire:* madrigals, Monteverdi period, 17th and 18th century *Perfs:* 15-20 *Touring:* Italy, Europe *Comments:* the artistic director also performs with Il Concerto delle Viole (q.v.);
Ensemble Guidantus

Via Trieste, 58, 43100 **Parma**
Tel: 0521-775 535 Fax: 0521-775 535
E-Mail: maxnegro@synet.it
contact Marco Pedrona
Size: 6 *Type/spec:* instrumental *Repertoire:* venetian and baroque music *Perfs:* 20 *Touring:* USA, Japan *Comments:* recording available on DATUM (Stradivarius) and Dynamic

Ensemble La Reverdie
c/o Claudia Caffagni, Cannareggio 1068, 30121 **Venezia**
Tel: 041-718 067/0335-600 0080 (mobile)
Fax: 041-718 067
contacts Livia & Claudia Caffagni, Raffaella & Elisabetta de Mircovich, Doron David Sherwin
Size: 5 *Type/Spec:* instrumental, vocal *Repertoire:* European medieval *Perfs:* 40 *Touring:* France, Germany, Spain, Austria, Italy, Belgium, Netherlands, Switzerland *Comments:* second address: Via Follinetta 17, 31051 Follina (TV), tel/fax: 0438-971 405

Ensemble Micrologus
via Porta Chiusa, 6, 06038 **Spello (PG)**
Tel: 075-815 183/0742-652 459/0348-872 2313 (mobile)
Fax: 0742-652 459
Internet: www.micrologus.it
E-Mail: micrologus@informanet.it
contact Silvia Cordovana; direzione artistica Patrizia Bovi, Adolfo Broegg, Goffredo Degli Esposti, Gabriele Russo
Size: 6-9 *Type/Spec:* vocal and instrumental (harp, lute, psaltery,flutes, bagpipe, shawn, symphonia, fiddle, rebec, lyra) *Repertoire:* Italian and Spanish music (13th/15th C.); Neapolitan music of the 15th C. *Touring:* France, USA, Spain, Italy, Poland *Comments:* radio and television recordings for Italian, French, German, Austrian and Japanese stations; records available on Opus 111 label, Paris; contact: Silvia Cordovana, Tel/Fax: +39 6-8720 0794, Mobile: +39 0348-310 9901, Email: esseci@hotmail.com

Ensemble Sanfelice
Piazza San Felice 5, 50125 **Firenze**
Tel: 055-741 527 Fax: 055-741 527
E-Mail: fede@fol.it
conductor Federico Bardazzi;
assistant Eleonora Tassinari
Size: 8-24 (8 permanent) *Type/Spec:* mainly vocal and instrumental with continuo; small ensembles to chamber orchestra; always original instruments *Repertoire:* sacred middle ages, baroque *Perfs:* 40 *Touring:* Switzerland, Germany, Poland, Italy, Sweden *Comments:* recordings with Planet Sound;
see also Choirs

fête rustique
c/o Fadini, Via Alciati 5, 20146 **Milano**
Tel: 02-415 1729/06-534 2313 Fax: 02-415 1729/06-534 2313
director Giorgio Matteoli; manager Maria Rosa Cúsmá
Size: 4 up to chamber orchestra (14) *Repertoire:* Italian baroque unprinted scores, baroque music with period instruments, vocal *Touring:* international *Comments:* second address: Via Valtellina 100, 00151 Roma; CD's available; managment: European Consulting Group, 69 rue des Rigoles, 75020 Paris, tel:+33 1-4358 0603, fax:+33 1-4358 0803

Gallus Consort
Via Besenghi N. 50, 34143 **Trieste**
Tel: 040-310 173 Fax: 040-310 173
contacts Irena Pahor, Milos Pahor, Dina Slama
Size: 3 *Type/Spec:* instrumental, vocal *Repertoire:* baroque, renaissance to contemporary *Touring:* Italy, Slovenia

Gli Ottoni Di Verona
Via Santa Eurosia 8, 37060 **Trevenzuolo (VR)**
Tel: 045-735 0213 Fax: 0376-371 511
president Sig. Bruno Brunelli; dir. artistico Giordano Fermi
Size: varies *Type/Spec:* brass ensemble (occasionally with organ and percussion) *Repertoire:* baroque, renaissance to contemporary *Perfs:* 20-25 *Touring:* Europe, USA, South America, Netherlands *Comments:* organise: Festival Internazionale Di Ottoni (international brass festival) held every two years

Gruppo Incontro
Via Mazzini 32, 34121 **Trieste**
Tel: 040-55257 Fax: 040-638 212
president Mauro Tagliaferro; artistic director Cristiana Spadaro
Size: 25 *Type/Spec:* vocal and instrumental *Repertoire:* 14th-20th century *Perfs:* 10 annually *Touring:* Hungary, Austria *Comments:* sing in 15 different languages

Gruppo Musica Insieme
Via Fulda 117, 00148 **Roma**
Tel: 06-653 5998 Fax: 06-653 5998
administration Antenore Tecardi; artistic directors Anne-Beate Zimmer, Antenore Tecardi
Size: 2-9 *Type/Spec:* instrumental, vocal *Repertoire:* medieval, renaissance, baroque *Perfs:* 20

I Madrigalisti Di Venezia
c/o Mario Vio, San Marco 3769, 30124 **Venezia**
Tel: 041-522 2215 Fax: 041-522 2215
artistic director/administration Mario Vio
Size: 6-7 *Type/Spec:* instrumental (on period instruments), vocal *Repertoire:* baroque, sacred music, renaissance *Touring:* worldwide

I Solisti Di Cremona
Via Villa Glori 18, 26100 **Cremona**
Tel: 0372-413 078 Fax: 0372-21256
artistic director/presidente Marco Fracassi
Size: 6 (soprano, 2 violins, viola, violoncello, clavincembalo) *Type/Spec:* instrumental, vocal *Repertoire:* renaissance (Monteverdi) and baroque *Perfs:* 20 *Touring:* USA, Germany, France, Greece *Comments:* second address: Via Aselli 63, 26100 Cremona; see also Choirs

Il Complesso Barocco
Giudecca 317, 30133 **Venezia**
Tel: 041-523 5595 Fax: 041-523 5595
director Alan Curtis
Size: 4-20 *Type/Spec:* vocal and instrumental *Repertoire:* Italian music (mostly vocal and opera) *Perfs:* 30 *Touring:* USA, Germany

Il Concerto Delle Viole
Via Castello, 20, 27010 **Bascapé (PV)**
Tel: 0382-66153 Fax: 0382-66153
E-Mail: rgini@tin.it
artistic director Roberto Gini
Size: 14 *Type/Spec:* instumental – viola da gamba *Repertoire:* Italian renaissance, English, German and French baroque *Perfs:* 30 *Touring:* Italy, Europe *Comments:* the artistic director also performs with Ensemble Concerto (q.v.)

Il Viaggio Musicale
Via Alzate 58, 22032 **Albese Con Cassano (CO)**
Tel: 031-426 168/049-681 086 Fax: 049-880 1576/031-426 168
artistic director Paolo Tognon
Size: 4-8 *Type/Spec:* instrumental *Repertoire:* 17th century Italian and German baroque *Perfs:* 20

L'Orfeo Ensemble – Gruppo musicale di Spoleto
via Beato Leopoldo 113, 06049 **Spoleto (PG)**
Tel: 0743-260 337 Fax: 0743-260 337
Internet: orfeo.ejb.net
E-Mail: orfeo.ensemble@altavista.net
responsabile artistico Fabrizio Ammetto; musicologa e pubbliche relazioni Gioia Filocamo
Size: 2-15 *Type/Spec:* instrumental, chamber *Repertoire:* baroque to contemporary *Perfs:* 25 *Comments:* CDs available; coorganise music seminars and courses, musicology conferences, publication of critical editions; see also Orchestras

La Morra
c/o Sabina Cassola, Via Cimone 93/A, 00141 **Roma**
Tel: 06-8680 0131 Fax: 06-8680 0131
contact Sabina Cassola
Size: 6 *Type/Spec:* instrumental, vocal *Repertoire:* renaissance, medieval *Perfs:* 20-30 *Touring:* Italy, Tunisia *Comments:* perform on copies of original instruments

LABYRINTO, consort of viols
Via Tor de Cenci 18, 00128 **Roma**
Tel: 06-508 6201/29234 Fax: 06-508 6201
E-Mail: ixjpa@tin.it
director Paolo Pandolfo (mobile: 347-360 3384)
Size: up to 8 *Type/Spec:* renaissance and baroque music *Perfs:* 30 *Touring:* USA

Mala Punica
Via Guido Reni 3, 40125 **Bologna**
Tel: 051-236 985 Fax: 051-236 985
director Pedro Memelsdorff; organisation Francesca Sofri
Size: 8-20 (8 fixed number of which 6 play instruments and 2 are vocals) *Type/Spec:* instrumental, vocal *Repertoire:* late medieval, 14th and early 15th century sacred and secular polyphony, esp. ars subtilior *Perfs:* 24 *Touring:* Italy, France, Switzerland, Spain, Portugal, Belgium, Germany, USA, Denmark, Austria *Comments:* most programmes are secular, Missa Cantilena & Sidus Preclarum are liturgical; specialises in Ars Subtilior; Agency: Ricercare, Via Filiberto, 4, 20052 Monza, Tel: 039-744 703, Fax: 039-744 797

Nova Cantica
Via Fontana 3, 32035 **Santa Giustina (BL)**
Tel: 0437-859 296 Fax: 0437-859 296
presidente e direttore Maria Silvia Roveri; vice presidente Renzo Pegoraro
Size: 4-8 *Type/Spec:* vocal and instrumental *Repertoire:* medieval *Perfs:* 10 *Touring:* Italy
Comments: 3 CDs available

Orchestra Barocca del Teatro Comunale di Guastalla
P.za Garibaldi 1, 42016 **Guastalla (RE)**
Tel: 0522-839 758 Fax: 0522-839 756
Internet: www.pobassareggiana.com/guastalla
E-Mail: serviziculturali@comunediguastalla.com
direttore artistico e musicale Sandro Volta; presidente Maurizia Barazzoni
Size: 20 *Type/Spec:* baroque ensemble/orchestra *Repertoire:* 17th-early 18th C *Perfs:* 10 *Touring:* Italy, France *Comments:* second address: c/o Teatro Comunale, via Verdi 7, 42016 Guastalla (RE), Italy; (contact Centro Culturale only in the morning tel: 0522-839 755); see also Venues

Sonatori de la Gioiosa Marca
Via Verga 5, 31100 **Treviso**
Tel: 0422-432 725 Fax: 0422-436 280
Internet: www.trevisotvol.it/sonatoritv
E-Mail: sonatoritv@tvol.it
Size: 7 *Type/Spec:* chamber ensemble *Repertoire:* Venetian composers, Vivaldi, Italian music from 17th, 18th centuries *Perfs:* 40 *Touring:* Italy, Europe *Comments:* CD's available

Venice Baroque Orchestra
Via Cà Venier 8, 30172 **Mestre (VE)**
Tel: 041-962 999 Fax: 041-982 037
E-Mail: vbo@musicinvenice.com
direttore Andrea Marcon
Size: 9-25 *Type/Spec:* instrumental/vocal *Repertoire:* 16-18th century, emphasis is on unknown Venetican composers *Perfs:* 30 *Touring:* Austria, Germany, France, UK, USA

LATVIA (+371)

Collegium Musicum Rigense
The Riga Early Music Centre, 85 Brivibas, 1001 **Riga**
Tel: 2-275 575 Fax: 2-278 060
director Maris Kupchs (mobile: 922 6271)
Size: 5 *Type/Spec:* vocal ensemble *Repertoire:* 17th/18th C Riga composers such as J.V.Meder & J.Fischer; works of German, French and Italian baroque composers

Early Music Ensemble Canto of the Latvian University
Brivibas 85, 1001 **Riga**
Tel: 2-275 575 Fax: 2-278 060
artistic director Irene Nelsone (tel: 2-296 589)
Size: 8 *Touring:* Poland, Czech Republic, France, Russia

Early Music Ensemble Ludus
Senas muzikas ansamblis Ludus
85 Brivibas, 1001 **Riga**
Tel: 2-275 575 Fax: 2-278 060
artistic director Marite Virdina (mobile: 950 7644)
Size: 6-7 *Type/Spec:* instrumental ensemble and voice (contratenor) *Repertoire:* late renaissance and early baroque *Comments:* artistic director's address: Tapsu 45/40, 1001 Riga

LITHUANIA (+370)

Chamber Ensemble of Early Music Musica Humana
Senosios muzikos Kamerinis ansamblis Musica Humana
Ausros vartu 5, 2001 **Vilnius**
Tel: 2-626 802/615 715
Fax: 2-622 859/615 715
artistic director Algirdas Vizgirda
Comments: see also Orchestras

Early Music and Dance Ensemble Banchetto Musicale
Senosios muzikos ir sokiu ansamblis Banchetto Musicale
Gedimino pr.9, 2600 **Vilnius**
Tel: 2-756 332/233 795/615 082
Fax: 2-226 412
artistic director Jurate Mikiskaite
Comments: see also Orchestras

MOLDOVA (+373)

Ars Poetica
153, 31 August, 2012 **Chisinau**
Tel: 2-248 578 Fax: 2-247 981
director Oleg Palynsky

Art-Folk Trio Trigon
V Lupu str, 4 ap.14, 2008 **Chisinau**
Tel: 2-627 596 Fax: 2-629 561
manager Natalia Stefanet
Size: 3 (viola, guitar, drums)

NETHERLANDS (+31)

Alhambra Ensemble
c/o I.Ganz, Middenweg 156-I, 1097 TZ **Amsterdam**
Tel: 20-463 3557
Fax: 20-463 1072
E-Mail: IGANZ@compuserve.com
director Isabelle Ganz
Size: 5 (tenor and mezzo voices + instruments) (ensemble of 4 available) *Type/Spec:* instrumental and vocal sephardic music using oud, kanun, shawm, nay, dumbek & other percussion *Repertoire:* world music – middle-eastern sound *Perfs:* 15-20 *Touring:* Europe, USA, Israel *Comments:* CDs available

Amsterdam Baroque Orchestra and Choir
P.O. Box 1163, 1400 BD **Bussum**
Tel: 35-692 6000 Fax: 35-692 6001
Internet: www.tonkoopman.nl
E-Mail: cdeklerk@abo.rem.nl
managing director Franco Panozzo; office manager Cecilia Deklerk; conductor Ton Koopman
Size: 30 (orchestra) + 30 (choir) *Type/Spec:* baroque, especially Bach *Perfs:* 40-50 *Touring:* international *Comments:* approx. 10 CDs per year; touring company; Agent: Franco Panozzo Artists Management, Via Valverde 32, 37122 Verona, Italy, Tel: +39 045-801 4041, Fax: +39 045-801 4980; see also Orchestras and Choirs

Amsterdam Loeki Stardust Quartet
Molenaarserf 60, 3991 KR **Houten**
Tel: 30-635 3134 Fax: 30-635 3905
E-Mail: bertho.driever@wxs.nl
contact Paul Leenhouts, Daniel Brüggen, Bertho Driever, Karel van Steenhoven
Size: 4 *Type/Spec:* recorder quartet *Repertoire:* medieval, renaissance, baroque, contemporary *Perfs:* 80-90 *Touring:* England, Spain, Israel, USA, India, Japan, Germany, Austria, Australia *Comments:* recordings with DECCA and Channel Classics Records

Barokorkest van de Nederlandse Bachvereniging
Postbus 12017, 3501 AA **Utrecht**
Tel: 30-252 4010/251 3413 (box office) Fax: 30-251 1639
E-Mail: bachvereniging@wxs.nl
managing director Maria Hansen; artistic director/principal conductor Jos van Veldhoven; production Chris van de Ven
Size: 20 *Type/Spec:* instrumental on p
riod instruments *Repertoire:* 17th,18th century *Perfs:* 30+ *Comments:* CD recordings with Gustav Leonhardt available;CD recording Bach–St. Matthew Passion with Jos Van Veldhoven

Biedermeier Quintet
Ruyschstraat 8, 1091 CB **Amsterdam**
Tel: 20-692 3974 Fax: 20-692 8868
E-Mail: 100327.15@compuserve.com
contact Marten Root
Size: 5 *Type/Spec:* woodwind quintet (flute, oboe, clarinet, horn, bassoon) *Repertoire:* complete 19th century romantic repertoire for woodwind quintet *Touring:* Japan *Comments:* the group is made up of principal players of the most outstanding early music ensembles: the Schönbrunn Ensemble, Het Orkest van de 18th Eeuw, the Academy of Ancient Music, the Amsterdam Baaroque Orchestra, La Petite Bande and the Hanover Band

Cappella Figuralis
De Nederlandse Bachvereniging, Postbus 12017, 3501 AA **Utrecht**
Tel: 30-252 4010/251 3413 (box office)
Fax: 30-251 1639
E-Mail: bachvereniging@wxs.nl
managing director Maria Hansen; artistic director/principal conductor Jos van Veldhoven; production Chris van de Van
Size: 10-16 *Type/Spec:* vocal and instrumental, soloist ensemble *Repertoire:* 16th -18th century *Perfs:* 4+ *Touring:* Netherlands, France *Comments:* CD recordings of Dutch 17th century composers

Combattimento Consort Amsterdam
Nooit Gedacht 118, 1398 EG **Muiden**
Tel: 294-262 341 Fax: 294-263 651
Internet: www.combattimento-consort-amsterdam.nl
E-Mail: office@cca-music.nl
general manager Albert Adams; artistic director Jan Willem de Vriend; assistant general manager Marcel Mandos; producer Diana Bohnenberger; press and pr Marco van Es; assistant artistic director Taco Stronks
Size: 12 *Type/Spec:* instrumental & vocal (soloist) *Repertoire:* baroque *Perfs:* 60 *Touring:* Japan, Italy, Austria, Belgium *Comments:* see also Orchestras

Ensemble Cristofori
Jacob Geelstraat 26, 3532 TS **Utrecht**
Tel: 30-294 7987
Fax: 30-294 7987
E-Mail: clcomte@worldonline.nl
artistic director Arthur Schoonderwoerd
Size: 3-12 *Type/Spec:* instrumental (fortepiano, strings, wind instruments) & vocal *Repertoire:* chamber music with fortepiano and other historical instruments from 18th and 19th century *Touring:* France, Netherlands, Germany, Belgium *Comments:* concerts are often organised in cooperation with the Dutch Fortepiano Foundation

Ensemble Schönbrunn
Ruyschstraat 8, 2nd floor, 1091 CB **Amsterdam**
Tel: 20-692 3974
Fax: 20-692 8868
E-Mail: 100327.15@compuserve.com
contact Marten Root
Size: 10+ *Type/Spec:* instrumental (flute, strings, pianoforte, harpsichord) *Repertoire:* baroque, renaissance, early classical, romantic *Perfs:* 25+ *Touring:* Spain, France, Netherlands, Germany, Austria, USA, Russia, Israel *Comments:* recording with Globe

Ensemble Zefiro
Bosboom Toussaintstraat 40hs, 1054 AT **Amsterdam**
Tel: 20-618 8687 Fax: 20-618 8687
E-Mail: zefiro@dueffe.it
contact Alfredo Bernardini
Size: 5-15 *Type/Spec:* instrumental (mainly woodwind-2 oboes and 1 bassoon + other instruments) *Repertoire:* late baroque and classical *Perfs:* 35 *Touring:* Spain, Austria, Germany, Italy, France, Israel *Comments:* winners of Grand Prix du Disque

La Primavera
Jacob Geelstraat 26, 3532 TS **Utrecht**
Tel: 30-294 9515 Fax: 30-294 9515
Internet: www.dse.nl/laprimavera
E-Mail: LaPrima@dse.nl
artistic director Clémence Comte
Size: 3-8 *Type/Spec:* instrumental (recorder, viola da gamba, theorbe, luth, guitar, harp, harpsichord)/vocal *Repertoire:* French, Italian Spanish 16th-18th century music *Touring:* France, Netherlands, German, Belgium, Austria

Landini Consort
Jacob Geelstraat 26, 3532 TS **Utrecht**
Tel: 30-294 9515
Fax: 30-294 9515
E-Mail: clcomte@worldonline.nl
contact Clémence Comte
Size: 3 *Type/Spec:* recorder ensemble *Repertoire:* early and modern music *Touring:* France, Belgium, Germany, Israel, Netherlands

Le Parnasse
Jacob Geelstraat 26, 3532 TS **Utrecht**
Tel: 30-294 9515 Fax: 30-294 9515
E-Mail: clcomte@worldonline.nl
artistic director Clémence Comte
Size: 3-6 *Type/Spec:* instrumental (recorders, viola da gamba, theorbe, chitarone, luth, guitar) *Repertoire:* French, Italian, German, Spanish 15th-18th century music *Touring:* France, Netherlands

Nederlands Historisch Dans-en-Theaterensemble
Het Ven 1, 6997 AX **Hoog Keppel**
Tel: 314-381 254 Fax: 314-381 254
artistic director Maria Angad Gaur
Size: variable number of musicians & actors + 8 dancers *Repertoire:* renaissance, baroque and dance & music, theatre *Perfs:* 20+ *Touring:* Germany, Netherlands, Czech Republic, Japan *Comments:* see also Dance

Orchestra of the Eighteenth Century
Orkest van de Achttiende Eeuw
Borneokade 301, 1019 XG **Amsterdam**
Tel: 20-626 8236 Fax: 20-620 5932
Internet: www.Orchestra18C.com
E-Mail: info@Orchestra18C.com
general director Sieuwert Verster;
music director Frans Brüggen
Size: 55 *Repertoire:* classical, specialising in 18th century *Perfs:* 40-50 *Touring:* Europe, Japan *Comments:* the Orchestra of the Eighteenth Century, an international group of musicians specializing in the performance of 18th century music, was founded in1981 by Frans Brüggen, with support of a number of friends from all over the world and subsidies from the Dutch Government and the Prins Bernhard Fund; from 1983 untill 1988 the orchestra was sponsored by IBM Europe; see also Orchestras;

Trio Passaggio
PO Box 362, 4000 AJ **Tiel**
Tel: 344-631 579 Fax: 344-631 479
contact Norbert Kunst
Type/Spec: early music chamber ensemble *Repertoire:* mainly baroque and pre-baroque *Touring:* international *Comments:* Cd's available; future projects include a children's opera

NORWAY (+47)

Barokkanerne
Gange Rolvs gt 2E, 0273 **Oslo**
Tel: 2244 5018
Fax: 2243 1697
contact Johan Nicoali Mohn
Size: 3-25 (varies) *Type/Spec:* baroque
Repertoire: chamber group and orchestra performing mainly baroque music 1600-1760 *Perfs:* 4-5

Bergen Barokk
c/o Frode Thorsen, Nygårdsgt . 63, 5008 **Bergen**
Tel: 5531 9338
Fax: 5558 6960
E-Mail: Frode.Thorsen@grieg.vib.no
contact Frode Thorsen
Size: 4 + occassionally lute, strings and vocal (soprano) *Type/Spec:* instrumental (recorder/traverso, viola da gamba/baroque cello, harpsichord/organ) *Repertoire:* baroque sonatas and cantalas etc (Veracini, Händel, Hotteterre a.o.) *Touring:* Norway, Finland *Comments:* recordings on CD – Händel : Sonatas for recorder and B.C., Veracini/Barsanti: Sonatas on Simax Classics, J. Chr. Pepusch: Cantatas on BIS

Christiania Consort
c/o Svein Egil Skotte, Inkognito terrasse 2, 0256 **Oslo**
Tel: 2244 5393 Fax: 2244 5393
E-Mail: s.e.skotte@notam.uio.no
contact Svein Egil Skotte; leader Knut Johannessen
Size: 3-6 *Type/Spec:* baroque *Repertoire:* 1600-1770 *Perfs:* 5-10 *Touring:* national

Norwegian Baroque Orchestra
Norsk Barokkorkester
Paul Fjermstads v.18, 7052 **Trondheim**
Tel: 7351 7210/7394 1751 Fax: 7351 7224
Internet: www.nbo.no
E-Mail: toreaune@nbo.no
managing director Tore Aaen Aune; principal conductors Andrew Parrot, Ketil Haugsand
Size: 12-40 *Type/Spec:* chamber orchestra *Repertoire:* baroque to classic *Perfs:* 6
Touring: Norway, Germany, France

Pro Musica Antiqua
Ekebergveien 54, 1181 **Oslo**
Tel: 2268 5983
Internet: www.nmh.no/~hog
E-Mail: hog@samson.nmh.no
director Hans Olav Gorset
Size: 3-8 singers and musicians *Repertoire:* medieval and renaissance *Touring:* international, national

Pro Musica Antiqua, Oslo
Ekebergv. 54, 1181 **Oslo**
Tel: 2268 5983
Internet: www.nmh.no/~hog/
E-Mail: hog@samson.nmh.no
director Hans Olav Gorset
Size: 3-8 *Type/Spec:* vocals, instrumental – recorders, viols, lutes *Repertoire:* medieval, renaissance *Perfs:* 20 *Touring:* Norway *Comments:* CD available

POLAND (+48)

Ars Nova
ul. Zakroczymska 2/2, 02-225 **Warszawa**
Tel: 22-831 2482 Fax: 22-831 2482
E-Mail: jurbi@friko7.onet.pl
director Jacek Urbaniak
Size: 5-12 *Repertoire:* medieval, renaissance *Perfs:* 14 *Touring:* Poland, Italy *Comments:* Polish and Spanish medieval music

Arte dei Suonatori
Os. Oswiecenia 66/29, 61-209 **Poznan**
Tel: 61-876 5842 Fax: 61-876 5842
E-Mail: arte@au.poznan.pl
directors Ewa and Aureliusz Golínski
Size: 4-15 *Repertoire:* baroque and classical *Perfs:* 8

Collegium Mamulianum
Os. Oswiecenia 62/15, 61-209 **Poznan**
Tel: 61-879 0621 Fax: 61-823 3704
director Dymitr Olszewski
Repertoire: baroque and classical

Concerto Polacco
Al. Niepodleglosci 71/38, 02-626 **Warszawa**
Tel: 22-844 3608
director Marck Toporowski
Type/Spec: baroque and classical

Dankwart Consort
ul. Sw Marcin 26/13, 61-805 **Poznan**
Tel: 61-823 1188
director Marcin Sompolinskí
Repertoire: baroque and classical

Fiori Musicali
ul. Sarego 12/14, 31-047 **Kraków**
Tel: 12-422 9062
director Zygmunt Kaczmarski
Repertoire: baroque and classical

Il Tempo
ul. Kanadyjska 4/7, 03-957 **Warszawa**
Tel: 22-617 1702 Fax: 22-617 1702
director Agata Sapiecha
Size: 4-22 *Type/spec:* instrumental, vocal, dance
Repertoire: early 17th – late 18th century

Kleine Cammer-musique
ul. Piotrkowska 145/21, 90-434 **Lodz**
Tel: 42-636 8370
director Jerzy Zak
Repertoire: renaissance and baroque

'Tutti e Solo' – Poznan Chamber Ensemble
Os. Jagiellonskie 12/71, 61-227 **Poznan**
Tel: 61-876 5801/601-767 993 (GSM) Fax: 61-876 5801
artistic director Barbara Mucha
Size: 4+ *Type/Spec:* baroque and early classical music
Repertoire: Polish baroque music; German, Italian, French, English and Scottish baroque and early classical works; *Touring:* national, international *Comments:* CD recorded by Dorian Discovery Ltd; performed music for the CD-ROM 'The Royal Castle in Warsaw'; made recordings for the Polish Radio &TV and Germany TV

RUSSIA (+7)

Barocco Ensemble
c/o Tim Yusupoff, ul Zorge 90-8, Rep. of Tatarstan, 420110 **Kazan**

E-Mail: root@ens-kust.kcn.ru
Size: 4 *Repertoire:* baroque *Touring:* national, Europe

Musica Petropolitana
House 16, apt. 13, Chervonnogo Kazachestva str., 198096 **St Petersburg**
Tel: 812-350 9442 Fax: 812-315 5785
contact Dimitry Sokolov
Size: 5 *Type/spec:* chamber quintet *Repertoire:* baroque music *Touring:* Europe, Israel, Turkey, USA

SPAIN (+34)

Al Ayre Español
Gran Via 80, Oficina 215-216, 28013 **Madrid**
Tel: 91-541 9642 Fax: 91-541 8470
Internet: www.artemusica.com
E-Mail: concerts@artemusica.com
managing director Eduardo Brenda; artistic director Raul Mallavibarrena; administrator Matilde Russo
Size: 6-25 *Type/spec:* vocal, instrumental *Repertoire:* Spanish baroque *Perfs:* 35 *Touring:* Central & South America *Comments:* second address: Plaza de Santa Cruz N° 13-15, Esc 1ffi, 1° dcha, 50003, Zaragoza; recordings for Deutsche Harmonia Mundi; managed by: Arte Música; see also Choirs and Agents & Producers

Alia Musica
Rincón 13, 1° B, Galapagar, 28260 **Madrid**
Tel: 91-858 2240/629-216 604 (mobile) Fax: 98-578 3417
Internet: www.aliamusica.com
E-Mail: miguel@aliamusica.com
director Miguel Sanchez
Size: 5-7 *Type/Spec:* instrumental, vocal *Repertoire:* medieval, Spanish-Jewish music *Perfs:* 30 *Touring:* Spain, Europe *Comments:* Agent: Adela Sanchez Producciones, Residencial Monsacro, Edificio C n°1, 1° B, 33162 Santa Eulalia de Morcín (Asturias) Tel: 98-578 3400/629-869 212 (mobile), Fax: 98-578 3417, Email: producciones@adelasanchez.com, Internet: www.adelasanchez.com, see also Agents & Producers

Atrium Musicae – Gregorio Paniagua
Museo Monasterio de Camorritos, Cercedilla, 28470 **Madrid**
Tel: 91-852 2086 Fax: 91-852 2086
E-Mail: e7600035@tsai.es
director and founder Gregorio Paniagua
Size: 1-12 *Type/Spec:* instrumental, vocal *Repertoire:* ancient Greek music, medieval, renaissance, baroque, contemporary and new works/compositions of Gregorio Paniagua *Touring:* Europe, USA, Asia, Australia *Comments:* extensive discography

Capella de Ministrers
Aptdo de Correos 115, 46450 **Benifaio (Valencia)**
Tel: 96-178 0015/929-618 411 (mobile) Fax: 96-178 0015
Internet: www.dkey.es/licanus
E-Mail: sincopa@ciberia.com
director artistico Carles Magraner
Size: 8-20 *Type/Spec:* vocal and instrumental Spanish music XIII, XIV C *Repertoire:* mainly Spanish and colonial American music from 16th-18th centuries, also baroque *Touring:* Spain, South America *Comments:* recordings with Harmonia Mundi

Conjunto Barroco Zarabanda
c/ Vallehermoso 34, 28015 **Madrid**
Tel: 91-448 7726 Fax: 91-448 7726
artistic director Alvaro Marías
Size: 4-10 *Repertoire:* baroque, renaissance and classical *Perfs:* 30 *Touring:* Spain, USA, Latin America *Comments:* touring in Spain with Teresa Berganza, and Charles Brett

Duo Nasarre
c/o Adela Sanchez Producciones, Residencial Monsacro, Edificio C n° 1, 1° B, 33162 **Santa Eulalia de Morcín (Asturias)**
Tel: 98-578 3400/629-869 212 (mobile)
Fax: 98-578 3417
Internet: www.adelasanchez.com
E-Mail: producciones@adelasanchez.com
administrator Adela Sanchez
Size: 2 (trumpet and organ) *Repertoire:* Spanish baroque music for clarin and organ *Touring:* Europe

Ensemble Instrumental Fontegara
Gran Via 80, Oficina 215-216, 28013 **Madrid**
Tel: 91-541 9642 Fax: 91-541 8470
Internet: www.artemusica.com
E-Mail: concerts@artemusica.com
managing director Eduardo Brenlla; artistic director Raúl Mallavibarrena; administrator Matilde Russo
Size: varies *Type/Spec:* instrumental, vocal *Repertoire:* baroque, renaissance *Perfs:* 20 *Touring:* national, Europe, South America *Comments:* performs with Musica Ficta (choir); represented by Arte Musica; recordings for Deutsche Harmonia Mundi; see also Choirs and Agents (Arté Musica)

Grupo de Musica Barroca La Folía
c/ Jesús del Valle 12, 1°/D, 28004 **Madrid**
Tel: 91-521 3244 Fax: 91-521 3244
artistic director Pedro Bonet
Size: 2-9 *Type/Spec:* instrumental, vocal *Repertoire:* 17th and 18th C Spanish baroque *Perfs:* 25 *Touring:* France, Spain, Portugal, Italy, Mexico *Comments:* special programme for 1999/2000: instumental music from Velazquez's times

Grupo S.E.M.A.
c/Olvega 13, 28033 **Madrid**
Tel: 91-562 0581 Fax: 91-766 4888
Internet: www.arrakis.es/~gru.sema
E-Mail: gru.sema@arrakis.es
artistic director Pepe Rey
Size: 10-18 *Repertoire:* medieval and renaissance *Perfs:* 15-20 *Touring:* Spain, Europe

HESPERION XX
Travesera de Gracia 18-20, 08021 **Barcelona**
Tel: 93-594 4760 Fax: 93-580 5606
E-Mail: 101617.3236@compuserve.com
admistration Irene Bloc; director Jordi Savall
Size: 2-16 *Type/Spec:* vocal and instrumental (viols, wind instruments, percussion, lute etc.) *Repertoire:* 12th-17th C *Perfs:* 40 *Touring:* Spain, Europe, North America and Argentina *Comments:* performs with La Capella Reial de Catalunya (choir); see also Choirs

La Stravaganza Asociación Musica Barroca
Calle Residencia, 25, Esc. B, 3° B, 28200 **San Lorenzo del Escorial (Madrid)**
Tel: 91-896 0359 Fax: 91-896 0359
manager Alicia García Alegre; artistic director Mariano Martín
Size: 4-20 *Type/Spec:* baroque and classical, instrumental, vocal *Repertoire:* specialise in Spanish theatrical music of 18th century *Perfs:* 20-30 *Touring:* Spain, Europe *Comments:* produced a CD monographic of Handel sonatas; also produces baroque opera

Musica Reservata de Barcelona
c/o Jordi Abello, Av. Meridiana 506-510, 1° 2ª, 08030 **Barcelona**
Tel: 93-346 2432 Fax: 93-346 2432
E-Mail: jordiabello@mixmail.com
contact Jordi Abello, Antoni Trigueros
Size: 6, up to 8 singers + continuo players (for large-scale works) *Type/Spec:* unaccompanied renaissance sacred music *Repertoire:* renaissance & baroque music, mostly unknown Spanish composers *Perfs:* 20 *Touring:* Spain, Italy *Comments:* radio broadcasts & recordings; second address: c/o Antoni Trigueros, Navas de Tolosa 369, 08041 Barcelona, tel & fax:93-351 8356

Schola Mozarábica
c/ cid 15, Majadahonda, 28220 **Madrid**
Tel: 91-638 3963 Fax: 91-593 0886
contact José Maria Allende
Size: 5 *Type/Spec:* vocal & instrumental *Repertoire:* mozarabic music (9th-10th-11th-12th C.) *Touring:* Spain, Europe

Scholars Baroque Ensemble, The
Romani 14, Altafulla, 43893 **Altafulla (Tarragona)**
Tel: 977-650 748 Fax: 977-650 748
E-Mail: dvan@tinet.fut.es
artistic co-ordinator David van Asch
Size: 12-26 musicians and singers *Type/Spec:* vocal and instrumental *Repertoire:* baroque *Perfs:* 15 *Touring:* Spain, Austria, France *Comments:* UK based ensemble administered by David van Asch from Spain

SWEDEN (+46)

Drottningholm Baroque Ensemble and Orchestra
Birger Jarisgatan 39, 111 45 **Stockholm**
Tel: 8-102 090 Fax: 8-102 090
managing director Lars Brolin
Size: 6-40 *Type/Spec:* chamber orchestra *Repertoire:* baroque-Viennese classics *Perfs:* 60-70 *Touring:* worldwide *Comments:* records for BIS, Musica Sveciae, Proprius, Caprice, EMI, Erato and RCA

Stockholm Baroque Orchestra
c/o Double Agent Artist Management, Aprikosgatan 29, 165 60 **Hässelby**
Tel: 8-471 9604 Fax: 8-471 9604
E-Mail: ann-charlott.hell@swipnet.se
contact Ann-Charlotte Hell
Size: 6-30 *Type/Spec:* chamber orchestra *Repertoire:* baroque-Viennese classics *Perfs:* 15

Swedish Baroque Orchestra, The
Svenska Barockorkestern
c/o Västmanlandsmusikeu, Hässlö Park, 721 31 **Västras**
Tel: 21-800 800/315 760 Fax: 21-800 801
E-Mail: me.miv@swipnet.se
contact Håkan Johansson; manager Håkan Wiskström
Size: 15-30 *Type/Spec:* instrumental *Repertoire:* baroque *Perfs:* 16 *Touring:* Sweden *Comments:* the orchestra consists of freelance musicians from Västeras Simfonietta, The Stockholm Philharmonic and other musicians; second address:
Visthusgatan 119, 72481 Västras

Wasa Baroque Ensemble
Gamla Björlandav 37, 417 20 **Göteborg**
Tel: 31-239 443
E-Mail: gabriel.bania@telia.com
musical leader and director Gabriel Bania
Size: 2-25 musicians *Repertoire:* 17th and 18th C. instrumental and vocal music *Comments:* the ensemble is one of the very few groups in the world experimenting with the original baroque stringing

SWITZERLAND (+41)

Chamber Players Luzern
Luegetenstr. 14, 6004 **Luzern**
Tel: 41-240 1114 Fax: 41-240 1114
E-Mail: paradise@swissonline.ch
members George Paradise, Rosemarie Paradise, Hans-Ulrich Stohler, Cyprian Meyer
Size: 4 *Type/Spec:* instrumental (oboe/ oboe d'amour, flute, violoncello, cembalo) *Repertoire:* baroque & contemporary music *Perfs:* 8-12 *Comments:* all of the members have done individual recordings

Inter City Flute Players, The
Monbijoustr. 37, 3011 **Bern**
Tel: 31-381 5723
Leitung Pierre-André Bovey
Size: 12-16 *Type/Spec:* flute consort *Repertoire:* original works for flute consorts and transcriptions *Perfs:* 10 *Touring:* Switzerland

Octomania (Bläseroktett)
Schaffhauserstr. 242, 8057 **Zürich**
Tel: 1-313 0331 Fax: 1-311 2585
E-Mail: marter@access.ch
director Matthias Arter
Size: 9 (wind octet + double bass) *Type/Spec:* instrumental- woodwind & brass *Repertoire:* classical, romantic, contemporary *Perfs:* 20 *Touring:* Switzerland, Germany, Italy, France

Quartetto Mobile
c/o Hans-Jakob Bollinger, Chutzenstr. 19, 3007 **Bern**
Tel: 31-372 4503 Fax: 31-372 4503
Internet: www.swissonline.ch/miclimusic
E-Mail: hjbollinger@datacomm.ch
manager/administrator Hans-Jakob Bollinger
Size: 4 *Type/Spec:* brass ensemble (trumpets, trombone) *Repertoire:* baroque, modern and own arrangements *Perfs:* 15 *Comments:* CD available

UKRAINE (+380)

Castrum Hung
vul. Berczeni 105, **Uzhorod**
Tel: 3122-34772
director Stepan Tykhonenko

Kiev Chamber Orchestra Archi
ulitsa Kreschatik 40, **Kiev (Kyiv)**
Tel: 44-229 2265 Fax: 44-224 1349
Size: 16 *Type/Spec:* string instruments *Repertoire:* baroque, classical *Touring:* Poland, Japan

Silva Rerum
vul. Mykilsko-Botaniczna 14/5, 252033 **Kiev (Kyiv)**
Tel: 44-244 2766
director Tetiana Trehub

UNITED KINGDOM (+44)

Academy of Ancient Music, The
10 Brookside, **Cambridge** CB2 1JE
Tel: 1223-301 509
Fax: 1223-327 377
Internet: www.aam.co.uk
E-Mail: administrator@aam.co.uk
general manager Christopher Lawrence; director Christopher Hogwood CBE; associate conductor Paul Goodwin; associate director & concert master Andrew Manze; concerts and tours manager Fiona Seer; administrator Madeleine Holmes
Size: 3-180 (including choir) *Type/Spec:* baroque and classical *Perfs:* 100 *Touring:* Europe, USA
Comments: see also Orchestra

Arcadia of London
60 Ashville Road, **London** E11 4DT
Tel: 20-8558 7723 Fax: 20-8558 7723
E-Mail: lottieman@aol.com
contact Maryann Tedstone
Size: 3-12 *Type/Spec:* baroque, popular renaissance *Perfs:* 10

Badinage
c/o Music Management (UK) Ltd., PO Box 1105, **London** SW1V 2DE
Tel: 20-7823 1111
Fax: 20-7823 1001
E-Mail: mm@musicmanagement.demon.co.uk
director Paul Carrol
Size: 3-15 *Type/Spec:* baroque & classical
Repertoire: baroque, classical, chamber & orchestra
Perfs: 50-80 *Touring:* international *Comments:* released 12 CDs through Meridian Records; now recording for Chandos Records

Baker Collection (Oxford 1672/83)– The oldest English Violin Consort
Lloyd-Wilson Musical Enterprises, Kenton Cottage, Burnt Hill Way, **Farnham** GU10 4RP
Tel: 1252-795 047
Fax: 1252-795 047
contact Brian Lloyd Wilson; presenter Peter Trevelyan
Size: 4-6 + soloists *Type/Spec:* instrumental + vocal *Repertoire:* 17th C *Perfs:* 15-25
Touring: Germany, Spain, UK *Comments:* strong historical emphasis including pre-concert talks

Bande Classique, La
38 Alric Avenue, **New Malden** KT3 4JN
Tel: 20-8942 1519/411-724 138 (mobile)
Fax: 20-8287 9284
musical director Jane Booth
Size: 3 *Type/Spec:* 17th/18th/19th/20th C. *Repertoire:* wind music *Perfs:* 4 *Comments:* workshops to tertiary level; full repertoire on request; lecture recitals

Baroque Brass of London
4 Hunter Road, **London** SW20 8NZ
Tel: 20-8946 2700 Fax: 20-8946 7272
directors Michael Laird, Robert Howes
Size: 10 (8 brass, timpani and organ) *Type/Spec:* 17th/18th C brass music on period instruments
Perfs: 20 *Touring:* Japan

Belfast Baroque
215 Stockmans Lane,
Belfast (Northern Ireland) BT11 9AQ
Tel: 28-9061 3384 Fax: 28-9061 3326
contact Dominic McHugh

Brandenburg Consort, The
5 Cornfield View, **Sleaford** NG34 7WF
Tel: 1529-304 130
Fax: 1529-304 131
Internet: freespace.virgin.net/roy.goodman
E-Mail: roy.goodman@virgin.net
musical director Roy Goodman;
administrator Steven Jones
Size: 6-36 *Type/Spec:* instrumental, choral
Repertoire: baroque, classical

Britten-Pears Baroque Orchestra, The
The Britten-Pears School for Advanced Musical Studies, High Street, **Aldeburgh** IP15 5AX
Tel: 1728-454 327/688 671
Fax: 1728-688 171
Internet: www.aldeburgh.co.uk
E-Mail: bpo@aldeburghfestivals.org
director Elizabeth Webb; administrator Ann Rawdon Smith; assistant administrator Julia Robinson; honorary president Ton Koopmann
Size: 15-40 *Type/Spec:* instrumental *Repertoire:* baroque *Perfs:* 2-5 *Touring:* national *Comments:* a unique training orchestra for post-graduate musicians and young professionals; welcome applications from the UK and Europe; see also Orchestras; Orchestra was planning to move in November 1999, no further details at time of going to print

Broadside Band, The
20 Leverton Street, **London** NW5 2PJ
Tel: 20-7267 7176
Fax: 20-7267 0127
E-Mail: JrmyBarlow@aol.com
contact Jeremy Barlow
Size: 4 *Type/Spec:* 17th C English popular music
Repertoire: popular and dance music c.1550-c.1750 *Perfs:* 12 *Comments:* more than a dozen recordings for EMI, Harmonia Mundi, Hyperion, Saydisc, Dorian etc.

Burning Bush, The
19 Patshull Rd, **London** NW5 2JX
Tel: 20-7485 3957
Fax: 20-7267 2957
E-Mail: Lucieskeaping@hotmail.com
director Lucie Skeaping
Size: 5-6 *Type/Spec:* traditional Jewish music *Repertoire:* Jewish music from Sephardi and Ashkenzi traditions – from medieval Spain to 19th C Europe, songs, dance & a great variety of traditional instruments from around the world *Perfs:* 30+ concerts plus educational workshops *Touring:* Germany, Belgium, Israel, UK, South America, Finland, Slovenia
Comments: TV appearances, radio documentries; director Lucie Skeaping is regular BBC broadcaster of Jewish music; 5 CDs available

Cambridge Baroque Camerata, The
6 Dane Drive **Cambridge** CB3 9LP
Tel: 1223-515 688
musical director Jonathan Hellyer Jones
Size: 2-30 *Type/Spec:* instrumental – harpsichord based adding string, wind and brass as required, chamber ensemble *Repertoire:* baroque *Perfs:* 10-25 *Touring:* France

Cardinall's Musick, The
1 Lorne Court, Whitehall Road,
Harrow on the Hill HA1 3BH
Tel: 20-8422 3119 Fax: 20-8423 9707
Internet: www.cardinall.demon.co.uk
E-Mail: admin@cardinallsmusick.demon.co.uk
artistic director Andrew Carwood; administration Irene Wears
Size: 5-16 *Type/Spec:* English and European renaissance *Perfs:* 15 *Touring:* UK, USA, Belgium *Comments:* specialise in UK festivals; recordings available on ASV's Gaudeamus label

Carnival Band, The
c/o Seaview Music, 28 Mawson Rd, **Cambridge** CB1 2EA
Tel: 1223-508 431 Fax: 1223-508 449
E-Mail: seaview@dial.pipex.com
manager Alison Page; leader Andy Watts
Size: 5-6 *Type/Spec:* instrumental & vocal *Repertoire:* renaissance *Perfs:* 50+ *Touring:* worldwide *Comments:* all members of the band belong to various orchestras, coming together as the Carnival Band throughout the year for occassional engagements

Chiaroscuro
71 Priory Road, Kew Gardens, **Richmond** TW9 3DH
Tel: 20-8940 7086 Fax: 20-8332 0879
manager Francesca McManus;
director Nigel Rogers (tenor)
Size: 6-30 *Type/Spec:* vocal ensemble + baroque orchestra *Repertoire:* late renaissance to baroque

Circa 1500
86 Avenue Road, **London** N15 5DN
Tel: 20-8802 7873 Fax: 20-8802 7873
director Nancy Hadden
Size: 3-5 *Type/Spec:* vocal and instrumental *Repertoire:* renaissance *Perfs:* 12-20 *Touring:* national, international *Comments:* 7 CDs – Virgin, CRD, Hyperion, Chandos, ASV; agent: Upbeat Management (London), contact: Maureen Phillips

Circa 1800
The Mill, Woodmancote, **Cheltenham** GL52 4QG
Tel: 1242-673 636
artistic director Kathleen Malet
Size: 2 *Type/Spec:* instrumental *Repertoire:* 17th/18th C

City Waites, The
Office, 19 Patshull Rd, **London** NW5 2JX
Tel: 20-7485 3957 Fax: 20-7267 2957
E-Mail: Lucieskeaping@hotmail.com
contacts Lucie Skeaping, Douglas Wootton, Mike Brain, Roddy Skeaping
Size: 4 *Type/Spec:* early English popular music + song *Repertoire:* music and broadside ballads of the streets, theatres and taverns of 17th C England, also medieval repertoire *Perfs:* 30-40 concerts + workshops per year *Touring:* Middle East, USA, Europe, South America, Philippines, Thailand, Germany *Comments:* visual/theatrical presentation, TV and radio broadcasts; over 16 CDs available; consorts for National Trust, Royal National Theatre, Shakespeare's Globe,

Clerkes of Oxenford, The
Ty Isaf, Llanilar, **Aberystwyth (Wales)** SY23 4NP
Tel: 1974-241 229
E-Mail: dww@aber.ac.uk
contact David Wulstan
Size: 6-22 *Type/Spec:* small ensemble for medieval music, larger group for renaissance, baroque and other music *Repertoire:* tudor, medieval, renaissance *Perfs:* 10+ *Touring:* international *Comments:* CD's available on Calliope, Music for Pleasure, and Proud Sound

Collegium Musicum 90
71 Priory Road, Kew Gardens, **Richmond** TW9 3DH
Tel: 20-8940 7086 Fax: 20-8332 0879
manager Francesca McManus; musical directors Richard Hickox, Simon Standage
Size: 10-60 *Type/Spec:* baroque, classical, choral and orchestral *Repertoire:* Telemann, Leclair, Bach, Handel, Haydn *Perfs:* 15-20 *Touring:* national *Comments:* regular recordings with Chandos Records on exclusive contract

Combattimento
55 Marmora Road, **London** SE22 0RY
Tel: 20-8299 1914 Fax: 20-8299 1914
E-Mail: Hirstpr@aol.com
director David Roblou; pr & arts administration Diana Hirst; Italian director Mark Tucker;
stage director Ian Caddy
Size: 3-35 *Type/Spec:* vocal and operatic (staged or semi-staged) *Repertoire:* ranges from late renaissance to 20thC *Touring:* national, international *Comments:* aims to promote a bel canto style of singing accompanied in a suitably flexible manner by period instruments where appropriate

Companie of Dansers – Trabocchetti, The
41 Talma Gardens, **Twickenham** TW2 7RB
Tel: 20-8892 9638
Fax: 20-8892 9638
artistic director Madeleine Inglehearn;
musical director Jean McCreery
Size: 8 (3 dancers, 5 musicians) *Type/Spec:* 17th-18th C dance and music *Repertoire:* English baroque *Perfs:* 10-30 *Comments:* offer educational programmes for schools; promotional video available

Concert Royal
25 Turners Croft, Heslington,
York YO10 5EL
Tel: 1904-410 298
Fax: 1904-421 109
Internet: www.classical-artists.com/concertroyal
E-Mail: r.garvey@easynet.co.uk
director Peter Harrison
Size: 4 *Type/Spec:* vocal and instrumental
Repertoire: baroque (English 18th C) *Perfs:* 50 *Touring:* national and international *Comments:* programme for 2000/2001: Jane Austen's Musical England

Concordia
46 Uplands Road, **London** N8 9NL
Tel: 20-8348 4295 Fax: 20-8292 7125
E-Mail: Sarah.Bm@btinternet.com
director Mark Levy;
administrator Sarah Bonner-Morgan
Size: 5 core members *Type/Spec:* viol consort (also perform with singers)
Repertoire: renaissance, baroque, contemporary *Perfs:* 30+ *Touring:* Netherlands, Belgium, Spain, Germany
Comments: record for Chandos, Metronome

Consort of Musicke
13 Pages Lane, **London** N10 1PU
Tel: 20-8444 6565
Fax: 20-8444 1008
E-Mail: consort@easynet.co.uk
contact Anthony Rooley, Emma Kirkby
Size: up to 6 *Type/Spec:* vocal *Repertoire:* 16th/18th C vocal music *Touring:* Europe, Israel, North America
Comments: over 100 recordings on various international labels, inc. most recently, ASV; see also Choirs

Convivium (Wallfisch/Tunnicliffe/Nicholson)
c/o Helen Sykes Artists Management, First Floor Parkway House, Sheen Lane, **London** SW14 8LS
Tel: 20-8876 8276 Fax: 20-8876 8277
E-Mail: helen@hsam.u-net.com
director Elizabeth Wallfisch
Size: 3+ *Type/Spec:* instrumental *Repertoire:* baroque, classical, early romantic *Perfs:* varies *Touring:* UK and abroad *Comments:* over 10 recordings on Hyperion

Dowland Consort, The
71 Priory Road, Kew Gardens, **Richmond** TW9 3DH
Tel: 20-8940 7086
Fax: 20-8332 0879
manager Francesca McManus; director Jakob Lindberg
Size: 6 *Type/Spec:* renaissance music for lutes and viols by John Dowland and his contemporaries *Touring:* international *Comments:* various CDs on BIS

Dragonsfire
9 Hillside Road, **Ashtead** KT21 1RZ
Tel: 1372-277 703 Fax: 1372-278 406
contact Nigel Perona-Wright
Size: 4 *Type/Spec:* vocal and multi-instrumental (use of up to 50 instruments) *Repertoire:* renaissance/Tudor and British traditional music and song *Perfs:* 200
Comments: 4 recordings currently available; annual recital at Purcell Room

Dufay Collective, The
19 Hillfield Road, Comberton,
Cambridge CB3 7DB
Tel: 20-8488 3947
Fax: 20-8488 3947
Internet: www.dufay.com
E-Mail: info@dufay.com
contacts Peter Skuce, William Lyons
Size: 5 *Type/Spec:* medieval and renaissance music
Repertoire: 12th-17th C *Perfs:* 40-50 *Touring:* Morocco, Spain, Brazil

Ecole d'Orphée, L'
c/o John Holloway, The Old Manse, Leafield,
Witney OX8 5NN
Tel: 1993-878 200
Fax: 1993-878 375
Internet: www.classical-artists.com
E-Mail: oldmanse@compuserve.com
director John Holloway
Type/Spec: baroque *Repertoire:* baroque

Elizabethan Consort of Viols
22 Crouch Street,
Banbury OX16 9PP
Tel: 1295-277 976 Fax: 1295-277 976
contact Peter Adams
Size: 3-5 *Type/Spec:* 16th C to present time
Repertoire: 17th C English *Perfs:* 25-30

English Bach Festival Baroque Ensemble
15 South Eaton Place,
London SW1W 9ER
Tel: 20-7730 5925
Fax: 20-7730 1456
E-Mail: english.bachfestival@which.net
director Lina Lalandi OBE
Size: 7-50 *Type/Spec:* instrumental, vocal *Repertoire:* early opera *Perfs:* 20 *Touring:* international
Comments: see also Opera and Festivals

English Baroque Soloists
Monteverdi Choir and Orchestra Ltd., 61 Wandsworth High Street, **London** SW18 2PT
Tel: 20-8871 4750
Fax: 20-8871 4751
Internet: www.monteverdi.co.uk
E-Mail: info@monteverdi.org.uk
acting general manager Howard Gough; artistic director Sir John Eliot Gardiner; administrator Jan Normanton; orchestra manager David Adams; project co-ordinator Andrew Hammond
Size: 20-45 *Type/Spec:* instrumental *Repertoire:* music up to and including Mozart *Touring:* UK, Europe, USA *Comments:* see also Orchestras

English Concert, The
8 St. George's Terrace, **London** NW1 8XJ
Tel: 20-7911 0905 Fax: 20-7911 0904
E-Mail: ec@englishconcert.co.uk
general manager Felix Warnock; artistic director Trevor Pinnock CBE; orchestral manager Sarah Fenn; administrator Victoria Atkinson
Size: 10-50 *Type/Spec:* chamber orchestra *Repertoire:* baroque, early classical *Perfs:* up to 50 *Touring:* Europe, South America, USA, Japan *Comments:* all recordings on DG Archiv; see also Orchestras

English Fantasy, The
25A Cleveland Road,
London SW13 0AA
Tel: 20-8876 1274
contact Fiona Huggett
Size: 5-6 *Type/Spec:* viol consort *Repertoire:* Elizabethan & Jacobean viol consort music; consort songs for soprano & counter tenor with 4-5 part viol settings *Perfs:* 3-15 *Comments:* CD available on ASV

Eroica Quartet
c/o Hazard Chase, Richmond House, 16-20 Regent Street, **Cambridge** CB2 1DB
Tel: 1223-312 400
Fax: 1223-460 827
Internet: www.hazardchase.co.uk
E-Mail: hilary.perrott@hazardchase.co. uk
contact Hilary Perrott
Size: 4 (string quartet)
Repertoire: classical and romantic
Touring: worldwide *Comments:* see also Orchestras

European Union Baroque Orchestra
Hordley, **Wootton Woodstock** OX20 1EP
Tel: 1993-812 111
Fax: 1993-812 911
Internet: www.eubo.org.uk
E-Mail: info@eubo.org.uk
general administrator Paul James; orchestral manager Emma Wilkinson; music director Roy Goodman; development director Nick Berry
Size: 24 (100% annual renewal) *Type/Spec:* baroque orchestra *Repertoire:* baroque *Perfs:* 40 *Touring:* UK, worldwide *Comments:* pre-professional training orchestra funded by European Commission and Matsushita Electric Europe (Headquarters) see also Orchestras

Ex Cathedra
Suite 303, 95 Spencer Street, **Birmingham** B18 6DA
Tel: 121-523 1025 Fax: 121-523 1026
general manager Justin Lee;
artistic director Jeffrey Skidmore
Size: 12-32 *Type/Spec:* vocal and instrumental *Repertoire:* music from 15th C. to present day, specialising in late renaissance and baroque *Perfs:* 30+ *Touring:* UK, Europe *Comments:* recordings available on ASV; extensive education workshops: reaching over 1000 people each year; projects can be tailored to promoters needs

Extempore String Ensemble
72 Sussex Way, **London** N7 6RR
Tel: 20-7272 9009
director George Weigand
Size: 3-7 *Type/Spec:* instrumental – 16th/18th C for string ensemble of lutes, viols, violin and harpsichord with optional singer, wind instruments and/or dancers *Repertoire:* emphasis on 16th & 17th century style improvisation *Touring:* UK, Europe *Comments:* CDs, radio and television recordings

Fiori Musicali
Bank Cottage, **Preston Capes** NN11 3TD
Tel: 1327-361 380 Fax: 1327-361 415
Internet: www.fiori-musicali.com
E-Mail: fiori@fiori-musicali.com
director Penelope Rapson; leader Kerskin Linder-Dewan
Size: 5-50 *Type/Spec:* instrumental and choral *Repertoire:* baroque and classical *Perfs:* 35-50 *Touring:* UK

Fioritura
38 Alric Avenue, **New Malden** KT3 4JN
Tel: 20-8942 1519/411-724 138 (mobile)
Fax: 20-8287 9284
administrator Jane Booth
Size: 4 *Type/Spec:* instrumental, vocal *Repertoire:* classical, romantic *Perfs:* 15 *Comments:* use both period and modern instruments; see also Les Aventuriers

Fretwork
c/o Askonas Holt Ltd., 27 Chancery Lane, **London** WC2A 1PF
Tel: 20-7400 1751 Fax: 20-7400 1799
E-Mail: info@holt.co.uk
contact Melanie Evans
Size: 4-9 *Type/Spec:* viol consort *Repertoire:* renaissance, baroque, contemporary *Perfs:* 40 *Touring:* North America, Europe *Comments:* 16 records on Virgin Veritas label

Frottola
79 Humber Doucy Lane, **Ipswich** IP4 3NU
Tel: 1473-718 811
Internet: www.btinternet.com/~Jennie.Cassidy/
E-Mail: Frottola@btinternet.com
contact Jennie Cassidy
Size: 3 *Type/Spec:* vocal and instrumental *Repertoire:* medieval, renaissance and baroque *Touring:* UK

Gabrieli Consort and Players
Room 13, The Annexe, Shoreditch Town Hall, 380 Old Street, **London** EC1V 9LT
Tel: 20-7613 4404 Fax: 20-7613 4414
Internet: www.gabrieli.com
E-Mail: gabrieliconsort@compuserve.com
general manager Anita Crowe; artistic director Paul McCreesh; administrator Lucy Miller; director of development Dawn Rotheram
Size: 12-60 *Type/Spec:* vocal consort, baroque choir, instrumental consort, baroque orchestra *Repertoire:* high renaissance, baroque (16th-18th C) *Perfs:* 40-60 *Touring:* Europe, South America, USA, Far East *Comments:* see also Orchestras

Georgian Music Room, The
33 Hartswood Road, **London** W12 9NE
Tel: 20-8749 3365 Fax: 20-8749 1201
contact Celia Harper; agent Blythe
Size: 3-5 *Type/Spec:* English music with contemporary readings *Repertoire:* 17th & 18th C English music *Perfs:* 5-40

Gesualdo Consort of London, The
112 Wordsworth Road, **Hampton** TW12 1ET
Tel: 20-8941 2684 Fax: 20-8941 2684
E-Mail: venosa@ndirect.co.uk
director Gerald Place
Size: 4-6 *Type/Spec:* vocal ensemble unaccompanied or with lute *Repertoire:* late renaissance, early baroque, 20th C. *Touring:* national, Italy, Netherlands, Belgium *Comments:* recordings for ASV, Cantoris, Libra, TV film on Gesualdo for Werber Herzog; see also Orchestras

Gothic Voices
c/o Leigh Nixon, 7 Mount Pleasant, West Horsley, **Surrey** KT24 6BL
Tel: 1483 285 395 Fax: 1483 285 395
E-Mail: leigh.nixon@ukgateway.net
contact Leigh Nixon
Size: 4-7 *Type/Spec:* vocal *Repertoire:* medieval *Perfs:* 20-30 *Touring:* Germany, Australia, Slovenia, Latvia, USA, UK

Hanover Band
The Old Market, Upper Market Street, **Hove** BN3 1AS
Tel: 1273-206 978 Fax: 1273-329 636
Internet: www.hanoverband.com
E-Mail: mailbox@hanoverband.co.uk
chief executive Stephen Neiman; artistic director Caroline Brown; marketing & communication manager David Orams; pa to artistic director Jane Saunders; promotions manager Kathy Audiev
Size: 15-60 *Repertoire:* baroque, classical, romantic; played on period instruments *Perfs:* 35-40 *Touring:* Germany *Comments:* patron: H.R.H. The Duke of Kent, KG; see also orchestras

Harp Consort, The
9 Cliff Street, St Peter Port,
Guernsey (Channel Islands) GY1 1LH
Tel: 1481-713 037 Fax: 1481-700 502
E-Mail: harp@compuserve.com
director Andrew Lawrence-King; manager Howard Baer
Size: 2-15 *Type/Spec:* instrumental/vocal *Repertoire:* medieval, renaissance, baroque *Perfs:* 50 *Touring:* USA, Germany, France, Finland, UK, Japan, Spain, Italy, Israel *Comments:* world early music and dance performed by improvising continuo-band

Hausmusik London
c/o Judith Hendershott, 4 Bennett Park,
London SE3 9RB
Tel: 20-8852 0823 Fax: 20-8852 0016
general manager Judith Hendershott
Size: 5-9 *Type/Spec:* chamber ensemble (Mendelssohn, Schubert, Brahms) *Repertoire:* 18th/19th C *Touring:* national *Comments:* recordings on Virgin; live broadcasts and recordings for BBC World Service and Radio 3

Hercules
87 Middle Lane, **London** N8 8NX
Tel: 20-8340 2156 Fax: 20-8340 2156
contact Keith McGowan
Size: 3-6 *Type/Spec:* instrumental (shawms, lutes, organ) *Repertoire:* music from 1400 – 1600 *Perfs:* 6 *Comments:* available for corporate functions and theatre

His Majestys Sagbutts and Cornetts
80 Vancouver Road, **London** SE23 2JA
Tel: 20-8473 0444 Fax: 20-8699 6926
Internet: www.pavilion.co.uk/paulnieman/hmsc.html
E-Mail: jwest@ic.ac.uk
general manager Jeremy West;
artistic director Timothy Roberts
Size: 7 *Type/Spec:* instrumental (wind and brass) *Repertoire:* renaissance & early baroque *Comments:* CDs available (mainly on Hyperion)

I Fagiolini
24, Salisbury Close, **Princes Risborough** HP27 0JF
Tel: 1844-345 957 Fax: 1844-345 957
Internet: www.philomel.demon.co.uk/fagiolini
E-Mail: robert.hollingworth@virgin.net
director Robert Hollingworth; agent Alan Coates; administrator Kathryn Coggins
Size: 5-10 *Type/Spec:* solo voice ensemble, often additional instrumental *Repertoire:* renaissance, early baroque, contemporary *Perfs:* 50 *Touring:* UK, Finland, Denmark, Norway, Spain, Hungary, Italy, USA, Germany, Belgium *Comments:* commission contemporary works

Joglaresa
31A Vestry Road, **London** SE5 8PG
Tel: 20-7708 3529 Fax: 20-7708 3529
director Belinda Sykes
Size: 4-5 *Type/Spec:* medieval and Arab-Andalusian music with instruments *Perfs:* 15
Touring: UK, Slovenia, Morocco

Jouissance des Dames
80 Denbigh Street, **London** SW1V 2EX
Tel: 20-7828 3090/600-740 433 Fax: 20-7828 3090
administrator Jessica Gordon
Size: 3 *Type/Spec:* vocal and instrumental *Repertoire:* renaissance *Comments:* also offer workshops/lecture-recitals

King's Consort, The
34 St Mary's Grove, **London** W4 3LN
Tel: 20-8995 9994 Fax: 20-8995 2115
Internet: www.the-kings-consort.org.uk
E-Mail: info@the-kings-consort.org.uk
artistic director Robert King; artistic manager Edward Hossack; development director Nicky Oppenheimer; tour manager Eugenia Pino;
administrator Elizabeth Baines
Size: 15-50 + 16-30 choir *Type/Spec:* baroque and early classical on period instruments with/without choir/soloists; also chamber ensemble *Perfs:* 75 *Touring:* Australia, Argentina, Belgium, Brazil, France, Germany, Hong Kong, Italy, Netherlands, New Zealand, Norway, Poland, Spain, Sweden, Switzerland, Turkey *Comments:* coming seasons also include fully-staged operas by Handel, Purcell, Rameau & Mozart

King/Heringman – Mezzo Soprano/ Lute Duo
41 Angles Road, **London** SW16 2UU
Tel: 20-8769 4833 Fax: 20-8769 4833
E-Mail: pellingman@compuserve.com
contacts Catherine King, Jacob Heringman
Type/Spec: instrumental, vocal *Repertoire:* renaissance to early baroque + contemporary *Perfs:* 12-15 *Touring:* USA

Kontraste
8 Pit Farm Road, **Guildford** GU1 2JH
Tel: 1483-563 096 Fax: 1483-563 096
contact Penelope Cave
Size: 3-5 *Type/Spec:* instrumental chamber music; flute, violin and harpsichord form the nucleus (thus no piano necessary) *Repertoire:* baroque and contemporary *Touring:* UK, Scotland, Germany

Kuijken Brothers
Allied Artists, 42 Montpelier Square, **London** SW7 1JZ
Tel: 20-7589 6243 Fax: 20-7581 5269
E-Mail: info@alliedartists.co.uk
contact Robert Slotover
Size: 3-4 *Type/Spec:* baroque, pre-classical to classical *Touring:* national and international *Comments:* played on original instruments

La Brigata
Billington Manor, Billington, **Leighton Buzzard** LU7 9BJ
Tel: 1525-372 516 Fax: 1525-851 649
manager Pat Hedges; musical director Peter Syrus
Size: 2-5 *Type/Spec:* music drama *Repertoire:* 1300-1600 in various European languages *Perfs:* 5 *Touring:* UK *Comments:* workshops with the able-bodied and disabled

Legrand Ensemble, The
Upbeat Management, Sutton Business Centre, Restmor Way, **Wallington** SM6 7AH
Tel: 20-8773 1223 Fax: 20-8669 6752
Internet: www.upbeat.co.uk
E-Mail: classic@upbeat.co.uk
contact Maureen Phillips
Size: 6 *Type/Spec:* early music and contemporary *Repertoire:* 16th-17th C. & contemporary *Perfs:* 6 *Comments:* many works commissioned by & written for the group; managed by Upbeat Management (see also Agents)

Les Aventuriers
38 Alric Avenue, **New Malden** KT3 4JN
Tel: 20-8942 1519/411-724 138 (mobile)
Fax: 20-8287 9284
musical director Jane Booth
Size: 5 *Type/Spec:* quintets for clarinet and strings
Repertoire: 18th/19th C *Perfs:* 20 *Comments:* workshops to tertiary level; full repertoire on request; see also Fioritura

London Baroque
Brick Kiln Cottage, Hollington, **Newbury** RG20 9XX
Tel: 1635-254 331
Fax: 1635-253 629
E-Mail: c.medlam@btinternet.com
contact Charles Medlam
Size: 4-6 *Type/Spec:* baroque chamber music *Repertoire:* from end of 16th century up to Mozart and Haydn with works of virtually unknown composers next to familiar masterpieces of the baroque and early classical eras
Perfs: 50 *Touring:* Japan, USA
Comments: US-Management: Joanne Rile Management Inc., 100 Old York Road – Benson East Suite 1206, Jenkintown PA 19046-3613,USA, tel: 215-885 6400, fax: 215-885 9929; see also Orchestras (Romantic Chamber Group of London)

London Handel Orchestra
The Coach House, Drury Lane,
Redmarley d'Abitôt GL19 3JX
Tel: 1531-650 616
Fax: 1531-650 616
contact Denys Darlow;
associate conductors Laurence Cummings, Jonathan Rees-Williams
Size: 20 *Type/Spec:* instrumental *Repertoire:* Handel and his contemporaries (European and English) oratorio; orchestral music *Perfs:* 19+ *Touring:* Tilford Bach Festival (May 99); St. Georges Chapel, Windsor Castle (spring & autumn) *Comments:* resident orchestra at the London Handel Festival; associated with the choir of St. Georges Chapel, Windsor Castle; see also Choirs

London Pro Arte Baroque Orchestra
17B St. Augustine Avenue, **Croydon** CR2 6JN
Tel: 20-8688 2890/802-429 235 Fax: 20-8688 2901
Internet: ds.dial.pipex.com/proarte
E-Mail: proarte@dial.pipex.com
orchestra manager Richard Thomas; artistic director/principal conductor Murray Stewart
Size: 14+ *Repertoire:* baroque, classical (authentic instruments) *Perfs:* 12 *Touring:* France *Comments:* venues include: South Bank Centre; Barbican; St. John's, Smith Square; Colston Hall, Bristol

London Pro Musica
15 Rock Street, **Brighton** BN2 1NF
Tel: 1273-692 974
Fax: 1273-622 792
contact Bernard Thomas
Size: 4-12 *Type/Spec:* voices, wind ensemble
Repertoire: renaissance, early baroque *Perfs:* 10
Comments: CD on Carlton label

London Wind Consort
Cantax House, Lacock, **Chippenham** SN15 2JZ
Tel: 1249-730 468
Fax: 1249-730 468
contact Andrew van der Beek
Size: 4-8 *Type/Spec:* renaissance, baroque *Perfs:* 20

Ludus Baroque
c/o Leithlofts, 8/1 Maritime Street,
Edinburgh (Scotland) EH6 6SB
Tel: 131-467 0066
Fax: 131-467 7333
Internet: www.leithlofts.co.uk/ludus
E-Mail: ludus@leithlofts.co.uk
musical director Richard Neville-Towle
Size: up to 16 singers and 18 instrumentalists; 5 is usual no. for touring ensemble *Type/Spec:* instrumental and vocal *Repertoire:* 17th/18th C music performed on period instruments *Perfs:* 30 *Touring:* highlands & islands of Scotland *Comments:* awarded lottery finance to purchase copies of various 18th C music and instruments; all will be available to interested parties

Maggie Cole & Friends
c/o Robert White Artist Management,
182 Moselle Avenue, **London** N22 6EX
Tel: 20-8881 6914
Fax: 20-8888 9662
E-Mail: rwhiteam@aol.com
contact Robert White; director & harpsichord Maggie Cole; leader Catherine Mackintosh
Size: 7-10 *Type/Spec:* music for harpsichord & single strings, with soloists *Repertoire:* baroque music, principally Bach *Perfs:* 10 *Touring:* Europe

Midland Baroque
3 Abbey Mill End, **St Albans** AL3 4HN
Tel: 172-784 3656
Fax: 172-784 3656
contact Diane Terry
Size: 5 *Type/Spec:* instrumental
Repertoire: baroque *Touring:* UK

Musica Antiqua of London
87 Olive Road, **London** NW2 6UR
Tel: 20-8452 3254 Fax: 20-8452 3254
E-Mail: alison.crum@which.net
administrator Alison Crum; director Philip Thorby
Size: 5 *Type/Spec:* renaissance – vocal & instrumental – viols, recorders, shawms, crumhorns, sackbut, flute, lute, harp with guest singers *Repertoire:* early 16th century secular music from Spain, Italy, France, Germany and England *Perfs:* 5 *Comments:* CD on Naxos label, and on Saydisc

Musica Dolce
Redwings Linden Chase, **Uckfield** TN22 1EE
Tel: 1825-760 046 Fax: 1825-760 046
contact Linda Brand
Size: 4 (harpsichord, cello, recorder, soprano)
Type/Spec: instrumental + vocal *Repertoire:* 18thC baroque *Perfs:* 20 *Touring:* USA

Musica Fiammante
c/o J. Audrey Ellison International Artists' Management, 135 Stevenage Rd., **London** SW6 6PB
Tel: 20-7381 9751 Fax: 20-7381 2406
manager J. Audrey Ellison
Size: 3 *Type/Spec:* soprano, cello, harpsichord *Repertoire:* Domenico Scarlatti, baroque *Touring:* national and international *Comments:* also lecture recitals; CDs available on Unicorn-Karchana

Musica Secreta
c/o Deborah Roberts, 9 Chalkers Lane,
Hurstpierpoint BN6 9LR
Tel: 1273-833 950 Fax: 1273-833 950
E-Mail: 101565.3033@compuserve.com
manager Deborah Roberts
Size: 3 singers (up to 6 singers for convent style polyphony) + 2 continuo players *Type/Spec:* female voices and continuo (up to 6 singers for convent style polyphony) *Repertoire:* renaissance + early baroque, inc. Italian, French, English and convent music *Touring:* national and international *Comments:* 4 CDs available (2 on Amon Ra, 2 on Linn)

Musicians of the Globe
12 Vathouse, Regents Bridge Gardens,
London SW8 1HD
Tel: 20-7735 8154 Fax: 20-7820 0801
E-Mail: Philip.Pickett@btinternet.com
director Philip Pickett
Size: 6-60 *Type/Spec:* instrumental, vocal *Repertoire:* renaissance, baroque, classical, romantic, esp. English 1590-1850 *Perfs:* 30 *Touring:* worldwide *Comments:* ensemble formed as associate of New Shakespeare Globe Theatre in London; provide period music for at least one authentic production each year and give regular concerts in the Globe; recordings on Philips

Musicke Companye, The
Neil Chaffey Concert Promotions, 9 Munts Meadow, **Weston** SG4 7AE
Tel: 1462-790 919 Fax: 1462-790 920
Internet: www.pinknoise.demon.co.uk/mc/
contacts Phillipa Hyde, Paul Esswood, Jennifer Janse, Helen Rogers
Size: 4 (+ occasional guest artists) *Type/Spec:* instrumental, vocal *Repertoire:* early to late baroque (1600-1780) *Perfs:* 20 *Touring:* Sweden, France, UK *Comments:* recordings available on Intim Musik, and Forties Recording

Músicos de Cámara
19 Linton Street, **London** N1 7DU
Tel: 20-7354 2973 Fax: 20-7354 2973
E-Mail: mjyakeley@yahoo.com
director M. June Yakeley
Size: 4-8 *Type/Spec:* baroque, chamber with voices
Repertoire: 17th C Spanish *Perfs:* 8-10 *Touring:* Spain
Comments: also works with theatre and dance groups

New London Consort
12 Vathouse, Regents Bridge Gdns.,
London SW8 1HD
Tel: 20-7735 8154
Fax: 20-7820 0801
E-Mail: Philip.Pickett@btinternet.com
director Philip Pickett
Size: 4-40 *Type/Spec:* instrumental, vocal *Repertoire:* medieval, renaissance, baroque *Perfs:* 70 *Touring:* worldwide *Comments:* recordings on Decca L'Oiseau – Lyre; see also Orchestras; associate of the South Bank Centre

Orchestra of the Age of Enlightenment
5th Floor, Westcombe House,
56-58 Whitcomb St., **London** WC2H 7DN
Tel: 20-7930 0646
Fax: 20-7930 0626
E-Mail: oae@premier.co.uk
general manager David Pickard;
artistic administrator James Ellis
Size: 20-60 *Type/Spec:* baroque, classical *Perfs:* 40
Touring: Austria, Spain, Italy, France, Germany, Switzerland *Comments:* operas at Glyndebourne; associate orchestra at South Bank Centre, London; see also Orchestras

Orchestra of the Renaissance
c/o Mary Taylor, The Old Manse, Leafield, **Witney** OX8 5NN
Tel: 1993-878 200 Fax: 1993-878 375
Internet: www.classical-artists.com
E-Mail: oldmanse@compuserve.com
director Richard Cheetham; adminsitration Mary Taylor
Size: 4-17 *Type/Spec:* renaissance *Repertoire:* renaissance
Touring: international

Orlando Consort, The
124 Westway, Raynes Park, **London** SW20 9LS
Tel: 20-8540 1633 Fax: 20-8542 8215
Internet:
ourworld.compuserve.com/homepages/Donald_Greig/
E-Mail: AngusSmith1@compuserve.com
contact Angus Smith
Size: 4 *Type/Spec:* vocal *Repertoire:* medieval, early renaissance *Perfs:* 30 *Touring:* USA, South America, France, Spain, Italy, Holland *Comments:* recordings available on Saydisc, Metronome and Deutsche Grammophon

Oxford Baroque
70 Hayfield Road, **Oxford** OX2 6TU
Tel: 1865-559 771 Fax: 1865-559 771
director Guy Williams
Size: 4-10 *Type/Spec:* mainly instrumental *Repertoire:* baroque & early classical *Perfs:* 10 *Touring:* UK
Comments: lottery funding for concert and recording

Palladian Ensemble
c/o Hazard Chase, Richmond House, 16-20 Regent Street, **Cambridge** CB2 1DB
Tel: 1223-312 400 Fax: 1223-460 827
Internet: www.hazardchase.co.uk
E-Mail: hilary.perrott@hazardchase.co.uk
contact Hilary Perrott
Size: 4 *Type/Spec:* instrumental (recorders, violin, viola da gamba, theorbo/archlute/guitar) *Repertoire:* 17th, 18th century *Touring:* worldwide *Comments:* record for Linn Records; educational programmes available

Parley of Instruments, The
c/o Helen Sykes Artists Management, 1st Floor, Parkway House, Sheen Lane, **London** SW14 8LS
Tel: 20-8876 8276 Fax: 20-8876 8277
E-Mail: helen@hsam.u-net.com
agent Helen Sykes; director Peter Holman
Size: 4-25 *Type/Spec:* instrumental *Repertoire:* renaissance + baroque violin, orchestral & vocal/choral music
Touring: UK and abroad *Comments:* over 40 recordings on Hyperion-label

Praetorius Consort of London
122 Wigmore Street, **London** W1H 9FE
Tel: 20-7935 1270
contact Christopher Ball
Size: 5-7 *Type/Spec:* specialise in renaissance period
Perfs: 45 *Comments:* recorded for EMI, CBS & BBC records

Purcell Quartet
Garth, Gwernogle, Nr. Brechfa, **Carmarthen** SA32 7RN
Tel: 1267-202 380 Fax: 1267-202 399
E-Mail: Richard@fretwork.demon.co.uk
contact Richard Boothby
Size: min. 4 expanding to a baroque orchestra under the name Purcell Quartet + *Type/Spec:* Purcell Quartet – trio sonata ensemble, Purcell Quartet + – baroque string consort/baroque orchestra *Repertoire:* baroque
Perfs: 30 *Touring:* UK, France, Germany, Austria, Slovenia, Hungary, Croatia *Comments:* 21 recordings for Chandos and 6 for Hyperion; new record exclusively for Chandos; French representative: Ian Malkin, Satirino, 118 rue Haxo, 75019 Paris, France, Tel: +33 1-4208 6814, Fax: +33 1-4003 8770, Email: Satirino@compuserve.com; German speaking representative: Keith Mayler MAM Management, Larnenseldgasse 26/33, 1120 Wien, Austria, Tel: +43 1-815 3733, Fax:+43 1-812 7167, E-mail: mam-vienna@netway.at

Raglan Baroque Players
140 Muswell Hill Road, **London** N10 3JD
Tel: 20-8444 2507 Fax: 20-8444 1795
E-Mail: raglanadmin@compuserve.com
director Nicholas Kraemer; manager Vicky Miller (tel: 171-704 9137)
Size: 12-25 *Type/Spec:* period instruments *Repertoire:* baroque-classical *Perfs:* 10 *Comments:* representation: Helen Sykes Artists Management, Tel: 20-8876 8276, Fax: 20-8876 8277

Red Byrd
c/o Robert White Artist Management, 182 Moselle Avenue, **London** N22 6EX
Tel: 20-8881 6914 Fax: 20-8888 9662
E-Mail: rwhiteam@aol.com
contact Robert White
Size: 2-6 *Type/Spec:* vocal chamber ensemble, early and new music *Repertoire:* medieval, renaissance, contemporary *Perfs:* 10 *Touring:* Europe *Comments:* recordings on various labels inc. Hyperion & Virgin Classics; see also Choirs

Red Priest
Upbeat Management, Sutton Business Centre, Restmor Way, **Wallington** SM6 7AH
Tel: 20-8773 1223 Fax: 20-8669 6752
Internet: www.upbeat.co.uk
E-Mail: classic@upbeat.co.uk
director Piers Adams; contact Maureen Phillips
Size: 4-8 *Type/Spec:* recorder, baroque strings & continuo *Repertoire:* baroque *Touring:* UK, USA, Germany, Ireland *Comments:* managed by: Upbeat Management (see also Agents & Producers)

Romanesca
c/o Andrew Manze, 25 Stephen Road, Headington, **Oxford** OX3 9AY
Tel: 1865-751 591
Fax: 1865-751 591
director Andrew Manze
Size: 3 + guest vocalists and/or instrumentalists *Type/Spec:* instrumental, vocal *Repertoire:* baroque, especially 17th C *Touring:* USA, Canada, Paris, Vienna, Barcelona *Comments:* highly successful CD productions (excl. Harmonia Mundi, France); address all correspondence to John Moeus (General Manager), Nassaukade 5, 1052 CE Amsterdam, Netherlands, Tel: +31 20-684 4322, Fax: +31 20-682 8799

Rose Consort of Viols
28 Wentworth Road, Scarcroft Hill, **York** YO24 1DG
Tel: 1904-652 736 Fax: 1904-652 736
Internet: www.plantcell.lu.se/rose
E-Mail: j.h.bryan@hud.ac.uk
artistic administrator John Bryan
Size: 3-6 viols+ solo voice, lute, organ as appropriate *Type/Spec:* viol consort *Repertoire:* renaissance, early baroque (mostly English) *Touring:* Arts Council of England Early Music Project Award (UK), USA, Canada *Comments:* 15+ recordings

Scholars Baroque Ensemble, The
aa
Comments: UK- based ensemble, administered by David van Asch, see entry under Spain

Sirinu
28 Mawson Road, **Cambridge** CB1 2EA
Tel: 1223-508 431 Fax: 1123-508 449
manager Alison Page; assistant manager Sarah Bruce
Size: 4 *Type/Spec:* vocal and instrumental consort *Repertoire:* early, ethnic and contemporary, world *Perfs:* 5-10 *Touring:* UK, Belgium

Sonnerie
71 Priory Road, **Kew** TW9 3DH
Tel: 20-8940 7086 Fax: 20-8332 0879
manager Francesca McManus;
director Monica Huggett
Size: 3-15 *Type/Spec:* instrumental *Repertoire:* Bach, Handel, French, English and Italian baroque *Perfs:* 25-30 *Touring:* worldwide *Comments:* recordings for Virgin Classics, ASV, Teldec, Harmonia Mundi USA, CPO

Sprezzatura
The Dormer Flat, High St., **Mayfield** TN20 6AL
Tel: 1435-872 187 Fax: 1435-872 187
Internet: www.landini.org/mayfield
E-Mail: m.fields@cwcom.net
contacts Evelyn Tubb, Michael Fields
Size: 2+ *Type/Spec:* instrumental, solo singers *Repertoire:* dramatic, virtuosic solo songs from the baroque period *Perfs:* 12 *Touring:* UK, Latvia, Spain, Italy, Poland *Comments:* Tubb/Fields duo also presents solo songs with accompaniment from 16th -19th century

St. James's Baroque Players
200 Broomwood Rd., **London** SW11 6JY
Tel: 20-7228 6388 Fax: 20-7738 1706
director Ivor Bolton; manager Delia Pye
Size: 5-50 *Type/Spec:* chamber choral and orchestral *Repertoire:* high baroque *Perfs:* 10-15 *Touring:* UK, Europe

Steinitz Bach Players
Bach House, 73 High St., **Old Oxted** RH8 9LN
Tel: 1883-717 372 Fax: 1883-715 851
secretary of London Bach Society/director of London Bach Festival Margaret Steinitz
Size: up to 30 *Type/Spec:* chamber orchestra, period instruments only *Repertoire:* music of J.S.Bach, especially the Cantatas *Perfs:* up to 12 *Comments:* at present all concerts are within the London Bach Festival

Symphony of Harmony & Invention, The
Enslow House, Station Road, Enslow, **Kidlington** OX5 3AX
Tel: 1869-331 544 Fax: 1869-331 011
Internet: www.the-sixteen.org.uk
E-Mail: info@thesixteen.org.uk
general manager Gijs Elsen; musical director Harry Christophers; development manager Peter Burrows; administrator Alison Stillman
Size: 6-50 *Type/Spec:* period ensemble *Repertoire:* baroque *Touring:* Italy, Spain, Portugal, USA, Austria, Germany, France, Belgium, The Netherlands, Australia, Far East *Comments:* agents: Lorenzo Baldrighi (Italy) + Carmen Prieto (Spain); see also Choirs (The Sixteen) and Orchestras

Tallis Scholars, The
c/o Hazard Chase, Richmond House, 16-20 Regents Street, **Cambridge** CB2 1DB
Tel: 1223-312 400 Fax: 1223-460 827
E-Mail: info@hazardchase.co.uk
administrator Sibyile Mager; musical director Peter Phillips
Size: 10 *Type/Spec:* unaccompanied renaissance sacred music *Perfs:* 60 *Touring:* USA, Europe, UK, Japan, China, Australia, New Zealand *Comments:* CD's available

Tapestry of Music
13 Tintern Ave., Ashton in Makerfield, **Wigan** WN4 9HY
Tel: 1942-720 323
contacts Brian Radford, Glynis Radford
Size: 2-4 *Type/Spec:* instrumental, vocal *Repertoire:* medieval to baroque *Perfs:* 150 *Touring:* UK, France *Comments:* also school performances, lectures, workshops and corporate entertainment; 3 CDs available

Taverner Choir, Consort and Players
Ibex House, 42-46 Minories, **London** EC3N 1DY
Tel: 20-7481 2103 Fax: 20-7481 2865
Internet: www.upbeat.co.uk
E-Mail: classic@upbeat.co.uk
administrator Victoria Newbert; artistic director/conductor Andrew Parrot; associate director Malcolm Bruno
Size: 5-60 *Type/Spec:* vocal orientated, small chamber to large-scale choral works *Repertoire:* 13th-20th century *Perfs:* 15-20 *Touring:* Germany, Switzerland, Spain, USA, Japan, Scandinavia

The Revolutionary Drawing Room
Upbeat Management, Sutton Business Centre, Restmor Way, **Wallington** SM6 7AH
Tel: 20-8773 1223 Fax: 20-8669 6752
Internet: www.upbeat.co.uk
E-Mail: classic@upbeat.co.uk
contact Maureen Phillips; artistic director Angela East
Size: 3-9 *Type/Spec:* late classical/romantic on period instruments

Timedance
10 Westside, 68 Fortis Green, **London** N2 9ES
Tel: 20-8444 0707 Fax: 20-8444 0707
E-Mail: anna.lejfelt-sahlen@dha.slu.se
director Jane Gingell
Size: 2-20 *Type/Spec:* period dance, music and theatre *Repertoire:* 12th-19th century, special period 1580-1740 *Touring:* UK, Sweden, Germany, Spain, Finland. Baltic States, Belgium *Comments:* sister group Timedance Hansa presents performance projects of 17th C masques and operas; programme on baroque ballerina Marie Sallé, Telemann baroque ballet, Commedia del Arte programme, and other

Tirami Su
7 Queensdown Road, **London** E5 8NN
Tel: 20-8985 2802 Fax: 20-8985 2802
Internet: www.tirami.freeserve.co.uk
E-Mail: 106325.1610@compuserve.com
director Erin Headley; agent Irene Witmer
Type/Spec: strings, voices *Repertoire:* 17th-century music including Monteverdi, Schütz, Purcell *Touring:* Sweden, Holland, Switzerland, Germany, Israel, Spain *Comments:* first recording: Che Soave armonia on Vanguard Classics –; Agent: Irene Witmer Management, 97 Kerkstraat, 1017 Amsterdam, Netherlands, tel & fax: 31 20-524 4040, email:witmeric@euronet.nl

Tragicomedia
7 Queensdown Road, **London** E5 8NN
Tel: 20-8985 2802
Fax: 20-8985 2802
E-Mail: 106325.1610@compuserve.com
directors Stephen Stubbs, Erin Headley;
agent Irene Witmen
Size: 5-15 *Type/Spec:* vocal & instrumental *Repertoire:* 17th C *Perfs:* 80-100 (including Operas) *Touring:* Netherlands, Germany, Switzerland, USA *Comments:* recordings with EMI, Virgin, Teldec, Vanguard; agent: Irene Witmen, 97 Kerkstraat, 1017 GD Amsterdam, Netherlands; Tel: +31 20-524 4040 Fax: +31 20-524 4044 Email: witmeric@euronet.nl

Trio Basiliensis
58 Redhill Drive, **Brighton** BN1 5FL
Tel: 1273-552 548 Fax: 1273-389 572
Internet: home.t-online.de/home/trio-basiliensis
E-Mail: simmonds.mezger@cwcom.net
contact Paul Simmonds
Size: 3 *Type/Spec:* instrumental (recorder, French flageolet, baroque musette, viola da gamba, harpsichord) *Repertoire:* late renaissance-late baroque, early classical 20th century *Perfs:* 20-30 *Touring:* Germany, Switzerland, Belgium, USA, France, Netherlands, England, South Africa *Comments:* specialise in lesser known composers, CDs with Ars Musici

Trio Holloway – ter Linden – Mortensen
c/o Mary Taylor, The Old Manse, Leafield, **Witney** OX8 5NN
Tel: 1993-878 200 Fax: 1993-878 375
Internet: www.classical-artists.com
E-Mail: oldmanse@compuserve.com
administration Mary Taylor; musical directors John Holloway, Lars Ulrik Mortensen, Jaap ter Linden
Size: 3 (violin, harpsichord, cello, gamba) *Type/Spec:* baroque *Touring:* international

Virelai
c/o Jacob Heringman, 41 Angles Road, **London** SW16 2UU
Tel: 20-8769 4833 Fax: 20-8769 4833
E-Mail: pellingman@compuserve.com
contacts Catherine King, Jacob Heringman, Susanna Pell, William Lyons
Size: 4 *Type/Spec:* instrumental, vocal *Repertoire:* late medieval/ early renaissance *Perfs:* 10-12 *Touring:* national and international *Comments:* 4 CDs, 1st on BBC Music Magazine cover, rest on Virgin

Virelai
c/o Robert White Artist Management, 182 Moselle Avenue, **London** N22 6EX
Tel: 20-8881 6914 Fax: 20-8888 9662
E-Mail: rwhiteam@aol.com
contact Robert White
Size: 4 plus guests *Type/Spec:* medieval, renaissance, contemporary; using period instruments *Repertoire:* neglected music of the late Middle Ages and renaissance, particularly from Italy and France *Perfs:* 10 *Touring:* Europe *Comments:* 3 CDs on Virgin Veritas

Wren Baroque Orchestra
Wren Music, 8 Park Lane, **Selsey** PO20 0HD
Tel: 1243-604 281 Fax: 1243-604 387
Internet: www.musiciansgallery.com
E-Mail: m.elliott@chihe.ac.uk
director Martin Elliott; leaders Susan Carpenter-Jacobs, Julia Bishop
Size: varies *Type/Spec:* Bach Passions, Caldara and Monteverdi Vespers *Repertoire:* baroque *Touring:* UK *Comments:* works in association with Wren Baroque Soloists

Wren Baroque Soloists
Wren Music, 8 Park Lane, **Selsey** PO20 0HD
Tel: 1243-604 281 Fax: 1243-604 387
Internet: www.musiciansgallery.com
E-Mail: m.elliott@chihe.ac.uk
director Martin Elliott
Size: 7 *Type/Spec:* baroque vocal ensemble and continuo *Repertoire:* Caldara, Peerson, Jeffreys, Purcell, Bach, Handel, Telemann, Ziani, Conti, Monerverdi, Schütz, Trumphs of Oriana *Touring:* Canada, USA, New Zealand, Australia, also Arts Council sponsored tours of England; Uk Early Music Network Tour for Millenium Celebrations *Comments:* recordings with Koch Schwann, Collins Classics, Unicorn Kanchana; also works in association with Wren Baroque Orchestra; exclusive American representation – Abbey Artist Management +1 802-948 2848

Wren Consort
Wren Music, 8 Park Lane, **Selsey** PO20 0HD
Tel: 1243-604 281 Fax: 1243-604 387
Internet: php.indiana.edu/~elliottp/Wren
E-Mail: m.elliott@chihe.ac.uk
contact Martin Elliott/Wren Music
Size: 5 *Type/Spec:* voice and trumpet, baroque and contemporary *Repertoire:* Purcell, Handel, Bach, Gardener and Pott *Touring:* Europe

York Waits, The
12 Woodsome Drive, Fenay Bridge,
Huddersfield HD8 0JR
Tel: 1484-602 460
E-Mail: sol_marsh@yahoo.com
contact William Marshall
Size: 6 *Type/Spec:* renaissance wind *Repertoire:* instrumental music 1450-1600 *Perfs:* 20-30 *Comments:* 5 CDs available from Saydisc & Brewhouse; performances range from formal concerts to education, workshops and events such as processions

Yorkshire Baroque Soloists
11 Bootham Terrace, **York** YO30 7DH
Tel: 1904-652 799 Fax: 1904-338 349
E-Mail: ps22@york.ac.uk
contact Peter Seymour
Size: 2-40 *Type/Spec:* baroque and classical *Perfs:* 30 *Comments:* recordings available on Carlton IMP

YUGOSLAVIA (+381)

Due to the war in Kosovo we have been unable to update the following entries for Yugoslavia

Musica Antiqua
Kosovska 32/3, 11000 **Belgrade**
Tel: 11-324 4736
artistic director Vera Zlokovic

Renaissance
29 novembra 102/20, 11000 **Belgrade**
Tel: 11-762 207
artistic director Miodrag Ristic

Customer Service Page

Dear colleague

All the staff here at Arts Publishing International are continually working to ensure that the PAYE is the most valuable and easy-to-use reference book for the European performing arts market. With your individual requirements you are in the best position to tell us if the PAYE meets your needs. We would therefore be most grateful if you could send us your suggestions and comments on the book.

As well as your suggestions we would appreciate your help in keeping our records as accurate as possible. Please use this page to request information, amend your editorial entry for the next edition or send us new editorial entries. Please direct your mail to: **Editorial Department, Arts Publishing International Ltd., Lime Wharf, Vyner Street, London E2 9DJ, England** or contact us by telephone **(+44) 20 8709 9050**, by fax **(+44) 20 8709 9080** or by e-mail on **paye@api.co.uk**

Amendments

1 Amendments to existing entries in the Performing Arts Yearbook for Europe 2000

Please note: You will receive our formal entry correction letter to update your entry for the PAYE 2001 in May 2000. This space should be used if your information changes after you have returned our request for correct information next May.

Section (eg opera, dance, services and suppliers) ____

Original company name ____

New company name (if applicable) ____

New address ____

____

New telephone numbers ____

New fax numbers ____

New e-mail address/web site ____

Changes to personnel ____

Comments ____

New Entries

2 New entries for Performing Arts Yearbook for Europe 2001

Please note: All entries are free of charge, but are included at the Editor's discretion

Section ____

Company name ____

Address ____

____

Telephone numbers ____

Fax numbers ____

E-mail address/web site ____

Personnel ____

Comments ____

Mailing

3 Please complete the following section if you want information on our other publications, conferences or special events*

Organisation ____

Name ____

Job Title ____

Address ____

____

Tel ____ Fax ____

E-mail ____

- The information you have provided may be stored and used under the provisions of the Data Protection Act. If you prefer not to receive mail from third parties please tick this box ☐

Choirs and Vocal Ensembles

Choirs and Vocal Ensembles
Information of Choirs/Vocal Ensembles in this section has been based on information received about engagements. We do not intend to pass judgement on quality. If you wish to be considered for inclusion, please send information regarding performances and touring engagements to the editor.
Within country the choirs and vocal ensembles are ordered alphabetically by ensemble name.

Chæurs et Ensembles vocaux
Les chæurs et ensembles vocaux inclus dans cette rubrique ont été selectionnés selon les informations reçuees quant à leurs engagements. Nous ne faisons ainsi aucun jugement qualitatif. Si vous désirez être inclus, veuillez nous envoyer des informations de vos répresentations et vos tournées au redacteur.
Dans chacque section nationale les chæurs et ensembles vocaux sont par ordre alphabétique selon le nom d'ensemble.

Chöre und Vokalensembles
Die in dieser Rubrik aufgeführten **Chöre und Vokalensembles** wurden aufgrund Ihrer Angaben über Engagements ausgewählt. Es liegt uns fern, mit dieser Auswahl eine qualitative Beurteilung auszusprechen. Falls Sie Interesse daran haben, ebenfalls in dieser Rubrik aufgeführt zu werden, senden Sie bitte Informationen betr. Auftritte und Engagements an die Redaktion.
Die Einträge sind innerhalb aller Staaten alphabetisch nach Namen geordnet.

Cori e Gruppi Vocali
La scelta dei gruppi vocali e dei cori in questa sezione é avvenuta dopo aver considerato il numero degli spettacoli al cui il gruppo ha partecipato. L'inclusione non puó, perció, essere considerato in giudizo sulla qualitá del gruppo. Se siete interessati ad essere inclusi vi preghiamo di inviare delle informazioni riguardo il numero di spettacoli e/o di tournee al redattore del PAYE.
I gruppi di musica antica sono ordinati alfabeticamente all' interno dei paesi.

Coros y Grupos Vocalos
Hemos incluido estos Coros y Grupos Vocalos de Música Antigua según información que investigamos sobre sus representaciones y calendarios, es decir si actuan a menudo o no/van de giras nacionales o internacionales o no/etc. No pretendemos asegurar de la calidad de los grupos. Si qualquier persona quiere que salgan datos de su grupo el la próxima edición, pongase en contacto con el redactor.
Dentro del país, se han ordenado los Coros y Grupos Vocalos alfabéticamente por nombre del grupo.

Choirs and Vocal Ensembles (합창단 및 성악그룹)
이 부문에 기재된 합창단/성악그룹에 대한 정보는 입수된 공연 정보에 기초한다.
그룹 수준에 대한 평가는 하지 않는다. 이 리스트에 포함되기를 원하면, 공연 및 순회 공연에 대한 정보를 편집자에게 보내시오.
리스트는 국가별로 단체명에 따라 알파벳순으로 기재되었다.

合唱团和声乐队
这一章节中的合唱团和声乐队的情报是根据已收到的有关演出节目的情报而列出的。我们无意对演出的质量作出评判。如果您想让我们将贵公司也考虑进去的话，请将有关演出和巡回演出的情报寄给编辑。**在每个国家里合唱团或声乐队是按该团名字的字母顺序来排列的。**

合唱団、コーラスグループ
この章には公演に関して提供された情報を基に合唱団、コーラスグループが掲載されています。各グループの水準を判断するものではありません。リストへの掲載を希望する合唱団、コーラスグループは公演に関する情報を編集者までお送り下さい。**リストは国別で、一国内ではアルファベット順に記載されています。**

ALBANIA (+355)

Choir of the Orthodox Church, The
Kisha Orthodhokse Autoqefale, **Tirana**
conductor Prof. Milto Vako

Choir of the State Opera Theatre, The
Sheshi Skenderbej, **Tirana**
Tel: 42-24753 Fax: 42-24753

Female Choir of the Academy of Arts, The
Sheshi Nene Tereza, **Tirana**
conductor Prof. Milto Vako

Female Choir of the Municipality of Tirana, The
Bashkia e Tiranes, Sheshi Skenderbej, **Tirana**
conductor Prof. Milto Vako

Pax Dei
Rr. K. Mema nr 14, **Tirana**
Tel: 42-31790 Fax: 42-48594
conductor Suzana Turku
Type: mixed choir

ARMENIA (+374)

Academic State Choir of Armenia
60 Poushkin Street, 375002 **Yerevan**
Tel: 2-505 773/586 322/303 Fax: 2-523 555
E-Mail: root@knar.arminco.com
artistic director & chief conductor Ohannes Tchekidjian
Size: 100

Chamber Choir of Radio Company of Armenia
26-39 Kievian Street, 375033 **Yerevan**
Tel: 2-563 616/232 920 Fax: 2-151 059
artistic director & conductor Tigran Hekekian

Hover Chamber Choir
4-4 Azatoutian Street, 375037 **Yerevan**
Tel: 2-254 493/2-525 840 Fax: 2-151 431/2-525 840
Internet: www.arminco.com/homepage/nab
E-Mail: nbart@arminco.com
artistic director and conductor Sona Hovhanisyan

Komitas Chamber Choir of Yerevan State Conservatory
Yerevan State Conservatory, 1a Sayat-Nova Street, 375001 **Yerevan**
Tel: 2-582 559/528 799 Fax: 3-907 079
E-Mail: mgy@armintel.com
artistic director & conductor Hovhanes Mirzoyan

Little Singers of Armenia
26-39 Kievian Street, 375033 **Yerevan**
Tel: 2-563 616/232 920 Fax: 2-151 059
artistic director & conductor Tigran Hekekian
Type: children's choir

Male Chamber Choir of Armenian National Opera
58 Tumanian Street, 375001 **Yerevan**
Tel: 2-247 196/2-525 840 Fax: 2-151 431/2-525 840
artistic director & conductor Karen Sargsian

Narek Male Chamber Choir
Chamber Music Hall, 1 Isahakian Street, 375025 **Yerevan**
Tel: 2-522 928/526 725/525 840 Fax: 2-525 840
artistic director Mkrtch Mkrtchian

AUSTRIA (+43)

A-Capella-Chor Villach
Bahnhofstr. 24, 9586 **Fürnitz**
Tel: 4242-3005-146
Fax: 4242-3005-341
manager Hannes Klammer;
choir director Prof. Helmut Wulz
Repertoire: madrigals, sacred, contemporary, folk songs
Size: 45 *Perfs:* 30

Amadeus Knabenchor Wien
Amadeus Boys Choir Vienna
Leebgasse 34, 1100 **Wien**
Tel: 1-602 0086 Fax: 1-602 0086
artistic director Mag. Peter Lang;
Obmann Gerhard F. Grainer
Type: boys choir – a cappella with piano/orchestra
Repertoire: standard choral repertorie & viennese classics *Size:* 40 *Perfs:* 40 *Comments:* performs as choir at the Vienna State Opera

ARNOLD SCHOENBERG CHOR
Prinz Eugenstr. 16/3, 1040 **Wien**
Tel: 1-504 2540
Fax: 1-504 2549
E-Mail: asc@asc.at
manager/administrator Dr Erich Schneider;
conductor/artistic director Erwin Ortner
Type: concert choir *Repertoire:* renaissance, baroque, contemporary, opera *Size:* 12-120 *Perfs:* 30-40
Touring: Europe, USA *Comments:* works closely with Nikolaus Harnoncourt, Claudio Abbado and other guests; were awarded 'Classical Music Award' in 1994; multiple CD productions, ie: Schubert Gesamtwerk, Weltliche Chöre at Teldec with Grammy Award in Japan, France, Germany, Belgium

Bach-Chor Wels
Sattledt 216, 4642 **Sattledt**
Tel: 7244-8786
conductor Thomas Huber; representative Paul Kiblböck; Bach-Chor-archives Erika Huemer
Type: a cappella & orchestral *Repertoire:* Bach to contemporary *Size:* 40 *Perfs:* min. 5 (Feb-June)

Belcanto Chor Salzburg
Heuberg 193, 5023 **Salzburg**
Tel: 662-452 658
Fax: 662-450 165
Obmann Dieter Schaffer;
Chorleiter Gertraud Steinkogler-Wurzinger
Type: a cappella & orchestral, mixed
Repertoire: early church music, early music, madrigal, modern, romantic *Size:* 35 *Perfs:* 40 *Touring:* Wales, Germany, France, Italy, Switzerland, Croatia, Czech Republic

Choral Society Young Vienna
Chorvereinigung Jung-Wien
Musikvereinsgebäude, Bösendorferstr.12, 1010 **Wien**
Tel: 2236-21443 Fax: 2236-21443
Vorstand Christiane Maresch;
Dirigent Manfred Schiebel
Type: a cappella & orchestra
Repertoire: mostly Viennese music *Size:* 40 *Perfs:* approx. 50 *Touring:* South Africa

Chorus Sine Nomine
Schönborngasse 6/7, 1080 **Wien**
Tel: 1-402 6434 Fax: 1-402 6434
Internet: members.aon.at/chorussinenomine
E-Mail: chorussinenomine@aon.at
director Johannes Hiemetsberger; manager Walter Drewes; press officer Christoph Brandner
Type: mixed, a cappella and orchestral *Repertoire:* sacred and secular music from renaissance to contemporary *Size:* 35-100 *Perfs:* 25 *Touring:* Germany, New Zealand, Philippines

Concentus Vocalis
Vivenotweg 12, 3411 **Weidling**
Tel: 2243-26626 Fax: 2243-38866
managing director Konstantin Moritsch; artistic director Herbert Böck
Type: a cappella and orchestral *Repertoire:* from early baroque up to 20th century *Size:* 16-40 *Perfs:* 21 *Touring:* Europe *Comments:* participating in the 'Grand Choirs of Europe' – series in London, Copenhagen and The Hague

Cosa Vocale Wien
Taborstr. 64/19, 1020 **Wien**
Tel: 1-216 7804
Fax: 1-216 7804
E-Mail: glassner@netway.at
conductor Alois Glaßner
Type: a cappella & orchestra *Repertoire:* contemporary and early music *Size:* 6-16 *Perfs:* 10-15

Großer Chor des Tiroler Landeskonservatorium
Paul Hofhaimer Gasse 6, 6020 **Innsbruck**
Tel: 512-508 6852 Fax: 512-508 6855
Internet: www.tirol.gv.at
E-Mail: KONSERVATDRIUM@Tirol.GV.AT
conductor Günther Simonott
Type: mainly orchestral, also a cappella
Repertoire: early music to romantic *Size:* 60-70 *Perfs:* 3-4

Kammerchor Walter von der Vogelweide
Innstr. 107, 6020 **Innsbruck**
Tel: 512-266 953 Fax: 512-266 953
Internet: www.tirol.com/vogel-weide
E-Mail: vogel.weide@tirol.com
music director Armin Kölbl
manager Norbert Lederbauer
Type: chamber, a cappella, sometimes with orchestra
Repertoire: early music, modern, romantic
Size: 40 *Perfs:* 10

Konzertvereinigung Wiener Staatsopernchor
Opernring 2, 1010 **Wien**
Tel: 1-512 4884
Fax: 1-512 4884
managing director Wolfgang Scheider;
chairman Prof. Walter Zeh; concert director Claudio Abbado; choir director Ernst Dunshirn
Size: 102 *Perfs:* 480 opera, 2 concerts
Comments: see also Opera

Singverein der Ges. der Musikfreunde in Wien (Wiener Singverein)
Bösendorferstr. 12, 1010 **Wien**
Tel: 1-504 3348
Fax: 1-504 3348
E-Mail: wiener.singverein@aon.at
Vorstand Hans Peter Pokorny;
Dirigent Johannes Prinz; Schriftführer Rainer Wolfbauer
Type: mixed *Repertoire:* classical to modern *Size:* 180
Perfs: 30 *Touring:* throughout Europe
Comments: CDs available; recording with Vienna Philharmonic, conductor Nikolaus Harnoncourt in April 2000 for Teldec

Vienna Boys Choir
Wiener Sängerknaben
Augartenpalais, 1020 **Wien**
Tel: 1-216 3942 Fax: 1-216 3942 53
Internet: www.wsk.at
E-Mail: office@wsk.at
artistic director Norbert Balatsch; managing director Manfred Seipt; deputy conductor Gerald Wirth
Type: a cappella, with piano and orchestra *Repertoire:* choral music from renaissance to the 20th century; musical theatre *Size:* 4 choirs with 25 boys *Perfs:* 300
Touring: worldwide

Wiener Jeunesse-Chor
Rossauergasse 3/3, 1090 **Wien**
Tel: 664-121 7203 Fax: 1-319 8128
E-Mail: ozbic@igm.net
conductor Marco Ozbic
Type: concert choir *Repertoire:* classical
Size: 80-100 *Perfs:* 5-7

Wiener Kammerchor
Tanbruckgasse 2/9, 1120 **Wien**
Tel: 1-504 4946/815 3298 Fax: 1-504 4946/815 3298
Internet: www.htlw4.kammerchor.ac.at
E-Mail: kammerchor@_mail.htlw4.ac.at
Management Margot Riess; Präsident Manfred Länger; künstlerischer Leiter Johannes Prinz
Type: mixed *Repertoire:* from renaissance to contemporary, sacred and secular music *Size:* 36-60 *Perfs:* 40
Comments: second address: Wohllebengasse 10/30, 1040, Wien

Wiener Konzertchor
Herbststrasse 19/10, 1160 **Wien**
Tel: 1-494 8483 Fax: 1-494 8483
Internet: www.wiener-konzertchor.at
E-Mail: m.thoma@wiener-konzertchor.at
manager Martin Thoma;
artistic director/conductor Gottfried Rabl
Type: mixed chamber and a capella choir *Repertoire:* contemporary choir music, 20th century and also standard repertoire *Size:* 40+ *Perfs:* 15
Touring: Italy, France

Wiener Lehrer-a-cappella-Chor
Fasangasse 4, 1030 **Wien**
Tel: 1-440 2037 Fax: 1-4402 0374
secretary Herr Laubhann
conductor Prof. Günther Knotzinger
Type: mainly a cappella, with orchestral oratories
Repertoire: standard choral repertoire including modern music *Size:* 70-75 *Perfs:* 8-12 *Touring:* New York
Comments: emphasis on Austrian composers in modern choral literature

Wiener Männergesangs Verein
Vienna Male Choral Society
Bösendorferstr, 12, 1010 **Wien**
Tel: 1-505 7362/713 0127 Fax: 1-504 5450
manager & executive director Kurt Schuh; music director Gerhard Track; 2.Vorstand Ing Erich Lebisch
Type: male choir *Repertoire:* Schubert, Strauß, Robert Stolz (all well-known Austrian composers) *Size:* 90
Perfs: 20-25 *Touring:* USA

Wiener Singakademie
Lothringerstr. 20, 1030 **Wien**
Tel: 1-712 4686/664-383 2988 (artistic director) Fax: 1-713 1709
Internet: www.singakademie.at
E-Mail: joseph.hofstaetter@singakademie.at
Präsident Joseph Hofstätter; artistic director Heinz Ferlesch
Type: orchestral and a cappella *Repertoire:* baroque to modern; symphonies, oratorios *Size:* 80-100 *Perfs:* 10
Touring: Hungary, Austria *Comments:* resident at Wiener Konzerthaus

BELARUS (+375)

Citovich State Academic Folk Choir of the Republic of Belarus
Gosudarstvennyj Akadjemichjeskij Narodnyj Khor Rjespubliki Bjelaruss, imjeni Citovicha
ul. E Pashkjevich 23, 220029 **Minsk**
Tel: 172-340 656
director Ivan I. Mazurin

Kamjerata Group
Ansambl Kamjerata
pr. Franciska Skoryny 50, 220005 **Minsk**
Tel: 172-319 551
director Alla N. Volk

Klassic-Avangard Soloist Group
Ansambl Solistov Klassik-Avangard
pr. Franciska Skoryny 50, 220005 **Minsk**
Tel: 172-844 422
director Vladimir A Bajdov

Kupalinka Folk-Song Group
Ansambl Narodnoj Pjesni Kupalinka
pr. Franciska Skoryny 50, 220005 **Minsk**
Tel: 172-845 258
director Aljena S Tjelkova

Pjesniary Belarussian State Group
Bjeloruskij Gosudarstvjennyj Ansambl Pjesniary
pr. Franciska Skoryny 50, 220005 **Minsk**
Tel: 172-843 332 Fax: 172-311 334
director Vladimir Muljavin
Type: national Belarussian music *Size:* 17

Shyrma State Academic Choir Capelle of the Republic of Belarus
Gosudarstvjennaja Akadjemichjeskaja Khorovaja Kapjella Rjespubliki Bjelaruss imjeni Shyrmy
pr. Franciska Skoryny 50, 220005 **Minsk**
Tel: 172-314 265 Fax: 172 314 265
director Mikhail I Litvin

State Chamber Choir of the Republic of Belarus
Gosudarstvjennyj Kamjernyj Khor Rjespubliki Bjelarus i
pr. Franciska Skoryny 50, 220005 **Minsk**
Tel: 172-317 471 Fax: 172-317 471
director Igor Matjukhov
Type: mixed *Repertoire:* sacred music *Size:* 28
Comments: 2 CDs on the Vienna Music Label of Belarussian and Slavonic sacred music

Sviata Belarussian State Folk Music Group
Bjelaruskij Gosudarstvjennyj Ansambl Narodnoj Musuki Svjata
pr. Franciska Skoryny 50,
220005 **Minsk**
Tel: 172-311 617
director Evgenij P Jelizarov

BELGIUM (+32)

Académie Marcel Désiron Groupe Amadea
Rue Yernawe 20,
4470 **St. Georges-sur-Meuse**
Tel: 4-259 6686
choir director Eric Polet
Type: girls' choir, a cappella and with piano accompaniment *Repertoire:* contemporary, English & French, sacred music *Size:* 18 *Perfs:* 5

Children's Choir of Wallonia
Choeur d'Enfants de Wallonie
Avenue Bovesse, 13/12, 5100 **Namur**
Tel: 81-305 528 Fax: 81-305 528
E-Mail: wcc@skynet.be
music director Bénédicte Dujardin
Type: childrens', mixed, a cappella or piano accomp. *Repertoire:* sacred and secular from Renaissance to contemporary *Size:* 40 *Perfs:* 40 *Touring:* Finland, Sweden, Germany

Choeur de Chambre de Namur
Avenue Jean Ier, No. 2, 5000 **Namur**
Tel: 81-742 752
Fax: 81-742 194
E-Mail: centredechantchoral.asbl@skynet.be
executive director Emmanuel Poiré; music director Menier Denis; manager Jean Marc Poncelet; administrator Jean Marie Marchal
Type: mixed (a cappella), they also have a baroque orchestra *Repertoire:* from renaissance to classical (from Lassus to Beethoven) +20th century
Size: 2 choirs: chamber 16-32, symphonic 100 *Perfs:* 25 *Touring:* Belgium, France, Spain, Italy, Netherlands, Hungary *Comments:* the guest conductors for the next season are : Jean-Caude Malgoire, Sigiswald Kuijken, Jean Tubéry, Wieland Kuijtieu, Philippe Pierlot, Jean-Paul Dessy

Choeur Symphonique de Namur et de la Communauté Française de Belgique
Avenue Jean Ier, no.2, 5000 **Namur**
Tel: 81-742 752 Fax: 81-742 194
E-Mail: centredechantchorale.asbl@skynet.be
executive director Emmanuel Poiré; music director Denis Menier; manager Jean Marc Poncelet; administration Jean-Nauie Marchal
Type: mixed with orchestra *Repertoire:* symphonic works from 19th and 20th centuries *Size:* 90
Perfs: 6 *Comments:* often works with the Liège Philharmonic Orchestra

Choraline, La
Rue de la Colline, 19, 5000 **Namur**
Tel: 81-740 611 Fax: 81-740 611
E-Mail: la.choraline@skynet.be
director Benoit Giaux
Type: mixed, equal voices (age 12-18) *Repertoire:* contemporary, classical, folk *Size:* 50 *Perfs:* 10-12 *Touring:* national, international *Comments:* looking for exchanges with other choirs

Collegium Vocale Gent
Drongenhof 42, 9000 **Gent**
Tel: 9-265 9050
Fax: 9-265 9051
manager Stephane Leys;
conductor Phillipe Herreweghe
Type: mixed choir *Repertoire:* baroque, some renaissance to romantic *Size:* 18-42
Perfs: 40-50 *Touring:* Europe, Japan
Comments: see also Early Music

Ensemble Vocal Féminin Hodie
Rue du Bois 2, 4280 **Bertrée-Hannut**
Tel: 19-513 551 Fax: 19-513 551
E-Mail: 100256.3252@compuserve.com
manager Jean-Claude Bossy;
conductor Jean-Claude Wilkens
Type: women's, a cappella *Repertoire:* 18th – 20th century *Size:* 18+ *Perfs:* 15 *Touring:* UK, France, Philippines, Spain, USA

Ex Tempore
Koninginlaan 22, 9820 **Merelbeke (Gent)**
Tel: 9-231 9712 Fax: 9-231 9712
E-Mail: yves.rosseel@skynet.be
manager Yves Rosseel;
music director/conductor Florian Heyerick
Type: mixed chamber choir/soloists with or without accompaniment (period instruments) *Repertoire:* 16th-20th C choral music, oratoria, cantatas, chamber operas *Size:* 4-24 *Perfs:* 40 *Touring:* Holland, Russia, France, Belgium, Netherlands *Comments:* managers address: Brusselsesteenweg 324, 9050 Ledeberg, Belgium, Tel: 32-9-232 1926, Fax: 32-9-232 0999, Mobile: 32-75-79 8561; see also Orchestras

Flemish Radio Choir
Vlaums Radioloon
Brusselsestraat 63, 3000 **Leuven**
Tel: 32-162 90319/ 175 530 503 (mobile)
choir co-ordinator Walter de Prey
Type: mixed choir *Repertoire:* contemporary Flemish, Belgian and forign composers

Kempische Oratorium Vereniging VZW
c/o Dageraadstraat 32, 2300 **Turnhout**
Tel: 14-413 730 Fax: 14-413 730
administrator Lydie Marien;
artistic director Werner Van Mechelen
Type: mainly vocal/instrumental productions *Repertoire:* mainly baroque to romantic *Size:* 12-50 (+ instrumental ensemble 20) *Perfs:* 10 *Touring:* Switzerland

Laudantes Consort, Choir & Players
63 Avenue Jonnart, 1200 **Brussels**
Tel: 2-771 2745 Fax: 2-771 2745
director Guy Janssens; contact Anne Marie Claeys
Repertoire: mainly renaissance – polyphonic *Size:* 12 (consort), 45 (grand choeur + 40 musicians) *Perfs:* 25 *Touring:* national, international

Octava Alta
Rue de la Colline, 19, 5000 **Namur**
Tel: 81-740 611 Fax: 81-740 611
E-Mail: la.choraline@skynet.be
director Benoit Giaux
Type: mixed youth choir (age 18-30) *Repertoire:* a cappella, baroque (with orchestra), classical, folk *Size:* 50 *Perfs:* 7 *Touring:* Poland, Spain *Comments:* looking for exchanges with other youth choirs

Terpsychore
Route de Jemeppe 7,
6950 **Harsin**
Tel: 84-344 492
contact Xavier Haag
Type: mainly vocal (hire musicians when necessary) *Repertoire:* Bach and others from the same era, 20th C. *Size:* 22-24 *Perfs:* 12-15 *Comments:* take part in international competitions; see also Early Music

BOSNIA & HERZEGOVINA (+387)

Choir of the Music Academy
Josip Stadler Str 1, 71000 **Sarajevo**
Tel: 71-200 299 Fax: 71-444 896

Choir Trebevic
c/o HKD Napredak, 56 Marsala Tita Str, 71000 **Sarajevo**
Tel: 71-472 349 Fax: 71-447 223
conductor Ognjen Bomostar

Youth City Choir
c/o Pane Skrbic, 23 Kulina Bana Str., 72000 **Zenica**
Tel: 72-417 335/417 334
Fax: 72-417 333
conductor Milenko Karovic

BULGARIA (+359)

Bulgarian National A Capella Choir Svetoslav Obretenov
1 Benkovski Str., 1000 **Sofia**
Tel: 2-468 257/2-943 4242
conductor Prof. Georgy Robev;
director Valentin Anguelov
Type: a cappella *Size:* 85 *Comments:* home venue cap 1134

Sredetz Chamber Choir
35 Dunav Str., 1000 **Sofia**
Tel: 2-833 594 Fax: 2-876 522
artistic director Alexandar Kouyumdjiev
Type: mixed (a cappella and with orchestra) *Repertoire:* orthodox sacred music (14th-20th C.), standard choral repertoire, oratorios *Size:* 18-30 *Perfs:* 25 *Touring:* Europe
Comments: recordings, CD; TV-films

CROATIA (+385)

Choir of Croatian RTV
Glazbena proizvodnja HRT
Dezmanova 10, 10000 **Zagreb**
Tel: 1-480 7111/480 48204 Fax: 1-480 7191
director Stanislav Mlinar

Mixed choir Zora
Mjesoviti pjevacki zbor Zora
Domobranska 1, 47000 **Karlovac**
Tel: 47-614 950/614 951
Fax: 47-614 951
director Ljerka Lackovic;
art director & conductor Aleksandar Radivojevic

Pjevacki zbor Ivan Goran Kovacic
Opatovina 11, 10000 **Zagreb**
Tel: 1-481 3320/481 332
Fax: 1-481 3320
dirigent Sasa Britvic

CZECH REPUBLIC (+420)

Childrens Choir of the Czech Radio
Detsky Pevecky Sbor Ceského Rozhlasu
Vinohradská 12, 120 99 **Praha** 2
Tel: 2-2409 4111/4410/4425/232 6889
Fax: 2-2424 2043/2322 8152
choirmasters Bohumil Kulínsky, Dr. Blanka Kulinská

Czech Childrens Choir Jitro
Wonkova 385, 500 02 **Hradec Králové**
Tel: 49-616 582 Fax: 49-616 582
manager Jaroslav Pridal; artistic director Prof Jiri Skopal
Type: mixed (aged 5-17) *Repertoire:* Czech and foreign sacred, secular and folk music *Size:* 300 including smaller groups for performance, the leading group being JITRO-45 *Touring:* France, Germany, USA
Comments: address Prof Jiri Skopal: Smotlachy 1522, 500 08 Hradec Králové, Tel/Fax: 49-622 018

Czech Philharmonic Chorus of Brno
Cesky filharmonicky sbor Brno
ARS KONCERT Ltd, Úvoz 39,
602 00 **Brno**
Tel: 5-4323 3116
Fax: 5-4323 3358
E-Mail: ars@arskoncert.cz
chorus master, conductor Petr Fiala
Type: mixed *Repertoire:* sacred music, oratorios, cantatas, operas *Size:* 80
Comments: see also Agents and Producers

Czech Radio Chamber Choir
Komorní sbor Ceského rozhlasu
Jugolávskych partyzánu 14/678, Bubeneé,
160 00 **Praha** 6
Tel: 2-875 969
Fax: 2-875 969
choir master Stefan Britvík

Czech Radio Choir
Pevecky Sbor Ceského Rozhlasu
Komunardu 47, 170 00 **Praha** 7
Tel: 2-805 591/603-234 727(mobile) Fax: 2-805 591
choirmasters Stanislav Bogunia (2-2431 4170), Stefan Britvik

Kühn Childrens Choir
Kühnov détskysbor
Ortenovo nám 34, 170 00 **Praha** 7
Tel: 2-6671 0263 Fax: 2-6671 0263
artistic director Prof. Jirí Chvála

Kühn Mixed Choir
Kühnuv smíseny sbor
Krakovská 10, 110 00 **Praha** 1
Tel: 2-267 9613
choirmaster Pavel Kühn

Madrigal Quintet Brno
Vancurova 24, 615 00 **Brno**
Tel: 5-4821 0947/602-547 530 (mobile)
Fax: 5-4421 3293
manager Jirí Pavlík;
artistic director Roman Válek

Prague Philharmonic Choir
Prazsky Filharmonicky Sbor
nám. Míru 9, 120 00 **Praha** 2
Tel: 2-2159 6536/7 Fax: 2-2424 7616
intendant Jirí Cízek (tel: 602-210 149);
choirmaster Jaroslav Brych

Schola Gregoriana Pragensis
Pod lysinami 13,
147 00 **Praha** 4
Tel: 2-402 2690
Fax: 2-402 2690
Internet: www.sdmusic.cz/sgp
E-Mail: sgp@seznam.cz
artistic chief David Eben (tel:2-9002 7687)
Type: medieval sacred music, contemporary music
Size: 9 vocalists

DENMARK (+45)

Capella Hafniensis
c/o Verik Soelberg, Traps allé 11, 2500 **Valby**
Tel: 3616 6212/21-656 015 (mobile)
Fax: 3616 6213
leader Ole Kongsted
Type: mixed choir *Repertoire:* late renaissance of Northern Europe *Size:* 8-10 *Perfs:* 15-20 *Touring:* Denmark, Germany, Sweden *Comments:* the repertoire is material discovered in libraries and archi
es all over Northern Europe and so is unperformed by other ensembles

Chamber Choir Gaia
c/o Carsten Seyer-Hansen, Skanderborgvej 86, 2, 8000 **Aarhus** C
Tel: 8614 9235 Fax: 8614 9235
conductor Søren K. Hansen;
administrator Carsten Seyer-Hansen
Type: mixed choir *Repertoire:* standard but also unknown music from all epochs *Size:* 24
Perfs: 15-20 *Touring:* Denmark

Copenhagen Royal Chapel Choir
Sjaelør Boulevard 135, 2500 **Valby**
Tel: 3646 6222 Fax: 3644 2112
Internet: www.KDK.DK
E-Mail: DRENGEKOR@KDK.DK
executive director Ebbe Munk;
tour manager Andreas Frey
Type: choral music composed for boys' and men's voices *Repertoire:* renaissance, baroque, classical, romantic and contemporary *Size:* up to 95 boys and 45 adult male singers for some tours although 38 boys/16 men is more usual *Perfs:* 40 *Touring:* Italy, Germany, France 2001:South America *Comments:* est. 1924 by Mogens Wöldike. Give concerts at Copenhagen Cathedral; extensive CD production

Danish National Radio Choir, The
Radiohuset, 1999 **Frederiksberg** C
Tel: 3520 6381/3040 Fax: 3520 6121
Internet: www.dr.dk/rk
general manager & artistic director Per Erik Veng;
executive producer Gordon Alsing,
chief conductor Stefan Parkman
Type: chamber, a cappella + orchestra *Repertoire:* standard choral repertoire *Size:* chamber: 31, full size: 75 *Perfs:* 45-50 *Touring:* national and international *Comments:* exclusive contract with the recording company Chandos

Kammerkoret HYMNIA
Rosenbamgets Alle 40B, 2100 **Copenhagen Ø**
Tel: 3542 6939
Fax: 3542 6939
Internet: www.hymnia.dk
E-Mail: hl.melbye@get2net.dk
chairman Henik Melbye;
conductor Flemming Windekilde
Type: chamber choir, contemporary a cappella *Repertoire:* Ravel, Poulenc, Britten, Brahms, Jolivet, Ligeti, Messiaen *Size:* 26 *Perfs:* 15-25 *Touring:* national, international

Musica Ficta
Wilhelm Marstrandsgade 28,
2100 **Copenhagen Ø**
Tel: 3538 4483/3323 0107
Fax: 3538 4480
Internet: www.ficta.dk/
E-Mail: nn@ficta.dk
conductor/composer Bo Holten; manager t.b.a
Repertoire: renaissance and contemporary music *Size:* 6-16 *Perfs:* 50 *Touring:* England, France, Germany, Sweden, Australia, Italy, Portugal *Comments:* Musica Ficta records internationally for Naxos, nationally for Exlibris and Dacapo

Royal Opera Chorus, The
Det Kongelige Operakor
Det Kgl. Teater, Tordenskjoldsgade 8, PO Box 2185, 1017 **Copenhagen** K
Tel: 3369 6933 Fax: 3369 6767
Internet: www.kgl-teater.dk
E-Mail: admin@kgl-teater.dk
chorusmaster Kaare Hansen;
chairman Hans Jorjen Lauresen
Type: opera choir *Repertoire:* operas at the Royal Theatre; occasional concerts *Size:* 60
Perfs: 130 (16 different operas) *Touring:* Denmark

Sokkelund Sangkor
Rudersdalsvej 74, 2840 **Holte**
Tel: 4542 5400
Fax: 4542 5400
Internet: www.natmus.min.dk/sokke.sokke.htm
E-Mail: schuldt-jensen@image.dk
conductor/artistic director Morten Schuldt-Jensen
Type: a cappella and with chamber orchestra *Repertoire:* European 19th-century, Scandinavian contemporary, Baroque era masses, passions and oratorios *Size:* 22-30 *Perfs:* 30 *Touring:* national and international *Comments:* CDs available

Tivoli Concert Choir
Rudersdalsvej 74, 2840 **Holte**
Tel: 4542 5400 Fax: 4542 5400
E-Mail: schuldt-jensen@image.dk
artistic director Morten Schuldt-Jensen; management also Tivoli Artists, Vesterbrogade 3, 1620 Copenhagen V
Type: a cappella and with symphony orchestra *Repertoire:* oratories, masses, Baroque Era Passions, opera, symphonies *Size:* 40-120 *Perfs:* 8-10 *Comments:* resident choir of Tivoli Concert Hall; CDs available

University Choir Lille MUKO
Strandvejen 611 B, 2930 **Klampenborg**
Tel: 3963 8151 Fax: 3963 8151
Internet: www.lillemuko.dk
E-Mail: lillemuko@email.dk
manager Tine Thelmann;
conductor Jesper Grove Jørgensen
Type: a cappella, mixed *Repertoire:* contemporary music and Danish choral music *Size:* 35 *Perfs:* 30-40 *Touring:* Australia, Latvia, Italy *Comments:* several recordings available (see homepage)

Vokalgroup Ars Nova
Kronprinsensgade 7, mezz., 1114 **Copenhagen** K
Tel: 3313 5770 Fax: 3313 5770
E-Mail: arsnova@post5.tele.dk
manager Thomas Kiørbye; chief conductor Tamás Vetö; guest conductor Paul Hillier
Type: chamber choir *Repertoire:* early and new music *Size:* 12 *Touring:* Scandinavia and Europe, USA *Comments:* have produced a series of internationally acclaimed CDs

ESTONIA (+372)

Chamber Choir ARSIS
Arsise Kammerkoor
Tina 4-1, 10126 **Tallinn**
Tel: 6-313 221
conductor Aivar Mäe
Type: a cappella and with Handbell Ensemble *Touring:* Canada, USA, Europe

Childrens' Choir Ellerhein
Lastekoor Ellerhein
Mustamäe tee 59, 10619 **Tallinn**
Tel: 2-532 785 Fax: 2-527 790
conductor Tiia-Ester Loitme
Type: children's, girl's, a cappella *Size:* 110 *Perfs:* 43 *Touring:* Japan, Belgium, Finland, Germany, Italy, Latvia, Norway, Switzerland

Estonian Boys' Choir
Eesti Poistekoor
Estonia pst. 4, 10148 **Tallinn**
Tel: 6-260 201 Fax: 6-260 299
conductor Vello Laul
Type: a cappella and orchestra *Size:* 100 *Perfs:* 23

Estonian National Male Choir
Eesti Rahvusmeeskoor
Estonia pst. 4, 10148 **Tallinn**
Tel: 6-446 296 Fax: 6-314 171
Internet: www.concert.ee
E-Mail: ram@concert.ee
chief conductor Ants Soots; manager Vello Mäeots
Type: male *Repertoire:* ca 1000 pieces including major forms by Sibelius, Stravinsky, Shostakovitch, Wagner, opera highlights etc. *Size:* 60 *Perfs:* 70 *Touring:* Europe, North America *Comments:* recordings available on Deutsche Grammophon, Sony Classics, Virgin Classics, Melodija

Estonian Philharmonic Chamber Choir
Eesti Filharmoonia Kammerkoor
Lühike jalg 9, 10130 **Tallinn**
Tel: 6-314 646 Fax: 6-313 179
Internet: www.epcc.ee
E-Mail: epcc@online.ee
chief conductor Tõnu Kaljuste
Type: a cappella and orchestra *Perfs:* 50 *Touring:* USA, Canada, Japan, Australia and majority of European countries

Mixed Choir Noorus
Segakoor Noorus
Pikk 26, 10133 **Tallinn**
Tel: 2-441 551 Fax: 6-311 558
conductor Raul Talmar
Type: mixed, a cappella and with orchestra *Size:* 40 *Perfs:* 14 *Touring:* Italy, Ireland

FINLAND (+358)

Candomino
Olarinluoma 4, 02200 **Espoo**
Tel: 9-452 2193
Fax: 9-420 8160
conductor/contact Tauno Satomaa;
choir manager Hannele Granö
Type: mixed youth choir *Repertoire:* Finnish folk songs, Finnish sacred music, modern compositions *Size:* 43 *Perfs:* 15+ *Touring:* Norway, Denmark, Sweden, USA, Canada *Comments:* collaborate with other groups; TV and radio broadcasts

EOL Chamber Choir, The
Lehdesniityntie 3F99,
00340 **Helsinki**
Tel: 40-546 4486 (mobile)
Fax: 9-294 4950
E-Mail: kari.turunen@lumenvalo.fi
conductor and contact Kari Turunen
Type: chamber choir *Repertoire:* renaissance, contemporary, baroque *Size:* 30 *Perfs:* 10-15

Finnish Radio Chamber Choir, The
PO Box 14, 00024 **Yleisradio**
Tel: 9-1480 4352/9-1480 4375
Fax: 9-1480 2089
Internet: www.yle.fl/radioylenykkonen/musiikki
E-Mail: outi.paananen@yle.fi
contact Outi Paananen; artistic director Timo Nuoranne
Type: chamber *Repertoire:* mainly contemporary, some renaissance and romantic, classical *Size:* 24 *Perfs:* 8 (productions) *Touring:* Finland, Sweden

Helsinki University Male Chorus, The
Vanha ylioppilastalo
Mannerheimintie 3B,
00100 **Helsinki**
Tel: 9-655 651 Fax: 9-455 8566
Internet: www.yl.fi
president Kari Haapamäki (tel:50-502 3130);
conductor Matti Hyökki
Type: male choir *Repertoire:* whole spectrum of male choir music, especially romantic and contemporary. Also large scale works *Size:* 80-100 *Perfs:* 15 *Touring:* Scandinavia

Jubilate Choir, The
c/o Astrid Riska, Suonionkatu 7B,
00530 **Helsinki**
Tel: 9-698 8145
Internet: vn.fi/vn/um/finfo/english/jubilcho.html
conductor Astrid Riska
Type: mixed chamber choir *Repertoire:* contemporary, romantic *Size:* 35 *Perfs:* 8

Kiimingin Kiurut
Niemeläntie 21, 90900 **Kiiminki**
Tel: 8-816 1444 Fax: 8-816 2120
conductor/contact Liisa Räisänen
Type: girls' choir *Repertoire:* classical, madrigals, choral and folk music from other countries, Finnish music inc. folk songs, works from various composers and modern choral music *Size:* 25-27/30 *Perfs:* 15-20
Touring: international

Kokkolan Nuorisokuoro
Vostrobothian Conservatory,
Pitkänsillankatu 16,
67100 **Kokkola**
Tel: 6-831 3400/6-831 5177 Fax: 6-831 5368
E-Mail: kari.pappinen@cop.fi
conductor Kari Pappinen; chairperson Hannu Salo
Type: girls' choir *Repertoire:* wide range from contemporary to pop, folk music *Size:* 40 *Perfs:* 10-20 *Touring:* Finland, Europe; in year 2000: USA

Polytech Choir, The
PO Box 69, 02151 **Espoo**
Tel: 9-468 3161 Fax: 9-468 3181
Internet: pk.tky.hut.fi
E-Mail: pk@otax.tky.hut.fi
choral director Tapani Länsiö;
chairman Mikkok Kontiainen
Type: male choir *Repertoire:* all kind of male choir music, especially Finnish contemporary *Size:* 70 *Perfs:* 15
Touring: Finland, Europe, North America

Sympaatti Choir, The
Kankurinkatu 9 A 4,
33230 **Tampere**
Tel: 3-223 4379 Fax: 3-212 8039
Internet:
info1.info.tampere.fi/a/pispa/choir/enchoir.html
E-Mail: apipeni@info1.info.tampere.fi
contact Marita Sahi; conductor Pekka Nikula
Type: youth choir *Repertoire:* new Finnish music, contemporary and traditional choir music, folk songs, church music, jazz and gospel *Size:* 55 *Perfs:* 25-30 *Touring:* South Africa, Germany *Comments:* TV and radio performances; concerts with Tampere Philharmonic Orchestra; alternative email: marita.sahi@hv.fi

Tapiola Chamber Choir
Kuhatienahde 4 A 4, 02170 **Espoo**
Tel: 9-412 6805
Fax: 9-682 2683
Internet: www.englishcentre.fi/tkk
E-Mail: juha.hovinen@kolumbus.fi
manager Juha Hovinen; musical director Hannu Norjanen; deputy conductor Jaakko Mantyjarvi
Type: chamber *Repertoire:* baroque, romantic, contemporary and works commissioned by the TCC *Size:* 24-36 *Perfs:* 20 *Touring:* Ireland, Germany, Czech Republic *Comments:* the TCC is a founding member & organizer of the annual Helsinki Chamber Choir Week, launched in 1994; recordings for Finlandia Records

Tapiola Choir
Ahertajankuja 4, 02100 **Espoo**
Tel: 9-455 0757 Fax: 9-455 1328
Internet: www.sci.fi/~tapiolas/
E-Mail: tapiolas@sci.fi
manager Heli Lampi; conductor Kari Ala-Pöllänen; founder Prof. Erkki Pohjola
Type: mixed children's *Repertoire:* standard choral repertoire, Finnish folk, international classical and contemporary *Size:* 40-60 *Perfs:* 40 *Touring:* Europe, USA

FRANCE (+33)

A Sei Voci
32, Rue Gambetta, 72300 **Sablé**
Tel: 2-4392 7658 Fax: 2-4392 7659
E-Mail: aseivoci@compuserve.com
directeur administratif Thomas Vasseur; directeur artistique Bernard Fabre-Garrus
Type: professional *Repertoire:* baroque, renaissance, specialise in unknown and unpublished works, contemporary *Size:* 4-50 *Perfs:* 60 *Touring:* main festivals in Europe, Russia, Canada, South Africa, Israel, Netherlands *Comments:* supported by the French Ministry of Culture

Accentus
51 Rue de Chabrol, 75010 **Paris**
Tel: 1-4246 2200 Fax: 1-4246 1303
Internet: www.accentus.asso.fr
E-Mail: accentus@wanadoo
direction Laurence Equilbey; administration Olivier Mantei; president Daniel Badaro
Type: chamber choir *Repertoire:* a cappella (19th & 20th C.) *Size:* 32 *Perfs:* 50 *Touring:* France, Germany, Switzerland, Italy, Sweden, Belgium, Netherlands
Comments: recordings available

Akademia-Ensemble Vocal Régional de Champagne Ardenne
BP 86, 51203 **Epernay** Cedex
Tel: 3-2655 7180/86 Fax: 3-2655 7187
E-Mail: akademia@orcca.fr
administreteur Luc Delpech; direction artistique Françoise Lasserre; Delègueé Genérale Magali Duverne
Repertoire: 16th-18th century *Size:* 4-40 *Perfs:* 25-30 *Touring:* national, international

Ars Musicae
196 bis Avenue de Versailles,
75016 **Paris**
Tel: 1-4735 8917
chef de choeur Mariana Yotova-Ducros; présidente Catherine Veillet-Michelet
Type: female *Repertoire:* contemporary, classical, romantic *Size:* 18-20 *Perfs:* 3-5 *Touring:* France, Europe
Comments: chef de choeur:
Mariana Yotova-Ducros: 13 rue de Sérigné, Montrouge 92120

Atelier Lyrique de Bretagne
33, Rue de Kérivin, 29490 **Guipavas**
Tel: 2-9884 6118
directeur Georges Lecoz
Type: lyric repertoire *Size:* 15 *Perfs:* 10-15 *Touring:* France, regional

Caecilia, Maitrise Féminine
19 rue Louis Ulbach, 92 400 **Courbevoie**
Tel: 1-4789 1520 Fax: 1-4789 1520
directrice Christiane Zunbo-Nozé
Type: girls aged 12 to 20 *Repertoire:* classical, contemporary with instruments *Size:* 16-24 *Comments:* girls must undertake an audition

Calliope
114bis Grande rue de St Clair,
69300 **Caluire**
Tel: 4-7808 0321
Fax: 4-7808 0321
directeur artistique Régine Theodoresco
Type: female *Repertoire:* contemporary, 20th C and 19th and 20th Century French music *Size:* 18 *Perfs:* 10

Choeur et Orchestre de Paris-Sorbonne
2, Rue Francis Croisset, 75018 **Paris**
Tel: 1-4262 7171 Fax: 1-4251 6911
E-Mail: musicsorbonne@magic.fr
directeur Jacques Grimbert; administrateur Jean-Marie Houdayer; chef de choeur Denis Rouger
Type: symphony orchestra with mixed choir
Repertoire: classical, romantic, baroque *Size:* choir 100, orchestra 90 *Perfs:* 10 *Touring:* Europe *Comments:* see also Festivals

Choeur Lyrique du Grand Théâtre de Tours
34, Rue de la Scellerir,
37000 **Tours**
Tel: 2-4705 3347
Fax: 2-4766 1192
chef des choeurs Claire-Marie Mille; directeur Michel Jarry; administration Luc Cavalier; directeur technique Jean Michel Roux; directeur musical t.b.a.;
relations publiques Stephane de Cker
Repertoire: opera *Size:* 20 *Touring:* France : q1

Choeur Régional D'Ile de France
4 Rue de la Michodière, 75002 **Paris**
Tel: 1-4265 0802 Fax: 1-4265 0596
E-Mail: Mpiquemal@aol.com
administrateur Yves Rousseau;
directeur artistique Michel Piquemal
Repertoire: standard choral repertoire, romantic – contemporary *Size:* 100 *Perfs:* 25 *Touring:* France, Canada, Italy, Eastern Europe

Choeurs de l'Union Philharmonique de Metz-Sablon
48, Rue Saint Bernard, 57000 **Metz**
Tel: 3-8766 9493 Fax: 3-8769 0789
directeur artistique Jean Remy;
chef de choeur Odette Remy
Repertoire: standard choral repertoire *Size:* 120: female (cantare) 60; male (fidelio) 60 *Perfs:* 20 *Touring:* England, Belgium, France

Choeurs et Solistes de Lyon – Bernard Tétu
149, Rue Garibaldi, 69431 **Lyon** Cedex 3
Tel: 4-7895 2940 Fax: 4-7862 2903
Internet: www.solisteslyontetu.com
directeur général Anne-Christine Taberlet; chargée de la communication Pascaline Maugat;
directeur artistique Bernard Tétu
Type: adult professional choir *Repertoire:* classical, romantic (19th-20th c.) *Size:* 2-100 *Perfs:* 47
Touring: France

Ensemble Fulbert de Chartres
22, Rue des Réservoirs, 28000 **Chartres**
Tel: 2-3728 3153 Fax: 2-3728 3153
E-Mail: ensemblefulbert@francemel.com
directeur artistique Nicolas Lhoste; chef de choeur Asnelo Cholsti; contact Monique Frichot
Type: male choir *Repertoire:* gregorian songs, renaissance, medieval, romantic *Size:* 10 *Perfs:* 6

Ensemble Perceval
9, rue de la Loire, 49730 **Varennes-sur-Loire**
Tel: 2-4151 4088 Fax: 2-4151 4088
Internet: www.atlanticMedialab.com/Perceval/
E-Mail: ensemble.perceval@wanadoo.fr
direction artistique Katia Caré;
direction générale Guy Robert
Repertoire: medieval, vocal and instrumental *Size:* 3-10 *Perfs:* 70 *Touring:* worldwide

Ensemble Polyphonique de Lorraine
4 Bd. Charles V, 54000 **Nancy**
Tel: 3-8337 0400 Fax: 3-8337 0400
directeur Pascal Desaux; président Dominique Vellard
Type: a cappella or with small orchestra (lutist)
Repertoire: renaissance *Size:* 4-6 *Perfs:* 4-6
Touring: France

Ensemble Proscenium
Le Mesnil, 27300 **Valailles**
Tel: 2-3244 0077 Fax: 2-3244 0077
directeur Pascal Hellot; president Pier Jean Larmignat
Repertoire: French 17th C *Size:* 12-22 *Perfs:* 25
Touring: France

Ensemble Vocal Arnaut-de-Mareuil
Chemin du Vert Gallan, 24310 **Brantôme**
Tel: 5-5305 7363
président Laborie Maurice; chef de coeur Patrice Gouysse (5-5309 1613)
Type: a cappella accompanied with piano *Repertoire:* classical, chansonettes, folk, sacred *Size:* 50 *Perfs:* 5-10 *Touring:* England *Comments:* second address: Patrice Gouysse, 60 av. du général De Gaulle, 24660 Coulouriex-Chamier

Ensemble Vocal Jean Sourisse
3 Rue Jean Bart, 75006 **Paris**
Tel: 1-4222 9817 Fax: 1-4222 9817
E-Mail: rswyer@artinternet.fr
directeur musical/chef de choeur Jean Sourisse; président Claire Lamboley
Type: a cappella, small instrumental accomp. (piano, organ) *Repertoire:* standard choral repertoire, specialise in 19-20th C French music *Size:* 25 *Perfs:* 10-12 *Touring:* national, international *Comments:* recordings available on label Syrius, distributed by Concord

Ensemble Vocal Michel Piquemal
4 Rue de la Michodière, 75002 **Paris**
Tel: 1-4265 0802 Fax: 1-4265 0596
E-Mail: Mpiquemal@aol.com
administrateur Yves Rousseau; directeur artistique Michel Piquemal
Repertoire: 19th-20th C standard choral repertoire *Size:* 12-24 *Perfs:* 30-40 *Touring:* France, Canada, Indonesia

Ensemble Vocal Sagittarius
6 Passage Lathuile, 75018 **Paris**
Tel: 1-4522 1481 Fax: 1-4522 1481
directeur Michel Laplenie
Type: a cappella and with orchestra *Repertoire:* renaissance, baroque, specialise in German baroque (Schütz), French baroque *Size:* 8-12 *Perfs:* 15-20 *Touring:* Italy, France *Comments:* 20 CDs with Erato, Accord, Ades, Montaigne Disques etc.

Ensemble Vocal Soli-Tutti
Université Paris VIII, 2 Rue de la Liberté
93526 **Saint-Denis** Cedex
Tel: 1-4940 6528 Fax: 1-4821 0446
E-Mail: aca@univ-paris8.fr
administrateur Jean Philippe Dequin; directeur artistique Denis Gautheyrie;
chargé de production Marc Valero
Type: a cappella *Repertoire:* 20th C *Size:* 12 *Perfs:* 20 (+30 creations) *Touring:* Brazil, Italy, Spain, Corsica, France, Germany, USA, Czech Rep., Portugal, Canada
Comments: work with instrumental ensemble Futures Musiques; there is also the Choeur of St Denis: amateur singing between 30 and 80 singers; see also Orchestras

Ensemble Vocal St. Petersbourg
23 Chemin des Hires, 95150 **Taverny**
Tel: 1-3960 3057
Fax: 1-3960 3057
directeur Bernard Houdy
Type: a cappella/with orchestra *Repertoire:* traditional Russian Orthodox *Size:* 7 *Perfs:* 40
Touring: Japan, Russia

Formation Lyrique du Languedoc
Impasse St Mathieu, 34430 **Saint Jean-de-Vedas**
Tel: 4-6777 0916/6742 7779
directeur artistique Louis Massal (2 rue de Fort, 34630 St. Thibery)
Repertoire: operetta, opera *Size:* 12 soloists + 2 pianists *Perfs:* 20 *Touring:* regional *Comments:* ex-artists from the Opera de Montpellier, Opera de Nice, Opera de Marseille

La Cigale de Lyon
131 Rue Challemel Lacour, 69008 **Lyon**
Tel: 4-7875 1919 Fax: 4-7498 2835
E-Mail: cigalelyon@aol.com
directrice Anne-Marie Cabut;
fondateur Christian Wagner
Type: children's *Repertoire:* Bach – Brassens, classical, modern *Size:* 70 *Perfs:* 30-40
Touring: Japan, Belgium, Germany

La Psallette de Lorraine
L'Institut Européen de Cholares, 56, rue Claude Bernard, 57070 **Metz**
Tel: 3-8730 5207 Fax: 3-8730 8784
administratrice Chantal Grandclair;
directeur Florent Stroesser
Type: a cappella and with orchestra *Repertoire:* from baroque to 20th C music *Size:* 30 *Perfs:* 10

Le Cantrel de Lyon
114 bis Grande Rue de Saint-Clair, 69300 **Caluire**
Tel: 4-7808 0321 Fax: 4-7808 0321
chef de choeur Regine Theodoresco
Type: a cappella, oratorio *Repertoire:* 20th century, musique française *Size:* 50 *Perfs:* 10-15 *Touring:* Lebanon

Les Jeunes Solistes
28, rue des Petites Écuries, 75010 **Paris**
Tel: 1-4247 1611 Fax: 1-4247 1612
E-Mail: jsoliste@cub_inernet.fr
administrateur Laurence Dune; directeur artistique Rachid Safir; contact Diane de Monteynard
type: polyphonic & soloists *Repertoire:* from Renaissance to contemporary, often specially commissioned work *Size:* from solo to chamber size *Perfs:* 30
Touring: France, Europe

Madrigal de Bordeaux
Polifonia – Eliane Lavail, Château Feydeau,
33370 **Artigues-Près-Bordeaux**
Tel: 5-5632 6956 Fax: 5-5632 6956
E-Mail: polifonia@aol.com
directrice Eliane Lavail; présidente Odette Drupin; députée vice-président Daniel Chrétien; trésorier/secrétaire général François Tabanous;
secrétaire Françoise Rouquié
Repertoire: renaissance to contemporary *Size:* 4-16 *Perfs:* 6 *Touring:* Europe, Asia, America *Comments:* professional singers; see also Orchestras (Ensemble Orchestral d'Aquitaine)

Maîtrise de Notre-Dame de Paris
18, rue de Poissy, 75005 **Paris**
Tel: 1-4441 4999
Fax: 1-4051 0611
E-Mail: msndp@aol.com
directeur général Jean-Michel Dieuaide; chefs de choeur Nicole Corti, Denis Rouger, Emmanuel Magat
Repertoire: whole sacred repertoire *Size:* 25 amateurs, 16-18 professional training, 28 children

Musicatreize
55, Rue Grignan, 13006 **Marseille**
Tel: 4-9155 0277 Fax: 4-9155 0393
Internet: www.musicatreize.com
E-Mail: Musicatreize@musicatreize.com
directeur artistique Roland Hayrabedian; administrateur Thierry Boblet; relations publiques Marthe Lemut
Type: professional lyrical soloists and instrumentalists
Repertoire: concerts for voices a cappella or accompanied by instrumental formations, concerts with orchestra and soloists, musical theatre, opera

Size: 12-80 *Perfs:* 30-40 *Touring:* Italy, Spain, Germany, Belgium, Russia, Czech Republic
Comments: Musicatreize is particularily involved in contemporary music and creation; winners of the most important prizes in France; see also Orchestras

Oldarra
17 Rue Duler, 64200 **Biarritz**
Tel: 5-5924 0967
Fax: 5-5924 5563
musical director Inaki Urtizberra;
production Martin Garat
Type: male *Repertoire:* traditional Basque music
Size: 55 *Perfs:* 25 *Touring:* France, international
Comments: CD available on Warner Classics

Pages et Chantres de la Chapelle, Les
22 Avenue de Paris, 78000 **Versailles**
Tel: 1-3920 7810
Fax: 1-3920 7810
Internet: www.cmbv.culture.fr
déléguée générale Graziella Valée;
directeur musical Oliver Schneebeli
Repertoire: French baroque music *Size:* 30 *Perfs:* 30 *Touring:* France, Poland, Switzerland, Germany

Paris National Opera Children's Choir
Maitrise des Hauts de Seine – Chœur d'Enfants de l'Opéra National de Paris
9, Boulevard Aristide Briant,
92150 **Suresnes**
Tel: 1-4772 3030 Fax: 1-4772 3131
E-Mail: mhs@club-internet.fr
directeur Monsieur Gaël Darcher; administrateur Mme Annick Harb; directeur tournées Marc Augé
Type: boys' choir; girls' choir; men's choir *Repertoire:* classical and standard choral repertoire, opera, special events *Size:* boys' choir: 200, girls' choir: 100, men's choir: 60 *Perfs:* 100 annually *Touring:* worldwide including: France, USA, South Africa

Sotto Voce
c/o Ecole de Musique-Ancien College, Place Omer Sarraut, 82100 **Castelsarrasin**
Tel: 5-6395 0181 Fax: 5-6395 1669
chef de choeur/directeur musical Jean-Pierre Berrié
Type: a cappella, musicians sometimes *Repertoire:* contemporary *Size:* 25 *Perfs:* 12 *Touring:* France

GEORGIA (+995)

Ensemble of Musical Parody Scerzo
25 Rustaveli av., 380023 **Tbilisi**
Tel: 32-990 456/995 642 Fax: 32-933 250
artistic director Gela Parchukidze; assistant of artistic director Sshalva Shaorshadze
Type: professional mixed choir *Repertoire:* opera performances *Size:* 80 *Perfs:* 70 *Touring:* Germany, Italy, Malta

Georgian State Choir
1 Gorgasali St,
380023 **Tbilisi**
Tel: 32-722 725/723 583
artistic director Givi Mundjishvili;
general manager Nato Mjoistsrapishvili
Type: professional mixed choir *Repertoire:* classical, early, contemporary *Size:* 70 *Perfs:* 50
Comments: recordings available;
performances with orchestra

Tbilisi National Opera Choir
25 Rustaveli av
380008 **Tbilisi**
Tel: 32-990 456/990 642
Fax: 32-933 250
artistic director Gela Parchukidze
Type: male choir *Repertoire:* classical, folk music, jazz, rock *Size:* 6 *Perfs:* 40-50 *Touring:* Poland, Germany, Sweden, France, Spain

GERMANY (+49)

Aachener Kammerchor e.V.
Oberforstbacher Str 10,
52076 **Aachen**
Tel: 2408-928 130 Fax: 2408-928 132
Internet: aachen.heimat.de/aachener_kammerchor
E-Mail: fux.ac@t-online.de
Geschäftsführer Heribert Schroeder
Leitung Martin te Laak
Type: mainly a cappella, sometimes orchestral
Repertoire: chamber *Size:* 30 *Perfs:* 10

Bachchor Würzburg
Hofstallstr. 597070 **Würzburg**
Tel: 931-322 8480
Fax: 931-322 8471
Internet:
www.datenautobahn.de/musik/bachchor.wuerzburg
E-Mail: stjohannis@t-online.de
contact Christian Kabitz
Type: a cappella and orchestral, opera, mixed
Repertoire: 16th-20th century, sacred music, oratoria
Size: 110 *Perfs:* 30 *Touring:* national, international
Comments: see also Festivals

Balthasar-Neumann-Chor
c/o Büro für Internationale Kulturprojekte GmbH, Schwarzwaidstr. 298a, 79117 **Freiburg**
Tel: 761-612 238 Fax: 761 62229
E-Mail: Bik@fmf.notes-net.de
Musikalische Leitung Thomas Hengelbrock
Type: chamber choir *Repertoire:* 17th and 18th C, also opera & semi-opera *Comments:* see also Orchestras, Agents and Producers

Berliner Konzertchor e. V. – Hauptchor
Starnberger Str. 3, 10781 **Berlin**
Tel: 30-218 5001 Fax: 30-213 8703
Geschäftsstelle Doris Rohrschneider;
künstlerischer Leiter Matthias Elger
Type: orchestral, mixed *Repertoire:* Mozart, Bach, Beethoven, Brahms, Bruckner, Bizet, B. Britten, Honegger *Size:* 115 *Perfs:* 5 in the Philharmonie *Touring:* Germany *Comments:* see also Promoters

Berliner Konzertchor e. V. – Jugendchor
Starnberger Str. 3, 10781 **Berlin**
Tel: 30-218 5001 Fax: 30-213 8703
Geschäftsstelle Doris Rohrschneider;
Leiter Jan Ulberg
Type: mainly a cappella, youth choir, sometimes orchestral *Repertoire:* mainly classical, some baroque *Size:* 30 *Perfs:* 4 *Comments:* also performances with the main choir

Berliner Konzertchor e.V. – Spatzenchor
Starnberger Str. 3, 10781 **Berlin**
Tel: 30-218 5001 Fax: 30-213 8703
Geschäftsstelle Doris Rohrschneider,
Leiter Rainer Stelzner
Type: a cappella, children's choir (6-14 years) *Repertoire:* children's songs, folk, modern music *Size:* 50 *Perfs:* 3 (1 summer, 1 christmas concert) + various small concerts

Braunschweiger Domchor, Der
Domplatz 5, 38100 **Braunschweig**
Tel: 531-46473 Fax: 531-125 065
Domkantor Gerd-Peter Münden
Type: a cappella *Repertoire:* sacred and secular: renaissance to contemporary *Size:* 140 *Perfs:* 3-4 (+ church services) *Touring:* Spain, Italy, Czech Republic
Comments: see also Orchestras

Bulgarian Voices – Angelite, The
c/o Jaro, Bismarckstr. 43, 28203 **Bremen**
Tel: 421-78080/705 772 Fax: 421-74066
Internet: www.jaro.de
E-Mail: mail@jaro.de
conductor Velkov Valentin; impressaria Tenja Andreeva
Type: female, a capella *Repertoire:* traditional and contemporary, orthodox church music from 10th to 18th century *Size:* 20-22 *Perfs:* 100 *Touring:* worldwide
Comments: several records + video available *Comments:* JARO has worldwide exclusive management

Chor der Bamberger Symphoniker
Mußstraße 1, 96047 **Bamberg**
Tel: 951-964 7100 Fax: 951-964 7123
Chorleitung Rolf Beck;
Geschäftsführerin Sabine Kus (tel: 951-96471-21)
Type: mixed, orchestral & a cappella *Repertoire:* sacred and secular: renaissance to contemporary *Size:* over 100 *Perfs:* 15 *Touring:* Spain, Italy, Chech Republic
Comments: is affiliated to Bamberger Symphoniker but also performs on its own; see also Orchestras

Chor der Christuskirche München
c/o Pfarramt Christuskirche z. Hd. KMD Roman Emilius, Dom-Pedro-Platz 5, 80637 **München**
Tel: 89-157 9040 Fax: 89-157 7900
Geschäftsführer/Verwaltungsleiter Pfarramt Christuskirche, Prodekan Manfred Jahnel;
Künstlerischer Leiter KMD Roman Emilius
Type: a cappella, oratoria *Repertoire:* 19th/20th century
Size: 100 *Perfs:* 5 *Comments:* CD available

Chor des Sorbischen National Ensembles GmbH
Äussere Lauenstr. 2, 02625 **Bautzen**
Tel: 3591-3580 Fax: 3591-43096
Chordirektor Ronald Monem; Musikalische Leitung Dieter Kempe; Geschäftsführer Meto Benad
Type: orchestral, ballet *Repertoire:* classics of German and international choir repertoire; specialising in Sorbian national repertoire *Size:* 30 *Perfs:* 150 *Touring:* Finland, Spain, Japan *Comments:* see also Dance, Drama, Puppets

Chöre der Hochschule für Musik und Theater München
c/o Hochschule für Musik und Theater in München, Arcisstraße 12, 80333 **München**
Tel: 89-289 03 Fax: 89-2892 7419
Internet: www.musikhochschule-muenchen.mhn.de
Präsident Prof. Robert M. Helmschrott (tel: 89-2892 7403; Kanzler Dr. Alexander Krause (tel: 89-2892 7410)
Type: 4 choirs: Großer Chor der Hochschule (main choir), Leitung Andreas Herrmann; Großer Kirchenmusik-Chor der Hochschule (church choir), Leitung Prof. Michael Gläser; Madrigalchor der Hochschule (madrigal choir), Leitung Prof. Max Frey; Opernchor (opera choir), Leitung Prof. Wilfried Koch
Perfs: various throughout the year (also guest perfs)

Dresdner Kreuzchor
Eisenacherstraße 21, 01277 **Dresden**
Tel: 351-315 3560 Fax: 351-315 3561
Internet: www.kreuzchor.de
E-Mail: buero@kreuzchor.de
Leiter Roderich Kreile; Manager Uwe Grüner
Type: youth and adult male choir *Repertoire:* standard choral repertoire, symphonic and church music *Size:* 150, touring choir of 40-80 *Perfs:* 90 *Touring:* France, Italy and Germany, USA, Hungary, Russia *Comments:* in Dresden performs in association with the Kreuzkirche

Flensburger Bachchor
Dietrich-Nacke Straße 28, 24939 **Flensburg**
Tel: 461-53597
Fax: 461-55418
Leiter Prof. Matthias Janz
Type: orchestra, a cappella and mixed *Size:* 120
Perfs: 15-20 *Touring:* Denmark, Hungary, Austria

Frankfurter Kantorei
Homburger Hohl 18, 60437 **Frankfurt am Main**
Tel: 69-5093 0041 Fax: 69-5093 0042
Internet: members.aol.com/ftkantorei/welcome.html
E-Mail: hohohl18@aol.com
artistic director Winfried Toll;
manager Johannes Kaballo
Type: a cappella and orchestral *Repertoire:* oratorios, Mahler – symphonies, a cappella-literature *Size:* 60-100
Perfs: 20 *Touring:* national and international

Junge Kantorei München
c/o Pfarramt Christuskirche z. Hd. KMD Roman Emilius, Dom-Pedro-Platz 5,
80637 **München**
Tel: 89-157 9040 Fax: 89-157 7900
Geschäftsführer/Verwaltungsleiter Pfarramt Christuskirche, Prodekan Manfred Jahnel;
Künstlerischer Leiter KMD Roman Emilius
Type: a cappella *Repertoire:* chamber, with emphasis on 20th C. repertoire *Size:* 30 *Perfs:* 5

Junges Collegium Vocale
Jungfernstieg 26, 24103 **Kiel**
Tel: 431-96145
Fax: 431-96145
contact Christian Becker
Type: a cappella, orchestral, youth choir *Repertoire:* sacred, early, also contemporary sacred & secular music *Size:* 50 *Perfs:* 10 *Touring:* Sweden, Germany

Kammerchor Stuttgart
c/o Stuttgarter Musik Podium, Christophstr 5,
70178 **Stuttgart**
Tel: 711-239 1390 Fax: 711-239 1399
E-Mail: smp@n.zgs.de
Geschäftsführer Gregory Johns;
Künstlerischer Leiter Frieder Bernius
Type: a cappella and orchestral *Repertoire:* baroque to contemporary *Size:* 16-60 *Perfs:* 30 p.a. *Touring:* worldwide *Comments:* have done more than 50 recordings and won 15 international recording awards

Kartäuserkantorei Köln
Hans-Gerd Kuxdorf, Rhodiusstr. 1,
51065 **Köln**
Tel: 221-614 141
Fax: 221-614 141
E-Mail: studmico@vox.tin.it
conductor Peter Neumann
Type: oratorio choir *Repertoire:* 17th-20th century, romantic works *Size:* 60-80 *Touring:* Germany, France, Italy *Comments:* management: Gianna Nicoletti, Vicolo Monviso 1, 20010 Canegrate (Milano), tel. +39 03-3141 1142, fax. +39 03-3140 1515

Knabenchor Hannover
Meterstrasse 3,
30169 **Hannover**
Tel: 511-882 388
Fax: 511-809 3613
Internet: www.knabenchor-hannover.de
director/conductor Prof. Heinz Hennig
Type: boy's choir *Repertoire:* mostly sacred, from early to 20th century *Size:* 140 *Perfs:* 30-40
Touring: Germany *Comments:* CDs available;
also school for young singers

Kölner Kammerchor
c/o Agnes Dohm, Oberborsbacher Str 6,
51519 **Odenthal**
Tel: 2202-70293 Fax: 2202-70294
conductor Peter Neumann
Type: chamber choir- a cappella and with orchestra
Repertoire: Monteverdi, Handel, Bach, Mozart, romantic, Italian baroque *Size:* 15-40 *Perfs:* 10 *Touring:* Germany, Italy, France, Netherlands
Comments: management: Gianni Nicoletti, Vicolo Monviso 1, 20010 Canegrate (Milano), tel. 39-03 31/41 1142, fax. 39-03 31/40 1515;
recorded Mozart Messen for EMI Classics and for Carus, Schumann – Messe op. 147 for MDG (Diapason d'or 1996), G.F. Haendel, Saul for MDG, professional performances; see also Orchestras
(Collegium Cartusianum)

Kölner Kurrende
Brabanter Str 6, 50674 **Köln**
Tel: 221-251 533 Fax: 221-251 533
contact Elke Mascha Blankenburg
Type: mixed *Repertoire:* renaissance to modern
Size: 80 *Touring:* national, international *Comments:* numerous broadcasts, several recordings, 4 annual concerts at the Köln Philharmonie; numerous TV & radio broadcasts; see also Orchestras (Clara Schumann Orchester Köln)

Landesjugendchor Baden Württemberg
c/o Landesmusikrat Baden Württemberg e.v., Ortsstraße 6, 76228 **Karlsruhe**
Tel: 721-947 670 Fax: 721-947 3330
Organisationsleiter René Schuh;
Chorleiter Dan-Oluf Stenlund
Type: a cappella, orchestral, youth choir *Repertoire:* sacred & secular of all periods *Size:* 60-70 *Perfs:* 6
Comments: Auswahlchor

Landesjugendchor Schleswig-Holstein
c/o Landesmusikrat Schleswig-Holstein, Nikolaistraße 5, 24937 **Flensburg**
Tel: 461-141 5113 Fax: 461-141 5120
Internet: www.landesmusikrat.de
E-Mail: fuerst@landesmusikrat.de
Referentin Barbara Fürst;
Leiter Kirchenmusikdirektor Prof. Matthias Janz
Type: a cappella, occasionally orchestral, youth choir, mixed *Repertoire:* rarely performed choral material from early to contemporary music, sophisticated a cappella repertoire *Size:* 60 *Perfs:* at least 4
Comments: Auswahlchor

MDR Chor-Leipzig
Springerstrasse 22-24, 04105 **Leipzig**
Tel: 341-300 5705 Fax: 341-300 5701
Internet: www.mdr.de/klangkoerper
Chordirector Howard Arman; management Holger Kruppe, Mario Plath, Helga Kuschmitz
Type: a cappella, symphonic, mixed *Repertoire:* classical
Size: 73 *Touring:* national and international *Comments:* see also Orchestras and Festivals

Münchener Bach-Chor e.V.
c/o Frau Bliese, Ganghofer Str. 128, 81373 **München**
Tel: 171-546 3734 (mobile)
Internet: www.muenchen.de/bachchor
Künstlerischer Leiter Hanns-Martin Schneidt;
Vorstandsvorsitzende und Manager Andrea Bliese;
Pressereferentin Barbara Jacobi
(tel: 89-985 195, fax: 89-982 7126)
Repertoire: classical to contemporary *Size:* 120 *Perfs:* ca. 15 *Touring:* national and international *Comments:* Bachfest 26.5-4.6.2000
(250th anniversary of death of J. S. Bach)

Neubeurener Chorgemeinschaft
Am Gasteig 5, 83115 **Neubeuern**
Tel: 8035 1031
Fax: 0835 8492
Internet: www.chorgemeinschaft.de
E-Mail: guttenberg@chorgemeinschaft.de
Leiter Enoch zu Guttenberg; Leitung Chorbüro Hildegard Eutermoser; Leitung Presse und Öffenlich keitsarbeit Richard Hartmann
Type: a cappella and orchestral repertoire *Repertoire:* specialise in oratorio repertoires by Bach, Händel, Mozart, Mendelsohn-Bartholdy, Verdi *Size:* 100 *Perfs:* 25 *Touring:* national, Europe, USA, Argentina, Brasil, Uruguay *Comments:* main concert site: Philharmonie am Gasteig, Munich; various TV productions on German television; CDS available with SONY, BMG and FARAO Classics

Philharmonischer Chor Dresden
c/o Dresdener Philharmonie, Postfach 120424, 01005 **Dresden**
Tel: 351-486 6365
Fax: 351-486 6283/6365
Internet: www.dresdnerphilharmonie.de
E-Mail: contact@dresdnerphilharmonie.de
Chordirektor Professor Matthias Geissler;
Choriuspizientin Angelika Ernst
Type: mixed concerts choir *Repertoire:* oratorias, opera and other sinfonia *Size:* 110 *Perfs:* 6-10 *Touring:* Germany, Czech Republic, Poland, Austria *Comments:* visiting address: Kulturpalast am Altmarkt, 01067 Dresden; CDs available

Philharmonischer Chor München e.v.
c/o Münchner Philharmoniker, Kellerstraße 4/III, 81667 **München**
Tel: 89-4809 8504
Fax: 89-4809 8526
Internet: www.muenchenerphilharmoniker.de
E-Mail: andreas_herrmann@magicvillage.de
Geschäftsführer/Verwaltungsleiter, Intendant Bernd Gellermann; Leitung Künstlerisches Betriebsbüro der Münchner Philharmoniker Roswitha Wetz;
Künstlerischer Leiter Andreas Herrmann
Type: mixed, mainly orchestral *Repertoire:* 19th and 20th century *Size:* 130 *Perfs:* 24 *Touring:* national & international guest performances

Philharmonischer Jugendchor Dresden
Postfach 120424, 01005 **Dresden**
Tel: 351-486 6347 Fax: 351-486 6283
Internet: www.dresdnerphilharmonie.de
E-Mail: contact@dresdnerphilharmonie.de
Chordirektor Jürgen Becker;
Assistentin/Inspizientin Barbara Quellmelz
Type: mixed youth choir (16-25) *Repertoire:* sacred and secular a cappella music ranging from 16th century to contemporary works as well as choral symphonies *Size:* 30-45 *Perfs:* 15 *Touring:* Switzerland, Germany
Comments: visiting address:
Kulturpalast am Altmarkt, 01067 Dresden

Philharmonischer Kammerchor Dresden
c/o Dresdener Philharmonie, Postfach 120424, 01005 **Dresden**
Tel: 351-486 6365 Fax: 351-486 6283/6365
Chordirektor Professor Matthias Geissler;
Chorinspizientin Angelika Ernst
Type: mixed chamber choir (soprano, alt, tenor, bass)
Repertoire: a cappella, 16th century to modern *Size:* 30
Perfs: 8-12 *Touring:* Austria, Italy, Netherlands, Spain, Malta, France, Germany *Comments:* visiting address: Kulturpalast am Altmarkt, 01067 Dresden; CDs available (weltliche Chormusik a cappella von Romantik bis Gegenwart)

Philharmonischer Kinderchor Dresden
Postfach 120424, 01005 **Dresden**
Tel: 351-486 6347
Fax: 351-486 6283
Internet: www.dresdnerphilharmonie.de
E-Mail: contact@dresdnerphilharmonie.de
Chordirektor Jürgen Becker
Type: children's (10-18) *Repertoire:* 16th century to contemporary, sacred and secular, choral symphonies
Size: 40-110 *Perfs:* 35 *Touring:* national and international
Comments: visiting address: Kulturpalast am Altmarkt, 01067 Dresden; address Jürgen Becker: Kronenstr. 11, 01558 Grossenhain

Renner Ensemble Regensburg
c/o Thomas Bauer, Taubengässchen 5, 93047 **Regensburg**
Tel: 941-55304
Fax: 941-55305
E-Mail: SingerPur@aol.com
contact & management Thomas Bauer; Musikalischer Direktor Bernd Englbrecht
Type: male, a cappella *Repertoire:* specialised in classics *Size:* 14 *Perfs:* 25 *Touring:* Asia

Rheinische Kantorei
Ostpreussenallee 5 , 41539 **Dormagen**
Tel: 2133-477 905
Fax: 2133-477 905
musikalische Leitung Hermann Max;
organisatorische Leitung Martin Kahl
Type: a cappella and orchestral *Repertoire:* 17th and 18th Century *Size:* 16-24 *Perfs:* ca. 10 *Touring:* Europe, Israel
Comments: note: Das kleine Konzert (baroque orchestra) performs exclusively with this choir; both groups are professional; several CDs on EMI Classics, Capricio and CPO

RIAS-Kammerchor in der Rundfunk-Orchester und - Chöre GmbH
Charlottenstr. 56, 10117 **Berlin**
Tel: 30-2029 8730
Fax: 30-2029 8740
Internet: www.rias-kammerchor.de
E-Mail: info@rias-kammerchor.de
managing director Frank Druschel; chief conductor Marcus Creed; guest conductors René Jacobs, Phillippe Herreweghe; public relations Ralf Schott; secretary Rosmarie Arndt, Ingrid-Karin Wallat
Type: chamber choir *Repertoire:* early and contemporary music, a cappella and with chamber orchestra *Size:* 35 *Perfs:* 30-40 own series in the Philharmonie Berlin *Touring:* Germany, France, Belgium, Austria, Switzerland, Spain *Comments:* recordings on harmonia mundi france, Berlin Classics, Capriccio, EMI Classics and Deutsche Grammophon; 28 international recording awards like Cannes Classical Awards, Edison Award, Preis der deutschen Schallplattenkritik,
Choc de l'Annee, Grammophone Radio Chart USA; see also Early Music

Rundfunkchor Berlin in der Rundfunk-Orchester und - Chöre GmbH Berlin
Charlottenstr 56, 10117 **Berlin**
Tel: 30-2030 92220
Fax: 30-2030 92261
Internet: www.rchb.de
E-Mail: rundfunkchor-berlin@rchb.de
Intendant Dr Dieter Rexroth;
Geschäftsführer Wolfgang Ogrisek; Chefdirigent Robin Gritton; Chordirektor Hans-Hermann Rehberg;
Chorbüro Brigitte Schöne, Antonia Zellmer
Type: mixed, professional *Repertoire:* a cappella, classical from all eras, symphony *Size:* 64 *Perfs:* 50 *Touring:* Germany, USA, France, Spain, Netherlands
Comments: ticket office: Charlottenstr. 56, 10117 Berlin, tel. 30-2029 8722; CDs available

Sächsisches Vocalensemble
Saxonian Vocal Ensemble
Pillnitzer Landstraße 59, 01326 **Dresden**
Tel: 351-268 4543 Fax: 351-268 3543
Vorsitzender Steffan Itzerott;
Künstlerischer Leiter Matthias Jung
Type: a cappella and with instruments *Repertoire:* early music, 20th C music, rarely performed works often related to Saxony *Size:* 20 *Perfs:* 27-32 *Touring:* national, international *Comments:* CD recordings available

Singer Pur
c/o Thomas Bauer, Taubengässchen 5, 93047 **Regensburg**
Tel: 941-55304 Fax: 941-55305
contact & manager Thomas Bauer
Type: mixed, a cappella *Repertoire:* classical, modern
Size: 6 *Perfs:* 100

Städtischer Musikverein zu Düsseldorf
c/o Connect Marketing, Itterstr. 35-39, 40589 **Düsseldorf**
Tel: 211-794 3118
Fax: 211-794 3112
Vorsitzender Klaus Exler
Type: mixed *Repertoire:* classical to contemporary *Size:* 120-140 *Perfs:* 10-15 *Touring:* USA, Germany, France
Comments: regularly performs with Düsseldorfer Symphoniker Orchester but also with other big German and European philharmonic orchestras

Symphonischer Chor Hamburg
Colonnaden 72, 20354 **Hamburg**
Tel: 40-351 156 Fax: 40-3571 9553
Leiter Prof. Matthias Janz; Vorsitzende Sabine Pletat; Öffentlichkeitarbeit Charlotte Allardt (Sandmoorweg 40, 22559 Hamburg, tel: 40-815733)
Type: oratorio choir *Repertoire:* oratorio, some operas
Size: 120-130 *Perfs:* 4 *Touring:* Denmark with Sønderfyllands Symfonieorkester and alone, Slovenia and Italy with Slovenian Philharmonic Orchestra Maribor *Comments:* performs with the Hamburg Symphoniker and other orchestras in Northern Germany

Tölzer Knabenchor
Kaminskistrasse 13, 83671 **Benediktbeuern**
Tel: 8857-9061
Fax: 8857-1470
Internet: info@knabenchor.de
E-Mail: info@knabenchor.de
director Prof. Gerhard Schmidt-Gaden;
organisation/management Helga Schmidt-Gaden, May-Britt Andresen, Tilo Pitz; PR Jürgen Bierbaum
Type: professional boys choir + boy soloists *Repertoire:* standard choral repertoire, specializing in authentic performance of early music, also symphonic repertoire
Size: 2 concert choirs (30) *Perfs:* 200-250 *Touring:* worldwide *Comments:* more than 100 CD recordings (Dt. Schallplattenpreis); see also Early Music

Windsbacher Knabenchor
Heinrich Brandstr. 18, 91575 **Windsbach**
Tel: 9871-708 200
Fax: 9871-708 222
Internet: www.windsbacher-knabenchor.de
E-Mail: chorbuero@windsbacher-knabenchor.de
organisation & management Christa Rey;
Künstlerischer Leiter Karl-Friedrich Beringer
Type: professional boys choir *Repertoire:* classical and modern *Size:* touring choir of 55-75 *Perfs:* 60-80 *Touring:* worldwide e.g. Australia, Israel *Comments:* emphasis on oratorias and a cappella concerts

GIBRALTAR (+350)

Calpe Singers
32 Prince Edward's Road, **Gibraltar**
Tel: 76196/40745/52082 (answerphone) Fax: 52082
E-Mail: calpehc@gibnynex
musical director Hector Cortes
Type: mixed chamber choir *Repertoire:* from polphony to popular *Size:* 20 *Perfs:* 12 *Touring:* Spain, France, Italy, Portugal, UK, USA *Comments:* host the millenium advent week – choirs' own performances (each visiting choir) and one massed orchestra and choir performance on 13th Dec. 1999

GREECE (+30)

Choir of the Greek Radio & Television Broadcasting Company (ERT)
Athens Broadcasting Musical Ensembles Directorate, 432 Mesoghion Ave., Aghia Paraskevi, 15342 **Athens**
Tel: 1-606 6094
Fax: 1-606 6099
director of Athens Broadcasting Musical Ensembles Directorate Alkis Baltas; musical director of choir Andonis Kontogeorgiou;
administration officer K. Demisticha
Type: mixed choir, a cappella & orchestral *Repertoire:* oratorios, sacred music, classical, opera, contemporary, operetta *Size:* 52 *Perfs:* 10 + performances with national opera *Touring:* Greece, Cyprus *Comments:* studio recordings; co-productions with national opera

HUNGARY (+36)

Banchieri Singers
Banchieri Énekegyüttes
PB 137 , 4401 **Nyiregyháza**
Tel: 42-402 890 Fax: 42-402 890
Internet: www.szabolcs.net/banchieri/
E-Mail: banchi@elender.hu
leader Szilárd Szilágyi
Touring: national, Europe, Japan *Comments:* alternative internet:www.elender.hu~banchi; visiting address: Eötvös utca 4, CDs available

Bartók Choir of Szolnok
Szolnoki Bartók Choir
Tancsics u. 6, 5000 **Szolnok**
Tel: 56-375 302 Fax: 56-375 302
artistic director Eva Molnar
Type: girl's chamber choir, a cappella
Repertoire: madrigals

Béla Bartók Choir
Bartók Béla Énekkar
Szerb utca 21-23, 1058 **Budapest** V
Tel: 1-266 3981/266 7152
Fax: 1-266 3981
Internet: ludens.elte.hu/zene
E-Mail: baross@ludens.elte.hu
artistic director Gábor Baross;
administrator Ferenc Rákosi
Repertoire: ranges from folk songs to contemporary choral music *Comments:* choir has won numerous choir compertions

Budapest Madrigal Choir
Budapesti Madrigál Kórus
c/o IAG Europe Becsi kapu ter 8, 1014 **Budapest**
Tel: 1-356 1866 Fax: 1-356 1866
artistic director Ferenc Szekeres
Type: chamber choir *Repertoire:* madrigals, motets and the great cyclical works of the great masters of polyphony, cantatas and oratorios *Comments:* special emphasis on the choral works by Bartók and Kodály

Children's Choir of the Hungarian Radio and Television
Magyar Rádió és Televizió Gyermekkórusa
Bródy Sándor u. 5-7, 1088 **Budapest**
Tel: 1-328 7161 Fax: 1-328 7907/328 7161
Internet:
www.bmc.hu/rtv.childrens.choir.index2_en.htm
director Janos Sziranyi; artistic director Gabriella Thész;
manager Tamás Kelen
Type: children's choir, a cappella *Repertoire:* oratorios, operas, classical to contemporary *Size:* 50-90 *Perfs:* 30 annually *Touring:* Europe, Japan, USA *Comments:* under the management of the Radio, cooperation with the Budapest Symphony Orchestra and the mixed choir of the Hungarian Radio; has its own elementary school for the children; recordings available;venue: Marble Hall 100, Studio G150, Ferenc Liszt Academy of Music

Ferenc Liszt Teachers Choir
Liszt Ferenc Pedagóguskórus
Mártírok tere 10, 7100 **Szekszárd**
Tel: 74-316 722 Fax: 74-316 722
Internet: www.port.hu/owa/kultura
E-Mail: ifipolip@terrasoft.hu
president Magdolna Kiszlerné Talabos;
general secretary József Gerse
Repertoire: specialising in Hungarian music *Size:* 44

Honvéd Male Choir
Honvéd Férfikar
Kerepesi út 29/B, 1087 **Budapest**
Tel: 1-333 5124 Fax: 1-334 3772
Internet: www.magyar.org/zsuratszki/
conductor Andras Toth; artistic director Ferenc Novak;
general director Károly Aranyos
Type: mens' choir, a cappella *Repertoire:* oratorios, madrigals, Gregorian to contemporary *Size:* 42

Hungarian National Choir
Magyar Nemzeti Énekkar
Vörösmarty ter 1, 1051 **Budapest**
Tel: 1-318 0104 Fax: 1-429 1099/318 0374
Internet: www.bmc.hu/nfz/inte2_en.htm
E-Mail: natphilharm@mail.matav.hu
artistic director Mátyás Antal;
managing director Géza Kovács
Type: mixed choir, a cappella *Repertoire:* oratorios, classical to contemporary *Size:* 85 *Perfs:* 62 *Comments:* cooperation with the Hungarian National Philharmonic Orchestra

Ilona Zrínyi Female Choir
Zrínyi Ilona Leánykar
Nagyváthy utca 5,
3530 **Miskolc**
Tel: 46-344 908
Fax: 46-344 917
Internet: www.zrinyi-misk.sulinet.hu
E-Mail: suli91@miskolc.sulinet.hu
conductor Zsuzsanna Engi;
head Ildikó Kovácsné Szegedi
Type: female choir *Touring:* national, Europe

Kodály Choir of Debrecen
Debreceni Kodály Kórus
Széchenyi u. 1, 4025 **Debrecen**
Tel: 52-419 199 Fax: 52-419 199
artistic director Peter Erdei; conductor Lajos Szücs;
managing director Árpád Joób
Type: mixed choir, girls choir, a cappella *Repertoire:* oratorios, madrigals *Size:* 65 *Perfs:* 60 *Touring:* national, international *Comments:* special emphasis on choral works of Kodály

Mixed Choir of the Hungarian Radio and Television
Magyar Rádió és Televizió Vegyeskara
Bródy Sándor u. 5-7, 1088 **Budapest**
Tel: 1-328 7161 Fax: 1-328 7569/328 7161
Internet: www.port.hu/owg/kultura
director Janos Sziranyi; artistic director Kalman Strausz;
manager Tamás Kelen
Type: mixed choir, a cappella *Repertoire:* oratorios, opera, classical to contemporary *Size:* 70 *Perfs:* 40 *Touring:* Europe *Comments:* under the management of the Radio, cooperation with the Budapest Symphony Orchestra

Mixed Choir of the Hungarian State Opera
Magyar Állami Operaház Vegyeskara
Andrássy út 22, 1061 **Budapest**
Tel: 1-331 2550 Fax: 1-331 9817
artistic director Aniko Katona
Type: mixed choir *Repertoire:* opera *Comments:* under the management of the Opera, serving 2 venues

Primavera Choir
Primavera Kórus
Donát utca 55, 8000 **Székesfehérvár**
Tel: 22-305 172 Fax: 22-328 733
leader Ottília Horányi; administrator Márta Mézes
Type: mixed youth choir

Siófok Children's Choir
Városi Gyermek és Ifjúsági Kórus
Wesselényi utca 5, 8600 **Siófok**
Tel: 84-312 201 Fax: 84-312 201
choir master Imre Tímár; director Beatrix Mátrai
Type: youth choir *Repertoire:* gregorian, old and new church music, classical, Hungarian and foreign folk music and spirituals *Perfs:* 25

Vándor Choir of Budapest
Budapesti Vándor Kórus
Füzfő utca 12, 1145 **Budapest** XIV
Tel: 1-363 4294
leader László Révész; artistic manager Elly Révész;
secretary Klára Perlstein
Repertoire: classical, contemporary, oratorios with symphony orchestras

Zoltán Kodály Cantemus Children's Choir
Kodály Zoltán Általános Iskola Cantemus kórusa
Luther u. 57, 4400 **Nyiregyháza**
Tel: 42-310 731 Fax: 42-310 731
E-Mail: cantemus@mail.matav.hu
choir leader Dénes Szabó
Type: children's *Comments:* Dénes Szabó leads also ProMusica Choir, Nyiregyháza; venue 200

ICELAND (+354)

Hallgrímskirkja Motet Choir
Mótettukór Hallgrímskirkju
Postbox 651, 121 **Reykjavík**
Tel: 510 1000 Fax: 510 1010
Internet: www.hallgrimskirkja.is
E-Mail: kirkjulist@simnet.is
director Hördur Áskelsson
Type: mixed church *Repertoire:* sacred music, ancient and modern *Size:* 60 *Perfs:* 20+ *Comments:* visiting address: Hallgrímskirkja, Skólavörduholt Reykjavík

Icelandic Opera Choir, The
Kor Islensku Operunnar
PO Box 1666, 121 **Reykjavik**
Tel: 552 7366 Fax: 552 5966
E-Mail: gardarc@centrum.is
conductor Gardar Cortes
Type: mixed *Repertoire:* opera, Icelandic music
Size: varies *Touring:* Canada, USA

Karlakórinn Fóstbræður
Nybylavejur 94, 200 **Kópavogi**
Tel: 564 1159/568 5206/896 5753 (mobile) Fax: 564 1159
contact/conductor Arni Hardarson
Type: Nordic/Icelandic *Repertoire:* mainly Nordic, Scandinavian classical, traditional works *Size:* 65-70 *Touring:* Europe, Scandinavia *Comments:* 1-2 productions per year; alternative address: 1092111 Langholtsvegur, 105 Reykjavik

Kársnesskórinn
c/o Thórunn Björnsdottir, Kópavogsbraut 18, 200 **Kópavogur**
Tel: 554 1567/1568/4548(summer) Fax: 564 4233
contact Thórunn Björnsdottir
Type: children's choir and youth choir (5 age groups)
Repertoire: Icelandic folk, modern and world *Size:* 250
Touring: Canada, Newfoundland

Langholt Church Chamber Choir, The
Kammerkór Langholtskirkju
Sólheimum 13, 104 **Reykjavík**
Tel: 520 1313 Fax: 520 1301
conductor Jón Stefánsson
Repertoire: church music of all kinds *Size:* 12

Langholt Church Youth Choir, The
Gradualekór Langholtskirkju
Sólheimum 13, 104 **Reykjavík**
Tel: 520 1300/13/894 1600 (mobile) Fax: 520 1301/24
Internet: Langholtskirkja.is/klang/
E-Mail: klang@kirkjan.is
conductor Jón Stefánsson
Repertoire: church music, a cappella, modern music
Size: 45 *Perfs:* 6-10 *Touring:* Canada

The Hamrahlid Choir
Hamrahlídarkórinn
Stórholt 41, 105 **Reykjavík**
Tel: 562 6239 Fax: 562 6239
conductor & founder Thorgerdur Ingólfsdóttir
Type: mixed youth choir (age 18-26) *Repertoire:* international and Icelandic ranging from the Middle Ages to the present day *Size:* 50-60 *Touring:* Europe *Comments:* the Hamrahlid Choir has stimulated many of Iceland's foremost composers to create music especially for the choir

The Langholt Church Choir
Kór Langholtskirkju
Sólheimum 13, 104 **Reykjavík**
Tel: 520 1300 Fax: 520 1324
Internet: langholtskirkja.is/klang/
E-Mail: klang@kirkjan.is
contact Jón Stefánsson
Repertoire: church music, oratoria *Size:* 85 *Perfs:* 4-6
Touring: Scandinavia

Voces Thules
c/o Sigurdur Halldórsson, Njálsgötu 75, 101 **Reykjavík**
Tel: 562 1028 Fax: 561 5889
E-Mail: siha@ismennt.is
contact Sigurdur Halldórsson
Type: male voice ensemble (a cappella & instr.)
Repertoire: Icelandic and other European medieval, renaissance & 20th C music *Size:* 5-8 *Perfs:* 10-15
Touring: national, international

Vox feminae
Ægisgata 7, 121 **Reykjavík**
Tel: 562 6460 Fax: 562 6468
Type: women's choir *Repertoire:* mostly church music, and early music *Size:* 35

Women's Choir of Reykjavík
Kvennakór Reykjavíkur
Skogarhild 20, 125 **Reykjavík**
Tel: 562 6460 Fax: 562 6468
music director Sigrún Thorgeirsdóttir (554 0688)
Type: women's choir, a cappella, piano and orchestral
Repertoire: whole spectrum of womens' choir music
Size: 120 *Touring:* national, international

IRELAND Republic of (+353)

ANÚNA
Box 4468, Churchtown, **Dublin** 14
Tel: 1-283 5533 Fax: 1-283 5533
Internet: www.anuna.ie
E-Mail: info@anuna.ie
director and founder Michael McGlynn
Type: mixed *Repertoire:* exploration of Celtic music from ancient to modern times, a cappella/instrumental *Size:* 14-17 *Touring:* national & international *Comments:* 7 CDs released

Cantairi Béal Atha h-Amhnais
c/o Pauline Mc Garry, Devlis, **Ballyhaunis (Co. Mayo)**
Tel: 907-30170 Fax: 907-730 679
musical director Pauline Mc Garry
Type: mixed *Repertoire:* madrigals, church music, secular music *Size:* 25 *Perfs:* 4-5 *Touring:* Ireland
Comments: winners of several internationally renowne- choral Festivals, winners of European Music Year Award

Cantairí Óga Átha Cliath
150 Páirc Chúlambair, **Dublin** 16
Tel: 1-494 6004
conductor/musical director Brian Ó Dubhghaill
Type: a cappella *Repertoire:* 16th century to contemporary, specialising in 20th century composers *Size:* 40 *Perfs:* 1-2 a month *Touring:* Europe *Comments:* international prizewinners

Cois Cladaigh Chamber Choir
Oranswell, **Galway (Co. Galway)**
Tel: 91-756 812/524 185
Fax: 91-756 888
E-Mail: aquafact@iol.ie
conductor Dr. Brendan O'Connor
Type: chamber choir, mixed, mostly a cappella
Repertoire: 16th century and contemporary; Irish choral repertoire *Size:* 20 *Perfs:* 10 *Touring:* Norway, France
Comments: recording CDs of renaissance and contemporary spiritual and secular choral music

Galway Baroque Singers
14 Montrose House, **Whitestrand (Co. Galway)**
Tel: 88-691 1460
musical director Audrey Corbett;
secretary Joan Armitage
Type: mixed, a cappella and with orchestra or organ *Repertoire:* standard choral repertoire *Size:* 70-75 *Perfs:* 4-6

Holy Rosary College Choir
Holy Rosary College, **Mountbellew (Co. Galway)**
Tel: 905-79222 Fax: 905-79438
Internet: www.iol.ie/hrc
E-Mail: hrc@iol.ie
conductor Carmel Vesey
Type: mixed; 3 part SAA; with accompaniment *Repertoire:* 1800-1950; classical and traditional *Size:* 45 *Comments:* school choir

Irish Youth Choir
c/o Assoc. of Irish Choirs, Drinan St., **Cork**
Tel: 2-131 2296 Fax: 2-196 2457
E-Mail: cnc@iol.ie
administrator Barbara Heas; conductor Geoffrey Spratt
Type: mixed voice ages 17-29 *Repertoire:* large scale choral works *Size:* 120 *Perfs:* 3 *Touring:* Ireland, Scotland

Lindsay Singers, The
87 Lindsay Rd.,
Dublin 9
Tel: 1-830 4320
director Ethna Barror
Type: a cappella *Repertoire:* religious, classical, light classical, musical, comedies *Size:* 30 *Perfs:* 10 *Touring:* UK *Comments:* the choir won the Nomination Choir of the Year 1996, 97 & 98 (at the Cork International Festival), and the Henry Schutz Prize for 1998

National Chamber Choir
Dublin City University, Glasnevin, **Dublin** 9
Tel: 1-704 5665 Fax: 1-704 5603
Internet: www.dcu.ie/chamber/index.html
E-Mail: national.chamber.choir@dcu.ie
manager Karina Lundström; artistic director Colin Mawby; administrative assistant Gerard Keenan; education officer/chorus master David Darcy
Type: professional chamber choir *Repertoire:* chamber music (early, baroque, contemporary) *Size:* 17 *Perfs:* 40-50 *Comments:* run composition workshops in schools; commission children's operas for primary schools; have large contract with RTE (National Broadcasting Co.) also contract with Opera Ireland for 2 opera seasons per annum; CDs available

RTE Philharmonic Choir
Dannybrook, **Dublin** 4
Tel: 1-208 4518
Fax: 1-208 2511
Internet: www.rte.ie
directorof music Niall Doyle;
concerts manager Claire Meehan
Type: philharmonic choir *Repertoire:* wide, philharmonic concerts *Perfs:* 5 *Touring:* Ireland *Comments:* also RTE Cor Na Nóg (Children's Choir)

ITALY (+39)

Academia di Musica e Canto Corale di Trieste
Via Torino 22, 34123 **Trieste**
Tel: 040-312 513 Fax: 040-312 513
president Maria Susovsky; director chamber choir & youth choir Cristina Semeraro
Type: a cappella and with orchestra; 3 choirs: children's (Piccoli Cantori della Cita' di Trieste), youth (Coro Giovanile della Citta' di Trieste), chamber (Coro da Camera) *Repertoire:* from madrigals to contemporary music *Size:* 3 choirs: 40, 25, 9 *Touring:* national, international

Almagesto Vocale
Via Kennedy no.5, 20060 **Ornago (MI)**
Tel: 039-601 0150 Fax: 039-601 0121
artistic director Bruno Raffaele Foti
Type: a cappella and with orchestra *Repertoire:* from late renaissance to early baroque (Holy Latin music) and up to 18th C *Size:* 22-24 *Perfs:* 10
Comments: see Early Music

Associazione Corale Luigi Tonini Bossi
Via F. Cavallotti 40, 60019 **Senigallia (AN)**
Tel: 071-792 0301 (PR)/63926 (director)
Fax: 071-668 009
Internet: www.netitalia.com/corale
E-Mail: corale@indi.it
artistic director Antonella Vento; presidente Daniela Polonari; direttore del coro M° Massimo d'Ignazio
Type: a cappella and with orchestra *Repertoire:* classical to contemporary, sacred and secular music, jazz *Size:* 50 *Perfs:* 20 *Touring:* France, Germany, Hungary, Poland

Associazione Corale Vox Julia
Via Brigate Partigiane 11/B,
34077 **Ronchi dei Legionari (GO)**
Tel: 0481-778 424 Fax: 0481-710 113
artistic director Maestra Denise Marcuzzi;
president Cristiana Pisano
Type: a cappella, mixed *Repertoire:* medieval to contemporary *Size:* 30 *Perfs:* 20 *Touring:* Italy *Comments:* masterclasses and seminars for choral conducting and singing

Cantori Della Resurrezione
Via Ariosto 7, 07046 **Porto Torres (SS)**
Tel: 079-514 261
Fax: 079-514 261
direttore M° Antonio Sanna; presidente Marco Ligas
Type: 4 choirs: 1 gregoriano; 1 female; 1 madrigalistico; 1 mixed (male and female) *Repertoire:* gregorian and medieval music, renaissance and contemporary *Size:* 50 *Perfs:* 35 *Touring:* Switzerland, Italy, France Czech Republic

Cantori di Santomìo
Via Cardinale de Lai no.2, 36034 **Malo (VI)**
Tel: 0445-602 221/404 278/671 777
Fax: 0445-602 221
Internet: www.novast.it/cantori
E-Mail: cantori@novast.it
director Nicola Sella; president Giorgio Penzo
Type: a cappella, mixed *Repertoire:* sacred and secular, Gregorian chant to contemporary vocal music and baroque music with instruments *Size:* 35 *Perfs:* 30 *Comments:* winners of male voices prize in the Arezzo Competition various times and winners of mixed voices at Tours Competition in France 1988

Capella Ducale Venetia (Venice)
via Emanuele Filiberto 4, 20052 **Monza**
Tel: 744 703 Fax: 744 797
Internet: www.askesis.it/ricmus
E-Mail: gc.ricercar@askesis.it
general manager Gabriella Castelli;
artistic director Livio Picotti
Type: vocal *Repertoire:* renaissance and baroque repertoire performed in St Mark Venice for the Doge
Size: 7-40 *Perfs:* 30 *Touring:* Europe, Israel
Comments: see also Early Music

Collegium Vocale et Instrumentale Nova Ars Cantandi
Via Carini 28/G, 29100 **Piacenza**
Tel: 0523-490 278/347-824 4013 (mobile)
Fax: 0523-490 278
director/president Giovanni Acciai
Type: vocal ensemble *Repertoire:* madrigals, secular, contemporary *Size:* 3-12 *Perfs:* 20 *Touring:* Netherlands *Comments:* CDs available

Complesso Vocale di Nuoro
Via della Magnolie, Lotto 80, 08100 **Nuoro**
Tel: 0784-38447
Fax: 0784-38447
E-Mail: cvocale@hotmail.com
director Franca Floris; president Luigi Pisano
Type: a cappella and with orchestra *Repertoire:* from Gregorian chant to contemporary *Size:* 4-40 *Perfs:* 25

Corale Citta di Parma
Vicolo Delle Asse 5, 43100 **Parma**
Tel: 0521-234 167 (evenings) Fax: 0521-270 816
direttore artistico e M° delle voci miste e cameristiche Matteo Pagliari (tel: 0521-831 956, fax: 0521-289 731); M° delle voci bianche Francesco Pedrini (tel: 0521-251 362); presidente Mario Barantani
Type: a cappella and with orchestra *Repertoire:* from baroque to contemporary, renaissance *Size:* mixed: 45; youth: varies; treble voices: varies *Comments:* collaborates with Orchestra Toscanini (Parma)

Corale Polifonica di Sommariva Bosco
Via Cavour 72, 12048 **Sommariva Bosco (CN)**
Tel: 0172-54974/493 875 Fax: 0172-54974
Internet: www.geocities.com/vienna/strasse6450
E-Mail: g.chiavazza@areacom.it
artistic director Claudio Chiavazza;
presidente Paolo Bulgarini
Type: mixed, a cappella *Repertoire:* from Gregorian chant to contemporary vocal music *Size:* 35 *Perfs:* 15-20 *Touring:* Italy *Comments:* the choir sometimes performs with the RAI orchestra of Turin under the name of Coro Filarmonico Ruggero Maghini which is an ensemble of 5 choirs; also works closely with Gli Affetti Musicali (see Early Music)

Coro Antonio Illersberg
Casella Postale 2077, Opicina, 34016 **Trieste**
Tel: 040-213 093
Fax: 040-213 093
director Tullio Riccobon; president Bruno Dapretto
Type: a cappella, mens' choir *Repertoire:* sacred & secular *Size:* 22 *Perfs:* 10 *Touring:* Portugal, Australia

Coro Citta di Forlí
Corso Garibaldi 96, 47100 **Forlí**
Tel: 0543-30045
Fax: 0543-30045
Internet: www.fcv.it/forli/cultura/coroforli
E-Mail: coro@fcv.it
director Nella Servadei Cioja
Type: a cappella *Repertoire:* popular choral from Romagna, folk, classic poliphony *Size:* 30 *Perfs:* 25 *Touring:* Argentina

Coro dell' Orchestra Sinfonica di Milano Giuseppe Verdi
Corso San Gottardo, angolo via Torricelli,
20136 **Milano**
Tel: 2-8901 3121 Fax: 2-7209 9819
Internet: www.orchestrasinfonica.milano.it
E-Mail: info@orchestrasinfonica.milano.it
general manager Luigi Corbani; artistic secretary Sievia Lomazzi; press office Gianni Testa;
director of choir Romano Gandolf
Repertoire: from classical to contemporary *Size:* 115 *Perfs:* 30 *Comments:* see also Orchestras; Orchestra Sinfonica di Milano Giuseppe Verdi;
venues:Auditorium di Milano

Coro Filarmonico di Pesaro
Strada Panoramica Ardizio, 95, 61100 **Pesaro**
Tel: 0721-55468/335-635 9499 (mobile) Fax: 0721-55468
artistic director Roberto Renili; president Flavio Angelini; vice president Giuseppina Mancinelli;
secretary Milena Renili
Type: mixed *Repertoire:* opera with orchestra, symphonic, oratoria, sacred *Size:* 60 *Perfs:* 30 *Touring:* Italy, Germany

Coro Jubilate
Via Milano, 3, 20025 **Legnano (MI)**
Tel: 0331-594 504/454 707 Fax: 0331-597 433
Internet: www.nemo.it/guests/jubilate/default.htm
E-Mail: amj@mail.nemo.it
director Paolo Alli; presidente Carlo Leonardi
Repertoire: secular music, gregorian chant, folk, Italian and foreign composers of 20th century *Size:* 45 *Comments:* CDs available; see also Promoters, Festivals

Coro Musica Antiqua
Via Trevi 43, 05100 **Terni**
Tel: 0744-59751 Fax: 0744-59751
E-Mail: musicantiqua@seinet.it
direttore Stefania Trabalza
Type: a cappella and with orchestra, mixed *Repertoire:* madrigals and opera *Size:* 41 *Perfs:* 25 *Touring:* Bulgaria

Coro Polifonico San Paolo di Reggio Calabria
Associazione Culturale, Casella Postale 206,
89100 **Reggio Calabria**
Tel: 0965-641 189 Fax: 0965-893 899
E-Mail: acalaberz@vol.iunet.it
artistic director Carmen Cantarella(tel: 0965-47621); president Franco Amoroso (tel: 0965-54626/302 739); consigliere amministrativo Giuseppe Laganà (mobile: +39 328-617 4290)
Type: a cappella, mixed, polyphonic *Repertoire:* classical, folkloric, spirituals *Size:* 40-45 *Perfs:* 50 *Touring:* Europe, Italy *Comments:* also Children's choir (Piccolo Coro San Paolo) 20 children 6-13 years old

Coro Polofonico Turritano
Via Sassari 65, Casella Postale 159, **Porto Torres (SS)**
Tel: 079-512 690 Fax: 079-512 690
E-Mail: coroturr@rentec.net
conductor Luca Sannai (address: via Pacinotti 1ᴧ Trav. 07046 Porto Torres (SS) tel: +39 079-501 821; presidente Graziano Sannai
Type: mixed, a cappella *Repertoire:* renaissance and baroque poliphony, romantic school, contemporary authors, Sardinian folk *Size:* 45 *Perfs:* 30 *Touring:* Italy, Germany, Greece *Comments:* 1st prize winners of 6 competitions in Arezzo, Gorizia,Tolosa (Spain); CD available; organisers of International Festival Voci D'Europe (Sept, annual)

Coro Rosetum
Via Pisanello no. 1, 20146 **Milano**
Tel: 02-4870 7203/4009 2195
Fax: 02-4009 2195
Internet: www.rosetum.it
E-Mail: info@rosetum.it
director Umberto Balestrini; orchestra chairman Adriano Bassi
Type: mixed, with orchestra *Repertoire:* sacred, secular and lyric *Size:* 80 *Perfs:* 15 *Touring:* Switzerland

Ensemble Sanfelice
Piazza san Felice 5, 50125 **Firenze**
Tel: 055-741 527
Fax: 055-741 527
E-Mail: fede@fol.it
conductor Federico Bardazzi;
assistant Eleonora Tassinari
Type: mainly voices with continuo and few instruments, chamber orchestra; alway period instruments
Repertoire: sacred middle age, baroque and contemporary music *Size:* 8 singers, 3 permanent players, 8-12 singers are not *Perfs:* 40 *Touring:* Italy, Switzerland, Germany, Poland, Germany, Sweden *Comments:* recordings with Planet Sound; see also Early Music

Ensemble Vocale Polivox di Trieste
Via dell'Eremo 148, 34142 **Trieste**
Tel: 040-415 867
Fax: 040-415 867
artistic director Sandro Marigonda;
president Giuliano Goruppi
Type: a cappella *Repertoire:* renaissance, traditional music, pop music *Size:* 6 *Perfs:* 20

Gruppo Corale Citta' di Sasso Ferrato
Via Pergolesi 4, 60041 **Sasso Ferrao (AN)**
Tel: 0732-21811 (director)/959 144 (presidente)
Fax: 0732-9467
direttore artistico M° marco Agostinelli;
presidente Giuseppe Zatti
Type: a cappella – vocal and instrumental *Repertoire:* polyphonic, sacred and secular from the 13th-20th C *Size:* 25 *Perfs:* 10 *Comments:* the choir organises a local festival of polyphonic music called 'A L'Entrada Del Temps Clar'

Gruppo di Canto Ambrosiano
Viale Gorizia 5, 20144 **Milano**
Tel: 02-8940 4670 Fax: 02-7202 2419
artistic director/president Luigi Benedetti
Type: a cappella *Repertoire:* sacred, medieval, Gregorian chants, Ambrosian chants *Size:* 12 *Perfs:* 10-15 *Touring:* Germany, Greece *Comments:* CD's available

Gruppo Polifonico Citta di Rovigo
Via Bruno Buozzi 71, 45100 **Rouigo**
Tel: 0425-25948 (secretary)/421 884 Fax: 0425-421 884
artistic director Vittorio Zanon;
president Franco Veronese
Type: mixed, and with orchestra, a cappella *Repertoire:* Gregorian chant, renaissance, baroque, sacred, secular, contemporary, romantic *Size:* 5-35 *Perfs:* 20 *Touring:* Hungary, Germany *Comments:* winners of 1st prizes at Arezzo Int. Competition

Gruppo Vocale Amici Cantores
Via P. Diacono 3, 20133 **Milano**
Tel: 02-236 3762 Fax: 02-236 3762
E-Mail: st.torelli@agora.stm.it
Type: a cappella *Repertoire:* renaissance, early Italian baroque *Size:* 12 *Perfs:* 6 *Comments:* recordings available (Edizioni Paoline, Roma)

Gruppo Vocale dell'Accademia Jaufré Rudel
Calle dei Macellai 2, 34072 **Gradisca**
Tel: 0481-531 326 Fax: 0481-531 326
Internet: www.accademia.it
E-Mail: dramsam@mail.seta.it
direttore Giuseppe Paolo Cecere;
presidente dott. Fabio Cavalli
Repertoire: medieval music *Size:* 4-8 *Perfs:* 30-40
Comments: work closely with Dramsam; see Promoters and Early Music

Gruppo Vocale Stirps Jesse
Via P. Diacono 3, c/o Amici Cantores, 20133 **Milano**
Tel: 02-3300 6047 Fax: 02-3300 5119
E-Mail: st.torelli@agora-stm.it
directors Enrico De Capitani, Stefano Torelli
Type: a cappella *Repertoire:* Gregorian chant/medieval (11th-13th C.) *Size:* 3-12 *Perfs:* 10 *Comments:* recordings available (Edizioni Paoline, Roma – Amadeus, Milano); agent: Alma Music Project, tel: 02-204 6930 fax: 02-2951 5644

Gruppo Vocale Strumentale Lieder Ensemble
via Pellegrino Matteucci 5, 00154 **Roma**
Tel: 06-5728 5318/0335 613 2598 (mobile)
Fax: 06-5728 5318
director/president Fausto Di Cesare
Type: choir + orchestra *Repertoire:* classical, contemporary, romantic, chamber music *Size:* 2-25 *Perfs:* 15
Comments: they are also an instrumental group playing music from Bach onwards

I Mastri Fini
Via Guerrazzi 12, 21052 **Busto Arsizio (VA)**
Tel: 0331-639 576 Fax: 0331-623 204
artistic director Paolo Fossati;
president Riccardo Armussi
Type: a cappella, mixed choir *Repertoire:* from renaissance to contemporary *Size:* 25 *Perfs:* 10

Madrigalisti di Magliano in Toscana, I
piazza dei Frantoi no.9, 58051 **Magliano in Toscana (GR)**
Tel: 0564-592 046 (president)/870 042 (director) Fax: 0564-870 042
director Walter Marzilli; president Gregori M. Teresa
Type: a cappella, mixed *Repertoire:* sacred, secular, polyphonic from 16th century – today *Size:* 30 *Perfs:* 15-20 *Touring:* Germany

Nova Cantica
Via Fontana 3, 32035 **Santa Giustina (BL)**
Tel: 0437-859 296 Fax: 0437-859 296
direttore artistico Maria Silvia Roveri
Type: vocal and instrumental *Repertoire:* medieval *Size:* 4-10 *Touring:* Italy

Nova Cantica – Coro Voci Bianche
Via Mur di Cadola 10, 32100 **Belluno**
Tel: 0437-932 251 Fax: 0437-932 251
presidente Tiziana Savasta; vice presidente Silvano Tormen; direttore artistico e del coro Maria Silvia Roveri; ufficio stampa Erica Moret
Type: children's choir/boys' choir *Repertoire:* sacred and secular music from the Renaissance to today *Size:* 25 *Perfs:* 10 *Touring:* Italy

Schola Cantorum del Santuario di Rho
Pzza del Santuario, Corso Europa, 20017 **Rho**
Tel: 02-931 6004
artistic director Achille Nava; president Luciano Maiano
Type: a cappella and with orchestra *Repertoire:* from Gregorian chant to contemporary music *Size:* 65 *Perfs:* 20

Schola Gregoriana di Cremona
Via Villa Glori 18, 26100 **Cremona**
Tel: 0372-413 078
Fax: 0372-21256
direttore artistico Antonella Soana;
presidente Alda Mottinelli de Giuli
Type: only female voices *Repertoire:* Gregorian chant *Size:* 10 *Perfs:* 20 *Touring:* Italy *Comments:* see also Early Music

Schola Gregoriana Mediolanensis
Via Masotto 30, 20133 **Milano**
Tel: 02-7010 0338 (office)/4245 (home)
Fax: 02-7010 0338/4245
Internet: www.xfiles.it./cantogregoriano
director Giovanni Vianini
Type: a cappella *Repertoire:* medieval, gregorian and ambrosian chant *Size:* 30 (15 female, 15 male) *Perfs:* 40 *Touring:* Italy *Comments:* 15 CD's available; organise free introductory courses to Gregorian chant

Società Corale E. Capetti
Via Roma 1, 52027 **San Giovanni Valdarno (AR)**
Tel: 055-940 468/912 0340
artistic director Don Giorgio Martellini; president Paolo Bonci; vice-artistic director Franco Berti
Type: a cappella *Repertoire:* medieval to 20th century; folkloric *Size:* 38 *Perfs:* 10-15 + religious functions

Solisti del Madrigale
Via Carini 28/G, 29100 **Piacenza**
Tel: 0523-490 278/347-824 4013/339-263 4026
Fax: 0523-490 278
director/president Giovanni Acciai
Type: vocal ensemble *Repertoire:* madrigals, secular, contemporary *Size:* 5 *Perfs:* 25 *Touring:* Australia

LATVIA (+371)

Chamber Choir Sacrum
Kamerkoris Sacrum
Rigas 88-3, 2160 **Saulkrasti**
Tel: 947-633 3125 (mobile) Fax: 7-055 481
conductor Andris Veismanis
Repertoire: renaissance, baroque

Chamber Choir Versija
Kamerkoris Versija
Blaumana iela 16/18 – 1, 1011 **Riga**
Tel: 7-285 777 Fax: 7-860 263
managing director Silvija Greste;
artistic director Vita Timermane
Type: mixed choir, a cappella, orchestra *Size:* 22 (up to 40) *Touring:* worldwide

Choir of the Latvian National Opera
Latvijas Nacionalas operas koris
3 Aspazijas Blvd., 1050 **Riga**
Tel: 7-223 436 Fax: 7-228 930
E-Mail: mail@opera.lv
artistic director and chief conductor Andris Veismanis
Comments: second E-mail: admin@opera.lv

Jazeps Medins Music School Boys Choir
Jazepa Medina muzikas skolas zenu koris
Miera iela 74 – 32, 1013 **Riga**
Tel: 7-326 900/332 058 (school)
Fax: 7-821 116
managing director Astrida Kronberga;
artistic director Romans Vanags

Latvian Radio Choir
Latvijas Radio koris
Doma laukums 8, 1050 **Riga**
Tel: 2-206 671 Fax: 7-213 488
E-Mail: guntars.kirsis@radio.org.lv
artistic director and principal conductor Sigvards Klava;
director Guntars Kirsis

Riga Chamber Choir AVE SOL
Rigas Kamerkoris AVE SOL
Citadeles 7, 1010 **Riga**
Tel: 7-287 302
Fax: 7-828 484
Internet: muza.lv/choirs/avesol
E-Mail: as@mail.bkc.lv
managing director Guntars Felsbergs;
artistic director Imants Kokars

Riga Dome Boys' Choir
Rigas Doma zenu koris
Kalnciema St 10/12, 1048 **Riga**
Tel: 7-611 950/925 4979 (mobile)
Fax: 7-246 9149
E-Mail: rdks@rdks.lv
managing director Ingrida Bondare; artistic director Janis Erenstreits; principal conductor Martins Klisans

State Academic Choir Latvia
Valsts akademiskais koris Latvija
Kalku 11a, 1050 **Riga**
Tel: 7-223 839 Fax: 7-223 839
conductor Maris Sirmais; director Maris Oslejs
Repertoire: orientated towards large forms of vocal-instrumental music symphonies, oratorios, also a capella pieces and compositions for choir and organ *Size:* 70 singers *Comments:*
argest professional choir in Latvia

Women's Choir Dzintars
Sieviesu Koris Dzintars
Kalku 11a, 1050 **Riga**
Tel: 7-216 806/332 426
music director Ausma Derkevica

LITHUANIA (+370)

Boys Choir Azuoliukas
Berniuku ir Jaunuoliu Choras Azuoliukas
Vilniaus 39/6, 2600 **Vilnius**
Tel: 2-623 621 Fax: 2-221 456
artistic director Vytautas Miskinis
Comments: Laiskams: PO Box 1114, 2001 Vilnius

Chamber Choir Cantemus
Kamerinis Choras Cantemus
Justiniskiu 31-9, 2056 **Vilnius**
Tel: 2-410 822
chief conductor Laurynas Vakaris Lopas

Chamber Choir of the Lithuanian Music Academy
Lietuvos Muzikos Akademijos Kamerinis Choras
Lietuvos Muzikos Akademija, Gedimino 42, 2001 **Vilnius**
Tel: 2-610 494 Fax: 2-220 093
chief conductor Tadas Sumskas

Chamber Choir Russian Classic
Kamerinis choras Rusu klasika
Zygimantu 6, 2600 **Vilnius**
Tel: 2-313 651 Fax: 2-313 651
artistic director Tatjana Rinkeviciene

Choir Jauna Muzika
Choras Jonna Muzika
PO Box 2659, 2009 **Vilnius**
Tel: 2-226 679 Fax: 2-226 679
Internet: www.jaunamuzika.lt
E-Mail: janna.muzika@post.omnitel.net
director Algis Gurevicius;
chief conductor Vaclovas Augustinas

Girls Choir Liepaites
Mergaiciu ir Merginu Choras Liepaites
M. Putino 5, 2009 **Vilnius**
Tel: 2-612 865 Fax: 2-612 865
chief conductor Liucija Palinauskaite

Kaunas State Choir
Kauno Valstybinis Choras
L. Sapiegos 5, 3000 **Kaunas**
Tel: 7-203 746 Fax: 7-229 208
E-Mail: kau.fil@kaunas.omnitel.net
artistic director Petras Bingelis

Lithuanian Choir of the Blind Vilnius
Lietuvos akluju choras Vilnius
Skroblu 19, 2015 **Vilnius**
Tel: 2-636 069
chief conductor Jurijus Kalcas

Siauliai State Chamber Choir Polifonija
Siauliu Valstybinis Kamerinis Choras Polifonija
Ausros al. 15, 5400 **Siauliai**
Tel: 14-39624 Fax: 14-39624
artistic director Sigitas Vaiciulionis

State Song and Dance Company Lietuva
Valstybinis dainu ir sokiu ansamblis Lietuva
Vytenio 50, 2600 **Vilnius**
Tel: 2-239 865 Fax: 2-239 860
artistic director Pranciskus Budrius

Vilnius Municipality Chamber Choir Jauna Muzika
Vilniaus miesto Savivaldybes Kamerinis Choras Jauna Muzika
J. Basanaviciaus 23-14, 2009 **Vilnius**
Tel: 2-227 784
Fax: 2-226 679
artistic director Algis Gurevicius;
chief conductor Vaclovas Augustinas

Vilnius Teachers House Chamber Choir Salutaris
Vilniaus Mokytoju Namu Kamerinis Choras Salutaris
Ausros vartu 5, 2001 **Vilnius**
Tel: 2-626 802 Fax: 2-622 859
chief conductor Martynas Staskus

Youth Chamber Choir Aidija
Jaunimo Kamerinis Choras Aidija
Valanciaus 1-2, 2009 **Vilnius**
Tel: 2-650 13
Fax: 2-457 448
artistic director and conductor Romualdas Grazinis

MOLDOVA (+373)

Academic Choir DOINA
78 Mitropolit Varlaam str, 2012 **Chisinau**
Tel: 2-233 509/224 016 Fax: 2-238 257
artistic director Veronica Garstea

Choir of National Radio-Television
1 Miorita str , 2072 **Chisinau**
Tel: 2-721 096 Fax: 2-238 257
artistic director Valentin Budilevschi

Choir Renesans of the Institute of Arts of Moldova
111 Mateevici str, 2001 **Chisinau**
Tel: 2-238 258 Fax: 2-238 257
artistic director Teodor Zgureanu

Musical Feast
21 Pushkin str , 2012 **Chisinau**
Tel: 2-238 258 Fax: 2-238 257
artistic director Eugenia Enache

NETHERLANDS (+31)

Amersfoorts Mannenkoor
Hellestraat 7 B, 3811 LK **Amersfoort**
Tel: 33-461 3019
secretary M Meester; director Marius Schouten; chairman J. Kaspers
Type: male voice choir *Repertoire:* musical 17th-19thC, several centuries and composers *Size:* 47 *Perfs:* 10-11 *Comments:* a CD available

Amsterdam Baroque Orchestra and Choir
PO Box 1163, 1400 BD **Bussum**
Tel: 35-692 6000
Fax: 35-692 6001
Internet: www.tonkoopman.nl
E-Mail: cdeklerk@abo.rem.nl
managing director Franco Panozzo; office manager Cecilia Deklerk; conductor Ton Koopman
Type: mixed baroque choir *Repertoire:* baroque (especially Bach) *Size:* 30 (+ 30 orchestra) *Perfs:* 40-50 *Touring:* worldwide *Comments:* second address: Franco Panozzo, Artists Management, Via Valverde 32, 37122 Verona, Italy, Tel: +39 045-801 4041, Fax: +39 045-801 4980; touring company; see also Orchestras and Early Music

Beeker Liedertafel
PO Box 14, 6190 AA **Beek**
Tel: 43-361 9776 Fax: 43-367 0932
E-Mail: a.vanderarend@zw.unimaas.nl
director D. Ritten; president H. Pinxt; vice-president A. H. G. Schlenter; secretary A.J.G. van der Arend
Type: male *Repertoire:* classical, operetta, musical *Size:* 80 *Perfs:* 15 *Touring:* Italy *Comments:* founded 1889

Boxmeers Vocal Ensemble
Sweelinck 128, 5831 KV **Boxmeer**
Tel: 485-574 988 Fax: 485-574 988
director G. A. Brand; secretary H. J. A. Bruckwilder
Type: male *Repertoire:* international *Size:* 40 *Perfs:* 5 *Touring:* international *Comments:* several recordings available

Cappella Palestrina
Nazarethstre 3A, 3061 KN **Rotterdam**
Tel: 10-452 3638
Fax: 10-452 3638
conductor Maarten Michielsen
Type: a cappella, mixed *Repertoire:* late 16th century Italian repertoire and Dutch composers who worked in Italy in the 16th century *Size:* 16 *Perfs:* 40-50 *Comments:* 2 recordings with Erasmus label

Cappella Pratensis
Bisschop Zwijsenstraat 5,
5038 VA **Tilburg**
Tel: 13-535 7750
Fax: 13-536 8580
manager Ludy Vrydag; artistic director Dr Rebecca Stewart; management assistant Ella Hermans
Type: a cappella, mixed *Repertoire:* renaissance Flemish and French composers *Size:* 8-11 *Perfs:* 40 *Touring:* Central Europe, US *Comments:* several recordings available

Christelijk Residentie Mannenkoor
Van Boetzelaerlaan 70, 2581 AL **Den Haag**
Tel: 70-354 8855 Fax: 70-354 8855
Internet: www.hacohxs40.nl
E-Mail: b.terhaar.wxs.nl
conductor Aad Van Der Hoeven; organist Aarnoud de Groen
Type: male *Repertoire:* from classical and sacred to popular *Size:* 200 *Perfs:* 10 annually *Touring:* Germany, Luxemburg, Southern Netherlands

De Troubadours
Haarspithoek 63, 7546 KH **Enschede**
Tel: 53-478 3583
E-Mail: h.boers@inter.nl.net
contact H Boers
Type: male, a cappella *Repertoire:* from renaissance to modern *Size:* 18 *Perfs:* 8 *Touring:* Netherlands

Fortissimo
Dunanp Str 26, 4624 XD **Bergen op Zoom**
Tel: 164-253 691
director Peter Priem; secretary A. Schuureng
Type: male *Repertoire:* modern, 20th century *Size:* 32 *Touring:* European tour every 2/3 years, next planned for 2001 *Comments:* often commission Dutch composers

Geleens Mannenkoor Mignon
Dr. Schaepmanstr. 37, 6162 XL **Geleen**
Tel: 46-474 8819
contact F. J. J. Storcken; chairman H. B. Ketelslegees; treasurer J. M. J. Spengee; public relations J. J. Korevaar; conductor J. M. Gerits
Type: male *Repertoire:* opera, operetta, musicals, ritual songs *Size:* 130 *Perfs:* 14 annually

Halsterens Mannenkoor
Schelpstr. 4, 4661 EM **Halsteren**
Tel: 164-684 639
contact M. J. H. Geers
Type: male, a cappella *Repertoire:* all *Size:* 33 *Perfs:* 10-15 *Touring:* Netherlands

Koninklijk Heerlens Mannenkoor St. Pancratius
Jan Maenenstr. 6, 6412 EE **Heerlen**
Tel: 45-572 4488
contact P.J.J. van Els
Type: male, piano accompaniment *Repertoire:* standard choral repertoire – classical, modern *Size:* 75 *Perfs:* 20 *Touring:* Netherlands

Koninklijk Mannenkoor Die Haghe Sanghers
Blauwroodlaan 41, 2718 JN **Zoetermeer**
Tel: 79-361 3472 Fax: 70-333 3272
secretary P.W. M. van Veen; director R. Verhoett
Type: male, a cappella *Repertoire:* 15th-20th C. *Size:* 100 *Perfs:* 5-20 *Touring:* Netherlands

Koninklijk Mannenkoor Gruno Groningen
Helmerdeik 54, 9765 JE **Paterswold**
Tel: 50-309 1722
contact Richard Velthoven
Type: male *Size:* 45 *Touring:* Netherlands

Koninklijk Schiedams Mannenkoor Orpheus
Vismarkt 1, 3111 BN **Schiedam**
Tel: 10-426 7067
director Pim Overduin; secretary Mevr. E. Stouthandel-de Vogel; president T. J. van Boerum
Type: male, a cappella, sometimes instrumental *Repertoire:* standard choral repertoire (all languages) *Size:* 66 *Perfs:* 5-7 *Touring:* Netherlands, England, France *Comments:* CD with Euro Sound; Royal Male Choir

Koninklijke Zangvereeniging Nijmegen Mannenkoor
Borneo Str 13, 6524 LA **Nijmegen**
Tel: 24-322 2142 Fax: 24-388 8941
contact Mr. Heshusius
Type: male *Repertoire:* classical to contemporary *Size:* 130-140 *Perfs:* 10-12 *Touring:* Netherlands, France, Germany, UK

Koninklijke Zangvereeniging Rotte's Mannenkoor
Vondellaan 26,
2902 AS **Capelle Aan Den Ijssel**
Tel: 10-284 7791
Internet: www.pietjebell.kw.nl/for_fun/guest/rottes
E-Mail: gboerma@xs4all.nl
director R. Verhoeff; secretary G. J. M. Boerma
Type: male choir, mainly a cappella *Repertoire:* standard choral repertoire (in various languages- Latin, Russian, Czech, English etc.) *Size:* 73 *Perfs:* 10-15 *Touring:* year 2000 (150th anniversary) world tour *Comments:* 3 CDs available

Koninklijke Zangvereeniging Venlona
PO Box 405, 5900 AK **Venlo**
Tel: 77-351 8841
director & choir master H. E. G. J. Zeelen; secretary B. Hafmans
Type: male *Repertoire:* classical *Size:* 104 *Perfs:* 120 *Touring:* Germany, Italy, Austria

Koor Nederlandse Opera
Waterlooplein 22, 1011 PG **Amsterdam**
Tel: 20-551 8922/625 5455 (box office)
Fax: 20-551 8311
E-Mail: info@nederlandse-opera.nl
chorus manager Bridget Kievits; choir master Winfried Maczewski
Type: opera choir *Repertoire:* opera *Size:* 60 *Perfs:* 100 *Comments:* almost exclusively opera

Koor van de Nederlandse Bachvereniging
Postbus 12017, 3501 AA **Utrecht**
Tel: 30-252 4010/251 3413 (box office)
Fax: 30-251 1639
managing director Maria Hansen; artistic director/principal conductor Jos van Veldhoven; production Chris van de Ven
Type: a cappella and with orchestra *Repertoire:* 17th,18th century *Size:* 20 *Perfs:* 30+ *Comments:* CD recordings with Gustav Leonhardt and Ton Koopman, J.S.Bach – St Matthew Passion with Jos van Veldhoven

La Bonne Esperance Koninklijk Mannenkoor
Ranonkelpad 4, 5582 AE **Waalre**
Tel: 40-221 6573
director F. v.d. Goor Pzn
Type: male *Repertoire:* classical, modern, folk, opera *Size:* 120 *Perfs:* 10-12 *Touring:* Belgium, Germany, Austria, Hungary, France, Poland

Lambardi Mannenkoor
Koolakker 7, 5708 JA **Helmond**
Tel: 492-535 362 Fax: 492-383 195
director Ton Slegers; secretary Jan C. Zuidervaart; chairman Harry Stoop
Type: male voice choir *Repertoire:* varied (church music, opera, musicals) *Size:* 70 *Perfs:* 30-40 *Comments:* 45th anniversary in 1997

Nederlands Theaterkoor
Houtvaartkade 28D, 2111 BS **Aerdenhout**
Tel: 23-524 7792 Fax: 23-524 8162
manager Bart Van Veen
Type: mainly orchestral, also chamber choir *Repertoire:* standard choral repertoire and special music *Size:* up to 80 *Perfs:* 20 *Comments:* works with the Dutch Dance Theatre and the National Ballet; can be booked for performances

Netherlands Chamber Choir
Nederlands Kamerkoor
Paulus Potterstraat 16, 1071 CZ **Amsterdam**
Tel: 20-578 7978 Fax: 20-578 7979
E-Mail: info@nederlandskamerkoor.nl
managing director Leontien A. M. Tiddens; principal conductor Tõnu Kaljuste; artistic director Ivar Munk
Type: a cappella, chamber, mixed *Repertoire:* early middle ages to present day *Size:* 26 *Perfs:* approx. 75 *Touring:* Irael, Spain, France, Poland, Germany, Hungary, Switzerland, Italy, Czech Republic *Comments:* CD catalogue with 40 CD's (labels: Philips, Globe, Accent, Deutsche HM, Erasmus, Donemus, Denon, Harmonia Mundi France, NM Classics), Electra Nonesuch, Virgin Classics, Sony Classical, Emergo Classics

Netherlands Radio Choir
Groot Omroepkoor
PO Box 125, 1200 AC **Hilversum**
Tel: 35-671 4120 Fax: 35-671 4171
E-Mail: m.damen@mco.nl
manager Monica H.M. Damen; chief conductor (20 weeks p.a.) Martin Wright; guest conductor dependent on repertoire
Type: a cappella *Repertoire:* standard choral repertoire, especially romantic and 20th century music; with orchestra, everything from Bach to contemporary *Size:* 79: 23 sopranos, 20 altos, 18 tenors, 18 basses *Perfs:* 35 *Comments:* close cooperation with the Netherlands Radio Philharmonic, the Netherlands Radio Chamber Orchestra, the Netherlands Radio Symphony Orchestra; concerts given in the Amsterdam Concertgebouw and recorded for radio and television

Noord-Netherlands Concertkoor
Palmslag 20, 9724 CS **Gronnigen**
Tel: 50-369 5800 Fax: 50-369 5815
E-Mail: nno@tref.nl
general manager H. B. van der Meer (until March 2000 G Vierkant)
Type: mixed choir *Size:* 100 *Comments:* associated with Noord-Netherlands Orchestra

Residentie Bachkoor
Leuvensestraat 44,
2587 GH **Den Haag**
Tel: 70-354 3746 Fax: 70-350 9395
conductor Jos Vermunt
Type: mixed choir, with professional orchestra, with organ, a cappella *Repertoire:* standard choral repertoire including contemporary works, specialised in works and cantates of J.S. Bach and his contemporaries *Size:* 100 *Touring:* Belgium, Germany, France, Italy, Poland *Comments:* CD on Prisma label; perform mostly with Residentie Bachorkest and occasionally for the Residentie Orkest (The Hague Philharmonic Orchestra); see also Residentie Kamerkoor (q.v.)

Residentie Kamerkoor
Leuvensestraat 44, 2587 GH **Den Haag**
Tel: 70-354 3746
Fax: 70-350 9395
conductor Jos Vermunt
Type: mixed choir, with professional orchestra, with organ, a cappella *Repertoire:* standard choral repertoire including contemporary works *Size:* 30 *Touring:* Belgium, France, Spain *Comments:* CD on Prisma label; perform mostly with the Residentie Bachorkest (q.v.)

Westfries Mannenkoor
Herenweg 37,
1718 AB **Hoogwoud**
Tel: 226-351 360
Fax: 229-253 354
secretaries Margret Mooij
Type: male *Repertoire:* opera, musical, classical *Size:* 75 *Perfs:* 10 *Touring:* Netherlands

NORWAY (+47)

Bergen Cathedral Choir
Bergen Domkantori
c/o Bjorgvin Kirkenmusikk AS, PO Box 765, 5001 **Bergen**
Tel: 5531 0470 Fax: 5555 8140
conductor Magnar Mangersnes (55-184 350); chairman Solveig Myrås Jensen (55-930 990); leader Astrid Kløve Graue
Type: amateur mixed cathedral choir, polyphonic *Repertoire:* sacred music, contemporary Norwegian music, folk tunes *Size:* 55 *Perfs:* 10 (TV, radio, recordings and concerts) *Touring:* Norway, Europe *Comments:* winner of Let The People Sing contest, EBU and a number of other national and international prizes

Gli Skapoli
c/o Stageway, Skutevigsboder 11, 5035 **Bergen**
Tel: 5555 9696 Fax: 5531 2046
conductor Reza Aghamir; secretary Jan Tore Saltnes
Type: male choir *Repertoire:* classical, gospel, soul, pop and contemporary music *Size:* 20 *Touring:* Europe *Comments:* several recordings for Phillips Classics

Grex Vocalis
c/o Carl Høgset, Sørkedalsveien 78, 0376 **Oslo**
Tel: 2252 0299 Fax: 2252 4738
conductor & artistic director Carl Høgset
Type: mixed choir *Repertoire:* early renaissance to modern *Size:* 40 *Perfs:* 10 *Touring:* Norway *Comments:* independent choir, not affiliated to any institution; sometimes commission works; latest CD Messiah by Handel performed and recorded with Oslo Baroque Orchestra

Kvinnekoret Concentus
PO Box 668, 4301 **Sandnes**
Tel: 5162 6679/9511 9699 (mobile)
director Randi Garathun-Hansen
Type: women's choir *Size:* 30

Mandate
c/o Stageway, Skuterigsboder 11, 5035 **Bergen**
Tel: 5555 9696 Fax: 5531 2046
E-Mail: Jan.sallesnes@stageway.no
secretary Jan Tore Sallesnes; chairman Heine Totland; conductor Reza Aghamir
Type: male choir *Repertoire:* classical, soul, pop, contemporary, folk *Size:* 7 *Perfs:* 10+ *Touring:* Europe

Norske Solistkor, Det
Norwegian Soloist Choir
Tollbugata 28, 0157 **Oslo**
Tel: 2241 3970 Fax: 2241 3971
conductor Grete Pedersen Helgerød (tel: 3128 7379, fax: 3128 1989); manager Siri Kathrine Rude
Type: semi professional *Repertoire:* baroque and contemporary *Size:* 12-28 *Perfs:* 30 *Touring:* Scandinavia, Europe *Comments:* see also Oslo Chamber Choir

Oslo Cathedral Choir
Oslo Domkor
Karl Johans gt. 11, 0154 **Oslo**
Tel: 2331 4640 Fax: 2241 1717
Internet: www.oslodomkirke.no
director of administration Ms Bente Johnsrud; artistic director/conductor Terje Kvam
Type: semi professional choir, mixed *Repertoire:* mainly church music *Size:* 45, sometimes enlarged to 60 *Perfs:* 15-20

Oslo Chamber Choir
Oslo Kammerkor
c/o Torunn E. Tjelle, Seterlivn. 1, 1162 **Oslo**
Tel: 2228 4790 Fax: 2228 4168
E-Mail: torunnet@bio.vio.no
conductor Grete Pedersen Helgerød (Tel:3128 7379/Fax: 3128 1989)
Type: chamber *Repertoire:* church music, Norwegian/Scandinavian folk music *Size:* 34 *Perfs:* 40 *Touring:* Nordic countries, Ireland, Cuba, Israel

Oslo Gospel Choir
c/o stageway, Skuterigsboder II, 5035 **Bergen**
Tel: 2246 0016/5555 9696 (bookings) Fax: 2246 0016
E-Mail: Jan.sallesnes@stageway.no
manager Ole Edward Reitan; choir leader Tore W. Aas; contact bookings Jan Sallesnes (tel: 5555 9696)
Type: mixed *Repertoire:* mostly gospel, but also hymns, pop music *Size:* 30 *Perfs:* 50 *Touring:* Norway, Switzerland, Germany, Netherlands *Comments:* recordings available

Oslo Philharmonic Choir
PO Box 1607 Vika, Haaton VIIs gt. 2, 0119 **Oslo**
Tel: 2201 4900 Fax: 2201 4901
chorus master Tore Erik Moen
Comments: associated with Oslo Philharmonic Orchestra

Oslo Vokalensemble
Krisitan Mikkelsensgate 34, 0568 **Oslo**
Tel: 2238 4825/2244 6405
Internet: www.no/home/karit/ove-web.htm
conductor Fredrik Otterstad
Type: chamber choir *Repertoire:* classical, renaissance and baroque works *Size:* 25

Quattro Stagioni
c/o Scott Campbell, Bjørnerabben 5, 0383 **Oslo**
Tel: 2250 0353 Fax: 2252 4738
E-Mail: campbell@online.no
contact Scott Campbell
Type: male quartet *Repertoire:* history of European music *Size:* 4 *Perfs:* 50 *Touring:* Europe, USA

SKRUK
c/o Per Oddna Hildre, Ehrauaien 2, 6100 **Uolda**
Tel: 5782 0375/7007 7618 Fax: 7007 8567
Internet: www.skruk.no
chairman Arne Haaberg;
conductor Per Oddnar Hildre (tel: 7007 7618)
Type: mixed choir *Repertoire:* music influenced by church, Jazz, popular folklore music from South America and Azerbaidzhan; choir produce own interpretation of this music in collaboration with traditional musicians *Size:* 50 *Perfs:* 25 *Touring:* Norway, Azerbaidzhan *Comments:* have made 17 recordings and frequent TV appearances

Stavanger Vocal Ensemble
c/o Jørn Snorre Andersen, Madlatua 16, 4045 **Hafrsfjord**
Tel: 5158 7101/9170 8528 (mobile)/5156 5550/5155 6591
E-Mail: jorn.snorre.andersen@c2i.net
contact Jørn Snorre Andersen, Jørn Ingebrigstsen, Trond Ole Paulsen, Johannes Bjerga
Size: 20

Trondheim Kammerkor
c/o Norunn Ilevold Giske, Njardarvollen 19, 7032 **Trondheim**
Tel: 7359 6566/7393 9528 Fax: 7359 6588
E-Mail: bjogiske@online.no
conductor Norunn Ilevold Giske;
chairman Robert Grande
Type: mixed *Repertoire:* madrigals, romantic, church, new music, baroque and new works written especially for the choir *Size:* 28 *Perfs:* 8 *Touring:* international *Comments:* recordings available; alternative E-mail: norunn.giske@hf.ntnu.no

POLAND (+48)

Alla Pollacca Children's Choir
Chór Dzieciecy Alla Pollacca
al Niepodleglosci 245m. 65, 02-009 **Warszawa**
conductor Sabina Wlodarska

Bornus Consort
ul. Promiennego Slonca 26, 05-540 **Zalesie Górne**
Tel: 22-756 5591
director Marcin Bornus-Szczycinski
Repertoire: medieval, renaissance and early baroque vocal music

Bydgoszcz Music Academy Choir
Chór Akademii Muzycznej w Bydgoszczy
ul. Siemaszkowej 19, 85-790 **Bydgoszcz**
Tel: 52-439 671
conductor Janusz Stanecki
Type: mixed

Cantus Firmus Chamber Singers
Szczesliwicka 2 M.8, 02-352 **Warszawa**
Tel: 22-8233 389
contact Wlodzimierz Soltysik

Catholic Univ. of Lublin Choir
Chór Katolickiego Uniwersytetu Lubelskiego
Al. Raclawickie 14, 20-950 **Lublin**
Tel: 81-533 2572 Fax: 81-533 2572
manager Zdzislaw Cieszkowski;
conductor Kazimierz Górski

Choir Mottet and Madrigal
ul. Zagonowa 11/2, 61-644 **Poznan**
Tel: 61-8200 965
Type: mixed

Choir of the Catholic Theology in Warsaw
Chor Akademii Teologii Katolickiej
ul. Zelazna 27/27, 00-806 **Warszawa**
Tel: 22-620 4703
conductor rev. Kazimierz Szymonik
Type: mixed

Collegium Musicum Chamber Choir
Chór Kameralny Collegium Musicum
ul. Zamkowa 1, 10-074 **Olsztyn**
conductor Jerzy Wilinski

Il Canto
ul. Baczynskiego 18/20, 05-092 **Lomianki**
Tel: 22-751 3701 Fax: 22-751 3701
director Michal Straszewski
Type: chamber vocal ensemble *Repertoire:* renaissance and early baroque vocal music

Pedagogic College Students Choir
Chór Akademicki Wyzszej Szkoly Pedagogicznej
ul. Chodkiewicza 30, 85-064 **Bydgoszcz**
Tel: 52-341 3203 Fax: 52-341 3533
conductor Sylwester Matczak

Polish Chamber Singers The Affabre Concinui
ul. Pradzynskiego 57/9, 61-527 **Poznan**
Tel: 61-833 9019 Fax: 61-833 0960
Type: male choir *Repertoire:* renaissance to contemporary *Size:* 6 *Touring:* national, international *Comments:* recording for radio and TV

Polish Nightingales
Polskie Slowiki
ul. Cegielskiego 1, 61-862 **Poznan**
Tel: 61-853 4444 Fax: 61-877 9188
conductor/director Wojciech A. Krolopp
Type: boys' choir

Poznan Philharmonic
Poznanskie Slowiki – Poznan Nightingales
ul. Sw. Marcin 81, 61-808 **Poznan**
Tel: 61-852 2266 Fax: 61-852 3451
conductor Stafan Stuligrosz
Type: boys and mens Choir

Resonans con Tutti Mixed Choir
Chór Mieszany Resonans con tutti
ul. 11 Listopada 26/a, 41-807 **Zabrze**
Tel: 32-171 3251 ext 313
artistic director Maria Kroczek

Silesian Philharmonic Choir
Chor Filharmonii Slaskiej
ul. Sokolska 2, 40-084 **Katowice**
Tel: 32-589 885 Fax: 32-589 885
choir master Jan Wojtacha
Type: mixed *Size:* 70

Technical Univ. Students Choir, Szczecin
Chór Akademicki Politechniki Szczecinskiej -CHAPS
ul. Wyspianskiego 1, 70-497 **Szczecin**
conductor Jan Szyrocki

Warsaw Choral Society
Warsaw
Tel: 22-625 1431/826 5316 Fax: 22-629 3233
director and conductor Tadeusz Olszewski
Type: male chamber choir *Size:* varies *Touring:* national, international *Comments:* recordings for Polish radio and TV

Warsaw Philharmonic Choir
Chor Filharmonii Narodowej
ul. Jasna 5, 00-950 **Warszawa**
Tel: 22-826 7281 ext.117 or 182 Fax: 22-826 5617
E-Mail: phil@pol.pl
choirmaster Henryk Wojnarowski; contact K. Kord
Type: mixed choir *Size:* 100

Wroclaw Technical Univ. Students Choir
Akademicki Chór Politechniki Wroclawskiej
ul. Kolista 14/6, 54-132 **Wroclaw**
conductor Piotr Ferensowicz

PORTUGAL (+351)

Coro da Sé Catedral do Porto
Terreiro de D. Afonso Henriques, 4050-573 **Porto**
Tel: 2-205 4084 Fax: 2-208 5680
E-Mail: cscp@ecclesia.pt
chairman Conego António Ferreira dos Santos; vice chairman of the board Manuel Dias Amorim; musical director and conductor Eugénio Amorim Resende
Type: mixed, a cappella and with instruments (mainly Orquestra do Porto) *Repertoire:* polyphonic, 16th C., contemporary sacred European (Portuguese) *Size:* 150 *Perfs:* 15-20 annually *Comments:* recording for Numerica Editors

Coro do Teatro São Carlos
Fundação do Teatro de S. Carlos, Rua Serpa Pinto 9, 1200 **Lisboa**
Tel: 1-346 8408 Fax: 1-347 1738/346 684
mestre do coro João Paulo Santos
Type: mainly opera, concerts *Size:* 80 *Perfs:* 30-40 *Touring:* Spain, Portugal *Comments:* see also Opera, Orchestras

Gulbenkian Choir
Coro Gulbenkian
Fundação Calouste Gulbenkian / Music Department, Ave. de Berna 45, 1067 **Lisboa** Codex
Tel: 1-793 5131 (music dept) Fax: 1-793 7296
Internet: www.telepac.pt/earte/gulbenkian
E-Mail: musica@gulbenkian.pt
principal conductor Michel Corboz; associate conductor Fernando Eldoro;
assistant director Jorge Matta
Size: 100 *Perfs:* 10 *Touring:* Europe *Comments:* see also National/Regional Minstries, Orchestras, Dance, Festivals (2), Promoters, Venues

ROMANIA (+40)

Madrigal
c/o Academy of Music Ciprian Porumbescu, str. Stirbei Voda 33, Sectorul I, 79551 **Bucharest**
Tel: 1-314 7490
conductor Marin Constantin
Type: chamber choir

Preludiv
c/o Central de Cultura Tinerimea Româna, Str. Gutemberg 16, **Bucharest**
Tel: 1-312 1962
conductor Voicu Enachescu
Type: chamber choir

Transilvania State Philharmonic Choir
St Emmanuel de Martonne 1, 3400 **Cluj-Napoca**
Tel: 64-430 060/3 Fax: 64-197 812
Internet: www.tyf.ro/filarmonicacluj/index.html
conductor Cornel Groza; general director Emil Simon
Type: mixed *Repertoire:* wide *Size:* 70 *Perfs:* 50 *Touring:* Europe, Israel *Comments:* orchestra of the hilarmonic Cluj-napoca

RUSSIA (+7)

Academic Choir
Arts Center, 2 Pirogova str., 630090 **Novosibirsk**
Tel: 3832-397 818/343 Fax: 3832-302 237
Internet: www.nsu.ru/art_center
E-Mail: artcen@nsu.ru

Academy of Children's Choir
Zheleznodorozhny ul. Smelchak 11, 143980 **Moscow**
Tel: 095-522 1017
director G. A. Struve
Type: children's choir

Bolshoi Theatre Children's Choir
Tetralnaya Square 1, 103009 **Moscow**
Tel: 095-228 4091/292 3108/3870
manager Boris Dergachev;
chief conductor Andrey Zaboronok
Type: mixed *Repertoire:* secular and sacred works *Size:* 80 *Touring:* Europe *Comments:* recordings on Collins Classics and Russian Seasons label

Bolshoi Theatre Choir
Tetralnaya Square 1, 103009 **Moscow**
Tel: 095-228 4091/292 3108/3870
artistic director Bela Rudenko;
chief conductor Stanislav Lykov
Type: mixed *Size:* 80 *Touring:* worldwide *Comments:* recordings on Eratio, Le Chant du Monde and Olympia

Children's Choir Luch
Pleshcheeva 20, 127560 **Moscow**
Tel: 095-902 6036
director V. Nikeshin
Type: children's choir

Choir Studio Druzhba
Stalevarov 16a, School 405, 111555 **Moscow**
Tel: 095-302 2546

Choir Studio Radost
Novopeschannaya 26, 125252 **Moscow**
Tel: 095-198 0421

Concert Choir of St Petersburg State Mussorgsky Opera and Ballet theatre
1 Arts Square, 191011 **St Petersburg**
Tel: 812-219 1988/85/89/43 Fax: 812-314 7284/3653/2774
artistic director Vladimir Stolpovskikh;
contact Victoria Gordievskaya
Comments: see also Opera, Dance

Ensemble of Wind Music and Chamber Choir
Naberezhnaya river Fontanka 41, 191011 **St Petersburg**
Tel: 812-110 4043 Fax: 812-311 2066
director Alexandre Stupnev
Comments: see also Orchestras

Glinka State Academic Choir of St. Petersburg
nab Moiki 20, 191186 **St Petersburg**
Tel: 812-110 6873/314 1073
Fax: 812-110 6913
artistic director & chief conductor Vladislav Chernushenko
Type: mixed *Repertoire:* classical, sacred music *Size:* 65 *Touring:* Japan, France, Spain, UK *Comments:* formed in 1479 by Tsar Ivan III; records for Teldec, Collins Classics and Melodiya

Great Children's Choir of the TV and Radio Company Ostankino
Diktiarsky per. 7, 103050 **Moscow**
Tel: 095-299 5722 (after 16.00pm)
artistic director Victor Popov

Lege Artis Chamber Choir
1a Mateev per, 190210 **St Petersburg**
Tel: 812-464 1251 Fax: 812-219 5295
artistic director Boris Abalyan

Male Chamber Choir
Varvarka 2, 103012 **Moscow**
Tel: 095-298 3790
Type: male chamber choir

Piatnitsky State Academic Russian Folk Choir
Tverskaya ul 31, 103050 **Moscow**
Tel: 095-299 6925 Fax: 095-299 0549
chief choirmaster Elena Goriacheva

Rosinka
Naberezhnaya river Fontanka 41, 191011 **St Petersburg**
Tel: 812-110 4043 Fax: 812-311 2066
director Nikolai Kornev

Rossica Choir of St Petersburg
St Petersburg
Comments: please see under Solihull, United Kingdom

St Petersburg Boys' Choir
Masterskaya ulitsa 4, 190121 **St Petersburg**
Tel: 812-114 0300
artistic director Vladimir Begletsov
Repertoire: Russian and Western choral music *Size:* 65 *Comments:* representation: Sonata, UK ;see also under Agents & Producers

St Petersburg Chamber Choir
Box 406, **St Petersburg**
Tel: 812-275 2001 Fax: 812-275 2001
manager Victoria Kobzieva;
chorus master Andrej Petrenko
Type: mixed *Repertoire:* sacred and secular, a cappella music *Size:* 28 *Touring:* Germany, France, Netherlands, UK *Comments:* recordings for Melodiya; premieres of contemporary sacred music

St Petersburg Male Choir
Fontanka River 41, 191011 **St Petersburg**
Tel: 812-393 6418/232 8576
Fax: 812-151 5520/232 0942
E-Mail: siti@mail.wplus.net
artistic director Vadim Afanasiev;
manager Alexandr Radev
Type: male *Repertoire:* a cappella works by Russian composers, folk songs, classical works by Western composers: J.S. Bach, Handel, Mozart, Haydn, Brahms *Size:* 12-60 *Comments:* recordings for EMI Classics

St Petersburg Mozarteum Choir and Chamber Orchestra
Liteiny pr 20, 191028 **St Petersburg**
Tel: 812-110 4022/278 8661
Fax: 812-279 7486
artistic director & principal conductor Arkady Shteinlukht
Comments: see also Orchestras

Sveshnikov State Academic Russian Choir
Tverskaya 31, 103050 **Moscow**
Tel: 095-299 6521/9842
artistic director t.b.a.
Type: mixed *Repertoire:* sacred, folk *Size:* 120 *Touring:* Germany *Comments:* made historical recording of Rachmaninov's Vespers (1964); recordings on Melodiya, Russian Disc, Olympia, Le Chant du Monde

Voskresenye Choir
Moscow
music director Dmitry Onegin
Type: mixed *Repertoire:* contemporary and old Slavonic sacred music *Size:* 12 *Comments:* represented by Sonata (please see Promoters and Agents & Producers, UK)

SLOVENIA (+386)

Slovenian Chamber Choir, The
Kongresni trg. 10, P.O. Box 156, 1000 **Ljubljana**
Tel: 61-213 554
Fax: 61-213 640
artistic director Dr Mirko Luderman
Comments: see also Orchestra (Slovenian Philharmonic)

SPAIN (+34)

Agrupación Coral de Cámara de Pamplona
C/San Antón 12, 31001 **Pamplona**
Tel: 948-223 405 (Banco Atlantico) Fax: 948-226 803
E-Mail: koldop@arrakis.es
director Koldo Pastor;
president Luis Felipe Sarasa Garciá
Type: chamber choir, contemporary, classical and traditional music *Repertoire:* specialize in contemporary music *Size:* 18 *Perfs:* 40-50 annually *Touring:* Spain, South America, USA, Europe, Africa

Agrupación Coral Santa Maria de Castro Urdiales
c/El Charillo 2, 5°E, 39700 **Castro Urdialles (Cantabria)**
Tel: 942-861 349
Fax: 942-861 599
director Begonà Goikochea;
president Francisco Javier Carrasco
Type: mixed, a cappella and with orchestra *Repertoire:* standard choral repertoire, Spanish regional music *Size:* 45 *Perfs:* 40 *Comments:* organises a season of choral music in summer called Estelas Musicales

Capella Reial de Catalunya, La
Travesera de Gracia 18-20, 08021 **Barcelona**
Tel: 93-594 4760
Fax: 93-580 5606
E-Mail: 101617,3236@compuserve.com
director Jordi Savall; administrator Irene Bloc
Repertoire: music from 13th-17th C. *Size:* varies *Perfs:* 45 *Touring:* Europe, USA *Comments:* perform with Hesperion XX (see Early Music)

Cor Ciutat de Tarragona
Conservatori de Musica de Tarragona, Carrer Caballers 14, 43003 **Tarragona**
Tel: 977-234 167/223 590 Fax: 977-223 590
director Josep Prats; assistant director Nùria Francino; coordination Beni Ramon; president Lluis Gili
Type: a cappella, with orchestra *Repertoire:* standard choral repertoire *Size:* 40-50 *Perfs:* 7 *Touring:* regional *Comments:* organises Semana Cantan: International Festival of Choirs

Cor dels Amics de l'Opera de Sabadell
Plaça Sant Roc 22, 2° 1ffi, 08201 **Sabadell**
Tel: 93-725 6734/726 5470 Fax: 93-727 5321
Internet: www.amic-opera-sabadell.es
E-Mail: aaoe@sumi.es
presidente y directora artistica Mirna Lacambra Domenéch; vicepresidente y prensa Xavier Gondolbeu
Type: opera *Size:* 55-60 *Perfs:* 4 *Comments:* choir of ' Opera a Catalunya';
see also Opera, Festivals, Competitions

Coral Agora Secovia
Plaza san Esteban 11-3, 40003 **Segovia**
Tel: 92-143 4423 Fax: 92-143 4423
E-Mail: kent@futurnet.es
administrator Jose McGuel Arranz;
director Marisa Martin
Repertoire: all *Size:* 45 *Perfs:* 50 *Touring:* Europe
Comments: courses in August on choral singing

Coral Asociacion Cultural Aires de Carral
Edif. Banco Bilbao Vizcaya, c/ General Franco 4, 15175 **Carral (Coruña)**
Tel: 981-670 039 Fax: 981-670 039
director José Gordillo Campelo;
president José Barreiro García
Type: a cappella *Repertoire:* religious, Italian 'Habaneras' *Size:* 36 *Perfs:* 12 *Touring:* national *Comments:* funded by regional government

Coral del Conservatori Professional de Musica de Badalona
C/Pare Claret 2, 08911 **Badalona**
Tel: 93-389 3957 Fax: 93-389 3254
director Joan Puigdellivols
Type: mixed choir, a cappella and with orchestra *Repertoire:* standard choral repertoire *Size:* 40-50 *Perfs:* 20 *Touring:* Spain *Comments:* also have children's choir, director Montserrat Pi

Coral Isidoriana de Léon
Colegiata de San Isidoro, Pz. de Santo Martino 5, 24003 **León**
Tel: 987-223 6600
director Todomiro Alvarez Garcia; president Victor Reyero
Repertoire: classical, Leonnais *Size:* 45 *Perfs:* 15

Coral Polifónica de Santa Cruz de Tenerife
Aptdode Correos 57, La Esperanza,
38290 **Santa Cruz de Tenerife**
Tel: 922-297 209/609571520 (mobile) Fax: 922-297 209
director Francisco Padrón Correa;
assistant director Ana Isabel Delgado
Type: polyphonic, mixed *Repertoire:* sacred with chamber orchestra, popular *Size:* 40 *Perfs:* 70 *Touring:* national

Coro Amici Musicae del Auditorio de Zaragoza
Eduardo Ibarra s/n, 50009 **Zaragoza**
Tel: 976-434 291/721 300 Fax: 976-350 514
director Andres Ibiricu; president Juan Garcia Mugica
Type: with orchestra *Repertoire:* 19th & 20th century, symphony *Size:* 90 *Perfs:* 10-12 *Touring:* Spain *Comments:* resident choir of Auditorio de Zaragoza; see also Venues

Coro Clásico de Vigo
C/Venezuela 11, 7° E, 36203 **Vigo**
Tel: 986-421 517
director Joaquin Carvajal Baños;
secretario Jose Benito Gonzalez Baez
Type: polyphonic *Repertoire:* renaissance, folk, 20th C *Size:* 24 *Perfs:* 12-20

Coro de Camara Francisco de Montanos
Padilla 20, 2-D, 47003 **Valladolid**
Tel: 983-310 564/266 315
E-Mail: jigfm@hotmail.com
conductor Jose Ignacio Farran; manager Juan Carlos Martinez; secretary Charo de Fuentes
Type: chamber *Repertoire:* classical and modern works, several styles mainly from the 15th, 16th and 17th centuries *Size:* 20 *Perfs:* 20

Coro de la Radio Television Española
Sala Lenx. Paseo de la Florida 13, 28008 **Madrid**
Tel: 91-542 6468 Fax: 91-559 6967
gerente artistico Pedro Botías; director invitado del coro Laszlo Heltay; delegado del coro y orquesta Francisco de Paula Bellbell
Type: classical to comptemporary *Size:* 60-70 *Perfs:* 30 *Touring:* Spain *Comments:* performs with Orquesta Sinfónica de la Radiiotelevision Española; see also TV, Radio and Orchestra

Coro de la Universidad Carlos III de Madrid
C/Madrid, 126 Despacho 16.S.03,
28903 **Getafe (Madrid)**
Tel: 91-624 9266/924 9764 Fax: 91-624 9592
Internet:
www.uc3m.es/uc3m/gral/IA/ASOC/CORO/coro/presenta.htm
E-Mail: coro@alumnos.uc3m.es
coordinadora actividades musicales Isabel Urueña Cuadrado; directora del coro Nuria S. Fernandez Herranz; presidente de la Asociación del Coro de la Universidad Carlos III Felipe Formariz Pombo; secretaria de la asociación Maria Rosa Moreno Sánchez
Type: a cappella *Repertoire:* standard choral repertoire *Size:* 45 *Perfs:* 15-20 *Touring:* Spain *Comments:* also organises Encuentro de Coros Universitarios

Coro de la Universidad Politécnica de Madrid
Av. Ramiro de Maeztu, 7, 28040 **Madrid**
Tel: 91-336 6695 Fax: 91-336 6173
Internet: www.datsi.FI.upm.es/~coros
E-Mail: gcoro@fqupm.upm.es
director José de Felipe Arnaíz; president Enrique Calderón; gerente Javier Roiz (tel: 91-336 5959)
Type: polyphonic music from 16th century to contemporary compositions *Repertoire:* standard choral repertoire, various major works with orchestra *Size:* 120 *Perfs:* 5 *Touring:* Spain, Europe

Coro de Valencia
Teatres de la Generalitat, Teatro Principal, C/Barcas, 15, 46003 **Valencia**
Tel: 96-386 9722 Fax: 96-386 6574
Internet: www.palauvalencia.com
E-Mail: palaudelamusica@resone.es
director artistico Francisco Perales
Repertoire: opera, oratorio, zarzuela, symphonic choral, contemporary *Size:* 70 *Perfs:* 30 *Touring:* Spain, Europe *Comments:* resident choir at Palau de la Musica i Congressos de Valencia; see also Promoters

Coro Jesús Guridi
C/Canceler Ayala 13, 01004 **Vitoria**
Tel: 945-120 641
director José Luis Aramburu
Type: a cappella *Repertoire:* standard choral repertoire *Size:* 45 *Perfs:* 15

Coro Manuel de Falla
Conservatorio Superior de Música, C/ Jesús del Gran Poder 38, 41002 **Sevilla**
Tel: 95-441 1914
Fax: 95-438 3357
director Ricardo Rodriguez; president Maria José Pérez
Type: a cappella *Repertoire:* renaissance to contemporary *Size:* 40 *Perfs:* 10-15 *Touring:* Spain

Escolania de la Abadia de Santa Cruz del valle de Los Caídos
28209 **Valle de los Caídos (Madrid)**
Tel: 91-890 5411 Fax: 91-890 5594/896 1542
director Laurentino Sáenz de Buruaga Ruiz de Gauna
Type: children's choir *Repertoire:* medieval, gregorian, classical and modern, polyphonic *Size:* 50 *Perfs:* 12 *Touring:* Spain *Comments:* CDs available; specializing in Gregorian chant

Musica Ficta
Gran Via 80, Oficina 215-216, 28013 **Madrid**
Tel: 91-541 9642
Fax: 91-541 8470
Internet: www.artemusica.com
E-Mail: concerts@artemusica.com
commercial director Eduardo Brenlla;
artistic director Raúl Mallavibarrena
Type: a cappella and with orchestra *Repertoire:* baroque, renaissance *Size:* varies *Perfs:* 20-30
Touring: national, international *Comments:* recordings available; performs with ensemble Instrumental Fontegara; managed by Arte Música; see also Early Music and Agents

Neocantes
C/Real 19, 1°, 28250 **Torrelodones (Madrid)**
Tel: 91-859 3962/853 4010/607-745 423 (mobile)
Fax: 91-859 4637
Internet: www.greencom.net/arte4
E-Mail: arte4@greencom.net-
director Germán Torrellas; producción Antonia Sánchez, Macarena Torrelles, M. Fueyo
Type: vocal chamber choir, sometimes performs with musicians *Repertoire:* renaissance, early baroque, especially Spanish music from the 15th, 16th and 17th centuries *Size:* 5+ 8-10 *Perfs:* 40 *Comments:* specialise in Spanish music; managed by Arte 4,
see also Agents & Producers

Orfeó Catala
C/San Francisco de Paula 2, 08003 **Barcelona**
Tel: 93-268 1000
ax: 93-268 1000/4824
director orfeó Josep Vila Casañas; director chamber choir Jordi Casas Bayer; director youth choir Conchita García; directors children choir Maria Jesus Culleré, Luis Vilamajó
Type: a cappella, symphonic music *Repertoire:* symphony, oratorios *Size:* orfeó catala: 60; youth choir: 80; 3 children's choirs: 30 each *Perfs:* 100 *Touring:* Spain, Europe, South America *Comments:* Titular Choir of Palau de la Musica Catalana, Fundació Orfeo Catalan; see also Promoters & Venues

Orfeón Cajasur
Obra Social y Cultural Cajasur, Ronda de los Tejares 22, 6°, 14001 **Cordoba**
Tel: 957-214 424 Fax: 957-214 420
Internet: www.cajasur.es
director Ramón Medina Hidalgo
Type: a cappella choir *Repertoire:* sacred, popular *Size:* 85 *Perfs:* 40 *Touring:* Spain, religious festivals in Europe *Comments:* belongs to Obra Social y Cultural Cajasur; see also Promoters

Orfeón de Sestao
Conservatorio Municipal de Música, Gran Via 17, 48990 **Sestao (Vizcaya)**
Tel: 94-423 9579/908-672 545/608672545 (mobile) Fax: 94-423 9579
director Santiago Allende; presidente Pablo Vélez
Type: mens' choir *Repertoire:* classical, folkloric *Size:* 40 *Perfs:* 20 *Touring:* Spain, Europe *Comments:* collaborates with Asociación Bilbaina de Amigos de la Opera

Orfeón Donostiarra Chorus
San Juan N° 6, 20003 **San Sebastian**
Tel: 943-422 239 Fax: 943-423 675
Internet: www.gipuzkoa.net/orfeon
E-Mail: orfeon@gipuzkoa.net
director José Antonio Sainz Alfaro; secretary general Ma. Jesús Muñoz-Baroja
Type: symphonic *Size:* 130 *Perfs:* 45 *Touring:* Germany, Canary Islands

Orfeón Xoán Montes
c/Río Neira 17, 27002 **Lugo**
Tel: 982-220 578/220 511
Fax: 982-220 578
director Enrique Alvarellos Iglesias
Type: mens' choir, a cappella, renaissance, baroque *Repertoire:* folklore, opera, sacred *Size:* 40 *Perfs:* 20-25 *Touring:* Spain *Comments:* only all male choir in Galicia

Polifonica de Girona
11 De Setembre No21, 17007 **Girona**
Tel: 972-215 289 Fax: 972-215 289
E-Mail: moviment@copd.es
director Jordi Bernardo Figueras;
president Ana Maria Viader
Repertoire: baroque, classical, folk catalan, sacred music, modern light *Size:* 35 *Perfs:* 20 *Touring:* Spain, Europe *Comments:* member of the European Federation of Choirs

Schola Cantorum de Alcalá de Henares
C/San Juan N° 2, 28801 **Alcalá de Henares (Madrid)**
Tel: 91-880 6213 Fax: 91-881 4813
director Nuria Matamala Pichoto ;
president Juan Carlos Moran Rey
Type: mixed, a cappella *Repertoire:* classical, religious, modern *Size:* 45-50 *Perfs:* 30 *Touring:* Spain, Europe

Scholars, The
Romani 14, Altafulla, 43893 **Altafulla (Tarragona)**
Tel: 977-650 748
Fax: 977-650 748
E-Mail: dvan@tinet.fut.es
director David Van Asch
Type: a cappella *Repertoire:* renaissance to contemporary *Size:* 4 *Perfs:* 50 *Touring:* Austria, Japan, Spain, UK, USA *Comments:* UK based ensemble administered by David van Arch from Spain

Sociedad Coral de Bilbao
C/ Alameda de Urquijo 13, 48008 **Bilbao**
Tel: 94-416 7148
Fax: 94-416 1899
E-Mail: corolbilbo@euskalalnet.net
director Gorka Sierra; gerente Jose Antonio Villasante; director of children choir José Luis Ormazabal; director youth choir Iñaki Moreno;
director mixed choir Gorka Sierra
Type: symphonic choral; 3 choirs: children's, youth, adults (mixed) *Repertoire:* symphony, lyric *Size:* 60-70 children's choir; 60 youth choir; 110 mixed choir *Perfs:* 100 *Touring:* Spain, Europe, South America *Comments:* also have 2 music schools, one for children and another for youth;

SWEDEN (+46)

Eric Ericson Chamber Choir
Teatergatan 3, 5tr, 111 48 **Stockholm**
Tel: 8-611 1070 Fax: 8-131 832
Internet: www.kammarkoren.org
E-Mail: eekk@swipnet.se
manager Per Korsfeldt; artistic director Prof. Eric Ericsson; chairman Thomas Jennefelt
Type: professional, freelance, a cappella and orchestra *Repertoire:* contemporary *Size:* 33 *Perfs:* 40 *Touring:* national, international

Orphei Drängar Chorus
Sångsällskapet OD
Västra Strandgatan 7 B, 753 11 **Uppsala**
Tel: 18-713 050 Fax: 18-121 194
Internet: www.od.se
E-Mail: info@od.se
secretary Josef Åhman (email: secretary@od.se); conductor Robert Sund (email: conductor@od.se); assistant conductor Folke Alin; president Per Sverredal (email: president@od.se); vice-president Jüri-Karl Seim; information secretary Göran Kåver
Type: male voice, a cappella and symphony *Size:* 80 *Perfs:* 16 per season *Touring:* USA, Canada *Comments:* CDs available

Stockholm Bach Choir
Adolf Frederiks Bachkör
Adolf Frederiks Church, PO Box 3270, 103 65 **Stockholm**
Tel: 8-411 2351/8128 Fax: 8-204 912
director Anders Öhrwall
Type: mixed *Repertoire:* baroque *Size:* 30 *Touring:* national, international

Swedish Radio Choir
Berwaldhallen, Swedish Radio Broadcasting Corporation, 105 10 **Stockholm**
Tel: 8-784 5000 Fax: 8-784 1343
Internet: www.sr.se/berwaldhallen
E-Mail: radiokoren@bwh.sr.se
general manager Michael Tydén; artist and programme manager Gunnar Andersson; principal conductor Tönu Kaljuste; touring manager Eva Bjurenhed; marketing manager Karin Adolfsson
Type: professional, mixed, mostly a cappella, some orchestra *Repertoire:* contemporary *Size:* 33 *Perfs:* 20 *Touring:* national, international *Comments:* recordings available

SWITZERLAND (+41)

Akademiechor Luzern und Mozart-Ensemble Luzern
Musikhochschule Luzern, Fakultät II, Obergrundstraße 13, 6003 **Luzern**
Tel: 41-240 4318 Fax: 41-240 1453
E-Mail: fakultaet2@musikhochschule.ch
Leitung Dr. Alois Koch; Kommunikation/Öffentlichkeitsarbeit/ Marketing Hanno Wyss
Type: mixed *Repertoire:* from Monteverdi to 20th century *Size:* 80 *Perfs:* 3-4 *Touring:* mainly Switzerland and German speaking countries

Basler Bach Choir
c/o Hiriam Spiess, Rainstrasse 43, 4416 **Bubendorf**
Tel: 61-692 6405
president Myriam Spiess; conductor Joachim Krause
Type: mixed, a cappella and with orchestra *Repertoire:* 17th-20th century *Size:* 80-100 *Perfs:* 3-6

Basler Madrigalisten
Gundeldingerstr. 93, 4053 **Basel**
Tel: 61-272 8333 Fax: 61-272 8338
Manager Rita Froesch; Musikalischer Leiter Fritz Näf
Type: professional; a cappella and with orchestra; mixed *Repertoire:* from early to contemporary music *Size:* 16-32 *Perfs:* 15-20 *Touring:* Europe *Comments:* singers are contracted per project; CDs available; scenic projects (e.g. Renaissance, madrigal comedy)

Berner Bach Choir
c/o Theo Schranz, Grauholz Weg 8, 3084 **Wabern**
Tel: 31-964 0450 Fax: 31-964 0451
director/conductor Theo Loosli; president Theo Schranz; secretary Veronika Batt
Type: with orchestra *Repertoire:* 17th century-contemporary, emphasis on Bach & Romantik *Size:* 130 *Perfs:* 10 annually *Comments:* CDs, radio recordings; Kulturpreis 1998 der Berner Bürgergemeinde

Cantate Chor and Cantate Kammerchor Basel
c/o J. Eichenberger, Pfeffergässlein 13, 4051 **Basel**
Tel: 61-261 5926
president Jürg Eichenberger;
conductor/director Jürg Rüthi
Type: orchestral, chamber, a cappella, mixed *Repertoire:* standard choral repertoire, especially 20th century music *Size:* 30 *Perfs:* 3-5 *Touring:* Switzerland, Italy, France

Choeur des XVI
CP 144, 1701 **Fribourg**
Tel: 26-322 2568 (président)/413 3936 (director)
Fax: 26-322 1936
E-Mail: boivin.nussbaumer@com.mcnet.ch
director André Ducret; président Albert Nussbaumer
Type: mainly a cappella, sometimes orchestral, mixed *Repertoire:* renaissance, romantic, contemporary *Size:* 30-35 *Perfs:* 12 *Touring:* Europe

Chor des Luzerner Theaters
Theaterstr. 2, 6002 **Luzern**
Tel: 41-210 3363 Fax: 41-210 3367
choir director Wolfgang Müller-Salow; Indendant Barbara Mundel
Type: orchestral *Repertoire:* operetta, opera, musical *Size:* 16 *Perfs:* 200

Collegium Cantorum
c/o Mario Schwarz, Rohrschacher Str. 107,
9006 **St Gallen**
Tel: 71-245 1158 Fax: 71-245 1168
E-Mail: collmus@dial.eunet.ch
Leitung Mario Schwarz
Type: a cappella, orchestral *Repertoire:* new music/Bach cantatas *Size:* 10-15 *Comments:* address Mario Schwarz: Wiedenhubstr. 17, 9305 Berg SG, Tel: 71-450 0088 Fax: 71-450 0089; see also Kammerchor Oberthurgau (Choirs and Vocal Ensembles)

Coro della Radio Suizzera, Lugano
Radio della Radio Suizzera Italiana, Casella Postale, 6903 **Lugano**
Tel: 91-803 5111 Fax: 91-803 9085
E-Mail: gclericetti@tinet.ch
director Diego Fasolis; produttore Giuseppe Clericetti
Type: a cappella and with orchestra *Repertoire:* early music *Size:* 12-32 *Touring:* national, international *Comments:* they collaborate very often with two early music ensembles: Ensemble Vanitas, and Isonatori de la Marca, and work with two record lables (Naxos, ARPS, ARTS); see also TV & Orchestras

Ensemble Vocal de Lausanne
Avenue du Grammont 11 bis, 1007 **Lausanne**
Tel: 21-617 4707
Fax: 21-617 4867
Internet: Fusions.ch/evl
E-Mail: sjollema@span.ch
manager Frederik Sjollema; music director Michel Corboz; administration assistants Vincent Lipp, Meuel Off
Type: a cappella and with orchestra *Repertoire:* from Monteverdi to Arthur Honegger and Frank Martin *Size:* 24-70 *Perfs:* 25 *Touring:* Europe, South America, Japan *Comments:* CDs available

Göteburg Symphony Orchestra Chorus
Stenhammars Gatam 1, 41256 **Göteburg**
Tel: 31-615 300 Fax: 31-203 3502
Internet: www.goteborgssymfoniker.com
director Par Fridberg
Type: mixed *Size:* 100 *Perfs:* 20 *Touring:* worldwide with orchestra *Comments:* associated with Swedish National Orchestra

Kammerchor Oberthurgau
Rohrschacher Str. 107, 9006 **St Gallen**
Tel: 71-245 1158 Fax: 71-245 1168
E-Mail: collmus@dial.eunet.ch
Präsident and Sekretariat t.b.a.; musikalischer Leiter Mario Schwarz (Wiedenhubstr. 17, 9305 Berg SG, tel. 71-450 0088)
Type: mainly orchestral, a cappella *Repertoire:* oratorios new and rare, contemporary *Size:* 50-60 *Perfs:* 8 *Comments:* CDs available; coproduction with Südwestrundfunk Baden-Baden (SWR); concerts in Switzerland and abroad; see also Collegium Cantorum (Choirs and Vocal Ensembles)

Kammerchor Schaffhausen
c/o G Helbling, Winkelriedstr. 11, 9200 **Gossau**
Tel: 71-385 8674
Fax: 71-388 5339
contact Guido Helbling
Type: mixed choir, a cappella, orchestral *Repertoire:* madrigals, oratorios *Size:* 89 *Perfs:* 4

Regio-Chor Binningen
Gustackerstraße 15, 4103 **Bottmingen**
Tel: 61-421 4458 (president)/701 6292 (secretary)
Fax: 61-421 4458
Internet: www.adr.ch/regiochor
president Elisabeth Ruegsägger; Dirigent Thüring Bräm
Type: mainly orchestral, chamber *Repertoire:* oratorio, 17thC-contemporary *Size:* 110 *Perfs:* 6 *Touring:* Switzerland *Comments:* main venues: Martinskirche, Basel 922; Casino Basel 1400

TURKEY (+90)

Chorus Istanbul State Opera and Ballet
Istanbul Devlet Opera ve Balesi Korosu
Istanbul
Tel: 212-243 2011
Fax: 212-245 3916
contact Mahmet Pervez
Comments: see also Opera, Dance, Orchestras

Chorus Izmir State Opera and Ballet
Izmir Devlet Opera ve Balesi Korosu
Izmir
Tel: 232-484 6450
Fax: 232-441 0173
contact Erdogan Sanal
Comments: see also Opera, Dance, Orchestras

Chorus Mersin State Opera and Ballet
Mersin Devlet Opera ve Balesi Korosu
Mersin
Tel: 324-238 0493
Fax: 324-274 7119
contact Erdogan Sanal
Comments: see also Opera, Dance, Orchestras

Chorus of the Ankara State Opera and Ballet
Ankara Devlet Opera ve Balesi Korosu
Ankara
Tel: 312-311 2430 Fax: 312-311 9731
contact Hasan Hüseyin Akbulut
Comments: see also Opera, Dance, Orchestras

Istanbul European Chorus
Istanbul European Choir
Ilyas Gelebi Sok. No: 5/5, Cihangir , 80060 **Istanbul**
Tel: 212-283 5480 Fax: 212-283 5609
contact Ismet Ok

UKRAINE (+380)

Boyan Ensemble
Basseyna St. 1/2, 252004 **Kiev**
Tel: 44-225 1214/224 5909
Fax: 44-225 1214/224 6071
artistic director Bohdan Antkiv
Type: male voice choir *Repertoire:* combination of orthodox music and Ukrainian folk songs *Size:* 27 *Touring:* international *Comments:* UK management: Marguerite Rolle: Tel:1684-892 343/Fax: 1684-572 734

Dudaryk Boys Choir
Kopernyka St. 42, 290000 **Lviv**
Tel: 322-722 948 Fax: 322-728 577
artistic director Mykola Katsal
Type: aged 9-29 *Repertoire:* Ukrainian church and folk music *Size:* 65 *Touring:* USA

Dumka State Choir
Shevchenko Blvd. 50/52, 252032 **Kiev**
Tel: 44-216 9708 Fax: 44-216 9708
artistic director Yevhen Savchuk
Type: mixed, a cappella and with orchestra *Repertoire:* standard choral repertoire; Ukrainian sacred music and folk songs, new Ukrainian compositions *Size:* 65

Kiev Chamber Choir
Ulyanovych St. 12, 252005 **Kiev**
Tel: 44-264 7786 Fax: 44-264 7786
artistic director Mykola Hobdych
Type: mixed *Repertoire:* Ukrainian folk songs, sacred music, Slavonic church music, Western classical works for chamber choirs *Size:* 20 *Touring:* USA *Comments:* recording of Taverner's Sviati won the 1997 Mercury Music Award

Kiev Radio and TV Choir
Kreschatik 26, **Kiev** 1
Tel: 44-229 1170 Fax: 44-229 3322
manager Evgeny Semchenko;
chorus master Victor Skoromny
Type: mixed *Repertoire:* classical, many Ukrainian world premieres, folk *Size:* 65 *Touring:* UK, Spain, Netherlands, Germany *Comments:* recordings on Melodiya and Russian Disc; represented by Sonata (please see Promoters and Agents & Producers, UK)

Kyiv Conservatory Choir
K. Marx St. 1/3, 252001 **Kiev**
Tel: 44-229 0792
artistic director Pavlo Muravsky

Legenda Chamber Choir
Franko St. 30, 293720 **Ivano-Frankivsk**
Tel: 3244-23373/21450
director Ihor Tysklinskyi
Type: mixed

NCIC Capella
c/o Timchenko Svetlana, National Chamebr for International Co-operation, Box 66, 270011 **Odessa**
Tel: 482-247 047 Fax: 482-247 047
conductor Alisa Serebri
Type: male and female choirs *Repertoire:* Ukranian folk song, classical, liturgy *Size:* 30

Oreya Chamber Choir
Sobornyi Maydan 1, 262014 **Zhytomyr**
Tel: 412-372 491/373 468
Fax: 412-372 491/373 468
artistic director Oleksander Vatysk

Revutsky Men's Choir
Basseyna St. 1/2, 252004 **Kiev**
Tel: 44-225 1214/224 5909
Fax: 44-225 1214/224 6071
artistic director Bohdan Antkiv

Shchedryk Children's Choir
c/o Natala Pylypenko, Potychina St. 14/27, 252127 **Kiev**
artistic director Iryna Sablina

State Bandurists Choir
Volodymyrskyj Uzviz 2, 252001 **Kiev**
Tel: 44-228 0330

Trembita State Choir and Orchestra
Sichovych Striltsiv 10, 290000 **Lviv**
Tel: 322-727 063
Fax: 322-727 063
artistic director Mykola Kulyk

Ukraine National Opera Chorus
Shevchenko boulevard, **Kiev**
Tel: 44-224 0424 Fax: 44-229 3819
artistic director Anatoly Mokrenko;
chief conductor Lev Venedictov
Size: 80 *Comments:* recordings on Melodiya

UNITED KINGDOM (+44)

A Capella Portuguesa
The Queen's College,
Oxford OX1 4BW
Tel: 1865-279 173
Fax: 1865-790 819
E-Mail: bnelson@hkucc.hku.uk
director Bernadette Nelson; director/conductor Owen Rees (owen.rees@queens.ox.ac.uk)
Type: a cappella *Repertoire:* 16th/17th C music from Spain and Portugal *Size:* 10-18 *Perfs:* 4-6 *Touring:* national, international *Comments:* 3 recordings for Hyperion; much of repertoire performed is a result of research by Bernadette Nelson and Owen Rees; alternative E-mail: owen.rees@queens.ox.ac.uk

Academy of St Martin in the Fields Chorus
Raine House, Raine Street,
London E1 9RG
Tel: 20-7702 1377
Fax: 20-7481 0228
Internet: www.academysmif.co.uk
E-Mail: info@academysmif.co.uk
general manager George Brown;
administrator Louise Allen
Type: a cappella and orchestral *Size:* 24-75 *Touring:* UK, abroad *Comments:* work together with the orchestra; recordings, concerts & international tours done annually; see also Orchestras

Allegri Singers, The
16 Hall Drive, **Sydenham** SE26 6XB
Tel: 20-8778 4760
musical director Michael Nicholas;
hon. secretary Malcolm Gale
Type: a cappella and chamber *Repertoire:* standard choral repertoire specialising in 20th C works *Size:* 30 *Perfs:* 6 *Comments:* recordings available from Continuum Ltd and Thames Publishing

Amaryllis Consort
34 Lebanon Court, Richmond Road,
Twickenham TW1 3DA
Tel: 20-8892 3484
Fax: 20-8892 3484
director Charles Brett
Type: madrigal ensemble *Repertoire:* renaissance, Schubert/Brahms, Purcell, Poulenc *Size:* 6-8 *Perfs:* 20 *Touring:* UK, France, Spain, Mexico, Switzerland *Comments:* record, work with instrumentalists occasionally

Ambrosian Opera Chorus
4 Reynolds Road, **Beaconsfield** HP9 2NJ
Tel: 1494-680 873
Fax: 1494-680 501
director John McCarthy OBE
Type: opera chorus *Repertoire:* English, French, Italian, German and Russian repertoire *Size:* up to 450 *Perfs:* 30-40 *Touring:* Europe *Comments:* see also Ambrosian Singers, and John McCathy Singers

Ambrosian Singers
4 Reynolds Road, **Beaconsfield** HP9 2NJ
Tel: 1494-680 873
Fax: 1494-680 501
director John McCarthy OBE
Type: male, a cappella, children's, female, mixed, chamber, polyphonic, madrigal, gregorian *Repertoire:* Gregorian, Mozarabic, Ambrosian and Hebraic chants *Size:* up to 450 *Perfs:* 30-40 *Touring:* Europe *Comments:* see also Ambrosian Opera Chorus, and John McCarthy Singers

Bach Choir, The
30A Evelina Road, **London** SE15 2DX
Tel: 20-7277 7100
Fax: 20-7277 7100
Internet: www.TheBachChoir.org.uk
E-Mail: richard@TheBachChoir.org.uk
general manager Richard Sadler;
musical director David Hill
Type: mixed a cappella to large scale orchestral *Repertoire:* Tallis to new commissions *Size:* 265 *Perfs:* 24 *Comments:* also promote many of their own concerts; CD's available on Decca, Chandos, Pickwick, EMI, ASV, Priory and Lyrata

BBC National Chorus of Wales
BBC Broadcasting House, Llandaff,
Cardiff (Wales) CF5 2YQ
Tel: 29-2032 2587
Fax: 29-2032 2575
E-Mail: david.lawrence@bbc.co.uk
artistic director Simon Halsey; assistant director Adrian Partington; chorus manager David Lawrence
Type: orchestral, mixed *Repertoire:* standard choral repertoire *Size:* 160 *Perfs:* 6-12 *Touring:* UK

BBC Singers
Room 24, BBC Studios, Delaware Road,
London W9 2LG
Tel: 20-7765 4370 (manager)/4522 (producer)
Fax: 20-7765 2762
E-Mail: stephenashley-king@bbc.co.uk
manager Stephen Ashley-King; co-ordinator Ruth Potter; producer Michael Emery; assistant Neil Varley; chief conductor Stephen Cleobury
Type: professional *Repertoire:* 16th century to present day *Size:* 24 (6,6,6,6) *Touring:* national and international *Comments:* only full time professional choir in the UK

BBC Symphony Chorus
BBC Studios, Delaware Road, **London** W9 2LG
Tel: 20-7765 4715
Fax: 20-7286 3251
Internet: www.bbc.co.uk/orchestras/so/chorus
E-Mail: graham.wood@bbc.co.uk
administrator Graham Wood; director Stephen Jackson
Type: mostly with orchestra *Repertoire:* standard choral repertoire, emphasis on rarities and contemporary *Size:* 150 *Perfs:* 15-20 *Comments:* CDs recorded in conjunction with the BBC Symphony Orchestra on Teldec label and on their own on ASV

Belfast Cathedral Choir
Belfast Cathedral, Donegall Street,
Belfast BT1 2MB
Tel: 28-9032 8332 Fax: 28-9023 8855
organist David Drinkell
Type: church music *Size:* 50 *Perfs:* every Sunday and additional concerts *Touring:* UK, USA, Canada, Norway *Comments:* performs music of all periods to a high standard in the context of divine sevice, broadcasts andrecordings

Belfast Philharmonic Choir
36 Eastleigh Dale, **Belfast** BT4 3DT
Tel: 28-9067 1820
contact Dorothea Kerr
Type: with orchestra *Repertoire:* Messiah, Verdi Requiem, Mahler etc. *Size:* 160 *Perfs:* 5 *Comments:* venue: The Waterfront Hall, Belfast 2000

Bournemouth Sinfonietta Choir
221 Queen's Park Avenue,
Bournemouth BH8 9HD
Tel: 1202-393 352
secretary Pat Williams; conductor Howard Ionascu
Type: a cappella and orchestral *Repertoire:* standard choral repertoire *Size:* 25 *Perfs:* 10 *Touring:* UK

Bournemouth Symphony Chorus
7 Southbourne Coast Road, **Bournemouth** BH6 4BC
Tel: 1202-423 429 Fax: 1202-423 429
E-Mail: carolyn@bschorus.dircon.co.uk
secretary Carolyn Date; chorus master Neville Creed
Type: symphony chorus *Repertoire:* large scale choral works *Size:* 180 *Perfs:* 15-20 *Comments:* performs regularly with the Bournemouth Symphony Orchestra, the Bournemouth Sinfonietta, and other orchestras; address may change in '99 to: 7 Southbourne Coast Road, Bournemouth BH6 4DE; no further details were known at time of going to print

Brighton Festival Chorus
42 High Street, **Worthing** BN14 7NR
Tel: 70107 06235 Fax: 1903-602 831
Internet: www.pavilion.co.uk/bfc
chairman Jane Davies; music director James Morgan; general manager Eric Thompson; artistic manager Gill Kay; chorus administrator Robert Smith
Type: mixed *Repertoire:* all including contemporary *Size:* up to 170 *Perfs:* 12-14 *Touring:* international *Comments:* freelance chorus (concerts and recordings); recent work with the Royal Philharmonic, Philharmonia, Boston Symphony, London Philharmonic, Budapest Symphony, Orchestre National d'Ile de France; second address: 12a Pavillion Buildings, North St Brighton, E Sx. BN1 1EE, Tel: 1273-700 747 Fax: 1273-707 505

Britten Singers
c/o Denny Lyster Artists Management, 25 Courthope Road, **London** NW3 2LE
Tel: 20-7485 5932
Fax: 20-7267 0179
manager Jolyon Dodgson; president Richard Hickox; artistic director Simon Wright; contact Denny Lyster
Type: a cappella *Repertoire:* all periods, specialities:18th/19th century and contemporary *Size:* 16+ *Touring:* worldwide *Comments:* recordings mainly on Chandos

Cambridge Singers
PO Box 172, Whittlesford,
Cambridge CB2 4QZ
Tel: 1223-832 474
Fax: 1223-836 723
Internet: www.collegium.co.uk
E-Mail: info@collegium.co.uk
music director John Rutter
Type: professional, mixed voice *Repertoire:* standard choral repertoire *Size:* 28 *Comments:* recording choir only; recordings available mainly on the Collegium label

Cambridge Taverner Choir
29 Denton House, Bingham Court, Halton Road,
London N1 2AE
Tel: 20-7359 5960 Fax: 20-7359 5960
E-Mail: Helen.Garrison@bbc.co.uk
director Owen Rees; administrator Helen Garrison
Type: a cappella *Repertoire:* European renaissance *Size:* 20 *Perfs:* 5+ *Comments:* regular concert series at Cambridge; CD recordings available from Herald; various festivals

Camden Choir, The
80 Berners Way, **Broxbourne** EN10 6NP
Tel: 1992-443 321 Fax: 1992-443 321
E-Mail: camdenchoir@geocities.com
chair Mavis Pickard; musical director Julian Williamson; membership Krystyna Kujawinska (tel: 20-8943 1712)
Type: a cappella *Repertoire:* choral work from 16th C – contemporary *Size:* 40-50 *Perfs:* 3-4 *Comments:* already performed 4 world premieres; concert and rehearsal venue in Primrose Hill

Cantabile
c/o Seaview Music, 28 Manson Rd.,
Cambridge CB1 2EA
Tel: 1223-508 431 Fax: 1223-508 449
manager Alison Page
Type: male vocal ensemble *Repertoire:* light classical *Size:* 4 *Touring:* Europe

Canterbury Cathedral Choir
Christ Church Cathedral, 6 The Precincts,
Canterbury CT1 2EE
Tel: 1227-765 219 Fax: 1227-865 222
E-Mail: daocjaflood@email.msn.com
master of choristers David Flood
Type: cathedral choir *Repertoire:* wide choral repertoire *Size:* 30 *Perfs:* daily *Touring:* Spain, France, Netherlands *Comments:* recordings available on Metronome and York Ambisonic

Canzonetta
266 Manor Avenue, **Sale** M33 4NB
Tel: 161-905 1218 Fax: 161-905 1218
administrator Fiona Clucas;
music director Jeffrey Wynn Davies
Type: chamber choir, a cappella *Repertoire:* mixed, mainly 20th century *Size:* 8-28 *Perfs:* 5+ *Touring:* country-wide *Comments:* regular performances at Bridgewater Hall; recordings available on Guild and Somm labels

Cappella Nova
1/R 172 Hyndland Road, **Glasgow (Scotland)** G12 9HZ
Tel: 141-552 0634 Fax: 141-552 4053
E-Mail: alan.tavener@strath.ac.uk
manager Rebecca Tavener; director Alan Tavener
Type: professional *Repertoire:* from early to contemporary, particularly Scottish *Size:* 3-16 *Perfs:* 30+ *Touring:* national, international *Comments:* radio and TV recordings, CD's available on ASV Gaudeamus and Linn; often commission work

Cardiff Polyphonic Choir
148 Westbourne Road, **Penarth (Wales)** CF64 5BQ
Tel: 29-2070 7827
Fax: 29-2070 7827
E-Mail: howard.goodfellow@virgin.net
manager Howard Goodfellow;
musical director Simon Lovell-Jones
Type: mixed *Repertoire:* madrigal motels to larger choral works *Size:* 45 *Perfs:* 15 *Touring:* Europe, Czech Republic, USA *Comments:* recordings available on Black Mountain and Qualiton

Choir of Christ Church Cathedral Oxford, The
c/o Val Fancourt Music Management, 16 Ranelagh Avenue, Barnes Common, **London** SW13 0BW
Tel: 20-8876 6509 Fax: 20-8876 2551
E-Mail: valfancourt@compuserve.com
director Stephen Darlington;
sub-organiser David Goode
Type: cathedral choir (boys and men) *Size:* 32 *Touring:* Japan, USA, Belgium, Germany *Comments:* CDs available; television work

Choir of New College Oxford, The
c/o E. Higginbottom, New College, **Oxford** OX1
Tel: 1865-279 519 Fax: 1865-279 590
E-Mail: edward.higginbottom@new.ox.ac.uk
director Edward Higginbottom
Type: collegiate choir (boys and men) *Repertoire:* standard choral repertoire, with special interest in 16th-18th centuries *Size:* 32 *Touring:* France, Netherlands, Belgium, USA, Japan

Choir of the Orchestra of St. John's Smith Square
The White House, Eltham College, Grove Park Road,
London SE9 4QF
Tel: 20 8857 8579
Fax: 20 8857 9340
chorus master Jeremy Jackman; artistic director John Lubbock; general manager Nicky Goulder
Type: chamber choir *Repertoire:* standard choral repertoire *Size:* 30-60 *Perfs:* 8-12 per year *Comments:* CD available on ASV; see also Orchestras

City of Birmingham Choir
3 Fallowfield Road, **Walsall** WS5 3BS
Tel: 1922-722 602
Fax: 1922-722 602
general secretary Sylvia Emberson;
conductor Christopher Robinson CVO
Type: adult; mixed choir *Repertoire:* standard choral repertoire *Size:* 180 *Perfs:* 6
Comments: perform with the City of Birmingham Symphony Orchestra in the Symphony Hall

City of Birmingham Symphony Chorus (CBSC)
CBSO Centre, Berkley Street, **Birmingham** B1 2LF
Tel: 121-616 6500
Fax: 121-616 6518
Internet: www.cbso.co.uk
E-Mail: information@cbso.co.uk
chorus manager Claire Walters; music director Sir Simon Rattle CBE; chorus director Simon Halsey; chorus secretary Julia Towers
Type: symphonic, a cappella *Repertoire:* classical to contemporary *Size:* 200 *Perfs:* 25
Touring: national, Europe, Canada, Australia *Comments:* the CBSC undertakes an extensive programme of independent tours and concerts; recent work with Leipzig Gewandhaus, Rotterdam Philharmonic, Vienna Symphony, Amsterdam Concertgebow

City of Birmingham Symphony Youth Chorus
CBSO Centre, Berkley Street, **Birmingham** B1 2LF
Tel: 121-616 6500
Fax: 121-616 6518
Internet: www.cbso.co.uk
E-Mail: information@cbso.co.uk
chorus manager Claire Walters; music director Sir Simon Rattle CBE; chorus director Simon Halsey; chorus masters Adrian Partington, Shirley Court; secretary Julia Towers
Type: children's choir, a cappella, symphonic
Repertoire: standard choral repertoire *Size:* senior chorus (65: age 12-18yrs), junior chorus (100: 8-12 yrs)
Perfs: 20 *Touring:* national *Comments:* membership 1 year only by audition/readuition

City of Birmingham Youth Voices
CBSO Centre, Berkley Street, **Birmingham** B1 2LF
Tel: 121-616 6500
Fax: 121-616 6518
Internet: www.cbso.co.uk
E-Mail: information@cbso.co.uk
manager Claire Walters; conductor David Lawrence; chorus secretary Julia Towers
Type: SATB youth choir (4 part: soprano, alto, tenor, bass) *Size:* 120 *Perfs:* 4-6 *Comments:* CBYV is a collaborative project between Birmingham Music Service and CBSO; free membership, no auditions

City of Glasgow Chorus
14 Hyndland Road, **Glasgow (Scotland)** G12 9UP
Tel: 141-339 6153
Fax: 141-339 6153
E-Mail: grataylorglas@btinternet.com
music director Graham Taylor
Type: mixed (both a cappella & with orchestra)
Repertoire: main stream choral repertoire with emphasis on less frequently performed work *Size:* 140
Perfs: 12 *Comments:* 5 recordings available & several broadcasts on BBC2; perform with City of Glasgow Symphony, Orchestra of Scottish Opera, Royal Scottish National Orchestra

City of London Choir
81b Copleston Road,
London SE15 4AH
Tel: 20-7639 2873
Internet: www.colc.org.uk
chairman Duncan Robertson;
musical director Hilary Davan Wetton; treasurer Alan Cathcart; concert manager Jenny Robinson
Type: orchestral *Repertoire:* oratorio *Size:* 100
Perfs: 6 *Comments:* recorded CD with BBC Concert Orchestra

Consort of Musicke, The
13 Pages Lane, **London** N10 1PU
Tel: 20-8444 6565
Fax: 20-8444 1008
E-Mail: consort@easynet.co.uk
musical director Anthony Rooley;
administrator Lindsay Richardson
Type: early music vocal ensemble *Repertoire:* renaissance *Size:* up to 6 *Touring:* Europe, Israel, North America *Comments:* see also Early Music

Coro Cervantes
Flat 5, 58 Cleveland Way, **London** E1 4UF
Tel: 20-7366 6909
Fax: 20-7366 6909
Internet: Carlos@corocerv.force9.co.uk
E-Mail: www.corocerv.f9.co.uk
director Carlos Fernández Aransay;
manager Debra Skeen
Type: chamber choir *Repertoire:* specialised in Hispanic (Iberic and Latin American) classical choral music, from medieval to contemporary

Corydon Singers
24 Kirdford Road, **Arundel** BN18 9EE
Tel: 1903-885 465
Fax: 1903-885 466
Internet: www.orchestranet.co.uk/corydon.html
E-Mail: corydon.office@BTinternet.com
general manager Linda Osborne;
artistic director Matthew Best
Type: mixed choir for chamber through to symphonic repertoire *Size:* 30-100 *Perfs:* 12 *Touring:* International *Comments:* Hyperion recording catalogue (extensive discography); see also Orchestras

Crouch End Festival Chorus
PO Box 17102, **London** N8 9WH
Tel: 20-8374 4463 Fax: 20-8374 4463
chair Pauline Hoyle; musical director David Temple; membership secretary Catherine Best; pr Naomi Fulop
Type: a cappella and orchestral, mixed *Repertoire:* 20th C choral *Size:* 175 *Perfs:* 8-10 *Comments:* affiliated to NFMS; recordings with BBC Symphony Orchestra; several CDs available

Croydon Bach Choir, The
83 Purley Downs Road, **South Croydon** CR2 0RJ
Tel: 20-8668 4372
Fax: 20-8668 4372
chair Donald Rose; music director Peter Nardone; membership secretary Sandie Roper (20-8669 0616)
Type: a cappella and orchestral *Repertoire:* standard choral repertoire and new works *Size:* 60-70 *Perfs:* 4 *Comments:* affiliated to NFMS

Croydon Philharmonic Choir
29 Sundown Avenue, **Sanderstead** CR2 0RQ
Tel: 20-8657 1631
music director James Gaddarn;
Hon. general secretary George Jalfon
Type: choral classic with orchestra
Repertoire: wide choral repertoire *Size:* 130-150 *Perfs:* 5+

Deller Consort
2 Rural Terrace, Wye, **Ashford** TN25 5AP
Tel: 1233-812 267
Fax: 1227-781 830
musical director Mark Deller
Type: a cappella, madrigal with 1 lute
Repertoire: 16th/17th C *Size:* up to 7
Comments: management: Bureau de Concerts Maurice Werner, 7 rue Richpance 75008 Paris,
Tel: 1-4015 9280, Fax: 1-4926 0507

Elizabethan Singers of London
Elder Cottage, Felixstowe Ferry, **Felixstowe** IP11 9RZ
Tel: 1394-282 306 Fax: 1394-282 306
Internet:
www.classical-artists.com/elizabethan-singers/
E-Mail: elizabethan@classical-artists.com
administrator Anthony Ratcliffe; artistic and music director Sam Laughton; accompanist Simon Nieminski
Type: chamber choir *Repertoire:* 16th century-present day *Size:* 16-20 *Perfs:* 10-12
Touring: Germany, France, Norway *Comments:* the Elizabethan Singers are noted for their stylistic performances, researched from original historical sources and for their tradition of commissioning works from leading contemporary composers; also when appropriate perform in period costumes
(from their own wardrobe)

English Baroque Choir
c/o Hilary Sillis, 33 Lavington Road,
London W13 9NN
Tel: 20-8579 4169
Fax: 20-8932 0897
Internet: www.btinternet.com/~sashdown/ebc
E-Mail: sillis@dircon.co.uk
musical director Leon Lovett; chairman Peter Dean; contact Hilary Sillis
Type: a cappella, orchestral and mixed *Repertoire:* baroque; 16th-20th century *Size:* 60 *Perfs:* 7 *Touring:* Germany (Bocholt) *Comments:* the 1999/2000 season: 21st birthday celebrations

English Chamber Choir
8 Alma Square, **London** NW8 9QD
Tel: 20-7286 3944 Fax: 20-7289 9081
E-Mail: ecc.protheroe@btinternet.com
administrator Ann Manly; musical director Guy Protheroe; chair Hugh Joslin
Type: a cappella and orchestral *Repertoire:* standard choral repertoire, from 1500 to the present day
Size: 40-45 *Perfs:* 12-15 *Touring:* international *Comments:* perform frequently for commercial recordings, eg. films, albums, TV, commercials

English National Opera Chorus
London Coliseum, St Martin's Lane,
London WC2N 4ES
Tel: 20-7836 0111 ext. 302
Fax: 20-7845 9250
chorus manager Charles Kraus;
chorus master Stephen Harris
Type: opera *Repertoire:* opera *Size:* 68 *Perfs:* 175+
Comments: occassional records for TV and videos

Felicitas
184 Selwyn Avenue, Highams Park, **London** E4 9NE
Tel: 20-7699 3845 (day) /20-8527 5978 (evening)
Fax: 20-7699 3769
conductor Simon Winters; secretary Chrina Jarvis; membership secretary Ruth Marshall-Jones
Type: mainly a capella *Repertoire:* main emphasis on music from 16th-17th centuries but also music from other periods *Size:* 17 *Perfs:* 3-4 *Touring:* France
Comments: home venue is mainly Waltham Abbey, capacity 200; CDs available

Finchley Choral Society
c/o Graham Turl, 22 Wolstonbury, Woodside Park,
London N12 7BA
Tel: 20-8445 6717
president Brian Rayner Cook; chairman Graham Turl; musical director George Vass; secretary Norma Leeb; treasurer Alan Nafzger
Type: standard chorus with orchestras and soloists
Repertoire: standard choral repertoire including oratorios and masses, with professional soloists *Size:* 70
Perfs: 4 *Comments:* affiliated to NFMS

Finzi Singers
4 The Close, **Lichfield** WS13 7LD
Tel: 1543-250 627 Fax: 1543-250 970
E-Mail: paul.spicer@tisl.co.uk
administrator Elizabeth Dibben; director Paul Spicer
Type: mixed, chamber, a cappella *Repertoire:* specialise in British 20th C. *Size:* 12-18 *Touring:* national, international *Comments:* recording for Chandos Records and BBC Radio; professional choir

Geoffrey Mitchell Choir
49 Chelmsford Road, Woodford, **London** E18 2PW
Tel: 20-8491 0962 Fax: 20-8491 0956
E-Mail: 113073.654@compuserve.com
manager & chorus director Geoffrey Mitchell
Type: mixed, a cappella & orchestral *Repertoire:* varied
Size: 8-76 *Perfs:* 4 *Comments:* work mostly, though not exclusively, in the recording studio; 35 complete operas in the catalogue, for such labels as Opera Rara, Chandos, Hyperion, EMI, BBC, Carlton Classics

Gesualdo Consort of London
112 Wordsworth Road, **Hampton** TW12 1ET
Tel: 20-8941 2684 Fax: 20-8941 2684
E-Mail: vernosa@ndirect.co.uk
director Gerald Place
Type: vocal ensemble unaccompanied or with lute
Repertoire: late renaissance & early baroque; 20th century *Size:* 4-6
Touring: national, Italy, Netherlands, Belgium
Comments: recordings for ASV, Cantoris, Libra, TV film on Gesualdo for Werner Herzog (ZDF); see also Early Music

Goldsmiths Choral Union
25 Ashlyn Grove, Ardleigh Green,
Hornchurch RM11 2EQ
Tel: 1708-472 252 Fax: 1708-472 252
Internet: www.harmony.demon.co.uk/gcu/gcuad
E-Mail: VictoriaWare@compuserve.com
secretary Victoria Ware; music director Brian Wright; chairman Timothy Maby
Type: classical music choir *Repertoire:* wide repertoire
Size: 120-140 *Perfs:* 4-6 *Comments:* do broadcasts; commission work

Guildford Cathedral Choir
Guildford Cathedral, Stag Hill, **Guildford** GU2 5UP
Tel: 1483-565 287
Fax: 1483-303 350
Internet: www.guildford-cathedral.org
E-Mail: jill@guildford-cathedral.org
conductor Stephen Farr; sub-organist Geoffrey Morgan
Type: men and boys, mostly accompanied by organ and a cappella *Repertoire:* sacred *Size:* 30
Perfs: 300 choral services + occassional concerts
Touring: Denmark *Comments:* recordings available on Heral, Crimson, Lammas, Priory

Hallé Choir
92 Brown Lane, Heald Green, **Cheadle** SK8 3RA
Tel: 161-437 5991 Fax: 161-437 5991
administrator William Golightly;
chorus master Keith Orrell
Type: symphony chorus *Repertoire:* classical – contemporary *Size:* 150 *Perfs:* 25 annually *Touring:* international including France, Switzerland

Hamilton Harty Ensemble
62 Ulsterville Av, **Belfast** BT9 7AQ
Tel: 28-9066 7009
contact Peter Scott
Type: backing, concert work *Repertoire:* modern, classical *Size:* 25

Hilliard Ensemble, The
c/o Hazard Chase, Richmond House, 16-20 Regent Street, **Cambridge** CB2 1DB
Tel: 1223-312 400 Fax: 1223-460 827
Internet: www.hazardchase.co.uk
E-Mail: info@hazardchase.co.uk
counter tenor David James; tenor Rogers Covey-Crump, John Potter; bass Gordon Jones
Repertoire: medieval, renaissance, contemporary, mostly a cappella, collaboration with Jan Garbarek (saxophone)
Size: 4 *Perfs:* 100 *Touring:* worldwide *Comments:* also joined by other singers & instrumentalists for particular works

Holst Singers
The Holst Office, PO Box 16090, **London** EC4Y 7HS
Tel: 20-7936 4762 Fax: 20-7936 4767
E-Mail: holst-singers@tisl.co.uk
president James Bowman; music director Stephen Layton
Type: mixed *Repertoire:* English romantic *Size:* 36 *Perfs:* 20 *Comments:* record for Hyperion Records

Huddersfield Choral Society
c/o Jennie Blythe Artists Management, Sunnyside,
Lower Swell GL54 1LG
Tel: 1451-830 059 Fax: 1451-832 357
chorus master Joseph Cullen; principal guest conductor Jane Glover; principal conductor Martyn Brabbins
Type: full choir S.A.T.B. performing with professional orchestras *Repertoire:* standard choral repertoire *Size:* 200 *Perfs:* 8-15 *Comments:* the Huddersfield Choral Society is one of the oldest in Britain-founded in 1836; since that date the Society has built itself not only a national but also an international reputation for excellence

Ionian Singers, The
54 Holmdene Avenue, **London** SE24 9LE
Tel: 20-7733 6719 Fax: 20-7733 6719
E-Mail: ionsing@netcomuk.co.uk
manager Ulla Gray; conductor Timothy Salter
Type: SATB chamber choir, mostly unaccompanied
Repertoire: renaissance to present; emphasis on contemporary *Size:* 30 *Perfs:* 6 *Touring:* USA *Comments:* new and neglected works from the past form an important part of their programmes;
regular commercial recordings

Janet Sødring Spectrum Singers
19 Coombe Road, **London** W4 2HR
Tel: 20-8994 8149
musical director Janet Sødring
Type: 1: choral, 2: upper voices *Repertoire:* baroque, madrigals, masterworks, unaccompanied from 16th-20th century *Size:* 1: 8, 2: 4 *Perfs:* 2 *Comments:* ISM registered private singing teacher

John Alldis Choir
c/o Allied Artists Agency, 42 Montpellier Square,
London SW7 1JZ
Tel: 20-7589 6243 Fax: 20-7581 5269
manager Geoffrey Mitchell; conductor John Alldis
Type: a cappella and orchestral *Repertoire:* contemporary, opera, standard choral repertoire *Size:* 16 (mixed); 60-80 for large recording projects *Comments:* The Opera Chorus have done 50 CD recordings including recordings with Pavarotti, Sutherland, Domingo etc.; The John Alldis Choir has made 6 recordings (contemporary music plus many others of choral/orchestral repertoire (16-20 songs); The Groupe Vocal de France has made 42 recordings of early 20th century music

John Currie Singers, The
The Old Schoolhouse, Ballintuim, **Blairgowire (Scotland)** PH10 7NJ
Tel: 1250-886 234 Fax: 1250-886 327
artistic director & administrator John Currie;
chairman Raymond Williamson
Type: professional ensemble of singers and instruments
Repertoire: all periods and including Messiah, Monteverdi Vespers, the great Passions, Magnificat, B minor mass of Bach, late masses of Haydn *Size:* 16
Perfs: 16-18 *Touring:* national and international
Comments: founded in 1968; commission and perform many works by British composers

John McCarthy Singers
4 Reynolds Road, **Beaconsfield** HP9 2NJ
Tel: 1494-680 873 Fax: 1494-680 501
conductor John McCarthy OBE
Type: male, female, chamber, polyphonic, children
Repertoire: all types of music including madrigal, pop and light music *Size:* 40-60 *Perfs:* 30-40 *Touring:* Europe
Comments: specialist at gregorian and ambrosian chants; see also Ambrosian Opera Chorus, and Ambrosian Singers

Joyful Company of Singers
c/o London Musicians Ltd., Cedar House, Vine Lane,
Hillingdon UB10 0BK
Tel: 1895-252 555 Fax: 1895-252 556
Internet: www.jeos.demon.co.uk
E-Mail: bridget@lonmus.demon.co.uk
conductor/music director Peter Broadbent; chairman Rosemary Day; administrator Bridget Howarth
Type: chamber choir, mostly a cappella sometimes with orchesta *Repertoire:* 16th-20th C emphasis on contemporary *Size:* 24-32, pool of 110 singers *Perfs:* 22 *Touring:* national, Europe, festivals *Comments:* alternative address: Peter Broadbent, 52 Edenbridge Road, Enfield, Middlesex EN1 2LW tel/fax: 20-8360 7281 e-mail:pb@jcos.demon.co.uk; prizes;
recordings EMI Classics

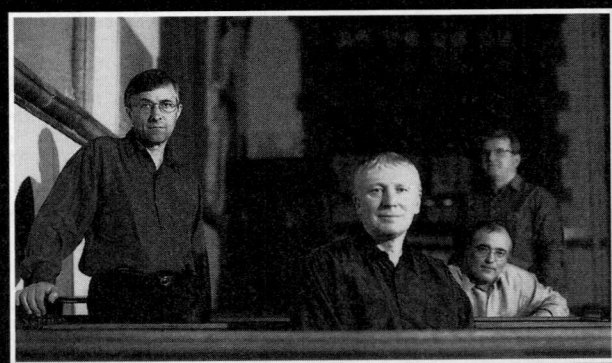

King's College Choir
King's College, **Cambridge** CB2 1ST
Tel: 1223-331 224
Fax: 1223-331 890
Internet: www.kings.cam.ac.uk
E-Mail: choir@kings.cam.ac.uk
director Stephen Cleobury
Type: all male collegiate choir *Repertoire:* church music *Size:* 30 *Perfs:* daily (except Monday), twice on Sunday during term-time + concerts & tours *Touring:* national, international *comments:* Agent: Intermusica Artists' Management Ltd, contact Peter Savory

Laudate Chamber Choir
81 Church Road, **Radley** OX14 3QF
Tel: 1235-543 066
Fax: 1235-543 034
E-Mail: HJPI@radely.org.uk
director Howard Ionescu; administrator Bella Pearson
Type: mixed, with orchestra *Repertoire:* chamber choral music *Size:* 16 *Touring:* France

Leeds Philharmonic Chorus
30 Jackman Drive, Horsforth,
Leeds LS18 4HS
Tel: 113-258 2744
secretary John Brodwell; president Lady Groves; chorus master Elisabeth Jill Wild
Type: amateur choral society *Repertoire:* standard choral repertoire *Size:* 200 *Perfs:* 4 *Touring:* UK *Comments:* CDs available on Chandos and BBC Classics

London Choral Society
c/o Jennie Blythe Artists Management, Sunnyside,
Lower Swell GL54 1LG
Tel: 1451-830 059
Fax: 1451-832 357
administrator Anne Howick; principal conductor Jane Glover; musical director Ronald Corp
Type: full S.A.T.B. choir performing with professional orchestra; mixed; sometimes a cappella *Repertoire:* standard choral repertoire; popular and operatic *Size:* 120 *Perfs:* 8 *Touring:* international *Comments:* patron: HRH The Duke of Gloucester; past conductors include Gennadi Rozdestvensky, Lord Menuhin, Pierre Boulez, Mstislav Rostropovich; works regularly with the New London Orchestra and the
Royal Philharmonic Orchestra

London Concert Choir
c/o Melanie Mehta, 6 Maxwell Gardens,
Orpington BR6 9QS
Tel: 1689-896 712/956-937 983 (mobile)
Internet: www.london-concert-choir.freeserve.co.uk
E-Mail: 100331.210@compuserve.com
conductor Mark Forkgen;
composer in association Simon Speare
Type: mixed *Size:* approx. 100 *Perfs:* 4-8
Touring: invited to perform in Cannes in Summer 1999
Comments: a series of vocal workshops will take place during each season in conjunction with the Composer in Association programme; welcome new members; for information about choir membership contact Melanie Mehta

London Concord Singers
126 Northchurch Rd., **London** N1 3PA
Tel: 20-7226 1392
music director Malcolm Cottle;
membership secretary Robert Hugill
Type: mixed chamber *Repertoire:* 16th-20th century *Size:* 25-30 *Perfs:* 3+ *Comments:* winners of PRS awards for Choral Enterprise

London Forest Choir
c/o Walthamstow Adult Education Centre, Greenleaf Rd.,
London E17
Tel: 20-8527 5978 Fax: 20-8688 2901
musical director Murray Stewart; secretary Chrina Jarvis (Tel: 20-8527 5978); membership secretary Joyce Giles
Type: mixed; with orchestra or organ
Repertoire: standard choral repertoire *Size:* 80-100 *Perfs:* 6 *Comments:* mostly perform with London Pro Arte Orchestra; CD available

London Handel Choir
The Coach House, Drury Lane,
Redmarley d'Abitôt GL19 3JX
Tel: 1531-650 616
Fax: 1531-650 616
conductor Denys Darlow; administrator Ann Senior (Tel: 20-8563 0618)
Type: mixed *Repertoire:* Handel and baroque period (also contemporary) *Size:* 18-22
Perfs: 15-20*Comments:* performs for London Handel Festival; see also Early Music

London Orpheus Choir
2 Tenby Mansions, Nottingham Street,
London W1M 3RD
Tel: 20-7486 1929
musical director James Gaddarn; chairman Colin Evans; secretary Judith Scammell
Type: mixed, with orchestra *Repertoire:* standard choral repertoire *Size:* 60 *Perfs:* 4+ annually *Comments:* recordings for the BBC

London Philharmonic Choir
13 Huntspill Street, **London** SW17 0AA
Tel: 20-8947 4355 Fax: 20-8947 4355
Internet: www.netlink.co.uk/users/lazuli/lpc
E-Mail: russ@dircon.co.uk
chairman Jane Hanson; secretary Anne Cotter; hon. treasurer Liz Cole; chorus master Neville Creed; auditions secretary Russell Scott (20-8953 4600)
Type: orchestral, mixed *Repertoire:* standard orchestral/choral repertoire *Size:* 140 *Perfs:* 12+ *Touring:* international *Comments:* rehearsals on Mondays and most Wednesdays in the city of London; patronage of HRH Princess Alexandra, president Sir Roger Norrington; large number of recordings available on labels such as Chandos, EMI and Decca

London Sinfonietta Chorus & Voices
22 St Mary's Avenue, **London** E11 2NP
Tel: 20-8989 4804 Fax: 20-8989 7389
general manager Paul Meecham;
director Terry Edwards
Type: a cappella *Repertoire:* 20th C *Size:* varies
Perfs: 6-10 *Comments:* see also London Voices

London Symphony Chorus
The Lodge, 70 Shooters Hill Road, **London** SE3 7BG
Tel: 20-7560 4030 Fax: 20-7560 4066
Internet: www.lsc.org.uk
E-Mail: pam_barker@tbg.focusnet.co.uk
principal conductor Richard Hickox; chorus director Stephen Westrop; chairman Pam Barker
Type: orchestral *Repertoire:* symphonic choral work *Size:* 220 *Perfs:* 30+ *Touring:* Australia, Israel, Italy, Singapore, France, Germany *Comments:* the LSC is an independent choir but a large percentage of its work is with the LSO and also the BBC National Orchestra of Wales; City of London Sinfonia and Royal Philharmonic Orchestra

London Voices
22 St Mary's Avenue, **London** E11 2NP
Tel: 20-8989 4804 Fax: 20-8989 7389
director Terry Edwards; secretary Jacqueline Peet
Type: a cappella, orchestral, opera, professional
Repertoire: standard choral repertoire *Perfs:* 6-10
Comments: see also London Sinfonietta Chorus & Voices

London Welsh Chorale
London Welsh Centre, 157-163 Gray's Inn Road,
London WC1X 8VE
Tel: 20-7278 7525 (secretary)
music director Kenneth Bowen; secretary Gerard Brouwer; chairman Nigel Wills;
treasurer Melissa Downes
Type: mixed, SATB, a cappella and with orchestra or organ *Repertoire:* standard choral repertoire & Welsh composers *Size:* 90-100
Perfs: 4-6 per year *Touring:* Wales *Comments:* committed to performing music by Welsh composers and music written in Welsh

Malcolm Sargent Festival Choir
26 Lamont Road, **London** SW10 0JE
Tel: 20-7602 6818
Fax: 20-7602 8162
E-Mail: malcom.sargent@virgin.net
director of music Dr. Charles Farncombe CBE;
chairman Sylvia Darley OBE
Type: drawn from members of choirs from every part of England performing voluntarily to raise money for charities *Repertoire:* perform major works at Royal Albert Hall, Royal Festival Hall, Barbican, Symphony Hall Birmingham and are invited to other opera and classical galas etc., oratorio & cathedral
Size: 350 *Perfs:* 15 *Touring:* Europe *Comments:* for an application form contact: 34 North End Road, London, W14 OSH, Tel: 20-7602 6818

Meljon Singers, The
3 Bloomfield Crescent, **Ilford** IG2 6DR
Tel: 1268 414 179 (secretary)
E-Mail: glynjon@aol.com
musical director Janette Ruocco; chair John Buckmaster; secretary Gill Fletcher
Type: chamber choir; a cappella *Repertoire:* extensive sacred + secular repertoire from 1500 to present
Size: 20 *Perfs:* 6

Middlesex Bach Choir
7 Bidesford Road, **South Ruislip** HA4 0UB
Tel: 7431-2317
chairman John Nodder; musical director Susan Digby; treasurer Dawn Pickett
Type: mixed chamber choir *Repertoire:* serious and light music from 16th – 20th centuries *Size:* 20 *Perfs:* 4 + various other engagements *Comments:* winners of PRS awards for unusual programming;
commission new works

Monteverdi Choir
Monteverdi Choir and Orchestra Ltd, 61-63
Wandsworth High Street, **London** SW18 2PT
Tel: 20-8871 4750
Fax: 20-8871 4751
Internet: www.monteverdi.co.uk
E-Mail: info@monteverdi.org.uk
acting general manager Howard Gough; artistic director Sir John Eliot Gardiner; administrator Jan Normanton; choir manager Christopher Foster; project co-ordinator Andrew Hammond
Type: mixed *Repertoire:* all periods *Size:* 20-75 *Perfs:* 10-20 *Touring:* USA, Europe

New London Chamber Choir
Bancroft, Rectory Lane,
Fringford (near Bicester) OX6 9DX
Tel: 1869-278 392 Fax: 1869-278 392
Internet: www.brailsford.demon.co.uk/nlcc.htm
E-Mail: nlcc@brailsford.demon.co.uk
conductor James Wood
Type: a cappella and with orchestra or ensemble
Repertoire: from early music to 20th century *Size:* 24-36
Perfs: 20-25 *Touring:* Europe (including Contemporary Music Festival) *Comments:* regularly record with Deutsche Grammophon and Hyperion

Orlando Chamber Choir, The
9a Woodside Lane, **London** N12 8RB
Tel: 20-8445 3819
contact Helen Cormack; conductor Brian Gordon
Type: a cappella, choral *Repertoire:* baroque & classical
Size: 40 *Perfs:* 2 concerts annually

Philharmonia Chorus
c/o Richard Thomas, 241 Shaftesbury Avenue,
London WC2H 8EH
Tel: 20-7333 1722 Fax: 20-7333 1769
E-Mail: richard@rhinegold.co.uk
chairman t.b.a.; airtistic director & chorus master Robert Dean; auditions secretary Hana Tiller
Type: orchestral, a cappella, mixed *Repertoire:* standard choral repertoire *Size:* up to 180 *Perfs:* 12-20 *Touring:* France, Spain, Germany *Comments:* works mainly with Philharmonia Orchestra, also frequently with other major orchestras, including The BBC S.O., The Royal Philharmonic, Orchestre Philharmonique de Strasbourg and The Orchestra of the Age of Enlightenment

Polly & the Phonics
25 Hailstone Close, **Rowley Regis** B65 8LJ
Tel: 1384-252 632 Fax: 1384-252 632
Internet: www.hecate.freeserve.co.uk
contact Heather Wastie, Kate Buttolph (tel: 121-458 6664), Alison Sabedoria (tel:121-523 9424)
Type: female vocal harmony plus keyboards, percussion & recorders *Repertoire:* fusion of cabaret & music theatre; early music & roots; popular & contemporary
Size: 3

Polyhymnia Choir Consort & Players
3 Paternoster House, Colebrook Street,
Winchester SO23 9LG
Tel: 1962-865 617
director Richard Lowell Childress
Type: professional chamber, mixed or all-male as required, usually a cappella *Repertoire:* Spanish renaissance, early North American, 15th-19th century sacred/secualr, 20th century *Size:* 8-18 as required
Comments: CD on Meridian label; ensemble in residence: The Winchester Early Music Festival

Polyphony
c/o Hazard Chase, 16-20 Regent Street,
Cambridge CB2 1DB
Tel: 1223-312 400 Fax: 1223-460 827
Internet: www.hazardchase.co.uk
E-Mail: info@hazardchase.co.uk
conductor Stephen Layton
Type: mixed voice ensemble *Repertoire:* medieval to contemporary *Size:* 10-24 *Perfs:* 25

Pro Cantione Antiqua
c/o Concert Directory International, Lyndhurst, Denton Rd., Ben Rhydding, **Ilkley** LS29 8QR
Tel: 1943-607 821 Fax: 1943-817 063
E-Mail: pca@ndirect.co.uk
contact Catherine Scott
Type: male voice ensemble *Repertoire:* medieval, renaissance *Size:* 5-16 *Perfs:* 40 *Touring:* Spain *Comments:* 100+ recordings; CD's available on Hyperion, Archiv, Teldec, ASV

Pro Musica Chorus of London
6 Durham Row, **London** E1 0NP
Tel: 20-7790 1004 Fax: 20-7790 1004
administration William Ryder
Type: a cappella and orchestral *Repertoire:* baroque to 20th century,opera and concert repertoire *Size:* 80-140
Perfs: 20-35 *Touring:* international
Comments: new work undertaken

Red Byrd
c/o Robert White Artist Management,
182 Moselle Ave., **London** N22 6EX
Tel: 20-8881 6914 Fax: 20-8888 9662
E-Mail: rwhiteam@aol.com
manager Robert White; dirs John Potter, Richard Wistreich
Type: vocal ensemble *Repertoire:* medieval, renaissance, contemporary *Size:* 2-6 *Perfs:* 10 *Touring:* Europe
Comments: recordings on various labels incl. Hyperion & Virgin Classics; see also Early Music

Rossica Choir of St Petersburg
12 Warren pr. Dorridge, **Solihull** B93 8JY
Tel: 01564-776 376 Fax: 01564-776 376
manager Jean Shearman
Size: 26

Rouss-land Soglasie Male Voice Choir of St Petersburg
c/o David Golightly, Modrana Music Promotions, 41 Parklands Way, **Poynton** SK12 1AL
Tel: 1625-875 389 Fax: 1625-875 389
E-Mail: david.f.golightly@bt.internet.com
conductor Alexander Govorov; manager David Golightly
Type: male *Repertoire:* Russian sacred and secular music, English contemporary music *Size:* 23 *Perfs:* 60 (all in Germany) *Touring:* Germany *Comments:* 2 CDs released with Carlton Home Entertainment

Royal Choral Society
Studio 9, 92 Lots Road, **London** SW10 0QD
Tel: 20-7376 3718 Fax: 20-7376 3719
Internet: go.ourworld.nu/royalchoralsociety
E-Mail: royalchoralsociety@compuserve.com
adminstrator Graeme Tonge; music director Richard Cooke; choir secretary Helen Body
Type: choral *Repertoire:* wide repertoire including opera and popular classics *Size:* 200 *Pers:* 20 *Comments:* see also Promoters & National Organisations

Royal Liverpool Philharmonic Choir
Philharmonic Hall, Hope St, **Liverpool** L1 9BP
Tel: 151-210 2895 Fax: 151-210 2902
Internet: www.plps.co.uk
E-Mail: RLPSociety@aol.com
administrator Eleanor Wright; chorus master Ian Tracey
Type: mixed *Repertoire:* wide spectrum of choral repertoire *Size:* 160 *Perfs:* 25-30 *Comments:* CDs available

Royal Opera Chorus
Royal Opera House, Floral Street, Covent Garden, **London** WC2E 9DD
Tel: 20-7212 9385 Fax: 20-7212 9444
chorus manager Gemma Barraclough; chorus director Terry Edwards; manager Dermot Agnew
Type: opera chorus *Repertoire:* full opera repertoire *Size:* 44

Royal Scottish National Orchestra Chorus
73 Claremont Street, **Glasgow (Scotland)** G3 7JB
Tel: 141-225 3553 Fax: 141-221 4317
Internet: www.scot-art.org/rsno
E-Mail: admin@rsno.org.uk
chorus manager Jill Mitchell;
chorus master Christopher Bell
Type: chorus performing regularly with the orchestra *Repertoire:* symphonic choral music *Size:* 200 *Perfs:* 6-8 with the RSNO, 6-8 own performances *Touring:* Australia, Northern Ireland

Saint Bartholomew's Hospital Choral Society
9 Berkeley Mews, Sandringham Court, **Burnham** SL1 6JD
Tel: 1628-664 157 Fax: 1628-664 157
honorary secretary Joan Harding;
conductor Ivor Setterfield
Type: mixed, with orchestra *Repertoire:* standard choral repertoire with emphasis on romantic late 19th and 20th centuries *Size:* 120-350 *Perfs:* 3+ *Touring:* Holland *Comments:* no audition; always welcomes new members; voice production, sight singing classes

Salisbury Cathedral Choir
33 The Close, **Salisbury** SP1 2EJ
Tel: 1722-555 125 Fax: 1722-555 117
director of music Simon Lole;
administrator Barry Makin
Type: cathedral choir *Repertoire:* church music *Size:* 16 boys, 19 girls, 6 men *Perfs:* 10 outside cathedral commitments *Comments:* boy and girl choristers trials annually Jan & Feb; visiting choirs welcome during Cathedral Choir's absence

Schola Cantorum of Oxford
c/o Faculty of Music, St Aldates, **Oxford** OX1 1DB
Tel: 1865-276 125 Fax: 1865-276 128
secretary Cathryn Miserandino;
conductor Mark Shepherd
Type: a cappella, mixed *Repertoire:* wide spectrum of choral repertoire including 20th C and specially commissioned works *Size:* 34 *Perfs:* 20+ *Touring:* international *Comments:* recordings for Naxos and Proudsound

Scholars, The
aa
Comments: UK-based ensemble, administered by David van Asch from Altafulla (Tarragona), see separate entry under Spain

South West Chamber Choir
18 Down Ham Gardens, Tamdrcon Foliot, **Plymouth** PL5 4QE
Tel: 1752-776 479 Fax: 1752-776 479
E-Mail: janet.clark@btinternet.com
publicity manager Janet Clarke
Type: mixed *Size:* 32 *Perfs:* 8 *Touring:* Ireland, England *Comments:* membership by audition -Devon & Cornwall only

St Cecilia Singers
The Old School House, 5 Picklenash Court, **Newent** GL18 1BG
Tel: 1531-822 361
Fax: 1452-415 824
E-Mail: ian.ball@gifford.co.uk
secretary Jean Hooper; conductor Ian Ball
Type: chamber mainly a capella *Repertoire:* 12th C to contemporary *Size:* 29 *Perfs:* 10 *Touring:* UK, Germany, Spain, USA *Comments:* Gloucester based, 2 concerts a year in Gloucester Cathedral

St George's Singers
St George's Church, High Street, **Belfast** BT1 2AG
Tel: 28-9023 1275
secretary D.A.R. Chillingworth (9085 2615)
Repertoire: classical, 17th-20th C

St. John's College's Choir
St. John's College, **Cambridge** CB2 1TP
Tel: 1223-338 600/612 (organist office)
Fax: 1223-766 419
Internet: www.joh.cam.ac.uk/
E-Mail: a.m.mansfield@joh.cam.ac.uk
director of music Christopher Robinson CVO; secretary to organist Angela Mansfield
Type: male, usually accompanied by organ *Repertoire:* mainly standard, some secular *Size:* 14 adults, 16 choristers *Perfs:* daily Tuesday-Sunday & twice on Sunday during term-time + concerts *Touring:* national, international *Comments:* recordings available on various labels including: Decca, Nimbus, Lindenberg, Chandos; list of recordings available from the Johnian Office at the college

St. Paul's Cathedral Choir
Music Department, 5B Amen Court, **London** EC4M 7BU
Tel: 20-7236 6883
Fax: 20-7248 2817
E-Mail: music.stpauls@dial.pipex.com
music secretary Jane Ruthven; director of music John Scott; assistant director of music Huw Williams
Type: cathedral choir *Repertoire:* sacred *Size:* 18 men, 30 boys *Perfs:* 20, apart from cathedral commitments *Comments:* recordings available mostly on Hyperion

Swingle Singers, The
Unit 32, Alpha Business Centre, 60 South Grove, **London** E17 7NX
Tel: 20-8509 9911 Fax: 20-8521 1825
administrator Susan Gregory
Type: a cappella *Repertoire:* light classical *Size:* 8 *Perfs:* 120 *Touring:* USA, Israel, Denmark, Belgium, Germany, Italy, Sweden, France, Japan *Comments:* CDs available

Tallis Chamber Choir
13 Albury Street, **London** SE8 3PT
Tel: 20-8691 8337
Fax: 20-8691 8337
Internet: www.classical-artists.com/tcc
director Philip Simms;
administrator Deborah Sandringham
Type: chamber choir, amateur *Repertoire:* early to 20th century *Size:* 12-60 *Touring:* France, UK, Poland

Taverner Choir
Ibex House, 42-46 Minories, **London** EC3N 1DY
Tel: 20-7481 2103
Fax: 20-7481 2865
administrator Victoria Newbert; artistic director/conductor Andrew Parrott;
associate director Malcolm Bruno
Type: range from chamber to choral choir *Repertoire:* 13th-20th century *Size:* 10-30 *Perfs:* 15-20 *Touring:* UK, Germany, Switzerland, Italy *Comments:* see also Early Music

The Sixteen
Enslow House, Station Road, Enslow, **Kidlington** OX5 3AX
Tel: 1869-331 711/544
Fax: 1869-331 011
Internet: www._the_sixteen.org.uk
E-Mail: info@thesixteen.org.uk
general manager Gijs Elsen; musical director Harry Christophers; development manager Peter Burrows; administrator Alison Stillman
Type: mixed choir, chamber, cathedral, polyphonic, madrigal etc *Repertoire:* renaissance, baroque, classical and 20th century music *Size:* 10-40 *Perfs:* 60 *Touring:* Italy, Spain, Portugal, USA, Austria, France, Belgium, The Netherlands, Germany, Australia, Far East *Comments:* see also Orchestras (The Symphony of Harmony and Invention)

Thomas Tallis Society
13 Albury Street, **London** SE8 3PT
Tel: 20-8691 8337
Fax: 20-8691 8337
administrator Deborah Sandringham;
director Philip Simms
Type: mixed *Repertoire:* early to 20th C *Size:* 40-50 *Perfs:* 4-6 *Comments:* concerts in Greenwich and London's main venues

Vasari Singers
c/o Julia Field, 89 Dovercourt Road, **London** SE22 8UW
Tel: 20-8693 5498 Fax: 20-8693 6319
Internet: www.vasarisingers.org
E-Mail: fieldjg@dulwich.org.uk
chairman Julia Field; conductor Jeremy Backhouse; agent J. Audrey Ellison (International Artists' Management); secretary Janet Clucas
Type: chamber *Repertoire:* standard choral repertoire *Size:* 25-40 *Perfs:* 12 *Touring:* international *Comments:* recordings with EMI/Guild

Wells Cathedral Choir
Wells Cathedral Office, Chain Gate, Cathedral Green, **Wells** BA5 2UE
Tel: 1749-674 483 Fax: 1749-677 360
organist & master of the choristers Malcolm Archer; assistant organist Rupert Gough
Type: male and boys choir, girls choir *Repertoire:* standard cathedral repertoire *Size:* 19 boys, 12 men, 18 girls *Perfs:* daily during term-times, 3 times on Sundays + concerts *Touring:* national, international *Comments:* recordings available on Griffin, Lammas, Hyperion and Cantaris

West Barnes Singers
16 Framfield Road, **Mitcham** CR4 2AL
Tel: 20-8648 5420
musical director Andrew Charity;
chairman Avril Shipton
Type: oratorio/choral/opera; mixed; with orchestra or organ *Size:* 65 *Perfs:* 5

Westminster Abbey Choir
The Chapter Office, Dean's Yard, **London** SW1P 3PA
Tel: 20-7222 5152 Fax: 20-7233 2072
Internet: www.westminster-abbey.org
E-Mail: precentor@westminster-abbey.org
organist and master of the choristers Martin Baker
Type: cathedral choir *Repertoire:* sacred *Size:* 24 boys, 12 men *Perfs:* 8 sung services per week in the Abbey plus concerts and tours *Comments:* CD's available on Sony, Griffen and Cantoris labels; boys educated at the Abbey Choir School

Westminster Cathedral Choir
Clergy House, 42 Francis Street, **London** SW1P 1QW
Tel: 20-7798 9057 Fax: 20-7798 9091
Internet: www.westminstercathedral.org.uk
E-Mail:
musicdepartment@westminstercathedral.org.uk
master of music t.b.a; secretary to master of music Joanna Driver
Type: boys and men *Repertoire:* church music from medieval to 20th century *Size:* 22 boys, 10 men *Perfs:* daily (except during August) *Touring:* international *Comments:* recording with Hyperion

Winchester Cathedral Choir
5 The Close, **Winchester** SO23 9LS
Tel: 1962-857 200 Fax: 1962-857 201
Internet: www.win.diocese.org.uk/cathedral.html
E-Mail: sandy.davis@dial.pipex.com
music office Sandy Davis, Sue Armstrong; organist and master of the music David Hill; assistant master of music Stephen Farr; assistant organist Sarah Baldock
Type: cathedral *Repertoire:* mainly sacred *Size:* 12 men, 20 boys *Perfs:* 6-12 apart from cathedral commitments *Touring:* international *Comments:* recordings available on Hyperion, Virgin and Herald labels,

Wren Singers of London
Wren Music, 8 Park Lane, **Selsey** PO20 0HD
Tel: 1243-604 281 Fax: 1243-604 387
Internet: www.musiciansgallery.com
E-Mail: m.elliott@chihe.ac.uk
director Martin Elliott
Type: professional chamber and cathedral/church mixed choir *Repertoire:* baroque, religious, serious and light music *Touring:* mainly UK *Comments:* works in association with Wren Baroque Soloists and Orchestra

Zemel Choir, The
c/o 26 Larch Close, Friern Barnet, **London** NW11 3NN
Tel: 20-8361 3389 Fax: 20-8361 3389
concert manager Marc Landsman; musical director Vivienne Bellos; chairman Rusty Davis
Type: mixed, a cappella and with accompaniment *Repertoire:* wide but specialise in Jewish liturgical and secular (eg. Ashkenazi, Sephardi & Israeli folk) music; also English and European traditional and popular works *Size:* 60 *Perfs:* 6 *Touring:* Israel, Poland, USA, Spain *Comments:* 2 CDs available on Olympia Records; new members always welcome; further recording plans

YUGOSLAVIA (+381)

Due to the war in Kosovo we have been unable to update the following entries for Yugoslavia

Musica Antiqua Serbiana
Kosovska 32/3, 11000 **Belgrade**
Tel: 11-324 4736
artistic director Vera Zlokovic
Repertoire: early music

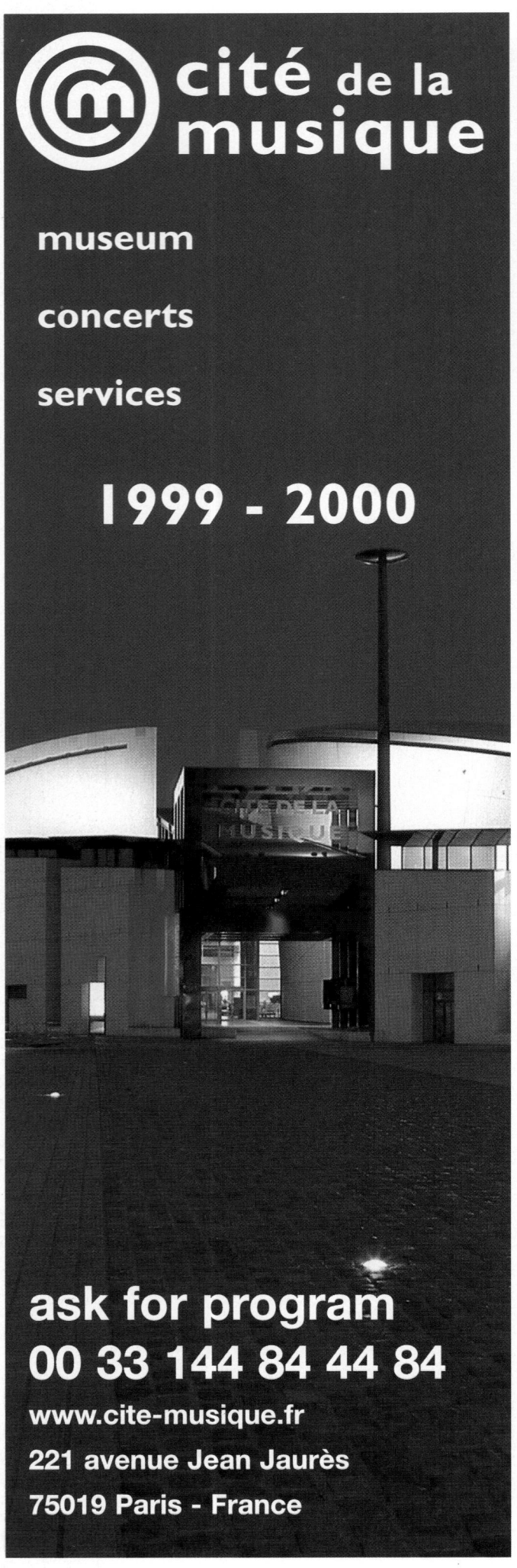

2000-2001

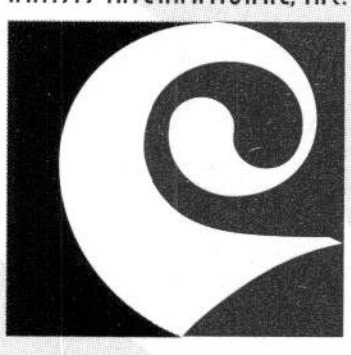

MICHAL SCHMIDT
PRESIDENT
STEPHEN LUGOSI
VICE-PRESIDENT
BARRY JORDAN
ADMINISTRATIVE DIRECTOR
ANTHONY BEZ
ADMINISTRATOR
STEVEN GOLDGLIT
COMPTROLLER
FRIEDA SERRANO
BOOKKEEPER

CONDUCTORS

Marin Alsop
Patricia Handy
Miguel Harth-Bedoya
Raymond Harvey
Takao Kanayama
Bernard Labadie
Fabio Mechetti
Roberto Minczuk
Kwamé Ryan
Uriel Segal *
Klauspeter Seibel *

COMPOSER/ CONDUCTOR

Peter Eötvös *

PIANISTS

Angela Cheng
Markus Groh *
Lee Luvisi
Pascal Rogé *
Alexis Weissenberg *
Lilya Zilberstein *

VIOLINISTS

James Buswell
Stephanie Chase
Glenn Dicterow
Brian Lewis

VIOLIST

Roberto Diaz

CELLISTS

Gustav Rivinius *
Sharon Robinson

FRENCH HORNIST

Marie Luise Neunecker *

CHAMBER ENSEMBLES

Diaz Trio
Vogler Quartet of Berlin *

CHAMBER ORCHESTRAS

Concerto Soloists of Philadelphia
Les Violons du Roy *

ORCHESTRA TOURS

Bundesjugendorchester – Germany *
Carl Nielsen Philharmonic – Odense, Denmark *
Orchestre de Bretagne *

SPECIAL ATTRACTIONS

Harlem Spiritual Ensemble
Ondekoza – Demon Drummers of Japan *
Yamato – Wadaiko Drummers of Japan *

* North American representation

59 EAST 54TH STREET, SUITE 83, NEW YORK NY 10022
TELEPHONE 212 421 8500 • FAX 212 421 8583
INFO@SCHMIDTART.COM • WWW.SCHMIDTART.COM

MWS@SCHMIDTART.COM
LUGOSI@SCHMIDTART.COM
BJOADAN@SCHMIDTART.COM
ABEZ@SCHMIDTART.COM

MICHAL SCHMIDT ARTISTS INTERNATIONAL, INC.

Askonas Holt is the new force in classical music

Formed from the merger of Lies Askonas and Harold Holt, Askonas Holt Limited provides representation for many of the greatest names in opera and classical music, as well as managing major international tours, projects and festivals.

Conductors & Instrumentalists

CONDUCTORS
Claudio Abbado
Yves Abel
Alexander Anissimov
David Atherton
Philippe Auguin
Rudolf Barshai
Daniel Barenboim
George Benjamin
Harry Bicket
Frans Brüggen
Sir Andrew Davis
Asher Fisch
Adam Fischer
Dietrich Fischer-Dieskau
Rafael Frühbeck de Burgos
Jane Glover
Paul Goodwin
Bernard Haitink
Daniel Harding
Eliahu Inbal
Graeme Jenkins
Emmanuel Krivine
Jan Latham-Koenig
Sir Charles Mackerras
Ion Marin
Wayne Marshall
Zubin Mehta
Tadaaki Otaka
Trevor Pinnock
Sir Simon Rattle
Leonard Slatkin
Patrick Summers
Robert Tear
Alexander Vedernikov
Marcello Viotti
Mark Wigglesworth

PIANO
Piotr Anderszewski
Emanuel Ax
Daniel Barenboim
Boris Berman
Peter Donohoe
Itamar Golan
Evgeny Kissin
John Lill
Wayne Marshall
Leon McCawley
Murray Perahia
Alfredo Perl
Maria João Pires
Kathryn Stott
Alexander Toradze
Lars Vogt

HARPSICHORD
Trevor Pinnock

ORGAN
Wayne Marshall

VIOLIN
Augustin Dumay
David Garrett
Ida Haendel
Jaime Laredo
Tasmin Little
Viktoria Mullova
Itzhak Perlman
Isaac Stern
Victor Tretyakov
Maxim Vengerov

CELLO
Natalie Clein
Yo-Yo Ma
Jian Wang

GUITAR
John Williams

FLUTE
Emmanuel Pahud

TRUMPET
Ole Edvard Antonsen

HORN
David Pyatt

ENSEMBLES
Ax/Stern/Laredo/Ma Quartet
Dumay/Pires Duo
Dumay/Pires/Wang Trio
Fretwork
Il Giardino Armonico
Kalichstein/Laredo/Robinson Trio
Orchestra Of The 18th Century
The Mullova Ensemble

Singers, Accompanists & Producers

SOPRANO
Mary-Louise Aitken
June Anderson
Lorna Anderson
Nancy Argenta
Dame Josephine Barstow
Kathleen Battle
Emma Bell
Christine Brewer
Rebecca Caine
Natalie Christie
Rita Cullis
Sophie Daneman
Nuccia Focile
Barbara Frittoli
Susannah Glanville
Clare Gormley
Galina Gorchakova
Susan Gritton
Maria Guleghina
Ying Huang
Gweneth-Ann Jeffers
Sumi Jo
Rosemary Joshua
Yvonne Kenny
Anna Korondi
Dame Felicity Lott
Geraldine McGreevy
Sylvia McNair
Lisa Milne
Heidi Grant Murphy
Tatiana Pavlovskaya
Elena Prokina
Dorothea Röschmann
Claire Rutter
Ines Salazar
Ruth Ann Swenson
Olga Trifonova
Valentina Tsydypova
Julia Varady
Janice Watson

MEZZO-SOPRANO
Irina Arkhipova
Teresa Berganza
Olga Borodina
Isabelle Cals
Anne Collins
Sarah Connolly
Michelle DeYoung
Stella Doufexis
Jane Henschel
Magdalena Kozená
Marjana Lipovsek
Nancy Maultsby
Irina Mishura
Ann Murray
Elena Obraztsova
Ruby Philogene
Mireia Pinto
Susan Quittmeyer
Eva Randova
Jean Rigby
Randi Stene
Ludmilla Schemshuk
Susanne Schimmack
Marianne Tarasova
Jard Van Nes
Sarah Walker
Louise Winter
Catherine Wyn-Rogers
Elena Zhidkova

COUNTER-TENOR
Brian Asawa
David Daniels
Derek Lee Ragin

TENOR
John Mark Ainsley
John Aler
Alfred Boe
Ian Bostridge
William Burden
Paul Charles Clarke
Richard Croft
Karl Daymond
Greg Fedderly
Jean-Paul Fouchécourt
Vsevolod Grivnov
Robin Leggate
Ilya Levinsky
Badri Maisuradze
Rhys Meirion
Chris Merritt
Daniel Norman
Iain Paton
Christoph Pregardien
Timothy Robinson
Anthony Rolfe Johnson
Peter Schreier
Daniil Shtoda
Toby Spence
Robert Tear

BARITONE/ BASS-BARITONE
Ildar Abdrazakov
Sir Thomas Allen
Neal Davies
William Dazeley
Dale Duesing
Vassily Gerello
Rodney Gilfry
Alan Held
Dmitri Hvorostovsky
Simon Keenlyside
Christopher Maltman
Earle Patriarco
Nikolai Putilin
Christopher Robertson
Jose Van Dam
David Wilson-Johnson

BASS
Askar Abdrazakov
Sergei Aleksashkin
Alexander Anisimov
Graeme Broadbent
Paata Burchuladze
Natale de Carolis
Aage Haugland
Mikhail Kit
Julian Konstantinov
Robert Lloyd
Tigran Martirossian
Kurt Moll
James Morris
John Relyea
Peter Rose
Stanislaw Schwets
Barseg Tumanyan
Richard Van Allan

MUSICALS
Kim Criswell
Brent Barrett

ACCOMPANISTS
Mikhail Arkadiev
György Fischer
Larissa Gergieva
Graham Johnson
Malcolm Martineau

PRODUCERS
John Cox
Martin Duncan
Nicholas Hytner
Stephen Lawless
Mikael Melbye
Deborah Warner
Rennie Wright

Please contact us for details of representation

Tours & Projects

Askonas Holt's Tours & Projects department works with some of the world's greatest orchestras and dance companies, presenting them at major venues in the UK and elsewhere, as well as managing tours and special projects around the globe. The company's expertise covers all areas of touring strategy, logistics, marketing, sponsorship and event management.

Askonas Holt also has a long and distinguished history in festival management and is recognised as one of London's leading concert promoters.

SOME RECENT AND FUTURE CLIENTS INCLUDE:

Accademia Nazionale di Santa Cecilia, Rome
Australian Chamber Orchestra
BBC Symphony Orchestra
Berlin Philharmonic Orchestra
Boston Symphony Orchestra
City of Birmingham Symphony Orchestra
Cologne Radio Symphony Orchestra
Detroit Symphony Orchestra
Dresden Staatskapelle of Saxony
National Symphony Orchestra, Washington DC
New York Philharmonic
Norwegian National Ballet
Orchestra of the Age of Enlightenment
Philadelphia Orchestra
Rotterdam Philharmonic Orchestra
Royal Philharmonic Orchestra
San Francisco Symphony
Staatskapelle Berlin
Sumo Association of Japan
Takarazuka Revue Company
Ulster Orchestra
Vienna Philharmonic Orchestra
Yomiuri Nippon Symphony Orchestra

STAFF

Sir Ian Hunter *President*
Sir Claus Moser *Chairman*
Martin Campbell-White *Joint Chief Executive*
Robert Rattray *Joint Chief Executive*
Peter Bloor *Director*
Mark Hildrew *Director*
Peter Martin *Director*
Jenifer Eddy *Consultant*

Annette Allen
Nicola-Fee Bahl
Jane Balmer
Lisa Battersby
Jan Burnett
Rupert Chandler
Ashley Chapman
Alison Charles
Jilly Clarke
Robert Clarke
Donagh Collins
Fabiana Dalpiaz
Miranda Demery
Aminah Domloge
Rona Eastwood
Melanie Evans
Jonathan Fleming
Gina Goldsmith
Errol Goldsworthy

Huw Humphreys
Nicola Huxley
Carol Kemp
Gaetan le Divelec
Gregoire le Divellec
June Mangan
Tim Menah
Claire Mudge
Alison Nethsingha
Jane Nicolson
Pip Pirie
Clare Seddon
Suzanne Spence
Joel Thomas
Constanze Vageler
Peggy White
Celia Willis
Nick Wilson
John Wise

Askonas Holt

Lonsdale Chambers, 27 Chancery Lane, London WC2A 1PF
Tel: 0171 400 1700 Fax: 0171 400 1799
E-mail: info@askonasholt.co.uk
Web site: www.askonasholt.co.uk

Barbara Hepworth: *Pelagos* (detail) 1943
© Alan Bowness, Hepworth Estate

Artists' List 2000

ATHOLE STILL
AS.
INTERNATIONAL MANAGEMENT LTD

CONDUCTORS

Guido Ajmone-Marsan	W
Dietfried Bernet	W
Noel Davies	W
Andrew Greenwood	W
Hilary Griffiths	W*
James Kelleher	W
Günter Neuhold	W*
Donald Runnicles	□

ENSEMBLES

Ensemble 415	W4

SOPRANOS

Maria Abajan	W*
Georgina Benza	W
Elena Brilova	W
Raphaelle Farman	W
Helen Field	W
Elena Filipova	W*
Jacquelyn Fugelle	W
Juliette Galstian	W
Cornelia Götz	W
Cynthia Haymon	W
Cynthia Makris	W*
Denia Mazzola	W
Karen Notare	W
Sue Patchell	W*
Nina Pavlovski	W*
Gail Pearson	W
Claire Primrose	W
Ashley Putnam	W1
Nina Rautio	W
Meryl Richardson	W
Soya Smolyaninova	W*
Penelope Thorn	W
Linda Watson	W*
Christine Weidinger	W

MEZZO SOPRANOS

Angela Hickey	W
Maria Jose Trullu	W*2
Natascha Petrinsky	W3
Ilia Aramayo Sandivari	W
Cécile Van de Sant	W
Gabriella Sborgi	W*2
Patricia Spence	W
Nuala Willis	W

COUNTER TENOR

Ricard Bordas	W
Martin Oro	W*

STAGE DIRECTORS/ DESIGNERS

Mike Ashman	W
Tim Coleman	W
Spyros Koskinas	W
Stefanos Lazaridis	W*
John Lloyd Davies	W
Stephen Medcalf	W
John Pascoe	W
Keith Warner	W

TENORS

Terje Andersen	W
Pietro Ballo	W*2
Edmund Barham	W
Evan Bowers	W
John Duykers	E
Francis Egerton	W
Bruce Ford	W1
Stuart Kale	W
Justin Lavender	W
Lars Magnusson	W*
Gianni Mongiardino	W*
Shalva Mukeria	W
Patrick Power	W
Graham Sanders	W
Jorma Silvasti	W*
Ian Thompson	W
Bradley Williams	E
Alan Woodrow	W
Charles Workman	W
Boiko Zvetanov	W*

BARITONES

Lado Ataneli	W*
Sigmund Cowan	W1
Mark Glanville	W
John Hancock	E
Carlos Marin	W
Anthony Marber	W
Daniel Mobbs	E
Louis Otey	W1
Stephen Owen	W
Malcolm Rivers	W
Andrew Rupp	W
Russell Smythe	W

BASSES

Mark Beesley	W
Eric Garrett	W
Manfred Hemm	W*
Brian Jauhiainen	W1
Jyrki Korhonen	W
Daniel Lewis Williams	W2
Frode Olsen	W
Matti Salminen	W*
Giovanni Tarasconi	W*
Tómas Tómasson	W

W = General Management
□ = GB/Sundry Territories
E = Europe
* = Non exclusive
1 = ex USA/CAN
2 = ex Italy
3 = ex Germ/Aust
4 = ex CH

ATHOLE STILL INTERNATIONAL MANAGEMENT LTD

FORESTERS HALL,
25-27 WESTOW STREET,
LONDON SE19 3RY
TEL: 0181 771 5271 (6 LINES)
FAX: 0181 771 8172
E-MAIL : ATHOLE@DIAL.PIPEX.COM

Drama

Drama
In this section the companies listed are primarily building-based or touring companies. However, the list does include some theatres which are also receiving venues for incoming tours at various times of the year. Only the most important young people's/children's theatre companies are included due to space constraints, though some of the large theatre companies mentioned also have children's and young people's companies. For more information about puppets see the appropriate section. **Within country companies are ordered by city and alphabetically within city.**

Théâtre
Dans son ensemble, cette rubrique englobe des compagnies à la fois essentiellement sédentaires ou qui font des tournées. Cependant, quelques théâtres d'accueil sont inclus; ils reçoivent des companies de l'extérieur pendant tout la saison. En raison de contraintes d'espace, seules quelques companies de théâtre Jeune Public parmi les plus importantes apparaissent ici. En ce qui concerne les marionnettes nos lecteurs sont priés de se reporter à la section appropriée. **Pour chaque pays les companies sont classées dans l'ordre des villes et par ordre alphabétique.**

Schauspiel
In diesem Kapitel sind Theaterensembles verzeichnet, die entweder Teil eines Mehrspartenbetriebs oder Tourneetheater/freie Gruppen sind. Eingeschlossen sind jedoch auch Theater, die zum Teil als Gastspieltheater tätig sind. Wegen der notwendigen Begrenzung des Umfangs konnten nur die wichtigsten der Kinder- und Jugentheater aufgeführt werden. Informationen über Puppentheater finden Sie im Kapitel 'Puppets'. **Die Einträge sind innerhalb aller Staaten alphabetisch nach Stadt und innerhalb der Stadt alphabetisch nach Namen geordnet.**

Compagnie di Teatro
Le compagnie di teatro elencate sono per la maggior parte compagnie stabili o di giro. Questa sezione include anche alcuni teatri che oltre ad avere una propria compagnia o delle proprie produzioni ospitano anche altri spettacoli durante vari periodi dell'anno. Per ragioni di spazio, sono state incluse soltanto le piú importanti compagnie di teatro ragazzi. Per piú informazioni riguardanti le compagnie di marionette consultare la sezione appropriata. **All'interno di ogni Nazione, le cittá seguono un ordine alfabetico e cosí a loro volta anche le compagnie.**

Teatro
En esta sección, la mayoría de las compañías son teatros estables o compañías itinerantes. Sin embargo, la lista incluye algunos teatros que también acogen a compañías itinerantes durante la temporada. A causa de la falta de espacio sólo se han incluido las compañías más importantes de teatro juvenil/infantil, aunque algunas de las grandes compañías de teatro también tienen compañías de teatro infantil y juvenil. Para más información sobre títeres véase la sección adecuada. **Las compañías están ordenadas por ciudades y alfabéticamente dentro de cada ciudad.**

Drama (연극)
이 부문에 기재 된 단체들은 일차적으로 한 곳에 주둔하거나 순회 공연하는 단체들이다. 그러나 일년 중 여러 번에 걸쳐 순회 공연 장소를 부여받는 몇몇 극장단들도 포함되었다. 이곳에 기재된 큰 단체들 중의 몇몇은 어린이/청소년 단체를 운영하고 있지만, 청소년/어린이 극장단들은 지면 관계상 가장 중요한 단체들만 포함되었다. 인형극단에 대한 정보는 관련부문을 참조하시오. **리스트는 국가별, 도시별, 그리고 다시 알파벳순으로 기재되었다.**

戏剧
本章节列出的公司主要是有固定办公楼或巡回公司。然而，该名单也包括一些在一年不同的时期中为来巡回演出团提供场所的戏剧院。尽管一些提到的大戏剧院公司有自己的儿童和年轻人公司，因为版面的限制、此处只包括了最重要的年轻人或儿童的戏剧公司。关于木偶戏详情，请阅有关章节。**在每个国家里公司是按城市顺序来排列的，而在一城市里公司又是按字母顺序来排列的。**

演劇
この章には劇場ベースあるいは巡回公演を行う劇団を主に掲載しました。また、リストには、一年を通して、団体観客を受け入れる劇団も含まれます。紙面が限られているので、青少年／児童劇団は主要なものに限りましたが、規模の大きな劇団にはこれらが付属している場合があります。人形劇に関する情報は該当する章をご覧下さい。**リストは国、都市別で、都市内ではアルファベット順に記載されています。**

ALBANIA (+355)

Aleksander Moisiu Theatre
Durres
Tel: 52-23466
director Vullnet Sabahu

Skampa Theatre
Elbasan
Tel: 545-3320

Apolonia Theatre
Fier
Tel: 642-2592
director Krenar Traka
Prods: 5 *Type:* repertory *Venues:* capacity 480

Theatre Andonzako Cajupi
Korça
Tel: 824-4878
director Sotiraq Tili

Theatre Migjeni
Shkoder
Tel: 224-3315
director Ndoc Cefa

National Theatre of Tirana
Place Skanderberg, **Tirana**
Tel: 42-23022/28933
director Gezim Kame
Prods: 6-7 *Type:* modern; new Albanian writing
Venues: capacity 540

Theatre Vlora
Vlora
Tel: 63-22455
general director Kristaq Skrami

ARMENIA (+374)

Kharazian Artashat State Dramatic Theatre
Dramteatr, 378240 **Artashat**

Kalantar Armenian Dramatic Theatre
Ul. Oktemberiana 2,
378630 **Gavar**

V. Adzhemian State Theatre Giumri
Giumr
Tel: 2-697 0723
Fax: 2-523 922
artistic director Akop Kazanchian

Shirvanzade Kafan Dramatic Theatre
Ul. Tumaniana 4,
377810 **Kafan**

Kumairi State Theatre
ul. Saiat-Nova,
377500 **Kumairi**

Abelian Vanadzor State Dramatic Theatre
Teatralnaia pl., 377200 **Vanadzor**
Tel: 2-523 922
artistic director Bagye Shakhverdian

Hrachja Kaplanian Yerevan City Council Dramatic Theater
28 Isahakian Street, 375025 **Yerevan**
Tel: 2-524 703
artistic director Armen Khandikian

Paronian Yerevan Theater of Musical Comedy
4 Khorurtaraneri Street, 375010 **Yerevan**
Tel: 2-580 075/101
artistic director Yervand Ghazanchian

Stanislavsky Russian State Dramatic Theatre
7 Abovian Street, 375010 **Yerevan**
Tel: 2-580 223
artistic director Alexander Grigorian

Sundukian National Academic Theater
6 Grigor Lusavorich Street, 375015 **Yerevan**
Tel: 2-520 610/525 700
artistic director Vahe Shahverdian

Yerevan Chamber Theatre
58 Mashtotz Street, 375009 **Yerevan**
Tel: 2-566 070 Fax: 2-589 383
artistic director Ara Yerinjakian; director Rouben Toroian

Yerevan State Theatre of Pantomine
36 Isahakian Street,
375025 **Yerevan**
Tel: 2-561 855
Fax: 2-524 437
artistic director Yuri Kostanian

Young People's Theatre
3 Moscovian Street, 375025 **Yerevan**
Tel: 2-565 153/531 974/581 974
artistic director Hakob Ghazanchian

AUSTRIA (+43)

Johann-Pölz-Halle-Theater
Hauptplatz 29, 3300 **Amstetten**
Tel: 7472-601 242/65706
Fax: 7472-601 249
Internet: www.avb.amstetten.at
E-Mail: avb@amstetten.at
Geschäftsführer Johann Kropfreiter
Perfs: 60 *Prods:* 1 *Type:* classical and modern
Venues: home 557 *Comments:* venue address: Stadionstraße 12, 3300 Amstetten tel: 7472-601 240, available for touring companies; no own ensemble

Stadttheater Baden Bei Wien
Theaterplatz 7, 2500 **Baden bei Wien**
Tel: 2252-48338
Fax: 2252-483 3850
Internet: www.baden-bei-wien.at/stadttheater
E-Mail: stadttheater@baden-bei-wien.at
Öffentlichkeitsarbeit Mag. Martina Malzer; VerwaltungsDirektor Reg. Rat. Wilfried Frankmann; Kunstlerischeleitung KS Elisabeth Kales-Wallwer
Actors: 40 + guests *Perfs:* 92 *Prods:* 12 *Type:* comedy, operetta, concerts *Venues:* home 702
Comments: established in 1718; see also Dance, Orchestras, Opera and Festivals

Stadttheater Berndorf
Kislingerplatz 6, 2560 **Berndorf**
Tel: 2672-82318/82470-21 Fax: 2672-85637
Internet: www.berndorf-stadt.at
E-Mail: kulturamt@berndorf-stadt.at
Intendant (during summer festival) Prof Felix Dvorak; Leiter Kulturamt Helga Hejduk
Actors: 30 *Perfs:* 70 *Prods:* 1 (for the annual July/August Sommerspiele) + several others *Type:* classic folkplay, comedy *Venues:* Stadttheater 475

Theater für Vorarlberg
Seestrasse 2, 6900 **Bregenz**
Tel: 5574-42870
Fax: 5574-48366
Intendant Harald F. Petermichel; Dramaturgie Andreas Hutter; Verwaltungsleiterin Barbara Haidlen
Actors: 10 permanent + 30 guest actors *Perfs:* 200 *Prods:* 13 *Type:* classical, modern *Venues:* Theater am Kornmarkt 556 *Touring:* Austria, Germany, Switzerland
Comments: see also Opera

Schauspielhaus Graz
Vereinigte Bühnen Graz, Hofgasse 11, 8010 **Graz**
Tel: 316-8005-0
Fax: 316-800 5495
Internet: www.buehnen-graz.com
E-Mail: info@buehnen-graz.com
Intendant Dr Gerhard Brunner; Schauspieldirektor Marc Günther; Dramaturgie Schauspielhaus Heike Frank (leitender Dramaturg), Peter Fuchs, Volker Bürger; Betriebsbüro Schauspielhaus Michael Tomec
Actors: 26 *Perfs:* 152 *Prods:* 11 (all new)
Type: all types *Venues:* Schauspielhaus 564 *Touring:* regional festivals *Comments:* see also Opera, Dance and Orchestras; features also a theatre for children and adolescents

Innsbrucker Kellertheater
Adolf-Pichler-Platz 8, 6020 **Innsbruck**
Tel: 512-580 743
Fax: 512-577 590
Intendanz Evelyn Fröhlich
Venues: capacity 80

Tiroler Landestheater
Rennweg 2, Postfach 134, 6010 **Innsbruck**
Tel: 512-52074
Fax: 512-5207 4333
Internet: www.landestheater.at
E-Mail: tiroler@landestheater.at
Intendant Brigitte Fassbaender; Betriebsdirektor Harald Mayr; künstlerisches Betriebsbüro u. Disposition Dieter Senft; Dramaturgie Dr Doris Happl; Schauspieldirektor Klaus Rohrmoser; Musikdirektor Georg Schmöhe; Chordirektor Claudio Büchler; technischer Direktor Werner Oberweger; Leiter des Tanztheaters Maria Luise Jaska
Actors: 28 *Perfs:* 100 *Prods:* 9 *Type:* classic to modern, emphasis on 20th C playwrights *Venues:* Grosses Haus 801, Kammerspiele 250, Werkraum 99
Comments: see also Opera, Dance

Stadttheater Klagenfurt
Theaterplatz 4, 9020 **Klagenfurt**
Tel: 463-55266
Fax: 463-5526 6724
Internet: www.stadttheater-klagenfurt.at
E-Mail: s.zoltan@stadttheater-klagenfurt.at
Intendant Dietmar Pflegerl; Dramaturgie Dr Maja Haderlap (Chefdramaturgin), Sylvia Brandl; Künstlerisches Betriebsbüro Erwin Zak; Besetzungsbüro für Musik Theater Heide Rabal; Chefdisponentin Emöke Szomraky
Perfs: 40-50 *Prods:* 3 *Type:* modern and classical theatre, dance theatre and musicals *Venues:* Stadttheater 757
Comments: see also Opera and Orchestras

Landestheater Linz
Promenade 39, 4020 **Linz**
Tel: 732-7611-0 Fax: 732-7611-308/333
Internet: linz.info.at/landestheater/
E-Mail: landestheater@linz.info.at
Intendant Dr Michael Klügl; kaufmännischer Direktor DDr Gerbert Schwaighofer; Schauspieldirektoren Gerhard Willert, Dagmar Schlingmann; Ballettdirektor Robert Poole; Kinder- und Jugendtheater Jutta Maria Staerk
Actors: 28 *Prods:* 21 (18 new) *Type:* classical, modern, contemporary etc. *Venues:* Grosses Haus 756, Kammerspiele 421, u\hof 100, Eisenhand 100
Comments: visiting address: Promenade 39, 4010 Linz; see also Bruckner Orchestra Linz; see also Opera, Dance and Orchestras (Bruckner Orchester Linz)

Theater Phönix
Wiener Str. 25, 4020 **Linz**
Tel: 732-662 641/666 500 (box office)
Fax: 732-6626 4130
Internet: www.servus.at/phoenix
E-Mail: theater.phoenix@servus.at
Leiter des Schauspiels Harald Gebhartl; Geschäftsführer/Leiter Kinder- und Jugendtheater und Sonderprojekte Stefan Kurowski; Dramaturgie und Öffentlichkeitsarbeit Alexander Kraus; Finanzen Sabine Belezanski, Margit Viechtbauer-Gruber; Technischer Leiter Peter Stangl
Actors: 10 *Perfs:* 300 *Prods:* 6-8 *Type:* Sprechtheater
Venues: Theater Phönix – stage A 380, stage B 100, stage C 80 *Touring:* German-speaking countries

Elisabethbühne
Petersbrunnhof, Erzabt-Klotz-Str. 22, 5020 **Salzburg**
Tel: 662-8085-0 Fax: 662-8085-33
E-Mail: ebuehne@salzburg.co.at
Direktion Renate Rustler-Ourth; Technischer Leiter Robert Kürbiß; Presse und Öffentlichkeitsarbeit Ingeborg Proyer; Spielleiter Robert Pienz; Dramaturgie Gerda Poschmann; Verwaltung Harald Fröhlich
Actors: 17 (permanent), 7 (part-time), 9 (students) *Perfs:* 300 *Prods:* 10 *Type:* literary theatre, classic and modern theater *Venues:* Großer Saal 240-350, Studio 100

Kleines Theater
Nonntaler Hauptstraße 39b, 5020 **Salzburg**
Tel: 662-872 154/830 813
Fax: 662-872 154-24/830 813-20
Internet: www.salzburg.com/kleinestheater
E-Mail: klm@ains.at
Intendant u. künstlerischer Leiter Claus Tröger; Geschäftsführer William E. Hayward
Actors: 9 *Perfs:* 250 *Prods:* 7 *Type:* comedy, cabaret, contemporary drama *Venues:* Metropolis 120 *Touring:* Austria, Germany *Comments:* member of Europäisches Theater Forum; address of administration: Nonntaler Hauptstraße 39a; venue Kleines Theater was shut down at the end of 1999

Salzburger Landestheater und Kammerspiele
Schwarzstraße 22, 5020 **Salzburg**
Tel: 662-871 512 Fax: 662-8715 1213
Internet: www.theater.co.at
E-Mail: service@theater.co.at
Intendant Lutz Hochstraate; Kaufmännischer Direktor Anton Schmidjell; Chefdisponent, Leiter des künstlerischen Betriebsbüros und persönlicher Referent des Intendanten Diethmar Straßer; Chefdramaturg Dr Christian Fuchs; Ballettdirektor Peter Breuer; Chordirektor Steffen Schubert
Actors: 40 *Perfs:* 58 *Prods:* 4 *Type:* modern, classical
Venues: Landestheater 711, Kammerspiele 137
Comments: see also Opera and Dance

Toihaus – Theater am Mirabellplatz
Franz-Josef-Strasse 4, 5020 **Salzburg**
Tel: 662-874 439 Fax: 662-874 439-4
E-Mail: toihaus@salzburg.co.at
Gesamtleitung Myrto Dimitriadou; Organisation Christoph Promberger; Theaterpädogogik/Schulkontakte Helga Gruber; Dramaturgie Werner Otte
Actors: 5 *Perfs:* 200 *Prods:* 5 *Type:* experimental children's and youth theatre, modern, concerts (modern music), performance productions *Venues:* capacity 75 *Touring:* national and international

Theater der Landeshauptstadt St Pölten – Theater für Niederösterreich
Rathausplatz 11, 3100 **St Pölten**
Tel: 2742-352 026
Fax: 2742-3520 2652
Internet: www.theater-stpoelten
E-Mail: intendanz@theater-stpoelten.at
Intendant Peter Wolsdorff; Intendant-Stellvertreter Pani Stamatopolos; Künstlerisches Betriebsbüro Peter Offner; Musikalische Oberleitung Klaus-Dieter Jung; Öffentlichskeitarbeit (PR) Pani Stamotopolos; Technischer Leiter Dipl. Ing. Edith Fellner
Perfs: 132 approx. (including operas, musicals, operettas) *Prods:* 9 *Type:* classical, modern, music theatre, comedy *Venues:* Theater der Landeshauptstadt 383 *Comments:* see also Opera; Österr Theatertreffen 13.05-20.05 2000

Studiobühne Villach
Postfach 168, 9500 **Villach**
Tel: 4242-27353 (office) 22129 (theatre)
Fax: 4242-273 534
E-Mail: studiobuehne@compu.etv.net
Obmann des Vereins Liselotto Buchacher; Künstlerische Leitung & Geschäftsführung Ingrid Ahrer; PR marketing Christa Dulcetta; Sekretariat & Buchhaltung Karin Tarmann; Techn Leitung/Technik Günther Zaworka; Regie Ingrid Ahrer, Thomas Birkmeir, Hans Escher, Hanspeter Horner, Erhard Pauer, Martin Polasek, Ernst M. Binder, Andreas Moldasch; I
Actors: varies *Perfs:* 220 *Prods:* 6-7 *Type:* contemporary *Venues:* Studiobühne Villach 100 *Touring:* national *Comments:* focus on topical issues

Akademietheater
Lisztstrasse 1, 1030 **Wien**
Tel: 1-514 440 Fax: 1-514 442 128
Direktor Klaus Bachler; Kaufmännischer Geschäftsführer Mag. Thomas Drozda; Stellvertreterin des Direktors Karin Bergmann; Stellvertreterin des kaufmännischen Direktors Mag Silvia Stantejsky; Leitung Dramaturgie Wolfgang Wiens; künstlerischer Generalsekretär Dr. Gerhard Blasche; Technischer Leiter Ing. Johann Bugnar; Pressebüro Konstanze Schäfer, Ulrike Spann
Actors: 97 *Perfs:* ca. 260 *Prods:* 8 *Type:* modern classics (emphasis on world premieres) *Venues:* Akademietheater 496 *Comments:* same management as the Burgtheater

Ateliertheater
Burggasse 71, 1070 **Wien**
Tel: 1-370 1108 (sekretariat)/524 2245 (theater)
Leiter Prof Dr Peter Janisch; Techn. Leitung Manfred Tscherne; Kostüme Mila Janisch; Buchhaltg Dr. Ewald Schwarz
Actors: varies *Perfs:* 4 *Prods:* 4 *Type:* mainly modern drama *Venues:* Ateliertheater 81 *Comments:* sekretariat: Eroicagasse 7/5/2, 1190 Wien

Burgtheater
Dr-Karl-Lueger-Ring 2, 1014 **Wien**
Tel: 1-51444-0 Fax: 1-5144 44107
Direktor Klaus Bachler; Kaufmännischer Geschäftsführer Mag. Thomas Drozda; Stellvertreterin des Direktors Karin Bergmann; Stellvertreterin des kaufmännischen Direktors Mag Silvia Stantejsky; Leitung Dramaturgie Wolfgang Wiens; Künstlerischer Generalsekretär Dr. Gerhard Blasche; Technischer Leiter Heinz Filar; Pressebüro Konstanze Schäfer, Ulrike Spann
Actors: 97 *Perfs:* ca. 260 *Prods:* 9 Pressereferat, Margit Schwarz, Andrea Köpke *Type:* classical and modern classics *Venues:* Burgtheater 1228, Akademietheater 496, Kasino 200, Vestibül 70 *Comments:* see also Opera and Dance (Wiener Kammer Oper / Wiener Staats Opern Ballet)

dietheater Künstlerhaus
Karlsplatz 5, 1010 **Wien**
Tel: 1-587 0504 (box office)/8774 (office)
Fax: 1-587 8774/31
Internet: www.dietheater.or.at/dietheater
E-Mail: dietheater@gmx.net
artistic director Christian Pronay; assistant to artistic director Anna Thier; press officer Elizabeth Drucker; chief technician Franz Strasser
Perfs: 400-500 *Prods:* up to 200 *Type:* contemporary drama, dance, performing arts etc. *Venues:* Künstlerhaus 198, dietheater Konzerthaus 89 *Comments:* venue for free groups of dance, theatre and performance; also rent practise rooms; no own ensemble; see also Festivals, Venues

Ensemble Theater am Petersplatz
Petersplatz 1, 1010 **Wien**
Tel: 1-535 3200 Fax: 1-532 7554
Leiter Dieter Haspel; Öffentlichkeitsarbeit und kaufmännische Leitung Christine Bauer
Actors: varies *Perfs:* 220 *Prods:* 5 per year *Type:* Sprechtheater *Venues:* home 150

Herbert Lederers Theater am Schwedenplatz
Franz-Josefs Kai 21, 1010 **Wien**
Tel: 1-535 7914 Fax: 1-535 7914
Leiter Herbert Lederer; Verwaltung Erna Perger
Comments: venue address: Steingasse 18, 1030 Wien tel: 1-713 6174

Kasino
Am Schwarzenbergplatz 1, 1030 **Wien**
Tel: 1-5144 44830
Direktor Klaus Bachler; Kaufmännischer Geschäftsführer Mag. Thomas Drozda; Stellvertreterin des Direktors Karin Bergmann; Stellvertreterin des kaufmännischen Direktors Mag. Silvia Stantejsky; Leitung Dramaturgie Wolfgang Wiens; Künstlerischer Generalsekretär Dr Gerhard Blasche; Technischer Leiter Heinz Filar; Pressebüro Konstanze Schäfer, Ulrike Spann
Actors: 97 *Perfs:* ca. 150 *Prods:* 4 *Type:* modern classics (emphasis on world premieres) *Venues:* Burgtheater 1228, Akademietheater 496, Kasino 200, Vestibül 70

Kleine Komödie
Mariahilfer Straße 115/1/7, 1060 **Wien**
Tel: 1-512 4280 (theaterkasse)/ 595 3295 (sekretariat)
Fax: 1-5953 29520 (secretary)
E-Mail: komoedie@aktiv.co.at
Leiter Helmut Siderits
Actors: 20-25 *Perfs:* 200 *Prods:* 3-4 *Type:* Boulevard Komödie *Comments:* visiting address: Walfischgasse 4, 1010 Wien

Komödie am Kai
Franz Josefs Kai 29, 1010 **Wien**
Tel: 1-533 2434 Fax: 1-535 3401 76
Direktor Erich L Koller; pers. Ref Sissy Boran
Perfs: ca.300 *Prods:* 2-3 *Type:* modern comedy *Venues:* home 160 *Comments:* Sekretariat: Obere Donaustrasse 3, 1020, Wien, tel: 1-332 7140

Löwinger-Bühne
Donaufelder Str. 2/4 – 2/29, 1210 **Wien**
Tel: 1-278 1042 Fax: 1-278 1802
Intendanz,Dramaturgie Paul Löwinger jnr, Sissy Löwinger
Actors: varies *Prods:* Volkstheater, 1 for touring company, 1 for TV *Type:* Volkstheater *Comments:* touring company

Theater Brett
Münzwardeingasse 2, 1060 **Wien**
Tel: 1-587 0663 Fax: 1-586 9155
Intendant Nika Brettschneider; Verwaltungsleiter Ludvik Kavin; Öffentlichkeitsarbeit Gerti Obermarzoner, Barbara Prinz, Martina Fuchs, Christine Fritz
Actors: 10-12 *Perfs:* 200 *Prods:* 5 *Type:* drama + movement theatre *Venues:* home 99 *Touring:* Germany, Switzerland, Czech Republic, Slovakia, Ukraine, Russia, Poland *Comments:* coproductions and exchange visits with alternative German, Czech, Slovakian, Hungarian and Yugoslavian directors and ensembles

Theater Gruppe 80
Gumpendorfer Strasse 67, 1060 **Wien**
Tel: 1-586 5222 Fax: 1-587 3672/11
Internet: www.gruppe80.nwy.at/gruppe80
E-Mail: gruppe80@netway.at
Künstl. Leit. Helmut Wiesner, Helga Illich;Verwaltungsleit. Monika Salamon; Techn. Leitung Edgar Fontanari
Actors: 15 *Perfs:* 160 *Prods:* 5 *Type:* classical and modern Austrian and German drama *Venues:* home 160

Theater in der Josefstadt
Betriebs-Ges m b H, Josefstädter Straße 26, 1080 **Wien**
Tel: 1-42700 Fax: 1-42700/60
Internet: www.josefstadt.org
Direktoren Helmuth Lohner, Robert Jungbluth; Prokurist u. Leiter d. Künstlerischen Betriebsbüro Josef Jurik; Dramaturgie Dr Rosina Raffeiner; pers. Referentin v. Helmuth Lohner Bertha Kammer; *Actors:* 100 *Perfs:* 1000 *Prods:* 19 *Type:* contemporary Austrian, classics, comedy *Venues:* Theater in der Josefstadt 774, Kammerspiele 528, Rabenhof 299 *Touring:* national

Theater Irwisch
Taubstummengasse 5/4, 1040 **Wien**
Tel: 1-504 3645 Fax: 1-504 3645-13
contacts Peter Hauptmann, Isabella Heugl
Actors: 4 *Perfs:* 50 *Prods:* 4 *Type:* street theatre *Comments:* touring company; managed by H2 – arts & acts

Theater Verein Odeon/Serapions Theater
Taborstraße 10, 1020 **Wien**
Tel: 1-216 5127/214 5562 (box-office) Fax: 1-216 5127-22
Internet: www.odeon-theater.at
E-Mail: odeon@odeon-theater.at
art. dirs/general managers Erwin Piplits, Ulrike Kaufmann; pr/press/adminstration Christa Tauss; technical manager Herbert Stangl;
Actors: varies *Perfs:* approx. 70 *Prods:* 1-2 *Type:* cross-over *Venues:* Odeon 300 *Comments:* Serapions Theater is the ensemble of Theater Verein Odeon; Odeon venue is also rented out to other companies and ensembles

Theater-Kabarett Simpl
Wollzeile 36, 1010 **Wien**
Tel: 1-512 4742 (box office) 512-3903 (9am-12pm)
Fax: 1-5123 9037
E-Mail: kabarett.simpl@netway.at
künstlerische Leiter Michael Niavarani; kommerzielle Leitung Albert Schmidleitner
Actors: 8 *Perfs:* 350 *Prods:* 2 *Type:* cabaret *Venues:* capacity 280

Vereinigte Bühnen Wien GmbH
Linke Wienzeile 6, 1060 **Wien**
Tel: 1-58830 Fax: 1-58830-33
Internet: www.musicalvienna.at
E-Mail: info@vbw.telecom.at
Intendant Rudi Klausnitzer; kaufmännischer Direktor Franz Häußler; künstlerische Produktion Barbara Quiehl-Masmeier; Dramaturgie Peter Back-Vega; Presse Ulli Stepan
Type: musical, revue, festival *Comments:* the organisation unites the following 3 theatres (see separate entries): Theater an der Wien (musicals, opera), Raimund-Theater (musicals), Ronacher Etablissement; see also Opera, Dance and Festivals; see also Orchester der Vereinigten Bühnen Wien GmbH

Volkstheater Wien
Neustiftgasse 1 am Weghuber Park, 1070 **Wien**
Tel: 1-5233 501-0/524 7263 (box office)
Fax: 1-5233 501242/333
Internet: www.volkstheater.at
E-Mail: ticket@volkstheater.at
Direktor Emmy Werner; Kaufmännische Direktion Dr Rainer Moritz; Dramaturg und Referent der Direktion Oliver vom Hove; Öffentlichkeitsarbeit und Produktionsbetreuung Brigitte Weidinger; Presse Mag. Barbara Pluch; technische Leitung Alfred Imrek
Actors: 40 *Prods:* 10 *Type:* classical drama, world premieres of Austrian writers *Venues:* Volkstheater 989 (10 wheelchair), Studiobühne am Plafond 40 *Comments:* Volkstheater special (readings, concerts, solo recitals, Matinees, discussions, events in the Spiel-'Bar/Balkonfoyer), exhibitions, guest performances; 7 productions per annum in the outer boroughs of Wien (20 different venues in Wien); alternative E-mail: info@volkstheater.at

AZERBAIDZHAN (+994)

Azerbaidzhan State Russian Drama Theatre
Hagani St. 7, 370000 **Baku**
Tel: 12-934 048
director Ibragimov Marat Faruk ogly

Azerbaidzhan State Theatre 'Youg'
Fizuli Square, 370001 **Baku**
Tel: 12-944 647
artistic director Gasanov Vagif Ibragim ogly

Azerbaidzhan State Young People's Theatre
Nizamy St. 72, 370000 **Baku**
Tel: 12-938 852
director Azizov Kamal Gabib ogly

Azerbaidzhan State Youth Theatre
Hagani St. 10, 370000 **Baku**
Tel: 12-932 963
director & artistic director Atakishiyev Guseinaga Agahusein ogly

National State Academic Theatre of Azerbaidzhan
Fizuli Square, 370000 **Baku**
Tel: 12-944 919
director Turabov Gasan Sattar ogly

Gazakh State Theatre
Gazakh
Tel: 12-89579/55277
director Mammedova Peri Aliyar Kizi

Giandja State Drama Theatre
A. Abbaszade St. 62, 374700 **Giandja**
Tel: 12-89522/25866
director Mammedov Nazim Kamil ogly

Nizamy Poetry Theatre
Baku St. 38, **Giandja**
Tel: 12-89522/25188

Lenkoran State Drama Theatre
28 May St. 16, 374311 **Lenkoran**
director Zeynalov Elshad Allahverdi ogly

Mingechaur State Drama Theatre
Gagarin St. 5,
374311 **Mingechaur**
Tel: 12-8247/33958
director Abbasov Zulfugar Gulu ogly

Nakchivan State Musical-Drama Theatre
A Javad St. 2,
373630 **Nakchivan**
Tel: 12-8236/52589
director Gummatov Mamed Tahir ogly

Sheki State Drama Theatre
Azadlyg St. 174, 374510 **Sheki**
Tel: 12-8277/3661
director Mustafayev Imamali Mushti ogly

Sumgait State Musical-Drama Theatre
Azadlyg Square 5,
373200 **Sumgait**
Tel: 12-8261/59121
director Shukurov Mehman Sakir ogly

BELARUS (+375)

Dunin-Marcinkevich Mogiljov Regional Theatre of Drama & Comedy
Mogiljovskij Oblastnoj Tjeatr Dramy i Komjedii imjeni Dunina-Marcinkjevicha
ul. Socialistichjeskaja 105, 213826 **Bobrujsk**
Tel: 2251-23066
director Jevgjenij A Gojko

Brest Regional Drama Theatre
Brjestskij Oblastnoj Dramatichjeskij Tjeatr
ul. Ljenina 21, 224005 **Brjest**
Tel: 162-266 440 Fax: 162-232 773
director Aljexandr A. Kozak

Gomel Regional Drama Theatre
Gomjellskij Oblastnoj Dramatichjeskij Tjeatr
pl. Ljenina 1, 226050 **Gomjell**
Tel: 232-534 375
director Valentina G. Ragovskaja

Grodno Regional Drama Theatre
Grodnjenskij Oblastnoj Dramatichjeskij Tjeatr
ul. Mostovaja 35, 230023 **Grodno**
Tel: 152-723 428 Fax: 152-723 428
director Nikolaj Jemjellianov

Belarussian Republican Young People's Spectator's Theatre
Bjelaruskij Rjespublikanskij Tjeatr Junogo Zritjelja
ul. Engjelsa 26, 220030 **Minsk**
Tel: 172-270 934 Fax: 172-270 934
director Jurij L Vutto

Dze-ja Minsk Drama Theatre
Minskij Dramatichjeskij Tjeatr Dzje-ja
ul. Chajkinoj 16, 220021 **Minsk**
Tel: 172-434 042
director Nikolaj Trukhan

Gorki Academic Russian Drama Theatre
Akadjemichjeskij Russkij Dramatichjeskij Tjeatr imjeni Gorkogo
Ul. Volodarskogo 5, 220050 **Minsk**
Tel: 172-203 825 Fax: 172-208 345
director Eduard I. Gjerasimovich

Janka Kupala National Academic Theatre
Nacionalnyj Akadjemichjeskij Tjeatr Mimjeni Janki Kupaly
ul. Engjelsa 7, 220030 **Minsk**
Tel: 172-276 081 Fax: 172-276 081
director Gjennadij B Davytko

Republican Theatre of Belarussian Drama
Rjespublikanskij Tjeatr Bjelaruskoj Dramaturgii
ul.Kropotkina 44, 220002 **Minsk**
Tel: 172-346 008
director Jurij V Kulik

Screen Actor's Theatre Studio
Tjeatr-Studija Kinoaktjora
pr. Mashjerova 13, 220004 **Minsk**
Tel: 172-230 811
director Nina N Shukan

State Youth Theatre of the Republic of Belarus
Gosudarstvjennyj Molodiozhnyi
Tjeatr Rjespubliki Bjelaruss
ul. Daumana 1, 220002 **Minsk**
Tel: 172-342 613 Fax: 172-342 613
director Virginia Tarnavskaite

Young Theatre of Estrade
Molodjezhnyj Tjeatr Estrady
ul. Moskovskaja 18A, 220001 **Minsk**
Tel: 172-228 071
director Aljexandr V Vnukov

Mogilev Regional Drama Theatre
Mogiljovskij Oblastnoj Dramatichjeskij Tjeatr
ul. Pervomajskaja 10, 212000 **Mogiljov**
Tel: 222-258 552
director Victor P Kurzhalov

Minsk Regional Drama Theatre
Minskij Oblastnoj Dramatichjeskij Tjeatr
ul Chkalova 7, 222310 **Molodjechno**
Tel: 273-54676
director Sjergjej B Valkovich

Meljezh Mozyr Drama Theatre
Mozyrskij Dramatichjeskij Tjeatr imjeni Mjeljezha
ul. Ljeninskaja 23, 247760 **Mozyr**
Tel: 2351-23278
director Marija I Potapjeva

Slonim Belarussian Drama Theatre
Slonimskij Bjelaruskij Dramatichjeskij Tjeatr
ul. Krasnoarmjejskaja 25, 231800 **Slonim**
Tel: 1562-25963
director A L Kljebanov

Jakub Kolas Belarussian State Academic Drama Theatre
Bjelaruskij Gosudarstvjennyj Akadjemichjeskiij Dramatichjeskij Tjeatr imjeni Jakuba Kolasa
ul. Zamkovaja 2, 210026 **Vitjebsk**
Tel: 2122-364 213 Fax: 2122-360 783
director Grigorij I Shatko

BELGIUM (+32)

Barre Weldaad
Lamorinièrestraat 252, 2018 **Antwerp**
Tel: 3-230 0273
Fax: 3-230 0273
director Stef Driezen
Actors: varies *Prods:* 2
ype: repertoire, new writing, contemporary
Touring: Belgium, Netherlands

Hetpaleis/Kjt
Meistraat 2, 2000 **Antwerp**
Tel: 3-202 8311 Fax: 3-202 8353
Internet: www.hetpaleis.kjt.be
E-Mail: hetpaleis.kjt@antwerp.be
director Barbara Wijckmans; administrator Ilse Scheers; public relations Dennis Meïer
Actors: 75 (freelance per production)
Perfs: 540 (130 in other cities) *Prods:* 10 *Type:* theatre for children and young people *Venues:* Municipal Theatre, minor auditorium 550 *Touring:* 4 productions tour in Belgium/Netherlands

Internationale Nieuwe Scène
New Scene International Collective
Zuiderpershuis Timmerwerfstraat 40, 2000 **Antwerp**
Tel: 3-216 4440 Fax: 3-248 0630
Internet: www.zuiderpershuis.be
E-Mail: ins@zuiderpershuis.be
management Christel Kersemans; artistic directors Charles Cornette, Hilde Uitterlinden;
press/public relations Ilke Festjens
Actors: 2 *Perfs:* 60 *Prods:* 4 *Type:* popular contemporary theatre with political undertones
Venues: Zuiderpershuis 360

Jan Fabre/Troubleyn
Italielei 56, 2000 **Antwerp**
Tel: 3-201 1300 Fax: 3-233 1501
E-Mail: barbara.deconinek@troubleyn.be
managing director Barbara De Coninck; artistic director Jan Fabre; financial manager Maai Meukns
Actors: varies *Prods:* 1 *Type:* contemporary *Venues:* Resident of deSingle (3 studios), Antwerp *Touring:* Europe, Columbia *Comments:* see also Dance

Nieuw Ensemble Raamteater
New Raam Theatre Ensemble
Lange Gasthuisstraat 26, 2018 **Antwerp**
Tel: 3-231 3444
Fax: 3-231 3509
director Marc Cnops
Actors: 14-15 *Perfs:* 300 *Prods:* 7 (6 new) *Type:* classical, modern, new writing, repertory
Venues: Teater Op't Zuid 200, Klein Raamteater 93
Touring: Belgium, Netherlands

Theater Zuidpool – R.V.T.
Theatre South Pole – Travelling People's Theatre
Lange Noordstraat 11, 2000 **Antwerp**
Tel: 3-231 5758/232 8104 Fax: 3-233 3618
director Peter Benoy; dramaturgist Bob Snijers; financial manager Fanny Scholliers;
public relations Ingrid van Kogelenberg
Actors: per production *Perfs:* 150 *Prods:* 8 *Type:* classical, with modern dramaturgy *Venues:* Zuidpool 150 *Touring:* Netherlands, Belgium *Comments:* touring company

Toneelhuis, Het
Jodenstraat 3, 2000 **Antwerp**
Tel: 3-224 8800 Fax: 3-224 8801
E-Mail: info@toneelhuis.be
artistic directors Luk Perceval; administrator Stefaan De Ruyck; public relations Johan van Steenkiste
Actors: 50 *Perfs:* 280 *Prods:* 14 *Type:* drama, music
Venues: Bourla theatre 1100, Cinema Tokio 100
Comments: a fusion between the former theatre companies Blauwe Maandag Compagnie and the Koninklijke Nederlandse Schouwburg; see also Venues

Zwarte Komedie
Black Comedy
Leguit 15-17, 2000 **Antwerp**
Tel: 3-233 4038/5678
Fax: 3-233 4038
manager Bert Verhoye; director Boris (the dog);
public relations Melke Coewerf
Actors: 9 *Perfs:* 150-160 *Prods:* 3 *Type:* cabaret and black theatre, satire *Venues:* 70, 145
Touring: Netherlands, Montréal
Comments: probably the only theatre company in the world to have a dog as a director

Stan Tg
Hossenplein 2, 2000 **Antwerpen**
Tel: 3-227 1381
Fax: 3-231 8058
E-Mail: stan@pophost.eunet.be
contact Renild van Bevel, Jolente de Keersmaeker, Frank Vercruyssen, Damiaan de Schrijver, Sara de Roderoo, Eska Sarif, Thomas Walgrava, Karin Damdts
Actors: 8 + *Perfs:* 130 *Prods:* 5 *Type:* contemporary theatre
Touring: Europe *Comments:* members regularly give theatre workshops in P.A.R.T.S.

Centre Dramatique d'Arlon
Maison de la Culture d'Arlon, Parc des Expositions, 6700 **Arlon**
Tel: 63-220 439
Fax: 63-219 789
directrice Marie-Claire Clausse
Perfs: 80 *Prods:* 1 *Type:* contemporary and modern (+ choreography) *Venues:* Maison de la Culture d'Arlon 613
Touring: Belgium, France, Luxembourg
Comments: see also Venues

Korre, De
Sint-Jakobsstraat 36, 8000 **Bruges**
Tel: 50-338 850 Fax: 50-335 197
manager Robrecht de Spiegelaere
Actors: 12 *Perfs:* 180 (50 in Bruges, rest in Flanders)
Prods: 5 *Type:* classical, contemporary *Venues:* De Korre 105, 180 *Touring:* Belgium, Netherlands

Area
47 rue de Locht, 1030 **Brussels**
Tel: 2-216 5315 Fax: 2-215 6997
directrice Pascale Tison
Actors: 3 *Prods:* 1 *Type:* modern – including performances of contemporary Belgian authors

BRONKS Jeugdtheater
Bialmontstraat 11, 1210 **Brussels**
Tel: 2-219 9921 Fax: 2-219 7554
E-Mail: bronks.jeugdtheater@skynet.be
artistic coordinator Oda Van Neygen
Type: contemporary theatre for young audience

Comédie Claude Volter
Av des Frères Legrain 98, 1150 **Brussels**
Tel: 2-762 0963 Fax: 2-763 2938
director Claude Volter;
administrators Sylvie D'Aney, Michelle Dewezeer
Actors: 30 *Perfs:* 112 *Prods:* 5 *Type:* classical *Venues:* La Comédie Claude Volter, stage A 152, stage B 119

Compagnie des Galeries
Galerie des Princes 6, 1000 **Brussels**
Tel: 2-513 3960 Fax: 2-512 6026
director Jean-Pierre Rey;
attaché de presse Fabien Gardin
Perfs: 150 *Prods:* 6 *Type:* comedy, classical, contemporary *Venues:* Théâtre Royal des Galeries 900 *Touring:* Belgium, France, Switzerland

Ensemble Leporello
Waversesteenweg 1139, 1160 **Brussels**
Tel: 2-223 1368 Fax: 2-646 4306
manager Els Smets; artistic director Dirk Opstaele
Actors: 15 *Perfs:* 70 *Prods:* 4 *Type:* classical repertoire, rythmical, movement theatre
Touring: France, Belgium, Holland *Comments:* performances in French, Dutch & English

Jan Lauwers/Needcompany
Hooikaai 35, 1000 **Brussels**
Tel: 2-218 4075 Fax: 2-218 2317
Internet: needcompany.vgc.be
E-Mail: needcompany@skynet.be
artistic director Jan Lauwers; managing director Christel Simons; production manager Carl Gydé; assistant managing director An Van der Donckt
Actors: 4-9 *Perfs:* 40-50 *Prods:* 3 *Type:* contemporary
Touring: Europe, America *Comments:* see also Dance

Kaaitheater
Quai des Péniches 2, 1000 **Brussels**
Tel: 2-201 5858 (admin)/5959 Fax: 2-201 5965
Internet: www.kaaitheater.cgc.be
artistic director Agna Smisdom; director Johan Rennies
Actors: varies *Venues:* Lunatheater up to 750

KVS – De Bottelarig
Royal Flemish Theatre
Delaunoy Street 58, 1080 **Brussels**
Tel: 2-412 7040 Fax: 2-412 7045
Internet: www.kvs.be
E-Mail: info@kvs.be
intendant/artistic director Franz Marijnen; directeur administratif Lieven Struye; public relations Jempi De Cooman; dramaturgie Paul Verduyckt; assitant Lieve Vande Velde; head of the technical crew Lucien Robbrechts; education Lieven Rossignol
Type: repertory theatre (modern & classical)
Touring: Netherlands *Comments:* De Bottelareg is the new venue; at the time of going to print the capacity had not been confirmed yet

Le Grand Midi
XL Théatre, 7a Rue Goffart, 1050 **Brussels**
Tel: 2-513 2178 Fax: 2-513 4053
E-Mail: theatre.grand.midi@skynet.be
directeur Bernard Damien
Actors: varies *Prods:* 1 *Type:* all types *Venues:* XL Théâtre 150 *Touring:* France, Switzerland

MOPA (Music in Relation with other Performing Arts)
39 rue Hôtel des Monnaies, 1060 **Brussels**
Tel: 2-534 5225 Fax: 2-534 5225
director Diane Broman
Actors: varies *Type:*
experimental voice & movement theatre

Rideau de Bruxelles
Palais des Beaux-Arts, 23 rue Ravenstein, 1000 **Brussels**
Tel: 2-507 8360 Fax: 2-507 8363
Internet: www.Rideaubxl.org
E-Mail: rideaubxl@gate71.be
directeurs Jules-Henri Marchant, Martine Renders;
administrateur Paul Rogie;
relations publiques Caroline Von Bibikow

Actors: varies *Perfs:* 300 *Prods:* 9 *Type:* contemporary *Venues:* Le Petit Theatre 150, Le Studio 200 *Comments:* some performances in sign language; publish translations of theatre scripts

Théâtre de la Balsamine
Avenue Félix Marchal 1, 1030 **Brussels**
Tel: 2-732 9618 (admin)/735 6468 (box office)
Fax: 2-733 2302
E-Mail: balsamine@skynet.be
director Christian Machiels; administrator Michel Van Slijpe; metteur en scène atachée a la compagnie Martine Wijckaert
Actors: per production *Perfs:* 100 (120 with dance) *Prods:* 4-5 *Type:* new writing, theatre, dance *Venues:* currently building a new theatre which will open in 2001; in 2000 performances will be in various venues *Touring:* Belgium, France *Comments:* co-produces and produces dance festival; see also Dance

Théâtre de la Vie
45 rue Traversière, 1210 **Brussels**
Tel: 2-219 1186 Fax: 2-219 3344
directeur Herbert Rolland; directeur administratif Myrian Buscema; directeur financier Léon Küpper; diffusion des spectacles Myriam Buscema
Actors: varies *Perfs:* 90 *Prods:* 2 *Type:* classical, contemporary, modern *Venues:* capacity 92 to 100 *Touring:* Belgium, Switzerland, France *Comments:* establishment of an actors' studio

Théâtre de Poche de Bruxelles
Chemin du Gymnase 1a, 1000 **Brussels**
Tel: 2-647 2726 Fax: 2-647 2822
Internet: www.poche.cediti.be
E-Mail: poche@gate71.be
director Roland Mahauden; assistant director Oliver Blim; technical director Avvedine Elbelghitti; secretary Giselle Remerie
Actors: varies per production *Perfs:* 253 *Prods:* 5-6 *Type:* contemporary *Venues:* Théâtre de Poche 240
Touring: France, Switzerland

Théâtre National de la Communauté Française de Belgique
Centre International Rogier, Rue Bertulot 3, 1210 **Brussels**
Tel: 2-203 4155 Fax: 2-203 2895
Internet: www.theatrenational.be
E-Mail: theatre.national@skynet.be
directeur Philippe van Kessel; administrateur délégué Myriam van Roosbroeck; directeur administratif et financier Jean-Pierre Braine;
attachée de presse Sophie Coppens
Actors: 120 *Perfs:* 450 *Prods:* 145 *Type:* modern, classical, new Belgian writing *Venues:* stage A 700, stage B 300
Touring: Belgium, France *Comments:* hires, promotes

Théâtre Royal du Parc
Rue de la Loi 3, 1000 **Brussels**
Tel: 2-512 5343/4823 Fax: 2-512 8098
director Yves Larec;
directruice adjointe Colette Lefèbvre
Actors: 50 (3 permanent) *Perfs:* 150 *Prods:* 5 *Type:* classical and comedy *Venues:* Théâtre Royal Du Parc 500 *Comments:* Tel. bookings 2-505 3030

Théâtre Varia
78 Rue du Sceptre, 1050 **Brussels**
Tel: 2-640 3550 Fax: 2-640 8835
directors Marcel Delval, Michel Dezoteux, Philippe Sireuil; administration Abdel Makoudi; secretaire génerale Sylvie Somen; relations publiques Christine Mawet, Anne Vandendorpe
Actors: varies *Perfs:* 130 *Prods:* 3 *Type:* contemporary
Venues: capacity 300 *Touring:* France, Switzerland

Théâtre-Cie Yvan Baudouin-Lesly Bunton
Avenue d'Auderghem 219-221, 1040 **Brussels**
Tel: 2-640 2760 Fax: 2-649 9253
E-Mail: theatre.baudouin-bunton@netsgo.be
director Yvan Baudouin; contact Lesley Bunton
Actors: 1-15 *Perfs:* 60-100 *Prods:* 2-4 *Type:* contemporary/creation *Venues:* Theatre Yvan Baudouin 83
Touring: national, international

Théâtre-Poème
Rue d'Ecosse 30, 1060 **Brussels**
Tel: 2-538 6358 Fax: 2-534 5858
directrice Monique Dorsel
Actors: 5 permanent + others *Perfs:* 150 *Prods:* 10-20 *Type:* contemporary + new perspective on classical texts *Venues:* 3 rooms: 20, 60, 70 *Touring:* national, international *Comments:* other activities of the company includes: literary meetings, philosophy, education programme and psychoanalysis

Théâtre de l'Ancre
Rue Montigny 122, 6000 **Charleroi**
Tel: 71-311 321
Fax: 71-304 382
director Jacques Fumière; press officer Sonia Bailly
Actors: varies *Perfs:* 85+ *Prods:* 1 *Type:* contemporary *Venues:* Théâtre de L'Ancre 120 *Touring:* Belgium, France, Switzerland

Arca Theatre
Sint-Widostraat 3, 9000 **Gent**
Tel: 9-225 1860 Fax: 9-223 0090
Internet: www.arca.be
E-Mail: arca.theatre@arca.be
director Jo Decaluwe; publice relations Luce Premer
Actors: varies *Perfs:* 200 *Prods:* 6 *Type:* modern *Venues:* Arca space: 45, 230, Théâtre Tennepot: Bomboniére 65, Becket up to 170, rehearsal room up to 150 *Touring:* Netherlands, Russia, South Africa, France *Comments:* twice a month, unpublished Flemish authors have the opportunity to present their work (some classical music as well)

Nederlands Toneel Gent (NTG)
Sint-Baafsplein 17, 9000 **Gent**
Tel: 9-225 1202/3208 (box office)
Fax: 9-224 4025/3317 (box office)
Internet: www.ntg.be
E-Mail: ntg@xntg.be
zakelijk directeur Maurice Vercauteren; artistiek directeur Jean-Pierre De Decker; productieleider Rudy Deraeve; communication Tom De Clercq
Actors: 13 permanent + 25 guests *Perfs:* 230 *Prods:* 10 *Type:* classical, modern, contemporary *Venues:* KNS Koninklijke Nederlandse Schouwburg 748, NTG2 (Minnemeers) 250, Minardschouwburg 300 *Comments:* simultanious translation available (French, English)

Speelteater Gent / De Kopergietery
Blekerijstraat 50, 9000 **Gent**
Tel: 9-266 1144 Fax: 9-224 2980
Internet: www.dekopezgietery.be
E-Mail: dekopergietery@skynet.be
business manager Anne Crevits; artistic director Eva Bal; technical contact Pascal Poissonnier; promotion t.b.a; drama & press Mieke Versyn;
vente et achat Nicole Petit
Actors: varies *Perfs:* 200+ *Prods:* 3 large, 5 small *Type:* children's, youth theatre, dance, music, literature *Venues:* De Kopergietery 200 *Touring:* Europe, Canada, Mexico *Comments:* professional actors making productions for children and youngsters; youngsters (aged 15 to 25) making productions for various age groups

Teater Taptoe
Forelstraat 91c, 9000 **Gent**
Tel: 9-223 6758 Fax: 9-223 5467
E-Mail: theater.taptoe@ping.be
commercial director Luk De Bruyker;
artistic director Freek Neirynck
Actors: 10 *Perfs:* 230 *Prods:* 6 *Type:* combination of actors, puppets and objects *Touring:* France, Spain, Poland, Netherlands, Japan *Comments:* touring company; see also Puppets

VICTORIA
Fratersplein 7, 9000 **Gent**
Tel: 9-225 3732/269 0969 Fax: 9-225 0076
Internet: www.victoria.be.compuserve.com
E-Mail: victoriatheatre@ompuserve.com
administrative director Katrien Laporte; artistic coordinator Dirk Pauwels; production manager Pat De Wit; promotional coordinator Koen Gisen
Actors: varies *Perfs:* 180-200 *Prods:* 5 *Type:* young people's & adult theatre + contemporary + dance *Venues:* Victoria 120, Mirard Schouwburg 220, Nieuwporttheatre 180 *Touring:* France, Switzerland, Netherlands, UK, Germany, Italy, Austria *Comments:* see also Festivals

Teater Antigone
Hazelaarstraat 5, 8500 **Kortrijk**
Tel: 56-226 870 Fax: 56-259 741
E-Mail: antigone@itinera.be
director Gosver Best; artistic director Jos Verbist
Actors: 1 *Perfs:* 100 *Prods:* 4 *Type:* classical, modern
Comments: touring company

Comédiens Associés
avenue Rogier, 7B Boite Postale 072, 4000 **Liège**
Tel: 4-223 7654
director Andrée Goffinet; contact Pierre Dubois
Actors: 8-10 *Perfs:* 32 *Prods:* 4 *Type:* vaudeville comedy
Venues: Théâtre du Trocadero 600

Groupov
26-28 rue Bois L'Evequestraat, 4000 **Liège**
Tel: 4-253 6123 Fax: 4-253 6094
E-Mail: groupov@hotmail.com
administrator Laurence Gay;
artistic director Jacques Delcuvellerie
Actors: 30 *Perfs:* 1 *Prods:* 1 *Type:* experimental *Venues:* Théâtre de la Place 600; Théâtre National (600-800)
Touring: France, Belgium *Comments:* runs 'project' teaching centre for professionals: 'Centre Experimental de Culture Active'

Théâtre Arlequin
Rue Rutxhiel 3, 4000 **Liège**
Tel: 4-222 1543/232 2082 (box office) Fax: 4-222 1715
director José Brouwers; président Jean Brumioul
Actors: varies *Perfs:* 200 *Prods:* 5 *Type:* classical, modern, comedy *Venues:* Théâtre Arlequin: stage A 60, stage B 80 *Touring:* Switzerland

Théâtre de la Place
Place de l'Yser 1, 4020 **Liège**
Tel: 4-344 7170 Fax: 4-341 3544
director J L Colinet; relations publiques Catherine De Michel; directeur technique Claude Santerre
Actors: varies *Prods:* 6 *Type:* theatre, baroque opera, classical, contemporary dance *Venues:* Théatre de la Place 600 *Touring:* Europe *Comments:* co-produces with Théâtre National de Belgium and others; booking Tel: 4-342 0000; see also Promoters

Théâtre de L'Eveil
Centre Culturel Régional de Mons, 8 rue des Arbalestriers, 7000 **Mons**
Tel: 65-349 704/2-705 7531 Fax: 2-705 3196
E-Mail: pion.g@skynet.be
directeur Guy Pion; administration Béatrix Feurauge
Actors: 4 *Perfs:* 168 *Prods:* 2 *Type:* contemporary *Venues:* Centre Culturel Régional de Mons 250 *Touring:* Belgium

Centre Culturel Régional de Namur
Avenue Reine Astrid 72, 5000 **Namur**
Tel: 81-256 161 (admin)/226 026 (box office) Fax: 81-256 160 (admin)/231 356 (box office)
director Patrick Colté; programmation Alain Bombaert; coordinateur technique Marc Noël; éducation permanente et vie assossiative Pierre-Jean Lacroix; communiation Laurent Cools
Actors: varies *Perfs:* 61 *Prods:* 23 *Type:* classical, contemporary *Venues:* Théâtre Marlagne 474, Maison de la Culture 450, Les Bateliers 100, Théâtre Royal de Namur 1000 *Comments:* see also Venues

Atelier Théâtre Jean Vilar
Ferme de Blocry, Place de l'Hocaille, 1348 **Ottignies/Louvain-La-Neuve**
Tel: 10-450 500 Fax: 10-453 234
director Armand Delcampe; assistant directors Cecile van Snick, Brigitte Tilliere; press & publicity Pascale Palmers; administration and finance Alain Abts; technical director Jann Bittner
Actors: 60 *Perfs:* 300 (tour included) *Prods:* 13 *Type:* classical, contemporary *Venues:* Théâtre Jean Vilar 594, Théâtre Blocry 140, Cirque Royal (Brussels) 1300
Touring: France, Switzerland, Belgium, Luxembourg

Baladins du Miroir, Les
Rue de la Porte, Champ Saint Roch, 1360 **Thorembais-Les-Béguines**
Tel: 10-888 329 Fax: 10-880 321
E-Mail: baladins@ipbelgium.com
international relations Gaspard Leclère; director & producer Nele Paxinou; programmation et communications Jean-Felix Tirtiaux;
technical director Xavier Decoux
Actors: varies (4 permanent) *Prods:* 1 *Type:* travelling theatre, fairground theatre (under marquee) *Venues:* marquee 350 *Touring:* Quebec
Comments: touring company; organisers of Festival de Arts Forains (Namur)

Theater Malpertuis
Malpertuis Theatre
Stationstraat 25, 8700 **Tielt**
Tel: 51-401 845 Fax: 51-400 149
E-Mail: malpertuis@unicall.be
director Herman Verschelden;
artistic director Sam Bogaerts
Actors: 5-13 *Perfs:* 150 *Prods:* 2-3 *Type:* different forms of new, experimental theatre, adaptations of classics *Venues:* Stadsschouwburg 500, Malpertuis 130 *Touring:* Belgium, Netherlands

Crea-Théâtre
47 rue Saint-Martin, 7500 **Tournai**
Tel: 69-889 130 Fax: 69-840 069
director Francis Houtteman;
administrator Nadia Vermeulen
Actors: 5 *Perfs:* 150 *Prods:* 3 new + 9 touring *Type:* children's theatre *Touring:* Belgium, France, Portugal
Comments: touring company

Gevolg, Het
The Consequence
Steenweg Op Oosthoven 168/1, 2300 **Turnhout**
Tel: 14-426 327 Fax: 14-428 236
Internet: users.skynet.be/het.gevolg
E-Mail: het.gevolg@skynet.be
artistic director Ignace Cornelissen; administrator Dirk Vanhaute; drama Alex Mallens; secretary Kristel Baeten; bookkeeper Viviane Der Kinderen; technical supervisor Paul Wilms; assistant Inge Thoré
Actors: 15 *Perfs:* 120 *Prods:* 4
Type: new writing, repertoire

Jonna Theatre
Aarschotsesteenweg 113, 3012 **Wilsele-Leuven**
Tel: 16-448 019 Fax: 16-447 820
Internet: www.digilife.be./schoolnet/scholen/jonna
E-Mail: jonna@digilife.be
director John Gysenburgh
Actors: varies *Perfs:* 50 *Prods:* 3 *Type:* clownery, street theatre *Venues:* Theatrehuis Jonna 300 *Comments:* theatre school for children and young people from 6-18 years old

BOSNIA & HERZEGOVINA (+387)

Croation National Theatre in Mostar
Hrvatsko narodno kazaliste u Mostaru
Trg hrvatskih velikana b.b., 88000 **Mostar**
Tel: 88-324 252
acting manager Ivan Ovcar

Mostar Youth Theatre
Alekse Santica 20, 88000 **Mostar**
Tel: 88-580 185 Fax: 88-580 185
E-Mail: mtm@cob.net.ba
director Sead Djulic

National Theatre Mostar
Brkica 2, 88000 **Mostar**
Tel: 88-562 437

Chamber Theatre '55
Marsala Tita Str. 56/II, 71000 **Sarajevo**
Tel: 71-214 908/214 633/209 041 Fax: 71-471 184
director Gradimir Gojer

National Theatre, Sarajevo
Obala Kulina Bana 9, 71000 **Sarajevo**
Tel: 71-663 647
Fax: 71-445 138
director Tvrtko Kulenovic

SARTR, Sarajevo War Theatre
Dalmatinska 2/III, 71000 **Sarajevo**
Tel: 71-664 070/665 189 Fax: 71-664 070
director Safet Plakalo

Youth Theatre
Kulovica 8, 71000 **Sarajevo**
Tel: 71-442 572/205 799
Fax: 71-442 572
director Nermin Tulic

Theatre Travnik
Skolska 23, 72270 **Travnik**
Tel: 72-818 443

National Theatre Tuzla
Kazan mahala 6, 75000 **Tuzla**
Tel: 75-251 646/251 647
Fax: 75-234 838
director Eldin Tabucic

Bosnian National Theatre
Trg BiH 3, 72000 **Zenica**
Tel: 72-31555/21142
Fax: 72-410 759
director Radovan Marusic

BULGARIA (+359)

Nikola Vaptzarov Drama Theatre
1 Dimitar Blagoev Square, 2700 **Blagoevgrad**
Tel: 73-23454 Fax: 73-25381
director Ivan Simeonov
Actors: 20 *Perfs:* 200 *Prods:* 5-6 *Venues:* Big stage 503, Chamber hall 110

Adriana Boudevska Drama Theatre
36a Tzar Assen Str, 8000 **Bourgas**
Tel: 56-841 494 Fax: 56-841 481
director Borislav Tchakrinov
Actors: 22 *Perfs:* 80 *Prods:* 4 *Venues:* Big Stage 420

Apostol Karamitev Drama Theatre
6400 **Dimitrovgrad**
Tel: 391-23312/24359
director Mladen Penkov
Actors: 20 *Perfs:* 80 *Prods:* 2-3 *Venues:* theatre hall 420

Yordan Yovkov Drama Theatre
9300 **Dobritch**
Tel: 58-25313 Fax: 58-25313
director Krassimir Rankov
Actors: 20 *Perfs:* 80 *Prods:* 3 *Venues:* Big stage 500, Chamber hall 250

Racho Stoyanov Drama Theatre
PO Box 81, 5300 **Gabrovo**
Tel: 66-26722
director Nevena Miteva
Actors: 15 *Venues:* Big stage 450, Chamber hall 100, Foyer-stage 90, Cafe-theatre 65

Satiric Variety Theatre
68 Bryanska Str., 5300 **Gabrovo**
Tel: 66-30093/30181
director Nikolay Georgiev
Actors: 7 + dancers *Perfs:* 150 *Prods:* 3-4 *Type:* variety, musicals *Venues:* Theatre Hall 180

Ivan Dimov Drama Theatre
40 Otets Paisiy Street, 6300 **Haskovo**
Tel: 38-32317/24233
director Venzeslav Assenov
Actors: 14 *Perfs:* 100 *Prods:* 4-5
Type: classical and contemporary *Venues:* Big stage 380, chamber hall 100

Dimitar Dimov State Theatre
1 Boulair Str., 6600 **Kardjali**
Tel: 361-22767/26481/22567
director Dimitar Ignatov
Actors: 18 *Type:* classical and contemporary *Venues:* Big stage 536

Drama Theatre Kazanluk
2500 **Kustendil**
Tel: 431-23796/23691
director Vassil Samarski
Type: classical, contemporary *Venues:* big stage 500

Kustendil Drama Theatre
28 Bulgaria Blvd, 2500 **Kustendil**
Tel: 78-27672 Fax: 78-27672
director Ilia Bogilov
Actors: 12 *Venues:* Big stage 720, Chamber hall 100, Café-theatre 200

Lovetch Drama Theatre
Bulgaria Square, 5500 **Lovetch**
Tel: 68-23630/25810
director George Mirchev
Actors: 12 *Perfs:* 80 *Prods:* 3-4 *Venues:* Big stage 435

Dragomir Assenov Drama Theatre
3400 **Montana**
Tel: 96-22014/22623 Fax: 96-22016
director Orlin Djakov
Actors: 15 *Perfs:* 130 *Prods:* 5-6 *Type:* classical drama
Venues: Big stage 580, Chamber stage with a garden 100

Konstantin Velichkov Drama Theatre
24 Kostadin Starev Str., 4400 **Pazardjik**
Tel: 34-20906/27535 Fax: 34-26533
director Vladlen Alexandrov
Actors: 19 *Perfs:* 90 *Prods:* 2 *Venues:* Big stage 680, Chamber hall 100

Boyan Danovski Drama Theatre
Palace of Culture, 2300 **Pernik**
Tel: 76-20535 Fax: 76-20500
director Angel Angelov
Actors: 20 *Perfs:* 70 *Prods:* 2 *Venues:* Big stage 490, Chamber Hall 100

Ivan Radoev Drama Theatre
5800 **Pleven**
Tel: 64-801 242 Fax: 64-44016
director Krassimira Filipova
Actors: 20 *Perfs:* 110 *Prods:* 4 *Venues:* Big stage 400, Chamber hall 100, Foyer-stage 60

N.O. Massalitinov Drama Theatre
36 Alexandre Batenberg St., 4000 **Plovdiv**
Tel: 32-624 867/632 364
director Emil Bonev
Actors: 22 *Perfs:* 150 *Prods:* 6 *Venues:* Big stage 550, Small summer Hall 150 to 250, 4th century open-air amphitheatre 4000

Anton Strashimirov Drama Theatre
Vazrajdane sq., PO Box 121, 7200 **Razgrad**
Tel: 84-25290/22638/29689
director Kosio Stanev
Actors: 15 *Perfs:* 150 *Prods:* 5 *Venues:* Big stage 530, chamber hall 80

Sava Ognianov Drama Theatre
3 Tzaribrod St, 7000 **Rousse**
Tel: 82-226 741/227 808
director Krum Gergizov
Actors: 30 *Perfs:* 80 *Prods:* 3 *Venues:* Big Stage 550, Chamber Hall Rousse 200, Conference Hall 400

Vassil Droumev Drama Theatre
9700 **Shoumen**
Tel: 54-57384/52241
director Radka Spasova
Actors: 20 *Perfs:* 120 *Prods:* 4 *Venues:* Big stage 600, Chamber hall 100 *Comments:* hall available to rent

Sava Dobroplodni Drama Theatre
PO Box 105, 7500 **Silistra**
Tel: 86-23101
director Stefan Staitchev
Actors: 16 *Perfs:* 110 *Prods:* 3-4 *Venues:* Big stage 555, Chamber hall 60

Stefan Kirov Drama Theatre
PO Box 164, 8800 **Sliven**
Tel: 44-23008/26939 Fax: 44-27094
director Elevteri Elevterov
Actors: 15 *Perfs:* 100 *Prods:* 6 *Venues:* Big stage 484, Chamber hall 120, foyer-stage 72, one actor stage 40
Comments: halls available to rent

Rhodopes Drama Theatre
PO Box 53, 8 Bulgaria Blvd., 4700 **Smolyan**
Tel: 301-25134 Fax: 301-25177
director Krastu Krastev
Actors: 15 *Perfs:* 120-150 *Type:* drama, comedy, musical
Venues: Big stage 683, Chamber hall A 120, Chamber hall B 80

199 Theatre
8 Slavianska Str., 1000 **Sofia**
Tel: 2-988 5319 Fax: 2-988 5319
director Valentin Stoichev
Actors: 2-5 *Perfs:* 100 *Prods:* 10 *Venues:* Theatre Hall 199

Aleko Konstantinov State Satiric Theatre
26 Stefan Karadja Str, 1000 **Sofia**
Tel: 2-988 5424
director Rachko Mladenov
Actors: 30 *Perfs:* 130 *Prods:* 5-6 *Type:* comedy and satire
Venues: Big Stage 583, Foyer-stage 90, Hall at the Hungarian Culture Centre 90
Comments: halls available to rent

Barbukov Theatre
Biser 7, **Sofia**
Tel: 2-650 270
contact Blagoi Stanoev

Credo Theatre
Kutlovitza str. 53, entr. B, fl. 8, apt. 22, 1505 **Sofia**
Tel: 489-44742/2-465 158 Fax: 2-465 158
E-Mail: credo@biscom.net
contact Nina Dimitrova

Free Theatre
ul. Krakra 2-a, 1504 **Sofia**
Tel: 2-449 487 Fax: 2-443 391
E-Mail: kala@bgnet.bg
contact Vesselin Kalanovski

Ivan Vazov National Theatre
5 Vassil Levski Str., 1000 **Sofia**
Tel: 2-987 7800/875 248 Fax: 2-877 066
director Prof. Vassil Stefanov
Actors: 53 *Perfs:* 150 *Prods:* 4-6 *Type:* classical and contemporary *Venues:* Big stage 220, Chamber hall 200, Second Chamber hall 80

La Strada First Private Theatre
c/o 6th September Str., 1000 **Sofia**
Tel: 2-878 433/981 1494/981 5215
director Nikolai Dodov; theatrical producer Stefan Moskov

National Army Theatre
98 Rakovski Str., 1000 **Sofia**
Tel: 2-872 303/884 356 Fax: 2-880 780
director Mitko Todorov
Actors: 38 *Perfs:* 130 *Prods:* 4 *Venues:* Big stage 200

National Youth Theatre
12 Narodno Sabranie Square, 1000 **Sofia**
Tel: 2-981 4617
director Georgi Kadurin
Actors: 30 *Perfs:* 100 *Prods:* 4 *Venues:* Big stage 400, Chamber stage 150

Off the Channal City Theatre
25 Yanko Sakazov Blvd, 1505 **Sofia**
Tel: 2-464 046/462 020/446 066/442 448 Fax: 2-462 020
director Bina Haralampieva
Actors: 22 *Perfs:* 120 *Prods:* 5 *Venues:* Big stage 400, Chamber stage 150

Pantdance
31 Skobelev Blvd, **Sofia**
Tel: 2-547 995/549 186 Fax: 2-542 832
director Nikolai Sotirov
Actors: 18 *Perfs:* 199 *Prods:* 4-5

Sfumato Theatre Workshop
14, Tzar Osvoboditel blvd., 1000 **Sofia**
Tel: 2-897 962 Fax: 2-897 962
directors Margarita Mladenova
Actors: 12 *Perfs:* 100 *Prods:* 4 *Venues:* capacity 50 to100

Sofia Drama Theatre
24 Yanko Sakazov Blvd., 1504 **Sofia**
Tel: 2-443 010 Fax: 2-443 512
director Doroteja Tontcheja
Actors: 25 *Perfs:* 100 *Prods:* 4 *Venues:* Big stage 496, Club-theatre 80, Arena-stage 70, Foyer-stage 80

Sofia Travelling Theatre
104 Sofronii Vratchanski Str., 1202 **Sofia**
Tel: 2-323 097/322 075
director Rumen Dimitrov
Actors: 23 *Perfs:* 110 *Prods:* 5 *Venues:* Big stage 500, Chamber stage 150

Tear and Laugh New Drama Theatre
5 Slavianska Str., 1000 **Sofia**
Tel: 2-882 373/880 681 Fax: 2-880 681
director Boyko Bogdanov
Actors: 30 *Perfs:* 100 *Prods:* 4 *Venues:* Big hall 630, Garden theatre 110, Foyer stage 170

Theatre 13
Tzarigradsko shose 81, bl. 106 vh B apt. 44, **Sofia**
Tel: 2-9166 2838 Fax: 2-963 0282
Internet: www.ejn.it/theatre13/
contact Radoslav Rachev

Theatre Alternativa
5 Gen. Gurko Str., 1000 **Sofia**
Tel: 2-878 533
director Dimitar Guranov

Theatre Dialog
127 G.S. Rakovski Str., 1000 **Sofia**
Tel: 2-814 799

Training Theatre of the Krastu Sarafov National Academy of Drama and Film Art
108/A Rakovski Str., PO Box 100, 1000 **Sofia**
Tel: 2-879 862/885 563 Fax: 2-897 389
directors Snejina Tankovska, Prof. Hristo Rukov
Actors: all graduate students *Perfs:* 50 *Prods:* 2 *Type:* training theatre – drama and puppetry *Venues:* Big Stage 440, Chamber Hall 75

Vuzrazdane Theatre
Central Library, 4 Slaveikov Blvd., 1000 **Sofia**
Tel: 2-875 411
director Georgy Georgiev

Geo Milev Drama Theatre
6000 **Srata Zagora**
Tel: 42-22273/39245 Fax: 42-22273
director Georgi Velev
Actors: 22 *Perfs:* 120 *Prods:* 3-4 *Venues:* Big stage 650

Drama Theatre
7700 **Targovishte**
Tel: 601-23377/22528
director Milko Nikodimov
Actors: 18 *Perfs:* 100 *Prods:* 3
Venues: Big stage 500, Chamber stage 150

Stoyan Bachvarov Drama Theatre
1 Nezavissimost sq., 9000 **Varna**
Tel: 52-222 544 Fax: 52-250 395
director Stoyan Alexiev
Actors: 22 *Perfs:* 230 *Prods:* 6-8
Venues: No.1 stage 425, No.2 stage 442

Veliko Tarnovo Drama Theatre
5000 **Veliko Turnovo**
Tel: 62-623 526
director Sava Dimitrov
Actors: 15 *Perfs:* 100 *Prods:* 3 *Venues:* Big stage 644, Chamber stage 100

Vladimir Trendafilov Drama Theatre
3700 **Vidin**
Tel: 94-23095/6/23127
director Krassimir Rangelov
Actors: 12 *Perfs:* 80 *Prods:* 3 *Venues:* Big stage 394

Drama Theatre Vratza
Hristo Botev Sq., 3000 **Vratza**
Tel: 92-26498/26571 Fax: 92-26498
director Anastas Popdimitrov
Actors: 18 *Perfs:* 100 *Prods:* 4
Venues: Big stage 750, Chamber stage 150

Drama Theatre Yambol
8600 **Yambol**
Tel: 46-243 824/22736
director Nikolai Valkonav
Actors: 15 *Perfs:* 60 *Prods:* 2 *Venues:* Big stage 326, chamber stage 150 *Touring:* national

CROATIA (+385)

Marin Drzic Theatre
Kazaliste Marina Drzica
Pred dvorom 3, 20000 **Dubrovnik**
Tel: 20-426 438/426 437 Fax: 20-411 434
manager Marin Gozze

Drama studio Zorin Dom
Dramski studio Zorin Dom
Domobranska 1, 47000 **Karlovac**
Tel: 47-614 950/614 951 Fax: 47-614 9513
director Ljerka Lackovic

Croatian National Theatre in Osijek
Hrvatsko narodno Kazaliste u Osijeku
Zupanijska 9, 31000 **Osijek**
Tel: 31-220 700/220 766 (publicity)/734 Fax: 31-220 734
director Zeljko Cagalj (31-220 726)

Istrian National Theatre
Istarsko Narodno Kazaliste
Matka Laginje 5, 52000 **Pula**
Tel: 52-216 796 Fax: 52-214 303
E-Mail: pula@pu.tel.hr
manager Davorka Lovrecic (52-22380)

Italian Drama of the Croatian National Theatre Ivan von Zajca
Talijanska drama Hrvatskog Narodnog Kazalista I. Pl. Zajca
Verdijeva 5 a, 51000 **Rijeka**
Tel: 51-336 592/212 322/211 268 Fax: 51-336 592
general director Srecko Sestan

Ivan von Zajca Drama of the Croatian National Theatre
Hrvatsko narodno Kazalista Ivana pl. Zajca
Uljarska 1, 51000 **Rijeka**
Tel: 51-337 888 Fax: 51-212 680
intendant Srecko Sestan (51-212 322/212 318)

Split Croatian National Theatre
Hrvatskog narodnog Kazalista Split
Trg Gaja Bulata 1, 21000 **Split**
Tel: 21-585 999/585 957 (publicity) Fax: 21-583 643
E-Mail: hnk-split@st.tel.hr
Intendant Ms. Mani Gotovac (21-361 216)

Croation National in Varazdin
Hrvatsko narodno Kazaliste u Varazdinu
Cesarceva 1, 42000 **Varazdin**
Tel: 42-214 688/211 218 Fax: 42-211 218
manager Marijan Varjacic

Virovitica Theatre
Kazaliste Virovitica
Trg Ljudevita Patacica 2, 33000 **Virovitica**
Tel: 33-721 330 Fax: 33-721 330
manager Miran Hajos

Croatian Theatre House
Hrvatska Kazalisna Kuca Zadar
Siroka Ulica 8, 23000 **Zadar**
Tel: 23-314 586/552 Fax: 23-314 590
E-Mail: hkk.zd@zd.tel.hr
acting manager Ms. Jadranka Svagusa

Bird of Paradise Theatre
Gradsko kazaliste Zar ptica
Bijenicka 97, 10000 **Zagreb**
Tel: 1-233 8961/1-233 8953/233 8954 (publicity) Fax: 1-233 8953/233 8954 (publicity)
manager Tomislav Milanovski

City Comedy Theatre
Zagrebacko gradsko kazaliste Komedija
Kaptol 9, 10000 **Zagreb**
Tel: 1-481 4566/481 3200 (publicity) Fax: 1-4381 2179
E-Mail: komedija@zg.tel.hr
manager Niko Pavlovic (1-481 2185)
Comments: Secretary Tel: 1-481 2100

City Theatre Cherry
Gradsko kazaliste Tresnja
Moscenicka 1, 10000 **Zagreb**
Tel: 1-363 8010 Fax: 1-363 8380 (publicity)/1-325 230
E-Mail: kazaliste-tresnja@zg.tel.hr
manager Ms. Vladimira Vrhovsek;
art director Hrvoje Hitrec

Croatian National Theatre in Zagreb
Hrvatsko narodno kazaliste u Zagrebu
Trg Marsala Tita 15, 10000 **Zagreb**
Tel: 1-482 8550/4828 530 (publicity)
Fax: 1-482 8531
Intendant Georgij Paro

Epilog Theatre
Epilog teatar
Park Ribnjak 1, 10000 **Zagreb**
Tel: 1-481 4719 (publicity)/1-388 1932 Fax: 1-388 1932
manager Ms. Davorka Juravic
(tel:1-481 4932/98-351 616 (mobile)

Exit Theatre
Teatar Exit
Ilica 208, 10000 **Zagreb**
Tel: 1-370 7626 Fax: 1-370 7626/370 4120
E-Mail: teatar-exit@zg.tel.hr
manager Matko Raguz

Gavella Drama Theatre
Dramsko Kazaliste Gavella
Frankopanska 6-8, 10000 **Zagreb**
Tel: 1-484 9222/484 8548/484 8541
Fax: 1-484 8541
manager Kreso Dolencic

Historion Theatre Company
Glumacka dru'ina Historion
Preradoiceva 24, 10000 **Zagreb**
Tel: 1-485 4713/485 4714
Fax: 1-485 4713/485 4714
manager Zlatko Vitez

Kerempuh Satirical Theatre
Satiricko kazaliste Kerempuh
Ilica 31, 10000 **Zagreb**
Tel: 1-424 509/424 120 (publicity)/431 734
Fax: 1-424 509
manager Dusko Ljustina

Little Stage Theatre
Kazaliste Mala scena
Medvescak 2, 10000 **Zagreb**
Tel: 1-468 3352
Fax: 1-468 3352/468 3370/468 3373/468 3374
Internet: www.ador.hr/mala-scena
E-Mail: mala-scena@zg.tel.hr
manager Ms. Vitomira Loncar

Theatre ETC
Teatar ITD
Savska 25, 10000 **Zagreb**
Tel: 1-459 3603/459 3677/459 3555 (publicity)
Fax: 1-484 3502
E-Mail: darko.lukic@zg.tel.hr
manager t.b.a.Darko Lukic (1-459 3613)

Travelling Theatre
Teatar U Gostima
Dolac 1, 10000 **Zagreb**
Tel: 1-481 6318/481 6319 Fax: 1-481 6291
art director Relja Basic; manager Stjepan Bahert

Zagreb Youth Theatre
Zagrebacko Kazaliste Mladih
Teslina 7, 10000 **Zagreb**
Tel: 1-431 444/487 2561/487 2562 Fax: 1-487 2568
director Leo Katunaric (1-487 2551)

CYPRUS (+357)

Ethal – Praxis Theatre
PO Box 58096, 3730 **Limassol**
Tel: 5-357 570 Fax: 5-341 112
director Doros Leropoulos
Actors: 5 (permanent) *Perfs:* 130 *Prods:* 5 per year *Venues:* Praxis Theatre, Limassol (210); Ancient Theatre of Curium, Limassol (1800); Municipal Theatre, Nicosia (1200), Melina Merkouri Hall, Nicosia (200); Makarios III Amphitheatre, Strovolos (1600); Municipal Theatre, Larnaka (400); Markideion Theatre, Pafos (380); Ancient Odeion, Pafos (500); Rialto Theatre, Limassol (560), Patticheion Municipal Theatre, Limassol (760)

Theatro Ena
Athina Avenue, **Nicosia**
Tel: 2-348 203
Fax: 2-344 270
artistic director Andreas Christodoulides

Satirikon Theatre
Athinon & Serron 3, Strovolos, 2040 **Strovolos**
Tel: 2-312 940/421 609 Fax: 2-493 450
Actors: 8 (permanent) *Perfs:* 200 *Prods:* 5 per year
Venues: Satiriko Theatre, Nicosia (360); Ancient Theatre of Curium, Limassol (1800); Municipal Theatre, Larnaka (400); Markideion Theatre, Pafos (380); Ancient Odeion, Pafos (500); Patticheion Municipal Amphitheatre, Larnaka (2100)

Theatre Organisation of Cyprus – State Theatre
Chalkanoros 2 & Liperti, 2000 **Strovolos**
Tel: 2-492 900 Fax: 2-492 923
chairman Michalis Loulloupis; director Antis Bargilly; president artistic committee Monica Kythreoti; administrative secretary Andreas Gabrielides
Actors: 23 (permanent) *Perfs:* 260 total
Prods: 8 per year (7 winter, 1 summer) *Type:* classical and modern, classical Greek – tragedy and comedy, youth theatre, experimental theatre *Venues:* Nicosia Municipal Theatre (1200); Markideion Theatre, Pafos (380), New Stage, Nicosia; Patticheion Municipal Theatre, Limassol (760); Ancient Theatre of Curium, Limassol (1800); Municipal Theatre, Larnaka (400); Patticheion Municipal Amphitheatre, Larnaka (2100); Ancient Odeion, Pafos (500) *Touring:* New York, Greece, various festivals including Athens festival, Epidauros festival, Israel, Germany, UK, Russia, Bulgaria

CZECH REPUBLIC (+420)

Brno City Theatre
Mestské divadlo Brno
Lidická 16, 657 51 **Brno**
Tel: 5-4532 1269 Fax: 5-4521 1443
Internet: www.mdb.cz
E-Mail: mdb@mdb.cz
director Stanislav Mosa
Actors: 30 *Perfs:* 300 *Prods:* 5
Venues: capacity 430, studio theatre 80

Brno National Theatre – Drama
Národní divadlo v Brne – cinohra
Dvoráková 11, 657 70 **Brno**
Tel: 5-4232 1285/1300 Fax: 5-4221 7045
Internet: www.ndbrno.cz
E-Mail: ndb@netbrno.cz
director Mojmír Weimann; drama director Zbynek Srba; manager Arnost Janek
Actors: 30 *Perfs:* 250 *Prods:* 6 *Venues:* Mahenovo divadlo 577, small stage 80
Comments: see also Opera and Dance

Centre for Experimental Theatre (CET)
Centrum experimentálního divadla (CED)
Zelny trh 9, 602 00 **Brno**
Tel: 5-4221 1630/1
Fax: 5-4221 0200
Internet: www.divadlo.cz/dhnp/ced
E-Mail: ced-dhnp@login.cz
director Petr Oslzly
Comments: parts of CET are Theatre Goose on a String (q.v.) and HaTheatre (q.v.)

HaTheatre
HaDivadlo
Sukova 4/6, 602 00 **Brno**
Tel: 5-4221 2761
Internet: www.hadivadlo.cz
E-Mail: hadi@hadivadlo.cz
Actors: 11 *Perfs:* 150 *Prods:* 4 *Venues:* Kabinet múz 100
Comments: part of CET (q.v.)

MARTA – Drama Studio of the Theatre Faculty JAMU
Studio MARTA – scéna divadelní fakulty JAMU
Bayerova 5, 602 00 **Brno**
Tel: 5-4121 3842 Fax: 5-4121 3842
artistic director Jaroslav Tucek;
manager Alena Plesáková
Perfs: 100 *Prods:* 7 *Venues:* home capacity 200
Comments: school theatre

Theatre at half past seven
Divadlo v 7 a pul
Svatopluka Cecha 35a, 612 00 **Brno**
Tel: 5-4124 0474
Fax: 5-4121 3206
artistic chief Matej T Ruzicka
Actors: varies *Perfs:* 150 *Prods:* 6
Venues: Divadlo Barka 150

Theatre Goose on a String
Divadlo HUSA na provázku
Zelny trh 9, 602 00 **Brno**
Tel: 5-4221 1630/1 Fax: 5-4221 0200
Internet: www.divadlo.cz/dhnp
E-Mail: ced-dhnp@login.cz
artistic chief Petr Oslzly
Actors: 13 *Perfs:* 200 *Prods:* 4 *Venues:* home venue 250, small stage 80 *Comments:* part of CET (q.v.)

South Bohemian Theatre – Drama
Jihoceské divadlo – cinohra
Dr. Stejskala 23, 370 47 **Ceské Budejovice**
Tel: 38-671 1111 Fax: 38-55640
Internet: mujweb.cz/www/jihocdivadlo
E-Mail: jihoceskedivadlo@iol.cz
director ing. Jan Mrzena; drama director Martin Hruska
Actors: 20 *Perfs:* 200 *Prods:* 6 *Venues:* capacity 240
Comments: see also Opera and Dance

TesínTheatre
Tesínské divadlo
Ostravská 67, 737 01 **Cesky Tesín**
Tel: 659-711 208/9 Fax: 659-713 372
Internet: www.tdivadlo.cz
E-Mail: info@tdivadlo.cz
director Roman Rozbrój; artistic chief (Czech stage) Ivana Wojtylova-Guziorová;
artistic chief (Polish stage) Jerzy Batzcki
Actors: 19 (Czech stage), 18 (Polish stage) *Perfs:* 170 (Czech stage), 120 (Polish stage) *Prods:* 7 (Czech stage), 7 (Polish stage) *Venues:* home capacity 458

West Bohemian Theatre
Západoceské divadlo
Divadelní námestí 1, 350 59 **Cheb**
Tel: 166-433 591/2 Fax: 166-310 079
director Frantisek Hromada
Actors: 18 *Perfs:* 220 *Prods:* 7
Venues: Theatre 300, Studio D 50

Klicpera Theatre
Klicperovo divadlo
Dlouhá 99, 500 01 **Hradec Králové**
Tel: 49-551 4590/1 Fax: 49-551 3782
Internet: www.hk.cesnet.cz/klicperovo-divadlo
E-Mail: k-divadlo@hk.cesnet.cz
director Ladislav Zeman
Actors: 20 *Perfs:* 220 *Prods:* 10 *Venues:* home capacity 464, Studio Beseda 120, Chamber Stage V podkroví 50

Mountains Theatre
Horácké divadlo
Komenského 22, 586 47 **Jihlava**
Tel: 66-732 1818/731 0179 Fax: 66-731 0179
Internet: www.webhouse.cz/hdj
E-Mail: hdj@jitel.cz
director Milos Stránsky; artistic chief Petr Zák;
manager Josef Fila
Actors: 22 *Perfs:* 230 *Prods:* 8 *Venues:* home capacity 450, small stage up to 100

Karlovy Vary City Theatre
Mestské divadlo Karlovy Vary
Husovo námestí 2, 360 21 **Karlovy Vary**
Tel: 17-322 3873
Fax: 17-322 9400
director Alois Jezek
Actors: 10 *Perfs:* 150 *Prods:* 5 *Venues:* home cap. 400

Theatre Dagmar
Divadlo Dagmar
Komorní scéna Tosca, Moravská 8,
360 01 **Karlovy Vary**
artistic chief Hana Franková
Actors: varies *Perfs:* 100 *Prods:* 3 *Venues:* Chamber stage Tosca 100 *Comments:* contact Mrs Hana Franková: Skroupova 5, 360 01 Karlovy Vary

Central Bohemian Theatre
Stredoceské divadlo
Divadelní ulice 1, 272 80 **Kladno**
Tel: 312-627 7123/4/5 Fax: 312-629 430
Internet: www.divadlo.cz/kladno
director Jaroslav Voelka; artistic chief Jirí Fréhar
Actors: 25 *Perfs:* 300 *Prods:* 11 *Venues:* home capacity 380, small stage 120, Club-Theatre 120

F. X. Salda Theatre – Drama
Divadlo F. X. Saldy – cinohra
Zhorelecká 344/5, 460 37 **Liberec**
Tel: 48-510 4288/4188 Fax: 48-510 4181
Internet: www.infolbc.cz/divadlo/uvodni.htm
E-Mail: mic@info.lbc.cz
director Frantisek Dána;
drama director Michaela Lohniská
Actors: 22 *Perfs:* 220 *Prods:* 10 *Venues:* home capacity 637, small theatre 120 to 200 *Comments:* see also Opera and Dance

Mladá Boleslav City Theatre
Mestské divadlo
Husova 214/8, 293 80 **Mladá Boleslav**
Tel: 326-21791 Fax: 326-28553
Internet: www.divadlo.cz/mdmb
director Frantisek Skrípek
Actors: varies *Perfs:* 300
Venues: home capacity 380, small stage 81

Most City Theatre
Mestské divadlo
PO Box 11, 434 11 **Most**
Tel: 35-610 0250/1 Fax: 35-25401
E-Mail: euroregion@traveller.cz
director Václav Hoffman; artistic chief Vlastimil Novák
Actors: 20 *Perfs:* 210 *Prods:* 8 *Venues:* Theatre 500
Comments: see also Puppets (Divadlo rozmanitostí)

Moravian Theatre – Drama
Moravské divadlo – cinohra
tr. Svobody 33, 771 07 **Olomouc**
Tel: 68-522 3651 Fax: 68-522 5781
Internet: mdo.olomouc.cz
E-Mail: mdo@olomouc.com
director Václav Kozusník; drama director Peter Gábor;
manager Marcela Arelyová
Actors: 24 *Perfs:* 200 *Prods:* 9 *Venues:* home capacity 504
Comments: see also Opera and Dance

Silesian Theatre – Drama
Slezské divadlo – cinohra
Horní námesti 13, 746 69 **Opava**
Tel: 653-621 156 Fax: 653-623 656
director Jiri Merínsky; drama director Bedrich Jansa
Actors: 24 *Perfs:* 200 *Prods:* 10 *Venues:* home capacity 416 *Comments:* see also Opera

Chamber Stage Arena
Komorní scéna Aréna
tr.28 rijna 23, 700 00 **Ostrava**
Tel: 69-611 5400 Fax: 69-611 4585
director Renata Huserová; artistic chief Pavel Cisovsky
Actors: 6 *Perfs:* 120 *Prods:* 3 *Venues:* capacity 150

Moravian and Silesian National Theatre – Drama
Narodní divadlo moravskoslezské – cinohra
Ceskoslovenskych legií 14, 701 04 **Ostrava**
Tel: 69-611 2821 Fax: 69-611 2881
Internet: www.ndm.cz
E-Mail: narodni_divadlo_ostrava@oasanet.cz
director Ludek Golat; drama director Juraj Deák
Actors: 25 *Perfs:* 220 *Prods:* 10
Venues: Divadlo Jirího Myrona 600, Divadlo Antonína Dvoráka 800, Foyer-Theatre 60 to 100
Comments: see also Opera and Dance

Petr Bezruc Theatre
Divadlo Petra Bezruce
trída 28., ríjna 120, 702 00 **Ostrava**
Tel: 69-611 2568 Fax: 69-234 766
director Michael Przebinda
Actors: 20 *Perfs:* 250 *Prods:* 8
Venues: home capacity 150, Márnice (Morgue) 40

East Bohemian Theatre
Vychodoceské divadlo
Divadelní 50, 531 62 **Pardubice**
Tel: 40-623 0000
Fax: 40-621 0224
director Gustav Skála
Actors: 30 *Perfs:* 250 *Prods:* 10 *Venues:* Theatre 597, Chamber stage 160

J K Tyl Theatre – Drama
Divadlo J.K. Tyla – cinohra
Prokopova 14, 304 11 **Plzen**
Tel: 19-722 6743
Fax: 19-220 190
Internet: www.central.cz/djkt
E-Mail: reditelstvi@djkt.plzen.city.cz
director Jan Burian; drama director Pavel Pavlovsky
Actors: 30 *Perfs:* 260 *Prods:* 7 *Venues:* Great Theatre 446, Chamber Theatre 440, Theatre in the Club 60
Comments: see also Opera and Dance

DISK – Drama Studio of the Theatre Faculty AMU
DISK – scéna divadelní fakulty AMU
Karlova 26, 11665 **Praha** 1
Tel: 2-2222 0055
Fax: 2-2222 0058
E-Mail: kolouskz@hamlet.damu.cz
director Otakar Kosek
Perfs: 100 *Prods:* 7
Venues: home capacity 200
Touring: school theatre

Drama Club
Cinoherni klub
Ve Smeckách 26, 110 00 **Praha** 1
Tel: 2-9622 2125/6/7
Fax: 2-9622 2124
director Vladimír Procházka
Actors: 25 *Perfs:* 200 *Prods:* 4 *Venues:* cap 180

Gaspar Kaspar
Spolek Kaspar
Celetná 17, 110 00 **Praha**
Tel: 2-232 6843 Fax: 2-2481 1452
Internet: www.divadlo.cz/kasper
artistic chief Jakub Spalek; manager Robert Hron
Actors: varies *Perfs:* 200 *Prods:* 4
Venues: Divadlo v Celetné 150

Jára Cimrman Theatre
Divadlo Járy Cimrmana
Stítného 5, 130 00 **Praha** 3
Tel: 2-2278 3260 Fax: 2-2278 0396
Internet: www.vol.cz/cimrman
E-Mail: cimrman@mbox.vol.cz
artistic chief Zdenek Sverák, Ladislav Smoljak
Actors: varies *Perfs:* 150 *Prods:* 1 *Venues:* Zizkovské divadlo Járy Cimrmana 300 *Comments:* contact Divadelní agentura ECHO – see under Agents

Prague Chamber Theatre
Prazské komorní divadlo
Liliová 18, 11000 **Praha** 1
Tel: 2-2222 0205
director Michal Hruby
Actors: varies *Perfs:* 80 *Prods:* 2 *Venues:* touring

Prague City Theatres
Mestská divadla prazská
Lazarská 6, 112 14 **Praha** 1
Tel: 2-2491 5342/3
Fax: 2-297 169
director Radka Pipkova
Comments: administration for the following three theatres: Theatre ABC (Divadlo ABC), Theatre of Comedy (Divadlo Komedie), Rokoko (q.v.)

Prague National Theatre – Drama
Národni divadlo – cinohra
PO Box 865, 112 30 **Praha** 1
Tel: 2-2421 4339 Fax: 2-2421 2149
Internet: www.anet.cz/nd
E-Mail: ntprague@ntprague.anet.cz
director Jiri Srstka; drama director Josef Kovalcuk
Actors: 45 *Perfs:* 350 *Prods:* 7 *Venues:* Národní divadlo 987, Stavovské divadlo 639, Kolowrat 80 *Comments:* see also Opera and Dance

Rokoko
Václavské nám 38, 110 00 **Praha** 1
Tel: 2-2421 7084 Fax: 2-2421 1260
Internet: www.rokoko.cz
E-Mail: rokoko@iol.cz
artistic chief Zdenek Potuzil
Actors: 12 *Perfs:* 200 *Prods:* 6 *Venues:* home capacity 220
Comments: one of the three theatres making up the Prague City Theatres (q.v.)

Semafor
V Jáme 1, 110 00 **Praha** 1
Tel: 2-2416 2585
director Jirí Suchy; manager Vladimír Hrabánek
Actors: varies *Perfs:* 180 *Prods:* 3 *Venues:* Semafor, Krizikova 10, 186 00 Praha 8, capacity 180

Studio Ypsilon
Spálená 16, 110 00 **Praha** 1
Tel: 2-2494 8124
Fax: 2-2494 6525
Internet: www.ypsilonka.cz
E-Mail: ypsilonka@software602.cz
director Jan Schmid
Actors: 18 *Perfs:* 230 *Prods:* 2 *Venues:* home capacity 200, small stage 100 to 180

Theatre ABC
Divadlo ABC
Vodickova 28, 110 00 **Praha** 1
Tel: 2-2421 2585
Fax: 2-2423 2275
Internet: www.ecn.cz/abc
E-Mail: divadlo.abc@ecn.cz
artistic chief Milan Schejbal
Actors: 20 *Perfs:* 200 *Prods:* 6 *Venues:* home capacity 636
Comments: one of the three theatres making up the Prague City Theatres (q.v.)

Theatre Ark
Divadlo Archa
Na Porící 26, 110 00 **Praha** 1
Tel: 2-232 7570 Fax: 2-232 2089/2481/2468
Internet: www.archatheatre.cz
E-Mail: archa@archatheatre.cz
director Ondrej Hrab
Perfs: 200 *Prods:* 3
Venues: large auditorium (arena and proscenium) 300-500; small auditorium 100-120
Comments: member of IETM (q.v.);
see also Venues and Promoters

Theatre Association CD 94
Divadelní sdruzení CD 94
Celetná 17, 110 00 **Praha** 1
Tel: 2-2480 9152
Fax: 2-2482 8327
Internet: www.cd94.cz
director Daniel Hrbek
Actors: varies *Perfs:* 150 *Prods:* 4
Venues: Divadlo v Celetné 150

Theatre below Palmovka
Divadlo pod Palmovkou
PO Box 36, 180 00 **Praha** 8
Tel: 2-6631 1708
Fax: 2-6631 0191
Internet: www.vol.cz/palmovka
E-Mail: palmovka@mbox.vol.cz
director Petr Kracik; manager Petr Nasic
Actors: 18 *Perfs:* 200 *Prods:* 5
Venues: home capacity 400,
Rehearsal Place Theatre 100

Theatre in Reznická
Divadlo v Reznické
Reznická 17, 110 00 **Praha** 1
Tel: 2-2223 0996
Fax: 2-2223 0996
manager Yvetta Srbová
Actors: varies *Perfs:* 150 *Prods:* 8 *Venues:* capacity 80

Theatre of Comedy
Divadlo Komedie
Jungmannova 1, 110 00 **Praha** 1
Tel: 2-2422 2484/5 Fax: 2-2421 6015
Internet: www.ecn.cz/komedie
E-Mail: komedie@mbox.vol.cz
artistic chief Michal Docekal
Actors: 19 *Perfs:* 150 *Prods:* 4 *Venues:* home capacity 319
Comments: one of the three theatres making up the Prague City Theatres (q.v.)

Theatre of Conservatoire THEC
Divadlo Konzervatore – DIK
Na Rejdisti 1, 110 00 **Praha** 1
Tel: 2-232 0967
Fax: 2-232 6406
Perfs: 100 *Prods:* 4 *Venues:* Zizkovské divadlo Járy Cimrmana 300(Stítného 5, 130 00 Praha 3 Tel: 2-628 4175 Fax: 2-627 8900 *Comments:* drama school theatre

Theatre of Dejvice
Dejvické divadlo
Zelená 15, 16000 **Praha** 6
Tel: 2-311 2365
Fax: 2-311 2359
Internet: www.divadlo.cz/dd
E-Mail: dejvicke@vol.cz
director Eva Merícková; artistic chief Miroslav Krobot
Actors: 10 *Perfs:* 180 *Prods:* 4 *Venues:* home capacity 150

Theatre on Dlouhá
Divadlo v Dlouhé
Dlouhá trída 39, 110 15 **Praha** 1
Tel: 2-2482 6807
Fax: 2-2482 6801
Internet: www.ecn.cz/dvd
E-Mail: divadlo.vdlouhe@ecn.cz
director Daniela Sálková
Actors: 15 *Perfs:* 200 *Prods:* 6 *Venues:* home capacity 580

Theatre on the Balustrade
Divadlo Na zábradlí
Anenské nám. 5, 115 33 **Praha** 1
Tel: 2-2222 2016
Fax: 2-2222 1622
Internet: www.periskop.cz/na-zabradli
E-Mail: dnz@comp.cz
director Doubravka Svobodová; artistic chief Petr Lébl
Actors: 11 *Perfs:* 200 *Prods:* 5
Venues: home capacity 208, Small Stage 80

Theatre on the Fidlovacka
Divadlo Na Fidlovacce
Kresomyslova 625/4,
140 00 **Praha** 4
Tel: 2-6121 5722
Fax: 2-6121 5721
Internet: www.fidlovacka.cz
E-Mail: fidlovacka@fidlovacka.cz
director Tomás Töpfer
Actors: varies *Prods:* 3
Venues: home cap. 400

Theatre on Vinohrady
Divadlo na Vinohradech
nám Míru 7, 120 00 **Praha** 2
Tel: 2-2425 7484 Fax: 2-2425 3870
Internet: www.alfa.sluzby.cz/dnv/
E-Mail: dnv@anet.cz
director Jirina Jirásková
Actors: 40 *Perfs:* 220 *Prods:* 5 *Venues:* home capacity 765, Rehearsal Place Theatre max. 80

Theatre Ungelt Divadlo
Malá Stupartská 1, 110 00 **Praha** 1
Tel: 2-2051 5621 Fax: 2-2482 8081
director Milan Hein
Actors: varies *Perfs:* 150 *Prods:* 3 *Venues:* home cap. 100

Theatre without the Balustrade
Divadlo Bez zábradlí
Palác Adria, Jungmannova 31, 110 00 **Praha** 1
Tel: 2-2449 4601 Fax: 2-2494 6436
Internet: web.iol.cz/dbz
E-Mail: hermanek@iol.cz
artistic chief Karel Hermánek
Actors: varies *Perfs:* 150 *Prods:* 2 *Venues:* home 300

Theatre Príbram
Divadlo Príbram
Legionáru 400, 261 02 **Príbram**
Tel: 306-25691
Internet: www.divadlo.pb.cz
E-Mail: divadlo@divadlo.pb.cz
director Jirí Slanec; artistic chief Jirí Zák
Actors: 15 *Perfs:* 230 *Prods:* 9 *Venues:* Great Stage 460, Chamber stage 140, Theatre after Curtain 120

North Moravian Theatre
Severomoravské divadlo
Komenského 1, 787 01 **Sumperk**
Tel: 649-214 062 Fax: 649-214 061
Internet: www.divadlo.cz/smdivadlo
director Petr Král
Actors: 12 *Perfs:* 300 *Prods:* 7 *Venues:* temporary theatre space 100, home capacity (reconstruction) 394

Theatre of Slovácko
Slovácké divadlo
Tyrsovo námestí 480, 686 12 **Uherské Hradiste**
Tel: 632-551 346 Fax: 632-552 167
Internet: www.uh.cz
E-Mail: sd@uh.cz
director Igor Stránsky
Actors: 18 *Perfs:* 220 *Prods:* 10 *Venues:* home capacity 385, small stage 100

Drama Studio
Cinoherní studio
Varsavská 767, 400 03 **Ústí nad Labem**
Tel: 47-553 1428 Fax: 47-553 1272
Internet: www.cs.usti.dtg.cz
E-Mail: cinoherak@pvtnet.cz
director Jaroslav Achab Haidler
Actors: 10 *Perfs:* 150 *Prods:* 4 *Venues:* capacity 150

Zlín City Theatre
Mestské divadlo
Tomáse Bati 4091/32, 761 87 **Zlín**
Tel: 67-763 6111 Fax: 67-763 6300
Internet: www.inext.cz/divadlozlin
E-Mail: divadlo@zl.inext.cz
director Antonín Sobek
Actors: 30 *Perfs:* 300 *Prods:* 10 *Venues:* home capacity 697, Z-Studio 100, theatre in club 80

DENMARK (+45)

Aalborg Teater
Jernbanegade 11, Postbox 1710, 9100 **Aalborg**
Tel: 9812 2744 Fax: 9813 8411/9816 7216
Internet: www.aalborg-teater.dk
E-Mail: aalborg-teater@adm
manager Marlene Schwartz;
press agent Helle Vagner Nielsen
Actors: 17+ guest appearances *Perfs:* 500 *Prods:* 12
Venues: Large Stage 460, Small Stage 120, Studio 50

Jomfru Ane Teatret
Jomfru Ane Gade 14, 9000 **Aalborg**
Tel: 9813 6044 Fax: 9813 1922
artistic director Inger Eilersen
Actors: 5 + freelancers *Perfs:* 15 *Prods:* 4 *Type:* modern; comedy; musical; new writing *Venues:* capacity up to 200 *Touring:* national

Aarhus Teater
Skolegade 9, 8000 **Aarhus** C
Tel: 8933 2300 Fax: 8933 2339
Internet: www.aarhusteater.dk
E-Mail: aateater@post3.tele.dk
theatre director Palle Jul Jørgensen;
marketing manager Leif Due
Actors: 34 *Perfs:* 450 *Prods:* 16 *Type:* classical, modern, musicals, comedies, cabaret *Venues:* 4 stages + 1 cabaret stage: Store scene 690, Scala 285, Studio 100, Stiklingen 100, Caberetscenen 80 *Comments:* permanent theatre company

Gruppe 38
Mejlgade 45, 8000 **Aarhus** C
Tel: 8613 5311
Fax: 8613 5188
directors Bodil Alling, Steen Noergaard; composer Soeren Soenberg; secretary Meike Mervig;
technition Kim Kirkeby Hansen
Actors: 4-5, 1 permanent *Perfs:* 3-4 *Prods:* 1-2
Type: children's theatre *Venues:* Auktionscenen (capacity 70 adults or 100 children) *Touring:* schools, theatres, Toronto: May 2000, Edinburgh: May 2000

Svalegangen
Rosenkrantzgade 21, 8000 **Aarhus** C
Tel: 8619 1944
Fax: 8618 2909
Internet: www.svalegangen.dk
E-Mail: svalegangen@svalegangen.dk
director Niels Andersen; administrator Tove Nielsen; producer Helge Kjems
Actors: varies *Perfs:* 200 *Prods:* 3-4 *Type:* modern, experimental, stand-up comedy, new writing *Venues:* capacity up to 210, Intimate stage 60
Touring: national *Comments:* offers workshops and educational programmes

Artibus Teater
Spillehuset, Vesterfælledvej 7 A, 1750 **Copenhagen** V
Tel: 3331 6095 Fax: 3331 6093
Internet: www.image.dk/~artibus
E-Mail: artibus@image.dk
contact Flemming Holk;
administrator Else Marie Mandøe
Actors: 4 *Perfs:* 100-150 *Prods:* 2 *Type:* children's and youth theatre, some adult
Venues: schools around Denmark

Danske Teater, Det
Hvidkildevej 64 indg 2,
2400 **Copenhagen** NV
Tel: 3834 5555 Fax: 3819 4456
Internet: www.detdansketeater.dk
artistic director & manager Peter Aude;
marketing director Milla Kær
Actors: varies *Perfs:* 400 *Prods:* 8-10 *Type:* from classical to contemporary *Touring:* Denmark *Comments:* national Danish touring theatre

Folketeatret
Peoples Theatre
Nørre Voldgade 50, PO Box 154,
1005 **Copenhagen** K
Tel: 3312 5445 Fax: 3393 9327
Internet: www.folketeatret.dk
theatre director Preben Harris; sub-director t.b.a; production manager Tommy Larsen; sales, information and press manager Mette W. Poulsen
Actors: 90 (for all stages) *Perfs:* 320 *Prods:* 10 *Type:* various from classical to modern, as well as musicals, puppets *Venues:* Grand Stage 600, Hippodrome 200, Cabaret Stage 100, Young Stage 50 *Touring:* large and small scale-Denmark, Russia, Hungary, Rumania

Hotel Pro Forma
Strandlodsvej 6, 2300 **Copenhagen** S
Tel: 3254 0217
Fax: 3296 9686
Internet: www.hotelproforma.dk
E-Mail: hotelproforma.@hotelproforma.dk
manager director Peter Hanke; artistic director Kirsten Dehlholm; project manager Lisa Aagesen;
technical co-ordinator Jørgen Kjer;
project co-ordinator Henriette Holm
Actors: various according to production, 1-700
Perfs: 40 *Prods:* 3 *Type:* site-specific work, museums, architectural sites, visual theatre
Touring: Australia, Europe, USA

Husets Teater
Halmtoret 9, 1700 **Copenhagen** V
Tel: 3322 7707
Fax: 3322 6150
E-Mail: husets.teater@image.dk
artistic director Sören Iversen;
adm. director Lísbeth Sjölin
Actors: varies *Perfs:* 130 *Prods:* 4 *Type:* modern, new writing *Venues:* capacity 120

Kongelige Teater, Det
Royal Theatre
Postbox 2185, 1017 **Copenhagen** K
Tel: 3369 6933
Fax: 3369 6519
Internet: www.kgl-teater.dk
E-Mail: admin@kgl-teater.dk
general manager Michael Christiansen; theatre director Klaus Hoffmeyer; opera director Elaine Padmore (from March 2000 Kasper Holten); ballet director Aage Thordal-Christensen
Actors: 50-60 *Perfs:* 656 *Prods:* 60-70
Type: plays, opera, ballet, concerts *Venues:* Old Stage (Gamlc Scene) 1300, Storekassen 775, – 2 spaces at Kgs. Nytorv; Turbinehallerne in Adelgade, Copenhagen 2 stages 200, 400 *Touring:* national, international
Comments: see also Opera and Dance

Mammutteatret
Livjaegergade 17 o.g., 2100 **Copenhagen** Ø
Tel: 3526 6234
Fax: 3526 6231
collective leadership: direction Claus Flygare, Tina Gylling Mortensen
Actors: varies *Perfs:* 30 *Prods:* 2-3 *Type:* modern and classical *Venues:* Kanonhallen up to 300, Mammutteatret 100

Ny Teater
Gl. Kongevej 29, 1610 **Copenhagen** V
Tel: 3325 6005
Fax: 3321 5006
Internet: www.detnyteater.dk
manager Niels-Bo Valbro
Perfs: 200 *Prods:* 6 *Type:* musical, classical, comedy *Venues:* Stage A 1000, Stage B 300

Privat Teatret
Nyropsgade 41, 1602 **Copenhagen** V
Tel: 3333 2333/3325 2517 (information)
Fax: 3321 5006
Internet: www.privatteatret.dk
manager Niels-Bo Valbro
Perfs: 400 per season *Type:* modern, classical, comedy *Venues:* Privat Teatret 650 *Touring:* national

Riddersalen (Jytte Abildstrøms Teater)
Allégade 7-9, 2000 **Copenhagen** F
Tel: 3887 1819 Fax: 3888 7204
Internet: www.webline.dk/riddersalen
E-Mail: jat.riddersalen@image.dk
artistic director Jytte Abildstrøm
Perfs: 300 *Prods:* 6 *Type:* mainly children's theatre, some classical *Venues:* capacity 201 *Touring:* national *Comments:* see also Puppets

Teatret ved Sorte Hest
Vesterbrogade 150, 1620 **Copenhagen** V
Tel: 3331 0606 Fax: 3323 0689
artistic directors Maria Stenz, Mickey Pheiffer
Actors: varies *Perfs:* varies *Prods:* 4-5 *Type:* experimental drama *Venues:* capacity 80 *Comments:* subsidised by Copenhagen Council and sometimes by the government

Betty Nansen Teatret
Asgårdsvej 2, 1811 **Frederiksberg** C
Tel: 3321 0755 Fax: 3331 4546
E-Mail: post@bettynansen.dk
administrative director Henrik Hartmann; artistic director Peter Langdal; dramaturgist Kitte Wagner; secretary Karin Gommesen
Actors: varies *Perfs:* 211 *Prods:* 5 *Type:* modern, classical, comedy and new writing *Venues:* Betty Nansen Teatret 501, Edison Stage 300 *Touring:* Denmark

Dr Dante
Frederiksberg Allé 102, 1820 **Frederiksberg** C
Tel: 3323 3100
Fax: 3323 3765
Internet: www.drdante.dk
E-Mail: dr.dante@drdante.dk
artistic director Nikolaj Cederholm; secretary Puk Linde
Actors: varies (no resident company) *Perfs:* 200 *Prods:* 3 annually *Type:* original Danish dramas (innovative) *Venues:* capacity 396

Vandrefalken
Travelling Falcon
sdr Vilstrup Bygade 8, 6100 **Haderslev**
Tel: 7458 2528
administrator Hans-Jøgen Lange
Actors: 1-3 *Perfs:* 175-200 *Type:* children's and young theatre *Venues:* schools throughout Denmark, Scandinavia *Comments:* also offers workshops

Team Teatret
Skolegade 12, 7400 **Herning**
Tel: 9712 5577 Fax: 9712 2550
Internet: www.teamteatret.dk
E-Mail: mail@teamteatret.dk
director Irene Hagerup
Actors: varies *Perfs:* 100 *Prods:* 3 *Type:* drama & 1 musical play per year *Venues:* 120 *Touring:* Denmark *Comments:* venue addresses: Stage 1, Bethaniagade 6-8, 7400 Herning, Stage 2, Nørregade 7, 7400 Herning

Odin Teatret/Nordisk Teaterlaboratorium
Box 1283, 7500 **Holstebro**
Tel: 9742 4777
Fax: 9741 0482
Internet: www.odinteatret.dk
E-Mail: odin@odinteatret.dk
theatre director Eugenio Barba; production manager Ulrik Skeel; tour manager Patricia Alves
Actors: 10 *Perfs:* up to 100 *Prods:* 10 *Type:* own repertoire *Venues:* indoor and outdoor *Touring:* Sweden, Norway, Denmark, Italy, Germany, Mexico, Spain, Brazil, France *Comments:* permanent company; other activities: ISTA – International School of Theatre Anthropology; Odin Teatret Publishing House; Pedagogy and Research; Odin Teatret Film; touring company; alternative e-mail: odinteat@post4.tele.dk

Hvidovre Teater
Hvidovre Strandvej 70 A, 2650 **Hvidovre**
Tel: 3649 1240 Fax: 3677 0203
E-Mail: hvteater@image.dk
theatre director Sejer Andersen
Actors: varies *Perfs:* 140 *Prods:* 5 *Type:* modern, contemporary *Venues:* Italian stage 305, Black box 500 *Touring:* Denmark, Sweden, Germany *Comments:* mainly touring company

Odense Teater
Jernbanegade 21, 5100 **Odense** C
Tel: 6613 2109
Fax: 6613 2119
Internet: www.odenseteater.dk
E-Mail: post@odenseteater.dk
theatre director Poul Holm Joensen; information officer Morten Kjaergaard
Actors: 30 *Perfs:* 24 plus guest performances *Prods:* 13 *Type:* classics to modern, musicals *Venues:* Store Scene 485, Sukkerkogeriet 200, Vaerkstedet 90 *Touring:* small tours at home, occasionally abroad *Comments:* subsidized regional theatre; pit-34 musicians

Gladsaxe Teater
Buddinge Hovedgade 81, 2860 **Søborg**
Tel: 3967 0500 Fax: 3966 3260
Internet: www.gladsaxeteater.dk
E-Mail: mail@galdsaxeteater.dk
theatre manager Flemming Enevold; deputy head Bjarne Skive; administration Agnege Waage Jensen; production manager Andreas Knudsen; secretary Gitte Stokholm; head of press Tatiana Vang
Actors: 30 *Perfs:* 143 *Prods:* 4 *Type:* musicals; modern and classic drama *Venues:* capacity 500 to 600

Baggård Teatret
Caroline Amalievej 26,
5700 **Svendborg**
Tel: 6221 4043
Fax: 6221 4301
Internet: www.baggaardteatret.dk
E-Mail: post@baggaardteatret.dk
Actors: 6 *Type:* theatre for children and young people *Venues:* mainly in schools *Touring:* Denmark, Germany, Switzerland, Scotland, Mexico

Boxigana Performance Theatre
Bjørnsonsvej 85, 2500 **Valby**
Tel: 3630 1691 Fax: 3630 1692
artistic directors Karin Sondergård, Kjell Yngve Petersen
Actors: varies *Perfs:* 20+ *Prods:* 2 *Type:* performance/media/installation mix forms/opera *Touring:* Denmark

ESTONIA (+372)

Endla Theatre
Pärnu Teater Endla
Keskväljak 1, **Pärnu**
Tel: 4-430 695 Fax: 4-430 692
Internet: www.styx.parnu.ee/endla/
E-Mail: teater@teater.parnu.ee
manager director Ain Roots;
artistic director Raivo Trass
Actors: 23 *Type:* classical, modern, comedy *Venues:* home capacity 593 *Comments:* state repertory theatre

Rakvere Theatre
Rakvere Teater
Kreutzwaldi Str. 2A, 44314 **Rakvere**
Tel: 3-223 429 Fax: 3-223 427
managing director Indrek Saar;
artistic director Üllar Saaremäe
Type: classical, modern, comedy *Venues:* home capacity 450 *Comments:* state repertory theatre

Estonian Drama Theatre
Eesti Draamateater
Pärnu mnt. 5, 10148 **Tallinn**
Tel: 2-443 976 Fax: 2-440 503
Internet: www.ee/draamateater/
E-Mail: draamateater@www.ee
managing director Tiit Laur;
artistic director Priit Pedajas
Actors: 43 *Type:* classical, modern, comedy *Venues:* home capacity stage A 542, stage B 126 *Comments:* state repertory theatre

Old Town Studio
Teater Vanalinnastuudio
Sakala 12-1, 10141 **Tallinn**
Tel: 2-448 408 Fax: 2-445 846
manager Jüri Karindi; artistic director Eino Baskin
Actors: 14 *Type:* comedy and satire *Comments:* state repertory theatre

Salong Theatre
Kaarli pst 9, 10119 **Tallinn**
Tel: 2-453 875
Internet: www.tallinn.ee/salong_teater/
E-Mail: salong.teater@tallinn.ee
artistic director Dajan Ahmetov
Comments: private theatre

State Russian Drama Theatre, The
Eesti Riiklik Vene Draamateater
Vabaduse väljak 5,
10141 **Tallinn**
Tel: 2-443 810
Fax: 2-443 810
manager Aleksander Iljin;
artistic director Eduard Toman
Actors: 29 *Perfs:* 181 *Type:* classical, modern, comedy *Venues:* home capacity 667
Comments: state repertory theatre

Tallinn Town Theatre
Tallinna Linnateater
Lai 23, 10133 **Tallinn**
Tel: 6-411 674
Fax: 6-411 672
Internet: www.ee/linnateater
E-Mail: linnateater@www.ee
managing director Raivo Põldmaa;
artistic director Elmo Nüganen
Actors: 24 *Perfs:* 279 *Type:* comedy, classical, modern *Venues:* home capacity: stage A 105, stage B 140 *Comments:* state and town repertory theatre

Theatrum
Vene tn 14, 10123 **Tallinn**
Tel: 6-446 889
Fax: 6-411 519
Internet: www.colleduc.ee/theatrum/
E-Mail: marius@colleduc.ee
artistic director Lembit Peterson
Actors: 9 *Perfs:* 6 *Type:* classical
Venues: theatre hall 80 *Comments:* independent, the aim is to carry out the substantial programme of the Early Music and Theatre Centre (planned into the former dominican St Catherine's monastery complex) in collaboration with the Dominican Order and the foundation Hereditas

VAT Theatre
VAT teater
PO Box 3242, **Tallinn**
Tel: 2-450 959
manager Hiie Fluss
Actors: 6 *Type:* special children's theatre

Von Krahl Theatre
Rataskaevu 10, 10123 **Tallinn**
Tel: 6-269 090 Fax: 6-269 099
Internet: www.vonkrahl.ee
managing director Priit Raud;
artistic director Peeter Jalakas
Actors: 5-10 *Prods:* 6 *Type:* contemporary, modern opera, multi-media *Venues:* capacity 200 *Touring:* England, Finland, Latvia, Lithuania, Germany, Netherlands *Comments:* independent

Tartu Theatre for Children
Tartu Lasteteater
Jaama 14, 51009 **Tartu**
Tel: 7-434 487
Internet: zen.estpak.ee/~renteks/lasteteater/
director Mart Kampus
Actors: 14 *Perfs:* 25 in month *Type:* based on fairy tales, legends, folklore; contemporary also for adults *Venues:* home capacity 56 *Touring:* Finland, Russia, Faroe Islands *Comments:* independent

Vanemuine Theatre
Teater Vanemuine
Vanemuine 6, 51003 **Tartu**
Tel: 7-439 012
Fax: 7-441 065
Internet: www.halo.ee/vanemuine
E-Mail: vanem@uninet.ee
managing director Jaak Viller
Type: classical, modern, comedy *Venues:* main stage 682, small house 440 *Touring:* Germany *Comments:* state repertory theatre, see also Opera, Orchestras and Dance

Viljandi Drama Theatre Ugala
Viljandi Draamateater Ugala
Vaksali 7, 71020 **Viljandi**
Tel: 4-333 718 Fax: 4-333 718
Internet: www.ugala.ee/
managing director Enn Kose;
artistic director Andres Noormets
Actors: 37 *Type:* modern, classical, comedy, musical *Venues:* home capacity 595
Comments: state repertory theatre

FINLAND (+358)

Unga Teatern
Klobbskogsvägen 9, 02630 **Esbo**
Tel: 9-524 277
Fax: 9-502 1746
artistic director Marjaana Castrén;
financial manager Toivo Jaakkola;
producer Vibeke Löfgrén
Actors: 6 *Perfs:* 260 *Prods:* 7
Type: children and young people *Venues:* Lillklobb Theatre *Comments:* permanent theatre company

Espoo Theatre
Espoon Teatteri
Revontulentie 8A, 02100 **Espoo**
Tel: 9-461 811 Fax: 9-467 550
Internet: www.espoo.fi/teatteri/
theatre director Maija-Liisa Márton (till 31.7.2000), Jussi Helminen (from 1.8.2000); financial manager Ulla Hämäläinen
Actors: varies *Perfs:* 130 *Prods:* 10 *Type:* guest performances (domestic and from abroad) and theatre's own productions *Venues:* Espoo Cultural Centre 141 to 304, Revontuli Hall (an old printing house) 100-280 *Comments:* theatre is also used for jazz concerts

Totem-teatteri
Ahertajankuja 4, II krs, 02100 **Espoo**
Tel: 9-464 505 Fax: 9-464 505
Internet: www.dlc.fi/~totem
E-Mail: totem@dlc.fi
artistic director Päivi Rissanen; producer Katriina Lahtinen
Perfs: 54 *Prods:* 3

Hämeenlinna City Theatre
Hämeenlinnan Kaupungin Teatteri
Palokunnankatu 1, 13100 **Hämeenlinna**
Tel: 3-616 9325 Fax: 3-616 9318
Internet: www.hameenlinnankaupunginteatteri.fi
E-Mail: riku.suokas@hameenlinnankaupunginteatteri.fi
theatre director Riku Suokas; financial manager Jukka Jokinen
Actors: 12 *Perfs:* 263 *Prods:* 8 *Venues:* big stage 247, small stage 100 *Comments:* permanent theatre company

Helsinki City Theatre
Helsingin Kaupunginteatteri
Ensi linja 2, 00530 **Helsinki**
Tel: 9-39401 Fax: 9-394 0244
Internet: www.hel.fi/citytheatre
theatre director Asko Sarkola; administrative director Reima Jokinen; producer Sanna Kangasluoma
Actors: 35 *Perfs:* 644 *Prods:* 13 *Venues:* large stage 936, small stage 200 to 350, studio 200
Comments: permanent theatre company

Helsinki Swedish Theatre
Svenska Teatern i Helsingfors
Pohjoisesplanadi 2, 00130 **Helsinki**
Tel: 9-616 211 Fax: 9-6162 1230
Internet: www.svenskateatern.fi
E-Mail: info@svenskateatern.fi
artistic director Lars Svedberg; financial manager Tuula Kankkonen
Actors: 17 *Perfs:* 426 *Prods:* 11 *Type:* repertory *Venues:* big stage 413 to 506, small stage 80 to 107, Nick 70
Comments: Swedish language theatre company

Improvisation Theatre
Stella Polaris
Tallberginkatu 1A 107,
00180 **Helsinki**
Tel: 9-694 4491
E-Mail: stella.polaris@nic.fi

Jurkka Theatre
Teatteri Jurkka
Vironkatu 7, 00170 **Helsinki**
Tel: 9-135 6166 Fax: 9-135 6898
Internet: www.sci.fi/~jurkka
E-Mail: jurkka@sci.fi
administrative manager Kalle Sandqvist
Perfs: 135 *Prods:* 2 *Venues:* main stage 50 *Comments:* permanent theatre company

KokoTeatteri
Hämeentie 1 E 43,
00530 **Helsinki**
Tel: 9-773 3312
Internet: www.kokoteatteri.fi
artistic director Anna Veijalainen (tel: 50-590 9813)

Kom Teatteri
Kapteeninkatu 26, 00140 **Helsinki**
Tel: 9-684 1841 Fax: 9-636 438
Internet: www.kom-teatteri.fi
theatre director Pekka Milonoff
Actors: 14 *Perfs:* 120 *Prods:* 4 *Type:* drama, music theatre *Venues:* capacity 150 to 250 *Comments:* permanent theatre company

Komediateatteri Arena
Hämeentie 2, 00530 **Helsinki**
Tel: 9-2709 0530
Fax: 9-774 1100
artistic director Ere Kokkonen
Venues: capacity 489

Lilla Teatern
Yrjönkatu 30, 00100 **Helsinki**
Tel: 9-647 490
Fax: 9-644 265
theatre director Tove Appelgren
Actors: 10 *Perfs:* 200 *Prods:* 4 *Type:* repertory *Venues:* Lilla teatern 263, Pikku-Lillan 100 *Comments:* permanent theatre company performing in Swedish and Finnish

Little Finnish Theatre
Teatteri Pieni Suomi
Junailijankuja 3, 00520 **Helsinki**
Tel: 9-229 3080 Fax: 9-229 30840
Internet: www.pienisuomi.fi
E-Mail: pienisuomi@pienisuomi.fi
theatre director Vilppu Kiljunen
Actors: 12 *Perfs:* 158 *Prods:* 6 *Type:* children's and youth theatre *Venues:* Pasila 330 *Comments:* permanent theatre company

National Theatre of Finland
Suomen Kansallisteatteri
Läntinen Teatterikuja 1B, 00100 **Helsinki**
Tel: 9-173 311 Fax: 9-1733 1200/1300
Internet: www.nationaltheatre.fi
E-Mail: suomen.kansallisteatteri@nationaltheatre.fi
director Maria-Liisa Nevala; chief stage director Antti Einari Halonen; chief dramaturgs Michael Baran, Eva Buchwald; information officer Paula Havaste
Actors: 46 *Perfs:* 730 *Prods:* 12 *Type:* modern, classical, new writing *Venues:* large stage 887, small stage 311, third stage 154, fourth stage 80-90 *Comments:* permanent theatre company

Performance Sikus
Vääksyntie 4C, 00510 **Helsinki**
Tel: 9-3487 0224 Fax: 9-773 1764
Internet: www.kolumbus.fi/performa
artistic director Vesa-Petteri Asikainen

Q-theatre
Q-teatteri
Tunturikatu 16, 00100 **Helsinki**
Tel: 9-4542 1311 Fax: 9-4542 1312
Internet: www.novision.fi/Q-teatteri
E-Mail: qtheatre@qteatt.pp.fi
chairman of the board Erik Söderblom
Actors: 15 *Perfs:* 200 *Prods:* 3-5 *Venues:* capacity Mainstage 172, Puoli Q 55, Varaulos Qäynti 30

Ryhmäteatteri
Pengerkatu 11, 00530 **Helsinki**
Tel: 9-718 655 Fax: 9-710 908
Internet: www.ryhmateatteri.fi
E-Mail: toimisto@ryhmateatteri.fi
artistic directors Esa Leskinen, Mika Myllyaho
Actors: 4 *Perfs:* 110-150 *Prods:* 2-4 *Type:* classics, new Finnish drama *Venues:* Ryhmäteatteri 300, Suomenlinna (summer theatre) 500 *Comments:* permanent theatre company

Teatteri Raivoisat Ruusut
office Iso Roobertink. 36-40, 00120 **Helsinki**
Tel: 9-630 400 Fax: 9-669 568
Internet: www.raivoisat-ruusut.fi
E-Mail: ruusu@raivoisat-ruusut.fi
artistic director Ritva Siikala; project manager Mari Nieminen
Actors: varies *Perfs:* 25 *Prods:* 1 *Comments:* the Raging Roses Theatre concentrates on the female/male structures of our culture

Teatteri Takomo
00180 **Helsinki**
Tel: 9-492 161
E-Mail: jkuitunen@teak.fi
director Kristian Smeds; producer Pirkko Peltola (040-517 1441); chairman of the board Rauno Ahonen (0400-906 114)

Theatre Open Doors
Teatteri Avoimet Ovet
Museokatu 18, 00100 **Helsinki**
Tel: 9-434 2510 Fax: 9-434 25110
Internet: www.avoimetovet.fi
E-Mail: hanna.arkio@teatteriao.inet.fi
artistic manager Liisi Tandefelt; producer Lea Launokari
Actors: 1 *Perfs:* 65 *Prods:* 3 *Comments:* touring company; performances in Finnish and German; second e-mail: Lea.Launokari@teatteriao.inet.fi

Universum
Lönnrotinkatu 32 A 28, 00180 **Helsinki**
Tel: 9-611 002 Fax: 9-6124 5700
director Annamari Karjalainen
Comments: umbrella organisation for small theatre groups, Aurinkoteatteri, Sirius Teatern, Teater Mars, Teater Venus

Viirus
Runeberginkatu 38, 00260 **Helsinki**
Tel: 9-7003 9031 Fax: 9-7003 9032
Internet: www.bookmark.fi/viirus
artistic directors Mats Långbacka, Johan Storgård; producer Göran Michelsson
Actors: 6 *Perfs:* 119 *Prods:* 9 *Type:* new interpretations of classics and new Scandinavian drama *Venues:* former purifying plant *Comments:* permanent theatre company, also used for comedy clubs

Teatteri Eurooppa 4
Saarijärventie 434, 44170 **Hietama**
Tel: 14-515 592 Fax: 14-515 593
theatre director Jukka Pääkkönen

Teatteri Imatra
Kallenkuja, 55100 **Imatra**
Tel: 5-681 6500
Fax: 5-681 6509
E-Mail: toimisto@teatteri-imatra.inet.fi
manager Risto Kekarainen
Type: repertory *Venues:* big stage 173, Summer theatre 484 *Comments:* permanent theatre company

Joensuu City Theatre
Joensuun Kaupunginteatteri
Kaupungintalo Rantakatu 4, 80100 **Joensuu**
Tel: 13-267 7111 Fax: 13-267 5275
Internet:
www.jns.fi/palvelut/kulttuuri/teatteri/ohjelmisto.htm
Actors: 13 *Perfs:* 210 *Prods:* 14 *Type:* repertory *Venues:* Salmisen sali 270, small stage 70 *Comments:* permanent theatre company

Jyväskylä City Theatre
Jyväskylän kaupunginteatteri
Vapaudenkatu 36, 40100 **Jyväskylä**
Tel: 14-624 211 Fax: 14-624 204
Internet: www.travel.ksp.fi/jklkaupunginteatteri/
theatre director Vesa Raiskio; dramaturg Hannele Ruotsalo
Actors: 21 *Perfs:* 320 *Prods:* 7 *Type:* repertory *Venues:* big stage 551, small stage 120 *Comments:* permanent theatre company

Kajaani City Theatre
Kajaanin Kaupunginteatteri
Kauppakatu 14, 87100 **Kajaani**
Tel: 8-615 5218 Fax: 8-613 1450
E-Mail: aila.lavaste@kajaani.fi
theatre director Aila Lavaste
Actors: 15 *Perfs:* 322 *Prods:* 8 *Type:* repertory *Venues:* stage 230, regional stage 150
Comments: permanent theatre company

Kemi City Theatre
Kemin Kaupunginteatteri
Marina Takalon katu 3,
94100 **Kemi**
Tel: 16-258 219
Fax: 16-258 235
Internet: www.kemi.fi/kulttuuri/teatteri
theatre director Olli-Pekka Ulkuniemi
Actors: 12 *Perfs:* 180 *Prods:* 8 *Type:* repertory *Venues:* big stage 303, small stage 120
Comments: permanent theatre company

Kokkola City Theatre
Kokkolan Kaupunginteatteri
Torikatu 48, 67100 **Kokkola**
Tel: 6-831 3153 Fax: 6-831 6123
Internet: www.teatteri.kokkola.fi
E-Mail: kokkolan.teatteri@kokkola.fi
theatre director Jari Ålander; financial director Helga Sarviranta-Vuotila
Actors: 10 *Perfs:* 150 *Prods:* 6 *Type:* repertory *Venues:* stage 220 *Comments:* permanent theatre company;

Kotkan kaupunginteatteri
Kotka City Theatre
Keskuskatu 15, 48100 **Kotka**
Tel: 5-234 4188
Fax: 5-218 3000
Internet: www.kulttuuri.kuopio.fi/teatteri
E-Mail: teatteri.kut@kuopio.fi
financial manager Matti Piipari
Actors: 16 *Perfs:* 269 *Prods:* 10 *Venues:* big stage 371, small stage 70 *Touring:* national *Comments:* permanent theatre company; second e-mail: eeva-liisa.virtanen@kotka.fi

Kouvola Theatre
Kouvolan Teatteri
Salpausselänkatu 38,
45100 **Kouvola**
Tel: 5-375 2162
Fax: 5-375 4124
Internet: www.kouvolanteatteri.fi
E-Mail: tuula.toijala@kouvolanteatteri.fi
theatre director Kari Suvalo; financial manager Tuula Toijala
Actors: 10 *Perfs:* 169 *Prods:* 5 *Type:* repertory *Venues:* big stage 353, small stage 120
Comments: permanent theatre company

Kuopio City Theatre
Kuopion kaupunginteatteri
Niiralankatu 2, 70600 **Kuopio**
Tel: 17-182 111 Fax: 17-182 431
Internet: www.kulttuuri.kuopio.fi/teatteri
E-Mail: teatteri.kut@kuopio.fi
theatre director Heikki Mäkelä; financial manager Jorma Karsikkoniemi
Actors: 24 *Perfs:* 300 *Prods:* 12
Type: modern, classical, comedy, new writing, music, puppetry *Venues:* large stage 414, studio stage 95
Touring: national *Comments:* permanent theatre company; theatre is one of the venues for Kuopio Dance and Music Festival

Lahti City Theatre
Lahden Kaupunginteatteri
Kirkkokatu 14, 15140 **Lahti**
Tel: 3-81411 Fax: 3-814 3145
Internet: www.lahti.fi/teatteri
E-Mail: teatteri@lahti.fi
artistic manager Jotaarkka Pennanen; administrative manager Helena Ahonen
Actors: 27 *Perfs:* 370 *Prods:* 10 *Type:* modern, classical, comedy, musical, new Finnish and foreign drama *Venues:* big stage 762, small stage 300, studio 80 *Comments:* permanent theatre company; theatre used for concerts, dance and congresses

Teatteri Vanha Juko
Vesijärvenkatu 16 pl 178, 15140 **Lahti**
Tel: 3-752 0585 Fax: 3-781 3409
Internet: www.phnet.fi/public/vanhajuko
E-Mail: vanha.juko@pp.phnat.fi
producer Jari Juutinen

Lappeenranta City Theatre
Lappeenrannan kaupunginteatteri
Valtakatu 56-58, 53100 **Lappeenranta**
Tel: 5-453 0675 Fax: 5-616 2300
Internet: www.lappeenranta.fi/teatteri
artistic director Helena Anttonen; stage director Teija Hyvärinen; manager of administration Pirkko Uitti
Actors: 14 *Perfs:* 162 *Prods:* 7 *Type:* repertory *Venues:* main stage 415, small stage 150 *Comments:* permanent theatre company

Klockriketeatern Helsinki
Antbacken 29/olsoni, 04150 **Mårtensby**
Tel: 9-239 1829/1890
artistic director Kristin Olsoni
Perfs: 30 *Prods:* 1

Mikkeli Theatre
Mikkelin Teatteri
Savilahdenkatu 11, 50100 **Mikkeli**
Tel: 15-35531 Fax: 15-355 3209
Internet: www.mikkeli.fi/teatteri
E-Mail: toimisto@mlinteatteri.inet.fi
theatre director Markku Savolainen
Actors: 10 *Perfs:* 315 *Prods:* 6 *Type:* repertory *Venues:* big stage 238, small stage 70, Open Air Stage 600 (summer theatre) *Comments:* permanent theatre company

Oulu City Theatre
Oulun Kaupunginteatteri
Kaarlenväylä 2, 90100 **Oulu**
Tel: 8-558 410 Fax: 8-5584 7099
Internet: www.ouka.fi/teatteri
E-Mail: teatteri@ouka.fi
director Maarit Pyökäri; manager Outi Sipilä
Actors: 23 *Perfs:* 300 *Prods:* 8 *Venues:* big stage 581, small stage 132, studio 65 *Comments:* permanent company

Pori Theatre
Porin Teatteri
Hallituskatu 14, 28100 **Pori**
Tel: 2-633 4400 Fax: 2-633 9872
Internet: www.pori.fi/tea
E-Mail: porin.teatteri@kolumbus.fi
theatre director Risto Ojanen
Actors: 16 *Perfs:* 259 *Prods:* 8 *Type:* repertory, including musicals and children's plays *Venues:* main stage 313, studio 120 *Comments:* permanent theatre company

Rakastajat – teatteriryhmä
Valtakatu 22, 28100 **Pori**
Tel: 2-633 0126 Fax: 2-633 0126
contact Angelika Meusel
Venues: stage 60-80

Rauma City Theatre
Rauman Kaupunginteatteri
Pursikatu 4, 26100 **Rauma**
Tel: 2-822 2155 Fax: 2-822 0847
artistic director Tommi Auvinen; financial manager Jari Nieminen
Actors: 7 *Perfs:* 111 *Prods:* 4 *Type:* repertory *Venues:* stage 100 *Comments:* permanent theatre company

Riihimäki Theatre
Riihimäen Teatteri
Hämeenaukio 1, 11100 **Riihimäki**
Tel: 19-732 502 Fax: 19-732 515
Internet: www.riihimaki.fi/teatteri
E-Mail: teatteri.riihimaki@kolumbus.fi
artistic director Jarno Hiilloskorpi; inancial manager Eeva Kokko
Actors: 6 *Perfs:* 143 *Prods:* 3 *Type:* repertory *Venues:* stage 206 *Comments:* permanent theatre company

Rovaniemi City Theatre
Rovaniemen Teatteri – Lapin Alueteatteri
Jorma Eton tie 8 A, 96100 **Rovaniemi**
Tel: 16-322 2500 Fax: 16-346 151
Internet: www.rovaniemi.fi/taide/teatteri/
E-Mail: ahti.ahonen@rovaniemi.fi
theatre director Ahti Ahonen
Actors: 17 *Perfs:* 265 *Prods:* 7 *Type:* repertory *Venues:* main stage 427, small stage 120

Savonlinna City Theatre
Savonlinnan Kaupunginteatteri
Olavinkatu 13, 57130 **Savonlinna**
Tel: 15-571 5100 Fax: 15-515 425
Internet: www.savonlinna.fi/sivistys/teatteri
theatre director Kimmo Lavaste; financial manager Päivi Korhonen
Actors: 8 *Perfs:* 150 *Prods:* 6 *Type:* repertory *Venues:* stage 228 *Comments:* permanent theatre company

Seinäjoki City Theatre
Seinäjoen Kaupunginteatteri
Alvar Aallonkatu 12, 60100 **Seinäjoki**
Tel: 6-416 2600 Fax: 6-414 1333
Internet: www.sjk.fi/teatteri
artistic director Tiina Puumalainen
Actors: 15 *Perfs:* 300 *Prods:* 7 *Type:* repertory *Venues:* main stage 429, small stage 100, studio 50 *Comments:* permanent theatre company

Ahaa Teatteri
Vellamonkatu 2, 33100 **Tampere**
Tel: 3-222 4870 Fax: 3-222 4872
Internet: www.tampere.fi/culture/ahaa
artistic director Virpi Koskela
Actors: 5 *Perfs:* 232 *Prods:* 4 *Comments:* permanent theatre company; touring company

Tampere Theatre, The
Tampereen Teatteri
Keskustori 2, 33100 **Tampere**
Tel: 3-216 0111 Fax: 3-216 0555
Internet: www.tampereenteatteri.fi
artistic director Heikki Vihinen; managing director Reino Bragge
Actors: 26 *Perfs:* 420 *Prods:* 13 *Type:* repertory *Venues:* Tampere theater 483, TT-Frenckell 233, Theater café 100 *Comments:* permanent theatre company

Tampereen Komediateatteri
Lapintie 3, 33100 **Tampere**
Tel: 3-276 0400 Fax: 3-273 0110
Internet: www.great.fi/~komedia
E-Mail: komedia@mailhost.great.fi
artistic director Tapio Parkkinen
Venues: stage 200, summer theatre 400

Teatteri 2000
Vellamonkatu 2, 33100 **Tampere**
Tel: 3-213 2555 Fax: 3-213 2350
E-Mail: teatteri2000@yritys.tpo.fi
theatre director Reima Vähämäki
Actors: 5 *Perfs:* 189 *Prods:* 6 *Type:* children's and young people *Comments:* permanent theatre company

Telakka
Tullikamarinaukio 3, 33100 **Tampere**
Tel: 3-225 0700 Fax: 3-225 0740
Internet: www.telakka.sci.fi
E-Mail: carneval@sci.fi

TTT – Theatre of Tampere, The
Tampereen Työväen Teatteri
Box 139, 33201 **Tampere**
Tel: 3-217 3111 Fax: 3-212 3825
Internet: www.sci.fi/~teatteri
E-Mail: ttt@ttt-teatteri.fi
theatre director Esko Roine; financial manager Seppo Soini
Actors: 30 *Perfs:* 382 *Prods:* 11 *Type:* repertory: modern, classical, comedy, new writing *Venues:* big stage 736, Eino Salmelainen stage 303, cellar stage 113, Kosti Elo hall 116 *Comments:* permanent theatre company

Åbo Swedish Theatre
Åbo Svenska Teater
Eerikinkatu 13, 20100 **Turku**
Tel: 2-251 1185 Fax: 2-231 9099
Internet: www.abo.fi/teater
E-Mail: tor.kreutzman@abo.fi
managing director Arn-Henrik Blomqvist; administrative director Sven Mattsson; marketing manager Tor Kreutzman
Actors: 18 *Perfs:* 200 *Prods:* 8
Type: repertory
Venues: main stage 311, studio 70-150
Comments: permanent theatre company

Turku City Theatre
Turun Kaupunginteatteri
Itäinen Rantakatu 14, 20800 **Turku**
Tel: 2-233 7177
Fax: 2-233 7101
theatre director Ilpo Tuomarila
Actors: 23 + 4 musicians *Perfs:* 245 *Prods:* 10 *Type:* repertory *Venues:* main stage 655, Sopukka 80-150, Pikkolo 45 *Comments:* permanent theatre company

Turku New Theatre
Turun Uusi Teatteri
Linnankatu 31, 20100 **Turku**
Tel: 2-232 1215
Fax: 2-250 1980
contact Sami Rannila
Actors: 5 *Perfs:* 278 *Prods:* 4

Vaasa Theatre
Wasa Teater
Kirkkopuistikko 16, 65100 **Vaasa**
Tel: 6-320 9300 Fax: 6-320 9350
Internet: www.svof.fi/wasateater
theatre director Erik Kiviniemi
Actors: 11 *Perfs:* 275 *Prods:* 6 *Type:* repertory *Venues:* big stage 270, small stage 60 *Comments:* permanent theatre company

Vaasan Kaupunginteatteri
Vaasa City Theatre
Pitkäkatu 53, 65100 **Vaasa**
Tel: 6-325 3960 Fax: 6-325 3969
Internet: www.vaasai.vaasa.fi/teatteris
E-Mail: vkt@pp.qnet.fi
theatre director Lasse Lindeman; administrative director Hannu Hakala
Actors: 16 *Perfs:* 245 *Prods:* 9 *Type:* repertory *Venues:* big stage 374, small stage 100-120 *Comments:* permanent theatre company

Teatteri Kehä III
Kuriiritie 36, 01300 **Vantaa**
Tel: 9-836 1919 Fax: 9-836 1226
contact Paula Huovinen
Actors: 1 *Perfs:* 102 *Prods:* 3

Varkauden Teatteri
Varkaus Theatre
Laivalinnankatu 29, 78200 **Varkaus**
Tel: 17-264 8800 Fax: 17-264 8899
Internet: www.dlc.fi/~varkteat/
E-Mail: varkauden.teatteri@dlc.fi
theatre director Tuomo Salmela
Actors: 9 *Perfs:* 166 *Prods:* 7 *Type:* repertory *Venues:* stage 250 *Comments:* permanent theatre company

FRANCE (+33)

Judith Production – La scène de l'autre
7 Rue Frédérique Mistral, 13100 **Aix-en-Provence**
Tel: 4-4221 2319 Fax: 4-4238 8345
contact Claudine Hunault
Actors: varies *Perfs:* 20 *Prods:* 1
Type: contemporary *Touring:* Europe
Comments: international co-productions

Nouveau Théâtre d'Angers
Centre Dramatique National, Maison de la Culture, 12 place Louis Imbach, BP 2107, 49021 **Angers** Cedex 2
Tel: 2-4188 9008 Fax: 2-4188 3780
E-Mail: nouveau.theatre@wanadoo.fr
directeur Claude Yersin; administrateur François Dugoujon; secrétaire général Daniel Besnehard
Actors: 1 (permanent) + hired actors as needed *Perfs:* 157 *Prods:* 3 *Type:* contemporary drama *Venues:* Théâtre Municipal 700, Theâtre Beaurepaire 530, Imbach 60, Atelier Jean Dasté 100 *Touring:* France, Switzerland, Germany *Comments:* see also Venues

Compagnie de Théâtre Le Sablier
Théâtre d'Angoulême, Scène Nationale Les Plateaux, BP 287, 16007 **Angoulême** Cedex
Tel: 5-4538 6161 Fax: 5-4538 6151
metteur en scéne Pascal Dubois; assistant Fred Saint-Pol
Actors: 2 *Type:* contemporary and classics *Venues:* Théâtre à l' italienne 730, Hall B 170 *Comments:* the Compagnie moved with the theatre to: Avenue des Maréchaux; see also Venues and Promoters

C.D.N. de Savoie
Bonlieu, 1 rue Jean Jaurès, 74000 **Annecy**
Tel: 4-5052 7674 Fax: 4-5052 9642
co-directeur Jean-Pierre Cazes; directeur artistique André Engel; directeur technique François Revol; secrétaire générale Anne Fisher
Prods: 2 + 3 co-productions *Type:* contemporary and classic theatre *Venues:* Bonlieu Scène National (Annecy 982) – Espace Malraux *Touring:* national

Vélo-Théâtre
Pepiniere d'Enterprises, Route de Buoux, 84400 **Apt**
Tel: 4-9004 8525 Fax: 4-9004 6384
directeurs Tania Castaing, Charlot Lemoine; relations publiques Marion Coste
Actors: 1 *Perfs:* 50 *Prods:* 4 *Type:* object theatre *Venues:* Théâtre 150 *Touring:* France, Belgium *Comments:* no text, show is only visual

Théâtre de la Commune Pandora
Centre Dramatique National d'Aubervilliers, 2 rue Edouard Poisson, BP 157, 93304 **Aubervilliers** Cedex
Tel: 1-4833 1616
Fax: 1-4834 3555
Internet: www.alegnia.fr/theatre-commune
directeur Didier Bezace; administratrice Nathalie Lemaire; direction communication Catherine Dan; relations publiques t.b.a.
Actors: no permanent company, hire actors as needed *Perfs:* 6 *Prods:* 1 *Type:* classical, modern
Venues: Théâtre de la Commune; large hall 530, small hall 230 *Comments:* also receiving house; see also Venues

Compagnie Gérard Gelas – Théâtre du Chêne Noir
8 bis rue Sainte-Catherine, 84000 **Avignon**
Tel: 4-9086 5811 Fax: 4-9085 8205
Internet: www.avignon-et-provence.com/chene-noir
directrice de gestion Eliane Brunet; directeur artistique Gérard Gelas; directeur technique Jean-Louis Cannaud; chargé de la presse et des relations publiques t.b.a; secretaire générale Katie Ricard
Actors: varies *Perfs:* 100-200 *Prods:* 1 *Type:* classical and contemporary, music *Venues:* salle John Coltrane 120, salle Léo Ferré 300 *Touring:* Europe *Comments:* rent, produce and co-produce

Compagnie Timar
Théâtre des Halles, 4 rue Noël Biret, 84000 **Avignon**
Tel: 4-9085 5257 Fax: 4-9082 9543
Internet: www.avignon-et-provence.com/theatre-halles
directeur Alain Timar; administrateur Laurette Paume; relations publiques Eve Ferragut
Actors: varies *Perfs:* 50 *Prods:* 1 *Type:* contemporary *Venues:* Théâtre des Halles 200 *Touring:* France

Théâtre des Carmes
6 place des Carmes, 84000 **Avignon**
Tel: 4-9082 2047 Fax: 4-9086 5226
Internet: www.perso.wanadoo.fr/Forum.Theatre
E-Mail: andre.benedetto@wanadoo.fr
secrétariat général Michèle Hoger; directeur artistique André Benedetto; administrateur Frances Ashley
Actors: 4 *Perfs:* 150 *Prods:* 2 *Type:* modern drama written by André Benedetto *Venues:* Théâtre des Carmes 200 *Touring:* France

Nouveau Théâtre de Besançon, Centre Dramatique National
Parc du Casino, Av Edouard Droz, 25000 **Besançon**
Tel: 3-8188 5511
Fax: 3-8150 0908
directeur Michel Dubois
Perfs: 74 *Prods:* 2 *Type:* classic & contemporary *Venues:* capacity 337 *Touring:* France *Comments:* see also Venues

Comédie de Béthune
Le Palace 138, rue du 11 novembre,
62412 **Béthune** Cedex
Tel: 3-2163 2900 Fax: 3-2163 2913
directeurs et metteurs en scéne Agathe Alexis, Alain Barsacq; responsable des ateliers de formation permanente et metteur en scène-associé Jean Lacornerie ; administrateur Didier Tridon; responsable de l'action artistique et de la diffusion Serge Basso; communication Fouad Bausba; relations publiques Philippe Momot; directeur technique Etienne Charasson
Perfs: 120 (theatre) + 150 (on tour) *Prods:* 3 *Type:* from classical to contemporary *Venues:* Studio Théâtre 156, Le Palace 350 *Touring:* France, Europe

Théâtre des Chimères – Les Découvertes
75 Avenue du Maréchal Juin, 64200 **Biarritz**
Tel: 5-5941 1819 Fax: 5-5923 4111
directeur Jean-Marie Broucaret; administration générale Marie-Julienne Hingant; communication Yves Mousset
Actors: varies *Prods:* 2 *Type:* classical, contemporary *Touring:* France, Bolivia *Comments:* ateliers – courses for children and adults, taught by the actors of the company; Festival de théâtre Franco-Iberique Bayonne Biarritz – see also Festivals

Compagnie du Hasard
8 rue du Lt Godineau, 41000 **Blois**
Tel: 2-5457 0570
Fax: 2-5457 0579
E-Mail: compagnie.hasard@wanadoo.fr
directeur artistique Nicolas Peskine; administratrice Catherine Amilcar; actrice et co-directrice Daniéle Marty; directeur technique Michel Druez; actrice et chanteuse Bénédicte Flatet;
relations publiques Tanja Horstmann
Actors: 15 *Perfs:* 40 *Type:* contemporary theatre, mobile theatre *Venues:* Théâtre des Provinces du Monde 200, tent 400 *Touring:* France, Europe *Comments:* company travels with own theatre, technical equipment and caravans; see also Venues

Compagnie Tiberghien
226, Bouvelard Albert 1er, 33800 **Bordeaux**
Tel: 5-5685 7090
Fax: 5-5685 9040
directeur Gilbert Tiberghien;
administration Karine Larrat
Actors: varies *Prods:* 1 *Type:* dramatic and contemporary, musicals *Venues:* Théâtre TNT (Tout Nouveau Théâtre) 100 *Touring:* France

Théâtre du Port de la Lune – Centre Dramatique National Bordeaux-Aquitaine – Théâtre National en Préfiguration
Square Jean-Vauthier, BP 7, 33031 **Bordeaux** Cedex
Tel: 5-5691 0181
Fax: 5-5692 8150
directeur Jean-Louis Thamin; directeur adjoint Gérard Lion; directeur technique Alain Pinel; chargée des relations extérieures Corinne Reboud
Perfs: 89 *Prods:* 2 *Type:* contemporary, classical *Venues:* Salle Jean Vauthier 484, Salle Les Essais 50

Quartz, Le
Centre National Dramatique et Chorégraphique, 2 et 4 Avenue Clehenceau, BP 411, 29275 **Brest** Cedex
Tel: 2-9844 1010 (public)/0807 (administration)
Fax: 2-9844 0066
E-Mail: dsabun.lequartz@wanadoo.fr
directeur Jacques Blanc; directeur technique Nicolas Hinssen; directeur communication Yves Leroy; assistante artistique Nadége Loir;
administrateur Claude Becker
Perfs: 150 *Prods:* 10 *Type:* classical, music, dance, theatre *Venues:* Centre Culturel de Brest stage A 1560 , stage B 314 *Touring:* France, Europe, Japan, USA *Comments:* dramatic and choreographic centre; congresses organised in the cultural centre; visiting address: 2-4 avenue Clemenceau, 29200 Brest; see also Promoters

Théâtre de l'émergence, Le
Centre Jules Verne, Place du Jeu de Paume,
60120 **Breteuil**
Tel: 3-4480 3544 Fax: 3-4480 3544
directeur & metteur en scène Bernard Habermeyer; relations publiques et
diffusions Marie-Anne Fizet-Gorin
Actors: varies (9) *Perfs:* 50+ *Prods:* 1 *Type:* all types *Venues:* Breteuil Theatre 300 *Touring:* Europe

Compagnie Hubert Jappelle – Théâtre De l'Usine
BP 82, Eragny-sur-Oise, 95612 **Cergy-Pontoise** Cedex
Tel: 1-3037 8457 Fax: 1-3464 1581
directeur Hubert Jappelle;
administration Patrick Herviou
Actors: varies *Perfs:* 40 *Prods:* 2 *Type:* classical, contemporary, experimental, marionnettes *Venues:* capacity 200 *Touring:* France

Théâtre de Saône et Loire
Théâtre Grain de Sel, 46 Grande Rue,
71100 **Châlon-sur-Saône**
Tel: 3-8548 6058 Fax: 3-8548 8692
directeur Jacques Bailliart;
administratrice Mireille Nichou
Perfs: 50-60 *Prods:* 1 *Type:* contemporary, classical *Venues:* Théâtre Grain de Sel 80 *Touring:* France *Comments:* administrative address: 5 rue des Cochons de Lait, 71100 Châlon-sur-Saône

Compagnie du Pain d'Orge
Théâtre de Champigny, 54 blrd du Château,
94500 **Champigny-sur-Marne**
Tel: 1-4880 5843 Fax: 1-4880 4827
directeur Jacques Guedj; président Georges Vriz; administratice Gina Oloa
Actors: 8 *Perfs:* 300 *Prods:* 2 *Venues:* Centre Gérard Philipe stage A 600, stage B 100 *Touring:* Europe, Africa

Influence Fievet-Palies
34 boulevand Nesles, 77420 **Champs-sur-Marne**
Tel: 1-6461 1077 Fax: 1-6461 0333
directeurs artistiques Claudine Fievet, Jean-Luc Palies; assistant direction Bruno Noury; sécrétaire Marie-Carmen Caron; assistante administration Florence Joly
Actors: varies *Perfs:* 50 *Prods:* 1 *Type:* baroque and contemporary *Touring:* France
Comments: see also Venues

Théâtre Régional des Pays de la Loire
4 bis rue Horeau, BP612, 53200 **Chateau-Gontier**
Tel: 2-4309 1670 Fax: 2-4307 5737
directeur Patrick Pelloquet; secrétaire générale Annie Guichard; secrétariat t.b.a.; régisseur général Jean Yves Laurendeau; administrateur Pascal Gilbert
Actors: varies *Perfs:* 80 *Prods:* 1 *Type:* modern, classic and contemporary drama *Touring:* France

Théâtre de Châtillon – Compagnie Serge Noyelle
15, rue de la Gare, 92320 **Châtillon**
Tel: 1-4657 2211 Fax: 1-4657 2692
E-Mail: theatre.châtillon@wanadoo.fr
directeur et metteur en scène Serge Noyelle; co-directeur Pedro Garcia; administrateur Frédéric Mazelly; communication Rachelle Mégissier
Actors: varies *Perfs:* 72 *Prods:* 2 *Type:* theatre, dance, street theatre *Venues:* Théâtre de Châtillon stage A 250, stage B 80 *Touring:* Europe, Quebec *Comments:* stage A visiting address: 3 rue Sadi Carnot, 92320 Châtillon; see also Venues

Théâtre du Pélican
12 rue Agrippa d'Aubigné, 63000 **Clermont-Ferrand**
Tel: 4-7391 5060 Fax: 4-7390 7800
directeur artistique Bruno Castan; directeur technique Pierre Mauchien; secrétaire générale, relations publiques et presse Dominique Delpeux
Perfs: 60 *Prods:* 1 *Type:* children's theatre *Touring:* France *Comments:* sponsored by Mairie de Clermont-Ferrand, Conseil Général du Puy de Dome, D.R.A.C Auvergne, Conseil Regional and some private companies

Clastic Théâtre
62 boulevard Victor Hugo, 92110 **Clichy**
Tel: 1-4106 0404 Fax: 1-4106 0403
directeur François Lazaro; administrateur Paul Rondin
Actors: 3 *Perfs:* 50 *Prods:* 1 *Type:* puppets/drama *Touring:* France, Europe *Comments:* see also Puppets

Atelier du Rhin – Centre Dramatique Régional d'Alsace
La Manufacture, 6 route d'Ingersheim,
68008 **Colmar** Cedex
Tel: 3-8941 7192 Fax: 3-8941 3326
E-Mail: info@atelierdurhin.com
directeur Matthew Jocelyn; directeur technique Jean-Claude Stephan; administrateur Frédéric de Beauair; directrice de la communication Michèle Gaujard
Perfs: 80-100 *Prods:* 3 *Type:* contemporary *Venues:* stage A 340, stage B 90 *Touring:* France and abroad
Comments: see also Opera, Venues and Promoters

Compagnie Daniel Dupont
46 rue de la Soie, 68000 **Colmar**
Tel: 3-8923 7901
directeur Daniel Dupont
Actors: varies *Comments:* company dormant at present

Théâtre de Corbeil – Essones, Le
20-22 rue Felicien-Rops, 91100 **Corbeil-Essonnes**
Tel: 1-6089 7547/6088 4899 Fax: 1-6089 7338
directeur André Pelliciari;
administrateur général Mahfoud Sadi
Perfs: min 50 *Prods:* 2-3 *Type:* contemporary *Venues:* capacity 525 *Comments:* policy: rent, present, co-produce, produce

Grenier de Bourgogne
Theatre Mansard, 94 bld Mansard, 21000 **Dijon**
Tel: 3-8063 8333 Fax: 3-8038 1275
directeur Jean Maisonnave; administration Gilles Foulet; relations publiques Gérard Berland
Perfs: 40 *Prods:* 1 *Type:* classical, contemporary, musical comedies *Touring:* France *Comments:* offers workshops and courses for children, teenagers and adults

Compagnie Jean et Colette Roche
73, rue de la Station, 93700 **Drancy**
Tel: 1-4832 2874
directeurs artistiques Jean Roche, Colette Roche
Perfs: 30-110 *Prods:* 1 *Type:* modern drama, contemporary, classical *Touring:* France, Europe

Compagnie des Opérations
Jacques Falguières-Théâtre d'Evreux, Place de Gaulle, 27000 **Evreux**
Tel: 2-3278 8525 (bookings)/8520 (admin)
Fax: 2-3278 8529
directeur Jacques Falguières
Perfs: 40 *Prods:* 1 *Type:* classical and contemporary, jazz, world music *Venues:* Théâtre
d'Evreux 400, Palais des Congrés 900 *Touring:* France
Comments: see also Venues

Théâtre de la Vache Cruelle
Le Ciella, Avenue docteur Tocheport, 24160 **Excideuil**
Tel: 5-5362 5319 Fax: 5-5362 5318
direction artistique Colette Froidefont; direction technique Fréderic Coustillas; administration Christiane Péninou, Samuel Ormaechea
Actors: 5 *Perfs:* 50 *Prods:* 1 (Echos sur le Sable D'algérie) *Type:* contemporary *Venues:* Le Ciella 209
Touring: France *Comments:* give courses for Baccalauréat students

Théâtre de Gennevilliers – Centre Dramatique National
41 Av des Grésillons, 92230 **Gennevilliers**
Tel: 1-4132 2610 Fax: 1- 4086 1744
directeur Bernard Sobel; directrice adjointe Nicole Martin; administrateur Philippe Grimm; directeur technique Yvernat Patrick; directrice communication et relations publiques Dominnique Landre
Perfs: 150 *Prods:* 2 *Type:* classical and contemporary *Venues:* 2 flexible halls: from 220 to 450 (with double stage) *Comments:* see also Venues

Centre Dramatique National Des Alpes
10 bis rue Ampere, 38000 **Grenoble**
Tel: 4-3812 1640
directeur Roger Caracache;
secrétaire general Elaine Baracetti;
metteur en scène (centre dramatique) Laurent Pelly
Perfs: 60 *Prods:* 1 *Type:* modern *Venues:* Maison de la Culture stage A 1200, stage B 500, stage C 300
Comments: Le Cargo will close for 2000

Compagnie Renata Scant
8 rue Pierre Duclot, 38000 **Grenoble**
Tel: 4-7644 6092 Fax: 4-7651 7427
Internet: www.neptune.fr/~scant/
directrice metteur en scène Renata Scant;
directeur technique du festival Pierre Auzas
Actors: 2 permanent, 20 for the season *Perfs:* 40 + 50 festival *Prods:* 2 *Type:* contemporary, classical *Venues:* Théâtre Prémol 250 *Touring:* Europe *Comments:* see also Festivals and Venues

Compagnie Yvon Chaix
Théâtre le Rio, 37 rue Servan, 38000 **Grenoble**
Tel: 4-7644 7011 Fax: 4-7644 7704
directeur Yvon Chaix; administration Elena Pastore; directeur technique Frédéric Biaudet
Perfs: 140 *Prods:* 1 *Type:* contemporary, modern *Venues:* Théâtre le Rio 134 *Touring:* France *Comments:* preparation for drama section of baccalauréat

Footsbarn Travelling Theatre
La Chaussée, 03190 **Herisson**
Tel: 4-7006 8484 Fax: 4-7006 8471
E-Mail: Footsbarn@compuserve.com
administrator John Kilby; assistante Natasha Hopkins; accountant Sylvie Falzone
Actors: 11 actors + 3 musicians *Perfs:* 100 *Prods:* 3 *Type:* popular theatre *Venues:* own theatre tent 450 to 650 *Touring:* worldwide *Comments:* videos and music cassettes/CDs available, workshop programme for professional theatricians throughout the year

Theatre National de Normandie Centu Dramatique – Comédie de Caen
BP 94, 14203 **Hérouville** Cedex
Tel: 2-3146 2727 Fax: 2-3146 2728
E-Mail: cdncaen@cybercable.tm.fr
directeur Eric Lacascade; directeur administratif Yvon Tranchant; conseiller artistique Philippe Lherbier; secrétaire générale Angelina Berforiui
Actors: 10 *Perfs:* 100 *Prods:* 3 *Type:* contemporary and classical theatre *Venues:* Théâtre d'Hérouville-Saint-Clair, Théâtre des Cordes *Touring:* Europe, South America, Asia *Comments:* see also Venues

Théâtre des Quartiers d'Ivry/La Balance
7 place Marcel Cachin, 94200 **Ivry-sur-Seine**
Tel: 1-4672 3743 Fax: 1-4671 2775
co-metteurs en scène Elisabeth Chailloux, Adel Hakim
Perfs: 75 *Prods:* 2 *Type:* contemporary *Venues:* Théâtre d'Ivry 240

Centre Dramatique de La Courneuve
21 Av Gabriel Péri, 93120 **La Courneuve**
Tel: 1-4836 1144 Fax: 1-4836 2383
directeur Dominique Brodin;
régisseur Christian l'Habitant
Actors: 7 *Perfs:* min 30 *Prods:* 1 *Type:* contemporary and classical *Venues:* Centre Culturel Municipal 200 *Touring:* France *Comments:* produce and co-produce; see also Venues

Cie José Manuel Cano Lopez
c/o Le Plessis, théatres Château de Plessis-Lès-Tours, Rue du Plessis, 37520 **La Riche**
Tel: 2-4738 2929
Fax: 2-4738 3565
directeur artistique José Manuel Cano Lopez;
administratrice Nathalie Zylbersztein;
responsable formation Alain Papillon;
responsable projeti artistiques Françoise Cano Lopez
Actors: 9 permanent *Perfs:* 130 *Prods:* 4 *Venues:* capacity 100 *Touring:* France *Comments:* see also Festivals

Théâtre de l'Utopie: Centre de Création théâtrale – Compagnie Nationale
39 rue Thiers, 1
000 **La Rochelle**
Tel: 5-4641 7133 Fax: 5-4627 1626
directeur artistique Patrick Collet;
co-directrice Denise Vlaneck
Actors: varies *Perfs:* 55 *Prods:* 1 *Type:* contemporary *Venues:* Théâtre de l'Utopie 40 up to 100 *Touring:* France, Africa, French speaking countries *Comments:* preparation for drama section of baccalauréat; work sometimes with job centres

Compagnie Humbert
Théâtre Municipal, Rue de la Comédie,
52200 **Langres**
Tel: 3-2573 9873 (Troyes)/3-2587 1304
Fax: 3-2573 9873 (Troyes)
directeur Michel Humbert; directeur adjoint Pierre Humbert; relations publiques Mèlamie Thy Tine Laugies, Berueplette Bouard Troyes;
régisseur Philippe Briot
Actors: 6-10 *Perfs:* 120 *Prods:* 3 *Type:* contemporary, classical *Venues:* Théâtre Municipal 300, Théâtre de la Madeleine à Troyes 550, open air in July 200 *Touring:* France *Comments:* in July the company organises an event called Rendez-vous de Juillet in Langres, in open-air venues; 2nd address: Théâtre de la Madeleine, rue Jules Lebocey, 10000 Troyes

Théâtre de l'Ephémère – Centre Dramatique du Maine
8 place des Jacobins, 72000 **Le Mans**
Tel: 2-4343 8989
Fax: 2-4343 9721
co-directeurs artistiques Jean-Louis Raynaud, Didier Lastère; administratrice Christine Vallée;
directeur technique Pascal Batard
Perfs: 100 *Prods:* 2 *Type:* contemporary *Venues:* Théâtre Paul Scarron 148 *Touring:* France, Europe

Théâtre du Radeau
2 rue de la fonderie,
72000 **Le Mans**
Tel: 2-4324 9360
Fax: 2-4328 5162
E-Mail: radeau@wanadoo.fr
co-direction François Tanguy, Laurence Chable; administration Françoise Furcy; régie générale Hervé Vincent
Actors: varies *Perfs:* 80 *Prods:* 1 (every 1.5 years) *Type:* créations, contemporary *Venues:* La Fonderie 130 *Touring:* Europe, France

Grand Bleu – Centre Dramatique National Jeunes Publics Lille/Nord-Pas de Calais, Le
36 Av Marx Dormoy, 59000 **Lille**
Tel: 3-2009 4550 Fax: 3-2009 2152
Internet: legrandbleu.com
E-Mail: grandbleu@nordnet.fr
directeur Bernard Allombert; communication Françoise Allombert; directeur technique Patrick Leroy;
administration Ariane Braun
Actors: varies *Perfs:* 300 *Prods:* 3 *Type:* contemporary drama for young people *Venues:* capacity 230 to 320 *Touring:* national, international *Comments:* two biennial festivals alternately: November 1999: Planetado: theater meeting for european teenagers with teenagers and professionals: performances, workshops, etc; October 2000: festival for young audience: international meeting for professionals; see also Venues and Festivals

Théâtre de la Découverte – La Verrière
28 rue Alphonse Mercier, 59800 **Lille**
Tel: 3-2054 9675
Fax: 3-2030 6309
E-Mail: theatredécouverte@nordnet.fr
administration Aline Haidon;
directeur artistique Dominique Sarrazin
Perfs: 65 *Prods:* 1 *Type:* contemporary, comedy *Venues:* La Verrière 150 *Touring:* France

Theatre du Nord – Tourcoing – Region Nord Pas De Calais
4 place du Général de Gaulle, BP 302, 59026 **Lille**
Tel: 3-2014 2400/2424 (booking) Fax: 3-2014 2414
Internet: www.nordnet.fr/tdn
E-Mail: tdn@nordnet.fr
directeur Stuart Seide;
communication Bruno De Visscher
Actors: varies *Perfs:* 100+ *Prods:* 4 *Type:* contemporary *Venues:* Théâtre National stage A 480, stage B 95, Théâtre de l'Idéal 400 *Touring:* France, Europe, Middle East

Théâtre de l'Union – Centre Dramatique National du Limousin
BP 206, 20 rue des Coopérateurs,
87006 **Limoges** Cedex
Tel: 5-5579 7479 Fax: 5-5577 3737
E-Mail: adm@theatre-union.fr
directeur Silriu Purcarete; administrateur Denis Triclot; directeur technique Yvon Truffaut;
conseiller artistique Alain Garlan
Perfs: 100 *Prods:* 2-3 *Type:* classical, contemporary *Venues:* Centre Dramatique 398 *Touring:* worldwide including: France, Europe *Comments:* produce and co-produce; see also Venues

Compagnie Christophe Perton
11, place Antonin Poncet, 69002 **Lyon**
Tel: 4-7838 2856
Fax: 4-7892 9772
metteur en scène, directeur artistique Christophe Perton; relations publiques Cendrine Forgemont; chargée de production Fadhila Mas;
administratrice Brigitte Duflau
Perfs: 30 *Prods:* 1-2 *Type:* contemporary *Touring:* France

Compagnie de la Satire
24, rue Saint Jean, 69005 **Lyon**
Tel: 4-7842 0401 Fax: 4-7842 0401
directeur artistique Bruno Carlucci;
administration Judith Bècle
Perfs: 60 *Prods:* 3 *Type:* contemporary, experimental theatre, inter-disciplinary venue *Touring:* France

Place Publique – théâtre et faits divers
22 rue Ornano, 69001 **Lyon**
Tel: 4-7829 6308
Fax: 4-7829 5661
administrateur Laurent Ribault;
direction artistique Patrick le Mauff
Actors: varies *Perfs:* 50 *Prods:* 1 or 2 *Type:* contemporary and classical *Venues:* tent 200 *Touring:* France, Europe

Théâtre des Jeunes Années – Centre Dramatique National (T.J.A.)
23 rue de Bourgogne, 69009 **Lyon**
Tel: 4-7253 1510
Fax: 4-7253 1519
directeurs artistiques Maurice Yendt, Michel Dieuaide; directeur technique Jean-Pierre Grosset
Actors: varies *Perfs:* 103 *Prods:* 4 *Type:* classical and contemporary drama *Venues:* Théâtre des Jeunes Années, Centre Dramatique National: Stage A: 450, Stage B: 100 *Comments:* produce and co-produce; see also Festivals and Venues

Théâtre du Point du Jour
7 rue des Aqueducs,
69005 **Lyon**
Tel: 4-7815 0180
Fax: 4-7815 0185
directeur administratif André Guittier; directeur artistique Michel Raskine; régisseur général Martial Jacquemet; attachée de presse Véronique Besançon
Perfs: 71 *Prods:* 1 *Type:* contemporary
Venues: Théâtre du Point du Jour 350 *Touring:* France

Théâtre les Ateliers
5 rue du Petit David, 69002 **Lyon**
Tel: 4-7837 4630
Fax: 4-7241 9302
directeur et metteur en scène Gilles Chavassieux; secrétaire générale Nicole Lachaise; relations publiques Marie-Françoise Renouprez, Nathalie Teboul;
administratice Danièle Martigny
Perfs: 180 *Prods:* 9 (incl 2 new) *Type:* contemporary *Venues:* capacity 100 and 230 *Touring:* France, Europe *Comments:* see also Venues

Théâtre 71 – Scène Nationale
3 Place du 11 Novembre, 92240 **Malakoff**
Tel: 1-4655 4345
Fax: 1-4655 1331
directeur Pierre Ascaride; secrétaire générale Agnès Célérier; administratrice Ghyslaine Schueller
Prods: 1 *Type:* contemporary *Venues:* Théâtre capacity 516 *Comments:* see also Venues

Théâtre Écoute
16 rue Raymond Fassin,
92240 **Malakoff**
Tel: 1-4655 6363/4542 5268 (admin. touring)
Fax: 1-4655 9222
metteur en scéne Jeanne Champagne;
administratrice Marika Hupé;
administratrice de production Huguette Kingué
Perfs: 100 *Prods:* 3 *Type:* contemporary and texts *Touring:* France, abroad *Comments:* drama courses, educational activities and work as a partner of the education minister in universities

Théâtre du Mantois
18 rue de Gassicourt, 78200 **Mantes-La-Jolie**
Tel: 1-3033 0226 Fax: 1-3094 5688
directeur Jean-Charles Lenoir; administrateur Natalié Guerin; relations publiques Nathalie Dubreuil
Actors: varies *Perfs:* 60 *Prods:* 3 *Type:* contemporary, classical, Francophone *Comments:* organise a biennial festival 'Francophonories Théâtrales pour la Jeunesse'; see also Festivals

Compagnie Chatot-Vouyoucas:Théâtre Gyptis
136 rue Loubon, 13003 **Marseille**
Tel: 4-9111 4150 Fax: 4-9111 4151
directeurs artistiques Andonis Vouyoucas, Françoise Chatot; régisseur général Olivier Le Tetour; accueil Noelle Hovanessian; secrétariat de direction Corinne Blanc; gestion Sandrine Rastello; attachée de presse Tatiana Brelet
Actors: varies *Perfs:* 9 *Prods:* 2 *Type:* classic and contemporary repertory *Venues:* capacity 700 *Touring:* France *Comments:* rent, produce, co-produce and present

Compagnie Richard Martin – Théâtre Axel Toursky
16 passage Léo Ferré, 13003 **Marseille**
Tel: 4-9102 5835/9158 5454 Fax: 4-9167 9964
administrature Bernard Urbain, Corinne Vallalta; directeur artistique et comédien Richard Martin; directeur technique Daniel Tzicuris; responsable communication Françoise Tremlet
Actors: varies *Perfs:* 40 *Prods:* 2 + 4 co-productions *Type:* contemporary, dance, jazz, variety, cinema *Venues:* capacity up to 800 *Comments:* see also Venues

Théâtre Demodesastr
7 Allées Leon G
mbetta, 13001 **Marseille**
Tel: 4-9150 0801 Fax: 4-9150 9754
artistic director Agnès Del Amo;
administrative director Sébastien Lauro-Lillo
Actors: 3 (fixed) *Perfs:* 15 *Prods:* 1 *Type:* visual theatre, contemporary dance theatre, poetry
Touring: France, Europe

Théâtre du Gymnase
4, Rue du Théâtre Français, 13001 **Marseille**
Tel: 4-9124 3524/3535 (bookings)
Fax: 4-9194 2180
E-Mail: Theatre.Gymnase@wanadoo.fr
directeur Dominique Bluzet; administratrice générale Alexia Peyronel; régisseur général Olivier Clot; secrétaire général Lionel Dahan; relations publiques Rabah Houia; directrice adjointe Sylvie Record
Actors: varies *Perfs:* 120 *Prods:* 3 *Type:* contemporary, classical *Venues:* Théâtre du Gymnase 680
Touring: France, Belgium, Switzerland

Théâtre du Point Aveugle
7 Allée Léon Gambetta,
3001 **Marseille**
Tel: 4-9195 6750
Fax: 4-9150 9754
secrétariat général Brigitte Gastaldi; directeur artistique François-Michel Pesenti; administrateur Franck Vernet; relations publiques André Gintzburger;
régisseur général Marc Vilarem
Actors: varies *Perfs:* 15-40 *Prods:* 3 *Type:* contemporary drama *Touring:* Europe, Asia, Switzerland, Taiwan, Hong-Kong, Singapore *Comments:* founded in 1979 – sponsored by the Marseille Town Hall, the Ministry of Culture, the Regional Council, and the General Council Department

Théâtre National de Marseille, La Criée
30 quai de Rive Neuve, 13284 **Marseille** Cedex 7
Tel: 4-9154 7454 Fax: 4-9154 2818
directeur Gildas Bourdet; administrateur Jean Laurent Paolini; relations publiques Bernadette Brissan, Stéphane de Bellevall; programation Marianne Epin; presse Béatrice Duprat
Prods: 14 *Type:* classical, contemporary *Venues:* Grand Salle 780, Petite Salle 250 *Touring:* France

Pascal Theatre
Appartement 92, Residence Le Vauban C, 59600 **Maubeuge**
Tel: 3-2764 5070 Fax: 3-2764 5070
E-Mail: pascal7038@aol.com
administrator Alain Carpentier; artistic director Julia Pascal; treasurer Madeleine Klotsche; collaborateurs Sarah Goldfarb, Thomas Kampe
Actors: 5-10 *Perfs:* 28-30 *Prods:* 3 in repertoire; 2 new plays *Type:* international physical theatre *Touring:* UK *Comments:* see also United Kingdom: Pascal Theatre Company, Tel: +44 171-383 0920, Fax: +44 171-419 9798

Opéra-Théâtre de Metz
4-5, Place de la Comédie, 57000 **Metz**
Tel: 3-8755 5171 Fax: 3-8731 3237
Internet: www.mairie-metz.fr.8080
directeur administratif Maria-Hélenè Metzinger-Nicolay; directeur artistique Danielle Ory; relations publiques Agnès Jacques; chef des chocurs Jean-Pierre Aniorte
Prods: 5 *Type:* all types *Venues:* capacity 750 *Comments:* see also Dance and Opera

Conpagnie Théâtre de l'Unité
Centre d'Art et de Plaisanterie, Hôtel de Sponeck, 54 rue Clémenceau, BP 236, 25204 **Montbeliard** Cedex
Tel: 3-8191 3711 Fax: 3-8191 1025
E-Mail: capsna@infrescom.fr
directeurs/metteurs en scéne/comédiens Jacques Livchine, Hervée De Lafond; scénographe Claude Acquart; secrétariat Sylvie Lalaude
Actors: varies *Perfs:* 15+ *Type:* contemporary *Venues:* Théâtre de Montbeliard 450 *Touring:* France, Belgium *Comments:* see also Venues

Théâtre des Fédérés – Centre Dramatique National de Création Région Auvergne
Espace Boris Vian, 03100 **Montluçon**
Tel: 4-7003 8618 Fax: 4-7005 8857
co-directeurs Olivier Perrier, Jean-Paul Wenzel; relations publiques Laurence Fleury
Actors: varies *Perfs:* 14+ *Prods:* 3 *Type:* contemporary *Venues:* Théâtre des Ilets 280, studio théâtre d'Hérisson (for rent) *Touring:* France *Comments:* see also Venues

Théâtre des Treize Vents – Centre Dramatique National Languedoc-Roussillon
Domaine de Grammont, 34965 **Montpellier** Cedex 2
Tel: 4-6799 2525 Fax: 4-6799 2528
E-Mail: theatre.des.13.vents@wanadoo.fr
directeur Jean Claude Fall; secrétaire générale Blandine Verhaverbeke; administrateur Benoit Joëssel; communication, directrice des relations publique Valérie Bousquet; directeur technique Gérard Espinoza
Perfs: 70 *Prods:* 2 *Type:* classical, modern and contemporary *Venues:* Théâtre de Grammont 591 *Touring:* France *Comments:* produce and co-produce

Théâtre des Jeunes Spectateurs – Centre Dramatique National
26 place Jean Jaurès, 93100 **Montreuil**
Tel: 1-4870 4890 Fax: 1-4859 6044
directeur Daniel Bazilier; directrice adjointe Patricia Giros; administratrice Régine Guillotin; relations publiques Brigitte Bertin, Christelle Faure, Jeanne Garcia; régie générale Pierre Hadef
Prods: 1 *Type:* children's theatre *Venues:* cap 340 *Touring:* France, Switzerland *Comments:* see also Venues

La Filature – Scène Nationale
20 allée Nathan Katz, 68090 **Mulhouse** Cedex
Tel: 3-8936 2828 Fax: 3-8936 2800
Internet: www.lafilature.asso.fr
E-Mail: mjl@lafilature.asso.fr
directeur général Christophe Crimes; chargée de production Nathalie Jugnet; delegué aux actions culturelles Francis Schaller; directeur technique Henri-François Monnier; attachée de presse Marie-Josée Lagarde; attachée de direction Cécila le Bomin; secrétaire générale Denise Benaberg
Perfs: 160 *Prods:* 2 theatre, 1 dance and 1 music *Type:* contemporary, classical and world music, video creations, theatre, opera, dance, circus *Venues:* Grande salle 1200, multi-purpose 120 to 380, petit salle cinema 100 *Comments:* Orchestre Symphonique de Mulhouse, Opera du Rhin, Ballet du Rhin; alternative e-mail: chc@lafilature.asso.fr; see also Venues

Scarface Ensemble
40 Rue Laurent, BP1082, 68051 **Mulhouse** Cedex
Tel: 3-8943 0641 Fax: 3-8943 0647
directrice artistique Elisabeth Marie
Actors: varies *Perfs:* 25 *Prods:* 1 *Type:* contemporary first productions and 20th century drama *Touring:* France

Théâtre 4 Litres 12
22 rue Sellier, 54000 **Nancy**
Tel: 3-8335 5710 Fax: 3-8337 3211
E-Mail: ginstburger@wanadoo.fr
directeurs Michel Massé, Odile Massé; administration Lydia Gorbatchew, Lional Dubut; directeur technique Jean-Christophe Cunat
Actors: 3 *Perfs:* 50 *Prods:* 1 *Type:* metaphysical buffoonery *Venues:* Salle Gentilly Nancy 100 *Touring:* France, Canada, Europe *Comments:* produce

Théâtre de la Manufacture – Centre Dramatique National Nancy-Lorraine
10 rue Baron-Louis, BP3349, 54014 **Nancy** Cedex
Tel: 3-8337 1299 Fax: 3-8337 1802
E-Mail: theatre.manufacture@wanadoo.fr
directeur Charles Tordjman; administration Gabrielle Kiffert; chargée de la communication Isabelle Villermain-Lécolier; directeur-adjoint Bernard Flevry
Perfs: 180-200 *Prods:* 1-7 *Venues:* Théâtre de la Manufacture 380 *Touring:* national, international

T et M Nanterre
Théâtre des Amandiers, 7 Av. Pablo Picasso, 92022 **Nanterre** Cedex
Tel: 1-4614 7019 Fax: 1-4725 1775
Internet: www.tem-nanterre.com
E-Mail: tem@tem-nanterre.com
directeur Antoine Gindt; assistante de direction Mireille Henne; administration Marie-Séverine Piard; directeur technique Bernard Jamond; relations publiques Isabelle Gaudfuey
Actors: varies *Perfs:* 100 *Prods:* 2 *Type:* contemporary theatre/music, contemporary opera *Venues:* Théâtre des Amandiers stage A 900, stage B 350, stage C 150 *Touring:* Europe

Théâtre Nanterre-Amandiers
7 Av Pablo Picasso, 92000 **Nanterre** Cedex
Tel: 1-4614 7070 Fax: 1-4725 1775
directeur Jean-Pierre Vincent; directeur technique Carlos Stavisky
Actors: varies *Perfs:* 255 *Prods:* 7-8 *Type:* modern/classical/contemporary *Venues:* Théâtre de Nanterre, halls A 900, hall B up to 500, hall C 150 *Touring:* national, international *Comments:* see also Promoters & Venues

Le Théâtre du loup
1 rue Suffren, 44000 **Nantes**
Tel: 2-4071 8070
Fax: 2-4069 6113
directeur artistique Yvon Lapous; president Pierre Perron; administratrice/secretaire comptable Liliane Djire
Perfs: 10+ *Prods:* 1 *Type:* contemporary *Touring:* France

Skené Productions
1 rue Suffren, 44000 **Nantes**
Tel: 2-4069 0909 Fax: 2-4069 1141
directeur artistique Hervé Tougeron; administration Aline Robin
Perfs: 20 *Prods:* 1 *Type:* contemporary, classical drama, musical *Touring:* Europe

Nouveau Théâtre de Nice – Centre Dramatique National Nice-Côte d'Azur
Promenade des Arts, 06300 **Nice**
Tel: 4-9313 9090 Fax: 4-9362 1946
directeur Jacques Weber; directeur administratif Yves Saussinan; relations publiques Dany Montiglio; directeur technique Yves Guérut; sécrétaire général Mady Leo
Prods: 7 *Venues:* salle Pierre Brasseur 1000, salle Michel Simon 300 *Touring:* France, Europe *Comments:* produce and co-produce, halls also used occasionally for dance, see also Venues

Centre National de Creation – Region Centre (CADO)
Carré Saint-Vincent, 45000 **Orléans**
Tel: 2-3854 2929 Fax: 2-3881 7764
directeurs Jean-Claude Houdinière, Loic Volard; administratrice Michèle Grandamas
Prods: 3 *Venues:* Centre National stage A 1000 , stage B 600 *Comments:* 2nd address: 103 rue de la Boétie, 75008 Paris, Tél: 1-4359 0676; Fax 1-4359 0448; see also Dance, Venues and Promoters (same address but different administration)

Atelier de Recherche et de Réalisation Théâtrale
Cartoucherie, Route du Champ de Manoeuvre, 75012 **Paris**
Tel: 1-4365 6654 Fax: 1-4365 5682
administratrice générale Marie-Noëlle Boyer; directeur artistique Philippe Adrien
Perfs: 100 *Prods:* 2 *Type:* contemporary and classical *Venues:* Théâtre de la Tempête 80 and 170 *Touring:* France, Luxembourg, Antilles *Comments:* produce, co-produce and offer job training for actors

Ateliers Contemporains, Les
68 rue Jean-Jacques Rousseau, 75001 **Paris**
Tel: 1-4887 9510 Fax: 1-4887 9501
directeur Claude Régy; administrateur Bertrand Krill
Perfs: 50 *Prods:* 1 *Type:* first productions, contemporary/modern, new playwrights *Touring:* France

Centre International de Création Théâtrale
13 bld Rochechouart, 75009 **Paris**
Tel: 1-4082 6200
Fax: 1-4222 2201
directeurs Peter Brook, Stephane Lissner; communication Anita Le Van
Perfs: 120 *Prods:* 1 *Type:* classical and modern *Venues:* Théâtre des Bouffes du Nord 510 *Touring:* international *Comments:* the administration will move out of their building in March 1998; the new address was not known at time of going to print; the Centre may be reached at: Théâtre des Bouffes du Nord, 37 bis Boulevard de la Chapelle, 750010 Paris; see also Venues

Chapeau Rouge, Le
95 rue du Faubourg St. Antoine, 75011 **Paris**
Tel: 1-4346 7070 Fax: 1-4347 0504
Internet: www.multimanice.com/chapeaurouge
E-Mail: chapeaurouge@aol.com
directeur artistique Pierre Pradinas; administrateurs Albert Prevot, Rosy Allery
Actors: 10 *Perfs:* 80 *Prods:* 2 *Type:* contemporary drama, comedy *Venues:* Théâtre la Piscine 400 *Touring:* France, Europe

Chimène
BP 425, 75527 **Paris** Cedex 11
Tel: 1-4259 8686 Fax: 1-4223 6250
directrice artistique Laurence Février; assistante Josseline Minet
Actors: 2 *Perfs:* 40 *Prods:* 1 *Type:* classical, modern, contemporary *Venues:* La Maroquinerie 250 *Touring:* France

Comédie Francaise
Salle Richelieu, 1 place Colette, 75001 **Paris**
Tel: 1-4458 1400/1515 (bookings) Fax: 1-4458 1550
Internet: www.comedie-francaise.fr
E-Mail: reservation@comedie-francaise.fr (booking only)
administrateur général et directeur artistique Jean Pierre Miquel; directeur administratif Bruno Ory-Lavollée; secrétaire général Florence Castera; attachée de presse Dominique Racle; relations publiques Paul Rens; administrateur délégué Denis May
Actors: 64 *Prods:* 15 *Type:* mostly classical, but some contemporary *Venues:* Salle Richelieu 892 (venue is a listed building-théâtre de l'Italienne-which dates from 1791), Théâtre du Vieux Colombier 300, Studio Théâtre 135 *Comments:* the only permanent company in France: Société des Comédiens Français. 2nd address-Théâtre du Vieux Colombier, 21 rue du Vieux Colombier, 75006 Paris, tél: 1-4439 8700; Studio Théâtre, place de la pyramide inversée, Carrousel du Louvre, 99 rue de Rivoli, 75001 Paris, Tel: 1-5558 9858 (information)

Compagnie Alain Rais
15 rue Titon, 75011 **Paris**
Tel: 1-4338 6085/4371 4821 Fax: 1-4357 7657
E-Mail: jack.salon@wanadoo.fr
directeur Alain Rais; administrateur Jack Salom
Actors: varies *Perfs:* 15
Type: contemporary, contemporary poetry theatre

Compagnie Artistic Athévains
Théâtre Artistic-Athévains, 45 bis Rue Richard Lenoir, 75011 **Paris**
Tel: 1-4356 3846
Fax: 1-4356 0897
directrice et metteur en scène Anne-Marie Lazarini; directrice administrative Dominique Bourde; directeur technique et scénographie François Cabanat
Prods: 1 *Venues:* Théâtre Artistic stage A 230, stage B 110 *Touring:* France

Compagnie Artistic Athévains
Théâtre Artistic-Athévains, 45 bis Rue Richard Lenoir, 75011 **Paris**
Tel: 1-4356 3846 Fax: 1-4356 0897
directrice et metteur en scène Anne-Marie Lazarini; directrice administrative Dominique Bourde; directeur technique et scénographie François Cabanat
Prods: 1 *Venues:* Théâtre Artistic stage A 230, stage B 110 *Touring:* France

Compagnie Bierry
75 blvd Montparnasse, 75006 **Paris**
Tel: 1-4544 5021
Fax: 1-4284 1291
directeur Etienne Bierry; contact Renée Delmas-Bierry (administratrice et directrice du théâtre de Poche)
Actors: varies *Perfs:* 240 *Prods:* 6 *Type:* contemporary and classical, discovery of new playwrights *Venues:* Théâtre de Poche Montparnasse 130 *Touring:* France *Comments:* see also Venues

Compagnie Christian Rist-le Studio Classique
23 rue Boyer, 75020 **Paris**
Tel: 1-4797 4200 (admin)/4500
Fax: 1-4797 4200
E-Mail: lelabo.paris@wanadoo.fr
directeur et metteur en scène Christian Rist; administratrice Françoise Lebeau
Perfs: 50-80 *Prods:* 2 every 3 years *Type:* classical and contemporary authors *Touring:* worldwide *Comments:* courses for professional actors

Compagnie Claude Confortès – Centre de Création Contemporaine
15 rue des Beaux Arts, 75006 **Paris**
Tel: 1-4326 1976 Fax: 1-4634 5041
administratrice Louisette Vayssettes; directeur artistique Claude Confortès; co-directeur Nicolas Erréra
Perfs: 96 *Prods:* 1 *Type:* contemporary, musical *Touring:* France, Belgium *Comments:* produce and co-produce contemporary authors

Compagnie des Claviers
3 rue du lieutenant Chauré, 75020 **Paris**
Tel: 1-4030 2171
Fax: 1-4030 2621
directeur artistique Jean-Paul Farré; administration Colette Bloesch
Actors: 1 *Perfs:* 70-80 *Prods:* 1 *Type:* musical burlesque *Touring:* France *Comments:* touring company

Compagnie Erzuli
9 Impasse des Jardiniers, 75011 **Paris**
Tel: 1-4348 1299 Fax: 1-4348 1299
administration Angela di Vincenzo; artistic director Jean-René Lemoine
Actors: varies *Perfs:* 45 *Prods:* 1 *Type:* contemporary *Touring:* France, Martinique *Comments:* see also Dance

Compagnie Françoise Pillet
13 rue Bourgon, 75013 **Paris**
Tel: 1-4581 5171 Fax: 1-4565 0835
directrice Françoise Pillet
Perfs: 200 *Prods:* 1 *Type:* classical and experimental theatre for young people *Touring:* France

Compagnie Jacques Mauclair
Théâtre du Marais, 37 rue Volta, 75003 **Paris**
Tel: 1-4278 0353 Fax: 1-4029 9252
directeur artistique Jacques Mauclair
Prods: 1 *Type:* classical and modern drama *Venues:* Théâtre du Marais 90
Comments: produce and co-produce

Compagnie Les Matinaux
L'Atalante, 10 place Charles Dullin, 75018 **Paris**
Tel: 1-4606 1190/4255 6941
directeurs artistiques Alain Barsacq
Actors: varies *Type:* modern and 19thC drama *Venues:* L'Atalante 50 *Touring:* France *Comments:* select and invite other companies to perform

Compagnie Marcel Marceau
32 rue de Londres, 75009 **Paris**
Tel: 1-4280 4832/4526 1170
Fax: 1-4874 9187
E-Mail: ncmmm@wanadoo.fr
directeur Marcel Marceau
Actors: 9 *Perfs:* 80 *Type:* classical mime
Touring: worldwide

Compagnie Philippe Fenwick-William Mesguich
42 rue de la Villette, 75019 **Paris**
Tel: 6-6248 9605 Fax: 1-5698 1431
chargé de production Patrick de Froidcourt; autear Philippe Fenwick; metteur en scenè William Mesguich; éclairagiste David Geoffrey
Actors: 12 *Perfs:* 65 *Type:* classic, contemporary, musicals *Touring:* France

Compagnie Philippe Genty - MPM International
21 rue du Grand Prieuré, 75011 **Paris**
Tel: 1-4923 8360
Fax: 1-4338 4314
management Marie-Pierre Paillard; directeur artistique Philippe Genty; administratrice Mireille Cappaert
Actors: 8 (dancers) *Perfs:* 100-110 *Prods:* 2 (1 new)
Type: a cross between dance, drama and marionettes
Touring: Africa, Israel, France, USA, Spain, Japan, Eastern Europe, Germany *Comments:* see also Dance, Puppets, Agents and Promoters

Compagnie TF2
2 bis Square du Croisic, 75015 **Paris**
Tel: 1-4567 9938
Fax: 1-4567 9938
E-Mail: jfpeyret@aol.com
directeur Jean-Francois Peyret
Perfs: 50 *Prods:* 1 *Type:* avant-garde *Venues:* MC93 Bobigny Théâtre, stage A 1000, stage B 250, TNT (Toulouse), TNT (Rennes) *Touring:* France
Comments: supported by the Ministry of Culture; project with Théâtre National de Bretagne

Compagnie – Théâtre des Évenements
14 rue neuve Popincourt, 75011 **Paris**
Tel: 1-4878 3966/614 370 086
Fax: 1-4878 3349
administrator Patrik de Froidcourt; artistic director Pierre Lacan
Actors: 7 *Perfs:* 30 *Prods:* 3 *Comments:* administration address: Ecce Bombo, 42 rue de la Villette, 75019 Paris; see also Dance and Drama

Compagnie Vicky Messica
Théâtre les Déchargeurs, 3 rue des Déchargeurs, 75001 **Paris**
Tel: 1-4236 0002/1029
Fax: 1-4236 5098
directeur Lee Fou Messica; président Marc Legrand; administrateur Christine Messica; régisseur Lurent Taffoureau; communication Jean-Philippe Azema
Actors: 4 *Perfs:* 60 *Prods:* 1 *Type:* poetry and new productions of contemporary works – work with the writers, in the Bohème: chanson française, chants lyriques, musicals, story telling, small plays
Venues: capacity 100, La Bohème 40 *Touring:* worldwide
Comments: rent, produce and co-produce

Compagnie Viviane Théophilides
27 rue du Fbg Montmartre, 75009 **Paris**
Tel: 1-4770 2232
Fax: 1-4770 3646
directeur artistique Viviane Théophilides
Actors: 3 musicians + 1 dancer *Perfs:* 22-23+ *Prods:* 1
Type: contemporary French drama, poetic international repertoire *Touring:* France

Deschamps et Deschamps
7 bis Avenue de Saint Mandé, 75012 **Paris**
Tel: 1-4345 8914
Fax: 1-4342 5219
E-Mail: deschien@cybercable.fr
administrateur Valérie Levy; directeurs artistiques Jérôme Deschamps, Macha Makeieff
Actors: 10 *Prods:* 1 *Type:* contemporary, classical
Touring: France *Comments:* produce and co-produce for television

G.R.A.T. – Compagnie Jean-Louis Hourdin
15 passage de la main d'or, 75011 **Paris**
Tel: 1-4700 4571 Fax: 1-4806 2465
directeur Jean-Louis Hourdin; administration Mireille Brunet
Actors: varies *Perfs:* 100 *Prods:* 1 *Type:* classical and contemporary *Touring:* France

Jean-Michel Ribes et Compagnie
2 bis rue Julien Lacroix, 75020 **Paris**
Tel: 1-4797 1930 Fax: 1-4797 1903
directeur Jean-Michel Ribes; administratrice Valérie Bouchez; secrétaire Nathalie Loiseau
Actors: varies *Prods:* 2-3 *Type:* contemporary *Venues:* Théâtre Tristan Bernard 480 *Touring:* France, Europe

L' Etoile du Nord
16 rue Georgette Agutte, 75018 **Paris**
Tel: 1-4226 4747 Fax: 1-4226 6398
directeurs artistiques Bernard Djaoui, Jean Macqueron; communication et relations publiques Virginie Fendler
Perfs: 180 *Prods:* 1+ *Type:* contemporary dance, drama
Venues: L' Etoile du Nord 203
Comments: see also Venues

Les Ateliers du Chaudron
31 passage de Menil Montant, 75011 **Paris**
Tel: 1-4361 1717 Fax: 1-4240 5997
responsable artistique Tanith Noble
Actors: varies *Perfs:* 10-15 *Type:* improvisation, visual and musical theatre *Comments:* also community work with the underpriviledged, theatre d'action visual, gestuel et musical; run workshops for all ages; help autistic children, people in hospitals

Les Grands Luminaires – Compagnie Micheline Uzan
253 blvd Raspail, 75014 **Paris**
Tel: 1-4335 0674 Fax: 1-4335 0412
directrice Micheline Uzan; secrétaire général Hugues Aubin
Perfs: 60+ *Prods:* 1 *Type:* contemporary *Touring:* France
Comments: produce and co-produce

Musique et Parole
APJA musique en scéne, Salle Pleyel, Studio 507, 252 rue du Fbg St Honoré, 75008 **Paris**
Tel: 1-5375 2067/4293 9112/6-1217 3221
Fax: 1-5375 2067
createurs Raymond Acquaviva, Brigitte Bladou
Actors: 5 *Perfs:* 50 *Prods:* 2 *Type:* musical theatre – biography of great composers: Satie, Ravel, Mozart put into music and drama *Touring:* international

Théâtre 14 Jean-Marie Serreau
20 Avenue Marc Sangnier, 75014 **Paris**
Tel: 1-4545 4977
Fax: 1-4044 5201
directeur Emmanuel Dechartre; administrateur Jean-François Guilliet; responsable collectivités Marie-Celine Fougère
Perfs: 126 *Prods:* 1 *Type:* classical-contemporary
Venues: capacity 200

Théâtre Aujourd'hui
31 rue Delambre, 75014 **Paris**
Tel: 1-4320 7059/1-4743 4002
Fax: 1-4538 5969
directeur artistique Jacques Seiler
Actors: varies *Prods:* 1 *Type:* contemporary
Comments: produce and co-produce

Théâtre de l'Aquarium
Cartoucherie, Route du Champ de Manoeuvres, 75012 **Paris**
Tel: 1-4374 7274 Fax: 1-4328 1360
administrateur Jean-Paul Perez; directeur artistique/metteur en scène Jean-Louis Benoit; directeur technique Dominique Fortin; relations publiques Christelle Cassard
Actors: varies *Prods:* 1 *Type:* use modern texts and adaptations of literary works such as novels and TV programmes, modern topics *Venues:* Cartoucherie hall A 250, hall B 200 *Touring:* France

Théâtre de l'Epée de Bois
Cartoucherie, Route du Champs de Manoeuvres, 75012 **Paris**
Tel: 1-4808 3974 Fax: 1-4328 5653
directeur artistique Antonio Diaz-Florian
Actors: 10-12 *Perfs:* 216 *Prods:* 13 *Type:* Ibero – Latin American bilingual theatre *Venues:* Cartoucherie hall A 300, hall B 164 *Touring:* Spain, France, Latin America
Comments: bilingual performances in French and Spanish; see also Espada de Madera, Madrid, Spain

Théâtre des Mathurins
36 rue des Mathurins, 75008 **Paris**
Tel: 1-5305 2706 (admin)/4265 6246
Fax: 1-5305 2708/4924 9169
président & directeur général Julien Vartet; régisseurs Pascal Vinet; administration Michèle Jolly
Prods: 1 *Type:* Boulevard (French plays by J Vartet)
Venues: Mathurins 500 *Comments:* see also Venues

Théâtre des Sources
100, ave Simon Bolivar, 75019 **Paris**
Tel: 1-4700 6632
E-Mail: teramoon@hotmail.com
artistic director Theresa Amoon
Actors: 5 (revolving) *Perfs:* 150 *Prods:* 2 *Type:* theatricalized versions of ancient legends & folk tales, using storytelling, dance & music *Venues:* various theatres in Paris & Paris region *Touring:* Europe, North America, South America, Asia *Comments:* also give workshops

Théâtre du Lierre
22 rue du Chevaleret, 75013 **Paris**
Tel: 1-4586 5583
Fax: 1-4586 8289
Internet: www.les-petits-ruisseaux.com/lierre/lierre.html
administratrice Michelle Dumont; directeur artistique Farid Paya; attachées de presse Anne Gueudré, Isabelle Mèglincky; attachée relations-publiques Maïa Vayne; communication t.b.a
Actors: 7 *Perfs:* 100 *Prods:* 1 *Type:* drama, dance, music, antique tragedies, lyric tragedies *Venues:* Théâtre du Lierre 200 *Touring:* France and abroad

Théâtre du Mouvement
21 rue du Grand Prieuré, 75011 **Paris**
Tel: 1-4806 4658
Fax: 1-4338 1399
E-Mail: tmouvement@aol.com
administration Marina Guglielmi; directeur artistique Claire Heggen, Yves Marc; diffusion internationale Danièla Litsoiu; directeur général Yves Marc
Actors: 10 *Perfs:* 100 *Prods:* 2 *Type:* movement theatre
Touring: France, Europe, Africa

Théâtre du Pont-Neuf
89 rue d'Aboukir, 75002 **Paris**
Tel: 1-4337 5765
Fax: 1-4337 5765
co-directeurs artistiques Philippe Mercier, Guy-Pierre Couleau
Actors: varies *Perfs:* 100 *Prods:* 1 *Type:* contemporary drama *Touring:* international *Comments:* produce and co-produce, supported by Ministry of Culture and Ville de Paris and sponsored privately

Théâtre du Rond-Point/Cie Marcel Maréchal
2 bis Av Franklin Roosevelt, Champs Elysées, 75008 **Paris**
Tel: 1-4495 980
Fax: 1-4075 0448
directeur Marcel Maréchal; directeur administratif Francois Collet; directeur artistique adjoint François Bourgeat; administrateur Jean Luc Grandie
Perfs: 200 *Prods:* 1 *Type:* contemporary *Venues:* Théâtre du Rond Point Champs Élysées: room A 754, room B 180 *Touring:* France, Europe *Comments:* also receiving venue in Gallery Auberti: Ateliers Theatre adults (courses)

Théâtre du Soleil
Cartoucherie, 75012 **Paris**
Tel: 1-4374 8763
Fax: 1-4328 3361
Internet: www.theatre-du-soleil.fr
E-Mail: thsoleil@worldnet.fr
directrice Ariane Mnouchkine; administrateur Pierre Salesne; presse et relations publiques Liliana Andreone
Actors: varies *Prods:* 2 *Type:* contemporary, classical
Venues: Cartoucherie 550

Théâtre Essaïon de Paris
6 rue Pierre au Lard, 75004 **Paris**
Tel: 1-4278 4642 (reservations)/4278 6173 (admin)
Fax: 1-4274 0454
directrice Alida Latessa; directeur artistique José Valverde; secrétaire Dabhia Maati
Perfs: 250-300 *Prods:* 1 *Type:* French drama by living authors *Venues:* salle 1 101, salle 2 80 *Comments:* 2-6 co-productions a season, second address (administration) 85 rue de la Verrerie, 75004, Paris tel:1-4278 6173

Théâtre International de Langue Française
Parc de la Villette, Pavillon du Charolais,
211 Av Jean-Jaurès, 75019 **Paris**
Tel: 1-4003 9390 Fax: 1-4239 1477
directeur artistique & directeur Gabriel Garran; directeur de communication Myriam Lothammer; assistantes communication Michéle Mabonzo, Florence Douez; directeur technique Georges Chaillan; p.r. Claire Gelineau
Perfs: 300 *Prods:* 1 *Type:* theatre by francophones authors *Venues:* Le Pavillon du Charolais 160, Parc de la Villette *Touring:* international *Comments:* rent, produce and co-produce

Théâtre National de Chaillot
BP 1007-16, 75761 **Paris** Cedex 16
Tel: 1-5365 3000 (booking)/5365 3100 (admin)
Fax: 1-4755 0800/4727 1031
(administration, communication)
Internet: www.theatre-chaillot.fr
directeur Jérôme Savary; administrateur Olivier Lombardie; directeur technique Didier Monfajon; attachée de presse Catherine Papeguay; responsable des relations avec le public Agnès Chemama; collaboration artistique Léonidas Strapatsakis
Actors: varies *Perfs:* 400 *Prods:* 10 *Type:* classical and contemporary *Venues:* Salle Jean Vilar 1350, Salle Gémier 418 *Touring:* France, abroad *Comments:* visiting address: 1 place du Trocadéro, 75116, Paris

Théâtre National de la Colline
15 rue Malte-Brun, 75020 **Paris**
Tel: 1-4462 5200
Fax: 1-4462 5290
directeur Alain Françon; administrateur général Alain Herzog; administrateur adjoint Pierre Yves Lenoir; conseil artistique Myriam Desrumeaux; conseil littéraire Laure Hémain; directeur technique Francis Charles; directrice des productions Anne Cotterlaz; directrice des relations extérieures Anne Goalard; presse Dominique Para
Actors: varies *Prods:* 10 *Type:* contemporary *Venues:* stage A 757, stage B 214 *Touring:* France, abroad *Comments:* see also Venues

Théâtre Ouvert – Centre Dramatique National de Création
Le Jardin d'Hiver, 4 bis Cité Véron, 75018 **Paris**
Tel: 1-4255 7440/4262 5949 (bookings) Fax: 1-4252 6776
directeurs Lucien Attoun, Micheline Attoun; administrateur Ricardo Marquez;
relations publiques Marlène Daniel
Actors: 5 *Perfs:* 70 *Prods:* 2 *Type:* contemporary *Venues:* stage A 200, stage B 100 *Touring:* France, Chile, Quebec, South America *Comments:* produce and co-produce; édition théâtre ouvert; see also Venues

Théâtre Silvia Monfort
106 rue Brancion, 75015 **Paris**
Tel: 1-4533 6670/4531 1096 (bookings) Fax: 1-4531 1571
directeur Régis Santon; administration t.b.a; comptable Guy Cartier; relations publiques Christophe Cauchi
Prods: 4 *Type:* classical and contemporary, classical music & dance *Venues:* capacity 456
Comments: see also Venues

Théâtre Tsai
66 rue Monge, 75005 **Paris**
Tel: 1-4201 4285 Fax: 1-4201 4285
E-Mail: tsai@wanadoo.fr
directrice Gilberte Tsai
Perfs: 40-50 *Prods:* 3 *Type:* contemporary *Touring:* France, Italy, Switzerland

Tréteaux de France – Centre Dramatique National, Les
11 rue Yvon Villarceau, 75016 **Paris**
Tel: 1-4501 9132 Fax: 1-4501 6937
directeur Jean Danet; administrateur, relations publiques Michel Clouet
Actors: 10 *Perfs:* 35 *Prods:* 1 *Type:* contemporary, classical, modern drama for teenage audiences *Venues:* tent 540 *Touring:* France *Comments:* presents dance, classical music, variety, children's events at the venue; see also Venues

Centre Dramatique Poitou-Charentes
4 impasse Arthur Ranc, BP 504,
86012 **Poitiers** Cedex
Tel: 5-4941 4390
Fax: 5-4941 0373
directrice Claire Lasne;
directrice adjointe/administratrice Daniele Jironès
Actors: varies *Perfs:* 70 *Prods:* 2 *Type:* contemporary, classical *Touring:* France *Comments:* touring company

C'est la Nuit
76, rue du Docteur Lemoine, 51100 **Reims**
Tel: 3-2677 0990/6-0863 4210
directrices artistiques Françoise Roche, Christine Berg
Perfs: 40 *Prods:* 2 *Type:* classical, contemporary *Touring:* France *Comments:* studio for drama courses

Comédie de Reims, La
3 Chaussée Bocquaine, 51100 **Reims**
Tel: 3-2648 4910 Fax: 3-2688 7695
directeur Christian Schiaretti; secrétaire général Christine Schmitt; administrateur Bernard Collet; chargé de production Vincent Marcoup; relations publiques Olivier Maby
Actors: 10-12 *Perfs:* 180 *Prods:* 3 *Type:* classical, contemporary *Venues:* La Comedie de Reims stage A 1000, stage B 200, Théâtre des Ateliers 50 *Touring:* France, Europe, Latin America, Africa, Morocco *Comments:* see also Venues

Théâtre National de Bretagne, Le
1 rue Saint-Hélier, BP 675, 35008 **Rennes** Cedex
Tel: 2-9931 5533 Fax: 2-9967 6619
directeur Francois le Pillouër; directeur administratif et financier Laurent Parigot; directrice adjoint Nathalie Solini; directrice communication Bernadette Kessler
Perfs: 220 *Prods:* 2 *Type:* mostly contemporary *Venues:* stage A 1150, stage B 350 *Touring:* France, Europe
Comments: see also Venues and Festivals

L'Athanor – Michel de Maulne
16 Av. du Docteur Vaillant, 93230 **Romainville**
Tel: 1-4843 3184 Fax: 1-4843 3184
directeur Michel de Maulne;
relations publiques Ophélie Orecchia;
directeur technique Jean-Pierre Chupin
Perfs: 60+ *Prods:* 1 *Type:* Théâtre Poésie Musique *Venues:* Théâtre Molière 200 *Touring:* France *Comments:* own the Théâtre Molière, Paris

Théâtre des Deux Rives – Centre de Création Dramatique de Haute-Normandie
48 rue Louis Ricard, 76000 **Rouen**
Tel: 2-3589 6341 Fax: 2-3570 5983
secrétaire générale Danièle Le Bihan; directeur artistique Alain Bézu; responsable pédagogique Catherine Dewitt; administrateur Jean-Marc Devaux; dir technique Patrick Delacroix; attaché de presse Eric Talbot
Perfs: 50 *Prods:* 3 *Type:* mainly contemporary *Venues:* Théâtre des Deux Rives 215 *Touring:* France *Comments:* courses for amateurs; see also Venues

Comédie de Saint-Etienne – Centre Dramatique National
7 Av Emile Loubet, 42000 **Saint-Etienne**
Tel: 4-7725 0124 Fax: 4-7741 9634
E-Mail: comedie.de.saint-etienne@wanadoo.fr
directeur Daniel Benoin; administrateur René Lévy; secrétaire générale Christiane Raia; régisseur général Daniel Cresisier; administrateur adjoint François Lecoq; directeur technique Jean-Pierre Laporte
Actors: 5 *Perfs:* 145 *Prods:* 9 *Type:* classic and contemporary *Venues:* Théâtre Jean Dasté 750, Théâtre en sous-sol 60, Théâtre du Parc Andrézieux-Bouthéon 370
Touring: France *Comments:* produce and co-produce, see also Venues

Cirkub'U
124 Cours Paul Doumer, 17100 **Saintes**
Tel: 5-4693 2732 Fax: 5-4697 2239
Internet: www.geocities.com/sotto/loftf/3559/
E-Mail: cirkubu@t3A.com
direction artistique Alain Le Bon;
marionettiste Michelle Gauraz
Actors: 1 puppeteer *Perfs:* 50 *Prods:* 2 *Type:* contemporary, puppetry *Touring:* Europe *Comments:* see also Puppets

Heyoka – Centre Dramatique National pour l'Enfance et la Jeunesse
Théâtre de Sartrouville, Place Jacques Brel, BP 93, 78505 **Sartrouville** Cedex
Tel: 1-3086 7777 Fax: 1-3914 8791
directeur Claude Sévénier; directrice adjointe Martine Spangaro; directeur de production Guy d'Hardivillers; auteus, metteus en scene Joel Jouanneau
Actors: varies *Perfs:* 37 spectacles, 166 representaions
Prods: 5 *Type:* theatre for young people *Venues:* Théâtre de Sartrouville 846, Espace Gérard Philipe 300 *Touring:* international *Comments:* see also Venues

Side One Posthume Théâtre
10 rue des Chéneaux, 92330 **Sceaux**
Tel: 1-4702 3232 Fax: 1-4661 8989
directeur Pascal Rambert; administration Gilles Mégret
Perfs: 20 *Prods:* 1 *Type:* contemporary *Touring:* France

Théâtre National de Strasbourg
1 avenue de la Marseillaise, BP 184/R5, 67005 **Strasbourg** Cedex
Tel: 3-8824 8800 (administration) Fax: 3-8837 3771
Internet: www.strasbourg.com/tns
directeur Jean Louis Martinelli; administrateur Philippe Buquet; press Anne-Laure Vesperini; communication Falienne Meyer
Perfs: 77 *Prods:* 6 (3 co-productions + 3 aceueils *Type:* classical, contemporary *Venues:* Grande Salle 600, Petite Salle 200 *Touring:* Europe *Comments:* invite European productions; set and costume design studio; Ecole Supérieure d'Art Dramatique du T.N.S.; see also Promoters

Théâtre Populaire de Lorraine
2 rue Pasteur BP 90-146, 57103 **Thionville** Cedex
Tel: 3-8253 3395 Fax: 3-8253 4055
directrice Stéphanie Loïk; administrateur Jean-Bastide Jacob; relations publicques Anaël Mayer;
directeur technique Jean-Claude Burg
Actors: varies *Perfs:* 45+ *Prods:* 1 *Type:* contemporary, classical *Venues:* Théâtre Municipal stage A 1200, stage B 130 *Comments:* produce and co-produce; courses for professionals and non-professionals;
courses for children

Théâtre National de Toulouse – Théiatre de la Cité
1, rue Pierre Baudis, BP 449, 31009 **Toulouse** Cedex 6
Tel: 5-3445 0500 (info)/05 (bookings)/10 (admin/20 (pr)
Fax: 5-3445 0511
E-Mail: entcihe@infornie.fr
directeur Jacques Nichet; directeur adjoint Richard Coconnier; directeur des relations publiques Valérie Held; directeur technique Pierre Crousaud
Perfs: 200 *Prods:* 5 *Type:* classical, contemporary *Venues:* hall A 900, hall B 240 *Touring:* France, Northern Europe, North Africa, Greece

Centre Dramatique Régional de Tours-Direction Gilles Bouillon
3 rue Léonard de Vinci, 37000 **Tours**
Tel: 2-4764 4864 Fax: 2-4720 1726
directeur Gilles Bouillon; administratrice Giovana Pacé; dramaturge Bernard Pico; regisseur Zavier Carré
Perfs: 80-100 *Prods:* 2 *Type:* classical, contemporary *Venues:* Grand Théâtre 1000, Théâtre Louis Jouvet 240
Touring: France *Comments:* see also Venues

Centre de Littérature Orale – CLIO
Quartier Rochambeau, 41100 **Vendome**
Tel: 2-5472 2676 Fax: 2-5472 2530
Internet: www.clio.org
E-Mail: clio@lenet.fr
directeur Bruno de la Salle; directrice adjonte Hélène Lavergne; présidente Evelyne Cevin;
relations publiques Valéryе Mordelet
Actors: 1 *Perfs:* 15 *Prods:* 1 *Type:* classical and contemporary epics *Venues:* Chapelle St. Jacques 200 *Touring:* France, Greece, Belgium, Switzerland, Netherlands
Comments: library on all books/documents about fairy tales and more generally tales;

Théâtre Montansier de Versailles – S.A. Scapin Productions
13 rue des Réservoirs, 78035 **Versailles** Cedex
Tel: 1-3920 1600 Fax: 1-3953 4321
directeur Francis Perrin; administratrice Elisabeth Levasseur; directeur technique Michel La Porta
Perfs: 55 *Prods:* 4 *Type:* classical *Venues:* Salle de Théâtre 633 *Touring:* France, Europe *Comments:* see also Venues

Théâtre de la Jacquerie
40, rue Georges Lebigot, 94800 **Villejuif**
Tel: 1-4726 4534 Fax: 1-4726 4543
directeur artistique Alain Mollot
Perfs: 50-80 *Prods:* 1 *Type:* comedy, drama *Venues:* Théâtre Romain Rolland 850 *Touring:* France, Europe

Théâtre National Populaire
8 place Lazare Goujon, 69627 **Villeurbanne** Cedex
Tel: 4-7803 3030 Fax: 4-7884 0320
directeur Roger Planchon; administrateur Dominique Delorme; communication Marie-José Fromont
Prods: 3 *Type:* contemporary, classical *Venues:* TNP 800
Touring: France, international

Compagnie La Goutte d'eau
13 rue Pierre -Sémard, 94400 **Vitry**
Tel: 1-4682 6190 Fax: 1-4681 2160
Internet: www.gare-au-web.com
E-Mail: contact@gare-au-web.com
directeurs Mustapha Aouaz, Anne-Marie Simonin
Actors: varies *Prods:* 3 *Type:* contemporary *Venues:* Gare au Théatre 220, home capacity 60 *Touring:* France

GEORGIA (+995)

Meskhetian Drama Theatre
10 King Tamar st., 883750 **Akhaltsikhe**
Tel: 265- 20568/20142/20592
manager Lia Suluashvili

Chavchavadze Hereti National Theatre
Village Alibeglo, **Azerbaijan**
Tel: 32-780 009/8-9955 1575 (mobile)
artistic director Anzor Dolenjashvili

Chavchavadze Batumi Drama Theatre
1 Rustaveli st., 384500 **Batumi**
Tel: 88222-74280/76114/74281
manager Levan Glonti; artistic director.Levan Mirtskhulava

Tsereteli Chiatura Drama Theatre
5 Chavchavadze str., **Chiatura**
Tel: 279- 52426/55262/52466
manager Iza Jishkariani; director Nana Demetrashvili

Dmanisi Drama Theatre Kvemo Kartli
56 St. Nino str., **Dmanisi**
manager Jumber Kopaliani (tel:32-985 124); artistic director Zina Kverenchkhiladze (tel: 32-952 266)

Eristavi Gori Drama Theatre
10 Chavchavadze st., 383500 **Gori**
Tel: 270-23740/23360
manager Kakha Beridze

Meskhishvili Kutaisi Drama Theatre
8 Agmashenebeli sq., 384000 **Kutaisi**
Tel: 231-55690/45747/77188
manager Avalo Kajaia; artistic director Jeiran Pachuashvili

Marneuli Drama Theatre Samshoblo
Marneuli
Tel: 357-291 023
manager Nana Bokuchava

Tsutsunava Ozurgeti Drama Theatre
1 Chavchavadze st., 384370 **Ozurgeti**
Tel: 296-65321/63373
manager Revaz Sarishvili; artistic director Otar Kutaladze; artistic consultant Giorgi Sabo

Gunia Poti Drama Theatre
1 Rustaveli st., 384690 **Poti**
Tel: 293-21544
manager, artistic director Aleko Janelidze

Rustavi Drama Theatre
7 Pirosmani str., 383040 **Rustavi**
Tel: 235-129 536
manager Jemal Maziashvilli

Rustavi State Youth Theatre
Shartava str., **Rustavi**
Tel: 235-122 747/152 754
manager Lali Tabagari;
artistic director Lomgul Murusidze

Khorava Senaki Theatre
2 Theatre sq., **Senaki**
Tel: 213-21023/22793
manager Vakhtang Salakaia

Sokhumi Russian Drama Theatre
4 Lenin str., **Sokhumi**
Tel: 300-21449

Chanba Abkhasian State Theatre
1 Pushkin st., 384900 **Sukhumi**
Tel: 300-23514/23515

Abashidze State Musical Theatre
182 Agmashenebeli Ave., 380012 **Tbilisi**
Tel: 32-342 773/348 090/347708
manager Nestor Chiladze; assistants Giga Lortkipanidze, Nugzar Kacharava

Adamian State Armenian Theatre
8 Ketevan the Martyr st. , 380003 **Tbilisi**
Tel: 32-741 764/741656/746295
manager Enok Tatevosyan; assistant Ahot Kazaryan; artistic director Armen Bainduryan

Chantladze Satire and Humour Theatre
65 Agmashenebeli Ave., 380002 **Tbilisi**
Tel: 32-960 656/955 676
manager, chairman of artistic board Amiran Meskhishvili; deputy manager Nino Japaridze; office manager Tea Chanturia

Film Actor's Theatre of Tumanishvili
164 Agmashenebeli Ave., 380012 **Tbilisi**
Tel: 32-340 937
artistic director Nugzar Bagration-Gruzinski; general manager Valerian Salukvadze; administrator Eliso Tabuashvili

Gamsakhurdia Sokhumi Theatre
17 Rustaveli ave., **Tbilisi**
Tel: 32-934 498/987 363/996 209/963 696
manager, artistic director Dimitri Jaiani; Lit. department Irma Gotsiridze

Georgian State Youth Theatre
127a Agmashenebeli Ave., 380064 **Tbilisi**
Tel: 32-960 903/950 309
manager Teimuraz Maisuradze; chairman of artistic board Giga Lordkipahidze; director Ketevan Kharshiladze

Griboedov State Russian Drama Theatre
2 Rustaveli Ave., 380007 **Tbilisi**
Tel: 32-936 256/931 923/933 301
manager Givi Baratashvili; assistant Revaz Gvineria; artistic director Avtandil Varsimashvili

Machabeli Tskhinvali Georgian Theatre
99/1 Agmashenebeli Av., 380064 **Tbilisi**
Tel: 32-943 641/953 881
manager Zaza Tediashvili

Marjanishvili State Academic Theatre
8 Marjanishvili st. 8, 380002 **Tbilisi**
Tel: 32-955 500/953 582/951 333
general manager Gaioz Kandelaki; managers Malkhaz Beburishvili, Akaki Kuchukhidze, Gia Buadze; artistic director Otar Megvinetukhutsesi

Metekhi Theatre
1 Metekhi str., 380003 **Tbilisi**
Tel: 32-740 464
head Sandro Mrevlishvili; manager Vakhtang Glonti

Mtskheta-Tianeti
Regional Theatre
Tbilisi
Tel: 32-986 591
manager Rezo Mgeladze

Pantomime State Theatre
37 Rustaveli Ave., 380008 **Tbilisi**
Tel: 32-982 506/936 634
manager, artistic director Amiran Shalikashvili; secretary Amiran Mujiri

Russian State Youth Theatre
91/1 Agmashenebeli ave., 380064 **Tbilisi**
Tel: 32-955 365/955 067/957 874
manager Tsisana Janashia; assistant Tamaz Urushadze; secretary Iza Bagdasarova

Rustaveli State Academic Theatre
17 Rustaveli Ave., 380004 **Tbilisi**
Tel: 32-931 894/999 864/936 583
manager Giorgi Tevzadze; artistic director Robert Sturua; administrator Shalva Nikolaishvili

Underbasement Theatre
42 Rustaveli ave., 380008 **Tbilisi**
Tel: 32-222 016 Fax: 32-001 127/001 027
general director Avtandil Varsimashvili; directors Levan Tsuladze, Otar Egadze

Vazha Pshavela Telavi Drama Theatre
3 Freedom sq., 383330 **Telavi**
Tel: 250-31528/31684
manager, artistic director Nukri Kantaria

Khetagurov Osetian Drama Theatre
21 Stalin st., 383550 **Tshinkvali**
Tel: 244-42840/42137
manager Tamerlan Dzotsoev

Chkheidze Zestaponi Theatre
23 Lenin str., **Zestaponi**
Tel: 292-52711/52760/55598
manager Rene Abesadze

Dadiani Zugdidi Drama Theatre
2 Theatre st., 384700 **Zugdidi**
Tel: 215-26590
manager Enver Pajava

GERMANY (+49)

Grenzlandtheater Aachen
Elisen Galerie, Friedrich-Wilhelm-Platz 5/6, 52062 **Aachen**
Tel: 241-474 610 Fax: 241-4174 6123
Direktor u. künstlerische Leitung Manfred Langner; Verwaltungsleitung u. Geschäftsführer Franz Hermanns; Dramaturgie u. Öffentlichkeitsarbeit Martina Kullmann
Actors: varies *Perfs:* c.a. 300 (70-80 touring) *Prods:* 8 *Type:* comedy, musical, drama *Venues:* capacity 218 *Touring:* Germany, Netherlands

Theater Aachen
Theaterplatz, 52062 **Aachen**
Tel: 241-47841 Fax: 241-478 4200
Internet: www.theater-aachen.de
E-Mail: pressestelle@theater-aachen.de
Generalintendant Claus Schmitz, (from 1/8/2000 Dr Paul Esterhazy); Leiterin PR Renate Faßbender; Schauspieldirektor Michael Klette; Dramaturgie Lukas Popovic; GMD Elio Boncompagni
Actors: 17 *Perfs:* 266 *Prods:* 35 *Type:* Schauspiel, theater for children & youths, opera, musical *Venues:* Grosses Haus 732 to 857, Kammerspiele 165, Mörgens 99 *Comments:* see also Opera and Orchestras

Theater der Stadt Aalen
Postfach 1740, Im Torhaus, 73430 **Aalen**
Tel: 7361-522 596 Fax: 7361-521 909
Intendant Udo Schoen; Dramaturg, Öffentlichkeitsarbeit Martin Vöhringer; Leiterin Kinder- u. Jugendtheater Gerburg Maria Müller; Verwaltungsdir. Tina Hofmann
Actors: 5 (permanent) *Perfs:* 200+ *Prods:* 9 *Type:* Sprechtheater *Venues:* Probebühne im Torhaus 180, Probebühne im Wiz 200, Studio im alten Rathaus 99 *Comments:* also hosts guest productions

Vorpommersche Landesbühne Anklam
Leipziger Allee 34, 17389 **Anklam**
Tel: 3971-2089-0 Fax: 3971-2089-24
Internet: www.theater-anklam.de
Intendant Dr Wolfgang Bordel; Dramaturgie Piet Oltmanns; Leiter des Ensembles Jürgen Verch; Technischer Leiter Hans-Jürgen Engel; Geschäftsführung Kerstin Baumbach
Actors: 11 *Perfs:* 300 *Prods:* 10
Type: Sprechtheater – children and youth theatre *Venues:* Theater im Zelt 240, Theater Anklam 205, studio 100, Theater Zinnowitz 340, Freilichtbühne Zinnowitz 1400 *Touring:* Germany

Eduard-Von-Winterstein-Theater Annaberg
Buchholzer Straße 67,
09456 **Annaberg-Buchholz**
Tel: 3733-1407-0
Fax: 3733-1407-180
Geschäftsführer Patrick Wasserbauer; Intendant & Oberspielleitung Prof. Hans Hermann Krug; Schauspielleitung Robert Strauß; Öffentlichkeitsarbeit Angelika Gläsemann; Chefdramaturg Michael Eccarius; Dramaturgie Schauspiel Silvia Giese
Actors: 10 *Perfs:* 250 *Prods:* 11 *Type:* Sprechtheater, musicals and operettas *Venues:* Stammhaus 300, Studiobühne 90, Freilichtbühne Grefensteine 1200 *Comments:* see also Opera

Theater Augsburg
Kasernstraße 4-6, 86152 **Augsburg**
Tel: 821-324 4912 Fax: 821-324 4544/4478
Internet: www.augsburg
Intendant Dr Ulrich Peters; Generalmusikdirektor Peter Leonard; Künstlerischer Betriebsdirektor Axel Peppermüller; Chefdramaturg Helmar von Hanstein; Oberspielleiter Schauspiel Holger Schultze; Leiter des Ausstattungsateliers Wolfgang Buchner; Kaufmännischer Direktor Dr Klaus Engert; Technischer Direktor Erwin Hammer
Actors: 20 *Prods:* 10 (9 new) *Venues:* Stadttheater 976, Kongreßhalle 1395, Komödie 310, Freilichtbühne Am Roten Tor 2117 *Comments:* see also Orchestras, Opera and Dance

Theater Baden-Baden
Goetheplatz, 76530 **Baden-Baden**
Tel: 7221-932 752 Fax: 7221-932 755
Intendant Peter Lüdi; Dramaturgie Herr Bachmeyer, Cornelia Bitsch; Verwaltungsleitung Angelika Borchert
Actors: 24 *Perfs:* 250 *Prods:* 16 *Type:* Sprechtheater + 2 music theatre productions per year *Venues:* Theater Baden-Baden 468, Kulissenhaus 50

E.T.A. Hoffmann-Theater
Schillerplatz 3-7, 96047 **Bamberg**
Tel: 951-871 431 Fax: 951-871 916
Internet: www.theater.bamberg.de
E-Mail: verwaltung.theater@stadt.bamberg.de
Intendant Rainer Lewandowski; Verwaltungsleiter Karl Fischer; Dramaturgie Rolf Ronzier, Karin Freymeyer; Disposition Stefan Dzierzawa; Öffentlichkeitsarbeit Verena Kögler
Actors: 18 *Perfs:* 400 *Prods:* 13 *Type:* Sprechtheater *Venues:* Großes Haus 372, Studio 99, Freilicht in der Alten Hofhaltung 900 *Touring:* USA, France *Comments:* see also Festivals

Deutsch-Sorbisches Volkstheater Bautzen
Seminarstrasse 12, 02625 **Bautzen**
Tel: 3591-584-215
Fax: 3591-44383
Internet: www.theater.bautzen.de
E-Mail: theater-bautzen@t-online.de
Intendant Lutz Hillmann; geschäftsführende Dramaturgin Eveline Günther
Actors: 29 *Perfs:* 800 *Prods:* 20 *Type:* Sprechtheater, puppetry *Venues:* Deutsch-Sorbisches Volkstheater 396, Probebühne 80 + regional venues, Puppet Theatre 120/60 *Touring:* regional *Comments:* see also Dance, Orchestra, Choirs and Puppets

Altstadt-Theater Spandau e.V
Zitadelle, Am Juliusturm, 13599 **Berlin**
Tel: 30-334 3000
Fax: 30-334 3010
Intendant Matthias Diem; Verwaltungsleiterin Barbara Cornelsen; Technischer Leiter Sylvo Pentz; Spielstättenleiterin Elke Braumann
Actors: no permanent ensemble *Perfs:* 200 *Prods:* 2 *Type:* modern and classic *Venues:* Freilichtbühne an der Zitadelle 600, neue bühne Zitadelle 74
Touring: Germany

Arthur Kuggeleyn u.a.
c/o Tom Horn, Naunynstr. 66,
10997 **Berlin**
Tel: 171-420 2978 (mobile)
Fax: 30-614 1808
Internet: www.subotnik.de
E-Mail: Arthurkugg@aol.com
art director Arthur Kuggeleyn; music Tom Horn; dj Exposito; dance Anne Rudelbach, Antoine Effroy
Actors: 2-10 *Perfs:* 30 *Prods:* 1-2 *Type:* multi-media dance performance & theatre *Touring:* national, international

Berliner Compagnie
Schillerstrasse 97, 10625 **Berlin**
Tel: 30-313 6134 Fax: 7462-7448 (Immendingen)
Direktor Gerhard Fries; Verwaltungsdirektorin Sybille Selwig; Öffentlichkeitsarbeit Elke Schuster
Actors: 6 *Perfs:* 85 *Prods:* 1 *Type:* Sprechtheater *Touring:* Germany, Italy, Switzerland, Austria *Comments:* administrative address: Brunnenstraße 6, 78194 Immendingen

Berliner Ensemble GmbH
Bertolt Brecht Platz 1, 10117 **Berlin**
Tel: 30-284 080 Fax: 30-284 8126/2840 8151
Internet: www.berliner-ensemble.de
E-Mail: berlinerensemble@bln.de
Geschäftsführer Peter Sauerbaum;
Künstlerische Leitung/Intendant Claus Peymann
Type: Sprechtheater *Venues:* Berliner Ensemble 680, Probebühne 100 *Comments:* theatre of young, contemporary authors like Wortz, Handke, Bernhard etc.

Berliner Kabarett-Theater Distel GmbH
Friedrichstr. 101, 10117 **Berlin**
Tel: 30-204 4704 (box office)
Fax: 30-208 1555/2030 0020 (box office)
Künstl Leitung Peter Eusikat;
Geschäftsführer Norbert Dahnke
Actors: 5 permanent, 3 temporary *Perfs:* 350-400 *Prods:* 1-2 *Type:* satire, political theatre *Venues:* Kabarett-Theater Distel 420 *Touring:* German speaking countries

Carrousel – Theater an der Parkaue
Parkaue 29, 10367 **Berlin**
Tel: 30-557 7520 Fax: 30-5577 5222
Internet: www.carrousel.de
E-Mail: info@carrousel.de
Intendant Manuel Schöbel; Stellv. Intendant u. Verwaltungsleitung Sigrid Eißfeller; Chefdramaturgin Odette Bereska; Technischer Direktor Gerhard Prengel; Chef-Marketing Dirk Neldner
Actors: 30 *Perfs:* 500 *Prods:* 10 *Type:* children's and young people's theatre *Venues:* Hauptbühne 420, kleine Bühne 70, Schiller-Theater-Werkstatt 90 *Touring:* Germany, Netherlands, Russia *Comments:* formerly Theater der Freundschaft; mainly perform children's and young people's theatre; co-organise the biennial Festival – Deutsches Kinder- und Jugendtheatertreffen

Department Theater GmbH & Jo Fabian
Borsigstraße 3, 10115 **Berlin**
Tel: 30-2838 8933 Fax: 30-2838 8933
Internet: www.jofabian.de
E-Mail: Traudl_Kupfer@compuserve.com
Regisseur und Choreograph Jo Fabian;
Management Traudl Kupfer;
Presse & Öffentlichkeitsarbeit Ralph Boock
Actors: variable *Perfs:* 50 *Prods:* 2-4 + film and CD-Rom *Type:* movement theatre *Venues:* Hebbel Theater 500 *Touring:* Germany, France, Austria, Netherlands

Deutsches Theater und Kammerspiele
Schumannstrasse 13a, 10117 **Berlin**
Tel: 30-284 410 Fax: 30-282 4117
Internet: www.deutsches-theater.berlin.net
E-Mail: pr@deutsches-theater.berlin.net
Intendant t.b.a.; Stell. Intendant Rosemarie Schauer; Verwaltung Christine Engelmann; Chefdramatung Susanne Thelemann; Öffentlichkeitsarbeit Klaus Siebenhaar; technische Leitung Stefan Kiefer
Actors: 66 *Perfs:* every day (Jan-June, Sept- Dec.) *Prods:* 5 (Deutsches Theater) + 5 (Kammerspiele) *Type:* from classic to modern (repertoire) *Comments:* box office Tel: 30-2844 1225

Freie Theateranstalten Berlin
Klausenerplatz 19, 14059 **Berlin**
Tel: 30-321 5889/325 5023 Fax: 30-321 5889
Intendant Adelheid Rogger; künstlerische Leitung Hermann van Harten
Actors: 8 *Perfs:* 300 *Prods:* 3 *Type:* political, Sprechtheater *Venues:* Freie Theateranstalten 99 *Touring:* guest performances mainly in Berlin, Europe

Freyer – Ensemble e.V.
Kadettenweg 53, 12205 **Berlin**
Tel: 30-833 9314
Fax: 30-843 0302
Künstlerische Leitung Achim Freyer, Maria-Elena Amos, Jakob Niedermeier; Produktionsleitung und Dramaturgie Sven Neumann
Actors: 14 + 1 singer *Perfs:* 30 *Prods:* 2-3 *Type:* cross over of music, dance, language and artistic-elements *Touring:* Germany, Austria, Switzerland, Italy *Comments:* touring company

Friends of Italian Opera
Fidicinstrasse 40, 10965 **Berlin**
Tel: 30-693 5692 (office)/30-691 1211 (box offce)
Fax: 30-691 3937
Internet: www.thefriends.de
E-Mail: info@thefriends.de
managing director Bernd Hoffmeister;
artistic director Günther Grosser;
project coordinator Tara McGowan;
PR officer Ulrike Dittrich
Actors: no permanent ensemble *Perfs:* 200-300 *Prods:* 12 *Type:* all genres of theatre ranging from classics to contemporary performance art *Venues:* one stage 75 *Comments:* established in 1989; the only English Theatre in Berlin; Friends of Italian Opera present around 12 to 15 different productions a year including guest performances from Great Britain, Ireland, Australia, USA, Canada etc; see also Venues

GRIPS Theater Berlin
Altonaer Strasse 22, 10557 **Berlin**
Tel: 30-393 3012 Fax: 30-393 3059
Internet: www.grips-theater.de
E-Mail: info@grips-theater.de
Direktor Volker Ludwig; Dramaturgie Odile Simon; Tourneeleiter u.technischer Leiter Peter Gilbert
Actors: 12 + guests *Perfs:* 240 *Prods:* 3-4 *Type:* Sprechtheater *Venues:* GRIPS Theater 360 *Touring:* Germany *Comments:* children's and young people's theatre- also adult theatre

Hansa Theater
Alt-Moabit 48, 10555 **Berlin**
Tel: 30-3984 7210/3984 7211 (box office)
Fax: 30-3984 7230
Internet: www.berlin.de
E-Mail: hansatheater@t-online.de
Direktor/Intendant Klaus J Rumpf;
Dramaturgie/stellvertr. Direktorin Sabine Thiesler;
Geschäftsleiter Dr Lutz Roggemann
Actors: 8-12 (no permanent ensemble) *Perfs:* 196 *Prods:* 4 *Type:* Volkstheater *Venues:* Hansa Theater 495 (8 wheelchair spaces) *:* alternative e-mail: www.th.net.de

Kleines Theater am Südwestkorso Berlin
Südwestkorso 64, 12161 **Berlin**
Tel: 30-821 2021/3030 Fax: 30-821 2417
Internet: www.kleines-theater.de
E-Mail: info@kleines-theater.de
Direktorin/Geschäftsführer/Künstlerische Leitung Sabine Fromm; Musikalische Oberleitung Rudolf Gäbler; Öffentlichkeitsreferat Anton Haberditzl; Verwaltungsleitung Rudolf Gäbler; Bühnenbild, Kostüme Norman Zechowski
Actors: no fixed ensemble *Perfs:* 140-150 *Prods:* 2 *Type:* Sprechtheater, parodistic music theatre
Venues: Kleines Theater 92

Komödie und Theater am Kurfürstendamm
Kurfürstendamm 206-209, 10719 **Berlin**
Tel: 30-885 911-0/4799 7440 (box office)
Fax: 30-8859 1140
Direktoren Jürgen Wölffer, Christian Wölffer;
Verwaltungsleiter Bert-Rainer Ott;
PR Jürgen Ross, Beatrix Ross
Actors: varies *Perfs:* 350 *Prods:* 10 (5 Kömodie, 5 Theater Kurfürstendamm) *Type:* boulevard theatre *Venues:* Theater am Kurfürstendamm 806, Kömodie 644 *Touring:* German speaking countries *Comments:* the two theatres share administration

Maxim Gorki Theater
Am Festungsgraben 2, 10117 **Berlin**
Tel: 30-20221-0 Fax: 30-20221-365
E-Mail: ticket@gorki.de
Intendant Dr. Bernd Wilms; Verwaltungsdirektor Klaus Steppat; Öffentlichkeitsarbeit Dr Carola Friedrichs-Friedlaender; Chefdramaturg Oliver Reese
Actors: 20-25 *Prods:* 10 *Type:* Sprechtheater *Venues:* Großes Haus 441, Gorkistudio 100 *Touring:* Germany

Renaissance-Theater
Knesebeckstrasse 100, 10623 **Berlin**
Tel: 30-315 973-0 Fax: 30-312 6369
Internet: www.renaissance-theater.de
E-Mail: tickets@renaissance-theater.de
Intendant u. Geschäftsführer Horst-H. Filohn; Direktionssekretariat Renate Koßmala; Dramaturgie Steffi Recknagel; Verwaltungsdirektor Horst Schäfer; technische Leitung Michael Jensen
Actors: varies *Perfs:* 270 *Prods:* 5 *Type:* Sprechtheater *Venues:* main theatre 545, studio 99

Schaubühne am Lehniner Platz
Kurfürstendamm 153, 10709 **Berlin**
Tel: 30-890 020 Fax: 30-8900 2190/89
Internet: www.schaubuehne.de
E-Mail: schaubuehne@bln.de
Direktion u. künstlerische Leitung Jürgen Schitthelm, Dr Friedrich Barner, Jens Hillje, Thomas Ostermeier, Jochen Sandig, Sasha Walz
Actors: 40 (including dancers) *Perfs:* 360 annually *Prods:* 10 (all new) *Type:* Sprechtheater + Tanztheater *Venues:* home 1500, Schaubühne Saal A 520, Saal B 400, Saal C 280, Probebühne Cuvrystraße 99 *Touring:* national and international guest performances

Schloßpark – Theater Berlin
Schloßstr. 48, 12165 **Berlin**
Tel: 30-793 5001/1515 (box office) Fax: 30-791 1212
Intendanz Heribert Sasse; Geschäftsführer Heribert Sasse, Frank Wisniewski; PR & Marketing Ulrika Poock
Actors: 1 + guests *Perfs:* 300-320 *Prods:* 5 *Type:* modern & classical drama *Venues:* capacity 460 *Touring:* Germany, Austria, Switzerland

Theater am Halleschen Ufer
Hallesches Ufer 32, 10963 **Berlin**
Tel: 30-251 0655 Fax: 30-251 2716
Internet: www.thub.de
E-Mail: info@thub.de
künstlerische Leitung Zebu Kluth; Leiter Tanz/Tanztheater Björn Dirk Schlüter; Leitung Producktion, management Nicola von Stillfried; Leitung Presse + Öffentlichkeitsarbeit Isabel Pflug
Actors: varies *Perfs:* 248 *Prods:* varies *Type:* contemporary dance, contemporary theatre *Venues:* Theatersaal 230, Foyer 99 *Touring:* national, international *Comments:* the THK is managing Jörg Lane/ LOSE COMBO and Anna Huber

Theater des Westens
Kantstr. 12, 10623 **Berlin**
Tel: 30-319 030 Fax: 30-319 03188
Internet: theater-des-westens.de
E-Mail: info@theater-des-westens
Intendant Künstlerischer Leiter Prof. Elmar Ottenthal; Stellvertreter Künstlerischer Leiter Jürg Burth
Actors: varies *Perfs:* 260 *Prods:* 3 *Type:* music, music-theatre *Venues:* Theater des Westens 1354 *Touring:* national guest performances *Comments:* see also Dance

Theater Skoronel
Grolmanstrasse 58, 10623 **Berlin**
Tel: 30-312 2695 Fax: 30-312 2695
Künstlerische Direktorin u. Regisseurin Judith Kuckart; artistic director Jörg Aufenanger
Actors: 1+ 7 dancers + 1 musician *Prods:* 2 *Touring:* national, international *Comments:* prods will be co-productions with the Berliner Ensemble; touring company

Theater Tribüne
Otto-Suhr-Allee 18, 10585 **Berlin**
Tel: 30-341 9001/2600 (box-office) Fax: 30-341 1686
Internet: www.tribuene.berlin.de
E-Mail: theater.tribuene@t-online.de
Direktion Ingrid Keller, Rainer Behrend; künstlerisches Betriebsbüro/Öffentlichkeitsarbeit Corinna Trempnau, Thomas Trempnau; technische Leitung Stefan Köhler
Perfs: 200 *Prods:* 4-5 *Type:* modern, classical, comedy, political *Venues:* home capacity 294-313

Theater Zum Westlichen Stadthirschen
Kreuzbergstrasse 37, 10965 **Berlin**
Tel: 30-785 7033 Fax: 30-785 8105
Verwaltungsleitung & Geschäftsführer Dominik Bender; Intendanz Dominik Bender, Johannes Herrschmann; Leitung Bühne & Licht Urs Hildbrand; Presse-und Öffentlichkeitsarbeit Annette Barner
Actors: 3-10 *Perfs:* 80-100 *Prods:* 2-4 *Type:* classical, modern *Venues:* Fabrik-Bühne 99

UFA – Circus Varieté
Internationales Kultur Centrum, Viktoriastr. 10-18, 12105 **Berlin**
Tel: 30-755030 Fax: 30-7550 3190/752 2344
Internet: www.ufafabrik.de
E-Mail: circus@ufafabrik.de
director Juppy Becher; communication Sigrid Niemer
Actors: 12-18 *Perfs:* 120 *Prods:* 3 *Type:* combination of Berlin varieté tradition with street culture of today *Venues:* Theatersaal 400, Varieté-Salon 200, W. Neuss-Salon 100, open air stage 700 *Touring:* national, international *Comments:* resident in International Kultur Centrum UFA-Fabrik Berlin

Vaganten Bühne Berlin
Kantstrasse 12a, 10623 **Berlin**
Tel: 30-312 4529 (box office)/ 313 1207 (administration)
Fax: 30-313 3483
Internet: www.Vaganten.de
E-Mail: Vaganten@t-online.de
Direktion Rainer Behrend und Jens-Peter Behrend;
Verwaltungsleitung Verena Aglassinger;
Dramaturgie Jens-Peter Behrend;
Technische Leitung Michael Gärtner
Actors: 12 *Perfs:* 240 *Prods:* 4 *Type:* modern drama, revue *Venues:* capacity 99

Volksbühne am Rosa-Luxemburg-Platz
Linienstraße 227, 10178 **Berlin**
Tel: 30-24065-5/ 24065 610 Fax: 30-24065-642/247 6759
E-Mail: 100631.2707@compuserve.com
Intendant Frank Castorf
Actors: 32 + dancers *Perfs:* 250 *Prods:* 10 *Type:* Sprechtheater, Choreographic Theater *Venues:* Großes Haus 843, Prater 96 *Touring:* national and international guest performances

Theater Bielefeld
Brunnenstr. 3-9, Postfach 100353, 33602 **Bielefeld**
Tel: 521-513 077/177 077 (box office)
Fax: 521-513 430/516 411 (box office)
Internet: www.bielefeld.de
Intendantin Regula Gerber; Dramaturgie Harald Sänger, Jan Hein (Autorenbühne Neue Szene); künstlerischer Betriebsdirektorin Sabine Schweitzer
Actors: 29 + guests *Prods:* 19 *Type:* Sprechtheater *Venues:* Bühnen der Stadt Bielefeld (Großes Haus 775, Kleines Haus 304), Theater am Alten Markt 330 *Comments:* see also Opera, Dance and Orchestra

Theaterlabor Bielefeld
Lerchenstr. 60A, 33607 **Bielefeld**
Tel: 521-287 856 Fax: 521-286 543
Organisation u. Management Gerlinde Behrendt; Regisseur Siegmar Schröder
Actors: 6 indoor/8-12 outdoor + guests *Prods:* 6 (4 indoor/2 outdoor) *Type:* experimental drama, including street theatre *Venues:* Theatersaal 99 *Comments:* host ISTA (International School of Theatre Anthropology) 2000; from september 2000 new venue address: August Bebel-Str. 135-145, 33602, Bielefeld

Euro Theater Central Bonn
PO Box 7245, 53072 **Bonn**
Tel: 228-652 951(box office)/637 026 Fax: 228-636 410
E-Mail: eurotheater@t-online.de
Direktion Gisela Pflugradt-Marteau; Dramaturgie und Öffentlichkeitsarbeit Gudrun Schäfer; Dramaturgie und Werbung Eleftheria Wollny-Pópota
Perfs: 250 *Prods:* 5 *Type:* classics, modern, experimental *Venues:* home 50 *Touring:* Pakistan, India, Ungarn, Rumania *Comments:* German co-ordinator of Zeittheater 2000 co-operative Festival; international productions on the cultural history of Europe; visiting address: Dreieck-Münsterplatz, Eingang Mauspfad, 53111 Bonn

Kleines Theater im Park
Koblenzer Strasse 78, 53177 **Bonn**
Tel: 228-362 839 Fax: 228-353 817
Direktor Walter Ullrich
Perfs: 300 *Prods:* 6 *Type:* comedy, drama, operetta *Venues:* Kleines Theater 161 *Comments:* Gastspiele in Germany-produce fairy-tale plays for children, also perform for schools

Schauspiel Bonn
Am Michaelshof 9, 53177 **Bonn**
Tel: 228-8001 Fax: 228-8126
Internet: www.schauspiel.bonn.de
E-Mail: schauspiel@bonn.de
General-Intendant Dr. Manfred Beilharz ; Verwaltungsdirektor Rolf Oltmanns; künstl. Betriebsdirektor Dr. Frieder Weber; Dramaturgin und Presseferentin Irma Dohn; Dramaturg Andreas Nattermann, Hermann Wündrich, John von Düffel; Dramaturgin Almut Wagner
Actors: 37 and guests *Perfs:* ca. 400 *Prods:* 16 *Type:* classical, contemporary *Venues:* Halle Beuel 650, Kammerspiel 473, Werkstattbühne 173, Alter Malersaal *Touring:* national, international *Comments:* promote Bonner BIENNALE – 22 June- 2 July 2000 (see also Festivals)

Brandenburger Theater
Grabenstrasse 14, 14776 **Brandenburg**
Tel: 3381-5110 Fax: 3381-511 120
Internet: www.fh-brandenburg.de/theater
Chefdramaturgin Bettina Bartz
Prods: 18 *Type:* music theatre with children and youth theatre *Venues:* Studiobühne 280, neue Probebühne 99 *Comments:* see also Opera, Dance, Puppets and Orchestras

Staatstheater Braunschweig
Am Theater, 38100 **Braunschweig**
Tel: 531-1234-0
Fax: 531-1234-114
Internet: www.staatstheater.braunschweig.de
E-Mail: service@staatstheater-braunschweig.de
Generalintendant Wolfgang Gropper; Verwaltungsleiter Thomas Fehrle; Leiter des Kinder-und Jugendtheaters Jörg Gade; Chefdramaturgin Ursula Werdenberg
Perfs: 500 approx. including all venues *Type:* children and youth theatre, classical, modern *Venues:* Großes Haus 906, Theaterspielplatz 99, Kleines Haus 330 *Comments:* also has children's and young people's company; see also Opera, Dance and Orchestra

bremer shakespeare company
Theater am Leibnizplatz, Postfach 10 66 65, 28066 **Bremen**
Tel: 421-500 333 Fax: 421-503 372
Internet: www.shakespeare-company.com
E-Mail: info@shakespeare-company.com
Organisation und Öffentlichkeitsarbeit Renate Heitmann, Peter Lüchinger, Erik Rossbander
Actors: 16 *Perfs:* 200 *Prods:* 4 *Type:* Sprechtheater (9 Shakespeare plays, 6 contemporary plays, repertory) *Venues:* Theatersaal 340, Falstaff 80 *Touring:* Europe *Comments:* founding the international 'Shakespeare Globe Centre Germany' – c/o the theatre; Visiting address: Leibnizplatz, 28199 Bremen

Bremer Theater
Am Goetheplatz 1-3, 28203 **Bremen**
Tel: 421-3653-0 Fax: 421-365 3415
Internet: www.bremertheater.com
E-Mail: info@bremertheater.com
Generalintendant Dr. Klaus Pierwoß; GMD Günter Neuhold; Tanztheater Susanne Linke; Chordirektor Theo Wiedebusch; Verwaltungsleiter Jens Walter
Actors: 23 *Prods:* 15 (5 children-youth-theatre) *Type:* Sprechtheater *Venues:* Theater am Goetheplatz 989, Schauspielhaus 330, Concordia 99, Brauhauskeller 60 *Touring:* Europe *Comments:* see also Opera and Dance

Waldau Theater
Waller Heerstraße 165, 28219 **Bremen**
Tel: 421-383 031/386 1755 (box office)
Fax: 421-381 947
Internet: www.waldau-theater.de
Intendant Michael Derda; Geschäftsführer Michael Derda, Helmut Zorn; technischer Leiter Frank Kulas
Actors: 40 *Perfs:* 320 *Prods:* 9 + 2 fairy tales + 1 children's theatre (Moki) + 2 cabarets
ype: Sprechtheater (Low and High German) *Venues:* Großer Saal/Hauptbühne 505, Tik Theater 70, Kleine Bühne 99 *Comments:* light theatre, folk theatre and children's theatre; private drama school; guest performances

Stadttheater Bremerhaven
Theodor-Heuss-Platz,
27568 **Bremerhaven**
Tel: 471-482 060
Fax: 471-4820 6274
Internet:
www.brem-de-info-bremerhaven-theater-index.htm
Intendant Peter Grisebach; Verwaltungsdirektor Jürgen Ahlf; Schauspieldirektor Holger Schultze
Actors: 14 *Perfs:* 200 *Prods:* 10 *Type:* modern, classical *Venues:* Stadttheater Grosses Haus 722, Kleines Haus 122, Theater im Fischereihafen 300 *Comments:* see also Opera, Dance and Orchestras

Badische Landesbühne Bruchsal
Am Alten Schloß 24, 76646 **Bruchsal**
Tel: 7251-7270
Fax: 7251-72746
Internet: www.dieBLB.de
E-Mail: blb-info@t-online.de
Intendant Carsten Ramm;
Verwaltungsleitung Norbert Kritzer
Actors: 20 *Perfs:* 400 *Prods:* 14
Type: Sprechtheater and children's and youth theatre *Venues:* Grosser Saal 680, Studio Hexagon 99 *Touring:* Germany

Westfälisches Landestheater
Europaplatz 10, 44575 **Castrop-Rauxel**
Tel: 2305-1618/17 Fax: 2305-18088
Internet: www.ndv.de/theater
E-Mail: WLTcastrop@aol.com
Intendanz Harald F. Petermichl; Verwaltung Gunter Wohlfarth; Dramaturgie Gösta Courkamp, Felicitas Mai, Regina Marx (Kinder- u. Jugendtheater); Öffentlichkeitsarbeit Ines Duda; Theaterpädagogik Heike Buderus-Prandekou
Actors: 18 *Perfs:* 309 *Prods:* 13 *Type:* Sprechtheater and children's and youth theatre *Venues:* Stadthalle 550, Studio 94 *Touring:* Germany

Schloßtheater Celle e.V.
Postfach 1333, 29203 **Celle**
Tel: 5141-905 080/12713 (box office) Fax: 5141-905 0844
Internet: www.schlosstheater-celle.de
Intendant Karin H. Veit; Geschäftsführer Klaus Tietje; Öffentlichkeitsarbeit Herr Behnke;
Sekretariat Frau Mehling
Actors: 15 + guests *Perfs:* 210 *Prods:* 20 *Type:* Sprechtheater *Venues:* main auditorium 330, Malersaal 45 *Comments:* visiting address: Schloßplatz 1, 29221 Celle; see also Venues and Promoters

1. Chemnitzer Kabarett
An der Markthalle 1-3, 09111 **Chemnitz**
Tel: 371-675 090
Fax: 371-675 0921
E-Mail: erstes_chemnitzer_kabarett@abo.freiepresse.de
Kabarettvorstand Andreas Zweigler
Actors: 4 *Perfs:* 250 *Prods:* 5 *Type:* political satire *Venues:* Kellerkabarett 180 *Touring:* Germany

Städtische Theater Chemnitz GmbH
Postfach 756, 09007 **Chemnitz**
Tel: 371-696 9710
Fax: 371-696 9799/699
Internet: www.freiepresse.de/theater-chemnitz
E-Mail: theater-chemnitz@abo.freiepresse.de
Generalintendant Rolf Stiska;
Schauspieldirektor Herbert Olschok
Actors: 24 *Perfs:* 350 *Prods:* 25
Type: Sprechtheater *Venues:* Schauspielhaus: Großes Haus 419, KAF 60, Foyer 60 *Comments:* visiting address: Käthe-Kollwitz-Straße 7, 09111 Chemnitz; see also Dance, Opera, Orchestras and Puppets

Landestheater Coburg
Großes Haus, Schlossplatz 6,
96450 **Coburg**
Tel: 9561-8850
Fax: 9561-793 979
Internet: www.coburg.baynet.de/veranstl/theater.htm
Intendant Norbert Kleine Borgmann;
Verwaltungsdirektor Wolfgang Vatke;
Chefdramatürg Peter Biermann
Actors: 15 *Perfs:* 400 (opera, drama, ballet)
Prods: 24 *Type:* classical to modern *Venues:* Grosses Haus 557, Theater in der Reithalle 99 *Touring:* guest performances *Comments:* see also Opera, Dance and Orchestras

Staatstheater Cottbus
Karl Liebknecht Strasse 136, 03046 **Cottbus**
Tel: 355-78240 Fax: 355-791 333
Intendant/Schauspieldirektor Christoph Schroth; Geschäftsführender Direktor Steffen Rohr; Leiter des Philharmonischen Orchesters und Chefdirigent GMD Reinhard Petersen; Operndirektor Martin Schüler; Public Relations /Marketing Anne Heym; Direktor für Ausstattung Joachim Vogler; Technischer Direktor Matthias Günther; Chordirektor Christina Möbius
Actors: 26 *Perfs:* 420 *Prods:* 20 *Type:* contemporary, new and classical theatre *Venues:* Großes Haus am Schillerplatz 678, Kammerbühne 140, Theaterscheune 140 *Comments:* see also Opera, Dance and Orchestra

Staatstheater Darmstadt
Marienplatz 2, 64283 **Darmstadt**
Tel: 6151-28111 Fax: 6151-281 1226
Intendant Gerd-Theo Umberg; Schauspieldirektor Davud Bouchehri; Spielleitung Thomas Grupper, Thomas Janßen, Bernarda Hórres
Actors: 30 *Perfs:* 170 *Prods:* 15 *Type:* Sprechtheater *Venues:* Grosses Haus 956, Kleines Haus 482, Werkstattbühne 99 *Comments:* see also Opera and Dance

Anhaltische Theater Dessau
Postfach 1203, 06812 **Dessau**
Tel: 340-2511-0 Fax: 340-251 1213
Internet: www.anhaltisches.theater.de
E-Mail: anhaltisches.theater.dnam@topmail.de
Generalintendant, Chefregisseur und Leiter des Musiktheaters Johannes Felsenstein;
Verwaltungsdirektor Joachim Landgraf;
Schauspieldirektor Helmut Straßburger;
Generalmusikdirector Carlos Kalmar
Perfs: 416 (+ opera, musical) *Prods:* 39 (16 new) *Type:* Sprechtheater, musical, opera, operetta *Venues:* Großes Haus 1096 , Studio 80, Foyer 150 *Comments:* visiting address: Friedensplatz 1a, 06844 Dessau; see also Opera, Dance and Orchestras; puppets

Landestheater Detmold
Theaterplatz 1, 32756 **Detmold**
Tel: 5231-97460 Fax: 5231-974 701
Internet: www.landestheaterdetmold.de
E-Mail: 113217.3637@compuserve.com
Intendant Ulf Reiher; Ltd. Dram. des Musiktheaters Elizabeth Wirth; Verwaltungsdirektor Volker Bierwirth; Leiterin Dramaturgie, Schauspieldrama Bettina Ruczynski; Geschäftsführer Musiktheater Rainer Worms; Oberspielleiter Schauspiel Ulrich Holle
Actors: 18 *Perfs:* 640 *Prods:* 7 + smaller prods *Type:* Sprechtheater (classic to modern) *Venues:* Großes Haus 650, Studiobühne 90 *Touring:* Germany, Benelux *Comments:* see also Opera, Dance and Orchestra

Fränkisch-Schwäbisches Städtetheater
Segringerstrasse 30, 91550 **Dinkelsbühl**
Tel: 9851-90273 Fax: 9851-90263
Intendant Christian Alexander Schnell; Technische Leitung Frieder Loew; Verwaltungsleitung Susanne Reinhardt, Ursula Gruß
Actors: 9 + guests *Prods:* 10 *Type:* Sprechtheater *Venues:* Fränkisch-Schwäbisches Städtetheater 200 *Comments:* 7 productions in winter season and 3 open-air performances

Burghofbühne Landestheater im Kreis Wesel e.V.
Luisenstrasse 173, 46537 **Dinslaken**
Tel: 2064-41100 Fax: 2064-411 022
Internet: www.burghofbuehne-dinslaken.de
E-Mail: burghofbuehne@t-online.de
Intendant Hanfried Schüttler; Dramaturgie Ursula Fröhlingsdorf , Stefanie Matuczak;
Verwaltungsleiter Winfried Cleve
Actors: 21 *Prods:* 7 (all new) *Type:* Sprechtheater with various elements *Venues:* Stadthalle 592, Burgtheater 2000 *Touring:* national

Theater Dortmund
Kuhstraße 12, 44137 **Dortmund**
Tel: 231-502 5547 Fax: 231-502 2461
Internet: www.dortmund.de/theater/
E-Mail: theater@dortmund.de
Generalintendant John Dew; Verwaltungsdirektor Wilhelm Scheer; Generalmusikdirector Anton Marik; Ballettdirektoren Jean Renshaw, Mei Hong Lin, Zoltan Ravasz; Öffentlichkeitsarbeit Rüdiger Beermann
Actors: 22 *Perfs:* 750 *Prods:* 42 (33 new) *Venues:* Opernhaus 1170, Schauspielhaus 496, Studio 100, children's and youth theatre 200 *Comments:* also has children's and young people's theatre; see also Opera, Dance, Orchestras

Dresdens Kabarett-Theater Die Herkuleskeule GmbH
Sternplatz 1, 01067 **Dresden**
Tel: 351-492 550 Fax: 351-492 5554
Internet: www.herkuleskeule.de
E-Mail: tickets@herkuleskeule.de
kaufmännischer Geschäftsführer Volker Arnold;
Intendant Wolfgang Schaller;
musikalischer Leiter Jens Wagner
Actors: 10 (actors and musicians) *Perfs:* 350 in house, 80 touring *Prods:* 2 *Type:* political, satirical, cabaret *Venues:* capacity 230 *Touring:* German speaking countries

Staatsschauspiel Dresden
Theaterstr. 2, 01067 **Dresden**
Tel: 351-491 350 Fax: 351-491 3910
Internet: www.staatsschauspiel-dresden.de
Intendant Prof Dr Dieter Görne; Oberspielleiter Hasko Weber; Geschäftsführender Direktor Hergen Gräper
Actors: 46 + guests *Perfs:* 400 *Prods:* 18
Type: modern, classic, comedy
Venues: Schauspielhaus 793, Schloßtheater 200, Theater Oben 99, TiF (Theater in der Fabrik) 99
Touring: Germany (e.g. Expo 2000, Hannover)

Theater Junge Generation
Meißner Landstrasse 4, 01157 **Dresden**
Tel: 351-429 120 Fax: 351-421 3200
Internet: www.cometo.tjg
E-Mail: TJG-service@t-online.de
Intendant Dietrich Kunze; Oberspielleiter Gerald Gluth; Verwaltungsdirektorin Karin Madel; musikalischer Leiter Matthias Thomser; Austattungsleiter Stefan Wiel; technischer Direktor Peter Rösner; Chefdramaturg Felicitas Loewe
Actors: 22 *Perfs:* 450 *Prods:* 11 *Venues:* Theatersaal 380, Theater auf der Treppe 99, Studiobühne 80

Düsseldorfer Schauspielhaus
Gustaf-Gründgens-Platz 1, 40211 **Düsseldorf**
Tel: 211-85230 Fax: 211-362 722
Generalintendantin Anna Badora; kaufm. Geschäftsführer Mathias Eichorn
Actors: 70 *Perfs:* 450 *Prods:* 20 *Type:* classical, Sprechtheater, modern *Venues:* Grosses Haus 968, Kleines Haus 300 *Touring:* international and national guest performances *Comments:* also has a children's and young people's theatre

Theater der Klänge
Winkelsfelderstr.21, 40477 **Düsseldorf**
Tel: 211-462 746 Fax: 211-467 722
Internet: www.folkwang.uni-essen.de/TdK/
E-Mail: theatre-der-klaenge@t-online.de
Direktor/künstlerische Leitung Jörg U. Lensing; musikalische Leitung Thomas Neuhaus; Ballettdirektoren Jacqueline Fischer, Kerstin Hörner
Actors: 8 *Perfs:* 40 *Prods:* 2 *Type:* new music, Tanztheater, Sprechtheater *Touring:* Europe *Comments:* acting, dance and music fusion; see also Dance

Tourneetheater Kontra-Punkt
Heyestrasse 116, 40625 **Düsseldorf**
Tel: 211-929 3578 Fax: 211-929 3574
Internet: www.kontra-punkt.de
E-Mail: theater@kontra-punkt.de
künstl. Leitung Annette Bieker, Frank Schulz; Betriebsbüro Gent Lazri, Horst Willi Groß
Actors: 11 *Perfs:* 110 *Prods:* 11 (2 new)
Type: new music theatre for adults and children
Touring: Netherlands, Germany, Hungary, Slovakia, Switzerland, Austria *Comments:* experimental touring theatre company, also mounts children's productions

Theater an der Rott
Pfarrkirchner Strasse 70, 84307 **Eggenfelden**
Tel: 8721-8181/10174(administration)
Fax: 8721-10174
Intendant Peter Nüesch
Actors: 7 + 32 guests *Perfs:* 145 *Prods:* 40
Type: opera, operetta, musical, children's theatre, drama, comedy *Venues:* 401/100

Landesbühne Sachsen-Anhalt
An Der Landwehr 5, Pf. 41,
06282 **Eisleben**
Tel: 3475-66990 Fax: 3475-669 921
Intendant Ulrich Fischer; Verwaltungsdirektorin Marga Curth; Leiter der Besucherservice Peter Kutsche; Schauspielleiterin Martina Bode; Leiter der Presseabteilung Nicola Genschorek
Actors: 17 *Perfs:* 300 *Prods:* 9 *Type:* modern, classical, comedy, children's and young people's theatre, open-air
Venues: Großes Haus 387, Foyer-Theater up to 99
Touring: Germany

Deutsche Kammerschauspiele
Verwaltung: Geyer-zu-Lauf-Strasse 26,
79312 **Emmendingen**
Tel: 7641-3272 Fax: 7641-43519
E-Mail: weth-dks@t-online.de
Geschäftsführende Direktorin Annette Greve; Künstlerischer Direktor Georg A Weth; Sekret Birgit Büker; Disposition Cordula März-Brendel
Actors: 21 (including guest performers) *Perfs:* 140 *Prods:* 4 *Type:* modern drama, fairy tales-drama, musicals, (Dia Musicana) *Comments:* touring theatre; see also Agents and Producers (Georg A. Weth)

Theater Erfurt
Postfach 244, 99084 **Erfurt**
Tel: 361-223 3100 Fax: 361-223 3120
Internet: www.theater-erfurt.de
E-Mail: alanger@theater-erfurt.de
Generalintendant Dietrich Taube; Chefdramaturg Dr Klaus Gronau; Oberspielleiter Schauspiel Peter Rein; Generalmusikdirektor Wolfgang Rögner; Leiter der Öffentlichkeitsarbeit Dr. Arne Langer
Actors: 22 + 9 *Perfs:* 160 + 200 *Prods:* 11 (drama) 14 (children's and young people's theatre) *Type:* Drama, children's and young people's theatre *Venues:* Kuppeltheater 685, Schauspielhaus 420, Kleine Bühne im Schauspielhaus 73, Domstufen 1000 *Comments:* visiting address: Walkmühlstraße 13, 99084 Erfurt; see also Opera, Dance and Orchestras

Theater Erlangen
Wasserturmstrasse 16, 91054 **Erlangen**
Tel: 9131-862 369 Fax: 9131-862 104
Intendant Hartmut Henne; Direktion Hartmut Henne, Inken Böhack, Peter N. Schultze, Dieter Welke; Dramaturgie Dieter Welke, Hartmut Henne; Öffentlichkeitsarbeit Bodo Birk; Grafik/Fotografie Dirk Bleicker; Künstlerische Betriebsdirektion Gerti Köhn; Technischer Leiter Carsten Schmid; Dramaturgie Johannes Blum, Lissy Schmidt
Actors: 8-10 *Perfs:* 300 (own + guest) *Prods:* 21 (13 new)
Type: classical and contemporary plays *Venues:* Markgrafentheater 570, Theater in der Garage 82
Touring: guest performances in Germany *Comments:* see also Venues

Grillo-Theater/Junges Schenspiel Casa Nova
II. Hagen 2, 45127 **Essen**
Tel: 201-8122-0
Fax: 201-8122-325/309/201-8
Internet: www.theater-essen.de
E-Mail: infogrillo@theater-essen.de
Geschäftsführer Otmar Herren; Schauspielintendant Jürgen Bosse
Actors: 40 (including guests) *Perfs:* 270 *Prods:* 18 *Venues:* Grillo-Theater 385, Junges Schauspiel; groß 300, klein 100, Studio 60, Café Central 120 *Touring:* Germany

Hermes Theater Gastspiele Marina Wickinghoff
Eiland 6, 45134 **Essen**
Tel: 201-473 434 Fax: 201-473 478
Direktor Marina Wickinghoff
Actors: varies *Perfs:* 190 *Prods:* 5 + 2 fairytales *Type:* from classical theatre to comedy, crime stories, children's theatre *Touring:* Austria, Switzerland, Germany
Comments: touring company

Theater und Philharmonie GmbH
Opernplatz 10, Schauspiel Essen im Grillo, II. Hagen 2, 45127 **Essen**
Tel: 201-8122-0 Fax: 201-8122-325
Internet: www.theater-essen.de
Intendant Jürgen Bosse; Stellv. Int. und Chefdramaturgin Susanne Abbrederis; Verwaltungsdirektorin Dieter Kükenhöner; Geschäftsführer Otmar Herren
Actors: 40 (incl. guest performers) *Type:* Sprechtheater
Venues: Grillo-Theater 385, Casa Nova Grossraum 300, Studio 60 and Cafe Central 90 *Comments:* also has a young people's theatre "Junges Schauspiel"; see also Opera and Dance

Württembergische Landesbühne
Postfach 100407, 73704 **Esslingen**
Tel: 711-3512 3050 Fax: 711-3512 3080
Intendant Peter Dolder; Organisationsleitung Christine Seger; Künstlerisches Betriebsbüro Frederike Maier; Verwaltungsdirektor Manfred P. Ernst; Öffentlichkeitsarbeit/ Sekretariat Jutta Ortelt
Actors: 24 *Perfs:* 700 *Prods:* 11 + 4 children's theatre, reprises 3 *Type:* Sprechtheater + 2 musicals *Venues:* Stadttheater 460, Studiotheater, Blarerplatz 80, Theater am Zollberg 200 *Touring:* Baden-Württemberg
Comments: visiting address: Ritterstr. 11, 73728 Esslingen

English Theater
Kaiserstrasse 52, 60329 **Frankfurt am Main**
Tel: 69-2423 1620 Fax: 69-2423 1614
Internet: www.virtualcity.de/englishtheater
E-Mail: Englishtheater@t-online.de
artistic/managing director Judith Rosenbauer; assistant managing director Marie-Luise Herbst
Actors: varies *Perfs:* 200+ *Prods:* 4 *Type:* English speaking theatre(English and American plays), classical and contemporary *Venues:* English Theater in Frankfurt 230 *Comments:* casts separately for each production from British actors, details from Caroline Funnell, 25 Rattray Road, London SW2 1AZ, Tel: +44-20-7326 4417, Fax:+44 20-7326 1713

Freies Schauspiel Ensemble Frankfurt
Hebelstr. 17, 60318 **Frankfurt am Main**
Tel: 69-596 9490 (info. and box-office)
Fax: 69-9552 0658
Intendant/künstlerische Leitung Reinhard Hinzpeter; Öffentlichkeitsarbeit Bettina M. Kaminski
Actors: 10 (+ 2 musician) *Perfs:* 95 *Prods:* 11 (2 new)
Type: Sprechtheater, Musiktheater *Venues:* Philanthropin 150

Fritz Rémond Theater im Zoo
Alfred Brehm-Platz 16,
60316 **Frankfurt am Main**
Tel: 69-444 004/435 166 (box office)
Fax: 69-495 0969
Direktor Prof. Claus Helmer
Perfs: 236 *Prods:* 6 *Venues:* capacity 342

Komödie, Die
Neue Mainzer Strasse 14-18,
60311 **Frankfurt am Main**
Tel: 69-284 330 Fax: 69-284 838
Direktor Prof Claus Helmer;
Direktions-Sekretariat Ursula Kion
Actors: ca. 40 *Perfs:* 300 *Type:* comedy *Venues:* home 319
Comments: new venue opens on October 1999

Schauspielhaus Frankfurt am Main
Neue Mainzerstraße 17, 60311 **Frankfurt am Main**
Tel: 69-2123 74293 Fax: 69-2123 7283
Intendant Prof. Peter Eschberg; künstlerischer Betriebsdirektor Wolfgang Stein; Leiter der Dramaturgie Hans-Joachim Ruckhäberle; Pressesprecher Dr. Jochen Zulang
Actors: 24 + guests *Perfs:* 380 *Prods:* 16
Type: classical, modern *Venues:* Schauspielhaus 712, Kammerspiel 193, Studiobühne 100 *Comments:* see also Opera and Dance (Ballett Frankfurt)

Theater am Turm
Städtische Bühnen Frankfurt, Das TAT, Bockenheimer Depot, Bockenheimer Warte, 60325 **Frankfurt am Main**
Tel: 69-2123 7288 Fax: 69-2123 9541
Intendant William Forsythe; Stellvertretende Direktoren Tom Kühnel, Robert Schuster; Ausstattungsleiter Jan Pappelbaum; Chefdramaturg Bernd Stegemann
Actors: 8 and guests *Perfs:* 120-150 *Type:* contemporary dance, theatre, live art, music, installations *Venues:* Theatersaal up to 450 *Comments:* see also Venues and Dance (Ballet Frankfurt)

Volkstheater Frankfurt-Liesel Christ
Großer Hirschgraben 21, 60311 **Frankfurt am Main**
Tel: 69-288 598(box office)/283 676 Fax: 69-20099
Direktion & Verwaltung Gisela Dahlem-Christ
Actors: 6-10 *Perfs:* 260 *Prods:* 6 *Type:* 'dialect' theatre
Venues: Cantatesaal 400, Freilichtbühne im Dominikanerkloster 400
Touring: guest performances in Germany

Antagon theaterAKTion
Orberstraße 57, 60386 **Frankfurt/ Main**
Tel: 69-417 041 Fax: 69-6414 7719
Internet: www.antagon.de
artistic director Bernhard Bub;
managing director Bernd Abraham
Actors: 6-25 *Type:* action theatre, street theatre, acts on stilts, dance *Venues:* outdoor and indoor
Touring: Europe, worldwide *Comments:* intercultural performances developing projects; workshop performance projects abroad; special events guiding performances; walk acts on stilts; studio training space; own tour bus, own special stage construction

Kleist/Theater Frankfurt (Oder)
Gerhart-Hauptmann-Strasse 3/4, 15234 **Frankfurt (Oder)**
Tel: 335-4141-0
Fax: 335-414 1215/433 5330
Intendant Manfred Weber; Verwaltungsleiterin Gertrud Roske; Chefdisponent und Leiter des künstlerischen Betriebsbüro Traudl Kupfer; Oberspielleiter Schauspiel Michael Funke
Actors: 18 *Perfs:* 438 *Prods:* 15 *Venues:* Hauptbühne 317, Theaterbahnhof 70, Theatercafe 64 *Comments:* theatre will close down on 30th June 2000

Mittelsächsische Theater und Philharmonie gemeinnützige GmbH
Borngasse 1, 09599 **Freiberg**
Tel: 3731-35820 Fax: 3731-23406
Intendant Dr Ingolf Huhn; Chefdramaturg Dr Roland Dreßler; Chefdisponentin Dr Yvonne Grunke; Leiter Öffentlichkeitsarbeit Dr Christoph Nieder; Schauspieldirektor Reinhardt Schuchart
Actors: 16 *Perfs:* 280 *Prods:* 24
Type: Schauspiel, musical, adult/youth *Venues:* Bühne Freiberg 295, Bühne in der Borngasse 60, Theater Döbeln 308 *Comments:* the theatre is a result of a merger between the former Stadttheater Freiberg and Stadttheater Döbeln; see also Opera and Orchestras

Alemannische Bühne Freiburg e.V.
Gerberau 15, 79098 **Freiburg**
Tel: 761-35782 Fax: 761-283 296
Künstl. Leiter Wolfgang Leppert
Type: Mundarttheater ('dialect' theatre)
Comments: above address will be valid from 2000; exact date was not known at time of going to print

Städtische Bühnen Freiburg
Bertoldstrasse 46, 79098 **Freiburg**
Tel: 761-201 2807/2950
Fax: 761-201 2999
Internet: www.uni-freiburg.de/theater/
Intendant Hans J. Ammann; Künstler. Betriebsdirektion Elke Hoch; Verwaltungsdirektor Henrik Huyskens; Öffentlichkeitsarbeit Heike Neumann
Actors: 26 (incl. guests) *Perfs:* 180 *Prods:* 14 (13 new)
Type: classical, modern *Venues:* Grosses Haus 850, Schauspielhaus Kurbel 350, Theatercafé 150, Kamera 99
Touring: Germany *Comments:* see also Opera, Dance, Orchestras and Festivals

Theater im Marienbad – Freiburger Kinder-und Jugendtheater e.V.
Marienstr. 4, 79098 **Freiburg**
Tel: 761-31470 Fax: 761-31560
Intendant/Geschäftsführer Dieter Kümmel; Verwaltung Hubertus Fehrenbacher;
Actors: 10 *Perfs:* 170-200 *Prods:* 11 (2 new) *Type:* Sprechtheater for all ages *Venues:* Theater im Marienbad 250 *Touring:* national, international

Wallgraben Theater
Rathausgasse 5a, 79098 **Freiburg**
Tel: 761-25656 (box-office)/25746 (dramaturgie)/25739 (direktion/verwaltung) Fax: 761-25166
E-Mail: 076172165@t-online.de
Direktoren Heinz Meier, Regine Effinger, Elmar Wittmann
Actors: varies *Perfs:* 330 *Prods:* 8 (6 new) *Type:* Sprechtheater *Venues:* cap 96 + Rathaus Innenhof 250

Stadttheater Fürth
Königstrasse 116, 90762 **Fürth**
Tel: 911-974 2410 Fax: 911-974 2444
Indendant Werner Müller; Verwaltungsleiter Thomas Reher; Öffentlichkeitsarbeit Günter Hallenberger; Dramaturgie Barbara Bredow; technische Leitung Manfred Datter
Actors: 50 *Perfs:* ca. 300 (including guests) *Prods:* 8 *Type:* Sprechtheater, Musiktheater *Venues:* Großes Haus 740. Studiobühne 120, Foyer 80, Freilichtbühne 300
Comments: see also Venues

Schillertheater NRW – Schauspiel
Kennedyplatz, 45881 **Gelsenkirchen**
Tel: 209-4097-0 Fax: 209-409 7111
Theaterleitung/Geschäftsführung Ludwig Baum, Holk Freytag, Peter Neubauer; Persönlicher Referent und Vertreter des Intendanten Jörg Maecker; Dramaturgie Martin Griesemer; Betriebsdirektor und Leiter des Künstlerischen Betriebsbüros Bjoern Peleikis; Öffentlichkeitsarbeit Oda Mahnke
Prods: ca. 18 *Venues:* Schauspielhaus 745, Kleines Haus 195 *Comments:* please see also Opera and Dance (Ballett Schindowski) and under Wuppertal in this section

Altenburg Gera Theater GmbH
Küchengartenallee 2, 07548 **Gera**
Tel: 365-82790 Fax: 365-827 9135
Internet: www.theater.altenburg.gera.de
E-Mail: boehme_pock@t-online.de
Generalintendant Michael Grosse; Chefdramaturgin Dagmar Kunze; Leiter des Kleinen Theater im Zentrum Arnold Bischinger; Schauspielleiterin Susanne Ebert; Technischer Direktor Thomas Stolze
Actors: 32 *Prods:* 17(15 new) *Type:* modern, classical *Venues:* Kleines Theater im Zentrum 170, Theatersaal 670, Konzertsaal 810, Kammerspiele 180 *Comments:* address Altenburg Theater: Theaterplatz 19, 04600 Altenburg; see also Opera, Dance and Orchestras, Tel: 3447-5850, Fax: 3447-585 186

Kabarett Fettnäppchen
Markt 1, 07545 **Gera**
Tel: 365-23131 Fax: 365-23131
Direktorin Eva-Maria Fastenau
Actors: 8 *Perfs:* 500 *Prods:* 3-4 *Type:* political, satirical, cabaret *Venues:* home 74, venue in Kapellendorf 120

Parktheater
Bliestalstrasse 40, 66453 **Gersheim**
Tel: 6843-8646 Fax: 6843-5265
Intendant Illon Astrid Hauck; Verwaltungsleitung Werner Beck
Actors: 4 *Perfs:* 50 *Prods:* 2 *Type:* Sprechtheater *Venues:* Klosterhof Blieskastel 300, Bliesgaufesthalle 500
Touring: German-speaking Europe throughout year

Stadttheater Gießen
Berliner Platz, 35390 **Giessen**
Tel: 641-7957-0 Fax: 641-795 780
Intendant Guy Montavon; Schauspieldirektoren Barbara & Jürgen Esser; Dramaturgie Christian Marten-Molnar, Carola von Gradulewski, Stefan Dehler
Actors: 17 *Perfs:* 145 *Prods:* 11 new + 6 readings *Type:* Sprechtheater *Venues:* Stadttheater am Berliner Platz 574, Theaterstudio 199 *Comments:* see also Opera, Dance, Orchestras and Venues

Tegernseer Volkstheater
Postfach 1127, 83701 **Gmund am Tegernsee**
Tel: 8022-93292 Fax: 8022-93248
Internet: www.volkstheater.de
E-Mail: volkstheater@online.de
Direktion und Künstlerische Leitung Florian Kern; Dramaturgie Regie Gerd Potyka, Ulrich Kern
Actors: 10 *Perfs:* 210 *Prods:* 3 *Type:* Sprechtheater *Venues:* capacity 260 *Touring:* Austria, Germany, Italy

Deutsches Theater in Göttingen
Theaterplatz 11, 37073 **Göttingen**
Tel: 551-49690 Fax: 551-496 958
Internet: www.goettingende/kultur/de
E-Mail: Deutsches-Theater@goettingen.de
Intendant Mark Zurmühle; Verwaltungsdirektor Ulrich Klötzner; Chefdramaturg Bernhard Glocksin
Actors: 39 *Perfs:* 420 + 40 guest performances *Prods:* 15 *Type:* classical, modern and contempary theatre *Venues:* Großes Haus 530, DT Studio 99, DT Keller 70 *Touring:* Poland, Germany, Russia

Junges Theater Göttingen
Hospitalstraße 6, 37073 **Göttingen**
Tel: 551-495 015 Fax: 551-495 0177
Internet: www.dabakus.de/jt
künstl Leitung Werner Feig; Öffentlicheitsreferat, Künstl. Betriebsbüro Christian Keim; Dramaturgie Ines Eggert
Actors: 7 + guests *Perfs:* 250 *Prods:* 8 *Type:* Sprechtheater, modern *Venues:* 280 *Touring:* Germany

Theater Vorpommern
Postfach 3114, 17461 **Greifswald**
Tel: 3834-57220/572 255 (box office) Fax: 3834-502 779
Internet: www.theatervorpommern.de
E-Mail: theater@t-online.de
Intendant/Geschäftsführer Rüdiger Bloch; Verwaltungsdirektor/Geschäftsführer Joachim von Trützschler; GMD Dorian Wilson; Kinder/Jugendtheater Tobias Ballnus, Marion Küster; Chefdisponent Martina Ehlert
Actors: 17 + 5 guests *Perfs:* approx. 100 *Prods:* 20 *Type:* Sprechtheater *Venues:* Großes Haus(Greifswald) 460, Großes Haus(Stralsund) 519, Brauhaus 50 *Comments:* see also Opera, Dance and Orchestras

RRRABATZZZ Theater GmbH
Krotzenburgerstr 42, 63512 **Hainburg**
Tel: 6182-7201 Fax: 6182-64418
Internet: www.rrrabatzzz.de
E-Mail: postmaster@rrrabatzzz.de
Intendanz Thomas Waldkircher, Anja Ihringer
Actors: 5 *Perfs:* 240 *Prods:* 3-4 *Type:* Sprechtheater, children's and youth theatre, dance theatre with speech *Venues:* Foyer 80, home 180 *Touring:* Austria, Finland, Turkey, Denmark, Sweden *Comments:* publish theatre plays from Scandinavia and other European countries, workshops and training, second website: www.VORHANGAUF.DE

neues theater – Schauspiel Halle
Große Ulrichstraße 50, 06108 **Halle (Saale)**
Tel: 345-2050-0 Fax: 345-202 6248
Internet: www.halleinfo.de/theater/nt
E-Mail: preuk@nt.hal.eunet.de
Intendant Peter Sodann; Verwaltungsdirektorin & stellvertretende Intendantin Dr Inge Richter; Chefdramaturg Erhard Preuk; 1. Spielleiter Hilmar Eichhorn; Schauspielkapellmeister Jan Trieder; Chefdisponent Andreas Stanicki
Actors: 35 *Perfs:* 500 *Prods:* 12 *Type:* Sprechtheater *Venues:* Theatersaal 450, Hoftheater 250, Kommode 207, das Tintenfaß 120 *Touring:* Germany, Switzerland

Thalia Theater Halle
Thaliapassage, 06108 **Halle (Saale)**
Tel: 345-204 050 Fax: 345-202 4357
Internet: www.halle-online.de/thalia
E-Mail: thaliatheater@t-online.de
Intendant Paula Bettina Mader; Kaufmännische Leitung Fera Schütze; Öffentlichkeitsreferat Frau Schreibeis
Actors: 20 *Perfs:* 400 *Prods:* 28 (14 new) *Type:* Sprechtheater, children's & young persons' theatre *Venues:* Großes Thalia Theater 300, Kleines Thalia Theater 80 *Touring:* German speaking countries
Comments: art & culture centre for children

Deutsches Schauspielhaus
Kirchenallee 39, 20099 **Hamburg**
Tel: 40-248 710 Fax: 40-2487 1410/411/412
Internet: www.maz.net/kultur/schauspielhaus.de
E-Mail: public@schauspielhaus.de
Intendant Frank Baumbauer (until summer 2000, Tom Stromberg (from summer 2000); Chefdramat Wilfred Schulz; Direktor Dr. Klaus Naseband; Kaufm. Geschäftsführer Peter F. Raddatz; techn. Direktor Eberhard Bothe
Actors: 60 *Perfs:* 500 *Prods:* 17-19
Type: modern (new authors) mix *Venues:* Schauspielhaus 1307, Malersaal 155, Kantine 99 *Touring:* national and international festivals

English Theatre of Hamburg, The
Lerchenfeld 14, 22081 **Hamburg**
Tel: 40-227 7089 Fax: 40-227 7927
Directors Robert Rumpf, Clifford Dean
Perfs: 230 *Prods:* 4 *Type:* modern and classical English repertoire *Venues:* capacity 160

Ernst Deutsch Theater
Ulmenau 25, 22087 **Hamburg**
Tel: 40-2270 1420 Fax: 40-2270 1435
Internet: www.cityvox.de/ernstdeutschtheater
E-Mail: info@ernstdeutschtheater.de
Intendantin Isabella Vértes-Schütter; Verwaltungsdirektor Wolfgang Borchert; Dramaturgie Juergen Apel; Presse-und Öffentlichkeitsarbeit Stefanie Weiss
Actors: 3 + guests *Perfs:* 420 *Prods:* 8 *Type:* modern, classical, fairytales *Venues:* home capacity 741; studio up to 70 *Touring:* German speaking countries

Kampnagel Hamburg
Jarrestrasse 20, 22303 **Hamburg**
Tel: 40-270 9490 Fax: 40-2709 4911
Internet: www.kampnagel.de
E-Mail: kampnagel@t-online.de
Kaufmänn. Direktor Jack Kurfess; Künstl Leiter Res Bosshart
Actors: varies (guest performances) *Perfs:* 100 *Prods:* 60 *Type:* Sprechtheater, Tanztheater, performances, musiktheater *Venues:* K1 200, K2 340, K6 820 *Touring:* national and international *Comments:* mounts own and co-prods and is a venue for visiting companies and festivals

Ohnsorg Theater
Große Bleichen 25, 20354 **Hamburg**
Tel: 40-350 8030 Fax: 40-3508 0343
Internet: www.ohnsorg.de
E-Mail: info@ohnsorg.de
Intendant Christian Seeler; Verwaltungsdirektor Heidrun Gellert
Actors: 20 + guests *Perfs:* 650-700 *Prods:* 8 *Type:* Volkstheater Niederdeutsche Bühne (dialect folk play) *Venues:* capacity 387 *Touring:* Germany, Austria, Switzerland *Comments:* touring company: Ohnsorg Tournee-und Medien GmbH

Schmidts-Tivoli
Spielbudenplatz 27-28, 20359 **Hamburg**
Tel: 40-317 788-0/78899 (box office) Fax: 40-317 788-74
Internet: www.tivoli.de
E-Mail: info@tivoli.de
Künstlerische Leitung Corny Littmann; Geschäftsleitung Corny Littmann, Prof. Norbert Aust
Actors: varies *Perfs:* 430+300 *Type:* 'schrilles Volkstheater' *Venues:* Schmidts Tivoli 620, Schmidt-Theater 230

Thalia Theater
Alstertor, 20095 **Hamburg**
Tel: 40-328 140 Fax: 40-3281 4201/2/4
Internet: www.thalia-theater.de
E-Mail: puplikum@thalia-theater.de
kaufmännischer Geschäftsführer Ulrich Khuon; Intendant Jürgen Flimm (until July 2000), Ludwig von Otting, Ulrich Khuon (from August 2000); Verwaltungsdirektor H-W Köster; Chefdramaturg Volker Canaris
Actors: 44 + guests *Perfs:* 550 *Prods:* 15 + 9 (new) *Type:* Sprechtheater *Venues:* Großes Haus 998, Tik 261
Touring: national and international

Theater Monsun und Institut
Friedensallee 20, 22765 **Hamburg**
Tel: 40-390 3148 Fax: 40-390 6441
Künstlerische Leitung Ulrike von Kieseritzky
Perfs: 140 *Type:* dance, movement & music theatre

Theater Scena Polska Hamburg
Bleicherstraße 50, 22767 **Hamburg**
Tel: 40-439 2790 Fax: 40-439 2790
Intendant/Künstlerische Leitung Aleksander Berlin; Öffentlichkeitsreferat Marzena Janiszewska-Hornowicz; Artdirektor Boris Sokolow
Prods: 2 *Type:* Spechtheater *Touring:* Eastern Europe
Comments: contact in Poland Tel: +48 601-394 981

YANCI
c/o Kaleidoscope Presentations, Kleiberweg 144a, 22547 **Hamburg**
Tel: 40-8407 9397
Internet: www.yanci.com
E-Mail: yanci@yanci.com
contact Julia Plückebaum
Actors: 4 *Type:* visual theatre
Comments: touring company

Commedia Futura
Eisfabrik, Seilerstr. 15-17, 30171 **Hannover**
Tel: 511-816 353 Fax: 511-816 353
Künstlerischer Leiter Wolfgang Piontek; Öffentlichkeitsarbeit u. Dramaturgie Peter Piontek
Actors: 5-10 *Perfs:* 80 *Prods:* 2-3 *Type:* multimedia dance theatre *Venues:* Schwarzer Saal 99, Zentralhalle 99
Touring: Europe *Comments:* see also Dance and Venues

Kittners Kritisches Kabarett
Bischofsholer Damm 88, 30173 **Hannover**
Tel: 511-851 333/161-252 4935 (mobile)
Fax: 511-283 4980/+43 3476-35224
Leitung Dietrich Kittner
Perfs: 182 *Prods:* 2 + 1 *Type:* political, cabaret *Venues:* Theater: Am Küchengarten 132 *Touring:* Germany. Austria, Switzerland,Belgium, Slovenia *Comments:* second address: Dedenitz 6, A-8490 Radkersburg, Austria

Landesbühne Hannover
Bultstrasse 7-9, 30159 **Hannover**
Tel: 511-282 8280 Fax: 511-2828 2888
Internet: www.landesbuehne-hannover.de
Intendant Gerhard Weber; Verwaltungsdirektor Jürgen Trieglaff; Chefdramaturgin Silke Schauer; Betriebsbüro Gudrun Urban
Actors: 26 *Perfs:* 430 *Prods:* 19 *Type:* drama, musicals, children's theatre *Venues:* Große Bühne 489, Dinner Theatre 90, Garten Theater Herrenhausen 904,
Touring: Germany

Niedersächsisches Staatsschauspiel Hannover
Prinzenstr. 9, 30159 **Hannover**
Tel: 511-999 900 Fax: 511-363 2536
Internet: www/staatstheater-hannover.de
E-Mail: gaby.schweer@staatstheater-hannover.com
Intendant Wilfried Schulz; künstlerische Betriebsdirektorin Christa Müller; Verwaltungsdirektor Knut Lehmann; Technischer Direktor Karl-Heinz Lins
Actors: 34 *Perfs:* 450 *Prods:* 14 *Type:* Sprechtheater, modern to classical *Venues:* Schauspielhaus 620, Ballhof 400, Probebühne Ballhof 100 *Touring:* national *Comments:* see also Opera and Dance

Rammbaff-theater
Windheimstraße 4, 30451 **Hannover**
Tel: 511-210 2267 Fax: 511-210 1499
Direktor u. künstlerische Leitung Holger Freudemann; musikalische Oberleitung Matthias Röse
Actors: 5 *Perfs:* 150 *Prods:* 2 (new) *Type:* children's/youth theatre *Venue:* cap 99 *Touring:* national, international

Theater an der Glocksee
Glockseestr. 35, 30169 **Hannover**
Tel: 511-131 518
Geschäftsführerin Claire Lütcke
Actors: 4-10 *Perfs:* 60-100 *Prods:* 2-3 *Type:* modern Sprechtheater *Venues:* Theaterraum 99 *Touring:* Germany *Comments:* experimental drama based on classical & modern literary works, and musicals

Theaterwerkstatt Hannover
Pavillion am Raschplatz, Lister Meile 4, 30161 **Hannover**
Tel: 511-344 104 Fax: 511-314 658
E-Mail: theaterwerkstatthannover@t-online.de
künstle Leitung/Geschäftsführung Martina van Boxen
Actors: 5 + guests *Perfs:* 45 *Prods:* 3 *Type:* movement, Music-und Sprechtheater *Venues:* Grosser Saal 99, Kleiner Saal 60 *Touring:* national, international

Theater der Stadt Heidelberg
Friedrichstrasse 5, 69117 **Heidelberg**
Tel: 6221-585 510 Fax: 6221-583 599
Intendant Dr Volkmar Clauß; PR Bertram Hacke; Schauspieldramaturgie Annette Hunscha, Matthias Schubert; Chefdisponentin Christa Oser; Leiter des Kinder- u. Jugendtheaters Hubert Habig
Actors: 19 *Perfs:* 500-600 (incl opera and ballet) *Prods:* 8 + 5 Kinder- und Jugendtheater *Type:* Sprechtheater *Venues:* Städtische Bühne 619, Kinder- u. Jugendtheater und Studio 130 *Comments:* Studio – Zwingerstr. 3-5 (tel: 6221-583 508), Kinder- u. Jugendtheater, Zwingerstr. 3-5 (tel: 6221-583 546): see also Orchestras, Dance and Opera

Theater der Stadt Heilbronn
Berliner Platz 1, 74072 **Heilbronn**
Tel: 7131-563 000 Fax: 7131-563 139
E-Mail: TheaterHN@gmx.de
Intendant Klaus Wagner; Verwaltungsdirektor Jürgen Frahm; Chefdramaturg Dr. Günter Ballhausen; Chefdisponent und stellvertretender Intendant Andreas Oberbach
Actors: 24 *Perfs:* 460 *Prods:* 19 *Type:* Sprechtheater (classical to modern) *Venues:* main auditorium 705, Kammerspiele 110-140; from the end of 2000: Das Komödienhaus 380 *Comments:* Gastspiele am Hause, opera, operette, ballet; see also Festivals (Tanztheater Tage); see also Venues

Theater Kohlenpott Produktion
Kronprinzenstr. 57, 44623 **Herne**
Tel: 2323-490 050 Fax: 2323-490 050
E-Mail: thomczyk@cityweb.de
Direktor & künstlerische Leitung Willi Thomczyk
Actors: 4-5 *Perfs:* 120 (60 on tour) *Prods:* 2-3 *Type:* experimental, youth theatre *Venues:* Flottmann Hallen 130 *Touring:* Germany *Comments:* member of Kooperative Freier Theater NRW e.v.

Stadttheater Hildesheim
Theaterstr. 6, 31141 **Hildesheim**
Tel: 5121-16930 Fax: 5121-169 393
Intendant Dr. Martin Kreutzberg; Dramaturgie Dr. Sabine Göttel, Susanne Bieler
Actors: 16 *Prods:* 9 *Type:* Sprechtheater *Venues:* Stadtheater Grosses Haus 607, Theo/Studiobühne 68, Foyer 65
Comments: see also Opera, Dance and Orchestras

Städtebundtheater Hof
Kulmbacherstr. 5, 95030 **Hof**
Tel: 9281-7070-0 Fax: 9281-707 0299
Internet: www.theater-hof.com
E-Mail: info@theater-hof.com
Intendant Uwe Drechsel; künstlerisches Betriebsbüro u. Disposition Petra Gorki; Chefdramaturg und stellv. Intendant in künstl. Angelegenheiten (Schauspiel) Thomas Schindler; Ref. für Werbung und Öffentlichkeitsarbeit Wolfgang Kerner; Musikdramaturg Michaela Peterseil; GMD Golo Berg; Marketing Leitung Petra Müller
Actors: 70 *Perfs:* 200 *Prods:* 5 + 1 Kinder u. Jugendtheater productions *Type:* Sprechtheater, Jugendtheater *Venues:* Stadttheater 567, Studio 99 *Touring:* Germany *Comments:* see also Opera and Dance

Stadttheater Ingolstadt
Schloßlände 1, 85049 **Ingolstadt**
Tel: 841-17801 Fax: 841-305 1809
Intendant Wolfram Krempel; Verwaltung Siegfried Ostermeier, Michael Schmidt
Actors: 26 *Perfs:* 400 *Prods:* 16 *Type:* Sprechtheater, musical *Venues:* Stadttheater 663, Werkstattbühne 99, Studio im Herzogskasten 60, theater am Turm Baur 99, Freilichtbühne Turm Baur 738 *Comments:* see also Festivals

Theaterhaus Jena
Schillergäßchen 1, 07745 **Jena**
Tel: 3641-88690 Fax: 3641-886 910
Internet: www.jena.online.de/theaterhaus
E-Mail: theaterhausjena@t-online.de
künstlerischer Geschäftsführer/Regie/Mitglied des Künstlerischen Stabes Sven Schlötcke; Kaufmännischer Geschäftsführer Klaus-Dieter Werner; Dramaturg/Mitglied des Künstlerischen Stabes Jan Kauenhowen, t.ba.; Ausstattung/Mitglied des Künstlerischen Stabes Katharina Tietze; Regieassistenz/Mitglied des Künstlerischen Stabes Janec Müller; Künstlerisches Betriebsbüro Kerstin Jonuschies; Öffentlichkeitsarbeit Andrea Hesse
Actors: 9 + guests *Perfs:* 190 *Prods:* 6 *Type:* speech, music and dance-theatre *Venues:* Hauptbühne 180, Seitenbühne 70, Unterbühne 70, Malsaal 30 *Touring:* Germany *Comments:* see also Venues

Pfalztheater
Willy-Brandt-Platz 4-5, 67657 **Kaiserslautern**
Tel: 631-3675-0 Fax: 631-307 5213
Intendant Wolfgang Quetes; Künstl. Betriebsdirektor chefdisponent Peter Bachmaier; Chefdramaturg Stephan Kopf; Verwaltungsdirektor Günter Albert; Presse u. Werbeorganisation Günther Fingerle
Actors: 32 *Prods:* 21 *Type:* Sprechtheater, Musiktheater, ballet *Venues:* Großes Haus 720, Werkstatt 200 *Comments:* see also Opera, Dance and Orchestras

Badisches Staatstheater Karlsruhe
76125 **Karlsruhe**
Tel: 721-3557-0 Fax: 721-373 223 (Verwaltung)
Internet: www.karlsruhe.de/kultur/staatstheater
E-Mail: kartenverkauf@bstaatstheater.bul.de
Generalintendant Pavel Fieber; Verwaltungsdirektor Wolfgang Sieber; Schauspieldirektor Peter Schroth; Ballettdirektor Olaf Schmidt;Technischer Direktor Harold Frlrinner; Oberspielleiter des Schauspiels Klaus Kusenberg; künstlerische Betriebsdirektorin Gudrun Pappermann; Presse- und Öffentlichkeitsarbeit Anna-Renate Sörgel, Gabi Oetterer; Assistent des Generalintendanten Carl Philip von Maldeghem
Actors: 31 (incl. guest actors) *Perfs:* 427 *Prods:* 22 *Type:* repertoire drawn from whole spectrum of world drama; classics, new plays, also shows for young people *Venues:* Großes Haus 1002, Kleines Haus 385, WSEL Studio 99, WSEL Werkstatt 200 *Comments:* venue address: Baumeisterstrasse 11, 76137 Karlsruhe; see also Opera, Dance, Orchestras and Festivals

Insel und Studio 84, Die
Karlstr. 49b, 76133 **Karlsruhe**
Tel: 721-356 330 Fax: 721-356 771
Direktion Werner Wederkind; Verwaltungsleitung Susanna Daferner; Künstl Betrietsbüro Madeleine Scharafat
Actors: 12 + 7 guests actors *Perfs:* 280-300 *Prods:* 8 *Type:* Sprechtheater, cabaret *Venues:* Die Insel 180, Studio 90

Kammertheater Karlsruhe am Rondellplatz
Karl-Friedrich-Strasse 24, 76133 **Karlsruhe**
Tel: 721-23111 Fax: 721-203 1138
Leiterin Heidi Vogel-Reinsch
Actors: 9 *Perfs:* 234 *Prods:* 7-8 (+1 children's production) *Type:* mainly Boulevard-Theater *Venues:* capacity 198

Theater in der Orgelfabrik e.V.
Amthausstr. 19, 76227 **Karlsruhe**
Tel: 721-401 443
E-Mail: ps.bel@t-online.de
Künstlerische Leitung Gabriele Michel, Dr. Franco Rosa
Actors: varies *Perfs:* 30 *Prods:* 3 *Type:* Sprechtheater *Venues:* Theater in der Orgelfabrik 99 *Comments:* summer theatre for 3 months a year

Komödie Kassel
Friedrich-Ebert-Straße 39, 34117 **Kassel**
Tel: 561-18383/284 325 Fax: 561-285 129
Direktion, Künstlerische Leitung Horst Lateika; Verwaltung, Dramaturgie – UA Dieter Ziermann
Actors: 10 *Perfs:* 440 *Prods:* 8 *Venues:* capacity 145 *Touring:* guest performances

Staatstheater Kassel
Friedrichsplatz 15, 34117 **Kassel**
Tel: 561-10940 Fax: 561-109 4204
Intendant Dr. Christoph Nix; künstlerische Betriebsdirektion Johannes Schwärsley; Chefdramaturg Ralf Fiedles; Generalmusikdirektor Roberto Paternostro; Schauspieldirektor Armin Petras; Studienleiter, Kapellmeister Hubert Dapp
Actors: 25 *Prods:* 13 *Venues:* Schauspielhaus 540, Frizz 99 Theater Im Fridericianum 99, Casanova 99, Opernhaus 953 *Comments:* see also Opera, Dance and Orchestras

Bühnen der Landeshauptstadt Kiel
Holtenauerstr. 103, 24105 **Kiel**
Tel: 431-886 680 Fax: 431-886 6815
Internet: www.kiel.de/buehnen
E-Mail: buehnen@lhstadt.kiel.de
Künstlerisches Leitungsteam Kirsten Harms, Raymund Richter
Actors: 22 *Prods:* 16 (14 new) *Type:* classical, modern *Venues:* Schauspiel 408, Kindertheater 120, Opernhaus 822 *Comments:* see also Opera and Dance

Polnisches Theater Kiel
Düppelstr. 61a, 24105 **Kiel**
Tel: 431-804 099 Fax: 431-84424
Internet: www.go-in.de/polnisches-theater-kiel
E-Mail: galia@t-online.de
Direktor Tadeusz Galia; Verwaltungsleitung u. Geschäftsführer Dr. Arnd Ziemke; Künstlerische Leitung Tadeusz Galia
Actors: 4 *Perfs:* 110 *Prods:* 3 *Type:* Sprechtheater, repertoire: contemporary stage literature with emphasis on Eastern Europe *Venues:* Polnisches Theater 45 *Touring:* national

Bleichgesichter
Hauptstr 14, 38274 **Klein-Elbe**
Tel: 5345-1984/171-475 1129(mobile)
Fax: 5345-622
E-Mail: stilvol@t-online.de
managing director Volker Stiehl
Actors: 1 + guests *Type:* movement theatre, pantomime *Comments:* also organise workshops, seminars and festivals; music production in own music studio; work for Expo 2000 in Hannover in workshop festivals

Theater der Stadt Koblenz
Clemensstr 1, 56068 **Koblenz**
Tel: 261-129 2870
Fax: 261-129 2800
Internet: www.koblenz.de/~kultur/theater
Intendantin Annegret Ritzel
Actors: 13 *Perfs:* 165 *Prods:* 11 *Type:* Sprechtheater *Venues:* Großes Haus am Deinhardplatz (501), Kammerspiele am Flonnsmarkt (151), probe-bühne 2 (70), Mittelfoyer (50) *Comments:* see also Opera and Dance

Atelier Theater
Roonstr. 78, 50674 **Köln**
Tel: 221-241 341/242 485 (ticket service)
Fax: 221-233 757
KünstlerischeLeitung Rosa K Wirtz; Verwaltungsdirektor & Öffentlichkeitsarbeit Sabine Heinrichs-Knab
Actors: varies *Perfs:* daily *Type:* cabaret, chansons, variety theatre *Venues:* Atelier-theater 99, Ateliercafe 80 *Comments:* cooperation with Kölner Festival (Frontfrauen Festival Köln Comedy); see also Festivals and Venues

Bühnen der Stadt Köln – Schauspiel
Offenbachplatz, 50667 **Köln**
Tel: 221-2212 8400 Fax: 221-2212 8210
Generalintendant Günter Krämer; Geschäftsführender Direktor und Stellvertreter des GI Bernd Fülle; Stellvertreter des GI in künstlerischen Fragen Dr. Ralf Hertling; Schauspieldirektion Torsten Fischer; Referentin für Öffentlichkeit Claudia Nola; Betriebsdirektorin Barbara Krauss
Actors: 36 *Perfs:* 500 *Prods:* 17 new, 10 repertoire *Venues:* Schauspielhaus 835, Halle Kalk; Schlosserei; Westend-Theater 60 *Comments:* see also Opera

Comedia Colonia Theater GmbH
Löwengasse 7-9, 50676 **Köln**
Tel: 221-247 650 Fax: 221-215 639
Internet: www.theaterszene-koeln.de
E-Mail: comedia@netcologne.de
Direktor & Geschäftsführer Klaus Schweizer; Künstlerische Leitung und Kinder- und Jugendtheater Andrea Gronemeyer; Verwaltungsleiterin Ursula Siedler; Öffentlichkeitsarbeit Jürgen Pohl
Actors: varies – only guest actors *Perfs:* 370 & 100 on tour *Prods:* 4 *Type:* children's and young people's theatre, comedy, cabaret, serious Sprechtheater *Venues:* Comedia Colonia 312 *Touring:* predominantly Germany – 80 performances for children & young people, 20 drama *Comments:* venue for independent theatre groups – 150 performances per year, theatre workshops; various entertainment forms for children and young people with typical children's and young people's subjects; see also Venues

Freies Werkstatt Theater
Zugweg 10, 50677 **Köln**
Tel: 221-327 817 Fax: 221-331 668
Internet:
www.theaterszene-koeln.de/werkstatt-theater/index.htm
E-Mail: fwt-koeln@t-online.de
Künstlerische Leitung Dieter Scholz u. Ingrid Berzau
Actors: varies *Perfs:* 240 *Prods:* 7 (5 new) *Type:* freies Schauspiel *Venues:* 2 stages, 99 each *Touring:* national, international *Comments:* professional theatre for children, young people and adults, non-professional theatre for elderly people; alternative internet: www.fwt-koeln.de

licht! theater
Xantener Straße 3, 50733 **Köln**
Tel: 221-976 3960 Fax: 221-976 3962
Internet: www.theaterszene-koeln.de/licht-theater/
E-Mail: licht-theater@t-online.de
Leitung Barbara Reineke, Jurgen Runkel
Type: contemporary drama incorporating dance and musical theatre, multi-media

MONTEURE
Geisselstr. 15, 50823 **Köln**
Tel: 221-510 3016 Fax: 221-510 3016
Künstlerische Leitung Joachim von der Heiden, Andi Lucas
Actors: 2 actors + 4 dancers + 4 musicians *Perfs:* 120 *Prods:* 1 *Type:* Music and dance theatre *Touring:* all year in all countries *Comments:* dance theatre with live music; own productions only; 3 coproductions with other theatres; see also Dance

Studiobühne der Universität Köln
Universitätsstr. 16a, 50923 **Köln**
Tel: 221-470 4513 Fax: 221-470 5150
E-Mail: georg.franke@uni-koeln.de
Direktor/Künstlerische Leitung Georg Franke; Verwaltung Andrea Schlitzer; Chef Choreographin Sandra Dieken; Öffentlichkeitsreferat Dietmar Kobboldt
Actors: 30-35 *Perfs:* 210-220 *Prods:* 8 *Type:* Sprechtheater and also some dance theatre *Venues:* Theater 320, Aula-Bühne 1200 *Comments:* see also Festivals (Kölner Universitätstheater Woche), second e-mail address: kobboldt@uni-koeln.de

Theater am Dom
Glockengasse 11, 50667 **Köln**
Tel: 221-258 0153/54 (box office)/55 (admin)
Fax: 221-258 0156
Direktoren Inge Durek, Barbara Heinersdorff; Verwaltungsleiter Oliver Durek
Actors: varies *Perfs:* 400 *Prods:* 4 *Type:* Sprechtheater *Venues:* capacity 376

theater der keller
Kleingedankstr. 6, 50677 **Köln**
Tel: 221-318 059/932 2959/960 Fax: 221-314 110
Internet: www.theaterszene-koeln.de/theater
E-Mail: theater-der-keller@t-online.de/der-keller
Direktor Meinhard Zanger; Dramaturgie, Öffentlichkeitsarbeit Ulrike Eiterich; künstlerisches Betriebsbüro Susanne Walker, Karin Pietsch; Technische Leitung Jürgen Pfliegner
Actors: varies *Perfs:* 300 *Prods:* 10 *Type:* literary, contemporary theatre *Venues:* theater der keller: 2 stages cap 100 each *Comments:* also drama school 'Schule des theaters'

Theater im Bauturm (TiB)
Aachener Str. 24-26, 50674 **Köln**
Tel: 221-524 242 (bookings)/951 443-1 (admin)
Fax: 221-951 4431
E-Mail: theater-im-bauturm@t-online.de
Theaterleitung Gerhardt Haag; Technik Georg Slobodzian; Dramaturgie Andrea Hoßfeld
Actors: guests (number varies) *Perfs:* 300 *Prods:* 7 (3 new) *Type:* Spechtheater *Venues:* capacity 146

Stadttheater Konstanz
Inselgasse 2-6, 78462 **Konstanz**
Tel: 7531-130 021 Fax: 7531-130 027
Internet: www.konstanz.de/theater
Intendant Rainer Mennicken; Verwaltungsleiterin Sabine Bilharz; Technischer Leiter Andreas Beilschmidt; Leiter Junges Theater Joachim Henn; Öffentlichkeitsarbeit Barbara Noth;
Referent d. Theaterleitung Florian Bolenius
Actors: 24 *Perfs:* 515 *Prods:* 20 *Type:* from classical to contemporary *Venues:* stadttheater 380, Werkstatt 99, Spiegelhalle 150, Sommertheater Meersburg 250

Vereinigte Städtische Bühnen Krefeld und Mönchengladbach
Theater Krefeld, Theaterplatz 3, 47798 **Krefeld**
Tel: 2151-8050 Fax: 2151-28295
Internet: members.aol.com/vsbühnen
Generalintendant Jens Pesel; Geschäftsführer Reinhard Zeileis; Generalmusikdirektor Anthony Bramall; Operndirektor Andreas Wendholz; Schauspieloberspielleiter Peter Hathazy; Ballettdirecktorin Heidrun Schwaarz
Actors: 29 *Perfs:* 550 *Prods:* 13 *Type:* Sprechtheater *Venues:* Theater Krefeld 832, Theater Mönchengladbach 811 *Comments:* see also Dance, Opera and Orchestras; see also Mönchengladbach; Stadttheater Krefeld, Theatre Mönchengladbach, Odenkirchner Str. 78, 41236 Monchengladbach, Tel: 2166- 6151-0 Fax: 2166-420 110; the theatre is also available for rent

Theater am Marienplatz (TAM)
Marienstr. 81/83, 47807 **Krefeld-Fischeln**
Tel: 2151-305 273 Fax: 2151 307 477
contact Pit Therre
Actors: varies *Perfs:* 40-45 *Prods:* 9 *Type:* contemporary literature and new music theatre including many premieres *Venues:* capacity 50-70
Touring: Germany, Europe

Südostbayerisches Städtetheater Landshut-Passau-Straubing
Ländtorplatz 2-5, 84028 **Landshut**
Tel: 871-922 080 Fax: 871-922 0834
Internet: www.suedostbayerisches-staedtetheater.de
E-Mail: stadttheater.passau@t-online.de
Intendant Johannes Reitmeier; Musikdirektor Roger Boggasch; Verwaltungsleiter Rudi Senff; Verwaltungsleiter der Musikalischen Abteilung/Passau Ralf Schützenberger; Dramaturgie (Musik) Andreas Frane; Dramaturgie (Schauspiel) Christiana Alexandridis, Brigitte Herrmann
Actors: 14 + guest actors *Prods:* 9 *Type:* Sprechtheater *Venues:* Stadttheater Landshut 365, Fürstbischöfliches Opernhaus Passau 350, Theater am Hagen-Straubing 374 *Comments:* see also Opera (Südostbayerisches Städtetheater, Passan); second e-mail address: stadttheater.Landshut@t-online.de

Kabarett Academixer
Kupfergasse academixer-Keller, 04109 **Leipzig**
Tel: 341-960 4848 Fax: 341-211 4258
Internet: www.academixer.com
E-Mail: info@academixer.com
Geschäftsführer Hans-Walter Molle, Rüdiger Thiele
Actors: 4 *Perfs:* 408 *Prods:* 4 *Type:* political and satirical cabaret, dialect programme *Venues:* academixer-Keller 250 *Touring:* Germany *Comments:* academixer – Keller is venue for the 1999 competition: Der Salzburger Stier

Kabarett Leipziger Pfeffermühle GmbH
Thomaskirchhof 16, 04109 **Leipzig**
Tel: 341-960 3253 (administration) 3196 (Box office)
Fax: 341-960 3107
E-Mail: kabarett.pfeffermuehle@t-online.de
Geschäftsführerin Dr. Heike Gebert
Actors: 6 *Perfs:* 325 *Prods:* 2 *Type:* political, satirical cabaret *Venues:* Kabarett Leipziger Pfeffermühle 157 *Touring:* national, international *Comments:* Pfeffermühlenclub, 70, eating and drinking place where readings, recitals etc. take palce

Schauspiel Leipzig
Bosestraße 1, 04109 **Leipzig**
Tel: 341-1268-0 Fax: 341-126 8159
Internet: www.schauspiel-leipzig.de
E-Mail: info@schauspiel-leipzig.de
Intendant Wolfgang Engel;\
Verwaltungsdirektor Gerhard Nodurft; Chefdramaturgin Dr. Dagmar Borrmann; Direckor Öffentlichkeitsarbeit Thorsten Weckherlin; künstlerische Betriebsdirektorin Anna Mülhöfer
Actors: 39 *Perfs:* 580 *Prods:* 15 *Type:* young and innovative *Venues:* Schauspielhaus 750, Spielstätte hinter dem Eisernen Vorhang des Schauspielhauses 120, Neue Szene 99, Horch und Guck 60 *Comments:* organise 'Lachmesse' – European Humour & Satire Festival; co-organiser/producer of 'Euro Scene' – European Festival of Avantgarde (q.v.)

Theater der Jungen Welt Leipzig
Lindenauer Markt 21, 04177 **Leipzig**
Tel: 341-486 600 Fax: 341-477 2994
E-Mail: theaterjw@t-online.de
Intendant Hanns Gallert; Verwaltungsdirektorin Erika Schulze; Spielleiter Norbert Solga; Dramaturgie und Regie Marion Firlus; Musikalische Leitung Tobias Rank; Öffentlichkeitsreferat Ulrike Linke; Theaterpädagogin Maria Knupp, Regina Vitzthum
Actors: 14 + 3 puppets *Perfs:* 600 *Prods:* 7 *Type:* drama, children & young people's theatre and puppet theatre *Venues:* Haus Leipzig max 120, Haus der Volkskunst (partly closed for renovation) 60 *Touring:* Germany *Comments:* member of ASSITEJ, workshops, joint projects with socio-cultural centres in the city

Bühnen der Hansestadt Lübeck
Beckergrube 16, 23539 **Lübeck**
Tel: 451-708 8112 Fax: 451-708 8177
Generalintendant Mark Adam; Leiter des künstlerischen Betriebsbüros Dr. Margrit Lindner; Verwaltungsleiter Peter Skrock; Generalmusikdirektor Erich Wächter; Leitung Schauspieldramaturgie Andreas Strähnz
Actors: 20 *Prods:* 8 (+ 3 studio) *Type:* Sprechtheater *Venues:* Kammerspiele 327, Studio 99 *Comments:* see also Opera and Orchestras

Theater Combinale
Hüxstr. 115, 23552 **Lübeck**
Tel: 451-78817 Fax: 451-706 3078
Internet: www.combinale.de
E-Mail: info@combinale.de
contact Ulli Haussmann
Actors: 3 + guests *Perfs:* 50-80 *Prods:* 4 *Venues:* home capacity 130 *Comments:* see also Venues

Prinzregententheater
Prinzregentenstrasse 45, 67063 **Ludwigshafen**
Tel: 621-525 240
Fax: 621-624 684
Direktor Bernhard Dropmann; Dramaturgie Ralf W. Zuber
Actors: 45 *Perfs:* 500 *Prods:* 7-8 *Type:* Sprechtheater, comedy *Venues:* Prinzregententheater 140 *Touring:* locally *Comments:* private theatre

Theater Lüneburg und Treffpunkt Neues Theater
Postfach 2829, 21318 **Lüneburg**
Tel: 4131-7520/42100 (box office) Fax: 4131-404 210
Internet: www.theater-lueneburg.de
E-Mail: dramaturgie@theater-lueneburg.de
Generalintendant Jan Aust; Verwaltungsdirektor Wolfgang Dannenfeld
Actors: 20-30 (mainly guest actors) *Perfs:* 100 *Prods:* 10 *Type:* Sprechtheater *Venues:* Theater 553 *Comments:* visiting address: An den Reeperbahnen 3, 21335 Lüneburg; see also Opera, Dance and Orchestras

Freie Kammerspiele Magdeburg Städtisches Schauspiel
Otto-Von-Guericke-Str. 64, 39104 **Magdeburg**
Tel: 391-5988-0 Fax: 391-598 8246
Internet:
www.magdeburg.de/kultur/kammerspiele.html
Intendant Wolf Bunge; Verwaltungsleiter Mathias Nowicki; Chefdramaturg Hans-Peter Frings; Stellv. Intendant u. künstlerischer Betriebsdirektor Jörg Richter
Actors: 21+ guests *Prods:* 32 (15 new) *Type:* Sprechtheater, children's and youth theatre *Venues:* Freie Kammerspiele 288 *Touring:* national, international

Theater der Landeshauptstadt Magdeburg
Postfach 1240, 39002 **Magdeburg**
Tel: 391-540 6500 Fax: 391-540 6599
Internet: www.theater-magdeburg.de
Generalintendant Max K Hoffmann; Verwaltungsdirektor Reinhard Odenstein; Chefdramaturg Dietmar Goergen; Oberspielleiter Schauspiel Helmut Palitsch
Actors: 21 *Prods:* 12 new *Venues:* Theater am Universitätsplatz 688, Podiumbühne ca. 40, Kabarett Die Kugelblitze 186 *Comments:* visiting address: Universitätsplatz 9, 39104 Magdeburg; see also Opera and Dance

Staatstheater Mainz
Gutenbergplatz 7, 55116 **Mainz**
Tel: 6131-28510 Fax: 6131-285 1333
Internet: www.staatstheater-mainz.de
E-Mail: theatmain@aol.com
Intendant Georges Delnon; künstlerischer Betriebsdirektor Hajo Fouquet; Chefdramaturg Martin Apelt; Schauspieldirektor Michael Helle; Kaufmännischer Geschäftsführer Lutz-Uwe Dünnwald
Type: classical to modern *Venues:* Phoenix-Halle 776, Tic-Theater im City 99, Kleines Haus 398 *Comments:* see also Opera, Orchestras and Dance (Mainz, Ballett des Theaters der Landeshauptstadt)

Klapsmühl' am Rathaus – Mannheimer Kleinkunstbühne
D6,3, 68159 **Mannheim**
Tel: 621-22488 Fax: 621-156 4436
Internet: www.klapsmuehl.de
Intendant/Künstlerische Leitung Klaus-Jürgen Hoffmann; Geschäftsführer Klaus-Wolfgang Schmitter; Musikalische Oberleitung Uli Preiß; Technische Leitung Hans Georg Sütsch
Actors: 5 + guest actors *Perfs:* 260 *Prods:* 7-8 *Type:* cabaret, chanson, comedy *Venues:* Klapsmühl 140 *Touring:* Germany *Comments:* also exhibitions

Nationaltheater Mannheim
Mozartstrasse 9, 68161 **Mannheim**
Tel: 621-168 0150 Fax: 621-168 0258
Internet: mannheim.nationaltheater.de
E-Mail: Nationaltheater.kassse@mannheim.de
Generalintendant Ulrich Schwab; Schauspieldirektor Bruno Klimek; Direktor des Künstl. Betriebs Joel Revelle; Dramaturgie Kekke Schmidt, Manfred Weiß, Antje Zajonz, Heike Dürscheid
Actors: 41 *Perfs:* 350 *Prods:* 28 (12 new) *Type:* Sprechtheater *Venues:* Schauspielhaus 639, Studiobühne 99 *Touring:* occassionally national *Comments:* also has children's and young people's theatre (SCHNAWWL);
see also Opera, Dance and Orchestras

Hessische Landestheater Marburg, Das
Theater am Schwanhof, Am Schwanhof 68-72, 35037 **Marburg**
Tel: 6421-990 231 Fax: 6421-990 241
Internet: www.hessisches-Landestheater.de
E-Mail: HLTMarburg@aol.com
Intendant Ekkehard Dennewitz; Dramaturgie Jürgen Sachs; Verwaltung Jürgen Schüßler; KBB Gabriele Kraft; Technische Leitung Fred Bielefeldt
Actors: 17 *Perfs:* 400 *Prods:* 20-25 (14 new) *Type:* drama, children's & youth theatre, musicals *Venues:* Theater am Schwanhof (Bühne 1 200, Bühne 2 99), Erwin Piscator-Haus 560, Fürstensaal 300, Deutschhauskeller 90, open-air stage *Touring:* Germany

Fränkisches Theater
Schloß Maßbach, 97711 **Maßbach**
Tel: 9737-235
Fax: 9735-1496
Direktion Lena Hutter, Herbert Heinz; Dramatwgie und Disposition Sebastian Worch
Actors: 20 *Perfs:* ca. 310 *Prods:* 11 *Venues:* Intimes Theater 87 *Touring:* national
Comments: see also Festivals

Das Meininger Theater-Südthüringisches Staatstheater
Bernhardstrasse 5, 98617 **Meiningen**
Tel: 3693-451-0 Fax: 3693-502 285
Internet: www.das-meininger-theater.de
E-Mail: kasse@das-meininger-theater.de
Intendantin Christine Mielitz; Verwaltungsdirektorin Regina Schwabe; Schauspieldirektor Karl Georg Kayser
Actors: 22 *Prods:* 10 *Venues:* Große Haus 740, Studiobühne Georgie's Off 90 *Comments:* see also Opera, Dance and Orchestras

Landestheater Schwaben
Postfach 1640, 87686 **Memmingen**
Tel: 8331-94590 Fax: 8331-80180
Intendant Walter Weyers; Verwaltungsleiter Volker Kraus; Dramaturgie Matthias Lösch, Monika Dobrowlanska; Leiter Öffentlichkeitsarbeit Peter Kesten
Actors: 15 *Perfs:* 300 *Prods:* 15 *Type:* classical, modern *Venues:* cap 416, Studio 90 *Touring:* Germany *Comments:* visiting address: Theaterplatz 2, 87700 Memmingen

Schauspiel Tournee Oenicke
Oberstr. 23, 52399 **Merzenich**
Tel: 2275-911 683 Fax: 2275-911 685
E-Mail: MOenicke@aol.com
Intendant u. Künstlerische Leitung Michael Oenicke; Verwaltungsleitung Dr. Werner Lothmann
Actors: varies *Perfs:* 200 *Prods:* 2 *Touring:* German speaking countries

Schloßtheater Moers
Kastell 6, 47441 **Moers**
Tel: 2841-201 732/1 Fax: 2841-201 350
Intendant Johannes Lepper;
Dramaturgie Stephane Gräve
Actors: 7 *Perfs:* 170 *Prods:* 8 *Type:* Sprechtheater, emphasis on new works *Venues:* Schloßtheater up to 120, Studio 60, Kapelle 60

Vereinigte Städtische Bühnen Krefeld und Mönchengladbach
Theater Mönchengladbach, Odenkirchener Strasse 78, 41236 **Mönchengladbach**
Tel: 2166-61510 Fax: 2166-420 110
Internet: members.aol.com/vsbuehnen
Comments: see entry under Krefeld; see also Opera, Dance and Orchestras; Theater Mönchengladbach is available for rent

META Theater München
Werkhaus Moosach, Osteranger 8, 85665 **Moosach**
Tel: 8091-3514 Fax: 8091-4695
Internet: www.meta-theater.com
E-Mail: meta-theater@t-online.de
Geschäftsführer u. Künstlerische Leitung Axel Tangerding
Actors: 5 *Perfs:* 50 *Prods:* 2 *Type:* intercultural projects, poetic theatre, based on movement and music *Venues:* Studio Werkhaus Moosach 99 *Touring:* Denmark, USA, France, India, China, Japan *Comments:* workshops and exchange with non-European theatre artists

Theater an der Ruhr GmbH
Akazienallee 61, 45478 **Mülheim a. d. Ruhr**
Tel: 208-59901-0 Fax: 208-59901-19
Internet: www.theater-an-der-ruhr.de
E-Mail: theater-an-der-ruhr@t-online.de
Management Renate Grimaldi; Direktor Roberto Ciulli; Dramaturgie Helmut Schäfer; Kaufm. Geschäftsführung Eberhard Wagner
Actors: 15 *Perfs:* 135 *Prods:* 2-3 *Type:* Sprechtheater – international co-productions *Venues:* Theater an der Ruhr im Raffelbergpark 200 *Touring:* Europe, South America, Middle East, Eastern Europe, Asia *Comments:* venue based and touring company

Bayerisches Staatsschauspiel
Postfach 100155, 80075 **München**
Tel: 89-218 501 Fax: 89-2185 2090
Internet: www.staatstheater.bayern.de/schauspiel
E-Mail: tickets@st-schauspiel.bayern.de
Intendant Eberhard Witt; Verwaltungsdirektorin Gisela Reiche; Künstlerischer Direktor Ulrich Wessel; Chefdramaturgin Dr Elizabeth Schweeger; Dramaturgie Frantiska Kötz, Dr. Bettina Schültke, Marion Jens Groß, Brigitte Fürle;
Presse und Öffentlichkeitsarbeit Goldmann PR
Actors: 70 *Perfs:* 500 *Prods:* 13-15 (about 35 plays in repertory) *Type:* Sprechtheater *Venues:* Residenztheater (Max-Joseph-Platz 1) 903, Cuvilliés Theater/Altes Residenztheater (Residenzstraße 1) 523, Theater im Marstall (Marstallplatz 4) 200 *Touring:* national, international *Comments:* visiting address: Max-Joseph-Platz 1, 80539 München; alternative email: presse@st-schauspiel.bayern.de; see also Opera, Dance, Orchestras and Festivals

Blutenburg-Theater, Münchens Kriminalbühne
Blutenburgstraße 35, 80636 **München**
Tel: 89-123 3071 Fax: 89-129 1270
E-Mail: blutenburg@aol.com
Direktor René Siegel-Sorell;
Dramaturgin Anne-Beate Engelke
Actors: 20 *Perfs:* 220 *Prods:* 3 *Type:* comedy, 'who-done-it' *Venues:* Boulevardtheater 99 *Comments:* only 'Kriminalbühne' in Germany

Das Schloss – Theaterzelt am Olympiaberg
Ackermannstr. 77, 80797 **München**
Tel: 89-300 3013 Fax: 89-300 8580
Künstl Leiter Gunnar Petersen; Tech Leiter Gregor Hermens
Actors: no permanent ensemble *Perfs:* 240 *Prods:* 4 *Type:* modern classics, literary theatre *Venues:* Theatre Tent cap 500 *Comments:* permanent circus tent available for hire

Kleine Komödie GmbH
Maximilianstrasse 47, 80538 **München**
Tel: 89-226 765 Fax: 89-291 3371
Direktion Inge Durek, Barbara Heinersdorff
Actors: varies *Perfs:* 300 *Prods:* 4 *Type:* comedy *Venues:* Kleine Komödie am Max II 577

Komödie im Bayerischen Hof
Promenadeplatz 6, 80333 **München**
Tel: 89-2916 0530/2916 1633 (reservations)/292 810 (box office) Fax: 89-2916 0531
Internet: www.iris-online.de
Direktorin Margit Bönisch; Stage Design Thomas Pekny; Presse und PR t.b.a
Perfs: 350 *Prods:* 6 *Type:* comedy *Venues:* Theater im Hotel Bayrischer Hof 570 *Comments:* private theatre; also musicals, concerts, musictheatre and special events

Münchner Kammerspiele
Hildegardstraße 1, 80539 **München**
Tel: 89-233 0368 Fax: 89-2333 6847
Internet: muenchner.kammerspiele
E-Mail: pr.kammerspiele@ems.muenchen.de
Intendant Dieter Dorn, (from 2001: Frank Bambauer); geschäftsführender Direktor Georg Wild; technischer Direktor Jürgen Höfer; künstl Direktor Michael Wachsmann
Actors: 50-60 *Perfs:* 600 *Prods:* 8-10 *Type:* Sprechtheater, classical & contemporary *Venues:* Schreinerei 99 *Touring:* national, international *Comments:* address of Schauspielhaus: Maximilianstr. 26-28, 80539 München; due to refurbishments the Kammerspiele will be closed from Jan -end of April 2000, the Schreinerei will be closed due to refurbishment from 31.12.99, from May 2000 all stages will be open again

Münchner Volkstheater GmbH
Augustenstr. 31, 80333 **München**
Tel: 89-523 550 Fax: 89-523 5539
Internet: www.muenchner-volkstheater.de
E-Mail: theater@muenchner-volkstheater.de
Intendant Ruth Drexel; Geschäftsführer Sebastian Feldhofer
Actors: guests *Perfs:* ca. 250 *Prods:* 6-8 *Type:* Schauspiel *Venues:* home capacity 609 *Touring:* Germany

Neue Schaubühne GmbH
Unsöldstr. 5, 80538 **München**
Tel: 89-242 8740 Fax: 89-293 773
E-Mail: neue.schaubuehne@t-online.de
Geschäftsführer Jürgen Angst
Actors: varies *Perfs:* ca. 200 *Prods:* 7 *Type:* Sprechtheater *Touring:* Austria, Germany, Switzerland, Liechtenstein *Comments:* touring theatre

Neue Werkbühne München GmbH
Barerstr. 49, 80799 **München**
Tel: 89-957 0768 Fax: 89-957 0768
Direktor Silvia Bartels; Verwaltungsdirektor Heide Lincke
Actors: 5-6 *Perfs:* 100 *Prods:* 4 *Type:* Sprechtheater *Touring:* Bavaria, Austria *Comments:* touring company visiting schools and other educational establishments

proT
Zenettistraße 34, 80337 **München**
Tel: 89-7466 3046 Fax: 89-7466 3047
Internet: www.proT.de
E-Mail: AlexeijSagerer@compuserve.com
Intendant Alexeij Sagerer; Öffentlichkeitsarbeit u. Organisation Christine Landinger
Type: direct theatre

Teamtheater Comedy
Am Einlaß 4, 80469 **München**
Tel: 89-260 6636 Fax: 89-260 5065
Theaterleitung Petra Maria Grühn
Actors: varies *Perfs:* 80 *Prods:* 2 *Type:* Sprechtheater, comedy *Venues:* capacity 50 *Comments:* share administration with Teamtheater Tankstelle e.V.

Teamtheater Tankstelle e. V.
Am Einlass 2 a, 80469 **München**
Tel: 89-260 4333 Fax: 89-260 5065
Theaterleitung Petra Maria Grühn;
Betriebsbüro Katharina Schöfl
Actors: varies *Perfs:* 150 *Prods:* 3 + 2 co-productions *Type:* Sprechtheater: modern, classical *Venues:* cap 99 *Comments:* share administration with Teamtheater Comedy

Theaterbetriebe Margit Bönisch GmbH
Komödie im Bayrischen Hof, Promenadenplatz 6, 80333 **München**
Tel: 89-647 253 Fax: 89-645 343
Geschäftsführerin Margit Bönisch
Actors: varies *Perfs:* 350 *Prods:* 10 *Type:* classical, modern drama, musical, comedies *Venues:* Komödie im Bayrischen Hof 570 *Touring:* Germany, Switzerland, Liechtenstein, Austria, Luxembourg *Comments:* venue based and touring theatre

Tourneetheater die scene GmbH
Von-der-Tann-Strasse 3, 80539 **München**
Tel: 89-293 047 Fax: 89-282 214
Direktor Hilde Kugelgruber
Actors: varies *Perfs:* 120 *Prods:* 3 *Type:* Sprechtheater *Touring:* Germany, Austria, Switzerland, Luxembourg, Italy *Comments:* touring company

Städtische Bühnen Münster
Neubrückenstrasse 63, 48143 **Münster**
Tel: 251-59090 Fax: 251-590 9202
Internet: www.muenster.de/stb/
E-Mail: staedt.buehnen@stadt-muenster.de
Generalintendant Thomas Bockelmann; Künstlerisches Betriebsbüro Burkhard Kolb; Chef-Dramaturgie Horst Busch; Chefdisponentin Bettina Reith; Generalmusikdirektor Will Humburg; Ballettdirektor Daniel Goldin; Chordirektor Peter Heinrich; Assistentin des Generalintendanten Anja-Brigitta Lucke; PR Tanja Gellermann
Actors: 22 *Perfs:* 500 *Prods:* 10 *Type:* Sprechtheater *Venues:* Grosses Haus 955, Kleines Haus 321 *Comments:* see also Opera, Dance and Orchestras

Spott-Licht-Satirisches Unterhaltungstheater
Löwengasse 24, 63263 **Neu-Isenburg**
Tel: 6102-89655 Fax: 6102-89655
Intendant/Geschäftsführer/ Künstlerische Leitung Michael Von Loefen; Verwaltungsleitung Christian Brauburger; Musikalische Oberleitung Armin Sturm
Actors: 5 *Perfs:* ca. 200 *Prods:* 2-3 *Type:* im Bereich Musical, Kabarett, Show-Comedy *Venues:* Kellertheater, Haus zum Löwen 80, Restaurant-Theater 80 *Touring:* local *Comments:* aditional Tel: 6102-25951/-38875 (box office)

Kammertheater im Schauspielhaus e.V.
Pfaffenstr. 22, 17033 **Neubrandenburg**
Tel: 395-544 2617/8/180-222 2617 (box office and information) Fax: 395-582 6179
E-Mail: kammertheater@t-online.de
Intendant Knut Hirche; Geschäftsführer Dieter Köplin; Dramatung Matthias Wolf
Actors: varies *Perfs:* 240 *Type:* puppetry, drama *Venues:* Schauspielhaus up to 280 *Touring:* Europe *Comments:* rent, produce, co-produce

Rheinisches Landestheater
Drususallee 8, 41460 **Neuss**
Tel: 2131-2699/0 Fax: 2131-269 944(Intendanz)/925(Dramaturgie)
Internet: www.rlt-neuss.de
E-Mail: 021312699/0004@t-online.de
Intendant Burkhard Mauer; Verwaltungsdirektor Dirk Gondesen; Dramaturgie Ulrike Schanko, Petra Biederbeck; Theaterpädagogin Bettina Maurer; Ausstattungsleitung Katharina Sichtling
Actors: 18 *Perfs:* 350 *Prods:* 10 *Type:* Schauspiel, children's & youth theatre, 1 musical *Venues:* Globe Theater 600, Studio 100, Theatre Drususallee 371 *Touring:* Germany *Comments:* new venue address from August 2000: Rheinisches Landestheater, Oberstrasse, 41460, Neuss

Landestheater Mecklenburg GmbH Neustrelitz
Friedrich-Ludwig-Jahn-Strasse 14, 17235 **Neustrelitz**
Tel: 3981-2770 Fax: 3981-205 435
Internet: www.landestheater-mecklenburg.de
E-Mail: info@landestheater-mecklenburg.de
Intendant Urs Leicht; Oberspielleiter Schauspiel Ralf-Peter Schulze; Chefdramaturg Hans-Jörg Grell; Öffentlichkeitsarbeit Dr. Christoph Dammann
Actors: 14 *Prods:* 6 (Großes Haus) *Venues:* Theater im Probenhaus 60, Theater im Foyer 60, Theatre im Club 60, Großes Haus 397 *Touring:* Germany *Comments:* see also Opera

Landesbühne Rheinland-Pfalz im Schloßtheater Neuwied
Schloßstraße 1, 56564 **Neuwied**
Tel: 2631-22288 Fax: 2631-20479
Direktion Walter Ullrich; Verwaltungsleitung Hans-Dieter Deckert
Actors: varies *Perfs:* 500 *Prods:* 9 *Type:* Sprechtheater + 1 operetta *Venues:* capacity 273 *Touring:* Germany

Theater Nordhausen/ Loh-Orchester Sondershausen GmbH
Käthe-Kollwitz-Strasse 15, 99734 **Nordhausen**
Tel: 3631-62600
Fax: 3631-626 0147
Internet: www.theater.nordhausen.de
E-Mail: theater@nordhausen.de
Intendant Dr Monika Pirklbauer; Personalleiterin Angela Kalus; Dramaturgie Karola Weil; Werkstattleiter Jürgen Bley; Technischer Direktor Ingo Laujer; Chefdramaturg Harald Blaschke; Leiter des Kinder-und Jugendtheater Petra Weimann; PR Susanne Benedek; Ausstattungsleiterin Annette Riedel
Actors: 12 *Perfs:* 400 *Prods:* 9 (5 new) *Venues:* Großes Haus 495, Theater unterm Dach 60, Foyer 50, hinter dem Vorhang 60, Haus der Kunst 381, Achteckhaus 320 *Touring:* GermanyComments: alternative Internet: loh-orchester.sondershausen.de; see also Opera, Dance and Orchestras; also do children's and youth theatre

Städtische Bühnen – Schauspiel Nürnberg
Richard-Wagner-Platz 2-10, 90443 **Nürnberg**
Tel: 911-231 3533 Fax: 911-231 3566
Internet: www.schauspiel.nuernberg.de
E-Mail: schauspiel@nuernberg.de
Schauspieldirektor Wulf Konold; Leiter der Öffentlichkeitsarbeit Jürgen Priebe; Dramaturgie Christian Gröschel
Actors: 24 *Perfs:* 350 annually *Prods:* 10 *Type:* classical and modern theatre *Venues:* Schauspielhaus 538, Kammerspiele 199
Comments: see also Opera and Dance

Theater Oberhausen
Ebertstraße 82, 46045 **Oberhausen**
Tel: 208-85780 Fax: 208-24292
Internet: www.theater-oberhausen.de
E-Mail: theaterob@cww.de
Intendant Klaus Weise; Verwaltungsdirektor Jürgen Hennemann; Chefdramaturg Helmut Postel; Pressereferentin Astrid Horst
Actors: 23 *Perfs:* 300 *Prods:* 15 new, 10 revivals *Type:* repertory *Venues:* Grosses Haus 450, Studio 99
Comments: particular emphasis on young people's theatre

Ensemble der Kulturetage
Kulturetage Oldenburg, Bahnhofstr. 11, 26122 **Oldenburg**
Tel: 441-924 8030 Fax: 441-924 8080
Internet: www.uni-oldenburg.de/kulturetage
E-Mail: ketage@unixen.htz.uni-oldenburg.de
ensemble manager Bernt Wach
Actors: 4+ guests *Perfs:* 80 *Prods:* 4 (2 new) *Type:* modern *Venues:* Kulturetage; stage A 199, stage B 99, and several other temporary venues *Comments:* see Venues and Festivals (Prisma Internationale Kulturtage)

Oldenburgisches Staatstheater
Theaterwall 28, 26122 **Oldenburg**
Tel: 441-22250 Fax: 441-222 5222(ticket service)
Internet: www.oldenburg.staatstheater.de
E-Mail: kasse@oldenburg.staatstheater.de
Generalintendant Stephan Mettin; Chefdramaturgie Matthias Schiffner, Georgia Eilert; Disponent des Künstlerischen Betriebsbüros Dr. Rüdiger Zagolla
Actors: 18+ about 8 guests *Prods:* 15 (10 new) + 4 (Children's theater + 3 (dialect theatre/Mundartbühne *Venues:* Großes Haus 881, Kleines Haus 350
Touring: national
Comments: see also Opera, Dance and Orchestras

Städtische Bühnen Osnabrück
Domhof 10-11, 49074 **Osnabrück**
Tel: 541-323 4310 Fax: 541-323 3297
Internet: www.theater-osnabrueck.de
E-Mail: theateros@aol.com
Intendent Norbert Hilchenbach; Generalmusikdirektor Jean-François Monnard; kaufmännischer Direktor Norbert Kronisch; Oberspielleiter Schauspiel Mario Andersen; Dramaturgie Dr Maria Hilchenbach, Stefan Klawitter, Herbert Hähnel, Verena Meyer; Chefdisponent Matthias Otto
Actors: 26, Sänger 12 *Perfs:* 270 *Prods:* 15 (Großes Haus) + 1 fairy tale; 8 (emma theater) + 3 children's + 7 Wiederaufnahmen *Type:* music theater, Schauspiel, dance theater, children's and youth theatre *Venues:* Grosses Haus 639, Emma theater 99 *Touring:* Germany
Comments: see also Opera, Orchestras and Dance (Osnabrück Tanztheater der Städtischen Bühnen)

WUM-Theatre
Postfach 4302, 49033 **Osnabrück**
Tel: 541-25228
contact Andreas Ottmer
Actors: 4 + guest actors *Type:* Sprechtheater + children's theater with music + cabaret *Touring:* Germany & Germany speaking parts of foreign countries (Goetheinstitut) *Comments:* touring company; agent: Her Classen, Büro für Kultur-und Medienprojekte (Tel/Fax: 40-390 1407)

Mecklenburgisches Landestheater Parchim
Blutstr. 16, 19370 **Parchim**
Tel: 3871-226 661 Fax: 3871-212 572
Intendant André Hiller; Buchhaltung Regina Hecht; technische Leiterin Stephanie Kniesbeck
Actors: 6 + guests *Perfs:* ca. 260 *Prods:* 10-12 *Type:* children's and youth theatre, classical, modern *Venues:* Bühnensaal 289, Malsaal up to 90, Theatergaststätte up to 40 *Touring:* national, international

Stadttheater Pforzheim
Am Waisenhausplatz 5, 75172 **Pforzheim**
Tel: 7231-391 488
Fax: 7231-391 485
Internet: www.pforzheim.de/theater
E-Mail: theater@stadt-pforzheim.de
Intendant Ernö Weil; Dramaturg und Leiter des Schauspiels Frank Wilmes; Dramaturgin und Leiterin des Musiktheater Beate Bucher-Heller; Ballettmeister Anthony J. Sterago
Actors: 17 *Prods:* 20 *Type:* Sprechtheater, music theatre, ballet *Venues:* Großes Haus 510, Podium 199 *Touring:* 15-20 guest performances (music theatre) *Comments:* see also Opera, Dance and Orchestras

Vogtland Theater Plauen
Theaterplatz , 08523 **Plauen**
Tel: 3741-291 2438 Fax: 3741-222 620
Internet: www.vogtlandtheater.de
Intendant Dieter Roth; Verwaltungsleitung Renate Wünsche; Direktor PR Christian Pöllmann; GMD Dieter-Gerhardt Worm; Künstlerische Leitung Klaus Krampe (Schauspiel); Chefdramaturgin Christa Stöß
Actors: 16 *Prods:* 8-10 *Type:* Sprechtheater, classical, modern *Venues:* Großes Haus 467, Kleines Haus 99, Festhalle Plauen 450 *Touring:* Germany *Comments:* see also Opera, Dance and Orchestra

Hans Otto Theater GmbH Potsdam
Berlinerstr. 27A, Schiffbauergasse, 14467 **Potsdam**
Tel: 331-98110/27571-0 Fax: 331-9811 180/981 1280
Internet: http:/hot.potsdam.de
Intendant Ralf-Günter Krolkiewicz; Leit Dramaturg Roland Bertschi; Leiterin Musiktheater Dr. Andrea Palent
Actors: 27 *Prods:* 23 *Type:* Sprechtheater, music theatre, children's & youth theatre *Venues:* Theater Am Alten Markt 600, Reithalle A (Schiffbauergasse) *Comments:* see also Opera

Kabarett Obelisk eV – Satire Theater Potsdam
Charlottenstr. 31, 14467 **Potsdam**
Tel: 331-280 710 Fax: 331-291 069
Internet: www.kabarett.potsdam.com
E-Mail: kabarett@potsdam.com
Ökonomische Geschäftsführerin Dagmar Neugebauer; künstlerischeGeschäftsführerin Gretel Schulze
Actors: 6 (+ guests) *Perfs:* 500 *Prods:* 3 *Type:* political satirical theatre *Venues:* Theatersaal up to 194, Cafe Koschweit 80, Hof 150 (in the summer) *Touring:* German speaking countries *Comments:* occasional work for T. V.; open air June-Sept, dance performances in Cafe Koschweit

Nordharzer Städtebundtheater – Halberstadt-Quedlinburg
Marschlinger Hof 17/18, 06484 **Quedlinburg**
Tel: 3946-96220/3941-6965-0 Fax: 3946-962 220/3941-442 652
Internet: www.halberstadt.de/theater
E-Mail: theater@halberstadt.de
Intendant Kay Metzger; Chefdramaturg Peter Oppermann; Verwaltungsdirektor Roland Hinkel; Oberspielleiter Schauspiel Malte Kreutzfelt; Oberspielleiter Musiktheater Horst Kupich;
Actors: 15 actors, 18 singers *Perfs:* 520 *Prods:* 30 *Type:* Sprechtheater, youth theatre, opera, musical *Venues:* Großes Haus Halberstadt 501, Kammerbühne Halberstadt 99, Großes Haus Quedlinburg 280, Neue Bühne Quedlinburg 70 *Comments:* second address: Intendanz-Spiegelstr. 20a, 38820 Halberstadt, Tel: 3941-6965-0, Fax: 3941-442 652, see also Opera and Dance

Landesbühnen Sachsen
Meißner Str. 152, 01445 **Radebeul**
Tel: 351-8954/0 Fax: 351-895 4201
Internet: www.dresden-theater.de
E-Mail: landesbuehnen.sachsen@dresden-theater.de
Intendant Christian Schmidt; Schauspieldirektor Andreas Knaup; Direktor Management, Öffentlichkeitsarbeit Till Wanschura; Verwaltungsdirektorin Barbara Kunz
Actors: 21 *Perfs:* 162 *Prods:* 16 (8 new) *Venues:* main venue: Theater Radebeul + various others in Saxony
Touring: Friedrichshafen *Comments:* see also Opera, Dance and Orchestras

Schloss Theater Rastatt
Museumstraße 6, 76437 **Rastatt**
Tel: 7222-37585 Fax: 7222-938 753
E-Mail: strrastatt@aol.com
Intendant, Geschäftsführer Edzard Schoppmann
Actors: 4 *Perfs:* 120 *Prods:* 3 *Type:* dance, music, movement theatre, Sprechtheater + children's and youth theatre *Venues:* Kellertheater 100, Theaterzelt up to 400 *Touring:* national, international *Comments:* educational projects, courses, seminars, drama, dance, music, art; in 2000 3 German/French productions

Theater Regensburg
Bismarckplatz 7, 93047 **Regensburg**
Tel: 941-507 1428 Fax: 941-507 4429
Intendantin Marietheres List; Kaufmännischer Direktor Holger von Berg; Geschäftsführende Schauspieldramaturgin Dr. Christa-Renate Thutewohl; Oberspielleiter Michael Bleiziffer; Disponent Johannes Fiedler; Referentin für Presse u. Öffentlichkeitsarbeit Kathrin Schäfer
Actors: 20 *Perfs:* 217 *Prods:* 11 *Type:* Sprechtheater *Venues:* Stadttheater (closed until 2001) 538, alternative venue: Velodrom 600; Theater am Haidplatz 138, Freilichttheater Im Hof des Thon-Dittmer-Palais 382
Comments: see also Opera, Dance and Orchestras

Westdeutsches Tourneetheater Remscheid GmbH
Bismarckstraße 138, 42859 **Remscheid**
Tel: 2191-32285 Fax: 2191-343 798
Intendant und Geschäftsführer Jaschi Jaschinski; Künstlerische Leitung Matthias Clauß
Actors: 5-6 + guest actors *Perfs:* 230 *Prods:* 3-4 *Type:* Sprechtheater + children's and youth theatre *Venues:* theater im Studio 99 *Touring:* Germany, Holland, Italy

Chiemgauer Volkstheater
Dorfstr. 4, 83083 **Riedering**
Tel: 8036-7158 Fax: 8036-3762
Intendant Bernd Helfrich; Verwaltungsleitung Mona Freiberg
Actors: 16 *Perfs:* 240 *Prods:* 8 *Type:* Sprechtheater *Venues:* capacity 220 *Touring:* central, south Germany
Comments: occassional work for T.V.

Volkstheater Rostock
Patriotischer Weg 33, 18057 **Rostock**
Tel: 381-2440 (Zentrale)/211 (Intendanz)/251/325 (Öffentlichkeitsarbeit/Marketing)/245 (Dramaturgie)
Fax: 381-244 213 (Intendanz)/251 (Öffentlichkeitsarbeit/Marketing)/492 3410 (Dramaturgie)
Intendant Dr. Michael Winrich Schlicht; Leitung des Betriebsbüros Walter Sänger; Leiter der Öffentlichkeitsarbeit Jürgen Opel; Leitender Dramaturg Peter Spuhler; Schauspieldirektion Alejandro Quintana; Verwaltungsdirektor Klaus-Dieter Hagen;
Actors: 21 + 2 puppeteers *Perfs:* ca. 550 *Prods:* 39 (19 new) *Type:* Sprechtheater & puppetry, music theatre, ballet, philharmonic concerts *Venues:* Spielstätten und Kapazitäten: Großes Haus 579, Barocksaal 167, Ateliertheater 40, Theater im Stadthafen 200, Kleine Komödie Warnemünde 68 *Touring:* national *Comments:* see also Opera, Dance and Orchestra

Thüringer Landestheater Eisenach-Rudolstadt-Saalfeld GmbH Haus Rudolstadt
Postfach 110, 07392 **Rudolstadt**
Tel: 3672-4500 Fax: 3672-450 114
Internet: www.thuringerlandestheater.de
Intendant und künstl. Geschäftsführer Johannes Steurich; Geschäftsführer Petra Mitdank; Künstlerischer Betriebsdirektor Gerhard Hentschel; Schauspieldirektor t.b.a; Chefdramaturg Bernhard Rohwedder
Actors: 23 *Perfs:* 205 *Type:* Sprechtheater *Venues:* Großes Haus 271, Studiobühne 50 *Comments:* see also Opera, Dance (Eisenach) and Orchestras

CARMILLA-Theaterproduktion
Auf der Adt 14, 66130 **Saarbrücken**
Tel: 6893-5312 Fax: 6893-986 095
Internet: www.villa-fledermaus.de/carmilla
E-Mail: carmillas@aol.com
Künstlerischer Leiter Friedhelm Schneidewind
Actors: 5 *Prods:* 1 *Type:* music, performance *Touring:* German speaking countries *Comments:* touring company

Resonanz-Theater
Mockenhübel 25, 66117 **Saarbrücken**
Tel: 681-583 816/171-530 2809 (mobile) Fax: 681-583 816
Direktor, Künst Leitung Jürgen Wönne; Regie Silvia Bervingas
Actors: 4 *Perfs:* 92 *Prods:* 2 *Type:* Sprechtheater, cabaret, comedy, children's theatre *Venues:* Kabarett im Ostviertel 80, Junge Bühne Homburg 60, KIK Wallerfangen 100 *Touring:* German speaking countries
Comments: see Agents and Producers (KIR-Resonanz-Theater)

Saarländisches Staatstheater
Postfach 102735, 66027 **Saarbrücken**
Tel: 681-3092-0 Fax: 681-309 2316
Internet: www.staatstheater.saarland.de
E-Mail: ssto2@t-online.de
Generalintendant u. Geschäftsführer Kurt Josef Schildknecht; Kaufmänn. Direktor u. Geschäftsführer Helmut Beckamp; Chefdramaturg Matthias Kaiser; Chefdisponentin Sylvia Prantscheff; Presse und Öffentlichkeitsarbeit Nicole Freyler
Actors: 29 *Perfs:* 240 *Prods:* 16 *Type:* Sprechtheater *Venues:* Staatstheater 875, Theater Arnual 99, Alte Feuerwache 240 to 300 *Comments:* visiting address: Schillerplatz 1, 66111 Saarbrücken; see also Opera, Dance, Orchestras and Venues

Schleswig-Holsteinisches Landestheater und Sinfonieorchester GmbH
Lollfuß 49-53, 24837 **Schleswig**
Tel: 4621-96700 Fax: 4621-967 083
Internet: www.landestheater.de
E-Mail: kontakt@landestheater.de
Generalintendant Dr Horst Mesalla (from 1.8.2000 Michael Grosse); künstlerischer Betriebsdirektor Lutz Erdmann; Verwaltungsdirektor Reiner Schmeckthal; Öffentlichkeitsarbeit Angela Möller; Chefdramaturg Dietmar Buchholz (from 1.8.2000 Christian Marten-Molnár); Oberspielleiter Werner Tietze
Actors: 25 *Perfs:* 560 *Prods:* 24 *Type:* Sprechtheater, children's and youth theatre *Venues:* Musiktheater Flensburg 459, Sprechtheater Rendsburg 510, Sprechtheater Schleswig 508, Schlosshofspiele-Freilichtbühne Im Schloß Gottorf-Schleswig 325
Comments: annual 'Schloßfestspiele' at Schloß Gottorf; see also Opera, Dance and Orchestras

Fränkisches Theater GmbH
Postfach 13, 97709 **Schloß Massbach**
Tel: 9735-235
Fax: 9735-1496
Direktor u. Verwaltungsleiter Herbert Heinz und Lena Heinz-Hutter; Dramaturgie Sebastian Worch; Künstl Leitung Lena Heinz-Hutter, Herbert Heinz
Actors: 22 *Perfs:* 329 *Prods:* 10 (including 2 children's and youth productions) *Type:* Sprechtheater *Venues:* Freilichtbühne 326, studio theatre 87 *Touring:* Germany

Uckermärkische Bühnen Schwedt
Berliner Strasse 46-48, 16303 **Schwedt /Oder**
Tel: 3332-538-0 Fax: 3332-538 124
Intendant Reinhard Simon; Verwaltungsleiter und 1. Stellvertreter des Intendanten Wilfried Peinke; Chefdramaturg und 2. Stellvertreter des Intendanten Wolfgang Bernert; Intendanzsekretärin und Personalbearbeiter Marga Lieder; Oberspielleiter Gösta Knothe; Direktor für künstlerische Produktion Peter Fabers; Leiterin Öffentlichkeitsarbeit Brigitte Hennig; Technischer Leiter Jörg Strutzke; Leiter Künstlerisches Betriebsbüro Dieter Wagner
Actors: 17 *Perfs:* 200 *Prods:* 10-12 *Venues:* Große Bühne 832, intimes theater 100, Berlischky-Pavillon 100, Naturbühne Schloßpark-Theater 400, Studio F 240, Podium 80, Theaterklause 80, Theaterzelt 180, Theater im Fahrstuhl 25 *Touring:* Germany
Comments: venue also for hire

Mecklenburgisches Staatstheater Schwerin
Alter Garten 2, 19055 **Schwerin**
Tel: 385-5300-131 Fax: 385-5300-137
E-Mail: presse@theater-schwerin.de
Generalintendant Joachim Kümmritz; Schauspieldirektor Peter Dehler;
Actors: 23+ guests *Perfs:* 280 *Prods:* 17 *Type:* classical, modern, comedy, contemporary theatre *Venues:* Großes Haus 640, E-Werk 99, Großes Haus 683, E-Werk 96
Touring: Germany, Austria, Switzerland *Comments:* see also Opera and Dance

Zweckverband NEUE BÜHNE – Niederlausitzer Theaterstädtebund Senftenberg
Rathenaustrasse 6-8, 01968 **Senftenberg**
Tel: 3573-8010 Fax: 3573-792 334
Intendant Heinz Klevenow; Verwaltungsdirektor Peter Kuzia; Chefdramaturg Karl-Heinz Gündel; Leiter Schauspielmusik Conrad Haase; Leiterin d. Öffentlichkeitsarbeit Silke Klaus
Actors: 22 *Perfs:* 300 *Prods:* 11 *Type:* children's/youth, musical *Venues:* Hauptbühne 295, Studio 90, Café 60
Touring: Germany

Theater Die Färbe
Schlachthausstraße 24, 78224 **Singen**
Tel: 7731-64646/62663 Fax: 7731-60596
Intendant u. Künstlerische Leitung Peter Simon; Ballettdirektor Milly van Lit
Actors: 6-8 *Perfs:* 110 *Prods:* 5 *Venues:* Kneipentheater (flexible stage) 90

Theater der Altmark Stendal
Karlstraße 6, 39576 **Stendal**
Tel: 3931-635 777 (box office)/6356 (switchboard)
Fax: 3931-635 707
E-Mail: tda.stendal@t-online.de
Intendant Goswin Moniac; stellv. Intendant Olga Wildgruber; Verwaltungsdirektorin Eva-Maria Sehnert
Actors: 19 + guests *Perfs:* 500 *Prods:* 28-29 (17-18 new)
Type: Sprechtheater, classical, modern *Venues:* Theater der Altmark Stendal Großes Haus-467, Kleines Haus-99, Rangfoyer-80 *Touring:* Netherlands

Theater Vorpommern
Postfach 1351, 18403 **Stralsund**
Tel: 3831-2646-0 Fax: 3831-292 896
Internet: www.theater-vorpommern.de
E-Mail: theater@t-online.de
kfm.Geschäftsführer Joachim v. Trützschler; Indendant Rüdiger Bloch ; Chefdramaturg Matthias Grätz; Oberspielleiter Schauspiel Matthias Nagatis; Chefdisponentin Martina Ehlert; Leiter für Presse und Öffentlichkeitsarbeit Marion Gerhardt; technischer Direktor Rainer Darr
Actors: 18 *Perfs:* 550 *Prods:* 21 *Type:* music theatre, ballet, Schauspiel *Venues:* Theater Greifswald 460, Theater Stralsund 520, Brauhaus Stralsund ca 60-80, Foyers (each 50), Theater im Penguin (max. 99) *Comments:* Theater Vorpommern, Postfach 3114, 17461 Greifswald, Tel: 3834-5722-0, Fax: 3834-2779

Altes Schauspielhaus
Postfach 10 01 61, 70001 **Stuttgart**
Tel: 711-225 940 Fax: 711-225 9419
Internet: www.schauspielhaus-comoedie.de
E-Mail: schauspielhaus-comoedie@t-online.de
Intendant Elert Bode; Künstlerisches Betriebsbüro Christa Bode; Dramaturgie Annette Weinmann; Verwaltungsleitung Ines Pieper
Actors: varies *Perfs:* 560 *Prods:* 13 (incl. theatre for children) *Type:* comedy and Sprechtheater *Venues:* Altes Schauspielhaus 486, Komödie im Marquardt 378
Touring: Germany, Austria, Switzerland

Makal-City Theater Internationales Pantomimentheater
Postfach 10 31 14, 70027 **Stuttgart**
Tel: 711-626 208 Fax: 711-612 124
Leitung & Geschäftsführung Gisela Schwenk, Peter Makal
Actors: 3 *Perfs:* daily *Type:* movement, pantomime, caberet, dance, clowning *Venues:* capacity 200 *Touring:* worldwide *Comments:* seminars for pantomime and body language; visiting address: Marienstr, 12(4 Obergeschoß), 70178 Stuttgart, second Tel:170-483 675; see also Festivals

Staatstheater Stuttgart
Oberer Schloßgarten 6, 70173 **Stuttgart**
Tel: 711-2032-0/202 090 (box office) Fax: 711-203 2516 (Intendanz)/ 203 2540 (Dramaturgie)
Internet: www.staatstheater.stuttgart.de
E-Mail: okretschmer.schauspiel@staatstheater.s.shuttle.de
Geschäftsführer/Direktor Hans Tränkle; Schauspielintendant Friedrich Schirmer; Stellvertretender Schauspielintendant Michael Propfe; Verwaltungsdirektor Andreas Bohrdt
Actors: 45 *Prods:* 9 *Type:* Sprechtheater (classic to modern) *Venues:* Kleines Haus 851, Kammertheater 160, Theater im Depot 119, Theaterkiste 48, *Comments:* see also Opera, Orchestras and Dance (Stuttgarter Ballett)

Theater tri-bühne
Eberhardstr. 61, 70173 **Stuttgart**
Tel: 711-236 4610 Fax: 711-236 0717
Internet: www.tri-buehne.de
E-Mail: stefanki@t-online.de
Intendantin und Künstlerische Leiterin Edith Koerber; Leiterin des Sekretariats Sabine Rodenhäuser; Musikalische Oberleitung Dietrich Lutz; Technische Leitung Oliver Schneider;
Dramaturg Géza Kirchknopf-Révay
Actors: 9 *Perfs:* 230 *Prods:* 3-4 *Type:* Sprechtheater
Venues: flexible stage 80 to 140 *Comments:* regular exchanges with partner theaters from Europe (Budapest, Prague, Moscow, Wales)

Theaterhaus Stuttgart
Ulmerstrasse 241, 70327 **Stuttgart**
Tel: 711-402 070 Fax: 711-427 363
Internet: www.theaterhaus.com
E-Mail: th@theaterhaus.com
Direktor Werner Schretzmeier; Verwaltungsleiter Willy Friedmann; technische Leitung Rüdiger Krazert; Öffentlichkeitsarbeit Michael Fohler, Nicole Kreja
Actors: 11 *Perfs:* 500 *Prods:* 3 *Type:* Sprechtheater *Venues:* Halle 1 620, Halle 2 300, Halle 3 150 *Comments:* multi-national ensemble; see also Venues

Theater Trier
Am Augustinerhof, 54290 **Trier**
Tel: 651-718 3464 Fax: 651-718 1468
Intendant Heinz Lukas-Kindermann; Generalmusikdirektor István Dénes; Chefdisponentin Anke Bergemann; Dramaturgie Anja Gewalt, Klaus-Dieter Köhler; Oberspielleiter des Schauspiels Klaus-Dieter Köhler; Öffentlichkeitsarbeit Philipp Förster
Actors: 15-17 *Perfs:* 60+50 children's theatre *Prods:* 10
Type: Sprechtheater *Venues:* Stadttheater 622, Studio 65 : *Comments:* see also Opera, Dance and Orchestra

Landestheater Württemberg-Hohenzollern
Eberhardstrasse 6, 72072 **Tübingen**
Tel: 7071-15920 Fax: 7071-159 270
Intendant Knut Weber; Verwaltungsdirektor Tilman Pröllochs; Leiter des Kinder – und Jugendtheaters Heiner Kondschak
Actors: 25 *Perfs:* 420 *Prods:* 12 (incl. children's+ youth theatre) *Type:* Sprechtheater, music theatre *Venues:* Große Saal 400, Werkstatt 150, UI 100, Musikproberaum 50 *Touring:* national, international
Comments: see also Venues

Tübinger Zimmertheater GmbH
Bursagasse 16, 72070 **Tübingen**
Tel: 7071-92730 Fax: 7071-927 322
Internet: www.cityinfonetz.de/zimmertheater
E-Mail: zimmertheater-tuebingen@t-online.de
Intendant Klaus Metzger
Actors: 7 + guests *Perfs:* 200 *Prods:* 4-5
Type: Sprechtheater
Venues: Gewölbe (Vaulted hall) 90, Zimmer 60

Ulmer Theater
Olgastr. 73, 89073 **Ulm**
Tel: 731-161 4450/10 Fax: 731-161 1619
Internet: www.theater.ulm.de
E-Mail: UlmerTheater@theater.ulm.de
Intendant Ansgar Haag (tel: 161-4400); Schauspieldramaturgie Christine Hoenmanns (tel: 161 4413), Henning Reinholz (161 4425); Generalmusikdirektor James-Allen Gähres; Presse und Öffentlichkeitsarbeit Frau Mayer (161 4410); Künstlerisches Betriebsbüro Frau Glathe (161 4434)
Actors: 20 *Perfs:* 166 *Prods:* 7 + 1 Wiederaufnahme
Venues: Ulmer Theatre 815, Podium 200 *Comments:* see also Opera, Dance and Orchestras

Deutsches National Theater Weimar
Postfach 3 + 5, 99401 **Weimar**
Tel: 3643-7550
Fax: 3643-755 218/307
E-Mail: dnt.service@weimar.net
Generalintendant Günther Beelitz; Chefdramaturg Thomas Potzger;
Presse- /Öffentlichkeitsarbeit Sylvia Obst
Actors: 28 + 8 students *Prods:* 24 *Type:* classic and contemporary *Venues:* Werkstattbühne 7/Erfurter Str. 76 176; Schloßkeller 99 *Touring:* national and international
Comments: visiting address: Theaterplatz 2, 99423 Weimar; see also Opera, Dance and Orchestras

Hessisches Staatstheater Wiesbaden
Postfach 3247, 65022 **Wiesbaden**
Tel: 611-132-1 Fax: 611-132 337
Internet: www.staatstheater-wiesbaden.de
Intendant Achim Thorwald; Schauspieldir Daniel Karasek
Actors: 25 *Prods:* 10 *Type:* Sprechtheater *Venues:* Staatstheater 1041, Kleines Haus 328, Studio-Souterrain 89 *Comments:* visiting address: Christian-Zais-Strasse 1-5, 65189 Wiesbaden; see also
Opera, Dance and Orchestras

Landesbühne Niedersachsen Nord GmbH
Virchowstr. 44, 26382 **Wilhelmshaven**
Tel: 4421-9401-0 Fax: 4421-940 145
Intendant und Geschäftsführer Gerhard Hess
Actors: 18 *Perfs:* 17 *Prods:* 16 *Type:* Sprechtheater *Venues:* Stadttheater Wilhelmshaven 475 to 525, Junges Theater in der Rheinstr. Studiobühne 99; open-air theatre 500
Touring: North Germany *Comments:* also has a young people's theatre (tel: 4421-940 134); see also Venues

Mitteldeutsches Landestheater
Thomas-Müntzer-Strasse 14-15, 06886 **Wittenberg**
Tel: 3491-47370 Fax: 3491-473 710
Internet: www.theater-wittenberg.de
E-Mail: theater-wb@t-online.de
Intendant Reinhold Stövesand; Oberspielleiter Musiktheater Markus Schuliers; Leiter Schauspiel Reinhold Stövesand; Chefdramaturg Eva Magdon; PR Hartmut Gorgs
Actors: 55 *Perfs:* 300 *Prods:* 18 *Venues:* Großes Haus 380, Studio 180, Brettl Keller 80 *Touring:* Germany
Comments: see also Opera and Orchestras

Schillertheater NRW – Schauspiel
Bundesallee 260, 42103 **Wuppertal**
Tel: 202-563 4261 Fax: 202-563 8077
Intendant Schauspiel Holk Freytag; Verwaltungschef Peter Neubauer; Künstlerischer Betriebsdirektor und Leiter des Künstlerischen Betriebsbüros Volker Seitz; Dramaturgen Barbara Müller, Gerold Theobalt (Stellvertreter des Intendanten), Kathrin Bieligk
Actors: ca. 27 *Perfs:* ca. 290 *Prods:* 11 *Type:* Sprechtheater
Venues: Schauspielhaus 745, Kleines Haus 195
Comments: see also Opera and Dance (Tanztheater Wuppertal Pina Bausch)

TiC (Theater in Cronenberg) e.V.
Bornerstrasse 1, 42349 **Wuppertal**
Tel: 202-472 211 Fax: 202-470 868
Internet: www.tic.wuppertal-one.de
E-Mail: tic@wtal.de
Direktor, Geschäftsführer Ronald F Stürzebecher; Verwaltungsleitung Edmund Willms; Dramaturgie Thomas Spielmann; Oberspielleiter Hans Richter
Actors: 35 *Perfs:* 320 *Prods:* 9 *Type:* Sprechtheater, musicals *Venues:* Studio 80, Podium 80, Theater 80, Tor I 150

Stadttheater Würzburg
Theaterstraße 21, 97070 **Würzburg**
Tel: 931-39080 Fax: 931-3908 102
Internet: www.theaterwuerzburg.de
E-Mail: info@theaterwuerzburg.de
Intendant Wolfgang Schaller; PR Jürgen Hartmann; Dramaturgie Dr. Michael Baumgarten; Kinder-und Jugendtheater Simone Sterr
Actors: 21 *Perfs:* 600 *Prods:* 27 (drama 12) *Venues:* Stadttheater 744, Kammerspiele 92, AKW 300
Comments: see also Opera, Dance and Orchestras

Theater Zeitz
August-Bebel-Strasse 2, 06712 **Zeitz**
Tel: 3441-216 707 Fax: 3441-216 707
Internet: www.theater-zeitz.de
E-Mail: info@theater-zeitz.de
Intendant und künstlerischer Leiter Wolfgang Eysold; Chefdramaturg u stellv. Intendant Karl-Heinz Möller
Actors: 38 *Perfs:* 385 *Prods:* 11 *Type:* cabaret, musical, comedy, modern *Venues:* Großes Haus 296, Schau-Fenster 50 *Touring:* national

Gerhart-Hauptmann-Theater Zittau GmbH
Theaterring 12, 02763 **Zittau**
Tel: 3583-770 512 Fax: 3583-512 179
Internet: www.kulturlick.de/ghtz
Intendant Klaus Stephan; Verwaltungsdirektor Ulrich Heinzelmann; Schauspielkapellmeister Erik Kross; Direktor Marketing, Presse Helmuth Meier
Actors: 19 *Perfs:* 250 *Prods:* 15 *Type:* Schauspiel, music productions, children's theatre *Venues:* Großer Saal 402, Waldbühne Jonsdorf 1121, Theater hinterm Vorhang 100, Theater im Foyer 75, Musiktheater Görlitz 675 *Touring:* Czech Republic, Poland

Theater zwickau GmbH
PF 201039, 08012 **Zwickau**
Tel: 375-834 600 Fax: 375-834 609
Internet: www.fh-zwickau.de/zwickau/theater/th/1.htm
E-Mail: theaterzwickau@abofreiepresse.de
Intendant und amtierender Schauspieldirektor Wolfgang Hauswald; Musikalischer Oberleiter Welisar Gentscheff; Verwaltungsdirektor Henry Klüglich
Actors: 13 *Perfs:* ca.235 *Prods:* 12 (9 new) *Type:* Schauspiel, Jugendtheater *Venues:* Gewandhaus 399, Theater in der Mühle (TiM) 68, Kleine Bühne 120
Comments: puppet theatre; see also Opera and Dance

GIBRALTAR (+350)

John Mackintosh Hall Theatre
308 Main Street, **Gibraltar**
Tel: 75669 Fax: 40843
E-Mail: gfjmh@gibnet.gi
director Geraldine Finlayson
Prods: 10-20 per year *Type:* mainly dance/drama, recitals, concerts *Venues:* John Mackintosh Hall Centre *Comments:* see also Venues

GREECE (+30)

Municipal Theatre of Agrinio
10 Charilaou Trikoupi, 30100 **Agrinio**
Tel: 641-21158/46452 Fax: 641-48498/21158
administration Dina Zorba-Grigoriades; artistic director Dimitris Pantazis (temporary);
chairman Giorgos Kostarelis
Actors: varies *Perfs:* 190 *Prods:* 4 (1 for small stage, 3 for main stage) *Type:* modern and contemporary Greek playwrights *Venues:* 'Panagopouleion' Municipal Theatre (winter) 364, Garden-Theatre 'Ellinida' (summer) 500 *Touring:* Greece *Comments:* also a department to support student theatre, a workshop for theatre in education and a puppets workshop

Amphi-Theatre
Adrianou 111, 10558 **Athens**
Tel: 1-323 3644/324 5445 Fax: 1-807 5694/324 5445
artistic director Spyros Evangelatos
Actors: 20 *Perfs:* 200 *Prods:* 4 *Type:* classical repertory – Greek renaissance-modern and international repertory *Venues:* Amphi-Theatre 200, Epidaurus ancient theatre 14000 *Touring:* worldwide *Comments:* during the last few years Amphi-Theatre has put emphasis on adapting and performing lesser known plays from the late Byzantine era and the Greek Rennaissance – the only company internationally to do so.

Anichto Theatro
Open Theatre
Kalvou 70 & Gyzi Str., 11474 **Athens**
Tel: 1-644 5749/223 4323 Fax: 1-646 0660
artistic director Giorgis Michailidis; adminstrator of the Months of Dance Doni Michailidou
Actors: 4 (core) *Perfs:* 250 *Prods:* 4 *Type:* classical, modern *Venues:* Anihto Theatro (winter) *Comments:* Open Theatre is also residence of the Months of Dance Festival organised by Doni Michailidou

Dionysos – Politistiko Somateio
Dionysos – Cultural Corporation
11 Knossou Str., 11253 **Athens**
Tel: 1-867 7070/862 4463 Fax: 1-862 9090
artistic director Lambros Tsagas
Actors: 6 (core) *Perfs:* 200 *Prods:* 3 *Type:* classical Greek drama, modern Greek and world drama *Venues:* Theatre Knossos – Italian Stage 600

diplous Eros Theatre Ensemble
7 Tournavitou Str., 10553 **Athens**
Tel: 1-325 5444 Fax: 1-321 9266
director Michael Marmarinos; artistic director Amalia Moutoussi; dramaturg Nikos Flessas; secretariat Marianna Vasilaki; public relations Helen Petassi
Actors: 8 *Perfs:* 200 *Prods:* 2-3
Type: modern, classical and avant garde
Venues: Theseum (a theatre for the arts) 120

Greek Theatre Company – Theatro Technis
Art Theatre
5 Pezmazoglou Str., 10564 **Athens**
Tel: 1-323 6732/322 760/ 322 6703/ 324 8738
Fax: 1-322 9703
artistic director Yorgos Lazanis; deputy general director Mimis Kougiounitzis; member of the board of directors and head actress Renee Pittaki
Actors: 6 (core) *Perfs:* 650 *Prods:* 10-12 per year *Type:* classical, modern and contemporary world drama *Venues:* Frynichou Str. Theatre; basement stage 210, Karloos Koun stage 230 *Comments:* also at: Theatre Karolos Koun, 4 Frynichou St., Plaka, 103 58 Athens; contact Renee Pittaki at Kodrou 13, 10558, Athens

National Theatre
Agiou Constantinou 24-26, 10437 **Athens**
Tel: 1-522 0585/87 Fax: 1-523 3371
artistic director Nicos Kourkoulos; deputy artistic director Katerina Kosmoc;
public relations Virginia Bakousi
Perfs: 300-500 *Prods:* 6 + 1 children's play *Type:* classic and modern drama, contemporary and experimental theatre *Venues:* National Theatre, Rex Theatre *Touring:* worldwide

Nea Skene
New Stage
Kykladon 11, 11361 **Athens**
Tel: 1-821 7877/724 8806
Fax: 1-821 3959/724 8806
director Lefteris Voyatzis
Actors: 11 *Perfs:* 300 *Type:* classical and modern drama *Venues:* Theatre Odou Kyladon (amphitheatre stage) *Touring:* national, international

Semeio Theatre Company
18 Ioustinianou Str., 11473 **Athens**
Tel: 1-922 9579/821 1847 Fax: 1-821 1847
artistic director Nick Diamandis; basic actor Ioanna Makri
Actors: 4 + extras *Perfs:* 200 *Prods:* 3 annually *Type:* avant-garde *Venues:* Theatre Semeio 125 *Touring:* Cyprus, Greece, Egypt

Stoa Theatre Company
55 Biskini Street, Zografou, 15771 **Athens**
Tel: 1-770 2830 Fax: 1-770 8828
E-Mail: thetstoa@otenet.gr
artistic director Thanassis Papageorghiou; resident dramatists Paulos Orkopoulos, Leda Protopsalti
Actors: 4 (core) *Perfs:* 300 *Prods:* 2-3 + 1 childrens play per season *Type:* contemporary Greek drama *Venues:* Theatro Stoa 310 *Touring:* Greece, Cyprus *Comments:* resident company at Theatre Stoa; see also Venues

Theatre Neo Rialto
Theatre Rialto, Kypselis 54 and Ag. Meletiou Str., 11362 **Athens**
Tel: 1-882 7000/821 8973/964 3951 Fax: 1-822 7921
E-Mail: mirka@eexi.gr
artistic directors Nana Nikolaou, Christo Kelandonis; press relations & management Mirka Droude
Actors: 11 *Perfs:* 150-200 *Prods:* 2 + 1 youth annually *Type:* classical, popular drama, comedy, musical for youth/children *Venues:* Theatre Rialto 450 *Touring:* Greece, Cyprus *Comments:* works with 2 stages one of which is for children/youth

Theatre Organisation Morfes
2 Riga Palamida, Plateia Ag. Apargyron, Psyrri, 10554 **Athens**
Tel: 1-323 8990/4713 Fax: 1-323 4713
artistic directors Tassos Bantis, Dimitri Kataleifos, Rania Economidou
Actors: 4 + 18 *Perfs:* 200 *Prods:* 3 *Type:* modern, contemporary *Venues:* Theatro Empros – 2 stages; Epano 88, Kato 155 *Touring:* Greece *Comments:* Morfes runs a drama school (3 year higher course in drama studies and acting)

Theatriki Etairia Erevnas
Ilission 21, Zografou, 15771 **Athens**
Tel: 1-775 1338 Fax: 1-775 1408
artistic director Dimitris Potamitis
Actors: 12 *Perfs:* 200-250 *Prods:* 3 *Type:* classical, modern and children's plays *Venues:* Theatre Erevnas 150 *Touring:* London, Cyprus, Greece

Theatro Apotheke
Sarri 40, Platea Ageon Asomaton, **Athens**
Tel: 1-325 3153
administration Aklis Charalambides
Actors: 9 *Perfs:* 200 *Prods:* 1-2 *Type:* modern comedy *Venues:* Apotheke Theatre 240

Theatro Exarchion
69 Themistokleous Street, 10683 **Athens**
Tel: 1-330 0879 Fax: 1-330 0937
manager Annita Decavalla; artistic director Takis Vouteris
Actors: 4 (core) *Perfs:* 230 *Prods:* 1-2 *Type:* contemporary Greek, European, American drama & classical *Venues:* Exarcheion theatre 120

Theatro Piraeos 131
Piraeus 131 Theatre
131, Piraeus Ave, **Athens**
Tel: 1-345 0922
directors Thanasis Papathanasiou, Michael Repas; administration Akis Charalambides
Actors: 8 *Perfs:* 160 *Prods:* 1 *Type:* modern comedy *Venues:* (own): Theatro Piraeus 300

Theatro Porta Theatre Company
Alkmanos 45-47, 11528 **Athens**
Tel: 1-724 0096 Fax: 1-724 0096
E-Mail: mporta@otenet.gr
artistic director & resident playwright Xenia Kalogeropoulou
Perfs: 100 per year (matinees only) *Type:* children's and youth drama *Venues:* Porta Theatre 480

Theatro Praxis
Praxis Theatre
16 Kefalinias Street, 11361 **Athens**
Tel: 1-883 8727 Fax: 1-723 3774
artistic director Betty Arvaniti;
producer Vassilis Poulaytzas
Actors: 14 *Perfs:* 200 *Prods:* 3 *Type:* modern, contemporary *Venues:* Theatro Kefalinias: main stage 180, second stage 50 *Comments:* every year organise a number of literary events

Theatro Tou Iliou
Theatre of the Sun Theatre Company
Frynichou 10, 10558 **Athens**
Tel: 1-323 1591/922 7784 Fax: 1-324 7509
artistic director Andreas Papaspyros; children's theatre's artistic director Daphni Vasiliadou
Actors: 7 (core) *Perfs:* 200 *Prods:* 2 + 1 children's *Type:* classical, modern, contemporary *Venues:* Theatro Tou Iliou 170 *Touring:* Greece and abroad

Theatro Tou Notou T.C.
Theatre of the South
Theatro Amore, 10 Pringhiponisson Street, 11474 **Athens**
Tel: 1-646 8009 Fax: 1-644 2869
E-Mail: amorenotos@otenet.gr
administrative director Aphrodite Christodolou; artistic director Yannis Houvardas; public relations Arghiro Bozoni; financial director George Sarafoglou; technical manager Adi Flutur; production manager Rena Poschaliss; assistant to artistic director Anna Houliara
Actors: 28 *Perfs:* 220 *Prods:* 5-7 *Type:* classical, modern drama, innovative theatre language, exchanges, co-productions *Venues:* Theatre Amore stage A 220, stage B 80 *Touring:* Europe *Comments:* interested in international co-production and projects

Tomee Theatre
3 Anatoliou Street, 11632 **Athens**
Tel: 301-726 0551 Fax: 301-726 0551
company director Maria Panoutsou
Actors: 14 *Prods:* modern production exploring classical texts in a modern style

Municipal Theatre of Crete
Nikiforou Foka 5, 73132 **Chanea**
Tel: 821-44256/57639 Fax: 821-45486
chairman Dimitris Kartakis;
artistic director Kapelonis Kostas
Actors: 10-20 *Perfs:* 100 annually *Prods:* 3-4 annually *Type:* classical, contemporary Greek *Venues:* Venizelio Odeion 360, Summer Eastern Moat Theatre (medieval venue) 3000 *Touring:* Crete, Greece

Omada Sygchronis Technis
Modern Art Company Ensemble
Haimanta 408, 15234 **Halandri (Athens)**
Tel: 1-684 9651/682 2360 Fax: 1-682 2360
artistic director Yannis Kalantzopoulos
Actors: 16 *Perfs:* 350 *Prods:* 4 *Type:* modern drama & comedy, experimental, children's theatre *Venues:* Aliki Theatre 600, Piraeus Municipal Hall 500 *Touring:* Greece *Comments:* works with three stages: Modern Curtain, Children's Curtain, Experimental Stage; permanent touring scheme

Municipal Theatre of Ioannina
Papazoglou 5, 45000 **Ioannina**
Tel: 651-25670 Fax: 651-73233
artistic director Georgos Tzerpos;
chairman Andreas Anagnostopoulos
Actors: 2 permanent *Perfs:* 200-300 annually *Prods:* 4-6 annually *Type:* classical, modern, contemporary, experimental and children's theatre *Venues:* Theatro Camberio 220, Theatre of Cultural Centre 600, Open Theatre of Company of Epiros Studies 3000, Ancient Theatre of Dodoni (summer) 10000 *Comments:* The Ionnian MTC freely distributes an architectural and feasibility study it has made for the construction of open air venues for summer performances

Omada Technis Polytheama
Polytheama Arts Ensemble
Sikelianou 3, 45333 **Ioannina**
Tel: 651-24144/48580 Fax: 651-33149
artistic director Dimitris Kostis
Actors: 7 *Perfs:* 50 *Prods:* 2 *Type:* contemporary world drama *Venues:* Theatre Polytheama 120 *Comments:* emphasis on contemporary and experimental forms; objective is to expand and encompass other art forms (performance art, dance-theatre etc.)

Theatriko Ergastiri Epirou
Garivaldi 26b, 54221 **Ioannina**
Tel: 651-36182/32642/36747 Fax: 651-36182/32642
artistic director Georgos Nakos
Actors: varies *Perfs:* 100 *Prods:* 2 per year *Type:* contemporary, experimental *Venues:* Theatre Logos 120 *Touring:* Greece, Albania *Comments:* established in 1983 with the co-operation of the Classical Studies faculty at the University of Ioannina; currently holds seminars and workshops for the study of classical Greek tragedy; see also Venues

Municipal Theatre of Kalamata
Mantiklou 17, PO Box 106, 24100 **Kalamata**
Tel: 721-28500/27976
Fax: 721-27976
artistic director t.b.a
Actors: 12 *Perfs:* 240 *Prods:* 3 + 1 childrens (winter); 1 in summer *Type:* Greek tragedy, classical, modern, contemporary and children's theatre *Venues:* Dimotiko Theatre; Central stage 300, New statge 300, Theatro Castrou (medieval castle venue) 1000
Touring: Cyprus, Greece

FASMA Art Organisation
Aplo Theatre, 4 Ch. Trikoupi Street, 17671 **Kallithea (Athens)**
Tel: 1-922 9605
Fax: 1-923 3526
E-Mail: FASMA@groovy.gr
artistic director Antonis Andypas (1-701 6723)
Actors: 10 *Perfs:* 220 *Prods:* 4 *Type:* modern and classical *Venues:* Aplo Theatro; central scene 188, new scene 125

Municipal Theatre of Komotini
30 Kondili street, 69100 **Komotini**
Tel: 531-27484/25970 Fax: 531-37770
Internet: www.depethe.kom/gr
E-Mail: info@depethe/kom.gr
production general manager Dimitris Katsimigas; artistic director Dimitris Papastamatis; secretary Theano Paschali; general manager Nikolaos Karambambas
Actors: 30 *Perfs:* 100 (25 in summer, 75 in winter) *Prods:* 3-4 *Type:* modern/ancient Greek, classical, contemporary, commedia dell'arte, children's *Venues:* old municipal library 145, open air summer theatre 1000
Touring: Greece

Municipal Theatre of Lamia
Ipsilantou 17, 35100 **Lamia**
Tel: 231-33325/32215 Fax: 231-32215
artistic director Panos Skouroliakos
Actors: varies *Perfs:* 70 (min) *Prods:* 2-4 *Type:* contemporary & modern Greek and classical *Venues:* Dimotiko Theatro Lamias 660, Dimotiki summer scene 1000, Kastrou Theatre 400 *Touring:* Greece *Comments:* season is dedicated to repertory of modern Greek comedy

Thessaliko Theatre
Municipal Theatre of Larisa, Roosevelt 59, 41222 **Larisa**
Tel: 41-621 209/210 Fax: 41-621 210
artistic director Giorgos Ziakas; chairman Anna Karamanoli-Glessi
Actors: 40-50 *Perfs:* 285 *Prods:* 6 *Type:* modern and contemporary Greek *Venues:* Milos Papa Theatre 183
Touring: Greece

Prova Theatre Company
106 Ermou Str., 10554 **Monastiraki (Athens)**
Tel: 1-321 4950/867 2087/964 0555
administration & artistic director Mary Razi
Actors: 8 *Perfs:* 150-180 *Prods:* 1-2 *Type:* modern, classical *Comments:* organises theatrical seminars and tuition classes for preparation for Drama School Te: 1-864 0555

Thiasos Epilogi T.C
Pylarinou 26, 15969 **Papagos**
Tel: 1-651 8982/93-587 700 (mobile) Fax: 1-651 8982
artistic director Nikitas Tsakiroglou
Actors: 18 *Perfs:* 150-200 *Prods:* 3 *Type:* contemporary drama, ancient Greek drama *Venues:* Diana Theatre 500, ancient Greek amphitheatres *Touring:* Greece (festivals), Portugal, UK, Cyprus

Municipal Theatre of Patras
17 Plateia, Georgiou A, 26110 **Patras**
Tel: 61-276 060 Fax: 61-276 060/623 730
chairman Victoria Ageopoulou; artistic director Giorgos Kimoulis; stage director P. Vasilopoulos
Actors: 5 (core) *Perfs:* 100 *Prods:* 4-5 (2-3 winter; 1 childrens theatre in summer) *Type:* classical and contemporary, Greek tragedy and comedy, renaissance theatre *Venues:* Theatre Apollon 450, Open Castle Theatre 1500, Ancient Odeon 3000
Touring: Greece, Cyprus

Municipal Theatre of Rhodes
1 Eleftherias Square, 85100 **Rhodes**
Tel: 241-30668
artistic director Michael Sdougos;
chairman Manoli Antonoglou
Perfs: 100-150 *Prods:* 3-4 + 1 childrens play *Type:* modern drama, children's theatre *Venues:* Rhodes National Theatre 900, Moat Amphitheatre 1500 *Touring:* Greece

Municipal Theatre of Serres
16 Orpheus Street, 62122 **Serres**
Tel: 321-66033/20500 Fax: 321-20500
artistic director Giorgos Siskos
Actors: 5 *Perfs:* 100 *Prods:* 3 *Type:* world drama *Venues:* Municipal Theatre 200, Koulas Hill Open Theatre 500 *Touring:* Greece *Comments:* focus on Greek drama (ancient-modern)

Kratiko Theatro Voreiou Hellados
National Theatre of Northern Greece
Ethnikis Amynis Str.2, **Thessaloniki**
Tel: 31-860 966/256 784/256 783 Fax: 31-860 458/256 782
Internet: www.ntng.gr
E-Mail: info@ntng.gr
artistic director Diagoras Chronopoulos
Actors: 109 actors and 12 dancers *Perfs:* 400-600 per year *Prods:* 15-25 *Type:* Greek tragedy, classical and modern drama, contemporary and experimental theatre, ballet, opera *Venues:* Macedonian Studies Society Theatre: Central stage 700, Royal Theatre (under construction): main theatre 800 and a studio, Forrest Theatre (open amphi-theatre) 3000; the Lazaristes monastery: 700, studio in Lazaristes 150 *Comments:* temporary address while theatre is being renovated: Vassilissis Olgas 136, 54645 Thessaloniki

New Theatre of Salonica T.C.
Themistokli Sofouli 67A, 55131 **Thessaloniki**
Tel: 31-417 068 Fax: 31-417 068
administration Dimitris Chalkias; art dirJenny Dalli-Chalkia
Actors: 7-10 *Perfs:* 130-150 *Prods:* 2 *Type:* Classical, Greek comedy *Venues:* resident at Pallas Theatre *Comments:* venue address: 73, Nikis Avenue, Thessaloniki

Piramatiki Skini of Thessaloniki
Amalia Theatre, 71 Amalia Str., 54640 **Thessaloniki**
Tel: 31-821 483 Fax: 31-360 708
general manager Natasha Papadimitriou; artistic director Nikiforos Papandreou
Actors: 12-15 *Perfs:* 150 *Prods:* 7 (5 new) *Type:* classical, modern *Venues:* Amalia Theatre 240 *Touring:* Greece, Norway, Sweden, UK, Egypt *Comments:* the company aims to promote research on theatre Practice and theory; financially supported by the Ministry of Culture; member of European Theatre Convention (ETC)

Municipal Theatre of Verria
Metropoleos 44, 59100 **Verria**
Tel: 331-74433 Fax: 331-74434
director Yiannis Karachisaridis
Perfs: 100-150 *Prods:* 2-3 *Type:* classical, modern *Venues:* Antoniadion Cultural Centre(winter) 300, Theatro Kallitheas (amateur sector) (winter) 250, Theatre Melina Merkouri *Touring:* Cyprus, Greece

GREENLAND (+299)

Silamiut
P.O. Box 1627, 3900 **Nuuk**
Tel: 299-329 232/299-577 756 (mobile) Fax: 299-327 156
Internet: www.silamiut.gl
E-Mail: silamiut@greennet.gl
direction H. C. Petersen; coreographer Indra Lorentzen
Actors: 5 *Prods:* 1 + 1 *Type:* mixing cabaret, music, dance, mask and video *Touring:* Europe *Comments:* theatre workshops

HUNGARY (+36)

Jókai Theatre of Békés County
Békés Megyei Jókai Színház
P.O.Box, 5601 **Békéscsaba**
Tel: 66-448 348 Fax: 66-441 730
art& managing director László Konter; art secretary Ila Szabó
Actors: 30 *Perfs:* 250 *Prods:* 7 + 1 studio, 2 for children
Type: modern, classical, comedy, children's play *Venues:* 400 *Comments:* address: Andrássy út.1, 5601, Békéscsaba

ARTUS
Kökörcsin u. 9, 1113 **Budapest**
Tel: 1-466 7505/209 0330 Fax: 1-209 0330
Internet: www.c3.hu/artus
E-Mail: artus@freemail.c3.hu
artistic directors Gabor Goda, Ildikó Mándy
Actors: 3-12 (dancers/actors) *Perfs:* 30-60 *Prods:* 1-2 in a year *Type:* contemporary *Touring:* Europe, Israel, New Zealand, Egypt, Tunisia *Comments:* see also Dance

Bárka Theatre
Bárka Szinház
Ullöi ut 82, 1082 **Budapest**
Tel: 1-303 6506 Fax: 1-210 5740
Internet: www.barka.hu
E-Mail: noe@barka.hu
director János Csányi; artistic secretary Zita Sallay
Actors: 10 *Perfs:* 300 *Produs:* 5 *Type:* drama, musical, tragedy, comedy *Venues:* 300, studio 100 *Comments:* visiting address: Ludovika tér 1, 1082 Budapest

Budapest Chamber Theatre
Budapesti Kamaraszinház
Asbóth u. 17, 1075 **Budapest**
Tel: 1-317 9769 Fax: 1-342 3393
E-Mail: badapestik@mail.matav.hu
director Miklós Szücs; artistic director József Ruszt; artistic secretary Eva Schön
Actors: 40 + 40 orchestra *Perfs:* 500 *Prods:* 12-15 – incl. opera & dance *Type:* modern, classical, chamber opera, dance, experimental *Venues:* theatres at: Nagymez (Budapest) 300, Asbóth (Budapest) 100, Castle Kiscell 350, Studio Shure 80

Comedy Theatre
Vigszinház
Szt. István Körut 14, 1137 **Budapest**
Tel: 1-340 5057 Fax: 1-329 2917
Internet: www.vigszinhaz.hu
E-Mail: vigszinhaz@euroweb.hu
director László Marton; artistic secretary Peter Várnai
Actors: 50 *Perfs:* main 261, chamber 253 *Prods:* 4 + 4
Type: modern, classical, comedy, musical *Venues:* home cap 1060, Pesti Theatre 540 *Comments:* Pesti Theatre, address: Váci u.9, 1052 Budapest, Tel: 1-266 5245/9932

Egyetemi Színpad
Universitas Stage
Szerb u. 21-23, 1056 **Budapest**
Tel: 1-266 3311 Fax: 1-266 3311
director András Hidvégi
Type: university theatre, experimental drama

Gaiety Theatre
Vidám Színpad
P.O. Box 82, 1366 **Budapest**
Tel: 1-332 8916 Fax: 1-332 0747
director Gyula Bodrogi; artistic secretary Károly Gévai
Actors: 25 *Perfs:* 250 *Prods:* 3 *Type:* comedy, musical
Venues: home cap 500, chamber theatre 190 *Comments:* visiting address: Révay u. 18, 1065, Budapest

Independent Stage
Független Színpad III
Vörösmarty Müvelödési Ház – Vörösmarty Cultural Centre, Golgota u.3, 1089 **Budapest**
Tel: 1-113 0607 Fax: 1-133 7190
artistic director Zoltán Molnár;
managing director Lajosné Kiss
Actors: 15 *Perfs:* 180 *Prods:* 4 *Type:* modern, classical, experimental *Comments:* no own theatre, guest performances only

József Attila Theatre
József Attila Színház
P.O. Box 107, 1389 **Budapest**
Tel: 1-350 1231/2/3/350 1313 Fax: 1-350 1313
Internet: www.irs.hu/jzsef.htm
director Péter Léner; secretary general László Pányoki
Actors: 30 *Perfs:* 400 *Prods:* 5-6 *Type:* classical, modern, musical *Venues:* home capacity 210 *Comments:* visiting address: Váci út 63 1134 Budapest

Karinthy Theatre
Karinthy Színház
Bartók Béla út. 130, 1113 **Budapest**
Tel: 1-203 8994 Fax: 1-385 8695/203 8994
managing & artistic director Márton Karinthy; artistic secretary Ibolya Potassy
Perfs: 100 *Prods:* 3-5 *Type:* modern, classical, comedy, experimental *Venues:* home capacity 210

Katona József Theatre
Katona József Színház
PO Box 116, 1364 **Budapest**
Tel: 1-318 3269 Fax: 1-266 2191
Internet: theatre.elender.hu/katona
E-Mail: katona@mail.elender.hu
director Gábor Zsámbéki; executive manager Tibor Téri; financial manager Katalin Dely; artistic secretary László Magyar; international relations Anna Veress
Actors: 37 *Perfs:* 350 *Prods:* 4 + 4 *Type:* modern, classical
Venues: main capacity 380, Kamra (chamber) 99
Touring: international *Comments:* visiting address: Petöfi Sándor u. 6, 1052 Budapest

Komédium Theatre
Komédium
Tüköry u. 5, 1054 **Budapest**
Tel: 1-332 5997 Fax: 1-332 5967
artistic director Gyula Radó; managing directors András Burger, Sándor Tóth
Comments: no permanent ensemble

Madách Theatre
Madách Színhaz
Erzsébet körút 31-33, 1073 **Budapest**
Tel: 1-322 0677 Fax: 1-322 8280
general & artistic director Imre Kerényi; financial manager Kálmánné Czobor;
artistic secretary Erzsi Balogh
Actors: 36 *Perfs:* 700 *Prods:* 4 + chamber theatre 4 + 2 studio *Type:* modern, classical, comedy, musical
Venues: home capacity 810, Madách Kamaraszínház (Madách studio) 90

Merlin International Theatre
Merlin Nemzetközi Színház
Gerlóczy u.4, 1052 **Budapest**
Tel: 1-317 9338/318 9844 Fax: 1-266 0904
Internet: www.c3.hu/~merlin/
E-Mail: merlin@c3.hu
director Tamás Jordán; director of the English section László Magacs; artistic secretary Ági Szakács
Venues: blackbox (variable theatre space) home capacity 220, club theatre (in the restaurant) 70 *Comments:* English language theatre

Microscope Theatre
Mikroszkóp Színpad
P.O. Box 658, 1399 **Budapest**
Tel: 1-312 2889/332 5322
Fax: 1-131 9942
director József Sas; managing director József Hámori; artistic secretary Éva Tuza
Actors: 9 *Perfs:* 260 *Prods:* 3 *Type:* comedy *Venues:* home capacity 192 *Comments:* visiting address: Nagymezö u 22-24, 1065 Budapest

Moving House Theatre Company
Mozgo Haz Tarsulas
Kisfaludy utca 28/b, 1082 **Budapest**
Tel: 1-313 3310
Fax: 1-313 3310
E-Mail: zoltan.imely@span.ch
artistic director Laszlo Hudi;
managing director Zoltan Imely
Actors: 14 *Perfs:* 50 *Prods:* 4 *Type:* new works, explores ways of working through diverse range of theatrical forms including live music, movement, text and strong visual content *Venues:* middle scale theatres, art centres, festivals *Touring:* national, international
Comments: independent touring company committed to developing new works with 1 commission per year; offers unique middle scale pieces on tour; also responds to invitations to create site specific one-off events; emphasis on international co-productions

MU Theatre
MU Színház
Körösy József u. 17, 1117 **Budapest**
Tel: 1-209 4014 Fax: 1-209 4014
director Tibor Leszták;
artistic director Gerzson Péter Kovács
Prods: 7 *Type:* contemporary dance and music *Venues:* home cap. 130 *Comments:* MU Theatre is one of the most important independent performing theatres in Hungary; the theatre is run by an independent art association supported by the Ministry of Culture, the National Cultural Fund, the City Council of Budapest and the Council of District 11th

National Theatre
Nemzeti Színház
P.O. Box 25, 1400 **Budapest**
Tel: 1-341 3849 Fax: 1-342 2559
managing director István Iglódy;
artistic secretary Béla Pethö
Actors: 70 *Perfs:* 200 + chamber theatre 200 *Prods:* 10 *Type:* modern, classical *Venues:* home capacity 660, Várszínház (Castle Theatre) 250, studio 99 *Comments:* visiting address: Hevesi Sándor tér 4,1077 Budapest

New Theatre
Új Színház
Paulay Ede u. 35, 1061 **Budapest**
Tel: 1-269 6021 Fax: 1-269 6020
Internet: www.szemtanu.hu/UJSzinhaz
E-Mail: UJSzinig@freemail.c3.hu
artistic director István Márta;
artistic secretary Antónia Juhász
Actors: 25 *Perfs:* 250 *Prods:* 6-7 *Type:* modern, classical *Venues:* home capacity 440, chamber hall 100

Ódry Stage
Ódry Színpad
Vas u. 2/C, 1088 **Budapest**
Tel: 1-318 8111 Fax: 1-338 4749
director/rector Péter Huszti;
general secretary Lajos Tiszeker
Venues: Odry Theatre 340, Odry Loft 100, Odry Színpad 170 *Comments:* stage of the Hungarian Academy of Dramatic and Film Arts

R.S.9 Studio Theatre
R.S.9 Stúdiószínház
Rumbach Sebestyén u.9, 1075 **Budapest**
Tel: 1-269 6610 Fax: 1-269 6609
Internet:
ourworld.compuserve.com/homepages/rs9theater
E-Mail: rs9theater@compuserve.com
directors Katalin Lábán, Dezsö Dobay
Type: experimental *Venues:* home 80 *Comments:* organisers of annual Festival of Alternatives Theatre

Radnóti Theatre
Radnóti Színház
P.O. Box 60, 1367 **Budapest**
Tel: 1-321 0660 Fax: 1-322 9496
E-Mail: radnotiszin@mail.detenet.hu
general manager András Bálint; artistic secretary László Muskát; financial manager József Csóti
Actors: 14 *Perfs:* 230 *Prods:* 4 *Type:* modern, classical, poetry *Venues:* home capacity 230 *Comments:* visiting address: Nagymez u 11, 1065 Budapest

Ruttkai Éva Theatre
Ruttkai Éva Színház
Üllöi ut 45, 1090 **Budapest**
Tel: 1-218 9380 Fax: 1-215 5020
director Miklós Nagy
Perfs: 50 *Prods:* 2-3 *Type:* chamber plays
Venues: capacity 90

Stage, The
Játékszín
Teréz körút 48, 1066 **Budapest**
Tel: 1-332 5532 Fax: 1-131 8749
Internet: www.jegymester.hu/
E-Mail: balazovits@jegymester.hu
artistic director Lajos Balázsovits;
artistic secretary István Lénárt
Type: modern, classical, comedy *Venues:* home capacity 300 *Comments:* no permanent ensemble

Studio K
Mátyás u. 9, 1093 **Budapest**
Tel: 1-216 7170 Fax: 1-216 7170
Internet: www.c3.hu/~studiok
E-Mail: studiok@mail.c3.hu
director Tamás Fodor
Type: experimental

Szkéné Theatre
Szkéné Színház
Müegyetem rakpart. 3, 1111 **Budapest**
Tel: 1-463 2451
Fax: 1-463 2450
E-Mail: ficzek@sc.bme.hu
artistic & managing director János Regös
Actors: varies *Perfs:* 150 *Type:* university theatre, experimental *Venues:* home capacity up to 160 : second e-mail: jregos@ccmail.bme.hu

Térszínház
Fö tér 1, 1033 **Budapest**
Tel: 1-388 4310 Fax: 1-388 4310
E-Mail: cobo@dunanet.hu
director Hunor Bucz
Touring: Hungary, neighbouring countries

Thália Ensemble
Thália Társaság
Stefánia út 34,
1143 **Budapest**
artistic director Imre Csiszár

Thália Theatre
Thália Színház
Nagymezö u. 22-24, 1065 **Budapest**
Tel: 1-312 4230/39
Fax: 1-311 8018
director László Megyeri; artistic secretary Zsuzsa Nagy
Actors: no resident company

Csokonai Theatre, Debrecen
Debreceni Csokonai Színház
P.O. Box 79, 4001 **Debrecen**
Tel: 52-417 811 Fax: 52-410 837
artistic & managing director György Lengyel; first associate director István Pinczés; music director Balázs Kocsár; general secretary Rozi Berényi
Actors: 39 actors, 17 singers, 12 dancers *Perfs:* 332 *Prods:* 14 *Type:* modern, classical, comedy, opera, operetta, musical, experimental studio plays *Venues:* home capacity 544, studio 50, chamber theatre in Kölcsey Cultural Centre 396, address: Hunyadi u. 1-3, 4026 Debrecen; Horvát Árpád Studio Theatre 70 *Comments:* visiting address: Kossuth u. 10, 4024 Debrecen

Gárdonyi Géza Theatre, Eger
Egri Gárdonyi Géza Színház
P.O. Box 193, 3301 **Eger**
Tel: 36-311 984 Fax: 36-313 838
director Sándor Beke; artistic secretary Melinda Varga
Actors: 37 *Perfs:* 425 *Prods:* 6 + 2 studio + 2 for children + 2 puppet *Type:* modern, classical, comedy, puppet *Venues:* home capacity 470, studio 60 *Comments:* visiting address: Hatvani kapu tér 1, 3300 Eger

National Theatre Györ
Györi Nemzeti Színház
P.O. Box 401, 9002 **Györ**
Tel: 96-312 167 Fax: 96-313 276
general manager György Korcsmáros; art director Géza Tordy; artistic secretary Attila Miksi
Actors: 85 *Perfs:* 230 *Prods:* 4 (drama), 3 (studio), 1 (opera), 3 (musicals), 2 (dance) *Type:* modern, classical, comedy, opera, dance *Venues:* home capacity 690, studio (Theatre on the Roof) 100 *Comments:* visiting address: Czuczor Gergely út 7, 9022 Györ

Csíky Gergely Theatre
Kaposvári Csíky Gergely Színház
P.O. B ox 13, 7402 **Kaposvár**
Tel: 82-320 833 Fax: 82-320 376
director László Babarczy; chief director Tamás Ascher; artistic secretary Márta Kamarell
Actors: 29 *Perfs:* 277 *Prods:* 6 *Type:* modern, classical, comedy *Venues:* home capacity 540 *Comments:* visiting address: Rákóczi tér 1, 7400 Kaposvár

Katona Joseph Theatre, Kecskemét
Kecskeméti Katona József Színház
P.O. Box 48, 6001 **Kecskemét**
Tel: 76-483 283 Fax: 76-481 417
Internet: www.kecskemet.szinhaz.hu
E-Mail: katonaj@mail.datanet.hu
director Géza Bodolay; general secretary Ibolya Simon
Actors: 31 *Perfs:* 260 *Prods:* 7 + 2 studio *Type:* modern, classical, comedy *Venues:* home capacity 600
Comments: visiting address:
Katona József tér 5, 6000 Kecskemét

National Theatre Miskolc
Miskolci Nemzeti Színház
POB 113, 3501 **Miskolc**
Tel: 46-344 711 Fax: 46-344 832
Internet: www.olh.hu/MiskolcNemzetiszinhaz
E-Mail: mszinhaz@mail.olh.hu
director Arpád Jutocsa Hegyi;
music director Gergely Keselyák
Actors: 36 actors, 26 musicians *Perfs:* 220 *Prods:* 7 + 2 studio *Type:* modern, classical, comedy, operetta *Venues:* home capacity 670, studio 50 *Comments:* visiting address: Déryné u 1, 3525 Miskolc

Móricz Zsigmond Theatre, Nyíregyháza
Nyíregyházi Móricz Zsigmond Színház
P.O. Box 53, 4401 **Nyíregyháza**
Tel: 42-311 333 Fax: 42-310 491
Internet: www.szabinet.hu/szinhaz
E-Mail: szinhaz@szabinet.hu
managing director Csaba Tasnádi;
artistic secretary Gyöngyver Kocsis
Actors: 27 *Perfs:* 340 *Prods:* 8 + 2 for children *Type:* modern, classical, comedy, children's theatre *Venues:* home capacity 500 *Comments:* visiting address: Bessenyei tér 13, 4400 Nyíregyháza

National Theatre Pécs
Pécsi Nemzeti Színház
P.O. Box 126, 7601 **Pécs**
Tel: 72-211 983 Fax: 72-411 986
director Tamás Baliko; managing director István Simon; artistic secretary Zita Csaba
Actors: 28 *Perfs:* 259 *Prods:* 7 + 3 chamber + 2 studio *Type:* modern, classical, comedy, opera, operetta, dance, puppet *Venues:* home capacity 530, studio 270 *Comments:* visiting address: Perczel u. 17, 7621 Pécs

Third Theatre in Pécs
Pécsi Harmadik Színház
Hajnóczi János u. 4, 7633 **Pécs**
Tel: 72-252 478 Fax: 72-251 340
director János Vincze;
artistic secretary Ágnes Muschberger
Prods: 2 *Type:* modern, classical

Croation Theatre in Pecz
Pécsi Horvát Horvát szinház
Anna ut. 17, 7621 **Pecz**
Tel: 72-210 197/211 019 Fax: 72-210 197/211 019
manager Toni Vidakovic; director Antal Vidákovics
Venues: home 67

Petöfi Theatre, Sopron
Soproni Petöfi Színház
Petöfi tér 1, 9400 **Sopron**
Tel: 99-511 700 Fax: 99-511 716
director Istvan Miko; managing director Ferenc Nyerges; artistic secretary Ildikó Domonkos
Actors: 30 *Type:* modern, classical, comedy *Venues:* home capacity 415

National Theatre Szeged
Szegedi Nemzeti Színház
POB 79, 6701 **Szeged**
Tel: 62-479 279 Fax: 62-475 562
Internet: www.jate.u-szeged.hu/csongrad/welcome/theatre.htm
E-Mail: szinhaz@tiszanet.hu
general director Károly Korognay; opera director Tamás Pál; general secretary Mária Hollandi
Actors: 41 *Perfs:* 341 *Prods:* 9 *Type:* modern, classical, comedy, operetta, dance *Venues:* home capacity 700, studio theatre 325 *Comments:* visiting address: Deák Ferenc u. 12, 6720 Szeged

Vörösmarty Theatre Székesfehérvár
Székesfehérvári Vörösmarty Színház
Föu. 8, 8000 **Székesfehérvár**
Tel: 22-311 296 Fax: 22-311 415
director Attila Péterffy; artistic secretary Zsolt Haraszty; artistic director Péter Horváth
Actors: 26

Deutsche Bühne/German Theatre
Szekszárdi Német Bemutatószínpad
Garay tér. 4, 7001 **Szekszárd**
Tel: 74-316 533 Fax: 74-316 725
artistic director Zsuzsa Dávid
Comments: German language theatre

Szigligeti Theatre Szolnok
Szolnoki Szigligeti Színház
P.O. Box 61, 5001 **Szolnok**
Tel: 56-342 633 Fax: 56-370 275
Internet: www.szigligeti.szolnex.hu
E-Mail: szinhaz@szolnex.hu
director György Schwajda; artistic secretary Éva Márton
Actors: 28 *Perfs:* 260 *Prods:* 9 *Type:* modern, classical, comedy, operetta *Venues:* home capacity 465
Comments: venue used for concerts; visiting address: Tisza-park 1, 5000 Szolnok

Jászai Mari Theatre, Tatabánya
Tatabányai Jászai Mari Színház
Népház u. 5, 2800 **Tatabánya**
Tel: 34-323 655/018 Fax: 34-323 090
artistic director Zoltán Zubornyák;
artistic secretary Zsuzsa Kovács

Petöfi Theatre, Veszprém
Veszprémi Petöfi Színház
POB 133, 8200 **Veszprém**
Tel: 88-424 064 Fax: 88-420 046
director László Vándorfi; artistic secretary Zsuzsa Egresi
Actors: 35 *Perfs:* 365 *Prods:* 6 + 1 for children + 1 dance *Type:* modern, classical, comedy, children's theatre, operetta, musical, dance *Venues:* home capacity 460, Latinovits Zoltán Studio Theatre 80 *Comments:* visiting address: Óváry Ferenc u.2., 8201 Veszprém

Hevesi Sándor Theatre, Zalaegerszeg
Zalaegerszegi Hevesi Sándor Színház
P.O. Box 129, 8901 **Zalaegerszeg**
Tel: 92-314 405 Fax: 92-314 408
Internet: zalaszam.hu/szinhaz/
E-Mail: szinhaz@matav.mail.hu
director Gábor Stefán; artistic secretary Emöke Salamon
Actors: 41 *Perfs:* 280 *Prods:* 12 *Type:* modern, classical, comedy, drama, musical *Venues:* home capacity 464
Comments: visiting address: Kosztolanyi tér 3, 8900 Zalaegerszeg

ICELAND (+354)

Akureyri Theatre
Leikfélag Akureyrar
Hafnarstraeti 57, PO Box 92, 602 **Akureyri**
Tel: 462 5073/1400 Fax: 461 1354
artistic director Sigurdur Hroarsson;
financial director Edda Johannes Dottir
Actors: 6 + 20 freelance *Perfs:* 80-100 *Prods:* 4-6 *Type:* modern, icelandic, musical, classical
Venues: home capacity 196

Ferdaleikhús
Light Nights-Summer Theatre
Baldursgata 37, 101 **Reykjavík**
Tel: 551 9181 Fax: 551 5015
Internet: cns.web.bu./edu/pub/snorrason/light.nights
director Kristín G. Magnus
Actors: 5 *Perfs:* 50 *Prods:* 2 *Type:* Episodes from folk stories; audio-visual presentations, also classical repertoire *Venues:* Tjarnarbio Theatre 245 *Touring:* Scotland (Edingburgh Fringe Festival)

Frú Emilía – leikhús
Frú Emilía – theatre
PO Box 447, 121 **Reykjavík**
Tel: 551 2233 Fax: 551 2224
director Guøjón Pedersen;
dramaturg Haflidi Arngrímsson
Actors: 8 *Perfs:* 80 *Prods:* 2 *Type:* classical, modern
Venues: capacity 100 *Touring:* Europe

Möguleikhúsid
Vid Hlemm, 105 **Reykjavík**
Tel: 562 2669/5060 Fax: 562 2669
E-Mail: ml@islandia.is
directors Pétur Eggerz, Bjarni Ingvarsson,
Alda Arnardottir
Actors: 2-6 *Perfs:* 100-190 *Prods:* 2-3 *Type:* children's theatre *Venues:* home capacity 130 *Touring:* mainly Iceland and occasionally Scandinavia *Comments:* produces new plays written especially for this group

National Theatre of Iceland
Thjódleikhúsid
Hverfisgata 19, 101 **Reykjavík**
Tel: 551 1204 Fax: 561 1200
Internet: www.theatre.is
E-Mail: stefbald@centrum.is
artistic director Stefán Baldursson; dramaturg Melkorka Tekla Olafsdóttir; production manager Sigmundur Örn Arngrímsson; administrative director
Gudrún Gudmundsdóttir;
marketing manager Gudrún Bachmann
Actors: 38 + freelance *Perfs:* 400 *Prods:* 10-14 *Type:* mixed repertory of new writing, modern, classical plays, musicals and opera *Venues:* main stage 530, small stage 100, studio scene 150 *Comments:* offices at: Lindargata 7, 101 Reykjavik; see also Venues

Reykjavik Theatre Company
Leikfélag Reykjavikur
Listabraut 3, PO Box 3390, 103 **Reykjavík**
Tel: 568 8000 Fax: 568 0383
manager Thorhildur Thorleifsdottir
Actors: 21 permanent, 60 in total *Prods:* 10-12 *Type:* modern, classical theatre *Venues:*
Stori 530, Litli up to 150

IRELAND Republic of (+353)

Yew Tree Theatre Company
Tone St., **Ballina (Co. Mayo)**
Tel: 96-71238/87-504 543(mobile) Fax: 96-71238/73113
Internet: www.yewtheatre.ie
E-Mail: yew@indigo.ie
artistic director John Breen
Actors: varies *Prods:* 3 per year *Type:* new writing from Irish and continental writers *Venues:* National Touring House, arts centre 200-300 *Touring:* national
Comments: regularly produce theatre for children

Corcadora Theatre Company
11/12 Marlboro Street, **Cork**
Tel: 21-278 326 Fax: 21-278 326
company manager Dyane Hanrahan; artistic directors Enola Walsh, Pat Kiernan
Actors: varies *Perfs:* 10 *Prods:* 3 *Type:* strong visual and physical presentations of original and devised scripts
Venues: Everyman Palace Theatre 600, UCC Granary Theatre 200, Triskel Arts Centre 100, also non-theatre venues, Opera House Cork 800, The Project 120

Graffiti Theatre Company
The Weighmaster's House, 2 Church Street,
Shandon, **Cork**
Tel: 21-397 111 Fax: 21-397 110
E-Mail: graffiti@tinet.ie
Financial Administrator Jennifer O'Donnell; Artistic director Emelie FitzGibbon
Actors: 12 *Perfs:* 200 *Prods:* 3 *Type:* predominately new work, theatre in education *Comments:* issue-based company , additional funding from FAS, Arts Council, Cork Corporation & City of Cork VEC, the Department of Education, the Southern Health Board

Abbey Theatre
26 Lower Abbey Street, **Dublin** 1
Tel: 1-887 2200 Fax: 1-872 9177
E-Mail: email@abbeytheatre.ie
general manager Martin Fahy; artistic director Patrick Mason; director of PR and marketing Madeline Boughton; managing director Richard Wakely
Actors: 10 permanent *Perfs:* 325 *Prods:* 14 *Type:* Irish plays and international classics *Venues:* capacity 628
Touring: Europe, USA, Australia, UK *Comments:* National Theatre of Ireland; produce and present; see also Peacock Theatre (Venues)

Barabbas...the company
7 South Great George Street, **Dublin** 2
Tel: 1-671 2013 Fax: 1-670 4275
E-Mail: barabbas@indigo.ie
company manager Enid Reid Whyte;
artistic director Veronica Coburn
Actors: varies *Perfs:* 60 *Prods:* 2 (1 new) *Type:* physical theatre with emphasis on company-devised and scripted work *Venues:* theatres and arts centres 150 to 900 *Touring:* national, USA *Comments:* may use words , does not rely on them, crosses language barriers providing international access to Irish culture; appears nightly on Teilfis na Gaeilge (Irish Language TV station)

Dublin Youth Theatre
23 Upper Gardiner Street, **Dublin** 1
Tel: 1-874 3687 Fax: 1-874 5189
E-Mail: dyt@iol.ie
administrator Valerie Bistany; chairperson Veronica Coburn
Type: drama for 14-22 year olds *Comments:* also runs theatre arts workshops; welcomes exchanges and projects with other youth groups

Focus Theatre
6 Pembroke Place, **Dublin** 2
Tel: 1-676 3071/660 7109 Fax: 1-660 7109
E-Mail: weakley@indigo.ie
administrator Etain Winder; artistic director Deidre O'Connell; assistant manager Kevin O'Brien
Actors: 30-40 *Perfs:* 307 *Prods:* 5 *Type:* contemporary Irish, European and American drama, classics, new Irish plays, improvisational theatre *Venues:* Focus Theatre 77 *Comments:* see also Venues

Gate Theatre Company
Cavendish Row, **Dublin** 1
Tel: 1-874 4368 Fax: 1-874 5373
director Michael Colgan; deputy directors Marie Rooney, Anne Clarke; theatre manager John Higgins; production manager Liam Pawley
Actors: varies *Perfs:* 300 *Prods:* 7-8 *Type:* classical plays, new Irish works *Venues:* Gate Theatre 371 *Touring:* Ireland, UK, USA, Europe, Australia

Íomhá Ildánach Theatre Company
The Crypt Arts Centre, Dublin Castle, Dame Street,
Dublin 2
Tel: 1-671 3387 Fax: 1-671 3370
E-Mail: crypt@clubi.ie
associate director Philip Gray; artistic director John O'Brien; executive director Niall Ó Sioradáin
Actors: 6 *Perfs:* 75 stage, 150 theatre-in-education, 2 special projects *Prods:* 3 *Type:* original written and devised work, using ancient and modern myth as source material in three main areas: stage, theatre-in-education and special projects (community, access projects etc.) *Venues:* The Crypt Arts Centre 100 *Touring:* Ireland, Europe, USA *Comments:* currently engaging in low-cost projects and co-productions; interested in contact with other like-minded companies/venues

PanPan Theatre
The Old School House, Eblana Avenue,
Dun Laoghaire, **Dublin**
Tel: 1-280 0544 Fax: 1-230 0918
Internet: ireland.iol.ie/arena/panpan
E-Mail: panpan@iol.ie
director Gavin Quinn; administrator Mary O' Donovan; production manager Aedín Cosgrove

Peacock Theatre
26 Lower Abbey Street, **Dublin** 1
Tel: 1-874 8741 Fax: 1-872 9177
E-Mail: press@abbeytheatre.ie
general manager Martin Fahy; artistic director Patrick Mason; managing director Richard Wakely
Actors: varies (all freelance) *Perfs:* 325 *Type:* experimental theatre of all kinds plus plays in the Irish language
Venues: capacity 157 *Touring:* Europe, USA, UK, Australia
Comments: Ireland's National Theatre; showcase for new Irish writers, further experimental theatre, encourage Irish language productions; see also Abbey Theatre; see also Venues

Rough Magic Theatre Company
5-6 South Great Georges Street, **Dublin** 2
Tel: 1-671 9278 Fax: 1-671 9301
Internet: www.iol.ie/~roughmag
E-Mail: roughmag@iol.ie
artistic director Lynne Parker; administrator Ciara McGlynn; executive producer Deborah Clydon; company manager Loughlin Deegan
Actors: 4-16 per production *Perfs:* 70 *Prods:* 2 *Type:* classical, new drama, new Irish writing *Venues:* Project Arts Centre 200, Gaiety Theatre 1500, Cork Opera House 1600, Civic Theatre 380, Town Hall Galway 286
Touring: Europe, USA, worldwide

TEAM Educational Theatre Company
4 Marlborough Place, **Dublin** 1
Tel: 1-878 6108
Fax: 1-874 8989
E-Mail: team@tinet.ie
administrator Jackie Ryan;
education officer Sharon Murphy
Actors: 5 *Perfs:* 220 *Prods:* 2-3 *Type:* theatre in education, writer-in-residence *Touring:* middle scale, permanent touring company. Ireland, festivals in Europe
Comments: list of scripts always available

Druid Theatre Company
Druid Lane, **Galway**
Tel: 91-568 617/660 (admin) Fax: 91-563 109
Internet: indigo.ie\~druidth
E-Mail: druidth@indigo.ie
general manager Louise Donlon; artistic director Garry Hynes; production services Maurice Power; production manager Bernard Walsh; administrator Maria Fleming
Actors: drawn from freelance market – approx. 32 per year *Perfs:* Galway: 180, Touring: 65
Prods: 4 evening productions; lunchtime and late night theatre in summer months *Type:* touring drama, new works, classic and contemporary Irish/European plays
Venues: capacity 120 *Touring:* national and international

Macnas
The Black Box, Dyke Road, **Galway**
Tel: 91-561 462
Fax: 91-563 905
Internet: www.macnas.com
E-Mail: macnas@iol.ie
general manager Declan Gibbons; PR Gary McMahon
Actors: 10-100 *Perfs:* 70+ *Prods:* 7 *Type:* street, stage theatre *Touring:* Ireland
Comments: community arts company

Island Theatre Company
Church Street, King's Island, **Limerick**
Tel: 61-410 433
Fax: 61-400 997
administrator Conor Nolan;
artistic director Terence Devlin
Actors: varies (freelance) *Perfs:* 50 *Prods:* 2-3 *Type:* classics, Irish writing, new Irish writing *Venues:* England, Italy, France *Touring:* Europe

Siamsa Tire – National Folk Theatre of Ireland
Siamsa Tire, The Town Park, **Tralee (Co. Kerry)**
Tel: 66-712 3055
Fax: 66-712 7276
manager Martin Whelan;
artistic director John Sheehan
Actors: 7 *Type:* Irish folk theatre *Venues:* Siamsa 355
Comments: see also Festivals and Venues

Red Kettle Theatre Company
33 O'Connell Street, **Waterford**
Tel: 51-879 688 Fax: 51-857 416
Internet: www.come.to/redkettle
E-Mail: rkettle@iol.ie
general manager Liam Rellis; artistic director Jim Nolan; administrator Catherine Collins
Actors: varies *Perfs:* 60 *Prods:* 3 + 2 children's show *Type:* modern drama, focus especially on new work by Irish writers *Venues:* Garter Lane 190, Andrews Lane Theatre, Dublin 220, Theatre Royal 650 *Touring:* minimum of 1 play per year throughout Ireland, Northern Ireland

ITALY (+39)

Dióscuri – Cooperativa Gruppo Folk
via Alessio di Giovanni 2, 92100 **Agrigento**
Tel: 0922-602 424/607 406
Fax: 0922-608 113/-602 424
presidente Eduardo Cicala; direttore artistico Enzo Gambino; direttore organizzativo Francesco Sodana; Ufficio Stampa Giovanni Lo Brutto
Actors: 8-15 *Perfs:* 100-120 *Prods:* 7 *Type:* musical comedy
Venues: Teatro Stabile di Palermo 1200 *Touring:* worldwide *Comments:* registered address: via Madonna delle Rocche, 28; 92100 Agrigento; the company writes and produces all productions

Teatro del Canguro
Via Trionfi 4, 60127 **Ancona**
Tel: 071-82805
Fax: 071-82805
Internet: www.fastnet.it/cultura/teatro/canguro
E-Mail: teatro.canguro@fastnet.it
direttore amministrativo Corrado Manzotti;
direttore artistico Lino Terra; direttore tecnico-organizzativo Cinzia Moreschi; ufficio stampa Mariella Ranieri
Actors: 10 *Perfs:* 200 *Prods:* 10
Type: children's theatre
Venues: Teatro Panettone, Teatro Sperimentale
Comments: Festival Internationa
– Linea di Confine – annual

TEE – Teatro Stabile Delle Marche
piazza Cavour, 29, 60121 **Ancona**
Tel: 071-200 442 Fax: 071-205 274
Internet: www.tee.it
E-Mail: info@tee.it
direttore artistico Giampiero Solari; presidente Paola Magliola; direttore Marco Morico; direttore amministrativo Barbara Marchetti; Il direttore organizzativo Tommaso Paolvcci; capo uff. stampa Beatrice Giongo
Actors: 20 *Perfs:* 30 *Prods:* 7 *Type:* prosa *Venues:* Teatro in Fiera 700 (Ancona), Teatro Sperimentale 'Lirico Arena 400 (Ancona), Teatro Alle Cave (Sirolo-An) *Touring:* Italy, France, Spain

Lanciavicchio – Soc. Coop. Teatrale, Il
via U. Maddalena, 4,
67050 **Antrosano di Avezzano (AQ)**
Tel: 0863-25933 Fax: 0863-33148
E-Mail: lanciavicchio@mail.dex-net.com
administrative director Giuseppe Cristoforo; artistic director Mario Fracassi;
technical director Antonio Silvagni
Actors: 7 *Perfs:* 60-70 *Prods:* 4 *Type:* youth and popular theatre, experimental *Venues:* Castello Orsini (Avezzano – AQ) 350, Il Lanciavicchio Auditorium 100 *Touring:* Italy *Comments:* organise workshops and a street theatre festival: Tra il Sole e la Luna

Teatro dei Colori –
Centro di Ricerca e Pedagogia Nello Spettacolo
Via La Marmora 8, 67051 **Avezzano (AQ)**
Tel: 0863-411 900 Fax: 0863-411 900
administrative director Gabriella Montuori;
artistic director Gabriele Ciaccia
Actors: 10 *Perfs:* 140 *Prods:* 5 new + 1 revival *Type:* youth theatre *Venues:* Teatro Comunale S. Francesco di Pescina 240, Centro Polivalente Castello Orsini-Colonna 300 *Touring:* Italy

Accademia Perduta Romagna Teatri
c/o Teatro Goldoni, 48012 **Bagnacavallo (RA)**
Tel: 0545-64330 Fax: 0545-64320
E-Mail: aprteatri@mail.asianet.it
artistic directors Ruggero Sintoni, Claudio Casadio
Actors: 1-6 *Perfs:* 400 *Prods:* 4-5 *Type:* comedy, drama, musicals, children's theatre *Venues:* Teatro Goldoni; Teatro Il Piccolo, Forlí; Teatro Comunale, Cervia; Teatro Masini, Faenza *Touring:* Italy *Comments:* registered address: Via Maggiore 65, 48100 Ravenna

Occupazioni Farsesche
c/o Teatro Comunale Barberino di Mugello, via della Repubblica N.3, 50031 **Barberino di Mugello (FI)**
Tel: 055-841 237 Fax: 055-841 6557
Internet: www.newnet.it
direttore Riccardo Sottili
Actors: varies according to show *Perfs:* 40 *Prods:* 2 *Type:* drama *Venues:* Teatro Comunale Barberino di Mugello 448 *Touring:* Portugal, Brasil, Ukraine

Compagnia Kismet
Strada San Giorgio Martire 22/F, 70123 **Bari**
Tel: 080-574 9254 Fax: 080-574 9228
E-Mail: kismet@pangeanet.it
presidente Augusto Masiello; direttore artistico (responsabile programmazione) Carlo Bruni; direttore artistico della programmazione musicale Antonio Princigalli; responsabile distribuzione Diane Guerrier; press office Marcella Chiummo
Actors: 8-25 *Perfs:* 210 *Prods:* 9 *Type:* contemporary and young persons theatre, theatre for the disabled (with disabled acting) *Venues:* Teatro Kismet 220 + 100 *Touring:* Israel *Comments:* conferences, exhibitions, many projects for children, courses; European projects with disabled actors; outreach programme with young offenders; see also Venues

Puglia-Teatro
Via Indipendenza 75, 70123 **Bari**
Tel: 080-579 3041 Fax: 080-579 3041
direttore Rino Bizzarro;
teatro scuola e administration Anna Brucoli;
rapporti com L'Universite Daniele Giancane
Actors: 6-7 *Perfs:* 80-100 *Prods:* 2 + 4 revivals *Type:* classical drama (focus on Southern Italian culture) *Comments:* touring company

Pandemonium Teatro
Via Camozzi 56, 24100 **Bergamo**
Tel: 035-235 039/440 Fax: 035-235 440
E-Mail: pandemonium@cyberg.it
direttore organizzativo Mario Ferrari;
direzione artistica Albino Bignamini
Actors: 5 *Perfs:* 150 *Prods:* 11 *Type:* children's and youth theatre, research *Touring:* Italy *Comments:* registered address:Via Ghislanzoni 41, 24100 Bergamo

Sezione Aurea
Via Pignolo 42/44, 24121 **Bergamo**
Tel: 035-211 211 Fax: 035-211 183
organisation director Tiziana Pirola; artistic directors Elisa Rossini, Maura Mandelli
Actors: 7 *Perfs:* 150 *Prods:* 12 *Type:* children's and youth theatre *Venues:* Auditorium Piazza Liberta' 298 *Touring:* Italy *Comments:* Regia Collettiva

Teatro Prova
via F. lli Calvi, 12, 24122 **Bergamo**
Tel: 035-225 847/-424 3079 (administration)
Fax: 035-336 623
E-Mail: il.teatro.prova@spm.it
direttore artistico Silvia Barbieri; direttore amministrativo Patrizia Geneletti; direttore tecnico Rita Ronzoni
Actors: 16 *Perfs:* 220 *Prods:* 2 + (11 revivals) *Type:* youth and children's theatre *Venues:* Teatro S. Giorgio 220

Teatro Tascabile di Bergamo (TTB)
via Colleoni 2, 24129 **Bergamo**
Tel: 035-235 350/210 281 Fax: 035-242 095
E-Mail: titibi@spm.it
artistic director Renzo Jescovi; organisation Antonella Baldi; administration Elena Donda
Actors: 8 *Perfs:* 100-130 *Prods:* 3-4 *Type:* street , oriental and chamber theatre *Venues:* Teatro Tascabile di Bergamo (home venue) *Comments:* see also Venues

Strumento Concerto
via Mancini, 3, 20030 **Birago di Lentate sul Seueso**
Tel: 0362-564 897 Fax: 0362-564 897
administrative director Sonia Milan;
artistic director Nicola Scarano
Actors: 2 permanent + guests per production *Prods:* 6 *Type:* musical theatre (world music) *Touring:* Italy, Switzerland *Comments:* run an interactive museum of 8000 musical instruments from all over the world and produce shows and exhibitions in different theatres; work closely with the 'Museo Teatrale alla Scala di Milano'

Banda Osiris
via Milazzo 5, 40121 **Bologna**
Tel: 051-252 718 Fax: 051-252 854
public relations Terry Cheggia
Actors: 4 *Perfs:* 100 *Prods:* 2 *Type:* comedy, music theatre *Touring:* Italy, Australia *Comments:* see also Opera

Baracca / Testoni Ragazzi, Centro Teatro e Arte per l'infanzia e la gioventù, La
Via Matteotti 16, 40129 **Bologna**
Tel: 051-379 000 Fax: 051-377 851
E-Mail: testrag@iperbole.bologna.it
presidente Lucio d'Amelio; vice presidente Roberto Frabetti; direzione artistica Valeria Frabetti; ufficio stampa Dott. Paolo Rubini
Actors: 10 *Perfs:* 396 *Prods:* 18 *Type:* children's and youth theatre *Venues:* Teatro Testoni: sala A 478, sala B 100 *Touring:* Italy, Germany, Spain, France, Netherlands *Comments:* see also Venues

Centro Culturale Teatroaperto
Via Libia, 59, 40138 **Bologna**
Tel: 051-342 934 Fax: 051-238 592
organisation director TizianoTommesani;
artistic director Guido Ferrarini;
administrative director Renata Fiorentini
Actors: 18 *Perfs:* 130 *Prods:* 4 *Type:* classical and contemporary theatre *Venues:* Teatro Dehon 500 *Touring:* Italy, Europe *Comments:* organisation of festival contemporary drama "La scritture incantata"; publish a quarterly magazine: La Scrittura Incantata; see also Venues

Compagnia di Andrea Adriatico
via del Pratello 90/92, 40122 **Bologna**
Tel: 051-522 032 Fax: 051-523 113
Internet: www2.comune.bologna.it/bologna/teatvita
E-Mail: teatvita@iperbole.bologna.it
director Andrea Adriatico;
production manager (abroad) Barbara Pulliero;
production manager (Italy) Monica Nicoli
Actors: 5 *Prods:* 2 *Type:* contemporary, physical, visual, site-specific productions *Venues:* Teatri di Vita 90 *Touring:* Italy, Europe *Comments:* see also Venues (Teatri di Vita)

Gruppo Libero Teatro, Il
Via Oberdan 25, 40126 **Bologna**
Tel: 051-224 671 Fax: 051-221 157
Internet: www2.comune.bologna.it/bologna/coopglt
E-Mail: coopglt@iperbole.bologna.it
artistic & organisational director Giorgio Bulla; theatre director Renzo Morselli; press office Cristina Radi
Actors: 7 (+ 11 according to the performance) *Perfs:* 110 *Prods:* 9 *Type:* youth and children's theatre, research theatre *Venues:* Sala Teatro San Martino 99, Chiostro 100-300 *Touring:* national, international *Comments:* collaboration with Fabula Rasa, and with Danza Eko Company (in Bologna); collaboration with Kauchemar Concret Teatro Firenze

Multimedia SRL
Via Novaro, 27, 40141 **Bologna**
Tel: 051-470 617 Fax: 051-470 617
artistic director/public relations Paola Fiore Donati; administrative director Giulio Corrente
Actors: 4 *Perfs:* 160 *Prods:* 4 *Type:* comic *Touring:* Italy

Nuova Scena SCRL – Teatro Stabile di Bologna
c/o Teatro Arena del Sole, Via Indipendenza 44, 40121 **Bologna**
Tel: 051-291 0911 Fax: 051-239 588
Internet: www.arenadelsole.it
E-Mail: info@arenadelsole.it
direttore artistico e organizzativo Paolo Cacchioli; presidente Massimo Terranova; vice presidente e direttore amministrativo Carla Magri; direttore della comunicazione Bruno Damini; condirettore organizzativo Natalino Mingrone
Actors: 50 *Perfs:* 450 *Prods:* 5 *Type:* prosa, dance *Venues:* Arena del Sole: Sala Grande 900, Sala InterAction (studio theatre) 180, Chiostro (open-air) 200 *Touring:* Italy, France, USA *Comments:* also student's theatre; see also Venues

Orchestra Stolpnik
via Francesco Barbieri 52, 40129 **Bologna**
Tel: 051-357 560 Fax: 051-357 560
Internet: geocity/balcony/4681
E-Mail: stolpnik@iperbole.bologna.it
artistic director Boris Bakal; administrative & press officer Pina Siotto; organisation Fabiana Milani
Actors: 7-15 *Perfs:* 50 *Prods:* 3 *Type:* experimental/contemporary *Touring:* Italy, Europe *Comments:* organises workshops with international artists (theatre, cinema, art)

Piccioni di Piazza Maggiore
via Milazzo 5, 40125 **Bologna**
Tel: 051-243 938 Fax: 051-252 854
direttore artistico e legale rappresentante Claudio Calabrò; attore unico Alessandro Bergonzoni; amministratore di compagnia e PR Riccardo Rodolfi
Actors: 1 *Perfs:* 93 *Prods:* 1 *Type:* comedy *Touring:* Italy, Switzerland, France

Teatrino Clandestino
Via Palmieri 33, 40138 **Bologna**
Tel: 051-649 2944/0335-631 0696 Fax: 051-649 2944
E-Mail: se10038@iperbole.bologna.it
producer, playwright, director, set designer, composer Pietro Babina;administrator Manuel Marcuccio; organisation, promotion Marcella Montanari, Sara Piombo
Actors: 3 (+ collaborators 6) *Perfs:* 70 *Prods:* 5 *Type:* contemporary *Venues:* Fratelli Rosselli *Touring:* Italy, France, UK, Yugoslavia, Belgium

Teatro di Leo (Centro Studi e Sperimentazione Teatro di Leo Snc)
via S.Vitale 63, 40125 **Bologna**
Tel: 051-234 822/233 546 Fax: 051-227 108
Internet: www.comune.bo.it/iperbole.tsanleon
E-Mail: tsanleon@iperbole.bologna.it
organisation director Paolo Ambrosino; artistic director Leone De Berardinis; administrative dir Claudia Manfredi
Actors: 10 *Perfs:* 70 *Prods:* 3 *Type:* experimental *Venues:* Teatro Laboratorio San Leonardo 142, Spazio Della Memoria 100 *Comments:* second E-mail: leonedeb@tin.it

Teatro Nuova Edizione
via delle Moline, 1, 40126 **Bologna**
Tel: 051-235 288 Fax: 051-226 767
Internet:
www.regione.emilia-romagna.it/culturaturismo/cul_cultura
E-Mail: tnuoved@iperbole.bologna.it
direttore Luigi Gozzi; organizzazione e uff. stampa Gloria Moretti, Isabella Scandaletti
Actors: varies *Perfs:* 100 *Prods:* 1 + 3 revivals *Type:* comedy, music-theater, contemporary drama *Venues:* Teatro Delle Moline 60 *Comments:* also workshops; administrative address: Via Milazzo N. 1, 40121 Bologna, Tel: 051-252 898; see also Venues

Teatro Perché – Compagnia D'Arte
via Borgonuovo, 11, 40125 **Bologna**
Tel: 051-239 221 Fax: 051-230 142
artistic dir Gabriele Marchesini; tech dir Massimiliano Sassi
Actors: 18 *Perfs:* 100 *Prods:* 3 *Type:* contemporary drama

Teatro Stabile di Bolzano
c/o Nuovo Teatro Comunale, Piazza Verdi,
39100 **Bolzano-Bozen**
Tel: 0471-304 111/304 113 (administration)/ 304 112 (box office) Fax: 0471-304 114
Internet: www.vol.it/alto-adige/teatrostabile/
presidente Giuseppe Negri; direttore artistico Marco Bernardi; press officers Gianfranco Benincasa, Saverio Ferragina
Actors: 11-17 *Perfs:* 150 *Prods:* 6 *Type:* classic to contemporary *Venues:* Nuovo Teatro Comunae, Sala Grande 810, Sala Polifunzionale 240 *Comments:* see also Venues (Nuovo Teatro Comunale)

Vereinigte Bühnen Bozen
c/o Neues Stadttheater Bozen, Verdiplatz, 39100 **Bozen**
Tel: 0471-981 777 Fax: 0471-980 360
E-Mail: vbbozen@tin.it
Künstlerischer Leiter Jörg Neumann (tel:0471-327 934); Kaufmännischer Leiter Dr MBA Pietro Callegari (tel: 0471- 327 934); Verwaltung Iiris Girardi (tel:0471-327 917); Künstlerisches Betriebsbüro Dr Carlo Nesler (tel:0471-327 933); Öffentlichbeitsarbeit Mag Stefan Nicdini (tel:0471-327 918)
Perfs: 120 *Prods:* 10 *Type:* drama, music theatre, folk theatre, children's and youth theatre *Venues:* Neues Stadttheater Bozen, Grosser Saal 810, Studio 160, Kloster Maria Heim (opem air stage) 160 *Comments:* see also Venues (Nuovo Teatro Comunale)

Centro Teatrale Bresciano
contrada delle Bassiche, 32, 25121 **Brescia**
Tel: 030-377 1111/2134 (press)
Fax: 030-293 181/377 0784 (press)
E-Mail: ctb@numerica.it
artistic director Cesare Lievi; secretary general Riccardo Piantoni; president Luigi Mahony; press officer Bianca Simoni
Actors: varies *Perfs:* 150 *Prods:* 6 *Type:* contemporary *Venues:* Teatro Grande 1100, Teatro Contrada Santa Chiara 154 *Touring:* Italy

Cooperativa Teatro Laboratorio
Via L. Balardini 10, Buffalora, 25129 **Brescia**
Tel: 030-230 6512 Fax: 030-230 2857
Internet: www.cityline/cutt/ctl/
direttore artistico e amministrativo e responsabile commerciale Cinzia Marmifero; vice direttore Vania Giacomelli; organisation Walter Forzani
Actors: 4 *Perfs:* 190 *Prods:* 6 youth theatre + 3 drama *Type:* youth theatre, drama and dance *Venues:* Centro Teatro Ragazzi, c/o comunitá Montana della val Sabbbia *Touring:* Italy *Comments:* they also run courses emphasising cross-cultural aspects

Akroama Teatro Stabile D'Arte Contemporanea e di Ricerca Della Sardegna
via La Palma, 09126 **Cagliari**
Tel: 070-341 322 Fax: 070-340 868
E-Mail: akroama@tin.it
administrative director Rosalba Piras; artistic director Lelio Lecis; management Stella Valentina Pecorella; press office Dafne Turillazzi
Actors: 52 *Perfs:* 180 *Prods:* 7 *Type:* total (drama, music, dance and visual arts) *Venues:* Teatro delle Saline, Teatro Akròama *Comments:* registered address: via Corsica 25, Cagliari 09100, tel & fax: 070-305474; legal address: Via Corsica 25, 09126, Cagliari

Teatro di Sardegna Soc. Coop. a.r.l.
Via Mameli 153, 09124 **Cagliari**
Tel: 070-275 899/276 220 Fax: 070-270 932
president Antonio Cabiddu; artistic director Paolo Bonacelli; press officer Giuseppe Murru
Actors: 12 *Perfs:* 220 *Prods:* 4 *Type:* classic and contemporary theatre *Venues:* Teatro Alfieri
Touring: Italy, Switzerland

Associazione Cult. Nave Argo
via Fisicara 7/A, 95041 **Caltagirone (CT)**
Tel: 0933-22436/52091 Fax: 0933-55989
E-Mail: prezzan@calatino.it
direttore artistico Nicoleugenia Prezzavento; responsabile legale Fabio Navarra
Actors: 5 *Perfs:* 20 *Prods:* 1 *Type:* contemporary *Venues:* Teatro Vitaliano Brancati 120 *Touring:* Italy *Comments:* produce international festival (Summer): Teatri in Città

Alfieri – Casa Degli Alfieri
Casa Degli Alfieri, Localita' Bertolina 1, 14030 **Castagnole Monferrato (Asti)**
Tel: 0141-292 572/583
Fax: 0141-292 572
E-Mail: alfierihouse@tin.it
direttore organizzativo Maurizio Agostinetto; direttore artistico Luciano Nattino
Actors: 15 *Perfs:* 120 *Prods:* 3 *Type:* experimental theatre (research theatre) *Venues:* Casa Degli Alfieri (summer season only); Open air 400-500 *Touring:* Italy, Europe *Comments:* also children's theatre; the Casa Degli Alfieri is a place for seminars, research, rehearsal and experimentation as well as a place for theatrical representation

Gruppo Iarba
piazza dei Martiri, 8, 95131 **Catania**
Tel: 095-535 453
Fax: 095-538 364
organisation director Giuseppe Maniscalco; artistic director Nino Romeo, Graziana Maniscalco
Actors: 8 *Perfs:* 100 *Prods:* 9 *Type:* research and experimental theatre *Touring:* Italy *Comments:* registered address: via Gramignani 46, 95121 Catania; organise workshops; see also Promoters

Piccolo Teatro di Catania
via F. Ciccaglione 29, 95125 **Catania**
Tel: 095-447 603/552 083
Fax: 095-552 083
artistic/administrative director Giovanni Salvo; technical director/press officer Luisa Fiorello
Actors: 20 *Perfs:* 110-120 *Prods:* 6 (incl 4 new) *Type:* contemporary *Venues:* Piccolo Teatro 242 *Touring:* Sicily *Comments:* also children's theatre; see also Venues

Teatro della Citta'
Via Sabotino nffl 2/C, 95129 **Catania**
Tel: 095-531 018/530 153
Fax: 095-530 044
direttore Orazio Torrisi; servizi amministrativi Isabella Costa; servizi organizzativi Marilina Scordo; coordinamento organizzativo Alessandro Alì; ufficio stampa Salvo La Rosa
Actors: varies *Perfs:* 30 *Prods:* 8 *Venues:* Teatro Brancati *Comments:* theatre address: Teatro Brancati, Via Sabotino 2-4, Catania, tel: 095-531 018

Teatro Stabile di Catania
Via Giuseppe Fava, 39, 90135 **Catania**
Tel: 095-354 466 Fax: 095-365 135/351 919
E-Mail: etsct@sicilia.pandora.it
presidente Prof. Giuseppe Giarrizzo.; direttore artistico Prof. Filippo Amoroso
Actors: 100 *Perfs:* 250-300 *Prods:* 6 *Type:* prosa *Venues:* Teatro Verga 700,, Teatro Angelo Musco 300 *Touring:* Italy *Comments:* run a 3 year theatre course for young actors, which is free:
Scuola di Teatro per Giovani Attori e Attrici

Societas Raffaello Sanzio
Via Serraglio 2, 47023 **Cesena (FO)**
Tel: 0547-25566 Fax: 0547-25560
Internet: www.raffaellosanzio.org
E-Mail: info@raffaellosanzio.org
organisation Gilda Biasini, Cosetta Nicolini; artistic director Romeo Castellucci; responsabile tecnico Fabio Sajiz
Actors: 20-25 *Perfs:* 80-90 *Prods:* 3 new, 5 revival *Type:* drama, children's theatre *Venues:* Teatro Comandini 100 *Touring:* Europe, Japan, South America, Australia *Comments:* registered address: sobborgo F. Comandini 52, 47023 Cesena , tel. 0547 29916; also run a school of theatre for youth organised by Claudia Castellucci, in collaboration with Romeo Castellucci and Chiara Guidi

Teatro della Valdoca SNC
via Aldini, 26, 47023 **Cesena (FO)**
Tel: 0547-24968 Fax: 0547-24968
E-Mail: valdoca@iol.it
artistic director Cesare Ronconi; organistion director Cristina Proserpio (0338-608 4150 mobile)
Actors: 17 *Perfs:* 65 *Prods:* 4 (incl 2 new) *Type:* contemporary *Venues:* Teatro Bonci (Cesena) *Touring:* Italy *Comments:* also publish their scripts and CDs of their shows

Teatro Città Murata
Piazzolo Terragni 1, 22100 **Como**
Tel: 031-269 175
Fax: 031-330 2781
Internet: tcmurata.it
E-Mail: tcmurata@tin.it
artistic director Mario Bianchi; organisation Alessandro Diliberto; president Daniele Braiucca; administrative director Franca Soldini; technical director Michele Napione
Actors: 12 *Perfs:* 120 *Prods:* 6 *Type:* youth theatre, contemporary theatre *Venues:* Teatro Nuovo Rebbio 320 *Touring:* France *Comments:* organises the festival of puppets and youth theatre: Tutti i Colori dell' Estate

Coop Centro RAT
Via Galluppi 15/19, 87100 **Cosenza**
Tel: 0984-73125 Fax: 0984-73125
Internet: www.linkey.net/acquario
E-Mail: cractcs@tin.it
presidente cooperative e direttore artistico Antonello Antonante; direttore artistico Massimo Costabile
Actors: 12-13 *Perfs:* 60-80 *Prods:* 2 *Type:* research theatre, children's theatre *Venues:* Teatro dell'Acquario 200 *Touring:* Italy *Comments:* see also Venues

Giallo Mare Minimal Teatro
via della Repubblica, 41, 50053 **Empoli (FI)**
Tel: 0571-81629/83758 Fax: 0571-83758
Internet: www.leonet.it/art/giallomare/
E-Mail: giallomare@leonet.it
administrative director Vania Pucci; artistic director Renzo Boldrini; technical director M. Teresa Delogu
Actors: 10 *Perfs:* 140 *Prods:* 10 *Type:* children's; youth theatre *Venues:* Sala Immaginazione 100, Teatro Comunale G. Verdi 300 *Touring:* Italy *Comments:* registered address: via Chiarugi 64, 50053 Empoli; research on the use of video for children's theatre

Teatro Due Mondi
Via Oberdan 9/a, 48018 **Faenza (RA)**
Tel: 0546-622 999 Fax: 0546-621 903
Internet: www.racine.ra.it/teatroduemondi
E-Mail: teatroduemondi@racine.ra.it
artistic director Alberto Grilli
Actors: 8 *Perfs:* 80 *Prods:* 6 *Type:* research theatre, street theatre and children's theatre *Venues:* Sala Teatro due Mondi, 50 (is going to be 100 hopefully for spring 2000) *Touring:* South America, national

TSR Produzioni E Servizi Del TeatroStabile in Rete – Coop arl
Corso Matteotti 4, 61032 **Fano (PE)**
Tel: 0721-826 462
Fax: 0721-830 146
Internet: www.gostec.it/teatrostabileinretejanocagli
E-Mail: fanoteatro@gostec.it
artistic director Massimo Pugliani; organisation directors Elisabetta Marsigli, Ivana Tomassini; press officer Elisabetta Marsigli
Actors: 7-12 *Perfs:* 80 *Prods:* 1 new + 3 revival *Type:* contemporary, research theatre, drama *Venues:* Teatro Della Concordia 250 (S. Costanzo), Teatro Della Fortuna 600 (Fano) *Touring:* Germany, Italy *Comments:* also run a children's theatre (Teatro Linguaggi Tansteatro); Tel. information centre: 0721-800 750; see also Festivals

Teatro Potlach
via S.Maria in Castello,10, 02032 **Fara Sabina (RI)**
Tel: 0765-277 080 Fax: 0765-277 210
E-Mail: potlach@uni.net
artistic director Giuseppe di Buduo; administration Marco Esposito; organisation Stefania Corallini
Actors: 5 *Perfs:* 180 *Prods:* 9 *Type:* experimental *Venues:* Sala Teatro Polach 100 *Touring:* Germany, Austria, Brazil, Switzerland *Comments:* registered address: via Anacapri 22, 00177, Roma; organises national and international workshops; also children's theatre – contact – Ivan Tanteri; organises festival – organises: the project Invisible Cities is a multi-disciplinary research project on city life and its memory

Teatri Comunicanti
Via Brunforte 42, 63023 **Fermo (AP)**
Tel: 0734-227 346/335 526 8147 (mobile)
Fax: 0734-227 873
artistic/administrative director Marco Renzi; technical director Cesanelli Oberdan
Actors: 6 *Perfs:* 100 *Prods:* 4 *Type:* children's theatre, comedy *Comments:* organises an international festival of children's theatre: Festival 'I Teatri del Mondo'

Aringa e Verdurini
Via Nuova de' Caccini, 1, 50121 **Firenze**
Tel: 055-234 6411/336-677 387 (mobile)
Fax: 055-234 3915/335-617 9402 (mobile)
E-Mail: leobrizzi@dada.it
responsabile organizzazione & direttore artistico Maria Cassi, Leonardo Brizzi
Actors: 2 *Perfs:* 100 *Prods:* 5 (new and revival) *Type:* musical comedy *Touring:* Spain, Portugal, Azores, France, Japan *Comments:* registered address: via San Damiano, 49, 50124 Firenze

ASTER
via dé Serragli, 5, 50124 **Firenze**
Tel: 055-213 320 Fax: 055-213 330
Internet: www.aster.fi.it
E-Mail: aster@ats.it
direttore artistico Enrica Maria Paoletti, Franco Paoletti; direttore organizzativo Enrica Maria Paoletti; ufficio stampa Rosalba Bartolotti; presidente Stefano Braschi
Actors: 9 *Perfs:* 78 *Prods:* 5 *Type:* youth and children's theatre *Venues:* Centro Icaro, Teatro Puccini

Chille de la Balanza
Centro Culturale Paolo Paoli via di San Salvi 12, 50135 **Firenze**
Tel: 055-623 6195 Fax: 055-623 6195
Internet: www.solecosta.it/chille.htm
E-Mail: chile@ats.it
artistic & administrative director Claudio Ascoli; technical director Sissi Abondanza
Actors: 30 *Perfs:* 120 *Prods:* 6 (New and revival) *Type:* street theatre, research theatre *Venues:* Centro Culturale Paolo Paoli Tracce di Vita Sensibile 150 *Touring:* Italy, France, Germany *Comments:* they organise a festival San Salvi La Citta' Nagata annual

CTM – Compagnia Teatrale I Magazzini
Via Domenico Maria Manni 55, 50135 **Firenze**
Tel: 055-600 218/609 450
Fax: 055-609 450
direzione organizzativa Patrizia Cuoco; direttore artistico Federico Tiezzi
Actors: 4-10 *Perfs:* 90 *Prods:* 5 *Type:* contemporary + prose *Touring:* Italy

Gruppo Teatrale Krypton
Borgo Pinti 89, 50121 **Firenze**
Tel: 055-234 5443
Fax: 055-234 5443
E-Mail: 0552345443@iol.it
direttore organizzativo Pina Izzi; direttore artistico Giancarlo Cauteruccio
Actors: 10 *Perfs:* 72 *Prods:* 6 *Type:* experimental *Venues:* Teatro Studio di Scandicci 400 *Touring:* Italy

Musica Meccanica
Borgo La Noce 7, 50123 **Firenze**
Tel: 055-917 9089/055-286 829/033-5592 5672 (mobile)
Fax: 055-917 9089
E-Mail: musica.meccanica@val.it
artistic director Massimo J. Monaco; administrative director Elena Patruno
Actors: 3 *Perfs:* 90 *Prods:* 3 *Type:* contemporary theatre, performance with machines and robots, street theatre, mechanic and automatic music, cabaret with songs and cruel ballads *Touring:* worldwide *Comments:* second E-mail: monaco@val.it; independent touring company; programme festival and special projects in Italy; in conjunction with visual artists to create performance with different language; publish a quarterly journal Musica Meccanica (q.v.)

Produzioni Teatrali Paolo Poli
c/o Essevuteatro sas, largo F.lli Alinari 15, 50123 **Firenze**
Tel: 055-238 1611/289 194
Fax: 055-238 1611
E-Mail: essevu@lam.it
artistic/administrative director Paolo Poli
Actors: 8 *Perfs:* 100 *Prods:* 1 *Type:* comedy *Touring:* Italy

Pupi e Fresedde-Teatro di Rifredi
via Vittorio Emanuele 303, 50134 **Firenze**
Tel: 055-422 0361/2 Fax: 055-422 1453
Internet: www.toxamateatro.it
E-Mail: staff@toxamateatro.it
organisation director Francesco De Biasi; artistic director Angelo Savelli;
egal representative Giancarlo Mordini
Actors: varies *Perfs:* 130 *Prods:* 3 *Venues:* Teatro di Rifredi 284 *Touring:* Italy, Turkey *Comments:* also youth theatre

Teatro Arcoiris
Via San Niccolò 63, 50125 **Firenze**
Tel: 055-234 6225 Fax: 055-234 6225
Internet: www.arcoiris.it
E-Mail: arcoiris@arcoiris.it
artistic/administrative director Pier Carlo Testa; technical director Corrado Mura
Actors: 15 *Perfs:* 82 *Prods:* 2/4 *Type:* experimental plays, children's theatre *Venues:* Teatro Sala Esse 260 *Touring:* Australia *Comments:* registered address: Via San Nicolo' 63, 50125, Firenze

Teatro Mascará
Via Palazzo dei Diavoli 83, 50142 **Firenze**
Tel: 055-711 31
Fax: 055-711 319
artistic director Gianfranco Pedullà; promotion, organisation and press office Marco Cannicci, Lauro Verrazzani, Laura Meini;
administrative director Tamara Rinaldi
Actors: 7 *Perfs:* 93 *Prods:* 3 new + 4 revival *Type:* drama and children's theatre *Touring:* Russia

Teatrombría
Via Fratelli Zeno 4, 50127 **Firenze**
Tel: 055-430 681 Fax: 055-430 681
artistic director Grazia Bellucci; artistic collaborator Corrado Sorbara
Actors: 2-4 *Perfs:* 60 *Prods:* 6 *Type:* shadow theatre *Touring:* Italy

SiciliaTeatro
Corso Vittorio Emanuele 292, 96014 **Floridia (SR)**
Tel: 0931-940 583 Fax: 0931-940 600
Internet: www.siciliateatro.it
E-Mail: info@siciliateatro.it
administrative director Santi Lo Monaco; artistic director Sebastiano Lo Monaco; press officer Isabella Micali Barattelli
Actors: varies *Perfs:* 175 *Prods:* 3 *Type:* classical, contemporary *Touring:* Italy *Comments:* second address: Via Nomentana 251, 00161 Rome, Tel: 06-4423 8641

Teatro dell'Arca
c/o Teatro G Testori, via Vespucci 13, 47100 **Forlì**
Tel: 0543-722 456
Fax: 0543-725 651
Internet: www.office.it
E-Mail: teatroarca@office.it
administrative and artistic director Franco Palmieri; technical director Sergio Cangini
Actors: 15 *Perfs:* 200 *Prods:* 2 + 4 revival *Type:* experimental, prosa, children & youth theatre *Venues:* Teatro Giovanni Testori 287 *Touring:* Italy, Europe *Comments:* see Venues

Lunaria – Associazione Culturale
Via XX Settembre 20 int.89,
16121 **Genova**
Tel: 010-592 838
Fax: 010-592 838
artistic & administrative director Daniela Ardini
Actors: 6 *Perfs:* 65-70 *Prods:* 4 *Type:* classical and contemporary *Touring:* Morocco,Austria, Germany, France, Spain

Teatro dell'Archivolto
c/o Teatro Gustavo Modena P.zza Modena ne 3, 16149 **Genova**
Tel: 010-65921
Fax: 010-659 2224
Internet: www.archivolto.it
E-Mail: info@archivolto.it
organizzatrice Giuseppina Rando; direttore artistico Giorgio Gallione; ufficio stampa Fulvia Bardelli
Actors: 19 *Perfs:* 120-130 *Prods:* 7 adult (4 new), 5 youth (2 new) *Type:* research on comic theatre and musical theatre, youth theatre *Venues:* Teatro Gustavo Modena 498 *Touring:* Italy *Comments:* also children's theatre; see also Venues

Teatro della Tosse
Piazza Negri 4, 16123 **Genova**
Tel: 010-248 7011 (switchboard)
Fax: 010-251 1275/261 488
E-Mail: tdtosse@money.it
presidente e direttore artistico Tonino Conte; direttore artistico Emanuele Luzzati; organizzazione Antonello Pischedda; ufficio stampa Maria de Barbieri, Laura Grendanin; vice direzione Sergio Maifredi
Actors: 20 *Perfs:* 400 *Prods:* 12 *Type:* visual & experimental theatre *Venues:* Teatro Sant'Agostino: Sala Aldo Trionfo 500, Sala Dino Campana 250, Sala Agorà 150 *Touring:* Italy *Comments:* see also Venues

Teatro Stabile di Genova
Piazza Borgo Pila 42, 16129 **Genova**
Tel: 010-53421 Fax: 010-534 2510
Internet: www.teatrodigenova.it.net
E-Mail: teatrodigenova@it.net
segretaria generale Carla Cannone; presidente avv. Giovanni Salvarezza; direttore artistico e amministrativo Ivo Chiesa; press office Rosanna Figliomeni
Actors: 45+ *Perfs:* 32 *Prods:* 4 *Type:* prose *Venues:* Teatro della Corte 1014, Teatro Duse 500 *Touring:* Italy *Comments:* also run a three year course for actors which is sponsored by the Region Liguria; see also Venues

Artisti Associati
via Carducci, 71, 34170 **Gorzia**
Tel: 0481-532 317 Fax: 0481-532 317
administrative director Gualtiero Mramor; artistic director Walter Mramor; press officers Paolo Sordini (Rome), Cristina Rastelli (Milano)
Actors: 15 *Perfs:* 100 *Prods:* 4 *Type:* classical and contemporary *Touring:* Italy

Teleme Teatro
Via F.lli Bandiera, 49, 58100 **Grosseto**
Tel: 0564-28341 Fax: 0564-420 252
E-Mail: teleme@tin.it
artistic director Francesco Tarsi
Actors: 15 *Perfs:* 80 *Prods:* 4 *Type:* poetry and fictional texts adapted for theatre, including Greek classical texts *Venues:* Anfiteatro Romano di Roselle (Grosseto)150 *Touring:* Italy, Europe *Comments:* organise workshops

Stalker Teatro
Via La Salle 2, 10095 **Grugliasco (TO)**
Tel: 011-786 946 Fax: 011-787 171
E-Mail: Stalker@alma.it
legale rappresentante Adriana Rinaldi; direttore artistico Gabriele Boccacini; segretarie di compagnia Antonella Eusebio, Robert Cipriani
Actors: 9 *Perfs:* 70 *Prods:* 8 (1 new) *Type:* performance theatre, events, visual installation, animation theatre for children, special events *Comments:* registered address: Via Frejus 29/A, 10095, Grugliasco (TO)

Teatro Stabile Abruzzese
Via Roma 54, 67100 **L'Aquila**
Tel: 0862-62946/413 200/414 269
Fax: 0862-414 269/62946/413 200
Internet: www.teatrostabile.abruzzo.it
E-Mail: tsa@webaq.it
commissario straordinario Arch. Renato Nicolini; direttore Federico Fiorenza; ufficio stampa Roberta Gargano
Actors: varies *Perfs:* 110 *Prods:* 5 : prosa *Venues:* Teatro Comunale 600 *Touring:* Italy *Comments:* see also Venues

Uovo – Centro Stabile Teatro Giovani D'Abruzzo, L'
Via dell'Oratorio 6, 67100 **L'Aquila**
Tel: 0862-410 416/411 331 (box office) Fax: 0862-28337
Internet: www.webaq.it/TeatroUovo
E-Mail: TeatroUovo@webaq.it
administrative director Antonio Massena; artistic director Maria Cristina Giambruno; president & legal representative Ezio Rainaldi
Perfs: 247 *Prods:* 9 *Type:* children's and youth theatre *Venues:* Teatro San Fillipo 272 *Comments:* carry out research, produce plays, work in the community and provide theatre training in the Centro Stabile Giovani D'Abruzzo

Koreja Coop – Cantieri Teatrali
Via Dorso 70, 73100 **Lecce**
Tel: 0832-242 000 Fax: 0832-242 000
E-Mail: koreja@tin.it
artistic & administrative director Salvatore Tramacere; technical director Franco Ungaro
Actors: 8 *Perfs:* 80 *Prods:* 4 *Type:* contemporary experimental theatre *Touring:* Italy *Comments:* organise a theatrical event which is held every year, Strade Maestre, which includes various national and international drama companies; it is held in Teatro Comunale Paisiello of Lecce – 320

Teatro Invito
Via Trieste 9, 23900 **Lecco**
Tel: 0341-287 128 Fax: 0341-287 114
E-Mail: alesspe@tin.it
artistic/administrative director Luca Radaelli; technical director and organisation Monica Martignoni
Actors: 8 *Perfs:* 140 *Prods:* 6 (3 new) *Type:* youth and children's theatre *Touring:* Italy *Comments:* registered address: Viale Turati 71, 22053 Lecco; organise adults courses and workshops in collaboration with public schools

Teatro d'Artificio
Strada Rivoltana 14 No 16, 20060 **Liscate (MI)**
Tel: 02-9535 0499/0347-423 5031 (mobile)
Fax: 0363-49000
Internet: www.clownitaly.com
E-Mail: carlopastori@ctraole.it
administrative director Roberto Abbiati;
artistic director Bano Ferrari
Actors: 3 *Perfs:* 130 *Prods:* 2 *Type:* children's theatre, clowns *Venues:* Teatro Degli Incamminati *Touring:* Europe *Comments:* registered address: Via Garibaldi 73, 20034 Giussano (MI)

C.E.L. – Teatro di Livorno
Via Goldoni 83, 57125 **Livorno**
Tel: 0586-889 111 Fax: 0586-899 920
Internet: www.comune.livorno.it/cel/home.htm
E-Mail: cel@mclink.it
amministrazione e produzione Isabella Bartolini; presidente Marco Bertini; affari generali Paolo Demi; comunicazione-immagine & responsabile ufficio stampa Antonella Peruffo; consulente artistico lirica Dott. Alberto Paloscia
Actors: varies *Perfs:* 18 *Prods:* 8 *Type:* operetta, prosa, lyric, ballet *Venues:* Teatro la Gran Guardia 1600 *Touring:* Italy *Comments:* see also Opera, Promoter and Venues

Teatro del Carretto SRL
piazza del Giglio 13, 55100 **Lucca**
Tel: 0583-48684
Fax: 0583-496 352
E-Mail: carretto@dada.it
administrative director Anna Maria Meo; artistic directors Maria Grazia Cipriani, Graziano Gregori
Actors: varies *Perfs:* 100 *Prods:* 1 + 3 revivals *Type:* prosa, research theatre *Touring:* Italy, France, Germany, USA (New York) *Comments:* curate not only the production but also the distribution; organization and production: Borgo Albizi 15, 50122 Firenze, Tel: 055-263 8303, Fax: 055-234 6002

Baracca Di Monza, La
via Paolo Sarti 28, 20052 **Macherio (MI)**
Tel: 039-463 070/480 613 Fax: 039-480 613
E-Mail: baraccam@tin.it
administrative director Roberto Sala;
artistic director Michele Ciarla
Actors: 10 *Perfs:* 200 *Prods:* 13 *Type:* children's and youth theatre *Touring:* Italy *Comments:* also educational activities

Teatro all' Improvviso
P. za Don E. Leoni 18, 46100 **Mantova**
Tel: 0376-221 705 Fax: 0376-222 723
E-Mail: t.improvviso@wnt.it
artistic director Dario Moretti;
responsible organisation Marina Lucchetta
Actors: 6 *Perfs:* 120 *Prods:* 6 *Type:* children's theatre *Venues:* Teatreno 140 *Touring:* Italy

Teatro la Ribalta Di Antonio Viganó
Via Montegrappa 17, Fraz. Sartirana, 23807 **Merate (LC)**
Tel: 039-952 0082 Fax: 039-952 0033
segreteria organizzativa Alessandra Sechi, Eugenia Neri; direzione artistica Antonio Viganó
Actors: 3 *Prods:* 1 *Type:* visual and dance theatre, young people's theatre *Venues:* Teatro Di Osmago 396 *Touring:* Italy, France *Comments:* also organise festival Campsirago Teatro (q.v.); they organise a festival which is held every year between January and April – sponsored by Regione Lombar

Agorà
via Friuli, 51, 20135 **Milano**
Tel: 02-5990 1578/5518 7465 Fax: 02-5518 7465
artistic director Milla Sannoner; legal representative Italia Ulivieri; press officer Fiorella Polli
Actors: 20 *Perfs:* 140 *Prods:* 2 new, 2 revival : prosa *Touring:* Italy, Prague

C.T.F.R. SRL
viale Piave,11, 20129 **Milano**
Tel: 02-783 204 Fax: 02-783 435
E-Mail: ctfr@micronet.it
artistic and administrative director Dario Fo; organisation director Franca Rame
Actors: 2 permanent *Prods:* 1 + 5 revivals *Type:* satirical and poetic theatre *Comments:* Dario Fo (artistic director) was awarded the 1997 Nobel prize for Literature

Compagnia del Teatro Carcano
corso di Porta Romana 63, 20122 **Milano**
Tel: 02-551 3211
Fax: 02-5518 1355
Internet: www.teatrocarcano.com
artistic director Giulio Bosetti; amministratore unico Nicoletta Rizzato; press office Brunella Portoghese
Actors: varies *Prods:* 4 *Venues:* Teatro Carcano 990 *Touring:* Italy *Comments:* see also Venues

Compagnia Picciola
Centro Culturele san Felice, Piazza san Fedele 4, 20121 **Milano**
Tel: 02-8635 2231 Fax: 02-8635 2233
director Maria Pia Pagliarecci
Prods: 10 in repertoire *Venues:* Teatro san Felice *Comments:* see also Venues

Compagnia Stabile del Teatro Filodrammatici
Via Filodrammatici 1, 20121 **Milano**
Tel: 02-8646 1670/869 3659
Fax: 02-8646 1884
responsabile amministrativo Marco Balbi; direttore artistico Claudio Beccari; press office & pr Silvia Pacciarini; organizzatore Emilio Russo
Actors: 6 *Perfs:* 250 *Prods:* 6 *Type:* prosa *Venues:* Teatro Filodrammatici 187 *Comments:* Accademia dei Fioldrammatici (tel: 2-8646 0849) organises two year courses for actors

Corona-Gherzi-Mattioli
L.Go Vulci 7, 20159 **Milano**
Tel: 02-744 002/689 6966/523 1160
Fax: 02-744 002/689 6966/523 1160
direttore organizzativo Roberto Corona; gestione artistica Monica Mattioli, Roberto Corona, Gianluigi Gherzi; organizzatrice per L'estero Annalisa Rossini (tel: 02-8950 3833)
Actors: 2 *Perfs:* 60-70 *Prods:* 5 (incl 2 new) *Touring:* Italy, Europe *Comments:* the group works mainly with youth organisations and community groups (centri sociali)

CRT Artificio SCRL
via Vincenzo Monti, 25, 20123 **Milano**
Tel: 02-4801 7050/7054 Fax: 02-4801 7077
E-Mail: artifici@tin.it
artistic & administrative director Franco Laera; press officer Lidia Gavana
Perfs: 130 *Prods:* 1 *Type:* prose, research, experimental
Touring: Italy, Europe

Fontana Teatro (Centro Teatro Ragazzi Giovani)
Via Boltraffio, 21, 20159 **Milano**
Tel: 02-688 6314 Fax: 02-688 7205
Internet: enter.it/fontanateatro/sf.html
E-Mail: fontana@enter.it
administrative director Gianmario Gatti; president Braschi Stefano; artistic directors Guido Clericetti, Stefan Braschi; press officer Elena Comoglio
Actors: varies *Perfs:* 160+ *Prods:* 4 *Type:* children's, youth theatre *Venues:* Sala Fontana 400 *Comments:* produce and support other youth theatre groups; organise: International Youth Theatre Festival in May, International Clown Festival in May-June

Grupporiani/Carlo Colla e Figli
via Neera, 24, 20141 **Milano**
Tel: 02-8953 1301 Fax: 02-846 1312
E-Mail: orian@tin.it
art dir Eugenio Monti Colla; prod manager Piero Corbella
Actors: 15 + orchestra *Perfs:* 150 *Prods:* 10 *Type:* traditional, animation, music, dance, marionettes *Venues:* Atelier Carlo Colla e Figli 200 *Touring:* Germany, Australia, USA, France *Comments:* see also Puppets

Mascherenere (Associazione-Laboratorio di Teatro)
via Rossini, 3, 20122 **Milano**
Tel: 02-7601 2132 Fax: 02-799 775
E-Mail: mascherenere@tiscalinet.it
administrative director Silvana Scandone; artistic director Leonardo Gazzola; technical director Rufin Doh; press officer Paolo Piseoldu;
chairman Modou Gueye
Actors: 8 *Perfs:* 50 *Prods:* 2 (new) *Type:* Afro-Italian theatre (narration, dance, music, dialogues etc. in mixed languages) *Touring:* Italy

Piccolo Teatro di Milano – Teatro d'Europa
Largo Paolo Grassi 2, 20121 **Milano**
Tel: 02-723 331 (switchboard)/8901 4202 (prod. office)
Fax: 02-874 836
Internet: www.piccoloteatro.it
E-Mail: info@piccoloteatro.org
general secretary GianMario Maggi; director Sergio Escobar; head of production & organization Rosanna Purchia; head of press Giovanni Soresi; dir art Luca Ronconi
Prods: 8-10 *Type:* classical, opera, experimental *Venues:* Teatro Giorgio Strehler 940, Teatro Paolo Grassi 600, Piccolo Teatro Studio 420 *Touring:* Italy, Europe, Far East *Comments:* administrative address: Via Rovello 2, 20121 Milano; see also Venues

Quelli di Grock
Via Emanuele Muzio N3, 20124 **Milano**
Tel: 02-6698 8993 Fax: 02-6698 8993
Internet: www.quellidigrock.com
E-Mail: quellidigrock@ntt.it
administrative and organisation director Francesco D'Agostino; artistic director Claudio Intropido
Actors: 13 *Perfs:* 200 *Prods:* 6 *Type:* dance theatre and children's theatre *Venues:* Teatro Greco 130, Teatro Verdi 200, Teatro delle Erbe 300 *Touring:* Austria, Germany, France, Italy

Teatri Possibili srl
Via Savona 10, 20144 **Milano**
Tel: 02-832 3126 Fax: 02-832 3264
E-Mail: cordel@tin.it
director Corrado d'Elia
Actors: 10 *Perfs:* 80 *Venues:* Teatro Libero 100
Comments: the theatre is available for hire; the season goes from Sept. to June; they run 2 + 1 year courses for actors and theatre directors

Teatridithalia – Elfo Portaromana Associati
Via Ciro Menotti 11, 20129 **Milano**
Tel: 02-7611 0007/0032/7010 8019(press office)
Fax: 02-7012 3851
Internet: www.elfo.org
E-Mail: info@elfo.org
organizzazione Fiorenzo Grassi, Rino de Pace; direttore artistico Ferdinando Bruni, Elio De Capitani; ufficio stampa Emanuela Caldirola; responsabile amministrativo Carmelita Scardamaglia;
press office Barbara Caldarini
Actors: 6 *Perfs:* 150 *Prods:* 12 *Type:* contemporary, classical *Venues:* Teatro dell'Elfo 580, Teatro di Portaromana 500 *Touring:* Italy *Comments:* see also Venues and Festivals

Teatro degli Incamminati
Via Ugo Foscolo 4, 20121 **Milano**
Tel: 02-875 365 Fax: 02-875 807
E-Mail: gmb@enter.it
administratie director & president Gianmario Bandera; artistic directors Emanuele Banterle, Franco Branciaroli
Actors: varies *Perfs:* 130 *Prods:* 3 *Type:* drama
Touring: Italy

Teatro dei Capovolti
Via F.Casati 8, 20124 **Milano**
Tel: 02-2940 1018/335-660 8177 (mobile)
Fax: 02-2940 1018
direttore Marco Bizzozero
Actors: 7 *Perfs:* 8-100 *Prods:* 2 *Type:* circus and theatre
Touring: Italy *Comments:* also has national school of theatre & circus at the same address

Teatro del Sole
Via San Elembardo 2, 20126 **Milano**
Tel: 02-255 2318 Fax: 02-255 0548
administration Giuseppe Meloni; artistic director Renata Coluccini; organiser Kristine Fahl; press office Chirtina Rimoldi; promotion Augusta M. Bariona
Actors: 6 *Perfs:* 100 *Prods:* 1 new + 6 revival *Type:* teatro d'attore for children and youth *Touring:* Italy, Europe
Comments: also runs a theatre school

Teatro Franco Parenti
Via Pier Lombardo 14, 20135 **Milano**
Tel: 02-5518 4075 Fax: 02-545 5929
presidente e direttore artistico Andree Ruth Shammah; capo ufficio stampa e responsabile culturale
Andrea Bisicchia
Actors: 20 *Perfs:* 172 *Prods:* 8 : prosa *Venues:* Teatro Franco Parenti 500, Spazio Nuovo 100 *Comments:* see also Venues

Teatro Litta SCRL
Corso Magenta 24, 20123 **Milano**
Tel: 02-805 5882/891/8645 4546 Fax: 02-7201 0640
E-Mail: teatrocitta1@galactica.it
organizer director Nicoletta Cardone Johnson; artistic director & producer Gaetano Callegaro; administrative director Giuliana Cidri; press office Giulia Tatulli
Actors: 8 *Perfs:* 140 *Prods:* 5 *Type:* research theatre, dance theatre, children & youth's theatre *Venues:* Teatro Litta 250 *Touring:* Italy *Comments:* funded by the Cultural Ministry as a center of theatrical research and experimentation; see also Venues

Teatro Out Off Sas Di B. Bertoldo & C
via G. Dupré 4, 20155 **Milano**
Tel: 02-3926 2282 Fax: 02-3921 5239
E-Mail: teatrooutoff@teatroitalia.com
artistic directors Beniamino Bertoldo; press officer Roberto Traverso; resident author Lorenzo Loris; directors Antonio Sixty, Antonio Latella, Lorenzo Loris
Actors: 10 *Perfs:* 110 *Prods:* 3 *Type:* research theatre
Venues: Teatro Out Off 100 *Touring:* Italy

Tuttoteatro (Società SRL)
via U. Foscolo 4, 20121 **Milano**
Tel: 02-805 6984/994 Fax: 02-805 6994
artistic & administrative director Roberta Milazzo; artistic director Nando Milazzo
Actors: 30 *Perfs:* 120-180 *Prods:* 2 *Type:* musical, prose
Touring: Italy

Emilia Romagna Teatro
Largo Garibaldi 15, 41100 **Modena**
Tel: 059-223 783
Fax: 059-234 979
E-Mail: erteatro@tin.it
direttore Pietro Valenti;
president Enzo Bioli; press officer Giobanna Botti
Actors: 60 *Perfs:* 150 *Prods:* 6 *Type:* classical to contemporary *Venues:* Teatro Storchi 960 *Touring:* Italy
Comments: also children's theatre

L'Albero – Centro Internazionale di Formazione Ricerca e Creazione Teatrale
via Casciani 3, 50025 **Montespertoli (FI)**
Tel: 0571-608 891
Fax: 0571-609 580
Internet: www.yve-lebreton.com
E-Mail: albero@yve_lebreton.com
artistic/administrative director Yves Lebreton
Actors: 1 *Perfs:* 60 *Prods:* 1 *Type:* physical theatre *Touring:* international *Comments:* also seminars and workshops

Compagnia Gli Ipocriti
Centro direzionale, Palazzo Esedra, Isola F 11, 80143 **Napoli**
Tel: 081-734 5222/5224
Fax: 081-734 5216
direttore artistico Carmela Trinchillo, Pasquale Scialò; legale representante Giuliano D'Alterio
Actors: varies *Perfs:* 16 *Prods:* 4 *Type:* contemporary mediterranean authors, classic *Touring:* Italy

Compagnia Prospect
Vico Vacche a S. Liborio 5, 80100 **Napoli**
Tel: 081-551 9733 Fax: 081-552 1495
administrative director Francesca Buzzurro; artistic director Mario Scarpetta; technical director Giuseppe Sabatino; legal representative Giovanni Pinto
Actors: varies *Perfs:* 80-100 *Prods:* 3 + 3 revivals *Type:* drama, children's theatre, youth theatre *Touring:* Italy
Comments: registered address: Via E. Arlotta 21, 80125 Napoli

Compagnia Teatrale di Enzo Moscato
Via Enea Zanfagna, 62, 80126 **Napoli**
Tel: 081-570 2288/0336-830994 Fax: 081-570 2288
artistic director Enzo Moscato; adm Claudio Affinito
Actors: 3-10 *Perfs:* 100-110 *Prods:* 2 + 4 revival *Type:* drama written by Enzo Moscato *Touring:* Italy, Germany, France *Comments:* Enzo Moscato's plays are translated and represented in different countries (especially in France)

Compagnia Teatro Nuovo – Il Carro
via Monte Calvario, 16, 80134 **Napoli**
Tel: 081-425 958 Fax: 081-406 062
administrative director Angelo Montella;
artistic director Igina di Napoli
Actors: 20 *Perfs:* 130 *Prods:* 10 *Type:* research *Venues:* Teatro Nuovo 300 *Touring:* Italy, Cuba, Germany

Compagnia Teatro Popolare
Via A Scarlatti 209, 80127 **Napoli**
Tel: 081-578 1905/556 0107 Fax: 081-556 0151
presidente Lucio Mirra; direttore artistico Luigi de Filippo; press office Claudia Mirra
Actors: 8-12 *Prods:* 1 *Type:* traditional Napolitan theatre
Venues: Teatro Diana 1000 *Touring:* Italy *Comments:* see also Venues

Consorzio 90
via Solimene 127, 80126 **Napoli**
Tel: 081-640 479/714 2499/549 1266
Fax: 081-714 1657/549 9656
legal representative Giuseppe Russo; artistic director Dalia Frediani; press officer Roberta Russo
Actors: 40 *Perfs:* 120+ *Prods:* 3 *Type:* prose, drama, variety *Venues:* Teatro Bellini 850 *Touring:* Italy, Europe

Cooperativa Il Teatro ARL
c/o Teatro Galleria Toledo, via Concezione a Montecalvario, 34, 80134 **Napoli**
Tel: 081-425 824/037 Fax: 081-415 935
artistic/administrativedirector Laura Angiulli; technical director Rosario Squillace; press officer Marita D'Elia
Actors: 20 *Perfs:* 120+ *Prods:* 3 *Type:* research drama
Venues: Teatro Galleria Toledo 300 *Touring:* Italy, France, Spain *Comments:* registered address: salita Tarsia, 56, 80135 Napoli; also children's theatre

Diana Organizzazione Italiana Spettacoli SNC
via L. Giordano, 64, 80127 **Napoli**
Tel: 081-578 1905 Fax: 081-556 0151
Internet: www.teatrodiana.it
E-Mail: teatro@teatrodiana.it
administrative & technical director Lucio Mirra; artistic directors Carlo Giuffré & Maria Caterina De Gaudio; press officer Claudia Mirra
Actors: 4+ *Perfs:* 300 *Prods:* 2+1 *Type:* variety (Napolitan tradition) *Venues:* Teatro Diana 1000 *Touring:* Italy, Switzerland, Germany *Comments:* see also Venues and Compagnia Teatro Popolare

Fondazione Teatro di Napoli – Teatro Del Mediterraneo
via Guglielrho Sanfelice 33, 80135 **Napoli**
Tel: 081-549 1266/9723 Fax: 081-549 9656
administrative director t.b.a.; artdirector Antonio Russo; tech director Aurelio Gatti; press officer Roberta Russo
Actors: varies *Perfs:* 200+ *Prods:* 7 *Type:* musical, operetta, drama *Venues:* Teatro Bellini di Napoli 950
Touring: Italy *Comments:* see also Venues

Gitiesse Artisti Riuniti
via San Pasquale a Chiaia, 55, 80121 **Napoli**
Tel: 081-407 898 Fax: 081-425 009
organisation director Lello Vianello; artistic director Giuseppe Gleijeses; admin. director Valeria De Liguoro
Actors: 109 *Perfs:* 285 *Prods:* 7 + 1 revival *Type:* drama and musical *Touring:* Italy, Switzerland

Il Sole e La Luna s.a.s.
Via Caravaggio, 144, 80126 **Napoli**
Tel: 081-549 1266 (teatro bellini) Fax: 081-549 9656
organisation & artistic director Roberta Russo; administrative manager Rosanna Calvanese
Actors: varies *Perfs:* 110+ *Prods:* 5 *Type:* traditional Napolitan drama *Venues:* Teatro Bellini (Napoli) 950
Touring: Italy *Comments:* see also Venues

Libera Scena Ensemble – Coop
via Galileo Ferraris 187, 80142 **Napoli**
Tel: 081-734 0364 Fax: 081-734 0364
administrative director Raffaele Serao; artistic director Renato Carpentieri; president Vincenzo Salomone
Actors: 13 *Perfs:* 100 *Prods:* 3 + 2 revival *Type:* research theatre *Venues:* Galleria Toledo 350; Teatro Nuovo 300
Touring: Italy *Comments:* also organise workshops from July-Oct; seminars

Nuvole, Le
V. le Kennedy 26, 80125 **Napoli**
Tel: 081-239 5653/714 6774 Fax: 081-239 5666/714 6774
Internet: www.geocities.com/atens/delphi/8257/
E-Mail: edc1512@iol.it
direttore artistica Michele Monetta; president and artistic director Luciana Florio; organizzatori artistici Morena Pauro; responsabile pedagogio Giovanni Petrone; amministratori Antonio De Maio, Franco Marchionibus
Actors: 25 *Perfs:* 150 *Prods:* 4 new + 4 revivals *Type:* mime, object theatre, youth theatre, children's theatre *Venues:* Teatro Edenlandia 280, Museo della Scienza 300, Museo di Capodimonte *Touring:* Italy *Comments:* registered address:Via Tasso 480, 80127 Napoli ; curates a programme ARTE E SCIENZA with international workshop Laboratorio Teatrale Scientifico

Riggiola (Comp. Teatrale La Riggiola Coop. a.r.l.), La
piazza S. Luigi 4a, 80123 **Napoli**
Tel: 081-769 0680/575 3037
Fax: 081-552 2761
artistic director Adriana Carli
Actors: varies *Perfs:* 130 *Prods:* 4 new + 3 revivals *Type:* experimental theatre *Venues:* La Riggiola 70 *Touring:* Italy *Comments:* interested in exchanges with international drama groups

Teatri Uniti
piazza dei Martiri 58, 80121 **Napoli**
Tel: 081-407 506/412 875/402 939 Fax: 081-402 939
Internet: www.teatriuniti.net
E-Mail: info@teatriuniti.net
administrative director Angelo Curti; artistic director Tony Servillo; press officer Sergio Marra
Actors: varies *Perfs:* 140 *Prods:* 2 *Type:* research *Touring:* Italy *Comments:* the group also produces films

Tam Teatro Musica (Ass. Cult)
Via XX Settembre 28, 35122 **Padova**
Tel: 049-654 669/656 692 Fax: 049-654 669
Internet: www.tamteatromusica.it
E-Mail: tam@intercity.it
administrative director Dario Nuzzaci; technical director Enrico Maso; artistic group Pierangela Amegro, Flavia Bussolotto, Laurent Dupont, Michele Sambin, Cinzia Zallekato
Perfs: 10 *Venues:* Teatro Maddalene 150

Associazione Teatro Biondo, Stabile di Palermo
Via Teatro Biondo 11, 90133 **Palermo**
Tel: 091-743 4300 (switchboard) Fax: 091-611 1947
presidente Rento Palazzo;
direttore artistico Pietro Carriglo
Actors: varies *Perfs:* 180 *Prods:* 6 *Type:* classical, contemporary *Venues:* Teatro Biondo 950, Sala Giorgio Strehler 130 *Touring:* Italy

Teatro Libero Palermo/incontroazione
Piazza Marima/ Salira Partamah, 90133 **Palermo**
Tel: 091-617 4040
Fax: 091-617 3712
Internet: www.telegest.it/teetislibero
E-Mail: libero@telefest.it
administrative director and organiser Giacoma Chiappara; artistic director Benedetto Mazzone, Lia Chiappara; press officer Angela Mannino
Actors: varies *Perfs:* 70 *Prods:* 3 + 3 new *Type:* research, dance theatre *Venues:* Teatro Libeno *Touring:* Italy

Associazione Teatrale Nautai Teatro
Via Massmio D'Azeglio, 13, 43100 **Parma**
Tel: 0521-200 798/335-589 9759 Fax: 0521-200 798
president & director Gigi Tapella;
organisation Sylviane Onken
Actors: 2 *Perfs:* 150 *Prods:* 7 *Type:* youth theatre *Touring:* Italy, Austria, France, Germany

Lenz Rifrazioni Ass. Cult.
via Trento, 49, 43100 **Parma**
Tel: 0521-270 141 Fax: 0521-272 641
Internet: www.lenzteat
E-Mail: lenzteat@tin.it
administrative director Marisa Bertolotti; artistic directors Maria Federica Maestri, Francesco Pititto;
press office Vivana Colla;
organizer & press office Simona Nobili
Actors: 14 *Perfs:* 75 *Prods:* 6 new *Type:* experimental, contemporary *Venues:* Teatro Lenz 100, Sala Est and Sala Majakowskj *Touring:* France, Germany *Comments:* Theatre and Dance workshops;
see also Festivals and Venues

Teatro delle Briciole
Parco Ducale, 1, 43100 **Parma**
Tel: 0521-992 044
Fax: 0521-992 048
Internet: www.briciole.it
E-Mail: briciole@tin.it
artistic director Roberto de Lellis;
responsabile settore estero Giacomo Scalisi
Actors: varies *Perfs:* 150 *Prods:* 10 *Type:* youth theatre, adult theatre *Venues:* Teatro al Parco: three halls 100, 200, 300 + summer venue 400 *Touring:* Europe, Italy, America

Teatro Stabile di Parma
Viale Basetti 12/A, 43100 **Parma**
Tel: 0521-208 088
Fax: 0521-231 232
Internet: www.teatrostabileparma.com
E-Mail: info@teatrostabileparma.com
presidente Paolo Donati; direttore artistico Walter Le Moli; press officer Laura De Stefano
Actors: 20 permanent ensemble *Perfs:* 200+ *Prods:* 4 *Type:* all types with particular attention to contemporary drama *Venues:* Teatro Due (same address): Sala Grande 500, Sala Bignardi 300, Piccola Sala 70, Spazio Minimo 100, Teatro Regio 1000 *Comments:* they will play host to 20 other companies with a total of 95 guest performances; see also Venues and Festivals

Donati-Olesen
via del Verzaro, 29,
06123 **Perugia**
Tel: 075-573 2400/06-581 7283/0348-445 5608 (mobile)
Fax: 06-5831 0896
E-Mail: sabinadetom@eolisons.it
artistic directors Giorgio Donati, Jacob Olesen
Actors: 3 *Perfs:* 100-120 *Prods:* 2 *Type:* comedy *Touring:* Italy, France, Germany

Fondazione Teatro Stabile dell'Umbria
Via del Verzaro 20, 06123 **Perugia**
Tel: 075-573 0105 Fax: 075-572 9039
Internet: www.teatrostabile.umbria.it
E-Mail: tsu@krenet.it
direttore Franco Ruggieri; presidente/legale rappresentante Bruno Buitoni; ufficio stampa Francesca Torcolini
Actors: varies *Perfs:* 200+ *Prods:* 3 new + 1 revivals *Type:* drama *Venues:* Teatro Morlacchi 850 *Comments:* see also Venues; they run a library and video library specialising in theatre, cinema and music -Centro Studi – Piazza Morlacchi 19 Tel/Fax: same as above

FonteMaggiore
Strada delle Fratte,
06071 **Perugia**
Tel: 075-528 9555/0348-601 4071
Fax: 075-528 7487
Internet: www.edisons.it/homepage/fontemaggiore
E-Mail: fontemaggiore@edisons.it
artistic director Giampiero Frondini; organization Stefano Cipiciani; press office Cinzia Spogli
Actors: varies *Perfs:* 170 *Prods:* 4 new + 8 revivals *Type:* drama and children's theatre *Venues:* Teatro S. Angelo (Perugia) 100, Teatro Concordia (Marsciano) 350, Teatro Susasio 172 *Touring:* Italy

Teatro di Sacco Ass. Ne Cul. Le
Via Santini 8, 06123 **Perugia**
Tel: 075-584 7731
Fax: 075-584 7222
president/organisation director & PR Enzo Cordasco; artistic director Roberto Biselli; administrative director Enzo Cordasco; operatori teatrali Robert Biselli, Carla Gariazzo
Actors: 4 *Perfs:* 30 *Prods:* 4 *Venues:* Sala Cutu *Touring:* Italy *Comments:* the group also works with schools and community projects

Aquarius Cooperativa
via Mazzini 44, 94015 **Piazza Armerina (EN)**
Tel: 0935-89500/360-650 423 (mobile) Fax: 0935-89500
direzione organizzativa Marco Avanzato; direttore artistica Claudio Folco Russo; ufficio stampa Francesco Urzí; registi Ezio Donato, Claudio Follo Russo
Actors: 8 *Perfs:* 50 *Prods:* 2
Type: youth theatre, comedy *Venues:* Teatro Garibaldi 157 *Touring:* Italy, (and either USA or Australia)

Pontedera Teatro Foundazione
Via Manzoni 22, 56025 **Pontedera**
Tel: 0587-57034/55720 Fax: 0587-213 631
Internet: www.pontederateatro.it
E-Mail: pontederateatro@pontederateatro.it
president Enrico Forte; artistic director Roberto Bacci; technical director Sergio Zagaglia; co-directors Luca Dini, Carla Pollastrelli; production Elina Pellegrini; organisation secretaries Gabriele Bientinesi, Daria Castellacci; administration Nicola Vespi, Stefania Paolini, Lisa Landi, Paola Vasarri;
promotion, Manvela Martinez
Prods: 5 *Type:* research theatre *Comments:* also produce and organise the festival Passaggio a Pontedera

Teatro Nucleo
Via Ricostruzione 40,
44038 **Pontelagoscuro (FE)**
Tel: 0532-742 339
Fax: 0532-744 119
Internet: www.pontederateatro.it
E-Mail: teatro@pontederateatro.it
organizzatore, presidente e ufficio stampa Antonio Tassinari; direttore artistico Horacio Czertok, Cora Herrendorf; amministratore Vanda Gregnanini
Actors: 8 *Perfs:* 40-50
Type: experimental and open space theatre *Comments:* organise training courses on theatre-therapy, called Teatro nella terapia, for working with ex-drug addicts and people with psychiatric problems

Erbamil Teatro
via Valbona, 73, 24010 **Ponteranica (BG)**
Tel: 035-573 876 Fax: 035-577 065
E-Mail: erbamil@iol.it
artistic & administrative director Fabio Comana; direttore organizzativo Nicola Cremaschi
Actors: 16 *Perfs:* 100 *Prods:* 1 *Type:* comedy and research *Venues:* Auditorium Comunale 140 *Touring:* Italy *Comments:* registered address: via Partigiani 4, 24121 Bergamo

Teatro di Piazza o D'Occasione
c/o Teatro Metastasio, Via Cairoli 59, 50047 **Prato**
Tel: 0574-608 533/531/536 Fax: 0574-608 531
Internet: www.tpo.it
E-Mail: tpo@comune.prate.it
presidente e legale rappresentante Edoardo Donatini
Actors: 28 *Perfs:* 200 *Prods:* 9 *Type:* children's theatre and youth theatre *Venues:* Teatro Fabbriocone 299, Teatro Metastasio 688 *Comments:* registered address: Corso Savonarola 9, 50047 Prato; see also Venues

Actores Alidos (Ass. Teatro Actores Alidos LST)
Via G. D'Annunzio 26, 09045 **Quartu S. Elena**
Tel: 070-822 842 (Teatro Centrale) Fax: 070-810 984
E-Mail: taatwm@tin.it
organisation director Tullia Agati; artistic director Gianfranco Angei
Actors: 15 *Perfs:* 80-85 *Prods:* 5 *Type:* modern and research *Venues:* Teatro Centrale 100 *Touring:* festivals in Spain, Switzerland, Egypt, Italy, France *Comments:* also administrates a data archive on performing arts (C.D.S) which offers different media including video, music tapes and CDs; organise Festival Internazionale del Teatro del Mediterrane; Visiting address: Teatro Centrale – Via Marconi 328/330, 09045, Quartu S. Elena; second address: P.za Republica 22, 09122, Cagliari

Teatro del Drago
Via Sant'Alberto 297, 48100 **Ravenna**
Tel: 0544-483 460/1 Fax: 0544-483 460
Internet: www.teatrodeldrago.it
E-Mail: drago@netgate.it
artistic/administrative directors Andrea & Mauro Monticelli
Actors: 6 *Perfs:* 200 *Prods:* 16 *Type:* object and animated theatre *Comments:* see also Puppets

Teatro delle Albe
c/o Ravenna Teatro, Via di Roma 39, 48100 **Ravenna**
Tel: 0544-36239/30227(box office) Fax: 0544-33303
Internet: www.netgate.it/ra.teatro
E-Mail: ra.teatro@netgate.it
artistic director Marco Martinelli;
contact Francesca Venturi
Actors: 10 *Perfs:* 10 *Prods:* 1 *Type:* research theatre *Venues:* Teatro Rasi 500, Teatro Alighieri 800 (only for drama season) *Comments:* the company has another site in Senegal: Guediawaye Theatre, Dakar, Senegal, Tel: 221-371 334, Fax: 221-371 335 – where the actors from Senegal perform annually between June-November, the artistic director is Mandiaye N'Diaye; see also Venues and Promoters

Centro Teatrale Meridionale – CTM
via Ricasoli,12, Rizziconi, 89016 **Reggio Calabria**
Tel: 0966-54555/53317 Fax: 0966-503 130
organisation director Francesca Papaleo; president & artistic director Domenico Pantano;
press officer Marina Rinaldo
Actors: 15 *Perfs:* 80 *Prods:* 2 *Type:* classical, contemporary and didactic *Venues:* Teatro Gioiosa 620 *Touring:* Italy *Comments:* also have educational outreach programme; theatre address: P.za Vittorio Veneto 8, Gioiosa Ionica, Tel: 0964-419 333

Antonio Panzuto T.E.E.
c/o ARTÉ, via San Carlo 1, 42100 **Reggio Emilia**
Tel: 059-847 033/338-669 0117 Fax: 059-847 014
E-Mail: siolenar@tin.it
artistic director Antonio Panzuto;
organization & pr Silvana Denaro
Actors: 1 *Perfs:* 4 *Prods:* 1 *Type:* youth theatre, installation, theatrical machines *Touring:* Italy, Switzerland *Comments:* registered address: Piazza Cavour 29, Ancona; the company interests are looked after by Arté, via S. Carlo 1, Reggio Emilia, contact Silvana Denaro Tel: 0522-437 443/ 0338 669 0117 (mobile)

Compagnia Teatro San Prospero
via Guidelli, 5, 42100 **Reggio Emilia**
Tel: 0522-439 346 Fax: 0522-452 455
organisation director Gianna Alfier; artistic director Alberto Cottafavi; administrative director Roberto Leoni
Actors: 12 *Perfs:* 1 + 5 *Prods:* 1 *Type:* dialect drama, classical, youth theatre in English *Venues:* Teatro San Prospero 192 *Touring:* Italy *Comments:* they run theatre courses; see also Venues; costumes history, dictions

Giardini Pensili (Compagnia Giardini Pensili)
via S. Aquilina, 23, 47900 **Rimini**
Tel: 0541-759 316 Fax: 0541-759 316
Internet: www.giardini.sm
E-Mail: lab@giardini.sm

artistic directors Roberto Paci Daló, Isabella Bordoni; organisation Floriana Paci
Actors: 3-15 (depending on production) *Perfs:* 85 *Prods:* 4 *Type:* new writing, music theatre, theatre and new technologies *Touring:* France, Austria, Germany, Italy, Spain

Atelier Envers Teatro
Village Preil 1, 11100 **Roisan (AO)**
Tel: 0165-50044/335-667 4862 (mobile) Fax: 0165-50044
E-Mail: envers@tin.it
artistic director Valeriano Gialli;
organisation Lauretta Cigolini
Actors: 7 *Perfs:* 70 *Prods:* 2 new + 2 revivals *Type:* contemporary theatre *Venues:* Teatro dela Ville 250 in Aosta *Touring:* Italy

Apas Produzioni SRL
via del Governo Vecchio, 91, 00186 **Roma**
Tel: 06-687 7463/689 2567 Fax: 06-689 2567
legal representative, organisation director & artistic director Sebastiano Calabrò; press officer Gianna Volpi
Actors: 8-20 *Prods:* 5 *Type:* prosa, comedy *Venues:* various throughout Italy *Touring:* Italy

Argot (Soc. Coop. Argot)
via Natale del Grande, 27, 00153 **Roma**
Tel: 06-589 8111/581 4023/588 2254 Fax: 06-589 8111
Internet: web.tiscalinet.it/argot
E-Mail: argo@tiscalinet.it
admin director Eleonora Bossi; art dir Maurizio Panici; scenographer Tiziano Fario; press officer Serena Grandicelli
Actors: varies *Perfs:* 200 *Prods:* 1 + 4 *Type:* contemporary and revised classical drama *Venues:* Sala Argot 50 *Touring:* Italy (incl. Festival del teatro Antico) *Comments:* the cooperative is particularly interested in new playwrights; organise theatrical events

Arte Spettacolo International
Via di Pallacorda 11/a, 00186 **Roma**
Tel: 06-687 4982 Fax: 06-4423 8661
president & artistic director Daniele Valmaggi;
organiser Sabine Frantellizzi
Actors: 10 *Prods:* 2 *Type:* classical, experimental *Comments:* theatre productions; innovative site-specific, large-scale events involving local artists; concerts; courses and workshops; festivals (international theatre, music); interested in international collaborations and cultural exchanges; see also Promoters

Associazione Culturale – Compagnia Teatro IT
c/o Teatro dell' Orologio, Via dei Filippini 17a, 00186 **Roma**
Tel: 06-6830 8735 Fax: 06-683 2764
organizzazione Daniela Rotunno; direzione artistica Mario Moretti; ufficio stampa Paola Ciccodicola
Actors: 25+ *Perfs:* 200+ *Prods:* 2 *Type:* contemporary, musical *Venues:* Sala Grande 100, Sala Caffe' Teatro 50, Sala Artaud 35 *Touring:* Italy *Comments:* see also Venues

Associazione Culturale Mondoteatro – Compagnia il Baraccone
Via Montefalco 40 Scala B Office N3, 00100 **Roma**
Tel: 06-3362 5210/335-607 8408 Fax: 06-3362 5210
president/artistic director Luigi Tani
Actors: 5 *Perfs:* 100 *Prods:* 4 *Type:* classical and modern drama *Touring:* Italy *Comments:* the company is well known for performing medieval and renaissance works; see also Agents & Producers; send all corespondance to: Via Clauzetto 61, 00188, Roma

Associazione Culturale Sala Orfeo
c/o Teatro dell' Orologio, via dei Filippini 17a, 00186 **Roma**
Tel: 06-6830 8330 Fax: 06-6830 8330
artistic & administrative director Orfeo Valentino; technical director Caterina Merlino
Actors: 8 *Perfs:* 85 *Prods:* 2 new + 1 revival *Type:* experimental theatre *Venues:* Sala Orfeo 100 *Touring:* Italy *Comments:* see Venues under Teatro Dell' Orologio

Associazione Culturale Teatro Drammatico
via Fratelli Ruspoli 8, 00198 **Roma**
Tel: 06-8530 2790 Fax: 06-841 7043
artistic director Franco Ricordi
Actors: 10 *Perfs:* 90 *Prods:* 3 *Type:* contemporary and classical with particular attention on Shakespeare *Touring:* Italy, Europe

Ata Teatro (Comp E. Cotta, C. Alighiero Gruppo Ata Teatro)
via Natale del Grande 8, 00153 **Roma**
Tel: 06-589 9934/361 0893 Fax: 06-589 9934/361 0893
artistic/admin director Carlo Alighiero; organisation dir Valeria Buffoni; press officers Olivia Alighiero, Valeria Buffoni
Actors: 15-30 *Perfs:* 130-150 *Prods:* 2-3 + 2-3 revival *Type:* contemporary *Venues:* Teatro Manzoni 430 *Touring:* Italy *Comments:* registered address: via Monte Zebio 14c, 00195 Roma, Tel/Fax: 06-361 0893

ATM
viale L. Da Vinci 65, 00145 **Roma**
Tel: 06-511 5992 Fax: 06-5160 2929
artistic director Gianni Pulone
Actors: 5-6 *Perfs:* 80 *Prods:* 1 *Venues:* Teatro dell' Orologio 100 *Touring:* Italy

Barberio Corsetti (Comp. Teat.di Giorgio Barberio Corsetti)
via dei Monti di Creta, 83, 00167 **Roma**
Tel: 06-662 4626 Fax: 06-662 3168
artistic director Giorgio Barberio Corsetti; technical director Luigi Grenna; press officer Viviana Ronzitti
Actors: 15 *Perfs:* 70-80 *Prods:* 2 *Touring:* Italy

Cerchio (Ass. Teatrale 'Il Cerchiò)
via Capo d'Africa, 32, 00184 **Roma**
Tel: 06-3972 5286/7904/7720 8917
Fax: 06-3973 2788/3927 7904
artistic /administrative director Riccardo Bernardini; technical director Stefano Bernadini
Actors: 12 *Perfs:* 70 *Prods:* 2 *Venues:* Teatro Elettra

Chi é di Scena (SNC)
P.zza Tuscolo 5, 00183 **Roma**
Tel: 06-700 5382/336-782 408 (mobile)
Fax: 06-700 5382
administrative director Valeria Salemme; legal representative Vincenzo Salemme
Actors: 8 *Perfs:* 110 *Prods:* 1 *Type:* contemporary *Touring:* Italy

Club Teatro
via Gaetano Mazzoni, 20, 00166 **Roma**
Tel: 06-624 3943 Fax: 06-624 3943
direttore organizzativo Gloria Caporossi; responsabili artistici Riccardo Caporossi, Claudio Remondi; direttore tecnico Fausto Moretti
Prods: 1 *Type:* contemporary drama *Comments:* the compant works with new actors for the realisationof origional drammaturgy

Collettivo Isabella Morra
Via Colleferro 9, 00189 **Roma**
Tel: 06-3036 1984 Fax: 06-3036 1984
presidente onorario Marta Marzotto; direttore artistico e legale rappresentante Saviana Scalfi
Actors: 14 *Perfs:* 100 *Prods:* 4 *Touring:* Italy *Comments:* a group dealing in particular with women's themes

Comp. del Teatro Moderno
piazza Melozzo da Forlì 16, 00196 **Roma**
Tel: 06-320 1851/324 1365 Fax: 06-324 0142
E-Mail: teatromoderno@srd.it
artistic/administrative director Claudio Padovani; technical director Roberto Rocchi
Actors: varies *Perfs:* 163 *Prods:* 3 *Type:* comedy, contemporary drama *Touring:* Italy, Switzerland

Compagnia del Meta-Teatro
via S. Francesco a Ripa, 129, 00153 **Roma**
Tel: 06-581 4723/588 0468/3937 6723
Fax: 06-581 4723
administrative director Anna Paola Bonanni; artistic director Giuseppe di Marca
Actors: 20 *Perfs:* 77 *Prods:* 5 new + 4 revivals *Type:* research *Venues:* Sala uno Teatro 150 *Touring:* Italy *Comments:* also workshops; funded by the state and local authorities

Compagnia dell' Atto
c/o A.T.C.L. Via Paolo Emilio 32, 00192 **Roma**
Tel: 06-321 3686 Fax: 06-321 3686
president Renato Campese
Actors: varies *Perfs:* 100-150 *Prods:* 3 *Type:* contempetary theatre *Touring:* Italy *Comments:* Indirizzo legale: Via Abruzzi N.5, 00187 Roma

Compagnia della Luna
Via Giulio Barrili 18, 00152 **Roma**
Tel: 06-5833 1503 Fax: 06-5833 1054
E-Mail: compluna@tin.it
artistic directors Vincenzo Cerami, Nicola Piovani
Actors: varies *Perfs:* 80 *Prods:* 2 *Type:* musical tale *Touring:* Italy *Comments:* registered address: via Lorenzo Valla 27, 00152, Roma

Compagnia di Progetto Teatroinaria-Stanze Luminose
Via Paolo Emilio 32, 00192 **Roma**
Tel: 06-321 3497 Fax: 06-323 0003
E-Mail: t.inaria@mix.it
artistic director Maria Teresa Imseng
Actors: 10 *Perfs:* 82 *Prods:* 3 *Type:* experimental, literary research *Touring:* Italy

Compagnia Diritto e Rovescio
via Parione, 17, 00186 **Roma**
Tel: 06-6880 5984 Fax: 06-689 7073
artistic directors Teresa and Massimo Pedroni
Actors: 20 *Perfs:* 80 *Prods:* 3, 2 new *Type:* new dramatisations, prose *Venues:* Teatro Belli Roma, Teatro Piccolo Eliseo *Touring:* Germany, Italy, Portugal

Compagnia Fascino PGT Ltd
c/o Teatro Parioli, Via G Borsi 20, 00197 **Roma**
Tel: 06-808 5303/807 2139
Fax: 06-807 4951
E-Mail: parioli@freemail.it
direttore artistico Maurizio Costanzo
Actors: varies *Perfs:* 150 *Prods:* 3 *Type:* light entertainment, drama *Venues:* Teatro Parioli 600 *Touring:* Italy *Comments:* registered address: Via Pietro Borsieri, 20, 00195 Roma, Fax: 06-372 0008

Compagnia Glauco Mauri SRL
Largo L. Antonelli 2, 00145 **Roma**
Tel: 06-540 2372
Fax: 06-541 0000
Internet: www.glaucomauri.it
E-Mail: gmauri@glaucomauri.it
direttore relazioni esterne ed organizzazione Giorgio Guazzotti; direttore artistico e legale rappresentante Roberto Sturno
Actors: 15 *Perfs:* 150 *Prods:* 2 *Type:* classical drama *Venues:* Teatro Eliseo *Touring:* Italy

Compagnia Micol SRL
Via Francesco Siacci 1, 00197 **Roma**
Tel: 06-534 2876/581 0875
Fax: 06-534 2876/581 0875
E-Mail: osolemio@tin.it
organisative director Enrico Porcaro; artistic director Pino Micol; legal representative Giuseppe Ciocia
Actors: varies *Perfs:* 120 *Prods:* 2 *Type:* Prosa *Touring:* Italy *Comments:* registered address: Via Alessandro Poerio, 140, 00152 Roma

Compagnia Stabile Del Teatro Tordinona
c/o Teatro Tordinona, Via Degli Acquasparta 16, 00186 **Roma**
Tel: 06-6880 5890 Fax: 06-6880 4982
E-Mail: tordinon@tin.it
direttore artistico Renato Giordano
Type: contemporary drama *Venues:* Teatro Tordinona 96 *Comments:* they run a school Trouiamoci Sul Parco a 3 yeartheatre course Oct-June

Compagnia Teatrale il Pantano
Viale G. Mazzini, 106, 00195 **Roma**
Tel: 06-3751 9868 Fax: 06-3751 9868
E-Mail: flyfly@iol.it
artistic director Claudio Frosi; organisation Marcella Bioccoli
Actors: 10 *Perfs:* 80 *Prods:* 3 *Type:* contemporary *Touring:* Italy

Compagnia Teatrale Moderno-Classico
via Iside, 2, 00184 **Roma**
Tel: 06-700 3495 Fax: 06-700 3495
administrative director & press officer Giancarlo Palombo; legal representative Federica de Vita; artistic director Franco Venturini
Actors: 4 *Perfs:* 100 *Prods:* 3 *Type:* modern, classic *Venues:* Teatro d'Oggi 50 *Touring:* Italy

Compagnia Teatrale Solari Vanzi
via Flaminia 259, 00196 **Roma**
Tel: 06-361 1669 Fax: 06-361 1669/5823 8115
E-Mail: ramarri@tin.it
artistic & administrative director Marco Solari; press officer Fiammetta Baralla; co-artistic director Alessandra Vanzi; organisation Rossana Marsili Libelli
Actors: 7-8 *Perfs:* 65 *Prods:* 3 *Type:* experimental theatre *Touring:* Italy *Comments:* registered address: via Flaminia 259, 00196 Roma, Tel/Fax: 6-361 1669; produces videos, records, CD-roms; runs workshops

Contemporanea 83 (Soc. Coop. La Contemporanea 83 RL)
piazza Tuscolo 5, 00183 **Roma**
Tel: 06-700 5382 Fax: 06-700 5382
E-Mail: contemporanea@tiscahnet.it
artistic & administrative director Sergio Fantoni; director Fioravante Cozzaglio;
artistic director Cristina Pezzoli
Actors: 14 *Perfs:* 120 *Prods:* 2 *Type:* contemporary *Touring:* Italy

Coop. Attori e Tecnici – Teatro Stabile di Interesse Pubblico
Piazza S. Maria Liberatrice 8/11, 00153 **Roma**
Tel: 06-578 1960/2314 Fax: 06-575 9935
direttore artistico e organizzativo Attilio Corsini; direttore tecnico Stefano Valle
Actors: varies *Perfs:* 200 *Prods:* 2 *Type:* comedy *Venues:* Teatro Vittoria 585 *Touring:* Italy & Europe *Comments:* manage the Teatro Vittoria; see also Venues

CPT Nuovo Politecnico
via G.B. Tiepolo 13a, 00196 **Roma**
Tel: 06-321 9891/361 1501
Fax: 06-361 1501
artistic & organisation director Mario Prosperi; administrative director Nicola Ciardi;
press officer Paola Sebastiani
Actors: 30 *Perfs:* 100 *Prods:* 1 + 2 revival *Type:* contemporary *Venues:* Teatro Politecnico 100 *Comments:* host annual contemporary playwrights' event in Sept/Oct; the annual event period varies from year to year

Dark Camera (Ass. Dark Camera)
via Camilla, 44, 00181 **Roma**
Tel: 06-7834 7348
Fax: 06-7834 7348
artistic & administrative director Marcello Sambati; press officer Sonia Secchi
Actors: 6 *Perfs:* 80 *Prods:* 2 *Type:* experimental *Venues:* Teatro Furio Camillo 99 (Rome) *Touring:* Italy

EAO Giglio SRL
via Clitunno 18, 00198 **Roma**
Tel: 06-884 1605 Fax: 06-884 1707
Internet: www.giglio.org
E-Mail: eaosrl@nbox.vol.it
artistic & administrative director Alessandro Giglio; pr Oriana Baciardi
Actors: 10 *Perfs:* 250 *Prods:* 3 *Type:* comedy *Touring:* Italy
Comments: also TV productions

Effeegi SRL Comp. del Teatro Ghione
via delle Fornaci, 37, 00165 **Roma**
Tel: 06-637 2294 Fax: 06-639 0578
Internet: www.ghione.it
E-Mail: ghione@pronet.it
artistic directors Christopher Axworthy, Ileana Ghione
Actors: 30+ *Perfs:* 140 *Prods:* 3+ *Type:* Prosa *Comments:* registered address: via di Monserrato 122, 00186 Roma, Tel: 06-637 2294, Fax 06-639 0578; the company also runs an international concert hall

Europa Duemila (Ass. Culturale)
via A. Ceriani, 1, 00165 **Roma**
Tel: 06-630 849/4423 6530 Fax: 06-630 849
artistic directors Massimo Belli , Giancarlo Cobelli
Actors: 15 *Perfs:* 80 *Prods:* 3 *Type:* research *Touring:* Italy

Fabbrica dell' Attore (Centro Stabile di Promozione di Ricerca Teatrale), La
via G. Carini 72/78, 00152 **Roma**
Tel: 06-589 8031/588 1021 Fax: 06-581 6623
E-Mail: teatrovascello@xwnet.com
artistic directors Giancarlo Nanni, Manuela Kustermann; ufficio stampa e pr t.b.a.; amministrazione Marco Ciuti
Type: research *Venues:* Teatro Vascello 400 *Touring:* Italy, Egypt, Canada *Comments:* registered address: via di Torre Argentina 44, 00186 Roma; staging of scenery is avant-garde; see also Venues

Gestione Spettacoli Teatrali Production F.R.L.
via Vicenza, 56, 00185 **Roma**
Tel: 06-445 1611 Fax: 06-494 0422
procuratore Mario Smeriglio; direttore amministrativo Claudio Perone; direttore artistico Antonella Steni
Actors: varies *Perfs:* 192 *Prods:* 4 *Type:* comedy, musical
Touring: Italy, Russia, France

Grande Opera, La
Via Cassia 1791, 00123 **Roma**
Tel: 06-3325 2746 Fax: 06-3325 2746
E-Mail: grandeopera@iol.it
administrator Ezio Barbetti;
artistic director Massimiliano Troiani
Actors: 6 *Perfs:* 90 *Prods:* 3 *Type:* contemporary *Touring:* Canada *Comments:* organisers of international festival Oltre L'Attore (Teatro di Figura)

Gruppo di Ricerca e Progett. Teatrale
via G. Gesmundo, 2, 00195 **Roma**
Tel: 06-3751 4662/372 4623 Fax: 06-372 4623
artistic director Giuliano Vasilicò;
admin & organisation officer Erica Talli
Actors: 8-10 *Perfs:* 90 *Prods:* 3 *Type:* experimental
Touring: Italy, France *Comments:* specialised in mise-en-scene of classic novals; they are concentrating on R. Musil at the moment

Il Globo – Associazione Culturale
via G. Parini, 7, 00152 **Roma**
Tel: 06-583 5896 Fax: 06-588 0094
administrative director Gabriele Pianese; artistic director Caterina Costantini
Actors: varies *Perfs:* 120 *Prods:* 3 *Type:* classical drama, contemporary *Touring:* Italy

Il Graffio (Comp. Sociale Il Graffio)
via R. Simoni, 73, 00157 **Roma**
Tel: 06-4173 0999/04 Fax: 06-4173 0904
organisation & administrative director Francesco Chiovenda; legal representative & artistic director Grazia Maria Scuccimarra; press officer Paolo Barca
Actors: 10 *Perfs:* 100 *Prods:* 6 *Type:* satirical theatre
Touring: Italy

L'Albero Associazione
Via Laurina 40, 00187 **Roma**
Tel: 06-323 4930
Fax: 06-323 4930
legal representative Gigi Angelillo; artistic directors Gigi Angelillo, Ludovica Modugno, Lorenzo Salveti
Actors: varies *Perfs:* 80 *Prods:* 1 new, 2 revival *Type:* contemporary *Touring:* Portugal, Ivory Cost, Belgium

La Bilancia Produzioni Teatrali e Cinematographiche – Societa' Coop.
via Principessa Clotilde 9, 00196 **Roma**
Tel: 06-324 3134
Fax: 06-323-6592
E-Mail: la.bilancia@tiscalinet.it
administrative director Stefano Marafante; press officer Carla Fabi, Barbara Ghinfanti; technical directors Alberto Cassarino, Stefano Marafante
Actors: 10 *Perfs:* 188 *Prods:* 8 *Type:* drama & experimental & comedy *Touring:* Italy, South America

Le Parole e le Cose (Assoc. Culturale)
via del Vascello 21, 00152 **Roma**
Tel: 06-589 8157 Fax: 06-589 8157
artistic/administrative director Lucia Poli; technical director Isabella Valoriani
Perfs: 80 *Prods:* 2 *Type:* contemporary, comedy *Touring:* Italy

Magnifico
via Firenze, 50, 00184 **Roma**
Tel: 06-486 000 Fax: 06-486 000
administrative dir Mario Gentili; artistic dirr Marco Mattolini
Actors: varies *Perfs:* 83 *Prods:* 4 *Type:* contemporary
Touring: Italy *Comments:* registered address: via Fra D. Buonvicini 17, 50132 Firenze; organise Todi Arte Festival, see also Festivals

Nuova Teatro Eliseo S.P.A.
Via della Consulta 1, 00184 **Roma**
Tel: 06-488 721 (switchboard) Fax: 06-485 600
E-Mail: teliseo@tin.it
artistic director Maurizio Scaparro;
legal representative Giampaolo Vianello
Actors: 29 *Prods:* 5 new + 5 revival *Type:* prosa *Venues:* Teatro Eliseo: Sala Eliseo 950, Sala Piccolo Eliseo 250
Touring: Italy *Comments:* have recently formed the jazz orchestra Eliseo Big Band; see also Venues

Plautina (Coop. La Plautina)
Teatro Anfitrione, via di S. Saba 24, 00153 **Roma**
Tel: 06-575 0827/7030 0994 Fax: 06-578 3116/702 8945
presidente Marcello Bonini Olas; direttore artistico Sergio Ammirata, Patrizia Parisi; direttore tecnico Isabella Sottovia; direttore organizzativo e ufficio stampa Patrizia Parisi
Actors: 40 *Perfs:* 120 min. *Prods:* 4 + 1 revival *Type:* comedy, classical and modern *Venues:* Teatro Anfitrione 200, Anfiteatro Della Quercia del Tasso 300 *Touring:* Belgium, Greece; see also Venues *Comments:* registered address: via Piccarda Donati 4, 00162 Roma ;

Plexus T. SRL
via di Vigna Murata 1, 00143 **Roma**
Tel: 06-591 9933/9867 Fax: 06-592 5522
artistic/administrative director Lucio Minunni Ardenzi; press officer Cristina Rastelli
Actors: varies *Perfs:* 200 *Prods:* 4 *Touring:* Italy *Comments:* production theatre; see also Agents & Producers

PRO. SIT Produzione Spettacoli Immagini Teatro
c/o Teatro Flaiano, Via Santo Stefano del Cacco N 15, 00195 **Roma**
Tel: 06-678 7424/679 6496 (box office)
Fax: 06-678 7424
Internet: www.pros.it
E-Mail: pros.it@pros.it
administrative director Gabriella Callea; artistic director Rossana Patrizia Siclari; stampa Gianna Volpi
Actors: 30 *Perfs:* 250 *Prods:* 8 (7 new) *Type:* prose, musical comedy *Venues:* Teatro Flaiano 200 *Touring:* Italy *Comments:* registered address: Piazzale Clodio 22, 00195 Roma

Rag Doll Produzioni Soc. Coop. SRL
via T. Macrobio 9, 00136 **Roma**
Tel: 06-3534 8780/360-240 448/3540 1108/6/9553
Fax: 06-3534 8780
Internet: www.ragdoll.it/teatro
E-Mail: f.verdinelli@ragdoll.it
artistic/administrative directors Roberta Lerici, Francesco Verdinelli; technical director Roberto Giannotti; organisation Linda Esdaile
Actors: 18-20 *Perfs:* 100-120 *Prods:* 5 + 3 revival *Type:* musical, comedy, experimental, internet theatre
Touring: Italy, USA, Europe *Comments:* registered address: via L. Pancaldo 26, 00147 Roma

Ruotalibera Teatro
Via Flavio Stilicone 134, 00175 **Roma**
Tel: 06-581 7004/7691 0288/761 5161 Fax: 06-7691 0289
responsabiledell' organizzazione Paola Meda; artistic director Tiziana Lucattini
Actors: 18 *Perfs:* 180 *Prods:* 2 *Type:* youth theatre *Touring:* France, Belgium, Switzerland, Germany *Comments:* also run a theatre school La pietra parta

Scuola di Tecniche dello Spettacolo
Via Monte Pollino 2, 00141 **Roma**
Tel: 06-817 4483 Fax: 06-817 4483
administrative director Sergio Cerquetti; artistic director Claretta Carotenuto; technical director Antonio Scalici; press officer Ettore Zocaro
Actors: 20 *Perfs:* 100 *Prods:* 2 *Type:* prosa, musical
Venues: Sala Tecniche Spettacolo 400 *Comments:* an institute of vocational training and production, legally acknowledged by the Presidenza del Consiglio dei Ministri – Dipartimento per lo Spettacolo

Società Cooperativa Teatro Artigiano s.r.q.
via Scipio Slataper 3, 00197 **Roma**
Tel: 06-321 6360 Fax: 06-321 6360
artistic director Pietro Longhi
Actors: 15 *Perfs:* 135 *Prods:* 1 *Type:* contemporary, comedy, youth theatre *Venues:* Teatro Manzoni 437
Touring: Italy *Comments:* 2nd address: c/o Teatre Manzoni, via Monte Zebio 14/c, 00195, Roma

Teatro Canzone (Coop Teatro Canzone)
via dei Vascellari 40, 00153 **Roma**
Tel: 06-581 4238 Fax: 06-581 2470
artistic director & press officer Adriana Martino; president Benedetto Ghiglia
Perfs: 90 *Prods:* 2 *Type:* contemporary *Touring:* Italy

Teatro Didattico Il Torchio
Via E. Morosini 16, 00153 **Roma**
Tel: 06-588 0810 Fax: 06-588 0810
administrative director Giovanna Longo;
artistic director Aldo Giovannetti
Actors: 6-7 *Perfs:* 100 *Prods:* 4 *Type:* youth theatre, didactic theatre, puppets *Touring:* Italy

Teatro e Società SRL
via S. Stefano del Cacco 16, 00186 **Roma**
Tel: 06-679 7496 Fax: 06-679 7496
director Pietro Mezzasoma
Actors: varies *Perfs:* 130 *Prods:* 2 *Type:* musical, prose
Touring: Italy, Europe

Teatro Popolare di Roma
Via Roma Libera 10, 00153 **Roma**
Tel: 06-588 1311 Fax: 06-580 0482
direzione organizzativa Fabio Castanello; coordinamento artistico Adriana Innocenti; presidente Piero Nuti
Actors: 1 to 15 *Perfs:* 110

Mago di Oz, Il
Arena Metato (Pisa), via Erbosa, 1,
56010 **S Andrea in Pescaiola**
Tel: 050-864 550 Fax: 050-864 550
artistic and administrative director Renato Baldasserini; technical director Francesco Borghini; organisation director Tommaso Iardella
Actors: 2-5 *Prods:* 1 *Type:* experimental theatre, children's theatre *Venues:* Teatro Ragazzi *Touring:* Italy, Europe

Arca Azzurra Teatro
Via Roma 47, 50026 **San Casciano V. P. (FI)**
Tel: 055-829 0137 Fax: 055-822 8422
presidente Luigi Frosali; direttore artistico Ugo Chiti; ufficio stampa Anna Giannelli; organizzazione generale Giorgio Guazzotti, Tiziana Ringressi, Costanza Gaeta
Actors: 5 *Perfs:* 100 *Prods:* 4 *Type:* contemporary *Venues:* Teatro Comunale Niccolini (San Casciando V. P.) 320
Touring: Italy

Associazione Culturale Katzenmacher
Via Machiavelli, 26 Roma 47,
50026 **San Casciano V.P. (FI)**
Tel: 055-820 280 Fax: 055-820 280
artistic director Alfonso Santagata; administrative director Laura Bagnoli; organisation director Maria Vittoria Nervi
Actors: 6 *Perfs:* 70 *Prods:* 2 new, 4 revival *Type:* experimental theatre *Touring:* Italy

Teatro Origine
via delle Boccette, 47, 63019 **Sant'Elpidio a Mare (AP)**
Tel: 0734-859 129 Fax: 0734-843 190
artistic/administrative director Cutini Marco
Actors: 3 *Perfs:* 12 *Prods:* 4 *Type:* contemporary *Venues:* Laboratorio Dell'Ingegno Teatrale 50

Teatro Stabile Ragazzi e Giovani La Botte E Il Cilindro
c/o Teatro il Ferroviario, Corso Vico, 14, 07100 **Sassari**
Tel: 079-263 3049 Fax: 079-263 3197
Internet: web.tiscalinet.it/bottecilindro
E-Mail: bottecilindro@ssnet.it
artistic/administrative director Pier Paolo Conconi; organisation director Sante Maurizi
Actors: 7 *Perfs:* 90 *Prods:* 2-3 *Type:* experimental and youth theatre *Venues:* Teatro Il Ferroviario 240 *Touring:* Italy *Comments:* also educational outreach programmes

La Dama Bianca
Piazza Martiri Partigiani 19, 41049 **Sassuolo (Modena)**
Tel: 0536-884 406 Fax: 0536-884 406
artistic director Marco Manchisi
Venues: Teatro D'Autore

Compagnia Laboratorio 9
Via Gramsci 426, 50019 **Sesto Fiorentino (FI)**
Tel: 055-440 852 Fax: 055-440 852
Internet: www.teatro-Limonaia.fi.it
E-Mail: info@teatro.Limonaia.fi.it
president & artistic directo Silvano Panichi; organisation Silvano Panichi; administrator Annamaria Gasti
Actors: 25 *Perfs:* 100 *Prods:* 2 new, 3 revivals *Type:* experimental theatre *Venues:* Teatro della Limonaia 100
Touring: Italy *Comments:* runs a school and master classes in collaboration with the European Union, also collaborate with the Intercity Festival; see also Venues and Festivals

Piccoli Principi
Via di Palastreto 11A, 50019 **Sesto Fiorentino (FI)**
Tel: 055-448 2735/442 916 Fax: 055-449 3122
E-Mail: piccoli.principi@dada.it
organisation director Chiara Fantini; artistic director Alessandro Libertini
Actors: 2 *Perfs:* 90 *Prods:* 1 *Type:* children's theatre, youth theatre *Touring:* France, Belgium, Italy, Switzerland

Laboratorio Teatro Settimo
Via Roosevelt 8/A, 10036 **Settimo Torinese (TO)**
Tel: 011-897 1746 Fax: 011-897 0851
artistic director Gabriele Vacis; officio stampa Ilaria Godino; organisation director Patrizia Coletta
Type: prose *Venues:* Garibaldi Teatro 200 *Touring:* Italy

Coop L'Arcolaio
via Degli Aranci 77, CP 171, 80067 **Sorrento (NA)**
Tel: 081-807 1814 Fax: 081-807 4375
general and artistic director Antonia Guida
Actors: 6 *Perfs:* 70 *Prods:* 5 *Type:* new authors, children's theatre *Venues:* Teatro D'Attore, Commedia Dell'Arte *Comments:* registered address: C. so Italia, 38, 80067 Sorrento

CREST (Collettivo Ricerche Espressive e Sperimentazione Teatrale)
Via Duomo 273, 74100 **Taranto**
Tel: 099-471 4520 Fax: 099-470 4792
E-Mail: c.r.e.s.t@iol.it
amministratrice Clara Cottino; direttore artistico Mauro Maggioni; coordinatore generale Giovanni Guarino
Actors: 20 *Perfs:* 130 *Prods:* 2 *Type:* experimentation and young peoples theatre *Venues:* Centro Teatro CREST 90 *Touring:* Italy *Comments:* registered address: Via Leonida 61, 74100 Taranto; see also Venues

Compagnia della Rancia
Via Filelfo 97, 62029 **Tolentino (MC)**
Tel: 0733-960 059 Fax: 0733-973 844
Internet: www.musical.it
E-Mail: rancia@musical.it
relazioni esterne e uff.stampa Massimo Zenobi; amministrazione Bruno Borraccini; organizzatore artistico Saverio Marconi; legale rappresentante Michele Renzullo
Actors: varies *Perfs:* 343 *Prods:* 4 *Type:* musical *Venues:* Teatro Vaccai 450 *Touring:* Italy *Comments:* second address: CP 112, 62029 Tolentino (MC); see also Venues and Agents & Producers

Alfa Folie and Ragazzi, L'
via Casalborgone, 16/i, 10132 **Torino**
Tel: 011-819 3529/5803 Fax: 011-819 3529
Internet: www.alfateatro.it
E-Mail: grilli@alfateatro.it
artistic dir Augusto Grilli; press officer & PR Claudio Bertoni
Actors: 18 *Perfs:* 120-130 *Prods:* 3-11 *Type:* operetta, youth theatre, puppets *Venues:* Alfa Teatro 300 *Touring:* Italy *Comments:* these are 2 different companies with 2 separate names

Ass. Teatro Stabile di Torino
Piazza S Carlo 161, 10123 **Torino**
Tel: 011-516 9411 Fax: 011-562 2033
Internet: www.teatrostabile.torino.it
E-Mail: info@teatrostabile.torino.it
direttore artistico Gabriele Lavia; presidente Agostino re Rebaudengo
Actors: varies *Perfs:* 228 *Prods:* 4 *Type:* prose *Venues:* Teatro Carignano 700 *Touring:* Italy *Comments:* run a three year drama school; also see Venues

Assemblea Teatro
Via Medail 36, 10144 **Torino**
Tel: 011-437 6230 Fax: 011-437 6272
Internet: www.assembleateatro.com
E-Mail: assteat@tin.it
presidente & direttore artistico Renzo Sicco; ufficio stampa Luisio Luciano Badolisani
Actors: varies *Perfs:* 200 *Type:* musical theatre, comic and dramatic *Venues:* Teatro Agnelli 374 *Touring:* worldwide *Comments:* collaborations with Peter Gabriel, David Sylvian, Mick Karn, Lindsay Kemp

Marcido Marcidorjs e Famosa Mimosa
via F. Aporti 27, 10131 **Torino**
Tel: 011-819 3522 Fax: 011-819 3522
artistic dir Marco Isidori; scenografa Daniela Dal Cin
Actors: 13 *Perfs:* 80 *Prods:* 4 *Type:* experimental *Venues:* Teatro San Gaetano, Teatro Sans Domenico *Comments:* registered address: Via F. Aporti 27, 10131 Torino

Sorelle Saburde, Le
c/o Teatro Juvarra, Via Juvarra 15, 10122 **Torino**
Tel: 011-540 675 Fax: 011-517 5084
Internet: www.quiaffari.it/juvarra
E-Mail: muliteatro@tin.it
president Luciano Capriolo; artistic director Sergio Martin; organisatin director Cesare Perotti
Actors: 4 *Perfs:* 70 *Prods:* 1 + 2 *Type:* modern *Venues:* Teatro Juvarra 222 *Touring:* Italy, Germany *Comments:* managed by M.A.S. Juvarra; see also Agents & Producers and Venues

Stilema
Corso Brescia 4 bis/2, 10152 **Torino**
Tel: 011-859 687/398 Fax: 011-859 398
Internet: www.clab.it
E-Mail: stilema@venturanet.it
administrative director Paola Elettro; artistic director Silvano Antonelli; technical directors Paola Elettro; organisation director Fabio Naggi
Actors: 9 *Perfs:* 100 *Prods:* 2 *Type:* children's theatre *Touring:* Italy, France

Teatro dell' Angolo
Via Industria 2, 10144 **Torino**
Tel: 011-489 676/482 343 Fax: 011-473 3102
Internet: www.arpnet.it/nangolo
E-Mail: angolo@arpnet.it
direttore artistico Graziano Melano; presidente Laura Emanuelli; direttore (Teatro Araldo) Massimo Calí
Actors: 5-15 *Perfs:* 250 (+ 150 of guest companies) *Prods:* 10 *Type:* contemporary, theatre for young people *Venues:* Teatro Araldo 214 *Touring:* France, Switzerland, Italy, UK *Comments:* occasionally rent theatre to other groups; see also Venues

TORINO SPETTACOLI
Piazza Solferino 4, 10121 **Torino**
Tel: 011-562 3800 Fax: 011-562 3435
Internet: www.torinospettacoli.it
E-Mail: tospett.tin.it
administrative director Gian Mesturino; artistic director Germana Erba
Actors: 30 (varies) *Perfs:* 200 *Prods:* 6 *Type:* prosa, comedy, musicals, concerts, operetta, cinema *Venues:* Teatro Alfieri 1512, Teatro Erba 400 *Touring:* Italy *Comments:* see also Venues

Gli Alcuni
via Corti 12, 31100 **Treviso**
Tel: 0422-421 142 Fax: 0422-421 151
E-Mail: alcuni@tin.it
artistic/administrative director Sergio Manfio; technical director Antonella Della Giustina
Actors: 4 *Perfs:* 150 *Prods:* 3 *Type:* cabaret, youth and children's theatre *Venues:* Teatro Sant' Anna 400 *Touring:* Italy

la contrada – Teatro Stabile di Trieste
c/o Teatro Cristallo, Via del Ghirlandaio 12, 34138 **Trieste**
Tel: 040-948 471/390 613 Fax: 040-946 460
E-Mail: contraola@spin.it
direttore organizzativo Ivaldo Vernelli; presidente Orazio Bobbio; direttore artistico Francesco Macedonio; responsabile teatro ragazzi Giorgio Amodeo
Actors: 20 *Perfs:* 200 *Prods:* 7 (3 new) *Type:* dialect, young theatre 3-14 yrs, drama *Venues:* Teatro Cristallo 752 *Touring:* Italy,Austria,Croatia *Comments:* resident company at Teatro Cristallo; see also Venues

Teatro Stabile del Friuli Venezia Giulia
Viale XX Settembre 45, 34126 **Trieste**
Tel: 040-567 201 Fax: 040-52447
Internet: www.comune.trieste.it/rossetti/lindex.htm
E-Mail: ts.rossetti@spin.it
direttore unico Dott. Antonio Calenda; presidente Prof. Roberto Damiani; direttore organizzativo dott. Franco Ferrari
Type: prosa *Venues:* Teatro Politeama Rossetti 1450

Teatro Stabile Sloveno di Trieste
Via Petronio 4, 34138 **Trieste**
Tel: 040-632 664
Fax: 040-368 547
presidente Dott. Filibert Beredelic; direttore artistico Marko Sosic
Actors: 11 *Perfs:* 200 *Prods:* 6 *Type:* classical drama, contemporary *Venues:* Kulturni Dom Theatre 550 *Touring:* Slovenia, Austria, Italy, Bosnia & Herzegovina

Centro Servizi E Spettacoli di Udine -Soc.Coop. ARL
via Crispi 65, 33100 **Udine**
Tel: 0432-504 765 Fax: 0432-504 448
E-Mail: direzcss@tin.it
administrative director Paolo Aniello; artistic director Alberto Bevilacqua; press office Fabriziz Maggi, Luisa Schiratti
Actors: 32 *Perfs:* 112 *Prods:* 8 *Type:* new Italian theatre, research, poetry *Venues:* Teatro Palamostre 500, Teatro Nuovo Giovanni da Udine 1500, various non-theatrical venues *Touring:* Italy *Comments:* organised a competition(L'Ecole De Maitre) for playwrights

Teatro Stabile Del Veneto Carlo Goldoni
Teatro Goldoni, San Marco 4650/B, 30124 **Venezia**
Tel: 041-520 5422 Fax: 041-520 5241
E-Mail: teatro@tin.it
direttore generale Mauro Carbonoli; presidente Francesco Raimondo Dona; coordinatrice Teatro Goldoni Cristiana Csermeliy; coordinatrice Teatro Verdi Marina Valenta
Comments: the company run another theatre in Padova, Teatro Verdi – they also run a school Scuola di Teatro – Goldoni, which has 20 students

Cooperativa del Teatro Scientifico
Via Tomaso da Vico 9, 37123 **Verona**
Tel: 045-803 1321
Fax: 045-803 1321
E-Mail: mscdc@tin.it
presidente Isabella Caserta; ufficio stampa e segreteria Cecilia Filippin; organisation Roberto Vandelli; direzione artistica Isabella Caserta
Actors: varies *Perfs:* 150 *Prods:* 10 *Type:* experimental; avantgarde; pantomime *Venues:* Teatro Laboratorio 150 *Touring:* Europe *Comments:* see also Venues and Festivals (Mimo e Dintorni Festival)

Fondazione AIDA – Centro Teatro Ragazzi
Vic. dietro Campanile Filippini, 16, 37121 **Verona**
Tel: 045-595 284/800 1471
Fax: 045-800 9850
Internet: www.f-aida.it
E-Mail: fondazione@f-aida.it
director Roberto Terribile; artistic director Gianni Franceschini
Actors: 30 *Perfs:* 250 *Prods:* 6 (4 new) *Type:* children's theatre, contemporary *Venues:* Teatro Filippini 280, Teatro Astra 500 *Touring:* France, Spain, Ireland, England, USA

Centro Stabile La Piccionaia – I Carrara Societa' Cooperativa ARL
Teatro Astra, Contra' Barche 53, 36100 **Vicenza**
Tel: 0444-541 819 Fax: 0444-327 562
Internet: www.goldnet.it
E-Mail: piccion@goldnet.it
artistic director Titino Carrara; presidente Pierluigi Cecchin; direttore organizzativo Annalisa Carrara; responsabile di produzione e progetto Coredana Chessa
Actors: 15 *Perfs:* 200 *Prods:* 14 *Type:* comedy, youth theatre *Venues:* Teatro Astra di Vicenza 414 *Touring:* Uruguay, Italy, Agentina

Teatro Evento
Via Selmi 2, 41058 **Vignola (MO)**
Tel: 051-613 2270 Fax: 051-757 0624
artistic/administrative director Sergio Galassi; technical director Vittorio Maraneoni; organisation manager Arianna Bortolotti
Actors: 8 *Prods:* 3 *Type:* youth theatre *Venues:* Teatro Testom Casacellio di Reno 600, Teatro La Venere Savig.Sul Panaro 350, *Touring:* Italy *Comments:* also organise courses

Teatro del Vento – Francini e Magri, Il
Via D' Adda 3, 24030 **Villa d'Adda (BG)**
Tel: 035-799 829/049-880 5660 Fax: 035-799 829
direttore artistico Lando Francini; direttore amministrativo Chiara Magri
Actors: 3 *Perfs:* 150 *Prods:* 4 *Type:* drama, mime, Chinese shadows *Touring:* Italy *Comments:* Lando Francini works as writer, scenographer

Associazione Culturale Porte Girevoli
c/o Claudio Cinelli, via dei Martiri 133, 50059 **Vinci (FI)**
Tel: 0571-729 128 Fax: 0571-729 128
artistic director Claudio Cinelli; coreografo Claudio Heloni; Ass. Palco Maneo Rigola; Attrice Paola Roman; Scenografo Milly Fiorini; organizzazione Birgit Noll, Valerio Chiarini
Actors: 13 *Perfs:* 100 *Prods:* 2 new, 2 revivals *Type:* drama and object theatre *Touring:* Italy, Europe, Canada, USA

LATVIA (+371)

Daugavpils State Theatre
Daugavpils Teatris
23a Saules, 5400 **Daugavpils**
Tel: 54-26700 Fax: 54-21941
artistic director Valentins Maculevics

Liepaja Theatre
Liepajas teatris
4 Teatra, 3400 **Liepaja**
Tel: 34-22514/26545 Fax: 34-22514
director Maruta Paveelsone

Daile Theatre
Latvijas Dailes Teatris
75 Brivibas, 1001 **Riga**
Tel: 2-270 463 Fax: 2-270 424
director Bertulis Pizics; artistic director Kârlis Auskaps

Independent Theatre Kabata (Pocket)
Neatkarigais teatris Kabata
19 Peldu, 1050 **Riga**
Tel: 7-211 341/225 334
directors Janis Holsteins, Dita Balcus

Independent Theatre Stage
Neatkarîtris Skatuve
Maskavas iela 108/110, 1003 **Riga**
Tel: 7-222 281
manager and artistic director Anna Eißvertiòa

Latvian National Theatre
Latvijas Nacionalais teatris
2 Kronvalda bulv., 1010 **Riga**
Tel: 7-322 828 Fax: 7-018 747
director Maris Jaunozols; artistic director Edmunds Freibergs

New Riga Theatre
Jaunais Rigas teatris
25 Lacplesa, 1050 **Riga**
Tel: 7-283 323
Fax: 7-282 945
E-Mail: fldrsltjrt@jrt.lv
artistic director Alvis Hermanis; managing director Gundega Palma

Riga Academic Russian Drama Theatre
Rīgas Akadēmiskais Krievu Drāmas teātris
Riga Academic, Kaïïu iela 16, 1050 **Riga**
Tel: 7-227 646 Fax: 7-229 692
E-Mail: art@trd.riga.lv
director Grigorij Cehoval;
artistic director Leonids Belavskis

Valmiera Drama Theatre
Valmieras Dramas Teatris
4 Lacplesa, 4200 **Valmiera**
Tel: 42-22284 Fax: 42-22031
managing director Peteris Sucis;
artistic director Varis Brasla

LITHUANIA (+370)

DZIUGENA Theatre
A. Mickeviciaus 18a, 3000 **Kaunas**
Tel: 7-201 206
director N. Narmontaite

Kaunas Small Theatre
Kauno Mazasis Teatras
M. Dauksos 34, 3000 **Kaunas**
Tel: 7-226 090
artistic director A. Lebeliùmas

Kaunas State Academic Drama Theatre
Kauno Valstybinis Akademinis Dramos Teatras
Laisvès Alèja 71, 3000 **Kaunas**
Tel: 7-224 198 Fax: 7-207 693
manager R. Staras; artistic director V. Bartulis

Menu Samburis
Kestucio 59-37, 3000 **Kaunas**
Tel: 7-756 967
director V. Masalskis

Klaipeda State Drama Theatre
Klaipèdos Valstybinis Dramos Teatras
Teatro 2, 5800 **Klaipèda**
Tel: 6-219 801 Fax: 6-219 804
managing director/artistic director P. Gaidys

Panevèzys J. Miltinis Drama Theatre
Panevèzio J. Miltinio Dramos Teatras
Laisves a. 5, 5300 **Panevèzys**
Tel: 5-468 691 Fax: 5-430 478
artistic director R. Teresas

Edmundo Studija 3
Unconventional Theatre Edmundo studija 3
Varpo 27-35, 5400 **Siauliai**
Tel: 14-21782
artistic director E. Leonavicius

Siauliai State Drama Theatre
Siauliu Valstybinis Dramos Teatras
Tilzes 155, 5400 **Siauliai**
Tel: 14-32641 Fax: 14-32614
managing director Nenekus; artistic director A. Venskus

Independent Actor Theatre
Nepriklausomo Aktoriaus Teatras
Gedimino 1, 2001 **Vilnius**
Tel: 2-619 084 Fax: 2-610 814
director A. Matulionis

Keistuoliai Theatre
Keistuoliu Teatras
Zvaigzdziu 38-76, 2050 **Vilnius**
Tel: 2-424 585 Fax: 2-424 585
director Haroldas Mackevicius

Lithuanian Folk Theatre
Lietuvos liaudies teatras
J. Basanaviciaus 13, 2600 **Vilnius**
Tel: 2-652 030
artistic director P. Mataitis

Lithuanian National Drama Theatre
Lietuvos nacionalinis dramos teatras
Gedimino pr. 4, 2600 **Vilnius**
Tel: 2-621 593 Fax: 2-620 051
artistic director R. Tuminas

Meno Fortas
Maironio St. 1,
2001 **Vilnius**
Tel: 2-612 766
director Eimuntas Nekrosius

Russian State Drama Theatre
Rusu Valstybinis Dramos Teatras
J. Basanaviciaus 13, 2600 **Vilnius**
Tel: 2-652 167 Fax: 2-652 167/221 801
artistic director L.M. Zaikauskas

Senamiescio Theatre
Senamiescio Teatras
V. Mykolaicio, Putino 5,
2009 **Vilnius**
Tel: 2-612 853
artistic director V. Pranulis

State Youth Theatre
Valstybinis Jaunimo Teatras
Arkliu 5, 2001 **Vilnius**
Tel: 2-625 556 Fax: 2-625 558
director K. Smoryginas; artistic director A. Latenas

The Whole World Plays Theatre
Visas Pasaulis Vaidina
Vytenio 6, 2009 **Vilnius**
Tel: 2-769 260
artistic director R. Urbonancaite

Vaidila Theatre
Vaidilos Teatras
A. Jaksto 9, 2600 **Vilnius**
Tel: 2-629 663 Fax: 2-629 663
director A. Arkauskas

Vaidilos Ainiai Theatre
Vaidilos Ainiai Theatre
A. Jaksto 9, 2600 **Vilnius**
Tel: 2-629 663 Fax: 2-629 663
artistic director A. Vecerskis

Vilnius State Small Theatre
Valstybinis Vilniaus Mazasis Teatras
Gedimino pr. 4, 2001 **Vilnius**
Tel: 2-613 195 Fax: 2-613 195
director E. Cenkus

LUXEMBOURG (+352)

Capuchin Theatre
Théâtre des Capucins
9 Place du Théâtre, 2613 **Luxembourg**
Tel: 4796 2433 Fax: 465 065
director Marc Olinger; technical director Remy Theisen
Actors: 12 *Prods:* 2 *Type:* spoken theatre (French, German), classical and contemporary *Venues:* capacity 269 *Touring:* Europe *Comments:* see also Venues

Centaur Theatre
Théâtre du Centaure
4 Grand Rue, BP 641, 2016 **Luxembourg**
Tel: 222 828 Fax: 371 116
administrative director Pierre Bodry; artistic director Marja-Leena Junker; treasurer t.b.a
Actors: 12 (varies) *Perfs:* 112 *Prods:* 4 *Type:* classical to modern *Venues:* Théâtre du Centaure 65 *Touring:* France *Comments:* perform mainly in French, but also in German, Luxembourg and English; 98-99 is the 25th anniversary of the company

Théâtre des Casemates
BP 452,
2014 **Luxembourg**
Tel: 291 281
président Pierre Capesius; artistic director Christine Reinhold; technical director Patrick Colling
Actors: 15 *Perfs:* 16 *Prods:* 4 *Type:* avant-garde, classic theatre *Venues:* 100 *Comments:* productions in German and Luxembourgeois; see also Venues

MACEDONIA (+389)

Folk Theatre Bitola
Naroden teatar Bitola
Marsal Tito 60, 97000 **Bitola**
Tel: 97-32416 Fax: 97-33970
director Blagoja Stefanovski

Folk Theatre Kumanovo
Naroden teatar Kumanovo
Kiril i Metodij bb, 91300 **Kumanovo**
Tel: 901-23950/26526
director Tomislav Spasovski

Folk Theatre Vojdan Cernodrinski
Naroden teatar Vojdan Cernodrinski
Borka Taleski br. 111, 98000 **Prilep**
Tel: 98-28644
director Stojan Damcevski

Drama Theatre
Dramski Teatar
Sekspirova 15, 91000 **Skopje**
Tel: 91-250 005/6 Fax: 91-256 598
director Blagoja Corevski
Perfs: 205 *Prods:* 6 new of 14

Macedonian National Theatre
Makedonski Naroden Teater
Kej Dimitar Vlahov bb,
91000 **Skopje**
Tel: 91-114 908/511 Fax: 91-114 060
managing director Ljupco Petrusevski;
drama director t.b.a.
Perfs: 154 *Prods:* 6 new of 14

Theatre for Children and Youth
Teatar za deca i mladinci
Bul. Kliment Ohridski bb, 91000 **Skopje**
Tel: 91-222 619
Fax: 91-223 118
director Ljubimir Cadikovski

Theatre of Minority
Teatar na narodnostite
Nikola Martinovski 41, 91000 **Skopje**
Tel: 91-111 017
Fax: 91-222 570
director of Turkish drama Saladin Bilal; director of Albanian drama Sefedin Nuredini

Folk Theatre Stip
Naroden teatar Stip
General Mihajlo Apostolski 21,
92000 **Stip**
Tel: 92-31366
director Gorgi Ustapetrov

Folk Theatre Anton Panov Strumica
Naroden teatar Anton Panov Strumica
Goce Delcev bb, 92400 **Strumica**
Tel: 902-26896
director Vanco Melev

Folk Theatre Jordan Hadzi Konstantinov Dzinot
Naroden teatar J.H.K. T. Veles
Titogradska bb, 91400 **Titov Veles**
Tel: 93-31750/21471
director Aleksandar Georgiev

MOLDOVA (+373)

National Theatre Vasile Alecsandri
Teatrul National Vasile Alecsandri
Piata Vasile Alecsandri 1, 279200 **Balti**
Tel: 31-25048
director Racila Anton Vasile

Bogdan Petriceicu Hasdeu Republican Theatre of Music and Drama
Teatrul Republican Musical Dramatic
Bogdan Petriceicu Hasdeu
B.P. Hasdeu str.6, 2830 **Cahul**
Tel: 39-20889
director Ignat Victor Mihai

Alexei Mateevici Theatre
Teatrul Alexei Mateevici
Sfatul Tarii str. 18, 2012 **Chisinau**
Tel: 2-237 671
director Vartic Andrei Vasile

Eugene Ionescu Theatre
Teatrul Eugene Ionesco
N Iorga Str. 16, 2012 **Chisinau**
Tel: 2-237 601
director Petru Butcaru

Musical Theatre Ginta Latina
Teatrul Musical Ginta Latina
Sfatul Tarii str. 18, 2012 **Chisinau**
Tel: 2-233 230
director Madan Veaceslav Tudor

National Theatre M. Eminescu
Teatrul National M. Eminescu
Stefan cel Mare Bil.79,
2012 **Chisinau**
Tel: 2-222 793
director Constantin Ceianu

Republican Theatre Luceafarul
Teatrul Republican Luceafarul
Veronica Micle Str. 7, 2012 **Chisinau**
Tel: 2-224 121
director Gheorghe Pirlea

State Russian Drama Theatre Anton Cehov
Teatrul Dramatic rus de Stat Anton Cehov
Vlaicu Pircalab str. 75, 2012 **Chisinau**
Tel: 2-221 695
director Veaceslav Madan

NETHERLANDS (+31)

Art & Pro (Artikelen & Projekten)
Rozengracht 117, 1016 LV **Amsterdam**
Tel: 20-627 6162 Fax: 20-624 8846
E-Mail: artenpro@euronet.nl
production manager t.b.a.; artistic director & author Frans Stryards; english-dutch translator Carina Meydam; finance director Roelf Huizenga
Actors: varies *Perfs:* 100 *Prods:* 3 *Type:* modern writing + repertoire *Venues:* Rozen Theatre 200 *Touring:* Netherlands, Belgium

Boom Chicago
Leidseplein Theater, Leidseplein 12,
1017 PT **Amsterdam**
Tel: 20-530 7300
Fax: 20-420 7423
Internet: www.boomchicago.nl
E-Mail: office@boomchicago.nl
producer Andrew Moskos; technical director Ken Schaefle; director of communications Jon Rosenfeld, Saskia Maas; artistic director Josephine O' Reilly
Actors: 11 *Prods:* 2 *Type:* comedy, improvisation *Venues:* Leidseplein Theater 280 *Touring:* national, international

Carver
Theaterzaken Via Rudolphi, Korte Leidsedwarsstraat 12, 1017 RC **Amsterdam**
Tel: 20-627 7555 Fax: 20-627 8541
E-Mail: info@viarudolphi.nl
artistic team Beppie Melissen, Rene vant Hof, Leny Breederveld; manager Marie-Anne Rudolphi
Actors: 4-5 *Perfs:* 50 *Type:* physical movement theatre, Dutch mime *Venues:* capacity 200

De Mexicaanse Hond en Orkater
Postbus 57145, 1040 BA **Amsterdam**
Tel: 20-606 0600/0601 (publicity) Fax: 20-606 0616
Internet: www.orkater.nl
E-Mail: info@orkater.nl
managing directors Marc van Warmerdam, Ton Schippers; publicity Wim Wentzel
Actors: varies *Perfs:* 200 *Prods:* 4 *Type:* music theatre *Venues:* capacity 200 to 800 *Touring:* Netherlands, Australia, France, Germany *Comments:* this company is a part of Orkater (q.v.); as writer, director and actor Alex Van Warmerdam has been responsible for seven Mexicaanse Hond performances and 3 films; perform in English, French and German; visiting address: Westergasfabriek, Haarlemmerweg 8-10, Amsterdam

Dogtroep
PO Box 15098, 1001 MB **Amsterdam**
Tel: 20-632 1139 Fax: 20-632 2253
Internet: www.dogtroep.nl
E-Mail: dogtroep@xs4all.nl
managing director Henk Keizer;
artistic director Titia Bouwmeester
Actors: 15-35 (including technicians and musicians) *Perfs:* 70 *Prods:* 4 *Type:* visual music theatre *Venues:* interesting spaces as well as theatres *Touring:* Netherlands, worldwide

Griftheater
Oostelijke Handelskade 33, 1019 BL **Amsterdam**
Tel: 20-419 3088 Fax: 20-419 1683
Internet: www.xs4all.nl/~grif
E-Mail: info@grif.nl
manager Jan Deinema;
artistic director Frits Vogels, John Taks
Actors: varies *Perfs:* 50 *Prods:* 2 *Type:* visual movement theatre *Touring:* USA, Netherlands *Comments:* site-specific work

House on the River Amstel
Huis Aan De Amstel
Lauriergracht 99c, 1016 RJ **Amsterdam**
Tel: 20-622 9328 Fax: 20-625 6609
E-Mail: hada@xs4all.nl
managing director Erica van Eeghen; artistic director Liesbeth Coltof; planning, production & publicity Corienne Nelissen
Actors: 5 *Perfs:* 175 *Prods:* 3 (2 new) *Type:* experimental, classical (Shakespeare) *Venues:* capacity 100 *Touring:* Netherlands, Belgium

Karina Holla
Bureau Berbee, Korte Leidsedwarsstraat 12, 1017 RC **Amsterdam**
Tel: 20-627 0455
Fax: 20-625 0616
artistic director Karina Holla
Actors: varies *Type:* modern mime *Venues:* capacity 200 *Touring:* Netherlands *Comments:* see also Promoters

Maatschappij Discordia
Keizersgracht 324, 1016 EZ **Amsterdam**
Tel: 20-627 1999 Fax: 20-639 3304
Internet: www.xs4all.nl/~discordi/index.html
E-Mail: discordi@xs4all.nl
art directors Jan Joris Lamers, Matthias de Koning
Actors: 10 *Perfs:* 150-170 *Prods:* 6-8 *Type:* repertory, music drama, experimental, performance art, children's theatre *Venues:* various capacities up to 100 *Touring:* Netherlands, Belgium, occasionally other European countries *Comments:* they are currently looking for a more permanent venue

Nieuw Amsterdam, De
Grote Bickerstraat 2-4, 1013 KS **Amsterdam**
Tel: 20-627 8672/8699 Fax: 20-620 0166
E-Mail: dnalab@xs4all.nl
business director Gerrit Wijnhoud;
artistic director Alida Neslo
Actors: 5 *Perfs:* 60 *Prods:* 2 (new) *Type:* non Western drama, own written repertoire *Venues:* de Nieuw Amsterdam 70 *Touring:* Germany, Netherlands, Surinam, Belgium, UK *Comments:* multi-cultural theatre group; also have full time international education department: ITS DNA; the education department differs from others by putting the emphasis on movement and the body as an instrument

Orkater
Postbus 57145, 1040 BA **Amsterdam**
Tel: 20-606 0600/0601 (publicity) Fax: 20-606 0616
Internet: www.orkater.nl
E-Mail: info@orkater.nl
managing directors Marc van Warmerdam, Ton Schippers; publicity Wim Wentzel
Actors: 4 (+ 8 musicians) *Perfs:* 60 *Prods:* 1 *Type:* new written music-theatre/musical theatre *Venues:* capacity 500-1000 *Touring:* national *Comments:* the Orkater Foundation explores different combinations of music (Orkest) and theatre (theater); visiting address: Westergasfabriek, Haarlemmerweg 8-10, Amsterdam; see also Opera

Suver Nuver
Theaterzaken Via Rudolphi, Korte Leidsedwarsstraat 12, 1017 RC **Amsterdam**
Tel: 20-627 7555 Fax: 20-627 8541
E-Mail: info@viaRudolphi.nl
artistic team Peer van den Berg, Henk Zwart, Dette Glashouwer; manager Marie-Anne Rudolphi
Actors: varies *Perfs:* 50 *Type:* physical movement theatre, Dutch mime *Venues:* capacity 200

Taller Amsterdam
Keizersgracht 607, 1017 DS **Amsterdam**
Tel: 20-624 6734 Fax: 20-627 1539
managing director Freek Van Kleij; artistic directors Armando Bergallo, Hector Vilche
Actors: varies *Type:* music theatre, contemporary opera and visual arts *Comments:* Taller Amsterdam is currently developing a new production for year 2000; see also Opera

Toneelgroep Amsterdam
Marnixstraat 427, 1017 PK **Amsterdam**
Tel: 20-523 7800 Fax: 20-626 8526
Internet: www.tga.nl
E-Mail: info@tga.nl
general manager Gerrit Korthals Altes; artistic directors Gerardjan Rijnders, Titus Muizelaar; publicity René van der Pluijm; technical supervisor Louis Janssen
Actors: 30 *Perfs:* 350 *Prods:* 15 *Type:* classical, modern and experimental *Venues:* Transformatorhuis Toneelgroep Amsterdam (TTA) 325, Bellevue Theatre 100-320, Stadsschouwburg, Amsterdam 800 *Touring:* Netherlands and Belgium, Germany, Denmark, Rumania, Czech Republic

Wederzijds
1e Nassaustraat 5, 1052 BD **Amsterdam**
Tel: 20-682 4854/686 4682 Fax: 20-686 6347
director Lieke Beijlsmit; artistic director Ad de Bont
Actors: 6 *Perfs:* 150 *Prods:* 3-4, 1new *Type:* youth theatre *Touring:* Netherlands *Comments:* Dutch touring company, performs regularly at festivals in Europe and the USA; performs sometimes in German and English

Werkteater, Het
Oostenburgergracht 75, 1018 NC **Amsterdam**
Tel: 20-627 0296 Fax: 20-627 7029
E-Mail: werteat@xs4all.nl
contact Hanz Looye
Actors: 11 *Perfs:* 100 *Prods:* 8 projects *Type:* based on improvisation *Venues:* Werktheater 400 + various others (hospitals, old factories) *Touring:* Netherlands, International *Comments:* some plays are performed in English

Youththeatrecompany Het Filiaal
Theaterbureau Slot, Gerda Slot, Plantage Muidergracht 155, 1018 TT **Amsterdam**
Tel: 20-422 7899 Fax: 20-624 0470
E-Mail: slot.theater@tref.nl
artistic director Monique Covers
Actors: varies *Prods:* 2 *Type:* children's theatre, music by Canadian composer Gabe Tarjan *Touring:* Europe *Comments:* Theaterbureau Slot, for children up to 8 years old; see also Puppets and Agents

Youththeatrecompany Saga
Theaterbureau Slot, Gerda Slot, Plantage Muidergracht 155, 1018 TT **Amsterdam**
Tel: 20-422 7899 Fax: 20-624 0470
E-Mail: slot.theater@tref.nl
artistic director Sylvia Valkenburg
Actors: varies *Prods:* 2-3 *Type:* children's theatre with song *Touring:* Europe

Theater van het Oosten
Rijnstraat 42, 6811 EX **Arnhem**
Tel: 26-443 7655 Fax: 26-442 0918
Internet: www.tuho.nl
E-Mail: info@tuho.nl
administrator Martin Scholten; artistic director Leonard Frank
Actors: no permanent company, all guests *Perfs:* 110 *Prods:* 3 *Type:* modern, classical *Venues:* capacity 93 *Touring:* Netherlands

Theatergroep Maccus
Rietveld 49, 2611 LH **Delft**
Tel: 15-212 2977 Fax: 15-213 1127
Internet: www.maccus.nl
E-Mail: maccus@maccus.nl
general manager Therese Adriaansens; artistic director Jos Van Kan; dramaturgy & education Berthe Spoelstra; booking & publicity Ilse van Dijk
Actors: 10 *Perfs:* 130 *Prods:* 3 *Type:* children's theatre *Venues:* theatres, schools capacity 200 *Touring:* Belgium, Austria, Netherlands, Germany

Appel, De
Duinstraat 6, Postbus 84260, 2508 AG **Den Haag**
Tel: 70-352 3344 Fax: 70-354 7417
E-Mail: appel@bart.nl
general manager Gerrit Dÿkstra; artistic directors Aram Adriaanse, Aus Greidanus
Actors: 7 *Perfs:* 280 *Prods:* 5-6 *Type:* broad repertoire *Venues:* De Appel Theatre Studio I 100, Studio II 100, Main Theatre 300 to 500 *Touring:* Netherlands

Nationale Toneel, Het
Schouburgstraat 8, 2511 VA **Den Haag**
Tel: 70-318 1473 Fax: 70-318 1488
E-Mail: onno@hnt.nl
managing director Evert de Jager; artistic directors Ger Thijs, Johan Doesburg; literary managers Karim Ameur, Martine Manten; publicity manager Arne Deen
Actors: no resident company *Perfs:* 380 *Prods:* 8 *Type:* modern/classical, comedy, new writing *Venues:* Koninklijke Schouwburg 700, Theatre Aan Het Spui A 300, B 150 *Touring:* Netherlands, Belgium

Theatre Company of the South, Het
Zuidelijk Toneel
PO Box 2185, 5600 CD **Eindhoven**
Tel: 40-233 3633 Fax: 40-246 0725
Internet: www.hzt.nl
E-Mail: email@hzt.nl
director Ivo van Hove; vice-director Hans Dowit; pr & marketing Max van Engen; producer Frank Carpentier
Actors: 7 + guests *Perfs:* 200 *Prods:* 6 (3 new) *Type:* modern & classical *Touring:* Germany, Scotland
Comments: second address: Fuutlaan 12, 5613 AB Eindhoven

Noord Nederlands Toneel
Postbus 7090, 9701 JB **Groningen**
Tel: 50-311 3388 Fax: 50-311 3141
Internet: www.nnt.nl
E-Mail: info@nnt.nl
director Evert de Jager; publicity Rein Bish, Petra van der Meer; production manager Freek Kramer
Perfs: 150 *Prods:* 3 *Touring:* Netherlands, Belgium
Comments: street address: Bloemstraat 38, 9712 LE Groningen, touring company

Tryater
Neptunusweg 34, 8938 AA **Leeuwarden**
Tel: 58-288 2335 Fax: 58-288 6824
general manager Ben van der Knaap; artistic director Jos Thie; head of press Antine Zÿlstra
Actors: 5 *Perfs:* 280 *Prods:* 5-6 *Type:* modern and classical *Touring:* Netherlands *Comments:* theatre for adults in the Frisian language and theatre for youth in Frisian and Dutch language

Theater aan het Vrijthof
Vrijthof 47, Postbus 882, 6200 AW **Maastricht**
Tel: 43-350 5555 Fax: 43-350 5522
Internet: www.theateraanhetvrijthof.nl
E-Mail: uitbalie@theateraanhetvrijthof.nl
director Piet van Hest; pr Elly Rietbroek; Schoenmakers; hoofd programma Jos Zwietink; hoofd fin. administratie Gerard Walraven
Venues: grote zaal 900

Teneeter
Daalseweg 262, 6523 CD **Nijmegen**
Tel: 24-360 0588 Fax: 24-360 5028
E-Mail: teneeter@wxs.nl
managing director Trees van Dijk; artistic director Rinus Knobel; communication & public relations Bernard Ellenbroek; education Nelleke Verweij
Actors: 6 *Perfs:* 120 *Prods:* 3 *Type:* youth theatre *Venues:* Badhuis Theatre 120 *Touring:* Netherlands, Belgium

FACT
S-Gravendijkwal 58b, 3014 EE **Rotterdam**
Tel: 10-436 7997 Fax: 10-436 7959
E-Mail: fact@fact.nl
publicity, production Lydia Buisman; artistic director Klemens Wannenmacher; financial director Harm Lambers; secretary, publicity Eveline Blok;
Actors: 8-10 per production *Perfs:* 60 *Prods:* 3-5 *Type:* modern theatre *Venues:* Rotterdamse Schouwburg 720/154 (small hall) *Touring:* Netherlands, Belgium
Comments: production house for young directors to perform at the Schouwburg Theatre and other theatres in the Netherlands

Independent Theatre
Onafhankelijk Toneel
Sint Jobsweg 3, 3024 EH **Rotterdam**
Tel: 10-478 0281/476 9029 Fax: 10-425 7915
Internet: www.ot-rotterdam.nl
E-Mail: ot@ot-rotterdam.nl
directors Mirjam Koen, Gerrit Timmers, Ton Luttering; administration Corry Prinsen; publicity Gerda Roest; choreographers Amy Gale, Ton Lutgerink;
Actors: varies *Perfs* 200 *Prods:* 4-9 *Type:* repertory, experimental, combined with dance, opera and visual arts *Venues:* O. T. Theatre up to 100, City theatres up to 600 *Touring:* national, international *Comments:* a collective of theatre-makers with varying backgrounds – visual arts, modern dance, acting – all of which are combined in productions; see also Dance and Opera

Ro-Theater
William Boothlaan 8, 3012 VJ **Rotterdam**
Tel: 10-404 6888 Fax: 10-414 7717
E-Mail: info@ro-theater.nl
managing & artistic director Guy Cassiers; technical director J Thÿssen; pr W Visser (Mrs); production controller B de Ronde
Actors: 10 + 6-7 free lance *Perfs:* 240 *Prods:* 8 *Type:* classical, new writing, literary adaptations *Venues:* Rotterdamse Schouwburg, Grote Zaal 960, Kleine Zaal 180, Ro-Theater 300 *Touring:* Netherlands, Belgium

Theater Sirkel
PO 214, 6130 AE **Sittard**
Tel: 46-452 5574 Fax: 46-452 6432
E-Mail: MALART@globalxs.nl
artistic directors Frans Malschaert, Anandi Teeuw; administration Maryke van Hout; technicians Dik Beets, Marc Claessens
Actors: 2-10 *Perfs:* 200 *Prods:* 6 (2 new) *Type:* unique blend of art and theatre, visual theatre for adults and children *Touring:* Netherlands, international *Comments:* second address: Putstraat 22, 6131 HL Sittard, Netherlands; see also Puppets and Venues

Theatergroep Hollandia
Oostzvjde 18, 1502 BG **Zaandam**
Tel: 75-612 7555 Fax: 75-670 1906
administrators Willy Smits, Jan Zoet; artistic directors Johan Simons, Paul Koek; publicity Annet Lekkenkerker, Rick Spaan; dramaturg Tom Blokdijk, Paul Slangen
Actors: 8 *Perfs:* 240 *Prods:* 6-7 *Type:* classical and modern, site specific, music theatre *Venues:* capacity 150 *Touring:* Netherlands, Belgium, Germany, France, Greece, USA *Comments:* the group works with young directors every year; performs at factories during worker's working hours

NORWAY (+47)

Musidra teater
Ringstabekkveien 112b, 1340 **Bekkestua**
Tel: 6753 0417 Fax: 6753 7584
director Camilla Tostrup
Prods: 37 *Type:* new theatre *Touring:* national, international *Comments:* oldest freelance professional theatre group in Norway

Bak-truppen
Postboks 598, 5806 **Bergen**
Tel: 2271 8833/2255 3022 Fax: 2271 8833/2255 3022
Internet: www.gbnett.no/theBAR
E-Mail: bak-truppen@notam.uio.no
co-directors Ingvild Holm, Trine Falch Johannessen
Type: music, text and movement, cross-over art collaborations *Venues:* perform in various open spaces *Touring:* Europe, Asia, USA *Comments:* visiting address: Dælengata 31, 0567 Bergen

Den Nationale Scene
Postboks 78, 5001 **Bergen**
Tel: 5554 9700 Fax: 5554 9790
Internet: www.den-nationale-scene.no
E-Mail: dns@den.nationale.scene.no
director Audun Hasti; artistic director Bemtein Baardson; head of board Dag Steinfeld; producer Øyvind Eskildsen; dramaturge Kirsten Broch; musical director Knut Skodvin; public relations manager Sverre Chr Wilhelmsen; marketing director Evy Fischer
Actors: 29 + 6 musicians *Prods:* 3 *Venues:* Lille Scene 90, Småscenen 150 to 250, Store Scene 450 *Comments:* It is the oldest theatre company in Norway and lists amongst its previous artistic directors Ibsen, Bjørnson & Heiberg

Prosjektteateret
Nygårdsgt 88, 5008 **Bergen**
Tel: 5527 0909
E-Mail: teatret@login.eunet.no
artistic director Tone Tjemsland; composer Maia Urstad; producer Grethe H. L. Melby
Actors: 6-8 *Perfs:* 20 *Prods:* 2 *Type:* project theatre group *Touring:* Norway, Poland, Sweden, Denmark

Sogn og Fjordane teater
Postboks 324, 6801 **Førde**
Tel: 5772 1850
Fax: 5782 2153
director Emte Stag
Prods: 2 major plays annually, 6-7 plays annually *Venues:* touring boat Innvik, theatre hall in Førdehuset *Touring:* mainly touring theatre *Comments:* visiting address: Førdehuset, Angedalsveien 5, 6800 Førde

Sami National Theatre Company
Sámi Beaivvás Teahter
Postboks 445, 9520 **Guovdageaidnu**
Tel: 7848 6811
Fax: 7848 6875
Internet: www.beaivvas.com
E-Mail: beaivvas@beaivvas.com
general director Alex Scherpf
Actors: 3-9 *Perfs:* 50-100 *Prods:* 3-4 *Type:* new writing, classical *Touring:* Finland, Norway, Sweden
Comments: touring company

Hedmark Teater
Postboks 4153, 2307 **Hamar**
Tel: 6259 8720 Fax: 6259 8721
artistic director Brit Lossius;
nstructer, writer Suerre Waage
Actors: 1 *Perfs:* 200 (incl co-productions) *Prods:* 6 *Type:* mainly new work, some traditional *Touring:* regional touring company *Comments:* present both children's theatre and co-productions; visiting address: Just Brochsgt. 13, 2307 Hamar; hires actors/performers on contract for most productions

Haugesund teater A/S
Postboks 603, 5528 **Haugesund**
Tel: 5273 4430 Fax: 5271 7013
E-Mail: jens.thordal@haugesund.kommune.no
director Jens Vagn Thordal
(tel: 5273 4430/ 9055 9671 mobile)
Type: mainly children's and youth theatre; repertoire mainly Norwegian and British drama with emphasis on musical theatre *Venues:* tour kindergardens, schools
Comments: visiting address: Knut Knutsensgate 4, 5528 Haugesund

Samovar teater
Parkveien 6, 9900 **Kirkenes**
Tel: 7899 2468 Fax: 7899 3753
Internet: home.newmedia.no/samovar
director Bente S. Andersen
Prods: 1-2 per year *Touring:* Scandinavia, Russia
Comments: also runs a theatre school for local children

Agder Teater
Kongensgate 2, Postboks 582,
4665 **Kristiansand**
Tel: 3812 2888
Fax: 3812 2880
Internet: www.agderteater.va.no
E-Mail: teateras@online.no
director Gunnar Grimstad
Actors: varies *Perfs:* 350 *Type:* new work, classics, traditional, puppet theatre, concerts, musicals *Venues:* Agder Theatre – Kristiansand 460, Agder Teater – Fjaereheia (open-air) 975 *Comments:* project theatre, no resident actors; hosts biannual international figure theatre festival

Nordland Teater A/S
Box 1263, 8601 **Mo i Rana**
Tel: 7513 4848
Fax: 7513 4860
E-Mail: nordlandteater@nordlandteater.no
director Frode Rasmussen
Actors: 7 *Perfs:* 150 *Prods:* 5 *Type:* classic drama, children's, contemporary writing and premieres, cabaret *Venues:* main house 400, small house 150 *Touring:* Nordland and Troms region

Teatret Vårt
Julsundvn 4, 6400 **Molde**
Tel: 7124 0280 Fax: 7124 0299
E-Mail: teatret.vart@moldenett.no
artistic director & manager Edvard Hoem
Actors: 10-14 *Perfs:* 200 *Prods:* 4 (2 new) *Type:* classical and contemporary author theatre *Touring:* Norway
Comments: regional touring company of Möre & Romsdal county

Menn i dress friteater
Men in Suits Fringe Theatre
c/o Ingvar Hopland, Furulund 1,
5221 **Nesttun**
Tel: 5513 9035
E-Mail: jopland@online.no
contacts Ingvar Hopland, Geir Amundsen
Type: mixture of theatre and puppets *Touring:* Norway

Boreas Teater
Norderhorgt 38, 0654 **Oslo**
Tel: 2268 2441 Fax: 2268 2441
artistic directors Annalisa Dal Pra, Patrick Shaw-Iversen
Actors: 1 + 1 full-time musician *Perfs:* 20-50 *Prods:* 1-2
Type: masques, gestures, improvisation Theatre of Music seeking to discover meeting points between modern music, sound, theatre *Venues:* Black Box Theatre; large stage 300, small stage 100 *Comments:* specialise in outdoor projects using unusual venues as the focus of the performance

Det åpne teater
Open Theatre
Tøyenbekken 34, 0188 **Oslo**
Tel: 2205 2800 Fax: 2205 2801
E-Mail: daat.teater@online.no
director Franzisca Aarflot
Type: workshop theatre for playwrights, contemporary plays

Grusomhetens teater
Theatre of Cruelty
Peter Aas vei 4a
0667 **Oslo**
Tel: 2275 5454
director Lars Øyno (tel: 9132 5639 mobile)
Prods: 8

Nationaltheatret
Ba Clemetsen, Box 1225 Vika, 0110 **Oslo**
Tel: 2241 1640 Fax: 2242 4343 (admin)/2200 1686 (marketing/information)
Internet: www.sol.no/nationaltheatret
managing director Gunnar Losseus; artistic, executive director Ellen Horn; marketing manager Thine Sletbak; press and information officer Ragnhild Samuelsbirg
Actors: 58 *Perfs:* 600 *Prods:* 12-15 *Type:* classical and contemporary foreign and Norwegian plays with a special attention on Ibsen and new Norwegian drama *Venues:* main stage 779, amphi stage 230, studio stage 80 *Comments:* hosting the Ibsen Stage Festival (biennial)

Nordic Black Theatre
Postboks 4621, 0506 **Oslo**
Tel: 2238 1262 Fax: 2238 2397
Internet: home.sol.no/theatre
E-Mail: theatre@online.no
director Cliff A. Moustache (tel: 9093 1038 mobile); venue bookings manager Jarl Solberg (tel: 9188 0613 mobile)

Norske Teatret, Det
Kristian IV's gt 8, 0164 **Oslo**
Tel: 2247 3800 Fax: 2233 6528
Internet: www.detnorsketeatret.no
E-Mail: info@detnorsketeatret.no
chief manager Vidar Sandem; press officer Signe Bjorvik; director of marketing Magnhild Arstein
Actors: 55 *Perfs:* 600 *Prods:* 14-18 *Type:* traditional and modern classics, European and Scandinavian children's theatre, musical theatre *Venues:* Main house 750-1000, second theatre 200, studio 90-120 *Touring:* Norway
Comments: Norwegian member of the European Theatre Convention

Oslo Nye Teater
Rosenkrantzgt. 10, 0159 **Oslo**
Tel: 2234 8600 Fax: 2234 8601
E-Mail: info@oslo-nye-teater.oslo.no
theatre director Kjetil Bang-Hansen; general manager Bjoern-Erik Kragstad; marketing director Haakon Lien
Actors: 30 permanent + 6 puppet players *Perfs:* 700 per annum *Prods:* 12 *Type:* all types of drama, comedy, musicals *Venues:* main stage 700, stage L 285, puppet theatre 180

Passage Nord Theatre
Stensgaten 32 C, 0358 **Oslo**
Tel: 2269 4428 Fax: 2269 4428
artistic director Kjetil Sköien
Actors: 8 *Perfs:* 100 *Venues:* Kanonhallen (Copenhagen), Black Box (Oslo), teatro Il Vascello, Rome *Touring:* Norway, Italy, Poland, France

Riksteatret – National Touring Company
Kongensgate 1, Postboks 724, Sentrum, 0105 **Oslo**
Tel: 2220 6015 Fax: 2220 6052
Internet: www.aftenposten.no/web/riksteat
artistic director Bente Erichsen; administrative director Gry Wie; marketing manager t.b.a.;
information consultant t.b.a.
Actors: 60 (permanent) *Perfs:* 626 *Prods:* 29 *Type:* classical/modern drama, puppets *Touring:* Norway

Thalias døtre
Thalia's Daughters
Olav Kyrresgate 3, 0273 **Oslo**
Tel: 2255 5997 Fax: 2255 5997
E-Mail: Agnetegh@online.no
artistic director Agnthe G Haaland
Type: interpret famous female characters in contemporary manner *Touring:* worldwide

Torshov Teatret
Johanne Dybwad Place 1, 0161 **Oslo**
Tel: 2222 4031 Fax: 2222 4151
manager Margrethe Aaby; artistic director Ellen Horn
Actors: 5 resident + 1-2 *Perfs:* 130 *Prods:* 4 major +2 small (incl. children's) *Type:* contemporary *Venues:* Torshov Theatre up to 150 *Comments:* Theatre-in-the-Round, visiting address: Vogtsgt. 64, 0466 Oslo

Verdensteatret
Marselisgt 27, 0551 **Oslo**
Tel: 2235 7949/9341 9289 (mobile) Fax: 2237 7663
Internet:
www.plato.no/doogie/verdensteatret/index.html
E-Mail: lisbethb@powertech.no
artistic leaders Lisbet J Bodd, Asle Nilsen
Actors: 6-8 *Perfs:* 15 *Prods:* 1 *Type:* visual/textual theatre, modern theatre *Venues:* BIT. teatret Garagen Begen 300, Black Box Theatre Oslo 200 *Touring:* international, national *Comments:* co-productions, touring company

Grenland friteater Norsk senter for fri scenekunst
Grenland Fringe Theatre
Huken 5, 3921 **Porsgrunn**
Tel: 3555 5169/9008 5696 (mobile) Fax: 3555 1940
E-Mail: grenfrit@online.no
administrator Trond Hannemyr
Type: various types of performances, including experimental, children and adults *Venues:* outdoor performances *Touring:* national, international *Comments:* company arranges courses, conferences and festivals

Teater Ibsen
Postboks 357, 3701 **Skien**
Tel: 3590 5050 Fax: 3590 5060
E-Mail: post@teateribsen.no
managing director Gry Wie; artistic director Morten Borgersen; technical director Per Haugen; sales manager Main Stensholt Holte; information/pr officer Maria Danielsen Qdah
Actors: 9 *Perfs:* 320-330 *Prods:* 4 (main), up to 50 (fringe) *Type:* concentrating mainly on Norwegian plays until 2002 *Venues:* Teater Ibsen Mainstage 180, Studio 60-100 *Touring:* South East Noway *Comments:* touring company

Rogaland Theatre
Kannikgt 2, 4005 **Stavanger**
Tel: 5191 9000
Internet: www.rogaland-teater.no
E-Mail: otskare@online.no
artistic director Eirik Stubø; business manager Geir Bergkastet; dramaturg Michael Evans; technical manager Oddgeir Kummen; sales manager Lillian Rødsten Alvarez; PR Olav Torbjørn Skare; accounts officer Merete Eik; production manager Leif Høiland
Actors: 20-25 (on one year contracts) *Perfs:* 400-450 *Prods:* 5 on main stage, 4 on studio stage, 2 in cellar theatre *Type:* varied repertoire *Venues:* main stage 370, studio stage 95, cellar theatre 55

Stella Polaris
Fossnes Centre, 3160 **Stokke**
Tel: 3333 9099/9283 4579 (mobile) Fax: 3336 6339
Internet: www.okkenhaug/com-web-stella.html
E-Mail: spolaris@online.no
administrator Merete Klingen; artistic director Per Spildra Borg; marketing Siw Pedersen
Actors: winter: 7-8; summer: 25 *Perfs:* 100 *Prods:* 9 (5 new) *Type:* gesture, ritualistic theatre, environmental, action theatre, story telling, (project theatre) *Venues:* public houses, main streets and squares of cities, outdoor theatres, church rooms, historic places *Touring:* Norway, Poland, Lithuania *Comments:* see also Puppetry

Hålogaland Teater
Postboks 840, 9258 **Tromsø**
Tel: 7766 5100 Fax: 7766 5101
theatre director Haukur J Gunnarsson; information officers Nils Kristian, Sørhiem Nilsen
Actors: 7 *Prods:* 3 *Type:* classic, musical, new work *Venues:* permanent stage (rented) in Kulturhuset Tromsø; 2 stages:, Lillescenen 180, Storscenen 661 *Touring:* north Norway

Totalteatret
Vestregt 48, 9008 **Tromsø**
Tel: 7765 7105 Fax: 7761 3686
Internet: www.totalteatret.com
E-Mail: adm@totalteatret.com
artistic director, information Kristin Eriksen
Actors: 3 *Perfs:* 100 *Prods:* 2 *Type:* text combined with a physical, outgoing style of acting *Venues:* Raadstua, Tromsø *Touring:* Norway, Europe

Cirka teater
Nedre allé 9, 7030 **Trondheim**
Tel: 7353 0733 Fax: 7353 0844
E-Mail: cirka.teater@online.no
contact Jorunn Dugstad
Type: physical theatre, use outdoor surroundings as settings *Venues:* homebase is Avantgarden Playhouse *Comments:* tours performances for adults and children; visiting address: Skippergata 10, 7000 Trondheim

Studio Teater a.s.
Olav Tryggvasonsgt. 5, 7011 **Trondheim**
Tel: 7353 4883 Fax: 7352 4732
actors Viggo Solum, Jørn Myrholdt, Sølvi Laugsand
Actors: 3 *Perfs:* 70-90 *Prods:* 2 *Type:* adult, children's theatre, in- and outside theatre including in ice and snow *Venues:* Teaterhuset Avant Garden (shared with 3 other groups) 100 *Touring:* Norway, Scandinavian countries

Teater Fusentast
Riddervoldsgate 28, 7016 **Trondheim**
Tel: 7351 8729/7284 6743 Fax: 7353 3026
Internet: home.c2i.net/comvlee/
E-Mail: comvlee@c2i.net
directors, actors Jaap den Hertog, Coby Omvlee, Karl Markus Reinert; publicity & admin Lillian Uran Todnem
Actors: 1-4 *Perfs:* 70-150 *Prods:* 7 *Type:* visual story-telling, puppets and puppeteers and/or actors interact with the audience, musical theatre, puppetry *Venues:* capacity up to 250 *Touring:* Norway, Netherlands, Russia, France *Comments:* plays for all age groups; also run courses and workshops on puppetry, clowning, acting skills

Trøndelag Teater
Trøndelag Teater, 7005 **Trondheim**
Tel: 7380 5100 Fax: 7380 5101
Internet: www.trøndelag/teater.no
E-Mail: webmaster@trøndelag/teater.no
theatre director Ola B Johannessen (until 16/8) (from August) Catrine Telle; information May Selmer
Actors: 28 permanent *Perfs:* 450 *Prods:* 10 *Type:* classic to contemporary *Venues:* Trøndelag Teater: main 524, old stage 320, studio 150, cabaret 100, small 60

Nord-Trøndelag teater
Stiklestad nasjonale kultursenter, 7650 **Verdal**
Tel: 7407 3104 Fax: 7407 7704
director Berit Vordal
Type: children's and youth theatre

POLAND (+48)

Aleksander Wegierko Theatre
Teatr im Aleksandra Wegierki
Elektryczna 12, 15-080 **Bialystok**
Tel: 85-7415 990 Fax: 85-7416 622
Internet: www.bialystok.telbank.pl/teatr
general and artistic director Andrzej Karolak
Actors: 18 *Type:* classical, modern *Venues:* Main stage 600, small stage 200 *Comments:* organises International Theatre Week, see also Festivals

Polish Theatre
Teatr Polski
1 Maja 1, 43-300 **Bielsko-Biala**
Tel: 33-8123 632/82451 Fax: 33-8123 632
Internet: free.polbox.pl/t/tpolbb
E-Mail: jlegon@polbox.com
general & artistic director t.b.a.
Actors: 17 *Type:* classical, modern
Venues: Main stage 581

Polish Theatre
Teatr Polski
Mickiewicza 2, 85-071 **Bydgoszcz**
Tel: 52-211 238/210 187 Fax: 52-211 168
Internet: www.psi.com.pl/tp/
E-Mail: tp@psi.com.pl
general and artistic director Andrzej Walden
Actors: 22 *Type:* classical, modern *Venues:* Main stage 728, small stage Teatr Kameralny (Grodzka 14) 254

Adam Mickiewicz Theatre
Teatr im. Adama Mickiewicza
pl. Teatralny 1, 43-400 **Cieszyn**
Tel: 33-8520 131
director Andrzej Lyzbicki
Comments: guest performance only

Adam Mickiewicz Theatre
Teatr im Adama Mickiewicza
Kilinskiego 15, 42-200 **Czestochowa**
Tel: 34-3245 075/3242 267 Fax: 34-3246 251
general and artistic director Marek Perepeczko
Actors: 17 *Type:* classical, modern *Venues:* Main stage 384, small stage 118

Dramatic Theatre
Teatr Dramatyczny
Pl Jagiellonczyka 1, 82-300 **Elblag**
Tel: 55-234 5616/234 4531
Fax: 55-234 5652
general director Dariusz Barton;
artistic director Antoni Baniukiewicz
Actors: 13 *Type:* classical, modern *Venues:* Main stage 600, small stage (Teatralna 1) 100

Sea Coast Theatre
Teatr Wybrzeze
Sw Ducha 2, 80-834 **Gdansk**
Tel: 58-301 7070/301 1836 Fax: 58-301 2046
general director Ewa Bonk-Wozniakiewicz; artistic director Krzytof Nazar
Actors: 37 *Type:* classical, modern, new writing *Venues:* Main stage 712, small stage – Czarna Sala (Black Room Kolodziejska 4) 80 *Comments:* includes: Teatr Kameralny, Boh. Monte Cassino 55/57, 81-767

City Theatre
Teatr Miejski
Bema 26, 81-381 **Gdynia**
Tel: 58-620 7846
Fax: 58-629 7123
general and artistic director Julia Wernio
Actors: 21 *Type:* classical, modern
Venues: capacity 300

Aleksander Fredro Theatre
Teatr im Aleksandra Fredry
Chrobrego 32, 62-200 **Gniezno**
Tel: 61-426 3993/426 2291 Fax: 61-426 2027
Internet: www.gniezno.top.pl/~teatr
general and artistic director Tomasz Szymanski
Actors: 15 *Type:* classical, modern *Venues:* capacity 457

Juliusz Osterwa Theatre
Teatr im Juliusza Osterwy
Teatralna 9, 66-400 **Gorzów Wlkp**
Tel: 95-722 5884/720 2610 Fax: 95-722 5884
general and artistic director Ryszard Major
Actors: 20 *Type:* classical, modern *Venues:* Main stage 461, studio stage 80

Culture Centre – Theatre
Centrum Kultury-Teatr
ul Marszalka Ferdinanda Focha 19, 86-300 **Grudziadz**
Tel: 56-462 4223 Fax: 56-462 3476
director Krystyna Nowak
Comments: includes: Scena Kameralna studio theatre

Cyprian Kamil Norwid Theatre
Teatr im Cypriana Kamila Norwida
Al Wojska Polskiego 38, 58-500 **Jelenia Gora**
Tel: 75-764 7695
Fax: 75-752 4730
general & artistic director Grzegorz Mrowczynski
Actors: 22 *Type:* classical, modern, new writing *Venues:* Main stage 600, studio stage 120
Comments: organises Jelemia Gôra Theatre Meetings and International Street Theatre Festival; see also Festivals

Wegajty Village Theatre
Teatr Wiejski Wegajty
Wegajty 18,
11-042 **Jonkowo (near Olsztyn)**
Tel: 89-512 9264
artistic director Waclaw Sobaszek
Actors: 8 *Type:* experimental

Wojciech Boguslawski Theatre
Teatr im Wojciecha Boguslawskiego
Pl. Boguslawskiego 1, 62-800 **Kalisz**
Tel: 62-502 3200 Fax: 62-502 3200
general and artistic director Jan Nowara
Actors: 22 *Type:* classical, modern *Venues:* capacity 409
Comments: organises Kalisz Theatre Meetings; see also Festivals

Cogitatur Theatre
Teatr Cogitatur
Gliwicka 9, 40-079 **Katowice**
Tel: 32-206 8343
Fax: 32-206 8343
Internet: www.promarcos.com.pl
E-Mail: cogitatur@promarcos.com
artistic director Witold Izdebski
Actors: 7 *Type:* experimental

Stanislaw Wyspianski Silesian Theatre
Teatr Slaski im Stanislawa Wyspianskiego
Rynek 2, 40-951 **Katowice**
Tel: 32-588 992
Fax: 32-598 976
general and artistic director Bogdan Tosza
Actors: 32 *Type:* classical, modern, new writing *Venues:* Main stage 410, small stage 80

Stefan Zeromski Theatre
Teatr im Stefana Zeromskiego
Sienkiewicza 32, 25-007 **Kielce**
Tel: 41-344 6048 Fax: 41-344 4765
general and artistic director Piotr Szczerski
Actors: 17 *Type:* classical, modern *Venues:* Main stage 351, small stage 100

Juliusz Slowacki Baltic Theatre
Teatr Baltycki im Juliusza Slowackiego
ul. Modrzejewskiej 12, 75-729 **Koszalin**
Tel: 94-342 2267 Fax: 94-342 2058
general director Zbigniew Kulagowski; artistic director Romuald Michalewski
Actors: 16 *Type:* classical, modern *Venues:* Main stage 439, small stage 90

Association Mandala
Stowarzyszenie Mandala
Os.II Putku Lotniczego 13/155, 31-868 **Kraków**
Tel: 12-647 8048 Fax: 12-647 8048
E-Mail: mandala@pp.com.pl
general and artistic director Andrzej Sadowski
Actors: 4 *Type:* experimental

Bücklein Theatre
Teatr Bückleina
Stowarzyszenie Instytut Bückleina, Lubicz 5a, 31-034 **Kraków**
Tel: 12-429 6616 Fax: 12-429 6616
Internet: www.bucklein.zine.net.pl/
E-Mail: teatr@bucklein.zine.net.pl
artistic director Adam Kwasny
Actors: 4 *Type:* experimental

CRICOTEKA
Kanonicza 5, 31-002 **Kraków**
Tel: 12-422 8332 Fax: 12-421 2840
Internet:
www.optimusnet.pl/miasta/kr/galerie/cricot.htm
general director Krzysztof Plesniarowicz
Comments: documentation and research work on Tadeusz Kantor's creativity, gallery

Helena Modrzejewska Old Theatre
Stary Teatr im Heleny Modrzejewskiej
Jagiellonska 5, 31-010 **Kraków**
Tel: 12-422 8566/421 2977
Fax: 12-421 3353
Internet: www.bci.krakow.pl/stary-teatr
E-Mail: stary.teatr@bci.pl
general director Ryszard Skrzypczak;
artistic director Jerzy Koenig
Actors: 72 *Type:* classical, modern, new writing *Venues:* 4 stages: Stary Teatr (main stage) 365, Scena Kameralna 281, Starowislna 21, Sala Heleny Modrzejewskiej 120, Piwnica przy Slawkowskiej 80, Slawkowska 15

Juliusz Slowacki Theatre
Teatr im Juliusza Slowackiego
Plac Swietego Ducha 1, 31-023 **Kraków**
Tel: 12-422 7703/422 4575 Fax: 12-422 3382
Internet: www.slowacki.krakow.pl
E-Mail: teatr@slowacki.krakow.pl
general and artistic director t.b.a.
Actors: 44 *Type:* classical, modern *Venues:* Main stage 483, small stage/Teatr Miniatura 110

Krakow Theatre – Scena STU
Krakowski Teatr – Scena STU
Krasinskiego 16, 30-513 **Kraków**
Tel: 12-422 2263 Fax: 12-422 6587
general director Aleksander Nowak; artistic directors Krzysztof Jasinski, Mikolaj Grabowski
Venues: cap 200 *Comments:* organises various theatre events

People's Theatre
Teatr Ludowy
Osiedle Teatralne 34, 31-948 **Kraków**
Tel: 12-644 3226/2766 Fax: 12-644 3226
Internet: www.gwc.com.pl/lud/
E-Mail: ludowy@teatry.art.pl
general and artistic director Jerzy Fedorowicz
Actors: 33 *Type:* classical, modern *Venues:* Main stage 399, small stage 52 *:* have a second stage in Nowa Huta

Tadeusz Boy-Zelenski Bagatelle Theatre
Teatr Bagatela im Tadeusza-Boya Zelenskiego
Karmelicka 6, 31-133 **Kraków**
Tel: 12-422 1237 Fax: 12-422 4544
Internet: www.bagatela.krakow.pl
E-Mail: info@bagatela.krakow.pl
general and artistic director Krzysztof Orzechowski
Actors: 16 *Type:* classical, modern *Venues:* capacity 440

Theatre KTO
Teatr KTO
Gzymsików 8, 30-015 **Kraków**
Tel: 12-633 8947
Fax: 12-633 8947
general and artistic director Jerzy Zon
Actors: 14 *Type:* experimental, open-air performances

Arts Centre – Dramatic Theatre
Centrum Sztuki – Teatr Dramatyczny
Rynek 39, 59-220 **Legnica**
Tel: 76-852 2948 Fax: 76-856 5238
general director Jacek Glomb
Actors: 14 *Type:* classical, modern *Venues:* Main stage 320, small stage 80

Common Theatre
Teatr Powszechny
Legionów 21, 91-069 **Lodz**
Tel: 42-632 3887 Fax: 42-636 1814
general director Ewa Pilawska; artistic directors Marcin Slawinski, Wojciech Adamczyk, Jacek Orlowski
Actors: 27 *Type:* classical, modern *Venues:* capacity 483

New Theatre
Teatr Nowy
Zachodnia 93, 90-402 **Lodz**
Tel: 42-633 8134/636 0592 Fax: 42-633 8134
general director Grazyna Wasilewska;
artistic director Mikolaj Grabowski
Actors: 45 *Type:* classical, modern *Venues:* Main stage 713, Wieckowskiego 15, small stage 207

Stefan Jaracz Theatre
Teatr im Stefana Jaracza
Jaracza 27, 90-261 **Lodz**
Tel: 42-633 9780/633 7585 Fax: 42-633 3035
Internet: www.teatr-jaracza.looz.pl/
general director Wojciech Nowicki; artistic director Waldemar Zawodzinski
Actors: 46 *Type:* classical, modern, new writing *Venues:* Main stage 514, small stage 130 *Comments:* offices Kilinskiego 45, 90-257 Lódz

Theatre 77 Centre of Artistic Imitiative
Teatr 77 – Osrodek Inicjatyw Artystyeznych
Zachodnia 56, 90-403 **Lodz**
Tel: 42-633 2641 Fax: 42-633 2641
general and artistic director Zdzislaw Hejduk
Type: experimental *Venues:* capacity 150

Centre of Theatre Practices Gardzienice
Osrodek Praktyk Teatralnych Gardzienice
Grodzka 5a, 20-112 **Lublin**
Tel: 81-532 9840/9637
Fax: 81-532 9840/9637
E-Mail: garden@dtm.lublin.pl
general and artistic director Wlodzimierz Staniewski
Actors: 10 *Type:* experimental

Juliusz Osterwa Theatre
Teatr im Juliusza Osterwy
Narutowicza 17, 20-004 **Lublin**
Tel: 81-532 2935
Fax: 81-532 0727
general and artistic director Cezary Karpinski
Actors: 30 *Type:* classical, modern *Venues:* Main stage 421, small stage 200

Teatr Grupa Chwilowa
ul Grodzka 36a/3, 20-112 **Lublin**
Tel: 81-743 6722
artistic director Krzysztof Borowiec
Type: experimental

Teatr Provisorium
c/o Centrum Kultury, ul. Peowiakòw 12, 20-007 **Lublin**
Tel: 81-532 7583/532 8700 Fax: 81-532 7583/532 8700
artistic director Janusz Oprynski
Actors: 2 *Type:* experimental

Teatr 'Scena 6'
c/o Centrum Kultury, ul. Peowiakòw 12, 20-007 **Lublin**
Tel: 81-532 7583 Fax: 81-532 8700
artistic director Henryk Kowalczyk
Actors: 8 *Type:* experimental

Visual Stage of the Catholic University of Lublin/KUL/
Scena Plastyczna Katolickiego Uniwersytetu Lubelskiego/KUL/
Al Raclawickie 14, 20-950 **Lublin**
Tel: 81-533 0392 Fax: 81-533 0433
general and artistic director Leszek Madzik
Actors: 19 *Type:* visual theatre

Stefan Jaracz Theatre
Teatr im Stefana Jaracza
1 Maja 4, 10-118 **Olsztyn**
Tel: 89-527 2963 Fax: 89-527 4446
general and artistic director Zbigniew Marek Hass
Actors: 19 *Type:* classical, modern, new writing *Venues:* Main stage 604, small stage 220

Jana Kochanowski Theatre
Teatr im Jana Kochanowskiego
Pl Teatralny 12, 45-056 **Opole**
Tel: 77-454 9082 Fax: 77-454 5942
Internet: www.opole.pol.pl/teatr-kochanowski/index.html
general and artistic director Adam Sroka
Actors: 21 *Type:* classical, modern *Venues:* Main stage 650, small stage 200 *Comments:* organises Opole theatre Confrontations-Polish Classics; see also Festivals

Jerzy Szaniawski Dramatic Theatre
Teatr Dramatyczny im Jerzego Szaniawskiego
Nowy Rynek 11, 09-400 **Plock**
Tel: 24-262 6071 Fax: 24-262 7377
general and artistic director
Zygmunt Marek Mokrowiecki
Actors: 22 *Type:* classical, modern *Venues:* Main stage 385, small stage 58

New Theatre
Teatr Nowy
Dabrowskiego 5, 60-838 **Poznan**
Tel: 61-848 4885/848 4949
Fax: 61-848 4933
Internet: www.info.poznan.pl/culture/Theatres
general and artistic director Eugeniusz Korin
Actors: 32 *Type:* classical, modern, new writing *Venues:* Main stage 327, small stage 80

Polish Theatre
Teatr Polski
27 Grudnia 8/10, 61-737 **Poznan**
Tel: 61-852 5628 Fax: 61-852 6495
Internet: www.quest.pl/teatr_polski/
E-Mail: teatr.polski@quest.pl
general and artistic director Waldemar Matuszewski
Actors: 28 *Type:* classical, modern *Venues:* Main stage 500, small stage 100

The Eight Day Theatre
Teatr Osmego Dnia
Ratajczaka 44, 61-728 **Poznan**
Tel: 61-852 7714 Fax: 61-852 2720
Internet: www.info.poznan.pl/culture/Theatres
director Tadeusz Janiszewski;
artistic director Ewa Wójciak
Actors: 4-6 *Type:* experimental *Comments:* also open air performances

Travel Office Theatre
Teatr Biuro Podrózy
c/o Osrodek Teatralny Maski, Niepodleglosci 26, 61-714 **Poznan**
Tel: 61-852 9083 Fax: 61-877 6866
Internet: www.info.poznan.pl/culture/Theatres
artistic director Pawel Szkotak
Actors: 8 *Type:* experimental, open air performances

Jan Kochanowski Common Theatre
Teatr Powszechny im Jana Kochanowskiego
Pl Jagiellonski 15, 26-600 **Radom**
Tel: 48-362 3723
Fax: 48-362 7927
Internet: www.radom.net/teatr
E-Mail: teatr@radom.net
general and artistic director Linas Marijus Zaikauskas
Actors: 12 *Type:* classical, modern *Venues:* Main stage 377, small stage 120 *Comments:* organises International Gombrowicz Festival; see also Festivals

Wanda Siemaszko Theatre
Teatr im Wandy Siemaszkowej
Sokola 7/9, 35-010 **Rzeszów**
Tel: 17-853 2748
Internet: www.rzeszow.biz.pl/teatr.htm
general director Zbigniew Rybka;
artistic director Henryk Rozen
Actors: 17 *Type:* classical, modern *Venues:* Main stage 363, small stage 100 *Comments:* organises Rzeszôw Theatre Meetings; see also Festivals

Chamber Orchestra and Impresarial Theatre
Orkiestra Kameralna i Teatr Impresaryjny
Walowa 3, 76-200 **Slupsk**
Tel: 59-428 434 Fax: 59-426 338
general and artistic director Bohdan Jarmolowicz
Venues: Main stage 364, small stage 80 *Comments:* only guest performances

Coal Field Theatre
Teatr Zaglebia
Teatralna 4, 41-200 **Sosnowiec**
Tel: 32-266 0791/494 Fax: 32-266 0791/494
general and artistic director Adam Kopciuszewski
Actors: 21 *Type:* classical, modern *Venues:* capacity 340

Foundation Wierszalin – Theatre
Fundacja Wierszalin – Teatr
Kossielna 4, 16-030 **Suprasl**
Tel: 85-745 4343 Fax: 85-745 4343
Internet: www.wierszalin.pl
E-Mail: wierszalin@wierszalin.pl
artistic director Piotr Tomaszuk
Actors: 6 *Type:* experimental, with puppets *Comments:* second address: P.O. Box, 20 00-951 Warszawa 41, Tel/Fax: 22-620 4369

Association-Kana Theatre
Stowarzyszenie-Teatr Kana
pl. Piotra i Pawla 4/5, 70-521 **Szczecin**
Tel: 91-433 0388 Fax: 91-433 0388
Internet: szpik.szczecin.art.pl/sztuka/teatr/kana.html
E-Mail: info@kana.art.pl
president Dariusz Mikula; artistic dir Zygmunt Duczynski
Actors: 5 *Type:* experimental

Contemporary Theatre
Teatr Wspolczesny
Waly Chrobrego 3, 70-500 **Szczecin**
Tel: 91-434 5414 Fax: 91-434 1777
Internet: www.dialcom.com.pl/thear-szczecin/
E-Mail: wspolczesny@dialcom.com.pl
general director Zenon Butkiewicz;
artistic director Anna Augustynowicz
Actors: 22 *Type:* classical, modern, new writing *Venues:* 455

Polish Theatre
Teatr Polski
Swarozyca 5, 71-601 **Szczecin**
Tel: 91-433 0075/0090
Internet: www.dialcom.pl/teatr-polski
E-Mail: teatr-polski@dial.com.pl
general and artistic director Adam Opatowicz
Actors: 18 *Type:* classical, modern *Venues:* Main stage 373, small stage 100 *Comments:* includes: Scena na Zamku studio

Ludwik Solski Theatre
Teatr im Ludwika Solskiego
Mickiewicza 4, 33-100 **Tarnów**
Tel: 14-210 200/221 251 Fax: 14-210 200
Internet: www.tarnow.pl/teatry/solski/
general and artistic director Stanislaw Swider
Actors: 16 *Type:* classical, modern *Venues:* Main stage 300, small stage 80

Wilam Horzyca Theatre
Teatr im Wilama Horzycy
Pl Teatralny 1, 87-100 **Torun**
Tel: 56-622 5222/21245 Fax: 56-622 3717
Internet: www.atm.com.pl/~kontakt/
E-Mail: kontakt@ikp.atm.com.pl
general director Jadwiga Oleradzka;
artistic director Andrzej Bubien
Actors: 29 *Type:* classical, modern, new writing *Venues:* capacity 436 *Comments:* Performances also in the former smoking room and foyer; organises International Theatre Festival KONTAKT last week of May, annual; see also Festivals

Jerzy Szaniawski Dramatic Theatre
Teatr Dramatyczny im Jerzego Szaniawskiego
Pl Teatralny 1, 58-300 **Walbrzych**
Tel: 74-25055/11
general and artistic director Wowo Bielicki
Actors: 8 *Type:* classical, modern *Venues:* Main stage 241, studio stage 50

Adequate Theatre
Teatr Adekwatny
c/o Artmedia, Kanonia 8/1, 00-258 **Warszawa**
Tel: 22-831 8567/635 0298
general and artistic director Henryk Boukolowski
Comments: no permanent actors company, guest performance at Teachers Culture Centre

Capital Dramatic Theatre of Warsaw
Teatr Dramatyczny Miasta Stolecznego Warszawy
Palac Kultury i Nauki, 00-901 **Warszawa**
Tel: 22-826 2684/2154 Fax: 22-826 2684
general director Anna Sapiego;
artistic director Piotr Cieslak
Actors: 38 *Type:* classical, modern, new writing *Venues:* Main stage 642, small stage 168, second small stage 122

Comedy Theatre
Teatr Komedia
Polnocne Centrum Sztuki, Slowackiego 19a, 01-592 **Warszawa**
Tel: 22-6331 584 Fax: 22-6339 610
general director Zenon Dadajewski
Venues: capacity 420 *Comments:* impresarial theatre

Contemporary Theatre
Teatr Współczesny
Mokotowska 13, 00-640 **Warszawa**
Tel: 22-825 1352 Fax: 22-825 5217
general and artistic director Maciej Englert
Actors: 38 *Type:* classical, modern *Venues:* Main stage 376, small stage 70

Ester Rachel Kaminska Jewish Theatre
Teatr Zydowski im Ester Rachel Kaminskiej
Plac Grzybowski 12/16, 00-104 **Warszawa**
Tel: 22-620 4954 Fax: 22-624 3233
general and artistic director Szymon Szurmiej
Actors: 37 *Type:* classical and modern Jewish repertoire *Venues:* capacity 381 *Comments:* includes: Warszawski Teatr Pantomimy/Warsaw Mime Theatre

Lothe Lachmann Videoteatr POZA
Palacyk Szustra, Morskie Oko 2, 02-511 **Warszawa**
Tel: 22-849 6856/849 5651
Type: experimental, video drama

Mermaid Theatre
Teatr Syrena
Litewska 3, 00-581 **Warszawa**
Tel: 22-628 5091/621 2441/628 2794 Fax: 22-629 5738
general and artistic director Barbara Borys-Damiecka
Actors: 27 *Type:* music comedy *Venues:* capacity 530

National Theatre
Teatr Narodowy
Plac Teatralny 3, 00-950 **Warszawa**
Tel: 22-692 0770/692 0200 Fax: 22-692 0741
Internet: www.korpo.pol.pl/narodowy/
general director Krzysztof Toronczyk;
artistic director Jerzy Grzegorzewski
Actors: 38 *Type:* classical, modern *Venues:* Boguslawski Hall 700 *Comments:* organises Warsaw Theatre Meetings; see also Festivals

New Theatre
Teatr Nowy
Pulawska 37, 02-508 **Warszawa**
Tel: 22-849 8491/849 3551
general and artistic director Adam Hanuszkiewicz
Actors: 17 *Type:* classical, modern, experimental
Venues: capacity 318

Ochota Theatre
Teatr Ochoty
Reja 9, 02-053 **Warszawa**
Tel: 22-825 8544/1478 Fax: 22-825 1478
Internet: www.teatrochoty.art.pl/
E-Mail: teatrochoty@art.pl
general and artistic director Tomasz Medrzak
Actors: 6 *Type:* classical, modern, new writing *Venues:* capacity 100 *Comments:* includes: Osrodek Kultury Teatralnej/Theatre Culture Centre

Old Powder House Theatre
Teatr Stara Prochownia
Bolesc 2, 00-259 **Warszawa**
Tel: 22-831 7355 ext. 21
general and artistic director Wojciech Siemion
Comments: no permanent actors' company

Polish Theatre
Teatr Polski
Karasia 2, 00-327 **Warszawa**
Tel: 22-826 4880/9271 Fax: 22-826 9278
Internet: www.teatr-polski.art.pl/
general director Jerzy Zaleski; artistic director Jaroslaw Kilian
Actors: 66 *Type:* classical, modern *Venues:* Main stage 967, small stage/Teatr Kameralny 357 *Comments:* second address: Foksal 16, 00-372 Warszawa, Tel: 22-826 4918, Internet: venus.ice.com.pl/teatry/polski

Presentation Stage
Scena Prezentacje
Zelazna 51/53, 00-841 **Warszawa**
Tel: 22-620 8288
Fax: 22-620 3490
general and artistic director Romuald Szejd
Type: contemporary *Venues:* capacity 100 *Comments:* no permanent actors' company, artists engaged for each production

Ramp Theatre
Teatr Rampa
Kolowa 20, 03-536 **Warszawa**
Tel: 22-679 3428/5051
Fax: 22-679 7100
general director Witold Olejarz; artistic director Krzysztof Miklaszewski
Actors: 11 *Type:* musical, cabaret *Venues:* Main stage 340, small stage 144

Square Theatre
Teatr Kwadrat
Czackiego 15/17, 00-043 **Warszawa**
Tel: 22-826 9637 Fax: 22-826 9637
general and artistic director Edmund Karwanski
Actors: 22 *Type:* comedy *Venues:* capacity 215

Stanislaw Ignacy Witkiewicz Art Centre and Studio Theatre
Centrum Sztuki im St I Witkiewicza i Teatr Studio
Palac Kultury i Nauki, 00-901 **Warszawa**
Tel: 22-620 4770 Fax: 22-620 0138
artistic director Zbigniew Brzoza;
general director Krzysztof Kosmala
Actors: 36 *Type:* classical, modern, new writing, experimental *Venues:* Main stage 342, small stage 200
Comments: Centrum Sztuki Studio includes: art gallery, documentation video centre, Teatr Studio

Stefan Jaracz Atheneum Theatre
Teatr Ateneum im Stefana Jaracza
Jaracza 2, 00-378 **Warszawa**
Tel: 22-625 3305 Fax: 22-625 3607
Internet: www.gdnet.pl/Ateneum
general director Zbigniew Libera; artistic director Gustaw Holoubek
Actors: 48 *Type:* classical, modern, new writing, literary cabaret *Venues:* Main stage 512, Scena 61 150, Scena Na Dole 110

Tadeusz Lomnicki Wola Theatre
Teatr na Woli im T. Lomnickiego
Kasprzaka 22, 01-211 **Warszawa**
Tel: 22-632 0005 Fax: 22-632 0370
general and artistic director Bogdan Augustyniak
Venues: capacity 400 *Comments:* no permanent actor's company, impresarial theatre

Teatr Maly
Plac Teatralny 3, 00-950 **Warszawa**
Tel: 22-828 6352 Fax: 22-826 1849
Internet: www.tab-tronik.com.pl/strong/teatr

Theatre Academy of Movement
Teatr Akademia Ruchu
c/o Centrum Sztuki Współczesnej, Zamek Ujazdowski, al. Ujazdowskie 6, 00-461 **Warszawa**
Tel: 22-628 1271/628 7683 Fax: 22-628 9550
general and artistic director Wojciech Krukowski
Actors: 5 *Type:* experimental, street performances, happenings *Comments:* organises film shows on theatrical research and other theatre events

Variety Theatre
Teatr Rozmaitosci
Marszalkowska 8, 00-590 **Warszawa**
Tel: 22-628 2864/4377
Fax: 22-628 0638
artistic director Grzegorz Jarzyna;
general director t.b.a.
Actors: 16 *Type:* modern, experimental

Zygmunt Hübner 'Common' Theatre
Teatr Powszechny im Zygmunta Hübnera
Zamoyskiego 20, 03-801 **Warszawa**
Tel: 22-818 1983/818 1575 Fax: 22-818 4304
general and artistic director Krzysztof Rudzinski
Actors: 38 *Type:* classical, modern, new writing *Venues:* Main stage 397, small stage 149 *Comments:* includes Teatr Montownia, Tel: 501-151 564

Impresarial Theatre
Teatr Impresaryjny
Wojska Polskiego 13, 87-800 **Wloclawek**
Tel: 54-411 5560
general director Jan Polak
Venues: capacity 417 *Comments:* no permanent actors' company, artists engaged for each production, also guest performances

Centre of Studies on Jerzy Grotowski's Work and Cultural and Theatre Research
Osrodek Badan Tworczosci Jerzego Grotowskiego i Poszukiwan Teatralno-Kulturowych
Rynek-Ratusz 27, 50-101 **Wroclaw**
Tel: 71-344 5320 Fax: 71-343 4267
general director Stanislaw Krotoski; artistic and research director Zbigniew Osinski
Venues: Theatre hall 100, lecture hall 70
Comments: Documentation and research work on Jerzy Grotowski's creativity, organisation of guest performances of experimental theatre groups, seminars, workshops, exhibitions, film and video shows; includes Teatr Piesn Kozla (experimental theatre)

Contemporary Theatre
Teatr Wspolczesny im Edmunda Wiercinskiego
c/o Edmund Wiereimski, Rzeznicza 12, 50-132 **Wroclaw**
Tel: 71-344 3276/343 8773 Fax: 71-344 3762
Internet: www.wroclaw.plan.pl
general and artistic director Krystyna Meissner
Actors: 28 *Type:* classical, modern *Venues:* Main stage 317, small stage 60

Gabriela Zapolska Polish Theatre
Teatr Polski im. Gabrieli Zapolskiej
Zapolskiej 3, 50-032 **Wroclaw**
Tel: 71-343 6963/6427 Fax: 71-343 6427
general and artistic director Jacek Weksler
Actors: 52 *Type:* classical, modern, new writing *Venues:* Main stage 1100, small stage/Teatr Kameralny 301, Swidnicka 28, Scena na Swiebodzkim, pl Orlat Lwowskich 20

Mime Studio Theatre
Teatr Studio Mimu
c/o Impart Art Centre, Mazowiecka 17, 50-412 **Wroclaw**
Tel: 601-756 808 Fax: 71-343 2962
E-Mail: impart@impart.art.pl
artistic director Jozef Markocki
Actors: 5 (mimes) *Type:* movement, modern pantomime
Venues: Impart State Art Centre *Comments:* touring company

Gustaw Morcinek New Theatre
Teatr Nowy im. Gustawa Morcimka
Powstancow 14, 41-800 **Zabrze**
Tel: 32-271 1508/2252
Internet: www.um.zabrze.pl/kulteatr.pl.html
E-Mail: zis@um.zabrze.pl
general and artistic director Jan Prochyra
Actors: 12 *Type:* classical, modern *Venues:* capacity 445

Stanislaw Ignacy Witkiewicz Theatre
Teatr im. Stanislawa Ignacego Witkiewicza
Chramcówki 15, 34-500 **Zakopane**
Tel: 18-206 8297 Fax: 18-206 8424
Internet: www.witkacy.zakopane.pl
E-Mail: teatr@witkacy.zakopane.pl
general and artistic director Andrzej Dziuk
Actors: 12 *Type:* classical in experimental mode, modern, new writing *Venues:* Main stage 150, small stage 80

Leon Kruczkowski Lubuski Theatre
Teatr Lubuski im. Leona Kruczkowiskiego
Niepodleglosci 3/5, 65-048 **Zielona Góra**
Tel: 68-327 2056 Fax: 68-327 1417
Internet: www.zgora.pl/teatr
general and artistic director Andrzej Buck
Actors: 20 *Type:* classical, modern *Venues:* Main stage 375, small stage 100, puppet stage 100 *Comments:* see also Puppets

PORTUGAL (+351)

Companhia de Teatro de Almada
Teatro Municipal de Almada, Rua Conde Ferreira, 2804-523 **Almada**
Tel: 1-275 2175/6567 Fax: 1-274 4856
director Joaquim Benite; administration Maria Laita; production & vice-director Vitor Gonçalves; technical direction Carlos Galvão
Actors: 12 *Perfs:* 232 *Prods:* 3 *Type:* classic drama, work on texts (contemporary or classic) *Venues:* Teatro Municipal de Almada main hall 119, studio 40 *Touring:* France, Spain, Africa, South America *Comments:* see also Festivals and Venues

Teatro Extremo
Apartado 124, 2801 **Almada Codex**
Tel: 1-273 0768 Fax: 1-273 0767
E-Mail: teatroextremo@mail.telepac.pt
artistic director Fernando Jorge Lopes, Paulo Duarte; production director Sofia Oliveira;
administration Rui Cerveira
Type: all types *Comments:* runs annual children's theatre festival; see also Festivals

Teatro Bárá
Praceta Gomes Eanes de Zurara 5, 5ffl Dta., Casal de S. Brás, 2700-427 **Amadora**
Tel: 1-493 3467/936-234 5488 (mobile) Fax: 1-493 3467
director Rui Pisco
Type: mostly children's theatre *Venues:* Sociedad de Instrução Guillerme Cossoul

Efémero – Companhia de Teatro Aveiro
Teatro Aveirense, Praça da Republica, 3810 **Aveiro**
Tel: 34-428 810 Fax: 34-22787
E-Mail: efemerco@esoterica.pt
director João Aidos
Type: all types *Venues:* Estaleiro Teatral 180

Arte Pública
Apartado 10, 7800 **Beja**
Tel: 84-327 153 Fax: 84-327 153
E-Mail: azinho.falante@ip.pt
producer José Barbieri
Comments: presents theater all over the Alentejo region; see also Promoters and Festivals

Braga Theatre Company
Teatro Circo, Avenida da Liberdade 697, 4700 **Braga**
Tel: 53-217 167/262 403 Fax: 53-612 174
E-Mail: ctb@mail.telepac.pt
director Rui Madeira
Actors: 10 *Type:* contemporary *Venues:* sala A 1200, sala B 100, sala C under construction *Touring:* Portugal *Comments:* concerts, dance, film festival, exhibitions, conferences, also support for local communities, school and universities; see also Venues; organises projects with Portuguese speaking African countries and Brasil

Teatro Em Movimento
Apartado 102, 5300 **Bragança**
Tel: 73-325 322 Fax: 73-325 322
director Leandro Vidal
Type: all types, including children's theatre *Venues:* Estúdio António Pedro 90

Teatro Público
Apartado 521, 2795 **Carnaxide (Lisboa)**
Tel: 1-325 0848/936-623 3932 Fax: 1-417 5770
director Scelso Cleto
Venues: Teatro Politema, Lisboa 500

Teatro Regional da Serra de Montemuro
Travessa Principal 1, Campo Benfeito, 3600 **Castro Daire**
Tel: 54-689 352/931-951 8393 (mobile) Fax: 54-689 160
contact Rita de Azevedo
Type: all types

Encerrado Para Obras
Rua de S. Teotonio 57 3ffl, 3000-377 **Coimbra**
Tel: 39-482 128
E-Mail: geraldo@mail.interacesso.pt
director José Geraldo
Type: street theatre, children's theatre, musicals, drama

Escola da Noite, A
Pátio da Inquisição, 3000 **Coimbra**
Tel: 39-827 261 Fax: 39-838 702
artistic director António Augusto Barros; directors António Jorge Dias, Rui Valente, Silvia Brito, Sofia Lobo
Actors: 8 *Perfs:* 120 *Prods:* 2-3 *Type:* classical to contemporary *Venues:* Pátio da Inquisição 156 *Touring:* Portugal, Africa, Europe, Brazil *Comments:* has co-productions with Portuguese speaking African groups and aims at networking with European groups; cultural interchange with Portuguese speaking groups from Africa and America is always a goal

O Teatrão – Teatro Parta a Infância de Coimbra
Rua Padro Monteiro 60, 3000 **Coimbra**
Tel: 931-461 7383
director Dr. Manuel Guerra
Type: children's theatre *Venues:* Cine-Theatro s. Teotonio *Comments:* will be moving in mid-2000, no further details available at time of going to print

Gicc Teatro das Beiras
Beco do Gameiro 5, Apartado 261, Centro Cívico, 6200 **Covilhã**
Tel: 75-336 133 Fax: 75-334 585
E-Mail: gicteatro@mail.telepac.pt
director Fernando Sena
Actors: 12 *Type:* all types *Venues:* Teatro Cinn Covilhã 1000 *Touring:* Portugal *Comments:* organises annual theatre festival; see also Festivals

Acto Theatre Company
Instituto de Arte Dramática, Apartado 158, 3860 **Estarreja**
Tel: 34-855 565 Fax: 34-855 423
E-Mail: acto@mail.telepac.pt
director José Filipe Pereira
Venues: Atelier Theatre 150

Teatro Experimental de Cascais
Av Fausto de Figueiredo, Monte Estoril, 2765 **Estoril**
Tel: 1-467 0320/486 7933
director João Vasco
Actors: 20 *Perfs:* 150 *Type:* contemporary, modern *Venues:* 120 *Touring:* Portugal, Europe, Japan, Brazil, USA *Comments:* see also Venues

Centro Dramático de Évora
Teatro Garcia de Resende, Praça Joaquim Antonio Aguiar, 7000-510 **Évora**
Tel: 66-705 533/703 112 Fax: 66-741 181
Internet: www.evova.net/cendrev
E-Mail: cendrev@mail.evora.net
directors José Russo
Actors: 13 *Perfs:* 200 *Type:* all types: contemporary, classical, modern *Venues:* Théâtre Garcia de Resende 300 *Touring:* Portugal *Comments:* produce and co-produce; offers drama courses from beginners to professionals; see also Puppets, Festivals and Venues

ACTA – A Companhia de Teatro do Algarve
Rua Antero de Quental 119, 8000 **Faro**
Tel: 89-878 908 Fax: 89-878 908
E-Mail: acta@mail.telepac.pt
director Luis Vicente

O Nariz – Teatro de Grupo
Rua Latino Coelho 12, 2400 **Leiria**
Tel: 44-832 312 Fax: 44-872 590
director Pedro Oliveira
Type: all types, including children's theatre *Venues:* Amphitheatre Orfeão de Leiria 130 *Comments:* organises annual festival, Festival Acaso (q.v.)

Chapito
Rua Costa do Castelo, 1, 1149-079 **Lisboa**
Tel: 1-887 8225/886 1410 Fax: 1-886 1463
director Teresa Ricou; artistic director t.b.a.; school director Helena Gelpi
Actors: 5 permanent (others depending on performances) *Perfs:* 200 *Prods:* 5 *Type:* theatre, circus, street performance, music, dance *Venues:* capacity 100 *Touring:* Cape Verde, France, Spain, Germany, Belgium, UK, Brazil *Comments:* circus school with various cultural activities; professional school of performing arts and jobs; Circus Arts and Techniques Course

Companhia Teatral do Chiado
Teatro Estúdio Mário Viegas, Rua António Maria Cardoso 40/50, 1200 **Lisboa**
Tel: 1-347 1279/342 2335/37
Fax: 1-342 9073/342 2340
Internet: www.cteatralchiado.pt
E-Mail: INFO@cteatralchiado.pt
director Juvenal Garcês; technical director Paulo Sabino; head of press and public relations Simao Rubim; assitant producer, production director Odete Viola; assistant production Maria José Sanros
Actors: 6 *Perfs:* 250 *Prods:* 4 *Type:* all types (comedy, drama, classic, modern) *Venues:* Teatro Estúdio Mario Viegas 128 *Touring:* Portugal, Europe South America, Africa

Comuna Experimental Theatre
Comuna Teatro de Pesquisa
Casarão Cor-De-Rosa, Praça de Espanha, 1070 **Lisboa**
Tel: 1-722 1770 Fax: 1-726 2616
director João Mota;
public relations Margarida Wellenkap
Actors: 10 *Perfs:* 300 *Prods:* 3-4 *Type:* classical, modern, comedy, mystery, musical *Venues:* Café Theatro 150, Sala de Novas Tendencias Senicas 102, Sala 1, Sala Nova *Touring:* Portugal, France

Cornucopia Theatre
Teatro da Cornucopia
Teatro do Bairro Alto, Rua Tenente Raul Cascais 1A, 1250 **Lisboa**
Tel: 1-396 9205/1515 Fax: 1-395 4508
directors Luis Miguel Cintra, Cristina Reis
Actors: 15 (permanent) + extras *Perfs:* 100 *Prods:* 4 *Type:* repertory company: experimental, classical, contemporary *Venues:* capacity 150 *Touring:* France, Belgium, Italy *Comments:* receive government funding

Grupo de Acção Teatral A Barraca
Cinearte, Largo de Santos 2, 1200 **Lisboa**
Tel: 1-396 5360/5275 Fax: 1-395 5845
directors Maria Do Céu Guerra, Halder Costa
Actors: 15 *Perfs:* 3 *Prods:* 3 *Type:* modern, classical, avant garde, comedy *Venues:* Cinearte, sala 1: 160, sala 2: 180 *Touring:* Brazil, Uruguai, Colombia, Mozambique, Mexico, Spain, France *Comments:* independent theatre group (20 years); present own and outside productions, also promotes Festival Vicentino Para a Juventude, a Portuguese festival for youth theatre on Gil Vicente's works

Grupo de Teatro Joana
Rua Luz Soriano 67 – 3ffl Sala 44, 1200 **Lisboa**
Tel: 1-342 6065
Fax: 1-342 6069
E-Mail: joanateatr@telepac.pt
directors Ana Mourato, Susete Bragança
Prods: 2-4 *Type:* emphasis on street theatre; theatre for children and young people; community theatre

New Theatre Group
Novo Grupo de Teatro
Teatro Aberto, Praça De Espanha, 1050-107 **Lisboa**
Tel: 1-797 0969/8898 Fax: 1-795 5822
directors João Lourenço, Francisco Pestana, Melim Teixeira, Irene Cruz;
public relations officer Maria Luis Capela
Actors: varies *Perfs:* 50 *Prods:* 4 *Type:* classical, avant garde, comic, experimental *Venues:* capacity 270 *Touring:* Brazil *Comments:* Government funded (Ministerio de Cultura)

O Bando, Cooperativa de Produçao Artistica Teatro de Animação
Sala Estrela, Rua St. Antonio a Estrela 60, 1350 **Lisboa**
Tel: 1-395 3289/90 Fax: 1-397 0626
director João Brites; producers Eduardo Henrique, Natercia Campos
Actors: 22 (+ guests) *Perfs:* 200-250 *Prods:* 4 *Type:* modern, street theatre, experimental, youth theatre *Venues:* capacity 101 *Touring:* Brazil, Mozambique, Italy, Switzerland, Morocco, Germany, Spain *Comments:* special focus on dramatists who write in Portuguese language; see also National Organisations

Sensurround Companhia de Teatro
Rua Dom Luis I 31, 1200 **Lisboa**
Tel: 1-397 6458 Fax: 1-347 9784
director Lucia Sigalho; producer Jorge Alonso
Type: alternative *Venues:* Warehouse size 1000msq. *Comments:* emphasis on alternative performance theatre

Teatro de Animação Os Papa-Leguas
Rua Professor Santos Lucas 36A, 1500-515 **Lisboa**
Tel: 1-714 1823 Fax: 1-714 2366
E-Mail: ospapaleguas@mail.telepac.pt
direcção Mário Jorge
Actors: 6-9 *Perfs:* 150 *Prods:* 2 *Type:* mostly children's theatre *Venues:* Sala Estudio Os Papa – Leguas 60, Cine-Teatro da Encarnação 374, *Comments:* the group runs drama courses/workshops for children and adults from Sept to June

Teatro Ibérico
Rua Xabregas 54, 1900-440 **Lisboa**
Tel: 1-868 2531 Fax: 1-868 6480
director Blanco Gil;
administrative director Fernando Viera
Perfs: 150 *Prods:* 2-3 *Venues:* 18th c Church 170 *Touring:* Portugal, Europe, USA, Mexico *Comments:* took part in International Festival in Miami, USA in 1999, with a 15th C Portuguese production

Teatro Infantil de Lisboa
Rua Bolgão-Pato 1B, 1700 **Lisboa**
Tel: 1-847 7853 Fax: 1-846 3168
direcção Kim Kachopo
Actors: 10 *Perfs:* 166 *Prods:* 2 *Type:* children's theatre *Touring:* Portugal

Teatro Meridional
Estrada da Luz 230, 8ffl esq, 1600 **Lisboa**
Tel: 1-716 7460 Fax: 1-716 7460
E-Mail: tmeridional@hotmail.com
directores Miguel Seabra, Álvaro Lavín, Julio Salvatierra
Actors: varies *Perfs:* 150 *Prods:* 2 *Type:* classical, modern, mediterranean character *Touring:* Spain, Portugal, Italy, South America, USA *Comments:* Spanish-Portuguese company; Spanish address: Paseo de la Chopera 49, 4ffl A, 28045 Madrid, Spain, Tel/Fax: +34 91-517 0951

Teatro Nacional Dona Maria II
Praça Don Pedro IV, 1100-201 **Lisboa**
Tel: 1-325 0800 Fax: 1-325 0938
director Dr Carlos Avilez; assistant director Mau Riçio; public relations Dra Cristina Martins; artistic producer Manuel Coelho; producer Antonino Folmer; publicity Rui Calapez
Actors: 30 *Prods:* 20 *Type:* classical, modern repertoire, musicals, drama, comedy, tragedy *Venues:* Sala Garrett 550, Sala Estudio Amelia Rey Colaço Robles Monteiro 80 *Touring:* Brazil, Spain, France, Germany *Comments:* present own, outside and international productions; government funded (national); see also Venues

Teatrus
Amoreira 172, 1200 **Lisboa**
Tel: 1-395 4676
contact Jorge Alonso
Type: Beckett, Kafka

Centro Cultural Malaposta
Centro Dramatico Intermunicipal Almeida Garrett/Teatro Malaposta
Rua de Angola Olival Basto, 2675 **Olival Basto**
Tel: 1-938 8407/8570 Fax: 1-938 9347
E-Mail: amascultura@mail.telepac.pt
director of CDIAG José Peixoto;
administrator Dra. Isabel Andrea
Actors: varies *Perfs:* 104 *Prods:* 4 *Type:* modern, street theatre, comedy *Venues:* Centro Cultural Malaposta stage A 206, stage B cinema 104; Stage C 70 *Comments:* also run documentary film festival in 3rd week of November

Teatro de Portalegre
Apartado 264, 7300 **Portalegre**
Tel: 45-207 894 Fax: 45-202 942
directors José Mascarenhas and Victor Pires
Actors: 8 *Perfs:* 150 p.a. *Prods:* 3-4 *Type:* children's and adult theatre, classical, comedy, contemporary, chamber theatre *Venues:* Sala Portolegre 80, Cineteatro Crissal 770 *Touring:* Portugal, Spain, France, Belgium *Comments:* see also Festivals

Pé de Vento – Colectivo de Animação Teatral
Rua da Vilarinha 1386, 4100 **Porto**
Tel: 2-610 8924
Fax: 2-617 8033
director João Luis
Type: young people's theatre *Venues:* Teatro de Vilarinha 116

Realist Art Theatre Studio
TEAR – Teatro Estudio de Arte Realista
Rua do Heroismo 86, 4300 **Porto**
Tel: 2-537 3265
directors Moura Pinheiro, Antonio Capelo and Luiz Batista
Comments: at present, school only

SAP Theatre Group/Theatre Vivo
Teatro Seiva Trupe – Teatro Vivo
Teatro Campo Aagre, Rua Das Estrelas, 4150 **Porto**
Tel: 2-606 3000 Fax: 2-606 3001
directors Julio Cardoso, Antonio Reis
Actors: 6 (varies) *Perfs:* 200 *Prods:* 3-4 *Type:* drama, comedy *Venues:* capacity 130, Teatro Campo Alegre A 320, Stage B 160 (3 spaces in total) *Touring:* Portugal, Europe *Comments:* state funded

Teatro Art' Imagem
Rua da Picaria 77A R/C, 4050-478 **Porto**
Tel: 2-208 4014 Fax: 2-208 4021
director José Leitão
Type: all types of theatre *Comments:* organises annual theatre festival Fazer a Festa (q.v.)

Teatro Bruto
Rua Mouzinho de Silvera 120 2ffl, 4050-146 **Porto**
Tel: 2-200 5587/936-883 446 (mobile) Fax: 2-200 5587
artistic directors Ana Luena, Mário Santos, Paulo Freixinho
Actors: 3 *Prods:* 3-4 *Type:* experimental, devised theatre *Venues:* varies *Comments:* carries out projects of thematically linked shows; emphasis on devised pieces

Teatro Experimental do Porto (TEP)
Rua Duque de Palmela 134, 4000 **Porto**
Tel: 2-536 9567 Fax: 2-536 9567
director Julio Gago
Venues: theatre under construction in Vila Nova de Gaia, capacity 200

Teatro Nacional S. João
Praça da Batalha, 4000-102 **Porto**
Tel: 2-208 6634/5/6/6392 Fax: 2-208 8282
Internet: www.tnsj.pt
director Ricardo Pais;
public relations officer Luisa Portal
Perfs: 150-200 *Prods:* 2-3 *Type:* all types *Venues:* capacity 500 *Touring:* Portugal, France *Comments:* co-produce, produce, present; dance theatre; see also Festivals

Cena Aberta, Companhia Teatral de Santarem
Largo Padre Francisco Nunes da Silva 3,
2000 **Santarem**
Tel: 931-985 0590/908 5154
director Alexandrina Baptista
Venues: various *Comments:* presents theatre for all ages

Setubal Animation Theatre
Teatro de Animação de Setubal
Largo da Misericordia 46, 1st floor, 2900-502 **Setúbal**
Tel: 65-229 130 Fax: 65-229 130
director Carlos César
Actors: 28 + guests *Perfs:* 100-200 *Prods:* 2-3 *Type:* comedy, classical, drama *Venues:* Forum Municipal Luisa Tody 1159 *Touring:* Portugal, France, Romania, Canada *Comments:* one of their actors won the prize of best actor (movie) of Spain & Portugal

Teatro do Mar
Rua Cândido dos Reis 51, 7520 **Sines**
Tel: 69-634 511 Fax: 69-860 0229
director Julieta Aurora E. Santos
Type: mostly young people's theatre

Companmia de Teatro de Sintra – Chão
Apartado 166, 2710 **Sintra**
Tel: 1-926 4168 Fax: 1-926 4611
director João de Melo Alvim
Venues: Theatre in Mammartins

Novo Teatro Construção – Companhia Profesional do Vale do Ave
Centro Cultural e da Juventude – Joane, Apartado 6007, 4760 **Villa Nova de Famalicão**
Tel: 52-993 423 Fax: 52-993 423
artistic director Xico Alves
Venues: theatre 204

ROMANIA (+40)

State Theatre of Arad
Bd. Revolutiei 103, 2900 **Arad**
Tel: 57-280 018 Fax: 57-280 016
artistic director Ovidiu Cornea
Actors: 15

George Bacovia Drama Theatre
Str. Iernii 7, 5500 **Bacau**
Tel: 34-118 335 (director)
artistic director Viorel Savin
Actors: 23

State Theatre of Baia Mare
Str. Crisan 4, 4800 **Baia Mare**
Tel: 62-411 124
artistic director Mircea Marin
Actors: 22

Victor Ion Popa Theatre
Str. Republicii 168, 6400 **Birlad**
Tel: 35-414 913
artistic director Marcel Anghel
Actors: 22

Mihail Eminescu Theatre
Teatrului Street No. 5, 6800 **Botosani**
Tel: 31-512 184 Fax: 31-516 925
artistic director Marius Rogojinschi
Actors: 17

Maria Filotti Theatre
B-dul Mihai Eminescu No. 2, 6100 **Braila**
Tel: 39-643 630 Fax: 39-647 336
artistic director t.b.a.
Actors: 20 *Venues:* capacity 349

Drama Theatre Brasov
Piata Teatrului No. 1, 2200 **Brasov**
Tel: 68-118 851/116 699 (deputy director)
Fax: 68-151 486
director Mircea Cornisteanu
Actors: 35

Bucharest Comedy Theatre
St. Mandinesti 2, 7008 **Bucharest**
Tel: 1-313 1791/315 9137 Fax: 1-312 0926
artistic director Dan Vasiliu;
assistant director Florin Necula
Actors: 35 *Venues:* capacity 427

I. L. Caragiale National Theatre
Blvd. Nicolae Balcescu 2, 70121 **Bucharest**
Tel: 1-613 9437/614 5692 Fax: 1-312 3169
general director Fanus Neagu;
artistic director Mihai Ispirescu
Actors: 60 *Venues:* Sala Mare 1187, Sala L. Rebreanu (Amfiteatru) 397, Sala Atelier 200, Studioul 99

Mask Theatre, The
Bd. N. Bálcescu 2, Sala Studio, **Bucharest**
Tel: 1-312 0929 Fax: 1-312 2863
artistic director Mihai Malai Mare
Actors: 7 *Type:* mime *Comments:* currently without an office; can be contacted via the Theatre Department of the Romanian Ministry of Culture (q.v.)

Romanian-French Theatre
Str. G. Enescu nr. 3 – 5, **Bucharest**
Tel: 1-615 3636 Fax: 1-612 0213
contact Ion Caramitru (UNITER)

State Jewish Theatre
Str. Iuliu Barasch 15, 74212 **Bucharest**
Tel: 1-323 3970/4035/625 4530 Fax: 1-323 2746
artistic director Harry Eliad;
assistant director J Waltman
Actors: 20 *Venues:* capacity 300

Studioul Casandra
Str. Iuliu Maniu 9, sect 3, **Bucharest**
Tel: 1-615 7259
director Valeriu Grama; rector Florin Mihailescu;
dean Gelu Colceag
Actors: varies *Type:* students theatre

Teatrul C. I. Nottara
Bd. Magheru 20, 70158 **Bucharest**
Tel: 1-659 5260/6070 Fax: 1-312 4480
artistic director Vlad Ràdescu
Actors: 50

Teatrul de Camera
Str. G. Enescu 3-5, **Bucharest**
Tel: 1-615 3636
Fax: 1-612 0213
contact Ion Caramitru (UNITER)

Teatrul Excelsior
Str. Academiei No. 28, 70109 **Bucharest**
Tel: 1-615 9736/9720 Fax: 1-210 0910
artistic director Ion Lucian
Actors: 14 *Type:* children & young people theatre
Comments: venue is currently closed for reconstruction work

Teatrul Inoportun
Str. George Enescu 3-5, **Bucharest**
Tel: 1-615 3636
director Victor Ioan Frunza

Teatrul Ion Creanga
Str. Pictor Verona 15, Sector 1, 70153 **Bucharest**
Tel: 1-650 2655/211 1169
Fax: 1-211 0061
artistic director Cornel Todea
Actors: 40 *Type:* children's theatre *Venues:* capacity 540

Teatrul Levant
Str. Eforie 8, 70623 **Bucharest**
Tel: 1-614 5141 Fax: 1-312 5333
artistic director Valeria Seciu
Actors: no fixed company *Comments:* private company

Teatrul Lucia Sturdza Bulandra
Str. Schitu Magureanu 1, Sect. 5,
70626 **Bucharest**
Tel: 1-614 9696/4592
Fax: 1-312 3897
director Victor Rebengiuc
Actors: 50

Teatrul Mic
Str. Constantin Mile 16, 70701 **Bucharest**
Tel: 1-614 1558 Fax: 1-614 7081/1558
artistic director Leopoldina Balanuta
Actors: 35 *Venues:* capacity 375

Teatrul Odeon
Calea Victoriei 16, Sect. 6, 77721 **Bucharest**
Tel: 1-617 0151/615 5053/614 5949 Fax: 1-312 2489
artistic director Alexandru Dabija
Actors: 40

Theatrum Mundi
Str. Mihai Eminescu 89, 72112 **Bucharest**
Tel: 1-210 4281 Fax: 1-210 5192
director Ion Cocora
Actors: 18 *Type:* special projects

Cluj-Napoca National Theatre
Piata Stefan cel Mare Nr. 24, 3400 **Cluj-Napoca**
Tel: 64-191 799 (director) Fax: 64-195 363 (director)
director Dorel Visan
Actors: 35 *Venues:* Scena Mare 928, Scena Studio 150

Hungarian State Theatre
Str. Emil Isac 26-28, 3400 **Cluj-Napoca**
Tel: 64-193 469 (director)
director Tompa Gabor
Actors: 24 *Venues:* capacity 857

Drama Theatre Constanta
Str. Mircea cel Batrin 97, 8700 **Constanta**
Tel: 41-611 744/619 453 Fax: 41-615 080/619 440
director Lucian Iancu; assistant Liviu Manolache
Actors: 25

Craiova National Theatre
Str. Al. I Cuza, No. 11, 1100 **Craiova**
Tel: 51-116 942/115 363/114 150
director Emil Boroghina; assistant director Cornel Baloi (Tel/Fax: 51-118 283)
Actors: 35 *Venues:* capacity 586

Galati Drama Theatre
Str. Domneasca Nr. 59, 6200 **Galati**
Tel: 36-412 745/330/460 703 Fax: 36-412 745
artistic director Adrian Lupu
Actors: 20 *Venues:* capacity 289

Teatrul Luceafarul
Centrul Civic 7, 6600 **Iasi**
Tel: 32-115 432/966/143 288 Fax: 32-115 966/212 662
artistic director Mircea Radu Iacoban
Actors: 12 *Type:* children's theatre & puppetry *Venues:* Sala Mare 450, Sala Mica 150

Vasile Alecsandri National Theatre in Iasi
Str. Agatha Barsescu No. 18, 6600 **Iasi**
Tel: 32-117 233/116 014 Fax: 32-116 778
artistic director Ioan Holban
Actors: 30 *Venues:* Sala Mare 746, Sala Studio 100

State Theatre of Oradea
Piata Republicii Nr. 6, 3700 **Oradea**
Tel: 59-130 885/720/136 592
director Petre Panait
Actors: 28 *Venues:* capacity 205

Teatrul I.D. Sârbu
Str. Mihai Viteazu 2, 2675 **Petrosani**
Tel: 54-541 154 Fax: 54-541 154
artistic director t.b.a.
Actors: 10 *Venues:* capacity 373

Teatrul Tineretului Piatra Neamt
Piata Stefan cel Mare 1, 5600 **Piatra Neamt**
Tel: 33-211 472 (director)/036 (bookings) Fax: 33-217 159
director Corneliu Dan Borcia
Actors: 18 *Type:* young people's theatre
Venues: capacity 350

Teatrul 'Alexandru Davilla'
Str. Victoriei 9, 0300 **Pitesti**
Tel: 48-624 044/636 793 (bookings)
artistic director t.b.a.
Actors: 15 *Comments:* County Culture Inspectorate, Fax: 48-634 893

Teatrul 'Toma Caragiu'
Str. Toma Caragiu 13, 2000 **Ploiesti**
Tel: 44-146 431/144 338
artistic director Lucian Sabados
Actors: 30 *Comments:* County Culture Inspectorate, Fax: 44-142 245

Teatrul 'C. A. Petculescu' Resita
str. 1 Decembrie 1918, 6, 1700 **Resita**
Tel: 55-215 080 Fax: 55-213 667
artistic director Ovidiu Cristea
Venues: capacity 361

Teatrul 'Anton Pann'
B-dul Tudor Vladimirescu Nr. 39, 1000 **Rimnicu-Vâlcea**
Tel: 50-717 320 Fax: 50-711 908
artistic director Gheorghe Marinescu

North Theatre, Satu Mare
St. Horea 3, 3900 **Satu Mare**
Tel: 61-715 876/711 337 Fax: 61-715 683/717 069
artistic director Cristian Ioan
Actors: 15 *Comments:* County Culture Inspectorate, Fax: 61-717 568

State Theatre Andrei Muresan of Sf. Gheorghe (Romanian)
Piata Libertatii Nr. 1, 4000 **Sf. Gheorghe (jud Covasna)**
Tel: 67-313 886 (Hungarian section)/312 104/315 324 (Romanian section)
director Radu Macrinici
Venues: capacity 400

State Theatre of Sibiu
B-dul Spitalelor Nr. 2, 2400 **Sibiu**
Fax: 69-210 092
director Mihai Bica
Actors: 18 *Venues:* capacity 210

German Theatre of Timisoara
Str. Marasesti 2, 1900 **Timisoara**
Tel: 56-134 638 Fax: 56-134 638
director Ildiko Zamfirescu

Hungarian Theatre "Csiky Gergely" of Timisoara
Str. Marasesti 2, 1900 **Timisoara**
Tel: 56-134 814/643 Fax: 56-194 029
director Andras Istvan Demeter

Teatrul National Timisoara
Str. Marasesti 2, 1900 **Timisoara**
Tel: 56-134 643/201 288 Fax: 56-134 643/199 908
artistic director Stefan Lordanescu
Actors: 30 *Venues:* capacity 711

Teatrul National Tirgu-Mures
Piata Teatrului Nr. 1, 4300 **Tirgu-Mures**
Tel: 65-114 835/240 Fax: 65-114 835
artistic director t.b.a.; assistant director t.b.a.
Actors: 35 *Venues:* Sala Mare 596, Sala Mica 100

Teatrul de Stat Turda
Str. Republicii Nr. 52, 3350 **Turda**
Tel: 64-311 952 Fax: 64-316 453
artistic director Mircea Ioan Casimcea

RUSSIA (+7)

Kazan Russian State Drama Theatre v. Kachalov
ul. Baumana 48, 420503 **Kazan (Tatarstan)**
Tel: 8432-327 751 Fax: 8432-321 869
director Grigori Pervine

Tatarian State Academic Drama Theatre Galiaskar Kamal
ul. Taterstan 1, 420021 **Kazan (Tatarstan)**
Tel: 8432-329 678

Chelovek Studio
Teatr-studiia Chelovek
Skaternyi per. 23a, 121069 **Moscow**
Tel: 095-291 2668/1656 Fax: 095-291 2668/1656
artistic director Lyudmila Roshkovan

Evgueni Vakhtangov Theatre
Arbat Ul. 26, 121002 **Moscow**
Tel: 095-241 0744 Fax: 095-241 2625
director Isidor Tartakovsky;
artistic director Mikhyail Ulyanov

Film Actor's Theatre Studio
Povarskaya Ul. 33, 121069 **Moscow**
Tel: 095-291 1461/290 5524 Fax: 095-290 6185
director Kozakow Uyri

Gogol Moscow Drama Theatre
Moskovskii dramaticheskii teatr im. Gogolia
Ul. Kozakova 8-A, 103064 **Moscow**
Tel: 095-261 3231 Fax: 095-261 3231
director Anastas Shlaustas

Kamernaya Stsena Theatre
Zemlyanoi Val Ul. 64, 109004 **Moscow**
Tel: 095-915 7521 Fax: 095-915 7136
director Tamara Baskina

Mayakovsky Theatre
UL. B. Nikitskaya 19, 103009 **Moscow**
Tel: 095-290 2725 Fax: 095-202 8006
administrative director Mikhail Zaitsev;
artistic director Andrei Goncharov
Comments: Branch: Khmeleva st. 21 2083196

Moscow Arts Theatre A P Chekhov (MKhAT)
Kamergerskij pere 3, 103009 **Moscow**
Tel: 095-229 3312/3874 (director)
Fax: 095-975 2196
director Vyacheslav Efimov; artistic director Oleg Yefremov (229 3312)
Comments: Moscow Arts Theatre was split by government into 2 companies with same name, but opposed to each other in terms of artistic principles and programmes

Moscow Arts Theatre Gorky
Moskovskii khudozhestvennyi teatr Soiuza SSR (MKhAT) im. Gorkogo
Tverskoy Boul. 22, 103009 **Moscow**
Tel: 095-203 7399/7466
Fax: 095-203 4449
artistic director Tatiana Doronina

Moscow Dramatic Theatre on the Malaya Bronnaya
Moskovskii dramaticheskii teatr na Maloi Bronnoi
Ul. Malaya Bronnaya 4, 103104 **Moscow**
Tel: 095-290 6731 Fax: 095-290 5767
director Ilya Kogan

Moscow Dramatic Theatre on the Taganka
Zemlyanoy Val. 76/21, 109004 **Moscow**
Tel: 095-915 1037 Fax: 095-274 0033
director Yuri Lyubimov

Moscow New Theatre Studio
Moskovskii novyi dramaticheskii teatr-studiia
Ul. Prokhodchikov 2, 129347 **Moscow**
Tel: 095-182 0347
Fax: 095-183 0398
director Alexandr Stulnev;
artistic director Boris Lwov-Anokhin

Moscow Theatre Lenkom
Moskovskii teatr Lenkom
Dmitrovka Mal. Ul. 6, 103006 **Moscow**
Tel: 095-299 7831 Fax: 095-234 9964
director Mark Zacharov

Mossoviet Theatre
Gosudarstvennyi akademicheskii teatr im. Mossoveta
Bol. Sadovaya Ul. 16, 103050 **Moscow**
Tel: 095-299 4437 Fax: 095-299 6421
director Lev Losev

Na Doskakh Theatre
Vspolnyi Per. 21 Kor.2, 103001 **Moscow**
Tel: 095-291 5365/200 1693 Fax: 095-200 1693
artistic director Serguei Kurginian

NA Yugo-Zapade Moscow Theatre
Vernadskogo pr.125, 117571 **Moscow**
Tel: 095-434 6000 Fax: 095-434 6000
artistic director Valery Belyakovich; director Boris Khvostov

Natalya Satz Children's Musical Theatre
Vernadsky prosp. 5, 117296 **Moscow**
Tel: 095-930 5243/5134 Fax: 095-930 5243
managing director Viktor Provorov;
artisitc director Viktor Ryabov
Actors: 178 + 80 orchestra

National Academic Maly Theatre of the Russian Federation
Teatralnaya pl. 1/6, 103009 **Moscow**
Tel: 095-925 9868 Fax: 095-921 0350
artistic director Yuri Solomine; general manager Viktor Korshunov

Oleg Tabakov Theatre Studio
Teatr-studiia pod rukovodstvom O. Tabakova
Chaplygina Ul. 1-A, 103062 **Moscow**
Tel: 095-923 6125/921 2480 Fax: 095-923 6125/921 2480

P. Fomenko Workshop Theatre
Arbat ul. 35, 121002 **Moscow**
Tel: 095-241 3941 Fax: 095-249 0170
Internet: www.theatre.ru/fomenko
E-Mail: fomenko@theatre.ru
director Piotr Fomenko
Actors: varies *Type:* adaptations of classical plays, new writing, Russian playwrights *Comments:* from Nov 98 own theatre venue at: Kutuzovskiy prospekt 30/32; tel: +7 095-249 1703

Pushkin DramaTheatre
Moskovskii dramaticheskii teatr im. A.S. Pushkina
Tverskoi b-r. 23, 103104 **Moscow**
Tel: 095-203 8587/203 4214 Fax: 095-203 2336

Romen Moscow Gypsy Theatre
Moskovskii tsyganskii teatr "Romen"
Leningradsky pr. 32/2, 125040 **Moscow**
Tel: 095-212 5092/0333 Fax: 095-214 8070

Saira Blansh Theater
Iakornaia 357, 115407 **Moscow**
Tel: 095-116 9121
E-Mail: saira@andrianov.msk.ru
director Oleg Soulimenko
Type: performance and dance, theatrical and dance experiments, free improvisation on stage *Comments:* see also Dance

Satire Theatre
Moskovskii teatr satiry
Pl. Triumfalnaya 2, 103050 **Moscow**
Tel: 095-299 4943/9813
Fax: 095-299 9483
artistic director Valentin Plutchek

Satiricon Theatre
Teatr Satirikon
Sheremetevskaya 8, 129594 **Moscow**
Tel: 095-289 7836/2330/1019 Fax: 095-284 4937
director Felix Margolin;
artistic director Konstantin Raikin

School of Dramatic Art
Teatr Shkola Dramatichesko Iskusstva
Povarskaya Ul. 20, 121069 **Moscow**
Tel: 095-291 4339/8568 Fax: 095-2033 3174
director Boris Likhtenfeld

SFERA Theatre
Moskovskii teatr miniatiur
Karetny riad Ul. 3, 103006 **Moscow**
Tel: 095-299 0677/0292 Fax: 095-299 9627
director Irina Tarasova

Sholom Jewish Drama Theater
Varshavskoe Shosse 71, 113556 **Moscow**
Tel: 095-113 2753 Fax: 095-113 2753
director Inna Suvorova

Sovremennik Moscow Theatre
Moskovskii teatr Sovremennik
Chistoprudnyi b-r. 19A, 101000 **Moscow**
Tel: 095-921 1790/2543 Fax: 095-921 6629
administrative director Leonid Erman;
artistic director Galina Voltchek

Spartac Square Moscow Theatre Studio
Moscovskii teatr-studia 'Na Spartakovskoi ploshadi'
Spartakovskaya Square 9/1-a, 107082 **Moscow**
Tel: 095-267 7187

Stanislavsky Moscow Drama Theatre
Moskovskii dramaticheskii teatr im. Stanislavskogo
Tverskaya Ul. 23, 103050 **Moscow**
Tel: 095-299 7621/3764
director Felix Demichev

State Academic Bolshoi Theatre of Russia
Teatralnaya Pl. 1, 103009 **Moscow**
Tel: 095-292 2600/7050 Fax: 095-292 9032
artistic director & general manager Vladimir Vassiliev;
executive manager Vladimir Kokonin;
ballet director Yuri Bogatyrev

State Academic Youth Theatre (RAMT)
Teatralnaya Pl. 2, 103009 **Moscow**
Tel: 095-292 0150/0154 Fax: 095-292 0150/0154
artistic director Alexei Borodin;
managing director Eduard Boyakov
Actors: 79 *Venues:* cap. 724

Theater Gitis
Gnezdnikovsky Bol. Per. 10, 103009 **Moscow**
Tel: 095-229 8661

Theatre of the Russian Army
Suvorovskaya Pl. 2, 129110 **Moscow**
Tel: 095-281 5120/2110/5719
director Victor Akimov

Ulysses Theatre Company
Dmitri Semakin, 8-47 Sportivny proezd, 109386 **Moscow**
Tel: 7-095 350 7293 Fax: 7-095 350 7293
E-Mail: ulysses@diona.msk.ru
Actors: 4

Youth Theatre (Moscow Theatre of Young Spectators)
Mamonovsky Per. 10, 103001 **Moscow**
Tel: 095-299 5360
director Mark Litvak;
artistic director Henrietta Yanovskaya
Type: new writing

Muchurinsk Dramatic Theatre
Gogolevskaya Ul. 55, 393740 **Muchurinsk**
Tel: 07545-53434

Andrei Mironov Theatre
Bolshoi Pr-t 75/35, 191011 **St Petersburg**
Tel: 812-346 1676 Fax: 812-346 1676
artistic director Rudolf Forshunov

Farces
St Petersburg
Tel: 7-812 275 5666 Fax: 7-812 271 2983
E-Mail: licedeie@mail.wplus.net
artistic director Victor Kramer; producer Valery Mineev
Actors: 6 + guests *Touring:* Europe *Comments:* company does not have a permanent address and is renting space meanwhile at the Baltic House theatre ; second E-mail: alex@kris.spb.su; Fringe First Award 1999 at Edinburgh

Komissarzhevskaya St Petersburg Theatre
Petersburgskii teatr im. Komissarzhevskoi
Ul. Utalianskaya 19, 191011 **St Petersburg**
Tel: 812-315 5355
Fax: 812-311 0853
artistic director Viktor Novikov (tel: 812-311 3388)

Maly Dramatic Theatre
Malyi dramaticheskii teatr
18 Rubinshteina str., 191002 **St Petersburg**
Tel: 812-113 2015 Fax: 812-113 3366
director Lev Dodin
Actors: 70 *Touring:* international

Regional Dramatic and Comedy Theatre
Oblastnoi teatr dramy i komedii
Liteinyi pr-t. 51, 191104 **St Petersburg**
Tel: 812-273 4458
director Galina Pavlovich

St Petersburg Academic Bolshoi Dramatic Theatre
Petersburgskii akademicheskii bolshoi dramaticheskii teatr
Nab.r. Fontanki 65, 191029 **St Petersburg**
Tel: 812-310 2005/310 7455 Fax: 812-110 4710
artistic director Kirill Lavrov

St Petersburg Open Theatre
Petersburgskii otkritij teatr
12 Vladimirsky pr., 191025 **St Petersburg**
Tel: 812-215 0896 Fax: 812-325 0325
artistic director Vladislav Pazi (tel: 812-164 4780); director Valery Gradkovsky (tel: 812-164 3965)

St Petersburg State Comedy Theatre
Petersburgskii gosudarstvennyi teatr komedii
56 Nevsky pr., 191011 **St Petersburg**
Tel: 812-215 6633/2565/314 2501 Fax: 812-314 2547/2501
artistic director Tatiana Kozakova;
conductor Anatoly Kovalev

St Petersburg State Theatre Baltiisky House
Alexandrovsky Park 4, 197198 **St Petersburg**
Tel: 812-232 0961/233 0932 Fax: 812-232 0961/233 9936
director Sergei Shub; artistic director Vladimir Tekke
Comments: organise Baltic International Festival

St Petersburg State Theatre of Musical Comedy
Petersburgskii teatr muzykalnoi komedii
13 Italianskaya str., 191011 **St Petersburg**
Tel: 812-314 6483 Fax: 812-311 7651
artistic director Alexander Belinsky (tel: 812-110 5982); director Vladimir Pashkov (tel: 812-210 4689)

St Petersburg Youth Theatre
Petersburgskii molodezhnyi teatr
Nab.r. Fontanki 114, 198005 **St Petersburg**
Tel: 812-251 6441/8166 Fax: 812-251 8015
Internet: www.theatre.dux.ru/fontanka
pr Roman Pavlouchev; artistic director Semen Spivak
Perfs: 320 *Venues:* capacity 222

St-Petersburg State Alexandrinsky Drama Theatre
Ostrovsky sq., 191011 **St Petersburg**
Tel: 812-315 4464 Fax: 812-311 5878
mamaging director Georgy Sashenko

Bashkirian Republican Russian Drama Theatre
pl. Lenina 1, 450075 **Ufa (Bashkortostan)**
Tel: 3472-343 235

National Theatre of South Ossetia
P.O. Box 1041, 36200 **Vladikavkaz**
Tel: 7-8672 42398/4235/42137 (evenings)
Fax: 7-8672 4235
director, artistic director Tamerlan Dzutsov; foreign affairs secretary Alan Sanakoev
Actors: 30 *Type:* all types of drama, Ossete also Western-European classics *Venues:* capacity 350
Comments: founded 1931, since 1977 very active in international links, also has a national foundation od culture support: Fortune-Arts

SAN MARINO (+378)

Piccolo Teatro Arnaldo Martelli, Il
c/o Eugenia Sammarini, Via Valserra, 4, **Murata**
Tel: 0549-997 125
presidente Enea Zani;
ufficio stampa & pr Eugenia Sammarini
Actors: 30 *Perfs:* 8 *Prods:* 3 *Venues:* various *Comments:* amateur company but receives state funds

SLOVAKIA (+421)

Many telephone and fax numbers in Slovakia are in the process of being changed. We have included all new numbers known at the time of going to print.

Theatre From the Passage
Divadlo z Pasáze
Cikkerova 5, 97401 **Banská Bystrica**
Tel: 088-412 4782/0905-266 180 (mobile)
Fax: 088-412 4782
artistic director Viera Dubacová

GUnaGU Theatre
Zadunajská 9, 851 01 **Bratislava**
Tel: 7-6224 6542 Fax: 7-6224 6542
Internet: kultura.gratex.sk/gunagu
E-Mail: anton.pisar@swh.sk
director Viliam Klimácek

New Stage Bratislava
Nová Scéna Bratislava
Zivnostenská 1, 812 14 **Bratislava**
Tel: 7-5292 3230 Fax: 7-5296 1431
Internet: kultura.gratex.sk/nscena
E-Mail: riaditel-ns@ba.entry.sk
general director Marek Tapák
(www.kura.gratex.sk/nscena); drama dir Bronislav Krizan
Actors: 30 *Perfs:* 250 *Prods:* 5 (drama) *Venues:* capacity 600, new stage Theatre Bratislava – Nová Scéna Bratislava *Comments:* see also Opera

Radosina Naive Theatre
Radosinské naivné divadlo
Bratislava – Agentura RND Bratislava, Skultétyho 5, 832 21 **Bratislava**
Tel: 7-5557 3169/ 0905-491 666 (mobile) Fax: 7-5557 4291
Internet: kultura.gratex.sk/rnd
artistic director Stanislav Stepka
Actors: 15 *Perfs:* 200 *Prods:* 3 *Venues:* home capacity 150

Slovak National Theatre
Slovenské národné divadlo
Gorkého 4, 815 86 **Bratislava**
Tel: 7-5413 1086/5443 3083/5441 2848 Fax: 7-5413 1020
general dir Dusan Jamrich; drama dir Juraj Slezácek
Actors: 53 *Perfs:* 470 *Prods:* 8-9 *Venues:* main stage 471, small stage 190 *Comments:* see also Opera and Dance

Stoka
Pribinova 1, PO Box 235, 810 00 **Bratislava**
Tel: 7-5292 4470/5292 4463 Fax: 7-5292 4470/5292 4463
Internet: www.stoka.sk
E-Mail: stoka@stoka.sk
director Blahoslav Uhlár
Actors: 10 *Perfs:* 120 *Prods:* 4 *Venues:* home capacity 100

Studio L + S
Námestie 1 mája 5, 811 06 **Bratislava**
Tel: 7-5292 1584/5296 3691 Fax: 7-5292 5082
Internet: www.snet.sk/studios
director Milan Lasica
Prods: 3 *Venues:* home capacity 150 to 300 *Comments:* contract guest performers

Theatre A. Ha
Divadlo a. ha
Skolská 14, 811 07 **Bratislava**
Tel: 0903-756 973 (mobile) Fax: 7-5443 4168
artistic director Viki Janousková

Theatre Arena
Divadlo Aréna
Viedenská cesta 10, 851 01 **Bratislava**
Tel: 7-6224 6875/6224 6864
Fax: 7-6224 6875/6224 6864
Internet: www.sknet.sk/arena
E-Mail: arena@sknet.sk
director Milan Sládek
Actors: 10 *Prods:* 1-2

Theatre Astorka Korzo '90
Divadlo Astorka Korzo '90
Suché myto 17, 814 99 **Bratislava**
Tel: 7-5443 2350/ 5443 1657 Fax: 7-5443 1657/ 5443 2983
Internet: kultura.gratex.sk/astorka
director Vladimír Cerny;
drama director Marián Zednikovic
Actors: 20 *Perfs:* 180 *Prods:* 4 *Venues:* capacity 146

Theatre LUDUS
Divadlo Ludus
Tupolevova 7/A, 851 01 **Bratislava**
Tel: 7-6383 3642 Fax: 7-6383 3389
director Pavol Paska
Type: children's and youth theatre

Theatre WEST
Divadlo WEST
Námestie SNP 14, 811 06 **Bratislava**
Tel: 7-5296 5831 Fax: 7-529 5832
director Lubo Roman

Jókai Theatre
Jókaiho divadlo
Petöfiho 1, 945 01 **Komárno**
Tel: 819-701 890/701 923 Fax: 819-701 923
director Jozsef Kiss
Actors: 20 *Perfs:* 235 *Prods:* 7 *Venues:* capacity 340
Comments: perform in Hungarian

State Theatre Kosice
Státne divadlo Kosice
Hlavná 58, 04272 **Kosice**
Tel: 095-622 7361 Fax: 095-622 8235

Thalia Theatre
Divadlo Thália
Timonova 3, 040 01 **Kosice**
Tel: 95-622 5866/1281 Fax: 95-622 5867
Internet: www.cassovia.sk/thalia
E-Mail: thalia@dodo.sk
director Ing. Peter Kolér; artistic director Tibor Fabo
Actors: 22 *Perfs:* 150 *Prods:* 3-4 *Venues:* capacity 300
Comments: perform in Hungarian

The Old City Theatre
Staromestské divadlo
Stará Bastová 1, 04101 **Kosice**
Tel: 95-622 1107/0903-605 315 (mobile)
Fax: 95-622 1107
artistic director Peter Rasev

Theatre Romathan
Divadlo Romathan
Stefánikova 4, 040 01 **Kosice**
Tel: 95-622 4980/0619 Fax: 95-622 4980
director Karol Adam

Slovak National Uprising Theatre
Divadlo Slovenského národného povstania
Divadelna' 1, 036 80 **Martin**
Tel: 842-224 098/0905-305632 (mobile phone)
Fax: 842-220 172
director Dr. Peter Kovác
Actors: 15 *Perfs:* 200 *Prods:* 5-6
Venues: main stage 385, studio 170

Andrej Bagar Theatre
Divadlo Andreja Bagara
Svätoplukovo nám 4, 949 01 **Nitra**
Tel: 87-772 1577/81
Fax: 87-524 871
director Svetozár Sprusansky
Actors: 25 *Perfs:* 230 *Prods:* 6
Venues: main stage 590, studio 150

Alexander Duchnovic Theatre
Divadlo Alexandra Duchnovica
Jarkova 77, 088 01 **Presov**
Tel: 91-723 261/732 700
Fax: 91-734 422
artistic director Jozef Tkác
Actors: 15 *Perfs:* 150 *Prods:* 3-4 *Venues:* capacity 160
Comments: performs in the Ruthenian language

Jonás Záborsky Theatre Presov
Divadlo Jonása Záborského v Presove
nám. Legionárov 6, 081 61 **Presov**
Tel: 91-723 888 Fax: 91-734 915
artistic director Milan Antol
Actors: 15 *Perfs:* 200 *Prods:* 3

The City Theatre Roznava
Mestské divadlo Roznava
Safárikova 29, 04801 **Roznava**
Tel: 0905-440 335 (mobile)
Internet: www.roznava.sk/kultura/actores
E-Mail: actores@award.sk
artistic director Tatiana Masníková

Spis Theatre
Spisské divadlo
Radnicne nám 4, 052 01 **Spisská Nová Ves**
Tel: 965-442 5801
Fax: 965-442 2986
director Jozef Lapsansky
Actors: 15 *Perfs:* 100 *Prods:* 3 *Type:* children's theatre
Venues: home capacity 320

Trnava Theatre
Trnavské divadlo
Trojicné nám 2, 917 01 **Trnava**
Tel: 805-5511 1353
Fax: 805-5511 1355
director Emil Nedielka; artistic director Ján Zavarsky
Actors: 30 *Perfs:* 200 *Prods:* 6 *Venues:* capacity 310

City Theatre of Zilina – Scene Maják Theatre
Mestské divadlo Zilina – Scéna Divadlo Maják
Horny val 3, 010 01 **Zilina**
Tel: 89-623 703 Fax: 89-623 802
director Elena Dikosová
Type: children's theatre

Jozef Gregor Tajovsky Theatre
Divadlo Jozefa Gregora Tajovského
Divadelná 3, 960 77 **Zvolen**
Tel: 855-532 0192
Fax: 855-532 5187
Internet: www.zv.psg.sk/prezenta/divadlo
E-Mail: divadlo@zv.psg.sk
general director Marcela Krsková;
artistic director Ivana Janáková
Actors: 20 *Perfs:* 150 *Prods:* 5 *Venues:* capacity 340

SLOVENIA (+386)

Slovene National Theatre Celje
Slovensko Ljudsko Gledalisce Celje
Gledaliski trg 5, 3000 **Celje**
Tel: 63-442 910
Fax: 63-441 850
manager Borut Alujevic; artistic director Matija Logar; P.R./marketing Jerneja Volfand; dramaturg Kristof Dovjak; director Franci Krizaj
Actors: 18 *Perfs:* 200 *Prods:* 6 *Type:* classic to modern drama (European and American) – including young peoples theatre, music, opera, dance; special emphasis on Slovene drama
Venues: large stage 356, small stage 70

Preseren's Theatre Kranj
Presernovo Gledalisce Kranj
Glavni trg 6, 4000 **Kranj**
Tel: 64-380 490 (management)/222 681 (box office)
Fax: 64-380 4933
Internet: www.pgk-gledalisce.si
E-Mail: presern-gled@s5.net
artistic director Marinka Postrak; performance organiser Jakob Kurat; managing director mag. Tomaz Kukovica
Actors: 8 + freelance *Perfs:* 120 (50 on tour) *Prods:* 5 *Type:* modern, classic, Slovene

Caffe Theater
Miklosiceva 2, 1000 **Ljubljana**
Tel: 61-125 6726/125 6726 Fax: 61-125 6726
E-Mail: cafe.teater@siol.net
artistic director Vita Mavric Strazisar; PR Branka Kraner
Perfs: 85 *Prods:* 1-2 *Type:* theatre, musical theatre, cabaret, poetry recitals *Venues:* coffee house 100 *Touring:* Slovenia

Cosmocinetic Cabinet Noordung
Kozmokineticni kabinet Noordung
Zupanciceva 10, 1000 **Ljubljana**
Tel: 61-214 958
Internet: www.absoizdelek.org
producer Breda Kralj; constructor of the united art Dragan Zivadinov; dramaturg Jordan Randzelovic

Cultural and Art Club France Preseren
KUD France Preseren
Karunova 14, Trnovo, 1000 **Ljubljana**
Tel: 61-332 288/299 Fax: 61-331 128
E-Mail: kud@kud-fp.si
president Jani Kovacic; secretary Zelko Pelicon; programme coordinator Tone Skrjanec
Type: theatre, puppet, contemporary dance, Cabaret, multimedia, poetry recitals, concerts, lectures *Venues:* hall capacity up to 200, gallery 150, patio 2500, club room 25 *Comments:* non-profit organisation promoting young, independent culture, own and coproductions; see also Promoters and Venues; organises festival of poetry and summer (open air)

Glej Theatre
Gledalisce Glej
Gregorciceva 3, 1000 **Ljubljana**
Tel: 61-216 679 Fax: 61-126 6162
general manager Lidija Jurjevec; artistic director Maks Sorsak; stage manager Andrej Meljo; secretary Maja Pavlin
Prods: 8 *Venues:* Venue and project centre, independent, capacity 75 *Touring:* USA, Europe

Mladinsko Theatre
Slovensko Mladinsko Gledalisce
Vilharjeva 11, 1000 **Ljubljana**
Tel: 61-310 610/301 286/296/133 5025 Fax: 61-133 5025
Internet: www.mladinsko-gl.si
manager Petar Jovic; artistic director Tomaz Toporisic; PR Dusan Pernat, Tomaz Toporisic; marketing Orbal Vito, Dusan Pernat; dramaturg Matjaz Berger
Actors: 22 *Perfs:* 180-220 *Prods:* 4 new of 12 *Type:* modern, experimental, performance theatre *Venues:* stage A 280, stage B 200 *Touring:* Spain, Venezuela, Colombia, Belgium, Italy *Comments:* produce, co-produce

Municipal Theatre of Ljubljana
Mestno Gledalisce
Copova 14, 1000 **Ljubljana**
Tel: 61-125 8222/214 188 Fax: 61-217 044
Internet: mgl.si21.com
artistic and managing director Boris Kobal; dramaturgs Alja Predan, Ira Ratej; director Zvone Sedlbauer; public relations Petra Zerovnik
Actors: 34 *Perfs:* 375 *Prods:* 6 (main stage) + 2 (small stage) *Type:* modern playwrights and comedies *Venues:* main stage 300, small stage 70 *Touring:* Austria, Italy, Czech Republic, Bulgaria *Comments:* regular exhibitions take place in the theatre's foyer, occasionally the house also hosts music, publishing and other cultural events

Museum – Associated for Atr Production and Publishing
Museum – Zavod za umetnisko produkcijo, posredovanje in zaloznistvo
Gornji trg 44, 1000 **Ljubljana**
Tel: 61-126 5681 Fax: 61-126 5681
E-Mail: museum@mail.ljudmila.org
artistic & managing director Barbara Novakovic Kolenc; PR & projects manager Dina Desman Vizintin
Prods: 3 *Type:* experimental, modern, visual theatre *Touring:* Scotland, Italy, Austria, Australia *Comments:* non-profit organisation, publishing & other cultural events; second address: office Novi trg 6, 1000 Ljubljana

Slovene National Theatre Drama Ljubljana
Slovensko Narodno Gledalisce Drama Ljubljana
Erjavceva 1, PO Box 27, 1000 **Ljubljana**
Tel: 61-221 462/492 Fax: 61-223 885
Internet: www.sngdrama-lj-si
E-Mail: sngdrama@sngdrama-lj-si
artistic & managing director Janez Pipan; dramaturgs Darja Dominkus, Diana Koloini, Mojca Kranjc; programme organizer Ljubinka Belehar; PR Valerija Cokan
Actors: 43 *Perfs:* 190 (main stage) + 200 (small stage) *Prods:* main stage: 14 (6 new), small stage: 13 (5 new) *Type:* classic, contemporary *Venues:* stage A 467, stage B 100 *Touring:* Slovenia and abroad *Comments:* member of ETC (European Theatre Convention)

Slovenian Chamber Theatre
Slovensko komorno gledalisce
Vodnikova 65,
1000 **Ljubljana**
Tel: 61-159 3395/161 1886
artistic director Evald Flisar

Spiritual Theatre
Spiritualno gledalisce
Gosposvetska 13, 1000 **Ljubljana**
Tel: 61-121 9012
E-Mail: aleksander.jurc@guest.arnes.si
artistic directors Aleksander Jurc, Mojca Türk
Type: contemporary author's theatre, performance

Drama of the Slovene National Theatre Maribor
Slovensko Narodno Gledalisce Maribor Drama
Slovenska Ulica 27, 2000 **Maribor**
Tel: 62-22840
Fax: 62-221 207/223 215
Internet: www.sng-mb.si
E-Mail: sng.maribor@sng-mb.si
general manager Blaz Rafolt; artistic director of drama Branko Kraljevic; dramaturg Andjelka Trkulja
Venues: Old Hall 380, New Big Hall 864, Small Scene 150, Kazinska Hall 200 *Touring:* Venezuela, Colombia, Austria, Russia, England, Spain : marleting e.mail: sng.maribor@sng-mb-si

Primorsko Drama Theatre
Primorsko Dramsko Gledalisce
Trg. E. Kardelja 5, 5000 **Nova Gorica**
Tel: 65-202 717 Fax: 65-21270
Internet: pdg-ng.si
E-Mail: pdg@siol.net
managing director Sergij Pelhan; artistic director Primoz Bebler; dramaturgs Martina Mrhar, tea Rogelj; PR Mirjam Drnovscek; programme organizer Branka Strukelj; language assistant Srecko Fiser
Actors: 23 *Prods:* 6 *Type:* modern focus, Slovene drama and Slovene premieres of foreign plays *Venues:* capacity 376 *Comments:* second E.mail: info@pdg.si

Ptuj Theatre
Gledalisce Ptuj
Slovenski Trg 13, 2250 **Ptuj**
Tel: 62-785 900/785 901/705 902
Fax: 62-785 900
Internet: www2.arnes.si/~mbgptuj
E-Mail: gledalisce.ptuj@guest.arnes.si
artistic & managing director Samo Strelec
Prods: 3-4 *Venues:* capacity 220

SPAIN (+34)

Teatro de Malta
c/Ricardo Castro 2, 2° dcha, 02001 **Albacete**
Tel: 967-218 231/970-885 999
Fax: 967-218 231
director Marta Torres Blanc; distributor Joseba Garcia (949-210 866/610-290 366)
Actors: varies *Perfs:* 75-80 *Prods:* 2 + 1 new *Type:* children's theatre, puppets, theatre for adults *Touring:* Spain *Comments:* postal address: Apdo Correos 731, 02080 Albacete; C/Ricardo Castro n 2 2 Dcha. 02001 Albacete

Teatro Fénix
Apdo Correos 431, 02080 **Albacete**
Tel: 967-287 382
Fax: 967-507 627
director Julián Herrero
Actors: 3 *Perfs:* 200 *Prods:* 3 (1 new) *Type:* theatre, dance and children's theatre *Venues:* Higuerela 200 *Touring:* Spain *Comments:* also runs workshops and courses for actors, and makes video promotions for other companies

El Tinglao
c/ Santa Ursula nffl 8,
28801 **Alcalá de Henares (Madrid)**
Tel: 607-694 706
E-Mail: jcerrato@teleline.es
artistic director David Ojeda Abolafia
Comments: work with disabled actors

Teatro de la Danza de Madrid
Ruperto Chapi 22,
28100 **Alcobendas (Madrid)**
Tel: 91-663 7163
Fax: 91-663 7029
Internet: www.infoescena.es/tdm
E-Mail: teatrodanza@teleline.es
administradores Roberto Alvarez Ruiz, Amelia Ochandiano; director artístico Luis Olmos
Actors: 10 *Perfs:* 150 *Prods:* 2 *Type:* contemporary, classic *Venues:* Centro Estable (own teaching centre) *Touring:* Spain *Comments:* resident company at Teatro Auditorio Ciudad de Alcobendas 950

Alquibla Teatro
c/ Mediodía, Edificio Sur 2ffi, 1fflE,
30157 **Algezares (Murcia)**
Tel: 968-844 889/629-602 174 (mobile)
Fax: 968-840 099
E-Mail: alquibla@distrito.com
director Antonio Saura; representant Nacho Vilar
Actors: 6-10 *Perfs:* 100-120 *Prods:* 2 *Type:* contemporary theatre *Touring:* Spain *Comments:* represented by: DADO Producciones Teatrales S.L., C/ Mediodía, Edificio Sur 2ffi, 1fflE, 30157 Algezares (Murcia)

Altair Teatre Estudi
Av. de Jijona 30,
03012 **Alicante**
Tel: 96-525 7690
E-Mail: altair@iponet.es
contacts Antoni Cuti, Oscar Rodríguez
Actors: varies *Perfs:* 50 *Prods:* 4 + 2 *Type:* children's theatre, theatre *Touring:* Spain, Portugal *Comments:* see also Producers

Taller de Teatro Axioma – Sociedad Cooperativa Andaluza
Apto de Correos 469, 04080 **Almería**
Tel: 950-290 501/617-020 431 (mobile)
Fax: 950-290 501
director Carlos Góngora; distribution Gloria Zapata
Actors: 9-13 *Perfs:* 60-70 *Prods:* 5 *Type:* theatre for the senses, indoors and street theatre, puppets
Touring: Spain, Europe

Markeline Theatre Company
Compania de Teatro Markeliñe
c/ Unamuno 9, 48340 **Amorebieta (Vizcaya)**
Tel: 94-673 3257/630 8013
Fax: 94-630 8013
commercial director Jose Ramón Martínez; artistic director Iñaki Egiluz
Actors: 6 *Perfs:* 70 *Prods:* 5 (2 new) *Type:* visual, mime, street theatre, comedy, children's theatre *Touring:* Spain, France, Belgium, Netherlands *Comments:* postal address: Aptdo de Correos 141, Amorebieta (Vizcaya)

Clunia Chamber Theatre
Clunia Teatro de Cámara
C/ Santa Lucia, 15, 09400 **Aranda de Duero (Burgos)**
Tel: 947-501 973
Fax: 947-500 373
director Julio López Laguna; sub-director Borja Peña; secretary Isabel Santos; programme director Sonia Martín; musical director Mario Lopez; choreography Ana Heras; public relations Rufino Delgado; dance Nacho del Cura
Actors: 35 *Perfs:* 40 *Prods:* 3 *Type:* classical, comedy, recitals, dance and musical theatre, poetry recitals *Venues:* Casa de Cultura 300, Teatro-Cine Aranda 900 *Touring:* Spain *Comments:* courses for actors and for young people

Cambaleo Teatro S.L.
Apartado de Correos 280,
28300 **Aranjuez (Madrid)**
Tel: 91-892 1793
Fax: 91-892 1877
Internet: www.arrakis.es/~/cambaleo/index.htm
E-Mail: cambaleo@arrakis.es
director Carlos Sarrio; press & promotion David Ruiz
Actors: 4 *Perfs:* 70-80 *Prods:* 3 *Type:* contemporary, children's theatre *Venues:* La Nave de Cambaleo 120 *Comments:* theatre courses and workshops for children and adults; presents productions of other companies; see also Venues

Teatro Guirigai, S.L.
C/ Rocío, 7, 28500 **Arganda Del Rey (Madrid)**
Tel: 91-870 3407
Fax: 91-870 0268
directors Agustín Iglesias
Actors: 10 *Perfs:* 80-90 *Prods:* 6
Type: street, stage, children's and adult theatre *Touring:* Spain, Portugal, USA, South America *Comments:* national & local funding, mainly by Comunidad de Madrid

Noa Teatro
Apto 728, 06080 **Badajoz**
Tel: 924-267 116
Fax: 924-267 116
director Pedro Luis Cortés;
producer Juan Carlos Anuncibai
Actors: 5 *Perfs:* 40-50 *Prods:* 2 (1 new)
Type: contemporary authors' theatre *Touring:* Spain
Comments: stage own productions

Suripanta Teatro
Carretera de Valverde km 2600, 06010 **Badajoz**
Tel: 924-267 572/400/606-319 383 (mobile)
Fax: 924-267 400
representante, dirección artística & técnica Pedro Rodríguez Ruiz
Actors: 3 + guests (depending on production) *Perfs:* 60 *Prods:* 2 (1 new) *Type:* contemporary versions of classics *Touring:* national, Portugal : visiting address: Apartado de Correos 419, 06080 Badajoz

Acteon
Valldonzella Nffl 52, Local 2, 08001 **Barcelona**
Tel: 93-317 0380/617-461 728 (mobile) Fax: 93-317 0380
Internet: www.cccbxaman.org/acteon
E-Mail: acteon@mail.cccbxaman.org
director Claudio Zulián; production Arantxa González; communication Montse Herrera
Actors: 5-7 *Perfs:* 25-30 *Prods:* 3 (1 new) *Type:* multi-media spectacles, contemporary theatre *Touring:* Spain, France, Italy *Comments:* managed by Acteon Productions; second address: Apdo. Correos 23349, 08080 Barcelona; see also Agents/Producers

Companyia Pepa Plana
C/ Carretes 1, 1ffl, 2ffl, 08001 **Barcelona**
Tel: 93-442 0048 Fax: 93-420 9464
Internet: www.barcelonet.com/pepaplana
E-Mail: cucutam@datalogic.es
director Pepa Plana; artistic director Joan Busquets; producer Oriol Blanchar
Actors: 3-5 *Perfs:* 80-100 *Prods:* 1 *Type:* contemporary clowns for adults/comedy *Touring:* Spain, Europe

Cònica – Lacònica Teatre D'Ombres, La
C/ Urgell 69 2ffl 2ffl, 08011 **Barcelona**
Tel: 93-323 7298 Fax: 93-454 7548
contacts Mercé Gost, Alba Zapater
Actors: varies (2) *Perfs:* 20 *Prods:* 2 *Type:* shadow theatre *Touring:* Europe, Spain *Comments:* shadow research with other artists, video; see also puppets

Dagoll Dagom, S.A.
Consell de Cent, 240 Pral 2ffl, 08011 **Barcelona**
Tel: 93-451 7206 Fax: 93-323 5531
artistic directors Joan Luis Bozzo, Miquel Periel Mitjana, Ana Rosa Cisquella
Actors: 18 *Perfs:* 150 *Prods:* 1 *Type:* classical, contemporary, musical *Venues:* Teatro Victoria 1250, Teatro Poliorama 636 *Comments:* manages Teatro Victoria with El Tricicle (drama) and Anexa Espectacles S.A. (agents); see also Venues and Agents

El Teatro Fronterizo
Alegre de Dalt, 55 bis, 08024 **Barcelona**
Tel: 93-284 5312 Fax: 93-219 7927
E-Mail: salabeckett@ctv.es
directors Tony Casares, Pep Far; contact Luis Miguel Climent
Actors: 1 *Perfs:* 30 *Prods:* 4 *Type:* experimental, contemporary *Venues:* Sala Beckett 80 *Touring:* Spain, Argentina *Comments:* organising acting and playwrighting workshops

Els Alquilinos Teatre
C. la lluna 23, entl 1ffi, 08001 **Barcelona**
Tel: 93-329 8756 Fax: 93-442 0658
E-Mail: aquilinos@ctv.es
director de producción Esther Prim; director artístico Miquel Alvarez
Actors: 4 *Perfs:* 80 *Prods:* 2 *Type:* puppets, experimental – children, family *Venues:* Teatre Regina Barcelona *Touring:* Spain, Europe *Comments:* funded by Gobierno Autónomo de Catalunya; see also Puppetry

Els Farsants SCP
C/ Encarnación, 115-117 ático 3ffl, 08024 **Barcelona**
Tel: 93-210 2856/630-970 953 (mobile)
Fax: 93-284 5748
directors José Gallardo, David Torras, Miguel Gelabert
Actors: 3 *Perfs:* 40 *Prods:* 4 *Type:* children's theatre including live music *Touring:* national

General Eléctrica
La Rambla 48, 08002 **Barcelona**
Tel: 93-317 8753 Fax: 93-317 8753
E-Mail: agee@jet.es
direction artistica Tomas Aragay, Roger Bernat; produccion y gestion Mónica Arùs
Actors: 10 *Perfs:* 35 *Prods:* 4 *Type:* contemporary theatre, dance *Touring:* Spain, France, Belgium *Comments:* centre of creation where performers, directors can develop their projects

La Cubana Accions Teatrals
Carmen 39 entlo., 08001 **Barcelona**
Tel: 93-412 3545
Fax: 93-301 0980
E-Mail: lacubana@ctv.es
director artístico Jordi Milan
Actors: varies *Perfs:* 300 *Prods:* 1 new (mid-2000) *Type:* theatrical actions, comedy *Touring:* Spain, South America *Comments:* managed by: Mama Mulata Productions, see also Agents and Producers

La Trepa
Jove Teatre Regina, Seneca 22, 08006 **Barcelona**
Tel: 93-218 1512/1474
Fax: 93-415 0098
directora María Agustina Solé i Riumalló
Actors: 6 *Perfs:* 125 *Prods:* 3 *Type:* children's theatre *Venues:* Jove Teatre Regina 435 *Touring:* Spain *Comments:* see also Venues

Las Caligulas
c/ Girona 35, 3ffl 2ffi, 08010 **Barcelona**
Tel: 93-318 7192/609-327 406 (mobile)
Fax: 9343-318 7192
Internet: www.seker.es/las_caligulas/
E-Mail: caligulas@seker.es
dirección artística y técnica Miguel Crespi; producción Maria Eugenia Sebastián
Actors: 5 *Perfs:* 37 *Prods:* 6 (4 street theatre + 2 stage) *Type:* comedy, street theatre, performance *Touring:* Europe, Australia, South America *Comments:* currently the company is doing mostly work for television and cinema; it also works for institutions and private companies devising animation spectacles for symposia, conferences, festivals and competitions

Lauta Independent Theatre Group
Grupo de Teatre Independiente Lauta
Camilo Rosell 58 bajo 1ffl, Santa Coloma de Gramanet, 08921 **Barcelona**
Tel: 93-392 6617 Fax: 93-386 9261
director Carlos García Quesada; gerente Lidia Montero Coss
Actors: 4 *Perfs:* 85 *Prods:* 1 *Type:* small-scale Spanish drama, poetic movement

Perillòs
Consejo de Ciento 369, 08009 **Barcelona**
Tel: 93-744 0028 Fax: 93-744 0028
contact Adelaida Borrás
Actors: 4-6 *Perfs:* 50 *Prods:* 1 *Type:* physical theatre, open-air performances *Comments:* also organise site specific projects and events for festivals

Pretérit Perfecte
c/ Cuba, 2, 08030 **Barcelona**
Tel: 93-274 1460 Fax: 93-274 1392
director Jordi Llop
Actors: 3 *Perfs:* 120 *Prods:* 1 + 1 *Type:* comedy *Venues:* Sala Nou Tantarantana – Barcelona 160 *Touring:* Spain *Comments:* performances in Catalan and Spanish

Rosa Sánchez and Konicthtr
C/ Borrell 130, 3, 1ffl, 08015 **Barcelona**
Tel: 93-453 7248 Fax: 93-453 7248
E-Mail: konic@mx3.redestb.es
directora administrativa Carmen Escardo; directora artística Rosa Sánchez
Actors: 3-5 *Perfs:* 30 *Prods:* 2 *Type:* experimental, visual theatre, installation performances, multi media *Touring:* Spain, Germany, France, UK, Netherlands *Comments:* organise workshops: theatre and technology interaction between body, sound and image

Teatre Gent
Rosselló 36, 5°, 3ffi, 08029 **Barcelona**
Tel: 93-322 4822
director Pere Daussá; administrator Neus Olivella
Actors: 10 *Prods:* 1 *Type:* children's theatre, classical catalan theatre

Teatre Lliure
Montseny, 47, 08012 **Barcelona**
Tel: 93-218 9251 Fax: 93-237 1243
director gerente Josep Montanyès; director artístico Lluis Pascual
Actors: 20 *Perfs:* 230 *Prods:* 5-6 *Type:* classical, contemporary drama *Venues:* Teatre Lliure 300 *Touring:* Spain, Europe *Comments:* collaborates with Institut del Teatre de Barcelona; see also Venues, Orchestras; member of U.T.E.

Teatre Nacional de Catalunya
Plaça de les Arts 1, 08013 **Barcelona**
Tel: 93-306 5700 Fax: 93-306 5701
Internet: www.cultura.gencat.es/tnc
E-Mail: info@tnc.es
director Domenec Reixach; administrador general Josep Maria Busquets
Actors: varies *Prods:* 20 (incl co-productions) *Type:* classical, avant-garde, prose, dance *Venues:* Sala Gran 896, experimental stage 500, ground for para-theatrical productions *Touring:* national *Comments:* see also Venues

Theatre Arca
C/Avella 4, Baixos, 08003 **Barcelona**
Tel: 93-319 1801
director general Jesús Roche; secretaria administrativa Teresa Pascuet; relaciones públicas Rosa Férez
Actors: 9 *Perfs:* 300 *Prods:* 6 + 2 *Touring:* Spain, Europe

Tricicle, El
Paseo de Gracia 20-4ffl 2ffi, 08007 **Barcelona**
Tel: 93-317 4747
Fax: 93-318 0806
Internet: www.trioicle.com
E-Mail: tricicle@compuserve.com
directora general Pilar Mir Maluquer; secretaria administrativa Silvia Sagué Arguimbau
Actors: 3 *Perfs:* 100 *Prods:* 1 + 1 *Type:* gestural theatre *Venues:* Teatro Victoria 1100 *Touring:* Spain, Europe *Comments:* manages Teatro Victoria with Dagoll Dagom and Anexa (agents); see also Agents & Producers and Venues

Vol Ras
C/ Salva 86-88, 08004 **Barcelona**
Tel: 93-442 3275 Fax: 93-442 3559
Internet: www.vol-ras.com
E-Mail: vol.ras@filnet.es
director Toni Alba; contact Roser Mané
Actors: 2 *Perfs:* 170 *Prods:* 1 *Type:* mime *Touring:* Europe *Comments:* funded by Ministrerio de Cultura and Generalitat de Catalunya

Tarima Theatre
Apartado de Correos 91, 48970 **Basauri (Vizcaya)**
Tel: 94-449 0665 Fax: 94-426 2029
director Francisco Hernando
Actors: 8 *Perfs:* 75 *Prods:* 1 *Type:* contemporary playwrights *Touring:* Spain *Comments:* organise theatre workshops for youth and adults

Adur Getxoko Antzerki
Plácido Careaga 5, 5ffl izda, 48014 **Bilbao**
Tel: 94-475 3454/616-079 075
director and coordinator Iñaki Urrutia
Actors: 4 *Perfs:* 50 *Prods:* 1 *Type:* street and stage, children's theatre *Touring:* Spain *Comments:* organise workshops for school children

Maskarada Antzerki Taldea SL
Quintana 8, 1fflizq, 48007 **Bilbao**
Tel: 94-446 7781/989-131 291/ 689-131 291
Fax: 94-446 7781
Internet: www.geocities.com/Broadway/5997/
E-Mail: maskarada@mail.com
director Karlos Panera Mendieta; administrator, manager & production Toño Pinto Segovia
Actors: 2 varies *Perfs:* 100 *Prods:* 2 *Type:* poetic theatre, comedy, author theatre *Touring:* Spain, Latin America *Comments:* performs in Basque and in Spanish

Teatro Estable de Cáceres
Aptdo. 481, 10080 **Cáceres**
Tel: 927-215 664/212 997/649-134 914
manager Asunción Morgado; artistic director Francisco Carrillo
Actors: 6 *Perfs:* 40-60 *Prods:* 1 + 3 street theatre *Type:* street theatre, children, contemporary

Comedians, Els
c/Las Palmas s/n, Apartado de Correos 2, 08360 **Canet de Mar (Barcelona)**
Tel: 93-794 1939/795 4666 Fax: 93-794 1858
Internet: www.2.scinet.es/comediants
E-Mail: 101725.677@compuserve.com
director Joan Font; gerente Francisca Sola
Actors: varies *Perfs:* 200-250 *Prods:* 3 *Type:* visual indoor theatre, street theatre *Touring:* Europe, South America, Australia

Xarxa Teatre
Apartado de Correos 268, Vila-Real, 12540 **Castellón (Valencia)**
Tel: 964-527 995 Fax: 964-530 918
Internet: www.xarxateatre.com
E-Mail: info@xarxateatre.com
director general Manuel Vilanova; director en gira Leandre Escamilla; secretaria de producción Rossanna Muñoz
Actors: 9 + 6 musicians *Perfs:* 150 *Prods:* 3 *Type:* street theatre, visual theatre and fireworks *Touring:* Spain, Europe, South America, Slovenia *Comments:* organise theatre workshops for young people; performances for special events

Teatro la Buhardilla S.L.
C/ José Cruz Conde Nffl 8, 2ffl, 14003 **Córdoba**
Tel: 957-481 904/929-553 486
Fax: 957-481 904/957-438 506
directora general Nieves Palma Galán; director artístico Francisco García Torrado; directoray administr Ricardo LunaNieves Palma
Actors: 5 + 2 technicians *Perfs:* 40-50 *Prods:* 2 + 1 *Type:* theatre of contemporary authors, visual and live theatre, children's theatre *Touring:* Spain *Comments:* theatre workshops for young actors and directors; funded by Junta de Andalucía

Oripando Teatro
c/o La Jaramilla, Av/ de la Constitución 47, 28820 **Coslada (Madrid)**
Tel: 91-669 5690 Fax: 91-673 0153
director Miguel Cubero Rodríguez; productores Alberto Gómez Pacios, Eva Navarro Navalon
Actors: 15 *Perfs:* 10 *Prods:* 1 *Type:* classical, cabaret *Venues:* La Jaramilla 250 *Touring:* national *Comments:* funded by local authority

Teatro Geroa
Apdo 291, 48200 **Durango (Vizcaya)**
Tel: 94-681 2481
Fax: 94-620 1177
presidente Alfonso Torregrosa; relaciones públicas y distribución Joseba Gil
Actors: 4 *Perfs:* 100 *Prods:* 1 *Type:* experimental theatre, only contemporary authors *Venues:* Teatro Principal (S. Sebastian), Círculo de Bellas Artes (Madrid) *Comments:* cooperative; provincial, regional & national funding

La Carátula (Asociación Cultural)
Aptdo. correos 236, 03280 **Elche (Alicante)**
Tel: 96-545 3571
Fax: 96-545 3571
director Antonio González Beltrán; Jefe de Producción José Manuel Garzón
Actors: 7 permanent *Perfs:* 6 (2) *Prods:* 6 *Type:* story telling, children and adult theatre, classical, avant-garde *Touring:* Spain, Latin America, North America *Comments:* the company has created the Carátula Jove Teatre Escola (School of Youth Theatre), with 30 students and 3 productions; theatre in Spanish and Catalan languages; also organise Festival de la Oralidad

Kilkarrak
c/ Puy 64 3°,
31200 **Estella (Navarra)**
Tel: 948-552 910
representante Pedro Echávarri
Actors: 14 *Perfs:* 20-25 *Prods:* 1 *Type:* comedy *Touring:* Navarra *Comments:* organise workshops, courses at schools

La Fura dels Baus
c/ de la Ciencia 21, 08850 **Gava (Barcelona)**
Tel: 93-662 4047
Fax: 93-662 4049
Internet: www.lafura.com
E-Mail: lafura@lafura.com
gerente Javier de Ramón Casanoba; administración Rosa Castells; directora comercial/venta en España y Latinoamerica Elena Blanco; venta en Francia Martina Gatell; venta resto del mundo Rosa Arnais; comunicación Sebastián Ruiz
Perfs: 150 *Prods:* 3 *Type:* avant-garde, performances with video & music, multi-media, opera *Touring:* worldwide *Comments:* funded by Generalitat de Catalunya and Ministerio de Cultura

Grupo de Teatro Telón de Fondo
Calle Puertu Ventana 10, 5°A, 33207 **Gijón**
Tel: 98-539 5049/516 2895 (theatre)/8-539 5049
director Xulio Vigil Parajón; director artístico Rosabel Berrocal García;
secretario administrativo Lluis Antón González
Actors: 12 *Perfs:* 60-70 *Prods:* 2 *Type:* street theatre, classical, realistic comedy *Venues:* El Glayiu 60 *Touring:* Spain, Portugal *Comments:* organise seminars on theatrical antropology, based on celtic culture

Semola Teatre
Plaça Sant Jaume 9, 17190 **Girona**
Tel: 972-226 031 Fax: 972-226 752
E-Mail: bitoteatre@aquired.es
director Joan Grau; representante José Domenech
Actors: 8 *Perfs:* 100 *Prods:* 1 *Type:* visual theatre *Venues:* Mercat de las Flors 700 *Touring:* Europe, Australia, Israel, South America

Talleret de Salt
Plaça Sant Jaume 9, 17190 **Girona**
Tel: 972-402 004 Fax: 972-400 084
E-Mail: bitoteatre@aquired.es
director Josep Domenèch i Pou
Actors: 11 *Perfs:* 120 *Prods:* 3 *Type:* theatre of text for adults and children *Venues:* Teatre de Salt 325 *Touring:* Europe, South America *Comments:* regional, national and municipal funding; plays open in Madrid, Teatro la Comedia 700 and in Barcelona, Mercat de las Flors 700

Teatre de L'Ull S.L
C/ Santísima Trinidad 18 Bajo, 46110 **Godella (Valencia)**
Tel: 609-648 282 (mobile)/96-384 2240
Fax: 06-363 8198
E-Mail: teatredelull@ctv.es
contact Juan José Benavent, Fernando Granell
Actors: 12 *Perfs:* 70 *Prods:* 2 + 1 *Type:* street theatre, contemporary theatre *Venues:* Sala Moratín, Teatro Rialto, various open-air venues, streets, parks, etc. *Touring:* Spain, Europe *Comments:* street theatre with fireworks and live music; also indoor productions

Fuegos Fatuos Teatro, S.L.
c/o Cardenal González de Mendoza, 27 Bajo Derecha, 19004 **Guadalajara**
Tel: 949-210 866/610 793 227 (mobile)
Fax: 949-210 866
director Fernando Romo; gerente Joseba García; dramaturgo Juan Andres Morillo-Velarde
Actors: 6 *Perfs:* 70 *Prods:* 1 *Type:* contemporary *Touring:* Spain

Compania de Teatro Andante
Av. Muntoz de Vargas 8. 5.B., 21006 **Huelva**
Tel: 959-226 139/366 735/630-022 088
Fax: 959-366 562
director artístico Jesus Domínguez
Actors: 5 *Prods:* 2 *Type:* contemporary texts, theatre for adults and children, classic theatre
Venues: Teatro Cine Colón 280 *Touring:* Spain
Comments: co-production Diputación Provincial de Huelva and Empresa Pública de Gestión de la Consejería de Cultura de la Junta de Andalucia; venue address: Teatro Cine Colon, C/ Cervantes Nffl 2, Bonares, 21003, Huelva

Legaleón-T Teatro
Apdo. 429, 20300 **Irún (Guipuzkoa)**
Tel: 943-610 304 Fax: 943-615 854
E-Mail: legaleon@arrakis.es
directora Ana Pérez; director artístico Oscar Gómez Mata; distribución Merche Tranche;
management Karmele Rivera
Actors: 3-5 *Perfs:* 70 *Prods:* 1-2 new *Type:* avant-garde, comedy *Touring:* national, Switzerland, France
Comments: coproduction with Swiss company L'Alakrán; also runs theatre courses

Artristras
Carrer Caritat 1, 08530 **La Garriga**
Tel: 93-871 7654
Fax: 93-871 7654
Internet: www.versin.com/usuaris/artristras
E-Mail: artristras@versin.com
director Quique Alcàntara; ténicos Jep Verges, Dolors Coll; oficina Lola Coll
Actors: 12 *Prods:* 2 *Type:* street theatre *Touring:* Europe

Companyia Teia Moner
Urbanizacion can Rovira, c/Can Rovira 33, 08186 **Lliça D'Amunt (Barcelona)**
Tel: 93-864 5834/609-310 371 (mobile)
Fax: 93-864 5834
Internet: www.quasar.es/teia
E-Mail: teiam@arrakis.es
direction Teia Moner;
music & light technician Miquel Espinosa
Actors: 1 *Perfs:* 60-70 *Prods:* 1 *Type:* object theatre, puppets *Touring:* national *Comments:* see also Puppets

Compañía Estable Teatro Guerra de Lorca
Plaza de Calderón de la Barca s/n,
30800 **Lorca (Murcia)**
Tel: 968-472 424/629-252 943 (mobile)/606-713 361
Fax: 968-460 212
Internet: www.zoom.es/~beraldo/
E-Mail: beraldo@zoom.es
director Miguel Angel Hernández García; president Adela Mendiola Rodríguez
Actors: 8 *Perfs:* 30-35 *Prods:* 2 *Type:* contemporary, classical and children's *Venues:* Teatro Guerra de Lorca 518 *Touring:* Spain *Comments:* resident company of Teatro Guerra Lorca; see also Venues

Teatro del Norte
c/ Conde de Santa Barbara 58,
33420 **Lugones (Asturias)**
Tel: 98-526 0103/514 2399/62-981 7657
Fax: 98-577 0825
director Etelvino Vázquez; director técnico Jesús Pérez
Actors: 6 *Perfs:* 50-60 *Prods:* 1 *Type:* avant garde, youth theatre, new interpretation of classical texts *Touring:* Italy, Spain, Portugal *Comments:* national and regional funding; educational activities

Carnicería Teatro, La
C/ Del Olivar 4, 5ffl, 28012 **Madrid**
Tel: 91-467 2413/913 080 004 Fax: 91-467 2413
dirección artistica Rodrigo García
Perfs: 50-60 *Prods:* 2 *Type:* avant-garde, experimental *Venues:* Sala Cuarta Pared 170 *Touring:* Spain, Europe *Comments:* national and regional funding

Cia Globo Teatro
Cale Embajaderes 6 1° 129, 28012 **Madrid**
Tel: 91-530 2859 Fax: 91-530 2859
E-Mail: elglobo@teleline.es
director Luis Garbán; general production Maria Fernandez H.
Actors: 7 *Perfs:* 70 *Prods:* 2 + 1 *Type:* avent-garde, magic-realism *Touring:* Spain, Middle East, South America

Compañía Calderón de la Barca
C/ Gavilán 18, Urbanización Cotorredondo, Arroyomolinos, 28939 **Madrid**
Tel: 91-812 2598 Fax: 91-812 2598
director general Máximo Martín; director artístico Martín Ferrer
Actors: 8-15 *Perfs:* 200 *Prods:* 3 (repertoire company) *Type:* all types of Spanish theatre (mainly classical, modern and comedy) *Touring:* national *Comments:* independent touring company

Compañía de Lina Morgan
Teatro La Latina, Plaza de la Cebada 2, 28005 **Madrid**
Tel: 91-365 0671 Fax: 91-366 6208
director Angel Gutiérrez
Actors: 8-10 *Perfs:* 10 a week (560 per annum) *Prods:* 1 *Type:* comedy/revista *Venues:* Teatro La Latina 960 *Comments:* participates in TV series and feature films

Compañía de Teatro Nuevo Repertorio
c/ Doctor Fourquet 31, 28012 **Madrid**
Tel: 91-539 5767 Fax: 91-539 5767
director Cristina Rota
Actors: 13 *Perfs:* 300 *Prods:* 2 *Type:* independent theatre, own productions, musicals, co-productions *Venues:* Sala del Mirador 160 *Touring:* Spain, South America, Europe *Comments:* also runs own theatre school Escuela de Teatro Cristina Rota, with 300 students and 15 teachers of 8 different subjects; see also Venues

Compañía de Teatro Nuevo Replika
Valdesangil 65, 7° B, 28039 **Madrid**
Tel: 91-373 9850/594 3882 Fax: 91-594 3882
director Socorro Anadón, Jaroslaw Bielski
Actors: 14 *Perfs:* 250 *Prods:* 2 *Type:* contemporary theatre *Touring:* Spain, Europe *Comments:* actors of several nationalities in the company

Compañía de Teatro Zascandil
C/ Discobolo 33, 28022 **Madrid**
Tel: 91-320 4699/908-522 013 (mobile)
Fax: 91-320 5759
Internet: www.readysoft.es/zascandil
E-Mail: zascandil@readysoft.es
administrador and distribución José María Adeva; director artístico Rafael Ruiz
Actors: 4 *Perfs:* 80 *Prods:* 2 *Type:* comedy, classical Spanish *Touring:* national

Compañía Lope de Vega
Marqués de Casa Riera 2, 28014 **Madrid**
Tel: 91-532 4438 Fax: 91-522 3181
director José Tamayo
Actors: 40 *Prods:* 3 *Type:* classical theatre *Venues:* Teatro Bellas Artes 455 *Touring:* Spain, Portugal *Comments:* home Company of Teatro Bellas Artes; see also Venues

Compañía Nacional de Teatro Clásico
Príncipe 14, 3° Izda, 28012 **Madrid**
Tel: 91-532 7928 Fax: 91-522 4690
E-Mail: tclasico@cntc.inaem.es
director Rafael Pérez Sierra; director adjunto Roberto Alonso Cuenca; jefe de producción Jose Manuel Gorospe; jefa de prensa Maria Jesus Barroso
Actors: 24 *Perfs:* 330-350 *Prods:* 2 *Type:* classical *Venues:* Teatro de la Comedia 600 *Touring:* Spain *Comments:* dependent on Ministry of Culture INAEM; manages Teatro de la Comedia; see also Venues

Cuarta Pared
c/ Ercilla, 17, 28005 **Madrid**
Tel: 91-517 2317/473 9666 Fax: 91-517 1144
dirección y programación Javier García Yagüe; gerencia Francisco García; promoción Amador González, Eva Gómez; coordinación técnica Richard Vázquez; secretaría Cristine García
Actors: 6 *Perfs:* 150 (100 + 50 touring) *Prods:* 2 + 2 (new) *Type:* contemporary *Venues:* Sala Cuarta Pared 172 *Touring:* national *Comments:* resident company at Sala Cuarta Pared; see also Venues

El Juglar Teatr

c/ Elisa 11, Hoyo de Manzanares, 28240 **Madrid**
Tel: 91-856 5922/7848
director Paco Angulo
Actors: 7 *Perfs:* 40-50 *Prods:* 1-2 *Type:* contemporary *Touring:* national

Ensayo 100
Raimundo Lulio 20, 28010 **Madrid**
Tel: 91-447 9486 Fax: 91-447 9486
Internet: www.usuarios.iponet.es/ensayo
E-Mail: ensayo100@iponet.es
artistic director Jorge Eines
Actors: 7 *Perfs:* 70 *Prods:* 2 + 1 *Type:* avant garde theatre *Venues:* Sala Ensayo 90, *Comments:* see also Venues

Espacio Abierto Centro de Producción Teatral
Colegiata 11 2ffi, 28012 **Madrid**
Tel: 91-369 2780 Fax: 91-369 2780
director Eusebio Lázaro;
assistant director Marina Saura
Actors: 10-20 *Perfs:* 30 *Prods:* 1 new *Type:* classical theatre with contemporary style *Touring:* Spain
Comments: regular participation in the annual festival of classic theatre of Mérida

Fundiciones Teatrales
Molino de Viento 4, 1° B, 28004 **Madrid**
Tel: 91-531 6761/617-667 277 (mobile)
Fax: 91-523 1351
director Jesús Cracio
Actors: 4 *Perfs:* 140 *Prods:* 1 (new) *Type:* contemporary *Venues:* Teatro Alfil 220, Teatro Lara 500, Circulo de Bellas Artes 300 *Touring:* Spain

Geografías Teatro
Malcampo 16, 3° 1ffi, 28002 **Madrid**
Tel: 91-519 2837
Fax: 91-519 2837
director Abel Vitón
Actors: 5 *Perfs:* 80 *Prods:* 2 *Type:* contemporary author's theatre *Touring:* Spain, Cuba

La Tartana Teatro de Títeres
Teatro Pradillo, Calle Pradillo 12, 28002 **Madrid**
Tel: 91-416 9011 Fax: 91-416 9968
director y programador Juan Muñoz Rebollo; administración and distribution Montse Ortiz;
jefe técnico Enrique Rodríguez
Actors: varies *Perfs:* 50 *Prods:* 2 *Type:* mainly contemporary, use of puppets (up to natural size), theatre for children *Venues:* Teatro Pradillo 100 *Touring:* Europe *Comments:* see also Puppets and Venues

Teatro de La Abadía
Centro de Estudios y Creación Escénicos de la Comunidad de Madrid, C/ Fernández de los Ríos 42, 28015 **Madrid**
Tel: 34-9144 81181/1338 Fax: 34-9144 81449
E-Mail: abadia@ctv.es
artistic director José Luis Gómez;
gerente Isabel Navarro
Venues: Sala Juau de la Cruz 300, Sala José Luis Alonso 206 *Touring:* Spain, Portugal, France, Italy, Germany, Poland, Columbia, Mexico, Brazil *Comments:* funded by national and regional authorities, runs annual course for professional actors; see also Venues; miembro de la Unión de los Teatros de Europa (U.T.E)

Teatro del Arte SL
Eguilaz 3, 28010 **Madrid**
Tel: 91-447 1603 Fax: 91-594 0877
dramaturgia y direccion Fernando Rojas
Actors: 10-15 *Perfs:* 100 *Prods:* 3 *Type:* classical, street theatre *Touring:* Spain, South America

Teatro del Centro Dramático Nacional
Teatro Nacional María Guerrero, Tamayo y Baus 4, 28004 **Madrid**
Tel: 91-310 2949 Fax: 91-319 3836
director Carlos Pérez de la Fuente; director de producción Julio Álvarez; gabinette di prensa José Ramón, Fernández & Rosa González
Actors: varies *Prods:* 4 *Type:* contemporary, universal *Comments:* resident company at Teatro María Guerrero; see also Venues

Teatro del Olivar
Menéndez Valdés 15, 4° izqu., 28015 **Madrid**
Tel: 91-447 0247 Fax: 91-593 8870/521 7927
director María Ruíz; assistant director Alba Vidal; dramaturgo Ronald Brouwer
Prods: 1 + 1 *Type:* Spanish classical, avant-garde *Touring:* Spain

Teatro Ibérico de Madrid
C/ Elisa N° 11, Hoyo de Manzanares, 28240 **Madrid**
Tel: 91-856 7848
director Paco Angulo
Actors: 5-6 *Perfs:* 200 *Prods:* 2 *Type:* comedy, children's theatre *Touring:* Spain *Comments:* independent theatre and street theatre

Teatro Impar
Calle Atocha 10 2ffi-3°, 28012 **Madrid**
Tel: 91-429 2911639-360 553 (mobile) Fax: 91-429 3201
E-Mail: teatroimpar@retemail.es
director/relaciones públicas Javier Veiga; relaciones públicas Maria José Zaragoza
Perfs: 60 *Prods:* 3 *Type:* musical comedy, children's theatre (musical), farce *Touring:* Spain

Teatro Meridional
Paseo de la Chopera 49, 4° A, 28045 **Madrid**
Tel: 91-517 0951/609-008 591 (mobile) Fax: 91-517 0951
E-Mail: tmeridional@hotmail.com
directores Miguel Seabra, Álvaro Lavín, Julio Salvatierra
Actors: varies *Perfs:* 2 *Prods:* 150 *Type:* classical, modern, mediterranean character *Touring:* Spain, Portugal, Italy, South America, USA *Comments:* Spanish-Portuguese company; Portuguese address: Estrada da Luz 230, 8° esq, 1600 Lisboa, Portugal, Tel/Fax: +351 1-716 7460 (q.v.)

Teatro Zampanó
Cuesta de las Descargas n° 12, 1° C, 28005 **Madrid**
Tel: 91-366 2847 Fax: 91-366 2847
directors José Maya, Amaya Curieses
Actors: 9 *Perfs:* 80 *Prods:* 2 *Type:* classical Spanish theatre *Touring:* Spain, South America

Triángulo Teatro
c/ Zurita 20, 28012 **Madrid**
Tel: 91-530 6891 Fax: 91-539 2518
Internet: salatriangulo@salatriangulo.com
E-Mail: www.salatriangulo.com
gerente y director artístico Alfonso Pindado; secretarias administrativas Melanie Pindado, Natalia Ortega
Actors: varies *Perfs:* 50 *Prods:* 3 *Type:* contemporary *Touring:* Spain, Europe *Comments:* resident company of Sala Triángulo; see also Venues and Festivals

Yacer Teatro
Navas Del Rey 23, 28011 **Madrid**
Tel: 91-526 0107/95-240 1100
contact Pablo Calvo (91-526 0107)
Actors: 6 *Perfs:* 30 *Prods:* 1 *Type:* contemporary *Touring:* Spain

Zaranda – Teatro Inestable de Andalucía la Baja, La
c/o Teatro La Zaranda, C/ Minas 9, 1° ext. A, 28004 **Madrid**
Tel: 91-532 0884
Fax: 91-532 1056
Internet: www.ctv.es/remesal
E-Mail: remesal@ctv.es
director Francisco Sánchez
Actors: 4 *Perfs:* 60 *Type:* contemporary theatre *Touring:* Spain, South America *Comments:* managed by: El Foro Espectaculos; see also Agents & Producers

Teatro Pikor
c/ Estación 2, 01120 **Maeztu (Alava)**
Tel: 945-410 060/629-323 322 (mobile) Fax: 945-410 060
E-Mail: pikor@clientes.euskaltel.es
contact Miguel Hormeda y Anna Rita Fiaschetti
Actors: 1-5 *Perfs:* 80 *Prods:* 6 *Type:* comedy, street theatre, comic theatre *Touring:* national *Comments:* street theatre workshops for amateurs

Acuario Teatro
c/ Chopera 8, Cerrado de Calderón, 29018 **Málaga**
Tel: 95-229 8959/656-331 175 Fax: 95-229 8959
E-Mail: dguzmano@nexo.es
empresario y director Diego Guzmán; secretaria Marisa Centeno; escenógrafo Pedro Vez; músico Patricia Quiroga
Actors: 5-6 *Perfs:* 160 *Prods:* 2-3 *Type:* musical theatre for all ages, much use of fantasy *Touring:* Spain *Comments:* special theatre for any kind of children's event

Brea Teatro
C/ Alférez Simo Castillo N°4, Bajo Dcha, 29007 **Málaga**
Tel: 95-228 7243/233 1991 Fax: 95-233 1991
director/author Mercedes León García; secretaria administrativa Ana Añoto
Actors: 2 *Perfs:* 30 *Prods:* 2 + 1 *Type:* black comedy, theatre of the absurd *Venues:* Sala Cánova (Málaga) 300 *Touring:* Spain

La Cort
Can Magi del Racó s/n, 08296 **Marganell (Barcelona)**
Tel: 93-835 7145 Fax: 93-835 7145
E-Mail: lacort@retemail.es
directors Ampar Roselló, Quentin Clemence
Actors: varies *Perfs:* 130 *Prods:* 4 *Type:* visual theatre, puppets, masks, dance, music *Venues:* La Cort 300, Teatro 150 *Touring:* Spain *Comments:* run workshops; funded by Instituto de Cultura de Barcelona

Sambhu Teatro
Avenida San Juan 48 bajo, 31253 **Miranda de Arga**
Tel: 948-737 136 Fax: 948-737 136
director y representante Juan Antonio San José
Actors: 3 *Perfs:* 155 *Prods:* 2 *Type:* circus, mime, clown, theatre, comedy for children *Venues:* Centro de Producción de Espectáculos de Miranda de Arga 100 & 125 *Touring:* Spain, Portugal *Comments:* funded by Govierno de Navarra

Los Locos International Theatre Company
Teatro Los Locos
C/ Alfaro 10, 4°, izq, 30001 **Murcia**
Tel: 968-215 434/284 817/619-086 203 Fax: 968-223 321
Internet: www.globalia.net/unidadmobil
E-Mail: u.movil@arrakis.es
director Enrique Martínez
Actors: 4 (varies) *Perfs:* 80-100 *Prods:* 2 + 1 *Type:* contemporary clown theatre, contemporary theatre *Touring:* South America, Spain *Comments:* organise international clown festival: Teatro Romea Murcia

Ridersi Gestión Cultural
c/o Carmen Conde EDF Venecia 2 1° E, 30002 **Murcia**
Tel: 968-341 422/609-617 318 (mobile) Fax: 968-341 422
dirección, administración y promoción José Manuel Ferrer García
Actors: 7-10 *Perfs:* 100 *Prods:* 3 *Type:* street theatre, children's theatre *Touring:* Spain *Comments:* adapts author works for children

Teatro Infantil Fábula
Carril Acequia de Alguazas 45, 30012 **Murcia**
Tel: 968-220 839/269 014/649-090 811 Fax: 968-222 290
E-Mail: fabulateatro@geocities.com
director Juan Pedro Romera; iluminación & sound Javi Parra; distribución Nuria Astillero;
producción Accion Teatral
Actors: 5 + 2 puppeteers *Perfs:* 100-140 *Prods:* 2 *Type:* children's theatre including music, puppets and dance *Venues:* Sala del Espinardo 600 *Touring:* Spain *Comments:* regional funding

Unidad Movil
c/ Alfaro, 10, 4°, Izq, 30001 **Murcia**
Tel: 968-215 434/284 817/619-086 203 Fax: 968-223 321
E-Mail: u.movil@arrakis.es
director Enrique Martínez
Actors: 6 *Perfs:* 50 *Prods:* 1 *Type:* contemporary theatre *Venues:* Sala Casablanca Alcantarilla 500 *Touring:* Spain, South America *Comments:* manages different companies

Teatro Margen, S.L.
C/ Hevia Bolaños s/n bajo, 33008 **Oviedo**
Tel: 985-213 578 Fax: 985-213 578
gerente y representante legal Arturo Castro Fernández
Actors: 8 *Perfs:* 125 *Prods:* 2 *Type:* street and classical Spanish *Touring:* Spain, Portugal, Belgium, UK

Anselm Turmeda
Calle 213, 27, 07015 **Palma de Mallorca**
Tel: 971-402 395
Fax: 971-700 608
director Pere Noguera
Actors: varies *Perfs:* 25 *Prods:* 1 *Type:* author theatre, contemporary and classical *Venues:* Teatro Principal 800, Auditorio de Palma 1300

Estudi Zero Teatre
C/Sans 5, 1°, 07001 **Palma de Mallorca**
Tel: 971-727 166 Fax: 971-723 597
director general Pere Mestre; directora administrativa Pepa Ramón; director técnico Dominic Hull; coordinador vestuario y utilleria Lourdes Erroz
Actors: 6-8 *Perfs:* 100 *Prods:* 3 + 1 *Type:* comedy, contemporary, street and stage *Venues:* Café Teatro Sans 90 *Touring:* Spain *Comments:* theatre under renovation – next season based on café theatre; theatre school also, providing 4 year-long theatre courses; see also Venues

Iguana Teatre, S Coop, Ltda
C/Ventada 27A, 07006 **Palma de Mallorca**
Tel: 971-246 200 Fax: 971-248 352/256 110
Internet: www.mallorcaweb
E-Mail: iguanateatre@balearkom.es
coordinador general Carles Molinet; director de escena Pere Fullana; director técnico Jordi Banal; departamento promoción Carme Ferret; administración Cati Fiol
Actors: 3 + extra *Perfs:* 80-90 *Prods:* 3 *Type:* repertory, street theatre, children's theatre *Venues:* Teatre del Mar 250 *Touring:* Spain, Europe *Comments:* funding by Ajuntament de Palma de Mallorca, Consell Insular de Mallorca, Ministerio de Cultura; see also Venues

Yllana
Jesus 20, 4°A, 07003 **Palma de Mallorca**
Tel: 971-207 410/609-604 923 Fax: 971-202 157
general manager Marcos Ottone
Actors: 8 *Perfs:* 200 *Prods:* 4 *Type:* comedy, visual theatre *Venues:* Teatro Alfil *Touring:* worldwide *Comments:* theatre and TV work; resident company of Teatro Alfil; second address: Teatro Alfil, C/ Pez 10, 28004 Madrid; see also Venues and Festivals

Teatro Estable de Navarra Pinpilinpauxa
C/ Andrés Gorricho s/n, 31015 **Pamplona**
Tel: 948-149 864/943-322 456 Fax: 948-133 718
director Angel Sagües; producción y venta Asun Abad
Actors: 3-9 *Perfs:* 100 *Prods:* 1 *Type:* children's theatre, street theatre and theatre for adults *Venues:* Escuela Navarra de Teatro 350 *Touring:* Spain *Comments:* regional funding from Dpto de Educación y Cultura del Gobierno de Navarra; own productions

Teatro Kollins Clown
C/ Isaba N° 32, 4° C, 31014 **Pamplona**
Tel: 948-121 033
representante Eloisa Martínez Gómez;
director artístico Javier Ibañez
Actors: 3 *Perfs:* 80 *Prods:* 6 *Type:* comedy (children – all ages) *Touring:* Spain

Teatro Trokolo
C/ San Nicolás 76, 4°, 31001 **Pamplona**
Tel: 948-225 032/610-883 075 Fax: 948-225 032
director Ramón Marcos; managers Belén Alvarez, Helena Amontarain
Actors: 4 *Perfs:* 60 *Prods:* 4 *Type:* comedy *Touring:* Spain *Comments:* represented by Truke Distribución, Tel: 948-225 032; see also Agents & Producers

Grupo de Teatro La Trapera
Paseo del Río Arga 3, 31350 **Peralta (Navarra)**
Tel: 948-751 474
Fax: 948-750 143
gerente Alfredo Castillo; productor Miguel Angel Lezáun; director Miguel Munarriz
Actors: 10-12 *Perfs:* 35 *Prods:* 1 *Type:* all types *Venues:* Casa Cultural de Peralta 150 *Touring:* Spain *Comments:* semi-professional group

Trapu Zaharra
Antigua Fabrica Niessen, c/ Alfonso XI s/n, 20100 **Rentería (Gipuzkoa)**
Tel: 943-219 855 Fax: 943-211 328
director gerente Bernar Rementería; director artístico Cesar Saratxu; relaciones públicas Conchi Soto; administrador José María Ocio
Actors: 5 *Perfs:* 50 *Prods:* 2 + 1 *Type:* humourous street theatre, indoor theatre *Venues:* Antigua Fabrica Niessen 300 *Touring:* Spain, France

Ur Teatro-Antzerkia S.L.
c/ Alfonso XI, Edificio Niessen 3°, 20100 **Rentería (Gipuzkoa)**
Tel: 943-528 548/340 548
Fax: 943-528 360
E-Mail: urteatro@facilnet.es
dirección artística Helena Pimenta; ayudante dirección Jose Tome; distribución-producción Angela Alejos
Perfs: 130 *Prods:* 3 *Type:* contemporary *Touring:* Spain, Portugal *Comments:* organize pedagogic programmes in schools about the presentation of each performance

Producciones Inconstantes
Plaza Valle del Nalón 13, 28529 **Ribas Vacia (Madrid)**
Tel: 91-369 4021/91-666 8775
Fax: 91-369 1516
E-Mail: cuartalinea@cuartalinea.es
productor Jesus Guzmán; directores Emilio del Valle, Carolina Solas
Actors: 3 + *Perfs:* 60 *Prods:* 2 + 1 *Type:* contemporary, realist, comedy *Touring:* Spain, South America

Eton Teatro
Paseo de los Robles 37-43, 2°H, 37004 **Salamanca**
Tel: 923-227 043
director Angel González Quesada
Actors: 6 *Perfs:* 40-50 *Prods:* 4 (3 new) *Type:* mime, commedia dell'arte, classical, poetry reading with voice effects, master of ceremonies, satire *Comments:* organise meetings, lectures and presentations for various types of theatre, theatrical investigation, actor's school

Ados Theatre
Ados Teatroa S.L.
c/ Egia 2, 5-E, 20012 **San Sebastián**
Tel: 943-278 109/639-978 688 Fax: 943-290 089
representante legal Jose Antonio Vitoria; distribuidor Koldo Losada; directora Garriñe Losada
Actors: 5 *Prods:* 1-2 *Type:* comedy *Venues:* Jareño (S. Sebastian) 290 *Touring:* Spain

Agerre Teatro Taldea Grupo de Teatro Aguirre Teatroa
Apartado de Correos 1509, 20080 **San Sebastián**
Tel: 943-471 106 Fax: 943-471 106
director administrativo Mielanjel Arana; directora artística Maite Aguirre
Actors: 4 *Perfs:* 40 *Prods:* 2 *Type:* experimental *Touring:* Spain, Europe *Comments:* Perform both in Basque & Spanish

Bederen 1
c/ Egia N° 8 3D, 20012 **San Sebastián**
Tel: 943-278 141
representante legal Jon Ezkurdia; subsecretarios Patxi Santamaría, Turbe Ormaetxe
Actors: 4 *Perfs:* 23 *Prods:* 1 *Type:* comedy *Touring:* Spain *Comments:* funded by Ayuntamiento San Sebastian

Tanttaka Teatroa
Paseo Salamanca 14 1- of 4, 20003 **San Sebastián**
Tel: 943-429 494/609-402 001 (mobile)
Fax: 943-422 212
E-Mail: tanttaka@produkzioak.com
gerente & director artístico Fernando Bernués
Actors: 15 *Perfs:* 360 *Prods:* 5 *Type:* contemporary author theatre *Touring:* Spain

Txalo Produkzioak
Paseo Ilumbre 7, 9° E, 20011 **San Sebastián**
Tel: 943-472 338/333 788 Fax: 943-474 008/333 788
E-Mail: tralo@clientes.euskattel.es
distribuidor y respresentante legal Javier Aguirre, Maribi Amieta; secretariz Gemz E. Tyeberria
Actors: 2 *Perfs:* 75 *Prods:* 2 + 1 new *Type:* comedy, classical *Venues:* Teatro Victoria Eugenia 1200 *Touring:* Spain *Comments:* local and regional funding

GTI Farándula
c/ Banus Alta 28,
08923 **Santa Coloma de Gramanet (Barcelona)**
Tel: 629-120 470 (mobile)
secretaria Rosa Viñas; director artístico Josep Navarro
Actors: 2 *Perfs:* 150 *Prods:* 1-2 *Type:* comedy, visual theatre, children's theatre *Venues:* Sala Segarra 500

Compañía de Danza-Teatro Española Dantea
C/ San Luis N° 36, 2° dcha, 39010 **Santander**
Tel: 942-376 921 Fax: 942-371 635
Internet: www.dantea.camerata.es
E-Mail: danteasl@camerdata.es
directores artísticos Miriam González-Gay, Gonzalo San Miguel; jefe de producción Belén González-Gay
Actors: 14 + 3 musicians *Perfs:* 80 *Prods:* 1 *Type:* dance theatre (Spanish and flamenco) *Touring:* Spain, Europe *Comments:* see also Dance

La Machina Teatro S.L.
Avda Cardenal Herrera Oria s/n, Facultad de Medicina, 39011 **Santander**
Tel: 942-201 913 Fax: 942-201 903
director Francisco Valcarce; distribución & Producción Rosa Lanza; gerente Pati Domenech
Actors: 7 *Perfs:* 135 *Prods:* 1 *Type:* contemporary, street theatre, children's theatre *Venues:* Sala Medicina 400, Palacio de Festivales de Cantabria, squares for street theatre *Comments:* funded by University; Francisco Valcarce is also director of El Aula de Teatro (Muestra de Teatro Internacional Contemporáneo)

Centro Dramatico Galego
Rúa do Villar 35, 1°, 15705 **Santiago de Compostela**
Tel: 981-581 111/572/738
Fax: 981-591 987
Internet: www.xumta.es/conselle/cultura
director Manuel Guede Oliva;
jefe producción Francisco Oti Rios
Actors: varies *Perfs:* 130 *Prods:* 4 *Type:* general repertory *Touring:* Spain, Portugal
Comments: all performances in Gallego; Centro has teaching rôle (related to IGAEM)

Chévere
rua San Lourenzo 51-53, 15705 **Santiago de Compostela**
Tel: 981-573 998 Fax: 981-573 998
E-Mail: salanasa@Interbook.net
gerente Jesús Ron; director John Eastham
Actors: 13 actors-musicians *Perfs:* 50-70 *Prods:* 1 new *Type:* musical theatre, clown theatre *Touring:* Spain, Portugal, Europe *Comments:* Chévere runs the venue Nasa, which is also used for art exhibitions; it is a non-institutional space for independent groups; they also collaborate and exchange with other artistic collectives; see also Venues

Teatro do Atlántico
Outeiro de Arriba 21, 15189 **Sesamo**
Tel: 981-678 103 Fax: 981-678 103
director Xulio Lago Alonso; co-directora María Barcala
Actors: 8-10 *Perfs:* 60 *Prods:* 2 *Type:* general repertoire *Touring:* Spain *Comments:* performs mostly in Gallego, national fundings

Centro Andaluz de Teatro (CAT)
C/ San Luis, 37, 41003 **Sevilla**
Tel: 95-490 1493/455 8870 Fax: 95-490 0707
Internet: cdaea.cica.es
E-Mail: cdaea@cica.es
director Emilio Hernández; gabinete de comunicación Raquel Fuentes
Actors: no fixed company *Perfs:* 200 *Prods:* 1 *Type:* contemporary, avant garde, classical *Venues:* Teatro Central 470 *Touring:* Spain, Portugal *Comments:* funded by Regional Directorate of Cultural Promotion; see National & Regional Ministries; organises workshops

La Cuadra de Sevilla
Polígono Navisa, Calle C, 27, 41006 **Sevilla**
Tel: 95-465 8181/492 0770/607-500 992 (mobile)
Fax: 95-465 9205
Internet: www.teatro.lacuadra.com
E-Mail: lacuadra2@compuserve.com
administración Federico González; director artístico Salvador Távora (670-660 307); prod Lilyane Drillon
Actors: 45 *Perfs:* 100 *Prods:* 1 + 1 *Type:* Andalusian roots combining live art forms including dance and music *Venues:* capacity 1000/5000 *Touring:* worldwide *Comments:* agent: Anexa (Barcelona) 93-451 6366 – La Cuadra de Sevilla 95-492 0770; Carmen: Andalusian Opera with bugles & drums, beyond the original legend told by old Cigarreras from Triana, opera by Salvador Tavora

Los Ulen
Federico Sénchaz Bedoya n° 20 3° IZQ., 41001 **Sevilla**
Tel: 95-422 5699 Fax: 95-422 9356
E-Mail: losulen@zoom.es
representante José Luis Díaz Cuero; distribución Victor García; administración Bis Producciones
Actors: 3 *Perfs:* 60 *Prods:* 1 *Type:* comic theatre *Venues:* Teatro Central (Sevilla) 850 *Touring:* Spain, South America *Comments:* funded by Junta de Andalucía; see also Agents & Producers (Bis Producciones)

Teatro Crónico
C/La María 6, 41008 **Sevilla**
Tel: 95-435 9343/573 8340/649-392 552 Fax: 95-435 2547
production and distribution manager Teresa Velázquez; director técnico y diseñador Antonio Domingo Alonso Hernández; administración María Domínguez Serrano
Actors: 4 *Perfs:* 50-60 *Prods:* 1 + 1 *Type:* experimental, comedy, physical theatre, street music with La Bande de la María *Venues:* Sala Imperdible 350 *Touring:* Spain, Portugal *Comments:* also run a multi-media, open space, called La Bande de la María, for proposals for music, dance and theatre productions

Teatro la Pupa – Producciones Imperdibles S.L.
Plz. S. Antonio Padua 9, 41002 **Sevilla**
Tel: 95-438 8219 Fax: 95-490 5380
E-Mail: imperdible@arrakis.es
directores José María Roca González, Gema López Torres; jefe de prensa y relaciones externas Alison Maia
Actors: varies *Perfs:* 73 *Prods:* 2 *Type:* avant-garde, visual, movement theatre *Venues:* Sala La imperdible 200, Cafe Teatro El Almacen 80 *Touring:* USA, Spain *Comments:* original productions; also organise festival – Mes de Danza; see also Festivals and Venues

Circ Crac
c/ Mayor 30, 08461 **St. Esteve de Palautordera (Barcelona)**
Tel: 93-848 0552 Fax: 93-848 2807
Internet: www.circ-crac.com
E-Mail: circ@circ-crac.com
director gerente Tortell Poltrona
Actors: 15-20 *Perfs:* 200 *Prods:* 1 *Type:* multi-media nomadic circus *Venues:* Carpa Circ Crac 500 *Touring:* Spain, Europe *Comments:* also home of Centre de Recerca de les Arts del Circ; also organising the future circus school: Escola de Circ

Centre Dramàtic del Vallès
Plaza Didó 1, 08221 **Terrassa (Barcelona)**
Tel: 93-788 7440 Fax: 93-788 7500
E-Mail: it.terrassa@diba.es
president Emili Matalonga; director Joan Anguera; producció & adminitració Montserrst Prat; producció & imatge Judith Figuerola
Actors: 26 *Perfs:* 150 *Prods:* 5 (3 new) *Type:* Catalan, international drama, performed in Catalan, mime *Venues:* Teatro Alegría 300, Sala María Plans 100 *Touring:* Spain, Andorra, France, Europe *Comments:* rep company

Hika Antzerki Taldea
Apdo 46, 20170 **Usurbil (Gipuzkoa)**
Tel: 943-472 688 Fax: 943-470 784
dir art Agurtzane Intxaurraga; gestión y distribución Belén Cruz
Actors: 5 *Prods:* 5 *Type:* musical comedy, children's and street theatre, documentary theatre *Touring:* Spain
Comments: some performances are in Basc language (Euskera)

Circo Gran Fele- Et Circulo Mágico
C/Pepita n°8-pta 2, 46009 **Valencia**
Tel: 96-347 7058 Fax: 96-347 7058
Internet: www.circogranfele.com
E-Mail: circo@bemarnet.es
producción Ane Carolós; PR/prensa Isebel R. Tena
Actors: 11 *Perfs:* 162 *Prods:* 2 *Type:* circus *Venues:* Tent 500 *Comments:* funded by Teatres da la Generalitat Valenciana, Ministerio de Cultura (INAEM) and IMPIVA; also run courses

Gerardo Esteve y Rafael Ponce
C/ San Jacinto 6, 5°, 46008 **Valencia**
Tel: 96-382 4970 Fax: 96-382 4970
director Gerardo Esteve Ibañez
Actors: 2 *Perfs:* 42 *Prods:* 1 *Type:* contemporary, personal creation movements *Venues:* Mercat de les Flors 600 – Barcelona *Touring:* Spain *Comments:* coproduce Conselleria de Valencia; Ministerio de Cultura INAEM; distribution: contact Paula Paz, El Buho; Servicios Teatrales, C/ Recoletos 12, 3° izda, 28001 Madrid, Tel: 91-576 7181, Fax: 91-576 7219

Pavana Producciones
Calle Caballeros, 16-2, 46001 **Valencia**
Tel: 96-315 5393 Fax: 96-315 5395
Internet: www.infoteatro.com
E-Mail: pavana@infoteatro.com
general manager José Alberto Fuentes; artistic director Rafael Calatayud; marketing Concha Catalán; pr Miguel Bea
Actors: varies *Perfs:* 200 *Prods:* 3 *Type:* contemporary *Touring:* Spain *Comments:* coproductions with Ministerio di Cultura and other institutions

Titola Teatre
Artes y Oficios 27 11°, 46021 **Valencia**
Tel: 609-147 317/96-346 3614 Fax: 96-346 3614
directors Susana Solly, Maite Villar
Actors: 5 *Type:* dance, theatre, contemporary mime & dance

Compañía de Teatro Juan Antonio Quintana – Teatro Íntimo
Paseo Zorrilla 99, 3° C, 47007 **Valladolid**
Tel: 983-472 423/689-031 309
director Juan Antonio Quintana;
escenógrafa Mery Maroto
Actors: 8-10 *Perfs:* 140-160 *Prods:* 1 *Type:* classical and contemporary theatre of authors *Venues:* Sala Lope de Vega 800, Teatro 500 *Touring:* Spain, Europe, USA

La Quimera de Plástico
c/ Cisterniga 9, bajo, 47005 **Valladolid**
Tel: 983-210 881/607-899 457(mobile) Fax: 983-201 191
directors Tomás Martín, Andrés Cienfuegos;
consejero delegado Juan Luis Sara
Actors: 8 *Perfs:* 100 *Prods:* 3 *Type:* classical, theatre for children *Venues:* Teatro Juan Bravo 600 *Touring:* Spain, Europe, South America *Comments:* see also Agents

Teatro Corsario
Panaderos 14, 4 dcha, 47004 **Valladolid**
Tel: 983-302 637 Fax: 983-302 637
Internet: www.gconta.es/corsario/
E-Mail: corsario@gconta.es
director Fernando Urdiales;
productor ejecutivo Luis Santana
Actors: 14 *Perfs:* 100 *Prods:* 4 repertory, 1 new annually *Type:* classical, mainly Spanish authors of the 'Golden Century' *Touring:* Spain, South America, Europe

Los Excéntricos Marceline, Sylvestre y Zaza
Passeig Violetes 52, 08190 **Valldoreix (Barcelona)**
Tel: 93-675 1566 Fax: 93-675 1566
artistic directors Marceline Kahn, Josep Ventura, Didier Armbruster; administrator Anna Tom
Actors: 3 *Perfs:* 140 *Prods:* 1 *Type:* contemporary clown, visual comedy, slapstick and music *Venues:* middle and small scale theatres *Touring:* worldwide

Els Joglars
Av. Països Catalans 5, 08500 **Vic (Barcelona)**
Tel: 93-883 2443 Fax: 93-885 3315
Internet: www.elsjoglars.com
E-Mail: elsjoglars@elsjoglars.com
gerente Josep Maria Fontseré; director Albert Boadella
Actors: 10 *Perfs:* 170 *Prods:* 1 *Type:* contemporary *Touring:* Spain, South America, Europe

Teatrapo
Av. Chile 11, Bloque 5, 3° D, 06700 **Villanueva de la Serena (Badajoz)**
Tel: 924-847 146/844 4033 Fax: 924-845628
director José Fernando Delgado Prieto
Actors: 7 *Perfs:* 130 *Prods:* 3 + 1 *Type:* street theatre, mime *Touring:* Spain, Europe, South America
Comments: funding by Consejeria de Cultra de la Junta de Extremadura

Bekereke
Carretera Vitoria Estella, km.24,
01128 **Virgala Menor (Alava)**
Tel: 945-410 168/629-463 668 (mobile) Fax: 945-410 168
director Elena Armengot;
lighting design Tom Donnellan
Actors: 6 *Perfs:* 50 *Prods:* 2 *Type:* contemporary street, multi-media *Touring:* Spain *Comments:* co-productions with dance companies and multi-media including one-off large scale site-specific events; also design lighting and scenography for other productions

Porpol S.C.L.
Beato Tomás de Zumarraga 98, 3°A,
01009 **Vitoria-Gasteiz**
Tel: 945-200 771/689-900 477 Fax: 945-285 645
directora Carmen Ruiz Corral
Actors: 5 *Perfs:* 250 *Prods:* 3 *Type:* avant garde, comedy *Touring:* Spain, Europe *Comments:* manages Taller de Artes Escénicas de Victoria, which runs courses for professionals of the performing arts; organises Festival de Teatro de Humor de Araia; see Festivals

Samaniego Grupo de Teatro
Monsenor Estenaga S/N, 01004 **Vitoria-Gasteiz**
Tel: 945-256 6585/271 496
director técnico Oskar Ruiz de Luzuriaga; director artístico Carlos González Petite
Actors: 12 *Perfs:* 22 *Prods:* 1+ 1 new *Type:* children's theatre, street theatre *Touring:* Spain *Comments:* own productions designed for children and young audiences; 1999-2000 is 30th anniversary of the company

Teatro Paraíso,
Centro de Creación Teatral para niños y jóvenes
Abechuco Pueblo 8° B, 01013 **Vitoria-Gasteiz**
Tel: 945-289 323 Fax: 945-269 184
E-Mail: teatro.paraiso@clientes.euskaltel.es
coordinadora Pilar López; director artístico Miguel Garrido, Y Toni Alba
Actors: 5-6 *Perfs:* 200 *Prods:* 4 *Type:* contemporary texts for children, adolescents and adults, comedy *Venues:* Sala de Vitoria 310, Sala de Bilbao 507 *Touring:* Spain, Europe *Comments:* company repertory consists of 6 different plays for children, young people of different age groups and adults; pedagogical team organises workshops for children's theatre and art installations

Achiperre Cooperativa teatro
Carretera de Almaraz, km. 1, 600, 49026 **Zamora**
Tel: 980-670 487 Fax: 980-670 611
Internet: www.gconta.es/achiperre
E-Mail: achiperre@gconta.es
secretario administrativo Fernando Pérez; director artístico Cándido de Castro
Actors: 6 *Perfs:* 120 *Prods:* 2 *Type:* theatre for youths, street theatre *Venues:* Teatro Principal Zamora 350 *Touring:* Egypt, Portugal, Cuba, Belgium, Italy, Russia *Comments:* provincial, regional and national funding

El Silbo Vulnerado
Poligono Malpica-Alfindén c/m, n° 4 La Puebla,
50171 **Zaragoza**
Tel: 976-568 589/107 353 Fax: 976-568 025/107 378
Internet: www.teatro.gi
E-Mail: silbo@teatro.gi
director artístico Luis Felipe Alegre
Perfs: 250 *Prods:* 4 (2 new) *Type:* performances created according to natural spaces, with audience participation; poetry, music, theatre *Touring:* Spain, South America, Cuba *Comments:* teaching programmes of music and theatre for secondary schools and universities; alternative address: Via Univérsitas 19, Casa 1-2° C, 50009, Zaragoza

Nuevo Teatro de Aragón
Poeta Leon Felipe 23, 3° C, 50015 **Zaragoza**
Tel: 976-533 312/327 388 Fax: 976-533 312
director Francisco Ortega Suárez;
gerente Benito de Ramón Pérez
Actors: 11 *Perfs:* 150 *Prods:* 1-2 *Type:* comedy, classical and contemporary *Touring:* Spain *Comments:* regional and national funding; own rehearsing venue not open for audiences

Promotora de Animación Infantil (PAI)
Calle Jaca 30-32, 50017 **Zaragoza**
Tel: 976-336 399
Fax: 976-536 796
E-Mail: pai@promi.es
representante María José Gorgojo
Actors: 9 *Perfs:* 2 *Prods:* 4 *Type:* street, audience participation (children play the main parts) *Venues:* open-air *Touring:* Spain, South America *Comments:* organize courses, work with teachers/schools

Tántalo Teatro de Zaragoza
c/ San Juan Bosco 58, 4° B, 50009 **Zaragoza**
Tel: 976-620 638
Fax: 976-620 638
director Danilo Nieto de Losada; gerente Juan Mohedano
Actors: 14-15 *Perfs:* 60 *Prods:* 2 *Type:* classical, contemporary *Venues:* Teatro Principal 1800 *Touring:* national

Teatro de la Ribera
Paseo de Cuellar, 4 (Villa Luna), 50006 **Zaragoza**
Tel: 976-276 113 Fax: 976-276 113
directora artística Pilar Laveaga
Actors: 10 *Perfs:* 100 *Prods:* 3 (1 new) *Type:* contemporary, Spanish, classical, foreign theatre *Touring:* Jordan, Morocco, Tunicia *Comments:* regional and national funding

Teatro del Temple
C/ Alfonso I, n° 2 bajo, 50003 **Zaragoza**
Tel: 976-298 865 Fax: 976-395 752
E-Mail: templesc.3021 @cajarural.com
dramaturgia (presidente de la Compañía) Alfonso Plou; dirección artística Carlos Martín; producción ejecutiva (secretario general) José Tricas
Actors: 3-13 *Perfs:* 100 *Prods:* 4 *Type:* contemporary *Touring:* Spain *Comments:* funded by regional government

Tranvía Teatro
Teniente Coronel Pueyo 8-10 Local, 50004 **Zaragoza**
Tel: 976-445 011
Fax: 976-445 127
E-Mail: rafat@redestb.es
director Rafael Campos; manager Cristina Yañez
Actors: 10-15 *Perfs:* 300 *Prods:* 10 *Type:* Spanish authors, comedy, children's theatre *Venues:* Teatro de la Estación 135 (own venue) *Touring:* Spain *Comments:* runs a drama school for young people; see also Venues

SWEDEN (+46)

Angereds Nya Teater
Triörgatan 1, 424 65 **Angered**
Tel: 313-315 408 Fax: 313-320 660
Internet: www.angeredsnyateater.se
E-Mail: info@angeredsnyateater.se
artistic director t.b.a.
Actors: 4-6 actors, 4 musicians *Perfs:* 100 *Prods:* 3-5 *Type:* contemporary drama aimed at 18-30 year olds; family entertainment, multi-cultural
Venues: Angereds Nya Teater 242

Älvsborgsteatern
Bryggaregatan 10, 503 38 **Borås**
Tel: 33-290 790 Fax: 33-290 799
director Ronnie Hallgren; choreographer Björn Elisson
Actors: 6-9 + 4 dancers *Perfs:* 160-200 *Prods:* 4-5 *Type:* classic, modern, mainly for youth, modern dance for young people *Venues:* Älvsborgsteatern 90-120 *Touring:* Sweden (mostly in the west of Sweden)

Borås Stadsteater
Box 55032, 50402 **Borås**
Tel: 33-357 000 Fax: 33-357 995
director Jarl Lindahl (33-357 653)
Actors: 16 *Perfs:* 250 *Type:* classical and modern *Venues:* Stadsteater: main stage 500, small stage 130

Dalateatern
Teatergatan 1, 791 62 **Falun**
Tel: 23-29050/16677 (ticket & programme info)
Fax: 23-10153
theatre director Hans Sjöberg; producer Mona Pettersson; marketing Krister Hell; finance & administration Leif Grundtman
Actors: 7 *Prods:* 4 own + 3 guest *Type:* classical, modern (Swedish and foreign) *Venues:* main stage 460, small stage (Black Box) 140 *Touring:* national, occassionally international *Comments:* see also orchestras

Folkteatern i Gävleborg
Norra Rådmansgatan 23, Box 146, 801 03 **Gävle**
Tel: 26-129 200 Fax: 26-126 282
Internet: www.gavlefolkteater.se
E-Mail: info@gavlefolkteater.se
director Tomas Lindström; producer Örjan Hans-Ers; stage manager Constantin Carlestam; dramaturg Joakim Stenshäll; administrator Kurt Nyander
Actors: varies *Perfs:* 450 *Prods:* 8-9 *Type:* plays about northern Sweden (Norrland), classical and contemporary *Venues:* Folkteatern (own stage) 200, The Wooden Theatre (Järvsö) 300, The Gasworks (Gävle) 300, stagefor children and youth (Bollnäs)150
Touring: Sweden

Atelierteatern
Erik Dahlbergsgatan 1, 411 26 **Göteborg**
Tel: 31-711 2088/138 901 Fax: 31-711 2051
Internet: www.algonet.se/~atelie
E-Mail: atelie@algonet.se
directors Ingela Clarholm, Mats Thorin;
artistic director Peter Wanselius
Actors: 4 + 2 musicians + 1 artist *Perfs:* 300 *Prods:* 4 *Type:* youth and children and family drama *Venues:* Atelierteatern 120 *Touring:* Sweden *Comments:* partly touring company (2 prods. at home, 2 prods. on tour); large part of work in form of 'improvisation theatre'

Folkteatern i Göteborg
Olof Palmes Plats, 413 04 **Göteborg**
Tel: 31-607 560 (admin)/607 575 (box office)
Fax: 31-607 599
Internet: www.folkteatern-goteborg.se
E-Mail: gugge.sandstrom@folkteatern.goteborg.se
manager and producer Gugge Sandstrøm
Actors: 12 permanent *Type:* mainly new written Swedish plays, also musicals, theatre for children, modern classic, Western drama *Venues:* Stora scenen 400, Lilla scenen 70 *Comments:* work permanently on small stage for 3-8 yrs, also have a touring company

Göteborgs Stadsteater
Box 5094, 402 22 **Göteborg**
Tel: 31-615 100 Fax: 31-615 114
Internet: www.culture.goteborg.se/gtheatre
E-Mail: info@stadsteatern.goteborg.se
managing director Gunwy Silander; technical manager Lars Garpenfeldt; marketing manager Malin Johansson
Actors: 12 *Perfs:* 200 *Prods:* 15 *Type:* Swedish and international, classical and modern, children's and youth theatre *Venues:* from studio 180 to auditorium 850 *Touring:* Western Sweden, Mozambique *Comments:* see also Venues

Teater Bhopa
Parkgatan 9, 411 24 **Göteborg**
Tel: 31-711 6069 Fax: 31-711 6068
E-Mail: bhopa@goteborg.mail.telia.com
director & artistic director Alexander Öberg;
producer Eva Lindberg
Actors: 10 *Perfs:* 70 *Prods:* 2 *Type:* modern and classical *Venues:* Teater Bhopa 100 *Touring:* national, international

Teater Uno
Stampgatan 4, 411 01 **Göteborg**
Tel: 31-159 990 Fax: 31-153 600

Helsingborgs Stadsteater
Karl Johans gata 1, 252 67 **Helsingborg**
Tel: 42-106 800/810 (ticket & info) Fax: 42-184 258
Internet: www.stadsteatern.helsingborg.se
theatre director Lars Svenson
Actors: 20 *Perfs:* 200 *Prods:* 7 *Type:* dramatic, classic and modern *Venues:* Stadsteater (main stage) 600,, small stage 100 *Touring:* Sweden, Denmark

Jönköpings Länsteater
Box 483, 551 16 **Jönköping**
Tel: 36-171 500 Fax: 36-171 501
Internet: www.jonkopings-lansteater.com
E-Mail: teater@jonkopings-lansteater.com
manager Bernt Lindkvist; finance director Per Brandt
Actors: 12 *Perfs:* 450 *Prods:* 8 *Type:* mainly new Swedish writers, some modern classics *Venues:* The Match Factory 165, The Black Room 50 to 200 *Touring:* south, mid. and northern parts of Sweden *Comments:* youth project: Sara Och Steinunn – musical for young people

Byteatern
Barlastgatan 8, 392 31 **Kalmar**
Tel: 480-085 602 Fax: 480-085 448
director Staffan Jonsson; admin Agneta Petersson
Actors: 5 + 2 musicians *Perfs:* 250 *Type:* modern, object theatre, mixed forms *Venues:* Kalmar theatre house (2 stages) *Touring:* international
Comments: theatre for the region

Nya Skånska Teatern
Östergatan 31, 261 34 **Landskrona**
Tel: 418-16555 Fax: 418-411 035
Internet: www.nyaskanskateatern.se
E-Mail: info@nyaskanskateatern.se
director Håkan Persson; producer Eva Omagbemi; economy Eva Rosberg
Actors: 12 *Perfs:* 135 *Prods:* 3-4 *Type:* cabaret, musical drama, drama for youth and children *Venues:* Landskrona Teater 180 to 280 *Touring:* Sweden *Comments:* performs extensively in schools

Norrbottensteatern
Box 50136, 973 24 **Luleå**
Tel: 920-243 400 Fax: 920-243 401
Internet: www.norrbottensteatern.bd.se
E-Mail: norrbottensteatern@nll.se
theatre director Rolf Degerlund
Actors: 8 + 3 musicians + freelance *Perfs:* 300 *Prods:* 6 *Type:* Swedish and international drama, classical and modern for adults and children *Venues:* Scen A 300, Scen B 120, Scen C 100 *Touring:* regional *Comments:* member of ETC (European Theatre Convention)

Expressteatern
Rörsjögatan 26, 211 37 **Malmö**
Tel: 40-124 111 Fax: 40-124 111
producer Ed Damron; art dirs Ed Damron, Vidisha Mallik
Actors: 2+ *Perfs:* 100 *Prods:* 1-2 *Type:* mixture of theatre, mime, mask and comedy *Touring:* national and international *Comments:* perform in Swedish and English

Malmö Musikteater
Box 175 20, 200 10 **Malmö**
Tel: 40-208 400
Fax: 40-208 423
managing & artistic director Lars Rudolfsson;
general director Philip Zanden
Actors: 40 choristers, 15 singers and guests, 63 orchestra *Perfs:* 10 *Prods:* 2-3 *Type:* opera, musicals, drama *Venues:* Storan 1460, Intiman 200 *Comments:* see also Venues and Opera

Proteus Theatre Company
Polgatan 56c, 216 11 **Malmö**
Tel: 40-160 986
administrator Maude Cantoreggi-Pederson
Actors: 3 + 2 musician *Perfs:* 70 *Prods:* 5-6 (incl. co-productions) *Type:* children's theatre, cabarets, classics, contemporary *Touring:* Sweden *Comments:* touring company

Östgötateatern
Box 3114, 600 03 **Norrköping**
Tel: 11-218 500 Fax: 11-199 752
Internet: www.ostgotateatern.se
E-Mail: info@ostgotateatern.se
managing director Lenny Carlsson; theatre director/artistic director Johan Celander; head of press and marketing Ricky Andreis; head of technique (stage and performance) Kent Blomberg; head of technique (construction) Kerstin Kalered; production co-ordinator Marie Wahlqvist
Type: classical and contemporary theatre, modern musical, youth and children's theatre, contemporary dance performances *Venues:* Stora Teatern Norrköping 600, Stora Teatern Linköping 400 *Comments:* see also Dance

Riksteatern – Swedish National Touring Theatre
Hallundavägen 30, 145 83 **Norsborg**
Tel: 8-5319 9100
Fax: 8-5318 3012
Internet: www.riksteatern.se
general manager Thomas Lyrevik;
information officer Eric Lindqvist
Actors: 50 *Perfs:* 2000 *Prods:* 50 *Comments:* Riksteatern includes: Tyst Teater (Theatre for the Deaf), Unga Riks (Theatre for Children and Youth) and the Cullberg Ballet; see also National Organisations (Riksteatern)

Tyst Teater
c/o Riksteatern, 14583 **Nörsborg**
Tel: 8-5319 9100 Fax: 8-5318 3012
Internet: www.riksteatern.se
E-Mail: barbro.gramen@riksteatern.se
artistic director Tom Fjordefalk;
administrator Barbo Gramén
Actors: 3 + guests *Perfs:* 115 *Prods:* 3-6 *Type:* repertoire theatre, from children's theatre to classical drama for adults *Touring:* worldwide *Comments:* origionally a theatre for the deaf; performances sometimes exclusively in sign language; sometimes mixed (sign + verbal); touring company for small and large venues

Länsteatern i Örebro
Änggatan 15, Box 8042, 700 08 **Örebro**
Tel: 19-215 900/908 (director)
Fax: 19-215 910
theatre director Leis Nilsson;
administration Lars Norling
Actors: 10 *Perfs:* 350 *Prods:* 6-7 *Type:* classical drama, musicals and modern theatre *Venues:* H Bergman Theatre 580, Old Theatre 200, Experimental Studio 120 *Touring:* Sweden

Västanä Teater
Västanä 63, 684 93 **Ransäter**
E-Mail: teaterprod@vastanateater.se
art director Leif Stinnerbom; PR Ewa Britt
Actors: varies *Perfs:* 60+ *Prods:* 3 *Type:* children's/youth theatre *Touring:* Sweden

Västerbottensteatern
Nordlandergatan 1,
931 33 **Skellefteå**
Tel: 910-37232
theatre director Ingrid Blidberg; information officers Monica Lindgren
Actors: 12 *Perfs:* 300 *Prods:* 4 largescale productions, 2 smaller *Type:* all types including theatre for children *Venues:* Nordanåteatern 421, Brunnsteatern 150 *Touring:* Sweden *Comments:* 98 season emphasizes children's theatre

Länsteatern Skaraborg
Eric Ugglas plats, 541 50 **Skövde**
Tel: 500-443 400 Fax: 500-443 432
Internet: www.skaraborgsteatern.se
E-Mail: post@skaraborgsteatern.se
theatre director Hans Berndtsson
Actors: 6 (permanent company) + 1 musician *Perfs:* 250-300 *Prods:* 7-10 *Type:* music theatre, drama (for adults & children) *Touring:* national, international *Comments:* occassionally go out to schools and do community work; cooperate with Stiftelsen Musik i Väst (see entry in Promoters); touring company but also own productions for special venues in Skövde
(e.g. in 2000 in Barn)

Boulevardteatern
Götgatan 73,
116 62 **Stockholm**
Tel: 8-642 9805
Fax: 8-642 9814
producers Annica Sigfridsson, Michael Sgerstrom
Perfs: 3 *Prods:* 3 *Type:* modern and classical
Venues: capacity 206

Group 98
Grupp 98
Teater Plaza, Odengatan 78, 113 22 **Stockholm**
Tel: 8-315 050 Fax: 8-310 151
Internet: www.teaterplaza.nu.se
E-Mail: info@teaterplaza.nu.se
theatre director Thorstern Flinck
Perfs: 100 *Prods:* 3 *Venues:* Teater Plaza 100 *Comments:* Group 98 is a non-profit organisation

Kungliga Dramatiska Teatern/Dramaten
Nybrogatan 2, Box 5037, 102 41 **Stockholm**
Tel: 8-665 6100 Fax: 8-663 8816
Internet: www.dramaten.se
E-Mail: ac.jernberg@dramatenise
theatre director Ingrid Dahlberg; deputy director Staffan Ryden; financial director Karin Unghanse; planning director Elisabet Holmström; information officer Ann-Christine Jernberg; production director Jan Lundberg
Actors: 80 *Perfs:* 1000-1500 *Prods:* 20-25 *Type:* classical, modern *Venues:* Stora scenen 800, Lilla scenen 350, Elverket 300, Målarsalen 200, Lejonkulan 70, Sibyllan 70, Fyran 80 *Touring:* Sweden, Scandinavia, Europe, USA

Orionteatern
Katarina Bangata 77, 116 62 **Stockholm**
Tel: 8-640 2960 Fax: 8-643 3004

Parkteatern Stadsteatern
Djurgardsv 42, Box 16412, 103 27 **Stockholm**
Tel: 8-5062 0292 Fax: 8-5062 0291
Internet: www.stadsteatern.stockholm.se
E-Mail: parkteatern@stadsteatern.stockholm.se
company director Benny Fredriksson
Actors: 6 wintertime, 20 summertime *Perfs:* 160 *Prods:* 15 *Type:* outdoor theatre, also musicals, ballet, dance, theatre for children + indoor performance during winter period *Comments:* free entry to all performances

Pocketteatern
Ringvägen 78, 118 60 **Stockholm**
Tel: 8-641 9370/5304 2214 Fax: 8-643 7339
E-Mail: forum@pocket-teatern.se
artistic directors Jöram von Euler, Birgitte Strand, Arsa Lundgren
Actors: 7 *Perfs:* 150 *Type:* new works, educational theatre, community work *Venue:* Forum Theatre *Touring:* Europe *Comments:* touring company

Södra Teatern
Mosebacke Torg 1-3, 116 46 **Stockholm**
Tel: 8-640 3334 Fax: 8-641 8068
E-Mail: info@sodrateatern.com
administration Catharina Clason; finance Ulla Wennerholm; marketing manager Eric Sjöström
Perfs: 50-60 *Prods:* 3 in-house, guest theatre for 20-25 other productions *Type:* all types: opera, ballet, drama, musicals, children's theatre *Venues:* Stora Scen 418, Kägelbanan 150, Caféteatern 120

Stockholms Stadsteater
Box 164 12, Beridarbansgatan 5, 103 27 **Stockholm**
Tel: 8-5062 0100 Fax: 8-5062 0101
Internet: www.stadsteatern.stockholm.se
E-Mail: info@stadsteatern.stockholm.se
theatre director Peter Wahlqvist; international director Christer Dahl; information officer Elisabeth Lindfors; planning director Bo Wahlström
Actors: 80 *Perfs:* 1400 *Prods:* 25 *Venues:* 6 stages, main house 750, smallest studio 80, the open air theatre Parkteatern *Touring:* Sweden, Europe

Teater Galeasen
Fri Scen, Skeppsholmen, Slupskjulsvägen, Hus 103,
111 47 **Stockholm**
Tel: 8-611 0030/0920 Fax: 8-611 0905
E-Mail: teater@galeasen.se
director Rickard Günther
Actors: varies *Perfs:* 80 *Prods:* 2 *Type:* modern *Venues:* Fri Scen cap. up to 100 *Touring:* national, international

Teatro Popular Latinoamericano
Hälsingegatan 3, 113 23 **Stockholm**
Tel: 8-315 250/328 290 Fax: 8-321 480
E-Mail: fhd420w@tninet.se
director Bernardo Llorens; producers Ana Maria Padilla
Actors: 5 *Perfs:* 200 *Prods:* 4 *Type:* Latin American and Spanish plays, Swedish drama *Venues:* Alias Teater 80 *Touring:* Sweden, Latin America, Spain, Northern Europe *Comments:* the company is mainly touring and presents Latin American and Spanish drama mostly, but also Swedish plays performed in Spanish and children's plays performed in both Spanish and Swedish; also performs Swedish and Latin American plays in Swedish with international actors

Theatre 3
Teater 3
Rosenlundsgatan 12, 118 53 **Stockholm**
Tel: 8-669 0060 Fax: 8-669 0058
E-Mail: teatertre@telia.com
producer Jenny Hagström; directors Hannu Book, Bengt Andersson, Lena Stefenson
Actors: varies *Perfs:* 130 *Prods:* 2-3 *Type:* mime, speech, movement, mainly children's theatre *Touring:* Sweden

Unga Klara
Stockholms Stadsteater, Box 164 12, 103 27 **Stockholm**
Tel: 8-5062 0375 Fax: 8-5062 0371
E-Mail: lotta.fristorp@stadsteatern.stockholm.se
artistic director Suzanne Osten; producer Peter Kollarik; dramaturg Nils Gredeby; marketing Anders Frennberg; press Lotta Fristorp
Actors: 10 + 4 *Perfs:* 60 + 50 *Prods:* 2 *Type:* modern & classical theatre (including children's theatre)

Friteatern
Bristol, Sturegatan 39, Box 1041, 172 21 **Sundbyberg**
Tel: 8-980 460 Fax: 8-291 546
Actors: 12 *Perfs:* 370 *Prods:* 4 (2 new) *Type:* mostly modern including children's theatre *Venues:* Bristol 130 *Touring:* Germany, Scandinavia, Cuba, Sweden *Comments:* produces highly successful children's theatre; the company writes and produces its own work and also collaborates with Swedish authors to produce new work; also invite guest theatre groups

Teater Västernorrland
Box 120, 851 03 **Sundsvall**
Tel: 60-180 300 Fax: 60-175 668
Internet: www.teater-vnorr.se
E-Mail: info@teater-vnorr.se
theatre director Tomas Melander
Actors: 16 *Perfs:* 400-500 *Prods:* 6 *Type:* classical, modern, children's theatre *Venues:* around Sundsvall 150 to 350 *Touring:* touring company, around county of Västernorrlands

AB Upsala Stadsteater
Box 1001, 751 40 **Uppsala**
Tel: 18-160 300 Fax: 18-160 301
Internet: www.uppsala.se/stadsteatern
E-Mail: stadsteatern@uppsala.se
theatre director Stefan Böhm;
administrative director Sverker Gawell
Actors: 15 permanent *Perfs:* 468 *Prods:* 12 new *Venues:* stage A 550, stage B 220, youth theatre 120

Teater Västmanlands
Slottsgatan 11, 722 11 **Västerås**
Tel: 21-108 500
Fax: 21-108 519
Internet: www.vltmedia.se/teater/web.html
managing & artistic director Anders Lerner;
budget & economics Göran Kihl
Actors: 12 + 3 musicians (additional per production)
Perfs: up to 400 *Prods:* 7 *Type:* classical, modern, children's *Venues:* stage A 400, stage B 100, children's/youth theatre 75 *Touring:* Sweden and international festivals *Comments:* regional theatre of Västmanland

Region Teatern Blekinge Kronoberg
PO Box 486, 351 06 **Växjö**
Tel: 470-10130 Fax: 470-13806
Internet: www.ltbleking.se/kultur/teatern
E-Mail: info@regimteatern.g.se
director Ingrid Kyrö; contact Margareta Berglund
Actors: 15-20 *Perfs:* 500 *Prods:* 12 *Type:* children's theatre, new and classics, adaptation of literary works *Venues:* home venue 10 *Touring:* mostly South Sweden; guest performances in Northern Eruope *Comments:* venue address: Västergatan 20, Växjö;
office at Kungsgatan 22, Växjö

SWITZERLAND (+41)

Theater Tuchlaube
Metzgergasse 18, 5000 **Aarau**
Tel: 62-824 2909
Fax: 62-824 2909
direction Urs Heller, Goy Krneta
Actors: 1-10 *Perfs:* 150 *Prods:* 12 (2 children's/youth theatre per year) *Type:* contemporary *Venues:* Theater Tuchlaube, two halls, each has a capacity of 130 *Comments:* no permanent ensemble

Jungbrunnen Theater Zürich
Loowiesenstr. 57,
8106 **Adlikon**
Tel: 1-840 3170
director and artistic leader Ernst Jenni, Doramaria Frey; general music director Simone Reymond
Actors: 12 *Perfs:* 60 *Prods:* 12
Type: drama, operetta, classical concerts *Comments:* touring company; company's productions are specifically for the elderly; touring is aimed at venues with an elderly audience

Theater Basel
Elisabethenstrasse 16, Postfach, 4010 **Basel**
Tel: 61-295 1100/1460
Fax: 61-295 1200/1590
general manager Michael Schindhelm; administrator Ivo Reichlin; ballett director Joachim Schlömer; opera director Albrecht Puhlmann; PR Kathrin Gartmann; general music director Julia Jones; choir director Henryk Polus; drama director Stefan Bachmann
Actors: 24 *Perfs:* 250 (+ opera and dance)
Prods: 20 *Venues:* Grosse Bühne 1015, Komödie 579, Kleine Bühne 322 *Comments:* see also Opera and Dance

Theater Spilkiste
St. Alban-Vorstadt 12, Postfach 124, 4009 **Basel**
Tel: 61-272 2343 Fax: 61-272 2308
E-Mail: imbos@magnet.ch
Theaterleitung Annette Rommel; Künstlerische Leitung Gerhard Imbsweiler, Ruth Oswalt; Technische Leitung Alex Götz; Ausstattung und Grafik Vincent da Silva; Theaterpädagogik Uwe Heinrich
Actors: 2-4 *Perfs:* 150 *Prods:* 1-2 *Type:* theatre for children to adults *Venues:* Vorstadt Theater 100 *Touring:* Germany, Austria, Tunisa, Switzerland

Kleintheater Krangasse 6
Postfach 589, 3000 **Bern** 8
Tel: 31-352 0278
Rechtsträger u. Leitung Thomas Nyffeler
Actors: varies according to project *Perfs:* 80 *Prods:* 2-4 *Type:* modern performance *Venues:* capacity 80, Kleintheater Krangasse 6 *Comments:* visiting address: Kramgasse 6, 3000 Bern 8; type: contemporary, literary, psychological small-scale theatre, cabaret and concerts

Stadttheater Bern
Nägeligasse 1, 3000 **Bern** 7
Tel: 31-312 1711 Fax: 31-311 3947/312 3670
Internet: www.stub.unibe.ch/kultw/stth/index.html
Direktor Eike Gramss; Stellv. Direktor & Chefdisponent Jochen Sostmann; Dramaturgin Nicola May; Regisseur Urs Schaub; Dramaturgieassistentin Christine Plank; Technischer Direktor Gino Fornasa; Öffentlichkeitsarbeit Karin Diem, Barbara Hauser;
Personaldirektorin Lucia Sternthal
Actors: 17 + 5 guests *Perfs:* 185 + 8 Gastspiele *Prods:* 9 new 1 reprisal *Type:* drama *Venues:* Stadttheater 730, Kornhausbühne 130 *Comments:* see also Opera and Dance

Theater am Käfigturm
Spitalgasse 4, 3011 **Bern**
Tel: 31-381 5050/311 6100 Fax: 31-381 7410
Intendant und Künstlerischer Leiter Roland Morgenegg; Bühnenmeister Christopher Mitton
Actors: 12-16 *Perfs:* 209 *Type:* drama, musicals, dance, cabaret *Venues:* Theater Am Käfigturm 330

Theater der Regionen / Théâtre des Régions – Biel/Bienne – Solothurn
Burggasse 13, Postfach, 2500 **Biel** 3
Tel: 32-328 8969 Fax: 32-328 8967
Direktor Peter Theiler; Verwaltungsleitung t.b.a.; Chefdisponent und persönlicher Referent des Direktors Mario Bettoli; Künstlerische Leitungs Schauspiel Peter Theiler, Sabine Hug; Dramaturgie Johann Casimir Eule; Öffentlichkeitsarbeit Markus Oswald; Leitende Regisseurin Schauspiel Sabine Hug
Perfs: 236 *Prods:* 8 *Type:* modern, classical *Venues:* Stadttheater Solothurn 280, Stadttheater Biel 280 *Touring:* Switzerland, Germany *Comments:* address Solothurn: Theatergasse 16-18, Ch-4500 Solothurn, tel:32-622 1182, fax: 32-623 1631; see also Opera, Orchestras and Promoters

Théâtre de Carouge
57 rue ancienne, case postale 2031,
1227 **Carouge-Genève**
Tel: 22-343 2555 Fax: 22-342 8795
Internet: www.theatredecarouge
E-Mail: tcarouge@iprolink.ch
directeur général Georges Wod-Wodzicki; administratice Thierry Gérard;
directeur technique Victor Trailescu
Actors: varies *Perfs:* 180-200 *Prods:* 5 *Type:* classical, comedy *Venues:* hall A 500, hall B 136 *Touring:* Switzerland, France, Russia, Vietnam, Canada

Goetheanum-Bühne
Rüttiweg 45, 4143 **Dornach**
Tel: 61-706 4242 Fax: 61-706 4251
Internet: www.goetheanum.ch
E-Mail: buehne@goetheanum.ch
Geschäftsführung Thomas Didden; Künstlerische Leitung Carina Schmid, Paul Klars Kor
Actors: 21 (+ 13 dancers) *Perfs:* 200 *Prods:* 4 *Type:* drama, puppets, concerts, eurythmie *Venues:* Grosser Saal 962, Schreinerei Saal 240, Kleiner Saal 460, Theater am Bahnhof 180 *Comments:* own ensemble, also organize festivals, conferences

Comédie de Genève
6 blvd des Philosophes, 1205 **Genève**
Tel: 22-320 5000/5001 (bookings) Fax: 22-320 0076
Internet: www.arlequin.ch/comedie
director Anne Bisang; administration Gisele Musy; public relations Vershique Marko-Batchinsky
Perfs: 7 *Prods:* 3 *Type:* contemporary, classical *Venues:* capacity 700 *Touring:* national, France

Compagnie du Revoir, La
Rue des mouettes 6, 1227 **Genève**
Tel: 22-343 3524/734 0782 Fax: 22-734 0782
direction et mise en scène Anne Bisang;
administration Gisèle Musy-Miche
Perfs: 25-40 *Prods:* 2 *Type:* contemporary *Venues:* Théâtre Saint-Gervais 200 *Touring:* China, France, Greec *Comments:* see also Venues (Théâtre Saint-Gervais)

Grand Théâtre de Genève
11 Blvd du Théâtre, 1211 **Genève** 11
Tel: 22-418 3000 Fax: 22-418 3001
Internet: www.geneveopera.ch
E-Mail: dirgen@geneveopera.ch
directrice générale Renée Auphan; secrétaire général François Duchêne; coordinateur artistique du ballet Giorgio Mancini; chef des choeurs Guillaume Tourniaire; directeur technique Jacques Ayrault; chef financier Martine Chevalier; attachée de presse et relations publiques Marie-Claire Mermoud; adjoint à la direction générale Marcel Quillévéré
Perfs: 100 (20 ballet) *Prods:* 10 + 5 recitals *Type:* ballet, opera, récitals *Venues:* Grand Théâtre 1488, Foyer 260, Bâtiment des Fances Dotricca 985 *Touring:* China, France, Greece, Turkey *Comments:* see also Opera and Dance

Studio d' Action Théâtrale (SAT)
3 rue Butini, 1202 **Genève**
Tel: 22-731 7227 Fax: 22-731 7227
secretary and public relations Clara Brancorsini; arts director Gabriel Alvarez
Actors: 5 *Perfs:* 45 *Prods:* 1 *Type:* experimental *Venues:* Rehearsal room 150, Salle de representation 100 *Touring:* South America

Théâtre am Stram-Gram
56 Route de Frontenex, 1207 **Genève**
Tel: 22-735 7924 Fax: 22-735 8041
Internet: www.regart.ch/amstramgram
director Dominique Catton;
administrative director Pierre-André Bauer
Actors: varies *Perfs:* 68 + 35 (scolaires) + 40 (touring) *Prods:* 3 *Type:* classical, contemporary *Venues:* capacity 330 *Touring:* France, Switzerland, Québec

Théâtre Le poche – Genève
4 rue de la Boulangerie, 1204 **Genève**
Tel: 22-310 4221 Fax: 22-781 3113
directeur Philippe Morand;
administrative director Maryvonne Joris
Actors: varies *Perfs:* 150-160 *Prods:* 7-9
Type: contemporary *Venues:* Théâtre Le poche 119

Théâtre Populaire Romand
case postale 1418, Rue Beau-site 30,
2301 **La Chaux-de-Fonds**
Tel: 32-913 1510 Fax: 32-913 1550
Internet: www.tpr.ch
director Charles Joris; administrative director Eric Lavanchy; public relations Claudine Blanchard
Actors: varies *Perfs:* 100 *Prods:* 2-3 *Type:* classical, contemporary *Venues:* capacity 200 *Touring:* Switzerland, France, Belgium, Luxemburg, French speaking Africa *Comments:* see also Festival of Neuchâtel

Crochet A Nuages, Le
Rue des Glaciers 2, 1004 **Lausanne**
Tel: 21-320 0534 (admin)/0120 (direction)
Fax: 21-320 0534
direction Armand Deladoey;
administration Roberto Betti
Actors: 4-10 *Perfs:* 15-30 *Prods:* 2-3 *Type:* classical, contemporary *Comments:* authors: W. Faulkner, Pasolini

Ensemble Théâtre Lausanne
Rue des Glaciers 2, 1004 **Lausanne**
Tel: 21-320 0534 Fax: 21-320 0534
direction Roberto Betti
Comments: theatre productions with invited directors

Théâtre Boulimie
Place Arlaud 1, 1003 **Lausanne**
Tel: 21-312 9700 Fax: 21 311 2689
directors Martine Jeanneret, Lova Golovtchiner
Actors: varies *Perfs:* 100-120 *Prods:* 2 *Type:* comedy *Venues:* capacity 152

Teatro Sunil
viale Cassarate 4, 6900 **Lugano**
Tel: 91-923 2850 Fax: 91-922 6285
E-Mail: sunil@ticino.com
direzione artistica e amministrazione Daniele Finzi-Pasca, Maria Bonzanigo
Actors: 7 *Perfs:* 150 *Prods:* 8 *Type:* drama, dance, clowning and experimental theatre *Touring:* worldwide *Comments:* experimental drama and dance group; perform in Italian, German, French, English, Spanish and Portugese; organise acting and dance seminars

Luzerner Theater
Theaterstrasse 2, 6002 **Luzern**
Tel: 41-210 3363 Fax: 41-210 3367
Internet:
www.centralnet.ch/kultur/luzernertheater/index.html
E-Mail: luzernertheater@centralnet.ch
Director Barbara Mundell; Dramaturgie Viola Hasselberg, Ann-Marie Arioli; Chefdisponent Jürgen Heene; Administrator Adrian Balmer; Musikdirektor Jonathan Nott; Ballettdirektor Walter Heun; Dramaturgin/Pressebeauftragte Ruth Schüann
Actors: 31 *Perfs:* 250 *Prods:* 5 + 3 in junge bühne *Type:* classical, new work *Venues:* Luzerner Theater 558, UG 80 *Touring:* Switzerland *Comments:* see also Dance and Opera

Centre Dramatique Chablais-Riviera
Théâtre du Vieux-Quartier, Rue du Pont 32,
1820 **Montreux**
Tel: 21-961 1132 Fax: 21-961 1133
E-Mail: cdcr-tvq@span.ch
directeur administratif et directeur artistique Jean-Philippe Weiss; administratrice Sylviane Vassy
Actors: 2-20 (Swiss, French and Belgian) *Perfs:* 100 *Prods:* 5 *Type:* all types especially comedy *Venues:* capacity 120, Théâtre du Vieux-Quartier, Montreux 1820 *Touring:* France *Comments:* perform in French

Théâtre Kléber-Meleau
Chemin de l'Usine à Gaz 9, 1020 **Renens**
Tel: 21-625 8400/29 (box-office) Fax: 21-625 8434
director Philippe Mentha;
administrative director Jacqueline Stettler
Perfs: 110-120 *Prods:* 3 *Type:* classical, contemporary *Venues:* capacity 323 *Touring:* Switzerland

Mummenschanz Stiftung
Trogenerstr. 80, Alt Stätten, 9450 **St Gallen**
Tel: 71-755 5547 Fax: 71-755 1254
contact Floriana Frassetto, Hans-Jürgen Tobler
Actors: 3-5 *Perfs:* 120 *Prods:* 1 *Type:* mix of theatre, mask, mime, comedy theatre *Touring:* worldwide

Stadttheater St Gallen
Museumsstrasse 1-24, 9004 **St Gallen**
Tel: 71-242 0505 Fax: 71-242 0506/7
Internet: www.stadttheuterstgallen.ch
Geschäftsführender Direktor Werner Signer; Schauspieldirektor Peter Schweiger; Chiefdisponent und Leiter des Künstlerischen Betriebs Rainer Schaub; Chefdramaturgin Madelaine Herzog; Dramaturgin Musiktheater Beale Breidenbach; Kinder und Jugendtheater Anja Horst; Öffentlichkeitsarbeit Christina Strobel
Actors: varies *Perfs:* 76 *Prods:* 5 (+ 1 children's play) *Type:* drama, opera, musicals, dance, ballet *Venues:* Stadttheater 741, Studiobühne 120 *Comments:* guest performances: Baden, Schaffhausen, Winterthur; also have a mobile children's theatre appearing in schools, kindergarden etc.; see also Opera and Dance

Sommertheater Winterthur
Stadthausstrasse 8a, Postfach 560, 8401 **Winterthur**
Tel: 52-212 3113 Fax: 52-212 7764
Intendant & Künstlerischer Leiter Hans Heinrich Rüegg
Actors: 40 *Perfs:* 80 *Prods:* 6 *Venues:* Sommertheater Garten up to 300, Saal up to 250

Theater Kanton Zürich
Postfach 385, 8400 **Winterthur**
Tel: 52-212 1442 Fax: 52-212 8819
E-Mail: theater.zuerich@tkz.ch
artistic director Jordi Vilardaga
Actors: 10 *Perfs:* 180 *Prods:* 4 *Venues:* Sidi Theater 150 *Touring:* Switzerland : visting address: St. Gallerstr. 40, 8400 Winterthur Switzerland

Bernhard-Theater
Theaterplatz, 8001 **Zürich**
Tel: 1-268 6689 Fax: 1-268 6696
directors Peter Schaerer, Wilhelmina Urech
Actors: 5-12 *Perfs:* 330 *Prods:* 9 *Type:* comedy, musical, dialect folkplay *Venues:* capacity 450 *Touring:* Switzerland

Bühne 64
Bellerivestrasse 3, 8008 **Zürich**
Tel: 1-382 2525 Fax: 1-382 2710
director Margot Medicus
Actors: 49 *Perfs:* 400 *Prods:* 6 *Type:* all types *Touring:* Germany, Austria, Lichtenstein, Switzerland, Luxemburg *Comments:* touring company

Neue Schauspiel AG
Zeltweg 5, Postfach, 8032 **Zürich**
Tel: 1-265 5757 Fax: 1-265 5800
Internet: www.schauspielhaus.ch
Intendant Dr Reinhard Palm; Künstlerischer Betriebsdirektor Annemarie Lang; Verwaltungsdirektor Marcel Müller; Leitender Dramaturg Bruno Hitz; PR Dramaturgie Marlies Lanker
Actors: 18 + guests *Perfs:* 13 *Prods:* 13 *Type:* classical, modern *Venues:* Große Bühne 823, studio 150 *Touring:* Germany *Comments:*
venue address- Rämistr. 34, 8001 Zürich

Off Off Stage
Off Off Bühne
Nordstr. 146, 8037 **Zürich**
Tel: 1-273 1692
E-Mail: vincentp@access.ch
Koproduzent, Regisseur, Autor Igor Bauersima; Koproduzenten, Schauspieler Ingrid Sattes, Alexander Seibt, Pascal Ulli
Actors: 3 *Perfs:* 10 + guest performances *Prods:* 1 *Venues:* Koproduktionshaus Theater an der Gessnerallee 400 *Touring:* German speaking countries *Comments:* for bookings – Pascal Ulli Tel:1-273 1692 E-mail:pascalulli@hotmail.com; German contact – Ingrid Sattes Tel:30-7870 6362 E-mail:isatt@aol.com; for press – Alexander Seibt Tel:1-262 5944

Ring-Theater
Aemtlerstr. 32, 8003 **Zürich**
Tel: 1-463 0294 Fax: 1 463 0294
director André Steger
Actors: 6-10 *Perfs:* 20-25 *Prods:* 1-2 *Touring:* Switzerland, abroad

Theater 58
Kanzleistrasse 127, 8004 **Zürich**
Tel: 1-291 0737 Fax: 1-241 0029
Bühnenleiter André Revelly;
Sekretariat Roswitha Würker
Actors: 8 *Perfs:* 110-140 *Prods:* 3-5 *Venues:* transportable touring stage 400 *Touring:* Switzerland, Germany, Austria

Theater Neumarkt
Neumarkt 5, 8001 **Zürich**
Tel: 1-267 6411 (Betriebsbüro)/6464 (Kasse)
Fax: 1-252 2439
Internet: www.theaterneumarkt.ch
Administrative Gabi Glesti; Verwaltungsratspräsident crescantia Dünsser, Otto Kukla; Technischer Leiter Norbert Marks; Dramaturgie Maren Rieger; Betriebsbüro Arlette Zimmermann; Öffentlichkeitsarbeit Uwe Heinrichs
Actors: 7 + guests *Perfs:* 200 *Prods:* 10 *Type:* mainly Sprechtheater, some music theatre *Venues:* seating capacity 220, Probebühne Werdinsel 90, Neumarkt-Separée 40 *Touring:* guest performances

TURKEY (+90)

Adana Devlet Tiyatrolari
Adana State Theatres
Adana
Tel: 322-359 0868

Ankara Devlet Tiyatrolari
Ankara State Theatres
Genel Müdürlük General Directorate, Mithatpasa Cad. 29/2, Kizilay, **Ankara**
Tel: 312-310 7225 Fax: 312-312 6507

Ankara Sanat Tiyatrosu – AST
Ankara Art Theatre
Izmir Cad. Ihlamur Sk. 7/4, Kizilay, **Ankara**
Tel: 312-425 0256

Antalya Devlet Tiyatrosu
Antalya State Theatre
Antalya
Tel: 242-248 1477

Bursa Devlet Tiyatrolari
Bursa State Theatres
Bursa
Tel: 224-221 2944 Fax: 224-222 5146

Diyarbakir Devlet Tiyatrosu
Diyarbakir State Theatre
Diyarbakir
Tel: 412-224 0007

Diyarbakir Sehir Tiyatrolari
Diyarbakir Municipal Theatres
Diyarbakir
Tel: 412-223 5160

Erzurum Devlet Tiyatrosu
Erzurum State Theatre
Erzurum
Tel: 442-234 8064

Ali Poyrazoglu Tiyatrosu
Ali Poyrazoglu Theatre
Oguzhan Cad. n° 19, Findikzade, **Istanbul**
Tel: 212-635 9587

Bakirköy Belediye Tiyatrolari
Bakirköy Belediye Municipal Theatre
Bakirköy Belediyesi, Yeni Mahalle-Bakirköy, **Istanbul**
Tel: 212-661 1941/42/43

BKM Oyunculari
Hasfiran Sok. n° 75, Besiktas, **Istanbul**
Tel: 212-260 1156

Dormen Tiyatrosu
Dormen Theatre
Ergenekon Cad. N°98, Pangalti, **Istanbul**
Tel: 212-241 2737 Fax: 212-248 9766

Dostlar Tiyatrosu
Dostlar Theatre
Baro Han Peremeci Sok., Tünel, **Istanbul**
Tel: 212-252 5935

Gönül Ülkü Gazanfer Özcan Tiyatrosu
Gönül Ülkü Gazanfer Özcan Theatre
Efe Sanatevi Bahceler Sok. n° 20, Mecidiyeköy, **Istanbul**
Tel: 212-212 9482

Hadi Caman Yeditepe Oyuncularia
Hadi Caman Yeditepe Variety Theatre
Tesvikiye Cad. n° 160, Nisantasi, **Istanbul**
Tel: 212-246 1777

Istanbul Devlet Tiyatrolari
Istanbul State Theatres
A.K.M., Taksim, **Istanbul**
Tel: 212-249 6944 (Taksim Stage)/245 2590 (Aziz Nesin Stage)
Fax: 212-243 7322 (Aziz Nesin Stage)

Istanbul Sehir Tiyatrolari
Istanbul Municipal Theatres
Genel Müdürlük, Harbiye, 30200 **Istanbul**
Tel: 212-240 2244
Fax: 212-248 2667
director Karabey Aydosan; artistic director Erol Keskin; theatre research laboratory Beklan Algan
Actors: 160

Kenter Tiyatrosu
Kenter Theatre
Halaskargazi Cad., Harbiye, **Istanbul**
Tel: 212-246 3589 Fax: 212-247 9295

Nejat Uygur Tiyatrosu
Nejat Uygur Theatre
Cavre Tiyatrosu, Kocamustafapasa, **Istanbul**
Tel: 212-585 5935/589 5759

Tiyatro Bakis
Efe Sanatevi, Bahceler Sokak n° 20, Mecidiyeköy, **Istanbul**
Tel: 212-212 9482

Tiyatro Istanbul
Profilo Kültür Merkezi, Mecidiyeköy, **Istanbul**
Tel: 212-216 4070

Tiyatro Kare
Abidei Húrriyet Cad. n° 227, Sisli, **Istanbul**
Tel: 212-230 1618

Tiyatro Oyunevi
Cihangir cad. Tansel apt., 33/5 Taksim, 80060 **Istanbul**
Tel: 212-251 2629/3942/6060
Fax: 212-252 7271
Internet: www.tiyatrooyunevi.com
E-Mail: info@tiyatrooyunevi.com
artistic director Mahir Gunsirayi (gunsiray@superon-line.com); designer Claude Leon; administrative director Ece Eroglu
Actors: 5-10 *Perfs:* 40-60 *Prods:* 2-3 *Type:* modern, classical, street, comedy, new writing etc. *Touring:* national and international

Izmir Devlet Tiyatrolari
Izmir State Theatres
Izmir
Tel: 232-489 0158
director Önder Alkim

Izmit Cevre Tiyatrosu ve Sanatevi
Izmit Art House and Theatre
Inönü Cad. Limonluk Gecidi 2/2, **Izmir**
Tel: 262-321 4111

Kocaeli Bölge Tiyatrosu
Kocaeli Bölge Theatre
Belediye Ishani Bati Blv. k. 5, **Izmir**
Tel: 262-324 1090

Konak Belediye Tiyatrosu
Konak Belediye Theatre
32 Sokak N° 4, Güzelyali, **Izmir**
Tel: 232-245 2367
general director Ali Haydar Erçig (51-357 319); stage manager Muammer Uz (51-151 129/774 587)
Actors: 15 *Perfs:* 200 *Prods:* 4 (2 for adults, 2 for children) *Type:* experimental, modern, new writing *Venues:* home capacity 200, Ahmetli-Manisa 300, Ankara ODTU University 300, Denizli 400 *Touring:* Ankara *Comments:* founded in 1982/83

Tiyatro Izmir
Izmir Theatre
1469 Sok 30/A, Alsancak, **Izmir**
Tel: 232-422 0354

Konya Devlet Tiyatrosu
Konya State Theatre
Konya
Tel: 332-350 0207

Sivas Devlet Tiyatrosu
Sivas State Theatre
Sivas
Tel: 346-225 7994

Trabzon Devlet Tiyatrolari
Trabzon State Theatres
Trabzon
Tel: 462-326 1479

Van Devlet Tiyatrosu
Van State Theatre
Van
Tel: 432-214 4106

UKRAINE (+380)

Dnepropetrovsk Ukrainian Musical-Dramatic Theatre T Shevchenko
Ul. Lenina 5, 320000 **Dnipropetrovsk**
Tel: 56-244 2735

Donetsk Ukrainian Musical and Dramatic Theatre ARTEMA
vul. Artema 74a, 340055 **Donetsk**
Tel: 62-293 2862/930 981

Lviv Regional Ukrainian Musical and Dramatic Theatre
Teatralna pl. 1, 293720 **Drohobych**
Tel: 3244-23264

Ivano-Frankivsk Ukranian Regional Musical and Dramatic Theatre
vul Radianska 42, 284000 **Ivano-Frankivsk**
Tel: 3422-31443/31087

Kharkiv Academic Ukrainian Dramatic Theatre T Shevchenko
vul Sumska 9, 310000 **Kharkiv**
Tel: 572-434 045

Kherson Ukrainian Musical and Dramatic Theatre
vul Horkoho 7, 325013 **Kherson**

Khmelnytskyi Ukrainian Musical and Dramatic Theatre
Ul. K. Libknekhta 40, 280000 **Khmelnytsky**
Tel: 3822-64362

Franko Kiev National Ukranian Academic Dramatic Theatre
Pl. I. Franko 3, 2520001 **Kiev (Kyiv)**
Tel: 44-229 3414/4842 Fax: 44-229 4010

Kyiv Drama and Comedy Theatre
Brovarskii pr. 25, **Kiev (Kyiv)**
Tel: 44-517 3669

Kirovohrad Ukrainian Musical and Drama Theatre
Ul. Lenina 4, 316000 **Kirovohrad**
Tel: 5222-41411

Volyns Ukrainian Musical and Dramatic Theatre T Shevchenko
Teatralna pl., 263000 **Lutsk**
Tel: 3322-26179

Lviv Academic Ukrainian Dramatic Theatre M. Zankovetsoyi
Ul. L. Ukrainky 1, 290000 **Lviv**

Mykolaiv Ukrainian Theatre of Drama and Musical Comedy
Ul. Dunaeva 59, 327017 **Mykolaiv**
Tel: 512-372 092

Odessa Ukrainian Musical and Dramatic Theatre
vul Pestera 15, 270057 **Odessa**
Tel: 482-235 566/235 486

Poltava Ukrainian Musical and Dramatic Theatre
vul Zhovtneva 23, 314601 **Poltava**
Tel: 5322-73392/72911

Rivne Regional Ukrainian Musical and Dramatic Theatre
Teatralna pl., 266000 **Rivne**

Krymskyi Ukrainian Musical Theatre
Pr. Kirova 17, 330000 **Simferopol**
Tel: 652-254 428

Tcherkasy Ukrainian Musical and Dramatic Theatre
vul Shevchenko 284, 257000 **Tcherkasy**
Tel: 472-474 418

Tchernivtsvi National Ukrainian Musical and Dramatic Theatre
Teatralna pl. 1, 274000 **Tchernivtsi**
Tel: 3700-25664/26525/27177

Tchernyhiv Regional Musical and Dramatic Theatre
Pl. Kuibysheva, 250000 **Tchernyhiv**
Tel: 4622-73030/40/29

Ternopil Ukrainian Musical and Dramatic Theatre T Shevchenko
vul. Shevchenko 6, 282000 **Ternopol**
Tel: 3522-23196/200 589

Zakarpatskii Regional Ukrainian Musical and Dramatic Theatre
Teatralna pl. 8, 294000 **Uzhhorod**

Vinnytsia Ukrainian Musical and Dramatic Theatre
Ul. Dzerzhinskoho 13, 286009 **Vinnytsia**
Tel: 4322-322 675

Zaporizzhia Ukrainian Music and Drama Theatre
Pr. Lenina41, 330063 **Zaporizzhia**
Tel: 612-645 726

Zhytomyr Ukrainian Musical and Dramatic Theatre
Pl. Lenina 6, 262000 **Zhytomyr**
Tel: 412-314 470

UNITED KINGDOM (+44)

Borderline Theatre Co
North Harbour Street, **Ayr (Scotland)** KA8 8AA
Tel: 1292-281 010 Fax: 1292-263 825
chief executive Edward Jackson; projects co-ordinator Helen Coughtrie; artistic director Leslie Finlay; secretary/bookkeeper Joyce Miller; education and outreach development officer Christine Woodburn
Actors: up to 30 *Perfs:* up to 180 *Prods:* 2 (1 new world premiere) *Type:* emphasis on new writing and young people's theatre *Touring:* Scotland *Comments:* touring theatre company

Guy Masterson Productions
Studio 7, The Bull Theatre
68 The High Street, **Barnet** EN5 5SJ
Tel: 20-8449 7800 Fax: 20-8449 5252
Internet: www.guymasterson.com
E-Mail: admin@guymasterson.com
director Guy Masterson;
general manager Jenny Sutherland
Type: small scale touring theatre, varied repertoire; all shows suitable for venues up to 1000 seats *Touring:* national, international

Scarlet Theatre, The
Studio 4, The Bull, 68 High Street, **Barnet** EN5 5SJ
Tel: 20-8441 9779
Fax: 20-8447 0075
Internet: www.scarlettheatre.co.uk
E-Mail: admin@scarlettheatre.co.uk
artistic director Gráinne Byrne; general manager Kate Littlewood; associate director Katarzyna Deszcz
Actors: up to 10 *Perfs:* 100 approx. *Prods:* average 2 *Type:* visual theatre that intergrates actors, design, lights, music and text as equal players on the stage space; texts are either improvised on adapted from classical modern or European plays *Venues:* theatre, art centres, small to middle scale *Touring:* national, international
Comments: alternative E-mail: grainne.byrne@scarlettheatre.co.uk; Scarlet interacts with art in galleries to create cross-art performances; actors training and residencies undertaken

Orchard Theatre
108 Newport Road,
Barnstaple EX32 9BA
Tel: 1271-371 475 Fax: 1271-371 825
Internet:
ourworld.compuserve.com/homepages/orchardtheatre
E-Mail: orchardtheatre@compuserve.com
administrator Frederica Notley;
artistic director Bill Buffery
Actors: up to 9 *Perfs:* 150 *Prods:* 3-4 *Type:* new plays and contemporary versions of classic texts, adult and children's shows *Venues:* capacity 700 (theatres to village halls) *Touring:* national, international, France, Canada *Comments:* touring company, small & middle scale venues; offer educational programmes from primary school to college age range; also have 3 youth groups

Haymarket Theatre Company
Haymarket Theatre, Wote Street,
Basingstoke RG21 7NW
Tel: 1256-323 073
Fax: 1256-357 130
Internet: www.haymarket.org.uk
E-Mail: info@haymarket.org.uk
theatre director Alasdair Ramsay;
theatre manager Tim Wills
Actors: varies *Perfs:* 288 *Prods:* 11 *Type:* classical and modern theatre *Venues:* Haymarket Theatre 426, Central Studio (Queen Mary's College, Basingstoke) 130
Comments: educational and community programmes; workshops also available; see also Venues

Natural Theatre Company (Bath Arts Workshop)
Widcombe Institute, Widcombe Hill, **Bath** BA2 6AA
Tel: 1225-469 131 Fax: 1225-442 555
Internet:
ourworld.compuserve.com/homepages/naturals
E-Mail: naturals@compuserve.com
general manager Dot Peryer; artistic director Ralph Oswick; tour co-ordinator Sandie Hurd
Actors: up to 30 *Perfs:* 200-300 *Type:* street theatre specialists *Touring:* worldwide

Dubbeljoint Productions Theatre Co. Ltd.
245 Lisburn Rd., **Belfast (Northern Ireland)** BT9 7EN
Tel: 28-9020 2222 Fax: 28-9020 2223
administrator Maura Brown; artistic director Pam Brighton; writer in residence Marie Jones
Actors: varies *Perfs:* 120 per year *Prods:* 3 *Type:* Irish drama, new writing, political drama *Venues:* capacity 200 to 1000 (incluidng purpose built theatres, community centres, town halls) *Touring:* UK, Australia, USA, Canada, Europe
Comments: creates work that addresses the unique political and social problems facing the whole of Ireland and touring that work as widely as possible

Lyric Theatre
55 Ridgeway Street, Stranmillis Embankment,
Belfast (Northern Ireland) BT9 5FB
Tel: 28-9066 9660/381 081 (box office)
Fax: 28-9038 1395
director of administration Liz McLean
Actors: varies *Perfs:* 250+ *Prods:* 12+ productions per season (season runs July-June) *Type:* modern European classics, new commissioned works, Irish classics *Venues:* Lyric Theatre 304 *Comments:* only full-time repertory theatre in Northern Ireland

Prime Cut Productions
McAvoy House, 17a Ormeau Av.,
Belfast (Northern Ireland) BT2 8HD
Tel: 28-9031 3156 Fax: 28-9031 3156
E-Mail: primecut.cbn@artservicesireland.com
artistic director Jackie Doyle;
general manager Russ Ogsgon
Actors: 5 *Perfs:* 60 *Prods:* 2 + readings *Type:* contemporary international *Touring:* Ireland

SHIBBOLETHeatre
89-91 Academy Street,
Belfast (Northern Ireland) BT1 2LS
Tel: 1247-853 258 Fax: 1247-853 258
E-Mail: shib@compuserve.com
co-artistic directors John McIlduff, Emily Mytton
Actors: 3-5 *Perfs:* 30 *Prods:* 1-2 *Type:* physical, visual theatre *Touring:* regional touring plans, Edinburgh Festival- August, Dublin Festival – October
Comments: current work is co-produced with Sinequanon Theatre Co company based in France and work is performed in French

Tinderbox Theatre Company
Mc Avoy House, 17a Ormeau Av.,
Belfast (Northern Ireland) BT2 8HD
Tel: 28-9043 9313 Fax: 28-9032 9420
E-Mail: tinder@darcam.co.uk
general manager Eamon Quinn
Prods: 3 + 1 *Type:* contemporary, classic, new writing
Touring: Ireland

Birmingham Repertory Theatre
Centenary Square, Broad Street, **Birmingham** B1 2EP
Tel: 121-236 6771 (administration)/4455 (box office)
Fax: 121-236 7883
Internet: www.birmingham/rep.co.uk
E-Mail: info@birmingham/rep.co.uk
executive producer John Stalker; artistic director Bill Alexander; associate director Tony Clark; head of marketing & development Annie Smart
Actors: varies *Perfs:* 200+ *Type:* classic, discovery & new plays *Venues:* Main House 800 approx., Studio up to 120 *Comments:* building-based producing company, occasional receiving venue, occassionaly takes tours out nationally and internationally; see also Venues; alternative E-mail: www.the/door.co.uk

Round Midnight
Unit 8 14-20 George Street, Balsall Heath,
Birmingham B12 9RG
Tel: 121-440 8188/961-313 449 Fax: 121-440 8188
Internet: welcome.to/rmtheatre
E-Mail: rmtheatre@yahoo.com
directors Stuart Lane, Claire Downes
Actors: 3 *Perfs:* varies *Prods:* 5 *Type:* community theatre, theatre in Education (TIE), small scale touring, youth theatre *Venues:* The Custard Factory 200 *Touring:* national *Comments:* produces dynamic new theatre for diverse audience; aims to be challenging and above all entertaining; funded by Regional Arts Board, Birmingham City Counciland has received National Lottery Funding; runs youth theatre; see Raw Talent (q.v.)

Octagon Theatre
Howell Croft South, **Bolton** BL1 1SB
Tel: 1204-529 407
Fax: 1204-380 110
head of marketing & sales Lynn Melville; press & marketing officer Rachel Bartholomew
Actors: varies *Perfs:* 60+ *Prods:* 10 *Type:* classical, modern *Venues:* Octagon Theatre 420, The Bill Naughton Theatre up to 100 *Comments:* building-based producing theatre; offers educational and outreach programmes, also youth theatre (age 8-30) with weekly free workshops, these activities come under the heading: activ 8; see also Venues

mind the ... gap
Queens House, Queens Road, **Bradford** BD8 7BS
Tel: 1274-544 683
Fax: 1274-544 501
Internet: www.mindthegap.demon.co.uk
E-Mail: arts@mindthegap.demon.co.uk
artistic director Tim Wheeler; administrative director Julia Skelton; company administrator Sally Bailey; associate director Dave Calvert; care coordinator Emma Potter; theatre development worker Matt Hargrave; production manager t.b.a.
Actors: 10 *Perfs:* 100 *Prods:* 6 per year *Type:* written and devised work, often site-specific *Touring:* national
Comments: mind the ... gap works with people who are traditionallly excluded from mainstream arts practice

Good Company Theatre Productions
46 Quebec Street,
Brighton BN2 2UZ
Tel: 1273-606 652
Fax: 1273-606 926
artistic director Sue Pomeroy;
adminstrator Emma Rees
Actors: 15-20 per production *Perfs:* 225
Prods: 2-4 *Type:* new writing, classics, Brecht
Venues: Bath Theatre Royal, Nottingham Theatre Royal, up to 1500 *Touring:* national and international
Comments: middle/large scale touring company with strong educational commitment

Bristol Old Vic
Theatre Royal, King Street,
Bristol BS1 4ED
Tel: 117-949 3993 (administration)/
987 7877 (box office)
Fax: 117-949 3996
Internet: www.bristol-old-vic.co.uk
E-Mail: bristol.old.vic@cableinet.co.uk
general manager Sarah Smith; artistic director Andy Hay; production manager Derek Simpson; assistant general manager James Taljaard; education director Heather Williams; press and development officer Phil Gibby; marketing officer Andrew Smaje
Actors: varies *Perfs:* performs daily (excluding Sundays)
Prods: 6-7 per season (Theatre Royal); 20 per year (New Vic Studio); 20 per year (The Basement)
Type: new and classical works *Venues:* Theatre Royal 650, New Vic Studio up to 200, The Basement 80
Comments: building-based company, occasionally available for hire; offers various educational programmes (6-20 age range), community outreach programmes, and workshops; see also Venues

Circomedia Centre for Contemporary Circus and Physical Performance
Kingswood Foundation,
Britannia Road, Kingswood,
Bristol BS15 8DB
Tel: 117-947 7288
Fax: 117-947 7288
Internet: www.circomedia.demon.co.uk
E-Mail: info@circomedia.demon.co.uk
administrator Kim Lawrence; course director Bim Mason; course deputy director Helen Crocker
Actors: 12-18 *Perfs:* 2 *Prods:* 1 *Type:* circus skills intergrated with performance and movement *Venues:* outdoor venues May-September 2000 *Comments:* Circomedia provides long term professional training for those who want to use circus skills with other forms e.g. dance, theatre, cabaret and street theatre

Forkbeard Fantasy
34 Balmoral Road, St Andrews,
Bristol BS7 9A7
Tel: 117-924 8141
Fax: 117-949 1178
company manager Janice May; artistic directors Tim Britton, Chris Britton, Penny Saunders
Actors: 3 *Perfs:* 100 *Prods:* 1 *Type:* comic, visual theatre, interaction with film *Venues:* small-medium scale and site-specific *Comments:* national and international touring company

Pentabus Theatre Company
Bromfield, near Ludlow SY8 2JU
Tel: 1584-856 564
Fax: 1584-856 254
E-Mail: tree@pentabus.prestel.co.uk
artistic director Theresa Heskins
Actors: 2-6 *Perfs:* 160 *Prods:* 4 (3 touring, 1 theatre in education, 1 new theatre) *Type:* small-scale rural touring and theatre in education *Venues:* mostly village halls
Touring: national

Churchill Theatre
High Street, **Bromley** BR1 1HA
Tel: 20-8464 7131 (administration)/
460 6677 (box office)
Fax: 20-8290 6968
adminsitrator Dominic Adams; head of marketing & publicity Colin Hilton; production manager Digby Robinson; producer Ian Ross;
theatre manager John Short
Actors: varies *Perfs:* 250 *Prods:* 8 *Type:* drama, musicals, dance, comedy, opera, children's shows *Venues:* Churchill Theatre 785 *Touring:* UK
Comments: see also Venues

Theatr Bara Caws
A1 Cibyn Industrial Estate, Gwynedd,
Caernarfon (Wales) LL55 2BD
Tel: 1286-676 335
Fax: 1286-676 335
E-Mail: tbaracaw@nascr.net
administrator Linda Brown;
artistic director Ian Rowlands
Actors: varies *Perfs:* 75-100 *Prods:* 3-4 (all new)
Type: touring community poductions *Venues:* small-mid scale community venues *Touring:* Wales
Comments: small-scale co-operative touring company; performs in Welsh language only

Brith Gof
Chapter Arts Centre, Market Road, Canton, **Cardiff (Wales)** CF5 1QE
Tel: 29-2022 2682 Fax: 29-2023 8741
Internet: www.brithgof.org.uk
artistic director Cliff McLucas;
executive director Alison Woods
Actors: up to 15 *Perfs:* 100 *Prods:* 4 (all new) *Type:* work in Welsh, English and bilingual, ranging from large site-specific pieces to small intimate studio productions *Venues:* capacity up to 2000 *Touring:* national, international *Comments:* touring company; creates unique pieces of visual/physical theatre from intimate one performer pieces to large scale site specific theatre works; offers smaller works on tour & also responds to invitations to create special one-off events; produces own TV programmes & publishes material about works and current theatre practices in Wales

Dalier Sylw
Chapter, Market Road, Canton, **Cardiff (Wales)** CF5 1QE
Tel: 29-2023 6650 Fax: 29-2023 6651
Internet: www.users.globalnet.co.uk/~dalsylw
E-Mail: dalsylw@globalnet.co.uk
administrator Mai Jones; artistic director Bethan Jones
Actors: 16-30 *Perfs:* 40-50 *Prods:* 3-5 *Type:* new writing and translations of contemporary & classical European plays *Venues:* theatres, community and site specific *Touring:* Wales *Comments:* productions in Welsh and English; school workshops based on Drama/Welsh A level curriculum

Made In Wales
Chapter, Market Road, **Cardiff (Wales)** CF5 1QE
Tel: 29-2034 4737 Fax: 29-2034 4738
E-Mail: madein.wales@mail.virgin.net
administrator Vicky Ferda-Riley; artistic director Jeff Teare; associate director Rebecca Gould
Actors: 15+ *Perfs:* 30+ *Prods:* 3-4 (all new) *Type:* new Welsh writing performed in English *Venues:* theatres 400, site-specific *Comments:* annual Summer youth project for 16-23 year olds

Sherman Theatre Company
Sherman Theatre, Senghennydd Road, **Cardiff (Wales)** CF24 4YE
Tel: 29-2064 6901 (stage door)/2064 6900 (box office)
Fax: 29-2064 6902
general manager Margaret Jones;
artistic director Philip Clark
Perfs: approx 400 per year *Prods:* 8 new per year *Type:* mixed, mainly young people's theatre *Venues:* Sherman Theatre 474, Studio Theatre 180 *Touring:* Wales, England *Comments:* see also Venues; has youth theatre which performs in the studio theatre

Everyman Theatre Company
Everyman Theatre, Regent Street, **Cheltenham** GL50 1HQ
Tel: 1242-512 515 (Administration)/572 573 (Box Office)/236 700 (press) Fax: 1242-224 305
Internet: www.everyman.u-net.com
E-Mail: admin@everyman.u-net.com
chief executive Philip Bernays
Perfs: 200+ *Prods:* 30+ *Type:* classical, modern, musicals, plays, comedy *Venues:* building-based company- Everyman Theatre 658 *Touring:* community touring *Comments:* see also Venues

Chester Gateway Theatre Company
Gateway Theatre, Hamilton Place, **Chester** CH1 2BH
Tel: 1244-344 238 Fax: 1244-317 277
Internet: www.gateway/theatre.org
administrative director Shea Connolly; artistic director Deborah Shaw; head of marketing Judith Edwards
Perfs: 200 *Prods:* 6 *Type:* classical, modern, musicals, new writings *Venues:* building-based company, occasionally receives in-coming productions; Gateway Theatre 440 *Touring:* national *Comments:* see also Venues

Chichester Festival Theatre
Oaklands Park, **Chichester** PO19 4AP
Tel: 1243-784 437 Fax: 1243-787 288
E-Mail: admin@cft.org.uk
theatre manager Janet Burton; director Andrew Welch; production manager Christopher Bush-Bailey
Actors: varies *Prods:* 8+ *Type:* May-Oct, classical, modern, musicals, Chichester Festival Youth Theatre *Venues:* main house 1374, Minerva Studio 280 *Touring:* national *Comments:* see also Venues

Mercury Theatre Company
Balkerne Gate, **Colchester** CO1 1PT
Tel: 1206-577 006 (admininstration)/573 948 (box office) Fax: 1206-769 607
E-Mail: mercury.theatre@virgin.net
chief executive Dee Evans; artistic producer Gregory Floy; marketing director Philip Bray;
production manager John Buckle;
press and marketing officer Toby Oliver
Actors: varies *Perfs:* varies *Prods:* 5-8 + studio productions *Type:* mix of modern plays, classics, new writing *Venues:* Mercury Theatre 499, Studio 80 *Comments:* the Mercury also runs an award winning programme of community activities including a playwright's group

Belgrade Theatre Trust
Belgrade Theatre, Belgrade Square, **Coventry** CV1 1GS
Tel: 24-7625 6431 Fax: 24-7655 0680
Internet: www.belgrade.co.uk
E-Mail: sdaykin@midnet.com
general manager David Beidas; director Bob Eaton; head of marketing Simon Daykin; associate producer Jane Hytch; head of production t.b.a.
Actors: varies *Perfs:* 420 *Prods:* 16+ *Type:* Studio Theatre: new writing, work for young people *Venues:* Main House 866, Studio 60 *Comments:* building-based producing theatre; occasional receiving venue; bar, restaurant & coffee bar; organise annual Coventry Festival (Coventry Arts Alive Festival – June); see also Venues and Festivals

English Touring Theatre
New Century Building, Hill Street, **Crewe** CW1 2BX
Tel: 1270-501 800 Fax: 1270-501 888
Internet: www.englishtouringtheatre.co.uk
E-Mail: press@englishtouringtheatre.co.uk
executive director t.b.a.; artistic director Stephen Unwin
Actors: 2-18 *Perfs:* 180-200 *Prods:* 3 *Type:* classics – traditional and modern, new plays (British & European) *Venues:* mid-large scale *Touring:* middle-scale, have toured to UK, Egypt, Pakistan, India, Turkey *Comments:* co-productions with other theatres; touring nationally 3 times per year

Welfare State International (Galactic Smallholdings Ltd)
Lanternhouse, The Ellers, Ulverston, **Cumbria** LA12 0AA
Tel: 1229-581 127 Fax: 1229-581 232
E-Mail: info@welfare-state.org
business manager Eileen Strand; artistic director John Fox; education and training coordinator Sue Gill; administrative assistant Dot Queen; centre manager Alec Bell; centre manager's assistant Vicky Halligan; financial assistant Julie Underwood;
warden Dave Hillman
Type: international celebratory arts company *Venues:* Lantern House, Ulverston and site specific *Comments:* Founded in 1968 in Yorkshire, England, have originated many prototypes of celebratory theatre which are now used extensively round the world

CTC
Arts Centre, Vane Terrace, **Darlington** DL3 7AX
Tel: 1325-352 004 Fax: 1325-369 404
Internet: www.stare.net/clevelandtheatre
E-Mail: ctc@clevelandtheatre.demon.co.uk
administrator Liz Clapham;
artistic director Paul Harman
Actors: 3-4 *Perfs:* 200+ *Prods:* 2 new + 2-3 in repertoire + Take Off Festival *Type:* theatre for children and young people *Venues:* capacity up to 200 (usually schools + national arts centre studios) *Comments:* organisers of annual Take Off Festival – England's showcase festival of theatre for children and young people (Take Off '2000 in Derventside, co Durham)

Derby Playhouse
Eagle Centre, **Derby** DE1 2NF
Tel: 1332-363 271 Fax: 1332-294 412
Internet: www.derbyplayhouse.demon.co.uk
E-Mail: admin@derbyplayhouse.demon.co.uk
executive director David W Edwards; artistic director Mark Clements; production manager Kit Lane; press and marketing manager Johnathan Saville;
associated director Pete Meakin
Actors: 6 (average) *Perfs:* 400 *Prods:* 8-9 (main house), 2-3 (studio) *Type:* repertory *Venues:* Main House 535, Studio 110 *Comments:* building-based company, receiving 10 visiting companies per year in studio and in the main theatre; subsidised regional theatre, own productions 40 weeks per year; Sunday concerts; see also Venues

Lone Twin
Dartington College of Art, Totnes, **Devon** TQ9 6EJ
Tel: 1803-862 224 Fax: 1803-862 724
contact Gary Winters (01426-187 005 pager), Gregg Whelan (01523-779 850 pager)
Actors: 2 *Perfs:* 7 *Prods:* 4 *Type:* performance, site specific live events *Touring:* mainly UK, some European *Comments:* most pieces are made to respond to the performance site

Dundee Repertory Theatre Ensemble Company
Tay Square, **Dundee (Scotland)** DD1 1PB
Tel: 1382-227 684/223 530 (box office)
Fax: 1382-228 609
administrative director Joanna Reid; artistic director and chief executive Hamish Glen; artistic director – Scottish Dance Theatre Janet Smith; theatre-based drama therapist Genevive Smyth (Tel: 1382-24 877); arts advocacy worker Rosalie Summerton; associate director of community arts Stephen Stenning
Actors: up to 12 *Prods:* 7 *Type:* repertory theatre; broad range of work *Venues:* stage 455 *Comments:* building-based producing theatre; touring dance co; occasional receiving venue; classical repertoire from round the world adapted and translated by contemporary playwrights mixed with new plays from local writers; rep. season and community based participatory work; home of Scottish Dance Theatre – Scotland's Contemporary Dance Company; see also Venues

Royal Lyceum Theatre
Grindlay Street, **Edinburgh (Scotland)** EH3 9AX
Tel: 131-229 7404/9697 (box office)/248 4848
Fax: 131-228 3955/221 9494 (box office)
Internet: www.infoser.com/infotheatre/lyceum/
E-Mail: royalyceumtheatre@cablenet.co.uk
general manager Nikki Axford; artistic director Kenny Ireland; external affairs manager Sadie McKinley; internal affairs manager Ruth Butterworth
Actors: varies *Perfs:* up to 240 *Prods:* 9-12 *Type:* wide variety of style; emphasis on Scottish work *Venues:* cap 659 *Touring:* UK and abroad, small and middle scale

Theatre Archipelago
2 Hill Street, **Edinburgh (Scotland)** EH2 3JZ
Tel: 131-624 4040 Fax: 131-624 4041
producer Linda Borthwick; artistic director Helena Kaat-Howson; marketing manager Maggie Mackay
Actors: varies *Perfs:* 120 *Prods:* 3-4 *Type:* new work, commissions and collaborative, also work on existing texts *Venues:* small-large scale *Touring:* national, international *Comments:* formaly known as Communicado; in conjunction with visual artists, composers, dancers etc. to create the most impact

Traverse Theatre
Cambridge Street, **Edinburgh (Scotland)** EH1 2ED
Tel: 131-228 3223/1404 (box-office) Fax: 131-229 8443
Internet: www.traverse.co.uk
E-Mail: admin@traverse.co.uk
artistic director Philip Howard;
administrative producer Lucy Mason
Perfs: 60-120 *Prods:* 6 per year *Type:* primarily new writing and foreign plays in translation *Venues:* available for touring international companies capacity up to 250 *Comments:* available for European co-productions, part of Edinburgh Festival Fringe
(submissions from preceding October for the following year); see also Venues

Northcott Devon Theatre and Arts Centre
Northcott Theatre, Stocker Road, **Exeter** EX4 4QB
Tel: 1392-256 182/493 493 Fax: 1392-499 641
Internet: www.ex.ac.uk/northcott
administrator John W Clarke; artistic director Ben Crocker; marketing director Sarah Dance
Actors: varies *Perfs:* 300 *Prods:* 9 *Type:* repertory theatre, wide variety of style *Venues:* Northcott Theatre 433, Studio Theatre 80 *Comments:* building-based producing theatre; receiving venue for dance, opera, concerts and jazz; see also Venues

Theatre Alibi
Northcott Studio Theatre, Emmanuel Road, **Exeter** EX4 1EJ
Tel: 1392-217 315 Fax: 1392-217 315
E-Mail: alibi@eclipse.co.uk
joint general managers Maggie Fisher, Annemarie MacDonald; artistic directors Daniel Jamieson, Nikki Sved
Actors: varies *Perfs:* 191 *Prods:* 3 *Type:* drama, song theatre, story-telling, touring theatre *Venues:* arts venues and community & educational venues *Touring:* regional, national *Comments:* contemporary story theatre; produce separate work for adults and for children

7:84 Theatre Company Scotland
333 Woodlands Road, **Glasgow (Scotland)** G3 6NG
Tel: 141-334 6686
Fax: 141-334 3369
E-Mail: 7.84-theatre@btinternet.com
artistic director Iain Reekie; general manager Tessa Rennie; outreach director Lorenzo Mile; marketing manager Joanna Lennie;
production manager Nick Millar
Actors: varies *Perfs:* 60 *Prods:* 3 (incl 2 new) *Type:* new writing, polictical theatre, outreach work *Venues:* small-middle scale *Touring:* Scotland *Comments:* small to middle-scale touring company; outreach programme, including workshops, usually accompanies productions, for all age ranges

Citizens' Theatre Company
Gorbals, **Glasgow (Scotland)** G5 9DS
Tel: 141-429 5561 (admin.)/0022 (box office)
Fax: 141-429 7374
Internet: www.citz.co.uk
E-Mail: boxoffice@citz.co.uk
general manager Sharman Weir; artistic directors Giles Havergal, Philip Prowse, Robert David MacDonald
Actors: varies *Prods:* 10 *Type:* British and foreign classics, Christmas show *Venues:* building-based company; Citizens Theatre 600, Circle Studio 120, Stalls Studio 60 *Comments:* free previews of all Citizen's company productions; see also Venues

Suspect Culture
128 Elderslie Street, **Glasgow (Scotland)** G3 7AW
Tel: 141-248 8052 Fax: 141-221 4470
E-Mail: suspect.culture@glasgow.almac.co.uk
artistic director Graham Eatough;
general manager David Smith
Actors: varies per production *Prods:* 3 (1 new per year) *Type:* new work *Touring:* UK, Italy, Brazil, Germany, Spain : international theatre company based in Scotland

Theatre Cryptic
Patrick Burgh Halls, 9 Burgh Hall Street,
Glasgow (Scotland) G11 5LW
Tel: 141-338 6929
Fax: 141-357 6924
Internet: www.theatrecyptic.demon.co.uk
E-Mail: claire@theatrecyptic.demon.co.uk
administrator Claire Findlay;
artistic director Cathie Boyd
Actors: varies *Perfs:* 30 *Prods:* 1 *Type:* music theatre, multi-cultural, cross-disciplined *Venues:* small-middle scale theatre *Touring:* Scotland, Hungary, Czech Republic, France, Croatia, Germany, Netherlands *Comments:* keen to establish links with other countries/companies with a view to future co-productions

Tron Theatre Company
63 Trongate,
Glasgow (Scotland) G1 5HB
Tel: 141-552 3748 Fax: 141-552 6657
Internet: www.tron.co.uk
E-Mail: neil@tron.co.uk
administrative director Neil Murray; artistic director Irina Brown; head of marketing & sales Damon Scott
Actors: up to 15 *Perfs:* 70-100 *Prods:* 2-3 *Type:* contemporary/international writers *Venues:* Tron 272
Touring: national *Comments:* small-scale building based company; available for tours to mid-large scale venues; Tron Theatre also used for music concerts, dance, jazz, comedy and visiting theatre companies;
see also Venues

Wildcat Stage Productions Ltd
c/o Creative (Scotland), 69 Buchanan Street,
Glasgow (Scotland) G1 3HL
Tel: 141-314 3732 Fax: 141-314 3738
artistic director David Anderson
Actors: varies *Perfs:* 64-128 *Prods:* 2 new *Type:* music theatre, emphasising accessible and populist Scottish writing *Venues:* from 1000 capacity theatres to studio/community venues *Comments:* available for national and international touring; company policy is to tour accessible theatre throughout the country

IOU Theatre
Dean Clough Industrial Park, **Halifax** HX3 5AX
Tel: 1422-369 217 Fax: 1422-330 203
E-Mail: iou@globalnet.co.uk
administrator Mel Rix; artistic director David Wheeler; administrative producer Richard Sobey
Actors: up to 14 *Perfs:* 100 *Prods:* 2-4 (incl 2 new) *Type:* visual and music based theatre; indoor and outdoor touring shows; site-specific productions, and installations as requested *Venues:* Theatre venues capacity 500, outdoor sites (parks, city squares etc.), site-specific (derelict buildings, beaches etc.) *Touring:* national, international *Comments:* touring company (indoor and outdoor); site-specific commissions as requested; runs short series of workshops on request ranging from 1day to 2 weeks

Harrogate Theatre Company
Oxford Street, **Harrogate** HG1 1QF
Tel: 1423-502 710 Fax: 1423-563 205
Internet: www.harrogatetheatre.co.uk
E-Mail: hgte-theatre@pop3.poptel.co.uk
executive director Sheena Wrigley; artistic director Rob Swain; marketing manager Rita Mulvey;
production manager Phil Day
Actors: 5-6 *Perfs:* 15 per production *Prods:* 5 + pantomime *Type:* full range of arts *Venues:* building based company-main theatre 500, studio theatre 50 *Comments:* has youth theatre for 6-14 year olds;
see also Venues

Queen's Theatre Company
Queen's Theatre, Billet Lane, **Hornchurch** RM11 1QT
Tel: 1708-456 118/443 333 (box office)
Fax: 1708-452 348
Internet: www.users.globalnet.co.uk/~queen's
E-Mail: queen's@globalnet.co.uk
administrative director Henrietta Duckworth; artistic director Bob Carlton; production manager Brod Mason; marketing manager Emma Wallis; house managers Dave Ross, John Kliber
Actors: 9 *Prods:* 9 (all new) *Type:* wide range *Venues:* building-based company capacity 506 *Touring:* national *Comments:* educational and community programes; workshops available; see also Venues

Hull Truck Theatre Company
Hull Truck Theatre, Spring Street,
Hull HU2 8RW
Tel: 1482-224 800 (admin)/323 638 (box office)
Fax: 1482-581 182
Internet: hulltruck.co.uk
E-Mail: admin@hulltruck.co.uk
executive director Simon Stallworthy; artistic director John Godber; education leader/director Peter Turner; general manager Joanne Gower
Actors: 1-8 *Perfs:* 500 *Prods:* 5 *Type:* contemporary, popular theatre *Venues:* capacity 50 to 2000 +, Hull Truck Theatre 300 *Touring:* UK *Comments:* based in Hull Truck Theatre; producing touring company; receiving venue; interested in co-productions; see also Venues

Eastern Angles Theatre Company
Sir John Mills Theatre, Gatacre Road,
Ipswich IP1 2LQ
Tel: 1473-218 202
Fax: 1473-250 954
administrator Rebecca Farrar; artistic director Ivan Cutting; assistant administrator Maggie Jones; marketing officer Andrew Burton;
stage manager Penny Griffin
Actors: 5-12 (varies) *Perfs:* 135 *Prods:* 3 *Type:* new writing, usually with a regional flavour + with live, orginal music *Venues:* Sir John Mills 120, tour to village, community & school halls, arts centres & main house stages up to 100 *Touring:* regionally *Comments:* touring company for Eastern England; residencies,
purchase of mobile seating unit

Wolsey Theatre Co
Civic Drive, **Ipswich** IP1 2AS
Tel: 1473-218 911
Fax: 1473-212 946
E-Mail: info@wolsey.eastern-arts.co.uk
contact Bryan Kempson
Comments: currently closed due to lack of funding; hopes to re-open May 2000

Cumbria Theatre Trust
Theatre by the Lake, Lakeside, **Keswick** CA12 5DJ
Tel: 17687-72282 (admin)/ 744 111 (box office)
Fax: 17687-74698
E-Mail: ctt@btinternet.com
artistic director Ian Forrest;
executive director Patric Guchnist
Actors: 10 *Perfs:* 110-140 *Prods:* 3 reps + up to 12 one off's *Type:* broad range of works
Venues: Theatre by the Lake 400, studio space 100
Comments: middle-scale producing company, all year round programme of popular plays presented in repertoire by resident professional company; receive occasional one night and touring productions

Dukes Playhouse Ltd
The Dukes, Moor Lane, **Lancaster** LA1 1QE
Tel: 1524-67461/66645 (box-office)
Fax: 1524-846 817
administrative director Amanda Belcham;
artistic director Ian Hastings
Actors: varies *Perfs:* 125-150 *Prods:* 5/6 *Type:* classics and new writing *Venues:* Duke's Theatre 320, Studio 198 *Comments:* Park Promenades June-Aug in Williamson Park 500, annual open-air event, one adaptation of a classic production and one family production; B.F.I. funded; regional film theatre

A Quiet Word
11 Hilton Place, **Leeds** LS8 4HE
Tel: 113-262 9303
Fax: 113-262 0740
E-Mail: quitword@msn.com
general manager Arthur Stafford;
artistic director Allison Andrews
Actors: varies per production *Type:* visual theatre
Touring: UK

Exponential Aerial Theatre
2A Hartley Crescent, Woodhouse, **Leeds** LS6 2LL
Tel: 113-244 0612
Fax: 113-244 0612
Internet: www.expo7.demon.co.uk
E-Mail: expo@expo7.demon.co.uk
artistic directors Rachael Nitz, Al Orange
Actors: 5 + 2 technicians *Perfs:* 10-20 *Prods:* 2 (1 new) *Type:* contemporary circus, aerial work, fire, music, acrobatic dance, large scale spectacle on outdoor aerial rig and stage *Touring:* outdoor tour with aerial rig: Europe (Summer 99) *Comments:* workshops and courses

Red Ladder Theatre Company
3 St Peters Building, York Street, **Leeds** LS9 8AJ
Tel: 113-245 5311 Fax: 113-245 5351
E-Mail: red-ladder@geo2.poptel.org.uk
artistic director Wendy Harris;
company administrator Janis Smyth;
touring and development manager Stef Gascoigne
Actors: 8-10 *Perfs:* 130 *Prods:* 2 *Type:* seeks to explore themes and issues relevant and accessible to young people (14+) *Venues:* youth and community centres and studio spaces as arranged *Touring:* national *Comments:* multi-racial actors, performers with disabilities; touring company committed to developing new writing with 2 commissions a year; offers arts based residencies during Spring and Autumn; working on exchange project in India

West Yorkshire Playhouse (Leeds Theatre Trust)
Playhouse Square, Quarry Hill, **Leeds** LS2 7UP
Tel: 113-213 7800 Fax: 113-213 7250
Internet: www.wyp.co.uk
artistic director (chief executive) Jude Kelly; managing director Maggie Saxon; director of community & education Maureen Rooksby; production manager Mike Brown; press officer Philip Meeks;
black arts co-ordinator Jackie Christie;
international co-ordinator Jude Kelly
Actors: up to 50 *Perfs:* 540 (per year) *Prods:* 16+ *Type:* British and International classics; new writing, community theatre, musicals, children's theatre *Venues:* Quarry Theatre 750, Courtyard Theatre 356 *Comments:* building-based producing company, receiving venue; both auditoria used for Sunday events/concerts (classical & jazz); producer of national and international touring work; also touring company to schools; see also Venues

Leicester Haymarket Theatre (Leicester Theatre Trust)
Belgrave Gate, **Leicester** LE1 3YQ
Tel: 116-253 0021 Fax: 116-251 3310
Internet:
www.netpresence.co.uk/leicesterhaymarkettheatre/
executive director Kathleen Hamilton; artistic director Paul Kerryson; Asian theatre initative contact Dr. Vayu Naidu
Actors: up to 25 *Prods:* 7 *Type:* drama, musicals, comedies, new writing *Venues:* Main House 752, Studio 120 *Touring:* some national and international touring, youth theatre, outreach and community; tours
Comments: building-based producing theatre, occasional receiving venue; also Asian theatre group; see also Venues; also runs Asian Theatre Initiative, which includes 3 Asian groups: Peacock (youth theatre), Aurat (womens), and a mens group

Everyman Theatre (Liverpool)
5-9 Hope Street, **Liverpool** L1 9B
Tel: 151-708 0338 Fax: 151-709 0398
Internet: www.everyman.merseyworld.com
E-Mail: info@everyman.org.uk
chief executive Rose Cuthberston; general manager Chris Ricketts; head of marketing Mike James; education officer Lisa Stam; press officer Paul Bell
Actors: up to 10 *Perfs:* 200 *Prods:* 4 *Type:* contemporary writing, experimental productions of modern and traditional classics *Venues:* Everyman Theatre 402
Comments: the company is in the process of merging with Liverpool Repertoire Theatre, at the time of going to print no more information was available;
see also Venues

Kaboodle Productions Ltd
15 Hope Street, **Liverpool** L1 9BQ
Tel: 151-709 2818 Fax: 151-709 2818
E-Mail: kaboodleproductions@btinternet.com
artistic director Lee Beagley
Actors: up to 20 *Perfs:* 150-300 *Prods:* 2 *Type:* innovative physical theatre (classics, adaptions, new works); emphasis on ensemble performance, physical presence and origional live music *Venues:* Everyman Theatre 400 *Touring:* national, international *Comments:* some educational programmes with tours,

Liverpool Repertory Theatre (Liverpool Playhouse)
Liverpool Playhouse, Williamson Square,
Liverpool L1 1EL
Tel: 151-709 8478/8363 (box office) Fax: 151-709 7113
artistic director Richard Williams; administrative director Jane Dawson; press & pr Lizzie Anne Meaghin
Actors: up to 25 *Perfs:* 200 + *Prods:* 10 *Type:* main theatre: drama, musicals, comedy; studio theatre: contemporary writing *Venues:* main Theatre 758, Studio 100 *Touring:* occasionally transfer to West End
Comments: the company is in the process of merging with Everyman Theatre (Liverpool), at the time of going to print no more information was available;
see also Venues

Theatr Powys
The Drama Centre, Tremont Road, **Llandrindod Wells (Wales)** LD1 5EB
Tel: 1597-824 444 Fax: 1597-824 381
E-Mail: theatr.powys@powys.gov.uk
general manager Colin Anderson;
artistic director Ian Yeoman
Actors: 3 *Perfs:* 150 *Prods:* 4 *Type:* varied styles, particular emphasis on devised and new writing *Comments:* small scale touring company catering for theatre in education and community

30 Bird Productions
Nelsons Row, **London** SW4 7JR
Tel: 20-7622 6745 Fax: 20-7622 6707
E-Mail: thirtybird.productions@virgin.net
artistic director/writer/director Mehrdad Seyf; artistic co-ordinator/performer Claire Summerfield; film production co-ordinator Maryam Seyf
Actors: 5 core members *Perfs:* 21 *Prods:* 1 *Type:* new writing, with a visual approach *Venues:* Riverside Studios, Studio 2 400 *Comments:* 30 Bird Productions is committed to producing high quality film and theatre productions from new writing with the aim of telling stories visually without sacrificing the oral tradition

Actors Touring Company
Alford House, Aveline Street, **London** SE11 5DQ
Tel: 20-7735 8311 Fax: 20-7735 1031
E-Mail: atc@cwcom.net
executive producer Gavin Barlow;
artistic director Nick Philippou
Actors: 6-9 *Perfs:* 100 *Prods:* 2 *Type:* ATC takes old stories and works with living writers to produce new theatre relevent and challening to audiences today
Venues: capacity 100 to 400 *Touring:* worldwide

Almeida Theatre Company Ltd., The
Almeida Theatre, Almeida Street, Islington,
London N1 1TA
Tel: 20-7226 7432 (administration)/7359 4404 (box office) Fax: 20-7704 9581 (administration)
Internet: www.almeida.co.uk
E-Mail: almeidatheatre@demon.co.uk
executive director Nick Starr; artistic directors Ian McDiarmid, Jonathan Kent; head of production Paul Clay; admin /asst. to director Amanda Rigali; production co-ordinator Kevin Fitzmaurice; education officer Jo Godwin; assistant to the directorate Anne Hudson
Actors: varies *Perfs:* 300+ *Prods:* 5+ *Type:* classical, foreign plays in translation, new writing *Venues:* Almeida Theatre 300 *Touring:* national and international *Comments:* International Theatre Season; hold Opera and Music Festival in July; see also Venues

Bush Theatre (Alternative Theatre Co Ltd)
The Bush Theatre, Shepherds Bush Green,
London W12 8QD
Tel: 20-7602 3703 Fax: 20-7602 7614
E-Mail: thebush@dircon.com
general manager Fiona Clerk;
artistic director Mike Bradwell
Actors: varies *Perfs:* 270 *Type:* new writing *Venues:* Bush Theatre 105 *Touring:* national and international *Comments:* see also Venues

Cherub Company London, The
Arch 5 and 6, Midland Road, **London** NW1 2AD
Tel: 20-7383 0947 Fax: 20-7383 0947
Internet: www.artsed.co.uk/cherub
director Andrew Visnevski; adminstrator Vi Marriott
Actors: varies *Prods:* 2 new per year *Type:* internationally acknowledged strikingly visual and unconventional approach to classics, new plays and adaptations *Venues:* small to middle scale

Donmar Warehouse at Thomas Neal's (Associate Capital Theatres Ltd)
41 Earlham Street, **London** WC2H 9LD
Tel: 20-7240 4882/7369 1732 (box office)
Fax: 20-7836 4099
executive producer Caro Newling;
artistic director Sam Mendes
Actors: varies *Prods:* 4 *Type:* contemporary classics, new works, music theatre, musicals *Venues:* studio 252 *Touring:* national *Comments:* Donmar Productions Ltd. produces its own work for 9 months of each year with occasional performances by visiting companies (3 per year); see also Venues

Dragonfly Mime Co
405 Kings Road, Chelsea, **London** SW10 0BB
Tel: 20-7739 1899 Fax: 20-7739 1999
E-Mail: dragonflymime@hotmail.com
tour manager Alexander Thompson
Actors: 2 *Perfs:* 150 *Prods:* 3 *Type:* poly-mime, physical theatre, Balinese masks, traditional chinese puppetry, shadowpuppets *Touring:* Mexico, New Zealand *Comments:* return UK for Summer season; see also Puppetry

English Shakespeare Company International Ltd
Unit 16 Archers Street Studios, 10-11 Archers Street,
London W1V 7HG
Tel: 20-7287 1113 Fax: 20-7287 0220
E-Mail: EngShakes@aol.com
education director Christopher Geelan;
artistic director Michael Bogdanov
Actors: 40 (education dept), 15-20 (large scale), 5 small scale *Prods:* 2 large-scale, 8 educational, 1 small/middle *Type:* classical *Venues:* large scale touring venues/small/middle scale *Touring:* national, international *Comments:* touring company; Education Dept address: 21-3 Meard St., London W1V 6PA

English Stage Company (Royal Court Theatre)
Royal Court Theatre, Sloane Square, **London** SW1W 8AS
Tel: 20-7565 5050/5000 (box office) Fax: 20-7565 5001
Internet: www.royal-court.org.uk
E-Mail: marketing@royal-court.demon.co.uk
executive director Vikki Heywood; artistic director Ian Rickson; head of marketing Stuart Buchanan
Actors: no resident group *Type:* new writing *Venues:* Theatre Upstairs 60 & 135, Theatre Downstairs 586 *Comments:* producing theatre; the aim of the English Stage Company is to develop and perform the best in new writing for the theatre, encouraging writers from all sections of our society to address the problems and possibilities of our time, and to promote its work vigorously to new and existing audiences; rebuilt and reburbished Royal Court, opened to the public in Autumn 1999 following a three year lottery project; see also Venues

Gate Theatre
11 Pembridge Road, **London** W11 3HQ
Tel: 20-7229 5387/0706 (box office) Fax: 20-7221 6055
general manager Sarah Preece; artistic director Mick Gordon; general producer Philippe Le Moine
Actors: varies *Perfs:* 240 *Prods:* 9 own, 3 visiting *Type:* world drama in translation, British premieres *Venues:* Gate Theatre 120 *Comments:* see also Festivals

Graeae Theatre Company
Interchange Studios, Dalby Street,
London NW5 3NQ
Tel: 20-7267 1959 (administration)/3164 (minicom)
Fax: 20-7267 2703
Internet: www.users.dircon.co.uk\~graeae
E-Mail: graeae@dircon.co.uk
administrator Tracy Brunt; artistic director Jenny Sealey; administrative director Kevin Dunn; associate director Mandy Colleran;
training development co-ordinator Carolyn Lucas
Actors: no resident group *Perfs:* 95
Type: new theatre writing – issues effecting the disabled community, classic texts adapted from a disability perspective *Venues:* capacity up to 300 *Touring:* national and international *Comments:* professional theatre company of disabled people; work examines issues surrounding disability through theatre training, outreach and education

Greenwich Theatre
Crooms Hill, **London** SE10 8ES
Tel: 20-8858 4447 (administration)
Fax: 20-8858 8042
executive director Hilary Strong
Actors: no resident group *Venues:* capacity 423
Comments: details unconfirmed at time of going to print; plans to re-open Nov. 1999 as producing and receiving theatre; see also Venues

Hampstead Theatre
Swiss Cottage Centre,
London NW3 3EX
Tel: 20-7722 9224/1189(production office)
Fax: 20-7722 3860
Internet: www.hampstead-theatre.co.uk
E-Mail: hampstead-theatre@atlas.co.uk
general manager James Williams; artistic director Jenny Topper; production manager John Titcombe; sales and marketing Vicky Biles;
technical director Alison Buchanan
Actors: varies *Perfs:* 300 + *Prods:* 6-7 per year *Type:* emphasis on new writing *Venues:* Hampstead Theatre 174 *Comments:* building-based company, occasional receiving venue; offer educational and community programmes; see also Venues

Heart and Soul
The Albany Theatre, Douglas Way,
London SE8 4AG
Tel: 20-8694 1632
Fax: 20-8694 1532
Internet: www.heartnsoul.co.uk
E-Mail: heartnsoul@compuserve.com
director Mark Williams; touring and marketing manager Michael Gaunt; financial & administrative manager Angela McNicholl
Actors: 12 + 4 musicians (core touring company)
Perfs: 30 p.a. *Prods:* 3 *Type:* music, music theatre *Venues:* The Albany Theatre, small, medium, large scale venues, open air festivals, arts centres, schools, theatres etc *Touring:* national, Europe, international *Comments:* also organise outreach programmes and workshops and courses in technical theatre, music and performance; Heart and Soul is a company of people with learning difficulties; run and produce the Beautiful Octupus Club, the only cabaret/nightclub run by and for people with learning difficulties in Europe

Jet Theatre
11 Clovelly Road, **London** W5 5HF
Tel: 20-8579 1029
Fax: 20-8566 2815
art director Kenneth Rea
Actors: 5-10 *Perfs:* 30 *Prods:* 1 + 1 new *Type:* physical theatre *Venues:* Riverside 355
Touring: England *Comments:* focusing on link between classical text and physical skills of actors and music

King's Head Theatre
115 Upper Street, Islington, **London** N1 1QN
Tel: 20-7226 8561
Fax: 20-7226 8507
artistic director Dan Crawford;
administrator Pam Mears
Actors: no resident group *Perfs:* 832 (16 per week, 52 weeks per year) *Prods:* 9-10 mainhouse + various different Sunday, Monday & matinee prods
Type: musicals, new plays, revivals *Venues:* King's Head Theatre 125 *Touring:* UK *Comments:* see also Venues

Lyric Theatre Hammersmith
King Street, Hammersmith,
London W6 OQL
Tel: 20-8741 0824
Fax: 20-8741 7694
chief executive Sue Storr; artistic director Neil Bartlett; finance director Pam Cooper;
administrative producer Simon Mellor
Type: classics, international work, music theatre, new work *Venues:* Main House 537, Studio 110 *Comments:* producing company; interested in co-productions; also receiving venue; Studio Theatre has regular programme of visiting companies; limited runs of new plays; see also Venues

MCC Productions/School of Physical Theatre
C/O 5 Lutwyche Road, **London** SE 6
Internet: www.physicaltheatre.com
E-Mail: school@physicaltheatre.com
director Ron East; administrator Lin Grist
Actors: 5 *Perfs:* 50 *Prods:* 3 (all New) *Type:* play/physical theatre *Venues:* various/rented *Comments:* main office is in Canada: P.O. Box 92503, 152 Carlton Street, Toronto ON M5A 4N9; see also MOD

Method & Madness
25 Short Street, **London** SE1 8LJ
Tel: 20-7450 1990/1998 (info. line)/1997 (minicom)
Fax: 20-7450 1991
E-Mail: methodandmadness@mcmail.com
executive producer Mary Caws;
artistic director Mike Alfreds
Actors: 10 + 7 stage management *Perfs:* 200 *Prods:* 5 *Type:* wide ranging repertoire *Venues:* middle scale *Touring:* national and international *Comments:* touring company; workshops available upon request

New Shakespeare Company
Open Air Theatre, Inner Circle, Regent's Park, **London** NW1 4NP
Tel: 20-7935 5884/5756/486 2431/1933 (box office) Fax: 20-7487 4562
artistic and managing director Ian Talbot; general manager Sheila Benjamin
Actors: hired per season *Perfs:* 110 *Prods:* 3 mainstage; 1 children's; numerous Sunday & late night prods *Type:* summer season of classical plays mostly by Shakespeare in rep, with a Broadway type musical *Venues:* Open Air Theatre 1187 *Touring:* national and international *Comments:* summer season May-Sept and Sunday events; fully accessible to wheelchairs; catering & bar facilities; sponsorship & corporate entertainment opportunites

Nitro
6 Brewery Road, 436 Essex Road, **London** N7 9NH
Tel: 20-7609 1331 Fax: 20-7609 1221
Internet: www.nitro.co.uk
E-Mail: black.theatreco-op@virgin.net
artistic director Felix Cross; general manager t.b.a.; administrative officer Natasha Graham
Actors: up to 7 *Perfs:* 100+ *Prods:* 2 per year *Type:* themes linked to the Black experience, emphasis on new writing and music theatre *Venues:* arts centres, studios, educational venues, festivals; up to 450 *Touring:* national *Comments:* small and middle scale touring company; also available for workshops and master classes; also manage 20 strong choir, jazz, soul, blues 'n gospel

Oily Cart Company Ltd
Smallwood School Annexe, Smallwood Road, **London** SW17 0TW
Tel: 20-8672 6329 Fax: 20-8672 0792
Internet: www.users.globalnet.co.uk/~oilycart
E-Mail: oilycart@premier.co.uk
general manager Joanna Ridout;
artistic director Tim Webb
Prods: 2 *Type:* children's theatre, visual, musical theatre, puppetry *Venues:* community venues, nurseries, schools, libraries, small-scale theatres, festivals *Touring:* national and Rebublic of Ireland *Comments:* motto – all sorts of shows for all sorts of kids, especially the very young and those with learning difficulties; see also Puppets

Old Vic, The
Waterloo Road, **London** SE1 8NB
Tel: 20-7928 2651 Fax: 20-7261 9161
general manager Michael Morris;
administrator Joan Moynighan
Prods: hire by outside productions, subscription series of own productions *Type:* classical and new play *Comments:* producing theatre, receiving venue, now run by Old Vic Theatre Trust (chair Alex Bernstein); policy is to produce or coproduce own plays and musicals; also available for rental; willing to premiere show; see also Venues

Paines Plough Theatre Co.
Fourth Floor, 43 Aldwych, **London** WC2B 4DA
Tel: 20-7240 4533 Fax: 20-7240 4534
E-Mail: paines.plough@dial.pipex.com
administrative director Belinda Hamilton; artistic director Vicky Featherstone;
literary manager Jessica Dromgoole
Actors: per show *Perfs:* 70 *Prods:* 2 per annum (both premieres) *Type:* to develop, produce & tour the most important & influential new plays by both established & unknown writers *Venues:* small to middle-scale theatres *Touring:* UK, Europe *Comments:* National touring company

Pan Project Intercultural Arts
c/o The City Lit, 16 Stukeley Street, **London** WC2B 5LJ
Tel: 20-7831 4399 Fax: 20-7831 5199
Internet: www.zyworld.com/panproject
E-Mail: panproject@compuserve.com
artistic director John Martin;
administrator Peter Vlachos
Comments: Pan Projec Intercultural Arts is dedicated to the presentation and exploration of culturally hybrid performance both locally and internationally

Parasol Theatre
Garden House, 4 Sunnyside, **London** SW19 4SL
Tel: 20-8946 9478 Fax: 20-8946 0228
director Richard Gill; associate director Mike McCormack; designer Elizabeth Waghorn
Actors: 6-18 *Perfs:* 200 *Prods:* 3 (incl. 1 new) *Type:* highly visual mixture of actors, mime and puppets (mainly light classical for young people and family audiences) *Venues:* mid-scale theatres *Touring:* national *Comments:* holders of Lord Mayor's Award for The Outstanding Contribution to the Cultural Life of Britain; touring company; workshops available depending on production

Pascal Theatre Company
35 Flaxman Court, Flaxman Terrace, **London** WC1H 9AR
Tel: 20-7383 0920 Fax: 20-7419 9798
E-Mail: Pascal7038@aol.com
administrator Graeme Braidwood; artistic director Julia Pascal; technical director Ian Watts; choreographer Thomas Kampe; composer in residence Kyla Greenbaum; fundraiser Ags Irwin
Actors: 5-10 *Perfs:* 120 *Prods:* 4 *Type:* mainly new writing with a multilingual emphasis and physical basis *Venues:* middle scale touring capacity 400 to 600 *Touring:* UK, France, Germany, Belgium, Sweden, Poland *Comments:* see also Drama (France)

People Show
People Show Studios, Pollard Row, **London** E2 6NB
Tel: 20-7729 1841 Fax: 20-7739 0203
Internet: www.peopleshow.ndirect.co.uk
E-Mail: people@peopleshow.ndirect.co.uk
producer Ruth Nutter; general manager Peter Staves
Actors: up to 10 *Perfs:* 30-50 *Prods:* 3 *Type:* interdisciplinary, innovative, physical theatre with a strong emphasis on visuals and sound *Venues:* small-mid scale, site-specific projects, residencies *Touring:* UK, Eire, Europe *Comments:* international touring alternative theatre company; company also has own rehearsal rooms available for hire

Polka Theatre for Children
240 The Broadway, Wimbledon, **London** SW19 1SB
Tel: 20-8543 3741/4888 (box office) Fax: 20-8542 7723
Internet: www.polkatheatre.com
E-Mail: polkabox@hotmail.com
administrative director Stephen Midlane; artistic director Vicky Ireland;
director of development Judy Vereker
Actors: 6 (main house), 7 (christmas production) *Perfs:* average 10 perfs per week during 11 month period *Prods:* 5 mainhouse; 2 studio *Type:* theatre for children *Venues:* Auditorium 300, Adventure Theatre 80 *Touring:* national *Comments:* building-based company, receiving venue (Adventure Theatre); touring is dependant on funding; see also Venues

Primitive Science
Hoxton Studios, Basement West, 23-28 Pem Street, **London** N1 5DL
Tel: 20-7739 0990 Fax: 20-7739 0990
directors Marc von Henning, Boz Temple-Morris
Actors: 3+ *Perfs:* varies *Prods:* 3-4 (all new) *Type:* integrated theatre of the senses *Venues:* varies including: Purcell Room, Young Vic, site-specific *Touring:* international

Red Shift Theatre Company
TRG2 Trowbray House, 108 Weston Street, **London** SE1 3QB
Tel: 20-7378 9787 Fax: 20-7378 9789
Internet: www.rshift.dircon.co.uk
E-Mail: rshift@dircon.co.uk
general manager Sophie Elliott; artistic director Jonathan Holloway
Actors: 5-10 *Perfs:* 150 *Prods:* 2 *Type:* accessible story-based theatre characterised by a strongly physical and visual approach, material includes adaptations, classics and new work *Venues:* small-mid scale up to 600 *Touring:* national *Comments:* normally 2 touring productions per year

Right Size, the
36 St. John's Lane, **London** EC1M 4BJ
Tel: 20-7490 1104
Fax: 20-7490 1105
E-Mail: mail@therightsize.demon.co.uk
artistic directors Hamish McColl, John Foley, Micheline Vandepoel; producer Christine Gettins
Actors: 2 (plus invited performers for some shows) *Perfs:* 150 *Prods:* 3 (incl. 1 new) *Type:* promote devised comic theatre, a collision of dance music, acrobatics and slapstick *Venues:* small-middle-scale venues *Touring:* national and international *Comments:* touring company; policy: equal opportunities employer; the company performs more than half of their works internationally; suitable for non-English speaking audiences

Royal Court Young People's Theatre
309 Portobello Road, **London** W10 5TD
Tel: 20-8960 4641 Fax: 20-8960 1434
E-Mail: ypt@royal-court.demon.co.uk
artistic director Ola Animashawun;
general manager Aoife Marrix
Prods: all new productions *Type:* promote young artists *Venues:* small-large scale *Comments:* run wide range of courses for young people to the ages 14-25, including writing for theatre and theatre skills; courses often develop into performance projects

Royal National Theatre
South Bank, **London** SE1 9PX
Tel: 20-7452 3333/3000 (box office)/3400 (ticket info.)
Fax: 20-7452 3344
Internet: www.nt-online.org
director Trevor Nunn; head of finance Lew Hodges; general manager Maggie Whitlum; theatre manager John Langley; head of public affairs Vivien Wallace; campaign director & director of development Breda Daly; head of touring Roger Chapman; head of studio Sue Higginson; head of press Fiona Walsh; head of marketing David Hamilton-Peters
Actors: varies *Perfs:* 1200 per annum *Prods:* 20 per annum *Type:* repertoire drawn from whole spectrum of world drama; classics, new plays, musical theatre, shows for young people *Venues:* Olivier Theatre 1160, Lyttelton 890, Cottesloe up to 400, Theatre Square (outdoors) *Touring:* extensive Uk and international touring *Comments:* building-based producing company; occasional receiving venue, especially for major international companies; early evening platform performances; foyers have a regular programme of live music and exhibitions; daily backstage tours and wide range of education activities; also wide range of events and activities front of house; see also Venues

Scarabeus
The Power Station, Coronet Street, **London** N1 6HD
Tel: 20-7739 7494 Fax: 20-7613 2894
Internet: www.scarabeus.co.uk
E-Mail: info@scarabeus.demon.co.uk
administrator Annette Loose;
artistic directors Daniela Essart, Soren Nielsen
Actors: up to 5 + 2 *Perfs:* 20-40 *Prods:* 1 *Type:* new circus, mime, dance, acrobatics, visual arts, emphasis on strong visuals, performance as spectacle, aerial work, strongly issue-based *Venues:* mid-large scale, festivals, communit/arts centres, theatres, street events, site-specific *Touring:* national, international *Comments:* extensive education programme available for all ages and levels of experience and ability

Shared Experience Theatre Company
The Soho Laundry, 9 Dufour's Place, **London** W1V 1FE
Tel: 20-7434 9248 Fax: 20-7287 8763
E-Mail: sharedexperience@compuserve.com
general manager Rachel Tackley; artistic director Nancy Meckler; marketing manager Darrell Williams; administrator Jane Claire; youth theatre director Becky Chapman; associate director Polly Teale
Actors: 6-10 *Perfs:* 100 *Prods:* 2 (usually new) *Type:* explores physical ways of working through a diverse range of theatrical forms; features in priority order existing work, new work, company-devised; also education and outreach programme with each production *Venues:* middle-scale venues *Touring:* international *Comments:* touring company, but also conducts actors workshops and youth theatre at its premises

Soho Theatre Company
c/o Soho Theatre and Writer's Centre, 21 Dean Street, **London** W1V 6NE
Tel: 20-7287 5060 Fax: 20-7287 5061
Internet: www.sohotheatre.com
E-Mail: mail@sohotheatre.co.uk
artistic director Abigail Morris; administrative producer Mark Godfrey; development director Carole Winter; literary manager Paul Sirett;
associate director Jonathon Lloyd
Actors: varies *Perfs:* 100 approx *Prods:* 4 *Type:* new writing exclusively *Venues:* Soho Theatre 200, studio space 100 *Touring:* occasionally in UK *Comments:* Soho Theatre and Writer's Centre due to open in Spring 2000; plus STC projects including showcases, co-productions, community and education work

Sphinx Theatre Co., The
25 Short Street, **London** SE1 8LJ
Tel: 20-7401 9993/4 Fax: 20-7401 9995
general manager Amanda Rigali;
artistic director Sue Parrish
Actors: varies *Perfs:* varies *Prods:* 1 *Type:* new writing, work by women writers *Venues:* small to middle scale venues, studios & art centres *Comments:* commissions women writers

Station House Opera
c/o Artsadmin, Toynbee Studios, 28 Commercial Street, **London** E1 6LS
Tel: 20-7247 5102
Fax: 20-7247 5103
E-Mail: Judith@artsadmin.co.uk
administration Judith Knight, Charlotte Aiken; press Martha Oakes (20-8293 1966)
Actors: 2 permananent + guests *Type:* physical and visual performance company *Touring:* on tour with their Roadmetal Sweetbread Show *Comments:* site-specific works, planning new works for the Straw House (Islington) and a major project for the millenium

Talawa Theatre Co
3rd floor, 23-25 Gt. Sutton St., **London** EC1V 0DN
Tel: 20-7251 6644 Fax: 20-7251 5969
E-Mail: hq@talawa.com
general manager Anthony Corriette; artistic director Yvonne Brewster; administrative assistant Joanna Lofthouse
Actors: varies *Perfs:* 40+ *Prods:* 2-3 *Type:* Black theatre, mixture of African, Carribean and British middle-scale work *Venues:* various UK venues capacity 250+ *Touring:* occasional touring, national and international *Comments:* policy: to provide middle-large-scale high quality productions both classical and contemporary, using Black culture, ritual and experience to enrich and influence British theatre; other activities: educational workshops, seminars, black women writers workshops and outreach work; also have an oral theatre history video project charting individual outstanding contributions to British theatre from black practitioners in the 1950's & 60's, called Blackground, which is housed at the Theatre Museum

Tara Arts Group
Tara Arts Centre, 356 Garratt Lane, **London** SW18 4ES
Tel: 20-8333 4457
Fax: 20-8870 9540
Internet: www.tara-arts.com
E-Mail: tara@tara-arts.com
administrator t.b.a.; artistic director Jatinder Verma
Actors: up to 8 + 2 musicians *Perfs:* 150 per annum *Prods:* 4+ *Type:* Asian theatre, storytelling, small/middle scale touring, multi-media *Venues:* small-middle scale *Touring:* national, international *Comments:* workshops and consultations available; also outreach programmes; see also Venues

Theatre Centre
Units 7 & 8, Toynbee Workshops, 3 Gunthorpe Street, **London** E1 7RQ
Tel: 20-7377 0379 Fax: 20-7377 1376
E-Mail: theacen@aol.com
director Rosamunde Hutt; administrator Julie Ellen; general manager Jackie Alexis
Actors: varies *Perfs:* 200 *Prods:* 4 *Type:* professional theatre for young people *Venues:* schools, theatres, arts centres, colleges *Touring:* national *Comments:* commissioning company with new writing laboratory; education and residency work undertaken

Theatre de Complicite
20-24 Eden Grove, **London** N7 8ED
Tel: 20-7700 0233
Fax: 20-7700 0234
E-Mail: email@complicite.co.uk
administrative producer Judith Dimant; artistic director Simon McBurney; education and marketing Kate Sparshatt
Actors: varies *Perfs:* 100-200 *Prods:* 1-2 *Type:* stunning visual and ensemble theatre explores devised work and English and European text *Touring:* UK, international *Comments:* touring company; workshops held Spring and Autumn, residencies undertaken

Theatre of Comedy Company
Shaftesbury Theatre, 210 Shaftesbury Avenue, **London** WC2H 8DP
Tel: 20-7379 3345 Fax: 20-7836 8181
chief executive Andrew Leigh;
theatre manager Christopher Flatman
Type: comedy/modern + classical plays/new plays for West End + touring *Venues:* Shaftesbury Theatre 1433 *Touring:* UK *Comments:* see also Venues

Theatre Royal Stratford East
Gerry Raffles Square, **London** E15 1BN
Tel: 20-8534 7374/0310 Fax: 20-8534 8381
general manager Nick Jones; marketing manager Kim Morgan; education director Danny Braverman; artistic director Philip Hedley
Actors: no resident company *Perfs:* 240 *Prods:* 10 *Type:* multi-cultural theatre, new writing *Venues:* theatre 470 *Comments:* refurbishments taking place so touring productions around London; offer workshops and educational programmes; will move in March '99 details were not known at time of going to print

Told by an Idiot
c/o BAC, Lavender Hill, **London** SW11 5TF
Tel: 20-7978 4200 Fax: 20-7978 5200
E-Mail: nsweeting@dial.pipex.com
artistic directors Hayley Carmichael, Paul Hunter, John Wright; producer Nick Sweeting; administrator Ghislaine Granger
Type: visual theatre, new productions devised by the company *Touring:* national, international

Unicorn Theatre For Children
Admin Offices, St Mark's Studios, Chillingworth Road, **London** N7 8QJ
Tel: 20-7700 0702 (admin.)/ 7609 1800 (box office)
Fax: 20-7700 3870
administrative director Christopher Moxon; artistic director Tony Graham; education officer Wendy Rouse; marketing Elly Crichton Stuart; development Eva Woloshyn; production Petius Bertschinger

Actors: up to 9 *Perfs:* 144 *Prods:* 4-5 per year + education projects *Type:* new plays, classical adaptations for children's/family audiences, schools *Venues:* The Pleasance Theatre 258 *Comments:* plays for schools during term time; public performances at weekends, half term and public holidays; performances mornings and afternoons; educational programme all year round, including outreach/community programmes and workshops

Young Vic Theatre, The
66 The Cut,
London SE1 8LZ
Tel: 20-7633 0133
Fax: 20-7928 1585
E-Mail: info@youngvic.org
administrative producer Caroline Maude; artistic director Tim Supple; director of communications Alex McGowan; finance director Elaine Lavelle; production manager Paul Russell; development director John Nicolls; artistic associate Sue Emmas
Actors: varies *Perfs:* 300+ *Prods:* 6-8 (incl. 3-4 new) *Type:* new versions of classic stories and seminal texts for audiences of all backgrounds and ages *Venues:* Main House up to 450, The Studio 60 *Touring:* national, international *Comments:* building-based producing company, occasional receiving venue, expanding touring program; offer educational and community programmes and workshops; apprentice programme and work experience available; see also Venues

Contact Theatre Company – Manchester Young People's Theatre Ltd
Oxford Road,
Manchester M15 6JA
Tel: 161-274 3434
Fax: 161-273 6286
Internet: www.contact-theatre.org.uk
E-Mail: info@contact-theatre.org.uk
executive producer Fiona Gasper; artistic director John E. McGrath; head of marketing and PR Lesa Dryburgh
Actors: 8 *Perfs:* 220 *Prods:* 6-7 *Type:* new writing, own productions, dance, music, multi-media, poetry, comedy *Venues:* space 1: 36c, space 2: 2-100, bar-cafe, foyer events *Comments:* see also Venues

Royal Exchange Theatre Co
St Ann's Square,
Manchester M2 7DH
Tel: 161-833 9333
Fax: 161-832 0881
Internet: www.royalexchange.co.uk
E-Mail: administration@royalexchange.co.uk
general manager Patricia Weller; artistic directors Braham Murray, Gregory Hersov, Matthew Lloyd; marketing manager Ivan Wadeson
Actors: varies *Perfs:* 280 *Prods:* 9 (main house) studio (t.b.a.) *Type:* producing broad range of work *Venues:* Main House 750, studio 100 *Touring:* community venues and theatres *Comments:* building-based producing theatre; cultural centre

Grand Theatre of Lemmings
38 High Street,
Manningtree CO11 1AJ
Tel: 1206-391 632
Fax: 1206-392 402
Internet: www.lemmings.dircon.co.uk
E-Mail: lemmings@dircon.co.uk
director Mr Rose; general manager Mandy Medlicott
Actors: 2-6 *Perfs:* 200 *Prods:* 2-3 *Type:* primarily street-theatre; visual shows, stilt characters, cabaret and rural arts touring *Venues:* small scale theatres and festivals *Touring:* worldwide *Comments:* collaborations with other groups; youth training workshops available

Torch Theatre
St Peter's Road,
Milford Haven (Wales) SA73 2BU
Tel: 1646-694 192
Fax: 1646-698 919/963 605 (marketing)
artistic director Peter Doran;
publicity & marketing manager Lesley Jones;
financial director Roland Williams
Actors: varies *Perfs:* 70 + visiting artistes *Prods:* 3+ *Type:* mixed programme *Venues:* Torch Theatre 297 *Comments:* building-based producing theatre and receiving venue; see also Venues

Clwyd Theatr Company
Theatr Clwyd,
Mold (Wales) CH7 1YA
Tel: 1352-756 331
Fax: 1352-758 323
E-Mail: drama@celtic.co.uk
general manager Sarah Holmes;
finance director Barry James
Actors: varies *Type:* classical, modern *Venues:* main theatre 582, Clwyd Room 350, Emlyn Williams Theatre 150 *Touring:* Wales *Comments:* there is an educational department that works independently from the Company, touring to schools; see also Venues

New Vic Theatre (Stoke-on-Trent and North Staffordshire Theatre Trust)
New Victoria Theatre, Etruria Road,
Newcastle-under-Lyme ST5 0JG
Tel: 1782-717 954 (administration)/717 539 (marketing)
Fax: 1782-712 885
Internet: www.uktw.co.uk/info/newvic.htm
artistic director Ewenda Hughes; general manager Ludo Keston; head of marketing & business development John Morton; production manager David Martin; theatre manager Judy Bowker
Actors: varies *Perfs:* 300 *Prods:* 10 (incl 1 new) *Type:* plays, concerts, exhibitions, fairs, special events *Venues:* New Vic Theatre-in-the-round 605, studio 100 *Comments:* building-based company; some concerts; each production has one sign language interpreted performance; see also Venues

Neighborhood Watch Stilts International
10 Ravenswork Terrace, **Newcastle-Upon-Tyne** NE4 5AU
Tel: 191-261 8987/411-656 759 Fax: 191-230 1012
Internet: www.nwsi.demon.co.uk
E-Mail: nwsi@nwsi.demon.co.uk
contact Paul Miskin
Actors: 23 *Perfs:* 100 *Prods:* 4 *Type:* street theatre *Touring:* USA, Europe, Korea, Brazil

Northern Stage Ensemble (Northern Stage Ltd)
Newcastle Playhouse, Haymarket, **Newcastle-upon-Tyne** NE1 7RH
Tel: 191-232 3366/230 5151 (box office) Fax: 191-261 8093
Internet: www.northernstage.co.uk
E-Mail: northern.stage@ncl.ac.uk
executive director Mandy Stewart; artistic director Alan Lyddiard; associate director Neil Murray; head of education and outreach Tony Harrington; director marketing & sales Mark Dobson; director of productions David Hayden
Actors: 13 *Perfs:* 300 *Prods:* 6 incl. 2 Christmas (usually all new) *Type:* new work, classic texts from international repertoire *Venues:* Newcastle Playhouse 512, Gulbenkian Studio 160 *Touring:* national, international *Comments:* extensive work in schools and community for most productions; workshops available; also receiving venue for most international companies

Royal Theatre and Opera House
15 Guildhall Road, **Northampton** NN1 1EA
Tel: 1604-638 343/624 485 Fax: 1604-602 408/250 285
administrative director Nigel Lavender; artistic director Michael Napier Brown; marketing manager Nina Desborough; directors' assistant Julie Martell; accountant Antony Watts
Actors: no resident company *Perfs:* 250/300 *Prods:* 9-10 (incl. 1 new) *Type:* broad range *Venues:* Theatre Royal 573 *Touring:* seperate touring and education departments that produce two community tours per season *Comments:* sunday concerts-dance, music, comedy; theatre in education does workshops; also have access for disabled theatre goers

Meeting Ground Theatre Co
4 Shirley Road, **Nottingham** NG3 5DA
Tel: 115-962 3009 Fax: 115-962 3009
artistic directors Tanya Myers, Stephen Lowe, Jonathan Chadwick
Prods: 1 *Type:* experimental *Venues:* small to middle-scale theatres, some site-specific work *Touring:* UK, Germany, Poland, France *Comments:* emphasis on international collaborations/production/touring

Nottingham Playhouse (Nottingham Theatre Trust)
Wellington Circus, **Nottingham** NG1 5AF
Tel: 115-947 4361 Fax: 115-947 5759
executive director Venu Dhupa; artistic director Giles Croft; admin dir Jim Robertson; head of marketing William Jones
Actors: varies *Perfs:* 95-130 *Prods:* 5 own new + visiting *Type:* repertory theatre company *Venues:* Main House 750-808 *Comments:* building-based producing company, receiving venue; see also Venues

Coliseum Theatre
Fairbottom Street, **Oldham** OL1 3SW
Tel: 161-624 1731 Fax: 161-624 5318
Internet: www.coliseum.demon.co.uk
chief executive Kenneth Alan Taylor; deputy chief executive Phil Clark; marketing director Jane Doxey; marketing & press manager Mark Llewellin
Perfs: 150 per 5 month season *Prods:* 9 in-house shows per annum plus Sunday night concerts/events *Type:* classics, modern, new plays, musicals *Venues:* main house 584, studio 60

Oxford Stage Company
13 High Street, 15-19 George Street, **Oxford** OX1 4DH
Tel: 1865-723 238 Fax: 1865-790 625
Internet: www.oxfordstage.co.uk
E-Mail: patrickmartin@oxfordstage.co.uk
general manager Patrick Martin; artistic director Dominic Dromgoole; marketing manager Gary Smith; production manager Katrina Gilroy
Actors: varies *Perfs:* 200 *Prods:* 4 *Type:* Shakespeare, 20th century drama *Touring:* UK, international *Comments:* middle-scale touring theatre company; all productions transfer to London after initial run in Oxford

Bash Street Company
35 Belgravia Street, **Penzance** TR18 2BL
Tel: 1736-360 795 Fax: 1736-360 795
Internet: www.users.dircon.co.uk/~bashst/home.htm
E-Mail: bashst@dircon.co.uk
artistic director Simon Pullum;
administrator Jojo Pickering
Actors: up to 5 *Perfs:* 150 *Prods:* 2 new per year *Type:* street, comedy, new circus *Venues:* middle to small scale, require suitable height for aerial work *Touring:* UK, Europe *Comments:* middle to small-scale company specialising in family entertainment, street theatre, walkabout characters for international festivals and events

Perth Repertory Theatre Company
Perth Repertory Theatre, 185 High Street, **Perth (Scotland)** PH1 5UW
Tel: 1738-472 700 Fax: 1738-624 576
Internet: www.perth.org.uk/perth/theatre.htm
E-Mail: theatre@perth.org.uk
general manager Paul Hackett; art dir Michael Winter
Actors: varies *Perfs:* 170 plays, 32 pantomime *Prods:* 10 plays, 1 pantomime *Type:* modern and classical *Venues:* Perth Repertory Theatre 490, Studio 120 *Comments:* see also Venues

Barbican Theatre
Castle Street, **Plymouth** PL1 2NJ
Tel: 1752-267 131
Fax: 1752-222 209
E-Mail: barbican@dircon.co.uk
general manager Sarah Pym;
artistic directors Mark Laville, Sheila Snellgrove
Actors: varies *Perfs:* 200 *Type:* theatre in education, theatre in health education, new writing, mime, physical theatre, dance, circus *Venues:* capacity 108

Theatre Royal
Royal Parade, **Plymouth** PL1 2TR
Tel: 1752-668 282 (administation)
Fax: 1752-671 179 (administration)/221 267 (marketing)
E-Mail: information@theatreroyal.demon.co.uk
chief executive Adrian Vinken; head of operations Margaret Garcia; artistic director Simon Stokes; head of production Alan Finch
Actors: no resident company *Perfs:* year round programme *Prods:* 36 *Type:* drama, musicals, opera, ballet, dance, pantomine, children's shows *Venues:* Theatre Royal 1296, The Drum 200 *Comments:* building-based producing theatre, receiving venue; have a youth theatre, The Young Company, for 13-25 year olds, 400 members; also have a community based company, The People's Company; see also Venues

Horse + Bamboo Theatre
Horse + Bamboo Centre, 679 Bacup Road, Waterfoot, **Rossendale** BB4 7HB
Tel: 1706-220 241 Fax: 1706-831 166
Internet: www.zen.co.uk/horse.bamboo/horse.htm
E-Mail: horse.bamboo@zen.co.uk
artistic director Bob Frith; administrative director t.b.a.
Actors: 6-10, incl musicians *Perfs:* 100 *Prods:* 2 *Type:* visual theatre and related activities; mixture of masked performers theatre, puppetry and live music *Venues:* from small village halls to small/mid scale touring venues *Touring:* UK, Eire, Europe, Eastern Europe *Comments:* new outdoor show for Summer 2000 planned as international collaboration with Nigerian playwright Sam Ukala; see also Puppetry

Salisbury Playhouse
Malthouse Lane, **Salisbury** SP2 7RA
Tel: 1722-320 117 (admin)/333 (box office)
Fax: 1722-421 991
executive director Rebecca Morland; artistic director Joanna Read; marketing manager James Gough; head of education Trevelyan Wright
Actors: no resident company *Perfs:* 269 Main Auditorium, 120 Salberg Studio, 50 education shows and workshops *Prods:* 14 Main Auditorium, 15 Salberg Studio, 26 education shows and workshops; 8 per season *Type:* repertory company, comedy, musicals, classics, new writing, children's shows, traditional pantomime *Venues:* Main House 517, Studio Theatre 140 *Comments:* building-based producing theatre, receiving venue; runs children's workshops and a youth theatre, Stage '65; see also Venues

Stephen Joseph Theatre
Westborough, **Scarborough** YO11 1JW
Tel: 1723-370 540 (administration)/541 (box office)
Fax: 1723-360 506
Internet: www.sjt.uk.com
E-Mail: response@sjt.uk.com
theatre manager Elizabeth Brown; artistic director Alan Ayckbourn; financial administrator Keith McFarlane; general administrator Stephen Wood; production manager Alison Fowler; press and marketing officer Andie Hawkes
Actors: 2-15 *Perfs:* 360 *Prods:* 12 (incl. 6 new) *Type:* new works by Alan Ayckbourn, new writers, new adaptations *Venues:* In-The-Round Auditorium 406, McCarthy Auditorium 165 *Touring:* national *Comments:* also has education department; workshops available at theatre and in schools; see also Venues

Compass Theatre Company
Carver Street Institute,
24 Rockingham Lane,
Sheffield S1 4FW
Tel: 114-275 5328
Fax: 114-278 6931
general manager Craig Dronfield; artistic director Neil Sissons; production manager Gareth Williams
Actors: 6 *Perfs:* 176 *Prods:* 2-3 *Type:* emphasis on the ensemble approach of classical theatre *Venues:* small, middle & large scale venues *Touring:* national, international *Comments:* small to middle-scale touring company; education workshops available

Crucible Theatre
55 Norfolk Street, **Sheffield** S1 1DA
Tel: 114-249 5999/6000 (box office)
Fax: 114-249 6003
chief executive Graham Morris; artistic director Deborah Paige; marketing director Angela Galvin; production manager Rob McKinney
Actors: varies *Prods:* 5+ *Type:* repertory *Venues:* Thrust Stage 1000, Studio 400 *Comments:* building-based producing theatre, receiving venue for a wide range of acitivities; all contact through Sheffield Theatres Tel: 114-249 5999; also have theatre in education and youth theatre; see also Venues

Forced Entertainment
Unit 102, The Workstation, 46 Shoreham Street, **Sheffield** S1 4SP
Tel: 114-279 8977
Fax: 114-221 2170
Internet: www.forced.co.uk
E-Mail: fe@forced.co.uk
writer/director Tim Etchells; artistic team Robin Arthur, Richard Lowdon, Claire Marshall, Cathy Naden, Terry O'Connor; general manager Deborah Chadbourn; administrator Verity Leigh
Actors: 5 *Perfs:* 35 in UK; 35 abroad p.a. *Prods:* 1 p.a. *Type:* new experimental theatre devised by the company *Venues:* up to 200 *Touring:* UK, USA, Scandinavia, Belgium/Holland, Germany

Nuffield Theatre Southampton
University Road, **Southampton** SO17 1TR
Tel: 23-8031 5500 Fax: 23-8031 5511
administrative director Mark Courtice; artistic director Patrick Sandford; production manager Julien Boast
Actors: no regular company *Prods:* 8 *Type:* emphasis on new and neglected works *Venues:* capacity 464 *Touring:* UK middle-scale *Comments:* building-based producing theatre, occasional receiving venue; see also Venues

Trestle Theatre Company
Birch Centre, Hill End Lane,
St Albans AL 4 0RA
Tel: 1727-850 950
Fax: 1727-855 558
E-Mail: trestle@dircon.co.uk
joint artistic directors Joff Chafer, Toby Wilsher
Actors: 4-5 *Perfs:* 200 *Prods:* 3 *Type:* mask, mime, new work *Venues:* small/middle scale *Touring:* UK, Ukraine, Brazil, Europe *Comments:* small to middle-scale touring company; Trestle is committed to an extensive education and outreach programme; and conducts workshops and residencies all over the country

Royal Shakespeare Company
Royal Shakespeare Theatre, Waterside,
Stratford-upon-Avon CV37 6BB
Tel: 1789-296 655
Fax: 1789-294 810
artistic director & chief executive Adrian Noble; executive producer Lynda Farran; general manager William Weston; financial controller David Fletcher; production controller James Langley; London manager Neil Constable; development director Jonathan Pope; head of operations Tana Wolf; head of marketing Kate Horton; head of press and PR Ian Rowley
Actors: 75 per season *Perfs:* 1000 *Prods:* 15 (all new) *Type:* Shakespeare & contemporaries and new writing & classical works *Venues:* Royal Shakespeare Theatre 1410, Swan Theatre 464, The Other Place 175, London: Barbican Theatre 1162, The Pit 200 *Touring:* national and international *Comments:* building-based, producing and touring company; 2nd address: Barbican Theatre, Barbican Centre, London EC2Y 8DS tel: 171-628 3351 fax: 171-374 0818; see also Venues

Green Ginger
32, The Norton, **Tenby (Wales)** SA70 8AB
Tel: 117-922 5599
Fax: 117-922 5599
E-Mail: greenginger@usa.net
director Terry Lee; artistic director Chris Pirie (Tel: 117-922 5599); technical director James Osborne
Actors: 3 *Perfs:* 70 *Prods:* 3 *Type:* low-language or non-language productions for all ages, life-size bunraku figures, streetwork, theatres, cabaret *Venues:* mid scale touring *Touring:* USA, Canada, mainland Europe, Indian Ocean *Comments:* perform in 12 languages (new languages attempted); also run workshops and masterclasses for children and adults; available for TV and film work; see also Puppets

Kneehigh Theatre Company
14 Walsingham Place, **Truro** TR1 2RP
Tel: 1872-223 159/1872-271 766 Fax: 1872-260 487
E-Mail: office@kneehigh.demon.co.uk
admin Julie Seyler; art dir Mike Shepherd, Bill Mitchell
Perfs: 120 *Prods:* 1 *Type:* all new productions, contemporary writers *Venues:* Rep. Studios & middle-scale Theatres *Touring:* national, international *Comments:* annual programme of theatrical events in communities in Cornwall; looking to extend into Atlantic Arc regions; interested in mutual collaborations

Palace Theatre Watford
Clarendon Road, **Watford** WD1 1JZ
Tel: 1923-235 455 Fax: 1923-819 664
administrative director Alastair Moir;
artistic director Lawrence Till
Prods: 9 *Type:* repertory *Venues:* cap 663 *Comments:* building-based producing theatre, receiving venue; see also Venues

Palace Theatre Centre
430 London Road, **Westcliff-on-Sea** SS0 9LA
Tel: 1702-347 816 Fax: 1702-435 031
artistic director Roy Marsden
Prods: 12 *Type:* drama, comedy, musical *Venues:* Palace Theatre Main House 603, Studio 100 *Comments:* provide sign performances and described performances for sight/hearing impaired audiences-wheelchair spaces, see also Venues

Hoodwink
High Point, Slab Lane, **Woodfalle** SP5 2NE
Tel: 172-551 2929
E-Mail: hwtheatre@aol.com

York Citizens' Theatre Trust
Theatre Royal, St Leonard's Place, **York** YO1 7HD
Tel: 1904-658 162 (administration)/623 568 (box office)
Fax: 1904-611 534
executive director Elizabeth Jones; artistic director Damian Cruden; ; production manager Matt Noddings; education & outreach officer Brian Higginson
Actors: varies *Perfs:* 250 *Prods:* 7+ *Type:* musicals, pantomime/,opera, dance, comedy, drama *Venues:* Theatre Royal 863 *Comments:* building-based producing theatre; receiving venue for theatre, dance; workshops for all age groups throughout the year, educational and community outreach programmes; see also Venues

YUGOSLAVIA (+381)

: Due to the war in Kosovo we have been unable to update the following entries for Yugoslavia

Belgrade Drama Theatre
Beogradsko dramsko pozoriste
Save Kovacevica 64 A, 11000 **Belgrade**
Tel: 11-413 155/423 183
manager Ljiljana Sedlar

Bitef Theatre
Bitef teatar
Terazije 29/1, 11000 **Belgrade**
Tel: 11-323 2437 Fax: 11-324 3966
general manager Olivija Mihajlovic-Domic; artistic director Ivana Vujic

Dah Theatre
Dah teatar
c/o Jadranka Andjelic, Nebojsina 41/26, 11000 **Belgrade**
Tel: 11-457 025 Fax: 11-457 025
directors Jadranka Andjelic, Dijana Milosevic

Little Theatre 'Dusko Radovic'
Malo pozoriste 'Dusko Radovic'
Aberdareva 1, 11000 **Belgrade**
Tel: 11-342 472/343 305 Fax: 11-332 982
director Stevan Koprivica

National Theatre
Narodno pozoriste
Francuska 3, 11000 **Belgrade**
Tel: 11-621 159 Fax: 11-622 560
general manager Nebojsa Bradic; drama director Radomir Putnik

Theatre KPGT
Pozoriste KPGT (Kazaliste, pozoriste, gledalisce, teatar)
Stara secerana, Radnicka 3, 11000 **Belgrade**
Tel: 11-558 840/541 247 Fax: 11-555 070/544 172 (Fax/modem)
director Ljubisa Ristic

Theatre on Terazije
Pozoriste na Terazijama
Trg Nikole Pasica 3, 11000 **Belgrade**
Tel: 11-334 037/345 677 Fax: 11-345 677
director Dusan Golumbovski

Theatre Studio 212
Atelje 212
Lole Ribara 21, 11000 **Belgrade**
Tel: 11-346 146 Fax: 11-336 215
manager Svetozar Cvetkovic

Torpedo Theatre Co: Ethno-Circus
Darijan Mihajlovic, Vojvode Stepe 106, 11000 **Belgrade**
Tel: 381-1146 9300 Fax: 381-1163 2750
E-Mail: asusa@eunet.yu

Yugoslav Drama Theatre
Jugoslovensko dramsko pozoriste
Srpskih vladara 50, 11000 **Belgrade**
Tel: 11-656 164/657 766 Fax: 11-687 854
general manager Jovan Cirilov; manager Branko Cvejic

Zvezdara Theatre
Zvezdara teatar
Milana Rakica 38, 11000 **Belgrade**
Tel: 11-417 687/419 360 Fax: 11-411 484
general manager Nenad Brkic; artistic director Dusan Kovacevic

Theatre Joakim Vujic
Teatar Joakim Vujic
Daniciceva 3, 34000 **Kragujevac**
Tel: 34-667 590/66591
director t.b.a.

National Theatre Krusevac
Krusevacko pozoriste
Mirka Tomica 26, 37000 **Krusevac**
Tel: 37-29919/21707
Fax: 37-29919/21707
director Jelena Ivanovic

National Theatre Nis
Narodno pozoriste
Vozdova 28, 18000 **Nis**
Tel: 18-22700 Fax: 18-22758
general manager Miladin Sevarlic

Serbian National Theatre
Srpsko narodno pozoriste
Pozorisni trg 1, 21000 **Novi Sad**
Tel: 21-621 411/23752 (drama department)
Fax: 21-623 391
general manager Stevan Divjakovic;
drama director Radoslav Milenkovic

Montenegro National Theatre
Crnogorsko narodno pozoriste
Stanka Dragojevica 18, 81000 **Podgorica**
Tel: 81-43293/45980 Fax: 81-51269
manager Stevan Kordic; drama director Igor Bojovic

Theatre DODEST
Pozoriste DODEST
Dom omladine Budo Tomovic, Vaka Djurovica 2, 81000 **Podgorica**
Tel: 81-45682/45345
Fax: 81-44563
director Ranko Vukovic

National Theatre Pristina
Narodno pozoriste
Vidovdanska 21, 38000 **Pristina**
Tel: 38-24406
Fax: 38-25165
general manager Radosav Stojanovic
Type: drama in Serbian and Albanian

National Theatre Ljubisa Jovanovic
Narodno pozoriste Ljubisa Jovanovic
Karadjordjeva 22,
15000 **Sabac**
Tel: 15-22762/22436
director Zlatica Popovic

National Theatre Sombor
Narodno pozoriste
Koste Trifkovica 2, 25000 **Sombor**
Tel: 25-37666/29466
Fax: 25-37666 ext 13
director Milivoje Mladjenovic

National Theatre Subotica
Narodno pozoriste – Nepszinhaz
Ive Vojnovica 2, 24000 **Subotica**
Tel: 24-53081/23431
Fax: 24-38081/33153
director Zuzana Erdudac

National Theatre Uzice
Narodno pozoriste
Trg partizana 12, 31000 **Uzice**
Tel: 31-26329 Fax: 31-26329
director Branko Popovic

National Theatre Sterija
Narodno pozoriste Sterija
Svetosavski trg 6, 26300 **Vrsac**
Tel: 13-813 289 Fax: 13-813 289
director Pavle Vlahovic

National Theatre – Zemun stage
Narodno pozoriste – Scena u Zemunu
Zmaj Jovina 1, 11080 **Zemun**
Tel: 11-618 084
director Bora Balac

Puppetry

Puppetry
This section includes puppet companies. Information about national organisations for puppets, puppet festivals, etc. will be found in the appropriate section. **Within country the companies are ordered by city and alphabetically within city.**

Art des Marionnettes
Cette rubrique englobe les compagnies de marionnettes. Les informations sur les organisations nationales, festivals etc. se trouvent dans les sections appropriées. **Pour chaque pays les compagnies sont classées dans l'ordre des villes et par ordre alphabétique.**

Puppenspiel
In diesem Kapitel werden Puppentheater und Puppenspielgruppen aufgeführt. Informationen über nationale Organisationen, Festspiele usw. finden Sie in den jeweiligen Kapiteln. **Die Einträge sind innerhalb aller Staaten alphabetisch nach Stadt und innerhalb der Stadt alphabetisch nach Namen geordnet.**

Marionette
Questa sezione include le compagnie di marionette. Informazioni su organizzazioni nazionali, festivals ecc. sono elencate nelle sezioni appropriate. **All'interno di ogni Paese, le compagnie sono ordinate per cittá ed in ordine alfabetico per ogni cittá.**

Marionetas
En esta sección se listan las compañías de marionetas. Los festivales de marionetas, organizaciones, etc. se encuentran en las secciones respectivas. **Están listadas alfabéticamente por ciudades dentro de cada país y alfabéticamente dentro de cada ciudad.**

Puppetry (인형극)
이 부문은 인형극단들을 포함한다. 인형극, 인형극 페스티발 등에 관계하는 국내 조직들에 대한 정보는 관련부문을 참조하시오. **리스트는 국가별, 도시별, 그리고 다시 알파벳순으로 기재되었다.**

木偶剧演出
本章节包括木偶剧团公司。有关木偶剧的国家性机构、木偶节等等可见于有关章节。**在每个国家里公司是按城市顺序来排列的，而在一城市里公司又是按字母顺序来排列的。**

人形劇
この章には人形劇団が記載されています。全国的な劇団や人形劇フェスティバル等に関する情報は該当する章をご覧下さい。**リストは国、都市別で、都市内ではアルファベット順に記載されています。**

ALBANIA (+355)

Puppet Theatre
Tirana
Tel: 42-2446
director Gjik Kurtiqi
Perfs: 400 *Venues:* capacity 200

ARMENIA (+374)

Hovhannes Toumanian State Puppet Theatre of Armenia
4 Sayat-Nova, 375001 **Yerevan**
Tel: 2-563 243/520 254
artistic director Rouben Babaian

Marionette State Theatre of Armenia
43 Mashtots Street, 375009 **Yerevan**
Tel: 2-562 450
artistic director Stepan Lusikian

AUSTRIA (+43)

Breitenfurter Marionettenbühne
Kardinal Piffl-Platz 1, 2384 **Breitenfurt -West**
Tel: 2239-5621
Leitung Rudolf Enter
Puppeteers: 4 + 1 technician *Perfs:* 12 *Prods:* 12 *Type:* fairy tale adaptations of Wiener Vorstadtkomödien *Venues:* capacity 60 *Touring:* German speaking countries *Comments:* second address: Rudolf Enter: Darnautgasse 10/4/13, 1120 Wien, Tel: 1-810 2841;

Puppetshow Rocking-Horse
Puppenbühne Schaukelpferd
Hauptstraße 9/6, 3153 **Eschenau**
Tel: 2762-67236 Fax: 2762-67663
Direktion Franz Walters
Puppeteers: 1 *Perfs:* 200 *Prods:* 5 *Type:* hand, stick, shadow, rolling marionettes *Venues:* nurseries, schools, cultural centres etc. capacity 100 to 200 *Touring:* national, international *Comments:* plays written by the director, with elements of new puppetry

Götzner Puppentheater
Puppentheater im Vereinshaus, 6840 **Götzis**
Tel: 5523-51160 Fax: 5523-53042
Leitung Mag. Elisabeth Wolber
Puppeteers: 8 *Perfs:* 40 *Prods:* 1 new *Type:* various forms of puppetry combined with black theatre; theatre for children and adults *Venues:* capacity 110 *Touring:* Austria, Germany, Switzerland *Comments:* commission music for performances; second address: Mag. Elisabeth Wolber, Zielstraße 28, 6840 Götzis

Kärntner Handpuppenspiele
St. Ruprechter Straße 57, 9020 **Klagenfurt**
Tel: 463-31183/664-252 4352 Fax: 463-31183
Leitung Willi Noll
Puppeteers: 2 *Perfs:* 250-300 *Prods:* 1 *Type:* hand *Touring:* Austria, Germany *Comments:* touring company; perform fairy tales (Grimm, Hauff, Andersen) with texts recorded by well-known actors

Marionettentheater Wilfried Popek
Thalsdorf 38, 9314 **Launsdorf**
Tel: 4213-2464/4212-6278
Leitung Wilfried Popek
Puppeteers: 1 *Perfs:* 30-40 *Prods:* 2 *Type:* marionette *Venues:* capacity 40 -45

Linzer Puppentheater
Langgasse 13, 4020 **Linz**
Tel: 732-602 258/664-102 0436 Fax: 7277-32104
E-Mail: chris.bs@online.edvg.co.at
Leitung Christa J. Koinig; Öffentlichkeitarbeit Jörg -D. Hanzhanz
Puppeteers: 5 *Perfs:* 100 *Prods:* 6 *Type:* hand & rod *Venues:* Kinder-Kulturzentrum Kuddelmuddel

Karin Schafer Figuren Theater
Josef Haydngasse 25, 7100 **Neusiedl am See**
Tel: 2167-3384 Fax: 2167-3384
E-Mail: H2@MAGNET.AT
director Karin Schäfer; management Peter Hauptmann
Perfs: 50 *Prods:* 2 *Type:* marionettes, different techniques, contemporary puppet theatre for adults *Touring:* international *Comments:* touring company; managed by: H2 – arts & acts

OÖ-Puppenbühne Pichler
Picassostraße 21, 4053 **Pucking**
Tel: 7229-88226 Fax: 7229-88226
Leitung Albin Pichler sen.
Puppeteers: 2 *Perfs:* 50+ *Type:* hand, rod, marionette *Venues:* schools, cultural centres *Comments:* about 800 puppets; following a long family tradition, second address: Albin Pichler jun., Buchengasse 5, 4616 Weisskirchen an der Traun, Tel: 7243-56667

Salzburger Marionettentheater
Schwarzstrasse 24, 5024 **Salzburg**
Tel: 662-872 406 Fax: 662-882 141
Internet: www.tcs.co.at/mario/
E-Mail: marionet@ping.at
Geschäftsführung Dr. Christoph Sebastian Schuchter; Künstlerische Leitung Frau Professor Gretl Aicher
Puppeteers: 14 *Perfs:* 150 *Prods:* 10 including new *Type:* Mozart operas, Tchaikovsky ballet, Strauss operetta, Prokoffief's Peter and the Wolf *Venues:* Marionetten Theater 353 *Touring:* France, Germany, Spain, Italy, Switzerland, USA, Japan

Salzburger Puppentheater-Le Parapluie
Krenzstr. 17, 5020 **Salzburg**
Tel: 662-453 574 Fax: 662-452 439
Leitung Herbert Just, Eva-Christine Just
Puppeteers: 2-8 *Perfs:* 250 *Prods:* 4 *Type:* hand, rod, marionette, shadow theatre (actors and puppets) *Comments:* Punch & Judy, workshops, performances in schools; 20% of performances for adults; mobile stage

Steyrer Kripperl
Grünmarkt 26, 4400 **Steyr**
Tel: 7252-52020
contact Mag. W. Bernhauer; Leitung Gerhard Nezbeda
Puppeteers: 8 *Perfs:* 25-30 *Type:* traditional 'Christmas' puppetry using early forms of mechanical puppet, rod puppets etc. *Venues:* Grünmarkt 26 *Comments:* texts are traditionally passed on orally; founded in c.1860; Bernhauer, Verein Heimatpflege, Stadtplatz 7, 4400 Steyr

Christoph Bochdansky
Zentagasse 39/1, 1050 **Wien**
Tel: 1-317 8898/548 6321 Fax: 1-317 8898
contact Christoph Bochdansky
Puppeteers: 1 *Perfs:* 80 *Prods:* 10 (2 new) *Type:* contemporary puppet theatre *Comments:* touring company

Figurentheater Lilarum
Göllnergasse 8, 1030 **Wien**
Tel: 1-710 2666 Fax: 1-710 4463
Internet: thing.at/lilarum/
E-Mail: lilarum@thing.or.at
Leitung Traude Kossatz; Techn. Leitung Paul Kossatz
Puppeteers: 5 *Perfs:* 270 *Prods:* 8-10 (2 new) *Type:* modern, hand, rod *Venues:* puppet theatre capacity 150 *Comments:* texts produced in co-operation with professional children's authors; for audiences of 3 years and above, including adults; the music is produced by professional avantgard composers; the voices of the puppets are famous Vienna actors and singers

Klaus Behrendt's Schattentheater
Invalidenstraße 3, 1030 **Wien**
Tel: 1-713 6675
Leitung Prof. Klaus Behrendt
Puppeteers: 1 *Perfs:* 70 *Prods:* 9 *Type:* rod puppets, shadow play *Venues:* home capacity 30 *Touring:* national, international *Comments:* Asiatic and European shadow theatre, myth and fairytales. Currently restoring historic puppet theatre in Austrian Theater Museum. Some performances given there by ensemble, tel. 1-512 8800

Märchenbühne – Der Apfelbaum
Stadtinitiative, Burgasse 28-32, 1070 **Wien**
Tel: 1-523 1729/20 Fax: 1-523 1729/21
contact Susanne Veres, Christa Horvat
Puppeteers: 9 *Perfs:* apprx. 180 per year *Prods:* 8 *Type:* marionettes, rod with live music accompaniement *Venues:* 99 *Touring:* Austria, Germany

Puppentheater Berta Klement
Buchengasse 170, 1100 **Wien**
Tel: 1-607 2476
Leitung Prof. Berta Klement; musikalische Leitung Prof. Renate Spitzner; Komponist Gerald Spitzner; Verwaltung Ingrid Irbinger
Puppeteers: 4 + musicians *Prods:* 20 *Type:* shadow, hand, marionettes, traditonal, but also puppet theatre as therapy *Venues:* capacity 70, universities, international conference halls, hospitals *Touring:* Austria, Slovenia, Switzerland, Germany, Poland

Wiener Handpuppenbühne – Herta Kindler
Geologengasse 9/6, 1030 **Wien**
Tel: 1-712 8353/663-820 232 (mobile) Fax: 1-712 8353
Leitung Herta Kindler
Puppeteers: 2-4 *Type:* hand *Venues:* Strandbad (summer), Gänsehäufel (out-door), schools, department stores, etc. *Touring:* Austria

Wiener Urania Puppentheater
Wiener Urania, Uraniastraße 1, 1011 **Wien**
Tel: 1-712 6191 Fax: 1-7126 19153
Leitung Manfred Müller
Puppeteers: 7-8 *Perfs:* 240 + 32 in 2nd venue *Prods:* 8 *Type:* hand, rod, mechanical puppets, fairy tales, Punch & Judy *Venues:* Urania 272, Puppentheater Pezi-Haus *Comments:* postal address – Postfach 881; 2nd venue address 3443 Rappoltenkirchen, Tel/Fax 2274-3434

AZERBAIDZHAN (+994)

Azerbaidzhan Abdulla Shaig State Puppet Theatre
Azerbaidzhan Avenue 36, 370004 **Baku**
Tel: 12-926 435
director Guliyev Rahman Ragim ogly

Giandja State Puppet Theatre
Djalil St. 195, 374400 **Giandja**
director Fataliyev Bayram Aprel ogly

Kahi State Puppet Theatre
Kahi
director Mahmudov Nazim Davud ogly

Nakchivan State Puppet Theatre
Nakchivan
director Kasimov Alekper Mamed ogly

Salyan State Puppet Theatre
Salyan
director Dadashov Faraj Ismail ogly

BELARUS (+375)

Brest Regional Puppet Theatre
Brestskij Oblastnoj Teatr Kukol
ul. Lenina 66, 224000 **Brest**
Tel: 162-263 359
director Mikhail A. Shavell

Gomell Regional Puppet Theatre
Gomelskij Oblastnoj Teatr Kukol
ul Pushkina 2, 246000 **Gomel**
Tel: 232-559 296
director Dmirrtyj A Gorelik

Grodno Regional Puppet Theatre
Grodnenskii Oblastnoj Teatr Kukol
ul. Derzhinskogo 1, 230023 **Grodno**
Tel: 152-440 340
director Nikolai I. Bardygo

State Puppet Theatre of the Republic of Belarus
Gosudarstvennyj Teatr Kukol Respubliki Belarus
ul. Engjelsa 20, 220030 **Minsk**
Tel: 172-271 365 Fax: 172-271 365
director Jevgjenij V. Klimakov

Mogilov Regional Puppet Theatre
Mogilevskii Oblastnoj Teatr Kukol
ul Pjervomajskaja 73, 212030 **Mogilev**
Tel: 222-228 683
director Oljeg O Zhugzhda

Batlejka Minsk Regional Puppet Theatre
Minskij Oblastnoj Teatr Kukol 'Batlejka'
ul Drozdovicha 5b, 222310 **Molodjechno**
Tel: 273-52861
director Alla V. Poliakova
Touring: national

Liallka Belarusian Theatre
Belaruskij Teatr Liallka
ul Pushkina 4, 210026 **Vitjebsk**
Tel: 212-360 239
director Gjerold B Osvjetinskij

BELGIUM (+32)

Poppentheater Mieke-Krik
Grote Beerstr. 43, 2018 **Antwerp**
Tel: 3-235 6116 Fax: 3-235 6116
directors Sonia Vandermaelen, Marc De Smet
Puppeteers: 4 *Perfs:* 200 *Type:* all types of puppetry, traditional and modern *Venues:* Sterretje 80

Ultima Thule
Steenbokstraat 36, 2018 **Antwerp**
Tel: 3-239 5305 Fax: 3-239 5305
director Joris Jozef
Puppeteers: 4-5 *Perfs:* 150 *Prods:* 2 *Type:* all kinds, except string puppets *Touring:* Belgium, Netherlands, France *Comments:* touring company; second address: Bis-Produkties, Liliestraat 61, 2540 Hove, Tel: 3-454 2737, Fax: 3-454 3435

Vlinders & Co (Butterflies and Company)
PB 32, 9120 **Beveren-Waas**
Tel: 3-755 2445/476-338 403 Fax: 3-755 2445
Internet: www.users.skynet/vlinders
E-Mail: ronny.aelbrecht@skynet.be
art dir Ronny Aelbrecht; chairman Peter D'Olislagers
Perfs: 250 *Prods:* 5 *Type:* modern, all forms except marionettes *Touring:* worldwide *Comments:* R Aelbrecht is also the secretary of the UNIMA - Flemish section

Théâtre Royal de Toone
Secrétariat du Théâtre Royal de Toone, Maison des Arts, Chaussée de Haecht 147, 1030 **Brussels**
Tel: 2-217 2753/0464 Fax: 2-218 5578
directeur administatif et artistique José Géal
Puppeteers: 6 +1 (voice) *Perfs:* 150 *Prods:* 8 *Type:* traditional, Brussels puppets (rod puppets) *Venues:* Théâtre Royal de Toone 140 *Comments:* perform in French, Flemish, German, English, Spanish; theatre address: 6 Impasse Schuddeveld, 21-23 Petite Rue des Bouchers 1000 Brussels, tel: 511 7137/513 5486 (bookings)

TOF Théâtre
9 rue Paul Emile Janson, 1050 **Brussels**
Tel: 2-537 3639/4421 Fax: 2-538 6158
director Alain Moreau
Puppeteers: 4 permanent *Perfs:* 120 *Prods:* 2 *Type:* modern, rod puppets *Touring:* Switzerland, France, Spain, Germany, Italy, Canada, Netherlands *Comments:* theatre address: TOF Theatre, 30 rue Louis Seculier, 1472 Vieux Gennape

Teater Taptoe
Forelstraat 91 C, 9000 **Gent**
Tel: 9-223 6758 Fax: 9-233 5467
E-Mail: theatre.taptoe@ping.be
commercial dir Luk de Bruyker; art dir Freek Neirynck
Puppeteers: 10 (and actors) *Perfs:* 250 *Prods:* 8 *Type:* puppets, actors and objects *Venues:* touring company *Touring:* France, Spain, Poland, Netherlands, Japan *Comments:* see also Drama

Al Botroûle
Rue Hocheporte 3, 4000 **Liège**
Tel: 4-223 0576 Fax: 4-223 0576
director Jacques Ancion
Puppeteers: 4 *Perfs:* 225 *Prods:* 16 (6 new) *Type:* traditional and contemporary *Venues:* Al Botroûle 42 *Touring:* Belgium, France, Spain, Germany, Czech Republik

Figurentheater Mechelen – De Maan
Minderbroedersgang 1-3, 2800 **Mechelen**
Tel: 15-200 200 Fax: 15-205 424
director Willem Verheyden
Puppeteers: 10 *Perfs:* 360 *Prods:* 5 *Type:* modern & traditional *Venues:* De Maan, Grote Zaal 186, De Blauwe Kamer 90 *Touring:* USA, Czech Republic, Netherlands, Germany, Luxembourg, Singapore, Japan

Poppentheater Kiekeboe-Pats (Antwerp)
Breda Baan 414 1er étage, 2070 **Merksem**
Tel: 3-646 3492 Fax: 3-646 3492
artistic director Walter Merholtein; administrator H. Scaoenmakers
Puppeteers: 2 *Perfs:* 25-30 *Prods:* 5 (2 new) *Type:* traditional puppetry

Poppentheater Jejem Piron VZW
Drabstr. 148, 2640 **Mortsel**
Tel: 3-440 5212 Fax: 3-440 5212
director Jean-Marie Piron
Puppeteers: 1 *Perfs:* 130 *Prods:* 1 out of 2 *Type:* modern *Venues:* small scale venues *Touring:* Netherlands

Poppentheater de Spiegel
Leemstraat 8a, 2861 **O.L.V. Waver**
Tel: 15-760 588/3-225 2839 Fax: 3-225 2839
director Karel Van Ransbeeck; direction Jeff Verschaeken; financial advice Danny Lievens; design Wouter Verhaart, Karel Van Ransbeeck
Puppeteers: 4 *Perfs:* 80-100 *Prods:* 4 *Type:* modern, rod puppets, objects, instruments, glove puppets, muppets, table puppets, Sicilian plastic puppets *Touring:* Belgium, France, Netherlands, Portugal, Hungary

Poppentheater Pico
Rozenlaan 61, 2840 **Reet**
Tel: 3-844 1076 Fax: 3-889 6890
E-Mail: koenvde@club.innet.be
technicians Tony Schilders, Koen Van den Eynde
Puppeteers: 3 *Perfs:* 20-30 *Prods:* 1-2 *Type:* modern *Touring:* Belgium, Netherlands

DRAAD – poppentheater vzw
Pater Pirestraat 11, 8800 **Roeselare**
Tel: 51-229 988 Fax: 51-229 988
E-Mail: alain.verhelst@skynet.be
chairman L. Vandeputte; secretary A. Verhelst
Puppeteers: 5-6 *Perfs:* 15-25 *Prods:* 1 *Type:* marionettes (strings) in wood *Touring:* Belgium, Netherlands

Panenka
Kerklei 49, 2960 **Sint-Job-in-'t-Goor**
Tel: 3-636 3026
director Wouter Wuyts
Puppeteers: 1-2 *Perfs:* 200 *Prods:* 4 *Type:* traditional puppet theatre for children *Venues:* 2 very small mobile theatres *Touring:* Belgium

Kinder- en poppentheater Propop
steenweg op oosthoven 114, 2300 **Turnhout**
Tel: 14-423 322 (reservations) Fax: 14-424 355
E-Mail: theater.propop@Pandora.be
director Ruud Alles; technician Paul Wouters; actress Kathlen van der Velde
Puppeteers: 3+ *Perfs:* 250 *Prods:* 2 *Type:* stick, hand and modern puppetry; also acting *Venues:* Poppenzaal, Turnhout 120 *Touring:* Flanders, Brussels, Netherlands

BOSNIA & HERZEGOVINA (+387)

School of Puppetry Art Sarajevo-Mostar
Dalamtinska 2/III, 71000 **Sarajevo**
Tel: 71-664 070 Fax: 71-664 070
manager Dubravka Zrnsc-Kulenovic

Youth Theatre
Kuloviceva 8, 71000 **Sarajevo**
Tel: 71-442 572/205 799 Fax: 71-442 572/205 799

BULGARIA (+359)

State Puppet Theatre
Profsayuzen dom na kulturata, 2700 **Blagoevgrad**
Tel: 73-21080 Fax: 73-25381
manager Ivan Daskalov
Puppeteers: 11 *Perfs:* 300 *Type:* various *Venues:* cap 250

State Puppet Theatre
8 Bogoridi Street, 8000 **Bourgas**
Tel: 56-842 998/840 735
manager Hristina Arsenieva

State Puppet Theatre Dora Gabe
9300 **Dobrich**
Tel: 58-22483/28810
director Petar Petkov
Puppeteers: 9 *Perfs:* 300 *Prods:* 4 *Venues:* cap 200

State Puppet Theatre
11 Kiril i Methodii Str., 5300 **Gabrovo**
Tel: 66-29051/29109 Fax: 66-29051
director Svetoslav Bonev
Puppeteers: 10 *Perfs:* 250 (120 on tour, 10 abroad) *Prods:* 4 *Type:* various *Venues:* capacity 150

State Puppet Theatre
6300 **Haskovo**
Tel: 38-20726/20626
director Georgi Nalbantov
Puppeteers: 8 *Perfs:* 300 (150 on tour) *Prods:* 4 *Type:* various *Venues:* capacity 220

State Puppet Theatre Philip Philipov
6600 **Kardjali**
Tel: 361-26766/22013
director Georgy Donchev
Puppeteers: 8 *Perfs:* 400 (300 on tour) *Prods:* 4 *Venues:* cap 200

State Puppet Theatre
4400 **Pazardjik**
Tel: 34-83175
director Marin Marinov
Type: various *Venues:* capacity 200

Sivina
Compl. 'Trakia' bl. 1 A, ap. 22, 4023 **Plovdiv**
Tel: 32-829 741
manager Ivan Sivinov
Puppeteers: 3 *Perfs:* 100 all on tour (20 abroad) *Type:* objects, materials etc.

State Puppet Theatre
14 Hristo G. Danov Str., 4000 **Plovdiv**
Tel: 32-625 840 Fax: 32-625 840
director Victor Boytchev
Puppeteers: 15 *Perfs:* 400 (50 on tour and 10 abroad) *Prods:* 5 *Venues:* 2 spaces; room A 200, room B 80

State Puppet Theatre
8 Knyajevska Str., 7000 **Rousse**
Tel: 82-225 273/804
manager Rositza Minovska

State Puppet Theatre
11 T. Ikonomov Str., 9700 **Shoumen**
Tel: 54-55062/50045
director Nely Dimitrova
Puppeteers: 9 *Perfs:* 300 (200 on tour) *Prods:* 4 *Type:* various *Venues:* capacity 200

State Puppet Theatre
10 Tzar Osvoboditel Str., 8800 **Sliven**
Tel: 44-22718/25186
director Svetlozar Gagov

Ariel Puppet Theatre
71 Ekzarh Yosif Str., 1000 **Sofia**
Tel: 2-833 353 Fax: 2-833 353
director Ruben Garabedian
Puppeteers: 2 *Perfs:* 250 (100 on tour, 50 abroad) *Prods:* 3

Atelie 313
Vassil Stoyanov Str., bl. 7, 1000 **Sofia**
Tel: 2-207 013/114
director Petar Pashov

Central State Puppet Theatre
14 Gurko str., 1000 **Sofia**
Tel: 2-873 815
director Alexander Tkachov
Puppeteers: 3 *Perfs:* 250 (50 on tour and 10 abroad) *Prods:* 3 *Type:* various

State Puppet Theatre
6000 **Stara Zagora**
Tel: 42-48095
director Dobrin Petkov
Puppeteers: 15 *Perfs:* 500 (300 on tour) *Prods:* 5 *Type:* various *Venues:* capacity 250

State Puppet Theatre
Hriso Botev St., PO Box 150, 7700 **Targovishte**
Tel: 601-25085/25401
director Mina Simeonova

State Puppet Theatre Varna
4 Dragoman Str., 9000 **Varna**
Tel: 52-607 844/607 841/607 842 Fax: 52-253 011
director Zlati Zlatev
Puppeteers: 15 *Perfs:* 550 (180 on tour and 50 abroad) *Prods:* 5 *Type:* various *Venues:* capacity 200

Sturche Puppet Theatre
Dom na Transportnite rabotnici, 9000 **Varna**
manager Rayko Raykov
Puppeteers: 15 *Perfs:* 150 (50 on tour, 10 abroad) *Prods:* 2 *Type:* various *Venues:* theatre capacity 350

State Puppet Theatre
48 Boyan Chonos Str., 3700 **Vidin**
Tel: 94-29182/29178
manager Pavlina Trifonova
Puppeteers: 9 *Perfs:* 250 (120 on tour) *Prods:* 4 *Type:* various *Venues:* capacity176

State Puppet Theatre
Hirsto Botev Sq., 3000 **Vratza**
Tel: 92-21083/21081
director Natacha Shamatova
Puppeteers: 6 *Perfs:* 200 (80 on tour, 10 of which abroad) *Prods:* 3 *Type:* various *Venues:* theatre capacity 100 *Touring:* national, international

State Puppet Theatre
8600 **Yambol**
Tel: 46-24701/24987
director Elena Doytcheva
Puppeteers: 10 *Perfs:* 250 (160 on tour) *Prods:* 3 *Type:* various *Venues:* capacity 250

CROATIA (+385)

Rijeka City Puppet Theatre
Gradsko kazaliste lutaka Rijeka
Blaza Polica 6, 51000 **Rijeka**
Tel: 51-212 090/51-211 381 Fax: 51-212 090/51-211 381
manager Ljerka Galic

Split City Puppet Theatre
Gradsko kazaliste lutaka Split
Kamila Toncica 1, 21000 **Split**
Tel: 21-46 099/21-356 925 Fax: 21-356 925
manager Ratko Glavina

Zadar Puppet Theatre
Kazaliste lutaka Zadar
Sokolska 1, 23000 **Zadar**
Tel: 23-430 158/23-311 122 Fax: 23-311 122
manager Davor Grzunov (tel: 23-212 754)

Puppet Stage I. B. Mazuranic
Lutkarska scena I. B. Ma'uranic
Vlaska 106, 10000 **Zagreb**
Tel: 1-464 0953 Fax: 1-464 0953
manager Sasa Greguric

Zagreb Puppet Theatre
Zagrebacko kazaliste lutaka
Trg kralja Tomislava 19, 10000 **Zagreb**
Tel: 1-434 430 Fax: 1-434 430
manager Nikola Cubela (tel/fax: 1-461 3484)

CYPRUS (+357)

George Idhalias
2836 **Korakou**
Tel: 2-932 116
Puppeteers: 1 *Perfs:* 50 *Type:* Karagiozi shadow figures *Venues:* capacity 300 *Touring:* Greece, Europe

Theatre Kourkoulianós
52 Amaranthe House, 37 J. F. Kennedy St., 3106 **Limassol**
Tel: 5-589 715
E-Mail: sitas@spidernet.com.cy
director and public relations Amaranth Sitas; stage manager and technical director Stelios Sitas
Puppeteers: 5 *Perfs:* 20 *Type:* glove and rod puppets, shadows *Venues:* Kourkoulianos Theatre (Limassol) 60; *Comments:* perform in Greek and English

Androulla Empedokleous-Puppet Theatre
2A Vassileos Constantinou Street, 1105 **Nicosia**
Tel: 2-772 627
Puppeteers: 1 *Perfs:* 60 *Type:* glove puppets and puppets that move their mouths, string puppets, modern puppets, rod puppets

CZECH REPUBLIC (+420)

Puppets Theatre Joy
Loutkové divadlo Radost
Cejl 29, 602 00 **Brno**
Tel: 5-4532 1273 Fax: 5-4521 0336
director Vlastimil Peska
Puppeteers: 14 *Perfs:* 280 *Prods:* 3 *Venues:* cap 220

Small Theatre
Malé divadlo
Hradební 18, 370 00 **Ceské Budejovice**
Tel: 38-635 5060
director Ivana Pribylová
Puppeteers: 8 *Perfs:* 200 *Prods:* 5 *Venues:* home cap 100

Studio dell' arte
Bedricha Smetany 2, 370 01 **Ceské Budejovice**
Tel: 38-25829 Fax: 38-25829
E-Mail: studio.dell.arte@iol.cz
artistic chief Katerina Melenová
Puppeteers: 4 *Perfs:* 100 *Prods:* 1 *Venues:* Divadlo pod cepici *Comments:* second address: Divadlo pod cepicí, Trznice IGY – Prazská 1258/30, 370 01 Ceské Budejovice

Theatre Drak
Divadlo Drak
Hradební 632, 500 02 **Hradec Králové**
Tel: 49-551 4721 Fax: 49-551 2510
Internet: www.divadlo.cz/drak
dir Jana Drazdáková; art dir Jakub Krofta
manager Lilian Morgan (France)
Puppeteers: 10 *Perfs:* 300 *Prods:* 3

Chinese Lantern Theatre
Divadlo Lampion
Nám. starosty Pavla 4, 272 51 **Kladno**
Tel: 312-622 732 Fax: 312-625 316
director Karél Brozek; manager Alois Tománek
Puppeteers: 12 *Perfs:* 440 *Prods:* 5 *Venues:* home cap 250

Naive Theatre
Naivní divadlo
Moskevská 18, 460 31 **Liberec**
Tel: 48-510 7282/7616 Fax: 48-510 7616
Internet: www.oasanet.cz/naive.theatre
E-Mail: naive.theatre@oasanet.cz
director Stanislav Doubrava
Puppeteers: 13 *Perfs:* 200 *Prods:* 4 *Venues:* home cap 250

Continuo Theatre
Divadlo Continuo
Malovice 35, 384 11 **Malovice**
Tel: 338-325 231/602-472 942 (mobile)
E-Mail: hafan@gego.cz
artistic chief Pavel Stourac
Puppeteers: 3 *Perfs:* 70 *Prods:* 2 *Comments:* second address: Agentura Hafan – Blanka Boruvková, Wüchterlova 16, 160 00 Praha 6, Tel/Fax: 2-2431 3151

Variety Theatre – Stage of the City Theatre Most
Divadlo rozmanitostí – scéna Mestského divadla v Moste
Topolová 1278/8, 434 00 **Most**
Tel: 35-41059 Fax: 35-29663
E-Mail: euroregion@traveller.cz
director Václav Hofman; artistic chief Antonín Klepác
Puppeteers: 12 *Perfs:* 180 *Prods:* 6 *Venues:* home capacity 190 *Comments:* see also Drama (Mestské divadlo Most)

Theatre of Puppets
Divadlo loutek
Masarykovo nám. 33, 729 82 **Ostrava**
Tel: 69-611 4884 Fax: 69-611 4322
E-Mail: loutky.ostrava@post.cz
director Jarmila Hájková
Puppeteers: 12 *Perfs:* 360 *Prods:* 4 *Venues:* home cap 176

Theatre Alpha
Divadlo Alfa
Rokycanská 7, 312 00 **Plzen**
Tel: 19-726 6520 Fax: 19-726 6736
E-Mail: alfa@pm.cesnet.cz
director Jirí Koptík
Puppeteers: 10 *Perfs:* 220 *Prods:* 4 *Venues:* home capacity 232

Buns and Puppets
Buchty a loutky
Ostrovského 24, 150 00 **Praha** 5
Tel: 2-541 9311 Fax: 2-541 9311
E-Mail: hafan@gego.cz
artistic chief Marek Becka; manager Blanka Boruvková
Puppeteers: 5 *Perfs:* 70 *Prods:* 3 *Venues:* home capacity 150 *Comments:* second address: Agentura Hafan-Blanka Boruvkova, Wüchterlova 16, 160 00 Praha 6, tel/fax: 2-2431 3151

Theatre Minor
Divadlo Minor
Senovászné nám. 28, 110 00 **Praha**
Tel: 2-2421 3241 Fax: 2-2421 4304
Internet: www.divadlo.cz/minor
E-Mail: minor@ms.easynet.cz
director Zdenek Pechácek
Puppeteers: 18 *Perfs:* 350 *Prods:* 5 *Venues:* home cap 226

Theatre of Formans Brothers
Divadlo bratrí Formanu
Hafan Studio- Blanka Boruvkoká, Wüchterlova, 16000 **Praha** 6
Tel: 2-2431 3151 Fax: 2-2431 3151
E-Mail: hafan@gego.cz
Puppeteers: 3 *Perfs:* 70 *Prods:* 1 *Venues:* touring

Theatre Spejbl and Hurvínek
Divadlo Spejbla a Hurvínka
Dejvická 38, 160 00 **Praha** 6
Tel: 2-312 1241/2431 6186 Fax: 2-312 2704
Internet: www.tradeweb.cz/ds/h
artistic director Martin Klásek; director Helena Stáchová
Puppeteers: 15 *Perfs:* 150 *Prods:* 1 *Venues:* home cap. 220

DENMARK (+45)

ALF-Dukketeater
v/Michael Svennevig, Viborggade 30, 5. tv., 2100 **Copenhagen** O
Tel: 3526 0564
contact Michael Svennevig
Puppeteers: 1 *Perfs:* 10-20 *Prods:* 1 *Type:* hand, rod, modern fairy-tales for children (4-9 years old) occassional performances for adults *Venues:* indoors and outdoor performances *Touring:* national & festivals in Latvia, Litthuania and Poland *Comments:* also performs without puppets (story-telling)

Det Lille Teater
Lavendelstraede 7, 1462 **Copenhagen**
Tel: 3312 1229 Fax: 3312 1529
Internet: www.detlilleteater.dk
E-Mail: dlt@detlilleteater.dk
contact Klaus Simonsen, Stig Dalum
Puppeteers: 3 *Perfs:* 300 *Prods:* 3 *Type:* puppets, shadow play, actors *Venues:* 2 stages: stage A 80, stage B 100

Jytte Abildstrøm's Children's Theatre
Allégade 7, 2000 **Copenhagen** F
Tel: 3887 1819 Fax: 3888 7204
Internet: www.webline.dk/riddersalen
E-Mail: jat.riddersalen@image.dk
artistic director Jytte Abildstrøm
Puppeteers: 25-30 *Perfs:* 365 *Prods:* 10 *Venues:* capacity 201 *Touring:* Denmark *Comments:* see also Drama

Maanegoegl
Baadsmandsstraede 8, 1407 **Copenhagen** K
Tel: 3257 7370 Fax: 3257 7370
artistic director Hanne Trolle
Puppeteers: 1 *Prods:* 1 *Type:* hand, rod, poetic, musical theatre *Touring:* Denmark, Europe *Comments:* perform for children 1-4 years; do shows in English and German

Paraplyteatret
Rådhusstraede 6C, 1466 **Copenhagen** K
Tel: 3313 3940/4054 3930 Fax: 3314 3960
Internet: www.paraply.dk
E-Mail: paraply@image.dk
artistic director Ray Nusselein; general administrator Lola Baidel
Puppeteers: varies *Perfs:* 130 *Prods:* 4 *Type:* object theatre, poetical theatre *Venues:* portable structure (size varies) *Touring:* Germany, France, Belgium, Finland, England

Theatre Comedievognen, The
Griffenfeldsgade 7A, 2200 **Copenhagen** N
Tel: 3536 6122 Fax: 3536 6522
E-Mail: comedie@unager.dk
management Eva Mannov, Vibeke Fabrin Lund, Bo Bertram, Niels Jørgensen
Puppeteers: 2 *Perfs:* 147 + 50 guest performances *Prods:* 4 (1 new) *Type:* stick, hand and puppets led by visible puppeteers and actors *Venues:* home capacity 100 *Touring:* Denmark *Comments:* many guest performers, designers and directors

Bjoerneteatret
Gl. Stationsvej 12, 4591 **Foellenslev**
Tel: 5926 8265 Fax: 5926 8281
managing director Carl Hartvetsen; artistic director Tom Nagel Rasmussen
Puppeteers: 2-12 *Prods:* 3 *Type:* hand puppets, open play, also with actors *Venues:* capacity 150 *Touring:* Denmark

Den Blaa Hest
Oddervej 80, 8270 **Højbjerg**
Tel: 8627 4944 Fax: 8627 4598
administrator Klaus Peterson; artistic director Aleksander Jochwed; press manager Annelise Larsen
Puppeteers: 1 + 5 actors *Perfs:* 30 *Prods:* 2 *Type:* object theatre and actors theatre *Venues:* Den Blaa Hest 150 *Touring:* Denmark, Europe *Comments:* caters for young children, adolescent and adult audiences

DRT – 1984
Sct. Nicolaigade 6, 6760 **Ribe**
Tel: 7542 2519
contact Ole Barkentin
Puppeteers: 2 *Perfs:* 135 *Prods:* 1 + 6 revivals *Type:* object theatre *Touring:* Denmark, Germany *Comments:* touring company

Pin Pon
Box 38, 8355 **Solbjerg**
Tel: 8653 1482 Fax: 8653 1518
contacts Ida Cafpillo, Marcio Igama
Puppeteers: 2 *Perfs:* 180 *Prods:* 3 *Type:* modern children's puppet theatre *Venues:* theatres, halls, schools cap 120 *Touring:* Denmark

ESTONIA (+372)

Estonian State Puppet Theatre
Eesti Riiklik Nukuteater
Lai St. 1, 10133 **Tallinn**
Tel: 6-411 614 Fax: 6-411 112
director Marge Kokk; artistic director Eero Spriit
Puppeteers: 15 *Prods:* 8 *Type:* all types *Venues:* home capacity 177 *Comments:* state repertory theatre

FINLAND (+358)

Teatteri Hevosenkenkä
Juhannusmäki 2, 02200 **Espoo**
Tel: 9-439 1220 Fax: 9-420 9508
director Kirsi Aropaltio; administrator Eila Koivula; secretary Johanna Bergmann
Puppeteers: 3 (permanent) *Perfs:* 300 *Prods:* 3 *Type:* all types except marionettes *Venues:* Teatteri Hevosenkenkä 111 *Touring:* national, international

Nukketeatteri Sampo
Klaavuntie 11, 00910 **Helsinki**
Tel: 9-336 968 Fax: 9-336 992
Internet: www.ntsampo.fi
E-Mail: ntsampo@ntsampo.fi
director Maija Baric; musical director Bojan Baric
Puppeteers: 3 *Perfs:* 260 *Prods:* 9 *Type:* marionettes, different types *Venues:* theatre capacity 80 *Touring:* national, international

Puppet Theatre Green Apple, The
Nukketeatteri Vihreä Omena
Eläintarhan huvila 7, 00530 **Helsinki**
Tel: 9-701 2483/712 818 Fax: 9-712 818
Internet: www.sgic.fi/unima
E-Mail: unima@sgic.fi
theatre director Ulla Raitahalme; sales manager Maiju Tavast
Puppeteers: 6 *Perfs:* 410 *Prods:* 8 *Type:* mixture of different techniques *Venues:* own theatre 60 *Touring:* Finland and abroad

Puppet Theatre Sytkyt
Nukketeatteri Sytkyt
Kalevank 17 C13, 00100 **Helsinki** 17
Tel: 400-575 968 Fax: 420-575 908
E-Mail: juha.laukkanen@sytkyt.inet.fi
theatre dir Juha Laukkanen; theatre prod Iiu Ruohonen
Puppeteers: 1 *Perfs:* 260 *Prods:* 10 *Type:* all types of puppets *Touring:* Finland and abroad

Teatteri MUKAMAS
Pispalan valtatie 30, 33250 **Tampere**
Tel: 3-212 0607/9197 Fax: 3-213 3809
Internet: www.mukamas.sci.fi/
E-Mail: mukamas@sci.fi
director Mansi Stycz; set designer Anna-Liisa Tarvainen
Puppeteers: 4 *Perfs:* 300+ (200 on tour) *Prods:* 3 *Type:* modern puppetry *Venues:* Theatre Hall 80, schools, libraries, kindergartens, festivals etc. in Europe *Touring:* Europe *Comments:* creative international cooperation with guest directors from Czech Republic, Sweden and Russia; also visiting companies from all over Europe

FRANCE (+33)

Caron
40 rue Blasset, 80000 **Amiens**
Tel: 3-2289 3745
director Lucien Caron
Puppeteers: 1 *Perfs:* 50+ *Prods:* 1 *Type:* marionettes, modern, traditional Guignol *Venues:* schools etc. *Touring:* France

Ches Panses Vertes
24 rue Saint Leu, 80000 **Amiens**
Tel: 3-2292 1932 Fax: 3-2291 1335
directrice Sylvie Baillon; administratrice Elise Lebossé; sécretaire Florence Baroiller
Puppeteers: 3 *Perfs:* 80 *Prods:* 5 per season *Type:* contemporary puppetry *Venues:* room A 130, room B 60; mobile show (tent) 250 *Touring:* France, Germany, Switzerland, Romania, Spain, Portugal *Comments:* courses and training for amateurs and professionals

Eclats D'Etats
8 rue d'assas, 80 000 **Amiens**
Tel: 3-2291 7085/6-8121 2844 Fax: 3-2292 7362
dir Antonakaki Katerrini, Jorand-Briquet Emmanuel
Puppeteers: varies *Perfs:* 20+ *Prods:* 2 *Type:* theatre of animated forms *Touring:* France

Théâtre de Chés Cabotans d'Amiens
31 Rue Edouard David, 80000 **Amiens**
Tel: 3-2222 3090 Fax: 3-2222 3094
Internet: www.oda.fr/aa/theatre_picard
directrice, relations publiques, metteur en scène et interprète Françoise Rose-Auvet; administrateur, scènographe, graphiste et interprète Jacques A.F. Auvet; secrétariat-comptable, informatique Francine Seguin
Puppeteers: 5-7 *Perfs:* 250 (exhibitions & performance animations) *Prods:* 1 *Type:* traditional, marionettes, rod *Venues:* Theatre Chés Cabotans d'Amien 133 *Touring:* national, international

Marionnettes D'Angoulême
Espace Marengo, 16000 **Angoulême**
Tel: 5-4569 3210
E-Mail: marionette@multimedia.com
directeur Michel Belezy
Puppeteers: 5 *Perfs:* 70 *Prods:* 2 *Type:* manipulation a vue *Venues:* Théâtre de Poche Marengo 120 *Touring:* France *Comments:* drama classes for young people and adults

Theatre de Mazade
27, bd de la Corniche, 07200 **Aubenas**
Tel: 4-7593 3156 Fax: 4-7593 3156
directrice artistique Alison Corbett; administration Carine Turbeaux, Nadia Pommaret
Puppeteers: varies + actors *Perfs:* 150 per season *Prods:* 1 new *Type:* modern, marionnette, rod, shadow, object theatre *Venues:* capacity up to 200
Touring: France and abroad

Compagnie Coatimundi
Maison IV de Chiffre, 26 rue des Teinturiers, 84000 **Avignon**
Tel: 4-9027 1060 Fax: 4-9086 1113
directeurs artistiques Jean-Claude Leportier, Catherine Kremer
Puppeteers: 2 *Perfs:* 100 *Prods:* 5 *Type:* mixed – actors, marionettes, objects – without dialogue *Touring:* USA, Kenya, Canada, national *Comments:* subsidised by the Ministry of Culture, the DRAC, the Office Régional de la Culture Provence/Alpes Côte d'Azur, Conseil Général du Vaucluse and L'AFAA

Theatre du Bambou Compagnie Fuhrmann
15, rue Paul-Chanson, 21200 **Beaune**
Tel: 3-8024 7756 Fax: 3-8024 0671
E-Mail: thbambou@club-internet.fr
directeur Irène de Nouaillan-Fuhrmann; régisseur général Laure Fuhrmann
Puppeteers: 3 *Perfs:* 100 *Prods:* 1 *Type:* contemporary *Venues:* 15, rue Paul-Chanson 90 *Touring:* France *Comments:* co-production with the Orchestra l'enfant et les Sortilèges

Manches A Balais – Korporation
136, Grande-Rue, 25000 **Besançon**
Tel: 3-8181 3331 Fax: 3-8180 7579
Internet: www.doubsinfo>com/marionnette
E-Mail: info@netconseils.com
directeur Jean-René Bouvret
Pupeteers: 3 *Perfs:* 70 *Prods:* 5 (2 new) *Type:* various puppet types *Touring:* France, international *Comments:* street puppet theatre

Compagnie du Théatrivore
8, av de la gare, 31360 **Boussens**
Tel: 5-6190 0238/607-114 705 (mobile) Fax: 5-6190 0238
directeur Philippe Olivier; administrateur Maurice Boisnard
Puppeteers: 1 *Perfs:* 220 *Prods:* 1 *Type:* shadow theatre, actors and marionettes *Venues:* shows for schools and cultural centres *Touring:* France

Theatre Bois Debout
8 bis, rue des Carrouges, 91800 **Brunoy**
Tel: 1-6939 5481 Fax: 1-6939 5481
directeur François Monestier
Puppeteers: 1-2 *Perfs:* 70 *Prods:* 2 *Type:* modern, symbolic, traditional *Venues:* 200 *Touring:* international *Comments:* also outside and street performances

Théâtre Foz
4 rue Lechartier, 14000 **Caen**
Tel: 2-3172 5409 Fax: 2-3183 2272
président Monique Calzas; directeur artistique Rowland Buys; relations publique Jean Truel
Puppeteers: 5 *Perfs:* 60 *Prods:* 2
Type: for young people *Venues:* Ailleurs 140
Touring: France, abroad

Arketal (Cie)
6 Impasse de la Chaumiere, BP 17, 06401 **Cannes** Cedex
Tel: 4-9368 9200 Fax: 4-9299 2507
directrice Sylvie Osman; scènographe Greta Bruggeman
Puppeteers: varies *Perfs:* 100 *Prods:* 1
Type: mixture of puppets and actors
Touring: France,Sweden, Norway, Switzerland

Pupella-Noguès
Boite Postale 2, 31460 **Caraman**
Tel: 5-6183 5926 Fax: 5-6183 5926
directeurs artistiques Noguès Joëlle, Pupella Giorgio
Puppeteers: 2-5 *Perfs:* 40+ *Prods:* 1
Type: marionette and shadow theatre for children and adults; repertoire: Beckett, Appleton, Kipling
Venues: Centres Culturels, Théâtres, Festivals
Touring: France

Clastic Theatre – Compagnie François Lazaro
62 Boulevard Victor Hugo, 92110 **Clichy**
Tel: 1-4106 0404 Fax: 1-4106 0403
directeur François Lazaro; administrateur Paul Rondin
Puppeteers: 1-8 *Perfs:* 50 *Prods:* 1
Type: modern theatre-marionnettes
Touring: Europe, France

Manimasc Théâtre
La Colle Concas, 06340 **Drap (Alpes Maritimes)**
Tel: 4-9354 8192
président Patrick Fromholtz; directrice Monique Bahrfeld
Puppeteers: 2 *Perfs:* 35 *Prods:* 1 *Type:* traditional, musical, creation & shadows shows
Comments: for all age groups

Compagnie Fifrelot Tailliez-Toutain
1 rue Gambetta, 95120 **Ermont**
Tel: 1-3072 1160 Fax: 1-3072 9902
directeur t.b.a.; directeur artistique Jean-Christophe Taillez; administratrice Patricia Dumoutier
Puppeteers: 5-6 *Perfs:* 200-250 *Type:* contemporary, shadows show & all types of puppets *Venues:* Ermont, Théâtre de l'Aventure 200 *Touring:* France, Europe
Comments: street theatre with musicians on stilts

Compagnie Jean-Pierre Lescot
9, rue Pasteur, 94120 **Fontenay-Sous-Bois**
Tel: 1-4876 5939 Fax: 1-4876 4685
directeur Jean-Pierre Lescot
Puppeteers: 5-6 *Perfs:* 100 *Prods:* 1 *Type:* marionettes, black theatre *Venues:* Salle Roublot 135 *Touring:* France, Europe *Comments:* also organise a biennial festival (1999); see also Festivals

Compagnie Théâtre Manarf
Le Moulin, 49220 **Grez-Neuville**
Tel: 2-4195 6929 Fax: 2-4195 6977
directeur Jacques Templeraud; contact Sylvie Monier
Puppeteers: 1-3 *Perfs:* 40 *Type:* marionettes, shadow puppets and actors *Venues:* home capacity 200 *Touring:* France, Europe, USA

Atelier de Creation des Marionnettes Dougnac
4, allée des Biches, 78170 **La Celle-Saint-Cloud**
Tel: 1-3969 1850/6-0905 8638 Fax: 1-3969 1850
directeur Michel Dougnac
Puppeteers: 2-4 *Perfs:* 80 *Prods:* 1 *Type:* modern *Touring:* France, abroad

Compagnie Daru
14, allée Tilleuls, BP 51, 91292 **La Norville** Cedex
Tel: 1-6490 6988 Fax: 1-6490 6988
directeurs Philippe Angrand, Christian Chabaud
Puppeteers: 6 *Perfs:* 25 *Prods:* 1 *Type:* contemporary
Touring: France

Les Bamboches
La Garenne et La Loze, 26160 **Le Poet-Laval**
Tel: 4-7546 8382 Fax: 4-7546 8382
contacts Katia Larvego
Puppeteers: 1-2 *Perfs:* 80 *Prods:* 1 *Type:* table puppets with song and music *Touring:* France, Switzerland
Comments: for young audiences and adults

Sainte Réparade
Maison des Association, Avenue de la Bourgade, 13610 **Le-Puy-Sainte-Réparade**
Tel: 4-4261 9036 Fax: 4-4261 9036
director Gui Baldet
Puppeteers: 1 *Perfs:* 100-120 *Prods:* 1 (for adults) *Type:* traditional (Guignol, Punch) *Venues:* cap. 50 *Touring:* France, Belgium, Switzerland *Comments:* shows adapted for toured countries

Ledun (Cie)
11 Rue Mariotte, 59000 **Lille**
Tel: 3-2053 5317 Fax: 3-2053 2497
contact Marcel Ledun
Puppeteers: 3 *Prods:* 1 *Type:* traditional, marionettes, string *Touring:* France, Canada, Japan, USA, Scandinavia, Europe *Comments:* organises exhibitions (1000 marionnettes); programmes for adults and children

Théâtre de l'Arc-En-Terre
14 Boulevard Boisson, 13004 **Marseille**
Tel: 4-9134 1939 Fax: 4-9134 2167
Internet: www.multimania.com/arkenter
E-Mail: theatrearc@aol.com
directeur Massimo Schuster; attache´de production Anne Magnet
Perfs: 80 *Prods:* 1 *Type:* varies *Touring:* national, international

Théâtre Du Fust
Chapelle des Carmes, 26200 **Montélimar**
Tel: 4-7501 1761 Fax: 4-7501 2018
E-Mail: theatre@lefust.com
régisseur général Gilles Richard; directrice artistique Émilie Valantin; administratice Laëtitia Pajot; relations publiques Guillemette Dubois
Puppeteers: 1-6 *Perfs:* 100 *Prods:* 2 *Type:* contemporary, traditional *Venues:* cap. 200-400 *Touring:* France, Europe *Comments:* audiovisual production work; emphasis on adult productions

Compagnie Philippe Juste
40, rue Paul-Signac, 93100 **Montreuil**
Tel: 1-4287 6561 Fax: 1-4287 6561
directeur Philippe Juste
Puppeteers: 1 *Perfs:* 90 *Prods:* 1 *Type:* modern, contemporary *Touring:* France

BLIN (Cie)
104 avenue Henri Ginoux, 92120 **Montrouge**
Tel: 1-4253 2324 Fax: 1-4253 2324
directeur Frédéric Blin
Puppeteers: 3 *Perfs:* 100-150 *Prods:* 1 *Type:* traditional, marionettes, à fils *Venues:* Le théâtre de Montrouge 250 *Touring:* France, abroad *Comments:* the oldest string puppet theatre in France, 3500 puppets

Les 4 Marionnettes de Nantes
8 rue garde Dieu, 44000 **Nantes**
Tel: 2-4047 6146/6-8698 2346 Fax: 2-4035 6270
president de l'association Loic Rousselot
Puppeteers: 4 *Perfs:* 100 *Prods:* 1 *Venues:* cap 300 *Touring:* France, Europe

Theatre d'Animation du Verseau
1 rue Miserey, 21401 **Noiran**
Tel: 3-2540 9561 Fax: 3-2582 5064
directeur Muriel Gaudiez
Puppeteers: varies *Perfs:* 100 *Prods:* 1 *Type:* animation theatre (with puppets) *Touring:* international *Comments:* shows for adults and children

Magic Turtle, The
Compagnie La Tortue Magique
2 rue du Bourdon Blanc, BP 1433, 45004 **Orleans**
Tel: 2-3854 6428 Fax: 2-3854 6529
E-Mail: jvszezak@cyber.cable.fr
directeurs Annie Korach, François Juszezak; directeur artistique Annie Korach; administratrice Nancy Tarrius
Puppeteers: 2 *Perfs:* 100 *Prods:* 4 *Type:* mechanical, glove, rod, for all ages; work with the help of cinema drama *Venues:* salle du théâtre du Parc Pasteur in Orléans 100 *Touring:* Europe, France *Comments:* organise festival; Festival du Parc Pasteur – puppets, theatre, music, annual Aug-Sept

Morisse et Compagnie
37, rue Pierre-Augustin-Caron, 77280 **Othis-Beaumarchais**
Tel: 1-6003 0478 Fax: 1-6003 0778
directrice Muriel Arnace; relations publiques Corinne Foucouin; compositeur Jean-Maurice Dutriaux; décorateur Georges Mosca
Puppeteers: 5 *Perfs:* 150 *Prods:* 1 *Type:* contemporary *Venues:* Centre Culturel Jacques Prévert de Villeparisis 1200 *Touring:* France *Comments:* for all age groups

Au Polichinelle Parisien
24 Villa Emile Loubet, 75019 **Paris**
Tel: 1-4842 5180 Fax: 1-4238 3992
directeur Philippe Casidanus
Puppeteers: 1 *Perfs:* 500 *Prods:* 1 *Type:* traditional, modern, glove puppets *Venues:* Polichinelle Parisien *Touring:* France, Italy *Comments:* family owned traditonal Champs Elysée puppets since 1818; Wed., Sat., & Sunday shows for all ages from 4 years – presente les farces de Polichinelle; visiting address: Parc Georges Brassens, 75015 Paris

Bululu Théâtre
4, rue des Ecouffes, 75004 **Paris**
Tel: 1-4278 5298 Fax: 1-4278 5298
E-Mail: bululu@wanadoo.fr
directeur Horacio Peralta; administrateur Richard Sutrie
Puppeteers: 3 *Perfs:* 50 *Prods:* 2 *Type:* all types except string *Touring:* France, Europe *Comments:* puppetry, theatre & street theatre

Compagnie Dominique Houdart – Jeanne Heuclin
58 rue de la Rochefoucauld, 75009 **Paris**
Tel: 1-4281 0928 Fax: 1-4463 0218
E-Mail: gintzburger@wanadoo.fr
directeurs Dominique Houdart, Jeanne Heuclin
Puppeteers: 6 *Perfs:* 80 *Type:* theatre, puppetry (classical, modern, musical) Bunraku, street puppets *Venues:* street theatre; various venues 300 to 700 *Touring:* Europe *Comments:* agent: André Gintzburger, 47 rue de Richelieu, 75001 Paris, tel. 1-4297 4536 fax. 1-4296 4299

Compagnie L'Olifant
82, rue des Vignolles, 75020 **Paris**
Tel: 1-4367 2253 Fax: 1-4367 8696
E-Mail: compagnie.olifant@wanadoo.fr
directeur Bernard Cordreaux
Perfs: 50+ *Prods:* 1 *Type:* modern, puppets and actors
Touring: France

Théâtre Aux Mains Nues – Compagnie Alain Recoing
37 rue de la Chapelle, 75018 **Paris**
Tel: 1-4461 8291/4205 3657 Fax: 1-4461 8295/4205 3657
directeur Alain Recoing
Puppeteers: 3-6 *Perfs:* 10 *Prods:* 1 *Type:* puppet and theatre *Touring:* France, abroad *Comments:* for all age groups; Alelier de Formation de L'acteur/marionnettists

Théâtre de L'Ombrelle
7 rue Robert et Sonia Delaunay, 75011 **Paris**
Tel: 1-4370 4219 Fax: 1-4370 5224
directeurs artistiques associés Florence de Andia, Sylvie Vallery-Masson, Colette Blanchet, Françoise Rouillon
Puppeteers: 5 *Perfs:* 100 *Prods:* 1 *Type:* shadow theatre using techniques such as puppets, masks and body forms *Touring:* France

Comments: performances especially for children; contact: Association de production et création, comme il vous plaira, Tel&Fax: 1-4343 5558

Théâtre du Petit-Miroir
5, rue Maurice-Bourdet, 75016 **Paris**
Tel: 1-4647 8015 Fax: 1-4050 1954
administration et contacts Sylviane Mossé; directeur artistique Jean-Luc Penso
Puppeteers: 2 *Perfs:* 80 *Prods:* 7 *Type:* traditional chinese and modern shadow puppets, modern puppets and traditional Chinese glove puppets *Venues:* capacity 150 to 400 *Touring:* France, Asia, USA, South Pacific, Europe, South America

Smala et Compagnie – La Compagnie Bleu-Théâtre
La Pepiniere, 6/8 Avenue Schuman, 64000 **Pau**
Tel: 5-5906 2405 Fax: 5-5906 2405
directeurs artistiques Marie-Hélène Godard, Jean-Louis Buecher
Puppeteers: 1 and 1 actor *Perfs:* 50-100 *Prods:* 2 *Venues:* cultural centres *Touring:* France *Comments:* also educational show in English

Brakabrik Théâtre – Compagnie Julie Dourdy
10, chemin St Patrice, 04860 **Pierrevert**
Tel: 4-9272 9042 Fax: 4-9272 9042
président Gérard Massen; animatrice Julie Dourdy
Puppeteers: 3 *Perfs:* 80 *Prods:* 1 *Type:* contemporary puppetry *Venues:* cultural centres, theatres, festivals *Touring:* France, Europe *Comments:* specialise in plays for young children

Compagnie Christian Griffoul
Théâtre de la Mouette, 4, av. de Bellevue, 91130 **Ris-Orangis**
Tel: 1-6906 1281 Fax: 1-6906 1281
directeur Christian Griffoul;
administration Francine Llounc
Puppeteers: 4 *Perfs:* 120 *Prods:* 1 *Type:* traditional *Touring:* France *Comments:* give classes in marionettes, manipulation and creation at University of Paris VIII, St Denis

Compagnie Des Balmes
3 rue Marceaux, 42300 **Roanne**
Tel: 4-7771 4025
directeur Jean-Louis Prebet
Puppeteers: 1-6 *Prods:* 2 *Type:* shadow and paper
Touring: France, abroad

Théâtre de la Courte Échelle
Quai Sainte-Claire, 26100 **Romans**
Tel: 4-7502 2076 Fax: 4-7570 9283
directeur Denis Donger; directrice artistique Claudine Serme; relations publiques Sophie Macel
Puppeteers: varies *Perfs:* 60 *Prods:* 1 *Type:* modern *Venues:* salle du théâtre 80 *Touring:* France

Théâtre Louis-Richard Armat
26, rue du Chateau, 59100 **Roubaix**
Tel: 3-2073 1010 Fax: 3-2073 7760
directeurs Alain Guillemin, Andrée Leroux
Puppeteers: 7 *Perfs:* 160 *Prods:* 2 *Type:* traditional and modern *Venues:* capacity 150 *Touring:* France, Europe

Atelier De L'Arcouest
Chemin de la Rivière, 76370 **Rouxmenil Bouteille**
Tel: 2-3584 1083/5024 (home) Fax: 2-3506 2068
directeurs Odile Mauviard
Puppeteers: 1 permanent *Perfs:* 10+ *Prods:* 1 *Type:* marionettes, masks, shadows and actors
Touring: France, Europe

Alain Le Boulaire
133 route de Vanne, 44800 **Saint Herblain**
Tel: 2-4076 4593 Fax: 2-4076 4912
directeur Alain Le Boulaire
Puppeteers: 1 *Perfs:* 70 *Prods:* 1 *Type:* shadow theatre
Touring: Europe *Comments:* adaption of the Greek shadow theatre & caragueuse

Théâtre de Mathieu – Compagnie Florence Thiebaut
Chemin des Combes, 34270 **St Matthieu de Treviers**
Tel: 4-6755 1526 Fax: 4-6755 1526
directrice Florence Thiebaut;
régisseur technique Daniel Landreau
Puppeteers: 2 *Perfs:* 50 *Prods:* 2 *Type:* contemporary
Touring: France *Comments:* for all age groups; visual shows – no speaking

Compagnie Amoros et Augustin
13 rue de Phalbourg, 67000 **Strasbourg**
Tel: 3-8835 1006/8889 9752 Fax: 3-8835 1085
directions Luc Amoros, Michèle Augustin; secrétariat Mathieu Desanlis; administrateur Bruno de Beaufort
Puppeteers: varies *Perfs:* 75 *Prods:* 2 *Type:* marionette, shadow theatre, painting and video *Touring:* France

Flash Marionnettes
54 Rue du Faubourg National, 67000 **Strasbourg**
Tel: 3-8823 1279 Fax: 3-8832 9911
contacts Corine Linden, Ismaïl Safwan; relation publique Cécile Bronner
Puppeteers: 3 *Perfs:* 150-160 *Prods:* 2 *Type:* modern
Touring: worldwide

Théâtre Tohu-Bohu
17 Rue des Foulons, 67200 **Strasbourg**
Tel: 3-8828 2000 Fax: 3-8828 2160
directeur artistique Gilbert Meyer; pr Delphine Brugger
Puppeteers: 3 *Perfs:* 50 *Prods:* 1 *Type:* object theatre, marionettes, sculptures, masks – for all ages
Touring: France

Théâtre de la Toupine – Spectacle de Rue et Spectacle de Marionnettes en Salle
5 imp. du Bastion, 74200 **Thonon**
Tel: 4-5071 6597 Fax: 4-5026 4455
contact Alain Benzoni
Puppeteers: 3 *Perfs:* 153 *Prods:* 1 *Type:* all types of marionettes, shadow theatre *Touring:* France, Europe
Comments: see also Festivals

Compagnie Mercy
48 rue de Liverdun, 54200 **Villey-Saint-Etienne**
Tel: 3-8362 9792 Fax: 3-8362 9792
E-Mail: cpt.rêve@wanadoo.fr
director Philippe Mercy
Puppeteers: 1 (permanent) *Perfs:* 80 *Prods:* 2 *Type:* all types – glove, life size, rod, table or castelet – for children & adults *Venues:* Aux Marionnettes de la Pépiniére (Nancy) +300, also own mobile theatre
Touring: France

Théâtre de Marionnettes de Metz
17 Place de l'abreuvoir, 57640 **Vrémy**
Tel: 3-8776 8048 Fax: 3-8776 8180
directeur Jean Poirson
Puppeteers: 5 *Perfs:* 90-100 *Prods:* 2 *Type:* contemporary (avantgarde) *Touring:* France, Europe *Comments:* shows for all age groups; research in different techniques, using actors and masks; mixture of huge (3m) & tiny (10cm) puppets; also street theatre

GEORGIA (+995)

Akhaltsikhe Puppet Theatre
19 King Tamar str.
Akhaltsikhe
Tel: 265-29073
manager Rusudan Sisauri; artistic director Nodar Ionatamishvili

Batumi Puppet Theatre
Stalin Ave. 40, 380450 **Batumi**
Tel: 88222-70592/76789
artistic director Tamaz Bolkvadze

Borjomi Puppet Theatre
9 Kostava str., **Borjomi**
Tel: 267-22815

Gogebashvili Puppet theatre
9 St. Nino Tamar str., **Gurjaani**
Tel: 231-55205/58090
manager Shalva Kebadze

Gurjaani Puppet Theatre
6 King Tamar st., 383300 **Gurjaani**
Tel: 253-20612/24280/23734/21644/22120
manager Givi Tabakhmelashvili;
artistic director Nodar Ionatamishvili

Marionette Theatre
26 Shavteli st., 380026 **Tbilisi**
Tel: 32-986 590/996 620 Fax: 32-986 593
managers Levan Guliashvili, Rezo Gabriadze
Puppeteers: 12

Puppet State Theatre
103 Agmashenebeli Ave., 380064 **Tbilisi**
Tel: 32-952 671
manager Vakhtang Maglaperidze; chief accountant Marina Kalatozishvili; administrator Tsiuri Chkhikvadze

GERMANY (+49)

Zapperlot – Die Bühne
Schloß Altmannshofen, 88317 **Aichstetten**
Tel: 7565-7971 Fax: 7565-7971
contacts K. Hoßfeld, A. Schilling
Puppeteers: 2 *Perfs:* 40 *Prods:* 2 *Type:* traditional, experimental *Venues:* touring company
Touring: Germany *Comments:* for all age groups, often works for TV productions; theatre projects with children;
own theatre productions

Theaterhaus Alpenrod Petra Schuff
Mittelstrasse 22, 57642 **Alpenrod**
Tel: 2662-50396
Fax: 2662-1788
künstlerische Leitung Petra Schuff
Perfs: 100 *Prods:* 6 *Type:* mobile theatre with puppets of different styles for all age groups
Venues: Theatre 80 *Comments:* supported by: Kunststiftung Baden-Württemberg; Kultusministerium, Mainz; Fonds darstellende Künste, Essen; Kultusministerium, Wiesbaden; Landesgirokasse, Stuttgart;
Westerwälder Volksbank; Naspa

Annes Bühne
Herderstr. 6, 26689 **Apen-Augustfehn**
Tel: 4489-3194 Fax: 4489-3109
Leiterin Anne Sudbrack
Puppeteers: 1 *Perfs:* 80-100 *Prods:* 7 *Type:* glove, rod, material and actors *Venues:* Annes Bühne in der 'Alten Tischler' *Touring:* Germany
Comments: theatre address: Annes Bühne in der 'Alten Tischler', Südgeorgsfehnerstr. 20a, 26689 Augustfehn

Augsburger Puppenkiste
Oehmichens Marionettentheater, Spitalgaße 15, 86150 **Augsburg**
Tel: 821-324 4976 Fax: 821-438 956
Internet: www.AugsburgerPuppenkiste.de
director Klaus Marschall
Puppeteers: 16 *Perfs:* 350 *Prods:* 2 *Type:* marionettes
Venues: home capacity 222
Touring: Germany *Comments:* office address: Ulmenweg 21, 86391 Stadtbergen, tel: 821-434 440

Theater Eggs Press
Eschenstr. 75, 53902 **Bad Münstereifel**
Tel: 2257-4414 Fax: 2257-4415
Internet: www.eggspress.de
E-Mail: mail@eggspress.de
Leitung Jojo Ludwig
Puppeteers: 1 *Perfs:* 150 *Prods:* 3 *Type:* object theatre, combination of puppetry and actors *Touring:* all Europe
Comments: also performs in French

Theater Christou
Meditatives Theater, Rathausstr. 5, 88410 **Bad Wurzach**
Tel: 7527-5393 Fax: 7527-5103
director Christian Christou;
artistic director Susanne Christou
Puppeteers: 2 *Perfs:* 80 *Prods:* 5 (1new) *Type:* table, rod, hand puppets; marionettes
Touring: Germany *Comments:* also poetry and adult puppet shows; often combined with/accompanied by live music, dance & theatre

Deutsch-Sorbisches Volkstheater Bautzen Puppentheater
Käthe-Kollwitz-Str. 17, Haus 10, 02625 **Bautzen**
Tel: 3591-584 280 Fax: 3591-584 280
amt. Intendant Lutz Hillmann; Dramaturg Hildburg Zschiedrich; künstlerische Leiterin Irene Barkow; technischer Leiter Martin Suschke
Puppeteers: 5 *Perfs:* 160 *Prods:* 18 *Type:* all types, combinations *Venues:* Puppentheater (belongs to Deutsch-Sorbisches Volkstheater); Großer Saal 250, Kleiner Saal 70 *Touring:* sorbischer Kulturraum, also national, international *Comments:* see also Drama, Choirs and Dance

Berliner Figuren Theater
Yorckstr. 59, 10965 **Berlin**
Tel: 30-786 9815 Fax: 30-786 9818
E-Mail: bft.harte@t-online.de
contact Tilman Harte
Puppeteers: 2 *Perfs:* 300 *Prods:* 5 *Type:* marionettes, open play (offenes Spiel), hand puppets
Venues: home capacity (children performances) 80, (adult performances) 50

DIE SCHAUBUDE Puppentheater Berlin
Greifswalder Str. 81-84, 10405 **Berlin**
Tel: 30-423 4314/428 6059 Fax: 30-423 4310
Internet: www.schaubude.bkv.org
E-Mail: info@bkv.org
artistic director Silvia Brendenal; technical director Steffi Ende; assistant to artistic director Silke Haueiß; secretary Martina Schnabel
Type: wide range of puppetry forms *Venues:* cap 147
Comments: international guest & local groups'perfs

Fliegendes Theater
Hasenheide 54, 10967 **Berlin**
Tel: 30-692 2100 Fax: 30-692 2100
Inhaber Rudolf Schmid; management/Öffentlichkeitsarbeit Tilman Leitzbach
Puppeteers: 3 *Perfs:* 150-200 *Prods:* 7 (1 new)
Type: all kinds and experimental *Venues:* home capacity 99 *Touring:* Germany

KOBALT Puppet Theatre
KOBALT Figurentheater
Sanderstr. 26, 12047 **Berlin**
Tel: 30-692 8340 Fax: 30-692 8340
Leitung Kristiane Balsevicius, Silke Technau
Puppeteers: 1-4 *Perfs:* 200 *Prods:* 10 *Type:* hand, experimental for children, for families, for adults
Venues: Die Schaubude Puppentheater Berlin 146, and other mobile venues 100 *Touring:* Germany, Spain, Switzerland, Austria, Prague

Theater Jaro
Schusterustr. 40, 10585 **Berlin**
Tel: 30-341 0442
Fax: 30-341 0442
contact Katja Behounek
Puppeteers: 5 *Perfs:* 120-130 *Prods:* 1 *Type:* mixture of drama, puppetry and music *Venues:* Das Charlottchen, Berlin 100 *Touring:* Germany

Theater Thomas Rohloff
Büro Kollwitzstr 53, 10405 **Berlin**
Tel: 30-4400 8274 Fax: 30-4400 8275
E-Mail: rohloff@snafu.de
Direktor Thomas Rohloff; Leiter der Öffentlichkeitsarbeit André Kraft
Puppeteers: 1 + guests *Type:* puppetry and theatre

Dagmar Selje Puppenspiele/Poetisches Puppentheater Bielefeld
Im Zentrum Bielefelder Puppenspiele, Ravensbergerstr. 12, 33602 **Bielefeld**
Tel: 521-179 605/60840(bookings) Fax: 521-1796 0335
Internet: www.bielefeld-info.de
E-Mail: LaDiva@t-online.de
Leiter Dagmar Selje Dagmar Selje
Puppeteers: 2 *Perfs:* 300 *Prods:* 2-3 *Type:* hand shadow *Venues:* Zentrum Bielefelder Puppenspiele 154 *Touring:* Germany, Austria *Comments:* for children only

Poetisches Puppentheatre Bielefeld
Im Zentrum Bielefelder Puppenspiele, Ravensbergerstr. 12, 33602 **Bielefeld**
Tel: 521-66344 Fax: 521-66346
Internet: www.poetisches-puppentheater.de
E-Mail: niekampTh@aol.com
Leiter Thomas Niekamp
Puppeteers: 4 *Perfs:* 180 *Prods:* 9 (2 for adults, 7 for children) *Type:* all types *Venues:* Zentrum Bielefelder Puppenspiele 154 *Touring:* Germany, Austria, Switzerland

Puppentheater Kieselstein
Postfach 600 203, 44842 **Bochum**
Tel: 2327-31812
Leitung Gisela u. Dieter Kieselstein
Puppeteers: 2 *Perfs:* 30 *Prods:* 2 adult series, 6 children series *Type:* every type except shadow *Venues:* touring company *Touring:* Germany, Europe

Guck mal – das mobile Figuren Theater
Georgstr. 16, 53111 **Bonn**
Tel: 228-633 601
Leitung Martina Hering
Puppeteers: 1 *Perfs:* 50 *Prods:* 3 *Type:* table puppets *Venues:* touring company *Touring:* Germany

Puppenbühne des Brandenburger Theaters
Grabenstraße 14, 14776 **Brandenburg**
Tel: 3381-511-0 Fax: 3381-511-0
contact Wolfgang Rudolph
Comments: see also Drama, Opera and Orchestras

Figurentheater Fadenschein
Bültenweg 95, 38106 **Braunschweig**
Tel: 531-340 845 Fax: 531-331 011
Internet: www.fadenschein.de
E-Mail: figurentheater@fadenschein.de
Managerin Angelika Rolle
Puppeteers: 3 *Perfs:* 100-150 *Prods:* 14 (children), 1 (adult) *Venues:* Theatre Fadenschein 100 *Touring:* national, international

Theater Im Wind
Liebermannstr. 16, 38106 **Braunschweig**
Tel: 531-343 633 Fax: 531-343 633
Direktor Enno Podehl, Anne Podehl
Puppeteers: 2 *Perfs:* 40-50 *Prods:* 1 *Type:* puppets, object theatre for adults only *Touring:* national, international *Comments:* perform in several languages andmainly for adults; touring company

Städtische Theater Chemnitz – Puppentheater
PF 756, 09007 **Chemnitz**
Tel: 371-696 9660/644 6431 Fax: 371-644 6432
Internet: www.in-chemnitz.de/lange/
Generalintendant Rolf Stiska; Direktor Puppentheater Manfred Blank
Puppeteers: 6 *Perfs:* 220 *Prods:* 18 *Type:* all types including: hand puppets, marionnette, shadow puppets, rod *Venues:* Cine Star Luxor Filmpalast 132 *Comments:* theatre address: Luxor-Filmpalast, Hartmannstraße 9, 09113 Chemnitz; see also Opera, Dance and Drama

Anhaltisches Theater Dessau Puppentheater
Friedensplatz 1a, 06844 **Dessau**
Tel: 340-212 401 Fax: 340-212 401
Leitung Jens Hellwig; Organisation Ilka Stritzel; Technik Detlef Marx
Puppeteers: 3 *Perfs:* 180 *Prods:* 11 (2 new) *Type:* all types *Venues:* Puppentheatersaal 135 *Touring:* national *Comments:* venue address: Ferdinand-von-Schillstr. 7; office address: Wolfgangstr. 13, see also Opera, Dance, Orchestras and Drama

Puppentheater der Stadt Dresden
Hebbelstr. 35 b, 01157 **Dresden**
Tel: 351-840 640 Fax: 351-840 644
Oberspielleiter Horst-Joachim Lonius; Leiter press Andrea Kuehl; Theaterpädagogin/Dramaturgie Bettina Seiler; künstl Betriebsbüro Sabine Nerad
Puppeteers: 7 *Perfs:* 250 *Prods:* 8 *Type:* marionettes, hand puppets, shadow puppets, mixed forms *Venues:* Sonnenhäusl (open air) 300, Saal 105 *Comments:* venue address: Rundkino, Prager Straße, 01069 Dresden

Figurentheater Hille Puppille
Am Hange 1, 48249 **Dülmen**
Tel: 2594-85912
Fax: 2594-85595
Internet: www.hille-puppille.de
E-Mail: post@hille-puppille.de
contact Hille u. Klaus Menning
Puppeteers: 2 *Perfs:* 150 *Prods:* 7 *Type:* large-scale figures, Tischfiguren *Venues:* mobile theatre *Touring:* Germany *Comments:* shows about racism, drug prevention, violence, friendship and courage

Düsseldorfer Marionetten-Theater
Bilker Straße 7, 40213 **Düsseldorf**
Tel: 211-328 432
Fax: 211-133 680
Internet: rp-online.de/duesseldorf/marionettentheater
E-Mail: marionettentheater@rp-online.de
Leiter Anton Bachleitner
Puppeteers: 5 *Perfs:* 220 *Prods:* 7 *Type:* marionettes, *Venues:* cap 100 *Touring:* Germany, worldwide

Tandem Theater
Postfach 1240, 69209 **Eppelheim**
Tel: 6221-764 604
Fax: 6221-764 604
Internet: www.tandemtheater.de
E-Mail: pkirsch.tandemtheater@t-online.de
Leiter und Direktor Peter Kirsch
Puppeteers: 1 *Perfs:* 100 *Prods:* 3 *Type:* various, mixed with acting *Comments:* touring company; visiting address: Wasserturmstr. 46, 69214 Eppelheim

Figurentheater Werner Knoedgen
Weimerstr. 15, 70734 **Fellbach**
Tel: 711-579 456 Fax: 711-578 3420
Direktor Prof. Werner Knoedgen
Puppeteers: 1 *Type:* combination of all types *Comments:* screenplay writer and puppeteer for TV series; Prof. W. Knoedgen is also head of university course 'Figurentheater' Stuttgart

Klappmaul Theater
Löwenhof Löwengasse 27 K, 60385 **Frankfurt am Main**
Tel: 69-9450 6178 Fax: 69-9450 6179
Internet: www.klappmaul.de
E-Mail: info@klappmaul.de
Leitungs Hg. Mahler, M. Kloss, Th. Korte, A Krein
Perfs: 200 *Prods:* 2 *Type:* puppetry and/or actors *Venues:* Freies Theaterhaus 100, Frankfurt, Mainzer Forumtheater Unterhaus 180, Mainz *Touring:* German-speaking countries *Comments:* TV and radio appearances; co-production with Stadttheater Luzern

Puppet Players
Jägerstr.1, 82131 **Gauting**
Tel: 89-850 1364 Fax: 89-850 1364
directors Susanne Forster, Stefan Fichert
Puppeteers: up to 14 *Perfs:* 100 *Prods:* 7 *Type:* innovative puppetry; music-theatre and shadow puppets, accustic figures *Touring:* Europe, Brazil *Comments:* touring company

Kleines Theater im Zentrum/Puppentheater
Gustav-Hennig-Platz 5, 07545 **Gera**
Tel: 365-8001 48415 Fax: 365-800 1486
Internet: www.gera-web.de/theater
E-Mail: martin@gera-web.de
Direktor Arnold Bischinger; Stellv. Direktorin/Dramaturgin Ingrid Fischer; Ausstattungsleiter Jan Hofmann; KBB/Leiter Öffentlichkeitsarbeit Wolfgang Martin
Puppeteers: 5 *Perfs:* 250 *Prods:* 5 *Type:* all types *Venues:* Das Kleine Theater in Zentrum 176, Probebühne 40 *Touring:* national, USA

Puppentheater der Stadt Halle
Mühlweg 12, 06114 **Halle**
Tel: 345-523 3531/3528
Fax: 345-522 2772
Intendant Rolf Voigt; Künstlerischer Leiter Christoph Werner; Leiter Öffentlichkeitsarbeit Ursula Bosch; Verwaltungsleiter Cornelia Kleinert
Puppeteers: 6 *Perfs:* 350 *Prods:* 6 new *Type:* marionettes, hand, rod, open, some cross over theatre *Venues:* home capacity 80 (both halls) *Touring:* festivals in Germany, Switzerland, Austria, USA, India, Kazakhstan

Mimomagic
c/o Kaleidoscope Presentations
Kleiberweg 144a, 22547 **Hamburg**
Tel: 40-8407 9397
Internet: www.yanci.com
E-Mail: yanci@yanci.com
contact Julia Plückebaum
Puppeteers: 4 *Type:* pantomime, marionet theatre, magic *Comments:* touring company

Figurentheater Seiler Hannover
Im Wiesenkampe 16, 30659 **Hannover**
Tel: 511-640 009
Fax: 511-640 009
Bühnenleiter Gerhard Seiler
Puppeteers: 1 *Perfs:* 150-200 *Prods:* 10 (1 new) *Type:* all types, except string puppets *Touring:* German-speaking countries *Comments:* touring company

Figurentheater Pappmobil
Behrensstr. 5, 44623 **Herne**
Tel: 2323-51110 Fax: 2323-51110
Internet: www.pappmobil.de
E-Mail: pappmobil@t-online.de
Leiter Bernd Staklies
Puppeteers: 2 *Perfs:* 120 *Prods:* 1 *Type:* hand, rod, music and actors *Venues:* Tiegerpalast 99 *Touring:* Germany *Comments:* mainly a touring company; visiting address: Heisterkamp 62, 44652 Herne, Tel: 2325-35632

Hohenloher Figurentheater
Dr.-Hans-Brüll-Str. 41, 56249 **Herschbach**
Tel: 2626-17045 Fax: 2626-17045
Leiter Harald Sperlich, Johanna Sperlich
Prods: 3 for adults, 8 for children
Type: traditional rod, glove *Touring:* national, international *Comments:* touring company

Fabula-Theater mit Figuren
Dorfstraße 23, 24879 **Idstedt**
Tel: 4625-7667 Fax: 4625-7289
Direktor Peter Röders
Puppeteers: 2 *Perfs:* 150 *Prods:* 1 *Type:* variety of types except string and shadow *Venues:* touring company *Touring:* Germany, Austria, Switzerland
Comments: performances for children, creates puppets for film productions

Marotte Figurentheater Karlsruhe
Kaiserallee 11, 76133 **Karlsruhe**
Tel: 721-841 555 Fax: 721-859 697
Internet: www.marotte-figurentheater.de
E-Mail: marotte-fig.theater@t-online.de
Direktor Thomas Hänsel; Organisation Ralph Bogdanowitsch
Puppeteers: 3 *Perfs:* 200-250 *Prods:* 2 *Venues:* home capacity 150 *Touring:* Germany *Comments:* performances for children and youth

Theater Laku Paka
Jakobstr. 17, 34260 **Kaufungen**
Tel: 5605-6891 Fax: 5605-70171
E-Mail: lakupaka@t-online.de
contact Günter Staniewski
Puppeteers: 2 *Perfs:* 150 *Prods:* 2 *Type:* all types *Venues:* touring company *Touring:* Germany, USA, Austria, Netherlands, Switzerland, Ireland *Comments:* performances for all age groups

Lübecker Marionnetten-Theater Fey
Kolk 20-22, 23552 **Lübeck**
Tel: 451-70060
Inhaberin Ingeborg Fey
Puppeteers: 5 *Perfs:* 520-540 *Prods:* 36 (1-2 new p.a.) *Type:* marionettes, shadow, traditional, experimental *Venues:* home capacity 100
Comments: shows for children and adults

Städtisches Puppentheater Magdeburg
Warschauer Str. 25, 39104 **Magdeburg**
Tel: 391-404 8164/2429/401 9755 Fax: 391-404 8164/2429
Intendant und Leiter Michael Kempchen
Puppeteers: 12 *Perfs:* 450 *Prods:* 25 *Type:* all types *Venues:* home capacity 193, 100 *Touring:* Germany, Japan, Greece, Bulgaria, Switzerland, Netherlands, Poland, Taiwan *Comments:* hosts the world congress and puppetry festival UNIMA 2000 from 24.06-02.07 2000

Fingerhuttheater
Wiedhöhe 14, 56581 **Melsbach**
Tel: 2634-2378 Fax: 2634-2378
Direktor Beatrix Berger
Puppeteers: 2 *Perfs:* 100 *Prods:* 8 *Type:* all types except string puppets, mixture of drama, puppetry and music *Venues:* touring company *Touring:* Germany
Comments: performances for children

Wodo-Puppenspiel
Cäcilienstr. 7, 45479 **Mülheim/Ruhr**
Tel: 208-424 043
Fax: 208-429 437
Internet: www.geocities.com/athens/academy/7151
E-Mail: wodo.puppenspiel@cityweb.de
contacts Dorothee Wellfonder, Wolfgang Kaup-Wellfonder
Puppeteers: 4 *Perfs:* 220-240 *Prods:* 15 *Type:* innovative, dramatised literary texts *Venues:* Kammermusiksaal der Stadt Mülheim a. d. Ruhr 200, Freilichtbühne der Stadt Mülheim a.d. Ruhr 2000 *Touring:* Germany

Kleine Bühne Naumburg
Theater für Schau,-Lust-und Figurenspiel, Am Salztor 1, 06618 **Naumburg**
Tel: 3445-776 265
Fax: 3445-776 265
Intendant Peter Stahl; Öffentlichkeitsarbeit Petra König; Techn. Leitung Detlef Hillmann
Puppeteers: 4 *Perfs:* 280 *Prods:* 18 *Type:* hand, rod, marionettes, modern, traditional
Venues: Puppentheater 80, Kleine Bühne 80, ART im Salztor 40, Sommerbühne Marientor 150 *Touring:* national, international *Comments:* shows for children and adults

Theater Laboratorium, Das
Wilhelmstr. 13, 26121 **Oldenburg**
Tel: 441-16464 Fax: 441-17155
Internet: members.aol.com/TheaLab
E-Mail: TheaLab@aol.com
contacts Pavel Möller-Lück, Barbara Schmitz-Lenders
Puppeteers: 3 *Perfs:* 200 *Prods:* 1 *Type:* drama, object theatre, puppets, Figurentheater *Venues:* home capacity 99 *Touring:* Netherlands, Switzerland, Israel, Austria, Russia, Germany

Regenbogen – Theater mit Puppen
Schanzendorf 29, 28870 **Ottersberg**
Tel: 4297-281 Fax: 4297-281
contact Eva Spilker
Puppeteers: 1 *Perfs:* 100-200 *Prods:* 10 *Type:* object theatre for children and adults *Touring:* Germany, Switzerland, Austria *Comments:* touring company

Figurentheatre Raphael Mürle
Kirchenstr. 6, 75172 **Pforzheim**
Tel: 7231-465 650 Fax: 7231-467 654
Internet: members.aol.com/figurthea
E-Mail: figurthea@aol.com
Leiter Dip. Figurenispieler Raphael Mürle
Puppeteers: 1 *Perfs:* 120 *Prods:* 7 (1 new) *Type:* marionettes, table- hand puppets, masks *Venues:* home capacity 100 *Touring:* Germany, Switzerland, Austria *Comments:* performances for adults and children

Marionettenbühne Mottenkäfig E.V. Pforzheim
Kirchenstraße 3, 75172 **Pforzheim**
Tel: 7231-463 234
Fax: 7082-2437
1.Vorsitzender, Organisation, Regie Wolfgang Bürger; 2.Vorsitzender, Figuren-und Szenographie Rainer Mürle
Puppeteers: 15 *Perfs:* 30 *Prods:* 1 *Type:* all types *Venues:* home capacity 100 *Touring:* national
Comments: performances for adults and children

Figurentheater Gingganz
Brackenbergstr. 4, 37127 **Scheden**
Tel: 5546-1303 Fax: 5546-97055
Internet
home.t-online.de/home/figurentheater.gingganz
E-Mail: figurentheater.gingganz@t-online.de
Leiter Michael Staemmler
Puppeteers: 2 *Perfs:* 120-140 *Prods:* 1 *Type:* all types, mixture between drama and puppetry *Touring:* national, international *Comments:* touring company

Wiener Masken – und Musiktheater
Am Buchenberg 6, Hofgut Ahlersbach, 36381 **Schlüchtern**
Tel: 6661-71823 Fax: 6661-72388
Leitung Angelika und Thomas Kippenberg
Puppeteers: 2-6 + 2-6 maskplayers *Perfs:* 50 *Prods:* 2 *Type:* over life-size masks and puppets, live music on stage for children and adults *Venues:* touring company *Touring:* Germany, Austria, Switzerland
Comments: professional musicians, entertainment with masks for festive occasions

Gerhards Marionetten
Leonhard-Kern-Weg 14, 74523 **Schwäbisch Hall**
Tel: 791-48536
contact Wolfgang Gerhards
Puppeteers: 6 *Perfs:* 120 *Prods:* 12 *Type:* marionettes, traditional *Venues:* Theater im Schafstall 180 *Comments:* theatre address: Theater im Schafstall, Im Lindach 9, 74523 Schwäbisch Hall, Tel: 791-48536

Steinauer Marionettentheater
Am Kumpen 4, 36396 **Steinau a.d.Strasse**
Tel: 6663-245
Direktor Karl Erich Magersuppe
Puppeteers: 6 *Perfs:* 450 *Prods:* 18 *Type:* traditional string puppets *Venues:* capacity 114 *Touring:* Germany
Comments: run the puppetry-museum at Schloß Steinau

Fantasia-Theater
Holz 11, 24409 **Stoltebühl**
Tel: 464-3979 Fax: 464-3112
Inhaber Stefan Teuber
Prods: 1 *Type:* modern *Touring:* Germany

Figurentheater Charlotte Wilde + Michael Vogel
Wunnensteinstr. 42, 70186 **Stuttgart**
Tel: 711-461 825
Fax: 711-461 825
contacts Charlotte Wilde, Michael Vogel
Puppeteers: 2 *Perfs:* 80 *Prods:* 4 (1 new) *Type:* marionettes, hand (live accompaniment), all types
Venues: small scale up to 200 *Touring:* national & international festivals *Comments:* touring company

Fitz-Figurentheater Stuttgart
Eberhardstrasse 61d, 70173 **Stuttgart**
Tel: 711-241 541 (box office)/236 8684 (admin)
Fax: 711-256 0422
E-Mail: figurentheater-stuttgart@t-online.de
Leitung Helmuth Pogerth, Katja Spiess
Perfs: 50-60 *Type:* all types *Venues:* Figurentheater 180
Comments: international and national guest performances; support of young artists

Gustaf und sein Ensemble
Urbanstraße 49, 70182 **Stuttgart**
Tel: 711-226 3509 Fax: 711-226 2586
Internet: www.hansen-creativ.com/raser
Direktor Prof. Albrecht Roser
Puppeteers: 2 *Perfs:* apprx 80 (only evening perfs for adults) *Type:* string puppets

Homunculus
Tübinger Str. 105, 70178 **Stuttgart**
Tel: 711-640 8497 Fax: 711-640 8497
contact Arne Bustorf
Puppeteers: 2 *Perfs:* 100-120 *Prods:* 1 *Type:* all types except shadow *Touring:* Germany, England, Ireland
Comments: also puppet maker, touring company

Materialtheater Stuttgart
Böblinger Str. 11, 70178 **Stuttgart**
Tel: 711-649 2449 Fax: 711-649 2449
E-Mail: emacluigi@ok.net
Leiter Sigrun Kilger, Hartmut Liebsch
Puppeteers: 2 *Perfs:* 50 *Prods:* 1-2 *Type:* experimental
Venues: Theaterhaus Stuttgart 100-250, Figurentheater Stuttgart 130 *Touring:* France, Switzerland, Italy, Austria
Comments: touring company

Optical-Figurenbühne
Spitalhofstraße 18b, 70437 **Stuttgart**
Tel: 711-847 784 Fax: 711-840 2052
contacts Crista Oeffler-Wöller, Bernhard Wöller
Puppeteers: 2 *Prods:* productions with music, figures, without language *Type:* marionettes, mainly table puppets, black theatre *Touring:* worldwide *Comments:* touring company

sepTeMBer FigurenTheater
Gartenstr. 26, 78532 **Tuttlingen**
Tel: 7461-12745 Fax: 7461-12745
contact Martin Bachmann, Cécile Legrand
Puppeteers: 2 *Perfs:* 80 *Prods:* 5 *Type:* table-rod-puppets, marionettes, shadow *Touring:* Europe *Comments:* touring company

Sparkassen-Puppenspiele
Stadionstraße 11, 78667 **Villingendorf/Rottweil**
Tel: 741-32630 Fax: 741-34624
contact Fred Bille
Puppeteers: 1 *Perfs:* 250 *Prods:* 1 *Type:* hand puppets
Touring: South Germany *Comments:* touring company

Velvets Black & Light Theater
Schwarzenbergstr.3, 65189 **Wiesbaden**
Tel: 611-719 971/6131-471 655
Fax: 611-719 971/6131-471 655
künstlerischer Leiters Bedrich Hanys, Dana Bufkova
Puppeteers: 6-8 (mimes) *Perfs:* 100-130 *Prods:* 4 (1 new)
Type: object theatre, pantomime, black theatre *Venues:* capacity 99 *Touring:* Germany, Netherlands, France

Theater aus dem Kessel – Worpsweder Figurentheater
Im Stillen Frieden 2, 27726 **Worpswede**
Tel: 4792-4610 Fax: 4792-4513
Internet: www.theater-aus-dem-kessel.de
E-Mail: info@theater-aus-dem-kessel.de
Inhaberin Barbara Theisen
Puppeteers: 2-3 *Perfs:* 100 *Prods:* 3 *Type:* innovative puppet theatre with music and poetic vision *Touring:* Germany *Comments:* touring theatre

Tranquilla
In den Birken 164, 42113 **Wuppertal**
Tel: 202-724 0823 Fax: 202-724 0823
Direktor Elke Richter
Puppeteers: 3 +1 musician *Perfs:* 20 *Prods:* 1 *Type:* shadow *Venues:* capacity 100 to 150 *Touring:* Germany
Comments: workshops/seminars in puppet-making

Plastisches Theater HOBBIT
Münzstr. 1, 97070 **Würzburg**
Tel: 931-59830/9366 6946 Fax: 9366-6653
contacts Bernd Kreußer, Jutta Schmitt
Puppeteers: 2 *Perfs:* 100 *Prods:* 3 *Type:* media theatre in creating and performing, graphic exhibitions *Venues:* cap 99 *Touring:* Germany, Europe *Comments:* workshop 'Hobbit-Bühne', Kirchheimerstr. 15, 97256 Geroldshausen

Puppentheater
am theater zwickau, Postfach 201039, 08012 **Zwickau**
Tel: 375-834 656/57
Fax: 375-834 609
Intendant Wolfgang Hauswald; Leiter Heinrich Schulze
Puppeteers: 5 *Perfs:* 270 *Prods:* 5 *Type:* all styles *Venues:* home capacity 120 to 180 *Touring:* Germany *Comments:* visiting address: Gewandhausstr. 7

GREECE (+30)

Ayusaya! Puppet Theatre
Kalypsous 16, 10435 **Athens**
Tel: 1-345 8978 Fax: 1-345 8978
E-Mail: ayusaya@hotmail.com
contact Stathis Markopoulos; scenographer Hermione Kontogoula
Puppeteers: 2 *Type:* all types *Venues:* streets, theatres, other venues *Touring:* national and international festivals

Charchout Puppet Theatre
Poseidonos 11, Metamorfosi, 14451 **Athens**
Tel: 1-283 0671/762 5006
contact Christos Autsides
Puppeteers: 1-3 *Touring:* Greece *Comments:* workshop address: Kostantinoupoleos 24, Plateia Ymmitou, Athens

Greek Puppet Theatre
34 Psaroudaki Str., 10445 **Athens**
Tel: 1-832 3714 (workshop); 1-861 4902 (home)
Fax: 1-832 3714
art director, President of the Board of the Group, Takis Sarris; public relations, Mina Sarris
Puppeteers: 6 + 1 light manager *Perfs:* 80 *Prods:* 1 + alternative repertory with 3 plays *Type:* big rod puppets, black theatre *Touring:* Greece (May-Oct); occasionally abroad *Comments:* traditional Greek puppetry; also run workshops

GRI Kouti (Andigoni Paroussi)
Andigoni Paroussi, Pat. Ioak, **Athens**
Tel: 1-721 1484 Fax: 1-722 4137
contact Alexia Alexiou, Eugenia Panagou, Anthie Vasiliov, Andigoni Paroussi
Puppeteers: 4 *Prods:* 2 *Type:* puppet theatre, object theatre *Touring:* Greece, Europe *Comments:* Andigoni Paroussi teaches puppet theatre at the University of Athens, and gives seminars and workshops to teachers and puppeteers

Kinoumeno Teatro
Emm. Benaki 118, 11473 **Athens**
Tel: 1-330 0328
dirs Antonakaki Katerini, Jorand-Briquet Emmanuel
Puppeteers: 2 *Perfs:* varies *Prods:* 1 per year *Type:* theatre with objects with emphasis on scenographic elements (formes animées) *Venues:* Greece, France *Touring:* participation at the Festival 2000 in Avignon
Comments: children and adult productions

Marionetes Laki Apostolide
Markou Botsari 10, Nea Penteli, **Athens**
Tel: 1-804 7026
contact Lakis Apostolides
Puppeteers: 1 *Perfs:* every day in summer; 1200 performances for Greek T.V. *Type:* all types, Russian and European *Venues:* Thetro Chan *Comments:* children and youth plays

Paraga Puppet Theatre
Kariotaki 5, 11131 **Athens**
Tel: 1-228 4804
directors Tzeni Pedefoundi
Puppeteers: 4 *Perfs:* 20 *Prods:* 1 *Type:* hand *Touring:* national, international

Theatro Skeon – Eugenios Spatharis
Argonafton St. 22, Maroussi, 15125 **Athens**
Tel: 1-802 7185/806 2950 Fax: 1-806 2950
director Eugenios Spatharis
Puppeteers: 1 (5 assistants, 3 musicians) *Perfs:* 300
Prods: 3 per year *Type:* shadow theatre *Touring:* Greece, Cyprus, Russia *Comments:* Theatro Skeon (Shadow Theatre) is an old traditional form of puppeteering

Theatro Skeon – Manthos Athineos
Shadow Theatre – Manthos Athineos
Salaminos 16, AG Dimitrios, 15235 **Athens**
Tel: 1-933 1184/935 9558
contact Manthos Athineos
Puppeteers: 2-3 *Perfs:* 150-200 *Type:* Karaghiozis – Greek folk shadow puppets *Venues:* Theatro Im. Athineou, Alsos Pagratiou (open theatre), Theatre Rialto *Touring:* Italy, Cyprus, Germany, France, Greece *Comments:* M. Athineos has adapted popular classic Greek plays of the 19th century

Theatro Skeon – Thiasos Athanasiou
Tsakalof 39, Piraeus, **Athens**
Tel: 1-9655 9681/901 1636 Fax: 1-994 6190
Kostas Athanasiou, Giannis Athanasiou, Argyris Athanasiou, Elena Athanasiou
Puppeteers: 4 *Perfs:* 200 *Type:* Karaghiozis – Greek folk shadow puppets *Venues:* Moscheto Municipal Cultural Centre *Touring:* various international festivals, national

Thiasos Skeon – Iason
Aeolou 30a, Palaio Falero, 17561 **Athens**
Tel: 1-983 2135 Fax: 1-984 6775
Jason Melissinos, Anna Melissinos, Alexander Melissinos
Puppeteers: 3 *Perfs:* 50-60 *Type:* Karaghiozis – Greek folk shadow puppets
Touring: Greece, Turkey, Pakistan, Russia

UNIMA (Crete) Puppet Theatre
EF. Polemiston 100, 73136 **Chanea (Crete)**
Tel: 821-97558
Fax: 821-97558
E-Mail: unima-crete@cha.forthnet.gr
contact Ariadne Novak
Puppeteers: 3-5 *Perfs:* 200 *Prods:* 2 *Type:* traditional marionettes, black light *Touring:* Greece, abroad
Comments: perform in Cretan dialect with subtitles in English and German

Puppet Theatre Tiritomba
Athinon 255, 41447 **Larissa**
Tel: 93-281 056 Fax: 93-281 056
director/puppeteer Konstantin Hatziandreou ; puppeteer Sophia Foutzopoulou
Puppeteers: 2 *Perfs:* 150 *Prods:* 2 *Type:* all types *Venues:* Puppet in MYLOS *Touring:* Greece, Italy, Czech Republic, Bulgaria, Turkey, Pakistan, Slovenia, Iran, Yugoslavia

Anna Santorinaiou
Fanarioton, 11472 **Neapoli (Athens)**
Tel: 1-644 0337 Fax: 1-642 0451
contact Anna Santorinaiou
Puppeteers: 1 *Prods:* 1-4 T.V. productions each year *Type:* muppets *Venues:* performs on television

Fatses Puppet and Mime Theatre
Tr. Artemidos 12, 26443 **Patras**
Tel: 61-434 246/93-781 056
contact Christos Anastasopoulos
Puppeteers: 2 *Perfs:* 150 *Prods:* 2 *Type:* hand puppets, mime, live music
Touring: Greece, Germany, Switzerland

Theatro Skion-Panos Kapetanidis
Premetes 12, Karatsini, 18756 **Piraeus**
Tel: 1-461 6664 Fax: 1-462 4098
director Panos Kapetanidis
Puppeteers: 2-3 *Perfs:* 200+ *Type:* Karaghiozis: Greek folk shadow theatre *Venues:* main venue: Cultural Centre of Council of Keratsini and other venues in Athens
Touring: Greece, Belgium, Netherlands, Germany, Turkey *Comments:* classical Karaghiozis repertory of adapted classical scripts

HUNGARY (+36)

ÁMK Children's Theatre
ÁMK Gyermek Színpad
Simon Bolivár sétány 4-8, 1214 **Budapest**
Tel: 1-276 2755 Fax: 1-276 2755
director Zoltán Tarcsa
Venues: 150 seat chamber theatre *Comments:* mainly for children; organise the International Festival of Lower Carpathian Basin

Budapest Puppet Theatre
Budapest Bábszínház
PO Box 69, 1400 **Budapest**
Tel: 1-321 5200/322 5051/342 2702
Fax: 1-342 4765
director Janós Meczner; artistic directors Pál Lengyel, Géza Balogh, Gyula Urbán; artistic secretary Ilma Götz
Puppeteers: 16 *Perfs:* 250 *Prods:* puppet 5, drama 4 *Type:* all types mainly rod and hand, bunraku, black theatre, drama *Venues:* home capacity 360 *Touring:* Taiwan, France, Italy *Comments:* visiting address: Andrássy út 69, 1062 Budapest

Kolibri Theatre
Kolibri Színház
Jókai tér 10, 1061 **Budapest**
Tel: 1-353 4633 Fax: 1-332 2585
Internet: www.c3.hu/~kolibri/
E-Mail: kolibri@mail.c3.hu
general director János Novák; secretary Zsuzsanna Pap
Puppeteers: 14 *Type:* experimental, rod, hand *Venues:* home capacity 222, Kolibri Cellar 60, Kolibri Nest 50

Vojtina Puppet Theatre
Vojtina Bábszinház
Piac 26A, 4024 **Debrecen**
Tel: 52-418 160 Fax: 52-418 160
E-Mail: vojtina@elender.hu
director Aniko Asboth

Harlequin Puppet Theatre
Harlekin Bábszínház
Bartók Béla tér 6, 3300 **Eger**
Tel: 36-310 151/413 073 Fax: 36-413 073
artistic director Károly Szíki
Puppeteers: 8 *Perfs:* 150 *Prods:* 4-5
ype: shadow, rod, black theatre

Iron Rooster Puppet Theatre
Vaskakas Bábszínház
Aradi Vértanúk útja 23, 9021 **Györ**
Tel: 96-320 316
Fax: 96-320 316
Internet: www.c3.hu/~vaskakas
E-Mail: vaskakas@mail.c3.hu
general manager Rozi Kocsis
Puppeteers: 8 *Perfs:* 240 *Type:* marionettes, glove, bunraku, shadow *Venues:* capacity 150 *Touring:* Slovakia *Comments:* hosts the International Festival of Puppet and Street Theatre

Ciróka Puppet Theatre
Ciróka Bábszinház
Budai u. 15, 6000 **Kecskemét**
Tel: 76-482 217/486 635
Fax: 76-486 635
director Agnes Kizely
Puppeteers: 8 *Perfs:* 223 *Prods:* 8 *Type:* all types

Miraculous Mill Puppet Theatre
Csodamalom Bábszínház
Kossuth Lajos ul. 11, 3525 **Miskolc**
Tel: 46-359 900 Fax: 46-359 469
artistic director Tibor Korzsényi
Puppeteers: 13 *Perfs:* 415 *Prods:* 6 *Type:* hand, rod and traditional

Bóbita Puppet Theatre
Bóbita Bábszínház
PO Box 126, 7601 **Pécs**
Tel: 72-210 301/211 791 Fax: 72-211 986
director Tamás Balikó; artistic director Gábor Sramó
Puppeteers: 6 *Perfs:* 150 *Venues:* home capacity 270
Touring: Spain *Comments:* visiting address: Pécsi Nemzeti Színház, Mária u. 18, 7621 Pécs

ICELAND (+354)

Brudubill – Puppet Car
Blonduhild 10, 105 **Reykjavík**
Tel: 552 5098 Fax: 552 5098
director Helga Steffensen
Perfs: 200 *Prods:* 2 *Type:* hand, rod, glove, marionettes & actors *Touring:* Iceland *Comments:* performances outdoors during the summer and indoors (schools, theatres) in winter

Leikbruduland
Frikirkjuvegi 11, 101 **Reykjavík**
Tel: 552 5098 Fax: 552 5098
contact Helga Steffensen, Erna Gudmarsdóttir, Hallveig Thorlacius, Bryndis Gunnarsdóttir
Puppeteers: 4 *Perfs:* 24 *Prods:* 2 *Type:* hand, rod, glove, marionette, shadow, black theatre *Comments:* Helga Steffensen is secretary of UNIMA Iceland – see National Organisations

IRELAND Republic of (+353)

Puppetoonz
4 Glatrimrd, **Bray (Co. Wicklow)**
Tel: 1-286 4404/086-834 5051 (mobile)
E-Mail: puppetoonz@tinet.ie
contacts Eva Lundin
Puppeteers: varies *Perfs:* varies *Prods:* 4 main ones *Type:* foam, latex, giant puppets, animatronics *Venues:* R.T.E. television, theatre and film festivals *Comments:* also produces puppetry for advertising

Lambert Puppet Theatre
Clifton Lane, Monkstown, **Dublin**
Tel: 1-280 0974/1863 Fax: 1-280 4772
E-Mail: puppet@iol.ie
director Eugene Lambert; pr Miriam Lambert
Puppeteers: 6 *Perfs:* 250 *Prods:* 12 *Type:* mostly rod, glove, some marionette and shadow *Venues:* Lambert Puppet Theatre 300, various venues (theatres, halls, hotels etc.) *Touring:* Ireland *Comments:* organizes International Puppet Festival Ireland (q.v.)

ITALY (+39)

Maninalto
Via Cardinal de Gambara, 32, 01031 **Bagnaia (UT)**
Tel: 0761-289 944/06-7047 5418 Fax: 0761-289 944
direttore artistico Augusto Terenzi; vice direttrice Luisa Piazza; management Birgit Noll
Puppeteers: 3 *Type:* object theatre for the young, bunraku
Touring: Italy *Comments:* management address: Steinring 47, 44789 Bochum, Germany

Comp. Granteatrino di Paolo Comentale
Via Crisanzio 5, 70122 **Bari**
Tel: 080-521 9974/534 4660 Fax: 080-572 0658
E-Mail: casadipulcinella@mail.clio.it
artistic director Paolo Comentale; administrative officer Maria Laterza; press officer Patrizia Fatuzzo
Puppeteers: 1 *Perfs:* 80 *Prods:* 1 *Type:* hand with glove; traditional and experimental *Venues:* Teatro Casa di Pulcinella 120 *Touring:* France, Germany, Italy
Comments: see also Festivals and Venues

Crear e' Bello – Teatro di Burattini di Pisa
Via Butese 7, 56011 **Calci (PI)**
Tel: 050-937 257
administrative director Piero Nissim; artistic directors Piero Nissim, Claudia Brambilla
Puppeteers: 2 *Perfs:* 80-100 *Type:* glove, marrot and coloured shadows, traditional Italian and European fables *Touring:* Italy *Comments:* organise Mattinate Burattine International Puppet Festival in Pisa (March); 200 puppets

Arrivano dal mare! Centro Teatro di Figura
via Cavour 12, 48015 **Cervia (RA)**
Tel: 0544-971 958 Fax: 0544-971 922
E-Mail: cts@queen.it
president and organiser Franco Belletti; direttore artistico Stefano Giunchi; organizzazione Paola Serafini; administration Stella Rossi
Puppeteers: 7 *Perfs:* 150-195 *Type:* all types *Venues:* Teatro Comunale di Cervia 250, Arena della Sirena 800, Magazzeni del Sale, Teatro di Cesena 300 *Comments:* see also Festivals; various courses throughout the year

Teatro Dei Burattini Di Como
via Tofane, 4, 22030 **Como**
Tel: 031-364 037 Fax: 031-364 007
president/ & legal representative Dario Tognocchi
Puppeteers: 5 *Type:* hand, carved wood *Venues:* Teatro S. Andrea (Brunate) 257

Pupi di Stac
Via Madonna delle Grazie 8, 50135 **Firenze**
Tel: 055-697 662/335 803 3322 (mobile)
Fax: 055-697 965
Internet: www.firenze.net/pupistac
E-Mail: pupistac@firenze.net
administrative director Monica Mani; artistic director Enrico Spinelli; technical director Laura Spinelli
Puppeteers: 6 *Perfs:* 200 *Prods:* 1 *Type:* traditional puppet theatre *Venues:* Teatro C.R.C. Antella-Firenze 250, Sala Vanni 192 *Touring:* Italy, Belgium *Comments:* can also play in English, French and Spanish

Teatro Pirata
Via Dei Saponari 4, 60035 **Jesi**
Tel: 0731-56590
Fax: 0731-56590
E-Mail: tpirata@indi.it
administrative director Silvano Fiordelmondo; artistic director Gianfrancesco Mattioni; technical director Diego Pasquinelli
Puppeteers: 3 *Perfs:* 90-110 *Prods:* 4 + 1 new *Type:* marionettes, traditional

Centro Teatrale Corniani
Via Romagnoli 9/C, 46100 **Mantova**
Tel: 0376-381 547
Fax: 0376-381 547
Internet: www.comune.mantova.it
E-Mail: corianiteatro@maynet.it
artistic director & legal agent Maurizio Corniani; organizzatore responsabile Monica Aga Rossi
Puppeteers: 2 *Perfs:* 85 *Prods:* 6 *Type:* glove puppets, marionettes, automations *Touring:* Europe *Comments:* workshops including story writing and puppet making with children; organiser of 'Animando Mantova', international exposition of Corniani's family collection of puppets; see also Festivals

Trovatore, Il
P.zza San Nicola no.3, 00013 **Mentana (Roma)**
Tel: 06-909 3885/0774-365 173
direttore artistico Giancarlo Santelli
Puppeteers: 3 *Perfs:* 40 *Prods:* 5 *Type:* glove *Venues:* Teatro dei Burattini 50 *Touring:* Italy

Carlo Colla e Figli
Via Neera 24, 20141 **Milano**
Tel: 02-8953 1301 Fax: 02-846 1312
E-Mail: comcolla@tin.it
artistic director Eugenio Monti Colla; production manager Piero Corbella
Puppeteers: 15 + orchestra *Perfs:* 150 *Prods:* 10 *Type:* marionettes *Venues:* Atelier Carlo Colla e Figli 200
Touring: Spoleto (Spoleto festival), Germany, Australia, USA, France *Comments:* three centuries of puppet tradition; management: Associazione Grupporiani; venue address: via Montegani 35/1 – 20141 Milano; see also Drama

Cooperativa Teatro del Buratto
Via Soffredini 75, 20126 **Milano**
Tel: 02-2700 2476 Fax: 02-2700 1084
E-Mail: teatrodelburatto@tin.it
direttore amministrativo Lucia Salvati; direzione artistica Monica Gattini ; organizzazione Enzo Guardalp; ufficio stampa Antonella Vitali
Puppeteers: 10 *Perfs:* 300 *Prods:* 12 *Type:* children's theatre – figure theatre *Venues:* Teatro Verdi 200, Teatro delle Erbe 300 *Touring:* Italy, France, Spain, South America *Comments:* registered address: Via Pastrengo 16, 20159 Milano

Teatro di Gianni e Cosetta Colla, Il
Via Tullo Ostilio 1, 20123 **Milano**
Tel: 02-468 260 Fax: 02-481 8490
artistic director Cosetta Colla; public relations & press Stefania Colla; administrative director & organisation Fabio Missana
Type: marionettes and actors *Venues:* Teatro delle Marionette, Milano 224

Teatro Laboratorio Mangiafuoco
via Grasselli, 4, 20137 **Milano**
Tel: 02-761 0491 Fax: 02-761 0491
presidenta Paola Bassani; organizzatore Claudio Borò; direttrice artistica Rosellina Leone
Puppeteers: 5 *Perfs:* 90 *Prods:* 4 *Type:* hand, shadow

Figli D'Arte Cuticchio
via Bara all'Olivella, 95, 90133 **Palermo**
Tel: 091-323 400
Fax: 091-335 922
president Girolamo Cuticchio; artistic director Mimmo Cuticchio; organisation Elisa Puleo
Puppeteers: 8 *Perfs:* 100 *Prods:* 3 *Type:* Sicilian puppets (old French epic poems) *Venues:* Teatro Santa Rosalia 100 *Touring:* Germany, Spain, France

Teatro Gioco Vita
Vicolo S. Matteo 6, 29100 **Piacenza**
Tel: 0523-332 613 Fax: 0523-338 428
Internet: www.teatrogiocovita.it
E-Mail: info@teatrogiocovita.it
director Diego Maj
Puppeteers: 10 *Perfs:* 300 *Prods:* 7 *Type:* shadow theatre: comic, jazz (especially for young people) *Venues:* Teatro San Matteo a Piacenza 204, Teatro Verdi a Castelsangiovanni 248 *Touring:* Italy, Canada, USA

Ravenna Teatro – Compagnia Drammatico Vegetale
c/o Teatro Rasi, Via di Roma 39, 48100 **Ravenna**
Tel: 0544-36239 Fax: 0544-33303
Internet: www.netgate.it/ra.teatro
E-Mail: ra.teatro@netgate.it
direttore artistico Piero Fenati
Puppeteers: 3 *Perfs:* 200 *Prods:* 1 *Type:* rod, animated theatre, youth and children's theatre *Venues:* Theatre Rasi 500, Teatro Alighieri 850 *Touring:* national, international *Comments:* see also Venues

Teatro del Drago
Via Sant' Alberto 297, 48100 **Ravenna**
Tel: 0544-483 460/1 Fax: 0544-483 460
Internet: www.teatrodeldrago.it
E-Mail: drago@netgate.it
artistic/administrative directors Andrea & Mauro Monticelli
Puppeteers: 4 *Perfs:* 150 *Prods:* 1 new *Type:* object and animation theatre *Comments:* see also Drama and Festivals

Nuova Opera dei Burattini
Largo Cristina di Svezia 12, 00165 **Roma**
Tel: 06-588 1194/588 2034 Fax: 06-589 6085
direzione artistica & amministrativa Giuseppina Volpicelli, Daniela Remiddi; direttore organizzativo Daniela Remiddi
Perfs: 109 *Prods:* 2 *Type:* rod, stick, glove, shadow and mixed theatre *Venues:* Teatro Verde 260 *Touring:* Italy, Morocco *Comments:* every year from Oct-May they present Italian and foreign companies in their theatre, als have workshops on animation and puppet making

Pupi Siciliani dei Fratelli Pasqualino
Via Luigi Arati 40, 00151 **Roma**
Tel: 06-5823 1066 Fax: 06-5823 1066
legale rappresentante e responsabile organizzativo Luigi Pasqualino; directore artistico Fortunato Pasqualino; regista Barbara Olson

Teatro Delle Marionette Degli Accettella
Piazza Gondar 22, 00199 **Roma**
Tel: 06-860 1733 Fax: 06-860 1733
organizzatore Vittoria Giorelli; legale rappresentante e direttore artistico Icaro Accettella
Puppeteers: 5 *Type:* marionettes, figure theatre *Venues:* Teatro Mongiovino, Roma 250 *Comments:* venue address: Via Giovanni Genocchi, 15, 00145 Roma, Tel: 06-513 9405

I Teatrini – Centro Campano Teatro d'Animazione
Via San Giorgio Vecchio, 31, 80046 **San Giorgio A Cremano (NA)**
Tel: 081-586 3451/6575 Fax: 081-586 3451
direttore artistico Bruno Leone; presidente Luigi Marsano; incaricato organizzativo Renato Rizzardi, Giovanna Faccicio
Puppeteers: 3 *Perfs:* 157 *Prods:* 7 *Type:* Guarrattelle (Pulcinella), traditional Napolitan puppets *Touring:* Germany, Austria, Spain, France, UK, Italy *Comments:* association of four different groups working with puppets; registered address: Via San Giorgio Vecchio 31, 80046 San Giorgio A Cremano (NA); also drama and children's theatre; member of UNIMA; office address: I Tran. Citta' Giardino 9, 80016 Marano (NA)

Gruppo Lucignolo
Via Sirio 91, 05100 **Terni**
Tel: 0744-243 279
direttore artistico Samuela Bonifazi; music consultant Maria Cristina Proietti; theatre consultant Manola Fiordalisa
Puppeteers: 2-3 *Prods:* 4 *Type:* puppets from all materials, glove puppets, shadows, foam puppets, mime *Touring:* Italy *Comments:* specialised in workshops in schools

Dottor Bostik, Il
via Maddalene 42, 10154 **Torino**
Tel: 011-200 528 Fax: 011-242 0767
president & artistic director Gavino Arru; administration Paola Lemetre
Puppeteers: 5 *Perfs:* 100 *Prods:* 2 *Type:* all types

Marionette Grilli
c/o Alfa Associazione Culturale, Via Casalborgone 16, 10132 **Torino**
Tel: 011-819 3529 Fax: 011-819 3529
Internet: www.alfateatro.it
E-Mail: grilli@alfateatro.it
administrator/legal representative Marco Grilli; artistic director Mariarosa Scalero; P.R. & public relations Claudio Bertoni
Puppeteers: 10 *Perfs:* 120 *Prods:* 30 *Type:* children's theatre *Venues:* Alfa Teatro 300, Le Serre 400 *Touring:* Italy, Europe *Comments:* also a puppetry school; see also Venues and Agents and Producers

Marionette Lupi
via Santa Teresa, 5, 10121 **Torino**
Tel: 011-530 238 Fax: 011-530 238
art dir Daniela Trezzi; legal representative Raoul Cristofoli
Perfs: 100 *Prods:* 3 *Type:* marionettes *Venues:* Sala Gianduja, Sala Giacometta *Comments:* registered address: via S. Teresa 5, 10121 Torino; 18th Century stage; 300+ marionettes

Teatro Stabile Del Friuli-Venezia Giulia – I Piccoli Di Podrecca
viale XX Settembre 45, 34126 **Trieste**
Tel: 040-567 201 Fax: 040-52447
Internet: www.comune.trieste.it/rossetti.lindex.htm
E-Mail: ts.rossetti@spin.it
direttore unico Antonio Calenda; organizzatore G.Paolo Andreutti
Puppeteers: 7-9 *Perfs:* 60 *Type:* giant puppets, early puppets *Touring:* Italy *Comments:* when possble also run puppeteering courses

Tiriteri Ass.ne Teatrale
CP 203, 50039 **Vicchio (FI)**
Tel: 055-849 7146 Fax: 055-849 7146
Internet: www.mugello.net/tiriteri
E-Mail: tiriteri@dada.it
administrative director Alberto Zoina; artistic director Anna Di Lena
Puppeteers: 3 *Perfs:* 80 *Prods:* 2 + 4 repertoire *Type:* marionettes-bunraku *Venues:* Teatro Comunale Giotto (Vicchio) 180 *Touring:* Italy, Germany, Australia

Teatro dell' Es
Via Pederzana n° 5, 40050 **Villanova di Castenaso (BO)**
Tel: 0151-605 3078 Fax: 0151-605 3078
Internet: www.teatrinodelles.com
E-Mail: vittorio@teatrinodelles.com
administrative director Rita Pasqualini; artistic director Vittorio Zanella
Puppeteers: 2 *Perfs:* 180 *Prods:* 15+ 1 new *Type:* rod, glove and shadow puppets, traditional and contemporary tales *Venues:* Teatro Consorziale di Budrio *Touring:* Europe *Comments:* organise Puppet Festival – Burattinado a Budrio; also exhibition of over 1300 puppets from 17th-20th C

LATVIA (+371)

Puppet Theatre
Valsl Iellu Teatris
K. Barona 16/18, 1011 **Riga**
Tel: 7-285 415 Fax: 7-285 415
director Valdemars Dziedatajs

LITHUANIA (+370)

Kaunas State Puppet Theatre
Kauno Valstybinis Leliu Teatras
Laisvès al. 87a, 3000 **Kaunas**
Tel: 7-227 158 (director) Fax: 2-610 814
director S. Klibavicius

Vilnius Puppet Theatre Lèlè
Vilniaus Lèlè Teatras
Arkliu 5, 2001 **Vilnius**
Tel: 2-628 159 Fax: 2-628 159
artistic director P. Svambaris

MOLDOVA (+373)

Puppet Theatre Licurici
68, Bucuresti Str, 2012 **Chisinau**
Tel: 2-244 725 Fax: 2-244 725
manager Titus Jucov

NETHERLANDS (+31)

Poppentheater Kameleon
c/o Kleine Spui Produkties, Kleine Spui 26, 3811 BE **Amersfoort**
Tel: 33-465 2660 Fax: 33-465 2618
Internet: www.kleinespui.demon.nl
E-Mail: ksp@kleinespui.demon.nl
managing directors kleine spui produkties Carla Kogelman, Prisca Maas; artistic director Dorris Boelaart (Tel/Fax: 78-616 6517)
Puppeteers: 1 *Perfs:* 100 *Prods:* 2+ 2 new *Type:* all types of puppets (hand-, marionettes etc.) and objects *Venues:* international puppet festivals, street performances, theatres up to 100 *Touring:* Netherlands, France, South Africa, USA, Israel, Belgium, Ireland, Germany *Comments:* puppet theatre for children's hospitals; performances for all ages

Poppentheater Toermalijn
Heiligenberger Weg 113, 3816 AJ **Amersfoort**
Tel: 33-470 0153 Fax: 33-475 5706
director Camilla Koevoeds
Puppeteers: 1 *Type:* hand puppets, marionettes *Touring:* Netherlands *Comments:* only for children

Stuffed Puppet Theatre, The
c/o Kleine Spui Produkties, Kleine Spui 26, 3811 BE **Amersfoort**
Tel: 33-465 2660
Fax: 33-465 2618
Internet: www.kleinespui.demon.nl
E-Mail: ksp@kleinespui.demon.nl
managing directors Kleine Spui Carla Kogelman, Prisca Maas; artistic director Neville Tranter
Puppeteers: 1 *Perfs:* 100 *Prods:* 3 + 1 new *Type:* hand and life-size puppets *Venues:* international festivals, theatres up to 700 *Touring:* worldwide *Comments:* performances in Dutch and English; registered association address: Stichting Stuffed Puppet Theatre, Postbus 8039, 1180 LA Amstelveen

TAMTAM, Objektentheater
c/o Kleine Spui Produkties, Kleine Spui 26, 3811 BE **Amersfoort**
Tel: 33-465 2660
Fax: 33-465 2618
Internet: www.kleinespui.demon.nl
E-Mail: ksp@kleinespui.demon.nl
artistic direction/puppeteers Gérard Schiphorst, Marije van der Sande
Puppeteers: 2 or 3 *Perfs:* 100-120 *Prods:* 5 *Type:* object theatre, street theatre *Venues:* small venues cap 10 to 100 *Touring:* Europe, South Africa *Comments:* touring company; second address: Boxbergerweg 35, 8121 PS Olst

Boschma
c/o Impresariaat Wim Visser, Kloveniersburgwal 47, 1011 JX **Amsterdam**
Tel: 20-623 3700
Fax: 20-620 8212
E-Mail: iwv@xs4all.nl
artistic director Feike Boschma; manager Wim Visser; assistant Hans Nass
Puppeteers: 3 *Perfs:* 50 *Prods:* 2 (1 new) *Type:* string, made of fabric *Touring:* Europe

St. Illusie/Ella Snoep
c/o Prima Rima, Nieuwe Herengracht 143, 1011 SG **Amsterdam**
Tel: 20-622 1257/620 4827
Fax: 20-622 1257
E-Mail: primarim@xs4all.nl
manager Els Wijmans, Dimph Verdiesen
Puppeteers: 1 *Perfs:* 90 *Prods:* 2 *Type:* string, rod, hand puppets *Venues:* small theatres, youth centres, schools, community centres *Touring:* Netherlands, Belgium *Comments:* see also Agents and Producers (Theaterbureau Prima Rima)

Theater Poging
c/o Van Baasbank & Baggerman, Keizersgracht 258, 1016 EV **Amsterdam**
Tel: 20-624 2631/627 6818
Fax: 20-622 7850
E-Mail: baasbank.baggerman@wxs.nl
founder Jan Goes
Puppeteers: 5 (including technicians *Perfs:* 40 *Prods:* 2 *Type:* live animation *Touring:* worldwide *Comments:* touring company; productions available in English, French, German, Spanish and Italian; see also Agents & Producers and Festivals

Theater Terra
c/o Teaterbureau Slot, Gerda Slot, Plantage Muidergracht 155, 1018 TT **Amsterdam**
Tel: 20-422 7899
Fax: 20-624 0470
E-Mail: slot.theater@tref.nl
artistic director Theo Terra
Puppeteers: 4 *Perfs:* 100 *Prods:* 2 *Type:* expressive and poetic theatre for children, based on the interplay between puppets and actors *Comments:* touring company; see also Drama and Agents and Producers

Damiet van Dalsum
Aardappelmarkt 9, 3311 BA **Dordrecht**
Tel: 78-614 0342
Fax: 78-614 1453
E-Mail: damiet@wxs.nl
artistic director Damiet van Dalsum
Puppeteers: 1 *Perfs:* 100 *Prods:* 5 *Type:* shadow, glove and marionettes *Venues:* Damiet Van Dalsum theatre, 60 *Touring:* international *Comments:* see also Festivals

Speeltheater Holland
Damplein 9, 1135 BK **Edam**
Tel: 299-372 295
Fax: 299-372 598
Internet: www.speeltheater.club.tip.nl
E-Mail: speeltheater@tip.nl
general manager Saskia Janse; artistic directors Onny Huisink; publicity Martien Langman; administration Hilda van der Wey; business manager Daphne Hartman
Puppeteers: varies *Perfs:* 100 *Prods:* 2 *Type:* modern *Venues:* small to large scale *Touring:* Netherlands, Belgium, Germany, Switzerland, Austria, France, USA *Comments:* different puppet techniques and other theatrical means are used for each production, but the visual element plays a prominent part in all performances

Flup & Ju Bedrijf
c/o Rob Maaskant, Nieuwlandseweg 11, 4339 NE **Nw. en St. Joosland**
Tel: 118-602 214
Fax: 118-602 214
artistic director/manager/props Rob Maaskant; costumes Christian Schop;
music director Harry V. D. Wekken
Puppeteers: 6 *Perfs:* 30-60 *Prods:* 2 *Type:* object theatre, street performances *Touring:* Netherlands, Germany, Belgium *Comments:* non-conventional performances, temporary monuments and environmental installations indoors and outdoors; some TV work

Theater Sirkel
PO 214, 6130 AE **Sittard**
Tel: 46-452 5574
Fax: 46-452 6432
E-Mail: MALART@globalXS.nl
artistic directors Frans Malschaert, Anandi Teeuw; management Serge Wetzels; technicians Dik Beets, Marc Claessens; administration Maryke van Hout
Puppeteers: 2-10 *Perfs:* 200 *Prods:* 6 (2 new) *Type:* blend of art and theatre, visual theatre *Touring:* Netherlands, abroad *Comments:* for all age groups; 2nd address: Putstraat 22, 6131 HL Sittard;
see also Drama and Venues

Poppentejater Otto van der Mieden
Kerkweg 38, 8193 KL **Vorchten**
Tel: 578-631 329
Fax: 578-631 329
director Otto van der Mieden
Puppeteers: 1 *Perfs:* 80 *Prods:* 1 *Type:* modern *Venues:* Poppenspe(e)l museum – Petit Théâtre 45 *Touring:* Netherlands, Switzerland, Italy, Belgium, Denmark, France, Germany, Sweden, Austria, Spain
Comments: also a puppetry museum at Kerkweg 38, 8193 KL Vorchten, Tel/Fax: 578-631 329

NORWAY (+47)

Levende dukker
Living Dolls
Bleikerfaret 84, 1370 **Asker**
Tel: 6678 0715 Fax: 6678 0242
director Agnes Schou

Commedia dukketeater
Postboks 8, Sentrum, 5803 **Bergen**
Tel: 5532 1846

Dukkenikkerne
Østre Murallmenning 2, 5012 **Bergen**
Tel: 5523 3030/9455 4884 (mobile)
Fax: 5523 3366
director Jack Markussen

Hordaland Teater
5047 **Fana**
Tel: 5591 6020
Fax: 5591 5945
Internet: www.spekter.no/nordaland.teater
director Vera Rostin Wexelsen
Puppeteers: 2-7 *Perfs:* 264 *Prods:* 4-8 *Type:* all types
Venues: Theatreboat 200, Anne Gullestad Theatre 200
Touring: national, international *Comments:* in charge of children's festival in cooperation with Bergen International Festival

Oslo Nye Dukketeatret
Frognerveien 67, 0266 **Oslo**
Tel: 2244 2122 (company)/429 075 (office)
Fax: 2244 4351
director Ketil Bang-Hansen; public relations Turid Wideroe; sales office Anne Winger
Puppeteers: 6 + 1 technician *Perfs:* 180-200 *Type:* various including glove, hand, rod, masks, bunraki *Venues:* home capacity 200 *Touring:* national, international
Comments: administrative address: Rosenkrantz Gate 10, 0159 Oslo; some TV work; mainly children's shows but also some adult shows; see also Venues

Riksteatret
Kongenst 1, Postboks 724, Sentrum, 0105 **Oslo**
Tel: 2220 6015
Fax: 2220 6052
Internet: www.aftenposten.no/web/riksteat
theatre director Bente Erichsen
Puppeteers: 5 *Perfs:* 6-25 *Prods:* 2-3 per year *Type:* various
Venues: touring company
Touring: national, international *Comments:* make their own puppets; see also Drama

Figurteateret i Nordland
8340 **Stamsund**
Tel: 7605 4050
Fax: 7605 4059
E-Mail: Figurteater@online.no
manager Marit Pedersen Omland; producer Line Andreassen; administration Ing Randi Johansen
Perfs: 150 *Prods:* 6-8 productions per year *Type:* all types
Touring: Nordland county *Comments:* professional theatre institution funded by Nordland county, Vestvågøy communicipality and the Cultural Dept. of Norwegian State; independent professional puppet theatre groups from all over Norway come here to produce their shows; also welcome at least one foreign production per year

Stella Polaris
Fossnes Centre, 3160 **Stokke**
Tel: 3333 9099/9283 4579 (mobile)
Fax: 3336 6339
E-Mail: spolaris@online.no
administrator Merete Klengen; art dir Per Spildra Borg
Puppeteers: 4 *Perfs:* 100 *Prods:* 6 *Type:* masks and big puppets *Venues:* small-mid scale indoor & outdoor spaces *Touring:* festivals in Sweden and Denmark
Comments: see also Drama

Cat in the Bag
Katte y Sekken
Adlersgt 31, 3116 **Tønsberg**
Tel: 3333 2889/9708 0265(moblile)
Fax: 3333 2585
contact Anne Helgesen
Puppeteers: 1 + actors + musician (when required) *Perfs:* 100 *Prods:* 2 + 1 new *Type:* all types *Venues:* small-large scale *Touring:* Norway *Comments:* publishes puppet magazine – And i Hanske, for UNIMA Norway

Petrusjka Teater
Olav-Tryggvasonsgate 5, 7011 **Trondheim**
Tel: 7351 0326 Fax: 7351 0364
artistic director Tatjana Zaitzow
Puppeteers: 1 *Perfs:* 30 *Prods:* 1 *Type:* rod, hand, modern and traditional marionettes, shadow, multi-media-shows *Venues:* The Theatrehouse Avant Garden *Touring:* worldwide *Comments:* has received several national and international awards for its plays and for its work for the promotion of puppet theatre as a genuine expression of art

Teater Fusentast
Scatterbrain Theatre
Riddervoldsgate 28, 7052 **Trondheim**
Tel: 7394 4200 Fax: 7394 4201
E-Mail: comvlee@c2i.net
directors/actors Jaap den Hertog, Coby Omvlee, Karl Markus Reinert, Trygve Faetten, Sivut Iversen; publicity/administration Lillian Uran Todnem
Puppeteers: 1-4 actors/puppeteers *Perfs:* 125-150 *Prods:* 7 current prods, 12 new prods each season *Type:* visual story-telling, puppets and puppeteers and/or actors interact with the audience, musical theatre, puppetry
Venues: capacity 55 to 250 *Touring:* Norway, Netherlands, France, Spain, UK *Comments:* plays for all age groups, also run courses and workshops on puppetry, clowning, acting skills; see also Drama

Dukkespilleriet
Postboks 365, 6390 **Vestnes**
Tel: 7118 9920 Fax: 7118 9921
Internet: www.dtsentrum.no
E-Mail: dukk@online.no
artistic director Jorunn Myhre; co-director Arild Karlsen

POLAND (+48)

Teatr Dzieci Zaglebia im. J. Dormana
Teatralna 4, 42-500 **Bedzin**
Tel: 32-267 3625/3668
director Michal Rosinski
Puppeteers: 13 *Perfs:* 240 *Prods:* 8 *Type:* classical *Venues:* capacity 314

Bialostocki Teatr Lalek
Kalinowskiego 1, 15-875 **Bialystok**
Tel: 85-7425 031/7428 631 Fax: 85-7428 631
Internet: www.btl.bialystok.pl
E-Mail: teatr@btl.bialystok.pl
director Wojciech Kobrzynski; artistic director Wojciech Szelachowski
Puppeteers: 19 *Perfs:* 240 *Prods:* 8 *Type:* classical *Venues:* main stage cap. 242, small stage cap. 50

Teatr Banialuka – Osrodek Teatralny
Mickiewicza 20, 43-300 **Bielsko-Biala**
Tel: 33-822 1047/812 3394/815 0914 Fax: 33-815 0915
Internet: www.banialuka.in.com.pl
E-Mail: banialuka@in.com.pl
director Krzysztof Rau
Puppeteers: 20 *Perfs:* 300-400 *Prods:* 4 *Venues:* capacity 265 *Comments:* co-produce International Puppet Theatre Festival in May (biennial) next 2000; see also Festivals

Miejski Teatr Miniatura
ul. Grunwaldzka 16, 80-236 **Gdansk-Wrzeszcz**
Tel: 58-341 0123/9483 Fax: 58-341 0123
director Konrad Szachnowski
Puppeteers: 15 *Perfs:* 300 *Prods:* 4 *Venues:* main stage cap. 260, small stage cap. 120

Jeleniogorski Teatr Animacji
ul. Wolnosci 159, 58-500 **Jelenia Góra**
Tel: 75-764 9615 Fax: 75-764 8514
director Bogdan Nauka
Puppeteers: 10 *Perfs:* 250 *Prods:* 4 *Type:* various but focus on modern puppetry *Venues:* capacity 100

Slaski Teatr Lalki i Aktora Ateneum
Sw. Jana 10, 40-012 **Katowice**
Tel: 32-253 8221/2 Fax: 32-253 7926
director Jarostaw Czypczar; art dir Bogumil Pasternak
Puppeteers: 13 *Perfs:* 300 *Prods:* 7 *Type:* modern and traditional *Venues:* main stage cap. 210, small stage cap. 96

Teatr Lalki i Aktora Kubus
ul Duza 9, 25-304 **Kielce**
Tel: 41-344 5836 Fax: 41-368 0293
director Irena Dragan
Puppeteers: 16 *Perfs:* 380 *Prods:* 3 *Venues:* cap 150

Teatr Lalki i Maski Groteska
ul Skarbowa 2, 31-121 **Krakow**
Tel: 12-633 9604/4822
Fax: 12-633 9965
director Adolf Weltschek
Puppeteers: 20 *Perfs:* 300 *Prods:* 5 *Venues:* 3 stages: main stage cap. 228, small stage cap. 200, second small stage cap. 100

Teatr Lalek Arlekin
ul. l Maja 2, 90-718 **Lódz**
Tel: 42-632 5899/633 0894 Fax: 42-632 5899/633 0894
Internet: www.teatr-arlekin.lodz.pl/
E-Mail: tarlekin@polbox.com
director Waldemar Wolanski
Puppeteers: 26 *Perfs:* 290 *Prods:* 8 *Type:* various *Venues:* capacity 208 *Comments:* includes Polish Centre of UNIMA (POLUNIMA) ul. Wólczanska 5

Teatr Lalek Pinokio
ul. Kopernika 16, 90-503 **Lódz**
Tel: 42-636 6690/636 2993 Fax: 42-636 5988
E-Mail: tliapn@triko2.onet.pl
director Waldemar Wilhelm
Puppeteers: 11 *Perfs:* 300 *Prods:* 4 *Type:* modern, traditional *Venues:* capacity 231

Theatre of Fire and Paper
Teatr Ognia i Papieru
Lisciasta 12/15, 91-357 **Lódz**
Tel: 42-658 5109
Internet: ewaka@box43.gnet.pl
E-Mail: iegogien@friko6.onet.pl
director Grzegorz Kwiecinski
Puppeteers: 11 actors *Type :* experimental *Comments:* 2nd e-mail: ewaka@box43.gnet.pl

Teatr Lalek
ul Sadowa 12, 18-400 **Lomza**
Tel: 86-216 5955 Fax: 86-216 5955
director Jaroslaw Antoniuk
Puppeteers: 6 *Type:* various

Teatr Lalki i Aktora im H. Ch. Andersena
ul. Dominikanska 1, 20-111 **Lublin**
Tel: 81-532 1628/3225 Fax: 81-534 3611
director Wlodzimierz Felenczak
Puppeteers: 14 *Perfs:* 300-400 *Prods:* 7 *Venues:* cap 197

Olsztynski Teatr Lalek
Glowackiego 17, 10-447 **Olsztyn**
Tel: 89-533 5440/6651
director Krzysztof Rosciszewski
Puppeteers: 12 *Perfs:* 300 *Prods:* 4 *Type:* various *Venues:* capacity 144

Opolski Teatr Lalki i Aktora im A Smolki
pl. Kopernika 1, 45-040 **Opole**
Tel: 77-453 7306 Fax: 77-453 7306
Internet: www.opole.pl/kultura/OTLiA
artistic director Krystian Kobylka
Puppeteers: 13 *Perfs:* 350 *Prods:* 5 *Type:* various *Venues:* capacity 272 *Comments:* organise Polish Puppet Theatre Festival mid October, biennial; see also Festivals

Poznanski Teatr Animacji
al. Niepodleglosci 14, 61-874 **Poznan**
Tel: 61-853 7220 Fax: 61-853 6402
Internet: www.teatr-animacji-poznan.com.pl/
E-Mail: info@teatr-animacji-poznan.com.pl
director Antoni Konczal; artistic director Janusz Ryl-Krystianowski
Puppeteers: 16 *Perfs:* 300 *Prods:* 4 *Type:* classical, experimental *Venues:* main stage cap. 240, small stage cap. 130

Teatr Wierzbak
Przybyszewskiego 45/7, 60-357 **Poznan**
Tel: 61-867 2907 Fax: 61-861 5814
directors Grazyna Wydrowska, Bohdan Wasiel
Puppeteers: 8 *Type:* experimental

Teatr Lalek Rabcio
ul Pocztowa 6, 34-410 **Rabka**
Tel: 18-267 7648/7170 Fax: 18-267 7515
director Pawel Stojowski
Puppeteers: 7 *Type:* classical *Venues:* capacity 150

Teatr Miejski Maska
Mickiewicza 13, 35-959 **Rzeszów**
Tel: 17-626 808/625 717 Fax: 17-622 407
director Maciej Tondera
Puppeteers: 11 *Perfs:* 350 *Prods:* 4 *Type :* classical
Comments: own stage under construction

Teatr Lalek Tecza
ul. Warynskiego 2, 76-200 **Slupsk**
Tel: 59-423 935/428 794
Fax: 59-427 724
director Malgorzata Kaminska-Sobczyk
Puppeteers: 11 *Type:* classical *Venues:* capacity 196

Teatr Lalek Pleciuga
ul. Kaszubska 9, 70-403 **Szczecin**
Tel: 91-433 2821/434 1002
Fax: 91-433 5804
Internet: www.europapress.com/pleciuga/index1.html
E-Mail: plecuiga@europapress.com
director Zbigniew Niecikowski
Puppeteers: 14 *Perfs:* 300 *Prods:* 5 *Type:* various *Venues:* capacity 240

Teatr Lalki i Aktora Baj Pomorski
Piernikarska 9, 87-100 **Torun**
Tel: 56-652 2424/2029
director Czeslaw Sienko
Puppeteers: 14 *Perfs:* 400 *Prods:* 4
Type: traditional, modern *Venues:* main stage cap 239, small stage cap 120

Teatr Lalek
Buczka 16, 58-300 **Walbrzych**
Tel: 74-24194 Fax: 74-24194
director Eugeniusz Koterla
Puppeteers: 11 *Perfs:* 250 *Prods:* 3 *Venues:* capacity 203

Teatr Lalek Guliwer
ul Rózana 16, 02-548 **Warszawa**
Tel: 22-845 1676/4616
Fax: 22-845 4613
director Miroslaw Korzeb;
artistic director Zbigniew Lisowski
Puppeteers: 12 *Perfs:* 300-350 *Prods:* 4 *Type:* various
Venues: capacity 235

Teatr Lalka
Palac Kultury i Nauki, Plac Defilad, 00-901 **Warszawa**
Tel: 22-620 4960
Fax: 22-624 8565
director Jan Woronko; artistic director Joanna Rogacka
Puppeteers: 16 *Perfs:* 300-350 *Prods:* 5 *Type:* various
Venues: capacity 280

Teatr Lalki i Aktora Baj
ul. Jagiellonska 28, 03-719 **Warszawa**
Tel: 22-619 8077/818 0201
Fax: 22-619 9096
director Krzysztof Niesiolowski
Puppeteers: 10 *Perfs:* 300-400 *Prods:* 5 *Type:* various
Venues: capacity 213 *Comments:* visit schools to perform

Wroclawski Teatr Lalek
pl. Teatralny 4, 50-051 **Wroclaw**
Tel: 71-344 1216
Fax: 71-344 4832
director Wieslaw Hejno
Puppeteers: 20 *Perfs:* 200-300 *Type:* classical, experimental *Venues:* capacity 310

Scena Lalkowa Lubuskiego Teatru im. L. Kruczkowskiego
Al Niepodleglosci 3/5, 65-048 **Zielona Góra**
Tel: 68-327 2056
Fax: 68-327 1417
Internet: www.zgora.pl/teatr
director Andrzej Buck
Puppeteers: 10 *Perfs:* 200-250 *Prods:* 5
Venues: capacity 100

PORTUGAL (+351)

S.A. Marionetas – Teatro E Bonecos
Apartdo 622, 2460 **Alcobaça**
Tel: 936-708 6609
Fax: 62-597 014
E-Mail: samarionetas@hotmail.com
director Sofia Vinagre
Venues: puppet theatre 70 *Comments:* shows for children and adults

Bonecos de Santo Aleixo
Teatro Garçia Resende, Praça Joaquim António Aguiar, 7000-510 **Evora**
Tel: 66-705 533/703 112
Fax: 66-741 181
Internet: www.evora.net/cenrev
E-Mail: cendrev@mail.evora.net
director José Russo
Puppeteers: 5 *Perfs:* 80 *Type:* marionettes, traditional rod puppets *Venues:* Teatro Garçia Resende 300 *Touring:* Portugal, Europe, Brazil
Comments: for all age groups, member of UNIMA; see also Drama, Festivals and Venues

A Tarumba – Teatro De Marionetas
Rua Do Sol Á Graça 18 R/C, 1170 **Lisboa**
Tel: 1-814 1588/931-920 7296 (mobile)
Fax: 1-814 1588
director Luis Viera
Venues: theatre 150

Marionetes de Lisboa
Av. República 101-A, 1600 **Lisboa** Codex
Tel: 1-796 5780
Fax: 1-795 5794
E-Mail: marionetas.de.lisboa@mail.telenet.pt
director Ildeberto Gama;
artistic directors José Ramalho, Cristina Pereira
Puppeteers: varies (none permanent) *Perfs:* 180 *Prods:* 8 *Type:* traditional and contemporary *Venues:* Casa das Marionetas 70, Amphytheatre 70 *Touring:* Eastern Europe *Comments:* 2nd address: Teatro Nacional D. Maria II, Praça D. Pedro II, 1100-201 Lisboa, tel. 1-325 0800; member of UNIMA

Teatro de Marionetas do Porto
Rua de Belomonte 57, 4050 **Porto**
Tel: 2-208 3341
Fax: 2-208 3243 (theatre)
Internet: www.tmp.sidereus.pt
E-Mail: tmp@mail.ip.pt
director João Paulo Cardosa
Puppeteers: 8 *Perfs:* 150 *Prods:* 7 (2 new) *Type:* various
Venues: capacity 60 *Touring:* Italy, France, Denmark, Spain, Asia, Brazil, England
Comments: see also Festivals

ROMANIA (+40)

Prichindel Puppet Theatre
Andrei Muresanu Str. 1, 2500 **Alba Iulia**
Tel: 58-811 752
artistic director Dan Purcelean
Puppeteers: 11 *Perfs:* 350 *Prods:* 3-4 *Venues:* capacity 160

Teatrul de Marionete
Str. Episcopiei no. 5, 2900 **Arad**
Tel: 57-212 974 Fax: 57-218 928
director Dan Antoci

Animations Theatre 'Licurici'
N. Balcescu Str. 90, 5500 **Bacau**
Tel: 34-145 565/122 763
director Stelian Preda
Puppeteers: 12 *Perfs:* 250 *Prods:* 3-4 *Venues:* capacity 200

Puppet Theatre of Baia Mare
Crisan Str. 8, 4800 **Baia Mare**
Tel: 62-471 419
director Alexandru Mociran
Puppeteers: 8 *Perfs:* 220 *Prods:* 3-4 *Venues:* capacity 160

Vasilache Puppet Theatre
Victoriei Str. 7, 6800 **Botosani**
Tel: 31-531 460/514 353
artistic director Mihai Elvadeanu
Puppeteers: 12 *Perfs:* 300 *Prods:* 3 *Venues:* capacity 182
Touring: Europe

Children Theatre Carabus
Polona Str. 12, 6100 **Braila**
Tel: 39-644 704
director Alexandrescu Liliana
Puppeteers: 12 *Perfs:* 250
Prods: 3 *Venues:* capacity 123

Teatrul Tandarica
Eremia Grigorescu Str. 24, Sector 1, 7000 **Bucharest**
Tel: 1-211 3288 (Sala Lahovary)/2377 (Sala Victoria)
Fax: 1-210 6294
artistic director and manager Mihaela Tonitza Iordache
Puppeteers: 24 *Perfs:* 800
Venues: capacity 350 and 400

Teatrul de Papusi Puck
Str. I.C. Bratianu no. 23, 3400 **Cluj-Napoca**
Tel: 64-195 992 Fax: 64-197 206
director Tudor Chirila
Venues: capacity 116

Puppet Theatre of Constanta
Aristide Karatzalis Str. 14, 8700 **Constanta**
Tel: 41-611 744/615 268/613 508
Fax: 41-615 080
artistic director Mona Chirila
Puppeteers: 10 *Perfs:* 200 *Venues:* capacity 300

Puppet Theatre Craiova
Al. I. Cuza Str. 16, 1100 **Craiova**
Tel: 51-412 473
Fax: 51-412 473
artistic director t.b.a.
Puppeteers: 12 *Perfs:* 270 *Venues:* capacity 132
Touring: national, international

Gulliver Puppet Theatre
Eroilor Str. 14, 6200 **Galati**
Tel: 36-412 302
director Dan Ganca
Puppeteers: 12 *Perfs:* 200 *Prods:* 3 *Venues:* capacity 120

Luceafarul Youth & Children's Theatre
Str. Stefan cel Mare n° 60, 6600 **Iasi**
Tel: 32-115 432/966/143 288
Fax: 32-115 966/212 662
director George Macovei

Puppet Theatre
Teatrul de Papusi
Str. V. Alecsandri n° 8, 3700 **Oradea**
Tel: 59-133 398
director Iuliu Moldovan
Venues: capacity 201

Aschiuta Puppet Theatre
Str. Domnita Balasa n° 13, 0300 **Pitesti**
Tel: 48-636 303
director Nicolae Banica

Ciufulici Puppet Theatre
Str. Teatrului n° 1,2000 **Ploiesti**
Tel: 44-146 431/114 455/144 338
director Mioara Pagîta

Puppet Theatre
Str. Al. Odobescu n° 4, 2400 **Sibiu**
Tel: 69-413 496/417 273
director Mihaela Grigoras
Venues: capacity 200

Teatrul de Papusi
B-dul Tineretii n° 3, 1900 **Timisoara**
Tel: 56-193 049/117 439/201 515
director Cornelia Pop

Puppet Theatre for Children and Youth 'Ariel'
Postei Str. 2, 4300 **Tirgu-Mures**
Tel: 65-120 428/165 537
Fax: 65-165 537
director Zeno Fodor
Puppeteers: 24 (12 Romanian and 12 Hungarian)
Perfs: 600-650 *Prods:* 3 Romanian, 3 Hungarian
Venues: capacity 167

RUSSIA (+7)

Astrakhan State Puppet Theatre
12 Phioletova Str., 414000 **Astrakhan**
Tel: 851-002 6392
director Vladimir Dolgopolov

Altai State Puppet theatre Skazka
41 Pushkin Str.,
656043 **Barnaul**
Tel: 3852-231 413/322 266

Belgorod State Puppet Theatre
5-b/8 Nekrasova Str., 308007 **Belgorod**
Tel: 0722-265 802
director Alexandr Kobelev

Birobijan Puppet Theatre Kudesnik
Shveinyi per. 5, 682200 **Birobijan**
Tel: 421-626 5253

Amur Region Puppet Theatre Amurchonok
60 Shevchenko Str.,
675011 **Blagoveshchensk (Amur Region)**
Tel: 416-222 8959

Briansk Region Puppet Theatre
12 Pushkina Str., 241021 **Briansk**
Tel: 083-222 1334
Fax: 083-257 7578
director Nina Mokovozova

Chuvash State Puppet Theatre
41 Uritzkogo Str., 428004 **Cheboksari**
Tel: 835-022 3840

Chita Regional Puppet Theatre
2 Verkholenskaya Str., 672039 **Chita**
Tel: 302-232 3077

Dzerzhinsk Puppet Theatre
Dzerzhinsk Square, 606000 **Dzerzhinsk (Nizhegorodski Region)**
Tel: 831-4033 0151

Ivanovski Puppet Theatre
Ivanovski teatr kukol
pl. Pushkina 2, Dvorets iskusstv, 153000 **Ivanovo**
Tel: 0932-327 668/412 352

Kaliningrad Regional Puppet Theatre
1 Prospect Pobedi, 236010 **Kaliningrad**
Tel: 0112-213 889/214 335/227 949
director Alexandr Perebeinos

Kazan Puppet Theatre
Kazanski teatr kukol
ul Lukovskovo 21,
420107 **Kazan (Tatarstan)**
Tel: 8432-389 471/044

Kemerovo Regional Puppet Theatre
18 Vesenniaya Str., 650099 **Kemerovo**
Tel: 34822-366 709/8549

Kirov State Puppet Theatre
73 Marx Str.,
610000 **Kirov**
Tel: 833-269 0511/622 806

Kostrom Puppet Theatre
Kostromskoi teatr kukol
ul Ostrovskovo 5, 156000 **Kostroma**
Tel: 09422-577 995/572 571

Krasnodarsk Puppet Theatre
Krasnodarski teatr kukol
ul Krasnaya 31, 350000 **Krasnodar**
Tel: 8612-524 488/525 411

Krasnoyarsk Puppet Theatre
Krasnoyarski teatr kukol
ul Lenina 119, 660017 **Krasnoyarsk**
Tel: 3912-234 679/5430

Kursk Puppet Theatre
2 Radishcheva Str., 305000 **Kursk**
Tel: 071-222 7656
Lipetsk State Puppet Theatre
Ul. Lenina 25, 398001 **Lipetsk**
Tel: 0742-778 601/240 146/240 106

Magadan State Puppet Theatre
20 Parkovaya Str., 685024 **Magadan**
Tel: 413-002 3068/27579

Daghestan State Puppet Theatre
40 Lenin Str., 367025 **Makhach-Kala**
Tel: 87200-671 669
artistic director Aminat Iakhjeva

Magic Theatre, Mikhail Chekhov International Cultural Centre
Floor 58, Snezhnaya St. 9, 129323 **Moscow**
Tel: 095-189 2390

Moscow Children's Chamber Puppet Theatre
Moskovski detski kamerni teatr kukol
ul. Bazhova 9, 129128 **Moscow**
Tel: 095-181 0193/5141
artistic director Vitalii Elseev

Moscow City Puppet Theatre
Moskovski gorodskoi teatr kukol
Spartakovskaya ul. 26, 107066 **Moscow**
Tel: 095-267 4481/4288 Fax: 095-261 3442
artistic director Viachaslav Kryuchkov;
director Yuri Dolgorukii

Moscow Region Puppet Theatre
Moskovski oblastnoi teatr kukol
Pestovsky per. 2, 109004 **Moscow**
Tel: 095-915 7922/5432

Moscow Shadow Theatre
Moskovski teatr tenei
Izmailovski Bulvar 60/10, 105077 **Moscow**
Tel: 095-465 6592 Fax: 095-465 5070
director Vadim Grigorjev;
artistic director Alexandr Krupenin

Moscow State Central Puppet Theatre im S.V. Obraztsova
Sadovo-Samotechnaya Ul. 3, 103473 **Moscow**
Tel: 095-209 4848/0904 Fax: 095-229 8910
artistic director Revaz Gabriadze

Moscow Theatre of the Children's Book The Magic Lamp
Moskovski teatr detskoi knigi 'Volshebnaya lampa'
Sretensky Bulvar, 9/2, 103045 **Moscow**
Tel: 095-928 2167/923 3984 Fax: 095-925 6993
artistic director Vladimir Shtein

Sergei Obrastzov Central Academic State Puppet Theatre
3, Sadovaya-Samotechnaya Str., 103473 **Moscow**
Tel: 095-299 7972 Fax: 095-299 8284
Comments: Obrastzov Central Puppetry Museum – Tel/Fax: 095-299 8910

Murmansk Regional Puppet Theatre
21-a, S.Perovskoi Str., 183038 **Murmansk**
Tel: 915-005 3357/56195

Kabardino-Balkarian State Puppet Theatre
16 Prospect Kaisina Kulieva,
360000 **Nalchik**
Tel: 86600-50476/8542

Neriungri State Actor and Puppet Theatre
Pionerskaya Ul. 4-A, 678922 **Neriungri (Sakha)**
Tel: 411-2224 4485/42658

Nizhnevartovsky Puppet Theatre "Barabashka"
60-letia Octiabria Str.,
62440 **Nizhnevartovsk (Tyumen Region, Khanti-Mansiysk Territory)**
Tel: 34566-238 951 Fax: 34566-238 951

Nizhegorodsky Puppet Theatre
Nizhegorodski teatr kukol
ul B. Pokrovskaya 39,
603600 **Nizhni Novgorod**
Tel: 8312-338 208/334 292

Nizhny Tagil Puppet Theatre
14 Lenina Str., 622034 **Nizhni Tagil (Sverdlovski Region)**
Tel: 343-525 5933/254 238

Oriol Regional Puppet Theatre
29 Sovetskaia Str., 302030 **Oryol**
Tel: 8600-56227

Penza Puppet Theatre
Penzenski teatr kukol
ul Chkalova 35, 440000 **Penza**
Tel: 8412-334 726

Perm State Puppet Theatre
65 K. Marx Str, 614039 **Perm**
Tel: 3422-442 167/444 566

Kamchatka Regional Puppet Theatre
42 Maksutova, 683032
Petropavlovsk-Kamchatski
Tel: 41500-26848/26347

Pskov Regional Puppet Theatre
3 Konnaya Str., 180007 **Pskov**
Tel: 811-246 007

Rostov Puppet Theatre
Rostovski teatr kukol
per. Universitetski 46, 340006 **Rostov-na-Donu**
Tel: 8632-654 591/652 528

Ryazan Puppet Theatre
Ryazanski teatr kukol
ul Esenina 31, 390023 **Ryazan**
Tel: 0912-771 589/442 673
director Askar Tager

Rybinsk Municipal Puppet Theatre
21 Krestovaya, 152909 **Rybinsk (Yaroslavski Region)**
Tel: 085-372 2054/22713

Samara Puppet Theatre
Samarski tear kukol
ul Tolstovo 82, 430041 **Samara**
Tel: 8462-320 824/344 980
director Vladimir Vorobiev

Mordovian Republican Puppet Theatre
90-A Volodarskogo Str., 430003 **Saransk**
Tel: 83422-52522/51598/75911

Saratov Puppet Theatre Teremok
16 Babushkin Vzvoz,
410002 **Saratov**
Tel: 852-261 966/262 228

Smolensk Regional Puppet Theatre
15-A Dzerzhinski Str., 214000 **Smolensk**
Tel: 081-003 3767/06

Bolshoi Puppet Theatre
Bolshoi teatr kukol
ul Nekrasov 10, 191104 **St Petersburg**
Tel: 812-272 9065/6657
artistic director Alla Polukhina;
director Vladimir Khalif (812-273 5303)

Fairy-tale Puppet Theatre
Kukolni teatr skazki
Mosovski prospect 121, 196006 **St Petersburg**
Tel: 812-298 5872/296 2496
director Vladimir Klimenko

Puppet-Marionette Theatre
Teatr kukol-marionetok
Nevski prospect 52,
191011 **St Petersburg**
Tel: 812-311 3557/310 0120
artistic director Natalia Luneva

Stavropol State Puppet Theatre
39 Prospect Octiabrskoi Revolutzii,
355000 **Stavropol**
Tel: 86522-269 733

Tambov State Puppet Theatre
15 Internatzionalnaya Str.,
392000 **Tambov**
Tel: 0752-221 158/7761

Togliatti Municipal Puppet Theatre
6, Ploshchad Svobodi,
445021 **Togliatti (Samarski Region)**
Tel: 8-1523 2082

Tomsk Regional Puppet Theatre
4 Kooperativni per.
634001 **Tomsk**
Tel: 382-222 5204/223 793

Tver Puppet Theatre
Tverskoi teatr kukol
pr. Pobedy 9,
170008 **Tver**
Tel: 08222-63740

Tyumen Puppet Theatre
Tyumenski teatr kukol
ul Kirova 36,
62503 **Tyumen**
Tel: 34522-267 605/267 679

Buryat State Puppet Theatre Ulger
46 Lenina Str., 670000 **Ulan-Ude**
Tel: 301-222 2292

Ulianovsk Puppet Theatre
Ulianovski teatr kukol
ul Goncharova 10, 432700 **Ulianovsk**
Tel: 8422-319 986

Vladimir Regional Puppet Theatre
7 Gagarina Str., 600000 **Vladimir**
Tel: 092-222 3141

Primorye Municipal Puppet Theatre
1-May Str. 8,
690091 **Vladivostok**
Tel: 423-0022 2021/225 041

Volgograd Regional Puppet Theatre
15 Prospect Lenina, 400066 **Volgograd**
Tel: 8442-335 698

Vologda Regional Puppet Theatre Teremok
21, Lenina Str.,
160035 **Vologda**
Tel: 817-222 4711/55682

Komi Republican State Puppet Theatre
2 Leningradskaya Str.,
169906 **Vorkuta**
Tel: 82151-41664/40632

Yaroslavl Puppet Theatre
Yaroslavski teatr kukol
pl. Yunocti 3, 150000 **Yaroslavl**
Tel: 0852-224 553/225 294

Mari Republican Puppet Theatre
87 Karl Marx Str., 424000 **Yoshkar-Ola**
Tel: 836-225 2522/51598

Sakhalin Regional Puppet Theatre
24 K. Marx Str., 693000 **Yuzhno-Sakhalinsk**
Tel: 424-223 1498

SLOVAKIA (+421)

Many telephone and fax numbers in Slovakia are in the process of being changed. We have included all new numbers known at the time of going to print.

Anton Anderle Traditional Puppet Theatre
Tradičné bábkové divadlo Anton Anderle
Nám. L. Stúra 22, 974 01 **Banská Bystrica**
Tel: 88-410 2096
Fax: 88-410 2096
manager, actor Anton Anderle
Puppeteers: 2 *Type:* string
Comments: also owns a collection of historical puppets

Puppet Theatre at the Crossroads
Bábkové divadlo na rázcestí
Kollárova 18, 975 90 **Banská Bystrica**
Tel: 88-412 5623/412 4193
Fax: 88-412 5623/412 4193
director Iveta Skripková
Puppeteers: 10 *Perfs:* 250 *Prods:* 3 *Type:* modern combined puppet theatre *Venues:* cap 100 to 200

State Puppet Theatre Bratislava
Státne bábkové divadlo Bratislava
Dunajská Ulica 36, 811 08 **Bratislava**
Tel: 7-5292 3668
Fax: 7-5296 6119
Internet: www.kultura.gratex.sk/sbd
manager Ján Brtis; artistic director Jozef Mokos
Puppeteers: 15 *Perfs:* 180 *Prods:* 2 *Type:* modern puppet theatre using different techniques *Venues:* cap 160

Puppet Theatre Kosice
Bábkové divadlo Kosice
Tajovského 4, 040 01 **Kosice**
Tel: 95-622 0455
Fax: 95-622 0049
director Katarína Procházková;
artistic director Ivan Sogel
Puppeteers: 10 *Perfs:* 240 *Prods:* 4 *Type:* combined puppet theatre *Venues:* home capacity 250, Scene Jorik 100 *Comments:* Scene Jorik is an experimental stage of drama for youth and adults

The Old Theatre Nitra
Stare divadlo Nitra
7 pesieho pluku cl., 949 01 **Nitra**
Tel: 87-524 092/525 003/522 586
Fax: 87-524 091/524 871
director Karol Spisák
Puppeteers: 12 *Perfs:* 240 *Prods:* 2
Comments: touring company

Theatre Piki
Divad bo Piki
L. Novomeského 25, 902 01 **Pezinok**
Tel: 704-404 341
Fax: 704-402 438
manager Lubomir Piktor

Puppet Theatre Zilina
Bábkové divadlo Zilina
Kuzmányho ul. 6, 011 37 **Zilina**
Tel: 89-562 0958
Fax: 89-562 3995
director Bibiana Tarasovicová
Puppeteers: 7 *Perfs:* 240 *Prods:* 3
Type: combined puppet theatre *Venues:* home cap 200

SLOVENIA (+386)

Paper Puppet Theatre Papilu
Papirnato Gledalisce Papilu
Hrvatini 204, 6280 **Ankaran**
Tel: 66-526 035
Fax: 66-526 035
directors Maja & Brane Solce
Puppeteers: 2 *Perfs:* 100-150 *Type:* paper puppetry exclusively *Venues:* capacity 150 *Touring:* Europe *Comments:* do performances and workshops with children and adults

Freyer Theatre
Freyer teater
Saranoviceva 13, 1000 **Ljubljana**
Tel: 61-323 621
Fax: 61-189 2233 (E Majaron c/o Faculty of Education)
E-Mail: edvard.majaron@guest.arnes.si
managing and artistic director Edvard Majaron
Type: marionettes, rod-puppets, toy-puppets
Touring: worldwide *Comments:* family shows; with music

Konj Puppet Theatre
Konj gledalisce lutk
KUD France Preseren, Karunova 14, 1000 **Ljubljana**
Tel: 61-332 288/332 299
Fax: 61-331 128
director Jan Zakonjsek;set and puppet design and technical issues Silvan Omerzu
Type: various types *Comments:* do performances for adults only

Puppet Theatre Joze Pengov Ljubljana
Lutkovno Gledalisce Joze Pengov
Draveljska 44, 1000 **Ljubljana**
Tel: 61-571 132
managing & artistic director Helena Sobar Zajc
Type: various traditional types of puppetry
Comments: incorporates actors in performances

Puppet Theatre Labirint
Lutkovno gledalisce Labirint
Rozna dolina c.II/9, 1000 **Ljubljana**
Tel: 61-268 908
E-Mail: sasa.jovanovic@siol.net
director Sasa Jovanovi
Puppeteers: 2-4 *Prods:* 1 annually *Type:* various techniques including shadow, projections, various hand puppets, rod puppets, Javanese puppets á la bunraku etc. *Comments:* do performances and workshops for adults and children

Puppet Theatre Ljubljana
Lutkovno Gledalisce Ljubljana
Krekov Trg. 2, **Ljubljana**
Tel: 61-300 0970
Fax: 61-314 795
general manager Ignacije Sunjic; technical manager Bozo Miler; literary manager Matjaz Loboda
Puppeteers: 17 *Perfs:* 450 minimum
Prods: 16 annually, 5 new + 2 special events annually
Type: all types including marionettes, hand puppets
Venues: main stage up to 300, Kulturnica (puppetry studio progamme) 70 , small stage 80, Podstreha (for miniature puppets) 35-50 *Touring:* national, international *Comments:* works with Slovene writers and producers; organizes puppetry education

Speakeasy Pictures
Beljaska 20, 1000 **Ljubljana**
Tel: 61-551 435
Fax: 61-551 435
authors Angus Reid, Bruce Reid, Barbara Bulatovic
Prods: 2 (artists in residence) projects annually *Type:* mulimedia performances, all types, mixed techniques (projections, shadows, film included) street puppetry

Maribor Puppet Theatre
Lutkovno Gledalisce Maribor
Rotovski trg 2,
2000 **Maribor**
Tel: 62-228 1970/228 1971
Fax: 62-227 412
E-Mail: mb-lutkgled@siol.net
director Tine Varl
Puppeteers: 6 *Perfs:* 400 *Prods:* 3 *Type:* all types, puppetry by Slovenian authors, mostly classical stories for children *Comments:* organise international puppet festival in the summer; member of UNIMA

SPAIN (+34)

Compañía Teia Moner
c/ Can Rovira, 33, Lliça d'Amunt, 08186 **Barcelona**
Tel: 93-864 5834/609 310 371(mobile) Fax: 93-864 5834
Internet: www.quasar.es/teia
E-Mail: teiam@arrakis.es
director Teia Moner; technician Miguel Espinosa
Puppeteers: 1 actor + 1 technician *Perfs:* 60-70 *Prods:* 5
Type: bunraku, rod, string and shadow puppets *Touring:* national *Comments:* performances in Catalan, Spanish and French; see also Drama

Cònica-La Cònica Theatre D'Ombres, La
c/ Urgel 69, 2° 2ª, 08011 **Barcelona**
Tel: 93-323 7298 Fax: 93-454 7548
contacts Mercé Gost, Alba Zapater
Puppeteers: varies *Perfs:* 20 *Prods:* 2 *Type:* shadow theatre *Touring:* Spain, Europe *Comments:* shadow research with other artists; video

Els Aquilinos Teatre
c/ de la Lluna, 23 entresuelo 1ª, 08001 **Barcelona**
Tel: 93-329 8756
Fax: 93-442 0658
E-Mail: aquilinos@ctv.es
director de producción Esther Prim;
director artístico Miguel Álvarez
Puppeteers: 3 *Perfs:* 80 *Prods:* 2 *Type:* various techniques: marionettes, glove, objects *Venues:* Teatre Regina
Touring: Spain, Europe *Comments:* funded by Gobierno Autónomo de Cataluña; see also Drama

L'Estenedor Teatre de Titelles
c/ Dalmau, 13 bajos izq., 08014 **Barcelona**
Tel: 93-296 7311/ 616 541 032 (mobile)
Fax: 93-296 7311
creador y manipulador David Laín i Devante; técnico de luz y sonido Jordi Monros
Puppeteers: 1 *Perfs:* 100 *Prods:* 15 + 1 *Type:* rod, glove, shadows, string *Touring:* Spain

La Fanfarra – Teatre de Marionetes
Teatre Malic, c/ Fusina 3, 08003 **Barcelona**
Tel: 93-310 7035 Fax: 93-319 5647
Internet: www.daucom.es/malic/
E-Mail: malic@pangea.org
contact Eugenio Navarro; directors Eugenio Navarro, Antoni Rumbau, Mariona Masgrau; administration Luisa Rodríguez
Puppeteers: 3 *Perfs:* 120 *Prods:* 6 *Type:* marionettes, glove, shadow and object theatre
Venues: Teatre Malic 50 *Comments:* managers of Teatre Malic; see also Venues

Rocamora
Argentona 30, 08024 **Barcelona**
Tel: 93-213 2344
Fax: 93-210 4206
director Carlos Cañellas;
producción Susanna Rodríguez
Puppeteers: 2 *Perfs:* 100 *Prods:* 2 (1 new) *Type:* string puppets for children and adults *Touring:* Spain, Italy
Comments: workshops for puppet making

Titelles Babi
c/ Marti Codolar 45-6°, 2° , L'Hospitalet del Llobregat, 08902 **Barcelona**
Tel: 93-331 9153/332 9997
Fax: 93-332 9997 (c/o Titelles Babi)
E-Mail: babi@ctv.es
responsable Carmen Calvet; director de programas Ferrán Albiol, Llorenç Albiol
Puppeteers: 3 *Perfs:* 90 *Prods:* 6 (1 new) *Type:* glove, rod, marionettes and actors *Touring:* Spain, Andorra
Comments: members of UNIMA Cataluña

Zootrop
Creu dels Molers 20, 4° 1ª, 08004 **Barcelona**
Tel: 93-301 1040 Fax: 93-301 1040
contact Esther Cabacés, Nuria Mestres

Taun Taun Teatroa
c/ Mizpildi s/n, 20570 **Bergara (Guipuzcoa)**
Tel: 943-765 837
Fax: 943-762 105
director Iñaki Mata Moz
Puppeteers: 5 *Prods:* 2 *Type:* avant-garde, objects *Venues:* Sala Nov Barris (Barcelona) 400 *Touring:* Spain
Comments: organise Festival Int. de Titeres para Adultos de Bergara; see also Festivals

Cobaya Teatro
Plaza Landabaso 3, 48015 **Bilbao**
Tel: 94-476 3723
Fax: 94-476 3723
director Javier Pérez
Puppeteers: 5+ *Perfs:* 50 *Prods:* 5 (1 estreno) *Type:* puppet theatre + actors *Touring:* festivals, international, salas alternatives *Comments:* have performed at 22 international puppet festivals in Spain; touring company

Los Titiriteros de Binéfar
c/ Lérida 23, 22500 **Binéfar (Huesca)**
Tel: 974-430 850/428 218 Fax: 974-430 850
director artístico Paco Paricio Casado; director ejectivo Pilar Amorós Muzas; secretaria Ana Tere Pedrós
Puppeteers: 6 actors, 2 musicians *Perfs:* 200 *Prods:* 1
Type: glove, marionettes and 'siluetas articuladas'
Venues: perform in provinces, in theatres, open-air venues: Teatro Regina de Barcelona 400
Touring: Spain, Europe

Gomes i Gomis Teatre
El Barru 7, 33529 **Buyeres Nava (Asturias)**
Tel: 98-571 8075/608-175 274 (mobile)
Fax: 98-571 8075
E-Mail: osoblanco-geoigeo@retemail.es
contact Amand Gomis i Romaguera; puppet maker Amalia Fernández Mayo
Puppeteers: 2 *Perfs:* 40 *Prods:* 3 + 1
Comments: puppetry and theatre workshops; also take commissions for sculpture, object making and props

Teatro de la Tía Norica
Apartado de Correos 2275, 11080 **Cadiz**
Tel: 956-221 680/211 123/227 624
Fax: 956-222 051
director José Bable Neira; producción Manuel Morillo González
Puppeteers: 12 *Perfs:* 50 *Prods:* 1 new every 2 years
Type: specialise in table and rod puppets, traditional puppetry, marionettes *Venues:* own venue: Baluarte de la Candelaria 150 *Touring:* Spain, Europe, South America
Comments: revival of 17th century company; give training in puppetry and puppet-making; contact José Bable Neira, c/ Pasquin 18-2° B, 11002 Cadiz, Spain, tel: 956-214 820

El Espejo Negro
Apdo. 127, 08950 **Esplugues (Barcelona)**
Tel: 93-473 8669
Fax: 93-372 5948
Internet: www.free-art.com
E-Mail: olivia@free-art.com
director, diseño y realización de marionetas Angel Calvente; vestuario y ayudante de taller Carmen Ledesma; management Free Art
Puppeteers: 4 *Perfs:* 70 *Prods:* 4 + 1 *Type:* marionettes for adults *Venues:* Teatro Goya 700 *Touring:* Spain, Europe
Comments: alternative E-mail: carles@free-art.com; see also Agents & Producers

Titeres Tiritando
Los Carambas 6, La Loma, 30565 **Las Torres de Cotillas (Murcia)**
Tel: 968-624 169
Fax: 968-624 169
E-Mail: tirita@cajamurcia.es
dirección Luis Ferrer Cuix; producción Antonia Navarro
Puppeteers: 5 *Perfs:* 80 *Prods:* 7
Type: various types including glove, objects, mixed actors and puppets *Touring:* Spain, Europe *Comments:* performances for children and adults

Companyia del Centre de Titelles de Lleida
Centro de Titelles de Lleida, Plaça de L'Hort de Sta Teresa 1, 25002 **Lleida**
Tel: 973-270 249
Fax: 973-264 515
co-direction & scenography Joan-Andreu Vallvé; co-direction & programming Julieta Agustí; secretary Ester Campavadal
Puppeteers: 15 *Perfs:* 200 *Prods:* 6 + 2
Type: table puppets, glove and shadows *Venues:* Teatre del Centre de Titelles de Lleida 200
Touring: Spain, Europe *Comments:* puppetry & theatre workshops and exhibitions; organise international fair of puppetry & the book fair of performing arts; see also National Organisations

Els Tres Tranquils
c/ San Antonio 88, 07620 **Llucmajor (Palma de Mallorca)**
Tel: 971-662 008/661 112/971 120 917
co-direction Joaquima Faidella
Puppeteers: 4 *Perfs:* 12 *Prods:* 1
Type: traditional hand glove puppets and pucinellas *Touring:* Spain, Europe

Compañía de Teatro la Gaviota
Gral. Pardiñas, 7-6°, 28001 **Madrid**
Tel: 91-577 1581
director Luis Alberto Ghiringhelli
Puppeteers: 2 *Perfs:* 100-150 *Prods:* 8
Type: glove, rod, muppets *Venues:* Teatro de Títeres del Retiro *Touring:* Spain *Comments:* member of Asociación Cultural Rayuela; see also Promoters

La Tartana – Teatro de Títeres
c/ Pradillo 12, 28002 **Madrid**
Tel: 91-416 9011
Fax: 91-416 9968
director y programador Juan Muñóz Rebollo; administración & distribución Montse Ortiz; jefe técnico Enrique Rodríguez
Puppeteers: 6 *Perfs:* 50 *Prods:* 2 *Type:* contemporary puppetry for children and adults *Venues:* Teatro Pradillo 100 *Touring:* Europe *Comments:* organise puppet manipulation workshops, see also Drama and Venues

Mar de Marionetas, La
Arriaza 18, 2° D, 28008 **Madrid**
Tel: 91-559 7540/970-723 360
Fax: 91-559 7540/970-723 360/910-385 198
E-Mail: earangof@nexo.es
director Marta Bautista; manager María Arango
Puppeteers: 1 *Perfs:* 120 *Prods:* 2 *Type:* all types
Comments: member of Asociación Cultural Rayuela; see also Promoters

Teatro de la Luna
C/ Alfonso XIII, 13 – esc. A 4° B, 28038 **Madrid**
Tel: 91-551 6618 Fax: 91-551 6618
contact Eulalia Domingo, Juan Manuel Recover
Puppeteers: 5 *Perfs:* 120 *Prods:* 4 *Type:* muppets, rod
Venues: Sala Cuarta Pared 250, Circulo de Bellas Artes 200 *Touring:* Italy, Germany, Spain *Comments:* combine elements of different artistic expressions such as literature, music, painting, sculpture and theatre; workshops for children in the national museum for contemporary art, Centro de Arte Reina Sofia (Madrid)

Teatro de Títeres – Peralta del Amo
c/ María Teresa 9, 6° A, 28028 **Madrid**
Tel: 91-355 7989/895 5703
E-Mail: micaela@ctv.es
responsable Francisco Peralta González
Puppeteers: 8 *Perfs:* 12 *Prods:* 1 *Type:* own technique
Touring: Spain

Mirapalo Teatro
Mirarte Producciones SL, c/ Portugal 12, 29017 **Málaga**
Tel: 95-229 4909 Fax: 95-229 4909
directors José António Triguero, Maite Serrano
Puppeteers: 3 + 2 *Perfs:* 40 *Prods:* 2 *Type:* combination of puppets and actors *Touring:* Spain *Comments:* produces plays, involving puppets and actors for adults and children; funded by Junta de Andalucía (Regional Government); programme and distribution of puppet companies for different venues in the city

Tan Tan Teatro
c/ Poeta Miguel Hernández 10, El Raal, 30139 **Murcia**
Tel: 968-870 154/670-321 227 (mobile)
Fax: 968-870 154
presidente Ángel Salcedo Santa; secretaria Mª Carmen Navarro García; tesorero Mariano Esparza Martinez; drección artística Carmen Navarro, Ángel Salcedo
Puppeteers: 2 *Perfs:* 90 *Prods:* 4 + 1 new *Type:* rod, table, glove, objects and actors *Touring:* national, festivals
Comments: puppets, street theatre, children theatre

Teatro del Urogallo
Plaza Tierno Galván 15, 5° C, 30009 **Murcia**
Tel: 968-283 420
responsables Fernando Vidal, Ramona Olivares
Puppeteers: 2 *Perfs:* 50 *Prods:* 6 *Type:* hand, bunraku and mixed technique *Venues:* Teatro Romea 1154

Títeres Los Claveles
c/ Río Arlanza 4, 2° A, 30007 **Murcia**
Tel: 968-248 124/244 634/670 984 129 (mobile) Fax: 968-248 124
E-Mail: jogargar@colon.net.es
contacts Paca García, Aniceto Roca
Puppeteers: 2 *Perfs:* 60 *Type:* rod, table *Venues:* Teatro Romea (Murcia) 1000 *Touring:* Spain

Hilando Titeres
c/ Jerez 476, Urb. Calypo Fado, 28600 **Navalcarnero (Madrid)**
Tel: 91-813 2533/ 670 723 340 (mobile) Fax: 91-813 2533
directors Mar Gasco García y Gonzalo Cardone
Puppeteers: 2 *Prods:* 3 *Type:* specialise in string, also shadow, glove, rod *Comments:* member of Asociación Cultural Rayuela; see also Promoters

Marimba Marionetas
c/o Bilbao 223, 28600 **Navalcarnero (Madrid)**
Tel: 91-813 2099 Fax: 91-813 2099
director José Luis García Suárez
Puppeteers: 3 *Perfs:* 150 *Prods:* 9 *Type:* varilla, hilo, marionetas *Touring:* Spain *Comments:* member of Asociación Cultural Rayuela; see also Promoters

Jordi Bertran
Ap. 47, 08460 **Palautordera (Barcelona)**
Tel: 93-848 0499 Fax: 93-848 0499
E-Mail: arts@abaforum.es
responsable Jordi Bertrán
Puppeteers: 3 *Perfs:* 60 *Prods:* 4 + 1 new *Type:* mixed (hilo, varilla) *Touring:* Spain, Europe, Asia, South America, USA *Comments:* 23 arts brothers projections; see also Agents & Producers

Tanxarina
c/ Eidos Nº 49, 36800 **Redondela (Pontevedra)**
Tel: 986-402 966
Fax: 986-402 966
representante Eduardo Rodríguez Cunha, Miguel Borines Fernández, Andrés Giraldez Rio
Puppeteers: 3 *Perfs:* 80 *Prods:* 3 *Type:* string, table puppets, glove, street theatre, shadow *Touring:* Mexico, El Salvador, Venezuela, Portugal *Comments:* own workshop, making puppets for regional television

Txotxongillo
Paseo Heriz 16, 5° A, 20008 **San Sebastian**
Tel: 943-215 869 Fax: 943-219 960
directors Encarni Genua, Manuel Gómez
Puppeteers: 2 *Perfs:* 100 *Prods:* 11 (1 new) *Type:* glove, marionette, objects, shadows, table *Touring:* Spain, Cuba, Europe, USA, Mexico

S'Estornell Teatre (Grup de Teresetes)
Sant Jordi 7, 07320 **Santa María del Cami, Mallorca (Baleares)**
Tel: 971-621 316 Fax: 971-140 419
director Josep Baño
Puppeteers: 3 *Perfs:* 25 *Prods:* 1 *Type:* string, glove, rod and shadow puppets *Comments:* perform in Catalan, Spanish, French and English; give classes in glove, rod and shadow puppetry; usually perform outdoors in village fairs, and in schools

Bihar
San Diego 12, 10°, 48910 **Sestao (Vizcaya)**
Tel: 94-495 9891/607 879 790 (mobile) Fax: 94-495 9891
director Felipe Garduño Hernández
Puppeteers: 2 *Perfs:* 150 *Prods:* 6 *Type:* glove, rod, bunraku, actors theatre for children *Touring:* Spain
Comments: repertory company for children and adults

Aldebarán
c/ Mandarina 10, 8° B, 41006 **Sevilla**
Tel: 95-452 1718
responsable Francisco Cornejo Vega
Puppeteers: 2 permanent *Perfs:* 50 *Prods:* 1 *Type:* string, rod and 'sobre peana' (ancient Andalusian technique)
Touring: Spain, international and national festivals

Sinsalabim
c/ Guajaraz 12, 45007 **Toledo**
Tel: 925-232 991
director Vicente Redondo
Puppeteers: 2 *Perfs:* 60 *Prods:* 3 *Type:* various types including hand, marionettes, childrens' events and magic *Venues:* regional cultural centres 120-500 *Touring:* Spain *Comments:* organise workshops for children

Sol Y Tierra
c/ Mayor 9, 28170 **Valdepielagos (Madrid)**
Tel: 91-841 6045/608-024 510 Fax: 91-841 6129
Internet: www.sinix.net/paginas/solytierra
E-Mail: solytierra@sinix.net
contact María José de la Rosa, Victor Torre
Puppeteers: 2 *Perfs:* 100 *Prods:* 1 *Type:* mixed technique between rod and bunraku *Venues:* Sala Pradillo (Madrid) 150, centro cultural de la villa (Madrid) 280
Touring: Spain *Comments:* themes of the plays relate to basic life values (peace, solidarity, ecology consumption, respect); also organise cooperative workshops with public interaction;

Bambalina Titelles
Cabillers, 3-Baix, 46003 **Valencia**
Tel: 96-391 1373/3989 Fax: 96-391 1373
E-Mail: bambalina@tecnovia.com
director Josep Policarpo
Puppeteers: 4-5 *Perfs:* 75-80 *Prods:* 2 + 3 *Type:* Bunraku, actors/puppets, children's and adults puppetry *Touring:* Germany, USA, Canada, Venezuela

Edu Borja, Teatre de Marionetes
c/ Mistral 71, Puerta 21, 46020 **Valencia**
Tel: 96-361 9406
contact Edu Borja
Puppeteers: 1 *Perfs:* 30 *Prods:* 2 (1 new) *Type:* kurumaningyio, objects, string *Touring:* Spain, Europe

NAIP
c/ Torras i Bages 10, 08500 **Vic (Barcelona)**
Tel: 93-886 0181 Fax: 93-886 0181
responsable Manel Ricart
Puppeteers: 4 *Perfs:* 50 *Prods:* 5 *Type:* marionettes, glove, object theatre, gigantic puppets *Touring:* Spain, Andorra
Comments: theatre for children, family and schools; organiser and artistic direction of the First International Puppetry Festival of Vic (Barcelona)

Compañía Arbolé
c/ Francisco Ferrer 7, 50015 **Zaragoza**
Tel: 976-734 466/629 622 687 (mobile) Fax: 976-734 466
E-Mail: arbole@ctv.es
dir Jose Ignacio Juarez Montolio; prod Esteban Villarocha
Puppeteers: 5 *Perfs:* 350 *Type:* traditional glove puppetry for children and adults *Venues:* Teatro de Marionetas Arbolé 140 *Touring:* Spain, South America, Europe
Comments: home company of Teatro Arbolé; also runs a publishing company for texts about puppetry called Titirilibros; see also Venues and Publications

Teatro de Medianoche
Lasala Valdés 21-23 bajo E, 50006 **Zaragoza**
Tel: 976-279 496
contact Domingo Castillo
Puppeteers: 3 *Perfs:* 50 *Prods:* 3 (2 new) *Type:* shadow, combination (string, rod, bunraku etc.) *Touring:* Spain
Comments: provide an educational programme in schools (shadow theatre)

SWEDEN (+46)

Picknickteatern
Högdalens Dockteater, Box 121, 124 21 **Bandhagen**
Tel: 8-647 6148
designer Margareta Lindgren; writer Karl-Erik Lindgren
Puppeteers: 2 *Perfs:* 120 *Prods:* 1 *Type:* traditional Kaspertheatre (Punch and Judy), modern *Venues:* capacity 60 *Comments:* performances mainly for children; organise seminars etc. venue used by other puppet groups

Dockteatern Sesam
Box 4177, 400 40 **Göteborg**
Tel: 31-248 023/705-485 639 (mobile)
Fax: 31-241 136
Internet: home.swipnet.se/sesam
E-Mail: sesam@swipnet.se
director Mansour. H. Shahpar;
artistic director Nasrin Barati
Puppeteers: 5 *Perfs:* 200 *Prods:* 2
Type: mainly modern shadow, but also rod, hand, marionette and bunrako *Venues:* permanent theatre house 90 *Touring:* Scandinavia, Germany, Russia, East Europe, Brazil *Comments:* performances for all age groups; original live accompaniment

Wasa Marionette Opera
Gamla Björlandav. 37, 417 20 **Göteborg**
Tel: 31-239 443
Fax: 31-239 443
E-Mail: gabriel.bania@telia.com
director Gabriel Bania; music director Mark Tatlow
Puppeteers: 6 *Perfs:* 10
Type: 17th and 18th century marionette opera, performed in a copy of a period puppet theatre, with copies of 18th century puppets *Touring:* Sweden, Europe

Raja-Teatern
Box 285, 871 26 **Härnösand**
Tel: 611-24020
Fax: 611-24020
Internet: home6.swipnet.se/~w-61995
E-Mail: info@raja.y.se
producer Lars Svedberg; puppet-maker Jonna Grimstoft; technical producer Anders Elfrén; music Stefan Nyberg; scenograf Ylva Varik; dir Eva Bygren
Puppeteers: 4 *Perfs:* 150 *Prods:* 2
Type: puppets, music and real actors *Touring:* Sweden, international *Comments:* performances for children and families, performances for the deaf

Puppet Theatre Workshop
Dockteater Verkstan
Prästavägen 7, 283 42 **Osby**
Tel: 479-13839/70-592 6648 (mobile)
Fax: 479-13839
artistic directors Cecilia Billing, Anders Lindholm
Puppeteers: 2 *Perfs:* 130 *Prods:* 4 (1 new)
Type: bunraku, marionettes, rod, glove, shadow, object theatre *Venues:* libraries, schools, theatres etc. *Touring:* national, international *Comments:* touring company; also puppet-makers

Urban Wahlstedt
Garnuddsvägen 10, 144 62 **Rönninge**
Tel: 8-5325 7131
contact Urban Wahlstedt
Type: educational puppetry; marionette models of dinosaurs, insects, birds; Javanese shadowplay 'wayang kulit', Sundanese rod puppetry 'wayang golek'

Dockteatern Långa Näsan
Stockholms Stadsteater, Box 164 12, 103 27 **Stockholm**
Tel: 8-5062 0223
Fax: 8-5062 0101
Internet: www.stadsteatern.stockholm.se
E-Mail: langanasan@stadsteatern.stockholm.se
artistic director Inger Jalmert-Moritz; public relations and group sales Lena Hellström; stage manager and lighting design Tomas Florhed; stage construction and crew Kurre Smedberg
Puppeteers: 6 *Perfs:* 160 *Prods:* 2
Type: marionettes and shadow play; also use a mixed format, combining hand and rod-mounted puppets, masked puppeteers and actors *Venues:* capacity 70
Comments: primarily aimed at children, but also perform for adults

Marionetteatern Sweden
Brunnsgatan 6, 111 38 **Stockholm**
Tel: 8-411 7112
Fax: 8-211 015
E-Mail: marionetteatern@stockholm.mail.telia.com
director Helena Alvarez; producer, administrator Carolina Fransson; public relations, info, producer Eva Kassander; museum exchange Elisabeth Beijer, Michael Meschke
Puppeteers: 3 *Perfs:* 200-300 *Prods:* 1-2
Type: all types, traditional, contemporary
Touring: world-wide *Comments:* Sweden's first professional puppet-theatre; runs 'Marionettmuseum' with one of Europes finest collections of Asian and contemporary puppets; occasionally perform in different languages

SWITZERLAND (+41)

Théâtre Antonin Artaud
Teatro San Materno, CP 566, 6612 **Ascona**
Tel: 91-791 8566 Fax: 91-791 8566
director Michel Poletti
Puppeteers: 3 *Perfs:* 60 *Prods:* 2 *Type:* all types, combined art forms (puppetry, dance, music) *Venues:* Teatro San Materno 150 *Touring:* France, Italy, Switzerland
Comments: see also Festivals (Festival Internazionalle delle Marionette

Basler Marionetten-Theater
Münsterplatz 8, 4051 **Basel**
Tel: 61-261 0612 Fax: 61-261 0655
dirs Wolfgang Burn, Marianne Marx; Sekr. Verena Kempf
Puppeteers: 25-30 *Perfs:* 100 *Prods:* 6 *Type:* all types except shadow *Venues:* home capacity 140
Touring: Switzerland

Berner Puppen Theater – Puppenbühne Demeng/Wirth
Postfach 652, 3000 **Bern** 8
Tel: 31-311 9585 Fax: 31-311 8849
Leitung Monika Demenga, Hans Wirth;
Sekretariat Regula Büsser
Puppeteers: 3 *Perfs:* 120 *Prods:* 10 *Type:* all types except string puppets *Venues:* cap 100 *Comments:* rehearsal space Tel: 31-351 0909 Fax 31-351 0950

Marionnettes de Genève
3 rue Rodo, CP 217, 1211 **Genève** 4
Tel: 41-84770
Fax: 41-84771
Internet: www.regart.ch/marionnettes
E-Mail: marionnettes@bluewin.ch
direction John Lewandowski; admin Markanda Imhof
Perfs: 180 *Prods:* 6-9 *Type:* string and other techniques
Venues: hall capacity 200 *Comments:* repertory theatre which invites companies to perform

Puppentheater Bleisch
Oberwilerstr. 6, 8444 **Henggart**
Tel: 52-316 1282
Fax: 52-316 1282
directors Ursula & Hans-Peter Bleisch
Puppeteers: 2 *Perfs:* 150 *Prods:* 8
Type: string, stick, hand puppets, mix puppetry and acting *Touring:* Switzerland, Germany, Austria

Das Theater-Pack
Hintere Bahnstr. 11, 5742 **Kölliken**
Tel: 62-723 1766
Fax: 62-723 1766
Internet: www.echo.ch/-xioux/theater-pack.html
Leiter Hansueli Trüb
Puppeteers: 7 *Perfs:* 50 *Prods:* 3 *Type:* shadow, rods, mechanical, free puppetry figure forms, drama, opera
Touring: Switzerland, Europe

Marionnettes de la Rose des Vents
Av. de Morges 155, 1004 **Lausanne**
Tel: 21-624 8570
Fax: 21-624 5477
E-Mail: brunnersd@bluewin.ch
director Daniel Brunner
Puppeteers: 6 *Perfs:* 60-80 *Prods:* 3 *Type:* shows for children, rod and string puppets + actors *Venues:* L'Aula du Collége des Bergières 400
Touring: Francophone Europe

Théâtre Globule
153 Av. de Morges, 1004 **Lausanne**
Tel: 21-624 5471
Fax: 21-624 5477
Internet: www.arlequin.ch/globule
E-Mail: mergren@bluewin.ch
directors Eric Mérinat, Isabelle Grenier
Puppeteers: 2 *Perfs:* 60 *Prods:* 1 *Type:* contemporary
Venues: capacity 180 to 400 *Touring:* Switzerland
Comments: touring company; performances for children and adults; specialise in paper puppets

Figurentheater Margrit Gysin
Wetterkreuz 3, 4410 **Liestal**
Tel: 61-921 5679
Fax: 61-921 5679
Leiterin Margrit Gysin (Ein-Frau-Theater)
Puppeteers: 1 *Perfs:* 200 *Prods:* 5 *Type:* experimental
Venues: various small theatres *Touring:* mainly Switzerland, Germany, worldwide *Comments:* Agents: Theateragentur, Barbara Ott, Rosenstrasse 14, 8400 Winterthur, Tel/Fax: 52-212 2077

Teatro dei Fauni
Muro della Rossa 26, 6600 **Locarno**
Tel: 91-751 1151
Fax: 91-751 1151
Internet: www.magnet.ch/Teatro_Fauni
E-Mail: pam@sma.ch
director Santuzza Oberholzer
Puppeteers: varies *Perfs:* 80 *Prods:* 3-4
Type: various types, combined art forms *Touring:* Switzerland, Italy, Germany, international festivals
Comments: organise mask, puppetry, Chinese shadow theatre and educational courses

Théâtre de la Poudrière
Quai Godet 18, 2000 **Neuchâtel**
Tel: 32-724 6519 Fax: 32-724 6517
director Yves Baudin;
administratrice Corinne Grandjean
Puppeteers: 3 *Perfs:* varies *Prods:* 1/2 years *Type:* all types
Venues: capacity 120 *Touring:* Switzerland, Belgium, France, Germany *Comments:* see also Festivals and Venues

Looslis Puppentheater/ Buccini Magic
Bubikstrasse 2, 8626 **Ottikon**
Tel: 1-935 4562 Fax: 1-975 2738
E-Mail: tolo@bluewin.ch
directors Trudi, Peter, Tobias und Lois Loosli
Puppeteers: 4 *Perfs:* 150 *Prods:* 7 *Type:* string, hand, mixed art forms, magic show *Venues:* cap. up to 300
Touring: Switzerland, Austria, Germany

Figurentheater VAGABU
Ob. Wenkenhofstr. 29, 4125 **Riehen**
Tel: 61-601 4113 Fax: 61-601 4131
director Christian Schuppli
Puppeteers: 1-7 *Perfs:* 80 *Prods:* 4 *Type:* modern, masks, various types *Touring:* national, international *Comments:* touring company, own rehearsal space and workshop

Tösstaler-Marionetten
Neschwilerstr. 43, 8486 **Rikon**
Tel: 52-383 2494 Fax: 52-383 3768
Leiter Werner Bühlmann
Puppeteers: 4 *Perfs:* 120-140 *Prods:* 8 *Type:* all types, combining modern and traditional puppetry forms
Touring: German speaking countries *Comments:* organise courses, performances for children and adults (open and closed performances)

Fährbetrieb
Kalabinth 11, 9042 **Speicher**
Tel: 71-344 1171 Fax: 71-344 1171
Leiters Kurt Fröhlich, Sylvia Peter
Puppeteers: 2 *Type:* shadow, traditional and experimental puppetry *Touring:* Switzerland, abroad
Comments: organise puppetry courses

St. Galler Puppentheater
Postfach, 9004 **St Gallen**
Tel: 71-223 1247/222 6060
Fax: 71-223 1247
director Tobias Ryser
Puppeteers: 16 *Perfs:* 120-140 *Prods:* 3 *Type:* traditional, modern, combined art forms *Venues:* home capacity 162
Touring: Germany speaking Switzerland

Pannalal's Puppets
61 route de Drize, 1234 **Vessy**
Tel: 22-300 0004
Fax: 22-300 0004
directors Tina und Michel Perret-Gentil
Puppeteers: 2 *Perfs:* 80 *Prods:* 1 *Type:* all types *Venues:* touring company *Touring:* Italy, Romania, Bulgaria, Germany, Austria, Switzerland

Black Theatre Zurich 'Black & Light'
Schwarzes Theater Zürich
Rigiweg 6, 8604 **Volketswil**
Tel: 1-945 5762
director Jiri Prochazka
Puppeteers: 8 *Perfs:* 60-70 *Prods:* 2-3 *Type:* string puppets, black theater, mask, shadow *Venues:* various venues 200 to 1200 *Touring:* Germany, Austria, Italy, Luxembourg, Switzerland

Winterthurer Marionettentheater
Waaghaus, Marktgasse 25, 8400 **Winterthur**
Tel: 52-212 1496 Fax: 52-212 8312
directors Ursula Bienz (tel: 52-212 8335)
Puppeteers: 5-8 *Perfs:* 70-100 *Prods:* 18 *Type:* traditional
Venues: cap 90 to 120 *Comments:* theatre is used by local and foreign ensembles on tour in Switzerland

Zürcher Puppen Theater
Krebsgasse 10, Postfach 23, 8024 **Zürich**
Tel: 1-252 9424 (theatre)/261 0207 (administration)
Fax: 1-261 0723
Internet: www.kulturinfo.ch/Theaterpuppentheater
E-Mail: zpt@bluewin.ch
director Ursula Pfister; administration Susan Pfammatter; sets and costumes Marianne Hollenstein
Puppeteers: 4-5 *Perfs:* 260 (ca 200 guest performances, ca 30 different productions of guest performances, ca 30 own-producations of Zürcher Puppen Theater) *Prods:* 1 *Type:* all types *Venues:* Zürcher Puppentheater 150
Touring: national

TURKEY (+90)

Hayali Torun Çelebi
Bahcelieveler 11, Sokak No. 41/5, 06490 **Ankara**
Tel: 312-223 0494/285 3030 Fax: 312-285 7333/213 3419
director Tuncay Tanboga
Puppeteers: 3 *Perfs:* 900 *Type:* traditional shadow and hand puppets *Venues:* capacity 300 *Touring:* 15 cities in Turkey, France, Germany, USA, Italy, Spain, Belgium, Greece, Japan, India, Finland, Netherlands, Uzbekistan, Taiwan

Theatre Tempo
Tiyatro Tempo
Büklüm Sokak, 105/A, Kavaklidere, 06700 **Ankara**
Tel: 312-426 7293 Fax: 312-426 7293
director Haluk Yüce; artistic direction Emine Kaygun, Aylin Özyatan, Erkan Bektas, Savas Bayram
Puppeteers: 4 *Perfs:* 200 *Prods:* 2 *Type:* traditional Turkish shadow puppetry, various techniques combined
Venues: capacity 200 *Touring:* Europe (Germany, Belgium, Italy, Finland, France, Spain) India, Canada, USA, Pakistan

Osman Ubuz
Kücükparmakkapi Sokak 44/6, **Beyoglu (Istanbul)**
Tel: 212-251 9737
director Osman Ubuz; artistic direction Tayfun Ubuz, Erban Ubuz
Puppeteers: 2 *Perfs:* 50 *Type:* hand and string puppets

Bursa Karagöz Theatre
Kapaliçarsi, Eski Aynaliçarsi içi N° 12, 16020 **Bursa**
Tel: 224-221 8727 Fax: 224-220 5350
director Sinasi Çelikkol; puppeteers Aysel Çelikkol, Ugur Çelikkol, Ibrahim Koca
Puppeteers: 3 *Perfs:* 100 *Type:* traditional shadow puppetry *Touring:* Belaurs, Greece, Finland

Art Centre of Müjdat Gezen
Müjdat Gezen Sanat Merkezi
Ziverbey Kayisdagi Caddesi N° 48, Kadiköy, **Istanbul**
Tel: 216-346 5109/348 8072
Fax: 216-348 8074
director Müjdat Gezen
Type: theatre, shadow, music *Touring:* plans: 30 cities in Turkey; Australia, Japan, USA, Germany, France, Italy, Spain

Cengiz ÖZEK
Akdeniz Cad. 38/4, Fatih, **Istanbul**
Tel: 212-631 5953 Fax: 212-246 3539
director Cengiz Özek
Perfs: 100 *Type:* traditional shadow puppetry *Touring:* Europe

Hayali Safderi Puppet Theatre
Hayali Safderi Golge Tiyatrosu
Marmara Cad 22/6, Daire 15, Senesenevler, Erenköy, 81090 **Istanbul**
Tel: 216-372 5420
director Metin Özlen
Puppeteers: 1 *Perfs:* 50 *Prods:* 3 *Type:* traditional shadow puppetry *Venues:* capacity 200 *Touring:* Turkey, England, USA, Japan, France, Germany, Belarus, Greece

Ihsan Dizdar Traditional Theatre Group
ihsan Dizdar Geleneksel Tiyatro Grubu
Ihsaniye Iskelesi Sokak 35/1, Üsküdar, **Istanbul**
Tel: 216-334 3452
director Ihsan Dizdar
Puppeteers: 2 *Perfs:* 100 *Prods:* 4 *Type:* traditional shadow puppetry, hand and string puppets *Venues:* capacity 200
Touring: 23 cities in Turkey

Istanbul Puppet Theatre
Istanbul Kukla Tiyatrosu
P.K. 46, Üsküdar, **Istanbul**
Tel: 216-323 1549
director Ünver Oral
Puppeteers: 2 *Perfs:* 60 *Prods:* 1 *Type:* tradtitional and modern Turkish shadow puppetry and hand puppets
Venues: cap 150 *Touring:* Turkey, Europe, Croatia, Iran

Orhan Kurt Karagöz-Puppet Theatre
Orhan Kurt Karagöz-Kukla Tiyatrosu
Mete Cad., Simitas Bloklari Blok 30/A D: 403, Merter, 34010 **Istanbul**
Tel: 212-556 1113 Fax: 212-556 1113
director Orhan Kurt
Puppeteers: 2 *Perfs:* 100 *Type:* traditional Turkish shadow puppetry *Venues:* capacity 200 *Touring:* 10 cities in Turkey, abroad-Tunisia, Germany, Italy, Austria, France, Greece, Romania

Tacettin Diker Karagöz-Puppet Theatre
Tacettin Diker Karagöz-Kukla Tiyatrosu
Halic Cad. 26/3, Fatih, 34260 **Istanbul**
Tel: 212-525 4410
director Tacettin Diker; puppeteers Selahattin Erener, M. Güneri Acar
Puppeteers: 2 *Perfs:* 150 *Type:* traditional shadow puppetry, string and hand puppets *Venues:* capacity 200
Touring: 10 cities in Turkey, Tunisia, Germany, Italy, Netherlands, Austria, France

Mehmet BAYCAN Karagöz-ibis Theatre
Mehmet Baycan Karagöz-ibis Tiyatrosu
Ege kent, 8847/1 Sokak, N° 2, Daire 3, Öykü Apt. Karsiyaka, **Izmir**
Tel: 232-329 7508
director Mehment Baycan
Type: taditional shadow and puppets

Golden Mask Teatre
Tiyatro Altin Maske
Mühürdar Cad. Haci Hüsam Sokak, N° 14/12, **Kadiköy (Istanbul)**

Tel: 216-336 9200
director Didar Semiramis Mutlukan
Puppeteers: 3 *Perfs:* 100 *Type:* hand puppets

Devlet Tiyatrosu – State Theatre Mustafa Mutlu
Dr. Besim Ömer, Cad. Adalararasi Sokak Yaprakli Apt. 4/16, **Keçiören (Ankara)**
Tel: 312-339 6547
contact Mustafa Mutlu
Perfs: 100 *Prods:* 2 *Type:* traditional and modern Turkish shadow puppets, hand puppets *Touring:* Turkey, Spain, Canada, Germany, Austria, Syria, Poland, France

Yeni Ankara Oyunculari
Turgutreis Mahallesi 428, Sokak N° 9, **Mersin**
Tel: 324-238 0963/326 6545
director Yasar Urasli
Puppeteers: 1 *Perfs:* 100
Type: traditional Turkish shadow puppetry

The Municipality of Ankara-Metropolitan Baskent Puppet Theatre
Ankara Buyuksehir Belediyesi Baskent Kukla Tiyatrosu
Büyüksehir Belediyesi Kültür Merzeki, Gençlik Parki, **Ulus (Ankara)**
Tel: 312-312 4025 Fax: 312-324 3858
dir Mehmet Tahir Ikiler; art dirs Oya Ikiler, Selim Basegmez
Puppeteers: 2 *Perfs:* 200 *Prods:* 5 *Type:* string *Venues:* cap 300 *Touring:* 20 cities in Turkey, Israel

Kültür Bakanligi Devlet Geleneksel Türk Tiyatrosu Toplulugu
The Traditional Theatre Community of State, Ministry of Culture
Mithatpasa Caddesi N° 18 Kat 5, 06420 **Yenisehir (Ankara)**
Tel: 312-431 5955/0320 Fax: 312-431 0297
director Mevlüt Özhan
Type: traditional theatre, shadow and puppet

UKRAINE (+380)

Cherkassy Puppet Theatre
vul.Lenina 4, 257000 **Cherkassy**
Tel: 472-457 049

Chernivtsi Puppet Theatre
vul. Mytna 22, 274000 **Chernivtsi**
Tel: 3722-26314

Dnipropetrovsk Puppet Theatre
vul. Moskovska 7, 320000 **Dnipropetrovsk**
Tel: 562-452 411

Donetsk Puppet Theatre
Prospect Ilitcha 18, 340003 **Donetsk**
Tel: 622-959 748

Ivano-Frankivsk Puppet Theatre
vul. Riadianska 10-A, 284000 **Ivano-Frankivsk**
Tel: 3422-23581

Kharkiv Puppet Theatre
Pl. Riadianskoyi Ukrayiny 24, 310057 **Kharkiv**
Tel: 572-225 232

Kherson Puppet Theatre
vul. 40-richchia Zhovtnia 8, 325013 **Kherson**
Tel: 5522-26361

Khmelnytskyi Puppet Theatre
vul Kirova 103, 280000 **Khmelnytskyi**
Tel: 3822-68093

Kyiv (Kiev) City Puppet Theatre
vul. Lunacharskoho 1-b, 252097 **Kiev (Kyiv)**
Tel: 44-517 4237

Kyiv (Kiev) State Puppet Theatre
vul. Sh. Rustaveli 13, 252023 **Kiev (Kyiv)**
Tel: 44-224 1125

Kirovohrad Puppet Theatre
vul. Libknechta 3-a, 316000 **Kirovohrad**
Tel: 5222-25172

Kryvi Rih Puppet Theatre
vul. Petrozavodska 5, 324000 **Kryvyi Rih**
Tel: 564-663 442

Luhansk Puppet Theatre
vul. 16-linia, 348016 **Luhansk**
Tel: 642-534 094

Volyn Puppet Theatre
vul. B. Khmelnytskoho 18, 263000 **Lutsk**
Tel: 3300-23163

Lviv Puppet Theatre
pl. Halytskoho 1, 290007 **Lviv**
Tel: 322-720 773

Odessa Puppet Theatre
vul. Pastera 62 , 270100 **Odessa**
Tel: 482-232 058

Poltava Puppet Theatre
vul. Pushkina 32, 314601 **Poltava**
Tel: 5322-79066

Rivne Puppet Theatre
vul. S. Petliury 15, 266000 **Rivne**
Tel: 3622-65684

Krymskyi Puppet Theatre
vul. Horkoho 9, 333000 **Simferopol**
Tel: 652-276 431

Ternopil Puppet Theatre
vul. Vatutina II, 282000 **Ternopil**
Tel: 3522-23196

Zakarpattia Puppet Theatre
Teatralna pl. 8, 294000 **Uzhhorod**
Tel: 3122-33049

Vinnytsia Puppet Theatre
vul. Tolstoho 6-a, 286018 **Vinnytsia**
Tel: 432-322 675

Zaporizzhia Puppet Theatre
vul. Hohola 60, 330063 **Zaporizzjia**
Tel: 612-642 364

Zhytomyr Puppet Theatre
vul. Plechanivska 7, 262000 **Zhytomyr**
Tel: 412-372 554

UNITED KINGDOM (+44)

International Purves Puppets, The
Biggar Puppet Theatre, Broughton Road, **Biggar (Scotland)** ML12 6HA
Tel: 1899-220 521 (administration Fax: 1899-220 750
Internet: www.puppets.freeserve.co.uk
E-Mail: purves@puppets.freeserve.co.uk
directors Jill and Ian Purves
Puppeteers: 3 or 4 per show *Perfs:* 150 *Prods:* 20 *Type:* all types of puppetry including very large-scale models, black-light show *Venues:* home capacity 100; also cap. up to 1500 when on tour *Touring:* UK and abroad *Comments:* venue address: Biggar Puppet Theatre, Broughton Road, Biggar, Lanarkshire, Scotland ML12 6HA, tel: 1899-220 631 (box office); offer multi-lingual performances

Major Mustard's Travelling Show
1 Carless Avenue, Harborne, **Birmingham** B17 9EG
Tel: 121-426 4329
E-Mail: MajorMustard@brum.com
director Mike Frost
Puppeteers: 1-2 *Perfs:* 200 *Prods:* 8 *Type:* glove, shadow *Venues:* community venues: schools, libraries, theatres, arts centres etc. *Touring:* Germany *Comments:* also TV work, commercials, etc.; puppetry shows 'Auf Deutsch' and also in English, suitable for various age ranges

Puppeteers' Company
PO Box 350, **Brighton** BN2 1TZ
Tel: 1273-687 183 (24hr) Fax: 87-0055 7853
Internet: www.puppco.demon.co.uk
E-Mail: admin@puppco.demon.co.uk
directors Peter Franklin, Steve Lee
Puppeteers: varies *Perfs:* 333+ annually *Type:* rods, marionettes, shadow *Venues:* arts festivals, theatres, cabaret *Touring:* UK, international *Comments:* TV appearances in 8 countries

Storybox Theatre
1 Bishops Road, Cleeve, **Bristol** BS49 4NQ
Tel: 1934-833 575 Fax: 1934-833 575
contact Tanya Landman, Rod Burnett
Puppeteers: 2 *Perfs:* 300 *Prods:* 1 *Type:* rod puppets *Touring:* national, international *Comments:* emphasis on visual; shows suitable for international audiences

Presto Puppet Theatre
Greenwood, 13 College Road, **Buxton** SK17 9DZ
Tel: 1298-77845
Fax: 1298-23946
general manager Nigel Lawton; artistic director Robin J Lawrence; production/technical manager John Baldock
Puppeteers: 3 *Perfs:* 340 *Prods:* 10 *Type:* puppets, large-scale theatre productions and adult marionette cabaret *Venues:* national touring houses, arts centres, educational venues, exhibition centres 300 to 1500 *Touring:* national *Comments:* cabaret, theatre in education; provides demonstrations of puppet making and manipulation

Pickleherring Theatre
6 Railbrook Court, Railway Street, **Crewe** CW2 7AD
Tel: 1270-257 973
artistic director Matthew Smith
Puppeteers: 2 *Perfs:* 100 annually *Prods:* 2 *Type:* puppets, mixed media *Venues:* arts centres, studio venues, festivals – up to 200 *Touring:* national *Comments:* commited to the promotion of new writing for puppet theatre and increasing the audience for puppet theatre;
funded by North West Arts Board, Crewe & Nantwich Borough Council

Edinburgh Puppet Company, The
81 Great Junction Street, Leith, **Edinburgh (Scotland)** EH6 5HZ
Tel: 131-554 8923 Fax: 131-554 1861
Internet: www.edinburgh-puppet.co.uk
E-Mail: puppet@ednet.co.uk
administrator Rick Conte; artistic directors Symon Macintyre, Kim Bergsagel
Puppeteers: 2-5 *Perfs:* 200 *Prods:* 2-3 *Type:* all types including mixed media, mask and mime *Venues:* small- and medium-scale *Touring:* Scotland, England, Ireland, Wales *Comments:* plans more joint productions and wants to continue with pageant work, creating large out-door spectacles; looking for partners to produce touring productions

No Strings Puppet Theatre
Archway House, Mansfield Road, **Edwinstowe** NG21 9HF
Tel: 1623-824 210/1629-582 063 (messages)
directors Alan Kirkpatrick, Sue Murray
Puppeteers: 2 *Perfs:* varies *Prods:* 2 *Type:* glove, rod puppets, giant & life size body puppets *Venues:* indoors and outdoors, small-scale venues *Touring:* national, international *Comments:* performances for all age groups ranging from children – adults; specialise in medieval fairs and other outdoor walk-about street events; flexible performers; workshops in puppet making and productions; schools programmes

Punchinello's Puppet Show
Punch's Oak, Cleobury Road, **Far Forest** DY14 9EB
Tel: 1299-266 634 Fax: 1299-266 561
Internet: www.punch-and-judy.com
E-Mail: glyn@punch-and-judy.com
contacts Glyn and Mary Edwards
Puppeteers: 2 *Perfs:* 250 *Prods:* 2 *Type:* glove, marionettes, giant body puppets
Venues: street performances, small theatres, fun fairs, but mainly festivals *Touring:* UK, worldwide *Comments:* specialise in traditional Punch & Judy

Parachute Theatre Company
Great Western House, 42 Portway, **Frome** BA11 1QR
Tel: 1373-465 510/467-668 009 (mobile)
creators/operators Nik Palmer, Lynne Porter
Puppeteers: 2 *Perfs:* 9 *Prods:* 3 (family show, late night cabaret, large-scale show *Type:* visual and musical, modern style puppetry of various types (large scale shows suitable for audiences of 5-6000)
Venues: theatres, festivals, community venues, schools etc. *Touring:* national, international *Comments:* 6 different performances for children and adults plus various workshops, workshop residence is a speciality; large-scale shows suitable for about 5000 spectators at festivals; perform without language

Ian Turbitt's Puppet Theatre
Parkfield Court, Flat H, 368 Langside Road, **Glasgow (Scotland)** G42 8XR
Tel: 141-423 5343
contact Ian Turbitt
Puppeteers: 1 *Prods:* 1 *Type:* hand, story-telling with puppets *Venues:* schools, small theatres, libraries, art galleries, historical properties, capacity 40 to 200
Touring: Scotland, England
Comments: has the rights to perform 'The Tales of Peter Rabbit'/Jemima Puddle-Duck

Scottish Mask and Puppet Theatre Centre
8-10 Balcarres Avenue, Kelvindale,
Glasgow (Scotland) G12 0QF
Tel: 141-339 6185 Fax: 141-357 4484
Internet: www.scot-art.org/smpc
E-Mail: sm010@post.almac.co.uk
director Malcolm Knight; administrator Lisa Daifuku; film & special effects Grant Mason; development officer John Clarke
Venues: receiving venue: saturday shows by visiting companies *Comments:* the centre houses an 80 seat studio theatre, cafe, shop, production design workshops, and office complex with reference library; it specialises in education, cultural animation projects, and service to professional puppeteers and film and TV; creative puppeteer documentation centre; promotes puppet & mask companies, exhibitions, conferences, master courses, international residences, and works; also has puppet and mask museum; permanet exhibition of puppets from around the world – The Magical World of Puppets, also The Miles Lee Collection; setting up the Anima Project, an international visitors centre comprising of theatre, museum and documentation centre, due to have opened at end of October 1999; see also National Organisations

Three Headed Man, The
c/o Andy Cunningham, Flat 8, 9 Brunswick Terrace, **Hove** BN3 1HL
Tel: 1273-326 684
Fax: 1273-326 684
contact Andy Cunningham
Puppeteers: 1 *Type:* bizzare perambulating act
Venues: outdoor venues, festivals
Comments: 'the wandering wonder' – walking and talking three-headed performer working indoors and outdoors, events, festivals

Faulty Optic Theatre of Animation
12 Savile Road, Lindley, **Huddersfield** HD3 3DH
Tel: 1484-536 027
Fax: 1484-536 027
E-Mail: faulty.optic@pop3.poptel.org.uk
directors Liz Walker, Gavin Glover
Puppeteers: 2-3 *Perfs:* 75-100 *Prods:* 3 (1 new) *Type:* mechanical theatre of the absurd using one-quarter- to three-quarter-life-size non-traditional figures, mutated toys, animated set and no words for an adult rather than a children's audience *Venues:* Blackbox, studio-theatres, art-centres, small theatres capacity 250 *Touring:* UK, Europe *Comments:* for performances in France contact: Yves Vasseur, 'Le Manège', Rue de la Croix, Maubeuge, France, Tel: +33 327-651 500 Fax: +33 327-659 380

Cap and Bells
13 Dartmouth Park Road, **London** NW5 1SU
Tel: 20-7267 8839
director Violet Philpott
Puppeteers: 2-4 *Prods:* 1 *Type:* glove, rod, shadow puppets, plus live mime & mask artist *Venues:* schools, libraries, theatres etc. capacity up to 400 *Comments:* TV appearances; also story telling for children and separate programmes for adults

Christopher Leith
25a Randolph Crescent, **London** W9 1DP
Tel: 20-7289 9653 Fax: 20-7289 9653
contact Christopher Leith
Puppeteers: varies *Perfs:* 80+ *Type:* all types – specialising in large marionettes *Venues:* art centres, theatres, churches capacity up to 500 *Touring:* national & international *Comments:* also teaches puppetry across the UK

Dragonfly Mime Co.
405 Kings Road, Chelsea, **London** SW10 0BB
Tel: 20-7739 1899
Fax: 20-7739 1999
E-Mail: dragonflymime@hotmail.com
tour manager Alexander Thompson
Puppeteers: 2 *Perfs:* 150 *Prods:* 3 *Type:* Balinese masks, traditional Chinese puppetry, shadow puppetry, shadow puppets, poly-mime, physical theatre *Touring:* Mexico, New Zealand *Comments:* return to UK for summer season; see also Drama

Improbable Theatre
c/o Nick Sweeting, Performing Arts Management, Battersea Arts Centre, Lavender Hill, **London** SW11 5TF
Tel: 20-7978 4200
Fax: 20-7978 5200
E-Mail: nsweeting@dial.pipex.com
artistic directors Julian Crouch, Phelim McDermott, Lee Simpson; producer Nick Sweeting; administrator Ghislaine Granger

Indefinite Articles
32 Henley Prior, Collier Street, **London** N1 9JU
Tel: 20-7278 4709
E-Mail: indart@lineone.net
contact Steve Tiplady
Puppeteers: 2 + musicians *Perfs:* 150 *Prods:* 1 *Type:* objects *Venues:* arts centres, schools, theatres *Touring:* UK, Slovenia, Hungary, France, USA

Little Angel Theatre
14 Dagmar Passage, Cross Street, **London** N1 2DN
Tel: 20-7226 1787 (box office)/7359 8581 (administration) Fax: 20-7359 7565
theatre producer Lorretta Howels; director Lyndie Wright; administrator Julia Bullock
Puppeteers: up to 15 *Perfs:* 400-450 *Prods:* 12 (2 new) *Type:* all types *Venues:* small- and medium-scale venues *Touring:* national, Europe *Comments:* courses held throughout the year; developing experimental methods for devising puppetry work for adult audiences; regular workshop with people with disabilities

Oily Cart
Smallwood School Annexe, Smallwood Road, **London** SW17 0TW
Tel: 20-8672 6329
Fax: 20-8672 0792
Internet: www.users.globalnet.co.uk/~oilycart
E-Mail: oilycart@premier.co.uk
general manager Joanna Ridout; art dir Tim Webb
Prods: 2 *Type:* all types, live music
Venues: community venues, nurseries, schools, libraries, small-scale theatres, festivals *Touring:* national and Republic of Ireland *Comments:* 'all sorts of shows for all sorts of kids' especially the very young and those with learning difficulties; see also Drama

Playboard Puppet Theatre
94 Ockendon Road, **London** N1 3NW
Tel: 20-7254 0416
Fax: 20-7254 0416
administrator/artistic director Ian Allen
Puppeteers: 1-12 according to production *Perfs:* 30+ *Prods:* 1-2 *Type:* hand puppets, rod puppets (with voices by actors) *Venues:* range from council halls – theatres cap. up to 800 *Touring:* national
Comments: also TV work

Professor Alexander's Punch & Judy Show
59 Wilton Way, **London** E8 1BG
Tel: 20-7254 0416 Fax: 20-7254 0416
proprietor John Alexander
Puppeteers: 1 *Perfs:* 200 *Type:* Punch and Judy *Venues:* small-scale theatres, street theatre, shopping malls *Touring:* national, international

Puppet Centre Trust
BAC, Lavender Hill, **London** SW11 5TN
Tel: 20-7228 5335 Fax: 20-7228 8863
E-Mail: pct@puppetcentre.demon.co.uk
director Loretta Howells; general admin Allyson Kirk
Comments: touring exhibitions, education liaison; see also National Organisations

Tim and Amanda Webb's Puppets
14 Third Avenue, **London** W3 7RT
Tel: 20-8749 1732 Fax: 20-8749 1732
Internet: www.premier.co.uk/webby
E-Mail: webby@premier.co.uk
Type: traditional Punch & Judy *Venues:* large- and small-scale, indoors & outdoors *Touring:* national, international

Doo Cot
4 Manley Units, 31 Range Road, **Manchester** M16 8FS
Tel: 161-232 0160 Fax: 161-232 0160
E-Mail: doocot@cssytems.net
co-artistic directors Nenagh Watson, Rachael Field
Puppeteers: 1 puppeteer & 1 on stage multi-media performer *Perfs:* 40 *Prods:* 3 (incl. 1 major tour & various site-specific) *Type:* computer animation, junkyard puppets from urban Manchester, shadow *Venues:* studio theatre 300, art galleries, site specific *Touring:* national, international *Comments:* offer workshops in performance, making skills and technology for youth and adults; specialise in working with adults with learning disabilities

Norwich Puppet Theatre
St James, Whitefriars, **Norwich** NR3 1TN
Tel: 1603-615 564 Fax: 1603-617 578
E-Mail: norpuppet@hotmail.com
general manager Ian Woods; artistic director Luis Boy; administrator June Hutton
Puppeteers: 2-8 *Perfs:* 500 *Prods:* 5 + 1 new *Type:* all types *Venues:* Norwich Puppet Theatre auditorium 198, studio 50; appearances include W. York Playhouse, Leicester Haymarket *Touring:* schools, festivals and theatres, national, international

Stephen Mottram's Animata
31 New High Street, Headington, **Oxford** OX3 7AJ
Tel: 1865-742 587
Fax: 1865-741 550
director Stephen Mottram; administrator Gill Jaggers
Puppeteers: 2 *Perfs:* 70-100 *Prods:* 2 *Type:* specially composed music by leading modern composers accompanying expertly manipulated puppet figures *Venues:* capacity 400 *Touring:* international *Comments:* performances for adults

Professor Dan Bishop's Traditional Punch & Judy
1 Bollowal Place, St. Just, **Penzance** TR19 7NE
Tel: 1736-788 308 Fax: 1736-788 353
contact Prof. Dan Bishop
Puppeteers: 2 *Perfs:* 300-400 *Type:* traditional glove puppetry *Venues:* street, theatres, schools *Touring:* France, Belgium *Comments:* Mr Punch's tragical comedy or comical tragedy presented in streets & theatres and at more than 30 international festivals worlwide; performed in eleven languages: French, Italian, Portuguese, Spanish, Japanese, Slovak, Slovene, Hungarian, Arabic, Polish, Russian; simple + compact to present

Horse & Bamboo Theatre
679 Bacup Road, Waterfoot, **Rossendale** BB4 7HB
Tel: 1706-220 241 Fax: 1706-831 166
Internet:
www.compnet.co.uk/bushome/~hobo/horse.htm
E-Mail: horse.bamboo@zen.co.uk
artistic director Bob Frith;
administrative director Simon Ruding
Puppeteers: 6-10, inc. musicians *Perfs:* 100 *Prods:* 2 *Type:* visual theatre and related activities; mixture of masked performers theatre, puppetry and live music *Venues:* from small village halls to small/mid scale touring venues, festivals and out door venues *Touring:* UK, Eire, Europe, Eastern Europe *Comments:* new outdoor show for Summer 2000/2001 planned as international collaboration with Nigerian playwright Sam Ukala; company base the centre for community and outreach work in E. Lancs. region; see also Drama

Freehand Theatre
1 Reynard Villas, Mayfield Grove, Baildon, **Shipley** BD17 6DY
Tel: 1274-585 277 Fax: 1274-585 277
E-Mail: freehandtheatre@pop3.poptel.org.uk
directors Lizzie Allen, Simon Hatfield
Puppeteers: 2 *Perfs:* 140 annually *Prods:* 2 (1 new) *Type:* rod, glove *Venues:* arts centres, festivals, schools, community centres max capacity 150 *Comments:* performances mainly for children

Professor John Styles, FRSA, MIMC
42 Christchurch Road, **Sidcup** DA15 7HQ
Tel: 20-8300 3579 Fax: 20-8300 3579
contact John Styles
Type: Punch & Judy *Comments:* see also Services

Hand-to-Mouth Theatre
51 Arnold Road, **Southampton** SO17 1TF
Tel: 1703-555 392 Fax: 1703-555 392
directors Martin Bridle, Su Eaton
Perfs: 200 *Type:* traditional and modern styles suitable for outdoors and indoors *Venues:* capacity 250 *Touring:* Austria, Greece, USA, Slovakia *Comments:* international performances; regular performer at the National Theatre, London; non-verbal shows for festivals, suitable for mixed (adult & children) audiences

Clydebuilt Puppet Theatre
4 Skene Street, **Strathmiglo Sise (Scotland)** KY14 7QL
Tel: 1337-860 337
Fax: 1337-860 337
director Stephen Smart;
designer/puppeteer Lee McCalister
Puppeteers: 2 *Perfs:* 200 *Prods:* 1 *Type:* rod, shadow, body *Venues:* small-scale theatres, schools, village halls, max. capacity 300 *Touring:* UK *Comments:* firmly established as one of Scotland's leading puppet theatres; very adaptable touring company, who develop and expand puppetry through visual, dramatic & entertaining interpretations of classic stories and contemporary work; workshops available; managed by No Strings Attached Agency, Tel: 20-7690 7449

Green Ginger
32 The Norton, **Tenby (Wales)** SA70 8AB
Tel: 117-922 5599
Fax: 117-922 5599
E-Mail: greenginger@usa.net
director Terry Lee; artistic director Chris Pirie; technical director James Osborne
Puppeteers: 3 *Perfs:* 200 *Prods:* 5 *Type:* low-language/non-language productions for all ages, life-size bunraku figures, street work, cabaret *Venues:* Black Box, cap. up to 350 *Touring:* USA, Canada, Europe, Far East, Indian Ocean *Comments:* perform in 11 languages including French, English and Italian; also run workshops and masterclasses for children and adults; available for TV and film work; commissions for production, design and animation projects always considered; see also Drama

Jacolly Puppet Theatre
Kirkella Road, **Yelverton** PL20 6BB
Tel: 1822-852 346
E-Mail: puppets@jacolly.freeserve.co.uk
co-directors Jacqueline Ilett, Holly Griffin; administration Sarah Berry
Puppeteers: 2 *Perfs:* 200 *Prods:* 1 *Type:* hand, rod and shadow *Venues:* Dogworthy Shows 150, Astra Show 250 *Touring:* national, international; small-scale theatres (including festivals except outdoors) *Comments:* puppet workshops for all ages

YUGOSLAVIA (+381)

Due to the war in Kosovo we have been unable to update the following entries for Yugoslavia

Puppet Theatre Kekec
Scena lutaka Kekec
Skojevska 75, 11000 **Beograd**
Tel: 11-536 078
director Jovan Kovacev

Puppet Theatre
Pozoriste lutaka
Brace Taskovic 7, 18000 **Nis**
Tel: 18-53962
director Stevan Bosnjak

Puppet Theatre Fenix
Lutkarska scena Fenix
Takovsa 4/18, 18000 **Nis**
Tel: 18-48392
directors Miroslava-Mima Jankovic, Branislav-Bane Jankovic

Children's Theatre
Pionirsko pozoriste
Trg Ivana Milutinovica 66, 81000 **Podgorica**
Tel: 81-43115
director Vanja Popovic

Puppet Theatre Pinocchio
Pozoriste lutaka Pinokio
Karadordeva 9, 11080 **Zemun**
Tel: 11-691 715
director Zivomir Jokovic

FEIKE
last production of the dutch godfather of puppetry
feike boschma
and company on tour till december 2000
contact:
impresariaat wim visser
phone +31 20 6233 700
fax +31 20 6208 212
e-mail art@iwv.nl

All year round the Baxter offers a wide range of local & international drama, music, dance & comedy - for all audiences including:
for our senior citizens
MORNING MELODIES
Monthly Morning Melodies with tea and biscuits
for youngsters
BAXKIDZ
BAXTEENZ
BaxKidz Theatre Club for 6-12 year olds
and BaxTeenz Theatre Club for 13-16 year olds
as well as Children's Theatre Musicals - every school holiday.
ALSO
A wide variety of multi-media musical courses for scholars and teachers.
AND
Facilities for: Conferences • Business Functions • Trade Fairs • Exhibitions • Seminars
PLUS
Invest in the Performing Arts as a 'Friend of the Baxter'. Enjoy Discounted Tickets
• Preferential Booking • Annual Gala Dinner • Lucky Prize Draws - and much more!
BAXTER THEATRE CENTRE
For more details contact:
The Baxter Theatre Centre
PO Box 297, Rondebosch 7701
(021) 685 7880 FAX (021) 689 1880
e-mail bxtms@protem.uct.ac.za
www.baxter.co.za

Festivals

Festivals
The emphasis of this list is on major festivals or those distinguished for other reasons, e.g. new work. Folk festivals have generally been excluded, as have festivals that are primarily amateur in intent. Preference has been given to events that are arranged for a short period, rather than a season of concerts spread over several months and usually inaccurately described as a 'festival'. However, exceptions have been made, especially where such events have a long established or significant reputation. **Within country the festivals are ordered by city, and alphabetically within city.**

Festivals
Nous avons mis l'accent sur les festivals les plus importants ou sur ceux qui sont remarquables pour d'autres raisons par exemple ceux qui promulguent des œuvres contemporaines ou nouvelles. En général les festivals de folklore ont été exclus ainsi que des festivals d'amateurs. Nous avons accordé la préférence à des festivals de courte durée plutôt qu'à des séries de concerts qui durent quelques mois mais qui portent le nom de 'festival'. Pourtant nous avons fait des exceptions, notamment pour les festivals établis de longue date ou qui jouissent d'une réputation établie. **Pour chaque pays les festivals sont dans l'ordre des villes et par ordre alphabétique pour chacune d'elles.**

Festspiele
Im Mittelpunkt dieses Kapitels stehen die größeren und renommierteren Festspiele (z.B. Festspiele die sich mit Welturaufführungen, neuer Musik usw. befassen). Folkloreveranstaltungen sowie Laienfestspiele werden kaum genannt. Festspiele, die für einen kurzen Zeitraum stattfinden werden gegenüber Konzertreihen, die im Laufe einiger Monate stattfinden und dennoch als Festival bezeichnet werden, bevorzugt. Es gibt aber Ausnahmen, besonders wenn solche Festspiele jahrelang stattgefunden haben und einen besonderen Ruf haben. **Die Einträge sind innerhalb aller Staaten alphabetisch nach Stadt und innerhalb der Stadt alphabetisch nach Namen geordnet.**

Festivals
Per quanto riguarda i festival abbiamo incluso i maggiori festivals o quelli che si sono distinti per una ragione particolare (es. nuovi festivals con tematiche particolari o nuove). I festivals di musica, teatro e danza popolare sono stati in gran parte esclusi essendo per la maggior parte amatoriali. La preferenza é stata data ad eventi di breve durata, e non ad eventi che, anche se vengono definiti festivals, si svolgono per svariati mesi e avendo tutte le caratteristiche di serie di concerti. Ad ogni modo sono state fatte delle eccezioni per quei festivals con una lunga tradizione alle spalle o di fama rinomata. **Sono ordinati alfabeticamente all'interno delle varie cittá e seguono lo stesso criterio all'interno dei vari Paesi.**

Festivales
En esta sección se recopilan grandes festivales o aquellos destacados por otras razones particulares tales como nuevos trabajos, arte vanguardista etc. Los festivales de folk han sido omitidos como norma general debido a su caracter aficionado. Se ha dado preferencia a aquellos acontecimientos organizados para un corto periodo de tiempo en vez de a temporadas de conciertos con una duración de varios meses que son generalmente incorrectamente denominados festivales. Sin embargo se han hecho algunas excepciones en los casos en los que tales acontecimientos tienen gran arraigo o destacada reputación. **Dentro de cada país, los festivales están ordenados por ciudades alfabéticamente.**

Festivals (페스티발)
주요 페스티발 및 어떤 이유로 인해, 예를 들어 전혀 새로운 시도를 한다거나 해서, 성격이 독특한 페스티발 등에 중점을 두었다. 민속 페스티발과 일차적으로 아마추어들을 위한 페스티발은 제외되었다. 행사 기간이 여러 달이고 행사의 성격에 부정확하게 '페스티발'이라고 명명되는 계절 콘서트보다 짧은 기간 동안 거행되는 행사에 우선권을 부여했다. 그러나 전통 있고 명성이 높은 행사에는 예외가 적용되었다. **리스트는 국가별, 도시별, 그리고 다시 알파벳순으로 기재되었다.**

艺术节
本名单的注重点为主要的艺术节或因为其它原因而与众不同的活动（例如新的艺术作品）。一般来讲民间艺术节并不包括在内，因为这类艺术节的意图主要是业余的。我们的侧重点为在一短时间里安排的事件，而并非那些持续数月之久并通常不确切地被描述为"艺术节"的音乐会季节。然而也有例外，特别是那些已长期被确认的或声誉显赫的事件。**在每个国家里艺术节是按城市顺序来排列的，而在一城市里艺术节又是按字母顺序来排列的。**

フェスティバル
ここでは主に、規模が大きいフェスティバルとネットワーク等、他に特徴があるフェスティバルを掲載しました。フォークフェスティバルやアマチュア色が強いものは原則的に除外してあります。特別に歴史があったり、評価がきわめて高いものは例外として、「フェスティバル」という名称でも、何カ月にもわたってコンサートが続くような性質の催しは避け、短期間のフェスティバルを優先的に掲載しています。**リストは国、都市別で、都市内ではアルファベット順に記載されています。**

ALBANIA (+355)

Days of New Albanian Music, The
c/o Academy of Arts, **Tirana**
Tel: 42-62899
general director Prof Fatmir Hysi
Period/Frequency: May, annual *Arts types:* contemporary music (composition & performance)

Nikolla Zoraqi Music Festival
c/o Academy of Arts, **Tirana**
Tel: 42-50396
general director Prof Zana Shuteriqi
Period/Frequency: annual *Arts types:* contemporary music

Ton de Leeuw Music Festival
c/o Academy of Arts, **Tirana**
Tel: 42-43673
general director Aleksander Pefii
Period/Frequency: annual *Arts types:* contemporary music *Comments:* international contemporary music festival for young composers under 30 years

Vocal Music Festival, The
Rr Myslym Shyri, P. 12, Shkalla 5, Ap. 38, **Tirana**
Tel: 42-34557
general director Prof Kozma Lara
Period/Frequency: December, annual *Arts types:* traditional vocal music

ANDORRA (+376)

Temporada de Música i Dansa d'Andorra La Vella
Plaça del Poble s/n , **Andorra la Vella**
Tel: 8-22242/64058
Fax: 8-64449
director artístico Josep Mª Escribano
Period/Frequency: Nov-May, annual *Arts types:* classical music, ballet, contemporary dance *Venues:* Sala d'Actes Del Centre de Congressos i Exposicions 300 to 1200 *Second Address:* Centre de Congressos i Exposicions, Plaça del Poble, s/n Andorra La Vella *Comments:* Festival organised by 'Comú d'Andorra La Vella' in collaboration with private firms of Andorra

Festival Internacional de Jazz d'Andorra, Escaldes-Engordany
Passeig del Valire 9, **Escaldes-Engordany**
Tel: 8-90890/75 Fax: 8-90886
directora de cultura Ana García Ricart;
conseller de culture Lydia Magallón Font
Period/Frequency: July, annual *Arts types:* jazz *Venues:* La Carpa 1500 *Comments:* Festival organised by 'Comú d'Escaldes-Engordany'. Also organise a free street festival of jazz & 'Art and Jazz', art exhibitions in different venues around Escaldes-Engordany

Festival Internacional Narciso Yepes
Iniciativas Turísticas de Ordino,
c/ Nou Vial s/n, **Ordino**
Tel: 8-36963 Fax: 8-839 225
Internet: www.andorra.ad/comuns/ordino/
E-Mail: ito@andorra.ad
director artístico Gerard Claret
Period/Frequency: Sept-Oct, annual *Arts types:* classical music *Venues:* Auditori Nacional d'Andorra, Ordino 500, Esglesia Parroquial d'Ordino 200
Comments: includes Conciertos Matinales (Sunday concerts in the church); organised by Iniciatives Turistiques D'Ordino and Credit Andorra

Festival Internacional Narciso Yepes
Iniciatives Turístiques de Ordino, c/Nou Vial s/n, **Ordino**
Tel: 8-737 080 Fax: 8-839 225
Internet: www.andorra.ad/comuns/ordino/
E-Mail: Ito@andorra.ad
director artístico Gerard Claret
Period/Frequency: Sept-Oct, annual *Arts types:* classical music *Venues:* Auditori Nacional d'Andorra, Ordino 500, Esglesia Parroquial d'Ordino 200 *Comments:* included Conciertos Matinales (Sunday concerts in the church); organised by Iniciatives Turistiques D'Ordino and Credit Andorra, which form the Associació Festivals d'Ordino

ARMENIA (+374)

Yerevan 2000 International Music Festival
4-4 Azatoutian Street, 375037 **Yerevan**
Tel: 2-254 493/525 840/562 735
Fax: 2-151 431 (AT&T)
Internet: www.arminco.com/homepages/nab
E-Mail: nbart@arminco.com
Period/Frequency: Sept-Oct 2000

Yerevan International Music Festival
4-4 Azatoutian Street,
375037 **Yerevan**
Tel: 2-254 493/525 840/562 735
Fax: 2-151 431
Internet: www.arminco.com/homepages/nab
E-Mail: nbart@arminco.com
president Nika Babaian
Period/Frequency: Sept/Nov, biennial (2001)

AUSTRIA (+43)

Achenseer Musiktage
Achenseer Tourismus, Rathaus, 6215 **Achensee**
Tel: 5246-5300 Fax: 5246-5333
Internet: www.achensee.com
E-Mail: info@achensee.tirol.at
Obmann des Achenseer Tourismus Johannes Entner
Period/Frequency: first week in July, annual *Arts types:* classical and modern dance music *Venues:* Pfarrkirche Pertisau up to 500, Veranstaltungszentrum Maurach 500

Operettenfestspiele Bad Ischl
Kongress & Theaterhaus, Kurhausstrasse 8,
4820 **Bad Ischl**
Tel: 6132-23839 Fax: 6132-238 3939
Internet: www.operette.badischl.at
E-Mail: info@operette.badischl.at
Geschäftsführer Dr Martin C Turba;
Musikdirektor Walter Erla
Period/Frequency: July-Aug, annual *Arts types:* operettas (staged and concert version), orchestral concerts, chamber music *Venues:* Kongress & Theaterhaus Bad Ischl 850 *Comments:* 26 performances; 2 operettas

Badener Beethoventage
Kulturamt der Stadt Baden, Hauptplatz 1,
2500 **Baden bei Wien**
Tel: 2252-86800/231 Fax: 2252-86800/210
Internet: www.baden-bei-wien.at
E-Mail: kultur@baden-bei-wien.at
Kulturamtsleiterin Christine Kranl;
Sachbearbeiterin Brigitte Schwarz
Period/Frequency: Sept-Oct (annual) *Arts types:* music *Venues:* Stadttheater Baden, Kaisersaal Grand Hotel Sauerhof, Beethovenhaus, Badener Saal und Casineum im Congress Casino

Sommerarena Baden
Stadttheater Baden bei Wien, Theaterplatz 7,
2500 **Baden bei Wien**
Tel: 2252-48339/36/48547 Fax: 2252-483 3840
Verwaltungsdirektor Reg. Rat. Wilfried Frankmann;
Künstlerische Leitung Elisabeth Kales-Wallner
Period/Frequency: June-Sept, annual *Arts types:* operetta *Venues:* Sommerarena 657 *Comments:* 3 operettas yearly, 55 performances; The Sommerarena has a retractable glass roof; see also Opera, Dance, Drama, Orchestras & Choirs

Bregenz Festival
Bregenzer Festspiele GmbH, Platz der Wiener Symphoniker 1, 6900 **Bregenz**
Tel: 5574-407-0 Fax: 5574-407 407
Internet: www.bregenzerfestspiele.com
E-Mail: info@bregenzerfestspiele.com
Intendant Dr Alfred Wopmann; Kaufmännischer Direktor Dkfm. Franz Salzmann; Künstlerisches Betriebsbüro Axel Renner, Eva Kleinitz (personal assistant to Dr. Wopmann); Festspielpräsident Dipl.-Ing.Günter Rhomberg; Kommunikation Bernd Feldmann, Evelyn Gmeiner, Monika Walter
Period/Frequency: July-Aug, annual *Arts types:* opera, orchestra, chamber music, sacred music, dance, drama *Venues:* Seetribüne 6800, Festspielhaus 1750, Theater am Kornmarkt 550, Palast Hohenems 300, Freilufttheater Martinsplatz 400 *Second Address:* postal address: Postfach 311, 6901 Bregenz

Haydnfestspiele
Schloß Esterházy, 7000 **Eisenstadt**
Tel: 2682-61866 Fax: 2682-61805
Internet: www.haydnfestival.at
E-Mail: office@haydnfestival.at
Intendant Dr Walter Reicher
Period/Frequency: Sept, annual *Arts types:* orchestra, chamber music, recitals, oratoria, operas *Venues:* Schloß Esterházy: Hadynsaal 600, Empiresaal 140 *Comments:* also weekly concerts at Schloss Esterházy (May-Oct); one weekend will feature works of Liszt

Schloßspiele Kobersdorf
Schloß Esterházy, 7000 **Eisenstadt**
Tel: 2682-66211 Fax: 2682-66211-14
Internet: members.eunet.at/schlosskobersdorf
E-Mail: schlosskobersdorf@EUnet.at
Intendanz K. Schsp. Prof. Rudolf Buczolich;
Geschäftsführung Eva Gold-Pirch
Period/Frequency: mid July-mid Aug, annual *Arts types:* theatre, European comedy
Venues: Schloßhof, Schloß Kobersdorf

Seefestspiele Mörbisch
Schloß Esterházy, 7000 **Eisenstadt**
Tel: 2682-66210/1
Fax: 2682-662 1014
Internet: www.seefestspiele-moerbisch.at
E-Mail: tickets@seefestspiele-moebisch.at
Intendant Prof. Harald Serafin;
Geschäftsführer Dietmar Posteiner
Period/Frequency: July-Aug, annual *Arts types:* operetta *Venues:* Seebühne Mörbisch (open-air) 4500 *Second Address:* Seebühne, 7072 Mörbisch am See *Comments:* 1 production, 33 performances; from July – August el: 2685-81810, Fax: 2685-818 140

Feldkircher Schloß-und Palaiskonzerte
Gesellschaft der Musikfreunde Feldkirch,
Schlossergasse 8, 6800 **Feldkirch**
Tel: 5522-304 272 Fax: 5522-304 279
E-Mail: kultur@rathaus.feldkirch.com
Leiter Prof. Michael Buchreiner
Period/Frequency: every Monday in July-Aug, annual *Arts types:* chamber music *Venues:* Schattenburg Feldkirch 120 *Comments:* orchestra concerts in spring and autumn

Forum Feldkirch – Musik des 20. Jhdts
Musikkreis Feldkirch, Schlossergasse 8, 6800 **Feldkirch**
Tel: 5522-304 272 Fax: 5522-304 279
E-Mail: kultur@rathaus.feldkirch.com
Leiter Prof. Walfried Kraher
Period/Frequency: Sept-Nov, annual *Arts types:* big band, jazz, contemporary *Venues:* venues throughout Feldkirch

Internationales Gauklerfestival Feldkirch
Herrengasse 10-12, 6800 **Feldkirch**
Tel: 5522-73467 Fax: 5522-79867
E-Mail: werbegemeinschaft@wtg.feldkirch.com
Leiter Andreas Schwarzmann, Hannes Jochum
Period/Frequency: August/September, annual *Arts types:* street theatre, jugglers, musicians, comedy, pantoimime, etc. *Venues:* Altstadt streets of Feldkirch

Festwochen in Gmunden
Theatergasse 7, 4810 **Gmunden**
Tel: 7612-70630 Fax: 7612-70638
E-Mail: kulturbuero.skokan@servus.at
Intendanz und Organisation Jutta Skokan
Period/Frequency: Aug-Sept, annual *Arts types:* drama, concerts, readings, exhibitions *Venues:* Stadttheater 428, Kongresshaus 680, Landschloß Ort 200, Seeschloss Ort 200 *Second Address:* Jutta Skokan (Geschäftsführ.) Eisenhowerstr. 12, 4600 Wels Tel. 7242-47494, Fax. 7242-52759

Eggenberger Schloßkonzerte
ORF, Radio Steiermark, Marburgerstraße 20, 8042 **Graz**
Tel: 316-470 224/227 Fax: 316-470 253
Intendant Kurt Bergmann;
Leitung Mag. Michael Agermann
Comments: there were no performances in 1999; the future of the festival is uncertain; no further information was available at time of going to print;
contact ORF for more details

musikprotokoll
c/o ORF Landesstudio Stmk.,
Marburger Straße 20, 8042 **Graz**
Tel: 316-4702 8224/8227 Fax: 316-4702 8253
Internet: radio-st.orf.at/musikprotokoll
E-Mail: musikprotokoll@orf.at
Intendant Dr Edgar Sterbenz; Programmdirektor Christian Scheib; Organisation Rosalinde Vidic
Period/Frequency: Sept/Oct, annual *Arts types:* contemporary music & performances *Venues:* Grazer Congress 1500-2000 *Comments:* part of Steirischer Herbst (q.v) – promoted by Österreichischer Rundfunk; tickets via E-mail; see also Eggenberger Schloßkonzerte

Open Music
Zeppelinstraße 41, 8055 **Graz**
Tel: 316-296 621/676-405 1589 (mobile)
Fax: 316-296 621
contact Wolfgang Hattinger
Period/Frequency: a total of 7 days throughout the year, annual *Arts types:* today's music (all styles including classical, pop, folk, rock); also various types of performing arts *Venues:*
Kulturzentrum bei den Minoriten

Steirischer Herbst 99
Sackstraße 17/I, 8010 **Graz**
Tel: 316-823 007 Fax: 316-835 788
Internet: www.stherbst.at
E-Mail: info@stherbst.at
Intendanz und Geschäftsführung Dr Peter Oswald
Period/Frequency: autumn (Sept-Oct: 5 weeks), annual *Arts types:* theatre, music theatre/musical, music, dance, exhibitions, cinema, literature, architecture, fine arts *Venues:* various in and around Graz

styriarte Graz
Palais Attems, Sackstraße 17, 8010 **Graz**
Tel: 316-812 941 Fax: 316-877 3836
Internet: www.styriarte.com
E-Mail: styriarte@styria.com
Festspielleitung Mathis Huber; Assistent Irmgard Heschl; Box Office Martin Exner (316-825 000); Press Office Monika Mertl (1-402 4272)
Period/Frequency: June-July, annual *Arts types:* chamber and orchestral concerts, opera *Venues:* Renaissance-Schloß Eggenberg 356, Stefaniensaal 1200, Schloßkirche Stainz 700, Minoritensaal 400

Raimundfestspiele Gutenstein
Marktgemeinde Gutenstein, 2770 **Gutenstein**
Tel: 2634-7220 Fax: 2634-8500
E-Mail: gdegutenstein@netway.at
administrator Fredrich Fischer
Period/Frequency: Aug, annual *Arts types:* theatre
Venues: open-air stage 600

Halbturner Schloßkonzerte
Budapesterstrasse 35, 7131 **Halbturn**
Tel: 2172-8580 Fax: 2172-8784
Vorstandsvorsitzer Ing. Josef Wagersreiter;
Künstlerische Leitung Robert Lehrbaumer
Period/Frequency: every Saturday in July/Aug, annual *Arts types:* chamber music, orchestral music, Liederabende, piano recitals; 8-10 different productions per festival *Venues:* Schloß 100 *Comments:* theme: chamber music and musical humour

Easterfestival – Music of Religions
Osterfestival Innsbruck – Musik der Religionen
Herzog-Otto-Str. 4, 6060 **Hall**
Tel: 5223-56706 Fax: 5223-45926
Internet: www.tirolkultur.at/g.st.barbara
E-Mail: g.st.barbara@tirolkultur.at
Art-Director Gerhard Crepaz;
Organizer Maria Crepaz & family
Period/Frequency: Easter, annual *Arts types:* dance, movement-theatre, workshops, concerts, liturgies, lectures, exhibitions, symposium *Venues:* Jesuitenkirche 800, Landestheater 850, Congress Innsbruck 500-1400, Stiftskirche Wilten

Schubertiade GmbH
Schweizerstr. 1, Postfach 100, 6845 **Hohenems**
Tel: 5576-72091 Fax: 5576-75450
Internet: www.schubertiade.at
E-Mail: info@schubertiade.at
Geschäftsführer Gerd Nachbauer
Period/Frequency: May/June/August/Sept, annual *Arts types:* Schubert recitals, lieder, chamber music, concerts, piano recitals *Venues:* Montforthaus Feldkirch 1000, Konservatoriumsaal Feldkirch 500, Angelika-Kauffmann-Saal, Schwarzenberg 430, Schloß Achberg 100, Hotel Post (Bezau) 800

Allegro Vivo International Chamber Music Festival Austria
Internationales Kammermusik Festival Austria
Festivalbüro, Wiener Strasse 2, 3580 **Horn**
Tel: 2252-89320/2982-4319
Fax: 2252-89320/2982 4319-4
Internet: www.allegro-vivo.music.at
E-Mail: office@allegro-vivo.music.at
Sekretariat Mag. Robert Berger;
Künstlerische Leitung Bijan Khadem-Missagh;
Summer Academy Dr. Margaret Ley
Period/Frequency: Aug-Sept, annual *Arts types:* from baroque to contemporary chamber music *Venues:* Waldviertel – Stift Altenburg, Schloss Breiteneich, Horn, Schloss Ottenstein, Stift Geras, Stift Zwettl, Gmünd, Waidhofen, Weitra, Eggenburg, Burg Rappottenstein, Burg Raabs *Second Address:* Germergasse 16, 2500 Baden bei Wien

Innsbruck Festival of Early Music
Innsbrucker Festwochen der Alten Musik
Haspingerstr. 1, 6020 **Innsbruck**
Tel: 512-571 032 Fax: 512-563 142
Internet: www.tiscover.com/fest-alte-musik
E-Mail: alte.musik@magnet.at
Direktorin Mag. Eva Schintlmeister;
künstlerische Leitung René Jacobs
Period/Frequency: July/Aug, annual *Arts types:* concerts (original instruments), 2 operas *Venues:* Schloss Ambras, Hofburg, Tiroler Landestheater, Congress Innsbruck, Hofkirche, Jesuitenkirche, Dom, Stiftskirche Wilten

Musik-Sommer-Klaus
Am Kirchenplatz 7 u 9, 4560 **Kirchdorf/Krems**
Tel: 7582-62450 Fax: 7582-64907/20
Internet: www.tiscover.com/pyhrn.eisenwurzen
E-Mail: pyhrn.eisenwurzen@upperaustria.or.at
Veranstalter Prof Wilfried Koch, Franz Limberger
Period/Frequency: July-Aug (every Saturday), annual *Arts types:* classical music *Comments:* candle-lit concerts in Bergkirche Klaus

Musikforum Viktring-Klagenfurt
Stift-Viktring, Stift-Viktring-Str 25,
9073 **Klagenfurt-Viktring**
Tel: 463-282 241 Fax: 463-281 626
Internet: www.happynet.at/musikforum
E-Mail: musikforum@happynet.at
Organisation/Öffentlichkeitsarbeit Mag. Werner Überbacher
Period/Frequency: July-Aug, annual *Arts types:* classical, jazz, composition, improvisation, contemporary & modern music, electronic *Venues:* Arkadenhof 1000, Fresken – Barocksaal 180, Stiftskirche 200 *Comments:* International Summer Master Courses – Concerts; also promotes young composers competitions; see also Competitions (Gustav Mahler Kompositionspreis der Stadt Klagenfurt)

ARS Electronica
c/o Ars Electronica Center, Betriebsgesellschaft mbH,
Hauptstraße 2, 4040 **Linz**
Tel: 732-7272-0 Fax: 732-72722
Internet: www.aec.at
E-Mail: info@aec.at
General Management Gerfried Stocker, Wolfgang Modera; Festival Coordinator Jutta Schmiederer; Assistant to CEO Romana Staufer; Ars Electronica FutureLab Horst Hörtner; System administration & technical maintenance Tom Teibler; Digital Economy Ursula Kürmayr; Museum of the Future Business Operations Birgit Wasmeyer
Period/Frequency: one week in Sept, annual *Arts types:* art, technology, society and science *Comments:* digital art/net art

Brucknerfest Linz
Brucknerhaus, Postfach 57,
Untere Donaulände 7,
4010 **Linz**
Tel: 732-7612 Fax: 732-761 2200
Internet: www.liva.linz.at
E-Mail: marketing@liva.co.at
Vorstandsdirektoren Ing. Mag. Wolfgang Lehner, Wolfgang Winkler
Period/Frequency: Sept, annual *Arts types:* orchestra, chamber music, opera, recitals *Venues:* Brucknerhaus Linz 1450 & 400, Stiftskirchen Wilhering & St Florian, Alter & Neuer Dom Linz *Comments:* see also Venues

Tanztage
Posthofstrasse 43, 4020 **Linz**
Tel: 732-770 548Fax: 732-782 652
Internet: www.posthof.at
E-Mail: office@posthof.at
marketing and promotion Karl Zabern
Period/Frequency: 6 evenings in March-April, annual *Arts types:* contemporary dance *Venues:* Großer Saal 630 (seated), 1300 (standing) *Comments:* see also Venues

Internationales Kammermusikfest Lockenhaus – Kremerata Musica
Hauptplatz 5, 7442 **Lockenhaus**
Tel: 2616-2224/2072
Fax: 2616-2023
Organisation Pfarrer Josef Herowitsch;
Künstlerischer Leiter Gidon Kremer
Period/Frequency: 10 days, first half of July, annual *Arts types:* chamber music and annual theme
Venues: Kirche 600, Burg 500 *Comments:* several single performances during the year

Internationale Barocktage Stift Melk
Kulturamt der Stadtgemeinde Melk,
Rathaus, 3390 **Melk**
Tel: 2752-52307/662-820 493
Fax: 2752-523 0727/662-820 493
Künstlerische Gesamtleitung Prof. Helmut Pilss
Period/Frequency: on Whitsun weekend, annual
Arts types: baroque, classical music
Venues: Stift in Melk 400 to 700

Musikwochen Millstatt
Postfach 27, 9872 **Millstatt/See**
Tel: 4766-202 235 Fax: 4766-3479
Internet: www.buk.ktn.gv.at/millstattmusik
E-Mail: musikwochen.millstatt@carinthia.com
Obmann Pater Paul Guntermann; Künstlerische Leiterin Gerda Gratzer; Organisation Elke Zervava
Period/Frequency: May-Oct, annual *Arts types:* classical music, jazz, music theatre, children's theatre, readings
Venues: Stiftskirche 350, Stiftshof 100, Rittersaal 200

International Puppettheatre Festival Mistelbach
Internationale Puppentheatertage Mistelbach
Hauptplatz 6, 2130 **Mistelbach**
Tel: 2572-251 5253
Fax: 2572-2515/217
Internet: www.nanet.at/mistelbach/index.htm
E-Mail: kultur@nanet.at
organisation Helga Ruso-Pawelka;
art director Dr Olaf Bernstengel
Period/Frequency: Oct, annual *Arts types:* puppetry
Venues: different venues in Mistelbach 100 to 400

muerz Werkstatt
Kunsthaus muerz GmbH, Wienerstraße 35,
8680 **Mürzzuschlag**
Tel: 3852-5620 Fax: 3852-56209
E-Mail: kunst@kunsthaus.muerz.at
Verwaltungsleiter Robert Lotter;
Musikalischer Leiter Ernst Smole
Period/Frequency: Oct, annual *Arts types:* contemporary music, jazz, classical music of the modern age, drama, exhibitions, literature *Venues:* Kunsthaus 300 and other venues in and around Mürzzuschlag *Comments:* muerz Werkstatt is part of Steirischer Herbst (q.v.)

Internationale Neuberger Kulturtage
Postfach 18, 8692 **Neuberg an der Mürz**
Tel: 7585-8421 Fax: 7585-8421
Internet: www.neuberg.at/kulturtage/
E-Mail: kulturtage@gmx.at
Organisation Christiane Wolfrum;
Musikalischer Leiter Stefan Vladar;
Koordination und Pressearbeit Gunda Fahrnberger
Period/Frequency: July, annual & 2 'Schumann Tage' in June *Arts types:* concerts, classical seminars, exhibitions, chamber music, church opera *Venues:* Stift Neuberg an der Mürz, Grünangerkirche *Second Address:* Tourismusverband Neuberg, 8692 Neuberg an der Mürz, Tel: 3857-8321, E-mail: tourismus@neuberg.at

Nickelsdorfer Konfrontationen
Jazzgalerie Nickelsdorf, Untere Hauptstraße 13a,
2425 **Nickelsdorf**
Tel: 2146-2359 Fax: 2146-2776
Internet: www.user.xpoint.at/jazzgalerie
E-Mail: jazzgalerie@xpoint.at
contacts Hans Falb, Reinhard Sdöger
Period/Frequency: 16-18 July, annual *Arts types:* contemporary, free jazz, improvised music *Venues:* Jazzgalerie/Cafe Restaurant Falb 2000-3000

Festival der Regionen
Postfach 43, 4100 **Ottensheim**
Tel: 7234-85285 Fax: 7234-85285/4
Internet: www.fdr.at
E-Mail: office@fdr.at.
contact Ferry Öllinger
Period/Frequency: June-July, biennial (2001) *Arts types:* drama, dance, music, exhibitions – only projects made for the festival *Venues:* indoor and outdoor venues cap up to 100

Perchtoldsdorfer Sommerspiele
Kulturabteilung, 2380 **Perchtoldsdorf**
Tel: 1-8668 3212 Fax: 1-8668 3133
Internet: www.markt-perchtoldsdorf.at
E-Mail: gemeinde@markt-perchtoldsdorf.at
Kulturabteilung Ursula Klein
Period/Frequency: July, annual *Arts types:* comedy
Venues: Burghof 630

Kunst und Kultur Raab
Raab 399, Postfach 24, 4760 **Raab**
Tel: 77-623 588 Fax: 77-623 588
contacts Rudi Wötzlmayr, Dieter Wagenbichler
Period/Frequency: June, annual *Arts types:* national and international jazz *Venues:* Musikschule Raab, clubconcerts at the 'LOGO' *Comments:* promoters: Kunst & Kultur raab

Jazzfestival Saalfelden
Brandstättengasse 1, 5760 **Saalfelden**
Tel: 6582-74963 Fax: 6582-749 634
Internet: www.jazzsaalfelden.at
E-Mail: jazzsaalfelden@netway.at
Direktor and Künstl. Leiter Gerhard Eder;
Öffentlichkeitsarbeit Ursula Windhager
Period/Frequency: Aug, annual *Arts types:* contemporary international jazz *Venues:* Capacity 2500

Aspekte Salzburg – Internationales Festival Zeitgenössischer Musik
Lasserstraße 6, 5020 **Salzburg**
Tel: 662-881 547 Fax: 662-882 143
Leiter Prof. Klaus Ager
Period/Frequency: May-June, annual *Arts types:* contemporary music *Venues:* Mozarteum,Grosses Studio 400

Fest in Hellbrunn
c/o Konzertagentur Steinschaden & Hiller, Nonntaler Hauptstraße 59/8, 5020 **Salzburg**
Tel: 662-828 695 Fax: 662-828 695/14
Internet: www.salzburg-concerts.com
E-Mail: office@salzburg-concerts.com
Künstlerisches Leitung Konstantin Hiller
Period/Frequency: Aug, annual *Arts types:* opera, drama, ballet, chamber music, recital *Venues:* Schloß Hellbrunn up to 200 *Comments:* see also Promoters

Internationale Orgelwochen
c/o Katholisches Bildungswerk, Kapitelplatz 6,
5020 **Salzburg**
Tel: 662-623 854 Fax: 662-623 854
Künstlerische Gesamtleitung Prof Stefan Klinda
Period/Frequency: July-Aug, annual *Arts types:* predominantly classical and romantic organ solos but also accompaniments with brass, woodwind, horn, trumpet and vocal *Venues:* St. Blasius 250 *Comments:* 12-15 prods

Internationale Salzburger Orgelkonzerte
Franziskanergasse 5, Postfach 292, 5010 **Salzburg**
Tel: 662-840 840 Fax: 662-840 840
Management Elvira Weinzettel; Künstl Dir Bernhard Gfrerer
Period/Frequency: July-Aug, annual *Arts types:* organ music, orchestral, choral *Venues:* Franziskanerkirche 500

Jazzfestival Salzburg
Kulturgelände Nonntal, Mühlbacherhofweg 5,
5020 **Salzburg**
Tel: 662-883 264/848 784 (tickets & info)
Fax: 662-883 264
E-Mail: jazzit@magnet.at
contact Andreas Neumayer
Period/Frequency: March, annual *Arts types:* international contemporary improvised music, new jazz, avantgarde
Venues: up to 300

JUVAVUM BRASS Festival – Salzburg
Gruberfeldsiedlung 219, 5023 **Salzburg**
Tel: 662-650 237 Fax: 662-650 237
Internet: www.juvavum.at
E-Mail: juvavum.brass@aon.at
contact Horst Hofer
Period/Frequency: Oct, annual *Arts types:* brass music (bands, ensembles, soloists, big bands) *Venues:* Grosser Saal – Mozarteum, Salzburger Dom, Stadtkinosaal, Braugewölbe *Comments:* also workshops

Mozartwoche Salzburg
Schwarzstr. 26, 5020 **Salzburg**
Tel: 662-889 4021 Fax: 662-872 996
Künstlerisches Betriebsbüro/Programmverantwortlicher Dr Josef Tichy; Presse-u. Öffentlichkeitsarbeit Dr Margit Skiaks; Präsident Dr. Friedrich Gehmacher; Geschäftsführer Wieland Lafferentz
Period/Frequency: Jan-Feb, annual *Arts types:* classical music with focus on Mozart, choir, orchestra, soloists, chamber music *Venues:* Mozarteum – Großer Saal 800, Mozarteum – Wiener Saal 200, Großes Festspielhaus 2111, Große Aula der Universität 734 *Comments:* promoted by Internationale Stiftung Mozarteum Salzburg; see also Venues and Promoters

Osterfestspiele Salzburg
Herbert-von-Karajan-Platz 9, 5020 **Salzburg**
Tel: 662-804 5328 Fax: 662-804 5790
Geschäftsführung Michael Dewitte; künstlerische Leitung Claudio Abbado
Period/Frequency: week before Easter until Easter Monday, annual *Arts types:* orchestra, choral, opera *Venues:* Großes Festspielhaus 2111, Mozarteum 800

Salzburger Festspiele
Postfach 140, 5010 **Salzburg**
Tel: 662-80450 Fax: 662-804 5700
Internet: www.salzburgfestival.at
E-Mail: info@salzburgfestival.at
kaufmännischer Leiter und Konzertreferat Prof. Dr. Hans Landesmann; Präsidentin Dr Helga Rabl-Stadler; Künstl Leitung u. Intendant Dr Gérard Mortier (until 2001); Leiterin des Künstl Betriebsbüros Eva-Maria Wieser
Period/Frequency: July-Aug, annual *Arts types:* opera, orchestra, chamber music, recitals, drama *Venues:* Felsenreitschule 1499, Grosses Festspielhaus 2111, Kleines Festspielhaus 1321, Landestheater 688, Domplatz 2111 (+ 400 standing), Perner Insel in Hallein 762, Mozarteum 799 *Comments:* see also Venues

Salzburger Festungskonzerte
Anton Adlgasser-Weg 22, 5020 **Salzburg**
Tel: 662-825 858 Fax: 662-825 859
Internet: salzburg.co.at/festungskonzerte
E-Mail: festungskonz@salzburg.co.at
Veranstalter Gerhard Papousek; Geschäftsführer Dr. Erich Berer
Period/Frequency: March – Jan *Arts types:* chamber music concerts (up to 14 musicians) *Venues:* Festung Hohensalzburg 180, Neue Residenz 150, Alte Residenz 400 *Comments:* concert works of great composers, particularly Mozart; 320 concerts; 60-80 different productions every year

Salzburger Kulturtage
Waagplatz 1a, 5020 **Salzburg**
Tel: 662-845 346 Fax: 662-842 665
Generalsekretär Dr Heinz Klier
Period/Frequency: the last two weeks of Oct, annual *Arts types:* opera, orchestra, ballet *Venues:* Großes Festspielhaus 2097 *Comments:* approx. 5 operas, 5 orchestra concerts, 2 ballets per year

Salzburger Mozart-Serenaden
Lieferinger Hauptstr. 136, 5013 **Salzburg**
Tel: 662-436 870 Fax: 662-436 970
Internet: www.austria.at/mozartserenaden/
E-Mail: mozart@salzburg.co.at
künstlerische Leitung Harald Nerat; Veranstalter Elisabeth Nerat
Period/Frequency: throughout the year, annual *Arts types:* Mozart – chamber music, some orchestra *Venues:* Gotischer Saal 250, Mozarteum/Grosser Saal 800 *Comments:* see also Promoters, Agents and Producers

Salzburger Schlosskonzerte
Griesgasse 6, 5020 **Salzburg**
Tel: 662-848 586 Fax: 662-844 747
Internet: www.esp.at/salzburger.schlosskonzerte
E-Mail: schlosskonzerte@EUnet.at
Geschäftsführender Leiter Luz Leskowitz; Press-und Öffentlichkeitsarbeit Mag. Silvia Span; Kartenbestellungen Brita Pobil; Buchhaltung Annemarie Göttlich
Period/Frequency: schedule for entire year (daily concerts during the summer season; 2-4 times a week during the winter season) *Arts types:* from piano concertos to chamber music *Venues:* Marble Hall of Mirabell Palace 180 *Comments:* 270 recitals a year

SommerSZENE
Anton Neumayer-Platz 2, 5020 **Salzburg**
Tel: 662-843 448 Fax: 662-846 808
Internet: www.salzburg.or.at/szene
E-Mail: szene@salzburg.or.at
Intendant Michael Stolhofer; Organisation Karin Buchauer; Koordination Brigitte Kühberger; Öffentlichkeitsarbeit Julia Fleischer; info desk Eva Forstenlechner; Produktion Eva Eckkrahmer
Period/Frequency: July, annual *Arts types:* dance, theatre, music *Venues:* Salzburg; Stadtkino 370, Tanzzentrum Sead 150, Schüttkasten 100, Truner Brauerei Obertrum 400, Gafe Gebäude 160, Künstlerhaus Salzburger Kunstverein 275, Lokal Bahnhof Salzburg 35 *Comments:* 17 productions + 1 free performance

Sonntagsmatineen im Schloss Mirabell
c/o Konzertagentur Steinschaden & Hiller, Nonntaler Hauptstraße 59/8, 5020 **Salzburg**
Tel: 662-828 695 Fax: 662-828 695/14
Internet: www.salzburg-concerts.com
E-Mail: office@salzburg-concerts.com
Leiter Georg Steinschaden, Konstantin Hiller
Period/Frequency: 20 concerts on Sundays (11am) throughout the year, annual *Arts types:* chamber music *Venues:* Marmorsaal, Schloß Mirabell 200 *Comments:* see also Promoters

Montafoner Sommerkonzerte
Stand Montafon, Postfach 6, 6780 **Schruns**
Tel: 5556-72132 Fax: 5556-721 329
E-Mail: Stand@Montafon.vol.at
Künstlerische Leitung Prof. Bernd Becher
Period/Frequency: June-Sept, annual *Arts types:* organ, chamber music, choir, orchestra, solo concerts, baroque, classical music *Venues:* various parish churches *Second Address:* Künstlerische Leitung, Burghalde 4, 6800 Feldkirch Tel: 5522-36954 *Comments:* 10-12 concerts

Klangspuren Schwaz – Tage Neuer Musik
Fuggergasse 2, 6130 **Schwaz**
Tel: 5242-73582 Fax: 5242-73582
Internet: www.klangspuren.com
E-Mail: bettina@netway.at
artistic director Thomas Larcher; executive director Maria-Luise Mayr; public relations Bettina Schlorhaufer
Period/Frequency: 10 days in Sept, annual *Arts types:* new music, contemporary classical

Komödienspiele Schloß Porcia
Verein Komödienspiele Porcia, Schloß Porcia, 9800 **Spittal/Drau**
Tel: 4762-42020 Fax: 4762-45163
E-Mail: komoedienspiel@carinthia.com
Künstlerischer Leiter Peter Pikl; Verwaltungsleiter Udo Kröll; Präsident Helmuth Drewes
Period/Frequency: July-Aug, annual *Arts types:* classical comedies, world literature *Venues:* Schloß Porcia (Renaissance castle) 367 *Second Address:* contact Direktorin Frau Paulitsch: Tourismusbüro Spittal an d. Drau Schloß Porcia, Burgplatz 1, 9800 Spittal, Tel: 4762-3420, Fax: 4762-3237

Attergauer Kultursommer
Attergaustraße 31, 4880 **St Georgen im Attergau**
Tel: 7667-8672 Fax: 7667-8918
Präsident ÖR. Baumann-Rott; Künstlerische Leitung Prof. Wolfgang Schuster; Verwaltung Margit Kienssberger
Period/Frequency: July-Aug, annual and 13 recitals *Arts types:* orchestra, chamber music, solo recitals, theatre, choral concerts, library *Venues:* Attergauhalle 1000, St. Georgen Pfarrkirche 600, Narzberger Gut 240, Pfarrkirche Vöcklamarkt 600, Pfarrkirche Schörfling 530 *Second Address:* Künstlerisches Betriebsbüro, Winzerstrasse 22, 1130 Wien, Tel: 1-5854 5312

Musica Sacra-Internationale Kirchenmusiktage in Niederösterreich
Prandtauerstr.2, 3100 **St Pölten**
Tel: 2742-333 2601/2600 (Dr Karl) Fax: 2742-333 2609
contact Dr Thomas Karl; Künstlerische Leitung Domkapellmeister Otto Kargl (tel: 324 342)
Period/Frequency: Sept-Oct, annual and 10-15 recitals *Arts types:* orchestra, solo, chamber concerts, church music *Venues:* Domkirche St Pölten, Stiftskirchen Lilienfeld, Herzogenburg

Stockerauer Festspiele
Rathaus, 2000 **Stockerau**
Tel: 2266-69518 Fax: 2266-69570
E-Mail: gdestockerau@netway.at
Intendant Alfons Haider; Verwaltungsleiter Peter Schlüter
Period/Frequency: July-Aug, annual *Arts types:* drama (mainly comedies), musicals *Venues:* Platz vor der Stadtpfarrkirche (open-air) 800 *Comments:* 2 productions, 28-30 performances

Musik Aktuell – Neue Musik in Niederösterreich
Musikfabrik, Wilhelmstr. 29, 3430 **Tulln**
Tel: 2272-65051 Fax: 2272-65052
Internet: www.arthoc.or.at/musikfabrik
E-Mail: musikfabrik@aon.at
Leiter Mag. Gottfried Zawichowski
Period/Frequency: annual, throughout the year *Arts types:* all forms of contemporary/modern music *Venues:* various in Lower Austria *Comments:* approx. 50 concerts

Ulrichsberger Kaleidophon
Badergasse 2, 4161 **Ulrichsberg**
Tel: 7288-6301
Fax: 7288-6301
Internet: www.netway.at/jazzatelier
E-Mail: afischer@netway.at
contact Alois Fischer
Period/Frequency: May, annual *Arts types:* new improvised music, jazz, new composed music *Venues:* Jazzatelier Ulrichsberg 300

Spectrum Villach
Postfach 214, 9500 **Villach**
Tel: 4242-287 164 Fax: 4242-287 164
Internet: www-buk.ktn.gv.at/spectrum
E-Mail: spectrum@carinthia.com
Leitung Michael Weger
Period/Frequency: May-June, biennial (2001) *Arts types:* drama, children & youth theatre, dance *Venues:* various venues in Villach *Comments:* International Theatreweek Festival, 45 performances & 20-25 different productions

Internationales Figurentheaterfestival Wels
Magistrat Wels Kulturverwaltung, Pollheimerstrasse 17, 4601 **Wels**
Tel: 7242-235 668 Fax: 7242-235 773
E-Mail: kranzl@wels.gv.at
Period/Frequency: March, annual *Arts types:* figure and object theatre for children and adults, special avantgarde section

Ballettzentrum Wolfsegg
Gesellschaft für Musiktheater, Türkenstraße 19, 1090 **Wien**
Tel: 1-317 0699 Fax: 1-310 8292 (Sept – July)
Intendant Prof. Franz Eugen Dostal; Ballettleitung Prof. Karol Tóth; Technische Leitung Klaus Lukesch, Pani Stamatopolos
Period/Frequency: Aug, annual *Arts types:* ballet, concerts, seminars *Second Address:* 4902 Wolfsegg Tel: 7676-6602 (Aug. only), Fax: 7676-835 113 (Aug. only) *Comments:* performances by international ballet school companies during the festival; offers training courses in ballet education (Balletpädagogik, Russian School); see also National Organisations

Carinthischer Sommer, Ossiach-Villach
Gumpendorfer Straße 76, 1060 **Wien**
Tel: 1-597 9492(Sept-May) Fax: 1-597 1236(Sept-May)
Internet: www.carinthischersommer.at
E-Mail: office@carinthischersommer.at
Intendantin Dr Gerda Fröhlich
Period/Frequency: July-Aug, annual *Arts types:* orchestra, chamber music, choral (lieder), recitals, (church) opera *Venues:* Stiftskirche Ossiach 700, Congress Center Villach 1000, Ossiach Barocksaal 250 *Second Address:* Sekretariat (June-Aug), Carinthischer Sommer, 9570 Ossiach 1, Tel: 4243-2510, Fax: 4243-2353 *Comments:* over 80 events; also lectures for adults; seminars for children

Chopin-Festival in der Kartause Gaming
Internationale Chopin-Gesellschaft in Wien, Biberstraße 4, 1010 **Wien**
Tel: 1-512 2374/6463 Fax: 1-512 646 375
Direktor Dr Theodor Kanitzer
Period/Frequency: third weekend of Aug, annual *Arts types:* solo, orchestra, concerts, piano recitals, chamber music, romantic, classical works *Venues:* Kartause Gaming, Marktgemeinde Gaming, Ötscherland (Niederösterreich) *Comments:* Oct-May concert series Gebäude der Bank Austria in Renngasse 2

Festival Wien modern
c/o Wiener Konzerthaus, Lothringerstraße 20, 1030 **Wien**
Tel: 1-7124 6860 Fax: 1-713 1709
E-Mail: wienmodern@konzerthaus.at
Organisation GS Christoph Lieben-Seutter, Dr Thomas Angyan, Prof. Lothar Knessl; Marketing & Öffentlichkeit Peter Polansky
Period/Frequency: end Oct-begin. Dec, annual *Arts types:* contemporary music *Venues:* 80% in the Konzerthaus 330 & 750 & 1800; and others including Musikverein, Odeon, Jugendstiltheater *Comments:* 30 different productions during the festival, see also Venues and Promoters

Festival Wiener Klassik
Bossigasse 76, 1130 **Wien**
Tel: 1-877 5208 Fax: 1-876 4623-17
E-Mail: haydn_sinfonietta@netway.at
Musikalischer Direktor Manfred Huss
Period/Frequency: July-Sept./Christmas, annual *Arts types:* chamber music, church music, orchestra *Venues:* in historic halls, theatres and churches up to 700 *Comments:* most concerts on period instruments; see also Orchestra (Haydn Sinfonietta Wien)

Fifth International Festival of New Music for Orchestra (2000)
c/o Vienna Modern Masters, Margaretenstrasse 125/15, 1050 **Wien**
Tel: 1-545 1778
Fax: 1-544 0785
Internet: www.xs4all.nl/~gdv/vmm
E-Mail: vmm@teleweb.at
president & festival director Clyd Smith PhD; vice president & artistic director of the festival Nancy Van de Vate
Period/Frequency: last 2 weeks of June, annual
Arts types: new (classical) music for orchestra
Venues: Philharmonic Hall, Olomouc, Czech Republic
Comments: at each festival the works selected are performed in concert and recorded for release on CD on The Vienna Modern Music label (q.v.)

Graben Fest Tage
c/o Österreichische Beamten Versicherung (ÖBV), Grillparzerstraße 14, 1016 **Wien**
Tel: 1-40120-0 Fax: 1-4012 01001
E-Mail: oebv@com.at
Generaldirektor Dipl. Kfm Dr. Johann Hauf; Musikalische Leitung Christoph Huber, Christoph Cech; Presse Herbert Maurer
Period/Frequency: June, annual *Arts types:* Austrian contemporary, improvised music, classic *Venues:* Grabenhof 100-150 *Comments:* venue address: Habsburger Gasse 1a, 1010 Wien

Hörgänge – Musik in Österreich
c/o Wiener Konzerthausgesellschaft, Lothringerstraße 20, 1030 **Wien**
Tel: 1-712 468 618 Fax: 1-713 1709
E-Mail: lepuschitz@konzerthaus.at
contact Rainer Lepuschitz; PR Peter Polansky
Period/Frequency: March/April (2-3 weeks), annual *Arts types:* focus on contemporary Austrian music
Venues: Wiener Konzerthaus – 3 Säle: 1800, 750, 330
Comments: see also Venues and Promoters

IM PULS-TANZ in Wien
PO Box 155, 1091 **Wien**
Tel: 1-523 5558 Fax: 1-5231 6839
Internet: tanzwochen.wien.at
E-Mail: ITW@magnet.at
Direktion Karl Regensburger, Guido Reimitz; Künstl. Leitung Andrée Valentin, Karl Regensburger; PR – Kontaktperson Rio Rutzinger
Period/Frequency: July/Aug, annual *Arts types:* performance festival featuring contemporary dance *Venues:* Burgtheater 1300, Volkstheater 950, Sofiensäle: Gr. Saal 450, Blauer Salon 250

imagetanz
dietheater Künstlerhaus, Karlsplatz 5, 1010 **Wien**
Tel: 1-587 0504 (box office)/8774 (office)
Fax: 1-5870 50431/877 431
Internet: www.dietheater.or.at/dietheater
E-Mail: dietheater@gmx.net
künstlerische Leitung Christian Pronay; Assistenz Anna Thier
Period/Frequency: Sept-Oct, annual *Arts types:* experimental, modern dance *Venues:* Künstlerhaus 198 *Comments:* also host fringe shows and guest performances; see also Drama and Venues

Internationale Tanzwochen Wien
Neustiftgasse 3/12, 1070 **Wien**
Tel: 1-523 5558 Fax: 1-5231 6839
Internet: tanzwochen.wien.at
E-Mail: ITW@magnet.at
Direktion Karl Regensburger, Guido Reimitz; Künstler. Leitung Ismael Ivo, Rio Rutzinger; PR – Kontaktperson Rio Rutzinger
Period/Frequency: Feb, July/Aug *Arts types:* all types of dance – contemporary dance theatre *Second Address:* postal address: PO Box 155, 1091 Wien
Comments: workshops

Internationales Musikfest
c/o Wiener Konzerthaus, Lothringerstr. 20, 1030 **Wien**
Tel: 1-7124 6860 Fax: 1-713 1709
E-Mail: keisch@konzerthaus.at
Generalskretär Christoph Lieben-Seutter; Marketing und Werbung Peter Polansky, Mag. Anja Reisch
Period/Frequency: June, annual *Arts types:* classical, opera *Venues:* Wiener Konzerthaus 1800 *Comments:* organised by Wiener Konzerthaus; see also Venues

Jazzfest Wien
Frankenberggasse 13/13, 1040 **Wien**
Tel: 1-503 5647
Fax: 1-503 5544
Internet: www.viennajazz.org
E-Mail: office@viennajazz.org
organizers Fritz Thom, Heinz Krassnitzer, Margit Rauner
Period/Frequency: June-July, annual *Arts types:* jazz, pop, blues, world music *Venues:* Staatsoper and various outdoor and indoor venues

Klangbogen Wien
Rathausstraße 4, 1010 **Wien**
Tel: 1-4000 8400 Fax: 1-4000-99-8400
Internet: www.klangbogen.at
E-Mail: info@festival-management.at
Musikintendant DI. Roland Geyer
Period/Frequency: July-Sept, annual (2000: 2 July-7 Sept) *Arts types:* orchestra, recitals, chamber music, operas, operettas *Venues:* various *Second Address:* tickets: Stadiongasse 9, 1010 Wien, Tel: 1-42717, Fax: 1-4000-99-8410

Laxenburger Kultursommer
Florianigasse 2/5, 1080 **Wien**
Tel: 1-406 5858
Fax: 1-406 5858
Intendant Prof. Jürgen Wilke
Period/Frequency: July-Aug, annual *Arts types:* Viennese comedies *Venues:* Komödienspiele in der Franzensburg *Second Address:* Marktgemeinde Laxenburg, Rathaus, 2361 Laxenburg

Laxenburger Meisterkonzerte im Schlosstheater Laxenburg
Reisnerstrasse 3, 1030 **Wien**
Tel: 1-714 8822 Fax: 1-714 8821
Internet: www.wiener-meisterkurse.music.at
E-Mail: wiener-meisterkurse@music.at
Organisation Elisabeth Keschmann; Künstl Leiter Prof. Günther Theuring; Präsident Prof. Dr. Hans Haselböck
Period/Frequency: July/Aug annual *Arts types:* soloists' concerts, masterclasses *Venues:* Schlosstheater Laxenburg, Konservatorium, Musik-Universität *Second Address:* Johannesgasse 4A, Konservatorium Wien, Tel: 1-512 7381/84 (only in July/Aug) *Comments:* great musical variety as the concerts depend on the members of the Wiener Meisterkurse; masterclasses in opera, singing, conducting, flute, cello, violin, piano, musical, lied; concerts and diplomas at the end of each class (15 classes, 2 weeks and 40 hourly lessons each)

Musikfestival Osterklang Wien
Rathausstraße 4, 1010 **Wien**
Tel: 1-4000 8400 Fax: 1-4000-99-8400
Internet: www.osterklang.at
E-Mail: info@festival-management.at
Muskintendant DI. Roland Geyer
Period/Frequency: April, annual (2000: 14-24 April) *Arts types:* chamber music, operas, orchestra *Venues:* various *Second Address:* tickets: Stadiongasse 9, 1010 Wien, Tel: 1-42717, Fax: 1-4000-99-8410

NEUER TANZ – Progress in Work
WUK-Werkstätten und Kulturhaus, Währingerstrasse 59, 1090 **Wien**
Tel: 1-401 2150 Fax: 1-405 4944
Internet: www.wuk.at
E-Mail: va.theater@wuk.at
künstl. Leitung Helmut Hartmann
Period/Frequency: June, annual *Arts types:* movement theatre, dance theatre, dance performance
Venues: Großer Saal 100-180 *Comments:* national and international platform for young choreographers to show work in progress; see also Tanzsprache – Festival im WUK, and Venues

Niederösterreichisches Donaufestival
Billrothstraße 58/2, 1190 **Wien**
Tel: 1-368 2356 (Intendanz Wien) Fax: 1-368 2356-19
Internet: www.donaufestival.at
E-Mail: office@dfg.co.at
kaufmännischer Leiter Mag Stephan Nistler; künstlerische Leitung Dr Alf Krauliz; Press & marketing Mag Martina Montecuccoli; Dramaturgie (Theater & Tanz) Dr. Beate Scholz; Dramaturgie (Musik) Regina Reisinger
Period/Frequency: mid-June-2nd week July, annual *Arts types:* theatre, dance performance, music-classical to pop, literature, circus, exhibitions, symposia, cabarets *Venues:* Krems: Stadtpark, Stadtsaal, Dominikanerkirche; St. Pölten: Festspielhaus *Second Address:* address June/July: Körnermarkt 13, 3500 Krems, Tel: 2732-75840, Fax: 2732-7584 222 (box office) *Comments:* between 40-60 different productions per festival; emphasis in last week is on theatre

Opern Air GmbH
Simondenkgasse 8/20, 1090 **Wien**
Tel: 1-310 2026 Fax: 1-319 1586
Intendant Karel Drgac
Period/Frequency: July-Aug, annual *Arts types:* opera *Venues:* Freilichtbühne auf der Burgruine Gars am Kamp 1300

Ost-West Musikfest Krems
Konzertbüro Ost-West Musikfest, Delugstraße 11, 1190 **Wien**
Tel: 1-320 8797 Fax: 1-320 8797
E-Mail: ost-west-musikfest@telecom.at
Künstlerischer Leiter Gernot Winischhofer
Period/Frequency: July-Aug, annual *Arts types:* classical concerts, international mastercourses *Venues:* Krems/Donau, Grafenegg, Heiligenkreuz-Gutenbrunn, St. Pölten, Herzogenburg, Dürnstein, Gotweig *Comments:* guests from all over Europe & overseas

Resonanzen
c/o Wiener Konzerthausgesellschaft, Lothringerstraße 20, 1030 **Wien**
Tel: 1-7124 6860 Fax: 1-713 1709
E-Mail: mail@konzerthaus.at
contact Christian Lackner
Period/Frequency: 1 week in January, annual *Arts types:* early music (renaissance & baroque) *Venues:* Wiener Konzerthaus, 3 Säle: 1800, 750, 330

SPECTACVLVM – Festspiele im Alten Wiener Universitätsviertel
Gesellschaft für Musiktheater, Türkenstrasse 19, 1090 **Wien**
Tel: 1-317 0699 Fax: 1-310 8292
Intendant Prof. Franz Eugen Dostal; Musikalische Leitung Prof. Bernhard Klebel, Dr. Gerhard Kramer, Mag. Thomas Schmögner; Dramaturgie Leo Wallner SJ
Period/Frequency: July, annual *Arts types:* concerts (also contemporary church ballet, baroque church opera) *Venues:* University Church 348 *Comments:* 5 performances; see also National Organisations

Tanzsprache
WUK-Veranstaltungsbüro, Währingerstrasse 59, 1090 **Wien**
Tel: 1-401 2149 Fax: 1-405 4944
Internet: www.wuk.at
E-Mail: va.pr@wuk.at
Leitung Veranstaltungsbüro WUK Vincent Abbrederis; künstlerische Leitung (Gesamtleitung Tanzsprache) Tatjana Langaskova
Period/Frequency: biennial (2001) *Arts types:* movement theatre, dance theatre, dance *Venues:* Großer Saal up to 200 *Comments:* see also Venues

Wiener Festwochen
Lehárgasse 11/1/6, 1060 **Wien**
Tel: 1-589 220/2222 (service/info during festival)
Fax: 1-589 2249
Internet: www.festwochen.or.at
E-Mail: festwochen@festwochen.at
Generalsekretär Wolfgang Wais; Schauspieldirektor Luc Bondy; Direktor für Musiktheater Dr Klaus-Peter Kehr; Tanzprojekte und Crossover Hortensia Völckers
Period/Frequency: May-June, annual *Arts types:* opera, operetta, theatre, symphony concerts, chamber music, exhibitions, guest performances, music on stage, symposia, dance *Venues:* Theater an der Wien 1161, other venues in the city *Comments:* each year about 30 prods

Wiener Tage der Zeitgenössischen Klaviermusik
Universität für Musik und darstellende Kunst, Abteilung Musikpädagogik, Rennweg 8, 1030 **Wien**
Tel: 1-798 5635 Fax: 1-7985 63528
E-Mail: grubauer@mhsw.ac.at
contact Otto Grubauer; künstlerische Leitungs Manon Liu Rennert, Johannes Marian
Period/Frequency: Feb, annual *Arts types:* contemporary piano music, workshops with composers, masterclasses and concerts *Comments:* alternative E-mail: m.l.rennert@magnet.at

Jazzfest Wiesen
Hauptstraße 140, 7203 **Wiesen**
Tel: 2626-817 690/816 480 Fax: 2626-816 4829
Internet: www.wiesen.at
E-Mail: info@jazzpub-wiesen.at
dirs Franz Bogner, Ewald Tatar, Alexander Swoboda
Period/Frequency: July, annual *Arts types:* jazz *Venues:* stage 8000 *Comments:* also other festivals: alternative rock (Forest Glade Festival), ethnic and world music

AZERBAIDZHAN (+994)

International Festival 'Musical September in Baku'
Azerbaidzhan Muslim Magomayev State Philharmonia
Government House, Azadlyg Square 1, 370016 **Baku**
Tel: 12-934 398 Fax: 12-935 605

International Folk Festival 'Hari Byul-Byul'
Government House, Azadlyg Square 1, 370016 **Baku**
Tel: 12-934 398 Fax: 12-935 605

Kara Karayev International Festival of Modern Music 'Music of the 20th Century'
Government House, Azadlyg Square 1, 370016 **Baku**
Tel: 12-934 398 Fax: 12-935 605

BELARUS (+375)

Paleski Karagod International Folk-Dance Festival
Mjezhdunarodnyj Fjestival Narodnogo
Tanca Paljeski Karagod
Brest
Tel: 162-266 021

Annual International Festival Belarussian Musical Autumn
Ezhjegodnyj Mjezhdunarodnyj Fjestival Bjelaruskaja Muzykalnaja Osjenn
Bjelgosfilarmonija, pr. Franciska Skoryny 50, 220005 **Minsk**
Tel: 172-319 050 Fax: 172-319 050
director Jurij Gildiuk
Period/Frequency: Nov, annual

Belaja Wiezha International Theatre Festival, Brest
Mjezhdunarodnyj Tjeatralnyj Fjestival Bjelaja Wiezha, Brjest
Ministjerstvo kultury (The Ministry of Culture), pr. Mashjerova 11, 220004 **Minsk**
Tel: 172-235 825 Fax: 172-235 825

Creative Youth's Festival of Music Theatre's Actors from countries of CIS
Fjestival tvorchjeskoj molodjozhi artistov muzykalnych tjeatrov ctran SNG
Ministjerstvo kultury (The Ministry of Culture), pr. Mashjerova 11, 220004 **Minsk**
Tel: 172-235 825 Fax: 172-235 825

International Festival December Musical Meetings, The
Mjezhdunarodnyj Fjestival Studzjenskija Muzychnyja Sustrechy
Ministjerstvo kultury (The Ministry of Culture), pr. Mashjerova, 11, 220004 **Minsk**
Tel: 172-235 825 Fax: 172-235 825

International Festival of Ancient and Modern Music – Polock
Mjezhdunarodnyj fjestival starinnoj i sovrjemjennoj muzyki – Polock
Ministjerstvo kultury (The Ministry of Culture), pr. Mashjerova 11, 220004 **Minsk**
Tel: 172-235 825 Fax: 172-235 825

International Festival of Children's Creative Work – The Voice of Childhood
Mjezhdunarodnyj fjestival djetskogo tvorchjestva Golos djetstva
Ministjerstvo kultury (The Ministry of Culture), pr. Mashjerova 11, 220004 **Minsk**
Tel: 172-235 825 Fax: 172-235 825

International Festival of Monoplays 2000
24-467 Russijanov str., 220141 **Minsk**
Tel: 172-607 313/310 758 Fax: 172-607 313/310 758
contact Antonina Mikhaltsova

International Festival of Organ Music – Polock
Mjezhdunarodnyj fjestival organnoj muzuki – Polock
Ministjerstvo kultury (The Ministry of Culture), pr. Mashjerova 11, 220004 **Minsk**
Tel: 172-235 825 Fax: 172-235 825

International Festival Regeneration of Belarussian Capelle
Mjezhdunarodnyj fjestival Vozrozhdjenije bjeloruskoj kapjelly
Ministjerstvo kultury (The Ministry of Culture), pr. Mashjerova 11, 220004 **Minsk**
Tel: 172-235 825 Fax: 172-235 825

International Folk Festival, Brest, The
Mjezhdunarodnyj Fjestival Folklora, Brjest
Ministjerstvo kultury (The Ministry of Culture), pr. Mashjerova 11, 220004 **Minsk**
Tel: 172-235 825 Fax: 172-235 825

International Jazz Festival
Mjezhdunarodnyj Dzhasovyj Fjestival
Ministjerstvo kultury (The Ministry of Culture), pr. Mashjerova 11, 220004 **Minsk**
Tel: 172-235 825 Fax: 172-235 825

International Music Festival The Golden Shlager – Mogilov, Minsk, The
Mjezhdunarodnyj Muzykalnyj Fjestival Zolotoj Chlagjer – Mogiljov, Minsk
Ministjerstvo kultury (The Ministry of Culture), pr. Mashjerova, 11, 220004 **Minsk**
Tel: 172-235 825 Fax: 172-235 825

International Puppet Theatre Festival
Mjezhdunarodnyj Fjestival Tjeatrov Kukol
Minsk
Tel: 172-271 365
director Jevgjenij Klimakov

International Youth Festival Young Belarus
Mjezhdunarodnyj molodjozhnyj fjestival Molodaja Bjelarus
Ministjerstvo kultury (The Ministry of Culture), pr. Mashjerova 11, 220004 **Minsk**
Tel: 172-235 825 Fax: 172-235 825

Ja International Monoperformance Festival
Mjezhdunarodnyj Fjestival Monospjektaklej Ja
Minsk
Tel: 172-366 982
director Alljeksjej Dudarjev

Minsk Spring International Arts Festival
Mjezhdunarodnyj Fjestival Iskusstv Minskaja Vjesna
Bjelgosfilarmonija, pr. Franciska Skoryny 50, 220005 **Minsk**
Tel: 172-319 050
Fax: 172-319 050
director Jurij Gildiuk
Period/Frequency: April

Slavianskie Teatralnye Vstrechi International Dramatic Theatre Festival
Mjezhdunarodnyj Fjestival Dramatichjeskikh Tjeatrov Slavianskie Tjeatralnye Vstrjechi
Ministjerstvo kultury (The Ministry of Culture), pr. Mashjerova 11, 220004 **Minsk**
Tel: 172-235 825 Fax: 172-235 825

Sozhski Karagod International Festival of Choreography Art, Gomell, The
Mjezhdunarodnyj Fjestival Khorjeografichjeskogo Iskustva Sozhski Karagod, Gomjell
Ministjerstvo kultury (The Ministry of Culture), pr. Mashjerova, 11, 220004 **Minsk**
Tel: 172-235 825 Fax: 172-235 825
Arts types: choreography

Spiritual Music Festival
Fjestival Dukhovnoj Muzyki
Ministjerstvo kultury (The Ministry of Culture), prosp. Mashjerova 11, 220004 **Minsk**
Tel: 172-235 825 Fax: 172-235 825

Zveniat Cimbaly i Garmonn Folk Music Festival
Fjestival Narodnoj Muzyki Zvjeniat Cimbaly i Garmonn
Ministjerstvo kultury (The Ministry of Culture), pr. Mashjerova 11, 220004 **Minsk**
Tel: 172-235 825 Fax: 172-235 825

Magutny Bozha Spiritual Music Festival
Fjestival Dukhovnoj Muzyki Magutny Bozha
Kostjol Svjatogo Stanislava, 212000 **Mogiljov**
Tel: 222-221 993 Fax: 222-220 283

Modern Choreography Festival
Fjestival Sovrjemjennoj Khorjeographii
Dirjekcija Fjestivalja (Festival Board of Directors), Park Frunzje, 210602 **Vitjebsk**
Tel: 212-374 902 Fax: 212-374 902
Period/Frequency: Nov

Slavianskij Bazar Variety Music Festival
Fjestival Estradnoj Muzyki Slavianskij Bazar
ul. Majakovskogo 1, 210000 **Vitjebsk**
Tel: 212-374 949 Fax: 212-374 949
Period/Frequency: July

Solertinski International Festival Chamber Music
Mjezhdunarodnyj Fjestival Kamjernoj Muzyki imjeni Soljertinskogo
Vitjebskoje Muzykalnoje Obshchjestvo (Vitjebsk Musical Society), pl. Ljenina 69, 210602 **Vitjebsk**
Tel: 212-372 171 Fax: 212-372 171
director Vladimir Pravilov
Period/Frequency: Dec

BELGIUM (+32)

De Beweeging
Gaastraat 90, 2060 **Antwerp**
Tel: 3-225 1066 Fax: 3-225 2135
Internet: www.debeweeging.be
E-Mail: mail@debeweeging.be
contact Antonio Jimenez
Period/Frequency: spring, summer, autumn, three times a year *Arts types:* dance, performance, fine art

Festival of Free Music
WIM, vzm, St. Vincentiusstraat 61, 2018 **Antwerp**
Tel: 3-230 6075 Fax: 3-281 5084
chairman Fred van Hove
Period/Frequency: first weekend of Aug (Thursday, Friday, Saturday), annual *Venues:* theater Zuidpool *Comments:* festival of free improvised music; venue address: Lange Noordstraat 11, Antwerp

Flanders Festival – Antwerp
Festival van Vlaanderen – Antwerp
Hessenhuis, Falconrui 53, 2000 **Antwerp**
Tel: 3-206 0367 Fax: 3-206 0370
Internet: www.dma.be/cultuur/festival/
E-Mail: flanders.festival@antwerpen.be
director Lieve Schaubroeck
Period/Frequency: Aug- polyphonic early music (15th – 16th century); Sept- contemporary & classical, annual *Arts types:* early, contemporary & classical music *Venues:* churches, museums & concert halls throughout Antwerp *Comments:* international guests booked

Junge Hunde Festival
Monty. Montignystraat 3, 2018 **Antwerp**
Tel: 3-238 6497 Fax: 3-238 0991
E-Mail: monty@village.uunet.be
contact Jeniffer Spricht
Period/Frequency: February *Arts types:* contemporary dance *Venues:* Monty 250-600 *Comments:* see also Venues (Monty)

Festival de Théâtre de Rue – Les Unes Fois D'un Soir
Rue des Ecriniers 5, 7800 **Ath**
Tel: 68-840 470 Fax: 68-840 721
E-Mail: 1x1soir@online.be
director Luc de Groeve
Period/Frequency: Aug, biennial (2000) *Arts types:* street theatre *Comments:* see also Agents (Walrus Productions)

Vlaams Poppen-en Figurentheaterfestival Beveren
Smisstraat 23, 9120 **Beveren**
Tel: 3-755 2445/476-338 403 Fax: 3-755 2445
E-Mail: ronny.aelbrecht@skynet.be
director Ronny Aelbrecht; PR Rudy Van Driessche
Period/Frequency: Aug, biennial (2001) *Arts types:* puppetry *Venues:* Beveren – theatres & open-air venues

Flanders Festival – Bruges
Festival van Vlaanderen – Brugge
Musica Antiqua Competitions, Collaert Mansionstraat 30, 8000 **Bruges**
Tel: 50-332 283 Fax: 50-345 204
Internet: musica-antiqua.com
E-Mail: musica-antiqua@unicall.be
festival director Robrecht Dewitte MBE
Period/Frequency: July-Aug, annual *Arts types:* early music, competitions: strings, winds, ensembles up to 1750; organ (2000); harpsicord & fortepiano (2001); *Venues:* historical halls and churches *Second Address:* Tourist Office, Burg 11, 8000 Bruges, Tel: 5044 8686, Fax: 5044 8600 *Comments:* see also Competitions

Brussels 2000 – European City of Culture
Capitale de l'Europe Ville culturelle de l'an 2000
Anspach Centre Boulevard Anspach 36, 1000 **Brussels**
Tel: 2-214 2000 Fax: 2-214 2020
Internet: www.brussels2000.be
E-Mail: admin@brussels2000.be
intendant Robert Palmer; programme coordinator dance & special events Guido Minne; programme coordinator literature & theatre Bernard Debroux; programme coordinator education & social activities Marcel De Munnynck; programme coordinator visual arts Annick de Ville; programme coordinator video, new media & cinema Dirk De Wit; programme coordinator infostructure Marie-Laure Roggemans; programme coordinator music Bert Schreusse
Period/Frequency: throughout the year 2000 *Arts types:* performing and visual arts, new media, education *Venues:* usual and unusual venues in Brussels, including launderettes *Comments:* Brussels is one of the 9 joint European Cities of Culture in the year 2000; pre-opening Sept '99; official opening last weekend of February 2000; closing event in 2001; plans to create a big black box

Festival Ars Musica
89 rue Royale, 1000 **Brussels**
Tel: 2-219 2660 Fax: 2-219 8814
Internet: www.arsmusica.be
E-Mail: secretariat@arsmusica.be
president Robert Wangermee; administrator Christian Renard; secrétaire général Virginie Civrais
Period/Frequency: 2000: 16 March-1April, annual *Arts types:* contemporary music, seminars, lectures and concerts by young European musicians *Venues:* Brussels and other cities in Belgium

Festival Couleur Café
c/o ZIG ZAG asbl, Ave. E. Claes 4, 1160 **Brussels**
Tel: 2-672 4912 Fax: 2-672 1291
Internet: www.couleurcafe.org
E-Mail: organisation@couleurcafe.org
direction et programmation Patrick Wallens; suivi contrats artistes Fabienne Borle; communication et promotion Michel Durieux
Period/Frequency: June, annual *Arts types:* world music, reggae, rap, salsa, samba, zouk, dub, funk, soul, raï, son, percussions *Venues:* 3 outdoor stages, 2 tents; cap. 1700 and 4000 *Comments:* also exhibitions

Festival des Midis-Minimes
c/o F.E. de Wasseige, Rue Grisar 21, 1070 **Brussels**
Tel: 2-527 3847 Fax: 2-520 7150
Internet: www.cyclone.be/midminim
E-Mail: F.E.de.Wasseige@cyclone.be
artistic director François-Emmanuel de Wasseige
Period/Frequency: July/Aug, annual *Arts types:* mainly chamber music, baroque & early music on period instruments, recitals, some traditional & jazz music: one concert a day except on Saturdays and Sundays; free entrance, noon concerts (42 performances/year) *Venues:* Eglise des Minimes (Brussels) 400, Royal Conservatory Concert Hall (Brussels) 600 *Comments:* see also Agents and Producers

Festival International Bellone – Brigittines
46 Rue de Flandre, 1000 **Brussels**
Tel: 2-506 4300 Fax: 2-503 1200
E-Mail: brigittines@skynet.be
artistic director Monique Duren, Patrick Bonté; administrator Jean-Marie Lemaître; promotion attachee Valerie Degauquier; technical director Pierre Stoffyn
Period/Frequency: second half of Aug – beg. of Sept, annual *Arts types:* contemporary dance, visual theatre *Venues:* Chapelle des Brigittines 160, Cour de la Bellone/Maison du Spectacle 120 *Comments:* venue address: Chapelle des Brigittines, Petite rue des Brigittines, 1000, Brussels; office address: Cour de la Bellone, 46 rue de Flandre, 1000 Brussels

Fête de la Musique en Communauté Française
Conseil Dela Musique, 236 rue Royale, 1210 **Brussels**
Tel: 2-226 1203 Fax: 2-219 6660
Internet: www.datanet.be/ConseilDeLaMusique
secrétaire général Georges Dumortier; coordinatice t.b.a.
Period/Frequency: June, annual *Arts types:* all types of music *Venues:* open-air all around the French speaking community (Brussels and Walloonia) *Comments:* all performances are free

Flanders Festival International – Brussels
Festival van Vlaanderen International
Rue Ravenstein, 60, 1000 **Brussels**
Tel: 2-548 9595 Fax: 2-548 9590
Internet: www.festival-vlaanderen.be
E-Mail: festival@skynet.be
general director Jan Briers jr.; programme manager Francis Maes; communications manager Paskal Deboosen
Period/Frequency: April-June: Kortrijk, May-July: Limburg, July-Aug: Bruges, Aug: Antwerp, Sept-Oct: Brussels, Gent, Oct: Mechelen, Leuven *Arts types:* baroque, classical, contemporary music, opera, ballet *Second address:* P.B.A.; Tel: 2-507 8200

Fondation Europalia International –Festival des Arts et de la Culture
10 Rue Royale, 1000 **Brussels**
Tel: 2-507 8550 Fax: 2-513 5488
Internet: www.europalia.com
E-Mail: europalia@skynet.be
general director Luc Stainier; musical, theatre and dance director Hadelin Donnet; external relations Colette Delmotte; director exhibitions Anne Mommens; financial manager Serge Symens; musical director Agnes Van Kerckhove; in charge of theatre & dance Dominique Daiwaille
Period/Frequency: Oct-Jan, annual *Arts types:* music, exhibitions, theatre, dance, literature, cinema *Venues:* Brussels, other cities in Belgium

Francophonies Théâtrales – Festival International de Théâtre Francophone
c/o ADAC, Rue Royale 10, 1000 **Brussels**
Tel: 2-507 8520 Fax: 2-507 8533
director Alain Leempoel;
communication & press relations Sophie Dupave
Period/Frequency: March-April, biennial (2000) *Arts types:* theatre from French-speaking countries *Venues:* Palais des Beaux-Arts (different halls) *Comments:* see also Promoters (ADAC)

International Summer Academy of Belgium (ISAB)
3 Ave H. Hollevoet, 1080 **Brussels**
Tel: 2-425 0022/420 0606
artistic director & president Hugues Navez
Period/Frequency: July-Aug, annual *Arts types:* instrumental, dance, theatre, musicals, vocal
Venues: Abbaye de Floreffe

Juillet Musical d'Aulne
12 Avenue Delleur, 1140 **Brussels**
Tel: 2-673 0353 Fax: 2-675 6444
président Christian Daubie; contact Dominique Cornil
Period/Frequency: last weekend June & 1st 2 weekends July *Arts types:* mostly classical music, 1 jazz festival, baroque *Venues:* Abbaye d'Aulne 500

kunsten Festival des Arts- Brussel
Brussels International Arts Festival
Quai du Commerce 18, Handelskaai, 1000 **Brussels**
Tel: 2-219 0707 Fax: 2-218 7453
E-Mail: kfda@innet.be
administrateur Jean-François Gerard; artistic director Frie Leysen; communication/presse Sophie van Stratum, Marc Toussait; dramaturge Claire Diez
Period/Frequency: May, biennial (2000) *Arts types:* contemporary arts – drama, dance, contemporary music, non-commercial film and video works, puppet theatre *Venues:* various venues throughout Brussels

Bis Arts
Centre Culture régional de Charleroi,
Boulevard Jacques Bertrand 3, 6000 **Charleroi**
Tel: 71-202 999 Fax: 71-308 541
E-Mail: ccvc@skynet.be
artistic directors Sylvano D'Angelo, Pierre Bolle
Period/Frequency: annual, 20 Oct-15 Nov 2000 *Arts types:* live performance art – music, dance, theatre, circus *Venues:* in and around Charleroi *Comments:* performing original arts

Festival d'Orgue de Châtelet
Eglise St. Pierre et Paul, 6200 **Châtelet**
Tel: 81-614 553
directeur Thierry Smets
Period/Frequency: Sept-Oct, annual *Arts types:* romantic, French symphonic *Venues:* Church St. Pierre et Paul 500
Second Address: 16, rue des Roses, 5030 Gembloux

Festival musical du Brabant Wallon
Rue Belotte 3, 1490 **Court St Etienne**
Tel: 10-615 777 Fax: 10-615 742
E-Mail: ccbw@euronet.be
coordinator Vincent Geens
Period/Frequency: Sept-Oct, annual *Arts types:* classical music *Venues:* churches and cultural centres throughout the Brabant Wallon *Comments:* member of Festival de Wallonie (q.v.)

Festival de l'Eté Mosan
35 rue Grande, 5500 **Dinant**
Tel: 82-225 924 Fax: 82-227 918
Internet: www.skynet.be/festival.html
president Emile Wauthy; administrator Ludovic de San
Period/Frequency: July-Sept, annual *Arts types:* classical music (orchestral, choir, chamber music concerts), jazz, recitals *Venues:* historic sites in Wallonie

Europees Figurenteatercentrum
Trommelstraat 1, 9000 **Gent**
Tel: 9-223 1215 Fax: 9-225 4545
E-Mail: eftc@skynet.be
co-ordinator Freek Neirynck; secretary Myriam Bodenghien
Period/Frequency: International Puppetbuskers Festival, July, biennial (2001); Figeuro, week of 21 July, biennial (even years) *Arts types:* puppetry and figurework *Venues:* Figurentheater Centre, 3 spaces 100 & 100 & 75
Comments: information centre for puppet theatre; see also National Organisations

Flanders Festival International – Gent
Festival van Vlaanderen International
Kleine Gentstraat 46, 9051 **Gent**
Tel: 9-243 9494 Fax: 9-243 9490
Internet: www.festival-vlaanderen.be
E-Mail: festival@skynet.be
general director Jan Briers jr.;
programme manager Francis Maes;
communications manager Paskal De Boosere
Period/Frequency: April-June: Kortrijk, May-July: Limburg, July-Aug: Bruges, Aug: Antwerp, Sept-Oct: Brussels, Gent, Oct: Mechelen, Leuven *Arts types:* baroque, classical, contemporary music, opera, ballet

Gentse Feesten Bij Sint-Jacobs
VZW Trefpunt, Bij Sint Jacobs 18, 9000 **Gent**
Tel: 9-225 3676 Fax: 9-233 1037
Internet: www.istf.be
E-Mail: trefpunt@netpoint.be
festival director Guido de Leeuw;
artistic direction Fabien Audooren
Period/Frequency: July, annual *Arts types:* mainly world music, classical, contemporary music, jazz *Comments:* within the festival also: dance workshops, children's festival, 1 classic film every evening (in cooperation with International Film Festival), debates/discussions with philosphers etc., dance hop

International Street Theatre Festival
Bij Sint-Jacobs 18, 9000 **Gent**
Tel: 9-225 3676 Fax: 9-233 1037
Internet: www.istf.be
E-Mail: street@istf.be
festival director Guido de Leeuw;
artistic director Fabien Audooren
Period/Frequency: July, biennial (2000) *Arts types:* movement theatre, street-theatre, street performance
Venues: Ghent *Comments:* co-produces street theatre

Victoria Festival
Fratersplein 7, 9000 **Gent**
Tel: 9-225 3732/269 0969
Fax: 9-225 0076
Internet: www.victoria.be
E-Mail: victoriatheatre@compuserve.com
general management Katrien Laporte; artistic coordinator Dirk Pauwels; production manager Pat de Wit; press and promotion management Koen Gisen; administration Linda Staelens, Mieke Declercq
Period/Frequency: end of April – beginning of May, annual *Arts types:* young people's & adult theatre, dance, video, plastic arts, music
Venues: Vooruit Arts Centre (8 halls), Minard Schouwburg 220, Victoria 120, and others *Comments:* see also Drama (Victoria Productions)

Vooruit Geluid Festival
Vooruit Arts Centre,
Sint-Pietersnieuwstraat 23, 9000 **Gent**
Tel: 9-267 2820 Fax: 9-267 2830
Internet: www.vooruit.be
E-Mail: wim.wabbes@vooruit.be
programme directors Wim Wabbes, Eva De Groote; coordinators Saskia Bovÿn; press Peter van den Eeden
Period/Frequency: beg. May, biennial (2000) *Arts types:* new music, avantgarde rock, improvised jazz, contemporary, ethnic and electronic music *Venues:* Salle de Concerts 1200 (standing), Salle de Théâtre 800, Salle de bal 500 (standing) 200 (seated), Salle du Dôme 200

Petits Concerts du Dimanche, Les
Organisation Edmond Cigrang, BP 18, 6720 **Habay**
Tel: 63-422 942 Fax: 63-424 050
E-Mail: Intart.M.Coppens@village.uunet.be
artistic director Marleen Coppens
Period/Frequency: Oct-May *Arts types:* chamber music
Venues: Villa Louvigny 300 (Luxembourg)

Flanders Festival – Kortrijk
Festival van Vlaanderen – Kortrijk
Jan Breydellaan 12, 8500 **Kortrijk**
Tel: 56-222 829 Fax: 56-220 502
Internet: www.yw3.com
E-Mail: kor@euronet.be
director Johan Denaux; prèsident Mme Denaux
Period/Frequency: March/June, annual *Arts types:* classical music (symphony, chamber, choral) *Venues:* various venues in Kortrijk and the surrounding area

Festival de Wallonie – Hainaut
33 Rue Paul Pature, 7100 **La Lousiere**
Tel: 64-226 340 Fax: 64-281 509
administrateur délégué Mme Rolin;
directeur artistique Frédéric Mariage
Period/Frequency: Sept/Oct, annual *Arts types:* classical music *Venues:* throughout Hainaut
Comments: member of Festival de Wallonie (q.v.)

Flanders Festival – Flemish Brabant
Brusselsestraat 63, 3000 **Leuven**
Tel: 16-200 540 Fax: 16-205 224
E-Mail: festival.vlaams.brabant@skynet.be
artistic director Prof Mark Delaere; responsable production Kathleen van den Eynde; financial director Luk Joly; resonsable communication Veerle Declerck
Period/Frequency: Sept-Oct, annual *Arts types:* even years: 20th century music, odd years: polyphonic music and every year: classical & romantic music; starting in Oct 2000: international avant-garde festival (3 days)
Venues: churches & different sites in the University of Leuven & important historical cities in the Province of Flemish Brabant

Klapstuk
E Van Evenstraat 2D, 3000 **Leuven**
Tel: 16-236 773 Fax: 16-224 676
Internet: www.stuc.kuleuven.ac.be/klapstuk
E-Mail: klapstuk@stuc.kuleuven.ac.be
production manager Kurt Lannoye; artistic directors An-Marie Lambrechts, Karolien Derwael, Griet Van Laer
Period/Frequency: Oct, biennial (2001) *Arts types:* contemporary dance *Venues:* different theatres in Leuven *Comments:* throughout the season Klapstuk invites choreographers to work in its studio for contemporary dance; see also Venues

Festival International de Durbuy
41 rue des Guillemins, 4000 **Liège**
Tel: 4-252 0701 Fax: 4-252 0701
president Jean Duchesne;
artistic director Emmanuel Koch
Period/Frequency: July-Oct, annual *Arts types:* classical music (symphonic, chamber, piano recitals, organ concerts) *Venues:* L'Eglise de Durbuy 300, L'Eglise de Hamoir 600, L'Eglisé d'Ocquier 300 *Second Address:* 176 Bvd d'Avroy, 4000 Liège Tel: 4-223 4630

Les Nuits de Septembre
Rue des Mineurs, 17, 4000 **Liège**
Tel: 4-223 3489 Fax: 4-222 1540
E-Mail: jmlg@arcadis.be
director Phillipe Vendrix; administrator Claire Ringlet
Period/Frequency: Sept, annual *Arts types:* early & baroque music *Venues:* churches and halls in Liège
Second Address: Université de Liège, Département de musicologie, Quai Roosevelt Ulg 4,
4000 Liège, Belgium, Tel: 4-366 5369
Comments: Thematic Festival: 1999 Metamorphoses

Rencontres d'Octobre – Festival International des Arts de La Scène
Palais des Congrès, Esplanade de l'Europe 2,
4020 **Liège**
Tel: 4-343 4247 Fax: 4-344 4966
Internet: www.moderne.org/rencontresoctobre/
directeur Robert Maréchal; relations publiques Geneviève Romijn; assistante Nathalie Nicosia
Period/Frequency: Oct, annual *Arts types:* theatre, dance, music *Venues:* different halls in Liège, Brussels and other towns in the French-speaking community

Flanders Festival – Mechelen
Festival van Vlaanderen – Mechelen
Stadhuis, Grote Markt 21, 2800 **Mechelen**
Tel: 15-297 822
Fax: 15-297 823
Internet: www.mechelen.be/stadsdienstenfestival.htm
E-Mail: festvlaan@mechelen.be
contact Marcel Kocken
Period/Frequency: Sept/Oct; annual *Arts types:* classical music, organ, bell-ringing *Venues:*
Mechelen and surrounding area

Festival de Chorales Paroissiales
Quai de l'Écluse, Résidence Lillas 6/45,
5000 **Namur**
Tel: 71-774 004 Fax: 71-740 412
directeur Fernard Legrain;
secrétaire Madelaine Laduron
Period/Frequency: Oct, annual *Arts types:* classical, sacred choral music *Venues:* L'Abbaye de Floreffe 1500
Comments: reunion of chorals; the festival is not open to the public, it is a festival for choirs only

Festival de Namur
42 Rue de fer, 5000 **Namur**
Tel: 81-246 420 Fax: 81-246 554
président Amand Dalem; vice-président Jean-Louis Close; directeur artistique Jean-Marie Marchal; administrateur-délégué Etienne Malherbe
Period/Frequency: July, annual *Arts types:* classical, mainly vocal *Venues:* churches and venues throughout the province of Namur *Second Address:* avenue Jean Premier 2, 5000 Namur, Belgium, Tel: 81-742 752
Comments: member of Festival de Wallonie (q.v.)

Festival de Wallonie (Federation)
Rue de l'Armée Grouchy 20, 5000 **Namur**
Tel: 81-733 781
Fax: 81-742 503
Internet: www.festival.wallonie.org
E-Mail: festival.wallonie@skynet.be
general secretary Baudouin Muylle;
artistic affairs Anne Hallet
Period/Frequency: June-Oct, annual *Arts types:* classical music *Venues:* various venues in Wallonie and Brussels
Comments: consists of 6 member festivals: Festival de Namur, Festival de Liège, Juillet Musical de Saint-Hubert, Festial de Stavelot, Festival musical de Brabant-Wallon and Festival de Wallonie-Hainaut

Namur en Mai – Festival des Arts Forains
Promotion des Arts Forains asbl,
rue des Brasseurs 156, 5000 **Namur**
Tel: 81-222 042 Fax: 81-222 042
Internet: www.seilles.arc.be/forains/webcam.htm
président du festival Jean-Louis Close;
présidente des Arts Forains Nele Paxinou;
production & organisation Jean-Félix Tirtiaux
communication & programmation Nathalie Tirtiaux
Period/Frequency: annual *Arts types:* fairground entertainers, exhibitions, street performers, theatre
Comments: alternative website: www.namur.be

Festival L'Espace du Son
c/o Musiques et Recherches, 3 Place de Ransbeck,
1380 **Ohain**
Tel: 2-354 4368 Fax: 2-351 0094
E-Mail: musiques.recherches@skynet.be
secretaire France Dubois; directeur artistique Annette Vande Gorne; administratrice Marianne Binard
Period/Frequency: annual, Oct 2000 *Arts types:* electroacoustic music, acousmatic music (on tape) *Venues:* XI – Theatre (Brussels) 250

Musica Antiqua Leuven VZW
Lostraat 235, 3212 **Pellenberg**
Tel: 16-257 099 Fax: 16-257 099
contact Luk Joly, Clara Buelens
Period/Frequency: Nov, annual *Arts types:* baroque
Venues: Aula de Somer, Leuven 800, St. Peters Church 200

Festival Musical des Raspes
22 Rue Gillard, 6043 **Ransart**
Tel: 71-352 258 Fax: 71-357 327
administration Jacques Cowez;
directeur artistique André Rulens (tel: 71-303 809);
directrice artistique et programmation Mme Promreur
Period/Frequency: May-June, annual *Arts types:* classical, jazz, music – especially chamber music *Venues:* L'Orangerie 500, La Chapelle 150, L'hôtel de Ville 150
Comments: see also Orchestras

Été Musical de Roisin
c/o Dr. Henri Bataille, 26 rue Prévost, 7387 **Roisin**
Tel: 65-759 503 (information & bookings)
Fax: 65-759 485
E-Mail: henri.Bataille@village.uunet.be
president Willy Decamps; treasurer Dr. Henri Bataille
Period/Frequency: Aug, annual *Arts types:* classical, baroque, chamber, choral *Venues:* L'Eglise St. Brice à Roisin 300

Juillet Musical de Saint-Hubert
Au Fourneau St Michel, 6870 **Saint-Hubert**
Tel: 61-614 138 Fax: 84-221 936
admin délégué Francis Tinchi
Period/Frequency: July, annual *Arts types:* classical
Venues: Basilic St Hubert and churches *Comments:* member of Festival de Wallonie (q.v.)

Festival musical D'Automne de Sivry-Rance
31 Grand Place, 6470 **Sivry**
Tel: 60-455 793 Fax: 60-456 280
président Philippe Hanon; animateur Claude de Kesel; coordinateur A. Philippe
Period/Frequency: Sep-Dec, annual *Arts types:* classical, jazz, harmony ensemble, folk dance *Venues:* Centre Culturel de Sivry 'Chemin des Amours' 280

Festival Théâtre Spa
Office du Tourisme, Place Royale, 4900 **Spa**
Tel: 87-775 652 Fax: 87-772 683
director general Armand Delcamp;
administrateur Mme Van Snick
Period/Frequency: Aug, annual *Arts types:* theatre *Venues:* Le Casino de Spa (various halls) 1000 and open air stages *Comments:* postal address to contact organisers: BP 80, 1200 Brussels, Tel: 2-731 3647

Festival de Stavelot
Ancienne Abbaye, 4970 **Stavelot**
Tel: 80-862 450 Fax: 42-233 752
director Raymond Micha; communication Suzanne Michard
Period/Frequency: Aug, annual *Arts types:* chamber music *Venues:* L'Ancienne Abbaye de Stavelot 300
Comments: member of Festival de Wallonie (q.v.)

Flanders Festival – Limburg Basilica Concerten
Festival van Vlaanderen – Basilica Concerten Limburg
Vlasmarkt 4, 3700 **Tongeren**
Tel: 12-235 719 Fax: 12-264 126
E-Mail: jovo@club.innet.be
president Camille Swinnen; co-ordinator Josian Vossn
Period/Frequency: May/June, annual *Arts types:* classical music, world music *Venues:* Basilica 800; various castles

BOSNIA & HERZEGOVINA (+387)

International Theatre Festival 'Days of Youth Theatre'
c/o Mostar Youth Theatre, Alekse Santica 20,
8000 **Mostar**
Tel: 88-580 185 Fax: 88-580 185
E-Mail: mtm@cob.net.ba
director Sead Djulic

International Theatre & Film Festival Mes Sarajevo
M. Tita Str 54/1, 71000 **Sarajevo**
Tel: 71-200 392/211 972/471 549 Fax: 71-211 972/471 549
director Edin Mustafic

Sarajevo Winter
c/o International Peace Center, Titova 7a,
71000 **Sarajevo**
Tel: 71-207 946/948/945 Fax: 71-207 946
E-Mail: ipc_sa@zamir.sa.ztn.zer.de
director Ibrahim Spahic
Period/Frequency: Feb-March, annual *Arts types:* theatre, concerts, fine arts, literary events, architecture, video
Comments: member of European Festivals Association

BULGARIA (+359)

International Biennale of humour and satire
PO Box 104, Dom na Humora & Satirata, 5300 **Gabrovo**
Tel: 66-27229 Fax: 66-26989
director Tatiana Tzankova
Period/Frequency: May, biennial (2001)

International Festival of Fair Games and Crafts
2300 **Pernik**
Tel: 76-20320/23890
director Georgy Atanasov

International Laureate Days Katia Popova
Music Agency, PO Box 273,
149 Vassil Levski Str., 5800 **Pleven**
Tel: 64-22918
director Aleko Antonov
Period/Frequency: Oct, biennial (2001) *Comments:* concerts with participation of young laureates from International competitions

European Cultural Month 99: Plovdiv
c/o Municipality Foundation,
22 Saborna str., 4000 **Plovdiv**
Tel: 32-269 402/621 503 Fax: 32-621 503
chairman Anastas Badev; executive dir Alexander Sekoulov

International Chamber Music
50/A Konstantin Stoilov Str., PO Box 548, 4000 **Plovdiv**
Tel: 32-222 897 Fax: 32-222 864
director Dimitar Malanshinov

International Folk Festival
4000 **Plovdiv**
Tel: 32-558 426
director Ivan Dimitrov

Verdiev Festival – Amfitheatre Plovdiv Old Town
4000 **Plovdiv**
Tel: 32-235 198/225 553
director Borislav Ivanov

International March Music Days
Zoya Alexandrova, 3 Tzaribrod, PO Box 464,
7000 **Rousse**
Tel: 82-223 064/230 290 Fax: 82-228 269
E-Mail: muisc_days@mlnk.net
director Iva Chavdarova
Period/Frequency: March, annual
Arts types: symphony, oratorio, chamber

Theatre Summer University
Stefan Kirov Drama Theatre, PO Box 164, 8800 **Sliven**
Tel: 44-27094 Fax: 44-22151
director t.b.a.
Period/Frequency: June, annual

International Apollonia Summer Festival of Arts – Sozopol
c/o Apollonia Art Foundation, 11 Slaveykov Sq.,
1000 **Sofia**
Tel: 2-980 5642/7833 Fax: 2-980 7833
E-Mail: apolonia@techno-link.com
president Prof. Dimo Dimov
Period/Frequency: Sept, annual *Arts types:* music, poetry, theatre, puppetry, films, exhibtions *Comments:* see also Promoters and Agents & Producers

International Sofia Music Weeks
National Palace of Culture, 1 Bulgaria Square, 1414 **Sofia**
Tel: 2-801 025 Fax: 2-543 041
director Dimitar Tapkov
Period/Frequency: May-June, annual *Arts types:* all musical genres *Venues:* National Palace of Culture

Musica Nova-Sofia International Festival of Contemporary Music, The
Evlogi Georgiev Blv. 149, 1504 **Sofia**
Tel: 2-442 780 Fax: 2-432 675
E-Mail: mproducers2@bnr.acad.bg
Period/Frequency: June, annual *Arts types:* composers, comptemporary music *Comments:* alternative E-mail: ludens@mail.bol.bg

ppIANISSIMO
16 V. Aprilov Str., 1504 **Sofia**
Tel: 2-944 1381 Fax: 2-650 921
E-Mail: ppianissimo@mailcom
Period/Frequency: annual *Arts types:* contemporary piano music

Sofia Summer
Bulgarian Chamber Music Agency,
1 Aksakov Street, 1000 **Sofia**
Tel: 2-801 189/876 522 Fax: 2-876 522
director Alexander Kouyumdziev
Period/Frequency: July-Sept, annual *Arts types:* chamber music concerts of soloists, vocal and instrumental ensembles *Venues:* museums and galleries

Television World Events
Television World Foundation,
2 Dunav Str., 1000 **Sofia**
Tel: 2-981 1668 Fax: 2-980 1625
E-Mail: goldena@serv.iinf.bg
director Georgi Kuzmov

Theatre in a Suitcase Festival
PO Box 1001, 1000 **Sofia**
Tel: 2-364 284/738 288 Fax: 2-364 284/738 288
contact Natasha Kourteva, Petar Todorov
Period/Frequency: May-June 2001

International Festival for Opera and Ballet
State Opera and Ballet, 30 Metodi Kusev Blvd.,
6000 **Stara Zagora**
Tel: 42-41015 Fax: 42-41015
director Rumen Neikov

Opera Festival – Stara Zagora
Music Agency, 6000 **Stara Zagora**
Tel: 42-29371/27196/95
director Tenko Kalaidjiev

Varna Summer International Music Festival
43 8th Primorski polk Str., 9000 **Varna**
Tel: 52-220 101/222 425/227 188
Fax: 52-220 101
director Lubomir Kutin; art manager Mincho Minchev
Period/Frequency: June-August, annual *Arts types:* symphony, chamber, opera, ballet, drama, jazz, folk, summer academy *Comments:* founded in 1926

Varna Summer International Theatre Festival
43 8th Primorski polk Str., 9000 **Varna**
Tel: 52-220 101/222 425 Fax: 52-253 011
Period/Frequency: June, annual *Arts types:* drama

Festival of Small Theatrical Forms
Drama Theatre Vratza, Hristo Botev Square,
3000 **Vratza**
Tel: 92-26498 Fax: 92-26498
Period/Frequency: May, annual

CROATIA (+385)

Dubrovnik Summer Festival
Dubrovacki Ljetni Festival
Poljana Paska Milicevica 1,
20000 **Dubrovnik**
Tel: 20-412 288 Fax: 20-427 944
E-Mail: direktor@dbk.festival.hr
director Franco Matusic; drama art director Josko Juvancic; music art director Valter Despalj
Period/Frequency: July/Aug, annual *Arts types:* drama, music, opera, dance, folklore *Comments:* alternative E-mail: program@dbk.festival.hr

Summer Performances on the Island of Krk
Ljetne priredbe Krk
Trg Svetog Kvirina 1, 51500 **Krk**
Tel: 51-221 249 Fax: 51-221 249
director Mladen Milovcic; art director Ivica Frleta

Music Festival Lubenice Music Evenings
Lubenicke glazbene veceri
c/o RIMI CO CONCERTS, Villa Frappart,
V.C. Emina 5, 51415 **Lovran**
Tel: 51-291 001 Fax: 51-292 313
director Ino Mirkovic; contact Silvana Sepic

Music Festival of Rab
Rapske glazbene veceri
c/o RIMI CO CONCERTS, Villa Frappart,
V.C. Emina 5, 51415 **Lovran**
Tel: 51-291 001 Fax: 51-292 313
director Ino Mirkovic; contact Silvana Sepic

Music Festival Summer on Pag
Pasko ljeto
c/o RIMI CO CONCERTS, Villa Frappart,
V.C. Emina 5, 51415 **Lovran**
Tel: 51-291 001 Fax: 51-292 313
director Ino Mirkovic; contact Silvana Sepic

Villa Frappart
c/o RIMI CO CONCERTS, Villa Frappart,
V.C. Emina 5, 51415 **Lovran**
Tel: 51-291 001 Fax: 51-292 313
director Ino Mirkovic; contact Silvana Sepic

Opatija Festival
Festival Opatija
Zert bb, pp 83, 51410 **Opatija**
Tel: 51-271 377/272 840 Fax: 51-272 840
director Raina Milos

Annale of Opera and Ballet
Anale Opere i Baleta
Croatian National Theatre, Zupanijska 9, 31000 **Osijek**
Tel: 31-220 700/734 Fax: 31-220 700/766
director Zeljko Cagalj

International Theatre Festival (PUF) – Pula, Porec
Medunarodni kazalisni festival, PUF – Pula, Porec
c/o Amateur Culture Club League – Pula,
Sergijevaca 32, 52100 **Pula**
Tel: 52-22881
Fax: 52-22881
artistic director Branko Susac (tel: 52-23915)
Period/Frequency: July *Arts types:* theatre *Comments:* organised by Amateur Culture Club League

Sibenik International Children's Festival
Medunarodni Djecij Festival Sibenik
c/o Sibensko kazaliste, Kralja Zvonimira 1
22000 **Sibenik**
Tel: 22-212 134/135/213 123/145
Fax: 22-212 134
director Dragan Zlatovic (tel: 22-213 145);
contact Jasenka Ramljak (tel: 22-213 145)
Period/Frequency: June/July *Arts types:* drama, music, puppetry, folklore

Split Summer Festival
Splitsko Ljeto
Croatian National Theatre,
Trg Gaje Bulata 1 21000 **Split**
Tel: 21-585 999 Fax: 21-583 643
director Mani Gotovac; manager Rade Perkovic
Period/Frequency: July-August
Arts types: drama, opera, ballet, concerts *Second Address:* Porinova 4, Split (Tel: 21-360 788, Fax: 21-360 789

Varazdin Baroque Evenings
Varazdinske Barokne Vecerí
Augusta Cesarca 1, 42000 **Varazdin**
Tel: 42-212 907 (Koncert office Varazdin)
Fax: 42-212 907
director Vladimir Kranjcevic

Musical Evenings in St. Donat's Zadar
Glazbene Veceri u Sv. Donatu Zadar
Concert Office Zadar, Trg Petra Zoranica 1,
23000 **Zadar**
Tel: 23-315 807 Fax: 23-315 807
E-Mail: kuz@lausa.com
artistic director Antun Dolicki
Period/Frequency: July

Contemporary Dance Week – Zagreb
Tjedan suvremenog plesa – Zagreb
Biankinijeva 5, 10000 **Zagreb**
Tel: 1-641 154 Fax: 1-641 154
art director Mirna Zagar;
producer Vladimir Stoisavljevic
Period/Frequency: June

Festival of New Theatre
Festival novog kazalista
KIC, Preradoviceva 5, 10000 **Zagreb**
Tel: 1-481 0736 Fax: 1-481 0735
artistic director Gordana Vnuk; producer Darko Putak
Period/Frequency: June *Arts types:* new theatre

Festival of New Theatres Eurokaz
Festival Kazalista Eurokaz
J. Gotovca 8, 10000 **Zagreb**
Tel: 1-487 2369 Fax: 1-487 2369
contact Gordana Vnuk

Festival of Rovinj
Festival Rovinj
Zvonimirova 23, 10000 **Zagreb**
Tel: 1-455 6785 Fax: 1-467 7571
director Katja Markotic
Period/Frequency: July-Aug *Second address:* Vlaciceva 8, 55210 Rovinj, Tel/Fax: 52-812 660

Folk Parade
Smotra folklora
Zagreb Concert Management,
Kneza Mislava 18, 10000 **Zagreb**
Tel: 1-461 1797/1807 Fax: 1-461 1709/1807
director Zorica Vitez

International Festival of Contemporary Music Zagreb
Tel: 1-423 463 Fax: 1-422 850
Internet: www.srce.hr/mbz/
E-Mail: hds@zg.tel.hr
Arts types: contemporary music

Light Music Festival ALTA
Alta Festival Zabavne Glazbe
Music Production,
Berislaviceva 9, 10000 **Zagreb**
Tel: 1-423 443
Fax: 1-422 850
director Drago Diklic
Second Address: Hrv Drus Skladatelja Alta Muz. Produkcija, 10000 Zagreb, Tel: 1-539 362

Music Biennale Zagreb
c/o Croatian Composers Society,
Berislaviceva 9, 41000 **Zagreb**
Tel: 1-423 463 Fax: 1-422 850
contact Ivo Josipovic
Period/Frequency: April, biennial *Arts types:* contemporary music *Comments:* see also National Organisations

Osor Music Evenings
Muzicke Veceri Osor
Hercegovacka 109, 10000 **Zagreb**
Tel: 1-173 743 Fax: 1-173 743
director Danijel Marusic

Zagreb Summer Festival
Zagrebacki Ljetni Festival
Zagreb Concert Management,
Kneza Mislava 18, 10000 **Zagreb**
Tel: 1-461 1709 Fax: 1-461 1807
director Erika Krpan

CYPRUS (+357)

Larnaka Festival
c/o Larnaka Municipality, PO Box 40045, 6300 **Larnaka**
Tel: 4-653 333/657 745 Fax: 4-653 384/627 244
mayor G Lycourgos
Period/Frequency: July, annual *Arts types:* music, dance, theatre (concerts, modern and classical dance, operas, theatrical performances etc) *Venues:* Larnaka Medieval Fort 700, Patticheion Municipal Amphitheatre, Larnaka 2100, Municipal Theatre of Larnaka 400

Limassol Municipality Summer Events
c/o Limsassol Municipality ,
PO Box 50089, 3600 **Limassol**
Tel: 5-745 919 Fax: 5-354 389
Internet: www.limassolmunicipal.com.cy
E-Mail: limassol.municipal@cytanet.com.cy
mayor Dr D Kontides
Period/Frequency: June-July, annual *Arts types:* music, dance, theatre, art exhibitions *Venues:* Municipal Garden Theatre, Ancient Theatre of Kourion 1800, Patticheion Municipal Theatre, Limassol 750, Medieval Castle Square, various others in Limassol

Kypria International Festival
Cultural Services – Ministry of Education & Culture,
20 Byron Avenue, 1437 **Nicosia**
Tel: 2-303 337/302 442 Fax: 2-673 565
acting director Stelios A. Hadjistyllis
Period/Frequency: Sept, annual *Arts types:* music, drama, dance, opera, cinema, art exhibitions *Venues:* Ancient Theatre of Curium (Limassol) 1800; Makarios III Amphitheatre (Strovolos) 1600, Municipal Theatre (Nicosia) 1200, Municipal Theatre (Larnaka) 400, Markideion Theatre (Pafos) 380, Ancient Odeion (Pafos) 500 *Comments:* arranged in cooperation with Cyprus Tourism Organisation

Pafos Aphrodite Festival
PO Box 60032, 8100 **Pafos**
Tel: 6-232 804/116 Fax: 6-234 762
Period/Frequency: August-September, annual *Arts types:* opera *Venues:* Pafos Castle Square *Comments:* organised by the Pafos Aphrodite Festival Cyprus Ltd

Paralimni Festival
c/o Paralimni Municipality,
PO Box 30033, 5310 **Paralimni**
Tel: 3-821 323 Fax: 3-825 023
mayor N. Vlittis
Arts types: international folklore festival *Venues:* Paralimni Stadium, Municipal Open Air Theatre 2000, Protaras

Strovolos Festival
c/o Strovolos Municipality,
PO Box 25694, 1388 **Strovolos**
Tel: 2-495 700 Fax: 2-494 738
mayor S. Heliophotou; contact Eleni Heracleous
Period/Frequency: April-May and Sept, annual *Arts types:* music, dance, theatre, cinema, art exhibitions *Venues:* Makarios III Amphitheatre 1600, Falcon School Amphitheatre (Strovolos) 900

CZECH REPUBLIC (+420)

Concentus Moraviae – International Music Festival & Information Center
Beethovenova 4, 602 00 **Brno**
Tel: 5-4221 9787 Fax: 5-4221 8450
E-Mail: concent@iol.cz
director David Diettrich; manager Lenka Foltynova
Period/Frequency: June-July, annual *Arts types:* classical music *Venues:* various venues in 13 cities of the Czech Republic *Comments:* every year there is a different theme

Easter Festival of Sacred Music
Velikonocní nl festival duchovnl hudby
c/o ARS/KONCERT s.r.o., Úvoz 39, 602 00 **Brno**
Tel: 5-4323 3116 Fax: 5-4323 3358
E-Mail: mhfb@arskoncert.cz
director Miroslav Stehlík
Period/Frequency: Easter, annual *Arts types:* sacred music *Comments:* see also Agents

Exposition of New Music
Expozice novè hudby
c/o ARS/KONCERT s.r.o., Úvoz 39, 602 00 **Brno**
Tel: 5-4323 3116 Fax: 5-4323 3358
E-Mail: mhfb@arskoncert.cz
director Miroslav Stehlík
Period/Frequency: Oct, annual (2000: 2-6 Oct) *Arts types:* contemporary, new music
Comments: see also Agents

Festival Radosti
Loutkove divadlo Radost, Cejl 29, 602 00 **Brno**
Tel: 5-4532 1273 Fax: 5-4521 0336
Period/Frequency: Nov, annual
Arts types: drama, puppets

Meeting
Setkání
Divadeln fakulta JAMU, Mozartova 1, 602 00 **Brno**
Tel: 5-4221 0136
Fax: 5-4221 2975
E-Mail: zahr.difa@jamu.cz
Period/Frequency: Feb, annual *Arts types:* drama
Comments: International Festival of Theatre Schools

Moravian Autumn
Moravsky podzim
c/o ARS/KONCERT s.r.l., Úvoz 39, 602 00 **Brno**
Tel: 5-4323 3116 Fax: 5-4323 3358
E-Mail: mhfb@arskoncert.cz
president of directorium Arnost Parsch;
director Miroslav Stehlik
Period/Frequency: Sept/Oct, annual *Arts types:* classical music to contemporary, opera *Comments:* theme for 2000 – Goodbye millenium; see also Agents

Musical Days
Dny Operety a Muzikalu
Narodni divadlo v Brne,
Dvorakova 11, 657 70 **Brno**
Tel: 5-4232 1285 Fax: 5-4221 7045
Internet: www.ndbrno.cz
E-Mail: ndb@netbrno.cz
Period/Frequency: Sept, annual
Arts types: musical theatre

Trialog
Narodni divadlo v Brne, Dvorakova 11, 657 70 **Brno**
Tel: 5-4221 3359 Fax: 5-4221 3359
Internet: www.ndbrno.cz
E-Mail: ndb@netbrno.cz
Period/Frequency: Feb, annual *Arts types:* drama

Emy Destinn Music Festival
Hudební slavnosti Emy Destinnové
Emy Destinn Festival Agency,
H. Kvapilové 36, 370 10 **Ceské Budějovice**
Tel: 603-720 300 Fax: 38-34526
director Antonín Kazil
Period/Frequency: Aug/Sept, annual *Comments:* vocal concerts, vocal courses and competition

Pleasant meeting
Príjemné setkání
Studio dell' arte – Divadlo pod cepicí, Prazská 1285/30, 370 01 **Ceské Budějovice**
Tel: 38-25829 Fax: 38-25829
E-Mail: studio.dell.arte@iol.cz
Period/Frequency: May, annual *Comments:* international festival of small theatres

Frontier Theatre Festival
Festival Divadlo na hranici
c/o Tesinske divadlo, Ostravská 67, 737 35 **Cesky Tesín**
Tel: 659-711 208/9 Fax: 659-713 372
Internet: www.tdivadlo.cz
E-Mail: info@tdivadlo.cz
Period/Frequency: Oct, annual *Arts types:* Czech, Slovak and Polish drama theatre *Comments:* run by: Tesínské divadlo and Teatr Polski Bielsko-Cieszyn

Festival One Man Show
Festival divadla jednoho herce
Západoceské divadlo,
Divadelní námestí 10, 350 59 **Cheb**
Tel: 166-433 591/2 Fax: 166-30510
Period/Frequency: Sept, biennial (2001)

Puppet's Chrudim
Loutkárská Chrudim
Muzeum loutkárskych kultur, 537 01 **Chrudim**
contact IPOS-ARTAMA
Period/Frequency: first week in July, annual *Second Address:* IPOS-ARTAMA, Kresomyslova 7, 140 00 Praha 4, Tel:2-6121 5684, Fax: 2-6121 5688 *Comments:* open festival of Czech puppet theatres

Theatre European Regions
Divadlo evropskych regionu
Klicperovo divadlo, Dlouhá 99, 500 01 **Hradec Králové**
Tel: 49-551 4590/1 Fax: 49-551 3782
Internet: hk.cesnet.cz/klicperovo-divadlo/
E-Mail: k-divadlo@hk.cesnet.cz
Period/Frequency: May, annual *Arts types:* open international festival provincial theatres (all forms)

Jirásek's Hronov
Jiráskuv Hronov
Mestsky úrad, 549 31 **Hronov**
contact Dr. M. Strotzer (at IPOS-ARTAMA)
Period/Frequency: Aug, annual *Second Address:* IPOS-ARTAMA, Kresomyslova 7, 140 00 Praha 4, Tel: 2-6121 5684, Fax: 2-6121 5688 *Comments:* special festival of Czech amateurs theatres (all forms)

Choir Music Festival
Festival sborového umeni
Dum kultury odboru, Tolstého 23, 586 01 **Jihlava**
Tel: 66-730 0861 Fax: 66-730 6760
Period/Frequency: June, annual (1999: 23-25 June)
Second Address: IPOS-ARTAMA, Dr. Jaroslava Macková, Kresomyslova 7, 140 00 Prague 4, tel: 2-612 15684-7, fax: 2-6121 5688 *Comments:* some of the concerts are held in Trebic and other towns in the surrounding area

Holidays in Telc
Prázdniny v Telci
c/o Ing. Milan Koláø, Komenského 30, 586 01 **Jihlava**
Tel: 66-739 2622 Fax: 66-739 2622
Internet: webhouse.cz/telc_folk
E-Mail: medved@jitel.cz
contact Ing. Milan Koláø
Period/Frequency: July-Aug, annual (2000: 29 July-13 Aug) *Arts types:* folk, rock, exhibitions, theatre, alternative arts *Comments:* the festival held in the south Moravian town Telc

Dvorák Autumn Festival Karlovy Vary
Dvorákuv Karlovarsky podzim
Karlovarsky symfonicky orchestr,
I.P.Pavlova 14, 360 01 **Karlovy Vary**
Tel: 17-22770/23310/28707-8 (switchboard)
Fax: 17-23753/23310
manager Jana Spirová
Period/Frequency: Sept, annual *Arts types:* concerts, chamber and orchestral music

Kmochuv Kolín / Frantisek Kmoch Festival of Kolín
Ateliér Longin, Karlova 30, 280 00 **Kolín** 1
Tel: 321-27854/24/2-2421 8399/603-439 769 (mobile)
Fax: 321-20263
E-Mail: longin@kolin.cz
Period/Frequency: June, annual *Arts types:* brass music
Comments: international

Kolín Memorial of Gaspard
Kasparuv kolínsky memoriál
Mestské divadlo v Kolíne,
Smetanova 557, 280 00 **Kolín** 4
Tel: 321-720 520 Fax: 321-720 781
Internet: www.divadlo-kolin.cz
E-Mail: email@divadlo-kolin.cz
Period/Frequency: Sept, biennial (2000) *Arts types:* International festival of nonverbal theatre, dedicated to the memory of Jean-Baptiste Gaspard Deburau

Forfest Kromeríz
Umelecká iniciativa, Kojetínská 1425, 767 01 **Kromeríz**
Tel: 634-24316/334 050 (conservatory) Fax: 634-24316
Internet: www.xs4all.nl/~ecpnm/
E-Mail: ck@snt.cz
manager Prof. Zdenka Vaculovicová
Period/Frequency: June, annual *Arts types:* contemporary sacred arts

Materinka
Naivní divadlo Liberec, Moskevská 18, 460 31 **Liberec**
Tel: 48-510 7282/92 Fax: 48-510 7616
Internet: www.oasanet.cz/naive.theatre
E-Mail: naive.theatre@oasanet.cz
director Stanislav Doubrava
Period/Frequency: June, biennial (2001) *Arts types:* festival of professional puppet theatre for children

FESMTH – Festival of Small Theatres
FEMAD – Festival Malych Divadel
Kulturní dum, 289 07 **Libice nad Cidlinou**
contact Dr M. Strotzer at IPOS-ARTAMA
Period/Frequency: Sept, annual *Arts types:* theatre for children, workshops *Second Address:* contact: IPOS-ARTAMA, Kresomyslova 7, 140 00 Praha 4, Tel: 2-6121 5684, Fax: 2-6121 5688

International Opera Festival Smetana's Litomysl
Mezinárodní operní festival Smetanova Litomysl
Smetanova Litomysl, Smetanovo nám 72,
POB 41, 570 01 **Litomysl**
Tel: 464-612 575 Fax: 464-612 575
Internet: www.ltm.cz/smetanovalitomysl
E-Mail: festsl@ltm.cz
director Jan Pikna
Period/Frequency: June-July, annual

Frédéric Chopin Festival
Festival Fryderyka Chopina
Kulturní a Informacní centrum, Hlavní trída 47,
353 01 **Mariánské Lázne**
Tel: 165-622 474/482 Fax: 165-622 617/5892
Period/Frequency: Aug, annual *Arts types:* chamber and symphonic music, exhibitions, every two years national piano competition (next: 2001)

International Guitar Festival
Mezinárodni Kytarovy festival
Castle Mikulov, 692 01 **Mikulov**
Tel: 5-573 769 Fax: 5-573 769
Internet: www.ihost.cz/guitarfest
E-Mail: mmyslivecek@telecom.cz
Period/Frequency: July, annual *Second Address:* Martin Myslivecek, Husova 51, 692 01 Mikulov, Tel: 625-513 128/603-485 250 (mobile)
Comments: also guitar seminars

International Organ Festival
Mezinárodní varhanní festival
Moravská filharmonie,
Horní nám. 23, 772 00 **Olomouc**
Tel: 68-522 8971/4922 Fax: 68-522 8511
Period/Frequency: Sept, annual

Olomouc Spring Festival
Olomoucké hudební jaro
Moravian Philharmonic,
Horní nam 23, 772 00 **Olomouc**
Tel: 68-522 8971/4922 Fax: 68-522 8511
Period/Frequency: May-June, annual
Arts types: serious music

Theatrical Flora
Divadelní Flora
Moravské divadlo, tr. Svobody 33, 771 07 **Olomouc**
Tel: 68-522 3651 Fax: 68-522 5727/81
Internet: www.mdo.olomouc.com
E-Mail: mdo@olomouc.com
manager Marcela Arelyová
Period/Frequency: spring, annual (2000: 25-30 April)
Arts types: drama, opera, operetta, dance *Comments:* festival meeting of theatres with more parts (drama, opera, operette, dance)

International Music Festival Janácek May
Mezinárodní hudební festival Janáckuv Máj
Ars Koncert Ostrava, Masná 10, 702 00 **Ostrava**
Tel: 69-611 4016/612 2300 Fax: 69-611 4016
Internet: www.mmo.cz/jm/index.htm
E-Mail: arsova@ova.bon.cz
manager Jaromír Javùrek
Period/Frequency: May-June, annual (2000: 26 May-15 June) *Arts types:* music, opera, musicological conference Janáckiana

Janácek's Hukvaldy – international Music Festival
Janáckovy Hukvaldy
Národní divadlo moravskoslezské-Fond Janáèkovy Hukvaldy, C.S. Legii 14, 702 00 **Ostrava**
Tel: 69-611 4326/2821 Fax: 69-611 21348/4326
E-Mail: narodni_divadlo_ostrava@oasanet.cz
contact Radmila Kotterbová, Alena Ivanková
Period/Frequency: June-July annual *Arts types:* opera, concerts *Venues:* open air (park and castle) *Comments:* this festival at Janacek's birthplace features music by Janacek and other central European composers

Spectaculo Interesse
Divadlo loutek, Masarykovo nám. 33, 729 82 **Ostrava** 1
Tel: 69-611 4884 Fax: 69-611 4322
E-Mail: loutky.ostrava@post.cz
Period/Frequency: Sept, biennial (2001) *Arts types:* puppetry *Comments:* also workshops

International Festival of Academic Choirs IFAS
Mezinárodní Festival Akademickych Sboru IFAS
Univerzita Pardubice, Studentská 84, 530 09 **Pardubice**
Tel: 40-603 6111/582 264 Fax: 40-626 2582/514 530
manager Ing A Mejstríková
Period/Frequency: June, biennial (2000: 26-28 June) *Arts types:* competitive festival with categories of mixed, female & chamber mixed choirs

International Festival of Childrens' Choirs
Mezinárodní festival detskychsboru
Cultural House of Dubina,
Jana Zajíce 983, 532 12 **Pardubice**
Tel: 40-626 2775/5461/606-804 651 (mobile)
Fax: 40-626 5462
Internet: www.ecn.cz/dubina
manager Gabriela Gutwirthová
Period/Frequency: Nov, annual

Skupa's Plzen
Skupova Plzen
c/o Divadlo Alfa, Rokycanská 7, 312 00 **Plzen**
Tel: 19-726 6520 Fax: 19-726 6736
E-Mail: alfa@pm.cesnet.cz
Period/Frequency: June, biennial (2000) *Arts types:* festival of professional puppet theatres

Smetana's Days
Smetanovské dny
KS Esprit, Sady Petatricátníku 1, 305 29 **Plzen**
Tel: 19-222 390/221 380/279 031
Fax: 19-226 372
Internet: www.central.cz/esprit
E-Mail: esprit@mmp.plzen-city.cz
Period/Frequency: March, annual
Arts types: concerts, theatre and literature performances, exhibitions, symposium

Alternative
Alternativa
c/o Divadlo Archa, Na Porící 26, 110 00 **Praha** 1
Tel: 2-232 7570 Fax: 2-232 2089
Internet: www.radio.cz/archa/
E-Mail: theatre@archa.anet.cz
manager Cestmír Hunát
Period/Frequency: Nov-Dec, annual (2000: 30 Nov-10 Dec) *Second Address:* Unijazz, Jindrisská 5, 110 00 Praha 1, Tel: 2-260 012, Fax: 2-269 276 *Comments:* festival of alternative cultures from all genres; alternative E-mail: unijazz@terminal.cz; alternative Internet: www.unijazz.cz

Between Fences
Mezi ploty
Sdruzení pro bezbariérovou kulturu Nedomysleno – Society for barrier-free culture,
Hrusická 2510, 141 00 **Praha** 4
Tel: 2-765 2725/9002 0115 Fax: 2-581 4601
E-Mail: nedomysleno@atlas.cz
Period/Frequency: May, annual *Arts types:* drama, music
Comments: festival is held in Brno and Prague

Czech Theatre
Ceské divadlo
Umelecka agentura FOIBOS, a.s.,
Atelier Trmalova vila, Vilova 11,
100 00 **Praha** 10
Tel: 2-7210 1121 Fax: 2-7210 1120
Internet: www.foibos.cz
E-Mail: info@foibos.cz
Period/Frequency: Sept-June, annual *Arts types:* drama

Dance Prague
Tanec Praha
Jirsíkova 4, 186 00 **Praha** 8
Tel: 2-2481 3899/7886/602-368 979 Fax: 2-231 9576
E-Mail: office@tanecpha.cz
festival director Yvonna Kreuzmannová-Nováková
Period/Frequency: June-July, annual (2000: 15 June-2 July) *Arts types:* contemporary dance *Venues:* Prague
Comments: international festival and conference for critics and theoreticians; also manages independent dance groups and seminars

Dance Theatre Festival 2000
c/o Déja Donné Production,
Nad Klikovkou 20, 150 00 **Praha** 5
Tel: 2-9004 3018 Fax: 2-9004 3018
Internet: www.osf.cz/dc
E-Mail: duncanct@mbox.vol.cz
artistic director Lenka Flory; administrators Michaela Skodova, Heather McGadie
Period/Frequency: Oct, annual *Arts types:* contemporary dance and dance theatre *Comments:* presenting small companies and solo works

Days of Contemporary Music
Dny soudobé hudby
Association of Music Artists and Scientists,
Radlická 99, 155 00 **Praha** 5
Tel: 2-531 271
Period/Frequency: Nov, annual *Arts types:* Czech contemporary music

Easter Days of Chamber Music
Velikonocní dny komorní hudby
Sonus, Pod Smukyrkou 1049, 150 00 **Praha** 5
Tel: 2-526 583/603-462 919 Fax: 2-526 583
Internet: www.piano.czerny.cz
E-Mail: czerny@czn.cz
director Zdenek Vokurka
Period/Frequency: Easter, annual (2000: 14-16 April)

Entrée to Dance
Entrée k Tanci
Tanec Praha, Jirsíkova 4, 186 00 **Praha** 8
Tel: 2-2481 3899/7886/602-368 979
Fax: 2-231 9576
Internet: www.tanecpha.cz
E-Mail: office@tanecpha.cz
Period/Frequency: April, annual *Arts types:* contemporary dance *Comments:* the festival is held in the east Bohemian town Hradec Králové

Festival of Progressive Personalities from European Dance Theatre
Festival Progresivních Osobností Tanecního Divadla
c/o Duncan Centrum, Branická 41, 140 00 **Praha** 4
Tel: 2-4446 1810 Fax: 2-4446 2354
E-Mail: theatre@archa.anet.cz
Period/Frequency: Oct, annual *Arts types:* contemporary dance *Second Address:* c/o Divadlo Archa, Na Porící 26, 110 00 Praha 1 Tel: 2-232 7570 Fax: 2-232 2089

Four Days in Motion
Ctyri dny v pohybu
Obcanské sdruzení Ctyri dny / Divadelni ustav,
Celetná 17, 110 00 **Praha** 1
Tel: 2-2480 9125
Fax: 2-2481 1452
E-Mail: ctyridny@login.cz
Period/Frequency: autumn, annual *Arts types:* contemporary European independent theatre

International Dance Week
Mezinárodní tyden tance
Tanecni Centrum Praha, U. Vitrniku 3, 162 00 **Praha** 6
Tel: 2-2422 9035/2061 0308/1980
Fax: 2-2061 0306
director Antonín Schneider
Period/Frequency: Jan and Nov, bi-annual *Arts types:* modern dance, seminars, workshops, video-productions, performances

International Festival Divadlo
Mezinárodni festival Divadlo
Mezinárodni festival Divadlo, Celetna 17, 110 00 **Praha** 1
Tel: 2-2481 8184 Fax: 2-2481 8184
Internet: www.festival.divadlo.cz
E-Mail: festival@divadlo.cz
directoro Lukas Matasek (tel: 2-2480 9716)
Period/Frequency: Nov, annual *Arts types:* best season performances of Czech theatres and foreign guests

International Festival of Marionette Theatre for Children
Mezinárodní festival loutkárského divadla pro deti
Mezinárodní institut loutkárského umení,
Karlova 12, 110 00 **Praha** 1
Tel: 2-269 383 Fax: 2-269 383
Period/Frequency: June, annual

International Music Festival in Cesky Krumlov
Mezinárodní hudební festival Cesky Krumlov
Auviex, Perlitová 1820/52, 140 00 **Praha** 4
Tel: 2-6126 1393/3700 Fax: 2-643 0525
Internet: www.auviex.cz
E-Mail: auviex@login.cz
manager Alexandrea Lufinková
Period/Frequency: Aug, annual (2000: 4-26 Aug)
Comments: the festival is held in the south Bohemian town Cesky Krumlov

Mozart Open 2000 – Prague Theatre Festival
Zatecká 1, 110 00 **Praha** 1
Tel: 2-232 3429/2536/4189
Fax: 2-232 3429/2536/4189
Internet: www.mozart.cz
E-Mail: festival@mozart.cz
chairman Dr. Jan Dvorák
Period/Frequency: April-Oct, annual *Arts types:* opera, drama, puppetry, film, exhibition, mime, moving theatre
Comments: see also Agents and Producers (VIA Praga Lmt)

Musica Iudaica
c/o Foundation Musica Iudaica SAI,
Besedni 3, 118 00 **Praha** 1
Tel: 2-5732 0008/9004 1651
Fax: 2-534 234/539 720
E-Mail: czmic@login.cz
secretary Marie Kounovská
Period/Frequency: Oct-Nov, annual
Arts types: Jewish music

Na Prahu!
Konzervator a vyssi odb. skola Jaroslava Jezka,
Roskotova 4/1692, 140 00 **Praha** 4
Tel: 2-4446 0397 Fax: 2-4446 6496
E-Mail: kjj@kjj.cz
Period/Frequency: June, annual *Arts types:* drama, school theatres

Next Wave
agentura VIA PRAGA, Zatecká 1, 110 00 **Praha** 1
Tel: 2-2481 9322/3 Fax: 2-2481 9324
Internet: www.nextwave.cz
E-Mail: festival@mozart.cz
Period/Frequency: Oct, annual *Arts types:* movement theatre and performances

Opera 2001 Festival of Czech Music Theatre
Opera 2001 Festival ceského hudebního divadla
Jednota hudebního divadla, K Vltave 18, 143 00 **Praha** 4
Tel: 2-402 2548 Fax: 2-402 2548
Internet: www.divadlo.cz
E-Mail: herman@ff.cuni.cz
secretary PhDr. Josef Herman, CSc.
Period/Frequency: autumn, biennial (2001: Oct-Nov)

Piano Festival in Cesky Krumlov
Klavirní Festival Cesky Krumlov
Auviex, Perlitová 1820/52, 140 00 **Praha** 4
Tel: 2-6126 1393/3700 Fax: 2-643 0525
Internet: www.auviex.cz
E-Mail: auviex@login.cz
manager Alexandra Lufinková
Period/Frequency: July, annual (2000: 9-22 July) *Arts types:* piano *Comments:* the festival is held in the south Bohemian town Cesky Krumlov

Prague Autumn Festival
Prazsky podzim
Príbenická 20, 130 00 **Praha** 3
Tel: 2-627 8740 Fax: 2-627 8642
Internet: www.prugueautumn.cz
E-Mail: festival@pragueautumn.cz
artistic director and festival administrator Pavel Spiroch; administrator Marie Holá
Period/Frequency: Sept, annual *Arts types:* classical music to contemporary and popular

Prague Choral Festival
Prazské dny sborového zpevu
BTI Travel Service, nám Míru 15, 120 00 **Praha** 2
Tel: 2-627 0411/6940/0427 Fax: 2-254 078/627 6926
director Ing Bedrich Plechác
Period/Frequency: Oct/Nov, annual *Comments:* international competitive review

Prague Confrontation
Prelet nad loutkárskym hnízdem
UNIMA (Divadelní ústav), Celetná 17, 110 00 **Praha** 1
Tel: 2-2480 9131/2 Fax: 2-2481 1452
Period/Frequency: first weekend in Oct, annual *Arts types:* ouppetry *Comments:* the best performances of Czech professional and amateur puppet theatre

Prague – European City of Culture 2000
c/o Prague City Hall, Námestí Republiky 5,
110 00 **Praha** 1
Tel: 2-2200 2383 Fax: 2-2200 2388
Internet: www.praha-emk2000.cz
E-Mail: praha2000@praha-emk2000.cz
Period/Frequency: throughout the year 2000 *Arts types:* performing and visual arts, includes many music, theatre and dance festivals, expositions and other events *Comments:* Praha is one of the 9 joint European Cities of Culture in the year 2000

Prague Spring – International Music Festival
Mezinárodní hudební festival Prazské jaro
Hellichova 18, 118 00 **Praha** 1
Tel: 2-533 474/530 293 Fax: 2-536 040
Internet: www.festival.cz
E-Mail: festival@login.cz
director Dr. Oleg Podgorny; president Libor Pesek
Period/Frequency: May-June, annual *Arts types:* classical music, opera, dance, music competition

Prague Theatre Festival of German Languages
Prazsky divadelní festival nemeckého jazyka
Karlovo nam. 28, 120 00 **Praha** 2
Tel: 2-2223 2303 Fax: 2-2223 2300
E-Mail: pratheaterfes@mbox.vol.cz
director Jitka Jilkova
Period/Frequency: Sept, annual *Arts types:* drama
Comments: international festival of theatres from German speaking countries

Roznov Festival
Roznovské slavnosti
Folklorní sdruzení CR,
Senovázné nám. 24, 118 47 **Praha** 1
Tel: 2-2410 2218 Fax: 2-2421 4647
Period/Frequency: July, annual (2000: 5-9 July) *Arts types:* folklore *Venues:* open-air museum *Comments:* the festival is held in the north Moravian town Roznov pod Radhostem

Slovak Theatre in Prague
Slovenské divadlo v Praze
Divadlo Bez zábradlí, Jungmannova 31, 110 00 **Praha** 1
Tel: 2-2494 6436 Fax: 2-2431 7579
Internet: web.iol.cz/dbz
E-Mail: hermanek@iol.cz
Period/Frequency: Feb, annual *Arts types:* drama
Comments: show of the best Slovak performances from last season

South Bohemian Music Festival
Jihocesky hudební festival
Apolinárská 3a, 128 00 **Praha** 2
Tel: 2-2491 0079 Fax: 2-2491 0079
E-Mail: pavel.janda@ecn.cz
secretary Pavel Janda
Period/Frequency: July, annual *Arts types:* concerts, interpretation courses, piano competitions, conferences, meetings of friends of chamber music *Venues:* Bechyne,Tyn nad Vltavou and other little South Bohemian towns *Second address:* Radoslav Kvapil: Hradecka 5, 130 00 Praha 2, Tel: 2-6731 2430

World Harp Congress
svetovy harfovy kongres
Prazsky podzim, Príbenická 20, 130 00 **Praha** 3
Tel: 2-627 8740/8657 Fax: 2-627 8657
Internet: www.pragueautumn.cz
E-Mail: festival@pragueautumn.cz
Period/Frequency: July

Young Podium
Mladé pódium
Fórum mladych, Radlická 99, 150 00 **Praha** 5
Tel: 2-531 271/603-761 300 (mobile) Fax: 2-539 720
E-Mail: his@vol.cz
manager Jan Machat
Period/Frequency: Aug, annual *Comments:* festival of young artists is held in the west Bohemian town Karlovy Vary; alternative E-mail: czmic@login.cz

Zlomvaz
DAMU – Katedra produkce, Karlova 26, 116 65 **Praha** 1
Tel: 2-2222 0053 Fax: 2-2222 0230
Period/Frequency: May, annual *Arts types:* drama
Comments: festival of theatre universities (Praha, Brno, Bratislava)

International Folklore Festival Stráznice
Mezinárodní folklóní festival Stráznice
Ústav lidové kultury, 696 62 **Stráznice – zámek**
Tel: 631-332 092 Fax: 631-332 101
E-Mail: ulk@brn.pvtnet.cz
manager Ludmila Horehledová
Period/Frequency: June, annual (2000: 23-25 June)
Arts types: folklore *Comments:* also folklore dance and singing competitions, exhibitions

Theatre in Park
Divadlo v parku
Severomoravske divadlo Sumperk,
Komenskeho 1, 787 46 **Sumperk**
Tel: 649-214 061
Internet: www.divadlo.cz/smdivadlo
Period/Frequency: June, annual
Arts types: theatre *Venues:* open-air

Meeting Zlín
Setkání Stretnutie
Mestské divadlo ve Zlíne,
Tomáse Bati 4091/32, 761 87 **Zlín**
Tel: 67-763 6111
Fax: 67-763 6300
E-Mail: divadlo@zl.inext.cz
Period/Frequency: June, biennial (2000)
Arts types: drama

DENMARK (+45)

Aarhus Festival, The
Officersbygningen, Vester Allé 3, 8000 **Aarhus** C
Tel: 8931 8270/2
Fax: 8619 1336
Internet: www.aarhusfestuge.dk
E-Mail: festugeinfo@aarhusfestuge.dk
artistic director Lars Seeberg
Period/Frequency: Sept, annual *Arts types:* opera, classical music, new music, rock, ballet, modern dance, film, theatre, exhibitions, symposia, sports, outdoor events *Venues:* various venues in Aarhus, i.e. The Concert Hall Århus

Aarhus International Jazz Festival
Musikhuset Århus, Thomas Jensens Allé,
8000 **Aarhus** C
Tel: 8931 8200
Fax: 8619 4386
Internet: www.musikhuset-aarhus.dk
E-Mail: musikhus@inet.uni-c.dk
festival coordinator Ilse Vestergaard;
marketing director Martin Lai
Period/Frequency: usually 3rd week in July, annual
Arts types: all types of jazz: international artists and local musicians in 250 concerts during one week
Venues: Musikhuset and various other venues in the city
Comments: other activities: exhibitions (record covers, jazz photos), street parades

NUMUS Festival
c/o Musikhuset Aarhus,
Thomas Jensens Allé, 8000 **Aarhus**
Tel: 8931 8200
Fax: 8619 4386
Internet: www.musikhuset-aarhus.dk
E-Mail: musikhus@inet.uni-c.dk
artistic director Karl Aage Rasmussen
Period/Frequency: late April, annual *Arts types:* new, experimental music *Venues:* Musikhuset Aarhus, other venues around Aarhus

Hans Christian Anderssen Festivalen
Fuglebakken 22, 5560 **Aarup**
Tel: 6443 3322 Fax: 6443 3324
E-Mail: ersv@post2.tele.dk
theatre director Erik Bent Svendlund
Period/Frequency: July-Aug, annual *Arts types:* musical based on a fairy-tale by Hans Christian Anderssen
Venues: Hans Christian Anderssen Performing Arts School, Old Village, Odense *Comments:* all performances are given by children at the Hans Christian Anderssen performing arts school

Ballerup Festival
Festivalsekretariatet, Musikhuset Lautrupgård,
Lautrupvej 2, 2750 **Ballerup**
Tel: 4484 5526 Fax: 4484 5932
E-Mail: festibal@dk-online.dk
director Jørgen Artby; administration assistant Birgit Steffensen; marketing assistant Tia Skov Larsen
Period/Frequency: end of Aug, biennial (2001) *Arts types:* big bands, rhythm, folk-dance, concerts, drum bands, small ensembles, theatre, dance, exhibitions, street parades *Venues:* Damgårdsparken (outdoor concerts), churches, concert halls, schools

Nordfyns Festival
Adelgade 44, 5400 **Bogense**
Tel: 6481 3889 (private)
contact Torben Juul
Period/Frequency: August 2000
Arts types: classical music, blues, jazz, ballet, folk songs, Danish poetry *Venues:* towh hall, cafes, art galleries and outdoors

Amager Musikfestival
Gammeltoftsgade 12A, 4,
1355 **Copenhagen** K
Tel: 3316 0131
E-Mail: nielshenrikjessen@get2net.dk
organiser Niels Henrik Jessen
Period/Frequency: Sept-Oct, annual *Arts types:* church, chamber music, contemporary (moderate), choral, early music *Venues:* 14 churches on the island of Amager

Composers Biennale
c/o Dansk Komponist Forening, Gråbrødretorv 16,1,
1154 **Copenhagen** K
Tel: 3313 5405 Fax: 3314 3219
E-Mail: danscore@inet.uni-c.dk
contact Niels Marthinsen, Svend Aaquist,
Klaus Ib Jørgensen
Period/Frequency: March, biennial (2000) *Arts types:* contemporary Danish music *Venues:* indoor concerts in central Copenhagen *Comments:* organised by the Danish Composer's Society

Copenhagen Choir Festival
c/o Greiff Music Gammeltofsgade 16,
1355 **Copenhagen** K
Tel: 3313 5570/5580 Fax: 3313 5540
E-Mail: info@greiff.dk
production manager Anja Reiff;
administrative manager Nicolai Gjessing
Period/Frequency: summer/autumn, annual *Arts types:* choral music *Venues:* Tivoli Concert Hall, Tivoli Gardens, churches, open-air

Copenhagen International Experimental Music Festival (CIEF)
Skræp, Kronprinsensgade 7, 1114 **Copenhagen** K
Tel: 3332 7222 Fax: 3332 7234
Internet: www.skraep.dk
E-Mail: skraep@skraep.dk
administrator Niels Winther
Period/Frequency: annual (17-26 August 2000) *Arts types:* experimental music *Venues:* Den Anden Opera, Kulturfabrikken + open air *Second address:* Tvær vej 10, 3390 Hundested

Copenhagen Jazz Festival
Nytoav 3, 1450 **Copenhagen** K
Tel: 3393 2013 Fax: 3393 2024
Internet: www.jazzfestival.dk
E-Mail: cjf@cjf.dk
chairman & managing director Anders Laursen;
secretary & programme manager Bodil Jacobsen
Period/Frequency: ten days from first Friday in July, annual *Arts types:* mainstream, swing, modern, fusion and avantgarde jazz *Venues:* indoor and outdoor venues in the city centre *Comments:* 500 concerts in 10 days

Golden Days in Copenhagen
Stockholmsgade 20, 2100 **Copenhagen Ø**
Tel: 3542 1432 Fax: 3542 1491
Internet: www.goldendays.dk
E-Mail: info@goldendays.dk
festival co-ordinator Ulla Tofte; chairperson Marianne Saabye; pr & marketing co-ordinator Jesper Moller
Period/Frequency: biennial (2000: 25 Aug-10 Sept) *Arts types:* chamber music, symphonic music, classical theatre, exhibitions *Venues:* National Museum *Comments:* festival focuses on the Danish Golden Age 1800-1850

Images of the World
c/o Danish Center for Culture and Development, DCCD, Vestergade 5, 1456 **Copenhagen** K
Tel: 3317 9700 Fax: 3317 9701
E-Mail: info@dccd.dk
Period/Frequency: Aug and Sept 2000 *Arts types:* music, theatre, dance, visual arts, literature, conferences, crafts, new media *Venues:* Copenhagen and other major towns in Denmark *Comments:* primary focus on the non-Western world; see also National Organisations

Fanø Musikfestival
Toftestien 21, Sønderho, 6720 **Fanø**
Tel: 7516 4429 Fax: 7516 4529
director Vibeke Schøtt
Period/Frequency: July-Aug, annual *Arts types:* recitals, chamber music, chamber orchestra *Venues:* Norby church

Sønderho International Guitar Festival
Gammel Byvej 4, 6720 **Fanø**
Tel: 7516 4383 Fax: 7516 4383
director Jørgen Bjørslev
Period/Frequency: July-Aug, annual *Arts types:* classical concerts with the guitar *Venues:* Sønderho Church 400

Contemporary Music in Suså
Tyvelsevej 26, Tyvelse, 4171 **Glumsø**
Tel: 5764 8102
Internet: www.webline.dk/nymususaa
E-Mail: nymususaa@adr.dk
contact Anne Kristine Smith; artistic director Hans-Henrik Nordstrøm
Period/Frequency: Aug, annual (2000: 26-27 Aug; 2001: 25-26 Aug; 2002: 24-25 Aug) *Arts types:* Danish contemporary music *Venues:* Suså Skolen, Skelly *Comments:* alternative Internet: www.nordstroem.dk

Bornholms Musikfestival
Jydeskæret 1, 3760 **Gudhjem (Bornholm)**
Tel: 5648 4180 Fax: 5648 4180
Internet: www.bornholms-musikfestival.dk
E-Mail: bmf@post7.tele.dk
chairman Mogens Rafn
Period/Frequency: July-Aug, annual *Arts types:* chamber music *Venues:* churches of the island of Bornholm

Vendsyssel Festival
Perikumvej 18, 9800 **Hjørring**
Tel: 9892 4588 Fax: 9891 1354
Internet: www.vendsysselfestival.dk
E-Mail: info@vendsysselfestival.dk
press secretary Bibbi Ungerskov (tel: 9842 3285); chairman of festival association Joergen Boe
Period/Frequency: July-Aug, annual *Arts types:* classical music *Venues:* churches, assembly halls, museums, mansion houses in Jutland *Comments:* around 60 concerts, international guests

Concerts at Louisiana
Gammel Strandvej 13, 3050 **Humlebæk**
Tel: 4919 0719 Fax: 4919 3605
artistic director Lars Fenger
Period/Frequency: all year *Arts types:* mostly chamber music *Venues:* Louisiana Concert Hall 330

Koncerter på Selsø Slott
c/o Mogens Friis, Langs Hegnet 39, 2800 **Lyngby**
Tel: 4593 0778 Fax: 4593 0778
Internet: hjem.get2net.dk/friis.schaeffer
E-Mail: friis.schaeffer@get2net.dk
contact Mogens Friis
Period/Frequency: June-Aug, annual *Arts types:* classical music *Venues:* Selsø Manor House 100 *Comments:* 8 performances per year

Staarup Hovedgaard
c/o Mogens Friis, Langs Hegnet 39, 2800 **Lyngby**
Tel: 4593 0778 Fax: 4593 0778
E-Mail: friis.schaeffer@get2net.dk
contact Mogens Friis
Period/Frequency: annual *Arts types:* classical music

Music Harvest
Musikhøst
c/o Carl Nielsen Academy of Music Odense, Islandsgade 2, 5000 **Odense** C
Tel: 6611 0663 Fax: 6617 7763
managing directors Bertel Krarup, Per Erland Rasmussen; secretary Anette Blauenfeldt
Period/Frequency: autumn, annual *Arts types:* contemporary music from Denmark and abroad *Venues:* Odense Koncerthus, Det Fynske Musikkonservatorium and other local venues

Oremandsgaard Kammermusikfest
Oremandsgaard Allé 2, 4720 **Praestø**
Tel: 5599 6110 Fax: 5599 6005
director Daniel Hage
Period/Frequency: end July-beg. Aug, annual *Arts types:* chamber music *Venues:* Oremandsgaard Husflidsskole *Second Address:* venue address: Oremandsgaard Husflidsskole, 4720 Praestø

Midtfyns Festival
Algade 54, 5750 **Ringe**
Tel: 6262 5624 Fax: 6262 5724
Internet: www.mf.dk
E-Mail: mfmusik@post1.tele.dk
director Nina Færgemann
Period/Frequency: first week of July for 5 days (Weds-Sun), annual *Arts types:* rock, folk music, blues, jazz, dance, techno *Second Address:* during festival: Dyrskuepladsen, Lombjergevej, 5750 Ringe *Comments:* 100 open-air performances

Summerconcerts in St Nicolai Church
St. Nicolai Church, Kirkepadsen 20, 3700 **Rønne**
Tel: 5695 9500 Fax: 5695 3495
Period/Frequency: June – Aug, annual *Arts types:* organ concerts on the famous four manual 51 stops Frobenius Organ *Venues:* Sct Nicolai Kirke *Comments:* 8 evening concerts, mainly organ, throughout June – August

Silkeborg Puppettheater Festival
Silkeborg Bibliotek, Hostrupsgade 41A, 8600 **Silkeborg**
Tel: 8682 0233 (library) Fax: 8680 2679
Internet: silkeborg.bib.dk
E-Mail: dengsoe@silkeborg.bib.dk
Silkeborg Library Ulla Dengsøeg
Period/Frequency: 2nd week in Nov, annual *Arts types:* all types of puppetry *Venues:* Lunden, Vestergade, 8600 Silkeborg *Comments:* performances for children and for adults, workshops, exhibitions in Silkeborg Library and Artscentre Silkeborg Bad

Busbjerg-Spillene
Danstrupvej 14, 8860 **Ulstrup**
Tel: 8668 2423
contact Lau Laursen
Period/Frequency: June-July, annual *Arts types:* theatre *Venues:* open-air *Comments:* 9 performances of one play; union founded 1945

ESTONIA (+372)

International Choir Festival Pärnu
Rahvusvaheline Koorifestival Pärnu
Nikolai 8, 80011 **Pärnu**
Tel: 4-445 801
director Alli Põrk
Period/Frequency: July *Arts types:* choral music

Watergate
c/o W-House Stuudio,
Esplanaadi 10, 80010 **Pärnu**
Tel: 44-42693 Fax: 44-42693
Internet: www.bates.ee/watergate
E-Mail: watergate@chaplin.ee
manager Priit Valkna
Period/Frequency: July, annual *Arts types:* all types of arts *Venues:* various places in Pärnu

Arvo Pärt Festival
Arvo Pärt Virumaal
c/o EESTI KONTSERT, Estonia pst.4, 10148 **Tallinn**
Tel: 6-443 198 Fax: 6-443 198
Internet: www.concert.ee/
E-Mail: eesti.kontsert@concert.ee
director Enno Mattisen; artistic director Peeter Vähi
Period/Frequency: Aug, annual *Arts types:* music from Arvo Pärt and others *Venues:* various in Virumaa County

August Dance Festival
c/o 2.tants, Rataskaevu 10, 10123 **Tallinn**
Tel: 6-269 090 Fax: 6-269 099
manager Priit Raud
Period/Frequency: August, biennal (2001) *Arts types:* contemporary dance, site specific performances *Venues:* theatre and venues in Tallinn

Baltoscandal – International theatre and dance festival
c/o ESP, Rataskaevu 10, 10123 **Tallinn**
Tel: 6-269 098 Fax: 6-269 099
Internet: www.baltoscandal.ee
managing director Valdo Kask; artistic director Peeter Jalakas; dance & workshops Priit Raud
Period/Frequency: June, biennial (2000) *Arts types:* contemporary theatre and dance *Venues:* theatres and open air venues in Rakvere

Baroque Music Days
c/o EESTI KONTSERT, Estonia pst. 4, 10148 **Tallinn**
Tel: 6-440 719 Fax: 6-443 198
Internet: www.concert.ee/
E-Mail: eesti.kontsert@concert.ee
artistic director Andres Mustonen
Period/Frequency: Jan, annual *Comments:* featuring performances from international artists

Eduard Tubin Festival
c/o EESTI KONTSERT, Estonia pst. 4, 10148 **Tallinn**
Tel: 6-446 255 Fax: 6-443 198
Internet: www.concert.ee/
E-Mail: eesti.kontsert@concert.ee
artistic director Neeme Järvi; producers Madis Kolk, Peeter Vähi
Period/Frequency: Aug, annual
Arts types: chamber and symphonic music

Estonian Dance Festival
Eesti Üldtantsupidu
Suur-Karja 23, 10140 **Tallinn**
Tel: 6-449 262 Fax: 6-449 147
manager Ilmar Moss
Period/Frequency: June, every 5 years (2004 *Venues:* Kalev Stadium 9000 dancers, audience 14000
Comments: run by Estonian Song and Dance Festival Foundation

Estonian Song Festival
Eesti Üldlaulupidu
Suur-Karja 23, 10140 **Tallinn**
Tel: 6-449 262 Fax: 6-449 147
manager Ilmar Moss
Period/Frequency: June, every 5 years (2004)
Venues: Song Festival Ground-stage 25000, audience 150000 *Comments:* run by Estonian Song and Dance Festival Foundation

Estonian Youth Song and Dance Festival
Noorte Laulu-ja Tantsupidu
Suur-Karja 23, 10140 **Tallinn**
Tel: 6-449 262 Fax: 6-449 147
manager Ilmar Moss
Period/Frequency: June, every 5 years (2002)
Venues: Song Festival Ground-stage 25000, audience 150000, Kalev Stadion 9000 dancers, audience 14000 *Comments:* run by Estonian Song and Dance Festival Foundation

EVOLUTSIOON Contemporary Dance Festival
c/o 2.tants, Rataskaevu 10, 10123 **Tallinn**
Tel: 6-269 094
Fax: 6-269 099
director Priit Raud; assistant Kaja Kann
Period/Frequency: biennial (2000) *Arts types:* contemporary and modern dance *Venues:* various theatres in Tallinn *Comments:* only East-European companies

Georg Ots Music Festival
Georg Otsa Muusikapäevad
c/o Eesti Kontsert, Estonia pst. 4, 10148 **Tallinn**
Tel: 6-260 260 Fax: 6-260 299
artistic director Arne Mikk
Period/Frequency: spring, annual *Arts types:* classical music and vocal concerts, chamber music

Haapsalu Early Music Festival
Haapsalu Vanamuusikafestival
c/o Concerto Grosso Concert Agency,
Rävala 12, 10143 **Tallinn**
Tel: 6-466 655 Fax: 6-466 676
E-Mail: tsiitan@estpak.ee
manager Egmont Välja; artistic director Toomas Siitan
Period/Frequency: July, annual *Arts types:* early music

International Festival for Contemporary Music-NYYD
Rahvusvaheline uue muusika festival NYYD
c/o Eesti Kontsert, Estonia pst. 4, 10148 **Tallinn**
Tel: 6-446 255 Fax: 6-443 198
Internet: www.concert.ee/
E-Mail: eesti.kontsert@concert.ee
artistic/managing director Madis Kolk
Period/Frequency: Nov, biennial (2001) *Arts types:* contemporary/avant garde music *Venues:* Estonia Concert Hall and various others *Comments:* organised by Eesti Kontsert, see also Promoters

International Music Festival Orient
Rahvusvaheline Muusikafestival Orient
c/o EESTI KONTSERT, Estonia pst.4, 10148 **Tallinn**
Tel: 6-443 670 Fax: 6-443 198
Internet: www.concert.ee/
E-Mail: eesti.kontsert@concert.ee
artistic director Peeter Vähi;
assistant artistic director Elle Himma
Period/Frequency: May, triennial (2001) *Arts types:* folk, sacred, contemporary and classical music from Asia
Venues: Estonia Concert Hall 410

Pärnu Raemuusika Festival
c/o EESTI KONTSERT,
Estonia pst. 4, 10148 **Tallinn**
Tel: 6-443 670 Fax: 6-443 198
Internet: www.concert.ee/
E-Mail: eesti.kontsert@concert.ee
artistic director Peeter Vähi; manager Tõiv Titts
Period/Frequency: Aug, annual *Arts types:* chamber music (recitals, chamber ensembles, small orchestras)
Venues: various in Pärnu

Tallinn International Choral Festival
Tallinna Rahvusvaheline Koorifestival
Suur-Karja 23, 10140 **Tallinn**
Tel: 6-449 262 Fax: 2-449 147
Period/Frequency: every 3 years (2000) *Arts types:* choral
Comments: organise competition as part of festival

Tallinn International Festival JAZZKAAR
Tallinna rahvusvaheline festival Jazzkaar
Gonsiori 21, 10147 **Tallinn**
Tel: 6-114 487 Fax: 6-114 487
Internet: er.ee/klassik/jazz
director Anne Erm
Period/Frequency: April, annual
Arts types: jazz and blues music

Tallinn International Organ Festival
Tallinna Rahvusvaheline Orelimuusika Festival
Niguliste 13, 10146 **Tallinn**
Tel: 2-443 198
Period/Frequency: July-Aug, annual
Venues: all churches in Estonia

Tallinn Old Town Days
Tallinna Vanalinna Päevad
Nunne tn. 18, 10133 **Tallinn**
Tel: 6-441 808 Fax: 6-313 552
Period/Frequency: June, annual
Arts types: mixed art forms *Venues:* various historic venues in the old town in Tallinn *Comments:* run by Tallinn Kesklinna Administration

Tallinn Summermusic
Tallinna Suvemuusika festival
c/o EESTI KONTSERT,
Estonia pst. 4, 10148 **Tallinn**
Tel: 6-443 670 Fax: 6-443 198
Internet: www.concert.ee/
E-Mail: eesti.kontsert@concert.ee
artistic director Peeter Vähi;
assistant artistic director Elle Himma
Period/Frequency: July-Aug, annual *Arts types:* contemporary, classical, chamber, folk music and song concerts

DIONYSIA Festival of Visual Arts
Dionsyia Visuaalsete Kunstide Festival
PO Box 105, **Tartu**
Tel: 7-434 122 Fax: 7-431 373
manager Egge Kulbok
Period/Frequency: May, biennial (2001)
Arts types: drama, contemporary theatre, dance, film, photo, contemporary visual arts *Venues:* theatres and venues in Tartu

Viljandi Early Music Festival
Viljandi Vanamuusikafestival
Linnu 2, 71020 **Viljandi**
Tel: 43-34617 Fax: 43-52993
Internet: www.ugala.ee/vanamuusika/
manager Tiit Jõgi; artistic director Neeme Punder
Period/Frequency: Aug, biennial (2001) *Arts types:* early music and dance *Venues:* various churches in Viljandi

FAROE ISLANDS (+298)

Summartónar – Faroe Islands Festival of Classical and Contemporary Music
Reynagøta 12, 100 **Torshavn**
Tel: 3-14815 Fax: 3-14825
administrating director Kristian Blak (tel: 3-14558)
Period/Frequency: June-July, annual *Type:* classical, contemporary *Venues:* various venues throughout the Islands including Nordic House, National Art Gallery
Comments: organised by Faroese Composers Association, Association of Musicians, the Nordic House & The Concert Society

FINLAND (+358)

Baltic Jazz, Marine Jazz Festival
Sparbacken 4, 25900 **Dalsbruk**
Tel: 2-466 2107
Fax: 2-466 2167
general director Magi Kulla
Period/Frequency: beginning of July *Arts types:* jazz

Hetta Music Event
Hetan Musiikkipäivät
Virastotalo, 99400 **Enontekiö**
Tel: 16-556 278 Fax: 16-556 229
E-Mail: kirjasto@enontekio.inet.fi
Period/Frequency: Easter, annual *Arts types:* sacred and baroque Easter music

April Jazz Espoo
Ahertajantie 6 B, 02100 **Espoo**
Tel: 9-455 0003 Fax: 9-465 172
E-Mail: espoo.big.band@kolumbus.fi
director Martti Lappalainen
Period/Frequency: biennial *Arts types:* jazz
Venues: Espoo Cultural Centre

Espoo International Piano Festival
Espoo Cultural Centre,
Kulttuuriaukio, 02100 **Espoo**
Tel: 9-430 7353 Fax: 9-430 7220
artistic directors Marita Viitasalo, Erik T. Tawaststjerna
Period/Frequency: biennial (2001)
Arts types: classical music *Venues:* Tapiola Hall 789, Louhi Hall 178 & 241 & 304

Häme Castle Children's Festival
Hämeen Linnan Lastentapahtuma
Hämeenlinna Arts Centre,
Keinusaarentie 13, 13110 **Hämeenlinna**
Tel: 3-621 3026 Fax: 3-621 2811
Internet: www.htk.fi/hml/kulttuurikeskus/childfes.htm
E-Mail: hll@htk.fi
general director Nina Hildén
Period/Frequency: July/Aug, annual *Arts types:* puppet theatre, drama, exhibitions, history, workshops, dance, concerts *Comments:* for children and families

Avanti! Summer Sounds
Suvisoitto
Avanti! Chamber Orchestra,
Tallberginkatu 1 B/80, 00180 **Helsinki**
Tel: 9-694 0091 Fax: 9-694 2208
Internet: www.avantimusic.fi
E-Mail: avanti@kaapeli.fi
managing director Kari Vase;
artistic director Sakari Oramo
Period/Frequency: June, annual
Arts types: baroque to avantgarde

Chamber Theatre Festival – 2000
Theatre Jurkka, Vironkatu 7, 00170 **Helsinki**
Tel: 9-135 6166/6898 Fax: 9-135 6166/6898
festival manager Ismo Knuuttii
Period/Frequency: autumn, 2000

Dance in November
Teatterikeskus,
Meritullinkatu 33, 00170 **Helsinki**
Tel: 9-135 7613 Fax: 9-135 5522
contact Riitta Aarniokoski
Period/Frequency: 1st week Nov, biennial (2000)
Arts types: contemporary dance *Venues:* several around Helsinki 100 to 300

Etnosoe!
Global Music Centre,
Mikkolantie 17, 00640 **Helsinki**
Tel: 9-752 3377
Fax: 9-752 3376
E-Mail: gmc@global.pp.fi
artistic director Anu Laakkonen
Period/Frequency: Oct, annual *Arts types:* world music
Venues: various clubs and concert halls in Helsinki

Forces of Light
Valon Voimat
Fredrikinkatu 61, A 44, 00100 **Helsinki**
Tel: 9-686 6810 Fax: 9-686 6811
Internet: www.hel.fi/valonvoimat
E-Mail: valon.voimat@netlife.fi
director Bo Karsten; producer Riitta Suomi;
project producer Elina Raitasalo;
information officer Kaarina Gould
Period/Frequency: Nov/Dec, annual *Arts types:* performing & visual arts

Helsinki 2000 – European City of Culture
Eteläranta 16, 00130 **Helsinki**
Tel: 9-169 3210 Fax: 9-169 3204
Internet: www.2000.hel.fi
director George Dolivo
Period/Frequency: throughout the year 2000 *Arts types:* performing and visual arts *Comments:* Helsinki is one of the 9 joint European Cities of Culture in the year 2000

Helsinki Act
Theatre Academy Continuing Education Centre,
PB 148, 00511 **Helsinki**
Tel: 9-431 361
Fax: 9-4313 6337
Internet: www.teak.fi/helsinkiact
E-Mail: helsinki.act@teak.fi
direction Marjatta Häti-Korkeila (9-4313 6242); sekretariat Jetta Kuitunen (9-4313 6241)
Period/Frequency: biannual, 2000 *Arts types:* theatre, dance *Venues:* Helsinki Hall of Culture, various venues

Helsinki Festival
Helsingin Juhlaviikot
Lasipalatsi, Mannerheimintie 22-24, 00100 **Helsinki**
Tel: 9-6126 5100 Fax: 9-6126 5161
Internet: www.helsinkifestival.fi
E-Mail: info@helsinkifestival.fi
director Risto Nieminen (e-mail: nieminen@helsinkifestival.fi); production manager Tuula Yrjö-Koskinen
Period/Frequency: Aug, annual *Arts types:* classical music, dance, theatre, visual arts, cinema, city events

Musica nova Helsinki
Lasipalasti, Mannerheimintie 22-24, 00100 **Helsinki**
Tel: 9-6126 5100 Fax: 9-6126 5161
Internet: www.helsinkifestival.fi
E-Mail: info@helsinkifestival.fi
artistic director Kimmo Haikolla
Period/Frequency: March, annual *Arts types:* contemporary music *Comments:* see also Helsinki Festival (q.v.)

Nordic Music Days
Society of Finnish Composers, Suomen Säveltäjät, Ry
Runeberginkatu 154, 11, 00100 **Helsinki**
Tel: 9-445 589 Fax: 9-440 181
Internet: personal.eunet.fi/pp/compose/
E-Mail: saveltajat@compose.pp.fi
artistic director Jarmo Sermalä;
secretary Annu Mikkonen
Period/Frequency: September, biennial *Arts types:* contemporary Nordic music *Venues:* different venues in Lahti, Turku and Helsinki *Comments:* in a different Nordic country every two years

Scandinavian Guitar Festival
Havsgatan 41A 10, 00150 **Helsinki**
Tel: 9-622 3990
Fax: 9-622 3920
artistic director Steve Sjöholm
Period/Frequency: Aug, annual *Comments:* competition, concerts and outdoor rock concert

Turku Play
c/o Helsinki International Theatre (H.I.T.) Productions,
Kukkaniityntie 17, 00900 **Helsinki**
Tel: 9-325 6981/950-346 0652 (mobile) Fax: 9-325 1697
Internet: www.kaapeli.fi/~jussiw/english.html
E-Mail: jussiw@netscape.net
festival director/head of operations Jussi Wahlgren
Period/Frequency: 2nd week of October 2000, annual
Arts types: text based drama *Venues:* small scale
Comments: alternative E-mail: jussiw@kaapeli.fi

WOMAD at Helsinki
Global Music Centre, Mikkolantie 17, 00640 **Helsinki**
Tel: 9-752 3377 Fax: 9-752 3376
E-Mail: gmc@global.pp.fi
artistic director Anu Laakkonen
Period/Frequency: Aug *Arts types:* world music, ethnotechno, dance and masks, music for children, circus

Sata-Häme Accordion Festival
PO Box 37, 39501 **Ikaalinen**
Tel: 3-440 0224 Fax: 3-450 1365
Internet: www.satahamesoi.sci.fi
E-Mail: toimisto@satahamesoi.sci.fi
general director Terhi Palonen;
artistic director Kimmo Mattila
Period/Frequency: end of June, annual *Arts types:* accordion music *Comments:* over 70 concerts and events during 7 days

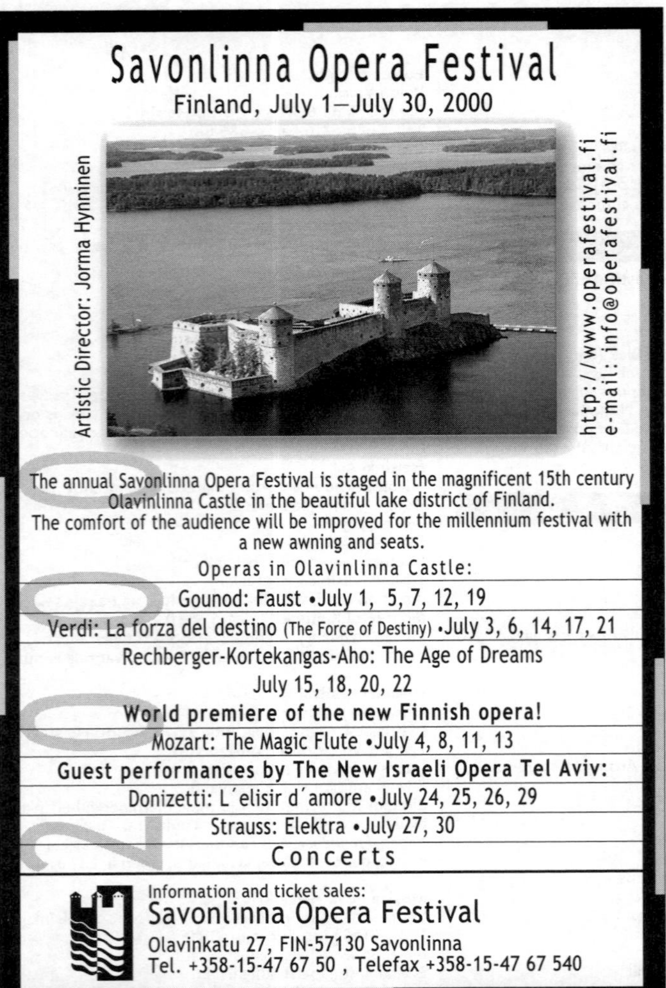

Savonlinna Opera Festival
Finland, July 1–July 30, 2000
Artistic Director: Jorma Hynninen
http://www.operafestival.fi
e-mail: info@operafestival.fi
2000
The annual Savonlinna Opera Festival is staged in the magnificent 15th century Olavinlinna Castle in the beautiful lake district of Finland.
The comfort of the audience will be improved for the millennium festival with a new awning and seats.
Operas in Olavinlinna Castle:
Gounod: Faust •July 1, 5, 7, 12, 19
Verdi: La forza del destino (The Force of Destiny) •July 3, 6, 14, 17, 21
Rechberger-Kortekangas-Aho: The Age of Dreams
July 15, 18, 20, 22
World premiere of the new Finnish opera!
Mozart: The Magic Flute •July 4, 8, 11, 13
Guest performances by The New Israeli Opera Tel Aviv:
Donizetti: L´elisir d´amore •July 24, 25, 26, 29
Strauss: Elektra •July 27, 30
Concerts
Information and ticket sales:
Savonlinna Opera Festival
Olavinkatu 27, FIN-57130 Savonlinna
Tel. +358-15-47 67 50 , Telefax +358-15-47 67 540

Ilmajoki Music Festival
Ilmajoen Musiikkijuhlat
Ilkantie 17, 60800 **Ilmajoki**
Tel: 6-424 7050 Fax: 6-424 7171
Internet: www.ilmajoenmusiikkijuhlat.fi
general dir Marjatta Eväsoja; artistic dir Lasse Lintala
Period/Frequency: June, annual *Arts types:* opera, concerts

Imatra Big Band Festival
Matinkatu 1 B, 2. kerr., 55100 **Imatra**
Tel: 5-436 6400 Fax: 5-436 6401
Internet: www.imedia.fi/ibbf
E-Mail: ibbf@imedia.fi
general manager Hannu Hokkanen; art dir Hannu Sopanen
Period/Frequency: July, annual *Arts types:* rock music *Comments:* jam sessions, courses and competitions, meeting of East and West, also bands from the US

Lakeside Blues Festival
Puistoblues
Järvenpään Blues-Jazz Diggarit r y,
PL 143, 04401 **Järvenpää**
Tel: 9-271 1305 Fax: 9-279 2550
Internet: www.puistoblues.fi
E-Mail: blues@sci.fi
general director Aki Keskinen
Period/Frequency: June, annual *Arts types:* music (blues-jazz)

Jyväskylä Arts Festival
Jyväskylän Kesä
Asemakatu 6, 40100 **Jyväskylä**
Tel: 14-624 385/387 Fax: 14-214 808
Internet: www.jkl.fi/festivaalit/kesa
E-Mail: tanja.rasi@jkl.fi
general manager Tanja Rasi
Period/Frequency: June, annual *Arts types:* chamber music, conferences, seminars, films

Kainuu Jazz Spring
Kainuun Jazzkevät
Pohjolankatu 16, 87100 **Kajaani**
Tel: 8-615 5514 Fax: 8-615 5664
Internet: www.kajaani.fi/
E-Mail: kajaani.info@kajaani.fi
director Unto Torniainen
Period/Frequency: May, annual *Arts types:* jazz and blues *Venues:* Kaukametsä Concert Hall, Hotel Kajanus and various venues throughout the city *Comments:* English language internet: www.kajaani.fi/english/events

Words and Music in Kajaani
Kajaanin Runoviikko Sana ja Sável
Pohjolankatu 16, 87100 **Kajaani**
Tel: 8-615 5555 Fax: 8-615 5664
Internet: www.kajaani.fi/tapahtum/runovko/index.htm
E-Mail: runo.viikko@kajaani.fi
admin dir Pekka Oikarinen; artistic dir Hannu Huuska
Period/Frequency: July, annual *Arts types:* poetry, theatre, music *Comments:* English language internet: www.kajaani.fi/english/events

Kangasniemi Music Festival
Kangasniemen musiikkiviikot
Cultural Office, Otto Mannisen tie 2,
51200 **Kangasniemi**
Tel: 15-780 1265 Fax: 15-780 1292
Internet: www.kangasniemi.fi/musiikkiviikot.html
E-Mail: irene.spannari@kangasniemi.fi
cultural secretary Irene Spännäri; art dir Markku Turunen
Period/Frequency: beg. of July, two weeks, annual *Arts types:* vocal and classical music, Kangasniemi Singing Competition and the Lied Pianist Competition *Venues:* capacity 200 to 1200

Kaustinen Folk Music Festival
PO Box 24, 69601 **Kaustinen**
Tel: 6-860 4111 Fax: 6-860 4222
Internet: www.kaustinen.fi/ktk/kfmf.htm
E-Mail: folk.fest@kaustinen.inet.fi
general director Pekka Leinonen;
programme director Jyrki Heiskanen
Period/Frequency: July, annual *Arts types:* folk music and dance, world music *Comments:* Scandinavia's largest international folk music and dance event

Kotkan meripäivät
Gutzatintic 14, 48100 **Kotka**
Tel: 5-234 4494 Fax: 5-217 190
Internet: www.kotka.fi/meripaivat/
E-Mail: kotkan.meripaivat@kotka.fi
Period/Frequency: July, annual *Arts types:* maritime dance, music

Kuhmo Chamber Music Festival
Kuhmon Kamarimusiikki
Torikatu 39, 88900 **Kuhmo**
Tel: 8-652 0936 Fax: 8-652 1961
Internet: www.kuhmofestival.fi
E-Mail: kuhmo.festival@kajak.fi
general dir Tuulikki Karjalainen; artistic dir Seppo Kimanen
Period/Frequency: July, annual *Arts types:* chamber music, recitals *Second Address:* Fredrikinkatu 77 A 2-4, 00100 Helsinki Tel: 9-493 867 Fax: 9-493 956 *Comments:* Kuhmo Chamber Music Competition every year in July, see also Competitions

Kuopio Dance Festival
Kuopio Tanssii Ja Soi
Torikatu 18, 70110 **Kuopio**
Tel: 17-282 1541 Fax: 17-261 1990
Internet: www.travel.fi/kuopiodancefestival
E-Mail: kuopio.dance.festival@travel.fi
festival director Anna Pitkänen;
artistic director Alpo O Pakarinen
Period/Frequency: June/July, annual *Arts types:* all types of dance and music *Venues:* Kuopio Music Centre 1000, Kuopio City Theatre 420, outdoor stage in the market square *Comments:* other activities: dance courses, exhibitions, international seminars on dance related subjects, medicine, minority cultures, movies

Kuusankoski International Children's Theatre Festival
Kuusankoski Theatre,
Kymenlaaksonk. 1, 45700 **Kuusankoski**
Tel: 5-374 7448/9-135 7074 Fax: 5-374 8937/9-135 7061
Period/Frequency: May, annual

Lahti Organ Festival
Lahden Kansainvälinen Urkuviikko
Kirkkokatu 5, 15110 **Lahti**
Tel: 3-782 3184 Fax: 3-783 2190
artistic director Kalevi Kiviniemi;
administrative director Auni Myohanen
Period/Frequency: July-Aug, annual *Arts types:* organ, chamber music, choral, recitals

Lappajärvi Music Days
Lappajärven musiikkipäivät
Hokmaninpolku 1, 62600 **Lappajärvi**
Tel: 6-62240 Fax: 6-62241
director Kalevi Olli;
chairman Matti Lampi (tel: 99-61152)
Period/Frequency: July-August, annual
Arts types: music, mainly vocal

Lieksa Brass Week
Lieksan Vaskiviikko
Koski-Jaakonkatu 4, 81700 **Lieksa**
Tel: 13-520 2055 Fax: 13-520 2044
Internet: musicfinland.com/lieksa
E-Mail: brass.week@lieksa.fi
marketing manager Tarja Tammia; art dir Jouni Auramo
Period/Frequency: July, annual *Arts types:* brass, chamber, wind, jazz, concerts, masterclasses *Venues:* Lieksa Culture Centre 400, Lieksa Church 1000, the Wooden Chapel belonging to the sculptress Eva Ryynänen (in Paateri)

Mikkeli International Amateur Theatre Festival
Cultural Office, Savilahdenkatu 10, 50100 **Mikkeli**
Tel: 15-194 2457 Fax: 15-194 2458
Internet: www.mikkeli.fi/tapahtumat/TNP
E-Mail: TNP@mikkeli.fi
Period/Frequency: Jan, annual

Mikkeli International Music Festival
Mikkelin Musiikkijuhlat
Vuonikatu 3A, 50100 **Mikkeli**
Tel: 15-162 076 Fax: 205-166 031
E-Mail: mikkeli.musicfestival@iwn.fi
managing director Kari Moring;
artistic director Valeri Gergiev
Period/Frequency: June/July, biennial (2000) *Arts types:* opera in stage productions, recitals

Korsholm Music Festival
Korsholman musiikkijuhlat
Keskustie 4, 65610 **Mustasaari**
Tel: 6-322 2390 Fax: 6-322 2393
Internet: www.korsholm.fi/music
E-Mail: music.festival@korsholm.fi
executive manager Rosmari Djupsund;
artistic director Frans Helmerson
Period/Frequency: June, annual *Arts types:* chamber music *Venues:* in Vassa: Town Hall 400, churches, art galleries etc *Second Address:* address during festival: Vaasa Town Hall, 65100 Vaasa *Comments:* cooperation with Umeå International Chamber Music Festival in Sweden under the name of Bothnic Music Festivals

Naantali Music Festival
Naantalin Musiikkijuhlat
PO Box 46, 21101 **Naantali**
Tel: 2-434 5363 Fax: 2-434 5425
Internet: www.naantalinmusiikkijuhlat.fi
E-Mail: info@naantalinmusiikkijuhlat.fi
executive director Tiina Tunturi;
artistic director Arto Noras
Period/Frequency: June, annual *Arts types:* chamber music, recitals *Venues:* churches 300 to 1000 *Second Address:* street address: Henrikinkatu 1

Bomba Festival
Bomban Juhlaviikot
Kötsintie 2, 75500 **Nurmes**
Tel: 13-681 6460 Fax: 13-681 6263
Internet: www.inet.fi/nurmes/juhlav
E-Mail: bomba.festivals@nurmes.fi
general manager Lauri Jánis
Period/Frequency: July, annual *Arts types:* Finno-ugrian theatre, music, folklore

Klemetti Summer Festival
Klemetin Kesä
Oriveden opisto, Koulutie 5, 35300 **Orivesi**
Tel: 3-336 6111 Fax: 3-335 2773
chairman of Klemetti Summer Festival Toini Hiukka;
head of Klemetti College Pirkko Partanen (9-491 833)
Period/Frequency: June, annual *Arts types:* choir music, symphony, chamber music, young rising stars *Venues:* concert hall of the Orivesi Institute (Oriveden Opisto) 400 *Second Address:* Museokatu 18A2, 00100 Helsinki, tel:0-441 725, fax:0-441 345 *Comments:* other activities during the festival: Klemetti Choir Competition (national); The Klemetti College Summer Course for choir conductors, singers, music teachers and young orchestral musicians in the Orivesi Institute

Oulainen Music Week
Oulaisten musiikkiviikot
Cultural Office,
Reservikomppaniankatu 4, 86300 **Oulainen**
Tel: 8-479 3272 Fax: 8-470 172
cultural secretary Sanna Pienihäkkinen
Period/Frequency: Oct- Nov, annual
Arts types: chamber music

Oulu Children's Theatre Festival
Oulun kaupunginteatteri
Pl. (xx), 90015 **Oulu**
Tel: 8-5584 7000 Fax: 8-5584 7099
Internet: www.ouka.fi/teatteri
Period/Frequency: February, annual
Arts types: children's theatre

Oulu Music Festival
Oulun musiikkijuhlat
Musiikkikeskus, Lintulammentie 1, 90150 **Oulu**
Tel: 8-336 830 Fax: 8-336 822
artistic director Ismo Sirén
Period/Frequency: April, annual *Arts types:* chamber, symphonic music *Venues:* Oulu Music Centre, Madetoja Hall 816, Tulindberg Hall 200

International Pori Jazz Festival
Pohjoisranta 11, 28100 **Pori**
Tel: 2-550 5550 Fax: 2-550 5525
Internet: www.porijazz.fi
E-Mail: festival@porijazz.fi
managing director Olli Kivelâ;
artistic director Jyrki Kangas
Period/Frequency: July, annual *Arts types:* jazz, rhythm and blues *Venues:* 15 different venues around the festival site

Fullmoon Dance Festival
Taydenkuun Tanssit Kaupungintalo
86800 **Pyhasalmi**
Tel: 8-780 547
Fax: 8-780 547
Internet: www.pyhajarvi.fi/tanssit
E-Mail: taydenkuun.tanssit@ppnet.fi
artistic director Katarina McAlester;
director Pirkko Hautala
Period/Frequency: July-Aug, annual
Arts types: contemporary dance

Kihaus Folk Music Festival
Rääkkylän Kansanmusiikki r y,
Kinnulantie 1, 82300 **Rääkkylä**
Tel: 13-666 1230 Fax: 13-684 3529
Internet: personal.inet.fi/tapahtuma/kihaus
E-Mail: Raakkylan.kansanmusiikki@kihaus.inet.fi
general director Seppo Mustonen
Period/Frequency: July, annual *Arts types:* folk music

Riihimäki Summer Concerts
Riihimäen kesäkonsertit
Kalevankatu 1, 11100 **Riihimäki**
Tel: 19-741 615 Fax: 19-732 626
Internet: www.riihimaki.fi/keskons/index.htm
general director Juha Pesonen
Period/Frequency: June, annual *Arts types:* classical and contemporary music, sometimes connected to visual arts *Venues:* Finnish Glass Museum

Savonlinna Opera Festival
Savonlinnan Oopperajuhlat
Olavinkatu 27, 57130 **Savonlinna**
Tel: 15-476 750
Fax: 15-476 7540
Internet: www.operafestival.fi
E-Mail: info@operafestival.fi
general director Paavo Suokko; artistic director Jorma Hynninen; marketing manager Helena Kontiainen
Period/Frequency: July, annual *Arts types:* opera, concerts, recitals *Comments:* approx. 20-25 opera performances in a season

Amateur Dramatic Festival
Harrastajateatterikesä
Keskuskatu 10 C 12, 60100 **Seinäjoki**
Tel: 6-423 2907
Fax: 6-423 6926
Internet: we.tietoraitti.fi/htkesa
project secretary Laura Junnila
Period/Frequency: Aug, annual *Arts types:* drama

Tango Festival in Seinäjoki
Tangomarkkinat
Seinäjoen Tangomarkkinat,
Kauppakatu 15 C, 60100 **Seinäjoki**
Tel: 6-420 1111 Fax: 6-414 2350
Internet: www.tangomarkkinat.fi
E-Mail: info@tangomarkkinat.fi
chairman Reijo Pitkäkoski; secretary Sirpa Latvala
Period/Frequency: July, annual *Arts types:* dance

Sysmä Summer Sounds
Sysmän Suvisoitto
PO Box 26, 19701 **Sysmä**
Tel: 3-843 1239 Fax: 3-717 2831
Internet: www.sysma.fi/sysma/suvisoitto.html
general director Sinikka Kemppainen;
artistic director Martti Wallen
Period/Frequency: 2 weeks at start of July, annual *Arts types:* classical music *Venues:* churches, mansions, schools & art centres throughout the local area 1000 to 1500

Pispala Schottische – Dance Mania
Pispalan Sottiisi
Vanha Kirjastotalo, Keskustori 4, 33100 **Tampere**
Tel: 3-212 2147 Fax: 3-3146 6756
Internet: www.sgic.fi/~sottiisi
E-Mail: sottiisi@sgic.fi
general director Jukka Heinämäki
Period/Frequency: July, annual

Tampere Biennale
Tullikamarinaukio 2, 33100 **Tampere**
Tel: 3-219 6172 Fax: 3-223 0121
Internet: www.tampere.fi/festival/music
E-Mail: music@tampere.fi
general director Aila Manninen
Period/Frequency: April, biennial (2000) *Arts types:* mainly Finnish contemporary music *Venues:* Tampere Hall 1800 and smaller halls and clubs

Tampere International Choir Festival
Tampereen Sävel
Tullikamarinaukio 2, 33100 **Tampere**
Tel: 3-3146 6136
Fax: 3-223 0121
Internet: www.tampere.fi/festival/music/choir.htm
E-Mail: music@tampere.fi
general director Aila Manninen; producer Eija Koivusalo
Period/Frequency: June, biennial (2001) *Arts types:* choirs and vocal ensembles, also contests for choirs and ensembles *Venues:* Tampere Hall 1800, cathedral 2000 and smaller churches, halls and clubs

Tampere International Theatre Festival
Tampereen Teatterikesä
Tullikamarinaukio 2, 33100 **Tampere**
Tel: 3-214 0992 Fax: 3-223 0121
Internet: www.tampere.fi/festival/theatre
E-Mail: theatre.festival@tt.tampere.fi
general director Raija-Liisa Seilo; artistic directors Kari Heiskanen, Reko Lundán, Maarit Pyökäri
Period/Frequency: Aug, annual *Arts types:* drama, comedy, street theatre, dance theatre, seminars etc. *Venues:* 49 venues all over city centre 50 to 1806 *Comments:* Finland's only annual festival of professional theatre, international guests

Tampere Jazz Happening
Tullikamarinaukio 2, 33100 **Tampere**
Tel: 3-3146 6136 Fax: 3-223 0121
Internet: www.tampere.fi/festival/music
E-Mail: music@tampere.fi
director Leena Korpinen
Period/Frequency: beginning of Nov, annual *Arts types:* contemporary international jazz *Venues:* Tullikamari Hall 800 and smaller clubs

International Kalott Jazz & Blues Festival
Tornio Cultural Office, Lukiokatu 10, 95400 **Tornio**
Tel: 16-432 424 Fax: 16-432 612
Internet: www.tornio.fi/kulttuur/jazz
E-Mail: helena.junes@tornio.fi
festival director Helena Junes
Period/Frequency: July, annual *Arts types:* jazz

Nordic Folkmusic, Accordion and Dance Festival
Kulttuuritoimisto, Lukiokatu 10, 95400 **Tornio**
Tel: 16-432 424/614/423 Fax: 16-432 612
contact Helena Junes
Period/Frequency: July, annual *Comments:* festival brings together musicians and the public from outside Scandanavia; also responsible for Calottjazz-Blues Festival, Tornio and Haaparanta (see separate entry)

Turku Music Festival
Turun musiikkijuhlat
Kauppiaskatu 11E 40, 20100 **Turku**
Tel: 2-251 1162 Fax: 2-231 3316
Internet: www.turkumusic.netti.fi
E-Mail: turku.music@tmf.netti.fi
executive director Alarik Repo;
artistic director Martti Rousi
Period/Frequency: Aug, annual *Arts types:* orchestral, light, chamber music, early music (on period instruments), recitals

Pentinkulma Days
Pentinkulman Päivät
Pentinkulman päivät, PL 33, 31761 **Urjala**
Tel: 3-541 4264
Fax: 3-541 4300
E-Mail: pentinkulmanpaivat@urjala.fi
general director Aulis Ruuska
Period/Frequency: July/Aug, annual

Crusell Week
Crusell-viikko
Kulttuuritoimisto, Rauhankatu 10, 23500 **Uusikaupunki**
Tel: 2-8451 5301 Fax: 2-8451 5442
Internet: www.wakkanet.fi/crusell/
E-Mail: crusell@wakkanet.fi
general manager Rauno Melos; artistic dir Petri Alanko
Period/Frequency: July-August *Arts types:* chamber music composed for woodwinds and a high standard of music teaching are central to Crusell Week *Venues:* most concerts, events and workshops take place in the Crusell Cultural Centre

Festival of Workers Music
Työväen Musiikkitapahtuma
Työväen Musiikitapahtuma r.y.,
Kauppatori 9, 37600 **Valkeakoski**
Tel: 3-585 0880 Fax: 3-584 9202
E-Mail: tyovaen.musiikkitapahtuma@co.inet.fi
general director Marianne Mihailow
Period/Frequency: late July, annual *Arts types:* music

Eteläeurooppalaista Barokkimusiikkia – Vantaan Barokkiviikko
Pl. 10, 01301 **Vantaa**
Tel: 9-830 6265
Fax: 9-830 6261
Internet: www.evl.fi/srk/vandasv/music/vantaabw.htm
E-Mail: vantaabw@yahoo.com
Period/Frequency: July-Aug, annual
Arts types: baroque music

Time of Music
Musiikin aika
Kunnantalo, Keskitie 10, 44500 **Viitasaari**
Tel: 14-573 195
Fax: 14-579 3515
Internet: www.viitasaari.fi/tom/
E-Mail: time.music@festival.fi
general director Markku Möttönen;
artistic director Jarmo Sermilä
Period/Frequency: July, annual *Arts types:* contemporary music *Venues:* various around Viitasaari 200 to 600

FRANCE (+33)

Aix en Musique
Espace Forbin, 3 place John Rewald, 13100 **Aix-en-Provence**
Tel: 4-4221 6969 Fax: 4-4221 9125
directeur Gérard Le Berre; administration Marylène LeQuesne; médiateur Eric Barbier
Period/Frequency: Oct-June, annual *Arts types:* contemporary music, jazz, lyrical, street performances *Venues:* churches, theatre, amphitheatres, hall between 300-800 *Comments:* majority of the concerts are free,

Festival Danse à Aix
Espace Forbin, 1, Place John Rewald, Cours Gambetta, 13100 **Aix-en-Provence**
Tel: 4-4296 0501 Fax: 4-4296 6530
E-Mail: danseaix@ten.fr
directrice Ginette Escoffier Carrere; administratrice Cathy Brun; co-ordination, relations publiques Annette Paulet; communication Dominique Berolatti
Period/Frequency: spring, annual
Arts types: contemporary dance

Festival International d'Art Lyrique et de Musique
Palais de L'Ancien Archevêché, 13100 **Aix-en-Provence**
Tel: 4-4217 3400/34 (bookings)
Fax: 4-4296 1261 (administration)
Internet: www.aix-en-provence.com/festarlyrique/
directeur Stéphane Lissner; communication Anita Levan
Period/Frequency: June-July (10 days), annual *Arts types:* lyrics, recitals, concerts, opera *Venues:* Archeveché open air theatre 1600, St. Sauveur Cathedral 800, Hotel Mayrier d'Oppede 400 *Comments:* also European Academy of Music

Festival d'Opérette
ex-Opérette, c/o Service Animation et Culture Théâtre de Verdure, BP 348, 73103 **Aix-les-Bains** Cedex
Tel: 4-7988 1436 Fax: 4-7988 4938
président Albert Arnould; directeur artistique Pierre Sybil
Period/Frequency: July, annual (2000: 10-25 July) *Arts types:* operette, contemporary, classical, viennoise
Venues: Théâtre du Casino Grand Cercle 832

Festival Théâtral d'Albi
Office du tourisme, Place Sainte Cécile, Palais de la Berbie, 81000 **Albi**
Tel: 5-6349 4880/4887 (direction) Fax: 5-6349 4898
président Jacques Bonnin;
directeur artistique Guy Vassal
Period/Frequency: June-July, annual
Arts types: theatre, classical, classic comedy *Venues:* Palais de la Berbie 500 (open-air)

Jazz en Ballade
Scène National de l'Albigeois, BP 49, 81002 **Albi** Cedex
Tel: 5-6354 1111 Fax: 5-6354 4647
directeur Ivan Morane;
responsable Alain Gonzalès (tel:5-6377 3216)
Period/Frequency: May, annual *Arts types:* jazz *Venues:* Le Vieux Carré in Albi 400 and throughout Albi *Comments:* see also Rebonds (Dance Festival)

Rebonds
Scène National de l'Albigeois, BP 49, 81002 **Albi** Cedex
Tel: 5-6354 1111 Fax: 5-6354 4647
directeurs Ivan Morane, Thierry Morlet (ADDA)
Period/Frequency: Feb (10 days), annual *Arts types:* dance: classical, contemporary, modern *Venues:* Théâtre d'Albi 600

Septembre Musical de l'Orne
BP 294, 61008 **Alençon** Cedex
Tel: 2-3380 4426 Fax: 2-3380 4423
Internet: www.cg61.fr
E-Mail: dumeige@wanadoo.fr
président Philippe Toussaint; conseiller artistique Jean-Pierre Wallez; chargée de mission Benedicte Dumeige
Period/Frequency: Augt/Sept, annual *Arts types:* classical, contemporary and chamber music, recitals, choir, opera, medieval music *Venues:* in historical sites of the department (l'Orne) 250-1000

Festival d'Ambert
la Planète , La Gare, 63600 **Ambert**
Tel: 4-7382 6843 Fax: 4-7382 3585
directeur et relations presse Angelina Berforini; directeur technique Pierre Fauchier; président de la Planète Bernard Lacroix; coordinatrice Armelle Cornet; conseillers artistíques Claire Lacroix, Patrick Belaubre
Period/Frequency: 1st week in Aug, annual *Arts types:* fairytales and storytelling, street theatre, cabarets, puppetry

Festival de l'Abbaye d'Ambronay
Bureau du Festival, Place de l'Abbaye, BP 3, 01500 **Ambronay**
Tel: 4-7438 7400/1004 (bookings) Fax: 4-7438 1093
Internet: www.fest-ambronay.com
E-Mail: fest.ambronay@wanadoo.fr
directeur Alain Brunet; chargée de production Antoine Manceau; chargé de communication Céline De Murcia; président Michel Cusin; admin Geneviève Rodriguez
Period/Frequency: Sept-Oct, annual *Arts types:* early music: baroque, classique (on period instruments), renaissance *Venues:* Abbatiale 1300, Tour Dauphine 200

Festival d'Amiens, Musique de Jazz et d'ailleurs
Maison de la Culture, Place Léon Gontier, BP 0631, 80006 **Amiens** Cedex
Tel: 3-2292 1548 Fax: 3-2292 5217
E-Mail: tdj@wanadoo.fr
admin Didier Ringalle; directeur artistique Michel Orier
Period/Frequency: March, annual *Arts types:* jazz, world music *Venues:* Cirque Municipal 2500, Place Gambetta open-air 3000, le petit théâtre 300, grand théâtre 1000, Le parvi 2000 (open-air), Les Magic Mirror

Festival des Cathédrales de Picardie
11 Mail Albert 1er, 80000 **Amiens**
Tel: 3-2297 3717 Fax: 3-2297 3742
E-Mail: festicat@neuronnexion.fr
directeur Jacques Bidart
Period/Frequency: Sept, annual *Arts types:* choral and orchestral music *Venues:* various cathedrals and churches in the area

Festival Estival du Centre Musical International d'Annecy
10 rue Jean Jacques Rousseau, 74000 **Annecy**
Tel: 4-5051 6767 Fax: 4-5052 9572
président Pascal Escande
Period/Frequency: August, annual *Arts types:* classical and contemporary music, dance, choral *Venues:* Château d'Annecy, Conservatoire (stages)

Fêtes Musicales de Savoie
16, rue Filaterie, 74000 **Annecy**
Tel: 4-5052 8743 Fax: 4-5045 8658
directeur artistique George Kiss
Period/Frequency: July-Aug, annual *Arts types:* classical, baroque, renaissance, romantic music
Venues: baroque churches

Noctibules, Bonlieu Scène Nationale, Les
1 rue Jean Jaurès, BP 294, 74007 **Annecy** Cedex
Tel: 4-5033 4400
E-Mail: bsn@cybercable.tm.fr
directeur Salvador Garcia
Period/Frequency: July, annual *Venues:* all around Annecy
Comments: see also Venues

Musicales du Château d'Ansouis, Les
Château d'Ansouis, 84240 **Ansouis**
Tel: 4-9009 8000 Fax: 4-9009 8000
fondateurs Michel Vasseur, Renaud Ceyrac
Period/Frequency: August, annual
Arts types: lyrical recitals and chamber music *Venues:* Terrase du Château 600

Festival International de Jazz Antibes/Juan les Pins
Maison du Tourisme, 11 place de Gaulle, 06600 **Antibes**
Tel: 4-9290 5300 Fax: 4-9290 5301
Internet: www.guide-azur.com
président Jacques Grima; directeur Victor Levy Perrault
Period/Frequency: 2nd half of July, annual (2000: 15-25 July) *Arts types:* jazz, blues, gospel, world, rock *Venues:* Pinede Gould – Juan les Pins 4500 *Second address:* 11 Place de Gaulle, 06600 Antibes

Festival Musique au Coeur d'Antibes
Direction des Affaires Culturelles, 15 rue Georges Clémenceau, 06600 **Antibes**
Tel: 4-9290 5460 Fax: 4-9290 5461
adjoint à la culture Jean Gismondi;
responsable des affaires culturelles Gérard Ghibaudo;
directeur artistique Eve Ruggieri
Period/Frequency: July, annual *Arts types:* opera, music
Venues: Chantier Naval Opera 1500

Rencontres du Sud, Les
Suds à Arles, BP147, 13631 **Arles** Cedex
Tel: 4-9096 0627
Fax: 4-9096 7948
Internet: www.suds-arles.com
E-Mail: contact@suds-arles.com
directrice artistique Marie José Justamond;
communication Corinne Falaschi
Period/Frequency: July, annual *Arts types:* world music
Venues: outdoor: Théâtre Antique d'Arles 2500, Arènes 8000, cours de l'Archeveché 350, Jardin d'été

Saison Musicale de Royaumont
Fondation Royaumont, 95270 **Asnières-sur-Oise**
Tel: 1-3035 5900 (admin)/3468 0550 (booking)
Fax: 1-3035 3945
Internet: www.royaumont.com
E-Mail: voix@royaumont.com
directeur général Françis Maréchal;
saison musicale administratrice Catherine Kollen
Period/Frequency: June-Sept, annual *Arts types:* vocal music (medieval to contemporary) *Venues:* l'Abbaye de Royaumont: hall 1 500, hall 2 250

Festival Européen d' Orgue d'Aubenas
45 rue G. Couderc, 07200 **Aubenas**
Tel: 1-3953 0096 Fax: 1-3953 0096
Internet: members.aol.com/orgaubenas/festival
E-Mail: orgaubenas@aol.com
directeur artistique et secrétaire André Siekierski;
président Claude Flory
Period/Frequency: every Sunday of July and first of August *Arts types:* organ, baroque and renaissance repertoire (99 focus on organ with instrument) *Venues:* Eglise St Laurent 500 *Second Address:* Bureau de Tourisme, bld Gambetta 4, Aubenas 07200, Tel: 4-7589 0203, Fax: 4-7589 0204 *Comments:* member of the Fédération Française des Festivals Internationaux de Musique; secretary: André Siekierski, 23 rue Champ Legarde, 78000 Versailles, Tel/Fax: 1-3953 0096; see also National Organisations (FFFMI)

International Street Theatre Festival of Aurillac
Festival d'Aurillac – Festival International de Théâtre de Rue
10 Rue de la Coste, 15000 **Aurillac**
Tel: 4-7145 4747 Fax: 4-7148 5225
Internet: www.aurillac.net
E-Mail: festival@aurillac.net
directeur artistique Jean-Marie Songy; président Jack Caldefie; coordinatrice générale Dominique Gruszczinski; responsable communication et presse Christophe Paris; directeur technique Olivier Desjardins
Period/Frequency: end of Aug, annual *Arts types:* street theatre *Comments:* see also Venues

Festival d'Auvers sur Oise
Manoir des Colombières, 95430 **Auvers-sur-Oise**
Tel: 1-3036 7777 (bookings)/7082
Fax: 1-3036 7155
Internet: www.festival-auvers.com
président Bernard Flye Saint-Marie;
directeur Pascal Escande
Period/Frequency: May-June, annual
Arts types: music, opera, classical and chamber music, chants, piano *Venues:* Eglise d'Auvers-sur Oise 600, Eglise Saint Denis á Méry-sur Oise 700, Château á Méry-sur-Oise 900

Nuits Musicales du Golfe du Morbihan
c/o Jean-Marc Bouré, 20 Rue Fécauderie, 89000 **Auxerre**
Tel: 3-8651 3171
Fax: 3-8651 3171
directeur artistique Jean-Marc Bouré
Period/Frequency: July/August, annual
Arts types: classical music (from the middle ages to the 20th C.) *Venues:* Chapelle de la Région de Vannes 250, Palais des Arts (Vannes) 800

Piano à Auxerre
12 avenue Gambetta, 89000 **Auxerre**
Tel: 3-8646 5542/8652 0619 (booking/info)
Fax: 3-8642 7713
directeur artistique Jean-Marc Bouré
Period/Frequency: Sept, annual *Arts types:* piano
Venues: Théâtre d'Auxerre 600

Avignon 2000 – European City of Culture
1 Avenue de la Foire, 84000 **Avignon**
Tel: 4-9027 2270
Fax: 4-9027 2279
directeur admin. Anne-Marie Roubaud
Period/Frequency: throughout the year 2000 *Arts types:* performing and visual arts *Comments:* Avignon is one of the 9 joint European Cities of Culture in the year 2000

Festival d'Avignon
8 bis rue de Mons, 84000 **Avignon**
Tel: 4-9027 6650
Fax: 4-9027 6683
Internet: www.festival-avignon.com
directeur Bernard Faivre d'Arcier; directeur-adjoint Christiane Bourbonnaud;
responsable communication et presse Olivia Lancelot
Period/Frequency: July, annual
Arts types: first productions of drama, contemporary dance *Venues:* prestigious sites of Avignon (la cour du Palais des Papes, salle Benoit XII) and throughout the town *Second Address:* 6 rue de Braque, 75003 Paris, Tel: 1-4461 8484, Fax: 1-4461 8527

Les Hivernales de Danse d'Avignon
La Manutention, 4 rue Escalier Saint Anne, 84000 **Avignon**
Tel: 4-9082 3312
Fax: 4-9014 0029
Internet: www.hivernales.asso.fr
E-Mail: hivernales@avignon.pacwan.net
directrice artistique Amélie Grand; co-directrice Catherine Bénard; administrateur Daniel Favier; attachée a la communication Anne Mathilde Guerin; chargée de diffusion Michéle Montesinos; attacheé aux relations europeénnes et internationale Céline Bréant
Period/Frequency: Feb, annual
Arts types: dance, contemporary *Venues:* Salle Benoît XII 450, Opera d'Avignon et des Pays de Vaucluse 1000, Théâtre du Cavaillon/Scéne Nationale 650, Auditorium du Thor 800, Chapelle des Pénitents Blancs 150
Comments: also organises the festival 'off' during the Festival d'Avignon in their studio (contemporary dance, jazz); other event: L'été des Hivernales, new dance companies perform during the festival d'Avignon in July

Piano aux Pyrénées
Office de Tourisme de Barèges, 65120 **Barèges**
Tel: 5-6292 1600 Fax: 5-6292 6913
Internet: www.classic_hall.com/festival/ppyrénées.html
directeur général Christophe Baillet;
directeur artistique Pierre Réach
Period/Frequency: July, annual *Arts types:* principally piano *Venues:* Les Termes (Barège) 300, La Maison de la Vallée (Luz St Sauveur) 150, the Roman Church (Sère Esquièze) 200, Résidence Continentale (Cautiets) 400, Church of St Savin 500, Abboye de l'Escaladieu 400 *Comments:* master classs and festival, Academie Internationale de Piano de Barèges

Festival de Jazz aux Remparts
18 ter, Bvd d'Alsace-Lorraine, BP 729, 64100 **Bayonne**
Tel: 5-5955 8505 (administration) Fax: 5-5955 2170
E-Mail: pnbayonne@aol.com
directeur Dominique Burucoa;
renseignement Sandra Rozier
Period/Frequency: July, annual *Arts types:* jazz and blues *Venues:* Rempart de Mousserolles 3000 *Second Address:* bookings: Tel: 5-5959 0727, Tuesday – Saturday (1-7 p.m.) *Comments:* see also Venues

Festival de Théâtre Franco-Ibérique et Latino-Américain
BP 411, 64104 **Bayonne** Cedex
Tel: 5-5925 7060 Fax: 5-5923 4111
administration général Marie-Julienne Hingant;
directeur artistique Jean-Marie Broucaret;
communication Yves Mousset
Period/Frequency: Oct, annual *Arts types:* French-Hispanic and Latin-American drama, musical theatre, dance, mime *Venues:* La Scène National de Bayonne 800, La Salle Lauga, Bayonne 1000 , Le Colisée, Biarritz 189, Théatre du Casino 900, Biarritz *Second Address:* 75 Avenue du Marechal Juin, 64200 Biarritz *Comments:* see also Drama – Théâtre des Chimères

Festival International de Musique Baroque
Office du Tourisme, Place de la Halle, 21200 **Beaune**
Tel: 3-8026 2130 Fax: 3-8026 2139
E-Mail: Blanchard.anne@wanadoo.fr
directeur administratif Kader Hassissi; directrice artistique Anne Blanchard; président Françoise Truchetet
Period/Frequency: July *Arts types:* baroque music, incl opera *Venues:* Basilique Notre Dame 1000, cour des Hospices de Beaune 1300, Salle des Pôvres 350 *Second Address:* 02 Square Saint Irénée, 75011 Paris, Tel: 1-4357 4697, Fax: 1-4700 1092

Rencontres Internationales d'ensembles de Violoncelles
Service Culturel, BP 330, 60021 **Beauvais** Cedex
Tel: 3-4406 3600 Fax: 3-4406 3605
Internet: www.re-violoncelle.com
E-Mail: contact@re-violoncelle.com
directeur artistique Jacques Bernaert; administratrice Nicole Wissotzky; directeur technique Gilles Caron
Period/Frequency: May, annual *Arts types:* cello *Venues:* Théâtre de Beauvais 700,
Cathédrale de Beauvais 380

Festival de Bellac
5 place Jean de la Fontaine, 87300 **Bellac**
Tel: 5-5568 1044 Fax: 5-5568 8819 (mention festival)
président et directeur Claude Bourdet
Period/Frequency: June-July annual *Arts types:* drama, music, jazz, exhibitions *Venues:* open-air 350 or indoor venue 350 (if it rains)

Journées Baroque sur Vienne
c/o L'Atelier du Musicien, Le Bourg, 16350 **Benest**
Tel: 5-4585 3502/4531 8023 Fax: 5-4585 3502/4531 8044
directrice générale L'Atelier du Musicien Françoise Besson; directeur artistique Journées Baroque sur Vienne Fedor Lederer
Period/Frequency: Sept, annual *Arts types:* classical music (17th and 18th C.) *Venues:* Churches of Confolens 100-500 and surrounding areas *Second address:* c/o Fedor Lederer, 5 rue Emile Roux, 16500 Confolens *Comments:* Directrice Générale: Françoise Besson, Atelier du Musicien, 16350 Benest

Festival International de Musique de Besançon et de Franche-Comté
3 bis, rue Léonel de Moustier, 25000 **Besançon**
Tel: 3-8125 0585 Fax: 3-8181 5215
Internet: www.besancon.com
E-Mail: festival.besancon@wanadoo.fr
directeur administratif Yvette Cussey; président Yves-Marie Lehmann; directeur general Michel des Borderies
Period/Frequency: Sept, annual *Arts types:* classical music: recital to symphonic music *Venues:* throughout Franche-Comté, Besançon Opéra Théâtre 1047 and churches up to 1200, Parlement room 200
Comments: member of Fédération Française de Festivals Internationaux de Musique

Jazz-en-Franche-Comté, Besançon
ASPRO Jazz, 6F Rue de la Vieille Monnaie, 25000 **Besançon**
Tel: 3-8183 3909 Fax: 3-8183 2511
Internet: www.multimania.com/asprojazz/
president Phillippe Romanoni; relations publiques/presse Marie-France Beuret
Period/Frequency: June-July, annual *Arts types:* jazz, improvisation, contemporary *Venues:* 15 concerts in 14 towns and outdoors in historical listed towns *Comments:* musical training courses with top jazz musicians

Le Temps d'Aimer
Biarritz Culture, Javalquinto, 64200 **Biarritz**
Tel: 5-5922 2021 Fax: 5-5922 4011
E-Mail: Btzculture@aol.com
directeur Filgi Claverie;
communication Marie-Héléne Lapasse
Period/Frequency: Sept, annual (2000: 3-19 Sept) *Arts types:* ballet *Venues:* La Gare du Midi (danse classique) 1400, le Théâtre du Casino Municipal (danse contemporaine) 700, Théâtre le Colysee 189 *Comments:* see also festival Les Fêtes Musicales and Promoters

Les Fêtes Musicales
Biarritz Culture, Javalquinto, 64200 **Biarritz**
Tel: 5-5922 2021 Fax: 5-5922 4011
E-Mail: Btzculture@aol.com
directeur Filgi Claverie; directeur artistique Micheline Banzet Lawton; communication Marie-Héléne Labasse
Period/Frequency: April, annual (2000: 26-30 April) *Arts types:* classical music *Venues:* La Gare du Midi 1400, Le Théâtre du Casino Municipal 700 *Comments:* see also festival 'Le Temps d'Aimer', see also Promoters

Polymusicales de Bollène, Les
Bureau du Festival, Espace Ripert, 84500 **Bollène**
Tel: 4-9040 5117 Fax: 4-9040 5147
directrice artistique Fabienne Lemonnier;
attachée de presse Céline Depeyre
Period/Frequency: July, annual *Arts types:* classical music, jazz, blues, variety *Venues:* outdoors: Cours Beroule 570, La Colléjiale

Ete Girondin
La Maison du Tourisme de la Gironde, 21 Cours de l'intendance, 33000 **Bordeaux**
Tel: 5-5652 6140 Fax: 5-5681 0999
Internet: www.tourisme-gironde.cg33.fr
E-Mail: tourisme@gironde.com
responsable Francis Larriba;
communication Marie-Claire Clémarès
Period/Frequency: beg. of June-end of Sept, annual *Arts types:* jazz (mainly), classical music, drama, traditional music, rock, plastic art *Venues:* all over Gironde

Festival de la Côte d'Opale
19 Boulevard Clocheville, 62200 **Boulogne-sur-Mer**
Tel: 3-2130 4033 Fax: 3-2130 5584
directeur Patrick Dréhan; secrétaire Valérie Rougemont
Period/Frequency: annual (2000: 2-25 July)
Arts types: variety *Venues:* throughout towns on the Pas de Calais coast

Music et Remparts
La Mairie, Service Culturel de la Ville Boulogne, Hotel de Ville, place Godrefroy-de-bouillon,
62200 **Boulogne-sur-Mer**
Tel: 3-2187 8143
Fax: 3-2187 8189
E-Mail: boulogne@tourisme.noroyo.fr
directeur Luc Tassart; responsable Catherine George; directeur artistique Jack Bornoff
Period/Frequency: April-May, annual *Arts types:* classical music, jazz *Venues:* historical places *Comments:* it is a 'Trans-manche' festival, half in France (Boulogne sur Mer, Bourboug, Montreval sur Mer...) and half in Great Britain (Ramsgate, Ashford, Folkstone...)

Festival de Noirlac
Association des Amis de l'Abbaye de Noirlac,
5, rue de Séraucourt, 18000 **Bourges**
Tel: 2-4867 0018
Fax: 2-4867 0144
Internet: www.berry.tm.fr
directeur André Margotin; président Philippe de Bonneval; président d'honneur Jean-François Deniau; président du comité d'honneur Michel Corboz
Period/Frequency: June-Aug, annual
Arts types: choirs, orchestras, chamber music *Venues:* Abbatiale 700, Le Cloître *Second Address:* Abbaye de Noirlac, 18200 Bruère Allichamps, Tel: 2-4896 2364
Comments: relations presse et administration Philippe Lorinquer, Régisseur: SEM 18, 10 Rue Georges Pompidou, 18021 Bourges Cedex, Tel: 2-4820 0862

International Festival for Electroacoustic Music
Festival International de Musique Electroacoustique Institute International de Musique Électroacoustic de Bourges ,Place André Malraux,
BP 39, 18001 **Bourges** Cedex
Tel: 2-4820 4187
Fax: 2-4820 4551
Internet: www.gmeb.fr
E-Mail: ime-bourges@gmeb.fr
directeurs Francoise Barrière, Christian Clozier
Period/Frequency: first two weeks of June, annual *Arts types:* electroacoustic music *Venues:* Palais Jacques Coeur; Théâtre Jacques Coeur; Maison de la Culture
Second Address: Bureau du Festival: Théâtre Jacques Coeur, rue Jacques Coeur, 18000 Bourges (only during the festival) *Comments:* see also Competitions

Très Riches Heures de L'Orgue en Berry
Les Amis du Grand Orgue,
22, rue Ranchot, 18000 **Bourges**
Tel: 2-4820 2524 Fax: 2-4820 5766
Internet: www.ville.bourges.fr
organisatrice Anne-France Pagenel-Aliquot
Period/Frequency: summer, annual *Arts types:* organ music *Venues:* Cathedrale Saint Etienne in Bourges
Second Address: Office du Tourisme, 21, rue Victor Hugo, 18003 Bourges cedex, Tel: 2-4823 0260
Comments: historic organ Joly-Cauchois from 1664 renovated in 1985 by Daniel Kern

Un Été à Bourges
L'Agence Culturelle, Théâtre Jacques Cour, BP 121, 18003 **Bourges** Cedex
Tel: 2-4824 9332 Fax: 2-4802 1083
Internet: www.ville-banges.fr
chargé de la programation Mr. Pobeau;
maire-adjoint chargé à la culture Margotin Narboux
Period/Frequency: June-Sept, annual *Arts types:* jazz, classical, world music *Venues:* throughout Bourges
Comments: 110 shows; managed by the town hall

Festival de la Vézère
11 place Jean-Marie Dauzier, 19100 **Brive-la-Gaillarde**
Tel: 5-5523 2509 Fax: 5-5584 8328
E-Mail: Festival.Vezere@wanadoo.fr
secretaire générale Claudine Delmas; présidente Isabelle de Lasteyrie du Saillant;
attaché de presse Aude de Jamblinne
Period/Frequency: July-Aug *Arts types:* classical music (chamber, opera etc) *Venues:* Château du Saillant 350, churches in the area

Aspects des Musiques d'Aujourd hui
Conservatoire de Caen, 1 rue du Carel, 14027 **Caen** Cedex
Tel: 2-3186 4200 Fax: 2-3186 1892
contact Mr Loviton
Period/Frequency: March, annual *Arts types:* concentrates on one particular composer

Juventus – Rencontres Européennes de Jeunes Musiciens
Théâtre de Cambrai, 59400 **Cambrai**
Tel: 1-4500 7576 Fax: 1-4500 9912
E-Mail: georges.gara@wanadoo.fr
directeur/directeur artistique Georges Gara;
chargée de communication Corinne Moncho (conseil général du nord)
Period/Frequency: July, annual *Arts types:* classical musical recitals by young Council of Europe laureates
Venues: Théâtre de Cambrai

Nuits Musicales du Suquet à Cannes
Parvis de l'Église Notre-Dame D'Espérance,
06400 **Cannes**
Tel: 4-9299 3108 (information)/9298 6277 (bookings)
Fax: 4-9298 9876
Internet: www.palais-festivals-cannes.fr
E-Mail: semcultu@imaginet.fr
attachée de presse Elisabeth Lara (tel: 4-9299 3135);
directeur artistique Gabriel Tacchino;
directeur de l'évènementiel Bernard Oheix
Period/Frequency: July, annual *Arts types:* chamber, classical, singing
Venues: Parvis of Notre-Dame d'Espérance 600 *Second Address:* administrative address: Palais des Festivals, BP 272, 06403 Cannes Cedex

Festival de Carcassonne – Languedoc – Roussillon
Théâtre Municipal, Rue Courtejaire,
BP 236, 11005 **Carcassonne** Cedex
Tel: 4-6877 7105 Fax: 4-6877 7073
Internet: www.festivaldecarcassone.com
président Philippe Boissonade; directeur Georges Bacou; directeur artistique Paul Barierre
Period/Frequency: July, annual *Arts types:* contemporary and classical music, drama, dance, opera, popular music *Venues:* Théâtre de la Cité 3000 *Comments:* bookings: 4-6877 7126

Festival d'été de Cargilesse
Office du Tourisme, le pigeonnier, 36190 **Cargilesse**
Tel: 2-5447 8506 Fax: 2-5447 7122
présidents t.b.a.; communication Marcel Pacaud
Period/Frequency: August *Arts types:* harp & chamber music *Venues:* Eglise Romane de Cargilesse 280

Chalon dans la Rue
5 place de l'Obélisque, 71100 **Chalon-sur-Saône**
Tel: 3-8548 0522 Fax: 3-8593 6862
Internet: chalondanslarue.com
E-Mail: festival@chalondanslarue.com
directeur artistique Pierre Layac; directeur administratif Jacques Quentin; relation presse Maximilien Sautai; coordination technique Olivier Brie,
Florence Dell' Accio, Laurent Folléat
Period/Frequency: 3rd week of July, annual *Arts types:* street theatre *Venues:* various parks, streets and building throughout Chalon
Second address: July – Maison du Festival, 16 rue de la Motte, 71100 Chalon-sur-Saône *Comments:* regional, national and international; most shows for all ages; most of the concerts are free

Festival d'art Sacré
1 rue des Champarts, 77720 **Champeaux**
Tel: 1-6066 9607 Fax: 1-6066 9607
directeur fondateur Michel Vauthrin
Period/Frequency: June, annual
Arts types: sacred music (gregorian to contemporary), dance, theatre *Venues:* Collégiale de Champeaux (XII th C.) *Comments:* produce and edit CD from the festival on own label 'Champeaux'

94 Coups de Théâtre
Association Défense et Promotion du théâtre jeune publique, Centre Culturel Gérard Philipe,
54 blrd du Château, 94500 **Champigny-Sur-Marne**
Tel: 1-4880 5507 Fax: 1-4880 4827
président Jacques Guedj;
administratrice de production t.b.a.;
administratrice Gina Oloa
Period/Frequency: March, biennial (2000) *Arts types:* theatre for children and young people *Venues:* throughout the Val de Marne

Festival Interculturel
Centre Youri Gagarine, 6 Av. du 11 novembre 1918, 94500 **Champigny-Sur-Marne**
Tel: 1-4880 9629
Fax: 1-4880 0031
directeur Thierry Pignot
Period/Frequency: Nov, annual *Arts types:* theatre, music, exhibitions, cinema *Venues:* Centre Culturel Youri Gagarine 300, Centre Culturel Gerard Philippe 800, Centre Culturel Jean Villard 250, Centre Culturel Olivier Messian 200, Mediathéque Jean-Jacques Rousseau 300 *Comments:* Festival has objectives every year: anti-racism and tackling the problems in the world; the profits are redistributed to different charity organisations

Musique au Coeur de la Tapisserie
Mr. Jorrand, 11 rue de l'Archevecher,
94220 **Charenton**
Tel: 1-4893 9811 Fax: 1-4893 9811
président Mr Jorrand
Period/Frequency: last week of July-Aug, annual
Arts types: classical music, organ
Venues: churches, up to 300

Festival Mondial des Théâtres de Marionnettes
BP 249, 08103 **Charleville-Mezières** Cedex
Tel: 3-2459 9494 Fax: 3-2456 0510
Internet: www.marionnette.com
E-Mail: festival@marionnette.com
président Jacques Félix
Period/Frequency: Sept, triennial (2000) *Arts types:* puppetry *Venues:* indoors as well as open air *Second Address:* visiting address of the administration: 25 rue du Petit Bois *Comments:* International Festival with 250 puppetry companies; see also National Organisation – UNIMA France

Journées Lyriques de Chartres
Office du Tourisme de Chartres, Place de la Cathédrale, BP 289, 28005 **Chartres** Cedex
Tel: 2-3721 5000 Fax: 2-3721 5191
présidente Charlotte Darmon;
directrice artistique Eve Ruggieri
Period/Frequency: September, annual *Arts types:* lyrical music *Venues:* Cathédrale de Chartres, Théâtre Municipal, Collégiale Saint-André
Comments: see also Promoters (FFFMI)

Floraisons Musicales, Les
Association les Floraisons Musicales, 12, avenue Charles de Gaulle, 84230 **Châteauneuf-du-Pape**
Tel: 4-9083 5757/7108/7292 Fax: 4-9083 5352/9086 3648
président Isabelle Laget;
directeur artistique Pierre Hommage
Period/Frequency: June, annual
Arts types: classical music *Venues:* Cellier du Château 200, Salle des Fêtes 400 *Comments:* see also National Organisations (FFFIM)

Grandes Heures de Cluny, Les
Office du Tourisme, 6, rue Merciére, 71250 **Cluny**
Tel: 3-8559 0534/2629 (bookings) Fax: 3-8559 0695
Internet: www.perso.wanadoo.fr/otcluny
E-Mail: cluny@wanadoo.fr
contact Jean-Claude Gosse
Period/Frequency: Aug, annual *Arts types:* chamber and sacred music, classical music *Venues:* 'Farinier', a XIIIth century granary 400 *Comments:* to promote Vins de Bourgogne; alternative Internet: www.bourgogne-tourisme.com

International Festival of Colmar, The
Colmar Tourist Office, 4 rue des Unterlinden,
68000 **Colmar**
Tel: 3-8920 6897 (festival office) Fax: 3-8941 3413
E-Mail: festival-international-de-colmar@at-colmar.fr
directeur Hubert Niess; direction artistique Vladimir Spivakov; responsable communication Sylvie Leroux; directrice-adjointe Anne Ledrich
Period/Frequency: July, annual *Arts types:* symphonic music, chamber music, recitals *Venues:* St Peter's Chapel 300, St Matthews Church 900, Decapole Hall (Koïfhus) 120

Festival des Forêts
6 Promenade St Pierre des Minimes, 60200 **Compiègne**
Tel: 3-4440 2899 Fax: 3-4440 2899
président du festival Brunó Ory Lavollée
Period/Frequency: annual (2000: 21 June-11 July)
Arts types: chamber and classical music *Venues:* Churches: l'Abbatiale de Saint Jean Aux-bois 400, Abbaye d'Ourscamp 380, Théâtre Imperial de Compiègne, Parc du Château *Comments:* some concerts are held in the forest

Festival de Théâtre de Rue
Théatre Simone Signoret, 12, Place Romagné,
78700 **Conflans-Sainte-Honorine**
Tel: 1-3490 9090/3972 5719
Fax: 1-3972 6177
E-Mail: Theatre.Signoret@wanadoo.fr
directeur Dominique Sautot
Period/Frequency: June, annual *Arts types:* theatre, music *Venues:* cap. 620, outdoors in the streets

Festival de Musique de Cordes-sur-Ciel
Maison Gaugiran,
40 Grand rue Raimond VII, 81170 **Cordes**
Tel: 5-6356 0075 Fax: 5-6356 2541
president Christian Urbita; directrice Valérie Follain
Period/Frequency: July-Aug, annual *Arts types:* chamber music, choral, spirituals, sacred music, orchestras, classical music, capella singers *Venues:* Église Saint-Michel Cordes 450, Maison Gaugiran 100, open-air: Place de la Bride, Vallee du Cerou *Comments:* other event: 3 Rencontre Europeenne Entre des Luthiers Archetiers et Musiciens (July)

Jazz Sous Les Pommiers
Les Unelles, BP 524, 50205 **Coutances** Cedex
Tel: 2-3376 7860 Fax: 2-3345 4836
Internet: www.oresia.com/jazzsouslespommier
E-Mail: jslp@oresia.com
directeur Denis Le Bas;
directeur adjoint Jean-Paul Lecoutour;
relations presse & administration Nicolas Jelansky
Period/Frequency: May, annual *Arts types:* jazz, blues, world music, street theatre *Venues:* Théâtre Municipal 700, Marcel Hélie 1500, Magic Mirrors 250 *Comments:* see also Venues

Festival Théâtral de Coye-La-Forêt
44 l'Orée des Bois, 60580 **Coye-La-Forêt**
Tel: 3-4458 6848/5239 Fax: 3-4458 6725
Internet: www.emroll.fr/tourisme.coye.html
E-Mail: festival-coye@hotmail.com
président Jean-François Gabillet; vice-président Claude Domenech; directeur artistique Jacques Bona
Period/Frequency: May, annual *Arts types:* all types of drama *Venues:* Centre Culturel 250 *Comments:* 16th festival; some shows also in other european languages, including English and German

Musique de Chambre à l'Orangerie de Bagatelle
8 rue Léonard Euler, 94000 **Créteil**
Tel: 1-4339 8907/4899 9311/6073 11718 (mobile)
Fax: 1-4980 9171
Internet: www.octuordefrance.com
président Daniel Naftalski; directeur musical Jean-Louis Sajot; communication Ariane Fournier
Period/Frequency: July-Aug, annual *Arts types:* contemporary & classical music *Venues:* in the Orangerie in the middle of the rose garden in Bagatelle 350 *Comments:* see also Orchestras (Octuor de France)

Festival Théâtral du Val d'Oise
21 BIS, Avenue de la division Leclerc,
95170 **Deuil-La-Barre**
Tel: 1-3417 9900
Fax: 1-3934 7068
directeur Alain Leonard
Period/Frequency: Oct-Nov, annual *Arts types:* contemporary drama *Venues:* 30 towns in the Val d'Oise *Second Address:* Abbaye de Maubuison, 95000, Saint Ouen l'Aumone *Comments:* young companies

Festival Est – Ouest
Place d'Hôtel de Ville, 26150 **Die**
Tel: 4-7522 1252 Fax: 4-7522 2247
Internet: www.est-ouest.com
E-Mail: festival.est-ouest@wanadoo.fr
directeur Ton Vink;
coordination programmation-administration Carole Rachet, Laurence Mundler;
relations presse Catherine Launay;
responsable European meetings Xavier Cazeneuve;
responsable Salon du livre d'Europe centrale
et orientale Agnès Boissy
Period/Frequency: Sept, annual *Arts types:* music, drama, literature, cinema, exhibitions, European meetings
Venues: open-air and in-doors in Die *Comments:* Multi-cultural festival with an East-European country; East-European Book Fair (French translations, 3500 titles)

Festival de Musique Ancienne de Dieppe
Ecole Nationale de Musique et de danse de Dieppe,
63, rue de la Barre, 76200 **Dieppe**
Tel: 2-3290 1334
Fax: 2-3506 0432
Internet: www.mairie-dieppe.fr
contact Christine Dufoise; directeur artistique Jean-Louis Charbonnier; administratrise Yäe-l Hassoun
Period/Frequency: Aug, annual *Arts types:* early music
Venues: Eglise Saint-Rémy 650, Eglise Arques-la-Bataille 500 to 600, Centre Jean Renoir 600, Auditorium 480, Eglise Saint-Jacques 500 , Chaveau Musée de Dieppe 60 *Comments:* also exhibitions, workshops, conferences and classes, masterclasses for all instruments and voices

Folkloriades Internationales et Fêtes de la Vigne
Festival de Musiques et Danses Populaires,
BP 1046, 21025 **Dijon** Cedex
Tel: 3-8030 3795 Fax: 3-8030 2344
E-Mail: folkloriades@axnet.fr
president Gérard Cunin;
secretaire general Robert Mutin
Period/Frequency: end of Aug-beg. of Sept *Arts types:* folklore: popular dance and music from all over the world – 25 different countries *Venues:* in the streets of Dijon, Grand Théâtre 900, Palais des Sports 5000, Auditorium 1611

L'Estivade
Mairie de Dijon, Direction des Affaires Culturelles, Hotel de Vogüé, 21000 **Dijon**
Tel: 3-8074 5374 Fax: 3-8074 5343
déléguée à l'action culturelle Michèle Curtil-Faivre
Period/Frequency: end of July – first week of August, annual *Arts types:* choir, shows, jazz, organ music, orchestras, dance, modern theatre *Venues:* throughout Dijon *Second Address:* during the festival: Hôtel Aubriot, 40 rue des Forges, 21000 Dijon,
Tel: 3-8030 3100 (booking & info)

Musiques Ultimes
Noise Museum, 19 rue Colson, 21000 **Dijon**
Tel: 3-8030 4273 Fax: 3-8030 4496
Internet: www.zone51.com/noisemuseum
E-Mail: NOISE.MUSEUM@wanadoo.fr
directeur artistique Yann Farcy
Period/Frequency: March *Arts types:* experimental & ambient music, sculpture, painting, installations
Venues: Maison de la Culture 1000, Nevers
Comments: European Festival

Opera d'Ete en Bourgogne
17 rue Amiral-Roussim, 21000 **Dijon**
Tel: 3-8030 6100
Fax: 3-8030 6152
président Jean-Michel Pelotte; directeur Daniel Linuesa
Period/Frequency: July-August, annual *Arts types:* lyrical art *Venues:* private mansions, castles and historic monuments of Bourgogne

Rencontre International de Théâtre
TNDB, 6 rue Rameau, BP 1230, 21029 **Dijon** Cedex
Tel: 3-8068 4747
Fax: 3-8068 4748
E-Mail: infotheatre@tndb.com
directeur Dominique Pitoiset (TNDB)
Period/Frequency: May, annual *Arts types:* theatre – contemporary *Venues:* Théâtre Parvis St. Jean 297
Comments: see also Drama and Venues

Festival International de la Musique de Chambre de Divonne les Bains
Domaine de Divonne, Avenue des Thermes,
01220 **Divonne-les-Bains**
Tel: 4-5040 3434 Fax: 4-5040 3424
directeur Jean Auberson
Period/Frequency: June, annual *Arts types:* chamber music, recitals *Venues:* Theatre du Domaine 260 *Second Address:* Festival de musique, Domaine de Divonne, 01220 Divonne les Bains

Les Météores
Festival International des Langues Françaises,
Place du Barlet, BP 79, 59502 **Douai** Cedex
Tel: 3-2799 6660
Fax: 3-2799 6661
Internet: www.etnet.fr/hippodrome
E-Mail: hippo@etnet.fr
directrice Marie Agnès Sevestre; directeur adjoint Jean Escher; administratrice adjointe Marie-Françoise Briez; conseiller artistique François Campana; secrétaire général Stéphane Konopczynski
Period/Frequency: March, annual
Arts types: drama, dance, variety, music theatre, rap, cinema (from francophone countries, 20 performances, 10 films), poetry *Venues:* l'Hippodrome, up to 1200, and other venues in Douai *Comments:* one of the aims is to show that there is not only one French language, but many; see also Venues

Larmes du Rire, Les
Direction des affaires culturelles, Mairie d'Epinal, BP 25, 88001 **Epinal** Cedex
Tel: 3-2968 5023
Fax: 3-2934 0612
Internet: www.ville_epinal.fr
directrice Pascale Valentin
Period/Frequency: Oct, annual
Arts types: drama (burlesque) *Venues:* Auditorium de la Louvière 500 *Comments:* booking: 3-2968 5067

Deferlantes, Les
Fécamp Scène Nationale, 54 rue Jules Ferry, BP 193, 76400 **Fécamp**
Tel: 2-3529 2281 Fax: 2-3528 5048
directrice Annick Bardol
Period/Frequency: beginning of April, annual *Arts types:* street arts (theatre, music & dance) *Venues:* Scene Nationale and outdoors, salle B 200, salle A 600 *Comments:* see also Venues

Harpes en Avenois (Mondial)
Service Culturel, Mairie de Feignies, 59750 **Feignies**
Tel: 3-2768 3902 Fax: 3-2768 3907
responsable David Deleye
Period/Frequency: Feb, annual *Arts types:* harp music, jazz, contemporary, classic, folk *Venues:* Espace Gerard Phillippe 330 *Comments:* all styles of harp music

Voyage en Marionnettes du Val de Marne
c/o Compagnie Jean-Pierre Lescot, 9, rue Pasteur, 94120 **Fontenay-Sous-Bois**
Tel: 1-4876 5939 Fax: 1-4876 4685
directeur artistique Jean-Pierre Lescot
Period/Frequency: Nov, biennial (2001) *Arts types:* puppetry for children and adults *Venues:* Salle Roublot, Fontenay-sous-Bois 135 *Comments:* see also Puppets

Abbaye Royale de Fontevraud
Centre Culturel de l'Ouest, 49590 **Fontevraud-l'Abbaye**
Tel: 2-4151 7352 Fax: 2-4138 1544
Internet: www.abbaye-fontevraud.asso.fr
E-Mail: abbaye.fontevraud@wanadoo.fr
président Olivier Guichard; vice-président Jean-Claude Groshens; directeur Jean-Paul Chaslus; dir art René Martin
Period/Frequency: Oct-June *Arts types:* sacred and secular music, world music *Venues:* Le Grand Refectoire 700, Le Haut Dortoire 400

rendez-vous musique nouvelle
Centre Culturel, 57600 **Forbach**
Tel: 3-8785 1231 Fax: 3-8785 1231
Internet: www.bplorraine.fr/RVMN/index.html
E-Mail: rdvmusiquenouvelle@bplorraine.fr
artistic direction Claude Lefebvre; electroacoustics Volker Böhm; communication, management Inge Borg
Period/Frequency: mid-November, annual *Arts types:* new music *Venues:* concerts at Forbach and in the region *Comments:* masterclasses throughout the year in analysis, composition, electroacoustics;

Festival de Marionnettes
Centre Culturel Marcel Pagnol, BP 181, Av. Rènè Cassin, 13774 **Fos-Sur-Mer** Cedex
Tel: 4-4211 0199 Fax: 4-4211 0247
directrice Catherine Simon; responsable de la programmation/ animation Dolores Fernández
Period/Frequency: Nov, biennial (2000) *Arts types:* world puppetry for young audiences and adults *Venues:* Centre Culturel 600, Petite salle 150

Festival de la Marionnette
Centre Georges Brassens, BP 8, 30300 **Fourques**
Tel: 4-9093 1447 Fax: 4-9049 7341
directeur J.M. Azema; animateur Emmanuel Patrick
Period/Frequency: end of Oct-beg. of Nov, annual *Arts types:* puppetry, animation *Venues:* Centre Georges Brassens 200

Festival de Gannat
4 Av. de la Rep, 03800 **Gannat**
Tel: 4-7090 1267 Fax: 4-7090 2264
Internet: cultures-traditions.com
E-Mail: 1063702762@compuserve.com
président Jean Roche;
directeur-adjoint Marie-Agnès Jacque
Period/Frequency: 7-10 days in July, annual *Arts types:* folkloric music, dance, crafts, games – cultures of the world *Venues:* all in Gannat including Place du Festival (a large space: Village of the World + a tent 20000)

Festival Musical des Grands Crus de Bourgogne
Centre Socio-Culturel, Avenue de Nierstein, 21220 **Gevrey-Chambertin**
Tel: 3-8051 8111/4350 4696 Fax: 3-8058 5155/4350 4696
Internet: www.mygale.org/00/csgev21/
E-Mail: coc-gevrey@ipac.fr
directeur artistique Yves Henri; vice-président Emmanuel de Malzieux; communication Christian Bon
Period/Frequency: April-October, annual *Arts types:* classical music, jazz *Venues:* all around Bourgogne *Comments:* 5 parts make up this festival: Musique en ChablisienLes Rencontres Musicales de Noyers, De Bach à Bacchus, Musiques au Chambertin, and Les Grands Heures de Cluny; ,

Musique en Grésivaudan
Mairie de Goncelin, 38570 **Goncelin**
Tel: 4-7608 2288
Fax: 4-7608 2288/1-4749 9536 (artistic director)
président et directeur artistiques Michel Moragues; directeur général Blandine Donot
Period/Frequency: August *Arts types:* chamber music *Venues:* 7-8 churches around the Grésivandan Valley, and the Espace Aragon (Villard Bonnot) 200-400

Festival de Théâtre Européen de Grenoble
Compagnie Renata Scant,
8 rue Pierre Duclot, 38000 **Grenoble**
Tel: 4-7644 6092
Fax: 4-7651 7427
Internet: www.neptune.fr/scant
E-Mail: scant@neptune.fr
directrice artistique et administratrice Renata Scant; directeur technique Pierre Auzas
Period/Frequency: last week June – 1st week in July, annual *Arts types:* theatre / street theatre
Venues: Théâtre de Grenoble 500, Théâtre "145" 275, Cour du Vieux Temple 500, Gymnase Vieux Temple 400, Théâtre Prémol 250, Le Théâtre Le Rio, streets and squares throughout Grenoble *Comments:* see also Drama and Venues

Festival de Pimpéan
Château de Pimpéan, 49320 **Grézillé**
Tel: 2-4168 9590
Fax: 2-4145 5193
Internet: pimpean.com
E-Mail: maryset@pimpean.com
agent artistique et
organisateur de spectacle Marie Tugendhat
Period/Frequency: Aug, annual *Arts types:* lyric festival *Venues:* church of the Château de Pimpéan (XV century) 60, Grenier aux Rentes 300 *Comments:* during the festival, there is a different concert everyday; also wine and food tasting: Fouaces

Festival d'Hardelot
23 av. de la Concorde, 62152 **Hardelot**
Tel: 3-2183 5102 Fax: 3-2191 8460
Internet: www.pas-de-calais.com
E-Mail: othardelot@nordnet.fr
président Bernard Delecour;
directeur Claude Desmarets
Period/Frequency: July/August, annual *Arts types:* orchestras, classical and chamber music *Venues:* Salle de l'Hôtel du Parc 1500, church 400

Moments Musicaux de L'Hermitage, Les
Hôtel L'Hermitage, 5 Esplanade Lucien Barrière, 44504 **La Baule** Cedex
Tel: 2-4011 4646
Fax: 2-4011 4635
E-Mail: hermitage@lucienbarriere.com
directeurs artistique René Martin;
présidente Cécile Combre
Period/Frequency: annual (2000: March) *Arts types:* chamber music, romantic and contemporary
Venues: capacity 450

Fêtes Romantiques de Nohant
Office du Tourisme, Square George Sand, 36400 **La Châtre**
Tel: 2-5448 2264
Fax: 2-5406 0915
Internet: www.berry.tm.fr
E-Mail: ot.la-chatre@wanadoo.fr
directeurs artistiques Jean-Yves Clément, Yves Henry
Period/Frequency: every weekend in June, annual *Arts types:* classical music and romantic literature *Venues:* Bergerie de Nohant 450 *Comments:* see also 'Rencontres de Frédéric Chopin'

Rencontres Internationales de Luthiers et maitres Sonneurs
Comité George Sand, 5 Place du Marché, BP 137, 36400 **La Châtre**
Tel: 2-5406 0996
Fax: 2-5448 2129
E-Mail: renc.saint-chartier@wanadoo.fr
commissaire general, directeur artistique Michelle Fromenteau; administrateur Maurice Bourg; regisseur general José Nedelec; president Nicolas Forissier
Period/Frequency: middle of July, annual *Arts types:* folk music *Venues:* Parc du Château de St. Chartier 36400 *Comments:* exhibitions of instrument makers (bagpipes, etc.), non-stop concerts, dance workshops

Rencontres Internationales de Frédéric Chopin
Office de Tourisme, 36400 **La Châtre-Nohant**
Tel: 2-5448 2264
Fax: 2-5406 0915
Internet: www.berry.tm.fr
E-Mail: ot.la-chatre@wanadoo.fr
directeurs artistiques Jean-Yves Clément, Yves Henry
Period/Frequency: mid-July, annual
Arts types: Chopin piano music *Venues:* Bergerie de Nohant 450 (George Sands' house), Théâtre de la Châtre 200 *Comments:* concerts, conferences, masterclasses. See also Fètes Romantiques

Festival Berlioz
69 rue de la République, BP 64, 38260 **La Côte-Saint-André**
Tel: 4-7420 3137 (admin)/2079 (booking)
Fax: 4-7420 2545
président Senateur Jean Boyer;
directeur Bernard Merlino
Period/Frequency: Aug, annual *Arts types:* classical music *Venues:* Les Halles de la Côte-Saint-André (XIII th C.) 1111, l'Église de la Côte-Saint-André (XI th C.) 250

Acteurs-Acteurs, International Film & Theatre Festival
Festival International Cinéma et Théâtre-Tours
Château de Plessis-lés-Tours,
Rue du Plessis, 37520 **La Riche**
Tel: 2-4738 2929
Fax: 2-4738 3565
directeur artistique José Manuel Cano Lopez; coordinatrice Marie-Laure Loisance
Period/Frequency: Oct, annual (8 days) *Arts types:* cinema, drama *Venues:* various in Tours
Comments: see also Drama

Printemps Théâtral
Association Vents et Marées, Théâtre Municipal, 85000 **La Roche-Sur-Yon**
Tel: 2-5136 0960
Fax: 2-5136 1571
E-Mail: vents.marees@wanadoo.fr
président Jean Lataillade;
responsable communications Pascale Lebard
Period/Frequency: May-June, annual
Arts types: drama *Venues:* Théâtre Municipal 440, Salle du Manége 800 *Second Address:* Centre Culturel des Salorges 85330 Noirmoutier

Francofolies de la Rochelle, Les
8 rue de l'Archimède, 17042 **La Rochelle** Cedex
Tel: 5-4628 2828
Fax: 5-4628 2829
Internet: www.francofolies.fr
E-Mail: francofolies@francofolies.fr
directeur Jean-Louis Foulquier; direction artistique Maryse Andrians, Ambre Foulquier; communication Kristine Kern, Delphine Lagache, Laurence Guinot Bourg; relations presse Maryse Bessaguet; administration Marie Dominique Bourdil, Christophe Bourdil
Period/Frequency: July, annual *Arts types:* French songs, rock, hip hop, world *Venues:* Esplanade Saint Jean d'Acre 15000, La Coursive – Grand Théâtre 1000, La Coursive – Salle Bleue 300, Carré Amelot 500, L'Encan 700, La Maki 1500

Roque d'Anthéron Festival International de Piano, La
Parc du Château de Florans,
13640 **La Roque d'Anthéron**
Tel: 4-4250 5115/16
Fax: 4-4250 4889
Internet: www.festival-piano.com
E-Mail: info@festival-piano.com
président Paul Onoratini;
directeur artistique René Martin
Period/Frequency: July-Aug, annual *Arts types:* piano – classical music presented in 44 concerts + 1 evening jazz *Venues:* Le Parc du Château de Florans 1854, l'Abbaye de Silvacane 800, Eglise de La Rogue 270, Théâtre Forbin 294, Etrang des Aulnes 1552, Jouques 200, Cueuron 363, Rognes 1312

Festival International de Musique et des Arts de La Tour de France et des Côtes du Roussillon Villages
Festival Office, Mairie,
Avenue Guy Malé, 66720 **La Tour-De-France**
Tel: 4-6829 0225/0934 (présidente) Fax: 4-6829 0594
directeur artistique John Bethell;
présidente Andrée Roulette
Period/Frequency: last week in July, annual
Arts types: baroque & sacred music, choir, opera, chamber music *Venues:* Eglise de la Tour de France 300, Notre Dame des Anges 100, Centre Culturel Martin Vivès 100, Théâtre de Verdure *Second Address:* Tel: 4-6829 4683 (during the festival) *Comments:* sponsored in part by the wine companies of the Languedoc Roussillon region

Festival International des Arts de Saint-Agrève
20 Paul Bruas, 07270 **Lamastre**
Tel: 4-7506 4392
Fax: 4-7506 3130/7530 2852
présidente Marie-Jeanne Sinz;
directeur artistique Paul Boucher
Period/Frequency: July-Aug, annual *Arts types:* chamber music, vocal, piano, chamber opera, jazz *Venues:* Grange de Clavières 300 *Comments:* rural setting, music, arts, masterclasses, exhibitions

Festival de l'Epau
Hôtel du Département,
7 rue des Maillets, 72072 **Le Mans** Cedex 9
Tel: 2-4381 4444 Fax: 2-4354 7102
Internet: www.sarthe.com/ccs
E-Mail: cecile.arthuis@cg72.fr
responsable Hervé De Colonbel
Period/Frequency: May-June, annual *Arts types:* chamber, choral and symphonic music *Venues:* l'Abbaye de l'Epau: Dortoire des Moines 600, l'Abbatiale 1000

Festival de l'Epau
Centre Culturel de la Sarthe, Hôtel du Département, 7 rue des Maillets, 72072 **Le Mans** Cedex 09
Tel: 2-4381 4444 Fax: 2-4354 7102
Internet: www.sarthe.com/ccs
président Louis-Jean de Nicolay; directeur Hervé de Colombel
Period/Frequency: May, annual *Arts types:* classical, chamber music *Venues:* Abbaye de l'Epau

Festival du Monastier
La Musique des Cuivres, La Vicairie, 43150 **Le Monastier**
Tel: 4-7103 9417 Fax: 4-7103 9500
Internet:
www.le-monastier-de-la musique-des-cuivres.net
E-Mail: mercier@club.internet.fr
président Roger Renault; directeur Roger Bertrand; directeur artistique Gilles Mercier
Period/Frequency: Aug, annual *Arts types:* from early music to contemporary music *Venues:* L'Eglise Abbatiale de Monastier 300, Chateau Abbatiale de Monastier 1000

Festival de Musique de la Chaise-Dieu
BP 150, 43004 **Le Puy-en-Velay** Cedex
Tel: 4-7109 4828 Fax: 4-7109 5558
Internet: www.leprogrès.fr/festival.chaise-dieu
E-Mail: festival-chaise-dieu@leprogres.fr
dir Guy Ramona; admin Denis Laurent; communication Cécile de Stredel; affaires extérieures Anne-Marie Giblin
Period/Frequency: end of Aug-beg. of Sept, annual *Arts types:* baroque, romantic, contemporary, church opera, sacred & secular *Venues:* Abbatiale St Robert , Salle Cziffra 280, La Chaise – Dieu *Second Address:* booking, Tel: 4-7100 0116 Fax:4-7100 0345 minitel: 3615 CASADEI *Comments:* visiting address: 12, bld Philippe-Jourde

Rencontres Internationales de Musique Médiévale du Thoronet
Plaine de Tarin, route du Luc, 83340 **Le Thoronet**
Tel: 4-9473 8500 Fax: 4-9473 8500
présidente Huguette Pourchet; directeur artistique Dominique Vellard; directeur administratif Daniel Bizien; attachée de presse Evelyne Pampin
Period/Frequency: July, annual *Arts types:* medieval music *Venues:* Abbaye du Thoronet 500

Les Nuits Pianistiques
680 chemin de la Tubasse, 13540 **Lignane-Puyricard**
Tel: 4-4292 6542 Fax: 4-4292 6542
directeur artistique Michel Bourdoncle
Period/Frequency: spring (Mar/April), annual *Arts types:* instrumental recitals, chamber concerts, symphonic concerts *Venues:* Salle du Bois de l'Aune 650

Festival Au Rayon Burlesque
Le Prato, Théâtre International de Quartier, 6 Allée de la Filature, 59000 **Lille**
Tel: 3-2052 7124 Fax: 3-2085 2894
responsable de la programmation Gilles Defacque; admin David Gadenne
Period/Frequency: May-June, annual *Arts types:* burlesque *Venues:* Salle du Prato à Lille 150 and venues in the region of Nord Pas de Calais

Planetado
Grand Bleu – Centre Dramatique National Jeunes Publics Lille/Nord-Pas de Calais,
36 Av. Marx Dormoy, 59000 **Lille**
Tel: 3-2009 4550 Fax: 3-2009 2152
Internet: www.legrandbleu.com
E-Mail: grandbleu@nordnet.fr
directeur Bernard Allombert; communication Françoise Allombert; administration Ariane Braun; directeur technique Patrick Leroy
Period/Frequency: Oct-Nov – the 2 festivals are biennial and take place alternately; Planetado in odd years, Vitrine Bleue in even years *Arts types:* drama for teenagers of Europe: Planetado, international meetings for professionals *Venues:* CDNJP 230-320 *Comments:* alternative E-mail: abraun@nordnet.fr; see also Venues and Drama

Rencontres, Les
Festival Les Rencontres, 17 rue de Thumesnil, 59000 **Lille**
Tel: 3-2052 6975 Fax: 3-2088 2146
Internet: www.Majt-lille.Asso.fr
E-Mail: Culture@majt-lille.Asso.fr
director general of la M.A.J.T. Jacques Herbaut; director of the festival Marc Menis; organisation of the festival Gaëlle Bruault, Sylvain Daudier, Renè-Marc Demaret, Bruno Lienard, Alexandre Marguet
Period/Frequency: 20-26 September *Arts types:* street theatre, visual arts, arts plastics expositions *Comments:* also organise arts exhibitions; management of artistic residential workshop La Fabrique where street theatre artistes can create, construct and do their rehearsal, also manage L' Atelier a center of creation in fine arts (paint, photos, video and sculpture)

Festival International des Francophonies en Limousin
11 avenue du Général de Gaulle, 87000 **Limoges**
Tel: 5-5510 9010 Fax: 5-5577 0472
Internet: www.fest-theatres-franco.com
E-Mail: fifl@wanadoo.fr
directrice Monique Blin; président Robert Abirached; secrétaire générale Béatrice Castaner; administrateur Nathalie Pousset
Period/Frequency: Sept-Oct, annual *Arts types:* mainly French speaking drama, music, poetry *Second Address:* 15 passage de la Main d'Or, 75011, Paris, Tel: 1-4700 3344, Fax: 1-4700 5591 *Comments:* over 200 artists from 15 different countries; conferences and meetings as well as performances and exhibitions

Biennale de la Danse
3 Rue Président Edouard Herriot, 69001 **Lyon**
Tel: 4-7207 4141 Fax: 4-7200 0313
Internet: www.biennale-de-lyon.org
E-Mail: info@biennale-de-lyon.org
administrateur Yves Le Sergent; directeur artistique Guy Darmet; directeur de la communication Didier Coirint; directeur général Henri Destezet
Period/Frequency: Sept-Oct, biennial (2000) *Arts types:* dance *Venues:* theatres in Lyon *Comments:* theme: festival invites companies from a specific country to perform, to promote understanding of different cultures

Biennale Théâtre Jeunes Publics – Lyon, La
Théâtre des Jeunes Années, Centre Dramatique National, 23 rue de Bourgogne, 69009 **Lyon**
Tel: 4-7253 1510 Fax: 4-7253 1519
secrétaire général Anne Robin; directeurs artistiques Maurice Yendt, Michel Dieuaide; directeur technique Jean-Pierre Grosset
Period/Frequency: June, biennial (2001) *Arts types:* young people's theatre *Venues:* various theatres throughout Lyon *Comments:* co-production with la Ville de Lyon et le Ministère de la Culture; see also Venues and Drama

Festival de Musique du Vieux Lyon
Bureau du Festival, 5 Place du Petit College, 69005 **Lyon**
Tel: 4-7838 0909 Fax: 4-7838 7262
directeur artistique & générale Eric Desnoues; president Jean-Philippe Lacroix; secretary Jean-Louis Mandon; contact presse Florence Maeso-Bessalel; communication/advertising-promotion Pascal Jullien; pr Eric Prost-Sydorak; édition Valérie Dal-Pino
Period/Frequency: Nov-Dec, annual *Arts types:* baroque, harpsicord, choir-sacred, renaissance, medieval *Venues:* Grand Salon de l'hôtel de Ville, Primatiale Saint-Jean, Auditorium, Musée des Tissus, Conservatoire National Superieur de Musique de Lyon, Opèra de Lyon, Chapelle Ampére *Comments:* see also Festival Estival du Vieux Lyon, Uzés Nuits Musicales, Académie Baroque de Lyon and Un Rendz-vous avec...

Festival Estival du Vieux Lyon
5, Place du Petit Collège, 69005 **Lyon**
Tel: 4-7838 0909 Fax: 4-7838 7262
contact presse Florence Maeso-Bessalel; director/founder (artistic director for festival d'Uzés Eric Desnoues); attacheé de direction Valèrie Dal Pino; pr Eric Prost-Sydorak; édition Valérie Dal-Pino
Period/Frequency: June-July, annual *Arts types:* baroque music, classical, serenades, sonatas, traditional music *Venues:* in the heart of the Vieux Lyon, Cour du Musée de Gadagne XVIth Century building (open-air), if it rains: Temple du Change, Musée des Tissus, Courde l'Hôtel de Ville *Second Address:* venue address: 10-14 Rue de Gadagne, Hôtel de Gadagne, 69005 Lyon *Comments:* see also Festival de Musique de Lyon, Uzès Nuits Musicales, Académie Baroque de Lyon and Un Rendez-vous avec....

Festival 'Musiques en Scène'
c/o GRAME, 9 rue du Garet, BP 1185, 69202 **Lyon** Cedex 1
Tel: 4-7207 3700 Fax: 4-7207 3701
Internet: www.grame.fr
E-Mail: grame@rd.grame.fr
directeur James Giroudon, Pierre Alain Jaffrennou; administratrice Florence Catrin; responsable recherche Yann Orlarey
Period/Frequency: March *Arts types:* contemporary music & musical theatre *Venues:* Théâtre de la Renaissance, up to 500, Musée d'Art Contemporain de Lyon 500, Maurice Ravel, Opera National de Lyon *Comments:* organised by GRAME, see also Venues & Promoters

Les Musicades
Musicalyon, 51 rue de l'Oeuvre, 69241 **Lyon** Cedex 4
Tel: 4-7200 2098 Fax: 4-7839 2841
Internet: www.perso.wanadoo.fr/musicades/
E-Mail: musicades@wanadoo.fr
président Dominique Henry
Period/Frequency: Sept, annual *Arts types:* chamber music (vocal and instrumental) *Venues:* L'opéra National de Lyon 1200, Salle Noliciè

Nuits de Fourvière, Les
1 rue Cléberg, 65005 **Lyon**
Tel: 4-7232 0000 Fax: 4-7257 1549
Internet: www.nuits-de-fourviere.org
adminstrateur Yves Girard; communication Jean-Luc Very (4-7257 1540)
Period/Frequency: June-Aug, annual *Arts types:* classical music, theatre, world music, rock, dance, cinema *Venues:* Théâtre Antique de Fourvière 4500

Francophonies Théâtrales Pour la Jeunesse
Théâtre du Mantois, 18 rue de Gassicourt, 78200 **Mantes-la-Jolie**
Tel: 1-3033 0226 Fax: 1-3094 5688
E-Mail: tmantois@clubinternet.fr
directeur Jean-Charles Lenoir; administrateur Nathalie Guérin; relations publiques Nathalie Dubruil
Period/Frequency: May, biennial (2000) *Arts types:* theatre for young audiences *Venues:* various throughout Mantes-la-Jolie *Comments:* see also Drama

Jazz in Marciac
Place de l'Hôtel de la Ville, BP 23, 32230 **Marciac (Gers)**
Tel: 5-6209 3198/3333 (reservations) Fax: 5-6209 3867
Internet: www.marciac.com
E-Mail: marciac@wanadoo.fr
président et directeur artistique Jean-Louis Guilhaumon; contact presse Gaetane Dupont-Bauverie
Period/Frequency: 10 days in mid-Aug *Arts types:* jazz *Venues:* Chapiteau 5000, Arenes 1000

Festival Lyrique en Marmandais
12 rue du Géneral Brun, 47200 **Marmande**
Tel: 5-5389 6875 Fax: 5-5389 6875
président Philippe Mestres; conseiller artistique Michel Herbé; communication Marie-Hélène Bonnauron
Period/Frequency: Aug, annual *Arts types:* lyric, classical music *Venues:* Théâtre Comœdia 600
Comments: see also Competition

Festival de Marseille
6 place Sadi Carnot, BP 2414, 13215 **Marseille** Cedex 2
Tel: 4-9199 0020 Fax: 4-9199 0022
E-Mail: info@festivaldemarseille.com
directeur Appoline Quintrand; directeur communication Sabina Canonica; chargée de production Marie Marmet; assistante de production Sophie Barbaux; assistante de communication Sabina Canonica
Period/Frequency: 3 weeks in July, annual *Arts types:* mainly dance, music, theatre, exhibitions, cinema *Venues:* Cour de la Vieille Charité 1500

Musiques à Bagatelle
Mairies des 6éme et 8éme , 125 rue du Cdt Rolland, 13008 **Marseille**
Tel: 4-9155 2834/1584
Fax: 4-9155 3778
hon. president Mayor Jean-Claude Gaudin; communication Miss Senes; attaché à la culture Paul Mercier
Period/Frequency: July, annual *Arts types:* orchestras (bass, jazz, organ), classical music *Venues:* Parc de Bagatelle, if it rains use: L'Eglise du Sacré-Coeur, avenue du Prado, 13008 Marseille *Comments:* all performances are free

Festival International d'Orgue à Masevaux
7 rue du Maréchal Foch, 68290 **Masevaux**
Tel: 3-8938 0418
Fax: 3-8982 4944 (office of tourisme)
artistic director Pierre Chevreau
Period/Frequency: Aug-Sept, annual *Arts types:* organ recitals, sacred music – (the festival revolves around one instrument: the organ) *Venues:* Eglise St Martin de Masevaux 1200 *Second Address:* Office du Tourisme (information & booking), 36 Fossé des Flagellants, 68290 Masevaux, Tel: 3-8982 4199

Folies de Maubeuge, Les
Le Manège, BP 105, 59602 **Maubeuge** Cedex
Tel: 3-2765 1500 Fax: 3-2765 9380
Internet: www.lemanege.com
E-Mail: manege1@worldnet.fr
directeur Didier Fusillier;
administrateur Yves Vasseur;
sécrétariat général Brigitte Briatte;
direction technique Frédéric Platteau;
relations publiques Gilles Bouckaert, Corinne Solini
Period/Frequency: June-July, annual *Arts types:* mainly street theatre, rock *Venues:* La Luna 2500, Salle Théophile Haut 2000, Centre Malraux 760, Théâtre du Manège 600, Salle Ferré 600, Salles Sthrau 2 x 150, Chapelle des Soeurs noires 90
Comments: working area: 3 towns: Maubeuge, Jeumont and Aulnoye; see also Venues

VIA
Le Manège, BP 105, 59602 **Maubeuge** Cedex
Tel: 3-2765 1500 Fax: 3-2765 9380
Internet: www.lemanege.com
E-Mail: manege1@worldnet.fr
directeur Didier Fusillier; administrateur Yves Vasseur; sécrétariat général Brigitte Briatte; directeur technique Frédéric Platteau; directeur communication Gilles Bouckaert; relations publiques Corinne Solini, Florence Laly, Fabien Lemdrie
Period/Frequency: end of March, annual *Arts types:* dance theatre & new technology *Venues:* La Luna 2500, Salle Théophile Haut 2000, Centre Malraux 760, Théâtre du Manège 600, Salles Sthrau 2 x 150, Chapelle des Soeurs noires 90, Salle Léo Ferré 700, Espace GP 300 *Comments:* working area: 3 towns; Maubeuge, Jeumont, Aulnoye,Feignies. Partnership of 22 towns sponsored by 33 companies

Festival du Comminges
31260 **Mazères-sur-Salat**
Tel: 5-6188 3200/6198 4535 (Bureau)
Fax: 5-6197 4560
Internet: www.festival-du-comminges.asso.fr
directeur fondateur Pierre Lacroix; directeur de programmation Jean Patrice Brosse (Tel: 1-4354 9580)
Period/Frequency: July-Aug, annual
Arts types: sacred music and chamber music *Venues:* Cathédrale de St Bertrand de Comminges 600, Basilique St Just Valcabrère 450, Collégiale de St Gaudens 500

Festival de Musique de Menton
Palais de l'Europe, Av Boyer,
BP 239, 06506 **Menton** Cedex
Tel: 4-9335 8222/9241 7650 Fax: 4-9241 7658
direction artistique Thomas Erdos;
présidente Jacqueline Schneider-Borocz
Period/Frequency: Aug, annual *Arts types:* chamber music *Venues:* Parvis Saint-Michel, Menton

Fruits de Mhère
Le Bourg, 58140 **Mhère**
Tel: 3-8622 7222 Fax: 3-8622 7571
Internet: www.multimania.com/mhere
E-Mail: mhere@multimania.com
président Jacques Di Donato; secrétaire Isabelle Duthoit
Period/Frequency: Aug, annual *Arts types:* contemporary music, theatre, improvised music

Heures Romantiques au pays de Monthodon, Les
Office du Tourisme, Mairie de Monthodon, M. Fermé, rue du 8 mai, 37110 **Monthodon**
Tel: 2-4756 2222 Fax: 2-4729 5170
adjoint au maire Pierre Fermé; dir art Udo Reinemann
Period/Frequency: July/August, annual *Arts types:* chamber and choral music *Venues:* churches 150-250

Festival du Périgord Noir
49 rue Général Foy, 24290 **Montignac**
Tel: 5-5351 9517 Fax: 5-5350 8700
Internet: www.cetoucom.com/festival
président et directeur artistique Jean-Luc Soulé;
attachée aux relations exterieurs et artistiques Véronique Iaciu; communication et attachée de presse Dominique Larmoyer (tel: 1-4067 6895/96, fax: 1-4067 9181)
Period/Frequency: July-Aug *Arts types:* baroque and chamber music *Venues:* churches and abbeys in Dordogne *Comments:* International Academy of Chamber Music, string quartet, quintet

L' Ete Musical en Bergerac
Office du Tourisme du Montpaziérois,
24540 **Montpazier**
Tel: 5-5322 6859 Fax: 5-5374 3008
E-Mail: siac@montpazier@wanadoo.fr
président Mr Chisson;
pr/responsable artistiques Isabelle Brunet
Period/Frequency: July-August *Arts types:* classical music, jazz, world music, opera, ballet *Venues:* La Bastide de Monpazier 300, Le Château de Biron 1200 to 1500, Abbaye de Cadouin 500, Le Château de Monbazillac 300, Le Cloître des Récollêts a Bergerac 400

Festival de Radio-France et Montpellier Languedoc-Roussillon
Le Corum, BP 9214, 34043 **Montpellier** Cedex 1
Tel: 4-6761 6681 Fax: 4-6761 6682
administrateur générale Jany Macaby; dir art René Koering; attachée de presse Fanny Decobert; pr Pascal Dufour
Period/Frequency: July-Aug, annual
Arts types: musique classique symphonique et lyrique, early music, jazz *Venues:* Opera Berlioz le Corum 2000, Cour Jacques Coeur 1200, Cour des Ursulines 800, Salle Pasteur-Le Corum 700 *Second Address:* Paris address: Radio France pièce 9433, 116 avenue du Président Kennedy, 75220 Paris Cedex 16

Festival International Montpellier Danse
Hôtel d'Assas, 6 rue Vieille Aiguillerie,
34000 **Montpellier**
Tel: 4-6760 8360 Fax: 4-6760 8306
Internet: www.montpellierdanse.com
E-Mail: info@montpellierdanse.com
directeur général Jean-Paul Montanari; directrice adjointe Gisèle Depuccio; chargée de communication, presse Françoise Bretton; admin Jacques Jaricot
Period/Frequency: June-July, annual *Arts types:* modern dance *Venues:* Opéra Comédie 900, Opéra Berlioz 2000, Cour des Ursulines 800, Studio Bagonet-Les Ursulines

Montpellier Danse
Association Festival International Montpellier Danse, Hôtel d'Assas, 6 rue Vieille Aiguillerie,
34000 **Montpellier**
Tel: 4-6760 8360
Fax: 4-6760 8306
Internet: www.montpellierdanse.com
E-Mail: info@montpellierdanse.com
Period/Frequency: end of June-July *Arts types:* contemporary *Venues:* Opera Berlioz, Opera Comedie, Théâtre Jean Villar, Cour des Ursulines

Printemps des Comédiens, Le
Parc Euromédecine, 34097 **Montpellier** Cedex 5
Tel: 4-6763 6667 Fax: 4-6704 2150
Internet: www.cge-ol.fr/printemps
E-Mail: printemps@cge-ol.fr
directeur général et artistique Daniel Bedos; directeur administratif Philippe Gayola
Period/Frequency: June-July, annual *Arts types:* drama, comedy, music, world music *Venues:* Parc du Chateau d'O, Cours Molière 1000 (18th century, open-air), Théâtre d'O 174, Bassin 600 *Second Address:* postal address: Domaine Départemental de Château d'O, 857 rue de Saint-Priest, 34090 Montpellier,
Tel: 4-6763 6666 (bookings)

Les Arts Jaillissants
Mairie, 63220 **Montsapey**
Tel: 4-7936 2352/2924 (tourist office) Fax: 4-7936 3895
président Bernard Villermet; administrateur & financier Jean-Pierre Ruffier; communication Gérard Trombert
Period/Frequency: July-August, annual *Arts types:* classic & baroque music, 18th & 19th centuries *Venues:* Eglise Classée du Montsapey 230 *Comments:* also painting exhibition during the festival

Festival Classique Junior
40 rue de Bourgogne, 03000 **Moulins**
Tel: 4-7044 6861 Fax: 4-7048 5049 (Mairie de Moulin)
président de l'association Jacques De Vergnette
Period/Frequency: June or July, annual *Arts types:* chamber music, classical music *Venues:* churches and châteaux in the area of Moulin
Comments: featuring best pupils from Conservatoires de Musique de Paris et de Lyon

Festival de Musique et D'Art Baroque en Tarentaise
Place Saint Pierre, 73600 **Moutiers**
Tel: 4-7924 4702 Fax: 4-7924 5980
president Josette-Elise Tatin;
artistic director Brigitte Haudebourg
Period/Frequency: 1st 2 weeks in Aug, annual *Arts types:* baroque music *Venues:* baroque churches *Second Address:* Josette-Elise Tatin, Grand Coeur, 73260 Villarberenger tel. 4-7924 4702 fax. 4-7924 5980, Brigitte Haudebourg 10 Av. F. Roosevelt, 92150 Suresnes tel. 1-4728 7652 fax. 1-4506 4125

Jazz à Mulhouse
BP 1335, 68056 **Mulhouse** Cedex
Tel: 3-8945 6395 Fax: 3-8956 2690
Internet: www.jazz-mulhouse.org
E-Mail: Jazz.A.mulhouse@wanadoo.fr
directeur Paul Kanitzer;
relations presse Christiane Stumps
Period/Frequency: Aug, annual *Arts types:* jazz dominance European, musiques improvisée et d'aujourd'hui *Venues:* throughout the south of Haut Rhin and in Mulhouse

Masquerades (Biennale des arts associés), Les
c/z Lasca, BP 301, 54006 **Nancy** Cedex
Tel: 3-8332 0225 Fax: 3-8337 8082
directeur Gilles Gosserez
Period/Frequency: August, biennial (2000) *Arts types:* puppetry (contemporary) *Comments:* European festival

Nancy Jazz Pulsations
BP 711, 54064 **Nancy**
Tel: 3-8335 4086 Fax: 3-8335 5644
Internet: www.nancyjazzpuls.com
directeur Patrick Kader; administration Raymond Sanna; président Michel Piotrkowski;
relations presse Emmanuelle Duchesne
Period/Frequency: Oct, annual *Arts types:* jazz, blues, rock, African music, pop, techno *Venues:* le Zenith 6000, Chapiteau de la Pépiniére 2000, Clubs 200/400, Magic Mirrors 400 *Comments:* exhibitions, cinema

Festival International de Théâtre Etudiant
Théâtre des Amandiers, 7 Ave. Pablo Picasso,
92022 **Nanterre** Cedex
Tel: 1-4614 7000/7044 Fax: 1-4725 1775
E-Mail: amandiers@aol.com
directeur Jean-Pierre Vincent; directeur délégué Marc Dondey; coordination du festival Céline Roblot;
relations avec le public Jocelyne Gougerot
Period/Frequency: June, annual
Arts types: theatre at a university level, young theatre companies *Venues:* Théâtre des Amandiers, various in Nanterre *Second Address:* Université Paris X – Nanterre, délégation aux Affaires Culturelles et Institut d'Etudes Théâtrales Tel: 1-4097 7418
Comments: participant universities from all the world: Goethe Universität of Frankfurt, University of Manchester, Zagreb, Belgium, Morroco

Festival d'Été de Nantes
Porte St. Pierre, rue de l'Évêché, 44000 **Nantes**
Tel: 2-4008 0100 Fax: 2-4048 1264
Internet: www.festival-ete-nantes.org
E-Mail: contact@festival-ete-nantes.org
directeur artistique Bertrand Delaporte;
assistante Fabienne Bernard
Period/Frequency: July, annual *Arts types:* world music, traditional songs from all continents, dance, cinema *Venues:* Ile Sainte Anne, Prairie aux ducs
Comments: information: Tel: 2-4008 0066

Fin de Siècle
CRDC, 2 rue de la Biscuiterie, BP 21304,
44013 **Nantes** Cedex 1
Tel: 2-5182 1500
Fax: 2-4020 2012
directeur Jean Blaise; président Daniel Briolet
Period/Frequency: end Dec-beg. Jan, annual *Arts types:* all arts types including music, dance, plastic arts, theatre, discussions *Venues:* L'Usine-Lu, salle 2000
Comments: every year there is a theme – 1999: New York; artists come from the country featured;
see also Venues

Folle Journée, La
Cité des Congrès, BP 24102, 44041 **Nantes** Cedex 1
Tel: 2-5188 2000 Fax: 2-5188 2020
Internet: www.Congres-Nantes.fr
E-Mail: infoculture@congres-nantes.fr
directeur général Jacques Tallut; directeur adjoint Jean-Baptiste Desbois; directrice de la communication et relations extérieures Michèle Guillossou; directeur artistique René Martin (CREA)
Period/Frequency: Feb, annual *Arts types:* classical music *Venues:* Cité des Congrès 20000 (including: Auditorium 2000, 800, 450, G. Halle 3000) *Comments:* organised by CREA (Centre de Réalisations et d'Etudes Artistiques); visiting address: 5 rue de Valmy, 44000 Nantes; see also Promoters

Printemps des Arts, Le
c/o Association PRINTEMPS DES ARTS,
2, rue Gaston Veil, 44000 **Nantes**
Tel: 2-4020 0300 Fax: 2-4012 0597
dir art Philippe Lénael; administrateur Elisabeth Moret
Period/Frequency: annual *Arts types:* early music, opera

Festival International de Musique du Haut-Bugey
39 rue du Collège, 01130 **Nantua**
Tel: 4-7475 2494 Fax: 4-7475 2494
président Hervé Vion-Delphin; dir art Guy Dangain
Period/Frequency: June-August, annual *Arts types:* classical music *Venues:* Abbatiale de Nantua (12th C.) 700

Festival de Musique en Bourbonnais
Château de Nassigny, 03190 **Nassigny**
Tel: 4-7006 7226 Fax: 4-7006 2245
Internet: persoweb.francenet.fr\~emmendoe\fest.htm
E-Mail: emmendoe@micronet.fr
présidente Bernadette Roux; vices-présidents Jean-Claude Renon, Annie Emmendoerffer; trésorier Pierre Devaux
Period/Frequency: July-Aug *Arts types:* chamber music *Venues:* Eglise de Châteloy, Hérisson, petite église romane 350, Anciennes Forges de Troncais, St Bonnet Troncais, Grange aménagée 440

Festival de Musique en Albret
Chemin de Ladevèze, 47600 **Nérac**
Tel: 5-5365 2120 Fax: 5-5365 6481
directeur artistique Jacques Casterede;
secrétariat Jacqueline D'Auriol
Period/Frequency: July-Aug, annual *Arts types:* chamber music, classical music *Venues:* throughout the Albret region, Lot-et-Garonne *Comments:* 10th festival

Festival Semaines Musicales de Tours
10 rue Ancelle, 92200 **Neuilly**
Tel: 1-4722 9708 Fax: 1-4640 0945
Internet: www.semaines-musicales.com
E-Mail: aidam99@hotmail.com
directeur Rollo Kovac
Period/Frequency: July, annual *Arts types:* opera, dance, classical music, masterclasses *Venues:* in Tours and Châteaux (nearby) 300-600 *Comments:* alternative Internet: www.iFrance.com/aidam99

Festival Semaines Musicales de Tours
AIDAM, 10 rue Ancelle, 92200 **Neuilly**
Tel: 1-4722 9708 Fax: 1-4640 0945
Internet: www.semaines-musicales.com
E-Mail: aidam99@hotmail.com
président Rollo Kovac; dir artistique Youri Bashnet
Period/Frequency: July, annual *Arts types:* classical music
Comments: see also Promoters (FFFMI)

Les Rencontres Internationales de Jazz
BP 824, 58008 **Nevers** Cedex
Tel: 3-8657 8851 Fax: 3-8657 9305
Internet: www.jazzfrance.com/nevers
E-Mail: nevers.djazz@wanadoo.fr
programmateur Roger Fontanel;
assistante Sabine Cersosimo
Period/Frequency: 6-13 Nov *Arts types:* jazz *Venues:* le PAC des Ouches 120, Maison de la Culture 1000, Salle du Théâtre 300

Festival Musiques Actuelles Nice Côte d'Azur (MANCA)
Centre National de Creation Musicale, 33 Av Jean-Médecin, 06000 **Nice**
Tel: 4-9388 7468 Fax: 4-9316 0766
E-Mail: firm_studio@compuserve.com
administration Olivier Enguchard;
attachée de presse Martine Danguy d'Alessandro
Period/Frequency: Nov, annual *Arts types:* contemporary music (electro-acoustique), exhibitions *Venues:* mainly in the Auditorium Musée d'Art Moderne 225, all around Nice and the region *Comments:* 20-25 concerts, also conferences and a mini MANCA for young audiences; see also Promoters

Festival de Châteauvallon
Châteauvallon, BP 118, 83192 **Ollioules** Cedex
Tel: 4-9422 7400
Fax: 4-9422 7419
information Nataly Bernard
Period/Frequency: July, annual *Arts types:* contemporary dance, drama *Venues:* Théâtre Couvert 500, Amphithéâtre 1200, Cinema 100, Videothèque 15
Comments: see also Dance, Venues and Promoters

Chorégies d'Orange
BP 205, 18 Place Silvain, 84107 **Orange** Cedex
Tel: 4-9034 2424 (bookings)/9051 8383 (admin)
Fax: 4-9011 0404 (bookings)/9034 8767 (admin)
Internet: www.choregies.asso.fr
directeur Raymond Duffaut; communication – presse nationale et international Colette Chaunu; responsable communication et presse régionale Colette Brivet
Period/Frequency: July-Aug *Arts types:* opera, classical and symphonic concerts, oratorio *Venues:* Théâtre Antique d'Orange 8600

Academie Internationale de Musique de Flaine
29 rue Desaix, 75015 **Paris**
Tel: 1-4229 2552/4324 8165/5090 8001 (bookings)
Fax: 1-4229 2552
directeurs Bruno Latouche, Jean Lenert
Period/Frequency: Aug, annual *Arts types:* chamber and classical music, symphony, recitals
Venues: Auditorium de Flaine 500

Africolor
145 rue de Menil Montant, 75020 **Paris**
Tel: 1-4797 6999
Fax: 1-4797 6544
E-Mail: Africolor@aol.com
directeur Philippe Conrath
Period/Frequency: annual (2000: July) *Arts types:* African music *Venues:* Théâtre Gérard Philipe, de Saint Denis

Châtillon-sur-Seine International Summer University and North Burgundy festival
110 quai Louis Blériot, 75781 **Paris** Cedex 16
Tel: 1-4525 3787 Fax: 1-4525 3787
Internet: www.cfpcommunication.com/univchat
E-Mail: amcc@club-internet.com
director Fernand Quattrocchi
Period/Frequency: July, annual *Arts types:* classical music, jazz, theatre, painting, sports *Venues:* Châtillon-sur-Seine, in Côte d'Or *Second Address:* 10 rue de la Liberation, 21400 Châtillon-sur-Seine, Tel: 3-8081 5276, Fax: 3-8081 5859

Festival d'Automne
156 rue de Rivoli, 75001 **Paris**
Tel: 1-5345 1700 Fax: 1-5345 1701
Internet: www.festival-automne.com
E-Mail: info@festival-automne.com
directeur général Alain Crombecque; directrice artistique musique Joséphine Markovits; directrice artistique théatre et danse Marie Collin; communication et relations avec la presse Patrick Duval; relations publiques Elisa Santos-Gros, Gérard di Giacomo
Period/Frequency: Sept-Dec, annual *Arts types:* contemporary dance, theatre, contemporary music, cinema, plastic art *Venues:* throughout Paris

Festival d'Ile de France
30 rue de Miromesnil, 75008 **Paris**
Tel: 1-4494 2888/2850 (bookings)
Fax: 1-4494 2858
Internet: www.cr-ile-de.france.com
E-Mail: info@festival-ile-de-france.com
directrice Charlotte Latigrat;
président du conseil rég. Jean-Paul Huchon;
administration Olivier Delsalle;
communication Laurence Lévi;
relations publiques Nathalie Andries;
vice-présidente culture Marie Pierre De La Gontrie
Period/Frequency: Sept-Oct, annual *Arts types:* classical music *Venues:* various historic monuments in the Ile-de-France 200 to 1500 *Comments:* also organise the Rencontres Musicales de Villarceaux; also Festival 93 Factory (9-17 Oct) electronic music

Festival d'Orgue de Chartres
75 rue de Grenelle, 75007 **Paris**
Tel: 1-4548 3174
Fax: 1-4549 1434
président fondateur de l'Association des Grandes Orgues de Chartres Pierre Firmin Didot;
directrice Colette Morillon
Period/Frequency: July-Sept, annual *Arts types:* organ, classical music *Venues:* Cathédrale de Chartres 1200
Second Address: Office de Tourisme de Chartres, Place de la Cathédrale, 28000, Chartres, Tel: 2-3721 5000, Fax: 2-3721 5191 *Comments:* performances on sundays; free admission; see also Competitions

Festival de l'Imaginaire
Maison des Cultures du Monde,
101 boulevard Raspail, 75006 **Paris**
Tel: 1-4544 7230 (admin)/4142 (booking)
Fax: 1-4544 7660
Internet: www.mcm.asso.fr
E-Mail: cultures.du.monde@wanadoo.fr
directeur Chérif Khaznadar; conseillers artistiques Françoise Gründ, Pierre Bois, Arwad Esber;
administratrice Martine Westphal
Period/Frequency: May/June, annual
Arts types: theatre, music, dance, exhibition, (contemporary & traditional) *Venues:* Théâtre de l'Alliance 360, Institut du Monde Arabe, Grande Halle de la Villette, Théâtre Equestre Zingaro 600 *Comments:* the Maision des Cultures du Monde organise events from abroad

Festival de Pau
9 Rue de Boccador, 75008 **Paris**
Tel: 1-4720 9540 Fax: 1-4952 0291
directeur Roger Hanin; administrateur Bernard Renan; sous la haute présidence de André Labarrère Député Maire de Pau; attachée de presse Tania Mimoun
Period/Frequency: June-July, annual *Arts types:* drama, music, dance, variety *Venues:* Théâtre St Louis 350, La Villa St Bazil, Le Zénith

Festival des Églises Romanes du Berry
Yves d'Argent, 11, rue Sedillot, 75007 **Paris**
Tel: 1-4555 7678 Fax: 1-4556 0647
Internet: www.france-villages.com
président Yves d'Argent
Period/Frequency: July -Aug, annual *Arts types:* chamber music, orchestras, early music, choirs, recitals *Venues:* in churches around the Berry region *Second address:* Yves d'Argent, Les Turaux, 18600, Vereaux, Tel: 2-4874 1051

Festival musique en l'Ile (Concertsolo)
CODA, 106 Bld Richard Le-Noir, 75011 **Paris**
Tel: 1-4355 4709 Fax: 1-4355 3517
administrateur Philippe Suzanne
Period/Frequency: July-Sept, annual *Arts types:* vocal sacred music, baroque *Venues:* L'Eglise St Louis 400, L'Eglise St Germain 600, and various other churches

Festival Musique en Sorbonne
Musique en Sorbonne,
2 rue Francis de Croisset, 75018 **Paris**
Tel: 1-4262 7171 Fax: 1-4251 6911
administrateur Jean Marie Houdayer;
directeur artistique Jacques Grimbert
Period/Frequency: June, annual *Venues:* Grand Amphithéâtre de la Sorbonne 1200, Amphithéâtre Richelieu 500 to 600 *Comments:*
see also Choirs & Orchestras

Festival Nord Bourgogne
110 Quai Louis Blériot, 75781 **Paris** Cedex 16
Tel: 1-4525 3787 Fax: 1-4525 3787
Internet: www.cfpcommunication.com/festivalnb
E-Mail: amcc@club-internet.fr
président Fernand Quattrocchi
Period/Frequency: July-Aug, annual *Arts types:* chamber music, recitals, orchestra, choir, opera *Venues:* Châtillon-sur-Seine and surroundings in Côte d'Or
Second Address: 10, rue de la Libération, 21400 Châtillon-sur-Seine Tel: 3-8081 5276 Fax: 3-8081 5859

Inaccoutumés, Les
Ménagerie du Verre, 12-14 rue Léchevin, 75011 **Paris**
Tel: 1-4338 3344 Fax: 1-4338 7456
Internet: multimania.com/menageri
E-Mail: menageri@club-internet.fr
directrice Marie-Thérèse Allier
Period/Frequency: Jan-Feb and May-June, annual
Arts types: contemporary drama and dance
Venues: Ménagerie de Verre, Etrange Carlo
Comments: see also Venues

Musicales d'Ajaccio
28 rue des Saules, 75018 **Paris**
Tel: 1-4257 3791 Fax: 1-4257 3791
E-Mail: musicales.dajaccio@wanadoo.fr
présidente, fondatrice Selice Borsari;
directeur artistique Bruno Peltre
Period/Frequency: July, annual *Arts types:* classical & contemporary music, masterclasses *Venues:* Salle des Congrès 350, Cathédrale d'Ajaccio 3000

Musique au Carrousel du Louvre
99 rue de Rivoli, 75001 **Paris**
Tel: 1-4316 4747 Fax: 1-4316 4740
E-Mail: info@carrousel-du-louvres.fr
contact Guillaume Snollaerts;
communication Vanessa Laporte
Period/Frequency: Aug, annual *Arts types:* classical music
Venues: Carrousel du Louvre salle Gabriel 550
Comments: booking: contact FNAC and Virgin

Orientales, Les
Bureau Parisien, 250 bd St.-Germain, 75007 **Paris**
Tel: 1-4222 6646/4172 7988 Fax: 1-4172 7990/6337
E-Mail: les.orientales@wanadoo.fr
directeur artistique Alain Weber;
directeur adjointe Delphine Boudon
Period/Frequency: June-July, annual *Arts types:* traditional music from the orient *Venues:* l'église Abbatiale *Second Address:* Hôtel de Ville, 49410 Saint-Florent-le-Vieil, Fax: 2-4172 5585

Paris Quartier d'été
5 rue Boudreau, 75009 **Paris**
Tel: 1-4494 9800 Fax: 1-4494 9801
Internet: www.quartierdete.com
E-Mail: pqe@claranet.fr
directeur Patrice Martinet; directeur adjoint Hélène Fulgence; directeur technique Alain Menuan; secrétaire générale Michelle Chanonat
Period/Frequency: mid-July/mid-August, annual *Arts types:* world music, classical music, jazz, dance, circus, street theatre, parade *Venues:* all around Paris, mostly open-air places *Comments:* most shows are free

Rencontres Musicales
c/o Association Academus,
41 rue de Voulle, 75015 **Paris**
Tel: 1-4828 6511 Fax: 1-4828 6511
E-Mail: cecilia.contact@wanadoo.fr
director Jacques Masson;
artistic director Gabriela Torma
Period/Frequency: 25 July-9 August *Arts types:* concert, chamber music, vocal music *Venues:* Abbaye St Colomban à Luxeuil-les-Bains 200

Rencontres Musicales D'Evian
152 boulevard Haussmann, 75008 **Paris**
Tel: 1-4435 2690 Fax: 1-4289 2650
directrice générale Elena Rostropovich; président Mstislav Rostropovich; admin Séverine Benetton
Period/Frequency: July, annual (2000: 2-11 July) *Arts types:* symphonic music, chamber music, recitals, masterclasses, competition: concours international le quatuor á cordes, jazz, Indian music *Venues:* du Casino 750, Théâtre Riboud 300, La Grange au Lac 1200 *Second Address:* Casino d'Evian, BP8, 74502 Evian Les Bains, Cedex, Tel: 4-5075 0410, Fax: 4-5026 8748 *Comments:* booking: Evian- 4-5075 0410 during April/ July; see also Competitions

Rencontres Musicales de Villarceaux
30 rue de Miromesnil, 75008 **Paris**
Tel: 1-4494 2878 Fax: 1-4494 2858
Internet: www.cr-ile-de-france.fr
E-Mail: info@festival-ile-de-france.com
directrice Charlotte Latigrat; coordination Dominique Boutel; administrice Stéphanie Devissaguet
Period/Frequency: Sept-Oct, annual *Arts types:* classical music *Venues:* Chateau de Villarceaux

De Bouche à Oreille – Festival de musiques traditionnelles et métissées
Maison des Cultures de Pays, 1 rue de la Vau St Jacques, BP 3, 79201 **Parthenay** Cedex
Tel: 5-4994 9070 Fax: 5-4994 9071
Internet: www.district-parthenay.fr/metive
E-Mail: metive@district-parthenay.fr
directeur Jany Rouger; administrateur Pierre-Olivier Launalle; coordinateur Elodee Robbe; attachée de presse Soizick Fonteneau, Dominique Passebon; directeur artistique Frédéric Pouget;
conseillé artistique Dominique Gauvrit
Period/Frequency: Aug, annual *Arts types:* traditional music, musique vivante *Venues:* Maison des Cultures de Pays 250, Palais des Congrés 600 and open-air concerts
Comments: concerts in the afternoon and evening

Festival Plurielles
c/o Théâtre Saragosse, 17 Av. de Saragosse, 64000 **Pau**
Tel: 5-5984 1193 Fax: 5-5984 9124
Internet: www.perso.wanadoo.fr/theatre.saragosse
E-Mail: theatre.saragosse@wanadoo.fr
directeur Michel Vincenot
Period/Frequency: March-April, annual *Arts types:* contemporary dance *Venues:* Théâtre Saragosse 260
Comments: see also Venues

Mimos Festival International du Mime
Centre Culturel de la Visitation et de la Maison du Mime, Rue Littré, 24000 **Périgueux**
Tel: 5-5353 5517/1871 (booking) Fax: 5-5304 3084/5335 0857
Internet: perso.wanadoo.fr/persona.grata/
E-Mail: persona.grata@wanadoo.fr
président Jacques Canton; président d'honneur Xavier Darcos; directeur artistique Peter Bu; attachée de presse Michèle Latraverse; organisation, administration Chantal Achilli, Roger Esposito; vice présidents Serge Salleron, Jean-Jacques Ratier; secrétaire Marie-Françoise Audrerie; trésorier Jean-Claude Cesaire; trésorier adjoint Gérard Millet;
conseiller technique Jacky Bonin;
conseiller pour la communication Maurice Melliet
Period/Frequency: July- Aug, annual *Arts types:* mime, dance, gesture theatre *Venues:* La Visitation 300, NTP 700, Le Palace 250, Gymnase 120 *Comments:* alternative Internet: www.preso.wanadoo.fr/presona.grata/

Sinfonia en Périgord
Boite Postale 1012, 24001 **Périgueux** Cedex
Tel: 5-5353 3295/1970 (bookings) Fax: 5-5303 7877
Internet: www.perigord.tm.fr/sinfonia.htm
E-Mail: sinfonia@perigord.tm.fr
directeur général fondateur Michel Theodorides;
directeur artistique Bernard Fabre Garrus
Period/Frequency: weekends in Sept, annual *Arts types:* baroque and classical music *Venues:* Nouvean Théâtre
Second Address: Espace Tourisme Perigord, 25 rue Wilson 24000 Périgueux Tel: 5-5335 5050 Fax: 5-5306 3094 *Comments:* venues address: 1 Avenue d'Aquitaine, 24000 Périgueux; see also Competitions

Festival de Musique de Chambre de Perros-Guirec
Mairie, Service Animation Culturelle,
Place de l'Hôtel de Ville, 22700 **Perros-Guirec**
Tel: 2-9649 0245 Fax: 2-9691 2384
directeur artistique et communication Marie Aude Roux; directeur administratif Erwan Henry
Period/Frequency: July/August, annual *Arts types:* chamber music *Venues:* Palais des Congrès 450

Festival de Pierrefonds
3 rue Notre Dame, 60350 **Pierrefonds**
Tel: 3-4442 8000 Fax: 3-4442 5606
E-Mail: festivalp@aol.com
président François Fron; directeur artistique Gilbert Langlois; administrateur Philippe Joyeux; attachée de presse Marie-Jo Picot-Mourgues
Period/Frequency: July-Aug, annual *Arts types:* theatre, classical music *Venues:* Chateau National de Pierrefonds: La Cours d'Honneur 500, Salle des Gardes 300, La Chapelle 100

Rencontres de Harpe Celtique de Dinan
CRIHC , La Gallerie, 22490 **Plouer**
Tel: 2-9686 8494 Fax: 2-9686 8940
Internet: www.eurobretagne.fr/HARPE_CELTIQUE
E-Mail: harp@wanadoo.fr
directeur artistique Myrdhin; secrétariat général Elisabeth Affolter; responsable des concours Dominique Bouchaud
Period/Frequency: July, annual *Arts types:* Celtic harp *Venues:* Théâtre des Jacobin in Dinan 600, and churches *Comments:* unique in Europe: during this festival there are two competitions – celtic harp improvisation and celtic harp composition – every three years; also during the festival there is Celtic harp training

Coups de Théâtre
Le Théâtre Scène Nationale, 1 place du Maréchal Leclerc, 86000 **Poitiers**
Tel: 5-4939 4000
Fax: 5-4955 1691
directeur Denis Garnier; administratrice Jocelyne Steffan; secrétaire générale Suzy Bely; directeur de projet Christian Chaignon; responsable des relations avec le public Sylvie Violan; coordinatrice de direction technique Valérie Bobin; responsable de l'information Monique Narciso
Period/Frequency: April, annual *Arts types:* contemporary drama *Venues:* throughout Poitiers *Comments:* booking from 13:00-18:30; free admission; see also Venues (Théâtre-Scene Nationale de Poitiers)

Rencontres Musicales Internationales de Pont-St-Esprit
Avenue Gaston Doumergue, 30130 **Pont-St-Esprit**
Tel: 4-6639 2831 Fax: 4-6639 2831
directrice Michèle Dimambro;
président d'honneur Ivry Gitlis
Period/Frequency: Aug, annual *Arts types:* chamber and choral music *Venues:* Collègiale de Pont St Esprit 450, la cour d'Honneur de la chartreuse de Valbonne 800-900 *Comments:* organised by Academie de Musique

Festival Pablo Casals
Rue Victor Hugo, BP24, 66502 **Prades** Cedex 2
Tel: 4-6896 3307 Fax: 4-6896 5095
Internet: pro.wanadoo.fr/festival.casals/
E-Mail: festival.casals@wanadoo.fr
administrateur Antonia Calm;
directeur artistique Michel Lethiec
Period/Frequency: July-Aug, annual *Arts types:* chamber music, choral *Venues:* Abbaye St Michel de Cuxa 700, Eglise St. Pierre de Prades 700, and small churches around Prades 200 *Comments:* 2 week course (Aug 1-15): stages de l'Académie Internationale de la Musique de Chambre; Festival is invited for co-production in the Théâtre des Champs-Elysees; three series, 2 concerts, in January, March and June for the Jubilee in 2000

Printemps Musical de Provins
Direction des Affaires Culturelles de Provins, 1 Cours des Bénèdictins, 77160 **Provins**
Tel: 1-6067 0260 Fax: 1-6067 0261
président Robert Chevalier; directeur artistique Pierre Reach; service culture Anick Michelet
Period/Frequency: May, annual *Arts types:* classical music *Venues:* churches
Comments: see also Promoters (FFFMI)

Semaines Musicales de Quimper
21 rue Pen Ar Steir, 29000 **Quemper**
Tel: 2-9895 3243/9890 5775
Fax: 2-9855 4772/9852 1590
Internet: www.bagadoo.tm.fr/smq
président Michel Le Grand; vice-président Philippe Destainville; affiche faite par Enrique Marine
Period/Frequency: Aug, annual *Arts types:* classical music, baroque, contemporary *Venues:* Eglise St Mathieu 800, Chapelle de Kerdevot 350, Orangerie de Lanniron 400, Théâtre Municipal, Théâtre de Cournaille 700, Eglise Locmaria 600, Théâtre Max Jacob

Flâneries Musicales d' Eté, Les
Office du Tourisme, 12,
Bld du Général Leclerc, 51100 **Reims**
Tel: 3-2677 4525 (information)/00 (administration)
Fax: 3-2677 4514/27
E-Mail: TourismReims@netvia.com
présidente Gabrielle Nguyen; directeur artistique Hervé Corre (Transat); attaché de presse Franck Peynimand (tel: 1-4567 9546, fax: 1-4567 5543)
Period/Frequency: July-Aug, annual *Arts types:* classical, contemporary, jazz *Venues:* throughout Reims *Second Address:* 2 rue Guillaume de Machault, 51100 Reims *Comments:* 120 free concerts

Mettre en Scène
Théâtre National de Bretagne, 1 rue St Hélier, BP 675, 35008 **Rennes** Cedex
Tel: 2-9931 5533 Fax: 2-9967 6619
directeur Francois Le Pillouër;
directeur administratif et financier Laurent Parigot; communication Bernadette Kessler
Period/Frequency: November, annual *Arts types:* drama, dance, contemporary *Venues:* Salle Jean Vilar 1130, Salle Jean-Marie Serreau 300, Théâtre de la Parcheminerie 250, and other places throughout Rennes *Comments:* booking: 2-9930 8888; see also Drama & Venues

Tombées de la Nuit, Les
Office du Tourisme,
11 rue St Yves, CS26410, 35064 **Rennes** Cedex
Tel: 2-9967 1111 Fax: 2-9967 1110
responsable de la programmation Jean-Bernard Vighetti; assistants Catherine Ferré, Maryline Honoré, Gérard Malard
Period/Frequency: July, annual
Arts types: all types of contemporary arts including music & street theatre of the Mediterranean *Venues:* open air (some shows are free)

Octobre en Normandie
3 rue Chéruel, 76000 **Rouen**
Tel: 2-3515 8787 Fax: 2-3515 2704
administration Philippe Naulot; directeur artistique Philippe Danel; vice président Pierre Weber
Period/Frequency: Oct, annual *Arts types:* contemporary music, contemporary dance, classical music *Venues:* Rouen, Le Havre, Dieppe *Comments:* nearly 60 concerts and dance performances

Festival de Sablé
16 rue Saint Denis, BP 177, 72305 **Sablé-sur-Sarthe**
Tel: 2-4395 4996 Fax: 2-4392 3437/1676
directeur artistique Jean Bernard Meunier
Period/Frequency: Aug, annual *Arts types:* baroque music *Venues:* Centre Culturel Joël le Theule 679, castles & churches around Sablé *Comments:* 3 or 4 concerts daily, international orchestras

Festival Art Rock
BP 4637, 22046 **Saint-Brieuc** Cedex 2
Tel: 2-9668 4623 Fax: 2-9668 4624
Internet: www.artrock.org
E-Mail: festival.artrock@wanadoo.fr
responsable de la programmation Jean-Michel Boinet; régisseur général Jean-Pierre Lucas; assistant de production Nicolas Letellier
Period/Frequency: June, annual *Arts types:* rock, dance, drama, music, street theatre, jazz, multimedia *Venues:* La Passerelle 1000, La Salle de Robien 2000, Scéne en Plein-Air 5000 *Comments:* see also Venues

Festival de Musique de Saint-Céré
18 Av du Docteur Roux, BP 59, 46400 **Saint-Céré**
Tel: 5-6538 2908
Fax: 5-6538 3594
Internet: www.opera-eclate.org
E-Mail: festival.saint.cere@wanadoo.fr
administrateur/communication François Boudeau; directeur Olivier Desbordes
Period/Frequency: July-Aug, annual *Arts types:* music, mainly opera *Venues:* le Château de Castelnau, Bretenoux 1200, le Château de Montal 400 (listed buildings) *Comments:* booking from May: 5-6538 2808

Festival de Musique Du Haut-Jura
3 rue Reybert, 39200 **Saint-Claude**
président Jacqueline Pesenti; directeur Didier Perret
Period/Frequency: July, annual *Arts types:* classical music *Venues:* Palais des Sports, lac d'Antre, Chapelle de St-Romain, also in Orgelet, Nyon (Suisse), Le Brassus *Second address:* Office du Tourisme: Tel: 3-8445 3424, Fax: 3-8441 0272 (bookings) *Comments:* see also Promoters (FFFMI)

Banlieues Bleues, Saint-Denis
49 boulevard Marcel Sembat, 93207 **Saint-Denis** Cedex
Tel: 1-4922 1015
Fax: 1-4922 1011
directeur Jacques Pornon; administration Anne-Marie Tinot; relations publiques & chargée de production Cécile Niasse; chargé de production Xavier Lemettre
Period/Frequency: March-April, annual
Arts types: jazz, blues, live music *Venues:* 30 concerts in 15 towns in 5 weeks

Festival de Saint Denis
6 place de la Légion d'Honneur,
93200 **Saint-Denis**
Tel: 1-4813 1210/0607 (bookings)
Fax: 1-4813 0281
Internet: www.festival-saint-denis.fr
E-Mail: festival.st-denis@wanadoo.fr
directeur Jean-Pierre Le Pavec; administratrice Nathalie Raporport; président Patrick Braouezec; communication, pr Nathalie Van Der Heyden
Period/Frequency: June, annual *Arts types:* music, choirs, oratorio *Venues:* La Basilique 1500, La Maison d'Éducation de la Légion d'Honneur A: 250 , B: 400 , C: 700, La Salle du Musée 250

Été Musical Loire en Rhone-Alpes
Conseil Général de la Loire, Direction de la culture, 2 rue Charles de Gaulle, 42000 **Saint-Etienne**
Tel: 4-7749 5810 Fax: 4-7749 5809
président Pascal Clement; conseiller artistique Daniel Kawka; directrice du service Jacqueline Bayon; député de la Loire,
vice-président chargé de la culture Daniel Mandon
Period/Frequency: July-August, annual *Arts types:* classical, world, traditional music, mainly vocals *Venues:* Hauts-Lîeux du Patrimoine Architectural du Départment 150 to 1400

Festival Massenet
l'Esplanade St-Etienne Opera, BP 237,
42013 **Saint-Etienne** Cedex 02
Tel: 4-7747 8347/40 (bookings) Fax: 4-7747 8369
président Alain Terrat; direction générale Jean-Louis Pichon; directeur musical Patrick Fournillier; administrateur Michel Fabre; directeur de la com Daniel Couriol
Period/Frequency: July-August, annual *Arts types:* classical music, recitals, dance, opera *Comments:* see also Promoters (FFFMI)

Festival Déodat de Séverac
Maison déodat de Séverac,
31540 **Saint-Felix-Lauragais (Toulouse)**
Tel: 5-6183 0183 Fax: 5-6218 9084
president/fondateur Gilbert Blacque Bélair; presidente Catherine Blacque Bélair; directeur artistique Jean-Jacques Cubaynes; communication Ruben Velazquez
Period/Frequency: June-July, annual *Arts types:* baroque music, opera, traditional singing *Venues:* around Saint Felix Lauragais, Toulouse and towns around

Musiques d'Automne
Mairie de Saint-Genest-Lerpt, Place de Charles de Gaulle, 42530 **Saint-Genest-Lerpt**
Tel: 4-7750 5188 Fax: 4-7790 1814
Internet: www.mus-automne.micioline.fr
président Louis Daurat;
directeur artistique Michel Tremoulhac
Period/Frequency: October, annual *Arts types:* baroque music *Venues:* churches in St Etianne or St Genest-Lerpt *Comments:* discographic production since 1996; see also Promoters (FFFMI)

Musique en Côte Basque
BP 212, 64502 **Saint-Jean-De-Luz**
Tel: 5-5951 1995 Fax: 5-5951 0781
président Jean-Michel Barate;
contact Mr Darfay;
pr Jeanine Dallavalle
Period/Frequency: September, annual *Arts types:* classical music *Venues:* Casino de Biarritz, churches

Festival de Saint Lizier
09190 **Saint-Lizier**
Tel: 5-6166 0789/6789 (booking) Fax: 5-6104 6614
directeur artistique David Lively; secrétaire Annie Saubion; président Roger Fauroux
Period/Frequency: Aug, annual *Arts types:* chamber music *Venues:* Cathedrale de St. Lizier 400

Festival de Musique Sacrée, Ancienne et Baroque
BP 18, 02830 **Saint-Michel-en-Thiérache**
Tel: 3-2358 8725 (booking)/2324 6009 (administration)
Fax: 3-2320 1198
directeur artistique Jean-Michel Verneiges;
service de presse Heike Schicke Tanz (tel: 1-5375 1770/4289 4366, fax: 1-4289 4225)
Period/Frequency: June-July, annual *Arts types:* sacred, ancient and baroque music, early music *Venues:* Abbey of Saint-Michel en Thiérache 900 *Comments:* original abbey founded in the 10th century; organ by Jean Boizard (1714), at the centre of the festival

Club des Cing, Le
Centre Culturel Le Fanal, Scène Nationale de Saint Nazaire, 33 boulevard Victor Hugo, BP 150, 44603 **Saint-Nazaire** Cedex
Tel: 2-4022 3938
Fax: 2-4022 9144
director Jean-Joël Le Chapelain; administratrice Maryvonne Bos; régisseur général Patrick Balaud; relations publiques Sylvette Magne;
information Christine Picout
Period/Frequency: May, annual *Arts types:* contemporary dance *Venues:* Théâtre Jean Bart 270, Théâtre Gérard Philipe 766 *Comments:* see also Venues

Consonances
Centre Culturel Le Fanal, Scène Nationale de Saint Nazaire, 33 boulevard Victor Hugo, BP 150, 44603 **Saint-Nazaire** Cedex
Tel: 2-4022 3938
Fax: 2-4022 9144
director Jean-Joël Le Chapelain;
artistic director Philippe Graffin;
régisseur général Patrick Balaud;
relations publiques Sylvette Magne;
administratrice Maryvonne Bos
Period/Frequency: Sept, annual *Arts types:* chamber music *Venues:* Galerie des Franciscains 200
Comments: see also Venues

Théâtre en Jeux
Centre Culturel Le Fanal, Scène Nationale de Saint Nazaire, 33 boulevard Victor Hugo,
BP 150, 44603 **Saint-Nazaire** Cedex
Tel: 2-4022 3938 Fax: 2-4022 9144
directeur Jean-Joël Le Chapelain; administratrice Maryvonne Bos; régisseur général Patrick Balaud; relations publiques Sylvette Magne
Period/Frequency: March, annual *Arts types:* contemporary drama *Venues:* all venues in Saint Nazaire including Théâtre Jean Bart 270, Théâtre Gerard Philipe 760, Centre Culturel 170 *Comments:* see also Venues

Organa
Festival Organa, Ecole de Musique,
Mas de l'argelier, 13210 **Saint-Rémy-de-Provence**
Tel: 4-9092 3617/0522 (bookings) Fax: 4-9092 3617
responsable Jean-Pierre Le Caudey
Period/Frequency: July-Sept, annual *Arts types:* recitals (organ), classical (organ), choirs *Venues:* Collégiale St. Martin 450 *Comments:* most concerts are free; 15 concerts; a concert every Saturday at 5.30pm

Été Musical de Saint Robert en Limousin
c/o Jean Louis Belliard, Le Vieux Logis,
19310 **Saint-Robert**
Tel: 5-5525 1133 Fax: 1-4534 0821
président Jean-Louis Belliard
Period/Frequency: July/August, annual *Arts types:* recital, chamber music, vocal music *Venues:* Eglise de St Robert 300 *Comments:* during the festival there is an exhbition held in the hall André Rousseau

Musiques dans les Vignes
Mairie, 84290 **Sainte-Cécile-Les-Vignes**
Tel: 4-9030 8017 Fax: 4-9030 7491
président Guy Penne; directeur artistiques Daniel Ceccaldi; presse et relations publiques Daniel Roubaud (tel: 4-9027 0423, fax: 4-9086 4610)
Period/Frequency: July/August, annual *Arts types:* classical music *Venues:* outdoor: Jardin de la Chapelle 200-300, Collègiale 200-300 (Bolène), Place des Arceaux 250 (Séguré), Place du Vieux Village 250 (Cairanne), Place de l'Eglise 250 (Camaret)

Académies Musicales de Saintes, Les
Abbaye aux Dames, BP 125, 17104 **Saintes** Cedex
Tel: 5-4697 4848/4695 9450 Fax: 5-4692 5856
Internet: www.lachapelleroyale.com
E-Mail: amf@t3a.com
administration Odile Pradem-Faure; président Alain De Pracomtal; direction artistique Philippe Herreweghe
Period/Frequency: July, annual *Arts types:* contemporary, baroque, romantic music; played on period instruments *Venues:* L'Abbaye aux Dames 600, l'Eglise Saint Vivien 490 *Comments:* 30 concerts in 10 days; one of the oldest festivals of baroque and romantic music; traditional concerts of Bach's Cantate at noon

Festival Méditerranéen
BP 4, 13129 **Salin-de-Giraud**
Tel: 4-4286 8686 Fax: 4-4286 8910
président François Pages;
organisation Claude Freissinier
Period/Frequency: July-Aug, annual *Arts types:* opera, classical music, jazz *Venues:* throughout the regions of Languedoc, Roussillon, Provence Alpes-Côtes d'Azur *Comments:* also organise concert series;
booking: 4-4286 8788

Saoû Chante Mozart dans la Drôme
26400 **Saoû**
Tel: 4-7576 0202
Fax: 4-7576 0228
Internet: saoumozart.ft-valence.net
E-Mail: mozart.saoû@wanadoo.fr
directeur Henry Fuoc; direction artistique Philippe Andriot, Philippe Bernold, Jacques Henry
Period/Frequency: July, annual *Arts types:* classical music (Mozart) *Venues:* Cour de Châteaux, Eglises Romanes (Provencal Drome)

Festival des Jeux du Théâtre de Sarlat en Périgord Creé en 1952
Hotel Plamon, Rue des Consuls, 24202 **Sarlat** Cedex
Tel: 5-5331 1083 Fax: 5-5330 2531
Internet: www.arachnis.asso.fr/jeux-theatre-sarlat
charge de programmation (actor directeur)
Jean Paul Tribout
Period/Frequency: July-Aug, annual *Arts types:* all types of theatre *Venues:* Place de la Liberté 1000, Jardin des Enfeux 500, Hotel Plamon 50 (for press conferences), Salle Paul Eluard 600, Abbaye Saint Claire 300 *Comments:* everything is performed in open-air theatres-spaces, if it rains performed at Salle Paul Eluard 600

Festival de l'Orangerie de Sceaux
BP 52, 92333 **Sceaux** Cedex
Tel: 1-4660 0779
Fax: 1-4660 1286
directrice Jacqueline Loewenguth
Period/Frequency: during weekends July-August-Sept, annual *Arts types:* chamber music *Venues:* Orangerie du Domaine de Sceaux 600 *Comments:* 25 performances

Rendez-Vous Chorégraphiques de Sceaux, Les
Scène Nationale Les Gémeaux, 49 Av Georges Clemenceau, 92330 **Sceaux**
Tel: 1-4660 0564 (administration)/
4661 3667 (bookings)
Fax: 1-4661 5455
directrice et programmation danse Françoise Letellier; administratrice Evelyne Abdelkader;
communication Nicolas Massadau
Period/Frequency: March-April, annual *Arts types:* contemporary dance *Venues:* Grande Salle 500, Petite Salle 180 *Comments:* see also Venues

Riches Heures Musicales de la Rotonde
Festival de Simiane, 04150 **Simiane-La-Rotonde**
Tel: 4-9275 9047/9014 (booking) Fax: 4-9275 9218
président et directeur administratif Marie-José Noël; vice-président et directeur artistique Jean Bascou
Period/Frequency: July/August, annual
Arts types: early music, medieval, baroque *Venues:* La Rotonde (12th C.) 150 *Comments:* see also National Organisations (FFFIM)

Nuits de la Citadelle
1 Alleé de Verdum, 04200 **Sisteron**
Tel: 4-9261 0600 Fax: 4-9261 2954
président Edith Robert; vice président Jacques Sauvair-Jourdan; relation presse Hélène Seranne
Period/Frequency: July-Aug, annual *Arts types:* music, dance, theatre *Venues:* Cloître St Dominique 700, Théâtre de la Citadelle 1500, Cathédrale Notre Dame des Pommiers 800

Viva Cité – Festival des arts de la rue
Mairie de Sotteville-lès-Rouen,
BP 19, 76301 **Sotteville-lès-Rouen** Cedex
Tel: 2-3563 6089 (Service Culturel) Fax: 2-3562 3557
directeur artistique Daniel Andrieu;
administration-accueil Carole Chrétien-Deperrois;
directeur technique Olivier Desjardins;
conseiller artistique Florence Fouchier
Period/Frequency: last weekend of June, annual *Arts types:* street theatre, sculpture, music, performances, dance, concerts *Venues:* Bois de la Garenne (park); Place de l'Hôtel de Ville *Comments:*
almost all performances are free

Semaine de la Liberté, La
L'Espace Georges Sadoul, 26-28 Quai Carnot,
88100 **St Dié-des-Vosges**
Tel: 3-2956 1409 Fax: 3-2955 1228
directeur Gérard Barbot
Period/Frequency: July, annual *Arts types:* contemporary & classical music, dance, song, theatre, street theatre *Venues:* open-air around the Tour de la Liberté 10000 *Comments:* free admission to all events

Malins Plaisirs, Les
Production 2M, 7 Place Sithieu, 62500 **St Omer**
Tel: 3-2198 1226
Fax: 3-2198 1226
E-Mail: malinsplaisirs@wanadoo.fr
directeur artistique Vincent Tavernier; administrateur Alain Nguyen; secrétariat général Tanette Lyoen
Period/Frequency: Aug, annual (except leap years) *Arts types:* theatre, opera *Venues:* Théâtre de Montreuil sur mer 300 *Comments:* see also Agents/Producers

Festival de Saint Riquier
BP3, 80135 **St Riquier**
Tel: 3-2228 8282 Fax: 3-2228 9018
directeur artistique Mikhail Rudy; directeur administratif Hughe Hairy; attachée de presse Heike Schiketanz
Period/Frequency: July, annual *Arts types:* classical music (vocal and instrumental) *Venues:* L'église Abbatiale de St Riquier 700-1000, Les Jardins de l'Abbaye 100

Festival de Musique de Strasbourg
Sté les amis de la Musique,
24 rue de la Mésange, 67000 **Strasbourg**
Tel: 3-8815 2929
Fax: 3-8824 0316
E-Mail: harry.lapp@wanadoo.fr
délégue general Harry Lapp; président René Géronimus
Period/Frequency: June-July *Arts types:* early music, classical, choral, opera and jazz *Venues:* Palais de la Musique et des Congrés *Second Address:* Bureau du Festival, Tel: 3-8832 4310, Fax: 3-8832 4238

Festival Voix et Route Romane
14, rue des Poules, 67000 **Strasbourg**
Tel: 3-8836 8932/8835 0065
Fax: 3-8836 8932
Internet: www.voix-romane.com
E-Mail: voix-romane@wanadoo.fr
directeur Jean-Paul Linder; conseiller artistique Klaus Gillessen; relations presse Veronique Bernard, Anna Kehl; président de l'association du festival Gilles Follea; conseiller musical Klaus Gillessen; administrateur délégué Daniel Walter; régisseur Thierry Codin; relations presse Jérôme Mallien
Period/Frequency: Aug-Oct, annual
Arts types: early music: medieval music *Venues:* churches and cathedrals *Comments:*
10 concerts & 2 conferences

MUSICA – Festival International des Musiques d'Aujourd'hui de Strasbourg
2 rue d'Ingwiller, 67000 **Strasbourg**
Tel: 3-8823 4646 (admin)/4723 (bookings)
Fax: 3-8823 4647
Internet: www.festival-musica.org
E-Mail: musica67@cybercable.fr
directeur Jean-Dominique Marco; administration Jérome Cloquet; déléguée artistique Virpi Nurmi; relations publiques Marie-Thérèse Muller; président Jérôme Clement; presse nationale et internationale /attachée de presse Valérie Samuel, Valérie Weill; coordination, information, documentation Emilie Le Squeren
Period/Frequency: Sept-Oct, annual *Arts types:* contemporary arts (concerts, operas, chamber music, dance) *Venues:* Palais de la Musique et des Congrés, Palais des Fêtes, Odysée, Eglise du Bouclier, Auditorium France 3 Alsace, Le-Maillon Théâtre de Strasbourg, L'Aubette, La Filature/scène nationale, Théâtre des Lisières, Pôle Sud

Festival de Sully
BP 58, Place Charles de Gaulle, 45600 **Sully-sur-Loire**
Tel: 2-3836 2946/800-452 818 (reservations)
Fax: 2-3836 4434
Internet: www.festival-sully.com
contact Didier Bidaux, 15 Av Montaigne, 75008 Paris, Tel: 1-4720 0478 Fax: 1-4952 0741; président Roger Guerre; directeur artistique François Serrette
Period/Frequency: June, annual *Arts types:* classical music and dance *Venues:* la Salle des Gardes du Château 400, l'Auditorium du Château 2000

Festival de Musique Sacrée de l'Abbaye de Sylvanès
Abbaye de Sylvanès, 12360 **Sylvanes**
Tel: 5-6598 2020
Fax: 5-6598 2025
Internet: www.sylvanes.com
E-Mail: abbaye@sylvanes.com
directeur fondateur Michel Wolkowitsky
Period/Frequency: July-Aug, annual *Arts types:* early music, sacred music and other *Venues:* Abbaye 1000 , and places near Sylvanès

Festival des Chemins de l'Imaginaire
Centre Culturel, 5 rue Marcel Michel,
24120 **Terrasson-la-Villedieu**
Tel: 5-5350 1380 Fax: 5-5350 4676
directeur Jean Paul Dumas
Period/Frequency: July, annual *Arts types:* street theatre *Venues:* Centre Culturel 200 and open-air, les Jardins de l'imaginaire *Comments:* see also Venues

Spectacles de rue de Thonon et Aix-Les-Bains et La Grand-Bornand
5, imp. du Bastion, 74200 **Thonon**
Tel: 4-5071 6597 Fax: 4-5026 4455
Internet: www.theatre-toupine.org
E-Mail: spectacles@theatre-toupine.org
responsable Alain Benzoni; assistants Françoise Mersch, Isabelle Naïm-Christin
Period/Frequency: Aug, annual *Arts types:* street theatre, puppets, parades, music, dance *Venues:* in the streets of Thonon and Aix-Les-Bains, Le Grand-Bornand *Comments:* most of the events are free. Thonon: 'Les Fondus du Macadum', Aix les Bains: 'Les Aoutiennes', Grand Bornand: 'Festival au Bonheur des mômes'

Festival de Musique de Toulon
117 Av. Lazare Carnot, 83000 **Toulon**
Tel: 4-9493 5545/680-856 363 (mobile)
Fax: 4-9424 1610
président Henri Tiscornia; directeur Claude-Henri Bonnet; pr Charlotte Hamel
Period/Frequency: June-July, annual *Arts types:* classical music *Venues:* Opera 1300, Musée de la Marine 300, Fort Lamalgue 4000 & 300, Abbaye du Thoronet 500, Collegiale Six Fours 400, Saint Louis de Hyeres 500, Saint Louis du Mourillon 400, Tour Royale, Saint Paul du Mourillon *Comments:* Concours International d'Instruments à Vent (May), for 1999: basson

Festival Piano aux Jacobins
61 rue de la Pomme, 31000 **Toulouse**
Tel: 5-6122 4005/6121 0900
Fax: 5-6121 7420
Internet: www.mairie-toulouse.fr
E-Mail: pianomail@aol.com
directeur Paul-Arnaud Pejouan; directeur artistique Catherine D'Argoubet
Period/Frequency: Sept, annual *Arts types:* piano concerts *Venues:* Cloître des Jacobins 1000 *Comments:* booking: Tel. 5-6122 4005

Journées de la danse, Les
Conservatoire Occitan 1 rue Jacques Darré, Espace St Cyprien, BP 3011, 31024 **Toulouse** Cedex
Tel: 5-6142 7579
Fax: 5-6142 1259
directeur Pierre Corbefin
Period/Frequency: November, biennial (2001) *Arts types:* French and foreign traditional dance and song *Venues:* Espace Bonnefoy (Toulouse) 400; Hall Commingues (Colomiers) 800, CREPS (stages) *Comments:* conferences, courses, workshops, shows

Marionnettissimo – Festival international de formes animées en région Toulousaine
54 Rue Milhes, 31300 **Toulouse**
Tel: 5-6149 6341 Fax: 5-6131 8201
Internet: www.chez.com/marionnettissimo
E-Mail: marionnettissimo@wanadoo.fr
programmations Jean Kaplan
Period/Frequency: Nov-Dec, biennial (2000) *Arts types:* international festival of puppetry and movement (for children and adults) *Venues:* 10 théâtres à Toulouse et region-capacities vary *Comments:* other activities: programme for children and adults – meetings, courses, informal parties

Choré – Graphique, Centre Chorégraphique National de Tours, Le
47, rue du Sergent Leclerc, 37000 **Tours**
Tel: 2-4736 4600 Fax: 2-4736 4601
Internet: www.ccnt-larrieu.com
E-Mail: info@ccnt-larrieu.com
programation Laurent Barré;
directeur artistique Daniel Barrieu
Period/Frequency: June (2 weeks), annual *Arts types:* contemporary dance *Venues:* venues in Tours *Comments:* 12 French & foreign dance companies, 12-15 performances; see also Dance

Fêtes Musicales en Tourraine, Les
Mairie de Tours, 37032 **Tours** Cedex
Tel: 2-4721 6508 Fax: 2-4721 6500
fondateur Richter Sveatoslav; directeur artistique René Martin; présidente Catherine Refabert
Period/Frequency: June-July *Arts types:* chamber music *Venues:* Grange de Meslay (built in 12th C) 1300

Festival du Pays d'Ans en Périgord
Théâtre et Musique au Pays d' Hautefort, Le Bourg, 24390 **Tourtoirac**
Tel: 5-5351 1363 Fax: 5-5351 1929
directrice Annie Fromentière
Period/Frequency: July-Aug, annual *Arts types:* theatre, music, jazz, classical music *Venues:* throughout the Perigord region in historic buildings, Canton d'Hautefort

Festival des Lacs d'Orient
Académie Musicale Européenne, 5 rue de Gambey, 10000 **Troyes**
Tel: 3-2573 9454 Fax: 3-2573 9454
directeur artistique Marie Christine Calvet
Period/Frequency: July, annual *Arts types:* classical music *Venues:* Domaine de Villehardouin 300 (outdoor)

Festival International les Nuits Musicales d' Uzès
Place Albert 1, BP 129, 30703 **Uzès** Cedex
Tel: 4-6622 6888 Fax: 4-6622 9519
E-Mail: otuzes@wanadoo.fr
présidente Yvette Doumens; hon. président Mayor Jean-Luc Chapon; direction artistique Eric Desnoues
Period/Frequency: July, annual *Arts types:* early music (middle-ages, renaissance, baroque) *Venues:* Cathedrale St-Théodorit d'Uzés, Duché d'Uzés, venues in Uzége, Lussan and Montaren *Second Address:* 5 Place du Petit College, 69005 Lyon, Tel: 4-7842 3904, Fax: 4-7842 3928 (press office) *Comments:* this festival is part of the idea: music and heritage (musical and architectural); see also Festival Estival du Vieux Lyon and Festival de Musique du Vieux Lyon

Festival de Boucard / L'Association les Amis de Boucard
BP 10, 18260 **Vailly-Sur-Fauldre**
Tel: 2-4873 8832 Fax: 2-4873 8832
Internet: www.perso.wanadoo.fr/festival.boucard/
E-Mail: Festival.Boucard@wanadoo.fr
président Bernard MacNab
Period/Frequency: July, annual *Arts types:* chamber music, orchestras, early music, choirs, recitals *Venues:* Grange du Château de Noyer 300, Eglise de Jares 400 *Comments:* 'Eurythmiques' is an association which presents 5 festivals in the Berry region; visiting address: Château de Boucard, 18260, Le Noyer; see also 'Festival de Noirlac' & 'Festival des Eglises Romanes du Berry'

Musique Action International
Centre Culturel André Malraux, Place de l'Hôtel de Ville, BP 126, 54504 **Vandoeuvre-les-Nancy** Cedex
Tel: 3-8357 5224 Fax: 3-8353 2185
Internet: www.services.worldnet.fr/ccam/
E-Mail: ccam@worldnet.fr
directeur Dominique Repecaud
Period/Frequency: May, annual *Arts types:* contemporary music *Venues:* salle André Malraux 230, salle des fêtes 500

Automne Musical du Château de Versailles
Centre de Musique Baroque de Versailles, Hôtel des Menus Plaisirs, 22 Avenue de Paris, 78000 **Versailles**
Tel: 1-3920 7810 Fax: 1-3920 7801
E-Mail: accueil@cmbv.com
directeur Vincent Berthier de Lioncourt
Period/Frequency: autumn, annual *Arts types:* baroque music *Venues:* Château de Versailles, Salon d'Hercule 300, Salon de Marengo 200, Le Grand Trianon 250-300, L' Opéra Royal 618, la Chapelle Royale

Nuits Musicales en Bourbonnais, Les
Association Musiques Vivantes,
3 Rue Jean-Jaurès, 03200 **Vichy**
Tel: 4-7031 1500 Fax: 4-7031 5766
secrétariat Lucile Nebout; président Jean-Michel Guerre; communication Ginette Coste
Period/Frequency: June-July, annual *Arts types:* classical music *Venues:* chateaux, churches & historic monuments in the Allier region
Comments: see also Promoters

Festival Jazz à Vienne
21 rue des Célestes, 38200 **Vienne**
Tel: 4-7478 8787 Fax: 4-7478 8788
Internet: jazzavienne.com
E-Mail: festival@jazzavienne.com
directeur Jean-Paul Bouteiller; administration Jacques Launay; attaché de presse Pierre Budimir; régisseur Dominique Bonvallet
Period/Frequency: July, annual *Arts types:* jazz *Venues:* in various open air places, Théâtre Antique 7000 *Second Address:* booking: 7485 0005
Comments: see also Venues

Festival de Ville D'Avray
10 rue de Marnes, 92410 **Ville d'Avray**
Tel: 1-4750 4428 Fax: 1-4750 5390
Internet: perso.club-internet.fr/jlpetit/
directeur artistique Jean-Louis Petit;
président Edmée Mottini
Period/Frequency: June, annual *Arts types:* French music of the early 20th Century (1999: Charles Gounod, 2000: Reynaldo Hahn) *Venues:* in the Château *Comments:* see also Competitions: Concours International d'interprétation

Rencontres Charles Dullin
Théâtre Romain Rolland, 18 rue Eugène Varlin, BP 11, 94801 **Villejuif** Cedex
Tel: 1-4958 1700 Fax: 1-4958 1710
directeur Michel le Gouill; administrateur Serge Millien; secrétaire générale Michèle Almeiras
Period/Frequency: Jan-Feb, biennial *Arts types:* contemporary theatre *Venues:* Théâtre Romain Rolland 840 + all theatres in the Val de Marne *Comments:* booking: 1-4958 1703; see also Venues

Biennale Nationale de Danse du Val de Marne
Domaine Chérioux, 4 route de Fontainebleau, 94407 **Vitry-sur-Seine** Cedex
Tel: 1-4686 1761 Fax: 1-4978 0290
E-Mail: Biennal.danse@wanadoo.fr
directeur Michel Caserta; administrateur Thierry Calonne; relations publiques Daniel Franchini
Period/Frequency: March-April, biennial (2001) *Arts types:* contemporary dance *Venues:* 21 theatres in the Val de Marne

Sons d'Hiver
Domaine Départemental Chérioux, 4 route de Fontainebleau, 94407 **Vitry-sur-Seine** Cedex
Tel: 1-4173 1165 Fax: 1-4687 4111
directeur Fabien Barontini
Period/Frequency: Jan-Feb, annual *Arts types:* jazz, world music *Venues:* all over the Val de Marne

GEORGIA (+995)

Georgian International Festival of Arts
CIC GIFT Office, 8, Marjanishvili str., **Tbilisi**
Tel: 32-223 591/940 090 Fax: 32-940 090
E-Mail: gift@osgf.ge
festival director Keti Dolidze
Period/Frequency: Oct *Arts types:* drama

International Annual Theatre Festival Theatre & Video
45 Chavchavadze av., 380062 **Tbilisi**
Tel: 32-294 306 Fax: 32-294 306/231 196
E-Mail: SCF@lingua.edu.ge
general director Levan Khetaguri
Period/Frequency: annual *Arts types:* theatre & video *Comments:* the aim of the festival is to show and signify the processes, which take place in the theatrical life; everyone can take part in the festival, professional theatre companies, which will send video recordings of their performances, automatically become participants of the festival; director of festivals

International Annual Theatre Video Festival Body Language
45 Chavchavadze av., 380062 **Tbilisi**
Tel: 32-294 306 Fax: 32-294 306/231 196
E-Mail: SCF@lingua.edu.ge
festival director Levan Khetaguri;
festival coordinator Tamta Berishvili
Period/Frequency: November *Arts types:* dance theatre *Comments:* organised by the Stichting Caucasus Foundation and IBCCP; the aim of the festival is to increase the visibility of dance, which has achieved a rapidly growing popularity within Georgian society and introduce dance as an art form to more people; everyone can take part in the festival: professional choreographers, dancers or companies, from classical ballet to modern dance, physical, movement and nonverbal theatre, which send video recordings of their performances, automatically become participants of the festival

International Guitar Festival Tbilisi
Tel: 32-380 052 Fax: 32-380 052
Internet: www.Orioni.com/ge/league
E-Mail: league@ORIONI.com.ge
Period/Frequency: October *Comments:* organised by the League of Professionals; alternative Internet: www.come.to/league.ge

International Music Festival Autumn Tbilisi
125 Agmashenebeli av., 380002 **Tbilisi**
Tel: 32-960 620/950 119 Fax: 32-958 996
president Jansug Kakhidze; organising committee Vato Kakhidze, Teona Kakhidze, Nino Sakvarelidze
Period/Frequency: second half of Sept, annual *Arts types:* classical, contemporary, folk music, jazz *Venues:* Tbilisi Centre for Music & Cultue

GERMANY (+49)

Aachener Bachtage
Aachener Bachverein, Michaelstr. 6-10, 52062 **Aachen**
Tel: 241-453-0
Fax: 241-453 100
Musikalische Oberleitung Wolfgang Karius
Period/Frequency: Nov- Dec, annual *Arts types:* choir, organ music, orchestral music *Venues:* churches in Aachen, Krönungsfestsaal

Augsburger Puppenspieltage
Kulturbüro der Stadt Augsburg,
Bahnhofstr. 18 1/3 a, 86150 **Augsburg**
Tel: 821-324 3254 Fax: 821-324 3252
Verantwortlich Fr. Pia Schaller
Period/Frequency: July, biennial *Arts types:* puppetry *Venues:* Kulturhaus Abraxas Saal 1: 150, Saal 2: 150 *Comments:* 30 performances, 20 groups

Deutsches Mozart Festival
c/o Deutsche Mozart Gesellschaft, Mozarthaus, Frauentorstraße 30, 86152 **Augsburg**
Tel: 821-518 588 Fax: 821-157 228
Internet: deutsche-mozart-gesellschaft.de
E-Mail: Deutsche-Mozart-Gesellschaft@t-online.de
contact Brigitte Loeder
Period/Frequency: annual *Arts types:* works by Mozart *Comments:* festival takes place in a different city every year, 2000: Hildesheim, 2001: Augsburg

Freilichtbühne am Roten Tor
Theater Augsburg, Postfach 111949,
Kasernstrasse 4-6, 86152 **Augsburg**
Tel: 821-324 4933 Fax: 821-324 4544
Intendant Dr Ulrich Peters; Kaufmännischer Direktor Dr Klaus Engert; Generalmusikdirektor Peter Leonard; Ballettdirektor Jochen Heckmann;
Chordirektor Edgar Hykel
Period/Frequency: June-July, annual *Arts types:* opera, musical *Venues:* Freilichtbühne am Roten Tor

Gandersheimer Domfestspiele
Amt für Kultur, Touristik und Stadtmarketing, Postfach 170, 37575 **Bad Gandersheim**
Tel: 5382-73427 Fax: 5382-73440
Internet: bad-gandersheim.de
Intendant Georg Immelmann; Verwaltungsleitung Nicole Kuprian (tel: 5382-73426)
Period/Frequency: June-Aug, annual *Arts types:* music, drama, children's theatre *Venues:* Stiftskirchenvorplatz Bad Gandersheim

Bad Hersfelder Festspielkonzerte – Oper in der Stiftsruine
Arbeitskreis für Musik e.V., Nachtigallenstraße 7, 36251 **Bad Hersfeld**
Tel: 6621-506 713 Fax: 6621-506 730
Künstlerischer Direktor Siegfried Heinrich;
Direktor Peter Lotschak
Period/Frequency: June-Aug, annual *Arts types:* opera, concerts, recitals *Venues:* Hersfelder Stiftsruine 1300, Ev. Stadtkirche 1000

Kissinger Sommer – Kultur in Europa – Internationales Musik Festival
Stadt Bad Kissingen,
Postfach 2260, 97672 **Bad Kissingen**
Tel: 971-807 110
Fax: 971-807 191
Internet: www.kissingersommer.de
Künstlerische Leitung Dr Kari Kahl-Wolfsjäger
Period/Frequency: June-July, annual *Arts types:* symphony, chamber music, opera, recitals, jazz, theatre *Venues:* Regentenbau with 4 halls, Großer Saal 1100, Theater (art deco) 540, various churches, castles and abbeys *Comments:* 60 different performances

Herbstliche Musiktage Bad Urach
Postfach 1240, 72563 **Bad Urach**
Tel: 7125-156 151
Fax: 7125-156 133
E-Mail: herbstliche-musiktage@t-online.de
Leitung Christian Lange, Andreas Schüle
Period/Frequency: Sept-Oct *Arts types:* opera, classical music, Lieder *Venues:* Residenzschloß, Amanduskirche, Festhalle

Burg-Festspiele Bad Vilbel
Klaus-Havensteinweg 1/2, 61118 **Bad Vilbel**
Tel: 6101-602 210 Fax: 6101-602 301
Internet: www.bad-vilbel.de
E-Mail: altemuehle@t-online.de
Festspielleitung Claus Kunzmann
Period/Frequency: June-Aug, annual *Arts types:* drama, literary readings, children's theatre *Venues:* Wasserburg Bad Vilbel 650

Rossini in Wildbad – Das Belcanto-Festival
Postfach 100201, 75313 **Bad Wildbad**
Tel: 7071-49040 Fax: 7071-49085
Internet: www.badwildbad.de/rossini/homepage.htm
E-Mail: josrossini@aol.com
Recherche Reto Müller; Künstl Gesamtleitung Jochen Schönleber; Pressereferat Annette Eckerle; Dramaturgie Dr. Annette Hornbacher; Organisation Carmen Bosch-Schairer
Period/Frequency: July *Arts types:* operas by Rossini, concerts, ballet, premieres *Venues:* Kursaal 400, König-Karls-Bad 225, Schwarzwaldhof 230 *Second Address:* winter address: Neckarhalde 38, 72070 Tübingen
Comments: seminars, radio recordings and a variety of other activities

Brahms Tage
Brahmsgesellschaft Baden-Baden e.V., Maximilianstr. 85, 76534 **Baden-Baden**
Tel: 7221-99872 Fax: 7221-71104
Präsident Dr. Werner Hoppe;
Geschäftsführung Ilka Hecker
Period/Frequency: May, biennial (2001) *Arts types:* symphony music, chamber music *Venues:* Kurhaus Baden-Baden, Festspielhaus Baden-Baden

Philharmonischer Sommer Baden-Baden
Schloß Solms, Solmsstraße 1, 76530 **Baden-Baden**
Tel: 7221-932 791 Fax: 7221-932 794
Admin Cornelius Grube; Künstl Leitung GMD Werner Stiefel
Period/Frequency: June/July, annual *Arts types:* music (opera, symphony, chamber music, concerts) *Venues:* Kurhaus, Baden-Baden 1000 & 500, Theater Baden-Baden 500 and other venues, some open-air *Comments:* International Baden-Baden masterclass for string instruments held in August – Carl Flesch-Akademie

Calderón-Spiele in der Alten Hofhaltung
E.T.A. Hoffmann-Theater, Schillerplatz 3-7, 96047 **Bamberg**
Tel: 951-871 433 (box office)/423 (public relations)
Fax: 951-871 967
Internet: www.theater.bamberg.de
E-Mail: verwaltung.theater@stadt.bamberg.de
Intendant Rainer Lewandowski; Verwaltungsleiter Karl Fischer; Dramaturgie und Öffentlichkeitsarbeit Rolf Ronzier, Karin Freymeyer, Verena Kögler;
Disposition Stefan Dzierzawa
Period/Frequency: July, annual *Arts types:* drama *Venues:* Alte Hofhaltung in Bamberg 900 *Comments:* theme for 2000: Berthold Brecht's Das Leben des Gallilei; see also Drama

Tage Alter Musik in Bamberg
c/o Musica Canterey Bamberg, obere Dorotheenstr. 3, 96049 **Bamberg**
Tel: 951-519 0041 Fax: 951-519 0041
direktor Gerhard Weinzierl
Period/Frequency: June, biennial (2000: 21-25 June) *Arts types:* music of 16th-18th century *Venues:* Kaisersaal der Residenz 300, Dominikaner Bibliothek 160, Schloß Seehof, various churches in the area *Comments:* theme for 2000: English music, late renaissance to light baroque

Bayreuther Festspiele
Postfach 100262, 95402 **Bayreuth**
Tel: 921-78780 Fax: 921-787 8130
Festspielleitung u. Geschäftsführer
Prof. Wolfgang Wagner
Period/Frequency: July-Aug, annual *Arts types:* opera (Wagner) *Venues:* Richard Wagner Festspielhaus 1925 *Second Address:* Festspielhügel 1-2, 95445 Bayreuth

Festival Junger Künstler Bayreuth
Äußere Badstr. 7a, 95448 **Bayreuth**
Tel: 921-980 0444 Fax: 921-98486
Internet: www.YoungArtistsBayreuth.org
E-Mail: info@das-treffen.de
Gesamtleitung Sissy Thammer
Period/Frequency: Aug, annual *Arts types:* musical workshops, symphony concerts, opera and courses *Venues:* different venues in own building, Europasaal up to 300, various halls/buildings in the region of Bayreuth

Musica Bayreuth
Ludwigstraße 26, 95444 **Bayreuth**
Tel: 921-67367 (Jan-June) Fax: 921-67367
Internet: www.musica-bayreuth.de
Intendanz Prof. Viktor Lukas, Elisabeth Lukas
Period/Frequency: first two weeks of May, annual *Arts types:* oratorio, opera, soloists concerts, orchestral concerts, baroque music *Venues:* Markgräfliches Opernhaus 500, Stadthalle 950, Stadtkirche 1000, Schloßkirche 600 *Second Address:* Bühlstraße 32, 95488 Eckersdorf *Comments:* promoted by Orgelwoche Bayreuth e.V.

Sommerspiele in der Eremitage
Röntgenstr. 2, 95447 **Bayreuth**
Tel: 921-764 360 Fax: 921-764 3622
Internet: www.bayreuth-online.de/studiob
E-Mail: studiobuehne@bayreuth-online.de
Direktor Werner Hildenbrand
Period/Frequency: June-Aug, annual *Arts types:* drama, classical & pop music, dance theatre, historical comedy, children's theatre *Venues:* Eremitage 230, Hof-Theater im Steingraeber-Palais, Naturgarten im Felsengarten zu Sanstareil *Comments:* see also Venues

Bach Tage Berlin
Kaiserdamm 31, 14057 **Berlin**
Tel: 30-301 5518 Fax: 30-301 9307
Internet: www.bachtage.de
Festspielleitung Dr Günther Wagner,Prof. Dr. Rudolf Stephan, Dieter Hauer; Geschäftsführung und Künstlerisches Betriebsbüro Marianne Arnold
Period/Frequency: July, biennial (2001) *Arts types:* chamber and choral music *Venues:* Philharmonie, Schauspielhaus, historic venues in Berlin, Potsdam and surrounding area including Berliner Dom

Berliner Festwochen
Berliner Festspiele GmbH, Budapester Straße 50, 10787 **Berlin**
Tel: 30-254 890 Fax: 30-2548 9111
Internet: www.berlinerfestspiele.de
Intendant Prof. Dr Ulrich Eckhardt; Geschäftsführung Hinrich Gieseler; Künstlerisches Büro Torsten Maß, Dirk Nabering (Konzerte)
Period/Frequency: Sept, annual *Arts types:* music, theatre, literature, exhibitions *Comments:* same address for following festivals: JazzFest Berlin, Theatertreffen Berlin, Theatertreffen der Jugend, Musikbiennale Berlin, Internationale Filmfestspiele, Treffen Junge Musik-Szene, Treffen Junger Autoren

Heimatklänge
c/o Piranha, Carmerstraße 11, 10623 **Berlin**
Tel: 30-318 6140 Fax: 30-3186 1410
Internet: www.piranha.de
E-Mail: womex@piranha.de
contact Brigitte Bieg, Christoph Borkowsky-Akbar
Period/Frequency: Aug-Sept, annual *Arts types:* world music *Comments:* see also Promoters (Piranha)

International Tanzwochen Münster
Lützenstr. 5, 10711 **Berlin**
Tel: 30-313 1644 Fax: 30-313 1644
artistic director Christine Gunnert-Möllmann
Period/Frequency: biennial (2000: 2-14 July) *Arts types:* contemporary dance, films, workshops, conferences *Venues:* Theater im Pumpenhaus 99 *Second address:* Kulturamt Münster, Ludgeriplatz 4, 48151 Münster

Internationales Tanzfest Berlin
TanzWerkstatt Berlin, Klosterstr. 68-70, 10179 **Berlin**
Tel: 30-2474 9756 Fax: 30-2474 9757
Internet: www.tanzwerkstaff.bkv.org
E-Mail: twb@bkv.org
art dirs Ulrike Becker, Nele Herling, André Thériault
Period/Frequency: Aug, annual *Arts types:* contemporary dance, performances, workshops, seminars *Venues:* Podewil Theater 185, Hebbel-Theater 600, Theater am Halleschen Ufer 220 and various other venues in Berlin

JazzFest Berlin
Berliner Festspiele, Budapester Strasse 50, 10787 **Berlin**
Tel: 30-254 890 Fax: 30-2548 9111
Internet: www.berlinerfestspiele.de/jazzfest
E-Mail: jazzfest@berlinerfestspiele.de
Produktionschef Ihno von Hasselt; Künstlerische Leitung Albert Mangelsdorff
Period/Frequency: Oct/Nov, annual *Arts types:* contemporary jazz *Venues:* Haus d. Kulturen d. Welt, Großes Auditorium 1000, Theatersaal 392

MusikBiennale Berlin – Internationales Fest für zeitgenössische Musik
Berliner Festspiele, Budapester Str. 50, 10787 **Berlin**
Tel: 30-254 890 Fax: 30-2548 9111
Internet: www.berlinerfestspiele.de
E-Mail: musikbiennale@berlinerfestspiele.de
Intendant Prof. Dr. Ulrich Eckhardt; Künstlerische Leitung Heike Hoffmann
Period/Frequency: biennial (2001: 9-18 June) *Arts types:* contemporary music *Venues:* Konzerthaus Berlin; Philharmonie; Hebbel-Theater, Neue Nationalgalerie; Hamburger Bahnhof – Museum für Gegenwart; KulturBrauerei; Podewil

Theatertreffen Berlin
Berliner Festspiele, Budapester Strasse 50, 10787 **Berlin**
Tel: 30-254 890 Fax: 30-2548 9111
Internet: www.berlinerfestspiele.de
E-Mail: artdir@berlinerfestspiele.de
Leitung Torsten Maß
Period/Frequency: May, annual *Arts types:* drama for German-speaking countries *Comments:* same address for following festivals: Berliner Festwochen, Internationale Filmfestspiele Berlin, Musikbiennale Berlin,Theatertreffen Berlin, Theatertreffen der Jugend, Treffen Junge Musikszene, Jazz Fest Berlin, Treffen Junger Autoren

Theatre of the World/Theater der Welt
Schloßstr. 48, 12165 **Berlin**
Tel: 30-791 1692 Fax: 30-791 1874
Internet: www.users.aol.com/itigermany/
E-Mail: itigermany@aol.com
Period/Frequency: June-July, triennial (2002) *Arts types:* international theatre and new, innovative performances in different languages
Comments: moving festival; for more information contact Martin Roeder-Zerndt from German ITI, Tel: 30-791 1777, or write to the above address

Moselfestwochen
Kultur & Kur GmbH,
Im Kurpark, 54470 **Bernkastel-Kues**
Tel: 6531-4066
Fax: 6531-3894
Internet: www.moselfestwochen.de
E-Mail: kultur-kur@aol.com
Geschäftsführer und künstlerischer Leiter
Hermann Lewen
Period/Frequency: April-Oct, annual *Arts types:* mainly classical music, some jazz *Venues:*
various venues in the area from Cochem to Trier (particularly the Kloster Machern, St Maximin Trier and various other cloisters and churches

Internationales Tanzprojekt Bielefeld
Kulturbüro, Niederwall 23, 33602 **Bielefeld**
Tel: 521-513 6786 Fax: 521-513 671
Organisator Rainer Schürmann;
künstlerischer Leiter Fred Traguth
Period/Frequency: July-Aug, annual *Arts types:* dance workshops, classical, modern and ethnic performances
Venues: Auditorium Maximum der Universitat 900

Figurentheater der Nationen FIDENA
Hattinger Str. 467, 44795 **Bochum**
Tel: 234-47720/29 Fax: 234-47735
Internet: www.dfp-fidena.de
E-Mail: info@dfp-fidena.de
Leitung Annette Dabs-Baucks; Wissenschaftliche Mitarbeit Anke Meyer; Sekretariat Elke Citrich
Period/Frequency: biennial *Arts types:* figure and object theatre *Venues:* various in Bochum *Comments:* see also National Organisations and Compeitions

Bonner Biennale
Schauspiel Bonn, Am Michaelshof 9, 53177 **Bonn**
Tel: 228-778 591/92 Fax: 228-778 598
Internet: www.schauspiel.bonn.de
E-Mail: biennale@bonn.de
Künstlerische Leitung Manfred Beilharz, Tankred Dorst, Almut Wagner
Period/Frequency: June, biennial (2000: 22 June-2 July)
Arts types: new European drama *Venues:* in different areas of Bonn and Bad Godesberg *Comments:* promoted by Schauspiel Bonn

Bottroper Märchentage
Postfach 101554, 46215 **Bottrop**
Tel: 2041-703 832 Fax: 2041-703 833
contact Herr Heinemann
Period/Frequency: Sept, biennial (2000) *Arts types:* music, theatre, story-telling, film, workshops, puppetry
Venues: schools, libraries, cultural centre *Second Address:* Blumenstraße 12-14, 46236 Bottrop

Festival Orgel PLUS Bottrop
Postfach 101554, 46215 **Bottrop**
Tel: 2041-703 831
Fax: 2041-703 833
Leiter Dieter Wollek; künstlerischer Leiter Dr. Stevens; Organisatorische Leitung Ursula Bannasch
Period/Frequency: Jan, annual *Arts types:* organ, chamber and orchestra music, masterclasses *Venues:* churches in Bottrop *Second Address:* visiting address: Blumenstr. 12-14, 46236 Bottrop

Figurentheatertage der Stadt Bottrop
Postfach 101554, 46215 **Bottrop**
Tel: 2041-703 832 Fax: 2041-703 833
contact Herr Heinemann
Period/Frequency: Sept, biennial (2001) *Arts types:* puppetry, object theatre *Venues:* cultural centre, schools, libraries *Comments:* workshops

Internationales Figurentheater Festival
Kulturinstitut der Stadt Braunschweig, Steintorwall 3, 38100 **Braunschweig**
Tel: 531-470 4860 Fax: 531-470 4809
Leitung Organisation und Öffentlichkeitsarbeit Wolfgang Hartwig; Künstlerische Leitung Enno Podehl
Period/Frequency: Nov., triennial (2000) *Arts types:* puppet theater *Venues:* various venues including open-air in Braunschweig

Tage Neuer Kammermusik
c/o Kulturinstitut der Stadt Braunschweig, Postfach 3309, 38023 **Braunschweig**
Tel: 531-470 4864 Fax: 531-470 4809
Internet: www.braunschweig.de
Organisation Verwaltung Dr. Annette Boldt-Stülzebach
Period/Frequency: Nov, biennial (2000) *Arts types:* contemporary chamber music

Musikfest Bremen
c/o Musikfest Bremen GmbH, Obernstraße 62-66, 28195 **Bremen**
Tel: 421-170 425 Fax: 421-18098
Künstlerischer Leiter Prof. Thomas Albert; Geschäftsführerin Rona Schiel
Period/Frequency: Sept, annual *Arts types:* classical and contemporary music, opera, cross-over projects *Venues:* concert houses, churches, theatres, spectacular venues like terminals *Comments:* music between traditional and avantgarde

Brühler Schloßkonzerte
Bahnhofstraße 16, 50321 **Brühl**
Tel: 2232-941 884 Fax: 2232-941 885
Internet: www.schlosskonzerte.de
E-Mail: info@schlosskonzerte.de
Geschäftsführer Robert Vogel; Künstlerischer Leiter Andreas Spering
Period/Frequency: May-Sept, annual *Arts types:* chamber, chamber orchestra concerts, staged and concert performances of oratorios and operas *Venues:* Treppenhaus von Schloß Augustusburg 470 *Comments:* venue Schloß Augustusburg is a unique baroque palace with a staircase designed by Balthasar Neumann & fresco-painted by Carlo Carlone. The palace is listed on UNESCO's "Liste des Weltkulturerbes"

Burghausen, Internationale Jazzwoche
Stadtplatz 110, 84489 **Burghausen**
Tel: 8677-1411 Fax: 8677-2441
E-Mail: info@b-jazz.com
1. Vorsitzender Herbert Hebertinger
Period/Frequency: March, annual *Arts types:* all types of jazz *Venues:* Wackerhalle 1450, Stadtsaal 700, Mautner Schloß 130 *Comments:* international jazz festival

Klosterspiele Hirsau
Marktbrücke 1, 75365 **Calw**
Tel: 7051-968 844 Fax: 7051-968 877
Intendant Ulrich Rothfuß; Geschäftsführung Hans-Martin Dittus; Verwaltungsleitung Kreisstadt Calw
Period/Frequency: July-Aug, annual (2000: 21 July-13 Aug) *Arts types:* open air theatre, concerts *Venues:* Aurelius Kirche, Klosterareal (open air theatre)

Musikalischer Herbst
c/o Kammerphilharmonie Merck, Frankfurter Str 250, 64290 **Darmstadt**
Tel: 6151-727 198 Fax: 6151-729 0198
Internet: www.merck.de/german/corporate/culture/ukphil.de.html
E-Mail: kammerphilharmonie@merck.de
general manager Stefan Reinhardt; artistic director Christian Rudolf Riedel
Period/Frequency: autumn (8 concerts, Sept-Dec), biennial (2000) *Arts types:* orchestral, chamber music, choral, symphony *Comments:* see also Kammerphilharmonie (Chamber Philharmonic) Merck

kurst weill fest dessau 2000
Kurt-Weill-Gesellschaft e.V., Ebertallee 63, 06846 **Dessau**
Tel: 340-619 595 Fax: 340-611 907
Internet: www.kurt-weill.de
E-Mail: weill-zentrum@t-online.de
managing director Andreas Attenhof; artistic director Patrik Ringborg; dramaturgy/production Kerstin Schweiger; marketing Jost Steinhausen
Period/Frequency: annual (2000: 18 Feb-5 March) *Arts types:* music theatre, concerts (jazz/rock), workshops, symposiums, readings, street theatre, films, exhibitions *Venues:* various in Dessau, Wolfen, Bernburg and Bitterfeld

Festliche Tage Alter Musik Knechtsteden
Ostpreussenallee 5, 41539 **Dormagen**
Tel: 2133-477 905 Fax: 2133-477 905
Geschäftsführung Martin Kahl; Künstlerischer Leiter Hermann Max
Period/Frequency: Sept, annual *Arts types:* chamber, choral, orchestral and oratorio concerts, music courses *Venues:* Klosterbasilika Knechtsteden 550

Burgfestspiele Dreieichenhain
Theater im Bürgerhaus, Fichtestr. 50, 63303 **Dreieich**
Tel: 6103-6000-0 Fax: 6103-600 077
E-Mail: buergerhaus@dialup.nacamar.de
contact Gustav Halberstadt
Period/Frequency: June-July, annual *Arts types:* drama, music-theatre, concerts *Venues:* Burggarten Dreieichenhain 1200 *Comments:* promoter: Burgfestspiele GmbH, Thomas Richter; atlernative E-mail: buergerhaus@dreieich.de

Dresdner Musikfestspiele
Postfach 20 27 23, 01193 **Dresden**
Tel: 351-47856-0 Fax: 351-471 7896
Internet: www.musikfestspiele.com
E-Mail: dmf@musikfestspiele.com
Intendant Prof. Dr. Michael Hampe (until 31 August 2000); Marketingdirektor und Pressesprecher Dirk Wagener; Programmdirektor Torsten Mosgraber (Intendant from 1 Sept 2000); Stellv. Intendant und Verwaltungsdirektor Kim Ry Andersen
Period/Frequency: May-June, annual *Arts types:* opera, ballet, dance theatre, orchestral and choir music, recitals and chamber music *Venues:* Semper Opera House, Culture Palace, churches in Dresden, Castle Pillnitz park, Hunting Lodge, Moritzburg, Albrechtsburg Meißen, Dresdner Zwinger, Kreuzkirche and Schauspiel Dresden *Second Address:* visiting address: Tiergartenstr. 36, 01219 Dresden

Dresdner Tage der zeitgenössischen Musik
Dresdner Zentrum für zeitgenössische Musik, Schevenstrasse 17, Schevenstrasse 17, 01326 **Dresden**
Tel: 351-26462-0 Fax: 351-26462-23
Internet: www.zeitmusik.de
E-Mail: ernesti@zeitmusik.de
Direktor Prof Udo Zimmermann; Verwaltungsleiterin Heike Höfer; Leiter des Bereiches künstlerische Produktion und Planung MD Jürgen Wirrmann; Leiterin des Bereiches Musikwissenschaft Marion Demuth; Leiter der PR & Öffentlichkeitsarbeit Marc Ernesti, BA
Period/Frequency: Oct, annual *Arts types:* contemporary music, dance, music theatre, performance *Venues:* Kulturpalast 2400, Semperoper 1300, Dreikönigskirche 450, Festspielhaus Hellerau 350, Dresdner Zentrum für zeitgenössische Musik 100, Dresdner Zentrum für zeitgenössische Musik Park und Villa, and others *Comments:* concerts, symposiums; archival & library facilities; enquiries into any aspect related to contemporary music welcome, see also National Organisation, Orchestras, Venues and Competitions

Duisburger Akzente
Rathaus, 47049 **Duisburg**
Tel: 203-283 2506 Fax: 203-283 3973
Kulturdezernent Gerd Bildau; Koordinator Helmut Linn (tel. 203-283 2716)
Period/Frequency: April-May, annual *Arts types:* theatre, opera, music, literature, film, exhibitions, jazz, world music *Comments:* 2000 theme: Cultural spaces in Europe (Niederrhein, Niederlande, Flanden)

Robert Schumann Festival
Robert-Schumann-Gesellschaft, Bilkerstr. 4-6, 40213 **Düsseldorf**
Tel: 211-133 240/899 6123 Fax: 211-892 9143
Internet: members.aol.com/schumannga/gesell.htm
E-Mail: schumann6a@aol.com
Direktorin Dr Gisela Schäfer, Robert Schumann GEs; Stadt Düsseldorf Vera van Hazebrouck (tel: 211-899 3606)
Period/Frequency: June, triennial (2000) *Arts types:* concerts, international Schumann symposium, international Clara Schumann competition *Venues:* Tonhalle, churches, open air *Second Address:* Tonhalle Intendantin, Ehrenhof 1, 40479 Düsseldorf, Tel. 211-899 3606, Fax: 211-892 9143
Comments: see also Competitions

Choriner Musiksommer e.V.
Schicklerstraße 3-5, 16225 **Eberswalde**
Tel: 3334-657 310 Fax: 3334-236 316
1. hauptamtliche Geschäftsführerin Irene Vahl; 1. Vorsitzender Prof. Dr. habil. Gunther Wolff; 2. Vorsitzender Dr. Klaus Höppner
Period/Frequency: June-Aug, annual *Arts types:* symphony, chamber, choral music from baroque to contemporary *Venues:* Zisterzienser-Kloster in Chorin bei Eberswalde 1400 (inside), 700 (outside) *Comments:* non-profit organisation; partly funded by Kulturministerium des Landes Brandenburg and by private sponsoring

Thüringer Bach-Wochen e.V.
Thuringian Bach-Weeks
Frauenplan 21, 99817 **Eisenach**
Tel: 3691-214 053 Fax: 3691-214 053
Vorsitzender Dr. Claus Oefner; Geschäftsführer Wolfgang Rewicki
Period/Frequency: 6 weeks around the birthday of Johann Sebastian Bach; March/April; annual (2000: 18 March-30 April) *Arts types:* concerts, lectures, exhibitions, guided tours *Comments:* Bach and his Thuringian contemporaries are the programme and the tenor of the Thuringian Bach-Weeks, all activities are at original places of the Bach-family in Thuringia

Festspiele auf Schloß Ellwangen
Kulturamt d. Stadt Ellwangen, Rathaus, 73479 **Ellwangen**
Tel: 7961-84246 Fax: 7961-84310
Internet: www.ellwangen.de
contact Anselm Grupp
Period/Frequency: June-Aug, annual *Arts types:* drama, classical music (orchestral) *Venues:* Schloßhof 400 *Second Address:* bookings: Tourist Information, Rathaus, 73479 Ellwangen, Tel: 7961-84303, Fax: 7961-84350

Internationales Musikfestival Ellwangen
Postfach 1112, 73471 **Ellwangen**
Tel: 711-715 6603 Fax: 711-715 7599
E-Mail: Viomusikus@aol.com
contact Gabriel Voicu
Period/Frequency: Aug, annual *Arts types:* instrumental and song recitals *Venues:* Schloß Ellwangen *Second Address:* Konzertagentur Strad, Europaplatz 20, 70565 Stuttgart *Comments:* also masterclasses

Europäisches Musikfest Münsterland e.V.
c/o Konzertdirektion Martin Müller, Vintrup 4, 59320 **Ennigerloh-Ostenfelde**
Tel: 2522-960 200 Fax: 2522-960 201
Internet: www.kulturnetz.muensterland.com/EMM
E-Mail: EMM@kulturnetz.muensterland.com
managing director Martin Müller; artistic director Reinbert Evers
Period/Frequency: Aug, annual *Arts types:* mainly classical music *Venues:* Schloß Nordkirchen *Comments:* 2000 theme: music of three regions from the Iberian peninsula

Klavier-Festival Ruhr
Initiativkreis Ruhrgebiet, Schinkelstr. 30-32, 45138 **Essen**
Tel: 201-896 6842 Fax: 201-896 6871
Internet: www.i-r.de
E-Mail: info@i-r.de
Künstlerische Ltg. Franz Xaver Ohnesorg; Leiter Künstl. Betriebsbüro Werner Heimlich
Period/Frequency: mid-June – mid-August, annual *Arts types:* piano recitals, piano concerts *Venues:* Ruhr area

Schloß-Festspiele Ettlingen
Postfach 0762, Kutschenplatz, 76261 **Ettlingen**
Tel: 7243-101 382 Fax: 7243-101 588
Intendant Dr Fritzdieter Gerhards; Künstlerisches Betriebsbüro Silvia Aumann
Period/Frequency: June-Aug *Arts types:* drama and music theatre (6 premieres) *Venues:* Schloß Ettlingen 873 *Comments:* since 1994 they also produce Festspiele für Kinder (FEFÜKI) (May-June/July)

Eutiner Sommerspiele GmbH/Oper im Schloßpark
Postfach 112, 23691 **Eutin**
Tel: 4521-2161/6140 Fax: 4521-3001
Intendant Siegfried Grote; Geschäftsführung Lothar Brandt; musikalische Leitung Hilary Griffiths; Chordirektor Friedeman Wieland
Period/Frequency: July-Aug, annual *Arts types:* opera, operetta, musical *Venues:* Schlosspark (open-air) 1900 *Comments:* visiting address: Jungfernstieg, 23701 Eutin

Deutsches Kinder- und Jugendtheatertreffen Berlin
Kinder- und Jugendtheaterzentrum in der Bundesrepubik Deutschland, Schützenstraße 12, 60311 **Frankfurt am Main**
Tel: 69-296 661 Fax: 69-292 354
Künstlerische Leitung Dr Gerd Taube, Henning Fangauf
Period/Frequency: April, biennial in Berlin *Arts types:* children and young people's theatre, puppets, dance-theatre, discussion sessions *Venues:* carrousel Theater an der Parkaue, Grips Theater (Berlin) *Comments:* organised by Kinder- und Jugentheaterzentrum in der Bundesrepublik Deutschland (q.v.)

Festival Neuer Tanz
AAK Freiburg, Im E-Werk Eschholzstr. 77, 79106 **Freiburg**
Tel: 761-207 570/48
directors Wolfgang Graf, Karin Hönes
Period/Frequency: 2000: Feb (2 weeks, 10-12 performances), 2001: May *Arts types:* dance

Internationales Freiburger Theaterfestival
Städtische Bühnen Freiburg, Bertholdstr. 46, 79098 **Freiburg**
Tel: 761-201 2807 Fax: 761-201 2999
Arts types: drama, visual, object theatre *Venues:* Freiburger Theater 909 & 300 & 190 & 99 and other venues *Second Address:* AAK im E-Werk, Eschholzstr. 77, 79106 Freiburg, Tel: 761-207 570 Fax: 761-207 5748
Comments: organised by Freiburg Theater

Bodensee-Festival GmbH
Olgastr. 21, 88045 **Friedrichshafen**
Tel: 7541-92320 Fax: 7541-33323
Internet: www.bodfest.de/
Geschäftsleiter Winfried Neumann, Hennu Faehndrich
Period/Frequency: May-June, annual *Arts types:* concerts, ballet, theatre, cabaret *Venues:* Friedrichshafen, more than 20 venues around the Bodensee

Münchner Klaviersommer
c/o LOFT Music, Wessobrunner Str. 4, 82131 **Gauting**
Tel: 89-8934 0894 Fax: 89-8934 0860
Leitung Dr. Manfred Frei, Karlheinz Hein
Period/Frequency: July, annual *Arts types:* jazz and classical music *Venues:* Gasteig Kulturzentrum, Muffathalle, Munich Philharmonic Hall 2100, Carl-Orff-Saal 600, Black Box 250, Festsaal Bayerischer Hof 800 *Second Address:* contact Karlheinz Hein, Friedensstr. 22, München, Tel: 89-408 828 *Comments:* also organise Richard Strauss Tage Garmisch-Partenkirchen

Richard-Strauss-Tage Garmisch-Partenkirchen
c/o LOFT Music, Wessobrunner Str. 4, 82131 **Gauting**
Tel: 89-8934 0894
Fax: 89-8934 0860
Leitung Dr. Manfred Frei, Christian Lange
Period/Frequency: June, annual *Arts types:* works by R. Strauss (including chamber music, song recitals, operas and premieres) *Venues:* Olympic Stadium 2800, Kongresszentrum up to 900 *Comments:* also organise Münchner Klaviersommer

Tage des Deutschen Puppenspiels
Revierpark Nienhausen GmbH, Feldmarkstrasse 201, 45883 **Gelsenkirchen**
Tel: 209-941 310 Fax: 209-941 3199
Programmleitung Herr Siebel
Period/Frequency: Jan, biennial (2000) *Arts types:* all forms of puppet theatre *Venues:* Gr. Saal Des Freizeithauses 300 to 350

Göttinger Figurentheatertage
Neues Rathaus, 37070 **Göttingen**
Tel: 551-400 2475 Fax: 551-400 2743
Internet: www.goettingen.de
E-Mail: kulturamt@goettingen.de
contact Roswitha Brauns
Period/Frequency: Jan-Feb, annual *Arts types:* puppetry *Venues:* Altes Rathaus 250, Lumcerè 150

Göttinger Händel-Festspiele
Hainholzweg 3-5, 37085 **Göttingen**
Tel: 551-56700 Fax: 551-45395
Internet: www.haendel.org
E-Mail: info@haendel.org
Leitung der Geschäftsstelle Benedikt Poensgen; Künstlerische Leitung Nicholas McGegan
Period/Frequency: annual (2000: 8-13 June) *Arts types:* Händel operas and baroque music
Venues: Deutsches Theater, churches in Göttingen, assembly hall, university *Comments:* 2000 theme: the cosmopolitan Händel; see Promoters

Mamu Butoh & Jazz
Gotmarstr. 3, 37073 **Göttingen**
Tel: 551-485 863/790 6245
Fax: 551-794 457
E-Mail: endo@mail.mpiem.gwdg.de
administrator (organisation, pr) Gabriele Endo; director Tadashi Endo
Period/Frequency: Jan *Arts types:* butoh, jazz *Venues:* Junges Theater 250 *Second address:* Gabriele Endo, Gehrenweg 3, 37130 Diemarden *Comments:* the festival is promoted by the Institut für Europäischen Bildungstransfer e.V. & the Kulturamt der Stadt Göttingen, supported by the Japan Foundation

Händel-Festspiele
Händel-Haus,
Große Nikolaistraße 5, 06108 **Halle (Saale)**
Tel: 345-5009 0222
Fax: 345-5009 0416
Internet: www.haendelfestspiele.halle.de
E-Mail: haendel@halle.de
Direktorin Dr. Hanna John
Period/Frequency: June, annual (2000: 2-11 June) *Arts types:* opera, oratorio, concerts, early music *Venues:* Opernhaus, Goethe-Theater, Händel-Haus, Dom, Franckesche Stiftungen, Marktkirche, neues Theater, Konzerthalle, Ulrichskirche, Galgenbergschlucht- open air concert with fireworks

Hamburger Ballett-Tage
John Neumeier Ballettzentrum Hamburg, Caspar-Voght-Straße 54, 20535 **Hamburg**
Tel: 40-2111 8816/5 Fax: 40-2111 8888
Internet: www.hamburgballett.de
E-Mail: presse@hamburgballett.de
Betriebsdirektorin Ulrike Schmidt; künstlerischer Direktor Prof. John Neumeier
Period/Frequency: May-July, annual *Arts types:* mainly classical ballet *Venues:* Staatsoper Hamburg 1675
Comments: booking: Tel: 40-351 721

Internationales Sommertheater Festival Hamburg
Jarrestraße 20, 22303 **Hamburg**
Tel: 40-271 131 Fax: 40-279 0098
Internet: www.sommertheater.org
E-Mail: info@sommertheater.org
künstlerische Leitung/Geschäftsführung Dieter Jaenicke; Kodirektorin Gabriele Naumann
Period/Frequency: July *Arts types:* dance and dance-theatre, performance and music *Venues:* Kampnagel Kulturfabrik *Comments:* new currents in international theatre and dance; will be dissolved after 2000

Tanzplattform Deutschland
c/o Kampnagel, Jarrestrasse 20, 22303 **Hamburg**
Tel: 40-270 9490 Fax: 40-2709 4911
Internet: www.kampnagel.de
E-Mail: kampnagel@t-online.de
Projektleitung Sabine Gehm
Period/Frequency: biennial (2000: 19-22 Jan) *Arts types:* dance *Venues:* Kampnagel Internationale Kulturfabrik
Comments: see also Venues

Brüder-Grimm-Märchenfestspiele
Olof-Palme-Haus,
Pfarrer-Hufnagel-Str. 2, 63454 **Hanau-Kesselstadt**
Tel: 6181-24670/77(March -Sept)/295 632(Jan-Dec)
Fax: 6181-24671
E-Mail: add.maerchenfestspiele.hanau@t-online.de
Leitung Dieter Stegmann; Verwaltungsleitung Dirk Steinmetz; Öffentlichkeitsarbeit Ulrich Siebert
Period/Frequency: summer, annual *Arts types:* drama, musical *Venues:* Park von Schloß Philippsruhe

Festival Theaterformen
Ballhofstraße 5, 30159 **Hannover**
Tel: 511-9999 2855 Fax: 511-9999 2950
Internet: www.theaterformen.de
E-Mail: info@theaterformen.de
Künstlerische Leitung Marie Zimmermann; Produktionsleitung Dr Jörg Scharpff
Period/Frequency: biennial (2000: 8 June-9 July) *Arts types:* drama *Venues:* various in Braunschweig and Hannover *Comments:* Festival accompanying Expo 2000

Festwochen in Herrenhausen, Die
Kulturamt der Landeshauptstadt Hannover, Friedrichswall 15, 30159 **Hannover**
Tel: 511-1684 6356 Fax: 511-1684 5073
Internet:
www.kulturserver.de/home/FestwochenHerrenhausen
Leitung Harald Böhlmann; Organisatorische Leitung Petra Mahramzadeh; Presse Karin S Schwarz (tel: 511-433 477, fax: 434 0060)
Period/Frequency: June-Aug, annual *Arts types:* classical music, opera, theatre, ballet, classical, street theatre, puppetry, comedy *Venues:* Gartentheater 900, Orangerie 500, Galerie 530, Großer Garten 2100

TANZtheater INTERNATIONAL
c/o Tanz und Theaterbüro Hannover, Roscherstr. 12, 30161 **Hannover**
Tel: 511-343 919 Fax: 511-331 965
Internet: www.tanztheater-international.de
E-Mail: tti@comlink.org
Festival Leitung Christiane Winter; künstl Leitung Dieter Jaenicke,Christiane Winter; Organisation Elke Weiler; presse & Öffentlichkeitsarbeit Angela Bosnjak
Period/Frequency: Sept, annual *Arts types:* contemporary dance *Venues:* Theater am Aegi 1100, Hochschule für Musik und Theater 460, Orangerie Herrenhausen 360 and various other venues

Schlossfestspiele Heidelberg
Theater der Stadt Heidelberg,
Friedrichstrasse 5, 69117 **Heidelberg**
Tel: 6221-583 514 Fax: 6221-583 599
Intendant Dr. Volkmar Clauß; Festspielleitung u. Geschäftsführung Prof Helmut Hein; Chordirektor Wolfgang Seeliger; Dirigenten Volker Christ, Joel Fried
Period/Frequency: July-Aug, annual *Arts types:* concerts (classical, wind, symphony), light American opera
Venues: Schloss Heidelberg: Schlosshof 800, Engl.Bau 300, Königssaal 590, Kaisersaal 220; others: Spiegelsaal/Prinz Carl Palais 180

Schwetzinger Mozartfest
c/o Michaela Simane,
Fritz-Frey Str. 6, 69121 **Heidelberg**
Tel: 6221-408 062 Fax: 6221-408 063
Präsident Gerhard Haeberlein; künstl Leitung Michaela Simane
Period/Frequency: Sept, annual *Arts types:* concerto, chamber music, sacred music, opera *Venues:* Schloss mit Rokokotheater 512, Konzertsaal

Opernfestspiele Heidenheim
Stadtverwaltung Heidenheim,
Postfach 1146, 89501 **Heidenheim**
Tel: 7321-327 387 Fax: 7321-327 688
Internet: www.opernfestspiele.de
E-Mail: oper@cmc-online.de
Künstlerischer Leiter u. Generalmusikdirektor Marco-Maria Canonica
Period/Frequency: July-Aug, annual *Arts types:* opera
Venues: Schloß Hellenstein in Heidenheim (open-air) 780

Tanz Theater Tage
c/o Theater Heilbronn,
Berliner Platz 1, 74072 **Heilbronn**
Tel: 7131-563 000 Fax: 7131-563 139
E-Mail: TheaterHN@gmx.de
contact Andreas Oberbach
Period/Frequency: June, annual *Arts types:* modern dance, dance theatre *Venues:* Theatre Heilbronn (Auditorium, Kammerspiele) *Comments:* international guests; see also Theater Heilbronn (Drama and Venues)

Walkenrieder Kreuzgangkonzerte
c/o Image Concert GmbH,
Heidestr.1, 37412 **Herzberg am Harz**
Tel: 5521-5610 Fax: 5521-72972
Internet: Image.Concert@t-online.de
contact Thomas Krause, Ilse Fischer
Period/Frequency: May-Sept, annual *Arts types:* classical concerts *Venues:* Zisterzienserkloster Walkenried (medieval Cistercian monastery), both inside and open-air venues

Schloßspiele Hohenlimburg
c/o Freundeskreis Schloßspiele Hohenlimburg e.V., Fabrikstraße 4, 58119 **Hohenlimburg**
Tel: 2334-2299 Fax: 2334-43251
E-Mail: gerdson@aol-com
Spielleitung Peter Schöne
Period/Frequency: July, annual *Arts types:* theatre, music (including classical music, jazz, rock), children's theatre and outdoor theatre *Venues:* Schloß Hohenlimburg 500, Barocksaal 100

Corveyer Musikwochen
Kulturkreis Höxter-Corvey GmbH, Stadthaus, Westerbachstr. 45, Moltkestrasse, 37671 **Höxter**
Tel: 5271-963 430
Fax: 5271-963 125
Internet: www.hoexter.de
E-Mail: info@hoexter.de
Geschäftsführer Rudolf Breul a.d., Maria Franke; Künstlerische Leitung Ronald Halsband (WDR, Köln); Durchführung Rudolf Lohmann (tel: 5271-31499)
Period/Frequency: May-June, annual *Arts types:* orch, chamber, choral concerts, song, piano recitals; 6 concerts each year *Venues:* Schloß Corvey bei Höxter, Kaisersaal 320, Abteikirche 650

Freilichtspiele im Turm Baur
c/o Stadttheater Ingolstadt, Schloßlände 1, 85049 **Ingolstadt**
Tel: 841-17801 Fax: 841-305 1809
Intendant Wolfram Krempel;
Verwaltung Sigfried Ostermeier, Michael Schmidt
Period/Frequency: June-July, annual *Arts types:* drama, music-theatre *Venues:* Turm Baur 750
Comments: see also Drama

Sommerkonzerte zwischen Donau u. Altmühl
Audi AG, 85045 **Ingolstadt**
Tel: 841-893 6194/6859
Fax: 841-893 1148
Internet: sommerkonzerte.de
E-Mail: steffen.mueller@audi.de
Leiter der Abteilung Public Relations Karl-Heinz Rumpf; Kultursponsoring Steffen Müller
Period/Frequency: June-July, annual *Arts types:* classical music, music theatre, modern music, world music
Venues: various venues in Leitheim, Ingolstadt, Neuburg, Eichstätt and Pfaffenhofen *Comments:* the festival is a co production between Bayerischer Rundfunk and Audi AG

Klang & Raum
c/o Swabian Conference Center, Kloster Irsee, Klosterring 4, 87660 **Irsee**
Tel: 8341-906 699 Fax: 8341-74278
Internet: www.kloster-irsee.de
E-Mail: Klang&Raum@kloster-irsee.de
managing director Harry Oesterle;
artistic director Bruno Weil
Period/Frequency: Aug/Sept, annual *Arts types:* classical and sacred music *Venues:* Kloster Irsee: Festival Hall 200, church 650; Marienkapelle Eggenthal 200
Comments: music on period instruments performed in original baroque settings

Burgfestspiele Jagsthausen
Heimat und Verkehrsverein Jagsthausen e.V., Schloßstr.12, 74249 **Jagsthausen**
Tel: 7943-912 345 Fax: 7943-912 440/450
Internet: www.jagsthausen.de
Intendant u. Künstlerischer Leiter Jochen Striebeck; Geschäftsführer Roland Halter;
musikalische Leitung Jean Hoffmann
Period/Frequency: June-Aug, annual *Arts types:* drama and musical, children's theatre (fairy tales) *Venues:* Götzenburg Jagsthausen 1000

Europäische Kulturtage Karlsruhe
Kulturreferat, Rathaus am Marktplatz, 76124 **Karlsruhe**
Tel: 721-133 4030/32/33 (information)
Fax: 721-133 4009
Internet: www.karlsruhe.de/kultur/ekt2000
E-Mail: kref@karlsruhe.de
Gesamtleitung Susanne Laugwitz MA;
Organisation und Werbung Sabine Mager
Period/Frequency: April-May, biennial (2000: 14 April-6 May) *Arts types:* theatre, music, exhibitions, literature, film *Second Address:* Badisches Staatstheater, Baumeisterstr. 11, 76137 Karlsruhe *Comments:* 2000 theme -Kunst Stück Zukunft

Händel-Festspiele
c/o Badisches Staatstheater, 76125 **Karlsruhe**
Tel: 721-3557-0 Fax: 721-373 223 (Verwaltung)
Internet: www.karlsruhe.de/kultur/staatstheater
E-Mail: kartenverkauf@bstaatstheater.bwl.de
Künstlerische Gesamtleitung Pavel Fieber, Ulrich Peters; Verwaltungsdirektor Wolfgang Sieber; Presse- und Öffentlichkeitsarbeit Anna-Renate Sörgel
Period/Frequency: Feb/March, annual (2000: 23 Feb-4 March) *Arts types:* G.F. Händel and his time – opera, oratorios and concerts, new works ref. to Händel
Venues: Großes Haus 1002, Kleines Haus 385, INSEL Studio 99, INSEL Werkstatt 200 *Comments:* venue address: Baumeisterstr. 11, 76137 Karlsruhe; see also Opera, Drama, Dance and Orchestras

Internationales Theaterfestival
c/o Sandkorn-Theater, Kaiserallee 11, 76133 **Karlsruhe**
Tel: 721-848 984 Fax: 721-853 321
Internet: www.sandkorn-theater.de
E-Mail: sandkorn-theater@t-oneline.de
Intendant Siegfried Kreiner;
Stellvertretende Intendantin Stefanie Lackner
Period/Frequency: August 2000 *Arts types:* cabaret, dance-theatre, music, dance *Venues:* Sandkorn-Theater; Fabriktheater 196, Studiotheater 120, theatre tents

Kasseler Musiktage
Heinrich-Schuetz-Allee 33, 34131 **Kassel**
Tel: 561-770 959 Fax: 561-780 987
Internet: www.kassel.de/musiktage
E-Mail: ksmusiktage@t-online.de
Geschäftsführerin Maren Matthes
Period/Frequency: end Sept, annual *Arts types:* classical, contemporary music *Venues:* Stadthalle 1700, Martinskirche 1400

Thespis, International Festival of Monodramas
Osloring 41, 24109 **Kiel**
Tel: 431-528 307
Fax: 431-528 307
contact Jolanta Kozak-Sutowitz
Period/Frequency: October

International Street Theatre Festival Holzminden
Kulturbüro Köln, Engelbertstr. 32, 50674 **Köln**
Tel: 221-241 3133 Fax: 221-240 3247
E-Mail: kulturbk@aol.com
künstlerische Leiter und Organisator Jürgen Ruppert
Period/Frequency: biennial (2000: 8-14 June) *Arts types:* street theatre *Venues:* various in Holzminden *Second address:* Stadt Holzminden, Kulturamt, Obere Str. 30, 37603 Holzminden *Comments:* see also Agents & Producers and Competitions

MusikTriennale Köln GmbH
Bischofsgartenstraße 1, 50667 **Köln**
Tel: 221-925 716-0
Fax: 221-925 716-395
Internet: www.MusikTriennalekoeln.de
E-Mail: mtk@koelnmusik.de
Geschäftsführender Direktor Dr. Albin Hänseroth; Aufsichtsratsvorsitzender Heinz J. Lüttgen; Künstlerische Leitung Gabriele Faust, Renate Liesmann-Baum, Reiner Michalke, Dr. Albin Hänseroth; Betriebsbüro Dr. Nicolette Schäfer
Period/Frequency: April-June, triennial (2000) *Arts types:* music *Venues:* various types of venues *Comments:* theme: music of the 20th century, cross-over in classical and popular music; in 2000 the focus will be on "human voice"

Pictures of (e)motion
Tanz Performance Köln, Melchiorstraße 3, 50670 **Köln**
Tel: 221-722 133 Fax: 221-739 2030
E-Mail: tpkoeln@pironet.de
director Madeline Ritter
Period/Frequency: autumn, biennial (2001) *Arts types:* dance, video, film and new media *Venues:* Kunst- und Ausstellungshalle der Bundesrepublik Deutschland Kunstmuseum Bonn *Comments:* collaboration with Interartes production centre for media design, film and total theater

Sommer-Köln
SK Stiftung Kultur, Im Mediapark 7, 50670 **Köln**
Tel: 221-226 2433/2423 Fax: 221-226 5743
Internet: www.sk-kultur.de
E-Mail: skkultur@aol.com
Referent Gisela Deckart (email: gisela.deckart@x400.kulturant.koeln.lio.de); PR Priska Höflich (email: skkulturpr@netcologne.de)
Period/Frequency: six weeks in summer, annual *Arts types:* avantgarde drama, children's theatre, comedy, street theatre *Comments:* open-air festival, free admission

Hohenloher Kultursommer
Postfach 1362, 74643 **Künzelsau**
Tel: 7940-18373 Fax: 7940-18363
Geschäftsführer Otto Müller; künstlerische Beratung Dr. Rosina Sonnenschmidt, Harald Knauss
Period/Frequency: June-Sept, annual *Arts types:* early music, classical, romantic, renaissance, dance, chamber music *Venues:* castles, churches, museums in Hohenlohe area

Landshuter Hofmusiktage
Verkehrsverein Landshut e.V.,
Altstadt 315, 84028 **Landshut**
Tel: 871-922 050
Fax: 871-89275
Internet: www.stadtlandshut.de
E-Mail: verkehrsverein@landshut.de
Intendant u. Künstlerischer Leiter Dr Franzpeter Messmer; Öffentlichkeitsarbeit Kurt A. Weinzierl
Period/Frequency: June-July, biennial (2000) *Arts types:* old and new music, commedia dell'arte *Venues:* Rathausprunksaal 500, Italienischer Saal 150, Burg Trausnitz 300, Stadtresidenz 550 *Comments:* exhibitions, concerts, workshops, historical meals and music, poetry readings international soloists invited

Bachfest der Neuen Bachgesellschaft e.V.
Neue Bachgesellschaft, Thomas Kirchhof 16,
04109 **Leipzig**
Tel: 341-960 1463
Fax: 341-960 1463
contact Herr Schmidt
Period/Frequency: March-Nov, annual *Arts types:* works by Bach *Comments:* organiser & location changes every year; 2000: Leipzig

euro-scene-Leipzig
Gottschedstr. 16, 04109 **Leipzig**
Tel: 341-980 0284 Fax: 341-980 4860
Internet: www.euro-scene.de
E-Mail: info@euro-scene.de
Direktorin Ann-Elisabeth Wolff; Presse und Künstl Mitarbeit Michael Freundt; Assistenz Dr Helga Müller
Period/Frequency: Nov, annual *Arts types:* avantgarde European theatre, dance, movement theatre *Venues:* Schauspielhaus 750, Neue Szene 100, Kellertheater in the Opera House up to 100, Schaubühne im Lindenfels 130, LOFFT Theaterhaus 100 *Comments:* also competition: The best German dance solo

Felix Mendelssohn-Festtage des Gewandhauses zu Leipzig
Augustusplatz 8, 04109 **Leipzig**
Tel: 341-127 0330/31 Fax: 341-127 0400
Internet: www.gewandhaus.de
E-Mail: gwhdir@gewandhaus.de
Gewandhausdirektor Andreas Schulz; Gewandhauskapellmeister Prof. Dr. Herbert Blomsteldt
Period/Frequency: end Oct-beg. Nov, annual *Arts types:* chamber music, lectures *Venues:* Gewandhaus zu Leipzig 1900, Mendelssohnhaus, Thomaskirche

MDR-Musiksommer
Mitteldeutscher Rundfunk, HA Klangkörper, Springerstr. 22-24, 04105 **Leipzig**
Tel: 341-300 5505 Fax: 341-300 5532
Internet: www.mdr.de/musiksommer
Leitung Mario Plath
Period/Frequency: June-Sept, annual *Arts types:* classical music *Venues:* historic venues in Saxony, Saxony-Anhalt & Thuringia *Comments:* see also Orchestras and Choirs

Internationales Tanzfestival NRW
Postfach 10 11 40, 51311 **Leverkusen**
Tel: 214-406 4117 Fax: 214-406 4102/03
E-Mail: tpkoeln@aol.com
Künstlerischerleiter Marc Jonkers
Period/Frequency: 1-18 June 2000, biennial *Arts types:* modern dance *Venues:* in Dortmund, Düsseldorf, Duisburg, Essen, Köln, Leverkusen, Remscheid *Second Address:* Tanz Performance Köln, Melchiorstr. 3, 50670 Köln, Tel: 221-722 133, Fax: 221-739 2030

Musiksommer Obermain
Landratsamt, Kronacher Str. 30, 96215 **Lichtenfels**
Tel: 9571-18283 Fax: 9571-18288
E-Mail: tourismus@musiksommer-obermain.htl.de
contact Frau Wich
Period/Frequency: May-Sept/Dec, annual *Arts types:* classical music

Internationales Fest der Puppen
c/o Theaterpädagogisches Zentrum,
Universitätsplatz 5-6, 49808 **Lingen (Ems)**
Tel: 591-91663-0 Fax: 591-91663-63
Internet: ece.eure.de
E-Mail: iata.ece@eure.de
Organisation Ingo Michael-Blunk; Dir Norbert Radermacher
Period/Frequency: Sept-Oct, biennial (2001) *Arts types:* puppetry *Venues:* Lingen, Professorenhaus und Theater an der Wilhelmshöhe

World Festival of Children's Theatre
Welt-Kindertheater-Fest
Stadt Lingen (Ems), TPZ, AITA/IATA,
Postfach 2060, 49803 **Lingen (Ems)**
Tel: 591-916 630 Fax: 591-916 6363
Internet: www.tpz-lingen.de
E-Mail: info@tpz-lingen.de
Künstlerischer Leiter Norbert Radermacher; Organisation Anne-Marie Jansen
Period/Frequency: biennial, but only every 4th year in Lingen *Venues:* Theater an der Wilhelmshöhe 753 (only in Lingen) *Comments:* coincides with symposia of experts in children's theatre; 2000 in Japan

Schleswig-Holstein Musik Festival
Postfach 2411, Jerusalemsberg 7, 23568 **Lübeck**
Tel: 451-389 570 Fax: 451-389 5757
Internet: www.shmf.de
künstlerischer Leiter Christoph Eschenbach; Direktor Rolf Beck; künstlerisches Betriebsbüro Dr Wolfgang Fink; Orchesterakademie Christian Lorenz; Orchesterkurse Prof Ulf Tischbirck; Presseabteilung Prisca Biermann; Konzertorganisation Markus Staeger
Period/Frequency: July-Aug, annual *Arts types:* orchestra, chamber concerts, piano, singing, opera recitals, jazz *Venues:* 35 venues in Schleswig-Holstein *Comments:* see also Orchestras

Ludwigsburger Schloßfestspiele – Internationale Festspiele Baden-Württemberg
Postfach 1022, 71610 **Ludwigsburg**
Tel: 7141-93960 Fax: 7141-939 677
Internet: www.festspiele.ludwigsburg.de
E-Mail: info@festspiele.ludwigsburg.de
geschäftsführende Direktorin Dr. Susanne Dieterich; künstlerische Leitung Prof Wolfgang Gönnenwein
Period/Frequency: June-Sept, annual *Arts types:* opera, ballet, classical and choir concerts, drama, chamber music, jazz, folk, exhibitions *Venues:* Residenzschloß, Theater im Forum 1200, Karlskaserne 500-600

Magdeburger Telemann-Festtage
Liebigstrasse 10, 39104 **Magdeburg**
Tel: 391-543 0290 Fax: 391-561 6421
Internet: telemann.magdeburg.de
E-Mail: telemann@magdeburg.de
Direktor Dr Wolf Hobohm
Period/Frequency: March, biennial *Arts types:* vocal works, unknown works, mostly Telemann, but also his contemporaries *Venues:* Konzerthalle Georg-Phillip-Telemann 350, Magdeburger Dom 800, Theater der Landeshauptstadt Magdeburg, and other venues

Internationales Theaterfestival Hambach
c/o Wolfgang Rademaker, Albinistrasse 13, 55116 **Mainz**
Tel: 6131-224 235 Fax: 6131-224 235
art director Wolfgang Rademaker
Period/Frequency: Sept, annual *Arts types:* drama, dance, cabaret, mime, puppets *Venues:* Hambacher Schloß Festsaal 400, Theaterzelt 300

Kölner Sommerfestival
c/o BB Promotion GmbH,
The Art of Entertainment, L7, 7a, 68161 **Mannheim**
Tel: 621-107 920 Fax: 621-13314
Internet: www.bb-promotion.com
E-Mail: zentrale@bb-promotion.com
Produzent Michael Brenner; Geschäftsführer Matthias Mantel, Ralf Kokemüller
Period/Frequency: June-Aug, annual *Arts types:* contemporary & modern dance, gospel, musicals, shows *Comments:* see also Promoters and Agents & Producers

BALANCE – Bewegungstheater International
Ketzerbach 14, 35037 **Marburg**
Tel: 6421-66308/177-660 9548 (mobile) Fax: 6421-66536
artistic directors Rainer Eble, Michael Küstermann
Period/Frequency: June/July, biennial (2000) *Arts types:* modern dance, dance theatre, movement theatre *Venues:* Stadthalle Marburg 925, Waggonhalle 99, TNT 99

Musica Sacra International
c/o Bayerische Musikakademie,
Kurfürstenstr. 19, 87616 **Marktoberdorf**
Tel: 8342-961 825 Fax: 8342-40370
Internet: www.modmusik.de
E-Mail: 100530.317@compuserve.com
director Gustav Adolf Rabus; manager Jeroen Schrijner
Period/Frequency: week around whitsun, biennial (2000) *Arts types:* sacred music *Venues:* churches in the region

Freilichtspiele Schloß Maßbach
Fränkisches Theater, Schloß Maßbach, 97711 **Maßbach**
Tel: 9735-235 Fax: 9735-1496
Direktoren Lena Hutter, Herbert Heinz; Dramaturgie und Disposition Sebastian Worch
Period/Frequency: June-Aug, annual *Arts types:* drama (classical-modern + comedy), children's theatre *Venues:* open air theatre 320 *Comments:* see also Drama

Klosterkonzerte Maulbronn
Evang. Seminar, Klosterhof 12-17, 75433 **Maulbronn**
Tel: 7043-7734 Fax: 7043-5702
Internet: www.maulbronn.de/klosterkonzerte
E-Mail: klosterkon@aol.com
Geschäftsführung Christa Köhler; Künstlerischer Leiter KMD & StD Jürgen Budday
Period/Frequency: May-Oct, annual *Arts types:* church music, chamber, choir music, oratorios, period music, serenades *Venues:* Kloster Maulbronn, Laienrefektorium 600, Klosterkirche 1000, Kreuzganggarten 900, Oratorium 200 *Comments:* Kloster Maulbronn is a UNESCO cultural monument

Ensemblia
Kulturamt der Stadt Mönchengladbach, Haus Westland,
Hindenburgstr. 201, 41061 **Mönchengladbach**
Tel: 2161-253 955/56 Fax: 2161-253 969
Internet: www.hbz-nrw.de/biblioteck/Moenchengladbach
E-Mail: ensemblia@topmail.de
Kulturamtsleiterin Bärbel Lenz
Period/Frequency: biennial *Arts types:* crosses boarders of various art forms

Mülheimer Theatertage
Kulturbetrieb Mühlheim an der Ruhr, Leineweberstr. 1,
45466 **Mülheim a. d. Ruhr**
Tel: 208-455 4112 Fax: 208-4555 84112
Internet: www.stuecke.de
E-Mail: balzer@stuecke.de
Intendant Udo Balzer-Reher
Period/Frequency: May-June, annual *Arts types:* drama *Venues:* Stadthalle Mühlheim a.d. Ruhr 707 *Comments:* premieres of works by living German-speaking authors; see also Veneus

Art Projekt
International Musikfestival GmbH, Widenmayerstr. 41,
80538 **München**
Tel: 89-290 7490 Fax: 89-2907 4999
Internet: www.art-concerts.de
E-Mail: art@art-concerts.de
managing director Franz Abraham
Period/Frequency: irregular *Arts types:* contemporary music, world, jazz, rock, symphonic, pop

Internationales Figurentheaterfestival
Gesellschaft zur Förderung des Puppenspiels, St. Jakobs Platz 1, 80331 **München**
Tel: 89-2332 4482 Fax: 89-2332 4482
Leiter Christoph Lepschy
Period/Frequency: annual, 2000: July *Arts types:* puppetry/all forms of animated theatre and visual theatre *Venues:* Münchner Stadtmuseum 180, Schauburg am Elisabethplatz 250 *Comments:* international festival for children and adults

Münchner Opern-Festspiele
Bayerische Staatsoper, Postfach 100148, 80075 **München**
Tel: 89-218 501 Fax: 89-2185 1133
Internet: www.bayerische.staatsoper.de
E-Mail: press@st-oper.bayern.de
Staatsintendant Peter Jonas; Geschäftsführender Direktor Dr. Roland Felber; Generalmusikdirektor Zubin Mehta; Operndirektor Gerd Uecker; Ballettdirektor Ivan Liska; Dramaturgie Dr. Hanspeter Krellmann; Pressesprecherin und Leiterin PR Dr. Ulrike Hessler
Period/Frequency: July, annual *Arts types:* opera, ballet, recitals, concerts (orchestra, chamber) *Venues:* Nationaltheater 2101, Cuvilliés Theater 450, Prinzregententheater 1100, Herkulessaal

Munich Biennale
Münchener Biennale
Kulturreferat der Landeshauptstadt München, 80313 **München**
Tel: 89-280 5607 Fax: 89-280 5679
Internet: www.muenchen.de/biennale
E-Mail: 100635.2504@compuserve.com
Veranstaltungsleiter Tilmann Broszat; Künstlerischer Leiter Peter Ruzicka
Period/Frequency: spring, annual *Arts types:* new music-theatre, new music *Venues:* Gasteig, Muffathalle, other venues *Second Address:* Ludwigstr. 8/III, 80539 München

Tanzwerkstatt Europa
Joint Adventures, Emil-Geis-Str. 21, 81379 **München**
Tel: 89-724 2515 Fax: 89-723 7782
Internet: www.tanznetz.de
E-Mail: jointadventures@t-online.de
Gesamtleitung Walter Heun; Administrationsleitung Ingrid Kalka; Presse Sarah Bergh
Period/Frequency: July/Aug, annual *Arts types:* contemporary dance, performances, workshops, lecture demonstrations, dance, videos *Venues:* Muffathalle 400, Neues Theater 100 *Comments:* European co-productions; also present biennial festival Tanzplattform Deutschland (q.v.);

Theaterfestival Spielart München
Ludwig Str. 8, 80539 **München**
Tel: 89-280 5607 Fax: 89-280 5679
Internet: www.spielmotor.de
E-Mail: info@spielmotor.de
contact Tilmann Broszat
Period/Frequency: Nov, biennial (2001) *Arts types:* new forms of theatre, both national and international *Venues:* all over Munich

TollWood Festival
Römerstr. 15, 80801 **München**
Tel: 89-383 850-0 Fax: 89-3838 5020
Internet: www.tollwood.de
E-Mail: info@tollwood.de
administration Mathias Schaettgen; artistic director Rita Rottenwallner; press Dieter Bork
Period/Frequency: 3 weeks in June-July, 4 weeks in Dec., (bi-annual) *Arts types:* music, circus, physical theatre, dance, variety, opera *Venues:* different circus tents up to 3500

6-Tage-Oper – Ein Marathon zugunsten der neuen Kammeroper
c/o Tafelhalle, Äußere Sulzbacher Str. 60, 90491 **Nürnberg**
Tel: 911-231 5297/329 047 (poc) Fax: 911-231 2310
Programmgruppe Dr. Brigitte Weinzierl, Werner Müller, Wulf Konold, Peter Beat Wyrsch, Harnut Henne, Wilfried Krüger, Franz Killer
Period/Frequency: autumn, 2001 *Arts types:* contemporary music, music theatre *Venues:* Tafelhalle, Stadttheater Fürth, Theater Erlangen, Städt. Bühnen Nürnberg, City Center Fürth *Second Address:* Kaiserstraße 177, 90763 Fürth *Comments:* introductory colloquiums are held for world premieres and German first performances, as well as follow-ups with the composers (called nachgehakt);
next festival in June 2000

Internationale Orgelwoche Nürnberg – Musica Sacra (ION)
Bismarckstraße 46, 90491 **Nürnberg**
Tel: 911-231 3528 Fax: 911-231 3510
Internet: www.ion.nuernberg.de
E-Mail: ion@nuernber.de
Geschäftsführer Dr Ekkehard Fellner; Künstlerischer Leiter Prof. Werner Jacob
Period/Frequency: June-July, annual *Arts types:* organ and sacred music *Venues:* Frauenkirche, St. Sebald, St. Lorenz, St. Egidien and other churches in the old town centre of Nürnberg, Meistersingerhalle

Rheingau Musik Festival
Konzertgesellschaft mbH, PO Box 1108, 65367 **Oestrich-Winkel**
Tel: 6723-91770 Fax: 6723-917 719
Internet: www.rheingau-musik-fesitval.de
E-Mail: rmf@rheingau-musik-festival.de
Künstlerischer Leiter u. Geschäftsführer Michael Herrmann; Leiter des künstlerischen Betriebsbüros Andreas Eckel; Veranstaltungsorganisation und -leitung Dana Döring, Martin Maruschka, Hartmut Schröder; Presse-u. Öffentlichkeitsarbeit Andrea Wattendorf
Period/Frequency: June-Aug, annual *Arts types:* music, cabaret, music theatre *Venues:* various venues in Wiesbaden and surrounding area up to 3000 *Second address:* Rheinallee 1, 65375 Oestrich-Winkel

Prisma Internationale Kulturtage
Kulturetage Oldenburg, Bahnhofstr. 11, 26122 **Oldenburg**
Tel: 441-924 8024 Fax: 441-924 8080
Internet: www.uni-oldenburg.de/kulturetage
E-Mail: ketage@uni-oldenburg.de
Künstl Gesamtleitung und Koordination Bernt Wach
Period/Frequency: Nov, biennial (2001) *Arts types:* dance, theatre, literature, film, music *Venues:* Kulturtage, 3 stages, and other venues *Comments:* also takes place in 2000 on a smaller scale; see also Drama and Venues

European Media Art Festival
Lohstr. 45, 49074 **Osnabrück**
Tel: 541-21658 Fax: 541-28327
Internet: www.emaf.de
E-Mail: info@emaf.de
Direktoren Alfred Rotert, Herman Nöring
Period/Frequency: May, annual *Arts types:* experimental film, video installations, interactive art, performances, CD-rom *Venues:* Lagerhalle- Großer Saal 250, Dominikaner Kirche-Kunsthalle 220 *Second Address:* postal address: Postfach 1861, PLZ 49008 Osnabrück *Comments:* the festival is organised by Internationaler Experimentalfilm Workshop e.V.

Paderborner Puppenspielwochen
Kulturamt der Stadt Paderborn, Mühlenstr. 15, 33095 **Paderborn**
Tel: 5251-881 499 Fax: 5251-882 041
Leitung t.b.a.; Organisation Margret Kosfeld
Period/Frequency: Jan-Feb, annual *Arts types:* international puppetry & figures *Venues:* Pader Halle 180, other small venues around Paderborn

Festspiele Europäische Wochen Passau
Dr-Hans-Kapfinger Str. 22, 94032 **Passau**
Tel: 851-560 960 Fax: 851-70994
Internet: www.pnm.de/ew
E-Mail: europaeischefestwochen@t-online.de
artistic director Dr Pankraz Freiherr von Freyberg; assistant Eva Eckert M.A.; public relations Angelika Hötzl
Period/Frequency: June-Aug, annual *Arts types:* opera, oratoria, orchestral and choir music, chamber music, theatre, recitals, film, exhibitions *Venues:* various venues in and around Passau, in Upper Austria, Czech Republic

Sandstein & Musik
Sandstone & Music
Klosterstraße 5a, 01796 **Pirna**
Tel: 3501-446 572 Fax: 3501-446 472
Internet: www.sandstein-musik.de
E-Mail: info@sandstein-musik.de
Chairman of the board Klaus Brähmig, MP; art director Prof. Ludwig Güttler
Period/Frequency: March-Dec, annual *Arts types:* classical music, especially baroque period music *Venues:* several churches, castles and museums in Saxon Switzerland/Saxony

Festival Mitte Europa Bavaria, Bohemia,Saxony
Friedensst.32, 08523 **Plauen**
Tel: 3741-214 302 Fax: 3741-214 301
Internet: www.Festival-Mitte-Europe.com
E-Mail: info-deutsch@festival-mitte-europa.com
Intendant Prof.Thomas Thomaschke; Geschäftsführer Martin Penzel; Konzeption Ivana Thomaschke-Vondrákáva
Period/Frequency: July-Aug, annual *Arts types:* music, theatre, workshop, dance, readings, drama, masterclasses *Second Address:* 2nd office: Schützenstr. 9f, 95028 Hof/Saale; tel: 9281-15502, fax: 9281-15503; 3rd office: Spalícek, nám. Krále Jirího 43, 350 02 Cheb, Czech Republic *Comments:* performances, workshops and exhibitions in 49 cities in Bavaria, Bohemia and Saxony

Musikfestspiele Potsdam Sanssouci GmbH
Wilhelm Staab Str 10-11, 14467 **Potsdam**
Tel: 331-293 866 (infomation)/270 9864 (admin)
Fax: 331-293 859
Internet: www.musikfestspiele.potsdam.de
E-Mail: musikfestspiele@potsdam.de
Geschäftsführer u. Künstlerisches Betriebsbüro Dr Andrea Palent; Künstlerisches Betriebsbüro Anke Derfert; Dramaturgie und Öffentlichkeitsarbeit Dr Christina Siegfried; Verwaltungsleitung Gudrun Mentler
Period/Frequency: June, annual *Arts types:* concerts, opera, dance *Venues:* palaces and gardens of Potsdam Sanssouci – 80 to 900 inside, & 2700 for open-air

Potsdamer Arkadien – Open-air Sommerkulturprogramm der Stadt Potsdam
Stadtverwaltung der Landshauptstadt Potsdam, Kulturamt, Hegelallee 9, 14467 **Potsdam**
Tel: 331-289 1941/942/944 Fax: 331-289 3113
Leiterin Brigitte Faber-Schmidt
Period/Frequency: May-Sept, annual *Arts types:* theatre, music, literature, exhibitions, comedy *Venues:* open-air in Potsdam *Comments:* free admission except Lichterfest (August)

Tête à Tête – International Street Theatre Festival
Stadt Rastatt – Hauptamt, Postfach 1263, 76402 **Rastatt**
Tel: 7222-972 112 Fax: 7222-972 108
Internet: www.rastatt.de
E-Mail: post@rastatt.de
Festivalkonzept und künstl Leitung Charlie Bick; Organisat Leitung Jürgen Pfeifer; Koordination Marion Künster
Period/Frequency: biennial (2000: 30 May-4 June) *Arts types:* street theatre *Venues:* squares & streets in the inner city

Ruhrfestspiele Recklinghausen
Europäisches Festival, Otto-Burrmeister-Allee 1, 45657 **Recklinghausen**
Tel: 2361-9180 Fax: 2361-13141
Internet: www.ruhrfestspiele.de
E-Mail: 101470.2375@compuserve.com
Festspielleiter Hansgünther Heyme; Stellv. Festspielleiter Hans Adalbert Karbe
Period/Frequency: May-June, annual *Arts types:* drama, music, dance *Venues:* Festspielhaus Recklinghausen (Kleine Bühne up to 500, Große Bühne 1023) and other venues in Recklinghausen
Comments: also art exhibitions

Tage alter Musik
Pro Musica Antiqua, Postfach 100903, 93009 **Regensburg**
Tel: 941-83009-48 Fax: 941-83009-39
Internet: db.allmusic.de/live/tage-alter-musik
E-Mail: 100721.2242@compuserve.com
Verwaltungsleitung Ludwig Hartmann, Stephan Schmid; Geschäftsführung Paul Holzgartner
Period/Frequency: annual (2000: 9-18 June) *Arts types:* early music on period instruments, from the middle ages to romantic *Venues:* concerts take place in historical sites throughout Regensburg *Comments:* includes instrument exhibition and talks, over 30 concerts take place over 10 days (including 'night' concerts); in 2000: Tage Alter und Neuer Musik 2000;
see also Publications

Kammeroper Schloss Rheinsberg
Kavalierhaus der Schlossanlage, 16831 **Rheinsberg**
Tel: 33931-38049 Fax: 33931-39707
E-Mail: kammeroper.schloss.rheinsberg@t-online.de
manager Dr Thomas Siedhoff; artistic director Prof. Siegfried Matthus; dramaturg Ilse Winter; press officer Ute Schindler; technical director Peter Seeber
Period/Frequency: July-Aug, annual *Arts types:* opera *Venues:* Schlosstheater, open-air performances in the Schloßpark Rheinsberg *Comments:* offer gifted young singers from around the world the chance to work with experienced professionals

Musik im 20. Jahrhundert
c/o Saarländischer Rundfunk, Funkhaus Halberg, 66100 **Saarbrücken**
Tel: 681-602 2041 Fax: 681-602 2243
director Dr Sabine Tomek
Period/Frequency: May, annual *Arts types:* new music, electro-acoustic music, orchestral music

Musikfestspiele Saarland e.V.
Rotenbühlerweg 28a, 66123 **Saarbrücken**
Tel: 681-397 359/938 6869 Fax: 681-372 310
Intendant & Künstlerischer Leiter Prof. Robert Leonardy
Period/Frequency: biennial (2001) *Arts types:* all types (focuses on a different country each festival) *Venues:* churches and other venues in Saar-Lor-Lux and Rheinland-Pfalz – Lorraine *Second Address:* Musikfestspiele Saarland, Karlsbergstr 74, 66424 Homburg

Perspectives Festival du Théâtre Français et de la Chanson
Passagestr. 2-4, 66111 **Saarbrücken**
Tel: 681-936 490 Fax: 681-32921
Internet: saarbruecken.de/sbnet/perspect.htm
E-Mail: ccaimacan@aol.com
Künstlerischer Leiter Christian Caimacan
Period/Frequency: May, annual *Arts types:* French drama, dance theatre and chanson, street theatre *Venues:* 6 different venues in Saarbrücken, 8000 seats in total

Sommer Szene – Internationale Strassentheatertage
Kultur Direkt e.V., Parkstrasse 8, 66111 **Saarbrücken**
Tel: 681-584 9367 Fax: 681-32803
E-Mail: KULDI@topmail.de
Organisatorische Leitung Marion Künster; Künstlerische Leitung Charlie Bick
Period/Frequency: Aug, annual *Arts types:* street theatre, music *Venues:* streets and squares in Saarbrücken, Völklingen, Dillingen and Illingen *Comments:* emphasis on innovative and international character

Festlicher Sommer in der Wies
Stadt Schongau, Marienplatz 7, 86956 **Schongau**
Tel: 8861-8173 Fax: 8861-200 861
Künstlerische Leitung MD Franz Brannekemper
Period/Frequency: end of June-beg. of Aug, annual *Arts types:* classical concerts

Festival Europäische Kirchenmusik Schwäbisch Gmünd
Stadtverwaltung Kulturbüro Europäische Kirchenmusik, Waisenhausgasse 1-3, 73525 **Schwäbisch Gmünd**
Tel: 7171-603 410 Fax: 7171-603 419
Internet: www.schwaebisch-gmuend.de/kirchenmusik
E-Mail: kulturbuero@schwaebisch-gmuend.de
Programmdirektor Dr Ewald Liska;
Leiter Kulturbüro Muchtar Al Ghusain
Period/Frequency: July-Aug (over 4 weeks), annual *Arts types:* sacred music, concerts, workshops, seminars *Venues:* old churches in Schwäbisch Gmünd and surrounding area *Comments:* also includes competitions for contemporary music and for organ improvisation

Freilichtspiele Schwäbisch Hall
Stadtverwaltung Festival, Am Markt 2,
Postfach 100225, 74523 **Schwäbisch Hall**
Tel: 791-751 418 Fax: 791-751 464
Internet: www.schwaebischhall.de
Intendant und Festspielleitung Achim Plato;
Geschäftsführung Udo Wittenbrock
Period/Frequency: June-Aug, annual *Arts types:* drama, musicals, singspiel, music-theater & theatre for children *Venues:* Große Freitreppe vor St Michael, Kleine Treppe Gelbinger Gasse, Theaterkeller am Hafenmarkt, Theaterscheune im Freilandmuseum Wackershofen *Comments:* in 2000 celebrating 75th anniversary

Internationale Kammermusikwoche im Radio Opera
Bayerische Kammeroper, Wengertspfad 2,
97523 **Schwanfeld**
Tel: 9384-8772 Fax: 9384-8678
Intendant Dr Blagoy Apostolov; GMD Prof Siegried Köhler
Period/Frequency: monthly in the Radio Opera *Arts types:* music, chamber opera, concerts *Venues:* varous in the Würzburg area, München *Comments:* also organise travels to opera festivals & opera houses in Europe, see also Opera (Bayerische Kammeroper)

Festspiele Mecklenburg-Vorpommern
Graf-Schack-Allee 10, 19053 **Schwerin**
Tel: 385-512 391 Fax: 385-512 392
Internet: www.festspiele-mv.de
E-Mail: service@festspiele-mv.de
Programmdirektor Dirk Matthiessen; Geschäftsführer und künstlerischer Leiter Dr Matthias von Hülsen; Pressereferentin Annette Dammann; Leiterin Kommunikation und Marketing Karen Ann Bode
Period/Frequency: June-Sept, annual *Arts types:* chamber, symphony, opera, exhibitions

ECLAT – Festival Neue Musik Stuttgart
c/o Musik der Jahrhunderte, Hasenbergstr. 31/2, 70178 **Stuttgart**
Tel: 711-629 0510 Fax: 711-629 0515
Internet: www.Musik-der-Jahrhunderte.de
E-Mail: mdjstuttgart@csi.com
Direktors KMD Prof Manfred Schreier und Hans Peter Jahn; Geschäftsführung Christine Fischer
Period/Frequency: Feb, annual *Arts types:* contemporary music linked to different art forms *Venues:* Theaterhaus 400, Kammertheater 250

Europäisches Musikfest Stuttgart/ Sommerakademie Johann-Sebastian Bach
Internationale Bachakademie Stuttgart, Johann-Sebastian-Bach-Platz, 70178 **Stuttgart**
Tel: 711-619 210 Fax: 711-619 2123
Internet: www.bachakademie.de
E-Mail: office@bachakademie.de
Geschäftsführung Andreas Keller; Künstlerische Leitung KMD Prof. Dr. h.c. Helmuth Rilling; Planung u. Realisation Dr. Christian Eisert; PR Rita Püpcke
Period/Frequency: Aug-Sept, annual (2000: 27 Aug-10 Sept) *Arts types:* concerts, courses, seminars, lectures etc. *Venues:* Liederhalle, Stuttgart, Hospitalhof, Kirchen *Comments:* theme 2000: Passion

Internationale Festwoche
Figurentheater Stuttgart,
Eberhardstrasse 61 d, 70173 **Stuttgart**
Tel: 711-241 541 (box office)/236 8684(admin.)
Fax: 711-236 0422
E-Mail: figurentheater-stuttgart@t-online.de
Leitung Helmuth Pogerth, Katja Spiess
Period/Frequency: March, annual *Arts types:* puppetry, object theatre, visual theatre *Venues:* Figurentheater 180

Metapher – Festival für Neue Vokalmusik
c/o Musik der Jahrhunderte,
Hasenbergstr. 31/2, 70178 **Stuttgart**
Tel: 711-629 0510 Fax: 711-629 0515
Internet: www.Musik-der-Jahrhunderte.de
E-Mail: mdjstuttgart@csl.com
Geschäftsführung Christine Fischer; Direktoren KMD Prof. Manfred Schreier, Hans Peter Jahn
Period/Frequency: biennial (2001) *Arts types:* contemporary vocal music *Comments:* co-production with SD Rundfunk

Putbus Festival
Rossini Festival GmbH,
Hohenheimer Straße 84, 70184 **Stuttgart**
Tel: 711-640 9357 Fax: 711-640 9774
Internet: putbus-festival.de
E-Mail: putbusfest@aol.com
Intendant Wilhelm Keitel;
Öffentlichkeitsarbeit Beate Neidhart-Keitel
Period/Frequency: Pentecost (3 weeks), annual *Arts types:* opera *Venues:* Theater Putbus 220, Marstall 580 *Second Address:* Alleestr. 14A, 18581 Putbus,
Tel: 38301-61987, Fax: 38301-61994

Schwetzinger Festspiele
Neckarstrasse 230, 70190 **Stuttgart**
Tel: 711-929 3038 Fax: 711-929 3315
Geschäftsführung und Konzertprogramm Peter Stieber; Künstl. Leitung Musik & Sprechtheater
Dr. Klaus-Peter Kehr
Period/Frequency: April-June, annual *Arts types:* opera, drama, concerts, dance, especially rarely performed masterworks *Venues:* Schwetzingen castle, opera held in Rokokotheater, concerts in adjoining galleries, open-air concerts in park *Comments:* composition commissions, workshops, premieres; the festival is held in conjunction with the Süddeutscher Rundfunk

World Festival of Sacred Music
c/o World Festival of Sacred Music e.V. D -Stuttgart, Froschweg 29, 70499 **Stuttgart**
Tel: 711-863 433 Fax: 711-860 1543
Internet: www.worldfestival-sacredmusik.de
E-Mail: worldsacredEurope@compuserve.com
chairman Europe Dr. Roland Haas;
vice president Laurance Nottellet
Period/Frequency: 2000 *Arts types:* sacred music *Venues:* Japan: Tokyo, Hiroshima; South India: Bangalore *Comments:* a global quest for unison; initiated by HH the Dalai Lama as a Millennium Project in 2000; alternative Internet: www.wfsm.org

Freilichtspiele Tecklenburg
Postfach 1143, 49537 **Tecklenburg**
Tel: 5482-220 Fax: 5482-1269
Intendant Radulf Beuleke; Geschäftsführung Fred Banse; Ballettdirektor Annette Fischer
Period/Frequency: May-Sept, annual *Arts types:* operetta, children's theatre, drama, musical *Venues:* Freilichtbühne 2500 *Second Address:* Schloßstr. 7, 49545 Teckleburg *Comments:* see also Opera and Dance

Puppentheatertage
Tandera-Theater, Dorfstrasse 30, 19246 **Testorf**
Tel: 38851-25302 Fax: 38851-25606
contact Dörthe Kiehn
Period/Frequency: Sept, annual *Arts types:* puppetry for children and adults *Venues:* Schloß Reinbek

Musiksommer zwischen Inn und Salzach
Landratsamt Traunstein, 83276 **Traunstein**
Tel: 861-58316
Fax: 861-58526
Geschäftsführerin Elisabeth Stadler;
Vorsitzender Jakob Strobl
Period/Frequency: May-Sept, annual *Arts types:* concerts of church and chamber music *Venues:* churches, abbeys, castles throughout Altötting, Berchtesgadener Land, Mühldorf, Rosenheim and Traunstein

Bürklins Summeropera
Weinkellerei, Gebr. Eckel GmbH, Weinstr. 65,
67157 **Wachenheim**
Tel: 6322-953 322
Fax: 6322-953 330
Internet: www.buerklin-wolf.de
E-Mail: bb@buerklin-wolf.de
Künstlerischer Leiter Christian Kabitz
Period/Frequency: 2001 *Arts types:* opera *Venues:* Englischer Garten des Weingutes (open air)

Dollart-Festival
Organeum Weener, Norderstraße 18, 26826 **Weener**
Tel: 4951-912 203 Fax: 4951-912 205
Internet: www.rheiderland.de/organeum
E-Mail: organeum@t-online.de
aritistic directors Prof. Harald Vogel (Germany), Peter Westerbrink (Netherlands)
Period/Frequency: Aug, biennial (2001) *Arts types:* early music & organ music on historic organs, concerts, lectures, exhibitions *Venues:* mainly churches in the region *Comments:* contact in the Netherlands: B.J.I Stagge, Spinolalaan 37, 9752 NR Haren, Netherlands, Tel: +31 50-534 6735, Fax: +31 50-534 0647

Weilburger Schlosskonzerte e.V. (Internationale Musikfestwochen in der fürstlichen Residenz)
Postfach 1329, 35773 **Weilburg**
Tel: 6471-41042
Fax: 6471-41917
1. Vorsitzender Horst Frey; Festspielleitung Karl Rarichs
Period/Frequency: June-July, annual *Arts types:* chamber, orchestra concerts, renaissance – modern *Venues:* Weilburger Schloß, Schloßkirche 900, Schloßhof 1200, Obere Orangerie 300, Alte Hofstube 240 *Second Address:* venue address: Postfach 1329, 35781 Weilburg

Kunstfest Weimar
c/o Weimar 1999 – Kulturstadt Europas GmbH,
Postfach 1999, 99403 **Weimar**
Tel: 3643-819 981 Fax: 3643-819 919/80
Internet: www.weimar1999.de
E-Mail: 1999@salve.com
Intendant Bernd Kauffmann
Period/Frequency: annual *Arts types:* theatre, dance, exhibitions, concerts, readings, symposia, puppetry *Venues:* Viehauktionshalle 750, Hetzerhalle 200, E-Werk 250-300, Kubus 250-300, Schlosspark Belvedere (open-air) 10000 *Comments:* the future of the festival was not certain at time of going to print; alternative E-mail: salve@weimar1999.de

Tage Neuer Musik in Weimar
Klang Projekte Weimar e.V.,
Paul Schneider str. 26, 99423 **Weimar**
Tel: 3643-53420 Fax: 3643-53420
Künstlerischer Leiter Michael von Hintzenstern
Period/Frequency: last week of Oct, annual *Arts types:* contemporary music *Comments:* music in relation to other artforms: dance, multi-media projects, film etc.; also organise new music concert series 'Neue Wege zur Musik, Wege zur Neuen Musik'

Bergwaldtheater Weißenburg – Festspielsommer der Heiteren Muse
Amt für Kultur und Touristik, Martin-Luther-Platz 3-5, 91780 **Weißenburg i. Bayern**
Tel: 9141-907 123 Fax: 9141-907 121
Internet: www.weissenburg.de
E-Mail: akut@weissenburg.de
Kulturreferentin S. Fucker
Period/Frequency: June-July, annual *Arts types:* operetta, opera, musicals, musical comedy, plays *Venues:* Ludwigshöhe 1191, standing room 500

Wernecker Schloßkonzerte
Kammerorchester Schloß Werneck e.V., Balthasar Neumann Platz 8, 97440 **Werneck**
Tel: 9722-91610 Fax: 9722-916 161
Internet: www.kammerorchester.de
E-Mail: kammerorchester@swin.de
Intendant u. Musikalische Oberleitung Ulf Klausenitzer
Period/Frequency: June-July, annual *Arts types:* music *Venues:* Schloßpark (open air), Schloßkirche 200 to 5000

Wetzlarer Festspiele eV
Domplatz 8, 35578 **Wetzlar**
Tel: 6441-22601 Fax: 6441-27101
Internet: www.wetzlarer-festspiele.de
E-Mail: wetzlarer-festspiele@t-online.de
Geschäftsführer Miguel Marcos Navas; Künstlerischer Leiter Dr. Fritzdieter Gerhards;
Vorsitzender Walter Froneberg
Period/Frequency: July-Aug, annual *Arts types:* concerts, ballet, musicals, drama *Venues:* Rosengarten 1500, Stadthalle 1000, Lottehof 400

Internationale Maifestspiele
Hessisches Staatstheater Wiesbaden,
Postfach 3247, 65022 **Wiesbaden**
Tel: 611-1321 Fax: 611-132 337
Internet: www.staatstheater-wiesbaden.de
Intendant Achim Thorwald
Period/Frequency: May, annual *Arts types:* opera, drama, dance, children and youth theatre *Venues:* Staatstheater (Großes Haus 1000, Kleines Haus 330, Studio 90, VESTI-Bühne 69)

Wiesbadener Puppenspielfestival
Kultur vor Ort, Amt für Soziale Arbeit, Dotzheimstr 97-99, 65197 **Wiesbaden**
Tel: 611-313 519 Fax: 611-313 952
contact Rainer Schmitt, Dieter Brunner, Dietmar Krah, Wolfgang Gunkel
Period/Frequency: Nov, annual *Arts types:* puppetry *Venues:* Kinderhaus Elsässer Platz, Wiesbaden 180

Wittener Tage für Neue Kammermusik
Stadt Witten – Kulturforum,
Bergerstrasse 25, 58452 **Witten**
Tel: 2302-581 2424 Fax: 2302-581 2499
Internet: www.witten.de
Leitung Harry Vogt (WDR); Sachbearbeitung Iris Müller
Period/Frequency: annual (2000: 5-7 May) *Arts types:* contemporary chamber music *Venues:* Saalbau Witten; Theatersaal 791, Festsaal 700 *Second Address:* venue address: Saalbau Witten, Bergerstrasse 25, 58452 Witten

Luisenburg-Festspiele
Jean-Paul-Strasse 5, 95632 **Wunsiedel**
Tel: 9232-99480 Fax: 9232-994 848
Internet: www.wunsiedel.de
E-Mail: willkommen@wunsiedel.de
Intendant Prof Hans Peter Doll; Künstlerisches Betriebsbüro Martha Baumeister-Boettge;
tourist-information Günter Stöhr
Period/Frequency: June-Aug, annual *Arts types:* drama, fairytales, Volksstücke, operetta, opera, tales for children *Venues:* open-air theatre, Luisenburg 2000 *Second Address:* Verkehrs-und Kulturamt Jean-Paul-Str. 5, 95632 Wunsiedel, Tel: 9232-602 162, Fax: 9232-602 169 *Comments:* oldest open-air theatre in Germany

IMPULSE 2000 – Off-Theater aus Deutschland, Österreich, Schweiz
Kultursekretariat NRW,
Friedrich-Engels-Allee 85, 42285 **Wuppertal**
Tel: 202-563 6803 Fax: 202-899 119
Internet: www.nrw-kultursekretariat.de
E-Mail: nrwkultur@aol.com
Geschäftsführer Dr Dietmar N Schmidt;
Verwaltungsleiter & Projektleitung Manfred Springer
Period/Frequency: Nov-Dec, annual *Arts types:* off-theatre *Venues:* various in NRW

Meeting Neuer Tanz NRW
Kultursekretariat NRW,
Friedrich-Engels-Allee 85, 42285 **Wuppertal**
Tel: 202-563 6803 Fax: 202-899 119
Internet: www.nrw-kultursekretariat.de
E-Mail: nrwkultur@aol.com
Geschäftsführer Dr Dietmar N Schmidt;
Verwaltungsleiter Manfred Springer;
Projektleitung Gianni Malfer
Period/Frequency: September, biennial (2001) *Arts types:* new dance *Venues:* various in NRW

Traumspiele – Kinder.Musik.Theater.Festival
Kultursekretariat NRW,
Friedrich-Engels-Allee 85, 42285 **Wuppertal**
Tel: 202-563 6803 Fax: 202-899 119
Internet: www.nrw-kultursekretariat.de
E-Mail: nrwkultur@aol.com
Geschäftsführer Dr. Dietmar N. Schmidt;
Verwaltungsleiter Manfred Springer;
Projektleitung Christine Post
Period/Frequency: biennial (2000: 10-19 March) *Arts types:* musical performances and theatre for children *Venues:* various in NRW

Bachtage Würzburg
c/o Bachchor Würzburg, Hofstallstr. 5, 97070 **Würzburg**
Tel: 931-322 8480 Fax: 931-322 8471
Künstlerischer Leiter Christian Kabitz
Period/Frequency: Nov, annual *Arts types:* chamber music, synthesis of classic and jazz, organ music, concert performance of oratorios *Venues:* St Johannis 1000, Großer Konzertsaal der Hochschule für Musik 800, Toskana-Saal from the residence 200 and other venues *Comments:* see also Choirs

Mozartfest Würzburg
Kulturamt, Rathaüs, 97070 **Würzburg**
Tel: 931-373 336 Fax: 931-373 399
Internet: www.mozartfest.de
E-Mail: kulturamt@wuerzburg.de
Organisation Klaus Heuberger; künstl Leiter Jonathan Seers
Period/Frequency: May-July, annual (2000: 31 May-2 July) *Arts types:* music of Mozart and his contemporaries *Venues:* Kaisersaal & Gartensaal der Residenz, Hofgarten der Residenz, Dom, Stadttheater, Neubaukirche

Tage der Alten Musik
Hochschule für Musik, Hofstallstr. 6-8,
97070 **Würzburg**
Fax: 931-321 8740
Initiator und Organisation Glen Wilson
Period/Frequency: Jan, biennial (2000) (alternate to Tage der Neuer Musik) *Arts types:* early music *Venues:* Großer Saal der Hochschule für Musik Würzburg 800, Kleiner Saal der Hochschule für Musik Würzburg 150

Tage der Neuen Musik
Hochschule für Musik, Hofstallstr. 6-8,
97070 **Würzburg**
Tel: 931-321 870 Fax: 931-321 870
Festspielleiter Prof Dr Klaus Stahmer
Period/Frequency: Jan, biennial (2000) *Arts types:* modern music, visual arts *Venues:* Großer Saal der Hochschule für Musik Würzburg 800, Kleiner Saal der Hochschule für Musik Würzburg 150, art galleries *Comments:* Theme 2000: Contemporary Music

Internationale Fasch – Festtage
c/o Internationale Fasch – Gesellschaft e.V., Wiekhaus, Postfach 1113, 39251 **Zerbst**
Tel: 3923-784 772 Fax: 3923-784 772
Internet: www.islandnet.com/~fasch
E-Mail: ifaschg@t-online.de
Geschäftsführerin Karin Spott (concerts), Susanne Baselt (international scholarly conference)
Period/Frequency: biennial (2001) *Arts types:* baroque music *Venues:* Stadthalle Zerbst mit Fasch-Saal, Coswig, Leitzkau *Second Address:* Stadtverwaltung Zerbst, Schloßfreiheit 19, 39261 Zerbst, Tel: 3923-754 156, Fax: 3923-754 158

GIBRALTAR (+350)

Gibraltar Drama Festival
c/o Ministry of Culture, 310 Main Street, **Gibraltar**
Tel: 41687 Fax: 52589
E-Mail: minculture@gibnynex.gi
minister for education, culture & youth affairs Dr. Bernard Linares; contact, director of culture Manolo Galliano
Period/Frequency: Nov, annual *Arts types:* theatre (one-act plays) *Venues:* Ince's Hall Theatre *Comments:* a week long festival established in 1947

Gibraltar National Week
Ministry of Culture, 310 Main Street, **Gibraltar**
Tel: 41687 Fax: 52589
E-Mail: minculture@gibnynex.gi
director of culture Manolo Galliano
Period/Frequency: Sept, annual *Arts types:* concerts, dance, exhibitions, theatre and annual fair *Comments:* 2 week long event culminates in National Day Parade

Gibraltar Spring Festival
c/o Ministry of Culture, 310 Main Street, **Gibraltar**
Tel: 41687 Fax: 52589
E-Mail: minculture@gibnynex.gi
minister for education, culture & youth affairs Dr. Bernard Linares; contact, director of culture Manolo Galliano
Period/Frequency: May, annual *Arts types:* dance, theatre, music, poetry, exhibitions, choirs

GREECE (+30)

Festival of Ancient Elis
Filikis Etaireias 6, 27200 **Amaliada**
Tel: 622-26030/27312 Fax: 622-25948
artistic director Dimitris Crallis
Period/Frequency: July-August, annual *Arts types:* ancient Greek tragedy, concerts (classical to contemporary music) *Venues:* Ancient Amphitheatre of Elis- drama; Chlemoutsi Castle – music *Comments:* organised by the Municipality of Amaliada in co-operation with Friends of Ancient Elis

Athens Festival
Greek Festival S.A., Voukourestiou 1, 10564 **Athens**
Tel: 1-323 0049/322 5904/3111/1459 (box office)/331 2618 (bookings) Fax: 1-323 5172
general director & president Georges Kouroupos; press officer Maria Panagiotopoulou (tel: 1-327 1129)
Period/Frequency: June-August, annual *Arts types:* drama, opera, dance- ballet, modern, performance art *Venues:* Herod Atticus Odeon (Roman-Hellenistic theatre in central Athens) 4980, Lycabettus (open air theatre on Lycabettus Hill in central Athens) 5000, Ancient theatre of Epidaurus 14000, Pirueus (industrial building in central Athens), Pnika (in hills in central Athens) *Comments:* other events: Epidaurus Festival, ancient Greek drama performances at the ancient theatre of Epidaurus – June-Aug; Sound & Light, illumination spectacle at Pnika nearby the Acropolis of Athens in English, French, German daily, Tel: 1-322 7944/922 6210

Epidaurus Festival
Greek Festival S.A., Voukourestiou 1, 10564 **Athens**
Tel: 1-323 1291/753-22006 (Epidaurus)
Fax: 1-323 5172/753-2208 (Epidaurus)
general director & president Georges Kouroupos; press officer Maria Panagiotopoulou (tel: 1-327 1129)
Period/Frequency: July-Aug, annual
Arts types: classical Greek and Latin drama (tragedy and comedy) *Venues:* Ancient Amphitheatre of Epidaurus 11000 *Comments:* mixed repertory of Greek and foreign productions

Festival Vironas
Festival under the Shadow of the Rocks
Kyprou and Evagelikis Scholis, 16232 **Athens**
Tel: 1-765 5748/766 2555
contact V. Marulianachi
Period/Frequency: Aug-Sept, annual
Arts types: 4 cycles: 1. Ancient Greek Drama, 2. Faces of Greek Singing, 3. Modern Dance, 4. Modern Drama, dramatized folk dance- contemporary music *Venues:* Theatro Vrachon Melina Mercouri & Anna Sinodinou- newly built amphitheatre situated in an old quarry *Comments:* the festival has started producing its own events and aims to be a co-producer in visiting events

Greek Folk Dances Festival
Dora Stratou Theatre, 8 Scholiou Street,
10558 **Athens (Plaka)**
Tel: 1-324 4395/6188
Fax: 1-324 6921
president Prof Alkis Raftis; art director G. Mavropoulos
Period/Frequency: May-Sept, every evening at 22.15 (Wed-Sun 20.15 & 22.15) *Arts types:* Greek folk dance, music, costumes *Venues:* Dora Stratou, Greek Dance Theatre *Second Address:* Philopappou Hill, Acropolis, Athens *Comments:* also organise workshops on traditional and ancient Greek dances; see also Dance

Heraklion Festival
Town Hall, Ag. Titou 1,
71202 **Heraklion (Crete)**
Tel: 81-399 399 (switchboard)
Fax: 81-227 180
Internet: www.heraklion-city.gr
E-Mail: neolaia@heraklion-city.gr
artistic director Giorgos Antonakis
Period/Frequency: July-Sept. annual
Arts types: dance, songs, music, opera *Venues:* Kipotheatro Kazantakis 2000, St Mark's basilica, Theatro M.Hatzidakis 500, medieval castle theatre Kovle 500 *Second address:* Cultural Youth Center, Androgeo 4, 71202 Heraklion, Tel: 81-399 211/2, Fax: 81-229 207 *Comments:* also lectures and seminars

International Puppet Theatre Days – Hydra
Evangelos Christidis, Paralia, 18040 **Hydra**
Tel: 298-53105/52952 Fax: 298-53622
contact Michael Meschke (298-52952),
Evan Christidis 9298-52740)
Period/Frequency: July, annual *Arts types:* puppets, shadow theater, gloves, mime, dance, workshops, lectures *Venues:* open stage, street shows *Second address:* c/o Antigone Parrousi, Patreorchou Loakim 48, Kolonaki, 10675 Athens *Comments:* free admission

Festival of Ioannina – Epirotika
55 Ag. Marinas, PO Box 1289, 45110 **Ioannina**
Tel: 651-20090 Fax: 651-77550
director Maria Stratsani; public relations Maria Vlachou; press officer Charis Kolios
Period/Frequency: July-Sept, annual *Arts types:* drama (classical, modern, contemporary); music (classical, contemporary, jazz), visual arts *Venues:* Cultural Center of the City of Jannina Theatre 700, open-air theatre of the town 3000, ancient amphitheatre of Dodoni 20000, medieval castle 1000

Kalamata International Dance Festival
c/o Kalamata International Dance Centre,
6, Pan. Kessari Street, 24100 **Kalamata**
Tel: 721-83086 Fax: 721-26966
Internet: dikeho.conxiou.gr
E-Mail: dikeho@conxiou.gr
artistic director Victoria Mairahgopoulou; production & communication Yianna Kambouridou; contact person Vassiliki Dadavassili; international contacts organisation, Kalamata Voula Lada
Period/Frequency: July/Aug, annual
Arts types: dance performances, parallel events of music, fine arts, etc *Venues:* Kalamata Castle Amphitheatre, Kalamata Municipal Regional Theatre, Kalamata National Stadium *Comments:* a contemporary dance seminar is organised every year within the framework of the festival

Olympus Festival
Estia Pieridon Mousson, PO Box 36, 60100 **Katerini**
Tel: 351-76041/29681 Fax: 351-76042/20681
contact Mr. Fourirniadis;
artistic director Kostas Kostantinidis
Period/Frequency: July-Sept, annual *Arts types:* music, dance, drama, concerts, exhibitions *Venues:* Ancient Theatre of Dion (open-air) 3000, Castle of Platamon

Festival of Philippi – Thassos – Macedonia
c/o Kavala Municipial Theatre, Kyprou 10, 65403 **Kavala**
Tel: 51-223 504
Fax: 51-220 510/223 504
president Achileas Nikolaidis; PR Eustratrou Teti
Period/Frequency: July-Aug, annual
Arts types: ancient Greek and renaissance drama, modern (up to 19th C.) Greek theatre *Venues:* amphitheatre of Phillipi 4000, Frourio Kavallas (medieval castle above the city port) 1500

International Festival of Patras
Old Municipal Hospital, Korilon 2,
PO Box 1184, 26110 **Patras**
Tel: 61-278 206/730/276 540 Fax: 61-225 948/226 567
president Ev Floratos; organising D. Papahristopoulou, A. Kokovika; artistic director Alexandros Myrat; press Victoria Agelopoulou
Period/Frequency: June-Aug, annual (2000: 24 June-1 Aug) *Arts types:* mainly classical music, jazz, dance and visual arts *Venues:* Archaeo Odeio (ancient open theatre); Theatro Kastrou (medieval castle at Patra Acropolis); Acilleon Cinmema, Old Municipal Hospital, Municipal Library

Festival Piraeus
c/o Municipal Enterprise for Cultural Development, Evripidou 79, 18532 **Piraeus**
Tel: 1-422 0483/4/5 Fax: 1-417 8595
director Liana Malamdreniote;
artistic director Nikos Galanos
Period/Frequency: summer, annual (2000: 20 days in Sept) *Arts types:* classical and modern drama, classical music, contemporary Greek popular music, classical and modern dance, cinema *Venues:* Veakion Theatre

Renaissance Festival of Rethymno
Leof. P. Kountouriotou 84, 74100 **Rethymno (Crete)**
Tel: 831-53311/53583 (festival)/51888 (city hall)
Fax: 831-53583/29879
administration Dimitris Z Arhontakis; artistic director Mayor Vangelis Stephanikis (tel: 831-29697)
Period/Frequency: July-Sept annual *Arts types:* drama, dance, music, visual arts, street theatre, comedy *Venues:* Erophili theatre, Fortezza (16th century Venetian castle) and various historic venues in the old town of Rethymno *Comments:* all events are related to Renaissance art and culture

Festival of Rhodes
Cultural Organisation of the Municipality of Rhodes, Plateia Elefterias 1, 85100 **Rodos**
Tel: 241-33343 Fax: 241-37149/33343
festival director Phillipos Papanicolaou; president Manolis Antonoglou

Period/Frequency: main time of festival July-end of Sept; *Arts types:* drama, dance, mime, puppetry, children's and youth theatre, opera, visual arts, music, literature *Venues:* medieval moat theatre in Rhodes' old city; Knight's Palace Theatre, Rodou (summer); National Theatre, DimotikouTheatre (winter); Rodiaki Epaulis

Dimitria – Thessaloniki
Theofilou 25, 54633 **Thessaloniki**
Tel: 31-228 414/281 068/286 780 Fax: 31-286 519
head of cultural sector N Makrantonakis
Period/Frequency: Sept-Nov, annual *Arts types:* classical-contemporary music, opera, classical- modern drama, ballet, modern dance, literature, cinema, visual arts (painting, sculpture, video, conceptual) *Venues:* Central Scene of the Association for Macedonian Studies; Auditorium-Aristotelian Univ. of Thessaloniki; Theatro Dasous 5000, State Theatre of Northern Greece *Comments:* International Festival of Film in November

Thessaloniki Spring Theatre Festival
Piramatike Skene of Thessaloniki
Amalia Theatre, 71 Amalias Str., 54640 **Thessaloniki**
Tel: 31-821 483 Fax: 31-860 708
general manager Natasha Papadimitriou;
artistic director Nikiforos Papandreou
Period/Frequency: April, annual *Arts types:* drama: experimental, avantgarde schemes, small scale theatre groups, one-man shows *Venues:* Amalia Theatre 240

HUNGARY (+36)

World Music Festival WOMUFE
Fodros 7B, 2040 **Budaörs**
Tel: 23-417 938 Fax: 23-417 007
E-Mail: mandel@mail.datanet.hu
director Robert Mandel
Period/Frequency: June-July, annual (8 concerts) *Art types:* world music *Venues:* Buda Park Stage

Art Festival of Zemplén County
Zempléni Müvészeti Napok
c/o Óbudai Tarsaskor, Kis Korona 7, 1036 **Budapest**
Tel: 1-250 0288/4937 Fax: 1-250 0340/387 8376
E-Mail: gandrasi@c3.hu
director Judit Merenyi
Period/Frequency: Aug, annual *Arts types:* classical music, spoken word, visual arts *Venues:* different venues in cities Sarospatak, Satoraljaujhely, Szerencs

Beethoven Concerts
c/o National Philharmonic Orchestra,
Vörösmarty tér 1, 1051 **Budapest**
Tel: 1-429 1090 Fax: 1-429 1099
director Géza Kovacs
Period/Frequency: June-Aug, annual *Arts types:* compositions for orchestra and concerti by Beethoven
Comments: held at Martonvásár

Budapest Autumn Festival
Budapesti Öszi Fesztivál
Budapesti Fesztiválközpont KHT,
Rákóczi út 65, 1081 **Budapest**
Tel: 1-210 1249/333 2337/210 2792 Fax: 1-210 5609
E-Mail: budfest@elender.hu
director Zsófia Zimányi
Period/Frequency: Oct, annual *Arts types:* contemporary music, dance, theatre, fine arts, film

Budapest Early Music Forum
Budapesti Régi Zenei Fórum
c/o Filharmonia Budapest, Jokai 6, 1066 **Budapest**
Tel: 1-331 2521/302 4961 Fax: 1-302 4962
director Gyorgy Igric
Period/Frequency: May, annual *Arts types:* early music *Venues:* Buda Castle, Budapest

Budapest International Choir Competition
Budapest Nemetközi Kórusverseny
Interkultur Hungaria, Rottenbiller utca 16-22, 1074 **Budapest** VII
Tel: 1-342 9362 Fax: 1-342 9362
E-Mail: basc@mail.matav.hu
director Gábor Hollerung
Period/Frequency: late March (4 days), biennial (2001, 2003) *Arts types:* choral *Comments:* Hungary's most important international choral festival

Budapest Music Week
Budapesti Zenei Hetek
Filharmonia Budapest, Jokai 6, 1066 **Budapest**
Tel: 1-331 2521/302 4961 Fax: 1-302 4962
director Györy Igric
Period/Frequency: Sept-Oct, annual *Arts types:* classical music

Budapest Open Air Festival
Budapesti Nyári Szabadtéri Fesztivál
c/o Szabad Tér Szinház Kht, Open Air Theatre, Varosmajor park 1, 1122 **Budapest**
Tel: 1-355 0175 Fax: 1-356 0998
director Ivan Gal; artistic director Gábor Koltay
Period/Frequency: June-Aug, annual *Arts types:* music, opera, rock-opera, musical, ballet, folklore *Venues:* open-air stages *Comments:* visiting address: Szabad Tér Színház, Városmajor, 1122, Budapest

Budapest Spring Festival
Budapesti Tavaszi Fesztivál
Budapesti Fesztiválközpont KHT,
PO Box 80, 1366 **Budapest**
Tel: 1-333 2337/210 1249/2792 Fax: 1-210 5609
Internet: www.bmc.hu/tavaszi/index2.htm
E-Mail: budfest@elender.hu
director Zsófia Zimányi
Period/Frequency: March, annual *Arts types:* music, dance, theatre, fine arts, film *Comments:* visiting address: Rákóczi út 65, 1081 Budapest

Budapest Summer Festival
Budapesti Nyári Fesztivál
Szabad Tér Színház Közhasznú Társaság,
PO Box 95, 1525 **Budapest**
Tel: 1-375 5922 Fax: 1-356 0998
managing director Gábor Koltay
Period/Frequency: July-Aug, annual *Arts types:* music theatre, ballet, concerts, folkloric arts *Venues:* Margaret Island open-air stage, Buda Park stage, Városmajor open-air stage

Farewell Festival
Budapesti Búcsú
Budapest Festival Centre, Rákóczi út 65, 1081 **Budapest**
Tel: 1-210 2792 Fax: 1-210 5609
E-Mail: budfest@elender.hu
director Zsófia Zimányi
Period/Frequency: last weekend in June, annual *Arts types:* folk, jazz & classical concerts, children's programmes

Ferencváros Summer Festival
Ferencvárosi Nyári Játékok
Ferencvárosi Nyári Játékok Kht,
Török Pál utca 3, 1093 **Budapest**
Tel: 1-218 0193 Fax: 1-218 0207
artistic director Antal Tóth; manager Miklós Kékesi
Period/Frequency: June-July (5 weeks), annual *Arts types:* classical music, opera, ballet, musicals *Venues:* Bakáts Square, Ferencváros

Haydn Festival
c/o Strem Bt, Bimbo 75, 1022 **Budapest**
Tel: 1-326 6152 Fax: 1-326 6152
director Kalman Strem
Period/Frequency: Sept, annual *Arts types:* classical music *Venues:* in city of Fertöd

Hungarian Festival of Theatres
Hungarian Theatre Society, Magyar Színházi Társaság, Városligeti Fasor 38, 1068 **Budapest**
Tel: 1-321 1120 ext. 159 Fax: 1-342 0146
managing director Marta Vajda

Interballett
PO Box 33, 1255 **Budapest**
Tel: 1-201 4407/8779 Fax: 1-201 5128
E-Mail: tforum@mail.c3.hu
managing director Tibor Galambos
Period/Frequency: March (8 days), biennial (2000, 2002) *Arts types:* ballet, folk dance, modern dance, jazz ballet *Comments:* visiting address:
Táncfórum, Corvin tér 8, 1011 Budapest

International Bartók Festival
Nemzetközi Bartók Fesztivál
PO Box 80, 1366 **Budapest**
Tel: 1-266 3108 Fax: 1-317 9910
E-Mail: beata@schanda.zpok.hu
director Beata Schanda
Period/Frequency: July, annual *Arts types:* 20th century music, emphasis on Bartók *Venues:* held at Szombathely *Comments:* visiting address: Interart Festivalcenter, Vörösmarty tér 1, 1051 Budapest, see also Agents & Producers

International Festival of Moving Theatres
IMT Nemzetközi Mozgásszínházi Talákozó
Szkéne Szinház, Müegyetem rakpart 3, 1111 **Budapest** X1
Tel: 1-463 2451/55 Fax: 1-463 2450
E-Mail: jregos@ccmail.bme.hu
director János Regös
Period/Frequency: October, biennial (2001, 2003) *Arts types:* experimental theatre

International Meeting of Moving Theatres
Nemzetközi Mozgasszinházi Talalkozó
Szkéné Theatre, Müegyetem rakpart 3, 1111 **Budapest**
Tel: 1-463 2451 Fax: 1-463 2450
directors János Regös, Pál Regös
Period/Frequency: Oct, annual *Comments:* it presents invited international companies of moving theatre

International Puppet Theatre Festival of the Lower Carpathian Basin
Kárpát Medencei Bábfesztivál
ÁMK Gyermek Szinpad,
Simon Bolivár sétány 4-8, 1214 **Budapest** XXI
Tel: 1-276 6622 Fax: 1-276 2755
director Imre Németh
Period/Frequency: June (3 days), annual
Arts types: puppet theatre

Kecskemét International Music Festival
Kecskeméti Nemzetközi Fesztivál
PO Box 80, 1366 **Budapest**
Tel: 1-266 3108 Fax: 1-317 9910
director Beata Schanda
Period/Frequency: July-Aug, biennial (2001) *Comments:* includes: Zoltán Kodály International Music Seminar; in cooperation with Kódaly Institute (Kéttemplom köz, 6000 Kecskemét) and Jeunesses Musicales de Hongrie; visiting address: Interart Festivalcenter, Vörösmarty tér 1

Kolbiri International Festival of Street Puppeteers
Kolibri Nemzetközi Utcai Bábjátékos Fesztivál
Jókai tér 10, 1061 **Budapest**
director János Novák
Period/Frequency: August, annual *Arts types:* puppetry, youth theatre, concerts

Mini Festival
Mini Fesztivál
c/o Magyar Zenemüvészeti Társaság (Hungarian Music Society), Bertalan 15, 1111 **Budapest**
Tel: 1-466 0543 Fax: 1-466 0543
president Janos Devich; secretary Eszter Judik
Period/Frequency: Jan, annual *Arts types:* new music

Music of our Age – contemporary music festival
Korunk Zenéje – Kortárs Zenei Fesztivál
Filharmonia Budapest, Jokai 6, 1066 **Budapest**
Tel: 1-331 2521/302 4961 Fax: 1-302 4962
director Gyorgy Igric
Period/Frequency: Oct, annual *Arts types:* contemporary music

National Theatre Encounter
Országos Szinházi Találkozó
Magyar Szinházmüvészeti Szövetség,
Városligeti fasor 38, 1068 **Budapest**
Tel: 1-342 0146 Fax: 1-342 0146
general secretary Marta Vajda
Period/Frequency: May-June, annual

Opera Viva Festival
Úri u. 40, 1014 **Budapest**
Tel: 1-356 0314 Fax: 1-356 0314
director & artistic advisor András Kürthy
Period/Frequency: June-July, annual
Arts types: opera, music theatre

Régi Zenei Napok, Sopron
Sopron Early Music Days
c/o Interart Festival Center,
Vörösmarty tér 1, 1051 **Budapest**
Tel: 1-266 3108 Fax: 1-317 9910
director Beata Schanda
Arts types: early music

Sopron Festival
Soproni Ünnepi Hetek
PO Box 80, 1366 **Budapest**
Tel: 1-266 3108 Fax: 1-317 9910
Internet: www.syneco.hu/kultura/sub
director Beata Schanda
Period/Frequency: June, annual *Arts types:* authentic interpretation of Baroque and early classical music, concerts, symposia, courses *Second Address:* Széchenyi ter 17-18, 9400 Sopron, Tel/Fax: 99-338 673; Pro Cultura Sopron, Liszt 1, 9400 Sopron, Tel/Fax: 99-511 700
Comments: visiting address: Interart Festivalcenter

Standard Festival
Mérték Fesztivál
c/o Budapest Chamber Opera,
Asbóth u. 24, 1075 **Budapest**
Tel: 1-375 8011 Fax: 1-356 4085
contact György Selmeczy
Period/Frequency: annual
Arts types: chamber opera and drama

Summer Opera and Ballet Festival
Budafest
Magyar Állami Operaház, Andrassy 22, 1061 **Budapest**
director Teodora Ban
Period/Frequency: Aug, annual *Comments:* visiting address: VIP Arts Management, Hajos 13-15, 1061 Budapest, Tel/Fax: 1-332 4816

SZÜNETJEL International Improvised Music Festival
c/o 4 ARTS/Beatrice Rossi, Eröd u. 20, 1027 **Budapest**
Tel: 1-201 6430 Fax: 1-201 6430
artistic directors/coordinators Albert Márkos, Gábor Tóth; managing director Beatrice Rossi
Period/Frequency: Dec, annual *Arts types:* improvised, noise, contemporary music *Venues:* MU Theatre Budapest, KAS Theatre Sopron, MASZK Szeged *Second address:* c/o Albert Markos, Brody S.U. 23A/III/15, 1088 Budapest; Tel-Fax: 1-338 3440

Bela Bartok International Choral Festival
Kolcsey Cultural Centre, Hunyadi 1-3, 4026 **Debrecen**
Tel: 52-326 288 Fax: 52-416 040
Internet: www.hbmo.hu/WEB1/MUVHAZ/muvhaz1.htm
E-Mail: kolcsey@c3.hu
director Andras Lukovics
Period/Frequency: biennial (2000: June/July)
Arts types: contemporary

Debrecen Spring Festival
Debreceni Tavaszi Fesztivál
Kölcsey Ferenc Megyei Városi Müvelödési Központ, Hunyadi János utca 1-3, 4026 **Debrecen**
Tel: 52-419 812/30-548 354 (mobile) Fax: 52-416 040
Internet: www.hbmo.hu/WEB1/MUVHAZ/muvhaz1.htm
E-Mail: kolcsey@c3.hu
manager Béla Szabó
Period/Frequency: late March (2 weeks), annual *Arts types:* classical music, ballet, folk dance, art, literature, opera, theatre *Venues:* 14 different venues,e.g : Bartók Hall, Kölcsey Cultural Centre, Academy of Music *Comments:* concurrent with Budapest Spring Festival

Györ Spring Festival
Györi Tavaszi Fesztivál
Györ Város Polgármesteri Hivatal, Városház tér 1, 9021 **Györ**
Tel: 96-442 020/500 241 Fax: 96-442 606/500 285
E-Mail: kultir@mail.gyor-ph.hu
manager Éva Nándorné Toth
Period/Frequency: late March (2 weeks), annual *Arts types:* chamber music, ballet *Venues:* National Theatre, Town Hall, Zichy Palace, Györ *Comments:* concurrent with Budapest Spring Festival

Györ Summer
Györi Nyár
International Cultural Festival, Árpád u. 44, 9022 **Györ**
Tel: 96-442 020/500 241 Fax: 96-500 285
director Nandorne Toth (city counsel)
Period/Frequency: annual

International Summer Cultural Festival, Györ
Györi Nyár Nemzetközi Kulturális Fesztivál
Györ Város Polgármesteri Hivatal, Városház tér 1, 9021 **Györ**
Tel: 96-442 020/500 241 Fax: 96-442 606/500 285
E-Mail: kultir@mail.gyor-ph.hu
manager Éva Nándorné Tóth
Period/Frequency: June-July, annual *Arts types:* ballet, folk dance, folk music, jazz & classical concerts, theatre, exhibitions, arts & craft fair, puppetry, street theatre *Venues:* 3 main venues: Embankment of the Rába River, Yard of the Xantus Museum, Széchenyi square

Iron Rooster International Puppet Festival, Ài Györ
Vaskakas Nemzetközi Bábfeszitvál
Aradi vértanúk útja 23, 9021 **Györ**
Tel: 96-320 316 Fax: 96-320 316
Internet: www.c3.hu/~vaskakas
E-Mail: vaskakas@mail.c3.hu
director Rozi Kocsis
Period/Frequency: June, annual *Arts types:* puppetry

Castle Theatre Gyula
Gyulai Várszinház
PO Box 30, 5700 **Gyula**
Tel: 66-463 148 Fax: 66-463 148
director József Gedeon; artistic adviser Imre Csiszár
Period/Frequency: July-Aug, annual *Arts types:* drama *Comments:* visiting address: Kossuth u. 13. 5700 Gyula

Kecskemét Spring Festival
Kecskeméti Tavaszi Fesztivál
PO Box 79, 6001 **Kecskemét**
Tel: 76-484 594 Fax: 76-328 522
E-Mail: efmk@c3.hu
contact Zsuzsanna Mészáros
Period/Frequency: late March (2 weeks), annual *Arts types:* concerts, theatre, dance, puppet theatre, ragtime, jazz *Venues:* Erdei Cultural Centre, Kodály Primary School of Music, Katona József Theatre, Kecskemét *Comments:* visiting address: Erdei Ferenc Megyei Müvelödési Központ, Deák 1 tér 1, 6001 Kecskemét

Hungarian Theatres Abroad, Kisvárda
Hataron túli Magyar Szinházak Fesztiválja, Kisvárda Fesztivál Iroda, Flórián tér 20, 4600 **Kisvárda**
Tel: 45-405 239 Fax: 45-405 238
director Béla Nyakó
Period/Frequency: June, annual

International Puppet Theatre Festival for Adults
Pécsi Nemzetközi Felnött Bábfesztivál
Mária u. 18, 7621 **Pécs**
Tel: 72-210 301/211 791
organizing committee Gábor Sramó
Arts types: puppetry

Pécs International Music Festival
Pécsi Nemzetközi Zenei fesztivál
Kiraly 19, 7621 **Pécs**
Tel: 72-324 350/242 793 Fax: 72-324 350
director Peter Szkladanyi
Period/Frequency: July-Aug, annual *Arts types:* classical music

Pécs Summer Theatre
Pécsi Nyári Színház
PO Box 289, 7621 **Pécs**
Tel: 72-410 834
director László Bagossy
Period/Frequency: June-Aug, annual *Arts types:* theatre, dance, classical music, puppets *Comments:* visiting address: Perczel u. 1, 7621 Pécs

Szeged Open Air Theatre
Szegedi Szabadtéri Játékok
Déak Ferenc 28, 6720 **Szeged**
Tel: 62-471 411/466 Fax: 62-471 322
director Karoly Korognai
Period/Frequency: July-Aug, annual
Arts types: opera, drama, musical *Venues:* home 3500

THEALTER Festival / International Meeting of Free Theatre
MASZK Association/Center for Hungarian Alternative Theatres, PO Box 905, 6701 **Szeged**
Tel: 62-312 303 Fax: 62-312 303
art dir József Balog; managing director Zsolt Fábian
Period/Frequency: July/Aug, annual *Arts types:* contemporary theatre, dance and movement theatre, street theatre, music (jazz, contemporary), exhibition, films

Szolnok Music Festival
Szolnoki Zenei Fesztivál
PO Box 222, 5001 **Szolnok**
Tel: 56-424 262/565 Fax: 56-424 262
director Lajos Vass
Period/Frequency: March-May, annual *Arts types:* orchestral, choral *Comments:* visiting address: Ars-in-Kom Müvészeti és Kommunikációs Kft, Kossuth Lajos tér 7, 5000 Szolnok

Müvészetek Völgye Valley of the Arts
Kossuth u. 39, 8295 **Taliándörögd**
Tel: 87-437 029/82-437 400 Fax: 82-437 029/87-437 039
artistic advisers Isván Márta, Balázs Golkó
Period/Frequency: July, annual *Arts types:* theatre, music, dance, children's programmes *Comments:* also excursions to the forest by bicycle, jeep or on horseback; the programme offers varied entertainment for the whole family, gives the opportunity to sample almost all the branches of the arts; every day the programmes last from early afternoon to dawn; second address: Kossuth u. 62, 8295 Kapolcs

ICELAND (+354)

Festival of Sacred Arts
Akureyrarkirkja, Postbox 442, 602 **Akureyri**
Tel: 462 7700 Fax: 461 2472
E-Mail: akirkja@nett.is
artistic director Björn Steinar Sólbergsson
Period/Frequency: April-May, biennial (2001) *Arts types:* emphasize the creation of new sacred art – especially church music, theatre and visual arts *Venues:* Akureyri Church

Summer Concerts in Akureyri Church
Akureyrarkirkja, PO Box 442, 602 **Akureyri**
Tel: 462 7700 Fax: 461 2472
E-Mail: akirkja@nett.is
manager Hrefna Hardardóttir;
artistic director Björn Steinar Sólbergsson
Period/Frequency: July-Aug, annual *Arts types:* classical contemporary music *Venues:* Akureyri Church 400
Comments: free perfs, Icelandic & international musicians

Skálholt Music Festival
Strönd, 225 **Bessastadahreppi**
Tel: 565 0859 Fax: 565 2985
E-Mail: sumartonleikar@kirkjan.is
director Mrs Helga Ingólfsdóttir
Period/Frequency: July-Aug, annual
Arts types: baroque music, 20th century sacred music

Dark Music Days
Myrkir Musikdagar
Society of Icelandic Composers, Laufásvegur 40, 101 **Reykjavík**
Tel: 552 4972 Fax: 562 6273
E-Mail: tonskald@centrum.is
president, director Kjartan Olafsson
Period/Frequency: Feb, biennial (2001)
Arts types: contemporary music

Festival of Sacred Arts
Kirkjulistahátíd
PO Box 651, 121 **Reykjavík**
Tel: 510 1000 Fax: 510 1010
Internet: www.hallgrimskirkja.is
E-Mail: kirkjulist@simnet.is
artistic director Hördur Askelsson
Period/Frequency: May-June, biennial (2001) *Arts types:* all types of sacred arts – in particular music – from all periods *Venues:* Hallgrímskirkja *Second Address:* Hallgrímskirkja, Skólavörduholt, Reykjavík *Comments:* chief instigator: Hallgrímskirkja Friends of the Arts Society; the Society also arranges concerts and other activities in Hallgrímskirkja during the ecclesiastical year; the activities often centre around the concert organ in Hallgrímskirkja

Northern Lights – Mordurljos
c/o Snorri Örn Snorrason, Mjóstraeti 10, 101 **Reykjavík**
Tel: 551 0033 Fax: 551 0033
contact Snorri Örn Snorrason
Period/Frequency: Oct-Nov, annual *Arts types:* early music *Venues:* various churches in Reykjavik
Comments: organised by Musica Antiqua; see also Promoters and Early Music

Rejkjavík 2000 – European City of Culture
c/o Thorunn Sigurdardottir, Athalstraeti 6, 101 **Reykjavík**
Tel: 575 2000 Fax: 575 2099
contact Thorunn Sigurdardottir;
communications officer Mrs Konradsdottir
Period/Frequency: throughout the year 2000 *Arts types:* performing and visual arts *Comments:* Reykjavík is one of the 9 European Cities of Culture in the year 2000

Reykjavik Arts Festival
Listahátíd i Reykjavík
PO Box 88, 121 **Reykjavík**
Tel: 561 2444 Fax: 562 2350
Internet: www.artfest.is
E-Mail: artfest@artfest.is
executive dir Marpa Björnsdòttir; art dir Sveinn Einarsson
Period/Frequency: May-June, biennial (2000) *Arts types:* visual, literature, theatre, dance, ballet, opera and all music from classical to pop *Venues:* various places in Reykjavík (Museums, Galleries, Theatres, etc.)
Comments: Iceland's largest festival, sponsored by City and State

Summer evening at the organ
Sumarkvöld viö orgellö
Pósthólf 651, 121 **Reykjavík**
Tel: 510 1000 Fax: 510 1010
Internet: www.hallgrimskirkja.is
E-Mail: kirkjulist@simnet.is
manager Eria Elín Hansdóttir
Period/Frequency: July and August *Second Address:* Hallgrímskirkja, Skólavöröuholt, Reykjavik
Comments: entrance free and free short lunch concerts Thursdays and Saturdays

IRELAND Republic of (+353)

West Cork Chamber Music Festival
1 Bridge Street, **Bantry (Co Cork)**
Tel: 27-52789/88 (bookings) Fax: 27-52797
Internet: www.vanbrughquartet.ie
E-Mail: westcorkmusic@eircom.net
festival director Francis Humphrys; artistic director Christopher Marwood; administrator Roisin McGuigan
Period/Frequency: June, annual (2000: June 24-July 2)
Arts types: chamber music *Venues:* Bantry House 254
Comments: young musicians masterclasses and related fringe performances

Music Festival at Great Irish Houses
First Floor, Black Rock Post Office, **Black Rock (Co Dublin)**
Tel: 1-278 1528/2506 (bookings) Fax: 1-278 1529
administrator Crawford Tipping;
artistic director Judith Woodworth
Period/Frequency: June, annual *Arts types:* chamber music, recitals *Venues:* capacity 100 to 400
Comments: closed until April 2000

Cork International Choral Festival
PO Box 68, **Cork**
Tel: 21-308 308 Fax: 21-308 309
Internet: www.musweb.com/CorkChoral.htm
E-Mail: chorfest@iol.ie
director John Fitzpatrick
Period/Frequency: spring, annual *Arts types:* choral, incorporating gala concerts, competitions, seminar on contemporary choral music, lunchtime concerts,church performances, programme of fringe events
Venues: City Hall 1200, Aula Maxima UCC 300, city churches, public areas

An tOireachtas
6 Harcourt Street, **Dublin** 2
Tel: 1-475 3857/478 1947 Fax: 1-475 8767
E-Mail: oireacht@indigo.ie
director Liam O' Maolaodha; executive officer Catrióṅna Breathnach; chairperson Stìofan O'Morian
Period/Frequency: Oct, annual *Arts types:* traditional Irish culture: music, storytelling in Irish, Céilt dancing, Irish songs, folk music, choirs, debates, art exhibition
Venues: capacity 500 to 600

Dublin International Organ and Choral Festival
Festival Office, Liffey House, Tara Street, **Dublin** 2
Tel: 1-677 3066 ext 416 Fax: 1-672 7279
Internet: www.iol.ie/~orga1/diocf
E-Mail: organs@diocf.iol.ie
artistic director Prof Gerard Gillen
Period/Frequency: June, triennial (2002) *Arts types:* organ, choral *Venues:* Christ Church Cathedral 500, St Patricks Cathedral 1000, National Concert Hall 1200
Comments: in off years, organise concerts of festival winners, during the festival there is also an organ competition

Dublin Theatre Festival
47 Nassau Street, **Dublin** 2
Tel: 1-677 8439/8122 Fax: 1-679 7709
Internet: www.iftn.ie/dublinfestival
E-Mail: dubfest@iol.ie
director Fergus Linehan
Period/Frequency: Oct for two weeks, annual *Arts types:* drama *Venues:* Dublin theatres: capacity 200 to 1200

Guinness Cork Jazz Festival
Guinness Ireland Group, St James's Gate, **Dublin** 8
Tel: 1-453 3645 ext 4015 Fax: 1-454 4253
Internet: www.guinness.com
E-Mail: jean.doyle@guinness.com
festival director Brian Brown; festival manager Philip Mangan; media relations Jean Doyle
Period/Frequency: Oct, annual *Arts types:* jazz, blues, funk *Venues:* throughout Cork City *Comments:* major sponsored event by The Guinness Ireland Group; in depth brochure with festival details/accommodation available from mid-Sept

Dun Laoghaire Festival
1 Northumberland Ave, **Dun Laoghaire**
Tel: 1-284 1864 Fax: 1-230 1656
Internet: www.dun.laoghaire.com
contact Breasal O'Caollai
Period/Frequency: June-July, annual *Arts types:* music, choral, folk dance, bands, emphasis on children's events, street music, circus acts, fireworks, carnival, Harbour Day *Venues:* various venues around Dun Laoghaire, indoor and outdoor *Comments:* main event on 4th July, dedicated to American culture

Baboró International Children's Festival
The Black Box, Dyke Road, **Galway**
Tel: 91-562 594 Fax: 91-562 642
Internet: www.iol.ie/baboro
E-Mail: gaf@iol.ie
executive director Jean Parkinson;
education & development officer Niamh Walsh
Period/Frequency: October, annual *Arts types:* all types *Venues:* varous *Comments:* Baboro programmes children's events for the Galway Arts Festival in July each year

Galway Arts Festival
Black Box Theatre, Dyke Road, **Galway**
Tel: 91-509 700 Fax: 91-562 655
Internet: www.failte.com/gaf/
E-Mail: gaf@iol.ie
director Ted Turton; manager Fergal McGrath
Period/Frequency: July, annual *Arts types:* theatre, popular music, classical music, film, readings, street spectacles, children's events *Venues:* capacity up to 1500 *Comments:* largest general arts festival in Eire

Kilkenny Arts Festival
92 High Street, **Kilkenny**
Tel: 56-63663 Fax: 56-51704
Internet: www.kilkennyarts.ie
E-Mail: kaw@iol.ie
administrator Maureen Kennelly
Period/Frequency: Aug, annual (2000: 11-20 Aug) *Arts types:* classical music, visual art, theatre, jazz, film, community arts *Venues:* St Canice's Cathedral 800, Kilkenny Castle 500, St John's C of I 150, St Mary's Cathedral 800, Watergate Theatre 300, Hibernan Hotel 100, New Park Hotel 300 *Second Address:* Grennan Mill, Thomastown

International Music Festival Killaloe (Co. Clare)
c/o Irish Chamber Orchestra, Foundation Building, University of Limerick, **Limerick**
Tel: 61-202 620 Fax: 61-202 617
E-Mail: ico@ul.ie
artistic director Fionnuala Hunt
Period/Frequency: July, annual *Arts types:* chamber music *Venues:* St Flannan's Catherdral *Comments:* see also Orchestras

Fleadh Cheoil Na h Eireann
32 Belgrave Square, **Monkstown (Co Dublin)**
Tel: 1-280 0295 Fax: 1-280 3759
Internet: www.comhaltas.com
E-Mail: enquiries@comhaltas.com
director general Labhras O'Murchu
Period/Frequency: Aug, annual *Arts types:* traditional Irish music, solo and unaccompanied singing, country and set dancing *Venues:* different town each year *Comments:* largest festival of traditional Irish music, song and dance

Fleadh Nua
Comhaltas Ceoltóiri Éireann, Belgrave Square, **Monkstown (Co Dublin)**
Tel: 1-652 4293/086-826 0300 (mobile) Fax: 1-280 3759
Internet: www.comhaltas.com
contact Frank Wheelan
Period/Frequency: Bank Holiday weekend in May, annual (2000: 25-29 May) *Arts types:* Irish traditional music, song, dance, folklore *Second Address:* festival address: Cois Nahabhna, Ennis, Co. Clare

International Puppet Festival Ireland
Clifton Lane, **Monkstown (Co Dublin)**
Tel: 1-280 0974/1863
Fax: 1-280 4772
E-Mail: puppet@iol.ie
director Eugene Lambert;
administrator Miriam Lambert
Period/Frequency: Sept, annual *Arts types:* puppetry *Venues:* regularly at Lambert Puppet Theatre 300 (q.v.) , and various others *Comments:* see also Puppetry

Sligo Arts Festival
The Model Arts Centre, The Mall, **Sligo**
Tel: 71-69802 Fax: 71-69802
administrator Danny Karrane
Period/Frequency: May-June, annual *Arts types:* all musics, theatre, comedy, children's shows, workshops, exhibitions, literature, street spectacles, fireworks, pub fringe *Venues:* St John's Cathedral 450, Hawkswell Theatre 280, Lagoon 300, The Factory Theatre 200, Model Arts Centre 20 to 150, Sligo Art Gallery 50, Festival Club 150, Hawkswele Theatre 350 *Comments:* also includes community arts projects

Waterford International Festival of Light Opera
60 Morrisons Avenue, **Waterford**
Tel: 51-375 437
general secretary Sean Dower; chairman Patrick Giles; vice chairman Colr Maurice Cummins; house manager Jack O'Donoghue; reception & transport manager Tom Murphy; PR officer Noel Grant; musical director Kevin Kavanagh; stage director Tony O'Regan
Period/Frequency: Sept-Oct, annual
Arts types: all types of musicals and light opera *Venues:* Theatre Royal 619 *Second Address:* Theatre Royal, The Mall, Waterford, Ireland *Comments:* competitive festival for amateur musical & operatic societies; entries come from Ireland, England, Scotland, Wales, France, Belgium, Switzerland & USA

Wexford Festival Opera
Theatre Royal, High Street, **Wexford**
Tel: 53-22400/22144 (box office)
Fax: 53-24289/47438 (box office)
Internet: www.wexfordopera.com
E-Mail: info@wexopera.iol.ie
chief executive Jerome Hynes;
artistic director Luigi Ferrari
Period/Frequency: Oct-Nov, annual *Arts types:* opera, chamber music, recitals, choral *Venues:* Theatre Royal 550 *Comments:* see also Opera

ITALY (+39)

Festival della Rotonda
c/o Comune di Albano Laziale, Piazza della Costit uente 1, 00041 **Albano Laziale**
Tel: 06-932 951/9329 5265
Fax: 06-9329 5281
Internet: www.municipium.com/comuni/albano_laziale
E-Mail: possenti@tiscalinet.it
artistic director Francesco Mario Possenti
Period/Frequency: beg. July to 1st Sunday of Aug *Arts types:* early music, sacred choral music of the XX century, ethnic music *Venues:* open air theatre *Comments:* organisers: Comune di Albano Laziale, Diocesi di Albano and Universitá Degli Studi di Roma Tor Vergata

Linea di Confine
c/o Teatro del Canguro,
Via Trionfi, 4, 60127 **Ancona**
Tel: 071-82805 Fax: 071-82805
Internet: www.fastnet.it/culture/teatro/canguro
E-Mail: teatro.canguro@fastnet.it
directtore amministrativo Corrado Manzoni; direttore artistico Lino Terra;
direttore tecnico-organizzativo Cinzia Moreschi
Period/Frequency: autumn, annual *Arts types:* all kinds of theatre *Venues:* Teatro Sperimentale 450, Teatro Panettone 450 *Comments:* festival to promote various types of theatrical activities aimed at young adults; see also Drama

Teatri Antichi Uniti
C.so Mazzini 148, 60121 **Ancona**
Tel: 071-207 5880/326 Fax: 071-54813
Internet: www.amat.marche.it
E-Mail: info@amat.marche.it
contact Prof. Aldo Amati (president of Amat Association/Municipio di Urbisaglia, Falerone AP)
Period/Frequency: July/Aug, annual *Arts types:* drama *Venues:* Anfiteatro Romano di Urbisaglia 1000, Teatro Romano di Falerone 450 *Second Address:* Municipio di Urbisaglia, Corso Giannelli, 62010 Urbisaglia (MC), Tel: 0733-50124, Fax: 0733-50367 *Comments:* the festival is organised by the Amat Association, the Comune di Urbisaglia, Comune di Falerone AP and Regione Marche

Festival Internazionale di Asolo – Incontri di Musica da Camera
c/o Asolo Musica, Via Browning 141, 31011 **Asolo**
Tel: 0423-950 150
Fax: 0423-529 890
presidente Dr Battista Parolin; vice presidente Ing. Carlo Torato; direttore artistico Mffl Federico Pupo; produzione Anna Lydia Dalla Rosa; amministrazione Maria Rosa Florian; segreteria artistica Gianfranco Spigolon Meneguzzo, Claudio Sartorato
Period/Frequency: Aug-Sept, annual
Arts types: chamber music *Venues:* Chiesa di San Gottardo, Teatro Eleonora Duse, churches, theatres, auditoriums, squares, etc. *Comments:* also master-classes; concerts, musical performances, etc. throughout the year

Asti Teatro
Via Al Teatro, Piazza Roma, 14100 **Asti**
Tel: 0141-399 341/342 Fax: 0141-355 723
Internet: www.comune.asti.it
E-Mail: asti.teatro@comune.asti.it
direzione e organizzazione generale Teatro Comunale Alfieri di Asti
Period/Frequency: June-July, annual *Arts types:* contemporary theatre, music, dance *Venues:* Sala Pastrone 150, Cortile del Palazzo del Collegio 700

Balletto Oggi
c/o Camerata Musicale Barese,
Via Sparano 141, 70121 **Bari**
Tel: 080-521 1908 Fax: 080-523 7154
presidente On. le Avv. Nicola Vernoła; vice-presidente On.le Prof Rosario Polizzi; direttore artistico Giovanni Antonioni; direttore organizzativo Dr Rocco De Venuto; ufficio stampa Dr Gustavo Delgado
Period/Frequency: Oct-July, annual *Arts types:* dance, ballet *Venues:* Teatro Piccinni 600, Teatro Team 2200, Nuovo Palazzo 750, Villa Romanazzi Carducci 450, Arena della Vittoria 4500 *Comments:* national, international guests

Mask and the Shadow, The
La Maschera e l'Ombra
Arena della Vittoria 4A, 70123 **Bari**
Tel: 080-521 9974/534 4660 Fax: 080-572 0658
Internet: www.aziendeonline.it/casadipuleinella/
E-Mail: casadipulcinella@mail.clio.it
amministrazione Maria Laterza;
direzione artistica Paolo Comentale;
ufficio stampa Emilia Brunetti, Patrizia Fatuzzo
Period/Frequency: Oct-April, annual *Arts types:* puppetry, children's and youth theatre, drama *Venues:* Teatro casa di Pulcinella 120 *Second Address:* Via Crisanzio 5, Bari 70122 *Comments:* overview of Italian puppetry; see also Venues and Puppetry

Time Zones
Via Abbrescia N.97, 70100 **Bari**
Tel: 080-558 1587 Fax: 080-558 1564
Internet: www.pangeanet.it/timezones
E-Mail: timezones@pangeanet.it
presidente onorario Ennio Morricone;
direttore artistico Gianluigi Trevisi
Period/Frequency: Sept/Oct *Arts types:* contemporary music, avantgarde *Venues:* various spaces depending on nature of event *Comments:* see Agents & Producers

Voci dell' Anima – Il Mediterraneo Tra Musica e Spiritualita, Le
c/o Princigalli Produzioni,
Lungomare Nazzario Sauro 13, 70121 **Bari**
Tel: 080-553 6542
Fax: 080-553 6542
E-Mail: princigalli@pangeanet.it
artistic director Antonio Princigalli;
organiser Gerardo Traetta;
press office Marcella Chiummo
Period/Frequency: annual *Arts types:* world/ethnic music *Venues:* old churches of the region

Festival di Batignano
Santa Croce, 58041 **Batignano (GR)**
Tel: 0564-338 096 Fax: 0564-338 085
direttore artistico Adam Pollock
Period/Frequency: July-Aug, annual *Arts types:* opera, early-contemporary music *Venues:* in the properties of Convento S Croce (Chiostro, old church ruins, Uliveto etc.) *Comments:* 2 new productions annually

Benevento Citta' Spettacolo
c/o Comune di Benevento,
Ufficio Cultura, 82100 **Benevento**
Tel: 0824-54305/21848 (theatre)
Fax: 0824-47774 (gen. segr.)
direttore artistico Maurizio Costanzo
Period/Frequency: Sept, annual
Arts types: drama, music, cinema *Venues:* theatres and historical settings in Benevento

Incontri Europei con la Musica
Via Borgo Palazzo 31, 24125 **Bergamo**
Tel: 035-242 287 Fax: 035-242 287
E-Mail: mabg@unibg.it
direttore artistico Pieralberto Cattaneo, Vittorio Fellegara
Period/Frequency: Jan-April, annual *Arts types:* classical, contemporary music *Venues:* Sala Piatti 300, Teatro Donizetti 1200, Teatro del Borgo 400 *Comments:* see also Promoters (Associazione Musica Aperta)

Angelica-Festival Internazionale di Musica
Via Fioravanti 14, 40129 **Bologna**
Tel: 051-374 877
Fax: 051-379 353
E-Mail: angelica@iperbole.bologna.it
direttore generale Mario Zanzani; direttore artistico Massimo Simonini; press officer Silvia Fanti
Period/Frequency: May, annual *Arts types:* contemporary music from various backgrounds and traditions *Second Address:* Via Cairoli 7, 40121 Bologna c/o ass. cult. Pierrot Lunaire

Bologna 2000 – European City of Culture
Via Oberdan 24, 40126 **Bologna**
Tel: 051-204 772/699/606 (press office)
Fax: 051-268 636/691
Internet: www.bologna2000.it
E-Mail: bo2000@comune.bologna.it
director cultural section Giordano Gasparini; information officer Laura Tagliaferri; press officer Francesca Puglisi (0335-597 2097, email: francesca.puglisi@comune.bologna.it)
Period/Frequency: throughout the year 2000
Arts types: performing and visual arts *Comments:* Bologna is one of the 9 joint European Cities of Culture in the year 2000; alternative E-mail: paola/zacchcroni@comune.bologna.it

Primavera E Autunno Musicale
Via Brigata Bolero 23, 40132 **Bologna**
Tel: 051-564 200
Fax: 051-575 120
presidente Dott.ssa Graziella Taglioli; direttore artistico Carlo Mazzoli
Period/Frequency: March-June and Oct-Dec, annual *Arts types:* concerts, opera, productions for children, piano and chamber music competitions, conferences
Venues: Teatro Comunale e Villa Griffone, Sasso Marconi *Comments:* 10th edition

Scrittura Incantata, La
Via Libia 59, 40131 **Bologna**
Tel: 051-342 934/344 772
Fax: 051-238 592
amministrazione Renata Fiorentini; direttore artistico Guido Ferrarini; ufficio stampa Tiziano Tommesani
Period/Frequency: April, annual
Arts types: contemporary drama *Venues:* Teatro Dehon, Bologna 500 *Comments:* see also Drama & Venues

Bolzano Estate
c/o Comune di Bolzano, Assessorato alla Cultura, Vicolo Gumer 7, 39100 **Bolzano**
Tel: 0471-997 392
Fax: 0471-997 387
Internet: www.comune.bolzano.it
assessore cultura Prof. Giuliano Gobbetti; responsabile organizzativo Renzo Caramaschi
Period/Frequency: July-Sept, annual *Arts types:* classical music, jazz, dance, comedy, cabaret, film club
Venues: Haus der Kultur 500, Palasport 1800, Teatro Comunale 810 & 240, and other various open air venues in Bolzano

Festival di Musica Contemporanea
Via Brennero 28, 39100 **Bolzano**
Tel: 0471-973 579/976 568
Fax: 0471-973 579/864
direttore artistico Hubert Stuppner
Period/Frequency: Nov-Dec, annual
Arts types: contemporary music concerts *Venues:* Haus der Kultur 520, Sala Concerti del Conservatorio 470

Festival Pianistico Internazionale Arturo Benedetti Michelangeli di Brescia e Bergamo
c/o Teatro Grande, Via Paganora 19/a, 25121 **Brescia**
Tel: 030-293 022/297 9333 (biglietteria)
Fax: 030-240 0771
Internet: numerica.it/festival
E-Mail: festivalpianistico@numerica.it
direttore artistico Mffl Agostino Orizio; ufficio stampa e segreteria artistica D.ssa Anna Bergonzelli
Period/Frequency: May-June, annual
Arts types: concerts *Venues:* Teatro Grande(Brescia), Teatro Donizetti(Bergamo) *Second Address:* Bergamo festival address: Via Zambonate 81, 24122 Bergamo, Tel: 035-240 140, Fax: 35-240 140

Girovagando in Musica – itinerari Turistici e Musicali
Via Rovigo, 28, 25125 **Brescia**
Tel: 030-353 2453
Fax: 030-354 7932
Internet: users.iol.it/gruppocaronte/girovagando.htm
E-Mail: gruppocaronte@iol.it
responsabile organizzatore Ricky Perlotti
Period/Frequency: June-Nov, annual *Arts types:* from medieval to contemporary music *Second Address:* Via Giovane Italia, 6, 25125 Brescia *Comments:* the festival takes place in approx. 80 different places in Italy and central Europe; it is organised by the Gruppo da Camera Caronte in collaboration with the support of Rappresentanza a Milano della Comunita' Europea (Representative in Milan of E.E.C.)

Estate Musicale Internazionale di Alghero
c/o Associazione Serate Musicali in Sardegna, Via Carducci 16, 09128 **Cagliari**
Tel: 070-443 621/0336-776 858
Fax: 070-43621
segretaria Barbara Lunetta Maggio; presidente e direttore artistico Franco Maggio Ormezowski
Period/Frequency: July-Sept *Arts types:* chamber music
Venues: Il Chiostro di San Francesco *Second Address:* venue address: Il Chiostro di San Francesco, Centro Artistico Culturale, Via Carlo Alberto 46, 07041 Alghero, Tel: 079-980 330

Festival Internazionale Nuova Danza Città di Cagliarie Sassari
Via Machiavelli 110, 09131 **Cagliari**
Tel: 070-492 645/494 281/0335-813 6666
Fax: 070-492 645
E-Mail: asmed@tiscalinet.it
direttore organizzativo Massimiliano Leoni; direttore artistico Paola Leoni; relazioni con l'estero Cristiana Camba; promozione Rosaria Tarantini; ufficio stampa Asmed
Period/Frequency: Sept-Oct, annual
Arts types: contemporary dance
Second Address: Via Pescara 2, 00182 Roma, tel & fax: 06-701 5559 *Comments:* organised by: ASMED (Associazione Sarda Musica e Danza): Sardinian choreographers, dance photography show, meetings, debates; see also Dance

Festival Spaziomusica
Associazione Spaziomusica, Via Liguria 60, 09127 **Cagliari**
Tel: 070-400 844
Fax: 070-485 439
Internet: www.festivalspaziomusica.it
E-Mail: smusica@tiscalinet.it
presidente Marcello Pusceddu; direttore artistico Franco Oppo
Period/Frequency: Nov-Dec, annual *Arts types:* contemporary music *Venues:* Cripta S. Domenico 100, Quartu Sant'Elena – Centrale Alidos 160, Auditorium Scuola Media, Teatro Civico

Festival Internazionale di Musica e Teatro da Camera
c/o Comune di Camerino, corso Vittorio Emanuele II, 62032 **Camerino (MC)**
Tel: 0737-636 245/636 041
Fax: 0737-636 041
Internet: www.unicam.it
E-Mail: camerinofestival@hotmail.com
direttore artistico e pr Francesco Rosati; responsabile organizzazione Daniele Antonozzi
Period/Frequency: Aug, annual *Arts types:* chamber music, drama, dance *Venues:* Teatro Filippo Marchetti 500 *Comments:* also masterclasses

Festival della Riviera Etrusca
Castello Pasquini, P.zza Della Vittoria 1, 57012 **Castiglioncello (LI)**
Tel: 0586-754 202/759 021
Fax: 0586-754 198
Internet: www.Luda.it/Armunia
E-Mail: Armunia@Luda.it
presidente Massimo Marini; direttore artistico Massimo Paganelli; uffico organizzaione Fabio Masi, Maria Paola Ganzerli; direttore amministrativo Simone Morfini; coordinamento artistico per la danza Stefania Bertolino; coordinamento artistico per il teatro Francesco Niccolini
Period/Frequency: June-Sept *Arts types:* dance, music, theatre *Venues:* dance: Castello Pasquini, Castiglioncello; music: Villa Guerrazzi 400, Cecina; opera: Teatro Musicale da Camera a Bolgheri 200, Castagneto Carducci, Teatro Comico di Strada
Comments: see Agents & Producers

Rassegna di Musica da Camera – Ceriale e Pietra Ligure
c/o Associazione F. Geminiani, Via Prae 2, 17023 **Ceriale (SV)**
Tel: 0182-990 717/932 492
Fax: 0182-932 492
president Mauro Borri; vice president Loredana Cardona; art director Luigi Giachino
Period/Frequency: June-Sept, annual *Arts types:* chamber, early music, sacred music, contemporary music *Venues:* Chiesa die SS. Giovanni Battista e Eugenio, Auditorium La Pietra *Comments:* see Competitions

Arrivano dal Mare! – International Puppetry Festival
Via Cavour n.12, 48015 **Cervia (RA)**
Tel: 0544-971 958
Fax: 0544-971 922
Internet: www.arrivanodalmare!.it
E-Mail: ctf@queen.it
amministrazione Stella Rossi; direttore artistico Stefano Giunchi; organizzazione Franco Belletti
Period/Frequency: Aug, annual
Arts types: international festival of puppetry and related arts *Venues:* Teatro Comunale di Cervia 270, Arena della Sirena 900, Magazzeni del Sale (ancient salt stores turned into theatre spaces 200 each), open air
Comments: see also Puppetry

Festival Internazionale di Musica da Camera di Cervo
Salita al Castello 15, 18010 **Cervo (IM)**
Tel: 0183-404 797/408 178 (July-Aug only)
Fax: 0183-404 796
Internet: www.cervo.com
E-Mail: festcervo@tin.it
direzione artistica Bruno Novella, Gustavo del Santo, Alja Vegh; organizzazione Comune di Cervo; consulente amministrativo Francesco Delbecchi
Period/Frequency: July-Aug, annual
Arts types: chamber music *Venues:* Piazza San Giovanni Battista, Cervo and other concerts in historic towns in Liguria *Comments:* masterclasses in September

Verucchio Festival
c/o Dell'Amore Management, Via Zeffirino Re 2C, 47023 **Cesena**
Tel: 0547-611 690 Fax: 0547-25895
Internet: www.ejn.it/verucchio-festival
E-Mail: amor@link.net.it
administration Carla Dell'Amore; artistic director Franco Dell'Amore; pr Lorenza Rossi; press office Daniela Montanari; secretary Giovanna Mazzoni
Period/Frequency: July, annual *Arts types:* ethnic music, world music, contemporary music
Venues: Arena Mura del Fossato 1000

Majellarte
Società Italiana della Musica del Teatro, Via L.Colazilli 5, 66100 **Chieti**
Tel: 0871-401 373 Fax: 0871-401 373
Internet: www.alicom.com/simt
E-Mail: simt@ch.alicom.com
president Antonello Pellegrini (tel: 0360 618 035); artistic director Maurizio Colasanti; press officer Stanisalo Liberatore (tel: 0338-612 6507)
Period/Frequency: mid July-Sept, annual; 'Chieti Musica': Jan-May, annual *Arts types:* classical and chamber music, theatre, jazz, symphony music, opera, multimedia *Venues:* Parco Nazionale della Majella in Abruzzo, Regione Verde d'Europa; the series of concerts are in Teatro Marrucino 500 *Comments:* also organises International Chamber Music Competition; see also Orchestras, Promoters (Societa Italiana della Musica e del Teatro) and Competitions

Festival delle Nazioni
Via Marconi 8/A, 06012 **Città di Castello (PG)**
Tel: 075-852 1142 Fax: 075-855 2461
presidente Franco Fontana; vice presidente Massimo Ortalli; direttore generale Vittorio Sabbatelli; responsabile settore cinema Laura Vichi
Period/Frequency: July-Sept, annual *Arts types:* chamber music, theatre, dance, cinema *Venues:* Parco di Palazzo Vitelli a San Egidio 500, Chiesa di San Domenico 400, Chiesa di San Francesco 300

Clusone Jazz Festival
Clusone Jazz Promotions, Via de Bernardi 6, 24023 **Clusone (BG)**
Tel: 0346-23823 Fax: 0346-23823
Internet: www.ejn.it/clusonejazz/
E-Mail: kicafg@tin.it
direttore artistico Livio Testa
Period/Frequency: July, annual *Arts types:* jazz *Venues:* Piazza dell'Orologio, Teatro Garden 350 *Comments:* first part of festival tours in Italy in Bergamo province; members of European Jazz Network; also www.ejn.it

Ballo é Bello
Palazzo Bellini, 44022 **Comacchio**
Tel: 0533-310 182 Fax: 0533-310 149
direttore Gianni Persanti; consulente artistico Vittoria Ottolenghi
Period/Frequency: July-Aug, annual *Arts types:* ballet, modern dance *Venues:* Teatro Estivo di Palazzo Bellini

Festival Internazionale Autunno Musicale a Como
Villa Olmo, Via Cantoni 1, 22100 **Como**
Tel: 031-571 150/572 800 Fax: 031-570 540
Internet: www.camtam.it
E-Mail: camtam@galactica.it
presidente fondatore Gisella Belgeri; presidente e direttore artistico Italo Gomez; direttore organizzatione artistica Bepi Morassi
Period/Frequency: Sept, annual *Arts types:* music, theatre, music-theatre, ballet, modern dance, seminars, exhibitions *Venues:* Teatro Sociale 1000, Villa Olmo 220
Comments: see also Promoters

Quadrivium Estate in Musica – Festival Internazionale
Associazione Culturale Quadrivium, Cas. Post. n. 159, 31015 **Conegliano (TV)**
Tel: 347-824 6624 (mobile) Fax: 010-247 2813
Internet: www.tmn.it/quadrivium
E-Mail: quadrivium@eudoramail.net
president & artisitic director Francesco de Zan
Period/Frequency: Aug/Sept, annual *Arts types:* chamber and symphony music *Venues:* di Follína in Musica [Abbazia de Follina (TV)], Conegliano in Musica [Convento di S. Francesco-Conegliano (TV)], Masterclasses Quadrivium [Convento di S. Francesco-Conegliano (TV)] *Comments:* masterclasses Quadrivium every year from 17 Aug-5 Sept during festival

Festival di Cremona Claudio Monteverdi
c/o Teatro Ponchielli, corso V. Emanuele 52, 26100 **Cremona**
Tel: 0372-407 275/4/3 Fax: 0372-460 180
Internet: www.rccr.cremona.it/doc_comu/tea/teaindex.htm
E-Mail: ponchielli@rccr.cremona.it
direttore artistico Angela Cauzzi; consulente artistico Cesare Mazzonis; addetto stampa e pr Arnaldo Bassini
Period/Frequency: May-June, annual *Arts types:* concerts of baroque music (in particular Claudio Monteverdi) and renaissance music *Venues:* churches in Cremona; Teatro Ponchielli 1246 *Comments:* box office: Tel: 0372-407 273/802; see also Venues

Incontro Internazionale Polifonico 'Città Di Fano'
Via Arco d'Augusto 39, 61032 **Fano (PS)**
Tel: 0721-805 052 Fax: 0721-805 052
E-Mail: s.alberico@flashnet.it
responsabile organizzativo Adele Maggioni;
responsabile del coro Alberico Sanchioni
Period/Frequency: September, annual
Arts types: choral *Venues:* Chiesa e Chiostro di San Paterniano, Teatro della Fortuna

Teatro Festival Orizzonti
Corso Matteotti 4, 61032 **Fano (PS)**
Tel: 0721-826 462 Fax: 0721-830 146
Internet: www.gostec.it/teatrostabileinretefanocagli
E-Mail: fanoteatro@gostec.it
amministrazione Ivana Tomassini; direzione artistica Massimo Puliani; ufficio stampa Elisabetta Marsigli
Period/Frequency: Feb-May, annual *Arts types:* contemporary drama, cultural meetings, performances, exhibitions *Venues:* Urbino, Pesaro, Fano *Comments:* organised in collaboration with the University of Urbino

Estate Fiesolana
Piazza del Mercato 5, 50014 **Fiesole (FI)**
Tel: 055-597 8308 Fax: 055-597 044
Internet: www.comune.fiesole.fi.it
E-Mail: efiesole@tin.it
direction Elisabetta Raolice, Massimiliano Vivoli; press office Lucia Pistola, Marco Guerrini
Period/Frequency: June-Sept, annual
Arts types: concerts, cinema, dance, drama *Venues:* Teatro Romano di Fiesole 1950

Camera di Espansione
Via Bolognese 16, 50139 **Firenze**
Tel: 055-484 608 Fax: 055-676 853
Internet: www.ecn.org/cpa/cde.htm
E-Mail: cde@ecn.org
contact Matteo Bambi, Massimo Conti, Nicola Guarneri, Duccio Brinati
Period/Frequency: April and November, bi-annual *Arts types:* contemporary dance, theatre, experimental music, video arts, multimedia, etc. *Venues:* C.P.A. Firenze and others *Comments:* organised by Kinkaleri; see also Dance

Fabbrica Europa, Territori d' Arte
Via Borgo degli Albizi n.15, 50122 **Firenze**
Tel: 055-248 0515/242 650 Fax: 055-247 9757
Internet: www.fabbricaeuropa.net
E-Mail: fabbrica.europa@firenze.net
direzione Maurizia Settembri, Andrés Morte
Period/Frequency: April-May, annual *Arts types:* theatre, dance, video, seminars, exhibitions, music, new technology and multi-media *Venues:* Ex. Stazione Leopolda, Porta al Prato Firenze *Comments:* multidisciplinary project aiming to create an international and permanent platform of exhibitions, research and cultural exchanges in the field of contemporary arts: see also Agents & Producers and Courses

Florence Dance Festival
Danza Contemporanea Internazionale
c/o Florence Dance Center,
Borgo della Stella 23R, 50124 **Firenze**
Tel: 055-289 276 Fax: 055-217 810
Internet: www.Florencedance.org
E-Mail: info@Florencedance.org
artistic directors Marga Nativo, Keith Ferrone; press office Alessandro Benedetti; secretary Francesca Tavassi; president Keith Ferrone
Period/Frequency: July, annual *Arts types:* contemporary, classic and folk dance, visual arts exhibitions
Comments: also has a choreography award; see also Competitions

Maggio Musicale Fiorentino
Teatro del Maggio Musicale Fiorentino,
Via Solferino 15, 50123 **Firenze**
Tel: 055-27791/211 158/213 535 (box office) Fax: 055-239 6954/277 9410 (box office)
Internet: www.maggiofiorentino.com
E-Mail: tickets@maggiofiorentino.com
sovrintendente t.b.a.; direttore artistico Cesare Mazzonis; direttore amministrativo Fabrizio Bini; ufficio stampa Susanna Colombo
Period/Frequency: April-July, annual *Arts types:* opera, symphonic, ballet, recitals, exhibitions and films
Venues: capacity 2004, Perpola 1000, Piccolo Teatro 520
Comments: alternative E-mail: stampa@maggiofiorentino.com; see also Opera, Dance, Orchestras and Venues

Donne in Musica: Gli Incontri al Borgo
Fondazione Adkins Chiti: Donne in Musica,
c/o Teatro Comunale,
Pza. Trento & Trieste, 03014 **Fiuggi Città (FR)**
Tel: 0775-549 071/177 Fax: 0775-549 071
Internet: www.rtmol.it/donneinmusica
E-Mail: donne.musica@rtmo/stt.it
president and artistic director Patricia Adkins Chiti; librarian t.b.a.; secretary t.b.a.; press office Anna Grignola (tel: 06-3549 6010, fax:06-3540 9378, email: stampamusica@pro.it), Anna Rita Piacentini (tel: 06-500 2666)
Period/Frequency: 1st & 2nd weeks Sept, annual *Arts types:* music of all kinds from early music to rock, contemporary, multi-media, avantgarde-international, must be composed by women, chamber music, recitals, symphonic, ballet, street spectacles; also art exhibitions, video and electronic productions and musicological symposium *Venues:* Borgo di Fiuggi (medieval village of Fiuggi), Municipal Theatre, squares, alleyways, cloisters, churches *Second Address:* Anna Grignola, Piazza della Balduina 59, 00136 Roma
Comments: linked to Festival is also an annual Symposium; principal interest: music by women composers of past and present; for the millennium the organisation has planned 150 concerts of sacred music compositions from 13th to 20th century, from all over the world, will be held in Rome-Anagni-Fiuggi, the event is named Donne in Musica – il Paradisso dell' Amore

Festival Teatri Possibili
Piazza Marconi 11, 71100 **Foggia**
Tel: 0881-772 914/774 640/709 194 Fax: 0881-709 194
direttore artistico & direttore Domenico Losavio; direttore organizzativo Lilly Carfagno; consulente musicale Giulio D'Angelo
Period/Frequency: Nov/Dec, annual *Arts types:* contemporary music and drama *Venues:* Teatro Rossini-Gioia del Colle *Comments:* see also Orchestras and Promoters

Progetto Musica – Primavera e Autunno Musicale
Piazza Marconi 11, 71100 **Foggia**
Tel: 0881-772 914/774 640 Fax: 0881-773 883
direttore artistico Domenico Losavio;
consulente musicale Giulio D'Angelo;
direttore organizzativo Lilly Carfagno
Period/Frequency: spring and autumn, bi-annual *Arts types:* classical music *Comments:* see also Promoters and Orchestras

Festival Internazionale del Balletto di Nervi
c/o Teatro Carlo Felice,
Passo Eugenio Montale 4, 16121 **Genova**
Tel: 010-53811 (press office)/538 1254/223
Fax: 010-538 1222 (press office)
Internet: www.carlofelice.it
E-Mail: cfstampa@tin.it (press office)
sovrintendente Nicola Costa; direttore artistico Alessio Vlad; consulente artistico Franco Bolletta; coordinatore attivitá di balletto Michele Corradi; direttore degli allestimenti scenici Carlo Savi
Period/Frequency: July, annual *Arts types:* ballet: classic and modern; complemented by concerts, exhibitions, conferences *Venues:* Teatro ai Parchi di Nervi 1200, Teatro Carlo Felice 2000 *Second Address:* Parchi di Nervi *Comments:* organised by Fondazione Carlo Felice e.a. Teatro Comunale dell' Opera di Genova; alternative E-mail: staff@carlofelice.it (theatre); see also Promoters, Venues and Orchestras

Genova Jazz
Via Savelli 37/39, 16143 **Genova**
Tel: 010-247 4471/4 Fax: 010-247 4507
Internet: www.pandd.it/genovajazz
E-Mail: elliclub@tin.it
organizzatori Marco Travagli, Lino Zero, Fabio Taddei
Period/Frequency: July, annual *Arts types:* jazz *Venues:* Zona Porto Antico, Area Expó, Teatro Piscina All'Aperto
Comments: programmes are based on touring groups and original productions of the festival, involving Italian, European and American musicians (established and young)

Festival dell'Infiorata – Rassegna di Danza e Musica
c/o Istituzione per il Servizio delle Attivitá Culturali – Comune di Genzano di Roma,
Via Belardi 81, 00045 **Genzano di Roma**
Tel: 06-9371 1315/307 Fax: 06-936 4816
Internet: www.pcg.it/infiorata
E-Mail: infioratadigenzano@pcg.it
presidente Gastone Verchiani
Period/Frequency: June-July, annual *Arts types:* classical, modern, contemporary dance and music
Venues: Parco Sforza-Censarini

Differenti Sensazioni – Festival Internazionale Delle Arti
Via La Salle 2, 10095 **Grugliasco (TO)**
Tel: 011-787 117/786 946 Fax: 011-787 117
E-Mail: stalker@alma.it
direttore artistico Gabriele Boccacini;
ufficio stampa t.b.a.
Period/Frequency: June-Sept, annual *Arts types:* drama, performance, visual arts, dance, video *Venues:* Città dell'Arte : venues address: sede Fondazione Pistoletto, Via Serralunga 27 Biella

Festival Internazionale del Jazz
Società dei Concerti O.N.L.U.S.,
Viale Italia 320, 19126 **La Spezia**
Tel: 0187-21927
Fax: 0187-510 481
presidente Prof Ernesto di Marino; vice presidente Prof Sergio Cozzani; direttore artistica Massimilinno Damerini; segretario Piero Barbareschi
Period/Frequency: July *Arts types:* jazz
Venues: Centro Allende, Piazza Mentana

Estate Musicale Frentana
c/o Associazione Amici Della Musica Fedele Fenaroli, Via F. Filzi 7, 66034 **Lanciano (CH)**
Tel: 0872-710 241 Fax: 0872-710 518
president Arch. Filomena di Renzo
Period/Frequency: May-Dec, annual *Arts types:* jazz, ethnic, classical music and related seminars *Venues:* Torri Montanare 1000 (open air), Auditorium Diocleziano 300, Cine-teatro Mazzini 150, Teatro Fenaroli 300 *Comments:* international seminars on orchestration, early music and jazz; see also Promoters

Festival Pontino di Musica
Campus Internazionale di Musica, c/o Università Pontina, Viale Le Corbusier 379, 04100 **Latina**
Tel: 0773-605 551 Fax: 0773-605 548
Internet: www.panservice.it/campusmusica
E-Mail: campus.musica@panservice.it
presidente onorario Goffredo Petrassi; direttore artistico per la musica contemporanea Prof. Raffaele Pozzi; presidente del Campus Internazionale di Musica Riccardo Cerocchi
Period/Frequency: June-July, annual *Arts types:* classical, contemporary music *Venues:* Castello Caetani (Sermoneta), Abbazia di Valvisciolo (Sermoneta), Infermeria dell' Abbazia di Fossanova (Priverno)
Comments: masterclasses are organised during the festival in Sermoneta (0773-30250/605 551)

Festival Corale Internazionale – La Fabbrica Del Canto
Via Milano 3, 20025 **Legnano (MI)**
Tel: 0331-594 504/454 707 Fax: 0331 597 433
Internet: www.nemo.it/guests/jubilate/default.htm
E-Mail: amj@mail.nemo.it
direttore artistico Giovanni Acciai
Period/Frequency: May-June, annual *Arts types:* choral
Venues: Basilica di S. Magno & other venues in Legnano and other cities *Comments:* see also Promoters: 'Associazione Musicale Jubilate' and Choirs

Macerata Opera
c/o Associazione Arena Sferisterio, Via Santa Maria Della Porta 65, 62100 **Macerata**
Tel: 0733-261 334/335 Fax: 0733-261 499
Internet: www.macerataopera.org
E-Mail: macerataopera@mercurio.it
sovrintendente Claudio Orazi;
technical & artistic director Bruno Carletti
Period/Frequency: July-Aug, annual *Arts types:* opera
Venues: Arena Sferisterio 2400, Teatro Lauro Rossi 300

Festival Animando Mantov – Figure d' Europe
Via Romagnoli 9/C, 46100 **Mantova**
Tel: 0376-381 547 Fax: 0376-381 547
Internet: www.comune.mantova.it
E-Mail: corianiteatro@maynet.it
Period/Frequency: June-Sept, annual *Arts types:* marionettes, puppets, shadow, glove puppets etc.
Comments: organised by: Centro Teatrale Corniani; artistic direction: Figure Teatrale

La Versiliana
Viale Morin 16, 55044 **Marina Di Pietrasanta (LU)**
Tel: 0584-23938/20668/20666 Fax: 0584-20022
Internet: www.versilia-toscana.it/versiliana
direttore artistico Franco Martini
Period/Frequency: July-Aug, annual *Arts types:* drama, dance, contemporary music, pop, art, exhibitions
Second Address: Gestione: Comune di Pietrasanta – Assessorato alla Cultura, Piazza Duomo, 55045 Pietrasanta, Tel: 0584-795 265 (Daniele Palchetti), Fax: 0584-795 310 *Comments:* space for children (puppets, clowns, baby sitting); free event 'Caffé' every day by Romano Battaglia, a series of conversations with culture protagonists

Festival della Valle d'Itria
c/o Centro Artistico Musicale Paolo Grassi, Palazzo Ducale, 74015 **Martina Franca (TA)**
Tel: 080-480 5100 Fax: 080-480 5120
E-Mail: Fvd@italiainrete.net
presidente Franco Punzi; direttore artistico Sergio Segalini; direttore amministrativo Roberto D'Arcangelo
Period/Frequency: July-Aug, annual *Arts types:* concerts, opera, ballet *Venues:* Palazzo Ducale 1000 and locations in the countryside

Festival di Musica Sinfonica
c/o Associazione Musicale Massese,
P.za San Martino 1, 54100 **Massa**
Tel: 0585-43732/791 625 Fax: 0585-791 625
presidente e direttore artistico Paolo Biancalana
Period/Frequency: July-Aug, annual *Arts types:* symphonic music *Venues:* Palazzo Ducale in Massa 400
Comments: see also Promoters

Lunatica
c/o Provincia di Massa Carrara, Ufficio Cultura, Via Cavour 17, 54100 **Massa**
Tel: 0585-816 620 (organiser)/616 (cultural officer)
Fax: 0585-816 624/25
cultural officer Eleonora Paglini
Period/Frequency: July-Aug, annual *Arts types:* music, theatre, dance *Venues:* historical and archeological sites in Lunigiana, Massa Carrara and Montignoso

Campsirago Teatro
Via Montegrappa 17, Fraz. Sartirana,
23807 **Merate (LC)**
Tel: 039-952 0082 Fax: 039-952 0033
direttore artistico Antonio Viganò;
ufficio organizzativo Eugenia Neri, Alessandra Sechi
Period/Frequency: July, annual
Arts types: dance, contemporary drama, music
Venues: in a small country town Campsirago *Comments:* see also Drama: Teatro la Ribalta di Antonio Vigané

Milano Estate
Associazione Milano Festival,
Via Monte Grappa 11, 20124 **Milano**
Tel: 02-2906 0978
Fax: 02-2901 9192
general managers/artistic directors Antonio Gnecchi Ruscone, Gianmario Longoni, Giancarlo Volpi
Period/Frequency: June/Sept, annual
Arts types: theatre, opera, ballet, street theatre *Venues:* Castello Sforzesco: Piazza delle Armi 2500, Cortile della Rocchetta 456 *Second Address:* Comune di Milano, Settore Cultura e Musei, Via Marino 7, 20121 Milano

Milanoltre
Via Ciro Menotti 11, 20129 **Milano**
Tel: 02-743 404
Fax: 02-7012 3851
E-Mail: miol@elfo.org
direttore amministrativa Barbara Sorani;
direttore artistico Fiorenzo Grassi
Period/Frequency: Oct-Nov, annual *Arts types:* theatre, dance, music *Venues:* Teatro di Porta Romana 500,Teatro Dell'Elfo 300 and other spaces
Comments: see also Drama and Venues

Musica e poesia a San Maurizio
c/o Comune di Milano, Settore Cultura,
Via T Marino 7, 20121 **Milano**
Tel: 02-6208 3856/862 418/795 393
Fax: 02-877 532/7601 4281
direttore artistico Sandro Boccardi
Period/Frequency: March-May, Sept-Dec, annual
Arts types: early music *Venues:* Coro di San Maurizio al Monastero Maggiore 200, Basilica di San Simpliciano 600, Santa Maria presso San Satiro

Aterforum Festival
c/o Ater , via Giardini 466/G, 41100 **Modena**
Tel: 059-340 221
Fax: 059-342 802
Internet: www.regione.emilia-romagna.it/ater
E-Mail: rer3@nettuno.it
president Maurizio Roi; direttore Roberto Giovannardi
Period/Frequency: Sept/Oct, annual
Arts types: early and contemporary music *Comments:* see also Agents & Producers, Promoters and Courses

Mundus – Linguaggi dell' Identita' e della Differenza
c/o ATER – Via Giardini 466/G, 41100 **Modena**
Tel: 059-340 221
Fax: 059-342 802
Internet: www.regione.emilia-romagna.it/ater
E-Mail: rer3@nettuno.it
president Maurizio Roi; direttore Ero Righi
Period/Frequency: July/Aug, annual *Arts types:* music, theatre, dance, worldmusic *Comments:* a festival of ethnic performing arts from all over the world; see also Agents & Producers, Promoters (ATER) and Courses

Festival Internazionale d'Organo di Cagliari
c/o E. Pasini Management,
Via Capo d' Orso n. 22, 09042 **Monserrato (CA)**
Tel: 070-572 707 Fax: 070-572 707
E-Mail: pasini.enrico@tiscalinet.it
president & artistic director Enrico Pasini; public relations Gianluca Frau; secretary Francesc Cocco
Period/Frequency: annual
Arts types: organ music *Venues:* St Rosalia Church

Cantiere Internazionale d'Arte
P.zza Grande n.7, 53045 **Montepulciano (Siena)**
Tel: 0578-757 089
Fax: 0578-758 307
Internet: www.cantiere.toscana.nu
E-Mail: cantiere@bccmp.com
direttore artistico Maestro Enrique Mazzola;
press office & artistic management Giovanna Lomazzi, Carlo Cavalletti
Period/Frequency: July-Aug, annual
Arts types: concerts, opera, drama, dance, seminars, exhibitions *Venues:* Teatro Poliziano 600, Piazza Grande, Tempio di S. Biagio, Chiostro della Fortezza, Salone dei Concerti Chiesa di San Francesco

Coreografo Elettronico, Il
c/o Ass. Napolidanza,
Via Nilo 28, 80100 **Napoli**
Tel: 081-422 118/0335-436 180
Fax: 081-404 722
Internet: www.napoli.com/napolidanza
E-Mail: vesuvio@synapsis.it
artistic director Marilena Riccio
Period/Frequency: autumn, annual
Arts types: videodance

Stagione di Concerti
Teatro di San Carlo, Via San Carlo 98 F, 80132 **Napoli**
Tel: 081-797 2111/2301 Fax: 081-797 2306/9
Internet: www.teatrosancarlo.it
E-Mail: infoteatro@teatrosancarlo.it
sovrintendente Francesco Canessa; direttore artistico Carlo Mayer; capo ufficio stampa Filippo Arriva
Period/Frequency: Sept-June, annual *Arts types:* symphony and chamber concerts, vocals (choirs)
Venues: Teatro di San Carlo 1400 *Comments:* plays host to other orchestras and conductors, Musicali Internazionali' and always performs an opera connected with the Neopolitan style of 1700; see also Orchestras, Venues, Opera and Dance

Festival Cusiano di Musica Antica
c/o Associazione Amici Della Musica V. Cocito,
Via Ravizza 6A, 28100 **Novara**
Tel: 0321-626 344 Fax: 0321-626 344
direttore artistico Elena Bollatto
Period/Frequency: June, annual *Arts types:* early music, soloists and ensembles, dance, ballads, madrigal
Venues: Chiesa di S Maria Assunta (Orta San Giulio) 250, Villa Tallone (Isola San Giulio) 100
Comments: see also Promoters

Festival G. Cantelli
c/o Associazione Amici della Musica V. Cocito,
Via Ravizza 6A, 28100 **Novara**
Tel: 0321-626 344 Fax: 0321-626 344
presidente e direttore artistico Folco Perrino;
direttore artistico Elena Bollatto
Period/Frequency: Nov/Dec, annual *Arts types:* concerts of symphonic and chamber orchestras *Venues:* Teatro Coccia (Novara) 950 *Comments:* see also Promoters

Festival Internazionale Città di Osimo – Rassegna di Danza e Balletto
Piazza Dante 7, 60027 **Osimo (Ancona)**
Tel: 071-723 1367/714 555 Fax: 071-713 2404
Internet: www.comune.osimo.an.it/ema
presidente Carlo Carletti; segretario Claudio Polenta
Period/Frequency: July, annual *Arts types:* dance
Venues: Piazza Duomo (open-air theatre)

Veneto Festival
Piazzale Pontecorvo 4/a, 35121 **Padova**
Tel: 049-666 128 Fax: 049-875 2598
manager Mirella Gualandi; direttore artistico Ugo Orlandi; presidente Luisa di San Bonifacio
Period/Frequency: May-July, annual *Arts types:* classical music *Venues:* Luoghi artistici del Veneto *Comments:* dedicated mainly to Veneto music and its influence on European music; see also Orchestras

Festival di Morgana
Via Butera 1, 90133 **Palermo**
Tel: 091-328 060/234 Fax: 091-328 276
E-Mail: mimap@telegest.it
ufficio stampa Giovannella Brancato;
president Marianne Vibaek
Period/Frequency: Nov-Dec, annual *Arts types:* puppetry
Venues: Museum of Puppets-Palermo

Festival di Palermo sul Novecento
Palazzo Zino, Via G. Despuches 1, 90141 **Palermo**
Tel: 091-580 982 Fax: 091-581 686
Internet: www.sispi.it/festival900
direttore artistico Roberto Andó; direttore organizzativo Gianni Valle; direttore tecnico Michele Russotto; promozione Ilaria Giaccone; segreteria organizzativa Sabina Lo Buglio; coordinamento organizzativo Giovannella Brancato
Period/Frequency: Oct -Nov *Arts types:* contemporary theatre, music and dance; visual arts *Venues:* Teatro Politeama, Cantieri Culturali alla Zisa

Incontroazione Teatro Festival
Piazza Marina/Salita Partanna 4, 90133 **Palermo**
Tel: 091-617 4040 Fax: 091-617 3712
Internet: www.telegest.it/teatrolibero
E-Mail: libero@telegest.it
presidente e direttore artistico Beno Mazzone; direttore organizzativo Giacoma Chiappara
Period/Frequency: April-May, annual *Arts types:* research theatre, contemporary dance *Venues:* Teatro Libero

Macchina dei Sogni, La
Via Bara all'Olivella 95, 90133 **Palermo**
Tel: 091-323 400 Fax: 091-335 922
organizzazione generale Elisa Puleo; direttore artistico Mimmo Cuticchio; ufficio stampa Sergio Marra
Period/Frequency: May, annual *Arts types:* European & Italian puppetry & animation

Festival Mozartiano
c/o Fondazione Arturo Toscanini, Via G. Tartini 13, 43100 **Parma**
Tel: 0521-2741/274 417 (marketing)/421 (secretariat)
Fax: 0521-272 134 (marketing/pr)/785 257
Internet: www.fondazione-toscanini.it
E-Mail: fondazione@toscanini.dsnet.it
general manager Prof. Gianni Baratta; artistic director Prof. Gian Paolo Minardi; music director of Toscanini Symphony Orchestra Patrick Fournillier
Period/Frequency: mid-Sept – mid-Oct, annual *Arts types:* symphonic repertoire, chamber music, recitals
Venues: Auditorium Europa, Palazzo dei Congressi, Salsomaggiore Terme (PR): 550 *Comments:* organised by Fondazione Arturo Toscanini

Natura Dèi Teatri
c/o Associazione Culturale Natura Dèi Teatri – laboratorio delle arti, via Pasubio 3/d, 43100 **Parma**
Tel: 0521-270 141(press office)
Fax: 0521-272 641(press office)
artistic direction Maria Federica Maestri, Francesco Pititto; press office Viviana Colla
Period/Frequency: Aug/Sept, annual *Arts types:* theatre, dance, music, poetry, art workshops, photography, visual arts, environmental issues *Second Address:* Lenz Rifrazioni, via Trento 49, 43100 Parma,
Tel: 0521-270 141, Fax: 0521-272 641

Teatro Festival di Parma – Meeting Europeo Dell'Attore
c/o Teatro Due, Viale Basetti 12 A, 43100 **Parma**
Tel: 0521-208 088/230 242 (info) Fax: 0521-231 232
Internet: www.teatrostabileparma.com
E-Mail: infofestival@teatrostabileparma.com
direttore artistico e presidente Giorgio Gennari; ufficio stampa Laura De Stefano, Carlotta Varga; segreteria generale Liliana Orsi; coordinamento produzioni e ospitalità Nicetta Cavalli; ufficio promozione pubblico Maria Rosa Bastianelli, Tiziana Pirondi; admin Pietro Bocchi, Giulia Horvath, Anna Maria Toscani
Period/Frequency: Oct, annual *Arts types:* mixed *Venues:* Teatro Due, other open air venues, and other theatres of the province*Comments:* see also Venues and Drama

Gospel and Soul Easter Festival
Associazione Umbria Jazz,
P.zza Danti N. 28, 06122 **Perugia**
Tel: 075-573 2432 Fax: 075-572 2656
Internet: www.umbriajazz.com
E-Mail: uj@krenet.it
presidente t.b.a.; vice presidente e amm unico Alba Peccia; responsabile organizzazione Sauro Peducci; direttore generale Virgilio Ambroglini;
cousulente legale Stefano Mazzi
Period/Frequency: Easter, annual *Arts types:* gospel & soul concerts *Venues:* Teatro Politeama 1000, Chiese A Terni

Sagra Musicale Umbra
Via Podiani 11, c/o Palazzo Della Penna, 06121 **Perugia**
Tel: 075-572 1374 Fax: 075-572 7614
segretario generale Francesco Maria Perrotta;
presidente Gian Franco Maddoli; dir art Carlo Pedini
Period/Frequency: Sept and Easter, biannual *Arts types:* concerts, opera, drama, ballet *Venues:* various throughout Umbria *Comments:* founded in 1937

Umbria Jazz
Associazione Umbria Jazz,
P.zza Danti n.28, 06122 **Perugia**
Tel: 075-573 2432 Fax: 075-572 2656
Internet: www.umbriajazz.com
E-Mail: uj@krenet.it
presidente t.b.a.; dir art e sovrintendente Carlo Pagnotta; direttore generale Virgilio Ambroglini; vice presidente e amm. unico Alba Peccia; responsabile organizzazione Sauro Peducci; consulente legale Stefano Mazzi
Period/Frequency: July (Perugia), Dec-Jan (Orvieto), annual *Arts types:* jazz concerts *Venues:* Umbria: Giardini del Fronotone 3500, San Francesco al Prato, Teatro Marlocchi e Piazze della Citta Perugia; Orvieto: Teatro Mancinelli, Duomo di Orvieto, Palazzo Sette, Palazzo del Popolo

Rossini Opera Festival
Via Rossini, 37, 61100 **Pesaro**
Tel: 0721-34435/30161 Fax: 0721-30979
Internet: www.rossinioperafestival.it
E-Mail: rof@rossinioperafestival.it
sovrintendente Gianfranco Mariotti;
direttore artistico Luigi Ferrari
Period/Frequency: Aug *Arts types:* opera, concerts
Venues: Teatro Rossini, Palafestival, Teatro Sperimentale, Auditorium Pedrotti *Comments:* member of Association Européenne des Festivals

Pescara Jazz – Festival Internazionale del Jazz
Ente Manifestazioni Pescaresi,
Via Liguria 6, 5th Floor, 65122 **Pescara**
Tel: 085-374 198/421 0112 Fax: 085-421 0757
Internet: www.pescarajazz.com
direttore artistico Lucio Fumo
Period/Frequency: July, annual *Arts types:* jazz *Venues:* Teatro Monumento Gabriele D'Annunzio 2000, Viale C. Colombo 122 (Pescara) *Comments:* the oldest jazz festival in Italy; see also Promoters

Festival Internazionale Inteatro (Polverigi)
Villa Nappi, Via Marconi 75, 60020 **Polverigi (AN)**
Tel: 071-909 0007 Fax: 071-906 326
Internet: www.fastnet.it/associazioni/inteatro
E-Mail: inteatro@tin.it
direzione artistica Velia Papa
Period/Frequency: July, annual *Arts types:* drama, music, dance *Venues:* Villa Comunale Nappi *Second Address:* Villa Comunale Nappi, 60020 Polverigi (AN)

La Luna è Azzurra Festival Internazionale del Teatro di Figura
Via della Gioventu 3, 56024 **Ponte a Egola (PI)**
Tel: 0571-485 078 Fax: 0571-485 078
direzione artistica Alberto Masoni, Alessandro Gigli
Period/Frequency: July, annual *Arts types:* puppetry, shadow theatre *Venues:* historical centre of San Miniato outdoors

Mercanzia, Festival Internazionale di Teatro di Strada – Certaldo
Via della Gioventú 3, 56024 **Ponte a Egola (PI)**
Tel: 0571-485 078 Fax: 0571-485 078
direzione artistica Alberto Masoni, Alessandro Gigli
Period/Frequency: July, annual *Arts types:* street theatre

Festival di Chitarra del Friuli Venezia Giulia
Via Caboto 1, 33170 **Pordenone**
Tel: 0434-41002/21367 Fax: 0434-41002/21367
Internet: www.farandola.it
E-Mail: scrivi@farandola.it
organizzazione Paolo Pegoraro, Angela Tagliariol; direttore artistico Francesco Carone; presidente Gabriella Bassignano
Period/Frequency: Sept-May, annual *Arts types:* music *Venues:* Auditorium 'A. Moro' 500 *Second Address:* Via Piave 15/A, 33170 Pordenone
Comments: see also Promoters

Festival Musica Ricerca
Via Caboto 1, 33170 **Pordenone**
Tel: 0434-21367/427-80176 Fax: 0434-21367/427-80176
Internet: www.farandola.it
E-Mail: serivi@farandola.it
organizzazione Gianpaolo Fagotto; direttore artistico Francesco Carone; presidente Gabriella Bassignano
Period/Frequency: Oct-May, annual *Arts types:* early music *Venues:* Auditorium Concordia 500, Abbazia di Sesto al Reghena 300, Duomo di Valvasone 500
Comments: see also Promoters

Cortili del Teatro, I
c/o Associazione Vesuvioteatro,
Corso Garibaldi 235, 80055 **Portici (NA)**
Tel: 081-480 384/273 152 Fax: 081-273 152
direttore artistico Giuseppe Liguoro
Period/Frequency: July, annual *Arts types:* contemporary drama, dance and music *Venues:* courts of monumental villas in Portici *Second address:* registered address: Via Roma 20, 80055 Portici (NA)

Festival Internazionale Teatro Per Ragazzi
Villa Murri, 63018 **Porto Sant' Elpidio (AP)**
Tel: 0734-909 278 Fax: 0734-906 105
Internet:
www.fastnet.it/associazioni/amat/festragazzi.htm
E-Mail: centridelmondo@mercurio.it
direttore artistico Marco Renzi; direttore organizzativo Giuseppe Nuciari; presidente Rosa Maria Saltarin
Period/Frequency: July, annual *Arts types:* drama, object theatre, shadow puppetry *Venues:* all open-air, Pineta Nord, Teatro del Mare, Teatro del Cielo;Parco di Villa Murri: Teatro della Villa, Teatro Galilei *Second Address:* Associazione Laboratorio Infanzia, Tel: 0734-909 278, Fax: 0734-992 346 *Comments:* the festival is organised by Associazione Laboratorio Infanzia

Festival di Teatro Filufilese
Via Cesare Battisti, 53, 73054 **Presicce (Lecce)**
Tel: 0833-727 040/726 635 Fax: 0833-726 635
organizzatrice Adele Legittimo; dir art Silvia Civilla
Period/Frequency: July/Aug, annual *Arts types:* children's and youth theatre, dance theatre, drama, concerts *Venues:* Atrio del Palazzo Paternó 300, Giardini Pensili 300, Cortile del Palazzo Comunale 400 *Second Address:* Rolando Civilla, Tel: 833-727 040 *Comments:* organised by Associazione Anteo-Teatro, Musica ed Arti Visive; see also Drama

Oltre i Confini Festival Internazionale del Teatro Mediterraneo – V Edizione
c/o Teatro Centrale,
Via Marconi 328, 09045 **Quartu Sant'Elena (Cagliari)**
Tel: 070-883 454/881 954/822 842 Fax: 070-880 270
E-Mail: TAATINM@tin.it
dir organizzativo Tullia Agati; dir art Gianfranco Angei
Period/Frequency: Oct/Nov/Dec, annual *Arts types:* theatre, music, dance *Venues:* Teatro Centrale 100 (Quartu Sant'Elena), Anfiteatro Romano 4000 (Cagliari), Teatro Alfieri 600 (Cagliari) *Second Address:* Piazza Repubblica, 22, 09122 Cagliari *Comments:* organisation: Via G. D'Annunzio 26, 09045 QuartuSant' Elena

Settimane Internazionali di Musica da Camera
Societá dei Concerti di Ravello, Via Trinitá
3, 84010 **Ravello**
Tel: 089-858 149/335
Fax: 089-858 249
Internet: www.res.amalficoast.it
E-Mail: info@res.amalficoast.it
presidente Palumbo Pasquale Antonio; direttore musicale Cantarella Maria Paola; segreteria Paola Amato
Period/Frequency: Sept-Oct, annual *Arts types:* chamber music *Venues:* Auditorium and Villa Rufolo Gardens in Ravello

Mister Jazz
Associazione Polifonica Ravenna, c/o Europe Jazz Network, Via Amalasunta 7, 48100 **Ravenna**
Tel: 0544-405 666/408 030 Fax: 0544-405 656
Internet: www.ejn.it
E-Mail: ejn@ejn.it
direttore artistico Filippo Bianchi,
Ufficio Stampa, Sandra Costantini
Period/Frequency: Easter period, annual *Arts types:* jazz *Venues:* Teatro Alighieri 1300, Teatro Rasi 500, Mama's 150 *Second Address:* Filippo Bianchi, Piazza Stefano Jacini 5, 00191 Roma *Comments:* mainly a series of workshops and concerts

Ravenna Festival
Via Dante Alighieri, 1, 48100 **Ravenna**
Tel: 0544-249 211 (switchboard)/237 (press office)
Fax: 0544-36303
Internet: www.ravennafestival.org
E-Mail: info@ravennafestival.org
presidente Cristina Mazzavillani-Muti
Period/Frequency: June-July, annual *Arts types:* music, opera, ballet, drama, ethnic music *Venues:* Basilica San Vitale, Teatro Alighieri 1300, Teatro Rasi 500, Basilica San Apollinare in Classe, Palazzo Mauro de André 2500, Basilica di Sant' Apollinare Nuovo, Teatro Rossini di Lugo 500, and other historical sites *Comments:* box office: c/o Teatro Alighieri, Via Mariani 2, 48100 Ravenna,Tel: 0544-32577 Fax: 0544-215 840

Ravenna Jazz Festival
Associazione Polifonica Ravenna, c/o Europe Jazz Network, Via Amalasunta 7, 48100 **Ravenna**
Tel: 0544-405 666/408 030 Fax: 0544-405 656
Internet: www.ejn.it
E-Mail: ejn@ejn.it
direttore artistico Filippo Bianchi;
ufficio stampa Sandra Costantini
Period/Frequency: end of July, annual
Arts types: jazz *Venues:* Rocca Brancaleone 800, others *Second Address:* Filippo Bianchi, Piazza Stefano Jacini 5, 00191 Roma

Di Nuovo Musica
Piazza Martiri 7 Luglio, 42100 **Reggio Emilia**
Tel: 0522-458 925/811 Fax: 0522-458 922/822
Internet: www.i-teatri.re.it
E-Mail: i-teatri@uffstampa@i-teatri.re.it
direzione organizzativa Giovanni Ottolini; direzione artistica Daniela Iotti, Paolo Perezzani
Period/Frequency: Oct/Nov, annual *Arts types:* 20th century and contemporary music *Venues:* Teatro Municipale Valli 1200, Teatro Cavallerizza 350, and other venues as required *Comments:* the festival is organised by Consorzio I Teatri (see Drama), Istituto Musicale A. Peri & Comune di Reggio Emilia; it attempts to conjugate music with the various languages of our age, from dance to visual arts; also seminars, conferences & debates, workshops and open rehearsals, especially aimed at young performers (musicians, composers, dancers or artists) and students of secondary schools

Reggio Emilia Jazz
Teatro Municipale 'R Valli',
P.zza Martiri VII Luglio, 42100 **Reggio Emilia**
Tel: 0522-458 811/6755 4222
Fax: 0522-458 922
Internet: www.nettuno.it/ejn/
E-Mail: ejn@ra.nettuno.it
direttore artistico Antonio De Rosa
Period/Frequency: April-May *Arts types:* jazz *Venues:* Teatro Municipale 'R Valli' 1200, Teatro Ariosto 800, Teatro Cavallerizza 450 *Comments:* Europe Jazz Network Tel: 0544-405 666 Fax: 0544-405 656; alternative E-mail: uffstampa@i-teatri.re.it (press)

Riccione TTV
v.le Vittorio Emanuele II, 2, 47838 **Riccione (RN)**
Tel: 0541-608 334/693 384/692 124
Fax: 0541-693 384/692 124
Internet: www.adhoc
E-Mail: riccionetestro@comune.riccione.on.it
direzione artistica Fabio Bruschi; organizzazione Sandra Angelini; documentazione Antonella Bacchini
Period/Frequency: end of May, annual
Arts types: TV programmes and videos about theatre, dance, opera, performing arts and new technologies *Venues:* Palazzo del Turismo *Second Address:* c/o Fabio Bruschi, Via Sacramora 48, 47811 Viserba di Rimini *Comments:* annual competition for Italian producers and videomakers specialised in the performing arts; prize: 10 m Lire; venue address: p.le Ceccarini 11, 47838 Riccione, Tel: 0541-608 333/332

Festival Internazionale di Interpretazione Pianistica
Associazione Amintore Galli,
Via Ceccarelli 37, 47900 **Rimini**
Tel: 0541-790 811/933 735/0425-938 419
Fax: 0425-938 419
president Pesaresi Simonetta;
vice president Ricciarelli Marco
Period/Frequency: Aug, annual *Arts types:* classical music *Venues:* Misano Adriatico, San Giovanni in Marignano, Gradara *Comments:* masterclasses for piano

International Meeting of Young Musicians – Musica Riva
Incontro Internazionale di Giovani Musicisti
Associazione Musica Riva, Via Maffei 7,
38066 **Riva del Garda (TN)**
Tel: 0464-554 073 Fax: 0464-520 900
Internet: www.garda.com
E-Mail: cmr@anthesi.com
presidente Milena Torboli;
direzione artistica Mietta Sighele
Period/Frequency: July, annual *Arts types:* symphonic, opera, chamber concerts, masterclasses *Second Address:* July only: Palazzo dei Congressi, Parco Lido, 38066 Riva del Garda, Tel: 0464-520 000, Fax: 0464-555 255

Festa Musica Pro Mundo Uno
Via Villa Maggiorani 20, 00168 **Roma**
Tel: 06-305 4141 Fax: 06-305 0117
presidente Maestro Giuseppe Juhar;
direttore artistico Dr Monika Ryba
Period/Frequency: Nov, annual *Arts types:* concerts, oratorio, opera, ballet, masterclasses *Venues:* every year in a different town in Italy (2000: Rome) *Comments:* see also Promoters: Academia Musicae Pro Mundo Uno

Festival D'Autunno
Eti Teatro Valle, via del Teatro Valle 23/a, **Roma**
Tel: 06-696 9049/687 7396
Period/Frequency: autumn, annual *Arts types:* contemporary theatre *Comments:* see also National Organisations

Festival Internazionale di Musica Antica
c/o Fondazione Italiana per la Musica Antica del SIFD, Via Col di Lana n.7, CP 6159, 00195 **Roma**
Tel: 06-321 0806 Fax: 06-321 0806
Internet: www.cilea.it/music/fima.fima.htm
segretaria amministrativa Francesca Maraschini, Roberta Mazza; presidente Renato Meucci
Period/Frequency: July, annual *Arts types:* early music, masterclasses, concerts, instrument exhibition, iconography seminar *Venues:* Urbino, various sites *Comments:* The Fondazione publishes the journal Recercare: journal for the study & practice of early music (direttore, Marco Di Pasquale); owns a library dedicated to organology based at centre in Rome

Fiati Festival
Via Macchiavelli 50, 00185 **Roma**
Tel: 06-4470 3055 Fax: 06-4470 3059
E-Mail: aifla@nexus.it
directors Gianluca Morseletto, Stefano Cioffi;
uff. stampa Susanna Persichilli
Period/Frequency: Nov, biennial *Arts types:* concerts of wind instruments only *Venues:* Museo Nazionale dell Arti e Tradizioni Popolari *Comments:* also masterclasses, exhibitions of wind instruments and publications; see also Publications and Competitions

Flautissimo – Festival Italiano del Flauto
Via Macchiavelli 50, 00185 **Roma**
Tel: 06-4470 3055 Fax: 06-4470 3059
E-Mail: aifla@nexus.it
directors Gianluca Morseletto, Stefano Cioffi;
uff. stampa Susanna Persichilli
Period/Frequency: Nov, biennial *Arts types:* classical flute music *Venues:* Museo Nazionale delle Arti e Tradizioni Popolari *Comments:* also exhibition of musical instruments, historical flutes, publications, masterclasses; see also Publications and Competitions

I Concerti nel Parco
Via Ugo Bassi 17, 00152 **Roma**
Tel: 06-581 6987/9 Fax: 06-581 6989
E-Mail: concerti.parco@pronet.it
presidente e direttore artistico Teresa Azzaro; vice presidente Maria Rosaria Calabrese
Period/Frequency: July, Sept, annual *Arts types:* classical, jazz, contemporary, ethnic, early music *Venues:* Chiostro del Sacro Cuore 600 in Trinita dei Monti, Chiostro del Bramante 400

Invito alla Danza
Invito alla Danza, piazzale Clodio 8, 00195 **Roma**
Tel: 06-3973 8323/06-4423 2525 Fax: 06-3973 8323
E-Mail: m.michetti@flashnet.it
presidente e direttore artistico Marina Michetti
Period/Frequency: July/Aug, annual *Arts types:* all types of dance including: classical & contemporary dance, tango *Venues:* Accademia Tedesca di Villa Massimo

Italian Riviera d'Ulisse Theatre Festival
Piazzale Sisto V n 2, 00185 **Roma**
Tel: 06-445 5659
Fax: 06-494 0858
Internet: www.agora.stm.it/italiafestival
amministrazione Nella Vano; direttore artistica Franco M. Portone; direzione tecnica Marco R Portone; segreteria Fondi la Pastora Fabio Baglioni; archivio fotografico Egidio Daniele
Period/Frequency: July-Aug, annual *Arts types:* new works by contemporary Italian authors *Venues:* Tempio di Giove Anxur (Terracina) *Second address:* Via di Porta San Lorenzo 4, 00185 Roma *Comments:* award 'Fondi la Pastora' for unpublished piece open to Italian and foreign authors who write in Italian – 10m Lire prize

Musicorum Tempora
c/o Arts Academy, Via G.A. Guattani 17, 00161 **Roma**
Tel: 06-4425 2208/2303
Fax: 06-4426 5224
Internet: www.artsacademy.com
E-Mail: artsacademy@mclink.it
artistic direction Maestro Francesco La Vecchia
Period/Frequency: July, annual
Arts types: classical music *Venues:* Villa Adriana di Tivoli

New Operafestival di Roma
c/o International Opera Academy,
Via dell' Idroscalo Nffl 2, 00121 **Roma**
direttore artistico Stefano Vignati; general direttore Marilyn Tyler; general manager Claudio Ferri
Period/Frequency: June-Aug, annual *Arts types:* opera, symphonic and chamber music *Venues:* Istituto S. Alessio up to 600 *Comments:* c/o Basilica di S. Clemente (p.zza S. Clemente), Tel/Fax: 06-991 2880

Nuovi Spazi Musicali – Festival di musica contemporanea
Via Divisione Torino 139, 00143 **Roma**
Tel: 06-502 1208 Fax: 06-502 1208
founder, president & artistic director Ada Gentile; vice-president & managing director
Dr Franco Mastroviti
Period/Frequency: Oct/Nov, annual *Arts types:* contemporary music (featuring many specially commissioned world premieres) *Venues:* Teatro dell'Acquario 350, Hungarian Academy Concert Hall 150, Polish Institute of Culture 150 *Comments:* member of the European Conference of Promoters of New Music

Romaeuropa Festival
Via XX Settembre, N. 3, 00187 **Roma**
Tel: 06-4890 4024
Fax: 06-4890 4030
Internet: www.romaeuropafestival.com
E-Mail: ROMAEUROPA@srd.it
direzione amministrativa Fabrizio Grifasi; direzione artistica Monique Veaute; responsabile organizativo Lucio Argano; presidente Sen. Giovanni Pieraccini
Period/Frequency: July, Oct, Nov, annual (2000: 25 June-8 July, 4 Oct-18 Nov) *Arts types:* contemporary dance, music *Venues:* Accademie, Embassy and theatres
Comments: alternative E-mails: fgrifasi@srd.it and largano@srd.it

Rumori Mediterranei – Festival Internazionale del Jazz di Roccella Jonica
c/o Associazione Culturale Jonica, Lungotevere Thaon di Revel,84 int.8, 00196 **Roma**
Tel: 06-322 2896/964-863 399/964-84473
Fax: 06-322 2896/964-84473
Internet: www.medianet1.it/roccellajazz/main.htm
E-Mail: acjr@tin.it
segretario generale Sergio Pinchera;
presidente Sisinio Zito;
artistic consultant Stefano Benni;
press office Paola Pinchera, Maurizio Quattrini;
adviser Vincenzo Staiano
Period/Frequency: last week of Aug, annual *Arts types:* jazz, recitals *Venues:* Teatro al Castello 2000, Auditorium Comunale 200 *Second Address:* Viale Degli Ulivi, 36-89047 Roccella Jonica (RC) *Comments:* American, European and Italian touring groups and original productions

Stagione Estiva
c/o Teatro dell'Opera di Roma Fondazione,
Via Firenze 72, 00184 **Roma**
Tel: 06-481 601 Fax: 06-488 1253
E-Mail: sovrintendenza@opera.roma.it
sovrintendente Francesco Ernani; presidente Francesco Rutelli; direttore artistico e musicale Giuseppe Sinopoli; maestro del coro Marcel Seminara
Period/Frequency: July-Aug, annual *Arts types:* opera, ballet, concerts *Venues:* Stadio Olimpico *Comments:* see also Opera, Dance, Orchestra and Venues

Todi Arte Festival
Via del Corso 530, 00186 **Roma**
Tel: 06-361 0892/3600 3435
Fax: 06-322 2873
direttori artistici e amministrative Simona Marchini, Walter Attanasi, Marco Marttolini; uffico stampa Gianna Volpi, Mila Sarti
Period/Frequency: Aug-Sept, annual *Arts types:* drama, dance, opera, video, cinema, exhibitions, poetry *Venues:* Piazza del Popolo, Sala del Capitano del Popolo, Sala delle Pietre, Monasterio delle Lucrezie – Teatro Comunale di Todi

Oriente Occidente
Incontri Internazionali di Rovereto,
Casella Postale 234, 38068 **Rovereto (TN)**
Tel: 0464-431 660
Fax: 0464-421 404
Internet: www.delta.it/oriente-occidente
E-Mail: oriente.occidente@pw.itnet.it
artistic director Lanfranco Cis, Paolo Manfrini; responsabile organizzazione Oriana Cescatti
Period/Frequency: Sept, annual *Arts types:* dance *Second Address:* Corso Bettini, 38068 Rovereto (TN)

Festival Musicale di Ravello
c/o Ente Provinciale Turismo,
Via Velia 15, 84100 **Salerno**
Tel: 089-231 432/800-213 289 (free phone)
Fax: 089-251 844
Internet: www.crmpa.it/ept
E-Mail: eptsa@xcom.it
amministratore generale dott. Antonio Pagano;
direttore artistico Roman Vlad;
direttore generale Vito Caponigro
Period/Frequency: June-July, annual *Arts types:* symphony and chamber music, ballet *Venues:* various venues in Ravello including Villa Rufolo (open-air) *Comments:* dedicated to R Wagner (operas)

Festival di San Gimignano
c/o Comune di S. Gimignano,
Piazza Duomo, 56037 **San Gimignano (SI)**
Tel: 0577-940 340/008 (tourist office)/941 269
Fax: 0577-940 112
Internet: www.sangimiano.com
E-Mail: prolocsg@tin.it
president dott. Stefano Del Seta
Period/Frequency: July-Aug, annual *Arts types:* music, opera *Venues:* Piazza del Duomo, churches

Festival di Santarcangelo dei Teatri
Associazione Santarcangelo dei Teatri, Contrada dei Fabbri 15, 47822 **Santarcangelo (RN)**
Tel: 0541-626 185/065 (press) Fax: 0541-620 560
Internet: www.santarcangelofestival.com
E-Mail: info@santarcangelofestival.com
direttore organizzativo Roberto Naccari; direttore artistico Silvio Castiglioni; codirettore artistico Massimo Marino; direttore organizzativo Roberto Vaccari
Period/Frequency: July, annual *Arts types:* contemporary theatre, Italian and foreign *Venues:* various theatres and venues thoughout the city

A L'Entrada del Temps Clar
Chiesa di San Bartolomeo, Via La Valle,
60047 **Sassoferrato (AN)**
Tel: 0732-21811/959 144
E-Mail: ago@pasena.it
presidente Giuseppe Zatti;
direttore artistico Marco Agostinelli
Period/Frequency: June, annual *Arts types:* polyphonic music, sacred & secular from 13th to 20th century
Venues: churches, main squares, local theatre

Festival Intercity Berlin
Via Gramsci 426, 50019 **Sesto Fiorentino (FI)**
Tel: 055-440 852 Fax: 055-440 852
Internet: www.teatro-limonaia.fi.it
E-Mail: info@teatro-limonaia.fi.it
amministrazione Annamaria Gasti; direzione artistica Barbara Nativi; ufficio stampa Bruno Casini; direzione organizzativo Barbara Nativi
Period/Frequency: Sept-Oct, annual *Arts types:* drama, meetings, readings *Venues:* Teatro Della Limonaia 100, different venues in Sesto F *Comments:* dedicated to a different city in the world every year: see also Venues

Festival Estivo di Musica da Camera
c/o Associazione Musicale "Ars Antiqua", casella postale 79, Via Vittorio Veneto 16/7,
16039 **Sestri Levante (GE)**
Tel: 0185-485 169 Fax: 0185-485 169
segretario generale Franca Campodonico; direttore artistico Vittorio Costa; direttore amministrativo Camilla Pigati; presidente Giulio Costa; vice presidente Francesco Gardella
Period/Frequency: July-Aug, annual *Arts types:* classical music, soloists, chamber, orchestras *Venues:* Auditorium Piazza Matteotti 200, Grand Hotel dei Castelli 200, Chiesa di S. Nicolò 500, Basilica dei Fieschi, Teatro Auditorium delle Clarisse *Comments:* organised by Associazione Musicale 'Ars Antiqua'; see also Promoters

Festival Settimana Musicale Senese
c/o Accademia Musicale Chigiana,
Via di Città 89, 53100 **Siena**
Tel: 0577-46152 Fax: 0577-288 124
Internet: www.chigiana.it
E-Mail: accademia.chigiana@chigiana.it
direttore amministrativo Mario Naldini;
presidente prof. Giovanni Grottanelli De'Santi;
direttore artistico Aldo Bennici
Period/Frequency: July, annual *Arts types:* classical music, chamber, symphony, opera *Venues:* Chiesa di Sant'Agostino 700, Cattedrale 1200, Teatro dei Rozzi 400 *Comments:* the first edition was in 1939;
see also Promoters

Ciclo Spettacoli Classici Teatro Greco
Istituto Nazionale Dramma Antico (Fondazione I.N.D.A.), Corso Matteotti 29, 96100 **Siracusa**
Tel: 0931-67415 Fax: 0931-21424
presidente Walter le Moli; direttore organizzativo t.b.a.
Period/Frequency: May/June, biennial (2000) *Arts types:* classical drama *Venues:* Teatro Greco di Siracusa 10000
Comments: performances of Greek classics in Italian; international meetings and courses on classical drama; see also Promoters

Spoleto Experimental Opera Season
Stagione del Teatro Lirico Sperimentale di Spoleto
Teatro Lirico Sperimentale di Spoleto 'A. Belli', Piazza G. Bovio n. 1, 06049 **Spoleto (PG)**
Tel: 0743-220 440/221 645 Fax: 0743-222 930
Internet: www.caribusiness.it/lirico
E-Mail: teatrolirico@mail.caribusiness.it
direttore organizzativo Claudio Lepore; president Carlo Belli; artistic director Michelangelo Zurletti; artistic assistant Nadia Nigris; administration Adele Capone; public relations Andrea Penna
Period/Frequency: Aug-Sept, annual *Arts types:* opera, chamber opera, concerts, lieder *Venues:* Teatro Nuovo, Teatro Caio Melisso, Teatri dell'Umbria *Comments:* the singers who perform are the winners of the European Community Competition, 1998/99; see also Promoters and Competitions

Spoleto Festival
Associazione Festival dei due Mondi,
P.zza Duomo n.8, 06049 **Spoleto (PG)**
Tel: 0743-45028/220 320/46644 (president)/223 041 (press) Fax: 0743-220 321/405/224 781 (press)
Internet: www.spoletofestival.com
E-Mail: pressoffice@spoletofestival.net
president & artistic director Francis Menotti; music section director Richard Hickox; press office Maria Bonmassar, christian Fousch, Leonardo Clausi
Period/Frequency: June-July, annual *Arts types:* opera, ballet, classical music, drama, exhibitions, cinema, crafts exhibitions *Comments:* alternative E-mails: artists@spoletofestival.net or tickets@spoletofestival.net;

Settimane Musicali di Stresa e del Lago Maggiore – Festival Internazionale
Via Canonica 6, 28838 **Stresa (VB)**
Tel: 0323-31095/30459 Fax: 0323-33006
Internet: www.stresa.net/settimanemusicali
E-Mail: settimanemusicali@stresa.net
president Giovan Battista Benvenuto
Period/Frequency: July-Aug-Sept, annual *Arts types:* classical music *Venues:* Theatre of the Conferences House – Stresa, The Tapestry Hall of Borromeo's Palace at Isola Bella, Loggia del Cashmere-Borromeo Gardens at Isola Madre, St. Ambrose's Church – Stresa, S.S. Gervasio e Protasio's Church – Baveno, Villa Pallavicino (Stresa), Collegio Rosmini (Stresa), Eremo di S. Caterina del Sasso (Leggiuno)and others
Comments: member of European Festivals Association

Festival Internazionale di Mezza Estate
Piazza Duca degli Abruzzi 35, 67069 **Tagliacozzo (AQ)**
Tel: 0863-614 202/3 Fax: 0863-614 227
direttore artistico Lorenzo Tozzi
Period/Frequency: July/Aug, annual *Arts types:* drama, dance, music and music theatre, opera *Venues:* Theatre Talia, outdoors, churches *Comments:* modern adaptations of rarely-performed operas and recupered operas

Taormina Arte
C.so Umberto 19, 98039 **Taormina**
Tel: 0942-21142 Fax: 0942-23348
Internet: www.taormina-arte.com
E-Mail: info@taormina-arte.com
segretario generale Antonino Panzera; direttore artistico musica e danza Gioacchino Lanza-Tomasi; direttore artistico teatro Giorgio Albertazzi; direttore artistico cinema Felice Laudadio
Period/Frequency: summer, annual *Arts types:* music, theatre, cinema, exhibitions, ballet *Venues:* Teatro Greco-Romano 5000, Palazzo dei Congressi 800/200

Festival Internazionale di Balletto Torino Danza
Piazza Castello 215, 10124 **Torino**
Tel: 011-88151 (switchboard) Fax: 011-881 5214
Internet: www.regio-torino.org
sovrintendente Teatro Regio di Torino Walter Vergnano; ufficio stamp Ugo Sandroni (tel: 011-881 5236, fax: 011-881 5268); direttore artistico Claudio Desderi; assistente alla direzione artistica per le attivita di danza Tiziana Tosco (tel: 011-881 5308)
Period/Frequency: October, biannual *Arts types:* classical, modern, contemporary dance *Venues:* Teatro Regio: Sala Grande 1592, Sala Piccola 388, cortile del palazzo Reale/ Teatro Carignano *Comments:* the festival is co-produced by Teatro Regio di Torino and the City of Torino, Via San Francesco da Paola 3, 10123 Torino

Festival Internazionale di Danza/Premio ACQUIDANZA (Acqui in Palcoscevco)
Compagnia di Danza Teatro di Torino,
Via Ormea 51, 10125 **Torino**
Tel: 011-473 0189
Fax: 011-473 2996
presidente e direttore artistico Loredana Furno; direttore organizzativo e segreteria ufficio cultura Aagni Terone, Bruno Ghione; tecnici di scena Franco d'Ambrosio, Enzo Galia
Period/Frequency: June/July/August *Arts types:* ballet, modern dance, music, opera *Venues:* Acqui Terme, Teatro all' Aperto *Second Address:* Comune di ACQUITERME assessrato alla Cultura Piazza Arrigo Levi 1 ACQUITERME (Alessandria) *Comments:* also organise award Aqui Danza, dance masterclass and competition, classical & contemporary dance concerts

Festival Internazionale di Musica Antica e Contemporanea Antidogma
c/o Antidogma Musica,
Via Cernaia 38, 10122 **Torino**
Tel: 011-542 936 Fax: 011-542 936
Internet: www.arpnet.it/~amusica
E-Mail: ecorreg@tin.it
presidente Dora Filippone;
direttore artistico Enrico Correggia
Period/Frequency: June-Oct, annual *Arts types:* concerts, performances *Venues:* Conservatorio G. Verdi 800 and various other historical venues around Piedmont *Comments:* organised by Antidogma Musica; Ensemble Antidogma tours abroad; see also Promoters

Gesto e l'Anima – Festival Internazionale di Danza, Il
c/o Fondazione Teatro Nuovo, Corso Massimo d'Azeglio 17, 10126 **Torino**
Tel: 011-650 0211/0256 (press office)
Fax: 011-650 0265
Internet: www.tntnuovo.it
E-Mail: nuovotnt@tin.it
direttore generale Gian Mesturino;
direttore amministrativo Lino Bongiovanni;
ufficio promozione Roberto Angi
Period/Frequency: Oct-May, annual *Arts types:* classical, modern, international dance *Venues:* Teatro Nuovo 1000, Torino; Teatro Civico 900, Vercelli; Teatro Comunale 500, Tortona *Comments:* organised by Fondazione Teatro Nuovo, see also Promoters and Agents & Producers

Settembre Musica
c/o Città di Torino, divisione Servizi Culturali, Via S. Francesco da Paola 3, 10123 **Torino**
Tel: 011-442 4715/4703 Fax: 011-442 4738
Internet: www.comune.torino.it/settembremusica/
E-Mail: settembre.musica@comune.torino.it
managing director Claudio Merlo;
artistic directors Enzo Restagno, Roman Vlad
Period/Frequency: Sept, annual *Arts types:* classical and contemporary symphonic and chamber concerts, seminars, jazz, avantgarde, ethnic

Vignale Danza – Festival Internazionale di Danza
c/o Fondazione Teatro Nuovo,
C.so Massimo d'Azeglio 17, 10126 **Torino**
Tel: 011-650 0211/0256 (press office)
Fax: 011-650 0265
Internet: www.tntnuovo.it
E-Mail: nuovotnt@tin.it
direttore generale Gian Mesturino;
direttore organizzativo Lino Bongiovanni;
ufficio promozione Roberto Angi;
ufficio stampa Alberto Angelino
Period/Frequency: June-Aug, annual *Arts types:* ballet, classical and modern dance, mime, drama, jazz, funk *Venues:* open-air theatre: Piazza del Popolo, Vignale, 1200 sitting & 2000 standing *Second Address:* summer address: Palazzo Callori, Vignale Monferrato, Tel: 0142-930 005, Fax: 0142-930 921 *Comments:* organised by Fondazione Teatro Nuovo; has dance stages, shows and competitions; see also Promoters, Agents & Producers

Itinerari Jazz a Trento
Centro Servizi Culturali Santa Chiara,
Via Santa Croce 67, 38100 **Trento**
Tel: 0461-986 488 Fax: 0461-231 044
direttore artistico Vincenzo Costa;
direttore Franco Oss Noser
Period/Frequency: April-May, annual
Arts types: jazz *Venues:* Auditorium Santa Chiara 838 seated, 100 standing

Trieste Operetta – Festival Internazionale Dell'Operetta
c/o Teatro Comunale Giuseppe Verdi,
Riva 3 Novembre 1, 34121 **Trieste**
Tel: 040-672 2111 Fax: 040-672 2249
Internet: www.teatroverdi-trieste.com
E-Mail: info@teatroverdi-trieste.com
sovrintendente Lorenzo Jorio;
segretario artistico Maestro Giovanni Pacor;
direttore del corpo di ballo Tuccio Rigano;
responsabile ufficio stampa e relazioni esterne Nicoletta Cavalieri;
direttore artistico Giandomenico Vaccari;
direttore di produzioni Gianni Gori
Period/Frequency: June-Aug, annual *Arts types:* operetta and musical theatre (musical) *Venues:* Teatro Giuseppe Verdi, Sala Tripcovich 934 *Comments:* see also Venues, Orchestras, Dance & Opera

Trieste Prima – Incontri Internazionali con la Musica Contemporanea
Chromas-Associazione Musica Contemporanea, Via Ponchielli 3, 34122 **Trieste**
Tel: 040-366 837 Fax: 040-366 837
Internet: www.tscont.trieste.it
E-Mail: paolocor@mailbox.iunet.it
presidente Adriano Martinolli;
direttore artistico Giampaolo Coral
Period/Frequency: Oct/Nov, annual *Arts types:* contemporary chamber music *Comments:* only dedicated to contemporary chamber music

Mittelfest
c/o Associazione Mittelfest, Stretta San Martino 4, Cividale del Friuli, 33043 **Udine**
Tel: 0432-730 793 Fax: 0432-701 099
Internet: www.regione.fvg.it/mittelfest
E-Mail: mittelfest@regione.fvg.it
presidente Avv. Giovanni Pelizzo
Period/Frequency: July, annual *Arts types:* drama, music, dance, cinema, puppetry & poetry from middle European countries, visual arts *Venues:* theatres, piazzas and streets around the city *Comments:* organised within the framework of the Central European Initiative; objective to promote vast cultural heritage of Central European countries, including 16 countries; see also Promoters

Estate Teatrale Veronese
Palazzo Barbieri, Piazza Bra 1, 37100 **Verona**
Tel: 045-807 7201/806 6489 (press office)
Fax: 045-806 6496 (press office)
Internet: www.comune.verona.it/home.html
E-Mail: estateteatrale@comune.verona.it
amministrazione Francesca Buniato; organizzazione e direzione artistica Gian Paolo Savorelli
Period/Frequency: June-Sept, annual *Arts types:* drama (Shakespeare), dance, music (jazz) *Venues:* Teatro Romano di Verona 2000 *Comments:* every year 2 Shakespeare productions and 1 Italian comedy of different authors

Festival dell' Arena di Verona
piazza Brà 28, 37121 **Verona**
Tel: 045-805 1811 (switchboard)/1891/1832 (press office)
Fax: 045-803 1443 (press office)/590 201/801 1566
Internet: www.arena.it
sovrintendente Renzo Giacchieri
Period/Frequency: June-Aug, annual *Arts types:* opera, ballet, concerts *Venues:* Arena di Verona 16000, Teatro Romano 3000 *Comments:* also conferences & exhibitions

Festival Internazionale Mimo e Dintorni
c/o Teatro Laboratorio,
Via Tommaso Da Vico 9, 37123 **Verona**
Tel: 045-803 1321/913 261
Fax: 045-803 1321
E-Mail: mscde@tin.it
direttore artistico Jana Balkan
Period/Frequency: Nov-Dec, annual *Arts types:* pantomime, mime, image theatre, dance
Venues: Teatro Laboratorio 200, Verona
Comments: see also Venues and Drama

LATVIA (+371)

International Piano Stars Festival
Pianisma zvaigßõu festivâls
Liepajas simfoniskais oríestris,
Graudu iela 50, 3401 **Liepaja**
Tel: 3-425 538 Fax: 3-481 478
E-Mail: lsovija@mail.anet.lv
Period/Frequency: annual

All Latvian Song and Dance Festival
Visparejie latviesu Dziesmu un Deju svetki
c/o E.Melngailis Folk Art Centre,
4 Pils laukums, 1050 **Riga**
Tel: 7-228 985 Fax: 7-227 405
E-Mail: festival@latnet.lv
Period/Frequency: quadrennial

International Baltic Ballet Festival
Starptautiskais Baltijas baleta festivals
Baznicas 4a, Floor 4, room 418, 1010 **Riga**
Tel: 7-220 513/9-288 318 (mobile)
Fax: 7-220 513
artistic director Lita Beiris
Period/Frequency: spring, annual *Arts types:* ballet

International Boys Choir Festival RIGAS DOMS
Starptautiskais zçnu koru festivals Rîgas Doms
Riga Dome Choir School,
10/12 Kalnciema, 1048 **Riga**
Tel: 7-611 950/246 9149/9-254 979 (mobile)
Fax: 7-246 9149
E-Mail: festival@rdks.lv
director Jânis Erenstreits
Period/Frequency: every five years

International Chamber Choir Festival Riga Dimd
Kamerkoru festivals Riga Dimd
Rigas domes Kulturas parvalde,
Valdemara iela 5, 1010 **Riga**
Tel: 7-320 941/944
Fax: 7-326 035
E-Mail: rdkp@latnet.lv
Period/Frequency: September, biennial
Arts types: chamber music, choral

International Early Music Festival
Starptautiskais Senas muzikas festivals
Riga Early Music Centre, 85 Brivibas, 1001 **Riga**
Tel: 2-275 575 Fax: 2-278 060
E-Mail: musbalt@com.latnet.lv
artistic director Solvita Sejane
Period/Frequency: July, annual

International Festival for Music Schools
Starptautiskais Bernu muzikas skolu audzekóu festivals
Culture Department of Riga City,
Valdemara iela 5, 1010 **Riga**
Tel: 7-320 941/944 Fax: 7-326 035
E-Mail: rdkp@latnet.lv
Period/Frequency: April, annual

International Festival of Contemporary Theatre HOMO NOVUS
Starptautiskais jaunâ teâtra festivâls HOMO NOVUS
The New Theatre Institute of Latvia, c/o RLB,
Meríéïa iela 13-426, 1050 **Riga**
Tel: 7-212 622 Fax: 7-212 471
E-Mail: jti@latnet.lv
director Peteris Krilovs; manager Edite Dancberga
Period/Frequency: October, biennial (2001)
Arts types: contemporary theatre

International Festival September Chamber Music Days
Starptautiskais festivals Septembra kamermuzikas dienas
Latvian Concert Agency, Kaïíu iela 11a, 1664 **Riga**
Tel: 7-213 426 Fax: 7-213 497
Period/Frequency: Sept, annual

International Folk Dance Festival Sudmalinas
Tautas deju festivals Sudmalinas
c/o E.Melngailis Folk Art Centre,
4 Pils laukums, 1050 **Riga**
Tel: 7-228 985 Fax: 7-227 405
E-Mail: festival@latnet.lv
manager of festival bureau Jânis Purviòs
Period/Frequency: triennial

International Folklore Festival Baltica
Folkloras festivals Baltica
c/o E.Melngailis Folk Art Centre,
4 Pils laukums, 1050 **Riga**
Tel: 7-228 985/326 589 Fax: 7-227 405
E-Mail: festival@latnet.lv
director of the festival Andris Kapusts
Period/Frequency: July, triennial

International J.S.Bach Music Week
Starptautiskâ J. S. Baha múzikas nedeïa
Latvian Concert Agency, Kaïíu iela 11a, 1664 **Riga**
Tel: 7-224 432 Fax: 7-213 497
Period/Frequency: before Easter, annual

International New Music Forum
Starptautiskais Jaunas muzikas Forums
Starptautiskais Jaunas muzikas centrs,
Jelgavas iela 25, 1004 **Riga**
Tel: 7-828 538 Fax: 7-828 538
artistic director Egils Straume
Arts types: contemporary music *Comments:* the largest contemporary music festival in the Baltics, comprises of more than 60 concerts, master classes and jazz music sessions

International Organ Music Festival Rîgas Doms
Starptautiskais erìeïmuzikas festivâls Rîgas Doms
Latvian Concert Agency, Kaïíu iela 11a, 1664 **Riga**
Tel: 7-224 432 Fax: 7-213 497
E-Mail: S.zake@bkc.lv
managing director Silvija Zaíe
Period/Frequency: July, annual

International Riga Jazz Festival – Jazz Forum
Rîgas dßeza festivâls – Dßeza forums
Starptautiskais Jaunâs mûzikas centrs,
Jelgavas iela 25, 1004 **Riga**
Tel: 7-828 538 Fax: 7-828 538
artistic director Egils Straume
Arts types: jazz

Nordic-Baltic Choir Festival
Ziemeïu un Baltijas valstu Dziesmu svetki
E. Melngailis Folk Art centre, Pils laukums 4, 1050 **Riga**
Tel: 7-228 985/227 405 Fax: 7-227 405
E-Mail: festival@latnet.lv
director Jânis Kurpnieks

Opera Music Festival in Sigulda
Opermuzikas svetki Sigulda
Biedriba Opermuzikas svetki Sigulda,
Kronvalda bulv. 2, 1929 **Riga**
Tel: 2-278 060 Fax: 7-222 384
managing director Dainis Kalns
Period/Frequency: July, annual *Type:* opera

Riga 2001 – European Cultural Month
Agency Riga 800, Torna 4, IB-103, 1050 **Riga**
Tel: 7-320 550
Fax: 7-320 609
Internet: www.riga800.lv
E-Mail: riga800@rcc.lv
director general Agency Riga 800 Inguna Ribena
Period/Frequency: August, 2001 *Arts types:* different types of arts *Comments:* the events are scheduled within the framework of the 800th anniversary of the City of Riga; the second organisation responsible is: Riga City Council Cultural Board, K. Valdemara 5, 1010 Riga, Latvia, Tel: 7-320 398, Fax: 7-326 035, E-mail: viktors@rcc.lv; Internet: www.rcc.lv

Riga Opera Festival
Rîgas Operas Festivâls
The Latvian National Opera,
Aspazijas bulv. 3, 1050 **Riga**
Tel: 7-223 927/1-225 747 Fax: 7-228 930
E-Mail: mail@opera.lv
project coordinator Dace Bula
Period/Frequency: June, annual

International Choir Music Festival
Starptautiskais koru muzikas festivals
Ventspils Kulturas centrs,
Kuldigas iela 18, 3600 **Ventspils**
Tel: 3-624 796 Fax: 3-623 796
Period/Frequency: July, biennial *Arts types:* choir music

LITHUANIA (+370)

International Festival of Young Musicians Kaunas
Tarptautinis jaunuju atlikeju festivalis Kaunas
L. Sapiegos 5, 3000 **Kaunas**
Tel: 7-222 558/626 802 Fax: 7-229 208/622 859
director of the festival Egidijus Miksys
Comments: only young musicians under the age of 16 years, winner of international competitions/festivals eligible

International Pazaislis Music Festival
Tarptautinis Pazaislio muzikos festivalis
Kaunas Philharmony, L. Sapiegos 5, 3000 **Kaunas**
Tel: 7-222 558 Fax: 7-229 208
E-Mail: kau.fil@kaunas.omnitel.net
director J Krépsta
Comments: organiser: Kaunas Philharmony

New Music Festival Kopa
Naujosios muzikos festivalis Kopa
Klaipeda Young Musicians Association,
Taikos pr. 73-7, 5810 **Klaipeda**
Tel: 6-230 037 Fax: 6-230 037
E-Mail: kjmd@klaipeda.omnitel.net
artistic director Loreta Budriuniene
Period/Frequency: May, annual

New Music Festival Mariu klavyrai
Naujosios muzikos festivalis Mariu klavyrai
Lithuanian Composer's Union, Klaipeda Department,
Kretingos 45-20, 5808 **Klaipeda**
Tel: 6-298 008 Fax: 6-298 008
artistic director Remigijus Sileika
Period/Frequency: October, annual

Thomas Mann Festival
Tomo Mano festivalis
Klaipedos apskr., **Neringa**
Tel: 59-52260/52622/2-220 841 Fax: 59-52856
E-Mail: mann@nida.omnitel.net
contact V Balciùnas

Baltic Modern Dance Festival
Baltijos siuolaikinio sokio festivalis
Totoriu St. 15-2, 2001 **Vilnius**
Tel: 2-223 641 Fax: 2-223 641
contact A Imbrasas
Period/Frequency: March, annual
Arts types: modern dance

Baltic Music Festival Gaida
Baltijos muzikos festivalis Gaida
Mickeviciaus 29, 2600 **Vilnius**
Tel: 2-223 611 Fax: 2-220 939
E-Mail: center@mipc.vno.osf.lt
chairman Gintaras Sodeika
Period/Frequency: Oct, annual *Arts types:* new music
Venues: Philharmonic Halls and other venues

Festival of Lithuanian Songs from all over the world
Pasaulio Lietuviu Dainu Svente
B Radvilaites 8, 2600 **Vilnius**
Tel: 2-611 190 Fax: 2-224 033
Comments: organiser: The Folk Cultural Centre

Festival of Music Action
Muzikinio veiksmo festivalis
Lithill Concert Agency, Universiteto 4, 2001 **Vilnius**
Tel: 2-220 304
Fax: 2-220 309
Internet: www.lithill.lt/festival/default.htm
E-Mail: public@lithill.lt
artistic director Tomas Ziburkus
Period/Frequency: December, annual

Festival of new music Jauna Muzika
Naujos muzikos festivalis Jauna Muzika
PO Box 2489, 2051 **Vilnius**
Tel: 2-263 291 Fax: 2-351 549
director Remigijus Merkelys
Arts types: new music

Folk Music Festival Skamba, Skamba Kankliai
Skamba, skamba kankliai Laudies Muzikos Festivalis
Gedimino pr 9, 2600 **Vilnius**
Tel: 2-791 287/971 288
Fax: 2-628 525
Comments: organiser: Ethnical Activity Centre

International Accordion Music Festival
Tarptautinis Akordeonistu Muzikos Festivalis
Vilniaus 39, 2001 **Vilnius**
Tel: 2-670 273/778 447/618 140 Fax: 2-226 982
president Ricardas Sviackevicius

International Festival of Ancient Music Banchetto Musicale
Tarptautinis Senosios Muzikos Festivalis
Gedimino pr.9, 2600 **Vilnius**
Tel: 2-615 084 Fax: 2-226 414
Comments: organisers:Cultural Department of the Vilnius City Council

International Festival of Piano Duets Siauliai
Siauliai Philharmony, Ausros Alèja 15, **Vilnius**
Tel: 1-435 743
contact B Mitkevicius

International Festival of the Young Performers Atzalynas
Tarptautinis jaunuju atlikeju festivalis Atzalynas
The National Philharmony, Ausros vartu 5, 2024 **Vilnius**
Tel: 2-626 802 Fax: 2-622 859
contact R Petraitis

International Folk Festival Baltica
Tarptautinis Folkloro Festivalis Baltica
B Radvilaites 8, 2600 **Vilnius**
Tel: 2-612 594/540 Fax: 2-224 033
E-Mail: lfcc@lfcc.lt

International Folk Festival of Instrumental Music
Tarptautinis Instrumentines Liaudies Muzikos Festivalis
B Radvilaites 8, 2600 **Vilnius**
Tel: 2-612 607 Fax: 2-224 033
manager of the festival Arturas Lunys
Comments: organisers: Vilnius Cultural Department, Folk Cultural Centre of Lithuania, Society of Lithuanian Musicians

Lithuanian International Theatre Festival (LIFE)
Lietuvos Tarptautinis Teatro Festivalis
J. Basanaviciaus str. 5, 2683 **Vilnius**
Tel: 2-625 158 Fax: 2-621 082
executive director Ruta Vanagaite
Comments: organiser: The Lithuanian International Theatre Festival LIFE

St Christopher's Summer Music Festival
Sv. Kristupo vasaros muzikos festivalis
Sv. Ignoto g 6, 2600 **Vilnius**
Tel: 2-623 114 Fax: 6-623 114
director Donatas Katkus
Period/Frequency: July/Aug, annual
Arts types: symphony music, contemporary chamber music, jazz, interdisciplinary projects

Trakai Festival
Traku festivalis
Basanaviciaus 5, 2683 **Vilnius**
Tel: 2-627 112/625 678 Fax: 2-625 678
E-Mail: petraitis@post.omnitel.net
managing director Romas Petraitis
Period/Frequency: July-Aug, annual *Arts types:* opera, ballet, symphony music, chamber music

Vilnius Festival
Vilniaus festival
c/o Lithuanian Philharmonic Society,
Ausros vartu 5, 2001 **Vilnius**
Tel: 2-626 802/627 094 Fax: 2-622 859
E-Mail: info@filharmonija.lt
festival director Gintautas Kevisas
Period/Frequency: May/July, annual *Arts types:* classical and contemporary music

Vilnius Jazz Festival
Vilniaus dziazo festivalis
PO Box 367, 2006 **Vilnius**
Tel: 2-230 448 Fax: 2-230 448
Internet: www.vilniusjazz.lt
E-Mail: office@vilniusjazz.lt
director Antanas Gustys
Arts types: jazz

Youth Chamber Music Days
Jaunimo kamerines muzikos dienos
Lithuanian Composers Union,
Mickeviciaus 29, 2600 **Vilnius**
Tel: 2-223 611 Fax: 2-220 939
E-Mail: center@mipc.vno.osf.lt
artistic director Gintaras Sodeika
Period/Frequency: May, annual

LUXEMBOURG (+352)

Echternach International Festival
Festival International d'Echternach (Luxembourg)
BP 30, 6401 **Echternach**
Tel: 728 347 Fax: 727 112
Internet: www.echternachfestival.lu
administrator Mariette Scholtes; art dir Cyprien Katsaris
Period/Frequency: May-June, annual *Arts types:* all types of classical music *Venues:* Basilique d'Echternach 750, Eglise St Pierre et Paul 450, Théâtre à Luxembourg 900, Conservatoire 600

Petits Concerts du Dimanche, Les Luxembourg
Comments: see entry in Belgium

World Music Days 2000 / ISCM
ISCM / LGNM, BP 828, 2018 **Luxembourg**
Tel: 225 821 Fax: 225 823
Internet: www.lgnm.lu
E-Mail: lgnm@lgnm.lu
art dir Marcel Wengler; administrator Luc Blasius
Period/Frequency: 29 Sept-8 Oct 2000
Arts types: contemporary music

European Festival of open air Theatre and Music in Wiltz
Festival Européen de Théâtre en plein air
et de Musique de Wiltz
Château de Wiltz, 9516 **Wiltz**
Tel: 958 145/957 441 Fax: 959 310
Internet:
www.restena.lu/culture/festival.de.wiltz.home.html
E-Mail: festival.wiltz@ci.culture.lu
président Roland Kinnen; conseiller artistique Fernand Koenig; secrétaire Nadia Breuer
Period/Frequency: July, annual *Arts types:* music, opera, operetta, jazz, dance (ballet), theatre in French, German and Luxembourgois *Venues:* hall omnisport 1200, amphithéâtre 3000, église basse 490, salles des fêtes de l'école primaire 320, église haute 310, salle des chevaliers 230 *Second Address:* Roland Kinnen, 33, route de Kautenbach, 9534 Wiltz, Tel: 352-957 057, Fax: 357-959 037

MACEDONIA (+389)

Ohrid Summer Festival
Ohridsko Leto
Kej Marsal Tito 1, 96000 **Ohrid**
Tel: 96-22304 (via operator) Fax: 96-21133
director Ljuben Batkovski
Period/Frequency: July-Aug *Arts types:* opera, music, drama

Theatre plays Vojdan Cernodrinski
Teatarski igri Vojdan Cernodrinski – Prilep
Marsal Tito bb, **Prilep**
Tel: 98-21703/25520/27308
Period/Frequency: June *Arts types:* theatre

Days of Macedonian music
Denovi na Makedonska muzika
Sojuz na kompozitori na Macedonian,
Maksim Gorki 18, **Skopje**
Tel: 91-220 567/234 953 Fax: 91-235 054
Period/Frequency: March/April, annual

Interfest – Bitola
Koncertna agencija Mak-Art – Skopje,
Nikola Grceto 6/15, **Skopje**
Tel: 91-611 051 Fax: 91-117 867
Period/Frequency: Oct *Arts types:* classical music

International Jazz Festival of Skopje
Internationalen Skopje dzez festival
Youth Cultural Center – Skopje,
Kej Dimitar Vlahov bb, 91000 **Skopje**
Tel: 91-111 508/115 225/233 401 Fax: 91-115 906
Period/Frequency: end of Oct *Arts types:* jazz

May Opera Evenings
Majski Operski Veceri
Kej Dimitar Vlahov bb, PF 153, 91000 **Skopje**
Tel: 91-114 908 Fax: 91-114 060
Period/Frequency: May *Arts types:* opera

Open Theatre Festival
Mlad otvoren teater
Kej Dimitar Vlahov bb, 91000 **Skopje**
Tel: 91-115 225 Fax: 91-115 906
director Ljubisa Nikodinovski
Period/Frequency: April/May; Aug/Sept, bi-annual *Arts types:* experimental, alternative theatre arts

Skopje summer
Skopsko leto
Kulturno-prosvetna zaednica na Skopje, Vasil Gorgov, baraka 4, PF 519, **Skopje**
Tel: 91-235 064
Period/Frequency: June/Aug, annual

Struga musical autumn
Struska muzicka esen
Union of Macedonian composers,
Maksim Gorki 18, 91000 **Skopje**
Tel: 91-220 567/234 953 Fax: 91-235 854
Period/Frequency: second part of Sept, annual

MALTA (+356)

Malta International Arts Festival
c/o Department of Culture, 230, Casa Gaspe, Republic Street, **Valletta** CMR 02
Tel: 231 914/232 515 Fax: 241 964
contact Joseph Mifsud
Period/Frequency: May-Set, annual *Arts types:* orchestral concerts and recitals, open-air theatre, ballet, folklore, jazz, folk singing

Malta International Choir Festival, The
c/o National Tourism Organisation-Malta, 280 Republic Street, **Valletta** CMR 02
Tel: 247 930 Fax: 220 401
Internet: www.tourism.org.mt
E-Mail: ntom.info@tourism.org.mt
director of events, chairman Piju Spiteri; secretary Janice Briffa
Period/Frequency: Nov, annual *Arts types:* choral music *Venues:* Mediterranean Conference Centre, Valletta 1400 *Comments:* see also Competitions

Malta Jazz Festival
Department of Culture, 230, Casa Gaspe, Republic Street, **Valletta** CMR 02
Tel: 231 914/232 515 Fax: 241 964
contact Joseph J. Mifsud
Period/Frequency: second half of July (3 days), annual *Arts types:* jazz – international performers *Venues:* Ta' Liesse, Valletta

MOLDOVA (+373)

International Festival of Opera and Ballet Stars Va invita Maria Biesu
Festivalul International al vedetelor de opera si balet Va invita Maria Biesu
Stefan cel Mare bld. 152, 2012 **Chisinau**
Tel: 2-238 258 Fax: 2-238 257
Period/Frequency: September, annual
Venues: National Opera Theatre

International Music and Dance Festival Martisor
21 Puskin str, 2012 **Chisinau**
Tel: 2-238 258
Fax: 2-238 257
manager Valentin Goga
Period/Frequency: March, annual
Venues: National Palace

MONACO (+377)

Printemps des Arts de Monte-Carlo
Direction des Affaires Culturelles, 4 bd des Moulins, 98000 **Monte Carlo**
Tel: 93-158 303/255 804
Fax: 93-506 694
directeur Rainier Rocchi; secrétaire général Rainier Rocchi; présidente S A La Princesse de Hanovre
Period/Frequency: April-May, annual *Arts types:* concerts, opera, ballet, théâtre *Venues:* Salle Garnier 550, Centre de Congrés Auditorium 1200, Salle des Variétes 350

NETHERLANDS (+31)

Delft Chamber Music Festival, The
Graaf Willemlaan 52, 1181 EH **Amstelveen**
Tel: 20-643 2043
Fax: 20-640 3961
Internet: www.cmr.nl/delftmusic
E-Mail: mbrinks@xs4all.nl
artistic director Isabelle van Keulen; managing director Marianne Brinks
Period/Frequency: Aug, annual (ten days)
Arts types: chamber music *Venues:* Van der Mandele Zaal, Museum Het Prinsenhof 350 *Comments:* ticket sales: Museum Het Prinsenhof Delft, Tel: 15-260 2602

Holland Festival
Kleine-Gartmanplantsoen 21, 1017 RP **Amsterdam**
Tel: 20-530 7110
Fax: 20-530 7119
Internet: www.hollandfestival.nl
E-Mail: info@hollandfestival.nl
festival director Ivo van Hove; managing director Jacques van Veen
Period/Frequency: June, annual *Arts types:* opera, concerts, dance, theatre, film, exhibitions
Venues: various in Amsterdam

International Gaudeamus Music Week
Swammerdamstraat 38, 1091 RV **Amsterdam**
Tel: 20-694 7349 Fax: 20-694 7258
Internet: www.xs4all.nl/~gaud
E-Mail: gaud@xs4all.nl
director Henk Heuvelmans
Period/Frequency: Sept, annual
Arts types: new music *Venues:* De Ijsbreker, Beurs van Berlage, Paradiso etc. *Comments:* organised by Gaudeamus Foundation, see also National Organisations and Competitions

International Percussion Festival The Big Bang
c/o The Office, Performing Arts Management, Keizersgracht 261, 1016 EC **Amsterdam**
Tel: 20-622 6979
Fax: 20-622 9081
E-Mail: kantoor@euronet.nl
contact E Willemsen, L Schipper, J de Heer
Period/Frequency: Jan/Feb, biennial (2000) *Arts types:* international percussion groups and soloists *Venues:* Den Haag, Utrecht, Amsterdam, Brussels, Hamburg e.o. *Second Address:* Keyser 18, Media Producties, Postbus 51169, 1007 ED Amsterdam
Comments: see also Agents & Producers

Julidans Festival
c/o Van Baasbank & Baggerman, Keizersgracht 258, 1016 EV **Amsterdam**
Tel: 20-624 2631/627 6818 Fax: 20-622 7850
Internet: www.xs4all.nl/~ssba/julidans.htm
E-Mail: baasbank.baggerman@wxs.nl
contact Jaap van Baasbank
Period/Frequency: July, annual *Arts types:* modern dance *Venues:* Stadsschouwburg, 3 spaces: 900, Theatre Bellevue 250, Paradiso 1200 (standing) *Comments:* organised in conjunction with Stadsschouwburg- contact address: Leidseplein 26, 1017 PT Amsterdam, Tel: 20-523 7700; Fax: 20-623 8685; see also Agents & Producers and Puppetry

Klap op de Vuurpijl
c/o Willem Breuker Kollektief, Prinseneiland 99, 1013 LN **Amsterdam**
Tel: 20-623 9799 Fax: 20-624 3534
Internet: www.xs4all.nl/~wbk/
E-Mail: wbk@xs4all.nl
manager Susanna von Canon; art dir Willem Breuker
Period/Frequency: Dec, annual *Arts types:* contemporary classical music, jazz *Comments:* see also Orchestras

Meervaart in de Knop
Meer en Vaant 300, 1068 LE **Amsterdam**
Tel: 20-410 7713 Fax: 20-410 7789
Internet: www.meervaart.nl
E-Mail: info@meervaart.nl
contact Sophie Lambo
Period/Frequency: February, annual *Arts types:* all performing arts, focus on new talents *Venues:* De Meervaart 850 *Comments:* also a contest Meervaart in de Knop Talenten Jacht; see also Venues

October Meeting
Bimhuis Oude Schans 73-77, 1011 KW **Amsterdam**
Tel: 20-623 3373 Fax: 20-620 7759
Internet: www.bimhuis.nl
E-Mail: bimhuis@bimhuis.nl
artistic director Huub Van Riel; publicity Karin Klooster; technician Marijn Philippona
Period/Frequency: every couple of years, not regular (depends on funds) *Arts types:* jazz, improvised music *Venues:* Bimhuis and small-mid scale venues in and around Amsterdam *Comments:* international meeting of leading jazz musicians; emphasis on performances of new unpublished compositions and improvised music; held irregularly but approximately every 4 years

Orlando Festival – International Chamber Music Festival – Kerkrade
Keizersgracht 261, 1016 EC **Amsterdam**
Tel: 20-623 0469 Fax: 20-622 9081
Internet: home.wxs.nl/~orlandofestival
E-Mail: orlandofestival@wxs.nl
manager Isabelle Bensa; artistic director Stefan Metz; organisation Evelyn Swemk
Period/Frequency: July/Aug, annual *Arts types:* chamber music *Venues:* Rolduc, Kerkrade 600, Wijngrachttheater 600 *Comments:* Chamber Music Academy during festival; also vocal course

Rotterdam Music Festival
c/o Gaudeamus Foundation, Henk Heuvelmans, Swammerdamstr. 38, 1091 RV **Amsterdam**
Tel: 20-694 7349 Fax: 20-694 7258
Internet: www.xs4all.nl/~gaud/
E-Mail: gaud@xs4all.nl
contact Arthur van der Drift
Period/Frequency: biennial (2001)

Triple X Festival
van Diemenstraat 410, 1013 CR **Amsterdam**
Tel: 20-420 5316 Fax: 20-638 9160
Internet: www.triplex.nl
E-Mail: triplex@xs4all.nl
contact, arts director Hay Schoolmeesters
Period/Frequency: August, annual *Arts types:* music, dance, theatre, performance art, visual arts exhibition, new media *Venues:* Westergasfabriek, Amsterdam

Festival Images
PO Box 1103, 6801 BC **Arnhem**
Tel: 26-370 3001 Fax: 26-443 4396
E-Mail: images@kref.nl
artistic and managing director Henk Boerhof
Period/Frequency: biennial (2000: 22-30 Sept)
Arts types: puppetry, object and visual theatre, mime & dance *Venues:* Schouwburg 600, 200, Museum of Modern Art & other venues in town *Second Address:* Koningsplein 12, 6811 BC Arnhem *Comments:* see also Promoters and Venues

International Choir Festival
2001 **Arnhem**
Tel: 30-231 3174 Fax: 30-231 8137
Internet: www.snk.nl
E-Mail: snk@euronet.nl
managing dir J Schrejner; musical dir Harold Lenselink
Period/Frequency: summer, quadrennial (2001) *Arts types:* all categories of choirs, standard repertoire, world music (50 concerts, 1 contest) *Venues:* Arnhem; various concert halls, churches, open air

North Sea Jazz Festival
PO Box 3325, 2601 DH **Delft**
Tel: 15-214 8900/215 7756 (information line)
Fax: 15-214 8393
Internet: www.northseajazz.nl
management Theo van den Hoek
Period/Frequency: second weekend in July, annual *Arts types:* jazz and jazz related music *Venues:* Netherlands Congress Centre Den Haag: one building – 15 stages plus roof terrace *Comments:* to order tickets in London phone +44 171-278 8623 (Mole Jazz)

Holland Dance Festival
Nobelstraat 21a, 2513 BC **Den Haag**
Tel: 70-361 6142 Fax: 70-365 0509
Internet: www.wxs.nl/~hdf
E-Mail: hdf@wxs.nl
general director Louise Helmer; artistic director Samuel Wuersten; office coordinator Aat Seger; project manager Martine van Dÿk
Period/Frequency: biennial (2001) *Arts types:* dance *Venues:* 5 venues, total 2601

International Micro Puppet Festival
International Micro Poppenfestival
Aardappelmarkt 9, 3311 BA **Dordrecht**
Tel: 78-614 0342 Fax: 78-614 1453
E-Mail: damiet@wxs.nl
manager Chris de Jong; artistic director & publicity Damiet van Dalsum
Period/Frequency: June, annual *Arts types:* all types of puppetry *Venues:* Damiet Van Dalsum Theatre 60, Kunstmin 180, Pictura 100, Houze Voorstraat N. 125, 80, Berckenpoort 90 *Comments:* see also Puppetry

Limburg Festival
Markt 1, 6161 GE **Geleen**
Tel: 46-478 4344
Fax: 46-475 8084
president Jan van den Berg; artistic administrator Tony Boersma; coordinator Charles Mersmans
Period/Frequency: Aug, annual *Arts types:* international professional street theatre, indoor theatre *Venues:* the province of Limburg in 44 cities, towns and villages, in Belgium, Germany and the Netherlands *Second Address:* Stichting Limburg Festival, PO Box 6835, 5975 ZG Sevenum Tel: 6-5398 0158 Fax: 77-467 2801

Noorderzon
PO Box 1736, 9701 BS **Groningen**
Tel: 50-314 0278 Fax: 50-312 0119
Internet: come.to/cultuurpaleis/
E-Mail: paleis@xs4all.nl
director Diederik van der Meide
Period/Frequency: Aug., annual
Arts types: theatre, music, dance

Cultura Nova
Stadsschouwburg Heerlen, PB 300, Burgemeester van Grunsvenplein 145, 6400 AH **Heerlen**
Tel: 45-576 8576
Fax: 45-571 8794
contact B. M.Schoonderwoerd; project manager H. J. W. N. Engelen
Period/Frequency: mid-Aug to mid-Sept, annual *Arts types:* modern theatre (new & contemporary), multi-media, modern dance, action theatre, exhibitions, film & lectures *Venues:* several locations in Heerlen

International Baroque Festival Amsterdam
PO Box 2277, 2301 CG **Leiden**
Tel: 71-514 0235
Fax: 71-566 3066
E-Mail: fredluiten@hetnet.nl
contact Fred Luiten
Period/Frequency: May, annual *Arts types:* baroque music, solo recitals, choir, orchestras, chamber music, opera, oratorio etc. *Venues:* Concertgebouw 2000, Beurs van Berlage 650, Westerkerk 1000, Engelse Kerk 350 *Comments:* see also Promoters (Fred Luiten Concert Series)

Musica Sacra
PO Box 882, 6200 AW **Maastricht**
Tel: 43-350 5546
Fax: 43-350 5522
Internet: www.theataraanhetvrijthof.nl
E-Mail: theataraanhetvrijthof@uitbalie.nl
director Piet van Hest; programming Jos Zwietink
Period/Frequency: third weekend in Sept, annual
Arts types: sacred music from various religious backgrounds; also dance, film *Venues:* mainly in churches in Maastricht *Comments:* each year the festival has a special theme

New Music Festival Maastricht
Stichting Intro, St Maartenspoort 2, 6221 BA **Maastricht**
Tel: 43-325 0511/3453
Fax: 43-325 7488
director Paul Coenjaarts
Period/Frequency: annual (different times each year) *Arts types:* new music, performance art *Venues:* theatres and parks in Maastricht *Comments:* see also Promoters

Festival Nieuwe Muziek
Centre for New Music, Kloveniersdoelen, Achter de Houttuinen 30, PO Box 15, 4330 AA **Middelburg**
Tel: 118-623 650
Fax: 118-624 754
Internet: www.zeelandnet.nl/cnnzld
E-Mail: cnnzld@zeelandnet.nl
director Ad van't Veer
Period/Frequency: June/July, annual
Arts types: contemporary music, improvisation *Venues:* concert hall, Kloveniersdoelen 160, Big Church, Veere 300-1000 *Comments:* see also Promoters

Muziek Festival Naarden
Prins Willems van Oranjelaan 4, 1412 GK **Naarden**
Tel: 35-678 1790 Fax: 35-678 1791
festival director Max Snijder
Period/Frequency: second weekend in May, biennial (2000: 11-14 May) *Arts types:* classical music, baroque-classical-romantic-contemporary, accent of vocal repertoire *Venues:* Grot Kerk 1500, Theaterzaal 200, The Old Cityhall 150, Katholic Curch 400

Rotterdam 2001 European City of Culture
Rotterdam 2001 Culturele Hoofdstad van Europa
PO Box 21362, 3001 AJ **Rotterdam**
Tel: 10-402 2001 Fax: 10-213 1160
Internet: www.rotterdam01.nl
E-Mail: rch@rotterdam01.nl
Intendant Bert van Meggelen; executive secretary Elisabeth Groot; programme council secretary Angélique de Meijer; business director Johan Moerman; marketing & communication Henze Pegman; responsible for the portfolio of the multicultural domain Mira Kho; responsible for the socio-cultural portfolio Carolien Dieleman *Comments:* visiting address: Mauritsweg 4, Rotterdam

Rotterdam Philharmonic Gergiev Festival
c/o Rotterdam Philharmonic Orchestra, de Doelen, Kruisstraat 2, 3012 CT **Rotterdam**
Tel: 10-217 1789
Fax: 10-411 6215
E-Mail: festival@repho.nl
artistic director Rotterdam Philharmonic Orchestra Kees Hillen; festival coordination Hans Verbugt
Period/Frequency: Sept, annual *Arts types:* symphony, chamber, opera *Venues:* de Doelen 2200

Boulevard s'Hertogenbosch
PO Box 1704, 5200 BT **s'-Hertogenbosch**
Tel: 73-612 4505(festival office)
Fax: 73-612 4544(festival office)
Internet: www.bossenova.nl
E-Mail: festival.boulevard@wxs.nl
festival director Wim Claessen
Period/Frequency: Aug, annual *Arts types:* theatre, music and dance performances, outdoor theatre, children's theatre *Venues:* Parade Square and several neighbouring locations *Second Address:* Colveniersstraat 4, 5211 AV, s'-Hertogenbosch (address office) *Comments:* during the festival hold a special project called La Strada, for art and theatre, held in cooperation with Belgium

Oerol Festival
Postbus 327, 8890 AA **Terschelling**
Tel: 562-448 448
Fax: 562-449 087
Internet: www.oerol.nl
E-Mail: oerol@frieslandnet.nl
artistic director Joop Mulder
Period/Frequency: June, annual *Arts types:* music, theatre, sculpture, street theatre, site-specific theatre *Venues:* various locations throughout the island

Festival a/d Werf
Boorstraat 107, 3513 SE **Utrecht**
Tel: 30-231 5355 (bookings)/53844 (office)
Fax: 30-233 2716
E-Mail: adwerf@wxs.nl
organiser/artistic director Jeffrey Meulman; financial director Koen van Dijk; theatre programme Marcel Bogers; visual arts programme Moritz Küng; music programme Jacqueline Oskamp; producer Esther Willemse; publicity Lian Rynga
Period/Frequency: May, annual
Arts types: theatre, music, art, dance, visual arts *Venues:* theatres all over Utrecht; Huis ald Werf – own venue; music marquee in town centre

Holland Festival Early Music Utrecht
Postbus 734, 3500 AS **Utrecht**
Tel: 30-236 2236
Fax: 30-232 2798
Internet: www.oudemuziek.nl
E-Mail: oom@oudemuziek.nl
executive producer Tineke de Ruiter van der Wal; director Casper Vogel
Period/Frequency: Aug-Sept, annual *Arts types:* early music, song recitals, chamber music, choral song recitals, opera & music theatre, world music *Venues:* various medieval and historic locations and Vredenburg *Comments:* also organise Network for Early Music, countrywide, October-June; 400 concerts in Festival and Network: see also Promoters

Springdance Festival
PO Box 111, 3500 AC **Utrecht**
Tel: 30-233 2032 Fax: 30-231 9364
Internet: home.wxs.nl/~spdance
E-Mail: springdance@wxs.nl
general & artistic director Guy Gypens; general manager Dianne Zuidema; production manager Yvonne Fuchs
Period/Frequency: April, biennial *Arts types:* modern dance, physical theatre, dance cinema *Venues:* in 5 or more venues in Utrecht

Streetfestival Vlissingen
Straatfestival Vlissingen
c/o Uit in Vlissingen, Postbus 5105, 4380 KC **Vlissingen**
Tel: 118-415 244/416 662 Fax: 118-412 648
E-Mail: uiv@zeelandnet.nl
organiser Klaas Overdam
Period/Frequency: 1st week of July, annual *Arts types:* street theatre, world music, outdoor theatre, small indoor theatre, projects *Venues:* indoor & outdoor up to 20000 *Comments:* applications to perform to be received before the end of each year

NORWAY (+47)

Autunnale Festival of Contemporary Music
Autunnale Festival for Samtidsmusikk
c/o Ny Musikk Bergen, Georgernes Verft 3, 5011 **Bergen**
Tel: 5556 0444/0374/5536 0656 Fax: 5556 0374/0444
director André Stene Johnsen
Period/Frequency: autumn, annual
Arts types: contemporary music

Bergen 2000 – European City of Culture
Postboks 434, Sentrum, 5001 **Bergen**
Tel: 5555 2000 Fax: 5555 2001
Internet: www.bergen2000.no
E-Mail: bergen.2000@bergen2000.no
director Terje Gloppen; marketing & information coordinator Mirella Bodini; admin. coordinator economy & programme Torill Nøstvåg; marketing director Kristian B. Jørgensen; information director Gina Winje; arts coordinator Ingebjørg Astrup, Tone Tjemsland, Harm-Christian Toulden, William Hazell
Period/Frequency: throughout the year 2000 (17 Feb-3 Dec) *Arts types:* performing and visual arts *Second Address:* Vagsallmenningen 1, 5001 Bergen
Comments: Bergen is one of nine European Cities of Culture in the year 2000

Bergen International Festival
Festspillene i Bergen
PO Box 183, 5001 **Bergen**
Tel: 5521 0630 Fax: 5521 0640
Internet: www.fib.no
E-Mail: info@fib.no
artistic and managing director Bergljót Jónsdóttir; manager press & public relations Henning Maalsnes (henning.malsnes@fib.no);
finance director Arnstein Drivenes
Period/Frequency: May, annual *Arts types:* orchestra, opera, recitals, ballet, theatre, dance, outdoor events/street performances *Venues:* Grieg Hall 1500, Bergen National Theatre 80-450, Kings Medieval Hall 430, Dance Theatre 300, Troldhaugen 200, Lysøen 90, Siljustøl 60, churches, Logen Chamber Music Hall *Second Address:* visiting address: Bryggen 9, 5th floor, 5003 Bergen *Comments:* Patron:
His Majesty King Herald V

Music Factory Contemporary Music Festival
Grieghallen, Edvard Griegs plass 1, 5015 **Bergen**
Tel: 5521 6120/2269 8342 Fax: 5521 6170
Internet: www.musicfactory.no
E-Mail: mail@musicfactory.no
director James Clapperton
Period/Frequency: May-June (10 days), annual
Arts types: contemporary music

Night Jazz International Jazz Festival
Nattjazz
Postboks 1957, Nordnes, 5817 **Bergen**
Tel: 5532 0976 Fax: 5556 0070
Internet: www.bgnett.no/nattjazz/
E-Mail: nattjazz@bgnett.no
co-directors Jon Skjerdal, Tom Svendsgård
Period/Frequency: May-June (10 days), annual *Arts types:* ranges from traditional jazz (bebop, hard bop, jazz rock, fusion & funk) to world music though the main focus is on the transition between modern jazz, rock and folk music

Oktober Dance Norway
Oktoberdans Norge
Nøstegaten 54, 5011 **Bergen**
Tel: 5523 2235
Fax: 5523 18115
Internet: www.bgnett.no/bit
E-Mail: bit@bgnett.no
artistic director Sven Åge Birkeland;
production directors Mette Helgesen, Lars Ove Toft
Period/Frequency: October, biennial (2000, 2002) *Arts types:* dance, contemporary dance, performances, masterclasses, symposiums

Nordland Music Festival
Nordland Musikkfestuke
PO Box 319, 8001 **Bodø**
Tel: 7552 2398 Fax: 7552 2387
Internet: www.nordland-musikkfestuke.no
E-Mail: nmfu@nordland-musikkfestuke.no
director Roar Leinan
Period/Frequency: July-Aug, annual *Arts types:* classical and other music, music theatre *Venues:* various

International Band Music Festival, Hamar
Janitsjarfestivalen Hamar
Postboks 65, 2301 **Hamar**
Tel: 6251 0530
festival secretary Kaja Gulden
Period/Frequency: June (10 days), biennial (2001, 2003)
Arts types: orchestras, choirs and bands, night concerts, shows, street theatre

International Church Music Festival in Kristiansand
Internasjonalt kirkefestspill
PO Box 321, 4601 **Kristiansand**
Tel: 3812 0940/3802 1311 Fax: 3812 0949/3802 7522
Internet: www.kirkefistspille.no
E-Mail: intkirke@online.no
senior administration Øystein Eidsaa; artistic director Andrew Wilder (cathedral organist, conductor)
Period/Frequency: May, annual *Arts types:* church music, chamber music, organ music, oratorios, art exhibition, seminar *Venues:* Kristiansand Cathedral 1600 *Second Address:* Gyldenløvesgate 9, 4611 Kristiansand

International Puppet Theatre Festival
Internasjonal figurteater festival
Postboks 582, 4601 **Kristiansand**
Tel: 3812 2888 Fax: 3812 2880
Internet: www.agderteater.va.no
E-Mail: teateras@online.no
general manager Nina Hammersmark
Period/Frequency: October (6 days), biennial *Arts types:* visual theatre, puppet theatre, there are also seminars, presentations, exhibitions, street theatre and parades, plays for children, adolescents and adults *Comments:* some of the plays for children tour the two Agder counties during the festival period; visiting address: Agder Teater, 4601 Kristiansand

Kristiansund Opera Festival
Operafestivalen i Kristiansund
Midt-Norsk Musikkteater,
King Olav Vs gate 1, **Kristiansund**
Tel: 7158 9960 Fax: 7158 9961
Internet: www.oik.no
E-Mail: opera@oik.no
director Olav Gridnes
Period/Frequency: February (14 days), annual *Arts types:* musical theatre, also conferences

Lillehammer Jazz Festival Døla-jazz
Postboks 566, 2601 **Lillehammer**
Tel: 6125 3297 Fax: 6128 8200
Internet: www.dolajazz.no
E-Mail: bjorn.norstegard@hil.no
director Trond Johnsen
Period/Frequency: October (4 days), annual
Arts types: mainly Norwegian and Nordic jazz, but also includes a range of performances by leading international performers

Molde International Jazz Festival
Sandvn. 1A, PO Box 261, 6401 **Molde**
Tel: 7120 3150/7121 6000/7125 5267
Fax: 7125 3635
Internet: www.moldejazz.no
E-Mail: moldejazz@moldejazz.no
director Thorstein Granly
Period/Frequency: July, annual *Arts types:* jazz and other related forms of rhythmic contemporary music *Venues:* capacity 100-400, largest concert hall 2500, outdoor venue 8500 *Comments:* member of: European Jazz Festival Organisation, Norwegian Jazz Federation Norway Festivals; a non-profit making organisation; free concerts at the outdoor venue

Du store verden! Multi Cultural Festival
Postboks 4642 Sofienberg, 0506 **Oslo**
Tel: 2211 6412
Fax: 2211 5123
Internet: www.du-store-verden.no
E-Mail: du.store.verden@online.no
director Kirsti Knudsen
Period/Frequency: Oct-Nov (22 days), annual
Arts types: foreign music, dance, theatre, literature, film and fine arts

Ibsen Stage Festival
Ibsen festivalen
Nationaltheatret, Johanne Dybwads Plass 1, 0161 **Oslo** 1
Tel: 2200 1400 (administration)/2241 1640/2242 4343
Fax: 2200 1699 (admin)/1686 (marketing/info)/2242 4343
Internet: www.sol.no/nationaltheatret
E-Mail: national@sn.no
artistic director Ellen Horn; programme director Gerd Stahl; info/press director Ragnhild Samuelsberg; marketing director Thine Slletbak

Period/Frequency: end Aug-beginning Sept, biennial (2000) *Arts types:* featuring Ibsen plays or performances based on Ibsen's work produced by Nationaltheatret and companies from all over the world in their local language; Festival also has a fringe with art exhibitions, films, concerts etc. *Venues:* Nationaltheatret, main stage 773, Amfiscenen 231, Torshovteatret 160, back stage up to 100 *Comments:* alternative E-mail: national@online.no

Oslo Chamber Music Festival
Oslo kammermusikkfestival
Grev Wedels Plass 2, 0151 **Oslo**
Tel: 2310 0730 Fax: 2310 0731
Internet: www.oslokammermusikkfestival.no
managing director Charlotte Winsnes;
artistic director Arve Tellefsen
Period/Frequency: August, annual *Arts types:* chamber music (in the widest sense of the term)
Venues: venues in Oslo

Oslo Jazz Festival
Tollbugata 28, 0157 **Oslo**
Tel: 2242 9120
Fax: 2242 9125
Internet: www.notam.uio.no/oslojazz/
E-Mail: oslojazz@notam.uio.no
director Aage Teigen
Period/Frequency: August (6 days), annual *Arts types:* jazz, traditional swing, modern and bebop styles

ULTIMA-Oslo Contemporary Music Festival
Tollbugata 28, 0157 **Oslo**
Tel: 2242 9999 Fax: 2242 4218
Internet: wwwl.ultima.no
E-Mail: info@ultima.no
head of production Howard Gamble; festival director Geir Johnson; information/public relations Beate Styri, Håvard Lund, Trine Vollan
Period/Frequency: Oct, annual *Arts types:* contemporary music, film, dance & related art forms, opera
Venues: Oslo Concert Hall, The Norwegian State Opera, Old Masonic Hall, Black Box Theatre, The University Auditorium, Rockefeller Music Hall, Oslo Cathedral, The Norwegian State Academy of Music, Cosmopolite Music Hall, Belleville and Det Norske Teatret
Comments: ULTIMA Oslo Contemporary Music Festival is Norway's largest contemporary music festival; it is a unique initiative within Norwegian cultural life; a foundation where sixteen of the largest institutions and organisations within the professional musical sphere co-ordinate their resources and contribute their expertise towards the attainment of a common goal

Porsgrunn International Theatre Festival
Porsgrunns Internasjonale teaterfestival
Huken 5, 3921 **Porsgrunn**
Tel: 3555 5169 Fax: 3555 1940
nternet: www.telemarksnett.no/friteateret/pit
:-Mail: grenfrit@online.no
.estival director Trond Hannemyr
Period/Frequency: May-June (8 days), annual
Arts types: popular theatre, avant garde, masterclass programmes, children's programmes and a large number of performances by companies from Norway, Belgium, Poland, Russia, Colombia, Wales and Italy

International Chamber Music Festival (ICMF)
Stavanger internasjonale kammermusikkfestival
Sandvigå 27, 4007 **Stavanger**
Tel: 5184 6670 Fax: 5184 6673
Internet: www.icmf.no
E-Mail: icmf@online.no
dept manager Sine Bjørnevik;
artistic director Truls Mørk
Period/Frequency: Aug, annual *Arts types:* chamber music *Venues:* 12th cent Stavanger Cathedral, Rogaland Art Museum, Bjergsted Music Complex and other unique locations such as the medieval Utstein Monastery *Second Address:* International Summer Academy, Sandvigå 27, 4007 Stavanger *Comments:* also masterclasses; alternative web-site: www.icmf.no/isa/isa.html

MaiJazz – Stavanger International Jazz Festival
MaiJazz – Stavanger internasjonale jazzfestival
Postboks 6, 4001 **Stavanger**
Tel: 5184 6667
Fax: 5184 6673
Internet: www.maijazz.no/maijazz99.htm
E-Mail: maijazz@sn.no
director Hasse Andersen
Period/Frequency: May (4 days), annual *Arts types:* jazz
Comments: alternative E-mail: stene@maijazz.no

Vestfold festspillene / Vestfold International Festival
PB 500, 3101 **Tønsberg**
Tel: 3330 8850
Fax: 3330 8860
Internet: www.vestfoldfest.no
E-Mail: info@vestfoldfest.no
director Birger Carlsen; artistic director Odd Terje Lysebo; administrator Kristin Saga
Period/Frequency: end of June – 2nd week July, annual
Arts types: music, theatre, dance

Northern Lights Festival
Nordlysfestivalen
PO Box 966, 9001 **Tromsø**
Tel: 7768 9070 Fax: 7768 9260/9301
Internet: www.nmok.org/nordfest
E-Mail: sundels@online.no
director Else Sundquist
Period/Frequency: Jan, annual *Arts types:* classical concerts-recitals, symphony, chamber music, music films, exhibitions, special concerts *Venues:* Kulturhuset in Tromsø 700, Bank Salen 150, Cathedral 750

Varanger Festival
Varangerfestivalen
Postboks 356, 9801 **Vadsø**
Tel: 7895 3120/3851 Fax: 7895 1490
Internet: www.home.eunet.no/~vadsjazz/
E-Mail: vadsjazz@eunet.no
director Kjell Magne Stålsett
Period/Frequency: August (5 days), annual

POLAND (+48)

Theatre Week
Tydzien Teatru
Teatr im Aleksandra Wegierki,
Elektryczna 12, 15-080 **Bialystok**
Tel: 85-741 5990 Fax: 85-741 6622
Internet: www.bialystok.telbank.pl/teatr
Period/Frequency: end of March, annual

International Festival of Puppetry Art
Miedzynarodowy Festiwal Sztuki Lalkarskiej
Osrodek Teatralny Banialuka,
ul. Mickiewicza 20, 43-300 **Bielsko-Biala**
Tel: 33-822 1047/812 3394/815 0914 Fax: 33-815 0915
Internet: banialuka.in.com.pl
E-Mail: banialuka@in.com.pl
director Krzysztof Rau
Period/Frequency: May, biennial (2000)

Bydgoszcz Opera Festival
ul. Gdanska 20, 85-006 **Bydgoszcz**
Tel: 52-224 985 Fax: 52-349 5050
Period/Frequency: May, annual

Musica Antiqua Europae Orientalis
ul. Libelta 16, 85-080 **Bydgoszcz**
Tel: 52-210 920 Fax: 52-210 752
E-Mail: fp@psi.com.pl
director Eleonora Harendarska
Period/Frequency: Sept *Arts types:* old music of all types

International Contemporary Dance Conference and Dance Art Festival
Miedzynarodowa Konferencja Tanca Wspólczesnego i Festiwal Sztuki Tanecznej
Slaski Teatr Tanca, ul. Zeromskiego 27, 41-902 **Bytom**
Tel: 32-281 8253/55 Fax: 32-281 8252
Internet: www.stt.art.pl
E-Mail: info@stt.art.pl
director Jacek Luminski
Period/Frequency: end of June-beg of July, annual
Arts types: dance

Gaude Mater International Festival of Sacred Music
Czestochowa ul. Dabrowszczakow 1,
42-200 **Czestochowa**
Tel: 34-324 3638 Fax: 34-365 1760
Period/Frequency: May, annual
Arts types: all types of music

International Chopin Festival at Duszniki Zdròj
Miedzynarodowy Festiwal Chopinowski
w Dusznikach Zdroju
Fundacja Miedzynarodowych Festiwali Chopinowskich, Rynek 10, 57-340 **Duszniki Zdroj**
Tel: 74-669 280 Fax: 74-669 280
director Piotr Paleczny
Period/Frequency: Aug *Arts types:* piano music
Comments: can also be contacted via Philharmonic Warsaw Artists (Tel: Warsaw 22-826 5711, Fax: 22-827-5263)

Musica Mariana Festival
Franziskans Culture Centre,
ul. sw. Trujcy 4, 80-822 **Gdansk**
Tel: 58-305 5796/60-262 8026 (mobile) Fax: 58-301 0752
director Marek Wysoczynski
Period/Frequency: end of May, annual *Arts types:* sacred, vocal, organ, chamber music, art exhibitions

Shakespeare Festival
Festiwal Szekspirowski
Funacja Theatrum Gedanense,
ul. Dlugi Targ 11/13, 80-828 **Gdansk**
Tel: 58-301 3411 Fax: 58-301 3411
E-Mail: fthgedan@gdansk.sprint.pl
Period/Frequency: August, biennial

International Organ Festival at Oliwa
Festiwal Muzyki Organowej w Oliwie
ul. Sarnial, 81-598 **Gdynia**
Tel: 58-413 073 Fax: 58-413 073
director Roman Perucki
Period/Frequency: July-Aug *Arts types:* organ music

International Festival of Eastern Orthodox Church Music
ul. Bialostocka 2, 17-200 **Hajnowka**
Tel: 85-682 3203
Period/Frequency: May, annual

Song of Our Roots International Early Music Festival
ul. Rynek 6, 37-500 **Jaroslaw**
Tel: 16-621 6451
director Marcin Szczycinski
Period/Frequency: August, annual

International Street Theatre Festival
Miedzynarodowy Festiwal Teatrów Ulicznych
Teatr im K. C. Norwida, al. Wojska Polskiego 38,
58-500 **Jelenia Góra**
Tel: 75-764 7695/7273 Fax: 75-752 4730
artistic director Grzegorz Mròwczynski
Period/Frequency: July or Aug, annual
Arts types: Polish and foreign street theatre

Jelenia Góra Theatre Meetings
Jeleniogórskie Spotkania Teatralne
Teatr im. C. K. Norwida, Wojska Polskiego 38,
58-500 **Jelenia Góra**
Tel: 75-764 7695/7273 Fax: 75-752 4730
director Grzegorz Mrówczynski
Period/Frequency: Sept-Oct, annual
Arts types: Polish productions of the season, guest performances from foreign companies

Kalisz Theatre Meetings
Kaliskie Spotkania Teatralne
Teatr im.W. Boguslawskiego, pl.W. Boguslawskiego 1,
62-800 **Kalisz**
Tel: 62-502 3200 Fax: 62-502 3200
director Jan Nowara
Period/Frequency: first week of May, annual
Arts types: Polish productions showing outstanding acting achievements

International Festival of Organ and Chamber Music
ul. Wolinska 9, 72-400 **Kamien Pomorski**
Tel: 91-382 5041
Period/Frequency: June-Sept, annual

Interpretations – Polish National Festival of Directing Art
Interpretacje – Ogólnopolski Festiwal Sztuki Rezyserskiej
Estrada Slaska, ul. Kosciuszki 88/90, 40-519 **Katowice**
Tel: 32-251 9338 Fax: 32-251 7527
Internet: www.um.katowice.pl/interpr.htm
director Kazimierz Kutz
Period/Frequency: March, annual

Swietokrzyskie Mountains Music Days, International Festival
Pl. Moniuszki 2b, 25-334 **Kielce**
Tel: 41-368 1140 Fax: 41-368 1191
Period/Frequency: March, annual

International Theatre Festival The Crash
Miedzynarodowy Festiwal Teatralny Zderzenie
Towarzystwo Teatralne Zderzenia, ul. Okrzei 14,
57-300 **Klodzko**
Tel: 74-672 440 Fax: 74-676 245
Internet: www.netgate.com.pl/zderzenie
E-Mail: zderzenie@netgate.com.pl
Period/Frequency: end of Nov, annual

Ballet Spring in Krakow
ul. sw. Ducha 1, 31-023 **Kraków**
Tel: 12-637 2760
Period/Frequency: May-July, annual

Cracow 2000 – European City of Culture
Cracow 2000 Festival Bureau, ul. Sw. Kryza 1,
31-028 **Kraków**
Tel: 12-421 8693/421 0435 Fax: 12-422 1381
Period/Frequency: throughout the year 2000 *Arts types:* performing and visual arts *Comments:* Krakow is one of the 9 joint European Cities of Culture in the year 2000

Cracow Theatre Keminiscences – International Festival of Alternative Theatre
Krakowskie Reminiscencje Teatralne – Miedzynarodowy Festival Teatròw Alternatywnych
Centrum Kultury, Oleandry 1, 30-060 **Kraków**
Tel: 12-633 3538/6160 Fax: 12-633 7648
Internet: www.reminiscencje.org
director Alina Pieta
Period/Frequency: mid-March, annual *Arts types:* Polish and foreign experimental theatres

International Audio Art Festival Cracow
c/o Art Society Muzyka Centrum, Marek Choloniewski,
ul. Starowislna 3, 31-038 **Kraków**
Tel: 12-167 6195
Fax: 12-167 6195
Internet: www.cyf-kr.edu.pl/-zbcholon/mch
E-Mail: zbcholon@cyf-kr.edu.pl
Period/Frequency: Nov, annual *Comments:* see also Promoters; alternative Internets: www.muzykacentrum.z.pl or www.audioart.z.pl or www.globalmix.z.pl

Music in Old Cracow Festival
Muzyka w Starym Krakowie
Ul. Zwierzyniecka 1, 31-103 **Kraków**
Tel: 12-422 7120 Fax: 12-422 4312
director Stanislaw Galonski
Period/Frequency: Aug *Arts types:* music; chamber recitals

Moniuszko Festival in Kudowa – Zdròj
Festiwal Moniuszkowski w Kudowje Zdroju
ul. Zdrojowa 29, 57-350 **Kudowa-Zdròj**
Tel: 72-661 926
director Maria Foltyn
Period/Frequency: June *Arts types:* vocal art

International Festival of Solo Puppeteers
Miedzynarodowy Festiwal Solistów Lalkarzy
Teatr Lalek Arlekin, ul. 1 Maja 2, 90-718 **Lódz**
Tel: 42-633 0894 Fax: 42-633 0894
Internet: www.teatr-arlekin.lodz.pl/
E-Mail: tarlekin@polbox.com
director Waldemar Wolanski
Period/Frequency: April, annual *Arts types:* puppetry

Lodz Ballet Meetings
Lódzkie Spotkania Baletowe
Teatr Wielki, Pl. Dabrowskiego, 90-249 **Lódz**
Tel: 42-636 2272/633 3186/9960 ext. 122
Fax: 42-631 9552
director Marcin Krzyzanowski
Period/Frequency: end of May, biennial *Arts types:* ballet

International Festival Theatre Confrontations
Miedzynarodowy Festiwal Konfrontacje Teatralne
c/o Centrum Kultury, Peowiaków 12, 20-007 **Lublin**
Tel: 81-532 7583/4507 Fax: 81-532 8700/7583
E-Mail: ck@ck.lublin.pl
Period/Frequency: mid-Oct, annual *Arts types:* Polish & foreign experimental theatres *Comments:* see also Promoters and Venues (Centrum Kultury Lublin)

Ada Sari Memorial Days of Vocal Art
ul. Dlugosza 3, 33-300 **Nowy Sacz**
Tel: 18-443 5215
Period/Frequency: May, annual

Opole Theatre Confrontation – Polish Classics
Opolskie Konfrontacje Teatralne – Klasyka Polska
Teatr im J. Kochanowskiego,
pl Teatralny 12, 45-056 **Opole**
Tel: 77-453 9082 Fax: 77-454 5942
Internet: www.opole.pol.pl/teatr-kochanowski/index.html
Period/Frequency: end of March, annual
Arts types: Polish classic drama works

Contemporary Dance Workshop
ul. Kozia 4, 61-834 **Poznan**
Tel: 61-852 4241
Period/Frequency: August, annual

International Theatre Festival Malta
Miedzynarodowy Festiwal Teatralny Malta
Towarzystwo Muzyczne im H. Wieniawskiego,
Swietoslawska 7, 61-840 **Poznan**
Tel: 61-852 2642 Fax: 61-852 2642
Internet: malta-festival.info.poznan.pl
E-Mail: office@malta-festival.info.poznan.pl
director Michal Merczynski; artistic director Lech Raczak; director Malta Off Wlodzinierz Mielcarek
Period/Frequency: June-July, annual *Arts types:* Polish and foreign street and experimental theatres

International Gombrowicz Festival
Miedzynarodowy Festiwal Gombrowiczowski
Teatr Powszechny im. J.Kochanowskiego,
Pl.Jagiellonski 15, 26-600 **Radom**
Tel: 48-362 3723 Fax: 48-362 7927
Internet: www.radom.net/teatr
Period/Frequency: September, biennial (2001)
Arts types: productions of Gombrowicz's plays and adaptations of his prose

International Music Festival in Lancut
Muzczny Festival w Lancucie
Rzeszow Philharmonic, ul Chopina 30, 35-959 **Rzeszów**
Tel: 17-628 507/622 333 Fax: 17-622 333
director Adam Natanek
Period/Frequency: May *Arts types:* music: orchestra, chamber, recitals

Rzeszów Theatre Meetings
Rzeszowskie Spotkania Teatralne
Teatr im. W. Siemaszkowej, Sokola 7/9, 35-010 **Rzeszów**
Tel: 17-853 2748
Fax: 17-853 2748
Internet: www.rzeszow.biz.pl/teatr.htm
director Zbigniew Rybka
Period/Frequency: mid-Nov, annual *Arts types:* Polish productions of the season

Polish Piano Festival
ul. S. Jaracza 6, 76-200 **Slupsk**
Tel: 59-426 487
Period/Frequency: September, annual

Tarnow Festival of Rediscovered and Forgotten Music
c/o IMPRESARIAT Inter Art Ltd.,
ul Narutowicza 15/45, 33-110 **Tarnow**
Tel: 14-217 267 Fax: 14-217 267
artistic directors Teresa Kaban, Henryk Blazej
Period/Frequency: April, annual *Arts types:* soloists, choirs, orchestras and chamber concerts, recently discovered and long forgotten music *Venues:* town hall, Mirror hall, cathedral, churches, museum *Comments:* under patronage of Ministry of Culture in Warsaw; pioneers recently discovered old music

International Theatre Festival Kontakt
Miedzynarodowy Festiwal Teatralny Kontakt
Teatr im. W. Horzyey, Plac Teatralny 1, 87-100 **Torun**
Tel: 56-622 5222/1245 Fax: 56-622 3717
Internet: www.atm.com.pl/~kontakt
E-Mail: kontakt@ikp.atm.com.pl
festival director Jadwiga Oleradzka; assistant to the festival director Andrzej Bubien
Period/Frequency: last week in May, annual *Arts types:* drama from Central and Eastern Europe *Venues:* Wilam Horzyca Theatre 400, Puppet theatre Baj Pomorski 200, Torun Exhibition Hall 400 *Comments:* takes the form of a competition with the participating plays judged by an international jury; also exhibitions, films, concerts etc.; simultaneous translation into Russian, English and Polish

Probaltica Festival of Chamber Music and Art of Baltic Countries
ul. Konstytucji 3 maja 76/34, 87-100 **Torun**
Tel: 56-648 8647
Period/Frequency: May, annual

Baroque Opera Festival in Warsaw
Warsaw Chamber Opera,
Ul. Nowogrodzka 49, 00-695 **Warszawa**
Tel: 22-628 3096 (general)/625 7510 (box office)
Fax: 22-629 3233
Period/Frequency: Oct-Nov, annual *Arts types:* early baroque, late Italian baroque, French & English opera *Venues:* Warsaw Chamber Opera Theater 150, Warsaw Historical Bdgs. Solidarnosti 766

Early Music Festival at the Royal Palace in Warsaw
ul. Zakroczymska 2 m 2, 00-225 **Warszawa**
Tel: 22-831 2482
E-Mail: jurbi@friko7.onet.pl
directors Jacek Urbaniak, Anna Kociecka
Period/Frequency: Nov-Dec, annual

Festival Okada
Warecka 4/6/m. 83, **Warszawa**
Tel: 22-826 2645 Fax: 22-826 2645
director Yoshiko Okada
Arts types: chamber, vocal, soloists and ensembles
Second Address: Alb. Kay Assoc. Inc., 58 West 58 Street (31E), New York, NY; tel; +1 212-593 1640, fax: +1 212=759 7329 *Comments:* the festival takes place in Zakopane

International Festival of Choral Song Miedzyzdroje
ul. Nowy Swiat 30/12, 00-373 **Warszawa**
Tel: 22-826 5170
Period/Frequency: June, annual

International Jazz Festival Jazz Jamboree
Miedzynarodowy Festival Jazzowy Jazz Jamboree
Fundacja Jazz Jamboree,
ul. Chmielna 20, 00-020 **Warszawa**
Tel: 22-827 8371/9575 Fax: 22-827 3926
managing director Jerzy Brize;
artistic director Henryk Majewski
Period/Frequency: Oct, annual *Arts types:* jazz: traditional, modern *Comments:* also concerts in jazz clubs

International Meetings of Action Art Crossroads
Miedzynarodowe Spotkania Sztuki Akcji Rozdroze
Centrum Szturki Współczesnej Zamek Ujazdowski, Al. Ujazdowskie 6, 00-461 **Warszawa**
Tel: 22-628 1271
Fax: 22-628 9550
E-Mail: csw@ikp.atm.com.pl
Period/Frequency: October, annual

Jazz Jamboree International Jazz Festival
ul. Chmielna 20, 00-020 **Warszawa**
Tel: 22-827 8371
Period/Frequency: October, annual

Mozart Festival
Festiwal Mozartowski
Warsaw Chamber Opera,
Ul. Nowogrodzka 49, 00-695 **Warszawa**
Tel: 22-628 3096
Fax: 22-625 7510
director & artistic director Stefan Sutkowski; festival office manager Magdalena Cybulska; booking manager Joanna Ogrodowczyk
Period/Frequency: June-July, annual *Arts types:* Mozart operas, concerts and pantomime performances to Mozart's music *Venues:* Warsaw Chamber Opera Theatre (al.Solidarnosci 76b), Royal Baths Gardens, Trinity Lutheran Church, Royal Castle, museums etc.

Street Art – International Meetings of Street and Outdoor Theatres
Sztuka Ulicy – Miedzynarodowe Spotkania Teatrów Ulicznych i Plenerowych
Staromiejski Dom Kultury,
Rynek Starego Miasta 2, 00-272 **Warszawa**
Tel: 22-831 2375 Fax: 22-831 2375
Period/Frequency: July, annual

Warsaw Autumn International Festival of Contemporary Music
Warszawska Jesien – Miedzynarodowy Festiwal Muzyki Wspolczesnej
Zwiazek Kompozytorow Polskich,
Rynek Starego Miasta 27, 00-272 **Warszawa**
Tel: 22-831 1634 Fax: 22-831 0607
Internet: www.warsaw-autumn.waw.pl
E-Mail: festival@warsaw-autumn.waw.pl
director Tadeusz Wielecki
Period/Frequency: Sept, annual
Arts types: contemporary music, all types

Warsaw Music Meetings
ul. Rynek Starego Miasta 27, ZKP, 00-272 **Warszawa**
Tel: 22-831 1634
director Wladyslaw Slowinski
Period/Frequency: May, annual
Arts types: early and contemporary music

Warsaw Theatre Meetings
Warszawskie Spotkania Teatralne
Teatr Maly-scena impresaryjna,
Pl. Pilsudskiego 9, 00-078 **Warszawa**
Tel: 22-635 6352 Fax: 22-826 1849
directors Mieczyslaw Marszycki, Pawel Konic
Period/Frequency: mid-March, annual

Witold Lutoslawski Forum
ul. Jasna 5, 00-950 **Warszawa**
Tel: 22-826 8311
Period/Frequency: March, annual
Arts types: contemporary music

Zakopane – Festival Okada
Warecka 4/6/ m. 83, 00-040 **Warszawa**
Tel: 22-826 2645 Fax: 22-826 2645
director Yoshiko Okada
Period/Frequency: July *Arts types:* chamber music, recitals *Venues:* in Zakopane *Second Address:* U.S.A. Albert Kay Associates, Inc.,
58 West 58 Street, Suite 31-E, New York, NY 10019-2510,
Tel: (212) 593-1640, Fax: (212) 759-7329

Early Music in May International Festival
ul. Szewska 19/12, 50-139 **Wroclaw**
Tel: 71-343 1513
Period/Frequency: May, annual

Festival of Stage Song Wroclaw
IMPART, ul. Mazowiecka 17, 50-412 **Wroclaw**
Tel: 71-343 2962
Period/Frequency: March, annual

Jazz on the Oder International Festival
ul. Odrzanska 2, 50-113 **Wroclaw**
Tel: 71-341 7101
Period/Frequency: May, annual

Understanding International Silesia Festival of Music
ul. Drzewieckiego 56/3, 54-129 **Wroclaw**
Tel: 71-674 520
E-Mail: msfm@polbox.com
Period/Frequency: April, annual *Arts types:* classical music

Wratislavia Cantans
c/o Panstwowa Instytucja Kultury,
ul. Kielbasnicza 5, 50-108 **Wroclaw**
Tel: 71-342 7257/343 0833 Fax: 71-343 0833
E-Mail: office@wratislavia.mtl.pl
director festival sites Lidia Geringer d'Oedenberg; artistic director Tadeusz Strugala
Period/Frequency: June and Sept, bi-annual *Arts types:* choral-instrumental concerts, fine arts exhibitions combined with chamber music, open-air concerts, lectures *Second Address:* ul. Piwna 4/3, 00-265 Warsaw, Tel/Fax: 2-635 0120, office manager- Monika Strugala

Wroclaw Meetings of One-actor Theatres and Small Theatres Forms
Wroclawskie Spotkania Teatrów Jednego Aktora i Malych Form Teatralnych
Wroclawskie Towarzystwo Przyjaciól Teatru,
Rynek-Ratusz 24, 50-101 **Wroclaw**
Tel: 71-441 046 Fax: 71-441 046
Period/Frequency: November, annual

Karol Szymanowski Music Days
ul. Kasprusie 19, 34-500 **Zakopane**
Tel: 18-201 4554
Period/Frequency: July, annual

East-West International Music Meetings
ul. Powstancow wielkopolskich 10, 65-075 **Zielona Gora**
Tel: 68-325 6512
Period/Frequency: March, annual

PORTUGAL (+351)

Almada International Theatre Festival
Festival Internacional do Teatro de Almada
Teatro Municipal de Almada, Rua Conde de Ferreira, 2804-523 **Almada**
Tel: 1-275 2175/6567 Fax: 1-274 4856
director Joaquim Benite; director adjunto Vitor Gonçalves; administracao Maria Laita
Period/Frequency: July, annual (2000: 4-18 July) *Arts types:* drama, music, dance, folklore *Venues:* open-air *Comments:* see also Drama & Venues

Festival X
Olho Associação Teatral, Apartado 285, Cova da Piedade, 2801-997 **Almada**
Tel: 1-273 1533/32 Fax: 1-273 1532
E-Mail: olho@mail.telepac.pt
art dir João Garcia Miguel; production Monica Samões
Period/Frequency: annual *Arts types:* theatre, dance, music, video, new artforms *Venues:* Espaço Ginjal (large warehouse divided into various performance spaces) *Comments:* see also Drama and Venues

Sementes-Mostra Internacional de Teatro Para o Pequeno Publico
Apartado 124, 2801 **Almada**
Tel: 1-273 0768 Fax: 1-273 0767
E-Mail: teatroextremo@mail.telepac.pt
director Rui Cerveira
Period/Frequency: May, annual *Arts types:* children's theatre *Comments:* organised by theatre company Teatro Extremo; see also Drama

Criativa
Apartado 10, 7800 **Beja**
Tel: 84-327 153 Fax: 84-327 153
E-Mail: azinho.falante@ip.pt
producer José Barbieri
Period/Frequency: annual *Arts types:* theatre *Comments:* see also Drama and Promoters

Estoril Jazz/Jazz Nun Dia de Verão
Rua D. Diogo de Menezes 153, 2750 **Cascais**
Tel: 482-7862 Fax: 482-7863
Internet: www.projazz.pt
E-Mail: projazz@mail.telepac.pt
artistic director Duarte Mendonça
Period/Frequency: first weekends of July, annual *Arts types:* jazz *Venues:* Teatro Auditorio, Parque Palmela

Altitudes Festival
Travessa Principal 1 – Campo Benfeito, 3600 **Castro Daire**
Tel: 54-689 352/931-951 8393 (mobile) Fax: 54-689 160
contact Rita de Azevedo
Period/Frequency: August, annual *Arts types:* theatre *Comments:* organised by Serra de Montemuro regional theatre company; see also Drama

Festival de Música dos Capuchos
Av. Alfonso de Albuquerque, 109-A, São João de Caparica, 2825 **Costa da Caparica**
Tel: 1-290 2520 Fax: 1-290 0210
artistic director José Adelino Tacanho
Period/Frequency: July-Aug, annual *Arts types:* music, dance, art exhibitions *Venues:* Convento dos Capuchos 300, Teatro Luisa Todi, Setubal 800, Igreja do Castelo de Palmela 500, Azeitaó 300, Convento da Arrábida – Arrábida 150, Centro Cultural de Belem, Mosteirio dos Jerónimos – Lisbon

Festival de Teatro da Covilhã
Beco do Gameiro 5, Apartado 261 – Centro Cívico, 6200 **Covilhã**
Tel: 75-336 133 Fax: 75-334 585
E-Mail: gicteatro@mail.telepac.pt
director Rui Sena
Period/Frequency: October/Nov, annual *Arts types:* theatre *Venues:* Teatro Cinn Covilhã 1000, Auditorio Unidos Tortosendo *Comments:* organised by theatre company GICC; see also Drama

Estoril Coast Music Festival
Festival de Música de Costa de Estoril
AIMCE, Casa Museu F/Erdades de Faria, Av. de Saboia, 1146, 2765 **Estoril**
Tel: 1-468 5199 Fax: 1-468 5607
E-Mail: festivaldoestoril@mail.telepac.pt
artistic director Pineiro Nagy
Period/Frequency: July-Aug, annual *Arts types:* classical music *Venues:* Hotel Palácio, Estoril; Auditorio Parque Palmela, Cascais; Capela da Penha Longa, Linhó

Bienal Internacional de Marionetas (BIME)
Centro Dramatico De Évora, Teatro Garcia de Resende, Praça Joaquim Antonio Aguiar, 7000-510 **Évora**
Tel: 66-705 533/703 112 Fax: 66-741 181
Internet: www.evora.net/cendrev
E-Mail: cendrev@mail.evora.net
director José Russo
Period/Frequency: May, biennial (2001) *Arts types:* puppetry *Venues:* Théâtre à l'Italienne 300 (teatro Garcia de Resende) *Comments:* see also Puppets & Venues

Festival Cenaz Novas
Pimtai, Associação Cultural, Malagueira, Apartado 176, 7000 **Évora**
Tel: 66-744 403 Fax: 66-744 403
E-Mail: pimtai@mail.evora.net
contact Alexandra Esperidião
Period/Frequency: May, annual *Arts types:* contemporary and alternative theatre *Venues:* various

Festival Internacional de Música do Algarve
Região de Turismo do Algarve, Av. 5 de Outubro, 8000-902 **Faro**
Tel: 89-800 400 Fax: 89-800 489
artistic director Dr. Luis Pereira Leal
Period/Frequency: May-July, annual *Arts types:* classic music, jazz, early music and ballet, modern & contemporary *Venues:* various throughout the Algarve

Festival da Madeira
Secretaria Regional do Turismo e Cultura, Direcção Regional dos Assuntos Culturais da Madeira, Avenida Arriaga 18, 9004-519 **Funchal (Madeira)**
Tel: 91-229 057 Fax: 91-232 151
E-Mail: drtpromarketing@mail.telepae.pt
regional director João Henrique da Silva; artistic dir Luís Pereira Leal; regional secretary (turismo è cultura) João Carlos Nunes de Abreu; director for culture t.b.a.
Period/Frequency: weekends in June, annual *Arts types:* concerts of classical music *Venues:* teatro Baltazar Dias, Casino do Funchal *Comments:* see also National & Regional Ministries of Culture & Funding Agencies

Festival Acaso
Rua Latino Coelho 12, 2400 **Leiria**
Tel: 44-832 312 Fax: 44-872 590
director Pedro Oliveira
Period/Frequency: May, annual *Arts types:* theatre, music, performance art, exhibitions *Comments:* partly organised by theatre company O Nariz; see also Drama

Festival de Música de Leiria
Av. 25 Abril, 8000-902 **Leiria**
Tel: 44-872 590 Fax: 44-823 870
artistic director Dr. Carlos de Pontes Leça; president of Orfeão de Leiria Dr. Henrique Manuel Correia Pinto; vice president Rui Alberto Antunes Gomes; secretaries Gracinda Moniz, Carminda Isabel Ribeiro
Period/Frequency: June-July, annual *Arts types:* dance, music, opera, ballet, classical, electroacoustic music, exhibitions, jazz *Venues:* Teatro José Lúcio da Silva 1000, Convento da Portela 1500, Mosteiro da Batalba 2000, Mosteiro de Alcobaça 600, Caslelo de Leiria 300, new Auditorium 250

Danças na Cidade
Rua Camilo Castelo Branco, 33 – 3°, 1150-083 **Lisboa**
Tel: 21-315 2267 Fax: 21-315 1368
E-Mail: dancasnacidade@mail.telepac.pt
direction Mónica Lapa, Mark Deputter
Period/Frequency: second half of Nov, biennial (2001) *Arts types:* contemporary dance *Venues:* Centro Cultural de Belém, Teatro da Trindade, Teatro Cinearte, Teatro Comuna, Teatro Taborda, ZDB *Comments:* also residencies, workshops, publications on performing arts, exchange projects with Africa and Brazil

Early Music Festival
Jornadas Gulbenkian de Música Antiga
Fundação Calouste Gulbenkian/Music Department, Avenida de Berna 45A, 1067 **Lisboa** Codex
Tel: 21-782 3000 Fax: 21-793 7296
Internet: www.gulbenkian.pt
E-Mail: musica@gulbenkian.pt
director Luís Pereira Leal
Period/Frequency: Oct, annual *Arts types:* early music, chamber music *Venues:* various venues *Comments:* see also Ministries, Dance, Orchestra, Choir, Venues, Promoters & 'Contemporary Music Festival'

Festival Atlântico
Associação zé Dos Bois, Trav. do Arco de Jesus, n° 24,R/C esq, 1200 **Lisboa**
Tel: 21-342 9882/397 0048 Fax: 21-347 6892
E-Mail: zedosbois@ip.pt
director Natxo Checa
Period/Frequency: May, biennial *Arts types:* performance art *Comments:* festival always has theme; see also Venues

Festival de Lisboa- Teatro, Danca e Música
Eutáxia, Assessoria Cultural, Rua de Santiago, 19, 1100 **Lisboa**
Tel: 21-443 2995 Fax: 21-441 3776
E-Mail: eutaxia@ip.pt
director Adolfo Gutkin; finance director Carmen Prast; technical director Carlos Gonçalues; design and architecture Adolfo Prast
Period/Frequency: Nov-Dec, annual *Arts types:* drama, dance and music *Venues:* varies, Teatro Municipal Maria Matos 700, IFICT Sala de Teatro 100, Teatro Municipal São Luiz 1000, Estufa Fria 1000, Convento do Beato 1000, Coliseu do Porto 2000, Teatro da Trindade 688 *Second Address:* Apdo Postal 4, Caxias 2780 Paço D'Arcos *Comments:* also organize talks with participating groups, exhibitions and other activities: see also Venues

Gulbenkian Contemporary Music Festival
Encontros Gulbenkian de Música Contemporânea
Acarte Department, Rua Dr. Nicolau Bettercourt, 1067 **Lisboa** Codex
Tel: 21-782 3000 Fax: 21-793 7296 (music dept.)
Internet: www.gulbenkian.pt
E-Mail: musica@gulbenkian.pt
music director Dr. Luís Pereira Leal
Period/Frequency: May, annual *Arts types:* contemporary music, jazz *Comments:* see also Ministries, Orchestras, Venues, Dance, Choirs, Promoters, 'Early Music Festival'

Lugar à Dança – Festival International de Dança em Paisagens Urbanas
Rua Presidente Arriaga, 29-1° esq., 1200 **Lisboa**
Tel: 21-397 0204 Fax: 21-397 0204
E-Mail: vo.arte@mail.teleweb.pt
artistic director Ana Rita Barata
Period/Frequency: May, annual *Arts types:* dance *Comments:* organised by Vo' Arte; see also Promoters

Festival de Teatro de Montemor-o-Velho
Apartado 7, 3140 **Montemor-o-Velho**
Tel: 39-680 836 Fax: 39-689 555
director Armando Valente
Period/Frequency: July-Aug, annual *Arts types:* theatre, music, cinema *Venues:* open-air, castles, churches, rivers, streets *Comments:* oldest theatre festival in Portugal; specifically use unconventional spaces

Early Music Festival of Obidos
Festival de Música Antiga de Obidos
Câmara Municipal de Obidos, Largo do S.Pedro, 2510 **Obidos**
Tel: 62-955 000 Fax: 62-955 001/014
artistic director Dr Luis Peireira Leal
Period/Frequency: 1st or 2nd week of Oct, annual *Arts types:* early music

Música Vivo International Festival
Miso Music Portugal, c/o P.M. Azguime, Rua do Douro 92, Rebelva, 2775 **Parede**
Tel: 1-457 5068 Fax: 1-458 7256
Internet: www.ip.pt/~ip00786/misomusic.html
E-Mail: miso.music@ip.pt
artistic director Miguel Azguime;
executive director Paula de Castro Guimarães
Period/Frequency: July, annual *Arts types:* music from young composers, electronic music & real time computer systems *Venues:* Instituto Franco-Protugues 280 (Lisbon) *Comments:* also organise exchanges between Portuguese ensembles and groups from other countries

Portalegre International Theatre Festival
c/o Teatro de Portalegre, Apartado 264, 7300 **Portalegre**
Tel: 45-207 894 Fax: 45-202 942
directors Dr. José Mascaranhas, Vitor Pires
Period/Frequency: Oct, annual *Arts types:* theatre *Venues:* Teatro de Portalegre *Comments:* see also Drama

Fazer a Festa – Festival Internacional de Teatro
Rua da Picaria 77A R/C, 4050-478 **Porto**
Tel: 2-208 4014 Fax: 2-208 4021
director José Leitão
Period/Frequency: April-May, annual *Arts types:* all types of theatre *Comments:* see also Drama

Festival Internacional de Marionetas do Porto
c/o Teatro de Marionetas do Porto, Rua de Belmonte 57, 4050 **Porto**
Tel: 2-208 3341 Fax: 2-208 3243
E-Mail: tmp@mail.ip.pt
contact Isabel Alves Costa
Period/Frequency: annual *Arts types:* puppetry *Venues:* Theatre 60 *Comments:* see also Puppetry

Festival Internacional de Teatro de Expressão Ibéria – FITE
Rua do Paraíso 217, 2° Sala 5, 4000 **Porto**
Tel: 2-208 2432 Fax: 2-200 4275
director Antonio Reis
Period/Frequency: May-June, annual *Arts types:* Iberian drama modern and classic

PORTO 2001, European Cultural City
PORTO 2001 SA, Edificio Península, Pç. Bom Sucesso, 127, 5°, Sala 505, 4150 **Porto**
Tel: 2-605 9400 Fax: 2-605 9450
E-Mail: AlvaroDomingues@porto.2001.pt
Period/Frequency: isolated event during 2001, including a pre-programmation during 1999 and 2000 *Arts types:* music, dance, drama, cinema, video, photography, fine arts, multimedia, literature *Venues:* Coliseu 3000; Teatro Nacional S. João 800; Teatro Municipal Rivoli 858 (large auditorium), 178 (small aud.), 180 (concert cafe); Auditorium Carlos Alberto 500, Europarque 1500, Teatro do Campo Alegre 350, Auditório da Biblioteca Almeida Garret 200; Fundação Eng. António Almeida 600, 300; Fundação Cupertino de Miranda 500, 220, 100; Auditório Helena Costa 200, Balleteatro 200, Teatro da Vilarinha 100, Sá da Bandeira 1000, Auditório Terço 900, Casa das Artes 195, 195; Auditório do Museu Arte Contemporanea de Serralves 300, Casa da Musica (projected building) 1500 (large auditorium), 400 (small auditorium)

Porto Natal Teatro Internacional
Teatro Nacional S. João, Praça da Batalha,
4000-102 **Porto**
Tel: 2-339 3038 Fax: 2-339 3037
Internet: www.ponti.pt
E-Mail: jlf@ponti.pt
director Ricardo Pais; contact José Luis Ferreira
Period/Frequency: Dec, biennial *Arts types:* drama, other performance arts *Venues:* Teatro Nacional S. João 500, Teatro Rivoli 1000, other venues in Porto *Comments:* initiative of the Ministry of Culture, in association with Oporto City Hall; see also Drama

Festival International de Música da Póvoa Varzim
Rua D. Maria I, 56, 4490 **Póvoa do Varzim**
Tel: 52-614 145 Fax: 52-612 548
Internet: www.cm-pvarzim.pt/festival-htm
director Prof. João Marques
Period/Frequency: July, annual *Arts types:* choral music, instrumental recitals, symphonic music *Venues:* Auditório Municipal 300, Casino da Póvoa 400, Igreja Matriz 400, Igreja S. Pedro de Rates 300 *Comments:* see also Venues

Sintra Music Festival
Festival de Música de Sintra
Praça da República 23, 2710 **Sintra**
Tel: 1-923 4895 Fax: 1-923 4845
artistic director Luis Pereira Leal;
coordinator of Sintra festival Ana Alcântara
Period/Frequency: June/July, annual *Arts types:* specialise in classical music for piano (romantic period) *Venues:* Palacios Nacionais da Pena, Queluz e Sintra, National Palaces of Pena 200, Queluz 400 and Sintra 300 *Second Address:* Fundaçáo Calouste Gulbenkian, Serviço de Musica Av de Berna, 45-a,1000 Lisboa, Portugal *Comments:* also promotes 'Ballet Nights' in the gardens of Seteais Hotel-Palace, in July/August

Festival de Música da Casa de Mateus
Casa de Mateus, 5000 **Vila Real**
Tel: 59-323 121 Fax: 59-326 553
Internet: www.utad.geira.pt/casa_mateus/
E-Mail: casa.mateus@utad.pt
contact Maria Amélia Albuquerque;
director artistico Adriano Jordáo
Period/Frequency: June-Sept, annual *Arts types:* jazz, baroque (opera, lied), classical *Venues:* about half the concerts are taking place in Casa de Mateus and the rest are in the North of Portugal and Galicia *Comments:* Casa de Mateus is also a music school; poetry readings as part of the festival, with a book published by the ed. Quetzal

ROMANIA (+40)

Festival of Contemporary Dance
Brasov
Tel: 68-418 850
director Mircea Cornisteanu

Festival of Contemporary Drama
Brasov
Tel: 68-418 850
director Mircea Cornisteanu

ARCHAEUS Festival – Contemporary Music Days Bacau
c/o Liviu Danceanu,
Vacaresti 267 bl. 63, ap. 49,
75176 **Bucharest**
Tel: 1-330 0359 Fax: 1-210 7211
contact Liviu Danceanu
Period/Frequency: annual *Arts types:* contempoary music – concerts, happenings, lectures

George Enescu International Festival
c/o Artexim, Calea Victoriei nr 155, bl D1, sc. 8, et.2, sect.1, 71012 **Bucharest**
Tel: 1-650 1806/7/8/9/10/11/12
Fax: 1-311 0200
Internet: www.pcnet.ro/enescu
E-Mail: artexim@pcnet.ro
general director Mihai Brediceanu;
artistic director Lawrence Foster
Period/Frequency: Oct-Nov,annual *Arts types:* chamber music, recitals, symphony orchestras, choral
Comments: see also Competitions

International Contemporary Music Festival
c/o ARTEXIM, Calea Victoriei 155 bl. D1,
Sc. 8, Et.2, 71012 **Bucharest**
Tel: 1-650 1806/12
Fax: 1-311 0200
Internet: www.pcnet.ro/enescu
E-Mail: artexim@pcnet.ro
Period/Frequency: May, annual

International ISCU Festival
c/o ARTEXIM, Calea Victoriei 155 bl. D1,
Sc. 8, Et.2, 71012 **Bucharest**
Tel: 1-650 1806/12
Fax: 1-311 0200
Internet: www.pcnet.ro/enescu
E-Mail: artexim@pcnet.ro
Period/Frequency: October

International Week of New Music
c/o Uniunea Compozitorilor si Muzicologilor din Romania, Dan Dediu, Calea Victoriei 141,
71102 **Bucharest**
Tel: 1-210 7211

Autumn Music Festival of Cluj
c/o Cluj-Npoca State Philharmonic Transilvania,
1 Emil de Martonne St., 3400 **Cluj-Napoca**
Tel: 64-430 060/63 Fax: 64-197 812
contact Adrian Pop
Period/Frequency: Sept/Oct, annual *Arts types:* contemporary music *Comments:* alternative contact: Academia de Muzica, Gheorghe Dima, Str. I. C. Bratianu 25, 3400 Cluj-Napoca, Tel/Fax: 64-193 879

Cluj Mozart Festival
c/o Societata Româna Mozart,
str. Voltaire 15, 3400 **Cluj-Napoca**
president Prof. Ferenc László
Period/Frequency: Dec, annual *Arts types:* symphony, chamber *Comments:* co-organised by Gheorghe Dima Music Academy, Transylvania State Philharmonic , Cultural Inspectorate of Cluj County

Nicolae Bretan Festival
Academia de Muzica Gheorghe Dima,
Str. I. C. Bratianu 25, 3400 **Cluj-Napoca**
Tel: 64-193 879 Fax: 64-193 879
Period/Frequency: March, biennial (2000)
Arts types: opera, arias *Venues:* Romanian State Opera, Philharmonic Hall of the Transylvanian Philharmonic Orchestra *Comments:*
see also Competitions and Promoters

Don Juan Festival
Iasi
Tel: 32-117 233/147 900
directors I. Holban, Benoit Vitse

Piatra Neamt Theatre Festival
1 Stefan cel Mare Square, 5600 **Piatra Neamt**
Tel: 33-211 472 Fax: 33-217 159
director Corneliu Dan Borcia
Period/Frequency: May, annual *Arts types:* drama
Venues: Piatra Neamtz Theatre

Romanian Drama Gala
Timisoara National Theatre International, **Timisoara**
Tel: 56-201 288
director Stefan Iordanescu

RUSSIA (+7)

Alternative Festival
Brusow per. 8/10 bld., 103009 **Moscow**
Tel: 095-229 1365/8101
contact Dmitri Ukhow
Arts types: contemporary music

December Evenings Festival
Volkhonka st. 12, 121019 **Moscow**
Tel: 095-203 7998/6978/6974
contact Irina Antonova
Period/Frequency: December *Arts types:* chamber music

Golden Mask
10 Otraotnoy Doul., 100001 **Moscow**
Tel: 095-229 9242/3039/209 2153/209 3450 Fax: 095-229 9242/3039/209 2153/209 3450
E-Mail: goldmask@orc.ru
director Alexey Malobrodsky
Period/Frequency: annual *Arts types:* dance

International Festival of One-Actor Plays
Secretary General, Russian ITI Centre, c/o Teatr Nacij, Petrovsky Pereulok 3, 103031 **Moscow**
Tel: 095-229 5672 Fax: 095-229 5672
Period/Frequency: October

International Music Festival Moscow
c/o Rosinterfest, Sadovaya Triumfalnaya Str 12/14, 103006 **Moscow**
Tel: 095-200 6585/209 2261 Fax: 095-209 2263
director Igor S Gourevich
Period/Frequency: Aug, annual *Arts types:* classical music, orchestra, vocal

International Theatre Festival Tchekhov
c/o MKTS, Leontievskii per. 21/1, 103009 **Moscow**
Tel: 095-229 3785 Fax: 095-229 2075
contact Valery Shadrine
Period/Frequency: March-July, biennial (2000)
Arts types: drama

Kuskovo summer Festival
Ul Lenintser 2, 111402 **Moscow**
Tel: 095-375 5252/370 0160
contact Tamara Nikonowa

Moscow Autumn Festival
Brusow per. 8/10 bld. 2, 103009 **Moscow**
Tel: 095-229 6760/1365/8101
contact Oleg Galakhow, Dmitri Ukhow
Arts types: contemporary music

Moscow International One Man Show Festival
c/o Russian National Centre of the International Theatre Institute, Theatre of Nations,
Petrovsky per. 3, 103031 **Moscow**
Tel: 095-229 5672/6585 (work hours)/429 7296 (evening)
Fax: 095-229 5672/6033 (work hours)/429 7296 (evening)
director Valery Khasanov
Period/Frequency: October, biennial (2001) *Arts types:* drama, dance, puppet, song and other genres

Moscow Stars Festival
Bolshaya Nikitskaya st. 13, 103009 **Moscow**
Tel: 095-229 9401/9436
contact Svetlana Gorbachowa
Period/Frequency: May, annual *Arts types:* Russian music, international artists

Ostankino Summer Festival
First Ostankinskaya st. 5, 129515 **Moscow**
Tel: 095-286 0288/1147/283 4645
contact Leah Lepskaya

Russian Winter Festival
Bolshaya Nikitskaya st. 13, 103009 **Moscow**
Tel: 095-229 9401/9436
contact Svetlana Gorbachowa
Period/Frequency: Dec-Jan, annual *Arts types:* Russian music, international artists

Baltic House
Baltiisby House
4 Alexandrovsky park, 197198 **St Petersburg**
Tel: 812-232 0961/233 0932
Fax: 812-232 0961/233 9936
executive director Inna Sterligova; director Serguey Shub; artistic director Vladimir Teble
Arts types: drama *Comments:* see also Drama

Children's Festival of Contemporary Music
St Petersburg
Tel: 812-311 3548
director Grigory Korchmar
Period/Frequency: April

Christmas in the Northern Palmyra
Rozhdestvenskie Vstretchy v Severnoi Palmire
St Petersburg
Tel: 812-273 0370 Fax: 812-273 0370
director Alexander Uteshev;
artistic director Yuri Temirkanov
Period/Frequency: Dec-Jan

Easter Festival
BO 13 Liniya 18, 199176 **St Petersburg**
Tel: 812-213 4103 Fax: 812-213 4704
director Valery Pavlov

Musical Spring in St Petersburg
St. Petersburg Composers Union, 45 Hertzen St., 190000 **St Petersburg**
Tel: 812-311 3548 Fax: 812-314 5818
E-Mail: Lobanov@ML1337.spb.edu
director Vladislav Uspensky
Period/Frequency: May

Paganini's Violin at the Hermitage
c/o Antonina Nabokova,
1319-59 Vladimivoky Prospect, 191002 **St Petersburg**
Tel: 812-164 3451 Fax: 812-273 2017
contact Antonina Nabokova
Period/Frequency: Sept, annual
Arts types: instrumental recitals

Stars of White Nights
c/o Irina Rudimova, Culture Committee of the Mayor's Office, Nevski Prospect 40, 191011 **St Petersburg**
Tel: 812-311 0688
Fax: 812-110 5993
executive director Natalia Eremina;
artistic director Valery Gergiev
Period/Frequency: June

Virtuosos 2000
St Petersburg
Tel: 812-311 0688
director Natalia Eremina
Period/Frequency: March/April
Comments: for young musicians

Festival of Contemporary Dance
1-2 Flatske Spusk, App. 82, 150028 **Yaroslavl**
Tel: 0852-294 218
E-Mail: podati@yaroslavl.ru
Period/Frequency: August, biennial (2000)
Arts types: contemporary dance

SAN MARINO (+378)

Festa Di Fondazione Della Repubblica
Ufficio Attività Sociali e Culturali, Contrada Omagnano 20, 47890 **San Marino**
Tel: 882 452 Fax: 882 300
E-Mail: statoturismo@omniway.sm

capo sezione cultura e spettacolo Manlio Gozi; dirigente Dott.ssa Gemma Cavalleri; capo sezione attività sociali dott.ssa Marilena Stefanoni; capo sezione amministrazione Fausta Casadei
Period/Frequency: 3rd Sept, annual *Arts types:* lyrical music, concerts, general entertainment, fireworks
Venues: open air. Theatres are only used in case of bad weather-Teatro Turismo, Teatro Titano

Stagione Concertistica di San Marino
Ufficio Attività Sociáli e Culturali,
Contrada Omagnano 20, 47890 **San Marino**
Tel: 882 410 Fax: 882 300
E-Mail: statoturismo@omniway.sm
capo sezione cultura e spettacolo Manlio Gozi; dirigente Dott.ssa Gemma Cavalleri; capo sezione amministrazione Fausta Casadei
Period/Frequency: spring-autumn, annual *Arts types:* classical and contemporary music *Venues:* mainly Teatro Concordia (Borgo Maggione)

Stagione teatrale di San Marino
Ufficio Attività Sociali e Culturali,
Contrada Omagnano 20, 47890 **San Marino**
Tel: 882 410 Fax: 882 300
E-Mail: statoturismo@omniway.sm
capo sezione cultura e spettacolo Manlio Gozi; dirigente Dott.ssa Gemma Cavalleri; capo sezione amministrazione Fausta Casadei
Period/Frequency: Oct-April, annual *Arts types:* drama
Venues: mainly Teatro Nuovo (Dogana)

SLOVAKIA (+421)

Many telephone and fax numbers in Slovakia are in the process of being changed. We have included all new numbers known at the time of going to print.

Music Days of Banská Bystrica
Banskobystrické hudobné dni
State Opera, Národná 11, 974 73 **Banská Bystrica**
Tel: 88-412 4418/5021 Fax: 88-415 3457
E-Mail: sobb@pcb.sk
director Rudolf Hromada
Period/Frequency: Oct-Nov, annual
Arts types: music, opera, recitals

Puppet Festival Banská Bystrica
Festival Bábkárska Bystrica
Bábkové Divadlo na Rázcestí,
Kollárova 18, 975 90 **Banská Bystrica**
Tel: 88-412 5623/4193 Fax: 88-412 5623/4193
director Iveta Skripková
Period/Frequency: September, biennial (2000)
Arts types: puppetry *Venues:* Puppet theatre 'Na Razcesti', regional cultural centre, Barbakan – castle courtyard *Comments:* organised by: Ministry of Culture, Theatre Institute and City Office B. Bystrice

Bratislava International Music Festival
Michalská 10, 815 36 **Bratislava**
Tel: 7-5443 0378/4546/4561/4538
Fax: 7-5443 2020/2652/2029
Internet: www.slovkoncert.sk
E-Mail: bhs@netlab.sk
artistic director Prof. Ladislav Burlas
Period/Frequency: Sept-Oct, annual
Arts types: music, opera, ballet

Central European Music Festival
Stredoeurópsky festival koncertného umenia
National Music Centre – Slovkoncert, Michalská 10, 815 36 **Bratislava** 1
Tel: 7-5443 1373/4561/4638 Fax: 7-5443 1373/2652
secretary Slávka Ferencová
Period/Frequency: April, annual *Arts types:* international music festival of young performers

Cultural Summer 2000
Kultúrne leto 2000
Ursulínska 11, 812 93 **Bratislava**
Tel: 7-5441 6548 Fax: 7-5441 2234
E-Mail: mksba@netlab.sk
director Dr Pavol Schwarz
Period/Frequency: July-Aug, annual *Arts types:* orchestral, chamber music, vocal, theatre

Evenings of New Music
Vecery novej hudby
International Society for Contemporary Music, Slovak Section, Music Information Centre of the Music Fund, Medená 29, 811 02 **Bratislava**
Tel: 7-5443 1380/1110 Fax: 7-5443 3569
Internet: www.his.sk
E-Mail: his@his.sk
directors Daniel Matej (7-5477 3713)
Period/Frequency: May-Sept, annual

Kaukliar – International Pantomime Festival
Theatre Aréna, Viedenská cesta 10, 851 01 **Bratislava**
Tel: 7-6224 6875 Fax: 7-6224 6864
Internet: www.sknet.sk/arena
E-Mail: arena@sknet.sk
director Prof Milan Sládek
Period/Frequency: June, annual

Melos – ÉTOS International Festival of the 20th Century Music
Melos – ÉTOS Medzinárodny festival hudby 20 storocia melosétos
Michalská 10, 815 36 **Bratislava**
Tel: 7-5443 1373/4561 Fax: 7-5443 1373/2652
Internet: www.slovkoncert.sk
E-Mail: slovkoncert@netlab.sk
artistic director Ivan Marton; secretary Slávka Ferencová
Period/Frequency: November, biennial (2001) *Arts types:* symphony, chamber, recitals, opera, choral seminars, discussions about contemporary music

Middle-European Festival of Interpretative Art Zilina
Stredoeurópsky festival interpretacného umenia Zilina
National Music Centre – Slovkoncert,
Michalská 10, 815 36 **Bratislava**
Tel: 7-5443 1373 Fax: 7-5443 1373
Internet: www.slovkonert.sk
E-Mail: slovkoncert@netlab.sk
artistic director Marián Lapsansky
Period/Frequency: April, annual

Old Music Days
Dni starej hudby
Centrum Starej hudby, Ra Ra musica,
Fandlyho 1, 811 03 **Bratislava** 1
Tel: 7-5441 8484 Fax: 7-5441 8484
Period/Frequency: October, annual *Arts types:* international music festival focusing on historically accurate 16th to 19th C. interpretation

Project Istropolitana- International Festival of the Drama Academies
VSMU, Ventúrska 3, 813 01 **Bratislava**
Tel: 7-5443 2579/2306 Fax: 7-5443 2579
E-Mail: dvvsmu@ba.sanet.sk
director Peter Mikulík
Period/Frequency: June, biennial (2000)

Slovak Historical Organs Festival
Festival Slovenské historické organy
National Music Centre – Slovkoncert,
Michalská 10, 815 36 **Bratislava**
Tel: 7-5443 1373 Fax: 7-5443 1373
artistic director Prof Ferdinand Klinda
Period/Frequency: August, annual

International Organ Festival
Medzinárodny organovy festival
State Philharmonic Kosice, Dom umenia,
Moyzesova 66, 041 23 **Kosice**
Tel: 95-622 4514 Fax: 7-622 4509
Internet: www.sfk.sk
director Julius Klein; artistic director Ivan Sokol
Period/Frequency: September, annual

Kosice Spring Musical Festival
Kosická hudobná jar
Dom umenia, Moyzesova 66, 041 23 **Kosice**
Tel: 95-622 4514/4509/7216 Fax: 95-622 4509/7216
Internet: www.sfk.sk
artistic director Július Klein
Arts types: classical music *Comments:* organised by the State Philharmonic Kosice

International Theatre Festival
Divadelná Nitra / Nitra Theatricals
Svatoplukovo nám. 4, 950 53 **Nitra**
Tel: 87-524 870 Fax: 87-524 870
Internet: kultura.gratex.sk/divadelna_nitra
E-Mail: festdn@nr.netax.sk
artistic & managing director Darina Kárová
Period/Frequency: annual *Comments:* organised by the Association of Nitra Theatricals, Theatre Institute

May Theatre Festival Nitra
Májová divadelná Nitra
Divadlo Andreja Bagara v Nitre,
Svätoplukovo nám 4, 949 01 **Nitra**
Tel: 87-772 1577/81 Fax: 87-524 871
E-Mail: dabnr@netlab.sk
director of festival & theatre Frantisek Javorsky
Period/Frequency: May, annual *Arts types:* theatre

Zvolen Castle Festival
Zámocké hry Zvolenské
Divadlo Jozefa Gregora Tajovského,
Divadelná 3, 960 77 **Zvolen**
Tel: 855-532 0192 Fax: 855-29698
Internet: www.zv.psg.sk
E-Mail: divadlo@zv.psg.sk
general director of J. G. Tajovsky Theatre Marcela Krsková
Period/Frequency: June/July, annual *Arts types:* drama, opera, children's theatre, interpretation courses

SLOVENIA (+386)

Days of Comedy
Dnevi Komedije
Gledaliski Trg 5, 3000 **Celje**
Tel: 63-442 910 Fax: 63-441 850
managing director Borut Alujevic
Period/Frequency: Jan-Feb, annual *Arts types:* theatre (comedy) *Venues:* Slovene National Theatre Celje

Summer Festival
Primorski Poletni Festival
Verdijeva 5, 6000 **Koper**
Tel: 66-271 912 Fax: 66-271 788
Internet: www.primorski-festival.si
E-Mail: pp.festival@siol.net
manager Neva Zajc; artistic director Primoz Bebler
Period/Frequency: June-Aug *Arts types:* theatre, dance, music *Venues:* open air locations on the slovene coast

Week of Slovene Drama
Teden Slovenske Drame
Glavni trg.6, 4000 **Kranj**
Tel: 64-380 490 (management)/222 681 (box office)
Fax: 64-380 4933
Internet: www.pgk-gledalisce.si
E-Mail: presern-gled@s5.net
Period/Frequency: Feb, annual *Arts types:* Slovene drama
Venues: Preseren's theatre, Kranj *Comments:* organise exhibitions in association with the festival; awards annual prize 'Prize of Slavko Grum' and every three years 'Grun -Filipic prize' for achievements in Slovene dramaturgy

City of Women – International Festival of Contemporary Arts
Mesto zensk, Kersnikova 4, 1000 **Ljubljana**
Tel: 61-329 184 Fax: 61-132 3092
Internet: www.sigov.si/uzp/city/
E-Mail: mesto.zensk@guest.arnes.si
prograame curator Koen Van Daele
Period/Frequency: October, annual *Arts types:* contemporary arts; all art disciplines (theatre, performance, music, film and video, fine arts, literature, multimedia etc) *Venues:* different veneus in Ljubljana *Comments:* presents work only created by women

Exodus – Festival of Contemporary Performing Art
Metelkova 6, 1000 **Ljubljana**
Tel: 61-131 3122/41-730 432 Fax: 61-133 5025
E-Mail: lj-exodos@guest.arnes.si
director Tomaz Toporisic;
artistic board Jedrt Jez, Jana Pavlic, Miran Sustersic
Period/Frequency: May, June, annual *Venues:* in Ljubljana and around Slovenia *Comments:* member of Network of Mediterranean Theatre Festivals

Festival Brezice
c/o Ars Ramovs, Slovenska cesta 1, 1000 **Ljubljana**
Tel: 61-125 3366 Fax: 61-174 1541
Internet: www.k-ramova.si/
E-Mail: info@k-ramovs.si
contact Klemen Ramovs
Period/Frequency: July, annual *Arts types:* early music
Comments: international early music festival

International Puppet Festival
c/o Ljubljana Puppet Theatre, Krekov Trg 2, **Ljubljana**
Tel: 61-314 966 Fax: 61-314 795
artistic director Mojca Kreft
Period/Frequency: June, annual

International Theatre Festival
Cankarjev Dom, Presernova 10, **Ljubljana**
Tel: 61-176 7100/222 835 Fax: 61-224 279
Internet: www.cd-cc.si
contact Ursula Cetinski; general director Mija Rotovnik
Period/Frequency: annual *Arts types:* theatre
Venues: Cankarjen Dom

Ljubljana Festival
Festival Ljubljana
Trg Francoske Revolucije 1-2, 1000 **Ljubljana**
Tel: 61-126 4340
Fax: 61-221 288
Internet: www.festival-lj.si/
E-Mail: info@festival-lj.si
general manager Darko Brlek; marketing manager Janja Rozman; secretary Sonja Vrhovec
Period/Frequency: July-Sept, annual *Arts types:* dance, ballet, drama, classical music, vocal recitals, musicals, contemporary Slovene music *Venues:* Krizanke complex: includes open-air stage 1400, churches, courtyard
Comments: organises International Summer Festivals, annually, and young musicians' concerts; member of the EFA-European Festivals Association

Ljubljana International Jazz Festival
Mednarodni Festival Jazza
c/o Cankarjev Dom Cultural and Congress Centre,
Presernova 10, 1000 **Ljubljana**
Tel: 61-176 7100
Fax: 61-224 279
head of jazz, rock, pop and entertainment music Bogdan Benigar(ext 157, email: bogdan.benigar@cd-cc.si)
Period/Frequency: June/July, annual *Arts types:* jazz
Venues: Cankarjev Dom *Comments:* see also Venues

Slovene Musical Days
Ljubljana
Tel: 61-126 4340
Fax: 61-221 288
Internet: www.festival-lj.si/
E-Mail: info@festival-lj.si
Period/Frequency: April

Borstnikovo Festival
Borstnikovo srecanje
Slovenska 27, 2000 **Maribor**
Tel: 62-213 982 Fax: 62-228 4051
director Olga Jancar; public relations Marko Vezovisek
Period/Frequency: Oct, annual *Arts types:* classic theatre

Lent Festival Maribor
Narodni dom Maribor, Kneza Koclja 9, 2000 **Maribor**
Tel: 62-229 4000 Fax: 62-225 376
Internet: www.nd-mb.si
E-Mail: nd@nd-mb.si
director & artistic director Vladimir Rukavina
Period/Frequency: June-July, annual *Arts types:* classic theatre, street theatre, ballet, opera, rock concerts, folk art, jazz, children's *Venues:* floating stage on rive Drava 3500, 8 smaller stages – open-air

Musical September Maribor
Glasbeni september
Narodni dom- Koncertna- poslovalnica,
Kneza Koclja 9, 2000 **Maribor**
Tel: 62-229 4000 Fax: 62-225 376
Internet: www.nd-mb.si
E-Mail: nd@nd-mb.si
director Vladimir Rukavina; general manager Brigita Pavlic
Period/Frequency: Sept *Arts types:* classical music (e.g. chamber) *Venues:* Stolnica church 350, Viteska Hall 200
Comments: organise concerts of classical and chamber music, Oct-June

Summer Dream Pier, International Puppet Festival
Poletni lutkovni pristan
Lutkovno gledalisce Maribor,
Rotovski trg 2, 2000 **Maribor**
Tel: 62-228 1970/71 Fax: 62-227 412
E-Mail: mb-lutkgled@siol.net
director Tine Varl
Period/Frequency: June-Sept, annual, (2000: 20 June-20 Sept) *Arts types:* puppetry *Comments:* puppet performances for children and adults

Festival of Monodrama Ptuj
Festival monodrame Ptuj
Slovenski trg 13, 2250 **Ptuj**
Tel: 62-785 900 Fax: 62-785 900
Internet: www2.arnes.si/~mbgptuj
E-Mail: gledalisce.ptuj@guest.arnes.si
director Samo Strelec
Period/Frequency: March, biennial (2001) *Arts types:* theatre *Venues:* Gledalisce Ptuj 200 *Comments:* award for best performance; organised by Gledalisce Ptuj

SPAIN (+34)

Festival del Sur – Encuentro Teatral 3 Continentes
Ayuntamiento de Agüimes, calle Joaquin Artiles 1, 35260 **Agüimes (Las Palmas de Gran Canarias)**
Tel: 928-784 100 ext. 223 Fax: 928-783 663/during festival: 928-180 534
director/concejal de cultura Antonio Lozano González; secretaría Maricarmen Ramírez
Period/Frequency: Sept, annual *Arts types:* theatre, companies from Africa, Europe and America *Venues:* Teatro Municipal de Agüimes 400, Casa de la Cultura del Cruce de Arinaga 400

Encuentro de Teatro: Joven Escena
Ayuntamiento de Albacete, 02071 **Albacete**
Tel: 967-596 100 Fax: 967-596 116
director administrativo Ginés Ortuño González
Period/Frequency: April, annual *Arts types:* independent theatre *Venues:* Auditorio Municipal 600 *Second address:* Plaza de la Catedral, sn, 02071 Albacete, Tel: 967-596 134

Festival de Albacete
Ayuntamiento de Albacete, Plaza de la Catedral s/n, 02071 **Albacete**
Tel: 967-596 100 Fax: 967-596 116
director administrativo Ginés Ortuño González
Period/Frequency: Aug, annual *Arts types:* theatre, dance, music *Venues:* Recinto ferial 2000, Caseta de los Jardinillos 1800, Plaza de Toros 10000

Mostra de Teatre D'Alcoi
Centre Cultural D'Alcoi, Av. País Valenciá 1,
03801 **Alcoi (Valencia)**
Tel: 96-554 4122/4434 Fax: 96-554 4425
Internet: www.ctv.es/mostra
director Jordi Botella; prensa Mila Moya
Period/Frequency: May, annual *Arts types:* theatre, street theatre *Venues:* Teatro Calderón 1000, Teatro Principal 600, Centre Cultural 200 *Comments:* organised by Centre Cultural D'Alcoi and Teatres de la Generalitat Valenciana; see also National Organisations

Festival Internacional de Música Clasica Cura
c/ Cavallers, 2-2°, 07210 **Algaida (Mallorca)**
Tel: 971-125 435 Fax: 971-125 374
director artistico Antonia Sitjar
Period/Frequency: July-Sept, annual *Arts types:* classical music *Venues:* various venues in 13 different villages: closing concert in Santuario de Cura 500
Comments: organised by Mancomunidad pla de Mallorca (971-830 441)

Festival Internacional de Títeres de Alicante Festitíteres
Apdo. 206, 03080 **Alicante**
Tel: 96-514 4525/9208 Fax: 96-514 4525/9233
E-Mail: artitere@teleline.es
dirección Angel Casado,César Garciá Juliá
Period/Frequency: Dec, annual *Arts types:* puppetry *Venues:* Parque 'el Palmeral' *Second Address:* Area de Cultura Ayto. de Alicante, C/Jorge Juan, 1, 03002 Alicante, Teatro Arniches 250, Teatro Principal 1000

Festival Internacional de Jazz
Casa de la Juventud, C/ Rambla Obispo Orbera 23, 04001 **Almería**
Tel: 950-620 585/90/95 Fax: 950-270 302/269 122
Internet: www.a2000.es/almeria
E-Mail: almeria@a2000.es
concejal de cultura del excmo ayuntamiento Esteban Rodriguez Rodriguez; jefe de servicio de cultura Juan Antonio Martín Cuadrado
Period/Frequency: spring, annual *Venues:* Auditorio Municipal Maestro Padilla 985, Auditorio de la Universidad de Almería 300 *Second Address:* during festival: Auditorio Municipal Maestro Padilla, Avda. del Mediterráneo s/n, Tel: 950-273 002, Fax: 950-276 923
Comments: organised by Area de Cultura del Ayuntamiento, Casa Municipal de la Juventud Almería

Jornadas de Teatro del Siglo de Oro
Dto de Literatura, Ies N° 1,
Carretera de Nítar Km 7, 04120 **Almería**
Tel: 950-291 440 Fax: 950-292 009
E-Mail: clplaza@larural.es
director Antonio Serrano Agulló
Period/Frequency: March, annual *Arts types:* theatre *Venues:* Auditorio Municipal Maestro Padilla 955, Teatro Apolo 300 *Second Address:* Casa de la Juventud, Area de Cultura del Ayuntamiento de Almería c/Rambla Obispo Orberá 23, 04071 Almeria Tel: 950-210 040 Fax: 950-270 302 *Comments:* funded by Inaem, Junta de Andalucía y Ayuntamiento de Almería and private organisations ; also have conferences and parallel exhibitions or cinema programmes every year

Avuimusica
Associació Catalana de Compositors, Passeig Colom 6, Espai IV, 08002 **Barcelona**
Tel: 93-268 3719 Fax: 93-268 1259
Internet: www.accompositors.com
E-Mail: acc@accompositors.com
director Agustí Charles Soler; sub-director Ramón Porter; secretary Alicia Coduras
Period/Frequency: Oct-May, annual *Arts types:* contemporary classical music *Venues:* Centre de Cultura Contemporanea de Barcelona 250 *Comments:* funded by Govern de la Generalitat de Catalunya, ajuntament de Barcelona, Societat d'Autors i Editors, Ministerio de Cultura

Castell de Peralada International Music Festival
Festival Castell de Peralada
c/ Pere de Montcada n° 1, 08034 **Barcelona**
Tel: 93-280 5868 Fax: 93-203 8700
Internet: www.festivalperalada.com
E-Mail: info@festivalperalada.com
director Luis López de Lamadrid
Period/Frequency: July-Aug, annual *Arts types:* classical music, opera, dance, symphonic music, theatre *Venues:* Castell de Peralada, Jardins del Palau 1600, Claustro 200, Iglesia 400 *Second Address:* during festival: Castell de Peralada, 17491 Perelada (Girona), Tel: 972-538 292, Fax: 972-538 292, Iglesia del Carmen 350

Cicle Joves & Classica Joventuts Musicals de Barcelona
Pau Claris 139 4° 1ª, **Barcelona**
Tel: 93-215 2918/3657 Fax: 93-487 2970
Internet: www.teleline.es/personal/jmb.bcn
E-Mail: jmb.bcn@suport.org
presidente Juan Milla
Period/Frequency: Oct-Dec, annual *Arts types:* classical music *Venues:* Casal de Metge *Second Address:* Casal del Metge, via Layetana 31, 08002 Barcelona, Tel: 93-319 7800 *Comments:* organised by Joventuts Musicals de Barcelona; see also National Organsiations and Competitions

Ciclo Musica XXI Joventuts Musicals de Barcelona
c/ Pau Claris 139 4T 1A, 08009 **Barcelona**
Tel: 93-215 2918/3657 Fax: 93-487 2970
Internet: www.teleline.es/personal/jmb.bcn
E-Mail: jmb.bcn@suport.org
presidente Juan Milla
Period/Frequency: Sept/Oct, annual *Arts types:* contemporary music *Second Address:* SGAE – Sociedad General de Autores, Paseo Colon 6, 08002 Barcelona
Comments: see also National Organsiations and Competitions

Dies de Dansa – International Festival of Dance in Urban Landscapes
Trafalgar 78, 1-1, 08010 **Barcelona**
Tel: 93-268 1868
Fax: 93-268 2424
E-Mail: marato.espect@cambrabcn.es
directores Arnau Vilardebó, Juan Eduardo López; producción Jectti Hoenisch, Montse Guiu, Ivette Vilar
Period/Frequency: July, annual *Arts types:* dance *Venues:* open-air locations, streets, parks, etc. *Comments:* also workshops for professional dancers and general public; organised by Associació Marató de L'Espectacle, co-produced by Associació Marató de L'Espectacle; forms part of Festival d'Estiu de Barcelona Grec; see also Promoters

Festival d'Estiu de Barcelona Grec
Institut de Cultura de Barcelona, Palau de la Virreina, La Rambla 99, 08002 **Barcelona**
Tel: 93-301 7775 Fax: 93-301 6100
Internet: www.grecbcn.com
E-Mail: smillet@mail.bcu.es
director festival Xavier Albertí; director gerente Institut de Cultura de Barcelona Ferran Mascarell; subdirector Biel Moll
Period/Frequency: June-Aug, annual *Arts types:* drama, music, dance, opera, cinema *Venues:* Plaza del Rey 800, Palau de la Musica, MACBA-CCCB, Teatro Grec 1900, Teatre Mercat de les Flors and other venues in Barcelona *Comments:* also organise Grec Metropolità Festival in the Metropolitan area of Barcelona (St. Adrià del Bessos, Sta. Coloma de Gramanet, Hospitalet del Llobregat, Badalona); alternative E-mail: infoicup@mail.bcn.es; see also Venues

Festival de Cadaqués
Arcs 8, 1er 2°, 08002 **Barcelona**
Tel: 93-301 9555 Fax: 93-302 2670
Internet: www.trito.es
E-Mail: trito@bcn.servicom.es
director Llorenç Caballero i Pàmies
Period/Frequency: Aug, annual *Arts types:* classical, contemporary music *Venues:* Iglésia Parroquial de Cadaqués (Cadaques Parish Church) 500 *Second Address:* address during festival: C/Cotxe 2, 17488 Cadaqués, Tel: 972-258 194, Fax: 972-258 074
Comments: see also Orchestras and Competitions

Festival de Música Antigua
Fundació la Caixa, Departamento Musical, Paseo de San Juan 108, 08037 **Barcelona**
Tel: 93-458 8905/06/07 (dept. music) Fax: 93-459 0662
Internet: www.fundacio.lacaixa.es
E-Mail: info.fundacio@lacaixa.es
director Maricarmen Palma
Period/Frequency: April-May, annual *Arts types:* early music *Venues:* Salon del Tinell 500, Centre Cultural de la Caixa 450 *Comments:* there is a section called 'Fringe' for young musicians (open submission); organised by Fundacion la Caixa, Dept-Musical; see also Promoters

Festival de Músicas del Mundo
Fundació la Caixa, Departamento Musical, Paseo de San Juan 108, 08037 **Barcelona**
Tel: 93-458 8905/06/07 (dept. music) Fax: 93-459 0662
Internet: www.fundacio.lacaixa.es
E-Mail: info.fundacio@lacaixa.es
director Maricarmen Palma
Period/Frequency: Oct, annual *Arts types:* ethnic music, mainly mediterranean area *Venues:* Salon del Tinell 500, Centre Cultural de la Caixa 450 *Comments:* organised by Fundacion la Caixa, Dept-Musical; see also Promoters

Festival de Músiques Contemporánies de Barcelona
Centre de Cultura Contemporanea de Barcelona, c/. Montalegre, 5, 08001 **Barcelona**
Tel: 93-306 4100
Fax: 93-306 4104
Internet: www.cccb.org
E-Mail: fmcb@cccb.org
director artístico David Albet
Period/Frequency: Oct-Dec, annual *Arts types:* contemporary music (classical, jazz, rock, electronic music)
Venues: Museo Arte contemporaneo de Barcelona, Centro de Cultura Contemporanea de Barcelona
Comments: organised by MACBA, ICUB, CCCB

Festival Internacional de Músika de Cantonigròs
c/ Muntaner 305, entl. 2ª, 08021 **Barcelona**
Tel: 93-201 5247/7711/852 5086/95
Fax: 93-201 7711
E-Mail: fimc@abaforum.es
president Josep M Busquets
Period/Frequency: 15-18 July, annual *Arts types:* choral, music, folk music, dance *Venues:* Esplanade in the village *Comments:* organised by FIMC in collaboration with Department de Cultura de la Generalitat de Catalunya and Diputació de Barcelona

International Puppet and Visual Theatre Festival of Barcelona
Festival Internacional de Teatre Visual i de Titelles de Barcelona
Institut del Teatre de la Diputació de Barcelona, c/ Sant Pere més baix, 7, 08003 **Barcelona**
Tel: 93-268 2078 Fax: 93-268 1070
E-Mail: i.teatre@diba.es
dirección Joan Baixas
Period/Frequency: Nov, biennial (2000) *Arts types:* puppets (adults and children), vsual theatre *Venues:* Teatro Adrià Gual 288, Teatro La Cuina 140
Comments: new building opening soon; see also National Organisations

Marató de L'Espectacle
Trafalgar 78, 1-1, 08010 **Barcelona**
Tel: 93-268 1868 Fax: 93-268 2424
E-Mail: marato.espect@cambrabcn.es
directores Arnau Vilardebó, Juan Eduardo López; producción Jectti Hoenisch, Montse Guiu, Ivette Vilar
Period/Frequency: May-June, annual *Arts types:* theatre, dance, music, video, film, street theatre, circus, shows, audience participation *Venues:* Mercat de les Flors de Barcelona, c/ Lérida 59, Barcelona, Tel: 93-426 1875 *Second Address:* Mercat de les Flors, c/ Lérida 59, Barcelona, Tel: 93-426 1875 *Comments:* organised and produced by Associació Marató de l'Espectacle; see also Promoters

Mostra Catalana de Música Contemporánea
Paseo de Colón 6, Espacio 4°, 08002 **Barcelona**
Tel: 93-268 3719
Fax: 93-268 1259
Internet: www.accompositors.com
E-Mail: acc@accompositors.com
director Agustí Charles Soler; sub-director Ramón Porter; secretary Ariadna Martin
Period/Frequency: Dec, biennial (2000) *Arts types:* contemporary classical music *Venues:* L'Auditori , SGAE *Comments:* funded by Gobierno de la Generalitat, Ayuntamiento de Barcelona, Sociedad de Autores y Editores, Ministerio de Cultura

Mostra de Video-Dansa de Barcelona
Apartat de Correus 2584, 08080 **Barcelona**
Tel: 93-319 8105/416 0957
Fax: 93-319 8105/416 0957
E-Mail: cdansa@arrakis.es
directoras Elisa Huerta, Nuria Font
Period/Frequency: Feb-March, biennial *Arts types:* video-dance *Venues:* Centro de Arte Sta Mónica *Comments:* organised by: Generalitat Dep Cultura, Portal Sta. Madrona, Barcelona; see also Recorded Media

Festival Int. de Titeres para Adultos de Bergara
c/ Mizpildi s/n, 20570 **Bergara**
Tel: 943-765 837 Fax: 943-762 105
directora Itsaso Azkarate
Period/Frequency: biennial (2000: April) *Arts types:* puppetry for adults *Venues:* Sala Zabalotegi 250 *Comments:* organsied by Taun Taun Teatroa; funded by Ayuntamiento de Bergara

Festival International de Musica Tropical
Ayuntamiento de Bilbao,
Plaza Ernesto Ercoreka s/n, 48007 **Bilbao**
Tel: 94-420 4430/22 Fax: 94-420 4403
Internet: www.bilbao.net
E-Mail: cultura@ayto.bilbao.net
director Ana Elejalde
Period/Frequency: July, annual *Arts types:* Latin and African music *Venues:* open air concerts: Parque dña Casilda *Comments:* organised by Ayuntamiento de Bilbao Area de Cultura y Turismo

International Puppet Festival of Bilbao
Festival Internacional de Titeres de Bilbao
PO Box 5090, 48009 **Bilbao**
Tel: 94-424 5902/0437
Fax: 94-424 2550
directora Concha de la Casa; prensa Carmen Torres; secretaria Marian Sanchez
Period/Frequency: Oct-Dec, annual *Arts types:* puppetry, object theatre, performance, dance *Venues:* Sala del Carmen 600, Sala Barrainkua 150 *Comments:* exhibitions, seminars, workshops; see also National Organisations and Publications: organised by Centro Municipal de las Artes de los Titeres; visiting address: Casa de Cultura, Barrainkua N°5, 48009 Bilbao

Temporada de Opera – Abao
c/ José María Olabarri n° 2/4, bajo, 48001 **Bilbao**
Tel: 94-435 5100
Fax: 94-435 5101
directora general Ana Esteban Arroyo; coordinator artístico Luis López Tejedor; presidente Francisco de Larracoechea; vice-presidente Otto Vargas Gold; secretario Juan José Matellanes
Period/Frequency: Sept-April, annual
Arts types: classical opera *Venues:* Teatro Euskalduno 2200 *Comments:* organised by Asociación Bilbaína de Amigos de le Opera (ABAO); see also Opera

Este es el Nombre del Festival
Fundació ACA/Àrea Creació Acústica,
Son Bielí, 07311 **Búger (Mallorca)**
Tel: 971-516 501
Fax: 971-516 502
E-Mail: fundacioaca@new-ton.com
presidente Antoni Caimari Alomar; coordinadora general fundació Beatriz Florit Rigo
Period/Frequency: Sept-Oct, annual
Arts types: music by national and international living composers, contemporary music *Venues:* Teatro Principal de Palma 700 *Comments:* also organise courses and lectures; organised by Fundació A.C.A. – Area Creació Musical; every year the festival is recorded and edited on CD by U.M. – Unió Music; see also Recorded Media and Promoters

Festival de Teatro Clásico
Instituto Municipal de Cultura,
Paseo del Espolón s/n, 09003 **Burgos**
Tel: 947-279 369 Fax: 947-271 250
coordinador cultural Ignacio Gonzàlez de Santiago; responsable de programación
Ignacio Javier de Miguel Gallo
Period/Frequency: Nov, annual *Arts types:* Greek, Roman, Golden age classical, drama *Venues:* Teatro Clunia 611, Teatro Principal 1000 *Comments:* incorporated in Otoñada Cultural

Festival International de Folklore Cuidad de Burgos
Apartado 352, 09080 **Burgos**
Tel: 947-277 896
Internet: www.render.es/Festival-Folclore-Burgos/
E-Mail: folclore@render.es
presidenta Concepcion Madorran Antoñanzas; secretario general Migul Alonso Gomez
Period/Frequency: July, annual
Arts types: folk dance, folk music, folk singing *Venues:* Plaza de San Juan (open air) *Second Address:* C/ Vitoria n° 60-7°, 09004 Burgos *Comments:* organised by Comite de Folclore Ciudad de Burgos

Otoñada Cultural
Instituto Municipal de Cultura,
Paseo del Espolón s/n, 09003 **Burgos**
Tel: 947-279 369 Fax: 947-271 250
coordinador cultural Ignacio Gonzàlez de Santiago; responsable de programación
Ignacio Javier de Miguel Gallo
Period/Frequency: Oct-Dec, annual *Arts types:* music, theatre, dance *Venues:* Teatro Principal 1000, Teatro Clunia, Casa de Cultura de Gamonal 600 *Comments:* includes Muestra Nacional de Teatro Principal 1000, Festival Internacional de Danza

Semana de Música Antonio de Cabezón
Instituto Municipal de Cultura de Burgos, Teatro Principal, Paseo del Espolón s/n, 09003 **Burgos**
Tel: 947-279 369 Fax: 947-271 250
coordinador cultural Ignacio Gonzàlez de Santiago; responsable de programación
Ignacio Javier de Miguel Gallo
Period/Frequency: Aug, annual *Arts types:* early music *Venues:* Capilla de Música de Bernardas 350, Teatro Principal 1000 *Comments:* incorporated in Reina Sofía Summer Festivals

Dansa València
Centre Coreogràfic, Parc de la Granja, s/n, 46100 **Burjassot (Valencia)**
Tel: 96-390 4774 Fax: 96-390 4772
E-Mail: fmedina@cult.gva.es
coordinación Inmaculada Gil Lázaro
Period/Frequency: Feb, annual *Arts types:* Spanish contemporary dance *Venues:* Teatre Principal 1072, Teatro Rialto 394, Teatre Talía 900
Comments: parallel activities: Mostra Internacional de Video Dansa, Congreso de la Federación Española de Profesionales de la Danza; see also National Organisations and Venues

Mostra Internacional de Mim. en Sueca
Centre Coreogràfic, Parc de la Granja s/n, 46100 **Burjassot (Valencia)**
Tel: 96-390 4774 Fax: 96-390 4772
director Abel Guarínos
Period/Frequency: September, annual *Arts types:* gestual theatre *Venues:* Teatro Bernat Baldobí 600, Casa de la Cultura 200 *Comments:* organised by Teatres de la Gen Valenciana, Ayuntamiento de Seuca y Fundacíòn Bancaixa

Festival de Teatro Clásico de Cáceres
Gran Teatro, c/ San Anton s/n, 10003 **Cáceres**
Tel: 927-212 949/215 651 Fax: 927-212 949
Internet: www.bme.es/granteatro
E-Mail: granteatro@bme.es
director Marceliano Solis Romero;
gerente Roberto García del Río
Period/Frequency: June, annual *Arts types:* open-air festival, classical theatre *Venues:* Plaza las Velatas, Plaza de San Jorge *Comments:* organised by Gran Teatro de Cáceres; see also Venues

Festival Iberoamericano de Teatro de Cádiz
Fundación Municipal de Cultura, c/ Isabel la Católica n° 12, 11004 **Cádiz**
Tel: 956-221 680/211 123/227 624
Fax: 956-222 051
E-Mail: fitdecádiz@ctv.es
director artístico and gerente José Bablé Neira
Period/Frequency: Oct, annual *Arts types:* theatre, music, dance, performance *Venues:* Gran Teatro Falla 1200, Sala La Lechera 250 , Sala Valcarcel 500, Palacio de Congresos 400 *Comments:* seminars, conferences, art exhibitions, forums, II Congress of Theatrical Pedagogy

Festival Internacional de Música 'Manuel de Falla'
Plaza de Falla s/n, 11003 **Cádiz**
Tel: 956-220 894 Fax: 956-220 354
tecnico cultura Vicente Ferrer; concejal cultura Francisco Carnota Acera
Period/Frequency: May, annual *Arts types:* contemporary and classical music *Venues:* Gran Teatro Falla 1200 *Second Address:* Fundación Municipal de Culutra, Isabel la Católica 12, 11003 Cadiz *Comments:* town hall fax: 56-222 051; funded by Fundacion Municipal de Cultura, Red Española de Teatros Y Auditorios, Unicaja

Festival de Música de Calonge
Plaça del Castell n°1, 17251 **Calonge (Catalunya)**
Tel: 972-660 476/660 481 Fax: 972-660 476
Internet: www.calonge-santantoni.com/festival
president Adrian Buckley
Period/Frequency: July-Aug, annual *Arts types:* jazz, classical music, popular music, flamenco *Venues:* Patio del Castillo de Calonge 500 (open air)

Festival de Teatro Ciudad de Cieza
Centro Cultural de Cieza,
Fernando III el Santo s/n, 30530 **Cieza (Murcia)**
Tel: 968-456 259 Fax: 968-762 761
director administrativo Bartolomé Avellanera; concejal de festejos Mª José Giménez
Period/Frequency: Aug, annual *Arts types:* all types of theatre *Venues:* Auditorio Municipal 1000 (open-air venue) *Comments:* organised by Concejalia de Cultura Ciudad de Cieza

Festival int. de la guitarra de Córdoba
F.P.M. Gran Teatro, Avda.
Gran Capitan 3, 14008 **Córdoba**
Tel: 957-480 644/237 Fax: 957-487 494
Internet: www.ayuncordoba.es
E-Mail: cpd@aix.ayuncordoba.es
director general Manuel Angel Jiménez Arévalo; producción Ana Linares; prensa Carmen Ruiz; pr Pablo Domínguez; jefe técnico José Antonio Figueola
Period/Frequency: July, annual *Arts types:* informative programme-seminars, conferences, lectures, master-classes, exhibitions, concerts, all types of music for guitar *Venues:* El Alcázar 4000, Gran Teatro 942
Comments: see also Venues

Charlie Rivel Memorial International Clown Festival
Festival Internacional de Payasos de Cornellá – Memorial Charlie Rivel
c/ Joan Maragall 44,
08940 **Cornella de Llobregat (Barcelona)**
Tel: 93-377 5454 Fax: 93-474 2850
Internet: www.intercom.es/cornella.festival-pallassos
director programacion Ramon Monserrat
Period/Frequency: May, biennial (2000) *Arts types:* classical, situation comedy, comedia dell'arte, picaresque, clowns, etc *Venues:* Teatro Auditorio de Cornellá 750, Patronat Cultural i Recreatiu 300
Comments: largest European event for clowning

Religious Music Week
Semana de Musica Religiosa
Apto de Correos 97, 16080 **Cuenca**
Tel: 969-178 857/8-046 200/06
Fax: 969-178 857
Internet: www.citelan.es/semana-musica-religiosa-cuenca
E-Mail: semana.musica.religiosa.cuenca@citelan.es
director artístico Ignacio Yepes; director técnico Ismael Barambio; coordinador general Claudio Nohales
Period/Frequency: during Holy Week, annual *Arts types:* sacred music *Venues:* Auditorio de Cuenca 800, Iglesia de S. Miguel 470, Iglesia de Los Paules 600 *Second address:* Glorieta González Palencia 2, 2ª, 16002 Cuenca

Festival Internacional de Deià
Alma Concerts, Davall Es Penyel, 07179 **Deiá (Mallorca)**
Tel: 971-639 178 Fax: 971-639 178
E-Mail: patrick@ctv.es
director Patrick Meadows; secretary Stephanie Shepard
Period/Frequency: 20-21 concerts once or twice a week from April-Oct, annual *Arts types:* chamber, classical, romantic, post romantic music, baroque with original instruments, flamenco *Venues:* Son Marroig 200, Iglésia de Deià 200 *Comments:* sponsors: Consell Insular de Mallorca and Ayuntamiento de Deià; organises concerts in spring of classical music of the 20th century in Palacio March

Udazkenean Folk (Festival de música folk-tradicional)
c/ Iparraguirre 8-2°, 20001 **Donostia-San Sebastian**
Tel: 943-291 747 Fax: 943-291 345
director Mikel Urbeltz
Period/Frequency: Oct, annual *Arts types:* folk music (folk groups from all over the world) *Venues:* Teatro Principal 700, Casa de Cultura de la Ciudad 350
Comments: Festival organised by Ikerfolk and funded by Diputacion de Gipuzkoa

Jornadas de Teatro de Eibar
Complejo Educativo-Centro de Residencias, Av. de Otaola 29, 20600 **Eibar (Guipuzkoa)**
Tel: 94-320 8444 ext 67
Fax: 94-320 3196
E-Mail: jmcornago@edunet.es
director Juan Ortega (ext 15); producer José Maria Cornago (ext 67); administration Manuel Murillo
Period/Frequency: Feb-March, annual *Arts types:* all types of theatre, some dance *Venues:* Teatro del Compleso Educativo Eibar 700

Festival de Teatre i Música Medieval d'Elx
Ayuntamiento de Elche, Placa de Baix, s/n, 03202 **Elche**
Tel: 96-661 1350 Fax: 96-661 0992
director Cesar Oliva;
coordinacion general & tecnica Vicente Perez
Period/Frequency: Oct-Nov, biennial (2000) *Arts types:* medieval theatre, dance and music, seminars with reference to El Misterio de Elche *Venues:* Basílica de Santa María 1500, Gran Teatre 1000, Iglesia de San José 500, Plaza del Congreso Eucarístico 3000 *Second address:* Teatres de la Generalitat Valenciana, c/ Barca 15, 46002 Valencia, Tel: 96-351 0051, Fax: 96-352 0287 *Comments:* organised by Teatres de la Generalitat Valenciana, Ayuntamiento de Elche, Diputacion de Alicante and Ministerio de Cultura

Festival Internacional de Jazz de Granada
Area de Cultura, Plza de los Girones nº 1,
18009 **Granada**
Tel: 958-247 383/72 Fax: 958-247 385
Internet: www.dipgra.es
E-Mail: cultura@dipgra.es
director Jesús Villalba; subdirector Juan de Dios Vico; productor tecnico Neil Doherty
Period/Frequency: Nov, annual *Arts types:* jazz and blues, cinema *Venues:* Palacio de Congresos 2000, Palacio Municipal de Deportes 10000, Teatro Isabel la Católica 800 *Comments:* local funding, Ayuntamiento de Granada, Diputación Provincial de Granada

Festival Internacional de Música y Danza de Granada
c/ Cárcel Baja, 19-3°, 18001 **Granada**
Tel: 958-276 200 Fax: 958-286 868
Internet: www.granadafestival.org
E-Mail: ofi@granadafestival.org
director Alfredo Aracil; coordinación artística Nina von Krong; jefe de prensa Teresa du Rio
Period/Frequency: June-July, annual *Arts types:* classical music, recitals, opera, ballet, flamenco *Venues:* Auditorium Manuel de Falla, Palacio de Carlos V, Teatro del Generalife, Catedral, Patio Arrayanes (Alhambra)

Festival Internacional de Tango
Ayuntamiento de Granada-Concejería de Cultura, Cuesta de Sta Ines Nº 6, 18010 **Granada**
Tel: 958-224 384/229 344/609-081 840 (mobile)
Fax: 958-227 778
Internet: www.granada.org
coordinador Horacio Rébora
Period/Frequency: April, annual *Venues:* Teatro Municipal Isabel la Católica 1300, Palacio de Congresos 2000 *Second Address:* Andart-La Tertulia. c/Pintor Lopez Mezquita, 3-18002 Granada Tel: 958-294 219/272 233 *Comments:* national and municipal funding, private funding – Argentinian Entities

Festival Internacional de Teatro de Granada
c/o Cultura de la Diputación Provincial de Granada, Plaza de los Girones 1, 18009 **Granada**
Tel: 958-247 380/383
Fax: 958-247 252
directors Alfonso Alcalá, Manolo Llanes
Period/Frequency: autumn, annual *Arts types:* avantgarde theatre, dance *Venues:* Teatro Alhambra 280, outdoors (street) *Comments:* organised and funded by Diputación Provincial de Granada, Ayuntamiento de Granada, Junta de Andalucía and Caja General de Ahorros de Granada

Jazz en la Costa
Area de Cultura Diputación Provinical de Granada, Plaza de Los Girones, 1, 18009 **Granada**
Tel: 958-247 372/383 Fax: 958-247 385
Internet: www.dipgra.es
director Jesús Villalba Lozano;
productor Francisco Guerrero
Period/Frequency: July, annual *Arts types:* concerts, jazz, blues, Latin jazz *Venues:* Parque El Majuelo 2000 *Second Address:* Ayuntamiento de Almuñecar, Casa Municipal de Cultura Almuñecar (Granada), Francisco Guerrero (958-838 605) *Comments:* courses, conferences, jazz workshops; organizer: diputación provincial de Granada, area de Cultura

Jornadas de Música Contemporánea
Area Cultural Caja de Granada, Reyes Católicos 51-2°, 18001 **Granada**
Tel: 958-225 459/244 403
Fax: 958-244 621
director de las Jornadas José García Román
Period/Frequency: March-April, annual *Arts types:* contemporary music *Venues:* Teatro Alhambra-Granada 300, Auditorio Manuel de Falla-Granada 1300 *Comments:* includes string quartet competition Luis de Narváez, prize 1250k pts: see also Competitions

Festival Iberoamericano de Huelva
Delegación de Cultura del Ayuntamiento de Huelva, Casa Colón, Plaza del Punto s/n, 21003 **Huelva**
Tel: 959-210 177/78/76
Fax: 959-210 180
organizador Juan López Cerezo
Period/Frequency: July, annual *Arts types:* all types of Latin American music *Venues:* open-air venues, Avenida de Andalucía

Festival Internacional de Teatro y Danza Castillo de Niebla
Diputación Provincial de Huelva, Area de Cultura, Calle San Salvador, 14 – 3°, 21003 **Huelva**
Tel: 959-494 696 (organisation) Fax: 959-494 699
E-Mail: dph2@otd1.otd.es
responsable area de cultura diputación Juan José Oña; técnica de cultura del ayuntamiento de niebla Juan Antonio Estrada
Period/Frequency: July-Aug, annual *Arts types:* theatre, dance *Venues:* Castillo de Niebla 1029, open air (castle courtyard) *Comments:* Javier Gutiérrez, Gran Teatro Tel: 959-494 696 (box office); organised by Diputación Provincial de Huelva Tel: 959-494 696, supported by Ayuntamiento de Niebla (Tel: 959-363 176) and Junta de Andalucía

Muestra Internacional de la Danza
Delegación de Cultura del Ayuntamiento de Huelva, Casa Colón, Plaza del Punto s/n, 21003 **Huelva**
Tel: 959-210 177/78/76 Fax: 959-210 180
programación Juan José López Cerezo
Period/Frequency: June-July, annual *Arts types:* world music, street dance and theatre *Venues:* open air venues: Calle del Centro, Avenida de Andalucía

Festival Internacional de Las Culturas Pirineos sur
Pirineo sur, Diputacion de Huesca,
Porches de Galicia 4, 22071 **Huesca**
Tel: 974-226 679/227 311/230 385 Fax: 974-243 112
Internet: www.aragon.net
E-Mail: dph@correo.aragon.net
director artistico Luis Calvo
Period/Frequency: July, annual *Arts types:* world music, workshops, exhibitions, cinema, world crafts market *Venues:* Auditorio Natural de Lanuza, Escenario de Sallent de Gallego, Valle de Tena, Huesca *Comments:* each year one week is dedicated to a different culture

Festival de Jerez
Fundación Teatro Villamarta,
Plaza Romeno Martínez s/n, 11402 **Jerez**
Tel: 956-329 313 Fax: 956-329 508
director gerente Francisco López Gumérrez; director de comunicación José Angel Bermejo
Period/Frequency: April, annual *Arts types:* flamenco *Venues:* Teatro Villamarta, Real Esurela Andaluzo del Arte Ecuestre, and other veneus in the city *Comments:* produced by Fundación Teatro Villamarta; see also Venues and Opera

Ciclo de Grandes Conciertos de Palacio
Teatro de la Ópera, Glorieta de Americas Nº 3,
15004 **La Coruña**
Tel: 981-252 021
Fax: 981-277 499
E-Mail: osg@lcg.servicom.es
manager Enrique Rojas Guillen;
musical adviser Victor Pablo Perez
Period/Frequency: Oct-May, annual *Arts types:* symphonic music, choral *Venues:* Palacio de Congresos – Auditorium, La Coruña *Comments:* see also Orchestra

Festival Mozart
Teatro de la Ópera, Glorieta de Americas Nº3, 15004 **La Coruña**
Tel: 981-252 021
Fax: 981-277 499
E-Mail: org@lcg.servicom.es
director Enrique Rojas Guillen; administrador Luciano Lago Padin; coordinador técnico Jose Queijo Rodriguez; director artistico Antonio Moral;
jefe de prensa Javier Alvarez Vizoso
Period/Frequency: May-June, annual *Arts types:* opera, symphonic music, chamber music *Venues:* Palacio de Congresos-Auditorio, Symphonic Hall 1746, Chamber Hall 475, Teatro Rosalia de Castro 700
Comments: funded by Ayuntamiento de la Coruña; see also Orchestras

La Coruña Music Festival
Festival de Musica de la Coruña
Teatro de la Ópera, Glorieta de America Nº 3,
15004 **La Coruña**
Tel: 981-252 021 Fax: 981-277 499
E-Mail: osg@lcg.servicom.es
director Enrique Rojas Guillén; administrador Luciano Lago Padín; coordinador técnico José Queijo Rodríguez; jefe de prensa Javier Alvarez Vizoso
Period/Frequency: Aug, annual *Arts types:* chamber, symphony and choral music *Venues:* Teatro de la Ópera, symphonic hall 1746, chamber hall 475, Teatro Rosalia de Castro 700

Estiu Musical a Castell-Platja d'Aro
c/ València 35 1°,
08430 **La Roca del Vallès (Barcelona)**
Tel: 93-879 5097
artistic director Josep Maria Sauret i Sumalla
Period/Frequency: July-Sept *Arts types:* classical music, chamber music and orchestra *Venues:* Iglesia Parroquial de Castell d'Aro 200, Iglesia Parroquial de Platja d'Aro 500 *Second Address:* c/ Mosser Cinto Verdager 4, 17250 Platja D'Aro *Comments:* organised by Associoació Musical Tempus; see also Promoters

Canary Islands Music Festival
Festival de Música de Canarias
Sociedad Canaria de las Artes Escénicas y de la Música (SOCAEM S.A.), León y Castillo 427, 3,
35007 **Las Palmas de Gran Canarias**
Tel: 928-247 442/3 Fax: 928-276 042
Internet: www.festivaldecanarias.com
E-Mail: festival@socaem.com
director del festival Rafael Nebot Cabrera; secretario del festival Nora Krozewski; gerente de SOCAEM
Luis Socorro Rodriguez
Period/Frequency: annual (2000: 7 Jan-2 March) *Arts types:* mainly classical music, but also some contemporary, chamber concerts and recitals *Venues:* Auditorio Alfredo Kraus (Gran Canaria) 1660, Teatro Guimera (Tenerife) 1000 *Second Address:* SOCAEM S.A. (Tenerife), Plaza 25 de Julio, nº 4, Edificio Roma 1°, 38004 Santa Cruz de Tenerife

Festival de Opera de Las Palmas
Asociaccion de Amigos Canarios de la Opera, Teatro Pérez Galdós, Plaza Stagno 1,
35002 **Las Palmas de Gran Canarias**
Tel: 928-370 125
Internet: www.canarias-internet.com/webf/opera
E-Mail: amigoscanarios@lpa.servicom.es
presidente Juan de Leon Suarez
Period/Frequency: Feb-May, annual *Arts types:* opera *Venues:* Teatro Pérez Galdós 1360, Auditorio Alfredo Krauss 1600 *Comments:* see also Opera

Festival de Otoño
Concejo Municipal de Cultura, León y Castillo 322, 4° planta, 35007 **Las Palmas de Gran Canarias**
Tel: 928-446 022/50/262 713/1391 Fax: 928-446 043/262 607
E-Mail: cultura@laspalmasgc.es
director Adela Martìn
Period/Frequency: Oct-Nov, annual *Arts types:* theatre, dance, musicals *Venues:* Teatro Perez Galdós, Teatro Coyás 1000, Auditorio Alfredo Krauss *Comments:* funded by Culture Ministrerio du Cultura and Canarias local government

Festival International de Canarias. Jazz & Mas
C/29 de Abril 39, 3°,
35007 **Las Palmas de Gran Canarias**
Tel: 928-220 407/473 Fax: 928-220 407
Internet: www.coloradoproducciones.com
E-Mail: info@coloradoproducciones.com
director Miguel Ramirez
Period/Frequency: July, annual *Arts types:* jazz, latin, ethnic, blues *Venues:* Auditorio Alfredo Krauss (Gran Canarias) 1600, Paraninfo Universitario (Tenerife) 600 *Comments:* see also Agents (Colorado Producciones)

Festival de Música Española
PO Box 1183, 24080 **León**
Tel: 987-213 844/639-826 460 (mobile director)
Fax: 987-213 844
director Daniel Gutierrez Sanz
Period/Frequency: July, annual *Arts types:* Spanish and Latin American music *Venues:* various venues in Leon up to 500, principal venues: Palacio de Los Guzmanes (XVI century) and Teatro Emperador

Festival Internacional de Órgano Catedral de León
Gran Avenida de San Marcos, 5-5° A, 24001 **León**
Tel: 987-246 303 Fax: 987-246 303
Internet: festorga.bornet.es
E-Mail: festorga@bornet.es
director del festival Samuel Rubio Alvarez; secretario general Fernando Quiñones Fidalgo; coordinadora Marta Martínez López
Period/Frequency: Sept-Oct, annual *Arts types:* mainly organ music, but includes all other types of classical music, orchestras, chamber music, choirs *Venues:* Cathedral of Leon 4000 and other churches in the province of Leon *Comments:* music seminars, courses; municipal funding with Caixa Galicia, funding by Caixa de Galicia, Diputación de León, Ayuntamiento de León and Junta de Castilla y León

Lleida International Puppet Theatre Festival
Fira de Teatre de Títelles de Lleida
Centre de Títelles de Lleida, Placa de L'hort de Sta Teresa, 1, 25002 **Lleida**
Tel: 973-270 249 Fax: 973-264 515
director de programación Julieta Agustí; director artistico Joan Andreu Vallvé
Period/Frequency: May, annual *Arts types:* puppetry *Venues:* Auditorio Municipal Enrique Granados, Audiotorio Fundacion la Caixa, Sede Teatro del Centro de Títelles, many other venues *Comments:* funded by Ayuntamiento de Lleida and the Generalitat de Catalunya; see also National Organisations and Puppetry

Festival Internacional de Música de la Villa de Llívia
Patronat del Museu Municipal de Llívia, Calle Forns, 4, 17527 **Llívia**
Tel: 972-896 313 Fax: 972-896 313
presidente José Vinyet i Estebanell
Period/Frequency: Aug, Dec, annual *Arts types:* all types of classical music, emphasis on chamber *Venues:* Iglesia Parroquial 750 *Second address:* c/ Coronel Molera 12-4°, 2ª, 17520 Puigcerdà

Musica als Patis
Carretera La Bisbal 5,
43712 **Llorenç del Penedés (Tarragona)**
Tel: 977-678 610 Fax: 977-678 313
E-Mail: mgyr@ctv.es
artistic director & organisation Santiago Gyr
Period/Frequency: July-Aug, annual *Arts types:* classical music, symphonic orchestras, soloists *Venues:* Vueltas del Circo Romano 200, Convento de las Carmelitas 250

Festival de Títeres de Logroño
Area de Cultura del Ayuntamiento,
Avenida de la Paz 11, 26071 **Logroño**
Tel: 941-277 000/012 Fax: 941-234 932
director Francisco Gestal
Period/Frequency: Dec, annual *Arts types:* puppetry *Venues:* Teatro Bretón 970, small venues, and various others throughout the province *Second address:* Consejería de Cultura, c/ Portales N° 2, 26071 Logroño, Tel: 941-291 100, Fax: 941-291 375 *Comments:* organised and funded by Ayuntamiento de Logroño and Consejería de Cultura

Agrupaciones Artísticas Once
c/ Prado 24, 28014 **Madrid**
Tel: 91-589 4600 Fax: 91-429 3118
Internet: www.once.es
E-Mail: soi@once.es
jefa del departamento de promoción artística Reyes Lluch
Period/Frequency: annual *Arts types:* music & theatre *Comments:* organised by O.N.C.E (National Org. for blind people); the festival alternates between music and theatre (one year theatre the next music); the actors and musicians are blind; every year the festival is held in a different city in Spain;
in 1999 it will be held in Almería

Alicante International Contemporary Music Festival
Festival Internacional de Música Contemporanea de Alicante
Centro de Arte Reina Sofia, Centro Para la Difusion de Musica Contemporanea, c/ St. Isabel 52, 28012 **Madrid**
Tel: 91-468 2310/2931 Fax: 91-530 8321
Internet: www.mcv.es/iem-cdme
E-Mail: consuelo.diez@cdmc.inaem.es
director administrativo y artístico Consuelo Diez; coordinadora CDMC Asunción Tirado
Period/Frequency: Sept, annual *Arts types:* contemporary music *Venues:* Castillo de Sta Bárbara 200, Sala de Conferencias de la Caja.A.M 100, Iglesia de San Nicholás de Bari 600, Auditorio de la C.A.M. 150, Aula de Cultura de la C.A.M. 350, Teatro Principal 1000 *Second Address:* Ayuntamiento de Alicante, Plaza del Ayuntamiento n° 11, 03002 Alicante, Tel: 96-514 9203/91-337 0310 *Comments:* co-organised by Fundacion Cultural de la C.A.M. (Alicante), SGAF, TVE, RNE; see also Promoters

Aranjuez Early Music Festival
Festival de Música Antigua de Aranjuez
c/o CP Conciertos,
Apodaca 9. Bajo Derecha, 28004 **Madrid**
Tel: 91-447 6400 Fax: 91-447 9699
promoter Javier Estrella
Period/Frequency: Nov, annual *Arts types:* early music on period instruments *Venues:* Auditorio Joaquin Rodrigo, Centro Cultural Isabel de Farnesio (Aranjuez) 400

Ciclo de Camara y Polifonía
Auditorio Nacional,
c/ Principe de Vergara 146, 28002 **Madrid**
Tel: 91-337 0259/63 Fax: 91-563 2907
Internet: www.coronacional.mcu.es
E-Mail: ocne@inaem.mcu.es
director tecnico Javier Casal Novoa;
coordinator general Antonio Serrano
Period/Frequency: Jan-July, annual *Arts types:* chamber music, recitals, vocal *Venues:* Auditorio Nacional, Sala Sinfonica 2280, Sala de Camara 707 *Comments:* organised by Orquesta y Coro Nacionales de Espana, Auditorio Nacional; alternative Internet: www.orquestanacional.mcu.es; see also Orchestras and Venues

Ciclo de Grandes Interpretes
c/ Cartagena 10, 1° C, 28028 **Madrid**
Tel: 91-356 7622/725 2098 Fax: 91-726 1864
E-Mail: scherzo@sinix.net
director Antonio Moral
Period/Frequency: 8 concerts from Jan-Nov, annual *Arts types:* classical music, especially piano music *Venues:* Auditorio Nacional (Sala Sinfonica 2700) *Comments:* funded by Scherzo Magazine and Canal + and Canal Satellite Digital; see also Publications

Conciertos de Semana Santa
Concejalía de Cultura del Ayuntamiento de Madrid,
Conde Duque 9 y 11, 28015 **Madrid**
Tel: 91-588 5279
Fax: 91-588 5839
coordinador de actividades musicales Daniel Velázquez; concejala de cultura Juan Antonio Gomez Angulo; programación Regino Mateo
Period/Frequency: Holy Week, annual *Arts types:* instrumental, vocal, symphony, church music (mostly chamber) *Venues:* churches in Madrid

DESVIACIONES
Julio Danvila 12, 28033 **Madrid**
Tel: 91-302 0615/527 4854 Fax: 91-302 0615
E-Mail: blancalvo@compuserve.com
contact Blanca Calvo
Period/Frequency: October (2 weeks), annual *Arts types:* new dance, conference, artist workshops *Venues:* Sala Cuarta Pared 200 *Comments:* organised by Blanca Calvo, La Ribot, Sala Cuarta Pared; alternative E-mail: laribot@compuserve.com; see also Dance and Venues

Festival Alternativo de Teatro Musica y Danza Madrid La Alternativa
Sala Triángulo, Zurita 20, 28012 **Madrid**
Tel: 91-530 6891 Fax: 91-539 2518
Internet: www.salatriangulo.com
E-Mail: salatriangulo@salatriangulo.com
programador Alfonso Pindado; organization Melanie Pindado; press Natalia Ortega
Period/Frequency: Feb, annual *Arts types:* independent theatre, also dance & music performances *Venues:* 30 venues in Madrid, Madrid Abierto (Theatre Fair) *Comments:* parallel programs: Alternativa Mujer Creadora (show produced and performed mainly by women), Europa Alterativa (european indepedent companies), Función Social del Teatro (performances in hospitals and prisions): see also Venues & Drama

Festival Internacional de Teatro Clásico
Principe 14, 1 °, 28012 **Madrid**
Tel: 91-521 0720 Fax: 91-521 2604
Internet: www.mec.es
director Luciano García Lorenzo
Period/Frequency: annual (2000: 8 July-1 August) *Arts types:* classical theatre *Venues:* Corral de Comedias 308, Teatro Municipal 250, Claustro de los Dominicos 516, Hospital de San Juan de Dios 700 *Second Address:* during festival: Ciudad Real, Tel: 926-882 420, Fax: 926-861 579; Parador de Turismo Ronda de San Francisco 31, 13270 Almagro, Ciudad Real *Comments:* founded and organised by Ministerio de Cultura, Junta de Castilla – La Mancha, Diputación Provincial de Ciudad Real and Ayuntamiento de Almagro

International Weeks of Children's Theatre
Semanas Internacionales de Teatro Para Niños Madrid y La Coruña)
c/o Acción Educativa, Luis Velez de Guevara 8, 28012 **Madrid**
Tel: 91-429 5029/8727 Fax: 91-429 5031
E-Mail: aeduca@pangea.es
dirección artistica Carlos Herans;
dirección técnica Pilar Amich
Period/Frequency: Nov/ Dec, annual *Arts types:* children's theatre including puppets *Venues:* Cultural Centres in Madrid and surroundings (500/200), Rosalia de Castro (La Coruña) 500, Forum Metropolitano (La Coruña) 250 *Second Address:* Carlos Herans, Sierra Bermeja 46, 28018 Madrid

Madrid Autumn Festival
Festival de Otoño de Madrid
Centro de Estudios y Actividades Culturales de la Comunidad de Madrid, Plaza de Espana 8, 28008 **Madrid**
Tel: 91-580 2575/7/0 Fax: 91-580 2565
director Alicia Moreno; coordinator Mora Apreda; press Mercedes Calvo, Beatriz de Torres
Period/Frequency: Oct-Nov, annual *Arts types:* theatre, music (mainly contemporary, also classical, opera and folk), dance, music theatre *Venues:* Teatro Albeniz 1080, Teatro de la Abadía, Circulo de Bellas Artes, Colegio de Medícos 545, Centro Cultural de la Villa, Auditorio Nacional and others *Comments:* Coordinator Tel: 91-580 2570

Madrid en Danza
Centro de Estudios y Actividades Culturales (CEyAC), Comunidad de Madrid,
Plaza de España, 8, 3°, 28008 **Madrid**
Tel: 91-580 2678 Fax: 91-580 2645
directora gerente Rosa Basante Pol; general coordination Dept. de Danza (see above address); asesory coordinador Raúl Cárdenes, Henrìque y Francisco Vega; directora festivales de Madrid Alicia Moreno
Period/Frequency: May-June, annual *Arts types:* dance, all types (contemporary, classical, spanish, flamenco) *Venues:* Centro Cultural de la Villa 700, Teatro Albéniz 1040, Teatro del Instituto Francés 254, Teatro Pradillo 96, Sala Cuarta Pared 250, Triángulo 180, Teatro de Madrid 900, open air spaces (street, squares, parks) *Comments:* organised by Centro de Estudios y Actividades Culturales (CEyAC), co-patrocinadores: Ministerio de Cultura (Inaem) and Ayuntamiento de Madrid

Festival de Teatro de Calle-Máglaga es Calle
Teatro Muncipal Míguel de Cervantes,
c/ Ramos Marín s/n, 29012 **Málaga**
Tel: 952-224 109 Fax: 952-212 993
Internet: www.teatrocervantes.net
E-Mail: info@teatrocervantes.com
director Angel Baena
Period/Frequency: May, annual *Arts types:* street theatre *Venues:* different places around Malaga

Festival de Teatro de Malága
Fundación Pública, Teatro Municipal Miguel de Cervantes, c/ Ramos Marín s/n, 29012 **Málaga**
Tel: 952-224 109/00/220 237 Fax: 952-212 993/224 545
Internet: www.teatrocervantes.com
E-Mail: info@teatrocervantes.net
director Francisco Rodríguez;
director teatro cervantes Salomón Castiel
Period/Frequency: Jan-Feb, annual *Arts types:* theatre *Venues:* Teatro Cervantes 1171 and other venues in Malaga *Comments:* festival organised by Teatro Cervantes, which depends on Ayuntamiento de Málaga: see also Venues

Festival de Verano – Julio en el Cervantes
Teatro Municipal Míguel de Cervantes, c/ Ramons Marín s/n, 29012 **Málaga**
Tel: 952-224 109 Fax: 952-212 993
Internet: www.teatrocervantes.net
E-Mail: info@teatrocervantes.com
theatre director Salomón Castiel;
programme Francisco Rodrìguez
Period/Frequency: July, annual *Arts types:* music, all types expect classical *Venues:* Teatro Cervantes 1171

Festival Internacional de Música de Matadepera
Casal de Cultura, Pere Aldavert 4,
08230 **Matadepera (Barcelona)**
Tel: 93-730 0132 Fax: 93-730 0600
Internet: www.culturamatadepera.es
E-Mail: patronat@culturamatadepera.es
director administrativo Josep M Pey Cazorla;
director artistico Francesca Marlet
Period/Frequency: July & Sept, annual
Arts types: classical music, other types of music *Venues:* Església de Sant Joan, Plaza de Montanyeta, Casal de Cultura 120

Merida Classical Theatre Festival
Festival Internacional de Teatro Clásico de Mérida
Espectáculos Ibéricos Producciones S.L.,
c/ Tarraco 19, 06800 **Mérida**
Tel: 924-330 312/007 Fax: 924-330 007
Internet: www.festival-de-merida.com
E-Mail: espib@ctv.es
co-dirección Damián Galán, Carlos Tristancho, Guillermo Galán
Period/Frequency: July-Aug, annual *Arts types:* mainly classical theatre and dance, opera *Venues:* Teatro Romano de Mérida (open-air) 2700 *Comments:* press: Pilar Caballero, Tel: 93-347 2955

Festival Internacional de Folklore en el Mediterráneo
Palacio Almudí, Plano de S. Francisco, 30004 **Murcia**
Tel: 968-214 488/294 135 Fax: 968-262 276
Internet: www.distrito.com/feaf
E-Mail: feaf@distrito.com
contact Milagros Carrasco (968-294 135)
Period/Frequency: Sept, annual *Arts types:* music, dance, theatre, art and craft exhibitions *Venues:* open-air auditorium 5000 *Second Address:* Torre de Romo 15, 30002 Murcia, Tel: 968-258 536 *Comments:* organised by Federacion Murciana de Folklore; funded by Ayuntamiento de Murcia

Festival Internacional de Jazz de Murcia
Palacio Almudi, Plano de S. Francisco, 30004 **Murcia**
Tel: 968-214 488/294 135
Fax: 968-216 248
Internet: www.distrito.com/feaf
E-Mail: feaf@distrito.com
contact Francis Armiñana Sanchez
Period/Frequency: May, annual *Arts types:* jazz *Venues:* in gardens or squares *Comments:* organised by Ayuntamiento de Murcia

International Festival of Youth Orchestras, Murcia
Festival Internacional de Orquestras de Jóvenes, Murcia
Universidad de Murcia, Campus de Espinardo, Edificio D, 30005 **Murcia**
Tel: 968-363 372 Fax: 968-363 389
Internet: www.um.es/fioj/
E-Mail: cayuelas@fcu.um.es
director artístico Juan Francisco Cayuelas Grao; coordinadora María Jesús Muñoz; director Antonio Narejos
Period/Frequency: March, annual *Arts types:* music, orchestral concerts, chamber, young pianists *Venues:* Teatro Circo (Cartagena) 800, Teatro Guerra (Lorca) 560, Teatro Vico (Jumilla) 525, Teatro Concha Segura (Yecla) 550, Auditorio y Centro de Congresos (Murcia) 1860 *Comments:* competitions: violin, viola, cello, double bass, composition

Murcia International Street Theatre Festival
Festival Internacional de Teatro en la Calle, Murcia
Palacio Almudi, Plano de S. Francisco, Concejalia de Festejos, 30004 **Murcia**
Tel: 968-214 488/210 815
Fax: 968-216 248
Internet: www.distrito.com.feaf
E-Mail: feaf@distrito.com
contact Armiñana Sánchez
Period/Frequency: week following Holy Week
Arts types: theatre *Comments:* organised by Ayuntamiento de Murcia

Fiesta del Títere de Los Veranos de la Villa
c/o Asociación Cultural Rayuela, c/ Jerez 476 – Urb. Calypo Fado, 28600 **Naval Carnero (Madrid)**
Tel: 91-577 1581/813 2533/2099/559 7540
Fax: 91-577 1581/813 2533/2099/559 7540
Period/Frequency: July, Aug, Sept, annual *Arts types:* puppets for children and adults in open-air venues *Venues:* Teatro Municipal de Títeres del Retiro 300 *Second Address:* Parque del Retiro, Entrada Plaza de la Independencia, 28013 Madrid *Comments:* organised by Asociación Cultural Rayuela; formed by 4 puppet companies: Teatro La Gaviota, Marimba Marionetas, La Mar de Marionetas and Hilando Titeres; see also Puppetry, Venues and Promoters

Festival Cueva de Nerja
Patronato Cueva de Nerja, Carretera de Maro s/n, 29787 **Nerja (Málaga)**
Tel: 95-252 9635/9535 Fax: 95-252 9646
Internet: www.bd-andalucia.es/cuevanerja.html
E-Mail: cuevanerja@vnet.es
gerente Antonio Rivas Areales
Period/Frequency: July, annual *Arts types:* ballet, flamenco, orchestra, lyrical *Venues:* Cueva de Nerja

Fórum de Teatre
Passeig d'en Blay, 5, 17800 **Olot (Gerona)**
Tel: 972-279 138 Fax: 972-267 351
Internet: www.garrotxa.net/forumteatre
E-Mail: teatre@olot.org
artístico director Xavier Ruscalleda; coordinacion general Tena Busquest; promoción Esther Forment; coordinación técnica Nino Costa, J A Montero
Period/Frequency: Oct, annual *Arts types:* mainly theatre, also dance, combined arts, visual arts *Venues:* Teatro Principal de Olot 550, Café Central 150, Centre Catolic 150, Orfeó Popular 100, Claustres de l' Hospìci 500, Claustres del Carme 250, Plaça de Braus 2500 *Comments:* each year has a different theme: 2000 – Water

Temporada de Ópera de Oviedo
C/ Melquíades Alvarez, 20, 1°E, 33003 **Oviedo**
Tel: 985-211 705/207 590 (theatre) Fax: 985-212 402
presidente Luis Alvanez Bartolomé
Period/Frequency: Sept-Jan, annual *Arts types:* opera *Venues:* Teatro Campoamor 1487 *Comments:* organised by Asociación Asturiana de Amigos de la Opera de Oviedo: see also Opera

Festival del Castell de Bellver
c/ Vicente Juan Roselló 22B, 07013 **Palma de Mallorca**
Tel: 971-287 565 Fax: 971-287 758
Period/Frequency: July, annual *Arts types:* classical music, opera *Venues:* Castell de Bellver 600 *Second address:* Castell de Bellver, 07013 Palma de Mallorca *Comments:* open air festival; see also Orchestras

Festival Internacional de Música Serenatas d'Estiú
Centro Cultural la Misericordia, Juventuts Musicals de Palma, Via Roma N° 1, 07012 **Palma de Mallorca**
Tel: 971-728 841 Fax: 971-728 841
responsable Concha Oliver
Period/Frequency: Aug, annual *Arts types:* chamber, symphony, choral, recitals *Venues:* Patio del Castell de Bellver, Palma 500-600 *Comments:* funded by Ayuntamiento de Palma de Mallorca, Tel: 971-727 744

Festival Internacional de Teatro de Humor de Madrid
Produciones Yllana S.L., c/ Jesus 20, 4° A, 07003 **Palma de Mallorca**
Tel: 971-207 410/609-604 923 (mobile) Fax: 971-202 157
general manager Marcos Ottone
Period/Frequency: April-May, annual *Arts types:* comedy *Venues:* Teatro Alfil 250 and other towns throughout the province of Madrid *Comments:* funded by Comunidad de Madrid (CEYAC) Regional Government: see also Drama and Venues (Yllana and Teatro Alfil), Agents & Promoters

Mallorca, Menorca and Eivissa International Organ Week
Setmana Internacional d'Orgue de Mallorca, Menorca i Eivissa
Departament d'Obra Social i Cultural, Caixa de Balears 'Sa Nostra', Carrer Ter N.16 del Poligon de son Fuster, 07009 **Palma de Mallorca**
Tel: 971-171 925 Fax: 971-171 795
E-Mail: aramis@sanostra.es
organisers Andreu Ramis Puig-gros
Period/Frequency: April (around Easter), annual *Arts types:* organ music *Venues:* Esglesia Santa Eulalia 600 (Mallorca), Esglesia de Santa Maria de Maó (Menorca) , Seu de Ciutadella (Menorca), Esglesia de Santa Creu (Eivissa), *Comments:* see also Promoters

Semana de Música Antigua de Estella
Dirección General de Cultura , c/ Santo Domingo, 6-3°, 31001 **Pamplona**
Tel: 948-426 066
Fax: 948-223 906
Internet: www.cfnavarra.es/cultura
E-Mail: yosesper@cfnavarra.es
coordinador Esperanza Asiáin
Period/Frequency: 2nd week in Sept, annual *Arts types:* early music *Venues:* Iglesia de San Miguel de Estella (Navarra) 400

Sonidos del Mundo Festivales de Navarra
Dirección General de Cultura, Institución 'Princípe de Viana', c/ Santo Domingo, 8, 31001 **Pamplona**
Tel: 948-426 058 Fax: 948-223 906
Internet: www.cfnavarra.es/cultura
E-Mail: yosesper@cfnavarra.es
director Tomás Yerro; programación Yolanda Osés
Period/Frequency: July-Aug, annual *Arts types:* world music, cinema, puppet, jazz *Venues:* various venues throughout Navarra *Comments:* to promote and introduce different cultures; also organises workshops and exhibitions

Festival Nuevas Musicas de San Sebastian
Syntorama, Barrio Castaño 19, Bajos, 20100 **Renteria (Gipuzkoa)**
Tel: 943-529 171 Fax: 943-516 292
E-Mail: syntorama@clientes.eskaltel.es
director Cruz Gorostegui
Period/Frequency: March/April, annual *Arts types:* new music *Venues:* Teatro Victoria Eugenia 1000 *Comments:* see also Agents and Producers and Recorded Media

Festival d'Opera de Sabadell – Opera de Catalunya
Plaça Sant Roc 22, 2° 1, 08201 **Sabadell**
Tel: 93-725 6734/726 5470 Fax: 93-727 5321
Internet: www.amics-opera-sabadell.es
E-Mail: aaos@sumi.es
presidente y directora artistica Mirna Lacambra Domenéch; vice-presidente y prensa Xavier Gondolbeu
Period/Frequency: Nov-May, annual *Arts types:* opera *Venues:* Teatro la Farandula Sabadell 1100, Teatro Fortuny-Reus 800, Teatro Municipal Girona 1000, Centre Cultural St. Cugat del Vallés 500, Auditori Enric Granados (Lleida) 800 *Comments:* organised by Associacio D'Amica de L'Opera de Sabadell; funded by: Inaem, Generalitat de Catalunya, Banco de Sabadell, Syuntamicnto de Sabadell; see also Opera, Choirs, Competitions and Courses

Cultural Salamanca
Servicio de Actividades Culturales, Palacio de Maldonado, Plaza San Benito 2, 37008 **Salamanca**
Tel: 923-294 480 Fax: 923-263 046
E-Mail: accult@cugu.usal.es
director Alberto Martín; coordinador Luis Barrio
Period/Frequency: Jan-Dec, annual *Arts types:* theatre, dance, music *Venues:* Colegio Mayor Fonseca 1200, Teatro Juan del Enzina 400 *Comments:* in the summer open-air night activities called 'Las Noches de Fonseca': funded by Junta de Castilla y Leon, Diputacion Provincial, Universidad de Salamanca, Ayuntamiento de Salamanca

Temporada Alta
Placa St. Jaume 9, 17190 **Salt (Girona)**
Tel: 972-402 004 Fax: 972-400 019
E-Mail: bitoteatre@arquired.es
responsable de programacion Salvador Sunyer
Period/Frequency: Oct/Nov, annual *Arts types:* theatre, dance and other performing arts *Venues:* Teatre Municipal Girona 740, Teatre de Salt 320, Sala la Planeta 200, Auditorio Casa Cultura 150, Aula Magna Universitat de Girona 300-600 *Comments:* see also Agents

Festival Internacional de Teatro, Música y Danza de San Javier (Murcia)
Concejalía de Cultura, Ayto. de San Javier, Martínez Tornell 2, 30730 **San Javier (Murcia)**
Tel: 968-573 700/191 617 Fax: 968-191 617
secretario consejo asesor de teatro Cesar Tárraga Baldó
Period/Frequency: July-Aug, annual *Arts types:* theatre, dance, music *Venues:* Auditorio Municipal 2500 *Second Address:* Ayuntamiento de San Javier Plaza Glorieta Garcia Alix, 3 30730 San Javier (Murcia) *Comments:* organised by Ayuntamiento de San Javier funded by Dirección General de Cultura Communidad Autonoma de Murcia

Bach Festival
Festival Bach Musikaldia
Diputación Foral de Gipuzkoa, Urdaneta 9, 20006 **San Sebastián**
Tel: 943-482 890/1 Fax: 943-482 765
Internet: www.guipozkoa.net
E-Mail: ialmagro@kultura.gipuzkoa.net
responsable José Antonio Enchenique, Itziar Almagro
Period/Frequency: Nov, annual *Venues:* Basilica Sta. Maria Del Coro 1500, Convento St. Teresa 500, Auditorio Kursaal 500 *Comments:* funded by Diputacion Foral de Guipuzkoa, Dpt de Cultura y Euskera, Ayuntamiento San Sebastian

Ciclo música de Azcoitia
Diputacìon Foral de Gipuzkoa, c/ Urdaneta, 9, 20006 **San Sebastián**
Tel: 943-482 890/1 Fax: 943-482 765
Internet: www.gipuzkoa.net/koldo-mitxelena/
E-Mail: ialmagro@kultura.gipuzkoa.net
responsable Itziar Almagro, José Antonio Enchenique
Period/Frequency: May, annual *Arts types:* classical music *Venues:* convento Santa Cruz 500 *Comments:* funded by Diputacion Foral de Guipuzcoa, Dpt Cultura y Euskera

Ciclo música de La Antigua (Zumarraga)
Diputacion Foral de Gipuzcoa, c/ Urdaneta, 9, 20006 **San Sebastián**
Tel: 943-482 890/1 Fax: 943-482 765
Internet: www.guipuzkoa.net
E-Mail: ialmagro@kultura.gipuzkoa.net
responsable Itziar Almagro, José Antonio Enchenique
Period/Frequency: Sept *Arts types:* classical & chamber music *Venues:* Ermita de La Antiqua 300 *Comments:* funded by Diputacion Foral de Guipuzkoa Dpt de Cultura y Euskera, Ayuntamiento San Sebastian

Ciclo Musical de Deba
Diputación Foral de Gipuzkoa, c/ Urdaneta, 9, 20006 **San Sebastián**
Tel: 943-482 890/1 Fax: 943-482 765
Internet: www.guipuzkoa.net
E-Mail: ialmagro@kultura.gipuzkoa.net
responsable José Antonio Enchenique, Itziar Almagro
Period/Frequency: Aug, annual *Arts types:* classical & chamber music *Venues:* Parroquia de Deba 500, Claustro de la Parroquia de Deba 500 *Comments:* funded by Diputacion Foral de Guipuzkoa, Dpt Cultura y Euskera, Ayuntamiento Deba

Ciclo Musical de Oñati
Diputación Foral de Gipuzkoa, c/ Urdaneta 9, 20006 **San Sebastián**
Tel: 943-482 890/1 Fax: 943-482 765
Internet: www.guipuzkoa.net
E-Mail: ialmagro@kultura.gipuzkoa.net
responsables Itziar Almagro, José Antonio Enchenique
Period/Frequency: May, annual *Arts types:* classical & chamber music *Venues:* Santa Ana Antzokia 300 *Comments:* funded by Diputacion Foral de Guipuzkoa, Dpt de Cultura y Euskera, Ayuntamiento Oñati

Ciclo musical de Zarautz
Diputación Foral de Gipuzcoa, c/ Urdaneta, 9, 20006 **San Sebastián**
Tel: 943-482 890/1 Fax: 943-482 765
Internet: www.guipuzkoa.net
E-Mail: ialmagro@kultura.gipuzkoa.net
responsable Itziar Almagro, José Antonio Enchenique
Period/Frequency: Aug *Arts types:* classical & chamber music *Venues:* Parroquia de Santa María La Real 500 *Comments:* funded by Diputacion Foral de Guipuzkoa, Dpt de Cultura y Euskera, Ayuntamiento Zarautz

Feria de Teatro de San Sebastian
c/ Republica Argentina N°2, 20004 **San Sebastián**
Tel: 943-481 150 Fax: 943-430 621/481 187
Internet: www.antzerki.com
E-Mail: udala_teatro@donostia.org
director Antton Azpitarte; pr Ane Segurado
Period/Frequency: July, annual *Arts types:* theatre *Venues:* Teatro Victoria Eugenia 1100, Teatro Principal 750 Casa de Cultura de Egia *Comments:* organised by Ayunamiento San Sebastian, Patronato de Cultura, Ministerio Educacion y Cultura

Maiatza Dantzan – Jornadas de Danza Contemporánea
Diputación Foral de Guipúzcoa, KM Kulturunea, c/ Urdaneta, 9, 20006 **San Sebastián**
Tel: 943-482 890/1 Fax: 943-482 765
Internet: www.guipuzkoa.net
E-Mail: maiatzadantzan@kultura.gipuzkoa.net
responsable Fco. Javier López Landatxe y Lide Arana
Period/Frequency: May, annual *Arts types:* contemporary dance *Venues:* Teatro Victoria Eugenia 1100

Quincena Musical/Musika Hamabostaldia
Teatro Victoria Eugenia, Reina Regente N° 9, 20003 **San Sebastián**
Tel: 943-481 238/9 Fax: 943-430 702
Internet: www.donsnsn.com
E-Mail: vdala_quincena@donostia.org
director José Antonio Echenique
Period/Frequency: Aug *Venues:* Auditorio Kursaal 1800, Salade Camara Kursaal 600, Conuento Santa Teresa 500, Salas Polivalentes Kursaal 250 *Comments:* funded by: Diputación, Ayuntamiento de San Sebantián and Gobierno Vasco

Festival de Jazz Ciudad de Sanlucar de Barrameda
Centro Cultural de Victoria Ayuntamiento de Sanlucar de Barrameda, Plza de la Victoria s/n, 11540 **Sanlúcar de Barrameda (Cádiz)**
Tel: 956-380 754 Fax: 956-380 754
director Jose Manuel Salas
Period/Frequency: July, annual *Arts types:* jazz *Venues:* Jardines del Palacio Municipal 800 *Comments:* funded by regional and provincial governments

Festival Internacional de Música 'A Orillas del Guadalquivir'
Centro Cultural de Victoria Ayuntamiento de Sanlúcar de Barrameda, Palacio Municipal, Plza de la Victoria s/n, 11540 **Sanlúcar de Barrameda (Cádiz)**
Tel: 956-380 754 Fax: 956-380 754
dirección artística Juan Rodríguez Romero; dirección programación José Manuel Salas Ibáñez
Period/Frequency: Aug, annual *Arts types:* classical music *Venues:* Auditorio de la Merced 400 *Comments:* funded by regional and provincial governments

Santander International Festival
Festival Internacional de Santander
Palacio de Festivales de Cantabria, c/ Gamazo s/n, 39004 **Santander (Cantabria)**
Tel: 942-210 508 Fax: 942-314 767
Internet: www.festival-int-santander.org
E-Mail: f_i_santander@mundivia.es
artistic and administrative director José Luis Ocejo García; ayunte direccion Emilia Levi
Period/Frequency: Aug, annual *Arts types:* dance, jazz, ballet, classical, music recitals, opera, exhibitions, lectures, street theatre *Venues:* Palacio de Festivales de Cantabria: Sala Argenta 1648, Sala Pereda 570, and historic venues throughout the region *Comments:* managed by Ayuntamiento de Santander & Diputacion Regional: receives private & regional funding

Compostela Millenium Festival
Auditorío de Galicia, Avda. Burgo das Nacións, s/n, 15705 **Santiago de Compostela**
Tel: 981-574 152/573 855/552 290
Fax: 981-574 250
Internet: www.audigal.es
E-Mail: info@audigal.es
director Xosé Denis Hombre
Period/Frequency: Aug, annual *Arts types:* opera, classical music, jazz, theatre, dance, lectures *Venues:* Auditorio de Galicia 1002, Plaza de la Catedral, Teatro Principal 400 *Comments:* management: Auditorio de Galicia, funded by 'Ayuntamiento Santiago de Compostela; see also Venues

Santiago de Compostela 2000 – European City of Culture
Oficina Compostela 2000, Rua do Vilar 67, 15705 **Santiago de Compostela**
Tel: 981-582 525 Fax: 981-557 246
E-Mail: info@compostela2000.com
director Pablo Martínez Saiz;
pr Maria José Porteiro (Incolsa)
Period/Frequency: throughout the year 2000 *Arts types:* performing and visual arts *Comments:* Santiago de Compostela is one of the 9 joint European Cities of Culture in the year 2000

Titirimundi Festival Internacional de Teatro de Títeres de Segovia
c/ Eulogio Martin Higuera, 6 B1, 40001 **Segovia**
Tel: 921-466 048
Fax: 921-466 148
Internet: www.nars.com/titirimundi
E-Mail: titirimundi@nars.com
director y realizador Julio Michel
Period/Frequency: May, annual *Arts types:* puppets *Venues:* Teatro Juan Bravo 489, Sala Alondiga 200, churches, historic buildings, streets

Verano Musical de Segovia
Fundación Juan de Borgón, Juan Bravo 7, 1°, 40001 **Segovia**
Tel: 921-461 400/416 Fax: 921-462 249
Internet: www.fundac-juandeborbon.com
E-Mail: fdjbluz@mx3.redestb.es
coordinador general Rodrigo Peñalosa
Period/Frequency: June-Aug, annual *Arts types:* international drama, music (symphony, choral, opera), dance *Venues:* Alcázar, Cathedral, church and historical places *Comments:* the festival comprises the Festival Internacional de Segovia, Semanas de Música de Cámara, Conciertos Entre dos Luces and the Festival Joven de Música; organised by Fundación Juan de Borbon; see also Promoters

Festival Internacional de Títeres de Sestao
c/o Ayuntamiento de Sestao, Departamento de Cultura, Edificio AISS – 2° Planta, Alameda de las Llanas, 4, 48910 **Sestao (Vizcaya)**
Tel: 94-496 4111 Fax: 94-495 7714
coordinador Angel Asensio Miranda
Period/Frequency: Nov-Dec, annual *Arts types:* puppetry *Venues:* Salón de Actos del AISS 350, Salón de Actos de la Escuela Municipal de Música 250 *Comments:* organised by Sestao Town Hall (Ayuntamiento de Sestao)

Acciones Por Hora
Plaza de S. Antonio de Padua N°9, 41002 **Sevilla**
Tel: 95-438 8219 Fax: 95-490 5380
E-Mail: mariag@sistelnet.es
director programas Gema Lopez; director artistico Fernando Lima; distribucion y produccion Pepa Muriel; director y coordinator Maria González
Period/Frequency: May, annual *Arts types:* video, dance, performances, installations, theatre *Venues:* Sala La Imperdible 200, open-air spaces and sites around the city *Comments:* see also Drama & Venues

Feria Internacional del Títere de Sevilla
Teatro Alameda, c/Crédito 13, 41002 **Sevilla**
Tel: 95-438 8312/490 0164/5 Fax: 95-490 5632
E-Mail: talameda@sitrantor.es
coordinador Guadalupe Tempestini Gnecchi
Period/Frequency: May, annual *Arts types:* puppetry for children and adults, street theatre *Venues:* open-air, Teatro Alameda 480 *Comments:* includes workshops, seminars, conferences

Festival de Italica en la Provincia
Diputacion Provincial de Seville,
Avda Menendez Pelayo 32, 41071 **Sevilla**
Tel: 95-455 0733/40 Fax: 95-455 0050
diputado del area de cultura y ecologia Manuel Copete; asesor ejecutivo cultura Jesus Cantero;
jefe de coordinacion Jesus Cosano
Period/Frequency: July, annual *Arts types:* theatre, dance and music *Venues:* 15 venues around various cities, including: Patio de Armas del Castillo (Alcalá de Guadaira), Plaza de Toros (Alcala del Rio), Patio de la Sede Central de la Diputación (Sevilla) 100
Comments: organised and funded by Diputacion Provincial de Seville

Festival de Música Antigua de Sevilla
Teatro Lope de Vega, Av. de Maria Luisa s/n, 41013 **Sevilla**
Tel: 95-459 0853/4 Fax: 95-459 0827
director Juan V. Rodríguez Yagües
Period/Frequency: March, annual *Venues:* Teatro Lope de Vega 750 *Second Address:* Area de Cultura del Ayuntamiento de Sevila, c/General Moscardó 1, 41001, Sevilla, Tel: 95-450 5656 *Comments:* funded by Ministerio de Educacion y Cultura y la Junta de Andalucia: see also Venues

Mes de Danza Sevilla
Plaza de S. Antonio de Padua N°9, 41002 **Sevilla**
Tel: 95-438 8219 Fax: 95-490 5380
E-Mail: mariag@sistelnet.es
director programas Gema Lopez; director artistico Fernando Lima; distribucion y produccion Pepa Muriel; director y coordinator Maria Gonzalez
Period/Frequency: Nov, annual *Arts types:* contemporary dance, video dance *Venues:* Sala la Imperdible 200, Almacen la Imperdible 100, Teatro Central 450 and sites around the city *Comments:* organised by Asociacion Andaluza de Danza, Pasaje Mallol 21, 3° C, 41003 Sevilla Tel: 95-453 9881/456 4396, and La Asociacion de Amigos de la Danza

Sitges Teatre Internacional
c/ Rafael Llopart 27, 08870 **Sitges**
Tel: 93-894 4561/4661 Fax: 93-894 8210
Internet: www.sitges.com/teatre
E-Mail: teasit@sitgestur.com
director Joan Ollé; coordinador Jaume Flor; manager Ramón Buxés
Period/Frequency: June, annual *Arts types:* theatre, music and dance *Venues:* Teatro Prado 450, Escorxodor 121, Mediterrani 209, Mercat 176, Espai de Mitsanit 250 *Second Address:* Plaça de l'Ajuntamen s/n 08870 Sitges (Patronat Municipal de Teatro de Sitges)

Mostra Internacional Folklórica de Sóller
Centro Cultural Can Dulce, Gran Vía 15, 07100 **Sóller (Mallorca)**
Tel: 971-630 099/753 Fax: 971-633 313
Internet: www.crecoco.es/samostra
E-Mail: oeugenio@mx3.redestb.es
director Joan Puigserver Arbona;
international secretary Willy Dons
Period/Frequency: last week of July, annual *Arts types:* folk song, folk dance, folk music *Venues:* Plaza de Sóller 4000, open-air Ses Voltes 4000 *Second Address:* Apto de Correos 39 07100 Sóller (Mallorca) *Comments:* tour to villages in Mallorca: Muro, La Puebla, San Lorenzo; organises workshops with the groups of The Mostra; non-competitve festival

Otoño Musical Soriano
Departamento Cultural Ayuntamiento de Soria, Plaza Mayor 8, 42071 **Soria**
Tel: 975-234 100 Fax: 975-234 115
E-Mail: teatrosoria@redteatros.inaem.es
director musical Odon Alonso; coordinador del festival José Manuel Aceña Diago
Period/Frequency: Sept, annual *Arts types:* classical music, exhibitions, lectures, courses *Venues:* Centro Cultural Palacio de la Audiencia 500

Fira de Teatre al Carrer de Tárrega
c/ de les Piques 1, 25300 **Tárrega**
Tel: 973-310 854 Fax: 973-501 528
Internet: www.firatarrega.com
E-Mail: firateatre@firatarrega.com
director gerente Pau Llacuna;
director artístico Joan Anguera
Period/Frequency: second week of Sept, annual *Arts types:* street theatre, text based theatre, dance, clowns, mime, puppets *Venues:* 10 venues comprising a range from 100 to 800 seats *Comments:* 80 groups, 200 performances

Course & International Music Festival Martin Codax
c/ Agen, Local 20, 45005 **Toledo**
Tel: 925-254 298 Fax: 925-254 298
E-Mail: rafacim@teleline.es
director Rafael Jiménez Herranz; subdirectores Francisco Javier Lara Lara, Juan Antonio Vicente Tellez; comunicacion Miguel Angel Serrano Masegoso
Period/Frequency: July, annual *Arts types:* instrumental recitals, chamber concerts *Comments:* courses for all instruments, singing and band conductors

Festival Internacional de Música de Toledo
Conservatorio Profesional de Música J. guerrero, c/ San Juan de la Penitencia 2, 45001 **Toledo**
Tel: 925-216 003
Fax: 925-256 265
E-Mail: FERMATA@teleline.es
artistic director Ludmil Anguelov;
administrative director Ana Sancho
Period/Frequency: May, annual *Arts types:* classical music, dance, jazz *Venues:* Teatro Rojas 478, Centro Cultural San Marcos 450, Museo Santa Cruz 1000, Museo Sefardí 250, Iglesia de San Julián 400 and other historic venues in Toledo *Comments:* funded by Diputación Provincial de Toledo; managed by Fermete Arts Management; see also Agents & Producers

Red de Teatros de Castilla-la Mancha
Consejeria Educacion y Cultura,
Plza Cardenal Siliceo s/n, 45071 **Toledo**
Tel: 925-267 400
Fax: 925-267 508
E-Mail: consej.edu.cultura@otfcampus.es
coordinadora de musica Ana Muñoz; responsable teatro Emilio Regio
Period/Frequency: spring & autumn, bi-annual *Arts types:* music, theatre *Venues:* all around the autonomic community of Castilla la Mancha

Festival Internacional de Marionetas
Centro de Iniciativas de Tolosa,
c/ Emeterio Arrese N°2, 20400 **Tolosa**
Tel: 943-650 414 Fax: 943-698 028
E-Mail: marreche@cittolosa.com
director Miguel Arreche
Period/Frequency: Nov-Dec, annual *Arts types:* puppetry *Venues:* Teatro Iparraguirre 560, Cine-Teatro Leidor 1300 *Comments:* funded by Diputacion Provincial de Guipuzcoa Ayuntamiento de Tolosa, Caja de Ahorros Guipuzecoa – San Sebastian, Gobierno Vasco

Theatre Showcase
Muestra de Teatro
Patronato Municipal de Cultura, Santa María 17, 23320 **Torreperogil (Jaén)**
Tel: 953-776 000/025 Fax: 953-776 025
director artistico Vicente Ruiz Raigal
Period/Frequency: Nov/Dec, annual *Arts types:* theatre, dance-theatre *Venues:* Centro Cultural Alfonso Fernandez Torres 250, Paseo del Prado (open-air) 1500, Caseta Municipal (open-air) 1000
Second Address: El Chirimbolo (Servicios Culturales) Santa Maria 27 Tel: 953-778 352

Torroella de Montgrí International Festival of Music
Festival Internacional de Música de
Torroella de Montgrí
Joventuts Musicals, C/ Codina, 28, 1°, Apartado 70, 17257 **Torroella de Montgrí (Girona)**
Tel: 972-760 605 Fax: 972-760 648
Internet: www.ddgi.es/tdm/fimtdm.html
E-Mail: jjmmtdm@ddgi.es
director Josep Lloret
Period/Frequency: July-Aug *Arts types:* chamber music, symphonic, recitals, early music, cinema, choral music, ethnic music *Venues:* Iglesia gótica de Sant Genis 700, Plaza de la Vila 1200, Sala de la Academia de Música 250 *Second Address:* C. D'Ulla 26, Torroella de Montgrí, Tel: 972-761 098, Fax: 972-760 648 *Comments:* other activities: masterclasses

Festival Internacional de Música y Danza 'Ciudad de Ubeda'
Palacio de Exposiciones y congresos 'Hospital de Santiago', Avda. Cristo Rey s/n, 23400 **Ubeda (Jaén)**
Tel: 953-750 191/750 842 Fax: 953-792 279
Internet: www.cibercentro.com
director, presidente de la Asociación Diego Martinez; jefe prensa Pedro Vago; coordinador Antonio Sanchez Montoya; administración Ántonia Atienza;
secretario Juan Ramón Martínez Elvira
Period/Frequency: May-June, annual *Arts types:* music, opera, jazz, dance, flamenco, celtic *Venues:* Auditorio del Hospital de Santiago 600, Patio de Columnas (open-air) 1200, Teatro Ideal 700, Iglesia Sto. Domingo 200, Archivo Historico Municipal 200 *Second Address:* Ayuntamiento de Ubeda, Plaza Vázquez de Molina s/n, 23400 Ubeda, Tel: 953-750 440 *Comments:* collaborator: Asociación cultural Amigos de la Música de Ubeda Tel: 953-752 875/0842; temporada de conciertos, desde el mes de octubre al mes de Abril de cada año

Festival Internacional d'Orquestres Juvenils
Consejería de Cultura Educacion y Ciencia, Avenida Campanar 32, 46015 **Valencia**
Tel: 96-386 9721 Fax: 96-386 6574
E-Mail: fcampillo@lettera.net
director general de promoción cultural, musica y bellas artes Consuelo Ciscar; director técnico actual, técnico del servicio de música Paco Campillo
Period/Frequency: July, annual *Arts types:* orchestral music *Venues:* Sala A del Palau de la Música y Congresos de Valencia 1790 *Comments:* Two orchestras from Valencia perform in the festival and others from abroad; the foreign orchestras then give 2 or 3 concerts in different cities in Valencia

Puppet's International Festival in La Vall d'Albaida
Mostra Internacional de Titelles a La Vall D'Albaida
Bambalina Titelles, c/ Cabillers 3 Baix, 46003 **Valencia**
Tel: 96-391 1373/3989 Fax: 96-391 1373
E-Mail: bambalina@tecnovia.com
organizer, Bambalina Titelles Josep Policarpo Bodi
Period/Frequency: Dec, annual *Arts types:* marionettes *Venues:* different villages in the valley *Second Address:* Mancomunitat de Municipis, Sant Francesc 8-3-6ª, 46870 Ontinyent (Valencia), Tel: 96-291 1532, Fax: 96-238 8545 *Comments:* also courses, conferences, workshops, etc.

Muestra Internacional de Danza de Valladolid
Fund. Mun. de Cultura, Casa Revilla, c/ Torrecilla 5, 47003 **Valladolid**
Tel: 983-426 246 Fax: 983-426 254
Internet: www.smova.org
E-Mail: mario@smcva.org
director Muestra Mario Perez; ayudante director Carlos Heredero; dep. prensa Pilar Ibarlucea
Period/Frequency: May, annual *Arts types:* dance *Venues:* Teatro Calderón (Valladolid)

Muestra Internacional de Teatro de Valladolid
Fund. Mun. de Cultura, Casa Revilla, c/ Torrecilla 5, 47003 **Valladolid**
Tel: 983-426 246
Fax: 983-426 254
Internet: www.smova.org
E-Mail: mario@smcva.org
director Muestra Mario Perez;
ayudante director Carlos Heredero;
dep. prensa Pilar Ibarlucea
Period/Frequency: Nov, annual *Arts types:* theatre *Venues:* Teatro Calderón (Valladolid)

Veladas de Pimentel, Las
Diputación de Valladolid,
c/Angustias 48, 47003 **Valladolid**
Tel: 983-427 100 ext. 682 Fax: 983-427 238
Internet: www.dip-valladoliz.es
E-Mail: educacion.cultura@dip-valladoliz.es
coordinador Oliva García; presidente diputacion Ramiro F. Ruíz Medrano
Period/Frequency: June-July, annual *Arts types:* music, theatre, dance *Venues:* Patio del Palacio de Pimentel 250 (open-air) *Second Address:* Servicios de Educación y Cultura, Ramón y Cajal s/n, 47071 Valladolid *Comments:* includes Semana de Musica Hispana, Noches de Teatro and Las Tardes de Pimentel

Valldemossa Chopin Festival
Festival Internacional Chopin de Valldemossa
Celda de Federico Chopin 2, Cartuja de Valldemossa, 07170 **Valldemossa (Baleares)**
Tel: 971-612 351 (box office) Fax: 971-612 351 (Jul-Aug)
E-Mail: sn1183@bitel.es
presidente Rosa Capllonc Ferrá; tesorero Jaime Capllonch Ferrà; secretario Joan Moll;
vice presidente Guillen Llabrés
Period/Frequency: the four sundays of Aug, annual *Arts types:* piano recitals, concerts in cloister of La Cartuja, contemporary photography, exhibitions *Venues:* Claustro de la Cartuja de Valldemossa 800, Habitaciones y Jardín de la Celda 150 *Second Address:* Tel/Fax: 971-715 636 (Oct-July)

Market of Live Music
Mercat de Música Viva de Vic
c/o IMPE Vic, Edifici el Sucre, H. Ramon d'Abadal i Vinyals, 5, 2a planta, 08500 **Vic**
Tel: 93-883 3100 Fax: 93-883 2626
Internet: www.mmvv.impevic.net
E-Mail: mmvv@impevic.net
director Carles Sala; presidenta de la comissión organizadora Montserrat Aliberch; gerente Xavier Mercadal; coordinadora Montse Portús
Period/Frequency: Sept, annual *Arts types:* music in all forms *Venues:* 14 venues around the city

Festival Internacional de Música Popular-Tradicional
Ajuntament de Vilanova i la Geltrú, Dpto. de Cultura, Plaça de la Vila, Nº 8, 08800 **Vilanova i la Geltrú**
Tel: 93-814 0000 Fax: 93-814 2425
Internet: www.solblau.net/fimpt
E-Mail: fimpt@vilanova.org
coordinador festival Carmen Silvestre; coordinador del dpto cultura Ricard Belascoain I Garcia
Period/Frequency: July, annual
Arts types: popular, folk music *Venues:* Teatro Principal 400, Recinto Moli de Mar 700

Festival of Street Theatre
Festival de Teatro de Calle de Vila-real
Departamento Cultura, Ayuntamiento,
12540 **Villa Real (Castellón)**
Tel: 964-521 919 Fax: 964-522 615
Internet: www.vila-real.com/teatre
E-Mail: teatre@vila-real.com
director Joan Raga Navarro
Period/Frequency: May, annual *Arts types:* street theatre *Venues:* streets of Vila-real *Comments:* funded by Ayuntamiento Vila-real, Generalitat Valenciana y Diputación de Castellón y Fundación Bancaixa

Festival de Teatro de Humor de Araia
Porpol Teatro, c/ Beato Tomas de Zumárraga 98, 3º A, 01009 **Vitoria**
Tel: 945-200 771/284 542/285 645
responsable de gestión Javier Alcorta
Period/Frequency: Aug, annual *Arts types:* comedy, theatre and street theatre *Second address:* Ayuntamiento de Aspárrenea, Herriko Emparantza 1, 01250 Araia (Alava), Tel: 945-304 006 *Comments:* organised by Ayuntamiento de Aspárrenea; managed by Porpol Teatro (q.v.)

Semana Coral Internacional de Alava
Fundacion Caja Vital Kutxa, c/ Postas 13, 01004 **Vitoria (Alava)**
Tel: 945-162 156 Fax: 945-162 190
Internet: www.vitoriagasteiz.org
E-Mail: jsannicolas@cajavital.es
responsable Paula Latorre; director fundación Caja Vital Kutxa Rafael Gomez-Escolar Mazuela
Period/Frequency: Sept, annual *Arts types:* choral music (8 foreign choirs) *Venues:* various churches in Alava and Vitoria, final concert in Teatro Principal 1000 *Comments:* organised and funded by Fundacion Caja Vital Kutxa

Vitoria-Gasteiz International Theatre Festival
Festival Internacional de Teatro de Vitoria Gasteiz
Palacio de Villasuso, Plaza del Machete s/n, 01001 **Vitoria Gasteiz**
Tel: 945-161 264 Fax: 945-161 276
Internet: www.vitoria-gasteiz.org
E-Mail: ayunti05@sarenet.es
director Enrike Ruiz de Gordoa; programador de espectáculos Felix Gonzalez Petite
Period/Frequency: Sept-Dec, annual *Arts types:* theatre, children's theatre, opera, dance *Venues:* Teatro Principal 1000 *Comments:* organised by Dept. de Cultura del Ayuntamiento de Vitoria-Gasteiz

Festival Internacional de Títeres y Marionetas
Teatro principal de Zamora, c/san vincente 1, 49001 **Zamora**
Tel: 980-534 719 Fax: 980-530 785
E-Mail: teaprinzamora@interbook.net
director gerente Daniel Perez Fernandez
Period/Frequency: May, annual *Arts types:* puppetry *Venues:* Teatro Principal de Zamora 367 and on the streets (Plaza El Fresco) *Comments:* regional funding

Feria de Teatro en Aragón
Diputación General de Aragón, Dpto. de Cultura y Educación, Paseo Mª Agustin 26B bajo, 50004 **Zaragoza**
Tel: 976-434 771 Fax: 976-282 661
Internet: www.aragon.net/feriahuesca.htm
E-Mail: circuito@correo.aragon.net
coordinación Anabel Salcedo; jefe de servicio Agustin Azaña Lorenzo; comisión técnica J L Melendo, Luis Calvo, Javier Brun
Period/Frequency: Nov, annual *Arts types:* theatre *Venues:* 8 theatres in Huesca 1000 to 1500, Teatro Olimpia (Huesca), Teatro Salesianos Carpa (Huesca), other venues in Huesca
Comments: regional and national funding

Festival Int. Castillo de Alcañiz
Dpto. de Cultura y Festivales,
Po. Mª Agustin 26 B, bajos, 50004 **Zaragoza**
Tel: 976-282 979 Fax: 976-282 661
Internet: www.aragon.net
E-Mail: info@correo.aragon.net
director José Luis Melendo;
jefe servicio Agustin Azaña Lorenzo
Period/Frequency: July-Aug, annual *Arts types:* theatre, music, dance *Venues:* Castillo de Alcañiz 1000, Teatro Municipal 400 *Second Address:* Ayuntamiento de Alcañiz, Plz. Espanña, 1, 44600 Alcañiz (Teruel) *Comments:* see also National & Regional Ministries

Festival Int. de Musica Castillo de Ainsa
Dpto. de Cultura y Festivales,
Paseo Mª Agustin 26, bajos, 50004 **Zaragoza**
Tel: 976-282 979 Fax: 976-282 661
Internet: www.aragon.net
E-Mail: info@correo.aragon.net
director José Luis Melendo;
jefe servicio Agustin Azaña Lorenzo
Period/Frequency: July-Aug, annual *Arts types:* exhibitions, music *Venues:* Recinto de Festivales Castillo de Ainsa *Second Address:* Ayuntamiento de Ainsa, Plz. Mayor 1, 22330 Ainsa (Huesca) *Comments:* Ciclo 'Festivales de Aragon' organised by La Diputacion General de Aragon (D.G.A); see also National & Regional Ministries

Festival Internacional de Jazz de Zaragoza
c/ Eduardo Ibarra 3, 50009 **Zaragoza**
Tel: 976-721 300
Fax: 976-350 514
E-Mail: auditoriozaz@sendanct.es
director tecnico y artistico Miguel Ángel Tapia
Period/Frequency: Nov, annual *Arts types:* jazz *Venues:* Auditorio Palacio de Congresos 1500 *Comments:* organised by Auditorio de Zaragoza

Festival Puerta al Mediterraneo
Dpto. de Cultura y Festivales, Paseo Mª Agustin 26, bajos, 50004 **Zaragoza**
Tel: 976-282 979 Fax: 976-282 661
Internet: www.aragon.net
E-Mail: info@correo.aragon.net
director José Luis Melendo;
efe servicio Agustin Azaña Lorenzo
Period/Frequency: Aug, annual *Arts types:* theatre, exhibitions, concerts *Second Address:* Ayuntamiento Rubielos de Mora, Plz. Hispanoamerica 1, 44415 Rubielos *Comments:* Ciclo ' Festivales de Aragon' organised by La Gobierno de Aragon (D.G.A.)

SWEDEN (+46)

Båstad Chamber Music Festival
Box 1014, 269 21 **Båstad**
Tel: 431-369 660 Fax: 431-371 210
Internet: www.bastad.se/musik
E-Mail: bastad.kammarmusikfestival@swipnet.se
artistic director Helen Jahren
Period/Frequency: week after Midsummer, annual *Arts types:* chamber music, choir *Venues:* Skottorp Castle, Apelryd Concert Barn, local churches including the medieval Maria church *Second Address:* The Bjäre Bookshop, Köpmansgatan 12, 269 35 Båstad *Comments:* also arranges a competition for young musicians, aged 18 and under; the winners are presented at one of the festival concerts and receive a cash prize

House of the Nobility Music with Stockholm Sinfonietta
Stockholm Sinfonietta Riddarhusmusik
c/o Kimby, Belevägen 10, 182 64 **Djursholm**
Tel: 8-755 5520 Fax: 8-755 5562
Internet: www.sinfoinietta.a.se
E-Mail: kimby@sinfonietta.a.se
manager Anders Kimby
Arts types: chamber orchestra: from baroque to the present days *Venues:* House of the Nobility 400, Stockholm Concerthouse 1800 *Comments:* see also Orchestras

Falun Folk Music Festival (FFF)
Box 387, 791 28 **Falun**
Tel: 23-83090 Fax: 23-63399
Internet: www.falunfolkfest.se
manager Hans Hjorth
Period/Frequency: week in July, annual *Second Address:* street address: Trotzgatan 10, 791 00 Falun *Comments:* presents the best of folk, traditional, roots, ethnic and world music from round the world; 400 artists from over 20 countries join 600 amateur musicians/course participants and 50000 visitors; feature concerts by top world artists, jam sessions, unexpected musical encounters in parks, on street corners and in public squares, programmes for children, courses and lectures, exhibitions, dance events, food and drink; ETHNO – a workshop and meeting place for younger folk musicians from all over the world, is arranged the week before FFF

Göteborg Dans & Teater Festival
Norra Hamngatan 8, 411 14 **Göteborg**
Tel: 31-611 273/4 Fax: 31-774 1187
Internet: w3.goteborg.se/kultur/dansteater
E-Mail:
dansteaterfestivalen@kulturnamuden.goteborg.se
director Birgitta Winnberg Rydh;
coordinator Pernilla Appelqvist
Period/Frequency: Aug, biennial (2000: 19-26 Aug) *Arts types:* dance, drama, opera, street theatre, seminars, workshops *Comments:* only festival in Sweden for international performing arts

Musik i Sommar-Gränna
Brahegatan 22, 563 32 **Gränna**
Tel: 390-10 520/704-167 580 (mobile) Fax: 390-10 520
Internet: www.welcom.to/musik-i-sommar-granna
E-Mail: barbar@algonet.se
festival director Hans Järeby
Period/Frequency: 1st week in July, annual *Arts types:* chamber music, early, symphony, choral music, instrumental recitals *Venues:* Gränna Church *Comments:* also run Bluegrass and Old Time Music Festival (q.v.)

Saxå Chamber Music Festival
Prästgatan 2, Grythyttans Gästgivaregård,
712 81 **Grythyttan**
Tel: 591-14140 Fax: 591-14124
Internet: www.musikfestivaler.se
E-Mail: peter.eriksson@konserthuset.se
artistic director Peter Eriksson
Period/Frequency: June, annual *Arts types:* chamber music, music *Second Address:* Peter Eriksson, Dalagatan 34, S-113 24 Stockholm Tel & Fax: 8-302 093, E-mail: peter@immanuel.se

Musik Vid Dellen
824 80 **Hudiksvall**
Tel: 650-19510 Fax: 650-38150
Internet: www.hudiksvall.se
E-Mail: barbro.sjoblom@hudiksvall.se
contact Barbro Sjoblom
Period/Frequency: July, annual *Arts types:* all types of music *Venues:* various around Hudiksvall

Junsele Festival of Music and Art
Musik – och konstveckan i Junsele
Pl. 944, 880 37 **Junsele**
Tel: 621-10279/10715 Fax: 621-10715
Internet: www.musik-konst.y.se
E-Mail: mok@cit.se
contact Erik Nordien
Period/Frequency: July, annual (2000: 8-15 July) *Arts types:* symphony, chamber music, recitals, vocal music, jazz, organ concerts, folk music, visual arts *Venues:* concert hall 500 to 600, forum 300, church, old homestead museum (open air concerts) *Comments:* musicians and ensembles from different countries and also exhibitions

Jazzfestivalen i Kristianstad/Åhus
Västra Storgatan 14, 291 32 **Kristianstad**
Tel: 44-126 805 Fax: 44-126 806
Internet: www.jazzfestival.org
E-Mail: info@jazzfestival.org
director Bengt B Månsson
Period/Frequency: July, annual (2000: 13-15 July) *Arts types:* jazz *Venues:* Tivoliparken 6000 and venues throughout Kristianstad and Åhus

Nordic Baroque Music Festival
Nordmalings Kommun, 914 81 **Nordmaling**
Tel: 930-14007 Fax: 930-14017
Internet: www.nordmaling.se/nordic.baroque
E-Mail: nordic.baroque@nordmaling.se
director and producer Tönu Puu;
administrator Sirpa Kärki
Period/Frequency: Aug, biennial (2001) *Arts types:* concerts with an early music repertory (high baroque), mainly chamber music, masterclasses *Venues:* 15thC church in Nordmaling 450 *Second Address:* Tönu Puu, Umeå University, 90187 Umeå, Tel: 90-786 5218, Fax: 90-22579

Chamber Music Festival
PO Box 88, 761 21 **Norrtelje**
Tel: 176-12726/71990 Fax: 176-12779/10618
director Gunnila von Barhr
Period/Frequency: July, annual *Arts types:* chamber music, art, jazz, symphonic music *Venues:* Norrtelje-Roslagen – famous archipelago north of Stockholm *Comments:* 2000: German composers

Music Festival of Piteå
Festspelen i Piteå
Framnäs folkhögskola, 943 33 **Öjebyn**
Tel: 911-231 100 Fax: 911-231 111
Internet: www.framna.fhsk.se/festspel
E-Mail: festspele.pitea@framna.fhsk.se
director Roger Noran; course leader Sven Erik Sandlund
Period/Frequency: July, annual *Arts types:* mostly classical, but also folk, pop, jazz, Afro-Carribean, gospel *Venues:* in and around Piteå *Comments:* also hold masterclasses in singing and different instruments; alternative E-mail: sven-erik.sandlund@m.h.luth.se

Oskarshamn International Choir Festival
Köpmangatan 4, 572 30 **Oskarshamn**
Tel: 491-77377 Fax: 491-10144
E-Mail: korfestivalen@adbc.se
chairman t.b.a.
Comments: the festival is currently undergoing structural changes, no further details known at time of going to print

Music Festival of Östersund
c/o Studiefrämjamdet, Kyrkgatan 59, 831 34 **Östersund**
Tel: 63-129 058/143 703 Fax: 63-122 239
chairman Per Söderberg; producer t.b.a.
Period/Frequency: last week June, annual *Arts types:* symphony, chamber music, string quartet, pop concerts, piano, folk music, jazz *Venues:* churches, theatres, salons *Comments:* the organisation is currently restructuring the festival; no further information was available at time of going to print

Östhammars Music Festival, The
Östhammars Musik Veckan
Kulturförvaltningen, Box 66, 742 21 **Östhammar**
Tel: 173-86000 Fax: 173-17537
Internet: www.osthammar.se
E-Mail: musikveckan@osthammar.se
contact Tippi Unge
Period/Frequency: 1st week July, annual *Arts types:* all kinds of music *Venues:* indoor and outdoor, churches and halls around Osthammars – up to 10000

Music at Lake Siljan
Musik vid Siljan
Box 28, 795 21 **Rättvik**
Tel: 248-10290 Fax: 248-51981
Internet: www.siljan.se
E-Mail: musik@siljan.se
adminstration Mrs Berit Helgesson; president & art director, producer Peter Waldemarsson;
public relations Hans Barksjo
Period/Frequency: June/July, annual *Arts types:* folk music, classical, jazz, choir, organ, orchestra *Venues:* open-air, medieval churches, herdsmen's chalets, museums, artists homes in Leksand and Rättvik *Comments:* Sweden's largest summer music festival; special activites and programmes for children

Kammarmusikfestivalen Sandviken – Högbo
Box 256, 811 23 **Sandviken**
Tel: 26-253 329/241 954 Fax: 26-272 721
Internet: sandviken.se/kmf
E-Mail: kmf@sandnet.se
contact Ove Jönsson; chairman of the board Elisabeth Harr; artistic directors Mats Widlund, Tobias Carron
Period/Frequency: Aug, annual *Arts types:* solo, duos, small ensembles with emphasis on string quartets, chamber orchestras *Venues:* Sandviken Baptist Church, Högbo Church *Second Address:* Elisabeth Harr, Hantverkarbacken 12, 81161 Sandviken, Sweden

Choir Festival in Skinnskatteberg
Körstämman i Skinnskatteberg
Kultur och Fritid, Box 101, 739 22 **Skinnskatteberg**
Tel: 222-45000 Fax: 222-45090
artistic director Ragnar Høkannson
Period/Frequency: June, annual *Arts types:* choral music, from folk and jazz to classical *Comments:* open-air festival with workshops

Elektronmusik Festvalen i Skinskatteberg
c/o EMS, Söder Mälarstrand, Box 101,
739 22 **Skinnskatteberg**
Tel: 222-45000/45131
Fax: 222-45090
E-Mail: us@ems.srk.se
festival organiser Ulf Stenberg (8-658 1995)
Period/Frequency: June, annual (23-25 June) *Arts types:* tape, instrument/tape, film/tape, music *Comments:* focus is on Karl-Heinz Stockhausen

Drottningholms Slottsteater
PO Box 27050, 102 51 **Stockholm**
Tel: 8-665 1400(office)/660 8225 (tickets)
Fax: 8-665 1473
Internet: www.drottningholmsteatern.dtm.se
E-Mail: dst@dtm.se
general manager Per Forsström;
artistic director Per-Erik Öhrn;
marketing manager Eva Lundgren (tel: 8-759 0406)
Period/Frequency: May-Sept, annual *Arts types:* opera, ballet, concerts (17th/18th century) *Venues:* Drottningholms Slottsteater 454 *Comments:* administrative address: Drottningholms teatermuseum, Box 27050, 102 51 Stockholm; no permanent opera or ballet company; the operas performed are 17th/18th century and the stage scenery and machinery is authentic 17th/18th century, as is the theatre building itself which is listed under the World Heritage; see also Operas

International Composers Festival
Stockholm Concert Hall, Box 7083, 103 87 **Stockholm**
Tel: 8-786 0200
Fax: 8-200 548 (pr)
festival and artistic director Åse Headström
Period/Frequency: Nov, annual *Venues:* Stockholm Concert Hall 1800, Grünewand Hall 460, Aulin Hall 150

International Vadstena Academy Foundation – Summer Opera Festival
Stiftelsen Internationella Vadstena-Akademien
Bergsgatan 57, 112 31 **Stockholm**
Tel: 8-652 6180 Fax: 8-650 8230
Internet: www.vadstena-akademien.org
E-Mail: info@vadstena-akedemien.org
administrative director Astrid Lande; artistic and research director Prof. Anders Wiklund
Period/Frequency: June-Aug, annual
Arts types: young prominent singers and musicians perform older operas that haven't been performed in the modern era; and operas written especially for the Academy *Venues:* Vadstena Slott (Vadstena Castle), Vadstena Gamla Teater(Old theater) *Second Address:* Lastköpingsgatan 5, 592 32 Vadstena, Tel: 143-12229, Fax: 143-12903

Royal Palace Music Festival, The
The Royal Palace, 111 30 **Stockholm**
Tel: 8-102 247
Fax: 8-215 911
Internet: www.royalfestivals.se
E-Mail: palace.concerts@royalfestivals.se
manager Mathias Walin; artistic director Mats Liljefors
Period/Frequency: July-Aug, annual *Arts types:* orchestral, chamber, operatic concert performances, jazz
Venues: Royal Palace of Stockholm: Hall of State 700, Royal Chapel 600, Museum of Antiquities 270, Karl XV Room 150

Stockholm Orient Festival – Re: Orient
Box 4215, 102 65 **Stockholm**
Tel: 8-640 0828 Fax: 8-702 1599
Internet: www.reorient.se
E-Mail: info@reorient.se
artistic director Ozan Sunar;
general manager Anders Lindblom;
producer Anna Ljungqvist; programming coordinator Jonas Elverstig; marketing manager Anneli Gunnar
Period/Frequency: June, annual *Arts types:* music, dance, children's activities, poetry and seminars focusing on traditional & currents trends of the Orient *Venues:* Sjöhistoriska museet: 2-3 tents capacities from 500 up to 1500 *Comments:* see also Promoters

Summer Night Concerts at the Museum of Fine Arts
Nationalmuseum, Box 16176, Södra Blasieholmshamnen, 103 24 **Stockholm**
Tel: 8-5195 4300/90 (press) Fax: 8-5195 4450
Internet: www.nationalmuseum.se
contact Agneta Karlstrom
Period/Frequency: June-Aug, annual *Arts types:* emphasis on classical music, some jazz & folk *Venues:* Museum of Fine Arts 600

Swedish Theatre Biennial
c/o Svensk Teaterunion – Svenska ITI, Box 15035, 104 65 **Stockholm**
Tel: 8-462 2530 Fax: 8-462 2535
E-Mail: swedish@iti.a.se
Period/Frequency: May, biennial (2001) *Arts types:* theatre *Comments:* the 2001 Biennial will take place on 24-27 May in Växjö

Ystad Opera Festival
PO Box 1013, 103 38 **Stockholm**
Tel: 8-411 6320 (until: 15.6.2000)/411 1 0519 (from: 16.6.2000) Fax: 8-411 9049
E-Mail: roa.bark@ystadoperan.se
contact Hans Ramberg
Period/Frequency: July, annual *Arts types:* opera
Venues: Ystad Theatre

Örebro Chamber Music Festival
Örebro KammarMusik Festspel
Solbergavägen 6A, 719 30 **Vintrosa**
Tel: 19-294 927 Fax: 19-294 997
Internet: www.srk.se/orebro/festspel
E-Mail: orefestspel@swipnet.se
artistic director Paul Morgan; chairman Siv Palgren; secretary Anders Nordqvist; treasurer Staffan Zika
Period/Frequency: Aug, annual *Arts types:* classical chamber music *Venues:* Örebro Konserthus 724, Stora Hotellets stora sal 250, St Nicolai kyrka 450, Örebro slott 200 *Second Address:* ticket office- Örebro Konserthus, Tel: 19-170 220

Lyckå Chambermusic Festival
c/o Berth Nilsson, Döbelnsgatan 14A, 271 31 **Ystad**
Tel: 411-65141 Fax: 411-65141
artistic director Berth Nilsson
Period/Frequency: 1st week in July, annual *Arts types:* chamber music (from experimental music to opera projects) *Venues:* various in Karlskrona

SWITZERLAND (+41)

Königsfelder Festspiel
Klosterkirche Königsfelden, 24 Promenade, 5200 **Arugg**
Tel: 56-441 0026 Fax: 56-441 1626
E-Mail: ch.dance@pop.agri.ch
commercial director Roman Kuhn;
artistic director Jean Deroc; GMD Peter Siegwart;
choreography James Sutherland
Period/Frequency: Aug-Sept, biennial (2000) *Arts types:* liturgic ballet-performance with singers, musicians, actors *Venues:* Königsfelden Abbey church 400

Ascona New Orleans Jazz
Casella postale 703, 6612 **Ascona**
Tel: 91-791 0090/0711 Fax: 91-792 1008/0711
Internet: www.asconajazz.ch
E-Mail: ascona@etlm.ch
Präsident Bruno Nötzli
Period/Frequency: last weekend June-first weekend July, annual *Arts types:* jazz, blues, gospel *Venues:* open-air
Comments: alternative E-mail: khe@jazzascona.ch

Festival de Danse de Neuchâtel
Dance Promotion Suisse, Via Collegio 16, 6612 **Ascona**
Tel: 91-791 7315/79-250 3974 Fax: 91-791 7315
contact Fernando Damaso
Period/Frequency: August, annual *Arts types:* jazz, modern, hip-hop, contemporary dance *Venues:* Théâtre de Neuchâtel 500 *Comments:* Stage International de Danse is also at the same time, an open stage for young choreographers with the support of the city

Settimane Musicali di Ascona
Lago Maggiore Turismo, Casa Serodine, 6612 **Ascona**
Tel: 91-791 0094 Fax: 91-792 1008
E-Mail: ascona@etlm.ch
president Prof Dino Invermizzi; sales Liliana Pensa
Period/Frequency: Aug-Oct, annual *Arts types:* classical music *Venues:* churches Collegio Papio in Ascona 400, San Francesco in Locarno 800

International Figura Theater Festival
Postfach 522, 5401 **Baden**
Tel: 56-221 7585 Fax: 56-221 7585
contact Arlette Richner
Period/Frequency: Sept, biennial (2000) *Arts types:* puppetry *Second address:* Postfach, 8401 Winterthur

Basel 2001 – European Cultural Month
Malzgasse 7A, 4010 **Basel**
Tel: 61-206 9000 Fax: 61-206 9009
E-Mail: info@basel2001.org
secretary Markus Bodmer
Period/Frequency: Oct-Nov 2001

Basel tanzt
Postfach, 4002 **Basel**
Tel: 61-639 1488 Fax: 61-631 1959
E-Mail: bata@baz.ch
Organisation Gerhard Althaus
Period/Frequency: autumn, biennial (2001) *Arts types:* ballet, dance *Venues:* Musical Theater Messe Basel

Festa dell' Opera a Castelgrande, Bellinzona
Casella postale 2111, 6500 **Bellinzona**
Tel: 91-830 1288/79-285 5047 Fax: 91-830 1555
direttore artistico Sergio Fontana;
coordinatrice Emilia Tonolla-Rosa
Period/Frequency: July-Aug, annual *Arts types:* opera *Venues:* Castelgrande 3500

Berner Tanztage
Verein Berner Tanztage, Postfach 317, 3000 **Bern** 14
Tel: 31-376 0303 Fax: 31-371 0333
Internet: www.tanztage.ch
E-Mail: info@tanztage.ch
director Reto Clavadetscher; press/public relations Claudia Rosiny, Anne Jäggi
Period/Frequency: Aug/Sept & end of Dec, bi-annual (twice a year) *Arts types:* dance, video *Venues:* Dampfzentrale – Kulturhallen am Aarelauf Aug/Sept 400, Dez 200 *Comments:* alternative E-mail: info@plusminus.ch; alternative Internet: www.plusminus.ch

Internationales Jazzfestival Bern
Hans Zurbrügg u. Marianne Gauer AG,
Engestr. 54A, 3012 **Bern**
Tel: 31-309 6171 Fax: 31-309 6151
E-Mail: zghotels@smile.ch
director Hans Zurbrügg
Period/Frequency: 1st week of May, annual (one week) *Arts types:* jazz, blues *Venues:* Kursaal Bern 1400, Marians Jazzroom 130

ktv/atp – Künstlerbörse (Artists Exchange)
Postfach 3350, 2500 **Biel/Bienne** 3
Tel: 32-323 5085 Fax: 32-323 5072
Internet: www.atp.ch
E-Mail: ktv-atp@bluewin.ch
president Peter Bissegger; director Denis Alber; secretaries Marianne Gschwind, Martin Clémence, Ursula Lehmann
Period/Frequency: last week of April, annual *Arts types:* theatre, pantomime, dance, music *Venues:* Schadausaal, Seestrasse, Thun *Comments:* visiting address: Obergasse 1, rue haute; events main purpose is to bring together artists, agents, events managers & promoters; see also atp artist & theatre promotion (ktv) (Promoters), Vereinigung für Künstler/innen, Theater-Veraustalter/inne (KTV/ATP) (National Organisations); alternative internet: www.ktv.ch

Semaines Musicales de Crans-Montana
case postale 112, 3963 **Crans-sur-Sierre**
Tel: 27-485 9999 Fax: 27-481 4671
E-Mail: cransmontana.life.scopus.ch
director François Barras;
secrétariat Daniéle Emery Mayor
Period/Frequency: summer/winter, bi-annual *Arts types:* classical music *Venues:* L'Eglise de Crans-sur-Sierre 450, L'Eglise de Montana 600, Le Régent 650

Internationales Musik Festival Davos 'young artists in concert'
Promenade 67, 7270 **Davos-Platz**
Tel: 81-415 2121 Fax: 81-415 2101
Internet: www.davos.ch
E-Mail: davos@davos.ch
Intendant Dirk Nabering
Period/Frequency: July-Aug, annual *Arts types:* classical and modern chamber music *Venues:* various venues in Davos including Congress Center and Kirchner Museum, churches and hotels *Comments:* Pre-bookings at Davos Tourismus (same address)

Belluard/Bollwerk International
case postale 120, 1701 **Fribourg**
Tel: 26-469 0900 Fax: 26-469 0901
Internet: www.bluewin.ch
E-Mail: belluard@bluewin.ch
directeurs Klaus Hersche, Olivier Suter; attachée de presse Sara Nyikus, Laurent Steiert
Period/Frequency: June-July, annual *Arts types:* all experimental types of the performing arts including video, young artists, mixed media, dance, music, performance art, installations, debates *Venues:* Belluard/Bollwerk

Festival de Musiques Sacrées de Fribourg
7, Rue des Alpes, case postale 292, 1701 **Fribourg**
Tel: 26-322 4800 Fax: 26-322 8331
E-Mail: sacredmusicfr@pingnet.ch
contact/festival administrator Nicole Renevey;
vice president François Page
Period/Frequency: July, biennial (2000: 7-16 July)) *Arts types:* sacred music, contemporary, early and baroque, renaissance, romantic music, lectures, workshops and classes on Gregorian chant and interpretation course *Venues:* Église du Collège St. Michel 500 *Comments:* European international festival

Rencontres Folkloriques Internationales Fribourg
Case postale 770, 1701 **Fribourg**
Tel: 26-321 3175 Fax: 26-322 3527
E-Mail: office.tourisme@fribourg.ch
président Christian Morard;
directeur de l'office du tourisme M. Bugnon
Period/Frequency: Aug, annual *Arts types:* folk art, music, dance, concerts, vocal *Venues:* l'Aula de l'Université *Second Address:* Tourist Office Fribourg

AMR Jazz Festival
AMR, 10 rue des Alpes, 1201 **Genève**
Tel: 22-716 5630 Fax: 22-731 4860
programming Dominique Wiedmer,
François Chevrolet, Joël Musy
Period/Frequency: April, annual *Arts types:* jazz *Venues:* Theatre Du Loup 300

Archipel – Festival des musiques d'aujourd'hui
8 rue de la Coulouvrenière, 1204 **Genève**
Tel: 22-329 4242 (admin)/2422 (info) Fax: 22-329 6868
Internet: www.archipel.org
E-Mail: festival@archipel.org
artistic director Jean Prevost;
administrator Michael Seum
Period/Frequency: 2 weeks in March, annual *Arts types:* contemporary music with concerts, films and conferences *Comments:* supported by the Dept of Culture, Geneva

Fête de la Musique, La
Service de l' Art Musical, 19, Route de Malagnou,
case postale 10, 1211 **Genève** 17
Tel: 22-418 6530 Fax: 22-418 6501
Internet: www.ville-ge.ch
E-Mail: beatrice.mawjee@dac.ville-ge.ch
chef de service Jean-Claude Poulin;
assistant Béatrice Mawjee
Period/Frequency: June, annual *Arts types:* all types of music *Venues:* Victoria Hall 1760, Le Grand Théâtre 1200, Hôtel de Ville 440, Eglise St. Germain 360, Temple de la Madeleine 400, Auditorie Calvin *Comments:* features more than 400 music groups

La Bâtie, Festival de Genève
Case Postale 1525, 1211 **Genève** 1
Tel: 22-908 6950 Fax: 22-738 5625
Internet: www.centreimage.ch/batie
E-Mail: batie@sgg.ch
administrator Bernard Laurent; director André Waldis; music programmer Eric Linder; public relations & press Alya Stürenbourg; theatre programmer Sandrine Kuster; dance programmer Claude Ratzé
Period/Frequency: Aug-Sept, annual *Arts types:* theatre, music (rock, jazz, ethno), dance, poetry, sonor poetry *Venues:* various venues in Geneva & border region *Second Address:* enquiries during the festival, 22-738 4032 (bookings)

Musiksommer Gstaad- Saanenland
Chalet Rialto, Postfach 65, 3780 **Gstaad**
Tel: 33-748 8338 Fax: 33-748 8339
Internet: www.musiksommer.ch
E-Mail: musiksommer@gstaad.ch
director Hans-Ueli Tschanz; president Leonz Blunschi; artistic director Dr. Peter Keller
Period/Frequency: July-Sept, annual *Arts types:* opera (concert versions), choir, orchestra, recitals, chamber music *Venues:* 5 churches in and around Saanen, Festival tent 2000

Interlaken Musicfestival Weeks
Interlakner Musikfestwochen
Postfach, 3800 **Interlaken**
Tel: 33-823 3800 Fax: 33-822 2219
Internet: www.InterlakenTourism.ch/musikfestwochen
Sekretariat Frau Rufener; president Peter Widmer; artistic director Martin Studer
Period/Frequency: Aug, annual *Arts types:* symphony and chamber music, matinees *Venues:* Casino Kursaal – Konzerthalle 1200, Theatersaal 680, Kirche Untersee 370, Ballsaal 350 *Comments:* the festival's main objective is to offer a stage to new artists

Kyburgiade
Schwandenstrasse 27, 8802 **Kilchberg**
Tel: 1-715 0559 Fax: 1-715 0814
Internet: www.kyburgiade.ch
E-Mail: jann.kilchberg@bluewin.ch
managing director Ruth Jann; art dirStephan Goerner
Period/Frequency: first 2 weeks in Aug, annual *Arts types:* chamber, early music *Venues:* Schloß Kyburg 1000 (open-air), Reithalle Winterthur 1000 *Second Address:* tel: 1-251 4044 fax: 1-251 4060

Festival de Neuchâtel
Théâtre Populaire Romand, CP ,
2301 **La Chaux-de-Fonds**
Tel: 32-913 1510 Fax: 32-913 1550
Internet: www.tpr.ch
director Charles Joris; administrative director Eric Lavanchy; general secretary Claudine Blanchard; technical director Géza Vadas
Period/Frequency: Sept, biennial (2000) *Arts types:* theatre, repertoire *Venues:* open-air (in Neuchâtel) *Comments:* own and guest productions; see also Drama

Internationale Musikfestwochen Luzern
Hirschmattstrasse 13, Postfach 3842, 6002 **Luzern**
Tel: 41-226 4400 Fax: 41-226 4460
Internet: www.lucernemusic.ch
E-Mail: lucernemusic@lucernemusic.ch
director Michael Haefliger; press & pr Martin Elbel
Period/Frequency: Aug-Sept, annual *Arts types:* symphony, chamber orchestra, chamber music, recitals, choral, masterclasses *Venues:* New concert hall in the Culture and Congress Centre Lucerne 1840, Lion Monument, Lucerne Theater, churches

Osterfestspiele – Internationale Musikfestwochen Luzern
Hirschmattstrasse 13, Postfach 3842, 6002 **Luzern**
Tel: 41-226 4400 Fax: 41-226 4460
Internet: www.lucernemusic.ch
E-Mail: lucernemusic@lucernemusic.ch
director Michael Haefliger; press & PR manager Martin Elbel (tel: 41-226 4443/44)
Period/Frequency: one week before Easter, annual *Arts types:* choral, sacred music, orchestra *Venues:* in two of the most splendid churches of Lucerne and the new concert hall in the Culture and Congress Centre Lucerne 1840

Piano 2000 – Lucerne Piano Festival
c/o Internationale Musikfestwochen Luzern,
Hirschmattstrasse 13, Postfach, 6002 **Luzern**
Tel: 41-226 4400 Fax: 41-226 4460
Internet: www.lucernemusic.ch
E-Mail: lucernemusic@lucernemusic.ch
director Michael Haefliger; press & pr Martin Elbel
Period/Frequency: Nov, annual *Arts types:* piano recitals, classical and jazz, combined with a festival of arts in relation with the piano *Venues:* new concert hall in the Culture and Congress Centre Lucerne

International Opera and Music Festival Montreux-Vevey
Festival International de Musique et d'Art Lyrique Montreux-Vevey
Rue du Théâtre 5, Case postale 353, 1820 **Montreux** 2
Tel: 21-966 8020 (main office)/8025 (bookings)
Fax: 21-963 2506
Internet: www.montreux-festival.com
E-Mail: courrier@montreux-festival.ch
general & artistic manager Christian Chorier;
executive manager Jean-Yves Rebourgeard
Period/Frequency: end of Aug-end of Sept, annual *Arts types:* 30 concerts, recitals, chamber music symphony orchestras, opera *Venues:* Auditorium Stravinsky 2000, Château de Chillon 340

Semaines Internationales de la Marionnette au pays Neuchâtelois, Les
Théâtre de la Poudrière, Quai Codet 18, 2000 **Neuchâtel**
Tel: 32-724 6519 Fax: 32-724 6517
directeurs Yves Bodin, Corinne Grandjean
Period/Frequency: Oct, biennial (2001) *Arts types:* puppet – contemporary (mainly), adult puppetry *Venues:* throughout the Canton of Neuchâtel from 50 to 600 *Comments:* 14 companies, 40 shows, international: see also Puppet companies & Venues

Far. Festival des Arts Vivants
Vy-Creuse 21, 1260 **Nyon**
Tel: 22-365 1550 Fax: 22-365 1551
Internet: www.festival.far.ch
E-Mail: far@festival-far.ch
administrator Véronique Ferrero;
artistic director Ariane Karcher
Period/Frequency: Aug, annual *Arts types:* drama, contemporary dance *Venues:* Usine à Gaz 150, Aula du Collège De Nyon 550

Paleo Festival, Festival de Nyon
route de St. Cergue 312, Case Postale 177, 1260 **Nyon**
Tel: 22-365 1010 Fax: 22-365 1020
Internet: www.paleo.ch
E-Mail: paleo@paleo.ch
directeur Daniel Rossellat; responsable de la programmation Jacques Monnier, Isabelle Primault;
presse Vincent Sager
Period/Frequency: July *Arts types:* rock, chanson, blues, classical, world music, hip-hop, trip-hop, electronic groove *Venues:* site de l'asse, outdoor – 5 stages 200,000 *Comments:* see also Agents

Engadiner Konzertwochen
Postfach 108, 7504 **Pontresina**
Tel: 81-842 6573 Fax: 81-842 6525
Internet: www.engadin.ch
E-Mail: info@engadin.ch
director Claudio Chiogna
Period/Frequency: July-Aug, annual *Arts types:* chamber music, 15-20 concerts *Venues:* 12 venues in Engadin

Internationale Bachfeste Schaffhausen
Kulturdienst, Stadthaus, 8200 **Schaffhausen**
Tel: 52-632 5287 Fax: 52-632 5274
E-Mail: rolf.mueller@stsh.ch
Kulturdirector Rolf C Müller; Direktor Bachgesellschaft Prof Diethard Hellman
Period/Frequency: May, triennial (2000) *Arts types:* 9 orchestras performing works by Bach *Venues:* St. Johann Church 1200

Internationales Fest der Volksmusik Schaffhausen
Kulturdienst, Stadthaus, 8200 **Schaffhausen**
Tel: 52-632 5288 Fax: 52-632 5274
director Arthur Ulmer
Period/Frequency: May, annual *Arts types:* folk music artists from Switzerland and international *Venues:* Stadttheater 690, St. Johann Church 1200

Musikfesttage der Internationalen Preisträger, Schaffhausen
Kulturdienst, Stadthaus, 8200 **Schaffhausen**
Tel: 52-632 5287 Fax: 52-632 5274
E-Mail: rolf.mueller@stsh.ch
kulturdirektor Rolf C Müller
Period/Frequency: May, triennial (2001) *Arts types:* concerts by international competition winners *Venues:* Stadttheater 690, St. Johann Church 1200

Festival International de l'Orgue Ancien et de la Musique Ancienne Valère
Château de Valère, case postale, 1950 **Sion** 2
Tel: 27-323 5767 Fax: 27-323 5767
Internet: www.novelliste.ch
director and organiser Maurice Wenger
Period/Frequency: July-Aug, annual *Arts types:* early unknown organ music played on the oldest organs in the world, choir music and early music groups *Venues:* Basilique du Château de Valère

Festival Tibor Varga, Sion, Valais, Suisse
Rue de Lausanne 22A, Case postale 1429, 1951 **Sion**
Tel: 27-323 4317 Fax: 27-323 4662
Internet: www.nouvelliste.ch/varga/tvarga.htm
E-Mail: festivargasion@vtx.ch
administrateur Pierre Gillioz;
directeur artistique Gilbert Varga
Period/Frequency: July-Sept, annual (30 concerts + open air) *Arts types:* classical music *Venues:* various in Sion and in Valois *Comments:* master courses, International Tibor Varga Violin Competition (9-18 August)

SNOW AND SYMPHONY – The St Moritz Music Festival
Snow and Symphony, Via Stredas 12, 7500 **St Moritz**
Tel: 81-834 4646 Fax: 81-834 4647
Intendant Peter Aronsky;
assistant manager Roman Grossrieder
Period/Frequency: March, annual (2000: 24 March-2 April; 2001: 23 March-1 April; 2002: 15-24 March) *Arts types:* classical music *Venues:* hotels in St Moritz cap. 220-560 (concert & dining halls)

Montreux Jazz Festival
CP 126, 1820 **Territet-Montreux**
Tel: 21-966 4444 Fax: 21-966 4448
Internet: www.montreuxjazz.com
E-Mail: info@mif.ch
founder & artistic director Claude Nobs; press and public relations Ingrid Walther (tel: 966 4439); promotion and sponsoring Cyril Zammit (tel: 966 4434); coordination Michaela Maioern (tel: 966 4450); infrastructure Jean Francois Chapuisat (tel: 966 4430)
Period/Frequency: July, annual *Arts types:* jazz, blues, gospel, Brazilian, African, rap, rock, pop, world; soloists, groups and orchestras *Venues:* Montreux Congress and Exhibition Centre- daily concerts in 2 halls: Auditorium Stravinski 1800 to 3000, Miles Davis Hall 1200 to 1800 *Second Address:* during festival: Centre des Congres et d'Expositions CCE, Grand Rue 95, 1820 Montreux *Comments:* important Off-Festival with over 300 open air concerts free of charge; workshops, clinics, acoustic concerts, exhibitions, market and food stalls, videos from MJF archives shown; see also Agents and Producers

Verbier Festival & Academy
4 rue Jean Jacques Rousseau, 1800 **Vevey**
Tel: 21-922 4010 Fax: 21-922 4012
Internet: www.verbierfestival.com
E-Mail: info@verbierfestival.com
directeur général Martin T:son Engström; administrateur Miguel Esteban; directeur artistique Avi Shoshani
Period/Frequency: July-Aug, annual *Arts types:* eclectic mix of music, dance, theatre, master classes, conferences, classical music, jazz *Venues:* Big Top 1300, church 600, open-air *Second Address:* Verbier Festival & Academy, Case postale 1936 Verbier

Jazz Festival Willisau
Postfach, 6130 **Willisau**
Tel: 41-970 2731
Fax: 41-970 3231
Internet: www.jazzwillisau.ch
E-Mail: troxler@centralnet.ch
contact Niklaus Troxler
Period/Frequency: from last Thursday of August for 4 days, annual *Arts types:* contemporary jazz *Venues:* Festhalle, Willisau 1600

Internationales Tanzfestival Schweiz Migros Kulturprozent
Migros-Genossenschafts-Bund / Performing Arts, Limmatstrasse 152, Postfach, 8031 **Zürich**
Tel: 1-277 2049 Fax: 1-277 2274
Internet: www.steps.ch
E-Mail: steps@mgb.ch
direction Isabella Spirig
Period/Frequency: April-May biennial (2000) *Arts types:* modern dance *Venues:* performances in about 20 towns in Switzerland

Tage für Neue Musik Zürich
Präsidialdepartement der Stadt Zürich, Abt. Musik, Stadthausquai 17, Postfach, 8022 **Zürich**
Tel: 1-216 3125/30 Fax: 1-212 1404
Internet: www.kultur.stadt-zuerich.ch
E-Mail: musik.literatur@prd.stzh.ch
artistic directors Walter Feldmann, Mats Scheidegger
Period/Frequency: mid-Nov, annual *Arts types:* contemporary music *Venues:* Säale der Tonhalle, Grosser Saal des Konservatoriums 400, Kleintheater 120 *Comments:* address artistic director: Wartstrasse 3, 8032 Zürich, Tel: 1-383 9580, Fax: 1-383 9516

Zürcher Festspiele
Info- u. Ticketoffice, Postfach 6036, 8023 **Zürich**
Tel: 1-269 9090 Fax: 1-260 7025
Internet: www.zuercher-festspiele.ch
Künstlerischer Geschäftsführer Alexander Pereira;
Kaufmännischer Geschäftsführer Jürg Keller
Period/Frequency: last week of June & 1st 3 weeks of July, annual *Arts types:* opera, concerts, drama, exhibitions *Venues:* Opernhaus, Tonhalle, Schauspielhaus, Kunsthaus and others *Second Address:* c/o Opernhaus Zürich, Falkenstr. 1, 8008 Zürich, Tel: 1-268 6400, Fax: 1-268 6640

Zürcher TheaterSpektakel
Stadthausquai 17, 8001 **Zürich**
Tel: 1-216 3551 Fax: 1-216 3574
Internet: www.theaterspekakel.ch
E-Mail: theaterspektakel@bluewin.ch
künstlerische Leitung Markus Luchsinger; administrative Leitung Cornelia Howald
Period/Frequency: Aug-Sept, annual *Arts types:* theatre, dance *Venues:* various in Zürich

TURKEY (+90)

Izmir International Festival
Uluslararasi Izmir Festivali
Izmir Foundation for Culture, Art and Education, 58 Sair Esref Bulvari, **Alsancak-Izmir**
Tel: 253-463 0300 Fax: 253-463 0077
president Filiz Eczacibasi Sarper
Period/Frequency: June-July, annual
Arts types: music, dance

Adpendos Opera & Ballet Festival (Antalya)
Ankara State Opera and Ballet, **Antalya (Ankara)**
Tel: 312-311 2430 Fax: 312-311 9731
director Hasan Hüseyin Akbulut
Period/Frequency: June, annual

International Bursa Festival
Uluslararasi Bursa Festivali
Bursa Kültür ve Sanat Vakfi, Bursa Foundation for Culture and Arts, Açikhava Tiyatrosu, Kültür Park, **Bursa**
Tel: 224-234 4911 Fax: 224-234 4911
Period/Frequency: June-July, annual *Arts types:* jazz, classical music, folk music, folk dance, ballet & dance

International Bursa Karagöz Festival
Uluslararasi Bursa Karagöz Festivali
UNIMA Türkiye Bursa Office, Kapali Carsi (Eski Aynali Carsi) ici No. 12-13, **Bursa**
Tel: 224-221 8727/220 5350
director Sinasi Celikkol
Period/Frequency: Oct, biennial

Akbank International Jazz Festival
c/o Pozitif Productions, Havyar Sok. No. 54, Cihangir, 80060 **Istanbul**
Tel: 212-252 5267/244 3394 Fax: 212-245 4176
managing directors Mehmet Ulug, Tcem Yegul, Ahmet Ulug
Period/Frequency: Oct, annual *Arts types:* contemporary jazz *Venues:* indoors

Assos Festival of Performing Arts
Galipdede Cad 149/9, Kuledibi, 80020 **Istanbul**
Tel: 212-249 2032 Fax: 212-243 2794
artistic director Hüseyin Katircioglu
Period/Frequency: end of September *Venues:* in the ancient ruins of Assos and the villages around
Comments: groups are given the opportunity to stay in the area for three weeks to create site-specific, inter-disciplinary work, co-productions between Turkish and overseas' groups are particularly encouraged

International Istanbul Jazz Festival
Uluslararasi Istanbul Caz Festivali, Istanbul Foundation for Culture and Arts,
Istiklal Cad. Luvr Ap No. 146 Beyoglu, **Istanbul**
Tel: 212-293 3133/34/35(ext: 42) Fax: 212-249 5667
Internet: www.istfest.org
E-Mail: jazz.fest@istfest-tr.org
president Sakir Eczacibasi;
general director Melih Fereli;
director Görgün Taner
Period/Frequency: July, annual

International Istanbul Music Festival
Uluslararasi Istanbul Müzik Festivali
Istanbul Foundation for Culture and Arts, Istiklal Cad. Luvr Ap. N° 146, Beyoglu, 80070 **Istanbul**
Tel: 212-293 3133/34/35/251 0541 Fax: 212-249 5667
Internet: www.istfest.org
E-Mail: music.fest@istfest-tr.org
president Sakir Eczacibasi; general director Melih Fereli; director Cevza Aktüze; assistant director Ahmet Erenli
Period/Frequency: June-July, annual *Arts types:* music, opera, dance, ballet

Istanbul International Theatre Festival
Uluslararasi Istanbul Tiyatro Festivali
Istanbul Foundation for Culture and Arts, Istiklal Cad. Luvr Ap. No.146, Beyoglu, **Istanbul**
Tel: 212-293 3133/34/35 (ext: 38) Fax: 212-249 5667
Internet: www.istfest.org
E-Mail: theatre.fest@istfest-tr.org
president Sakir Eczacibasi; general director Melih Fereli; director Dikmen Gürün Ucarer
Period/Frequency: May, annual *Arts types:* drama

International Ankara Music Festival
Uluslararasi Ankara Müzik Festivali
Sevda Cenap and Music Foundation, Tunali Hilmi Cad. 114/43, 06700 **Kavaklidere (Ankara)**
Tel: 312-427 0855 Fax: 312-467 3159
E-Mail: scavakfi@ada.com.tr
president of foundation Mehmet A Basman; coordinator of foundation Erik Basman
Period/Frequency: April-May, annual *Arts types:* classical & modern music and dance *Venues:* Presidential Symphony Orchestra Concert Hall 800, Opera House 723 *Comments:* Sevda Cenap Foundation organises concerts, recitals, competitions, symposia, see also Promoters

International Festival of Traditional Theatre
Uluslararasi Geleneksel Tiyatro Festivali
Mithatpasa Cad. No: 18/7, **Yenisehir (Ankara)**
Tel: 312-431 0320/5955/433 4527 Fax: 312-431 0297
Period/Frequency: biennial *Comments:* touring festival organized by the Ministry of Culture and UNIMA Türkiye

UKRAINE (+380)

Kyiv Summer Musical Evenings
31 Tolstoy Str, 252032 **Kiev**
Tel: 44-244 3238 Fax: 44-244 3268
E-Mail: kdmu@naverex.kiev.uz
general director Yuri Zilberman;
artistic director Ivan Karabits
Period/Frequency: annual *Comments:* orchestras, soloists, perfomers, conductors and compoers are invited to take part in a concert programme

Vladimir Krainev Invites
c/o Natalia Doushtchenko, International Vladimir Krainev Charity Fund, Tchelabyinskaya, 11 – Apt 12, 253002 **Kiev**
Tel: 44-517 8598 Fax: 44-517 8598
contact Natalia Doushtchenko
Comments: contact in France: Catherine Petit, Agence Artistique Catherine Petit, 26 rue de la Libération, 92210 Saint-Cloud, France, Tel: +33 1-4602 3336, Fax: +33 1-4602 2725, E-mail: aacp@wanadoo.fr; see also Agents & Producers (Agence Artistique Catherine Petit) and Competitions (International Vladimir Krainer's Young Pianists Competition)

International Festival "Musical Dialogues"
c/o Composers Union of Ukraine, **Kiev (Kyiv)**
Tel: 44-225 1337
contact Ihor Shcherbakov
Period/Frequency: May, annual *Venues:* in Kiev

International Festival of Organ Music
c/o Organ & Chamber Music Hall, Krasnoarmiyska Str. 77, **Kiev (Kyiv)**
Tel: 44-2698 6117
contact Volodymyr Lebedev
Period/Frequency: Sept, annual *Venues:* in Kiev

Kyiv (Kiev) International Music Fest
Pushkinska St. 1-3/5, apt. 12, 252003 **Kiev (Kyiv)**
Tel: 44-229 3161 Fax: 44-229 3161
director Ivan Karabyts
Period/Frequency: first week in Oct, annual *Arts types:* classical, mostly contemporary music
Venues: various halls in Kiev

Music Premieres of the Season International Festival
c/o Composers Union of Ukraine, **Kiev (Kyiv)**
Tel: 44-225 1337
contact Ihor Sherbakov
Period/Frequency: March-April *Venues:* in Kiev

Virtuosi – International Music Festival
Tchaikovsky St. 7, 29005 **Lviv**
Tel: 322-741 022
Fax: 322-726 725
director Serhiy Burko
Period/Frequency: May, annual

Contrasts
Volodymyr Syvokhip, Ukrainian Composers, Union Lviv Branch, Tchaikovsky str. 7, 290000 **Lviv-center**
Tel: 322-742 349
Fax: 322-725 847
E-Mail: olia@lim.lviv.uz

International Festival of Modern Arts
Association New Music (Ukraine sectionof the ISCM), 48 Bazarna str, apt. 1, 270011 **Odessa**
Tel: 482 -225 283/261 689
Fax: 482 -225 283/261 689
E-Mail: new_music@paco.net
Period/Frequency: annual *Arts types:* new music, visual arts, sound, video *Comments:* alternative E-mail: alex_vidr@paco.net or office_vidr@paco.net or karmella@paco.net; see also National Organisations

Organum – International Festival of Organ & Chamber Music
PO Box 1165, 244030 **Sumy**
Tel: 542-240 510/225 575/221 125
Fax: 542-225 575/221 125
director Orest Koval
Period/Frequency: April & Oct, bi-annual

UNITED KINGDOM (+44)

Aldeburgh Easter Festival
Aldeburgh Productions, High Street,
Aldeburgh IP15 5AX
Tel: 1728-452 935/453 543 (box office)
Fax: 1728-452 715
guest artistic director Robert King
Period/Frequency: April, annual *Arts types:* early music

Aldeburgh Festival of Music and the Arts
Aldeburgh Productions, High Street,
Aldeburgh IP15 5AX
Tel: 1728-452 935 Fax: 1728-452 715
Internet: www.aldeburgh.co.uk
E-Mail: enquiries@aldeburghfestivals.org
chief executive Jonathan Reekie;
artistic director Thomas Ades
Period/Frequency: June, annual
Arts types: opera, orchestra, chamber music, soloists and many more *Venues:* Snape-Maltings Concert Hall, Jubilee Hall, and various historic churches
Comments: Snape Maltings Proms in August, year-round programme of music; Easter, October and winter concert series

Armagh Arts Festival
The Market Place, Armagh Theatre and Arts Centre, Market Street, **Armagh (Northern Ireland)** BT61 7AT
Tel: 28-3752 1800 (tourist info centre)
E-Mail: armagh.arts@dnet.co.uk
contact, programme coordinators Lenny Mullan, Kate Bond
Period/Frequency: Oct, annual *Arts types:* classical and traditional music, theatre, talks, workshops, exhibitions, children's performances *Venues:* various venues in Armagh *Comments:* the festival is moving to the above address in early 2000, they can be contacted through the Tourist Info Centre on the above telephone number

Music in Armagh Chamber Music Series
Tourist Information Centre, 40 English Street, **Armagh (Northern Ireland)** BT61 7BA
Tel: 28-3752 1805 Fax: 28-3751 0180
E-Mail: armagh.arts@dnet.co.uk
coordinator Kate Bond
Period/Frequency: Sept-May, annual *Arts types:* professional chamber concerts *Venues:* The Market Place, Theatre and Arts Centre (Armagh) *Comments:* Sept-May, monthly concert in Armagh

Arundel Festival
Arundel Festival Society, The Mary Gate,
Arundel BN18 9AT
Tel: 1903-883 690/889 900 (info) Fax: 1903-884 243
Internet: www.argonet.co.uk/arundel.festival
E-Mail: arundel.festival@argonet.co.uk
festival coordinator Victoria Moles;
chairman Judith Buckland
Period/Frequency: Aug-Sept, annual (10 days) *Arts types:* open-air theatre, recitals, symphonic and chamber music, film literature, jazz, fireworks, art gallery trail, open-air spectaculars, small scale drama, street theatre *Venues:* Open Air Theatre Arundel Castle 900 to 2000, cathedral 500, churches 200 to 500 *Comments:* active fringe, historic town

Sidmouth International Festival
PO Box 296, **Aylesbury** HP19 3TL
Tel: 1296-433 669 Fax: 1296-392 300
Internet: www.mrscasey.co.uk/sidmouth
E-Mail: sidmouth@mrscasey.nildram.co.uk
festival director Steve Heap;
artistic director Alan Bearman;
press officer Paul Saunders;
office manager Louise Haynes
Period/Frequency: Aug, annual *Arts types:* international folk arts including music, dance and song *Venues:* Arena 6000, and other venues 30 to 1000

26th Barmouth Arts Festival 2000
1 Epworth Terrace,
Barmouth (Wales) LL42 1PN
Tel: 1341-280 392
administrative secretary Mair Jones
Period/Frequency: early Sept, annual *Arts types:* opera, dance, drama, welsh choir, classical music, light music & comedy, exhibition *Venues:* Dragon Theatre 237

Bath Fringe 2000
103 Walcot Street, **Bath** BA1 5BW
Tel: 1225-480 079 Fax: 1225-480 079
Internet: www.bathfringe.co.uk
E-Mail: admin@bathfringe.co.uk
administrator Wendy Matthews
Period/Frequency: annual, May-June *Arts types:* theatre, music, dance, comedy, street performance *Venues:* parks and streets all over the city *Comments:* also children's arts festival and a festival of contemporary art

Bath International Music Festival
c/o Bath Festival Trust, 5 Broad Street, **Bath** BA1 5LJ
Tel: 1225-462 231/463 362(box office)
Fax: 1225-445 551/310 377(box office)
E-Mail: bathfestivals@btconnect.com
director Tim Joss; head of fund raising Anne Strathie; head of marketing & community relations Tim Martienssen; financial controller Ian Morrison; literature festival programme director t.b.a.
Period/Frequency: May-June, annual *Arts types:* classical music, jazz, contemporary music, early music, world music, opera *Venues:* Assembly Rooms 529, Guildhall 361, Forum 1500, Wells Cathedral 992, Pavilion 763, Bath Abbey 934, Pump Room 316, St Johns Church (Keynsham) 472, Prior Park Chapel 402 *Comments:* also promote Bath Literature Festival (Feb/March)

Belfast Festival at Queen's
Festival House, 25 College Gardens,
Belfast (Northern Ireland) BT9 6BS
Tel: 28-9066 7687 Fax: 28-9066 3733
Internet: www.qub.ac.uk/festival
E-Mail: festival@qub.ac.uk
executive director Robert Agnew; programme director t.b.a.; assistant director Rosie Turner;
marketing manager Margaret McKee
Period/Frequency: Nov, annual *Arts types:* theatre, classical music, ballet, opera, cabaret, dance, folk, jazz, world music, comedy, film, children's *Venues:* 15 major venues including: Ulster Hall 1400, Grand Opera House 1000, Whitla Hall 1200, Elmwood Hall 500, Art Theatre 500, Waterfront Hall, 2200 *Comments:* largest arts festival in Ireland

Castleward Opera Festival
737 Lisburn Road, **Belfast (Northern Ireland)** BT9 7GU
Tel: 28-9066 1090
Fax: 28-9068 7081
manager Hilde Lugan
Period/Frequency: June, annual *Arts types:* opera (2 productions a year) *Venues:* Castleward Theatre, Strangford, County Down *Comments:* the venue is the property of the National Trust

Stratford Festival
Stratford Festival Company, Cotson Leys House, Burnell Close, **Bidford-on-Avon** B50 4AY
Tel: 1789-772 702 Fax: 1789-772 702
E-Mail: SBeare1010@aol.com
trustees Stuart E. J. Beare, Roger Rippin
Period/Frequency: 1-2 weeks early July, annual (events throughout the year) *Arts types:* classical music, jazz, pop, folk, theatre, street theatre, light entertainment variety, children's events *Venues:* Civic Hall 400, Town Hall 200 *Comments:* local festival involving all ages; particular policy to provide performance platform for young and emerging arts talents; some events throughout the year

ArtsFest
Birmingham Arts Marketing, Essex House,
31 Horse Fair, **Birmingham** B1 1DD
Tel: 121-622 1234
Fax: 121-622 1905
Internet: www.birminghamarts.org.uk
E-Mail: bam@agency-net.co.uk
co-director Paul Kaynes;
programmes manager Anne-Marie Pope;
marketing & sponsorship manager Clare Jepson-Homer
Period/Frequency: September *Comments:* a festival showcasing the arts of the West Midlands, all events free to the public

Birmingham International Jazz Festival
PO Box 944, Edgbaston, **Birmingham** B16 8UT
Tel: 121-454 7020
Fax: 121-454 9996
director and artistic director Jim Simpson; assistant director Tim Jennings; art director John Keetley; head of press & PR Louise Rose; talent buyer Val Wiseman; marketing director Catherine Ewart
Period/Frequency: 10 days starting 1st Friday in July, annual *Arts types:* jazz, blues, R & B *Venues:* various venues throughout the city from 100 to 2200
Comments: 200 shows; 90% free to the public

Voices in the City
c/o Cadbury Ltd, PO Box 12, Bournville,
Birmingham B30 2LU
Tel: 121-451 4032 Fax: 121-451 4395
E-Mail: b.g.chapman@voicesinthecity.homeserve.co.uk
general manager Basil Chapman;
artistic director Simon Halsey
Period/Frequency: October, annual *Arts types:* international choral festival *Venues:* in and around Birmingham *Comments:* the Festival exists to celebrate the central role played by choral music in the life of Birmingham, and to feed the resident skills by exposing the City and its musicians to the world's other choral traditions

St. Endellion 41th Festival of Music
Churchtown Farm House, Michaelstow, **Bodmin** PL30 3PD
Tel: 1208-850 463
conductor Richard Hickox; administration Anne Spicer
Period/Frequency: Easter & Summer, annual *Arts types:* choral, chamber, orchestral music *Venues:* St. Endellion Church 300 *Comments:* 27th Easter Festival: 16-23 April 2000; 42nd Summer Festival: 1-11 August 2000

Wadebridge Folk Festival, Cornwall
Yew Cottage, Rosehill, Lanivet, **Bodmin** PL30 5ES
Tel: 1208-831 123
E-Mail: wadebridgefolk@hotmail.com
tickets, information Sue Sedgwick (831 123); press/P.R. Clare Wilson (840-770 946); artists & programme Stephanie Nørgaard (1752-847 963)
Period/Frequency: Aug (bank holiday weekend), annual *Arts types:* folk music, dance and song, traditional Irish, English & European; morris and clog dance, workshops, children's entertainers, street performers *Venues:* Town Hall 300 , local pubs 200, Community Rooms 200, Local Schools 300 *Second Address:* during festival – Town Hall, The Platt, Wadebridge, Tel: 1208-812 643 *Comments:* workshops in singing, dancing & instruments for all age ranges

WOMAD Festival
World In The Park Ltd, Mill Lane, **Box Corsham** SN13 8PN
Tel: 1225-744 494 Fax: 1225-743 481
Internet: www.womad.org
E-Mail: womad@realworld.on.net
artistic director Thomas Brooman; financial administrator Karen Coghlan; events coordinator Geraldine Roule; event co-ordinator Paula Henderson; production director Steve Hadrell; education & WOMAD Foundation Mandy Macfarlane; production coordinator Lesley Kingsley; marketing & media manager Mandy Craine; Friends of WOMAD co-ordinator Annie Menter
Period/Frequency: 10 festivals a year internationally *Arts types:* music, dance and art from all over the world *Venues:* touring organisation working in Australia, Spain, UK, USA, Sicily, Singapore, Greece, Czech Republic, South Africa *Comments:* constituted aim is to excite and inform; and to make a wider audience aware of the worth and potential of a multi-cultural society; usual format for a WOMAD festival is one of performance on several stages and participatory workshops; crafts and foods from around the world ; most festivals also offer a range of activities for children; majority of festivals are outdoors, and settings have included railway stations, revamped cinemas and circus big-tops; see also Promoters

Bracknell Festival
South Hill Park Arts Centre, **Bracknell** RG12 7PA
Tel: 1344-427 272 Fax: 1344-411 427
E-Mail: marketing@southhillpark.org.uk
festival director Tim Brinkman; programming director David Fry; festival officer Simon Chatterton
Period/Frequency: July, annual *Arts types:* jazz, blues, folk, rock, Indie and reggae music *Venues:* South Hill Park 3000 *Comments:* 3 stages, national & international artists; alternative E-mail: festival@southhillpark.org.uk

Bradford Festival
The Wool Exchange, Hustlergate, **Bradford** BD1 1RE
Tel: 1274-309 199 Fax: 1274-724 213
Internet: www.bradfordfestival.yorks.com
E-Mail: info@bradfordfestival/.yorks.com
director Mark Fielding; press & marketing Rob Walsh
Period/Frequency: June/July, annual *Arts types:* folkloric, modern dance, modern theatre, jazz, multi-media, visual arts, world music, street theatre *Venues:* Peel Park 170,000, Centenary Square 2000

Canizarro Park Festival, The
Opera Box Ltd, Rhydyberi Cottages, Merthr Cynog,
Brecon (Wales) LD3 9SA
Tel: 1874-690 339 Fax: 1874-690 254
Internet: www.operabox.freeuk.com
E-Mail: opera-box@international. freeserve.co.uk
directors Brendan Wheatley, Bridgett Gill
Period/Frequency: July-Aug, annual (month long festival) *Arts types:* opera, dance, concerts *Venues:* Canizarro Park *Second address:* Canizarro Park, Wimbledon Common, London SW19 *Comments:* run by Classical Management Services; see also Promoters and Agents & Producers (Opera Box)

Brighton Festival
12a Pavilion Buildings, Castle Square, **Brighton** BN1 1EE
Tel: 1273-700 747
Fax: 1273-707 505
Internet: www.brighton-festival.org.uk
E-Mail: info@brighton-festival.org.uk
general manager John Lucas; artistic director Christopher Barron; head of marketing Lisa Wolfe
Period/Frequency: May, annual *Arts types:* theatre, music, opera, jazz, rock, comedy, cabaret, dance, performance, film, literature, street theatre *Venues:* Dome 1923, Theatre Royal 951, Gardner Arts Centre 498, Corn Exchange Theatre 300

visions
c/o Alexandra Curran, University of Brighton Gallery, Grand Parade, **Brighton** BN2 2JY
Tel: 1273-643 012 Fax: 1273-643 038
E-Mail: visionsfest@btinternet.com
artistic and managing director Sharon Kivity; administrator Alexandra Curran; executive producer Colin Matthews; marketing & pr consultant Sarah Heyworth
Period/Frequency: Oct/Nov, biennial (2000) *Arts types:* international animated theatre including live theatre, film and video, exhibitions, workshops and masterclasses *Venues:* in and around Brighton plus touring and satellite festivals throughout the U.K. eg. Belfast, Wales, Oxford, Farnham *Comments:* visions is promoted by the University of Brighton, the largest festival of its kind in the UK; accent on contemporary puppetry for adults as well as children; alternative E-mail: clm1@brighton.ac.uk

Buckingham Summer Festival
1 Poplars Close, Preston Bissett,
Buckingham MK18 4LR
Tel: 1280-848 275/823 334 (box office)
Fax: 1280-848 275
contact Robert Secret
Period/Frequency: July, annual *Arts types:* recitals, orchestral, choral *Venues:* The Radcliffe Centre 140, The Chancery Chapel 60, Buckingham Parish Church 400

Stowe Opera
1 Poplars Close, Preston Bissett,
Buckingham MK18 4LR
Tel: 1280-823 334/848 275 (admin)
Fax: 1280-848 275
managing director Robert Secret
Period/Frequency: Aug, annual *Arts types:* opera *Venues:* Roxburgh Theatre 470

Burnley National Blues Festival
The Burnley Mechanics Arts & Entertainment Centre, Manchester Road, **Burnley** BB11 1JA
Tel: 1282-430 005/055 (box office) Fax: 1282-457 428
arts developments & tourism officer David Peirce; operations manager Jon Yull
Period/Frequency: Easter, annual *Arts types:* full spectrum of traditional and contemporary blues styles *Venues:* Burnley Mechanics Arts & Entertainment Centre 300 to 425 *Comments:* regular performing arts programme throughout the year including theatre, dance and music; owned and operated by Burnley Borough Council's Arts Entertainment and Tourism

Buxton Festival
1 Crescent View, Hall Bank, **Buxton** SK17 6EN
Tel: 1298-70395/72190 (box office) Fax: 1298-72289
Internet: www.buxtonfestival.freeserve.co.uk
E-Mail: info@buxtonfestival.freeserve.co.uk
general manager Glyn Foley; artistic director Aidan Lang; chairman Lord Hattersley; head of communications Lee Barnes; development coordinator Jean Ball
Period/Frequency: July, annual *Arts types:* opera, recitals, concerts, young artists, talks, fringe *Venues:* Opera House 943, St John's Church 400, Palace Hotel 400, Octagon 600, Old Clubhouse 100 *Comments:* Buxton Festival Society have other events throughout the year for their members, contact Festival Society Chairman Jim Robinson at the above address; they were planning to move at the end of 1999, new address not known at time of going to print, please contact festival at the phone number above for further details

Beverley Chamber Music Festival
c/o Hazard Chase Ltd, Richmond House, 16-20 Regent Street, **Cambridge** CB2 1DB
Tel: 1223-312 400
Fax: 1223-460 827
Internet: www.hazardchase.co.uk
E-Mail: info@hazardchase.co.uk
festival management James Brown, Helen Poole; artistic director Martin Roscoe
Period/Frequency: Sept, annual *Arts types:* chamber music *Venues:* St Mary's Church, Beverley 452, Beverley Minster 600 *Comments:* also features Beverley inter@ctive, events for children and young people

Canterbury Festival
Christ Church Gate, The Precincts, **Canterbury** CT1 2EE
Tel: 1227-452 853 Fax: 1227-781 830
festival director Mark Deller; administrative assistant Miranda Manning-Press; marketing & publicity Jo Tuffs; sponsorship Patricia Ebden
Period/Frequency: Oct (200 events in a fortnight), annual *Arts types:* opera, dance, music, mime, drama, new circus, poetry recitals, cabaret comedy, jazz, rock, puppetry, street theatre masterclasses, workshops, outreach programme, community and education, visual arts *Venues:* Cathedral 1250, Marlowe Theatre 980, Gulbenkian Theatre 342, Margate Theatre Royal, other local theatres/halls *Comments:* brochures available from Canterbury Festival Office, Tel: 1227-455 600 (festival box office)

Lower Machen Festival
46 Richmond Road, Roath, **Cardiff (Wales)** CF24 3AT
Tel: 29-2048 2183 Fax: 29-2048 2183
artistic director Peter Reynolds;
administrator Aidan Plender
Period/Frequency: six day festival during last week of June, annual *Arts types:* concerts of classical chamber and vocal music *Venues:* St Michael's Church (Lower Machen) *Second address:* Administrator: 12 Woodford Close, Radyr Way, Llandaff, Cardiff CF5 2PH

Royal National Eisteddfod of Wales
40 Parc Ty Glas, Llanishen, **Cardiff (Wales)** CF14 5WU
Tel: 29-2076 3777 Fax: 29-2076 3737
Internet: www.eisteddfod.org.uk
director Elfed Roberts;
marketing officer Betsan Williams
Period/Frequency: Aug, annual *Arts types:* dance, music, theatre, folk *Venues:* travelling festival, held at a different location every year

Chelmsford Cathedral Festival
Chelmsford Cathedral Festival Office, Guy Harlings, New Street, **Chelmsford** CM1 1TY
Tel: 1245-359 890 Fax: 1245-280 456
festival director Dr Graham Elliott;
administrator Hilary Simmonds
Period/Frequency: May, annual *Arts types:* music & visual arts *Venues:* cathedral 700

Cheltenham International Festival of Music
Town Hall, Imperial Square, **Cheltenham** GL50 1QA
Tel: 1242-521 621 Fax: 1242-573 902
Internet: www.cheltenhamfestivals.co.uk
E-Mail: tobys@cheltenham.gov.uk
festivals administrator Jeremy Tyndall; artistic director Michael Berkeley; festivals organiser Toby Smith
Period/Frequency: July, annual *Arts types:* classical and contemporary music, symphony, chamber, opera, dance, jazz, film, fringe, exhibitions *Venues:* Town Hall 1000, Everyman Theatre 658, Pittville Pump Room 369

Chester Summer Music Festival
8 Abbey Square, **Chester** CH1 2HU
Tel: 1244-320 722 (administration)/700 (box office)
Fax: 1244-341 200
E-Mail: csmf@dial.pipex.com
administrator Fiona England;
artistic director Andrew Burn
Period/Frequency: July, annual
Arts types: classical, opera, jazz, blues, folk, pop *Venues:* Cathedral 1030, Town Hall 440, St John's Church 450, St Mary's Centre 150, Grosvenor Park 3000 *Comments:* children's workshops available; children's concerts; free entry community day

Chichester Festival Theatre
Chichester Festival Theatre, Oaklands Park,
Chichester PO19 4AP
Tel: 1243-784 437/781 312 (box office)
Fax: 1243-787 288
Internet: www.cft.org.uk
E-Mail: admin@cft.org.uk
festival director Andrew Welch; theatre manager Janet Burton; production manager Christopher Bush-Bailey; press & pr Vicky Edwards
Period/Frequency: May-mid-Oct, annual *Arts types:* theatre, musicals *Venues:* Chichester Festival Theatre 1374, Minerva Studio Theatre 250 *Comments:* also receiving venue out of festival season – orchestras, ballet, jazz, theatre, films (in Minerva Studio theatre); occassional painting & sculpture exhibitions; see also Drama and Venues

Chichester Festivities
Canon Gate House, South Street, **Chichester** PO19 1PU
Tel: 1243-785 718
Fax: 1243-528 356
administrator Amanda Sharp
Period/Frequency: July, annual *Arts types:* classical and chamber music, jazz, opera, dance, theatre *Venues:* Cathedral 900, Goodwood ballroom 230, small venues around the cathedral *Comments:* also painting and sculpture exhibitions

Lacock Abbey Festival
The Box Office, Lacock Abbey,
Chippenham SN15 2LG
Tel: 1249-730 042
artistic director Petronella Dittmer
Period/Frequency: annual or biennial, spring/summer *Arts types:* classical music, solo and small vocal and instrumental ensembles *Venues:* The Great Hall, other rooms at Lacock Abbey

Coventry Arts Alive
Belgrade Theatre, Belgrade Square, **Coventry** CV1 1GS
Tel: 24-7625 6431|
Fax: 24-7655 0680
Internet: www.belgrade.co.uk
arts alive co-ordinator Claire Maddocks;
associate producer Jane Hytch;
arts alive assistant Isobel Reynolds
Period/Frequency: May-July, annual
Arts types: theatre, performance, workshops, visual arts, puppetry, street theatre, dance *Venues:* Belgrade Theatre, open-air spaces *Comments:* features work by international, national and regional artists: see also Drama & Venues

Dumfries and Galloway Arts Festival Ltd
Gracefield Arts Centre, 28 Edinburgh Road,
Dumfries (Scotland) DG1 1NW
Tel: 1387-260 447
Fax: 1387-260 447
chairman B Jago; publicity Madam McKerrell of Hillhouse; treasurer S Mitchell
Period/Frequency: May-June, annual
Arts types: theatre, dance, classical music, jazz, Scottish music, folk, exhibitions, poetry, children's events, workshops *Venues:* various schools, theatre and churches throughout the region, Easterbrook Hall, Dumfries, Theatre Royal, Dumfries *Comments:* art and poetry competitions and mid year link concerts

Concerto Festival
PO Box 100, **East Horsley** KT24 6WN
Tel: 1483-282 666 Fax: 1483-284 777
E-Mail: nick@bomford.com
contact Nick Bomford
Period/Frequency: annual (through the year between Feb and Nov) *Arts types:* classical music *Venues:* St Martin-in-the-Fields, Barbican Centre, South Bank Centre, St John's Smith Square *Comments:* N B Management is also an artists agency

Edinburgh Festival Fringe
Festival Fringe Office, 180 High Street,
Edinburgh (Scotland) EH1 1QS
Tel: 131-226 5257
Fax: 131-220 4205
Internet: www.edfringe.com
E-Mail: admin@edfringe.com
director Paul Gudgin
Period/Frequency: Aug, annual *Arts types:* all performing arts *Venues:* various in Edinburgh up to 3500
Comments: festival with open access policy, open to all performances

Edinburgh International Festival
The Hub, Edinburgh Festival Centre, Castle Hill, Royal Mile, **Edinburgh (Scotland)** EH1 2NE
Tel: 131-473 2099 Fax: 131-473 2002
Internet: www.eif.co.uk
E-Mail: eif@eif.co.uk
festival director Brian McMaster; associate director James Waters; director of marketing & public affairs Joanna Baker; administrative director Nicholas Dodds; sponsorship director Nicola Pritchett-Brown
Period/Frequency: Aug-Sept, annual *Arts types:* music, symphony, recital, opera, theatre, dance *Venues:* Kings Theatre, Royal Lyceum Theatre, Playhouse Theatre, Usher Hall, Queen's Hall, Edinburgh Festival Theatre, Edinburgh International Conference Centre, plus other venues

Edinburgh International Jazz & Blues Festival
29 St Stephen's Street, **Edinburgh (Scotland)** EH3 5AN
Tel: 131-225 2202 Fax: 131-225 3321
administrator James Thomson; artistic director Michael Warner Hart; press Fiona Alexander (tel: 131-553 4000)
Period/Frequency: Aug, annual *Arts types:* jazz, blues
Venues: major theatres, cabaret venues, open air up to 2000 *Comments:* some performances free

Mendelssohn on Mull Festival
10 Gloucester Place,
Edinburgh (Scotland) EH3 6EF
Tel: 131-225 8282
Fax: 131-225 6889
Internet: www.bweb.co.uk
E-Mail: m.jeffcoat@ukonline-co.uk
administrator Marilyn Jeffcoat
Period/Frequency: July, annual *Arts types:* classical music including early music and contemporary music

Puppet and Animation Festival
The Netherbow Arts Centre, 43 – 45 High Street,
Edinburgh (Scotland) EH1 1SR
Tel: 131-557 5724/9579 (box office)
Fax: 131-556 7478
E-Mail: puppetfest@erlnet.co.uk
director Simon Hart
Period/Frequency: March-April, annual *Arts types:* puppetry & animation *Venues:* small-scale venues up to 200 *Comments:* festival covers Edinburgh, East Lothian, Midlothian, West Lothian, South Lanarkshire, Stirling & Fife, North Lanarkshire, Scottish Borders, Dumfries & Galloway; film & live performances, workshops available for all ages

Scottish International Children's Festival
45A George Street, **Edinburgh (Scotland)** EH2 2HT
Tel: 131-225 8050/220 6602 (box office)
Fax: 131-225 6440
director Tony Reekie; administrator Katie Stewart; marketing director Abigail Carney
Period/Frequency: May, annual *Arts types:* theatre, music, dance, puppetry *Venues:* mainly small-mid scale venues throughout Edinburgh *Comments:* commissions new Scottish work for young audiences; guest companies from Scotland and around the world: Commission operates own UK touring; small educational workshops for schools available during festival

Exeter Festival
Festival Office, Rm 4, 46A, Civic Centre, Paris Street, **Exeter** EX1 1JJ
Tel: 1392-265 200 Fax: 1392-265 366
festival manager Lesley Maynard; marketing Gerri Bennett
Period/Frequency: first 2 weeks in July, annual *Arts types:* most types of visual and performing arts with emphasis on music *Venues:* University Great Hall 1439, Cathedral 1096, Northcott Theatre 430 *Comments:* specific community involvement encompassing most forms of the performing arts

Fishguard International Music Festival
Festival Office, **Fishguard (Wales)** SA65 9BJ
Tel: 1348-873 612 Fax: 1348-873 612
Internet: fishguardonline.co.uk/festival
E-Mail: fishguard-imf@mwcom.net
co-ordinator Marion Butler; artistic director John S Davies
Period/Frequency: July, annual *Arts types:* classical music, recitals, orchestra, jazz, choral *Venues:* St David's Cathedral 600, School Concert Hall 800

Glasgow International Jazz Festival
18 Albion Street, **Glasgow (Scotland)** G1 1LH
Tel: 141-552 3552 Fax: 141-552 3592
Internet: www.jazzfest.co.uk
E-Mail: glasgow@jazzfest.co.uk
artistic director Olive May Millen; general manager Jill Rodger; marketing manager Alison Mussett; administrator Gillian Garrity
Period/Frequency: 5 days June-July, annual *Arts types:* jazz, blues *Venues:* Glasgow Royal Concert Hall 2000, The Old Fruit Market 700, City Halls 400, Tron Theatre 272, Princes Square 400 *Comments:* aims to provide the broadest range of jazz in Britain and the most accesible festival

New Moves
8 John Street, **Glasgow (Scotland)** G1 1GQ
Tel: 141-564 5552 Fax: 141-564 5553
E-Mail: devos@newmoves.co.uk
contact, director Nikki Milton (141-564 5554)
Period/Frequency: spring, annual *Arts types:* dance

Gorleston St Andrew's Festival
1 Middleton Gardens, Gorleston, **Great Yarmouth** NR31 7AE
Tel: 1493-601 167
correspondent Kathleen Plane; coordinator Harold H Taylor
Period/Frequency: Nov, annual *Arts types:* music, dance, theatre, opera, ballet *Venues:* Marina Leisure Centre, Yarmouth 1000, Ocean Room, Gorleston 700, Yarmouth Town Hall 300, Gorleston Chapter House 180 *Comments:* summer concerts

RNCM Manchester International Cello Festival
The Grange, Clay Lane, **Handforth** SK9 3NR
Tel: 1625-530 140 Fax: 1625-530 140
administrator Alison Godlee; assistant administrator Diane Syddall; artistic director Ralph Kirshbaum
Period/Frequency: biennial (2001: 2-6 May) *Arts types:* recitals, orchestral concerts, master classes, workshops, films, exhibitions, cello and bow making competition *Venues:* Royal Northern College of Music, Bridgewater Hall *Comments:* Patron – Her Royal Highness The Duchess of Kent; Honorary Patron – Daniel Barenboim

RNCM Quartet Fest 2000
The Grange, Clay Lane, **Handforth** SK9 3NR
Tel: 1625-530 140 Fax: 1625-530 140
artistic director Christopher Rowland; administrator Alison Godlee
Period/Frequency: January, annual *Arts types:* chamber music: recitals, masterclasses, seminars, instrument exhibition; also educational project *Venues:* Royal Northern College of Music (Manchester)
Comments: future themes: 2000 – Twentieth Century chamber music, 2001 – Beethoven chamber music (Beethoven Fest 2001)

Harrogate International Festival
1 Victoria Avenue, **Harrogate** HG1 1EQ
Tel: 1423-562 303 Fax: 1423-521 264
Internet: www.harrogate-festival.org.uk
E-Mail: info@harrogate-festival.org.uk
administrator Fiona Goh; festival director William Culver Dodds
Period/Frequency: 2 weeks in July-Aug, annual *Arts types:* recitals, concerts, theatre, opera, cabaret, street theatre, jazz, dance, comedy, talks *Venues:* 10 different venues all over Harrogate up to 2000

Jewish Music Festival (London International)
PO Box 232, **Harrow** HA1 2NN
Tel: 20-8909 2445 Fax: 20-8909 1030
E-Mail: jewishmusic@jmht.org
festival director Geraldine Auerbach
Period/Frequency: biennial autumn (2000: June-July) lasting up to 4 weeks with events every day; also one-off events outside of Festival times *Arts types:* Jewish music, liturgical, cantorial, folk & ethnic, popular and classical, concerts, recitals, workshops, masterclasses, symposia, talks, Yiddish theatre, comedy *Venues:* major concert halls in London – Barbican, Queen Elizabeth Hall, Purcell Room etc, also synagogues; concerts in other centres *Comments:* festival run by registered charity; Jewish Music Heritage Trust London; also run the Jewish Music centre for information, recordings and sheet music, tel: 20-8909 2445, fax: 20-89091030; see also National Organisations

Haslemere Festival
Festival Office, Jesses, Grayswood Road, **Haslemere** GU27 2BS
Tel: 1428-643 818 Fax: 1483-416 143
E-Mail: brian@be-blood.demon.co.uk
administrator Peter Andrews; artistic director Jeanne Dolmetsch; assistant artistic director Marguerite Dolmetsch
Period/Frequency: July, annual *Arts types:* 16th-18th century chamber music *Venues:* Haslemere Hall 375, St. Bartholomews 300, Haslemere Museum 100 *Second Address:* Haslemere Hall, Bridge Road, Haslemere, Tel: 1428-164 2161 (box office) *Comments:* Administrator: Tel: 1483-416 143, E-mail: andrews@highrise-1.freeserve.co.uk

Hay Festival, The
The Sunday Times Hay Festival of Literature and the Arts Ltd, **Hay-on-Wye** HR3 5BX
Tel: 1497-821 217 Fax: 1497-821 066
Internet: www.litfest.co.uk
E-Mail: peter@litfest.co.uk
festival director Peter Florence; publicity & marketing Midas PR (tel: 20-7584 7474)
Period/Frequency: May-June, annual *Arts types:* theatre, music, literature, comedy

Henley Festival of Music and the Arts
14 Friday Street, **Henley-on-Thames** RG9 1AH
Tel: 1491-843 400/404 (box office) Fax: 1491-410 482
Internet: www.henley-festival.co.uk
E-Mail: info@henley-festival.co.uk
chief executive Sam Gordon Clark; artistic director Stewart Collins
Period/Frequency: July, annual, 4 nights plus family event on 5th day *Arts types:* opera, cabaret, visual arts, young musicians, orchestra, jazz, mime, fireworks, street theatre *Venues:* The Stewards' Enclosure of the Henley Royal Regatta, outdoor, riverside 4500 each night *Comments:* seeks to promote young artists

Three Choirs Festival
Festival Office, The Canon's House Flat, The Close, **Hereford** HR1 2NG
Tel: 1432-274 455 Fax: 1432-851 773
artistic directors Adrian Lucas (Worcester), Roy Massey (Hereford), David Briggs(Gloucester); festival administrators Peter Dolby (Worcester), Elizabeth Pooley (Hereford), Bill Armiger (Gloucester)
Period/Frequency: Aug, annual *Arts types:* English choral tradition, new works, orchestral concerts and recitals, active fringe *Venues:* rotates between Worcester, Hereford and Gloucester Cathedrals, 2000: Hereford *Comments:* administrative address rotates respectively

Huddersfield Contemporary Music Festival
Department of Music, Huddersfield University, Queensgate, **Huddersfield** HD1 3DH
Tel: 1484-425 082/472 103 Fax: 1484-472 957
Internet: www.hud.ac.uk/events/hcmf/
E-Mail: hcmf@hud.ac.uk
general manager Luke O'Shaughnessy; artistic director Richard Steinitz OBE
Period/Frequency: Nov, annual *Arts types:* contemporary music, dance, theatre, improvised music, multi media *Venues:* Huddersfield Town Hall 1000, Lawrence Batley Theatre 450, St. Pauls Hall 300 *Comments:* Yorkshire Arts Young Composers Award

Highland Festival, The
40 Huntly St, **Inverness (Scotland)** IV3 5HR
Tel: 1463-719 000/711 112 (festival info)
Fax: 1463-716 777
Internet: www.highlandfestival.demon.co.uk
E-Mail: info@highlandfestival.demon.co.uk
administrator Morven MacLeod; festival director Alastair McDonald; fundraising officer Shona Arthur; marketing Emma Henderson; business manager Ian Middleton
Period/Frequency: May-June, annual *Arts types:* all types of art forms *Venues:* various range from village halls – castles, outdoors

King's Lynn Festival
27 King Street, **King's Lynn** PE30 1ET
Tel: 1553-767 557 Fax: 1553-767 688
administrator Joanne Rutterford; artistic director Ambrose Miller
Period/Frequency: July, annual *Arts types:* music, theatre, jazz, dance, lectures, exhibitions, literature, folk, opera *Venues:* Corn Exchange 738, St George's Guildhall 349, St Margarets Church 400, Town Hall 180

St Magnus Festival
Strandal, Nicolson Street, **Kirkwall, Orkney (Scotland)** KW15 1BD
Tel: 1856-872 669 Fax: 1856-871 170
administrator Dorothy Rushbrook; artistic director Glenys Hughes
Period/Frequency: June, annual *Arts types:* music, theatre, dance and visual arts, literature *Venues:* St. Magnus Cathedral 350 and various other venues *Comments:* educational and community programmes; workshops for schools

Leicester International Music Festival
New Walk Museum, 53 New Walk, **Leicester** LE1 7EA
Tel: 116-247 3043 Fax: 116-247 3043
artistic director Graham Oppenheimer; admin. director Sue Carverhill
Period/Frequency: June, annual *Arts types:* chamber music *Venues:* New Walk Museum 200, Guildhall 100

Glyndbourne Festival
Lewis
Comments: see entry under Opera

Lichfield International Arts Festival
7 The Close, **Lichfield** WS13 7LD
Tel: 1543-257 298 Fax: 1543-415 137
Internet: www.lichfieldfestival.org
E-Mail: lichfield.fest@lichfield-arts.org.uk
director Paul Spicer; administrator Ruth Hardingham; sponsorship Philip Davies; education coordinator Gill Jones; box office manager Claire Tetley; assistant administrator Linda Bradley; accounts Judy Grew
Period/Frequency: July, annual *Arts types:* music, theatre, opera, dance, films, workshops, talks, fringe *Venues:* Cathedral 1200, Civic Hall 400, Guildhall 200, St. John's Chapel 120, Cathedral Lady Chapel 300, town and country churches throughout Staffordshire *Second Address:* box office (mid May- mid July), Tel: 1543-257 557 Donegal House, Bore Street, Lichfield WS13 6NE

Africa Oye Music Festival
2A Franceys Street, **Liverpool** L3 5YQ
Tel: 151-708 6344/708 6200 Fax: 151-709 7102
project director Kenny Murray
Period/Frequency: June, annual *Arts types:* performing festival, music (mainly African) *Venues:* various in and around Merseyside *Second Address:* 2a Franceys Street, Liverpool L3 Tel: 151-708 6200 *Comments:* also do a concert series Sept-April and UK tours

Brouhaha International Festival
Gostins Building, 32-36 Hanover Street, **Liverpool** L1 4LN
Tel: 151-709 3334 Fax: 151-709 4994
Internet: www.brouhaha.demon.co.uk
E-Mail: admin@brouhaha.demon.co.uk
director Francisco Carrasco; administrator Karen Miller
Period/Frequency: Street Theatre Festival *Arts types:* various arts types including theatre, music, dance etc., features performances (city centre + suburbs), workshops and seminar *Venues:* various outdoor venues throughout Merseyside *Comments:* see also Services; community programmes & workshops

Gwyl Llanfyllin Festival
Pendyffryn, **Llanfyllin (Wales)** SY22 5LA
Tel: 1691-648 227 Fax: 1691-648 227
contact Pauline Page-Jones
Period/Frequency: June-July, annual *Arts types:* chamber music *Venues:* St Myllins Church 300 *Second Address:* Box Office: Wychwood House, Llanfyllin, Powys, Tel: 1691-648 125 :

Llangollen International Musical Eisteddfod
Eisteddfod Office, **Llangollen (Wales)** LL20 8SW
Tel: 1978-860 236 Fax: 1978-861 300
Internet: www.lime.com.uk
E-Mail: info@lime.com.uk
director of marketing Maureen A. Jones; artistic director Gwawr Owen
Period/Frequency: July, annual (2000: 3-9 July) *Arts types:* folk song and dance, choral, choir of the world *Venues:* Royal International Pavilion *Comments:* also new competition: Llangollen International Singing, 1st prize £15k

Vale of Glamorgan Festival
St Donats Arts Centre, St Donats Castle, **Llantwit Major (Wales)** CF61 1WF
Tel: 1446-792 151/162/794 848 (box office)
Fax: 1446-794 711
E-Mail: david.ambrose@which.net
director John Metcalf; associate director David Ambrose; administrator Brian van Duyn

Period/Frequency: Sept, annual *Arts types:* music by living composers *Venues:* throughout the Vale of Glamorgan, small – large scale venues capacity 60-1000 *Comments:* alternative E-mail: boxoffice@sdac.which.net

Aberdeen International Youth Festival (Scotland)
3 Nutborn House, Clifton Road, **London** SW19 4QT
Tel: 20-8946 2995 Fax: 20-8944 6507
E-Mail: nicola.wallis@virgin.net
festival director Nicola Wallis; administrator Evie Ayers; marketing director Roy Thomson; music director Michael Beeston; dance director Kenn Burke
Period/Frequency: Aug, annual *Arts types:* symphony, chamber music, visual arts, choral, jazz, modern dance, ballet, folk music & theatre *Venues:* Music Hall 1200, His Majesty's Theatre 1700, Mitchell Hall (Marischal College) 400, Lemon Tree 150, Arts Centre 350 *Second Address:* Town House, Broad Street, Aberdeen AB10 1AH, Tel: 1224-522 000

Austro-Hungarian Music Festival
c/o Martin Randall Travel Ltd,
10 Barley Mow Passage, Chiswick,
London W4 4PH
Tel: 20-8742 3355 Fax: 20-8742 7766
E-Mail: info@martinrandall.co.uk
managing director Martin Randall; festival organisers Sheila Taylor, Emma Duffield
Period/Frequency: 5-12 August 2000 *Venues:* private concerts in historical palaces, churches, country houses and theatres *Comments:* between 100-140 participants; see also Agents & Producers and Services

Barbican Festivals
c/o Barbican Press Office, Silk Street,
London EC2Y 8DS
Tel: 20-7638 5403
Fax: 20-7382 7252
Internet: www.barbican.org.uk
Period/Frequency: various throughout the year; different themes each year *Arts types:* performing and visual arts *Venues:* Barbican *Comments:* for further information please contact the press office

BBC Promenade Concerts
Broadcasting House, Portland Place,
London W1A 1AA
Tel: 20-7765 5575
Fax: 20-7765 0619
Internet: www.bbc.co.uk/proms/
E-Mail: proms@bbc.co.uk
director Nicholas Kenyon;
marketing manager Kate Finch
Period/Frequency: July-Sept, annual
Venues: Royal Albert Hall 5000

BOC Covent Garden Festival
Unit 47, The Market, The Piazza, Covent Garden,
London WC2E 8RF
Tel: 20-7379 0870 Fax: 20-7379 0876
Internet: www.cgf.co.uk
E-Mail: dim@cgf.co.uk
director Kenneth Richardson; administrator Anna Simpson; chairman of board Laurence Isaacson; chairman executive committee Neville Abraham; marketing manager Paul Gray
Period/Frequency: May/June, annual
Arts types: opera, music theatre *Venues:* Freemasons Hall 1300, Bow St. Magistrates Court 60, St. Pauls 375, St. Clement Danes 350, Royal Opera House Crush bar 180, Theatre Museum 100, The Cochrane Theatre 314, Arts Theatre 340 and many others each year

City of London Festival
Festival Office, Bishopsgate Hall,
230 Bishopsgate, **London** EC2M 4HW
Tel: 20-7377 0540/7638 8891 (box office)
Fax: 20-7377 1972
Internet: www.city-of-london-festival.org.uk
E-Mail: cityfest@dircon.co.uk
festival director Michael MacLeod; marketing manager Nick Bodger; events manager Jenny Smith; finance manager Carol Butler; sponsorship administrator Sue Hutchison; festival assistant Lucy Mayfield
Period/Frequency: June/July, annual *Arts types:* orchestra, recitals, opera, theatre, mime, street theatre literary events, jazz, city walks, open-air events
Venues: 70 venues from St Pauls to small churches, City Livery Halls , Bridewell Theatre, Mansion House, Guildhall, Barbican

Covent Garden May Fayre and Puppet Festival
Alternative Arts, 47a Brushfield Street,
London E1 6AA
Tel: 20-7375 0441
Fax: 20-7375 0484
contacts Maggie Pinhorn, Liz Weston
Period/Frequency: 2nd Sunday in May, annual
Arts types: puppetry *Venues:* St. Pauls Church Garden *Second Address:* venue address: Bedford St, Covent Garden, London WC2 UK *Comments:* celebrates the art of puppetry near the spot where Samuel Pepys first saw Mr Punch in 1662; free addmission to the public; see also National Organisations and Promoters

Dance Umbrella
20 Chancellor St, **London** W6 9RN
Tel: 20-8741 4040/7813 4803 (press)
Fax: 20-8741 7902/7813 4805 (press)
Internet: www.danceumbrella.co.uk
E-Mail: mail@danceumbrella.co.uk
artistic director Val Bourne; marketing manager David Pratt; programme director Betsy Gregory; administrator Toby Beazely; press Tony Shepherd (email: tonyshep@sheppr.demon.co.uk)
Period/Frequency: Oct-Nov, annual *Arts types:* British and international contemporary dance *Venues:* I.C.A. 160, The Place 300, Riverside Studio 300, Queen Elizabeth Hall 900, Sadlers' Wells 1200, Barbican

English Bach Festival
15 South Eaton Place, **London** SW1W 9ER
Tel: 20-7730 5925 Fax: 20-7730 1456
E-Mail: english.bachfestival@which.net
director Lina Lalandi OBE
Period/Frequency: throughout year *Arts types:* baroque opera, dance, classical music *Venues:* The South Bank and touring, Sadlers Wells Theatre, The Royal Opera House Studio Theatre *Comments:* see also Opera & Early Music

Feet First
Arts Worldwide, 309A Aberdeen House,
22 Highbury Grove, **London** N5 2DQ
Tel: 20-7354 3030 Fax: 20-7354 8404
Internet: www.artsworldwide.org.uk
E-Mail: artsworldwide@dial.pipex.com
artistic director Anne Hunt;
festival manager Anna Clancy
Period/Frequency: June-July 2000 *Arts types:* dance *Venues:* various in London and touring, culminates in Finsbury Park

Gate Theatre – Gate Biennale
11 Pembridge Road, **London** W11 3HQ
Tel: 20-7229 5387/0706 (box office) Fax: 20-7221 6055
manager Sarah Preece; artistic director Mick Gordon; producer Philippe Le Moine
Period/Frequency: 12 month programme, summer festival of international artists *Arts types:* international work in new English translations *Venues:* Gate Theatre 100 *Comments:* see also Drama

Greenwich & Docklands Festivals
6 College Approach, Greenwich, **London** SE10 9HY
Tel: 20-8305 1818 Fax: 20-8305 1188
Internet: www.festival.org
E-Mail: info@gdfest.co.uk
artistic director Bradley Hemmings; executive director Christine Mathews-Sheen; production administrator Jenny Lambert; marketing manager Sam McAuley; projects coordinator Nicky Bashall
Period/Frequency: bi-annual, July & 31 Dec *Arts types:* classical music, folk, jazz, rock, world music, theatre, cabaret, comedy, dance, art, literature *Venues:* Old Royal Naval College 700, Greenwich Theatre 400, The Space, Greenwich Dance Agency 700 *Comments:* also youth arts training programme – Gallery 37 – which employs up to 100 young people for 6 weeks during the summer festival

INTERFACE Festival
c/o pan Project, The City Lit, Stukeley Street,
London WC2B 5LJ
Tel: 20-7405 6702 Fax: 20-7831 5199
E-Mail: panproject@compuserve.com
artistic director John Martin;
admin director Peter Vlachos
Period/Frequency: bi-annual *Arts types:* theatre, dance, music, visual arts *Comments:* international festival showcasing the best intercultural companies

International Workshop Festival
Battersea Arts Centre, Lavender Hill, **London** SW11 5TN
Tel: 20-7637 0712 Fax: 20-7350 2137
Internet: www.i-w-f.demon.co.uk
E-Mail: i-w-f@i-w-f.demon.co.uk
artistic director Dick McCaw; administrative director Louise Coles; finance officer Bryan Lloyd
Period/Frequency: Sept & Oct, annual *Arts types:* theatre, dance, animation, circus, emphasis on visual rather than text-based theatre *Venues:* London, Leeds, Belfast, Glasgow *Comments:* focus on cross-over arts; publishes International Training Opportunities (Europe); organises masterclasses with artists who are the internationally acknowledged experts in their fields

London International Festival of Theatre (LIFT)
19-20 Great Sutton Street, **London** EC1V 0DR
Tel: 20-7490 3964/5 Fax: 20-7490 3976
Internet: www.lift-info.co.uk
E-Mail: info@liftfest.org.uk
administrative producer Angela McSherry; festival directors Rose De Wend Fenton, Lucy Neal
Period/Frequency: June-July, biennial (2001) *Arts types:* international contemporary theatre performance
Venues: Royal Court, SBC, other theatres & outdoor sites in London *Comments:* LIFT presents, co-commissions & creates events all over the city together with an adventurous education programme which connects international artists with communities, especially young people, thus linking the local with international

London International Mime Festival
35 Little Russell Street, **London** WC1A 2HH
Tel: 20-7637 5661 Fax: 20-7323 1151
E-Mail: limf@joseph.seelig.easynet.co.uk
directors Joseph Seelig, Helen Lannaghan
Period/Frequency: Jan, annual *Arts types:* mime, visual theatre, clowns, circus skills *Venues:* South Bank Centre, ICA, Pleasance London, BAC, Circus Space and selected touring *Comments:* 16-18 companies selected each year, approx. half international and half British; shows with little or no text are preferred; participation is by invitation only; work should be at least London if not British premiere;

Lufthansa Festival of Baroque Music
200 Broomwood Road, **London** SW11 6JY
Tel: 20-7228 6388/7222 1061 (box office)
Fax: 20-7738 1706
manager Delia Pye; artistic director Kate Bolton
Period/Frequency: June, annual *Arts types:* baroque and classical music *Venues:* St John's Smith Square 780, St James's Church, Piccadilly 475

Meltdown
South Bank Centre, **London** SE1 8XX
Tel: 20-7960 4242 Fax: 20-7921 0821
contact Rob Lynden (tel: 20-7921 0615); artistic director Liz McCudden (tel: 20-7921 0615); Meltdown producer David Sefton (tel: 20-7921 0615)
Period/Frequency: June-July, annual *Arts types:* music, film, visual arts & multi-media with contemporary music as its driving force *Venues:* Royal Festival Hall 2900, Queen Elizabeth Hall 917, Purcell Room 379, plus foyers & outdoors *Comments:* the artistic director is different each year

Music on a Summer Evening
Portland House, Stag Place, **London** SW1E 5EE
Tel: 20-7973 3427 Fax: 20-7973 3429
organiser Ann Christie
Period/Frequency: July-Sept, annual *Arts types:* classical music, jazz, opera *Venues:* Kenwood House (Hampstead), Marble Hill (Twickenham), Audley End (Essex), Wrest Park (Bedfordshire)

Presteigne Festival of Music and the Arts
17 Parliament Hill, **London** NW3 2TA
Tel: 20-7435 5965 Fax: 20-7435 9166
Internet: www.cadenza.org/presteigne
secretary Joan Hughes; festival director George Vass
Period/Frequency: last week of Aug, annual *Arts types:* predominantly classical music, also poetry, exhibitions, lectures *Venues:* venues in and around Presteigne mainly in village churches, St Andrew's Church 350 *Second Address:* festival box office in Presteigne open from early July, Tel: 1544-267 800

Re: Orient – Festival of Chinese Theatre and Dance from the Asian Pacific Rim
The Place Theatre, 17 Duke's Road, **London** WC1H 9AB
Tel: 20-7380 1268/7387 0031 Fax: 20-7383 2003
E-Mail: placetheatre@easynet.co.uk
festival director Pit Fong Loh; theatre director John Ashford; associate director Emma Gladstone; marketing manager Nicole Matthews; administrator Colette Hansford; project co-ordinator Anna Scott; technical manager Ian Richards
Period/Frequency: autumn, annual *Arts types:* contemporary dance and theatre *Venues:* The Place Theatre 300

Royal Court Young Writers' Festival
Royal Court Young Writer's Programme, Sloane Square, **London** SW1W 8AS
Tel: 20-7565 5050 Fax: 20-7565 5001
E-Mail: ywp@royalcourttheatre.com
associate director Ola Animashawun;
general manager Aoife Mannix
Period/Frequency: 2001 *Arts types:* production of plays written by young people under the age of 26 *Venues:* Royal Court Theatre Upstairs *Comments:* to encourage young people throughout Britain to write plays and to present a range of plays reflecting their work; the next festival will be in 2001; for further details contact the General Manager

Spitalfields Festival
75 Brushfield Street, **London** E1 6AA
Tel: 20-7377 0287/1362 (box office) Fax: 20-7247 0494
E-Mail: spitfest@easynet.co.uk
festival manager Judith Serota;
artistic director Judith Weir CBE
Period/Frequency: June & Dec, bi-annual *Arts types:* mainly western classical music, world music, education concerts, concerts by and for children
Venues: Christ Church 400

Windsor Festival
60 Ashworth Mansions, Grantully Road,
London W9 1LW
Tel: 20-7286 8811 Fax: 20-7286 0866
festival director Jane Krivine;
artistic director Lucie Skeaping
Period/Frequency: Sept-Oct, annual *Arts types:* classical music, jazz, talks, tours, children's events, words & music *Venues:* Windsor Castle, Eton College, Windsor Parish Church and surrounding area, *Comments:* box office – Tel: 1753-623 400 open from July

Woking Dance Umbrella
20 Chancellor Street, **London** W6 9RN
Tel: 20-8741 4040 Fax: 20-8741 7902
artistic director Val Bourne; Woking community dance development coordinator Jenny Lowde (tel: 1483-726 448); Woking Council David Vince (tel: 1483-755 855)
Period/Frequency: March, biennial (2001) *Arts types:* contemporary dance *Venues:* Ambassadors Theatre 200 *Comments:* Woking community dance development: Jenny Lowde, Info Centre, Crown House, Crown Square, Woking GU21 1HR, Tel: 1483-726 448

Ludlow Festival
Castle Square, **Ludlow** SY8 1AY
Tel: 1584-875 070 Fax: 1584-877 673
administrator Chris Garret; chairman Patricia Sibcy; acct/business manager Ray Sykes
Period/Frequency: June-July, annual *Arts types:* classical concerts, jazz, opera, comedy, theatre, recitals, dance, children's events *Venues:* The Castle 1195, Parish Church 620 and various other venues in the area *Comments:* organise lecture, guided tours, children's events; festival includes a large-scale professional production of a Shakespeare play performed in Ludlow Castle

Glories of the Keyboard – RNCM Broadwood International Festival
134 Kingsbrook Road, **Manchester** M1 68WG
Tel: 161-881 9320
Fax: 161-881 9320
artistic director Renna Kellaway;
festival administrator Carolyn Howlett
Period/Frequency: Nov, biennial (2001) *Arts types:* from baroque to contemporary, from solo to chamber music and concertos, master classes, talks and exhibitions *Venues:* Royal Northern College of Music *Comments:* patron: Her Royal Highness the Duchess of Kent

Manchester Festival, The
Central Library, St Peter's Square, **Manchester** M2 5PD
Tel: 161-234 1964/44
Fax: 161-236 7952
E-Mail: mcrfest@libraries.manchester.gov.uk
administrative director t.b.a.
Period/Frequency: annual *Arts types:* all arts and television focusing on popular culture, music, comedy, club culture, electronic art *Venues:* over 60 venues in Manchester *Comments:* working with the private sector on behalf of Manchester City Council

Manchester Irish Festival
Central Library, St. Peter's Square, **Manchester** M2 5PD
Tel: 161-236 1995
Fax: 161-236 7952
Internet: www.manchester-festival.org.uk
E-Mail: lheald@libraries.manchester.gov.uk
festival co-ordinator Linsey Heald
Period/Frequency: March, annual *Arts types:* all art forms including largely music, comedy, theatre & films, St Patrick's Day parade *Venues:* various across Manchester *Comments:* co-promoted by Manchester City Council in conjuncture with Manchester Irish Community

RNCM Broadwood International Festival: Glories of the Keyboard
Royal Northern College of Music, 124 Oxford Road, **Manchester** M13 9RD
Tel: 161-907 5282 (press)/5278 (box office)
Fax: 161-907 5367
E-Mail: info@rncm.ac.uk
artistic director Renna Kellaway;
festival administrator Carolyn Howlett;
assistant administrators Jane Thompson, Polly Beck
Period/Frequency: Nov, biennial (2001) *Arts types:* piano (chamber music) *Venues:* Royal Northern College of Music, Bridgewater Hall *Second address:* Festival Office: 134 Kingsbrook Road, Manchester M16 8WG, Tel: 161-881 9320 *Comments:* incorporates the RNCM Broadwood Piano Trio Competition; see also Competitions, Venues and Promoters

Streets Ahead Manchester
3 Birch Polygon, **Manchester** M14 5HX
Tel: 161-224 0020
Fax: 161-248 9331
E-Mail: mia@mcrl.poptel.org.uk
directors Jeremy Shine, Anne Tucker
Period/Frequency: May, annual (2000: 24 April-29 May) *Arts types:* street festival, music, dance, spectacular events, fireworks
Comments: Streets Ahead is the official Millennial Festival for Greater Manchester and will stage over 30 events; Britains most important showcase of street performances X.trax – 2nd week in May

Teeside International Eisteddfod
28 Gipsy Lane, Nunthorpe,
Middlesbrough TS7 0DX
Tel: 1642-316 258
Fax: 1642-316 258
secretary Mavis Lloyd
Period/Frequency: July, biennial (2001) *Arts types:* folk song, dance, choral *Venues:* various venues in Teeside *Comments:* competitive music festival featuring groups from all over the world

Ross-on-Wye International Festival
The Mews, **Mitcheldean** GL17 0SL
Tel: 1594-544 446/1989-563 330 (box office)
Fax: 1594-544 448
Internet: www.festival.org.uk
E-Mail: ross_festival@compuserve.com
artistic director Helen Wragg;
festival coordinator Megan Sparks
Period/Frequency: August, annual *Arts types:* performing arts *Venues:* festival pavillion 1300, Pheonix Theatre 70, The Baptist Church 150, Nimbus Concert Hall 600

International Fiesta
Lancaster City Council, Arts Events Office, The Platform, Station Buildings, Central Promenade, **Morecambe** LA4 4DB
Tel: 1524-582 803 Fax: 1524-831 704
head of arts & events Jon Harris
Period/Frequency: summer, annual *Arts types:* folk song, dance, world music, African, street theatre *Venues:* Morecambe Bay Arena 5000, The Platform up to 1000, plus outdoor performances *Comments:* production based educational activities and arts development all year

Longborough Festival
Longborough Festival Opera, New Banks Fee Longborough, **Moreton-in-Marsh** GL56 0QF
Tel: 1451-830 292 Fax: 1451-830 605
E-Mail: longboroughfestivalopera@btinternet.com
directors Martin & Lizzie Graham; pr & marketing Tei Williams (tel: 1865-883 139/884 240, email: tei@artsmarketing.demon.co.uk); sponsorship manager Susan Foster (tel: 1865-735 201)
Period/Frequency: June-July, annual *Arts types:* opera *Venues:* converted barn with pink palladian frontage 470 (370 stalls, 100 boxes) *Comments:* see also Venues

Newbury International Spring Festival
1 Bridge Street, **Newbury** RG14 5BE
Tel: 1635-32421/528 766 Fax: 1635-528 690
administrator Bronwen Sutton; artistic director Mark Eynon; marketing manager Phillipa Regan
Period/Frequency: May, annual *Arts types:* classical, orchestral, choral, chamber music, jazz, opera, recitals, theatre, dance, art lectures, exhibitions, open studios/workshops, masterclasses, educational and schools programme *Venues:* St Nicolas Church 630, various in and around Newbury, Corn Exchange 400, parish churches, country houses & hotels *Comments:* box office run by Newbury Corn Exchange on Tel: 1635-522 733

Milton Keynes Interntional Festival
30 St John Street, **Newport Pagnell** MK16 8HJ
Tel: 1908-610 564 Fax: 1908-610 564
Internet: users.powernet.co.uk/padlock/mkif.htm
E-Mail: mkintfestival@msn.com
artistic director & chairman Don Allison
Period/Frequency: annual, (2000: 30 June-2 July) *Arts types:* dance, music, song, concerts, dance workshops *Venues:* Milton Keynes Theatre 1300 and others *Comments:* information on all events and tickets from Milton Keynes Theatre, box office: Tel: 1908-606 090; information and leaflets from festival office

Norfolk & Norwich Festival
Festival Office, 42-58 St George's Street, **Norwich** NR3 1AB
Tel: 1603-614 921/764 764 (box office)
Fax: 1603-632 303
Internet: www.eab.org.uk/festivals
E-Mail: info@nnfest.demon.co.uk
festival director Peter Baldwin; general manager Nick Wells; marketing manager Fiona Carter; projects officer Ellen Bridgeland; administrative officer Melanie Gosling; economic development officer Sheila Hoyle
Period/Frequency: Oct, annual *Arts types:* recitals, chamber music, orchestra, choral, jazz, theatre, dance, mime, puppets, visual arts, film, comedy, lectures *Venues:* St Andrew's Hall 913, Blackfriars Hall 400, Norwich Cathedral 300 to 800, Theatre Royal 1300, Norwich Playhouse 308

Norwich Jazz Festival
c/o Norwich Arts Centre,
Reeves Yard, St Benedict's Street,
Norwich NR2 4PG
Tel: 1603-660 387
director and artistic director Pam Reekie; administrator Alison Schofield; publicity Rob Lockwood
Period/Frequency: Nov, annual *Arts types:* jazz *Venues:* different venues in Norwich while the Norwich Arts Centre 120 is being renovated *Comments:* year round theatre, music and comedy, workshop and education work

NOTT Dance Festival
c/o Dance 4 Ltd, @ Preset, 3-9 Hockley,
Nottingham NG1 1FH
Tel: 115-941 0773
Fax: 115-941 0776
Internet: www.innotts.co.uk/~preset
E-Mail: dance4@innotts.co.uk
director Jane Greenfield; administrator Rachel Emmett
Period/Frequency: May, annual *Arts types:* dance *Venues:* various in Nottingham cap. up to 200

Now Festival, The
Dept of Leisure & Community Services, Nottingham City Council, 55 Castle Gate, **Nottingham** NG1 7AF
Tel: 115-915 3534 Fax: 115-915 3599
Internet: www.nowfestival.org.uk
E-Mail: xdg71@dial.pipex.com
director Andrew Caleya Chetty;
production manager Tom Hall
Period/Frequency: Oct/Nov, annual *Arts types:* live art, new theatre and dance, new music, installations, film, video, inter-disciplinary work, new technology *Venues:* various in and around Nottingham, traditional and site specific spaces *Comments:* festival commissions approximately two thirds of its programme

Garsington Opera
Garsington Manor, **Oxford** OX44 9DH
Tel: 1865-368 201 Fax: 1865-361 545
chairman Leonard Ingrams; associate director Rachel Dominy; press/public relations Clare Adams
Period/Frequency: June-July, annual *Arts types:* opera *Venues:* grounds of Garsington Manor 440 *Comments:* open-air performances

Oxford Festival of Contemporary Music
25A Cave Street, **Oxford** OX4 1BA
Tel: 1865-791 355 Fax: 1865-432 674
E-Mail: davidbass@ofcm.ndirect.co.uk
general manager David Bass;
artistic directors Philip Cashian, Stefan Asbury;
honorary president Oliver Knussen
Period/Frequency: spring & autum, bi-annual *Arts types:* chamber orchestra, chamber music, choral, early music, new music, electronic music, jazz, multi-media, song & instrumental recitals, modern dance, opera, operetta, music theatre, sacred music, puppetry,world music *Venues:* Oxford Playhouse, Museum of Modern Art, Holywell Music Room, Jacqueline du Pré Music Building, Churches, Sheldonian Theatre, capacities 200 up to 1000

Perth Festival of the Arts
3-5 High Street, **Perth (Scotland)** PH1 5JS
Tel: 1738-475 295 Fax: 1738-475 295
Internet: www.perth.org.uk/perth/festival.htm
E-Mail: artsfestival@perth.org.uk
administrator Sandra Ralston
Period/Frequency: second half of May, annual *Arts types:* music, theatre, dance, opera, jazz, blues, stand-up comedy *Venues:* Perth City Hall 1300, St John's Kirk of Perth 600, Perth Theatre 500

Oundle International Festival and Summer School for Young Organists
The Old Crown, Glapthorn, **Peterborough** PE8 5BJ
Tel: 1832-272 026 Fax: 1832-272 026
director James Parsons; administrator Patricia Ryan
Period/Frequency: July, annual *Arts types:* symphony, chamber, vocal, jazz, organ recitals, fringe events, drama *Venues:* Oundle School Chapel 700, Oundle School Great Hall 550, country houses, village churches and Cambridge colleges *Comments:* festival with a unique formula incorporating summer school for young organists

Mananan International Festival of Music and the Arts
Erin Arts Centre, Victoria Square,
Port Erin (Isle of Man) IM9 6LD
Tel: 1624-835 858 Fax: 1624-836 658
Internet: homepages.enterprise.net/erinartscentre
E-Mail: erinartscentre@enterprise.net
founder and director John Bethell
Period/Frequency: June-July, annual *Arts types:* recitals, orchestra, opera, theatre, jazz, workshops, lectures, guided walks, exhibitions *Venues:* Erin Arts Centre, Port Erin *Comments:* Lionel Tertis International Competition-triennial (August 2000); twinned with the La Tour De France International Festival of Music and the Arts, France

Southern Cathedrals Festival
Department of Liturgy & Music, Ladywell, 33 The Close, **Salisbury** SP1 2EJ
Tel: 1722-555 125 Fax: 1722-555 117
contact & director Simon Lole (festival director)
Period/Frequency: July, annual (2000: 19-22 July) *Arts types:* sacred, choral and organ music *Venues:* rotates between Chichester, Salisbury and Winchester Cathedrals *Comments:* 2000 festival will be in Salisbury

Salisbury Festival
75 News Street, **Salisbury** SP1 2PH
Tel: 1722-323 883 Fax: 1722-410 552
Internet: www.salisburyfestival.co.uk
E-Mail: info@salisburyfestival.co.uk
general manager Caroline Peacock;
festival director Helen Marriage;
sponsorship & development Anita Odor
Period/Frequency: May/June, annual *Arts types:* multi-arts festival *Venues:* Cathedral 1200, City Hall 1000, Salisbury Playhouse 516, Arts Centre 400, other city churches, medieval hall, arts centre and external venues *Second Address:* Box office: Salisbury Play House, Malthouse Lane, Salisbury, Wiltshire, SP1 7RA, Tel: 1722-320 333

Music in the Round Festival
The Workstation,
15 Paternoster Row, **Sheffield** S1 2BX
Tel: 114-221 2182/249 6000 (box office)
Fax: 114-221 2183
administrator Tracey Waters;
artistic director Peter Cropper
Period/Frequency: May, annual *Arts types:* chamber music *Venues:* Crucible Studio Theatre 400
Comments: established autumn and spring programme of events from October through to March

Solihull Festival
c/o Ms B Chapple,
108 St Bernards Road, Olton,
Solihull B92 7BL
Tel: 121-706 8383
administrator Brenda Chapple;
artistic director Geoffrey Gibbons
Period/Frequency: May, annual *Arts types:* chamber orchestra, instrumental & choral recitals, organ recitals *Venues:* Solihull Library Theatre 430, St Alphege Church 350 *Second Address:* Mr Gibbon's address: Lottery Cottage, Hob Lane, Burion Green, Kenilworth CV8 1QA, Tel: 1676-535 818

International Organ Festival (IOFS)
PO Box 80, **St Albans** AL3 4HR
Tel: 1727-844 765 Fax: 1727-844 765
E-Mail: iofs@aol.com
general manager Ken Chapronierè;
artistic director Peter Hewitt
Period/Frequency: July, biennial (2001) *Arts types:* organ music (early to contemporary), orchestral/choral concerts, recitals, jazz, cabaret *Venues:* St Albans Cathedral, St Saviour's Church, St Albans, St Albans School, and other venues around St Albans

North Wales International Music Festival
Festival Office, High Street, **St Asaph (Wales)** LL17 0RD
Tel: 1745-584 508
Fax: 1745-584 508
administrator Jill Mort; artistic director Geraint Lewis
Period/Frequency: Sept, annual *Arts types:* orchestra, recitals, soloists, choral music *Venues:* St Asaph Cathedral 750 *Comments:* programme available June

Billingham International Folklore Festival
Festival Office, Leisure Department, Gloucester House, 72 Church Road, **Stockton-on-Tees** TS18 1YB
Tel: 1642-393 907
Fax: 1642-393 911
artists contact Joe Maloney; administration contact Carol Croft (1642-393 907)
Period/Frequency: Aug, annual *Arts types:* international folk, music, dance and song *Venues:* Open Air Arena 1200, College Theatre 450, Forum Theatre 631
Comments: workshops, craft fairs, children's club, parades, firework displays

Stockton International Riverside Festival
c/o ARC, Dovecot Street, **Stockton-on-Tees** TS18 1LL
Tel: 1642-611 625
Fax: 1642-666 668
E-Mail: frank@tremens.demon.co.uk
director Frank Wilson
Period/Frequency: July-Aug, annual *Arts types:* theatre, dance, music *Venues:* ARC Theatre, Trinity Gardens
Second address: Stockton Borough Council, Gloucester House, Church Road, Stockton-on-Tees, TS18 1LD
Comments: see also Venues

Stratford-upon-Avon English Music Festival
34 Scholars Lane, **Stratford-upon-Avon** CV37 6HE
Tel: 1789-261 561 Fax: 1789-261 577
E-Mail: londartist@aol.com
chairman Revd. Peter Holliday;
artistic director Michael Emmerson;
administration t.b.a.
Period/Frequency: Oct, annual *Arts types:* classical, folk, jazz, exhibitions *Comments:* a 10 day festival with an emphasis on English music with major concerts of classical music plus folk, jazz and exhibitions

Stratford-upon-Avon Flute Festival
PO Box 7, **Stratford-upon-Avon** CV37 9GB
Tel: 1789-269 247 Fax: 1789-269 843
E-Mail: stratflute@aol.com
director Elena Durán; chairman Michael Emmerson
Period/Frequency: July, annual *Arts types:* chamber music with flute *Venues:* Civic Hall 500, Town Hall 200, Guild Chapel 150 *Comments:* concerts and workshops showcasing the flute and young flutists

Gower Festival
c/o I J Campbell (secretary), Cruachan, Reynoldston, **Swansea (Wales)** SA3 1BR
Tel: 1792-390 404 (administration) Fax: 1792-390 404
E-Mail: gowerfestival@hotmail.com
music officer and artistic director G.J. Harries (tel: 860-725 934); publicity manager N King (tel: 1792-233 124); sponsorship P Price (tel: 1792-403 520)
Period/Frequency: July, annual *Arts types:* mainly chamber music *Venues:* various churches on the Gower Peninsula

Swansea Festival of Music and the Arts
9 Gabalfa Road, Sketty,
Swansea (Wales) SA2 8NF
Tel: 1792-411 570 (administration)
Fax: 1792-411 570 (administration)
chairman, councillor Howard Morgan;
festival administrator Susan Croall ;
artistic director John Metcalf (tel: 1570-493 576)
Period/Frequency: Oct, annual
Arts types: classical music, opera, theatre, ballet, exhibitions, films, educational projects *Venues:* Brangwyn Hall 1198, Grand Theatre 1019, Glynn Vivian Art Gallery, Taliesin Arts Centre 330, St. Mary's Church, Dylan Thomas Centre 150

Dartington International Summer School
The Gallery, Dartington hall,
Totnes TQ9 6DE
Tel: 1803-865 988(bookings) /867 068 (admin)
Fax: 1803-868 108
Internet: www.dissorg.u-net.com
E-Mail: brochure@dissorg.u-net.com
administrator Lisa Warren;
bookings administrator Jenny Pink;
artistic director Gavin Henderson;
sponsorship Lisa Hillman;
assistant administrator Deborah Dickens
Period/Frequency: last week of July-end of Aug, annual
Arts types: mainly music, music theatre, dance, opera, exhibitions, lectures *Venues:* Dartington Great Hall 400, Barn Theatre 200
Comments: over 40 major courses, over 60 masterclasses, numerous workshops, over 100 concerts

Charlecote Park Mid-Summer Music Festival
Northgate Music, Northgate, **Warwick** CV34 4JL
Tel: 1926-492 468
Fax: 1926-407 606
director and artistic director Richard Phillips
Period/Frequency: June, annual *Arts types:* chamber music *Venues:* The Great Hall 120

Warwick & Leamington Festival
Warwick Arts Society Office, Northgate,
Warwick CV34 4JL
Tel: 1926-410 747 Fax: 1926-407 606
director and artistic director Richard Phillips
Period/Frequency: May and July, annual *Arts types:* chamber music, early music, theatre, spoken word, exhibition *Venues:* St Mary's Church 400, Royal Pump Room 250, Warwick Castle 150 to 1000's, Royal Spa Centre 800 *Comments:* winter concerts String Quartets & Early Music Sept-March, Church Concerts series April-June; also organise a Theme Weekend (1st weekend in May) 2000: Haydn Festival Weekend in Leamington Spa

Northlands Festival
Whitechapel Road, **Wick** KW1 4EA
Tel: 1955-606 660 Fax: 1955-606 660
E-Mail: info@northlandsfestival.freeserve.co.uk
chairman Innes Miller; artist director Mary Miller;
festival manager Sally Body
Period/Frequency: Sept, annual *Arts types:* cross-media work, recitals, music, drama, dance, visual arts; all with Nordic/Scottish theme *Venues:* Caithness with exchanges to Nordic countries *Comments:* exchange of artists moving through Sweden, Denmark and Scotland

Dorset Opera
26 Central Acre, **Yeovil** BA20 1NU
Tel: 1935-479 297 Fax: 1935-412 210
E-Mail: D2303289@infotrade.co.uk
presdient Lady Digby DBE, DC; chairman Tim Lee;
treasurer Michael Burton-Brown; secretary Elisabeth Lang Brown; artistic director Patrick Shelley
Arts types: opera *Venues:* Sherborne (Dorset) 500 *Second Address:* 13 The Stables, Dragoon Way, Christchurch, Painton BH23 2TY, Tel: 1202-481 856, Fax: 1202-481 858, E-mail: dorsetopera@cult21.com

Beverley & East Riding Early Music Festival
PO Box 226, **York** YO30 6ZU
Tel: 1904-645 738 Fax: 1904-612 631
Internet: www.yorkearlymusic.org
E-Mail: yemf@netcomuk.co.uk
artistic and administrative director Delma Tomlin
Period/Frequency: May, annual *Arts types:* early music
Venues: Beverley Minster 750, St Mary's Church 500, Bainton Church 200

Northern Aldborough Festival
Aldborough Manor, Boroughbridge, **York** YO51 9EP
Tel: 1423-324 899 Fax: 1423-323 223
Internet: www.aldborough.com/festival
E-Mail: festival@aldborough.com
artistic director Martin Dreyer; chairman Andrew Lawson-Tancred; treasurer Christopher Tuffs;
administrator Adrian Smith
Period/Frequency: early-mid July (2000: 8-15 July)
Arts types: classical music, some jazz, emphasis on young performers, English music
Venues: churches in/around Aldborough/Boroughbridge cap. 100-250, Ripon Cathedral 500, festival marquee 300
Second address: 22 Huntington Road, York YO31 8RL, Tel: 1904-636 111, Fax: 1904-658 889, E-mail: martin@philipmartin.demon.co.uk *Comments:* occasional concerts promoted by Friends of Northern Aldborough Festival

York Early Music Festival
Festival Office, PO Box 226, **York** YO30 5ZU
Tel: 1904-658 338 Fax: 1904-612 631
Internet: www.yorkearlymusic.org
E-Mail: yemf@netcomuk.co.uk
administrative director Delma Tomlin; artistic advisers Anthony Rooley, John Bryan, Peter Seymour, Kate Bolton, David Fallows
Period/Frequency: July, annual *Arts types:* music performed on period instruments, choral, chamber music, solo recitals *Venues:* various 100 to 700

YUGOSLAVIA (+381)

Due to the war in Kosovo we have been unable to update the following entries for Yugoslavia

Bar Summer Festival
Barski ljetopis
Kulturnu centar Bar, 85000 **Bar**
Tel: 85-12431
director t.b.a.
Period/Frequency: July-Aug

BELEF – Belgrade Summer Festival
BELEF – Beogradski letnji festival
Belgrade Cultural Centre, Knez Mihailova 5,
11000 **Belgrade**
Tel: 11-622 058
Fax: 11-623 853
Period/Frequency: July-Aug

BEMUS – Belgrade Music Festivities
BEMUS – Beogradske muzicke svecanosti
Jugokoncert, Terazije 41, 11000 **Belgrade**
Tel: 11-324 303
Fax: 11-324 0479
director Eduard Ille
Period/Frequency: Oct

BITEF – Belgrade International Theatre Festival
BITEF – Beogradski internacionalni teatarski festival
Terazije 29/I, 11000 **Belgrade**
Tel: 11-324 3108
Internet: www.bitef.co.yu
artistic director Jovan Cirilov
Period/Frequency: Sept *Arts types:* avantgarde & experimental performing arts

International Review of Composers
Medunarodna tribina kompozitora
Misarska 12-14, 11000 **Belgrade**
Tel: 11-334 0894
Fax: 11-323 8637
E-Mail: sokojmic@EUnet.yu
director Milan Mihajlovic
Period/Frequency: May

Lucky Strike – International Summer Jazz Festival
Lucky Strike – Medunarodni letnji dzez festival
Sava Centre, Milentija Popovica 9,
11000 **Belgrade**
Tel: 11-311 4322 Fax: 11-311 1091
Period/Frequency: July

Theatre City Budva
Grad teatar Budva
Mediteranska 4, 86000 **Budva**
Tel: 86-51194/421 Fax: 86-52316
director Branislava Lijesevic
Period/Frequency: July-Aug

Sterijino pozorje – Yugoslav Theatre Festival
Sterijino pozorje – Jugoslovenske pozorisne igre
Zmaj Jovina 22/I, 21000 **Novi Sad**
Tel: 21-27255 Fax: 21-615 976
director Mileta Radovanovic
Period/Frequency: May-June

FIAT – Festival of International Alternative Theatre
FIAT – Festival internacionalnog alternativnog teatre
Vaka Djurovica 2, 81000 **Podgorica**
Tel: 81-45682 Fax: 81-44563
director t.b.a.
Period/Frequency: Feb

Festival of Mime and Monodrama
Festival pantomime i mondrame
Zmaj Jovine 1, 11080 **Zemun**
Tel: 11-618 031
Period/Frequency: May

International Orthodox Music Festival 'Choirs Beneath Frescoes'
Medunarodni festival duhovne muzike 'Horovi medu freskama'
Gospodarska 8, 11080 **Zernun**
Tel: 11-324 6167 Fax: 11-610 141
director Predrag Stamenkovic

GABOR MESZAROS

IVANO TORRE

Strumentisti

- ELISAVETA BLUMINA, piano
- •• MARIA LUISA CANTOS, piano
- • OLIVIER DARBELLAY, corno e violoncello - *french horn and cello*
- • BRUNO GROSSI, flauto
- MARC LAFORET, piano
- • GABOR MESZAROS, fagotto - *bassoon*
- • HANNES MEYER, organo
- BRANIMIR SLOKAR, trombone
- • MARC TEICHOLZ, chitarra - *guitar*

Attrazioni speciali

- KOL SIMCHA, contemporary Klezmer, piano-clarinetto-flauto contrabbasso-percussioni
- • IVANO TORRE, percussioni e composizione, incontro-scontro-incrocio tra musica classica e jazz. Diversi ensembles: percussioni-saxofoni-violoncello-fisarmonica-tuba-trombone-clarinetto-conchiglie
- • QUARTETTO TORRES E LA MAYA, chitarra classica e danza
- ENSEMBLE OF FOLK MUSIC DIVOGRAY, musica folcloristica, classica e moderna dall'Ucraina
- TRIO OF BANDURA PLAYERS UKRAINKA, canti folcloristici e classici accompagnati con il "bandura"

**Circolo Musicale
Emilia Tonolla-Rosa
6558 Lostallo
Switzerland**

Tel. +41 91 / 830 12 88
Fax +41 91 / 830 15 55
etonolla@ticino.com

THE ZAGREB SOLOISTS

Ensembles

- DUO EISENHOFFER-SLOKAR, arpa-trombone
- 21ST CENTURY DUO, piano-violoncello
- JESS-TRIO-WIEN, piano-violino-violoncello
- SPILLER TRIO, piano-violino-violoncello
- • TRIO ADORJÁN-CHUMACHENKO-LYSY, flauto-violino-viola
- • QUARTETTO TORRES, chitarre, *guitars*
- SLOKAR QUARTET, tromboni
- • IL NONETTO SVIZZERO-THE SWISS NONET, violino-viola-violoncello-contrabasso-flauto oboe-clarinetto-fagotto-corno
- I FIATI ITALIANI-SOLISTI TEATINI, oboi-clarinetti-fagotti-corni-pianoforte a quattro mani *oboes-clarinets-bassoons-horns-four-hands piano*
- I CAMERISTI LOMBARDI, orchestra da camera
- HUNGARIAN VIRTUOSI, orchestra da camera
- KIEV CHAMBER ORCHESTRA, orchestra da camera
- THE ZAGREB SOLOISTS, orchestra da camera

Conductor

PEI-YU CHANG

senza segno : in certi Paesi questi musicisti o ensembles sono rappresentati da altre agenzie. Diamo informazioni.
Unmarked : these musicians or ensembles are represented in some Countries by other agencies.Information on request
• : rappresentanza generale - general representative
• • : Europa

1994
1997
2000

The Sound of this Century

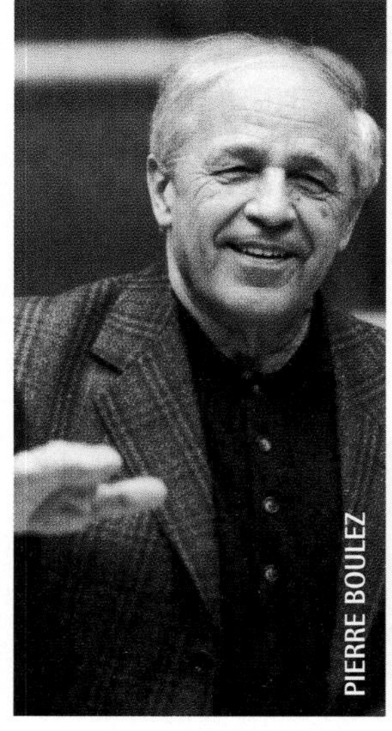

PIERRE BOULEZ

SIMON RATTLE

The sound of this century! As a grand finale to this music festival series held in Cologne during 1994, 1997 and 2000, MusikTriennale Köln is presenting a fireworks display of internationally celebrated artists performing the music of this century: the orchestras from Chicago, New York, Boston, Cleveland and Philadelphia with Pierre Boulez, Daniel Barenboim, Seiji Ozawa, Christoph von Dohnányi and Wolfgang Sawallisch, the Vienna and the Berlin Philharmonic Orchestras with Sir André Previn and Claudio Abbado, the City of Birmingham Symphony Orchestra with Sir Simon Rattle and Sakari Oramo, the Royal Concertgebouw Orchestra with Riccardo Chailly, and naturally the WDR Symphony Orchestra of Cologne under Semyon Bychkov, as well as the Gürzenich Orchestra under Cologne's General Music Director, James Conlon! Internationally celebrated soloists - among them Christine Schäfer, Barbara Bonney, Jennifer Ringo and Marianne Faithfull - and an "anthology of the Lied" in the 20th century will lend a distinctive character to the festival's theme, "La voix humaine". Concerts in the genres of jazz and experimental music, too, will reflect the diversity and richness of our era's music in fascinating performances.

JAMES CONLON

25 April to 12 June 2000

CHRISTINE SCHÄFER

Advance ticket sales start on 1 December 1999!

Plan your musical journey to Cologne - we would be pleased to send you the programme booklet free of charge! All you need to do is call us or send us an e-mail.

Köln Ticket
Information & Tickets
TriennaleHotline 0221/280 281
www.MusikTriennaleKoeln.de

KÜNSTLERAGENTUR Dr. RAAB & Dr. BÖHM
Opera, Operetta und Concert Ltd.

SOPRANO
Laura AIKIN (C/ST)
Karan ARMSTRONG (A)
Christiane BOESIGER (A/ST)
Elizabeth CONNELL (A/ST)
Lynne DAWSON (C/A)
Natalie DESSAY (C/A)
Maria GULEGHINA (ST)
Ingrid HABERMANN (A/ST)
Malin HARTELIUS (A/ST)
Soile ISOKOSKI (C/A)
Yvonne KENNY (C/A)
Hellen KWON (A/ST)
Ellen VAN LIER (A/ST)
Felicity LOTT (A)
Alessandra MARC (ST)
Sylvia McNAIR (C/A)
Christiane OELZE (C/A)
Luba ORGONASOVA (C/A)
Michele PATZAKIS (A/ST)
Adrienne PIECZONKA (C/A/D/ST)
Françoise POLLET (A/D/ST)
Amanda ROOCROFT (A)
Andrea ROST (ST)
Christine SCHÄFER (C/A)
Petra-Maria SCHNITZER (A/ST/*)
Cyndia SIEDEN (C/ST)
Cheryl STUDER (ST)
Lùbica VARGICOVÁ (ST)
Deborah VOIGT (C/A/ST)
Elizabeth WHITEHOUSE (A/ST)
Cornelia ZACH (A/ST)
Ruth ZIESAK (C/A)

MEZZOSOPRANO / CONTRALTO
Agnes BALTSA (ST)
Daphne EVANGELATOS (A/ST)
Bernarda FINK (A/ST)
Eugenie GRUNEWALD (A/D/CH)
Margareta HINTERMEIER (A/ST)
Barbara HÖLZL (A/ST)
Marjana LIPOVSEK (C/A)
Elisabeth VON MAGNUS (A/ST)
Hana MINUTILLO (ST)
Yvonne NAEF (A/D/CH/ST)
Natascha PETRINSKY (ST)
Jadwiga RAPPÉ (A/ST)
Gabriele REINHOLZ (A/ST)
Ludmila SCHEMTSCHUK (ST)
Iris VERMILLION (C/A)
Anne Sofie VON OTTER (C/A)
Dolora ZAJICK (A)

TENOR
John ALER (A)
Kurt AZESBERGER (A/D/ST)
Lando BARTOLINI (A/ST)
Ian BOSTRIDGE (C/A)
Joseph CALLEJA (ST)
Vladimir GALOUZINE (ST)
Paul GROVES (C/A/D)
Thomas HARPER (A/ST)
Jörg HERING (A/D/CH/ST)
Herbert LIPPERT (ST)
Jorge LOPEZ-YANEZ (A/ST)
Janez LOTRIC (E)
Thomas MOSER (C/A)
Dennis O´NEILL (A/ST)
John OSBORN (A)
Christoph PRÉGARDIEN (A/ST)
Kenneth RIEGEL (A)
Anthony ROLFE JOHNSON
Michael SCHADE (C/A)
Martin THOMPSON (A/ST)
Glenn WINSLADE (A/D/ST)
Heinz ZEDNIK (ST)

BARITONE
Olaf BAER (A/ST)
Gregg BAKER (E)
Vladimir CHERNOV (ST)
Alain FONDARY (A/ST)
Gottfried HORNIK (A/ST)
Simon KEENLYSIDE (C/A)
Jochen SCHMECKENBECHER (ST)
Andreas SCHMIDT (A/ST)
Alan TITUS (C/A)
Oliver WIDMER (C/E)
Ludwig WOLFRUM (A/ST)

BASSBARITONE / BASS
Sergej ALEKSASHKIN (ST)
Roland BRACHT (A/ST)
Paata BURCHULADZE (A/D/CH/ST)
Albert DOHMEN (A/ST)
Robert HOLL (A/D/ST)
James JOHNSON (E)
Günter MISSENHARDT (A/ST)
Anthony MICHAELS-MOORE (C/A)
Alfred MUFF (A/ST)
Jewgenij NESTERENKO (ST)
Thomas QUASTHOFF (A)
Kurt RYDL (ST)
Harald STAMM (A/ST)

PIANO
Valery AFANASSIEV (W)
Dmitri ALEXEEV (A/ST)
Ingeborg BALDASZTI (*)
Tzimon BARTO (A/ST)
Boris BEREZOVSKY (A/ST)
Ronald BRAUTIGAM (A/ST)
Peter DONOHOE (A/D)
Andrei GAVRILOV (A/ST)
Cyprien KATSARIS (E except D/F)
Zoltán KOCSIS (A)
Oleg MAISENBERG (A/ST)
Émile NAOUMOFF (A)
Ursula OPPENS (A/D/CH/*)
Cécile OUSSET (A/ST)
Anthony & Joseph PARATORE (A/ST)
Dezsö RÁNKI (A)
Markus SCHIRMER (A/ST)
Lisa SMIRNOVA (W)
Claudius TANSKI (W)
André WATTS (A)
Elisso WIRSSALADZE (A)
Christian ZACHARIAS (A/*)
Lilya ZILBERSTEIN (A/*)

ORGAN
Marie-Claire ALAIN (A/ST)
Jennifer BATE (W)
Daniel CHORZEMPA (A/ST)
Martin HASELBÖCK (W)
Elisabeth ULLMANN (*)
Gillian WEIR (A)

VIOLIN
David GARRETT (A)
Daniel HOPE (A)
Václav HUDECEK (E)
Chantal JUILLET (A)
Isabelle VAN KEULEN (A)
Shlomo MINTZ (A/ST)
Vadim REPIN (A/ST)
Benjamin SCHMID (A/ST)
Dmitri SITKOVETSKY (A/ST)
Sergej STADLER (W)
Viktor TRETJAKOV (A/ST)
Nikolaj ZNAIDER (A)

VIOLA
Yuri BASHMET (A)
Gérard CAUSSÉ (A/ST)
Nobuko IMAI (A/ST)
Thomas RIEBL (*)

CELLO
David GERINGAS (A/ST)
Miklós PERÉNYI (A/ST)

HARP
Maria GRAF (E)

GUITAR
Manuel BARRUECO (A)
Göran SÖLLSCHER (*)

CLARINET
Sharon KAM (A)
Paul MEYER (A)
Sabine MEYER (*)
Richard STOLTZMAN (A/ST)

FLUTE
Robert AITKEN (*)
Irena GRAFENAUER (E)

BASSOON
Klaus THUNEMANN (E)

OBOE
François LELEUX (A)

HORN
Marie Luise NEUNECKER (A/ST)

TRUMPET
Håkan Hardenberger (A/CH/ST)

TROMBONE
Christian LINDBERG (A/CH/F)

BRASS QUINTET
Brassissimo (E)

CHAMBER MUSIC
Ahn Trio (E)
Arditti Quartet (*)
Auer Quartet (A)
Bartók Quartet (A/ST)
Beaux Arts Trio (A)
Chilingirian Quartet (A/ST)
Emerson String Quartet (A/ST)
Giora Feidman Trio / Quartet (A/ST)
Juilliard String Quartet (A/ST)
Kavakos/Kashkashian/Perényi Trio (A/ST)
Leipziger Streichquartett (A)
Neunecker/Gawriloff/Aimard (A/ST/*)
Philharmonia Quartett Berlin (A/ST)
Takács Quartet (A/ST)
Tokyo String Quartet (A/ST)
Vogler Streichquartett (A)
Wiener Brahms Trio (W)
Wiener Eichendorff Quintett (A/ST/*)
Wiener Streichquartett (A/ST/*)

ANCIENT MUSIC / VOCAL ENSEMBLES
Harlem Spiritual Ensemble (*)
Hilliard Ensemble (*)
Musica Antiqua Köln (A/ST/*)
Tallis Scholars (A/ST)

CHAMBER ORCHESTRAS
Academy St. Martin in the Fields (A/ST)
Camerata Academica Salzburg (*)
Concerto Köln (A/ST/*)
English Baroque Soloists /Monteverdi Choir (A/ST)
English Chamber Orchestra (A)
I Fiamminghi (A/ST)
Moscow Soloists (Yuri Bashmet) (A/ST/*)
Münchner Kammerorchester (A/ST)
I Musici di Roma (A)
Orchestra of the Age of Enlightenment (A/ST)
Orpheus Chamber Orchestra (E)
Prague Philharmonia (A)
Stuttgarter Kammerorchester (A)
Tafelmusik Baroque Orchestra (A)
Wiener Akademie (ST/*)
Wiener Johann Strauss Kammerorchester (ST/L/*)

CHOIRS (SELECTION)
Eric Ericson Chamber Choir (A/ST)
Hungarian Radio Choir Budapest (A/ST)
Prague Philharmonic Choir (A/ST)
Swedish Radio Choir (A/ST)
Vienna Singverein (A/ST)

ORCHESTRAS
(exclusive representations)

Bamberg Symphony Orchestra
(Principal conductor: Jonathan Nott)

Bruckner Orchestra Linz
(from the saison 2000/2001 only / Principal conductor: Dennis Russell Davies)

ORCHESTRAL TOURS
(see tour roster)

CONDUCTORS (SELECTION)
Petr ALTRICHTER (A)
Christian BADEA (A/D/ST)
Mathias BAMERT (A)
Rudolph BARSHAI (A/ST)
Serge BAUDO (A/ST)
Jiri BELOHLAVEK (A)
Jean-Claude CASADESUS (A/ST)
Aldo CECCATO (A/ST)
Misha DAMEV (W)
Dennis Russell DAVIES (E)
Vladimir FEDOSEJEV (E)
Ádám FISCHER (*)
Iván FISCHER (*)
Claus Peter FLOR (A/ST)
Rafael FRÜHBECK DE BURGOS (A/ST)
Jane GLOVER (A/D/ST)
Theodor GUSCHLBAUER (A/D/ST)
Leopold HAGER (A/ST)
Martin HASELBÖCK (W)
Richard HICKOX (A)
Tetsuji HONNA (E)
Marek JANOWSKI (A/ST)
Mariss JANSONS (A)
Sir Neville MARRINER (A/ST)
Michel PLASSON (A/ST)
Georges PRÊTRE (W)
Sir André PREVIN (A)
Peter SCHNEIDER (ST)
Michael SCHØNWANDT (A/ST)
Martin SIEGHART (W)
Steven SLOANE (A)
Saulis SONDECKIS (A/ST)
Vladimir VERBITSKY (A)
Ralf WEIKERT (A/ST)
Bruno WEIL (A/ST)

REPRESENTATIONS

(A)	AUSTRIA
(ST)	SUNDRY TERRITORIES
(C)	CONCERTS ONLY
(D)	GERMANY,
(CH)	SWITZERLAND
(F)	FRANCE
(E)	EUROPE
(W)	WORLD
(*)	CERTAIN CONTRACTS
(L)	SUNDRY OVERSEA COUNTRIES

ORCHESTRAL TOURS (SELECTION)

2000

Berlin Symphony Orchestra / R. Weikert / M. Faithful	12 – 16 February
London Symphony Orchestra / Sir C. Davis	18 – 25 September
Orchestre National du Capitole de Toulouse / M. Plasson	29 Oct. – 8 Nov.
Philharmonia Orchestra / Ch. v. Dohnanyi	13 – 20 November

2001

Zürcher Bach Collegium / F. Welser-Möst (J.S. Bach: St. Matthew-Passion)	31 March – 5 April
Gewandhausorchester Leipzig / H. Blomstedt	May & 23 – 26 September
Danish National Radio Symphony Orchestra G. Albrecht / L.O. Andsnes / B. Skovhus	15 May – 1 June
German Symphony Orchestra Berlin / K. Nagano	5 – 10 June
Bamberg Symphony Orchestra / M. Gielen (Schönberg: Gurre-Lieder)	July
Gustav Mahler Youth Orchestra / Vienna Singverein **Prague Philharmonic Choir** / F. Welser-Möst (Mahler: Symphony Nr. 8)	August – September
City of Birmingham Symphony Orchestra / S. Oramo	2 – 8 November
Bruckner Orchestra Linz / D. R. Davies	on request
German Symphony Orchestra Berlin / K. Nagano	5 – 10 June

2002

Academy St. Martin in the Fields / Sir N. Marriner	25 – 28 January
Radio SO Stockholm / Swedish Radio Choir / M. Honeck	1 – 15 February
St. Petersburg Philharmonic / Y. Temirkanov	1 – 15 February
Royal Concertgebouw Orchestra / Riccardo Chailly	March
Dresdner Philharmonie / R. Frühbeck de Burgos	2 – 8 May
Radio Symphony Orchestra Cologne / S. Bychkov	7 – 17 May
Oslo Philharmonic Orchestra / M. Jansons	5 – 9 June

A-1010 Vienna, Plankengasse 7, Phone: +43-1/512 05 01, Fax: +43-1/512 77 43, e-mail: raab.boehm@magnet.at

Skyinbow Ltd
The Workshop
Vidlin
Shetland Isles
Scotland
ZE2 9QA

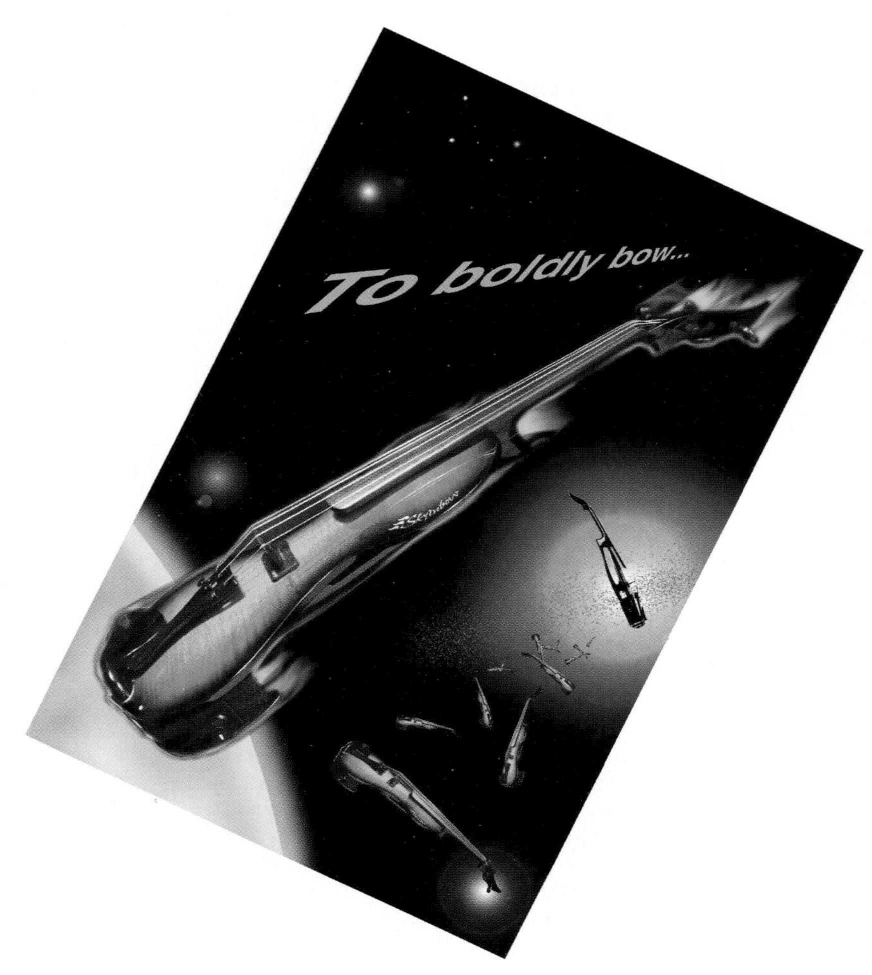

Skyinbow's uncompromising approach to playability
and tone have made our Pro and S1 violins
the choice of professionals.

Skyinbow violins are hand made in Scotland.

Skyinbow Pros are 'Lord of The Dance'

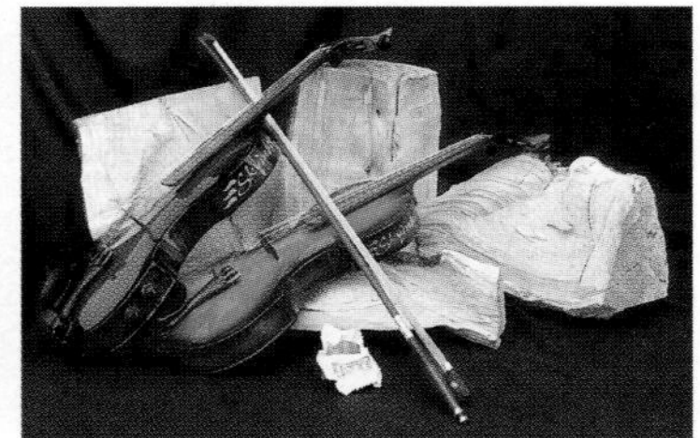

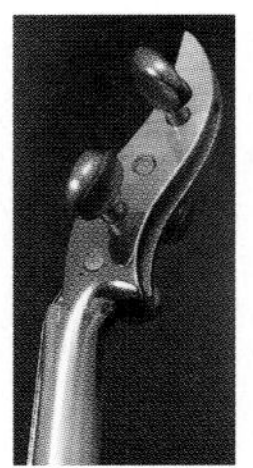

Tel: +44 (0) 1806 577 234
Fax: +44 (0) 1806 577 336
Email: sales@skyinbow.com
Website: www.skyinbow.com

Design and imaging by force10.co.uk

NOVART
Ballet Novart a.s.b.l. - Av. de l'Europe, 74 - 6000 Charleroi - Belgium
Contact: Spiro Dhimoïla - Tél. +32(0)71/32 39 91
Fax +32(0)71/30 27 42 - http://www.uniscene.org/novart - E mail: novart@uniscene.org
Photo: Laurence Van Rechem©

safe hands
... trust ours in handling
classical orchestras and musicians
SPECIALISED
TRAVEL
LIMITED
IATA
ABTA
ATOL
2178
telephone 020 8799 8320 facsimile 020 8998 7965 email admin@stlon.com

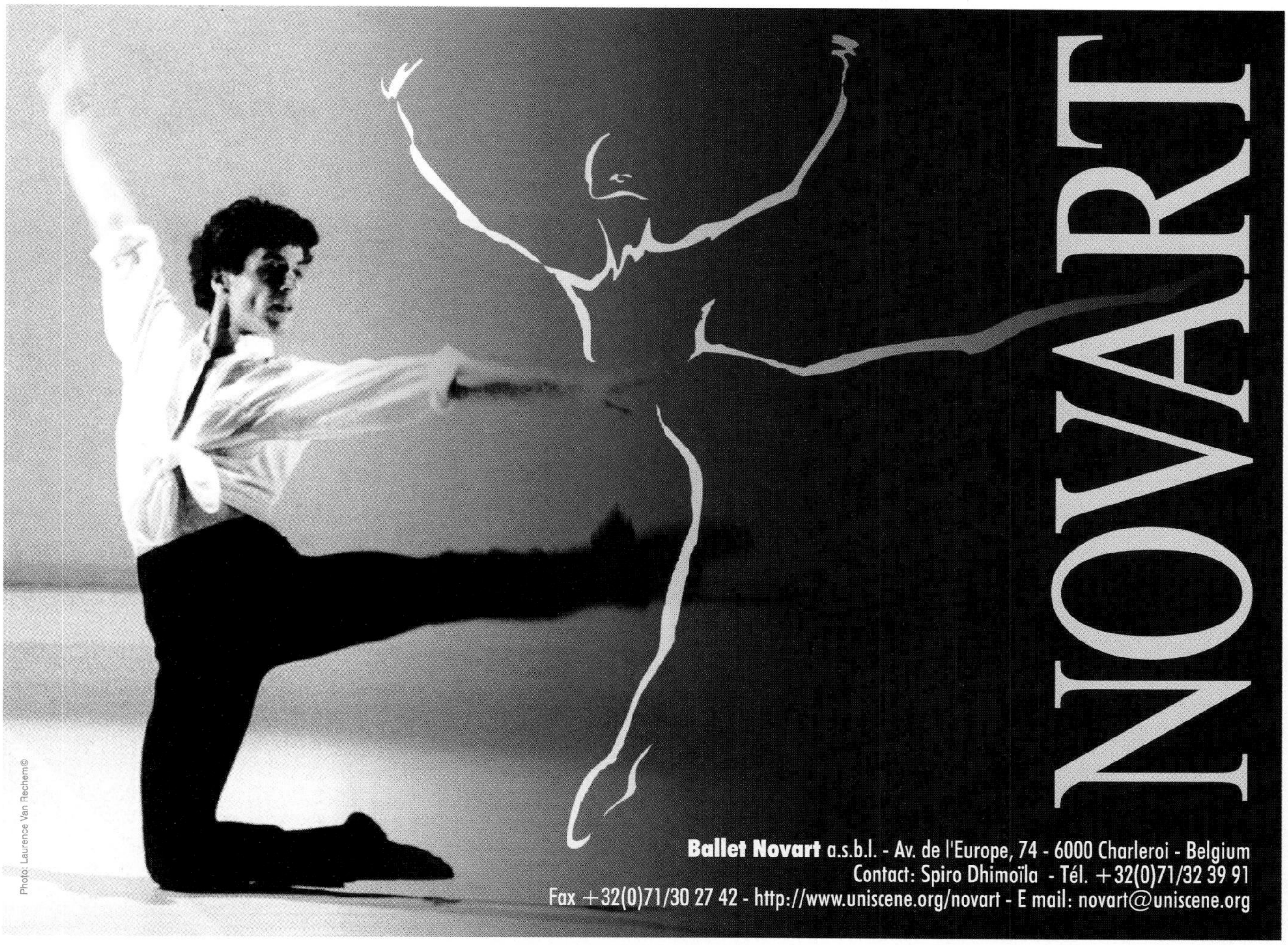

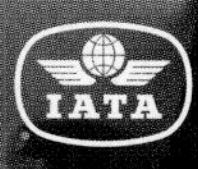

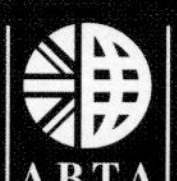

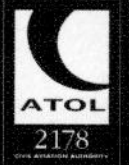

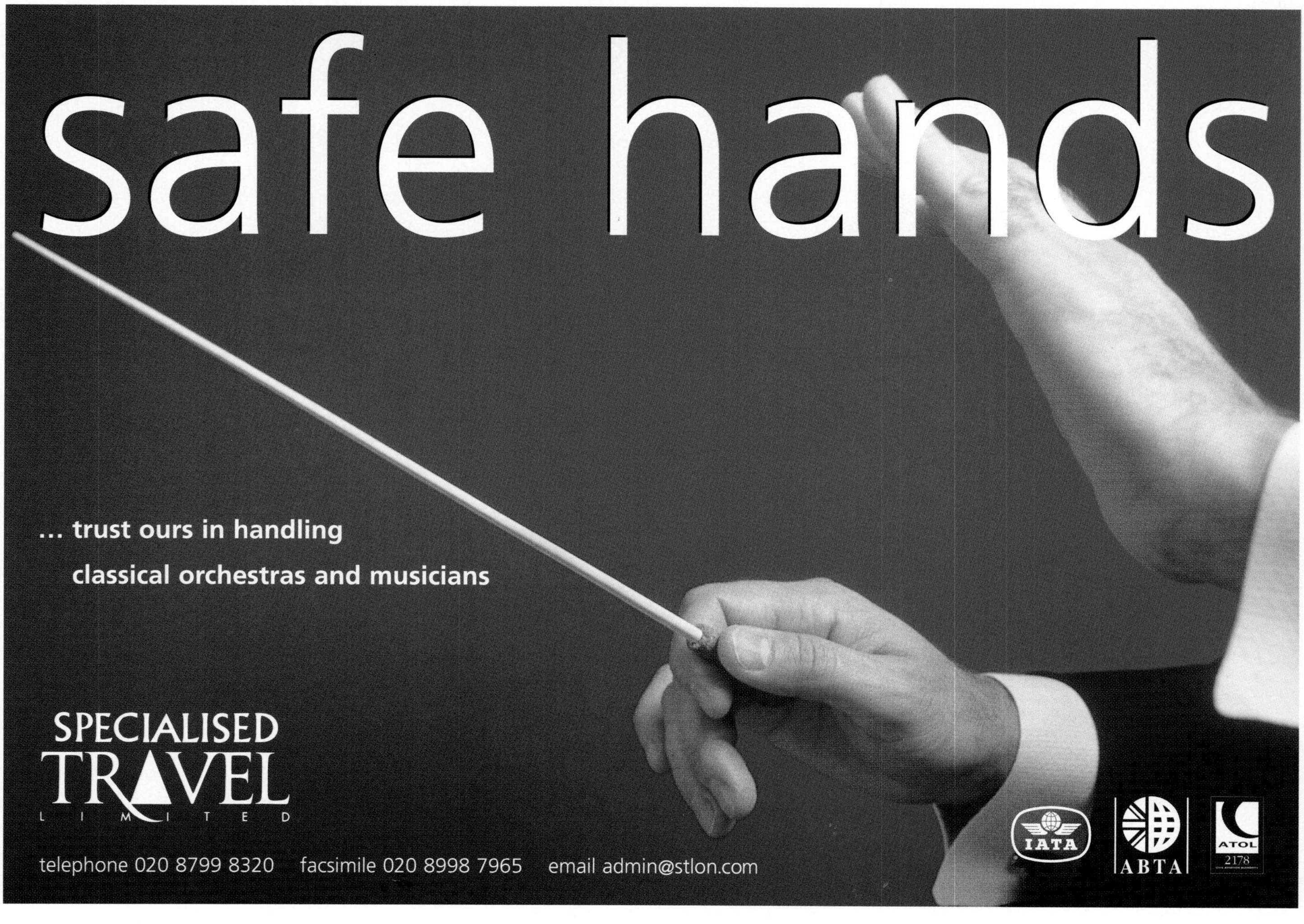

Venues

Venues
This list includes venues which present, and/or are available for hire/rent for a significant period of the year and/or are interested in co-productions. The commercial theatres of London's West End and the boulevard private theatres of Paris are also included here rather than in the Drama Section. **Within country the venues are ordered by city, and alphabetically within city.**

Salles de Spectacle
Cette rubrique englobe les lieux qui accueillent des spectacles et/ou qui sont disponibles à la location pour une certaine période de l'année et/ou qui s'intéressent à des co-productions. Les théâtres commerciaux du 'West End' de Londres et les théâtres de boulevard privés de Paris sont également inclus dans cette liste plutôt que dans celle des 'Théâtres'. **Pour chaque pays les salles sont classés dans l'ordre des villes et par ordre alphabétique.**

Spielstätten
In diesem Kapitel werden Spielstätten verzeichnet, die entweder Konzerte usw. veranstalten oder die Räumlichkeiten vermieten, sowie diejenigen, die sich mit Koproduktionen befassen. Die Londoner West End Theater und die privaten Boulevard Theater in Paris werden daher in diesem Kapitel und nicht im Kapitel 'Drama' aufgeführt. **Die Einträge sind innerhalb aller Staaten alphabetisch nach Stadt und innerhalb der Stadt alphabetisch nach Namen geordnet.**

Teatri, Auditorium ecc.
Questa sezione include tutti i teatri/auditorium/sale che presentano, ospitano, che possono essere affittati o che sono interessati a co-produzioni di spettacoli. Sono inoltre qui inclusi – anziché nella sezione 'drama'- i teatri commerciali londinesi del West End ed i teatri privati di Parigi. **Le cittá sono in ordine alfabetico e cosí anche i luoghi all'interno di esse.**

Salas de espectáculo
La lista incluye salas que presentan espectáculos y/o que son disponibles para alquilar por un periodo significativo del año y/o están interesadas en coproducciones. Los teatros comerciales del 'West End' de Londres o los teatros privados del 'boulevard' de Paris también están incluidos en esta sección en vez de en la de Drama. **Las salas están ordenadas por ciudades y en orden alfabético dentro de cada ciudad.**

Venues (공연장소)
이 리스트에는 연중 상당 기간을 대여하거나, 공동/합작 기획에 관심이 있는 현존하는 공연장소가 나와 있다. 런던의 웨스트 엔드에 있는 상업적 극장들과 파리의 개인 극장들도 연극 부문이 아니라 이 부문에 포함되었다. **리스트는 국가별, 도시별, 그리고 다시 알파벳순으로 기재되었다.**

场所
本名单列出了那些上演剧目和（或）在一年中的相当长时期可供租赁/租用和（或）有意于共同制作的场所。伦敦West End的商业性剧院和巴黎的娱乐性私人剧院也包括在本名单上，而不是包括在“戏剧”一节中。**在每个国家里场所是按城市顺序来排列的，而在每一城市里场所又是按字母顺序来排列的。**

会場
ここでは上演を行う会場、年間を通じて長期的に借りられる会場、そして共同製作に関心のある会場を掲載しています。ロンドンのウェストエンド、パリのブールヴァール等商業劇場は、劇団の章ではなく、この章に記載されています。**リストは国、都市別で、都市内ではアルファベット順に記載されています。**

ALBANIA (+355)

Aleksander Moisiu Theatre
Durrës
Tel: 52-23466
director Skonder Myshketa
Capacity: 400

Skampa Theatre of Elbasan
Elbasan
Tel: 545-3320
director Astrid Cerma
Capacity: 400

Apolonia Theatre
Fier
Tel: 64-22592
director Krenar Traka
Capacity: 480 *Comments:* see also Drama

Bylis Theatre
Fier
Tel: 64-22592
director Krenar Traka
Capacity: 400

Theatre Andon Zako Cajupi
Street Themistokli Germenji, **Korca**
Tel: 824-2100
director Sotiraq Tili
Capacity: 400

Migjeni Theatre
Theatre Migjeni Shkodra, **Shkodër**
Tel: 224-3315
director Cefa
Capacity: 500

International Culture Centre
Tirana
Tel: 42-28588
manager Zofina Kukh
Venue type: cultural centre *Capacity:* 400 *Policy:* rent *Arts types:* symphony and chamber music concerts, recitals and choral concerts

National Theatre of Tirana
Place Skanderbeg, **Tirana**
Tel: 42-23022/28933
director Gezim Kame
Venue type: theatre *Capacity:* 540 *Comments:* 200 performances annually

Puppet Theatre
Tirana
Tel: 42-22446
director Gjok Kurilul
Capacity: 200 *Arts types:* puppetry (200 perf. annually)

Theatre of Opera and Ballet Tirana
Sheshi Skenderbeu, PO Box 8368, **Tirana**
general (executive) director Vasil S. Tole (tel/fax: 42-27471); artistic director Bujar Llapaj (tel/fax: 42-24753)
Venue type: theatre *Capacity:* 800 *Policy:* rent *Arts types:* opera, operetta, dance, ballet, folk dance, symphony and chamber music, choral concerts *Comments:* various professional groups in Tob: Symphony Orchestra, Chorus, Ballet; see also Opera, Orchestras and Dance

Theatre of the Art Academy
Tirana
Tel: 42-25488 Fax: 42-25488
general director Kastriot Caushi; assistant general director Bujar Sykja
Venue type: theatre *Capacity:* 640 *Policy:* rent *Arts types:* symphony and chamber music concerts, recitals, operetta, choral music

Theatre of Vlora
Vlora
Tel: 63-22455
director Kristaq Skrami
Capacity: 250

ARMENIA (+374)

Aram Khachaturian Concert Hall
46 Mashtots Avenue, 375019 **Yerevan**
Tel: 2-580 701/564 965/581 572 Fax: 2-151 055/581 142
artistic director Loris Tyeknavorian

Small Philharmonic Concert Hall
2 Aboviana Street, 375010 **Yerevan**
Tel: 2-582 773 Fax: 2-562 324
director Gagik Ter-Kazarian

Sport & Concert Hall (SCC)
Tsitsernakaberd, 375028 **Yerevan**
Tel: 2-399 911/223 463/398 125 Fax: 2-390 001
general director Simon Khachatourian

Yerevan Chamber Music Hall
1, Isahakian Street, 375025 **Yerevan**
Tel: 2-526 725/780/718 Fax: 2-151 431
director Andranik Harutyunian

AUSTRIA (+43)

Bregenzer Festspiel- und Kongresshaus
Platz der Wr. Symphoniker 1, 6900 **Bregenz**
Tel: 5574-413-0 Fax: 5574-413 413
Internet: www.FestspielhausBregenz.at
E-Mail: ruth.gasser@fkh.at
Geschäftsführer Dipl. Kaufm. Franz Salzmann (Bregenzer Festspiele), Dr. Ruth Verena Gasser (Festspiel- und Kongresshaus)
Venue type: theatre *Capacity:* up to 1780, open-air 7000 *Policy:* promote, rent *Arts types:* opera (in and outdoors), theatre, ballet, orchestra, chamber music, social events, conferences, congresses, seminars

Kulturhaus Dornbirn
Rathausplatz 1, 6850 **Dornbirn**
Tel: 5572-27770 Fax: 5572-27770-11
E-Mail: kulturhaus@dornbirn.ool.at
Geschäftsführer Klaus Lingg; Verwaltung Fritz Ortner
Venue type: culture and congress house *Capacity:* 730 *Policy:* rent *Arts types:* opera, operetta, theatre, symphony, chamber music, recitals

Kultur- u Kongresszentrum
Schubertplatz 6, 7000 **Eisenstadt**
Tel: 2682-6468-0 Fax: 2682-646 803
Internet: www.burgld.at/kuz
E-Mail: kuz@burgld.at
Geschäftsführer ORGR Dr. Josef Wiedenhofer; Sekretariatsleitung Rosa Marie Ferschich
Venue type: multi-purpose *Capacity:* 780 *Policy:* rent, own productions and co-productions, especially with state co-operation *Arts types:* theatre, concerts, opera, readings, exhibitions, conferences *Comments:* one of the 5 cultural centres – in Eisenstadt, Mattersburg, Oberschützen, Güssing, Jennersdorf (all q.v.) – of the Burgenländische Kulturzentren, the central office being Mattersburg

Montforthaus Feldkirch
Vorarlberger Kultur- u. Kongresszentrum, Postfach 564, 6803 **Feldkirch**
Tel: 5522-76001 Fax: 5522-76002
Internet: www.vol.at/congressvorarlberg
E-Mail: montforthaus@monthforthaus.feldkirch.com
Geschäftsführer Arnold Ess
Venue type: multi-purpose *Capacity:* 1160 *Policy:* rent *Arts types:* concerts, festivals, dance, social events, conferences, conventions

Convention Center Graz – Grazer Congress
Schmiedgasse 2, 8010 **Graz**
Tel: 316-8049-0 Fax: 316-804 975/826 467
Internet: www.grazercongress.co.at
E-Mail: office@grazercongress.co.at
Geschäftsführer Dr. Nikolaus Breisach; Marketing manager Elisabeth Hansa; Reservation & Organisation Eva Puchwein
Venue type: multi-purpose, conference centre *Capacity:* Stefaniensaal 1100, Kammermusiksaal 400, Steiermarksaal 400 *Policy:* rent *Arts types:* conferences, concerts, banquets, seminars, shows *Comments:* the Convention Center consists of a total of 18 venues, all of which are available to hire

Kulturzentrum bei den Minoriten
Mariahilferplatz 3, 8020 **Graz**
Tel: 316-713 170 Fax: 316-713 170-4
Internet: kulturzentrum.minoriten.austro.net
E-Mail: minoriten@austro.net
Rektor Josef Fink; Vermietung Traute Radl; Theatre-Literature Dr. Birgit Pölzl; Music, Performance, Film/Video, Fine Art (Ressortleiterin) Mag. Ute Pinter; Science, Dance, Performance, Spirituality Dr. Johannes Rauchenberger
Venue type: multi-purpose
Capacity: Großer Saal 342, Kleiner Saal 100
Policy: promote, rent
Arts types: concerts, theatre, exhibitions, dance, experimental film, literature, performance, science

Kulturzentrum Jennersdorf, Büro Güssing
Schulstrasse 6, Postfach 40, 7540 **Güssing**
Tel: 3322-421 460 Fax: 3322-421 4619
Internet: www.burgld.at/kuz
E-Mail: kuz@burgld.at
Geschäftsführer w.Hofrat Dr. Josef Wiedenhofer
Venue type: multi-purpose *Capacity:* 500
Policy: rent, also own productions and co-productions, especially with state co-operation
Arts types: theatre, concerts, readings, exhibitions
Comments: one of the 5 cultural centres – in Eisenstadt, Mattersburg, Oberschützen, Güssing, Jennersdorf (all q.v.) – of the Burgenländische Kulturzentren, the central office being Mattersburg. Güssing is the office for Jennersdorf, which has a capacity of 380

Congress Innsbruck
Rennweg 3, 6021 **Innsbruck**
Tel: 512-5936-0 Fax: 512-59367
Internet: www.congress-innsbruck.at
E-Mail: congress.innsbruck@congress/innsbruck.at
Manager Georg Lamp; stellv. Manager Prok. Hans-Peter Brix
Venue type: multi-purpose *Capacity:* Tirolhall 1500, Doganahalle up to 2000, Innsbruck-hall 600 *Policy:* rent, promote *Arts types:* symphony, chamber music, plays, musicals, dance, ballet, exhibitions
Comments: promoter of congresses, exhibitions and social functions

Konzerthaus Klagenfurt
Miesstalerstrasse 8, 9020 **Klagenfurt**
Tel: 463-54272 Fax: 463-502 303
Verwaltungsdirektor Kurt Berger
Venue type: concert hall *Capacity:* Großer Saal 680, Mittlerer Saal 300 *Policy:* rent
Arts types: classical music concerts, jazz, folk

Brucknerhaus Linz
Untere Donaulände 7, Postfach 57, 4010 **Linz**
Tel: 732-7612
Fax: 732-761 2200
Internet: www.brucknerhaus.Linz.at
Vorstandsdirektoren Wolfgang Winkler (künstlerischer Leiter), Ing. Mag. Wolfgang Lehner (kaufmännischer Leiter); Marketing/Presse Karin Beate Kraml; Organisation Wolfgang Kohl; Technik Ing. Wolfgang Schützeneder
Venue type: concert hall
Capacity: Brucknersaal 1450, Stiftersaal 400, Keplersaal 100-250 *Policy:* present, rent
Arts types: symphony, chamber music, soloists, recitals, opera in concert, jazz, modern music
Comments: see also Festivals

Posthof, Zeitkultur im Hafen
Posthofstrasse 43, 4020 **Linz**
Tel: 732-770 5480 Fax: 732-782 652
Internet: www.posthof.at
E-Mail: office@posthof.at
administration manager Artur Matt; art director (music) Werner Ponesch; marketing and promotion Karl Zabern
Venue type: culture centre of contemporary art *Capacity:* Großer Saal – seated 630, standing 1300, Mittlerer Saal – seated 450, standing 900, Kleiner Saal-130 *Policy:* promote, rent *Arts types:* dance, theatre, cabaret, festivals, concerts (rock, pop, reggae, jazz, etc.) *Comments:* see also Festivals

Kulturzentrum Mattersburg
Wulkalände 2, 7210 **Mattersburg**
Tel: 2626-62096 Fax: 2626-65019
Internet: www.burgld.at/kuz
E-Mail: kuz@burgld.at
Geschäftsführer HR Dr. Josef Wiedenhofer; Bereich Theater Eva Gold-Pirch; Bereich Kinder- und Schülertheater Anita Gruber
Venue type: multi-purpose
Capacity: 430 *Policy:* rent, own producitions and co-productions, especially with state co-operation
Arts types: theatre, concerts, cabaret, readings, exhibitions *Comments:* Mattersburg is the central office of the 5 cultural centres of the Burgenländische Kulturzentren, the others at Eisenstadt, Oberschützen, Güssing, Jennersdorf (q.v.)

Kulturzentrum Oberschützen
Hauptplatz 8, 7432 **Oberschützen**
Tel: 3353-6680-0 Fax: 3353-66803
Internet: www.burgld.at/kuz
E-Mail: kuzo@burgld.at
Geschäftsführer ORGR Dr. Josef Wiedenhofer
Venue type: multi-purpose
Capacity: Takács Saal 600, Chamber music hall 120
Policy: rent, also own productions and co-productions, especially with state co-operation
Arts types: theatre, concerts, cabaret, readings, exhibitions *Comments:* one of the 5 cultural centres – in Eisenstadt, Mattersburg, Oberschützen, Güssing, Jennersdorf (all q.v.) – of the Burgenländische Kulturzentren, the central office being Mattersburg

Festsaal Saalfelden
Feuerwehrplatz, 5760 **Saalfelden**
Tel: 6582-7930
Fax: 6582-79378
Internet: www.tiscover.com/hindenburg
E-Mail: hotel.hindenburg@salzburg.co.at
Geschäftsführer Konrad Mittelberger
Venue type: multi-purpose
Capacity: 1000 *Policy:* rent, promote
Arts types: opera, cabaret, film, lectures, concerts, congresses, seminars, balls
Comments: also promoters of small concerts

International Stiftung Mozarteum
Schwarzstraße 26, 5020 **Salzburg**
Tel: 662-88940-21
Fax: 662-872 996
Geschäftsführer Wieland Lafferentz; Präsident Dr. Friedrich Gehmacher; Leiter Konzertbereich Dr. Josef Tichy
Venue type: Concert hall
Capacity: Großer Saal 800, Wiener Saal 200
Policy: present
Arts types: orchestra, chamber-music, lieder, recitals
Comments: offer subscription series; see also Festivals and Promoters

Salzburger Festspiele
Hofstallgasse 1, 5010 **Salzburg**
Tel: 662-80450 Fax: 662-804 5700/760
Internet: www.salzburgfestival.at
E-Mail: info@salzburgfestival.at
Kaufmännischer Leiter und Konzertreferat Dr Hans Landesmann; Präsidentin Dr Helga Rabl-Stadler; künstlerische Leitung & Intendant Dr Gérard Mortier (until: 2001); Leiterin des Künstlerischen Betriebsbüros Mag Eva-Maria Wieser
Capacity: Großes Festspielhaus 2111 *Policy:* rent & produce *Arts types:* predominantly concerts, opera, drama *Comments:* see also Festivals

Bühne im Hof, Die
Linzer Straße 18, 3100 **St Pölten**
Tel: 2742-352 291 Fax: 2742-352 294
Internet: www.bih.at
E-Mail: office@bih.at
Künstlerische Leiterin Mimi Wunderer; Dramaturg Rupert Klima
Venue type: multi-cultural production venue *Capacity:* seated 500, standing 800 *Policy:* promote, rent, also own productions *Arts types:* own productions are musicals and drama, other productions include dance theatre, children's/youth theatre, music, cabaret, concerts (world music, pop, reggae, jazz etc.), contemporary art *Comments:* see also Drama

AKZENT
Theresianumgasse 18, 1040 **Wien**
Tel: 1-5016 53302 Fax: 1-5016 53366
Geschäftsführer Dr Alfred Schleppnik
Venue type: culture centre *Capacity:* Theatre 449, Studio 80 *Policy:* rent, present *Arts types:* drama, dance, concerts etc.

Austria Center Vienna
Am Hubertusdamm 6, 1220 **Wien**
Tel: 1-26069-0 Fax: 1-26069-303
Internet: www.acv.at
E-Mail: office@acv.at
Generaldirektor Dr. Michael Auracher; Presse & PR Mag. Antonia Lang; Marketing Mag. Renate Dobler; Durchführung Alice Baor; Betrieb und Technik Geráld Schütz; Rechnungswesen/Personal Alfred Kubesch
Venue type: conference centre *Capacity:* fourteen halls seating up to 4200, 170 offices and conference rooms
Policy: rent *Arts types:* symphony, theatre, dance

dietheater – Konzerthaus
Lothringerstrasse 20, 1030 **Wien**
Tel: 1-587 8774 Fax: 1-587 8774-31
Internet: www.dietheater.or.at/dietheater
E-Mail: dietheater@gmx.net
manager & artistic director Christian Pronay; assistant to art director Anna Thier; press Elisabeth Drucker; chief technician Franz Strasser
Venue type: theatre *Capacity:* 89 *Policy:* present *Arts types:* fringe theatre, performance *Comments:* see also Drama and Festivals

dietheater – Künstlerhaus
Karlsplatz 5, 1010 **Wien**
Tel: 1-587 0504 (box office)/8774 (office)
Fax: 1-5870 50431/877 431
Internet: www.dietheater.or.at/dietheater
E-Mail: dietheater@gmx.net
manager & artistic director Christian Pronay; assistant to art director Anna Thier; press Elisabeth Drucker; chief technician Franz Strasser
Venue type: multi-functional theatre *Capacity:* 198 *Policy:* present *Arts types:* contemporary drama, dance, performance, modern theatre, mime, puppet theatre
Comments: see also Drama and Festivals

Musikverein, Gesellschaft der Musikfreunde in Wien
Boesendorferstrasse 12, 1010 **Wien**
Tel: 1-505 8681 Fax: 1-505 9409
Internet: www.musikverein.at
E-Mail: office@musikverein.at
Generalsekretär Dr. Thomas Angyan; künstl. Betriebsbüro Alessandra Seledec; Pressebüro Thomas Mittermayer
Venue type: concert hall *Capacity:* Großer Saal 1750 + 300 (standing), Brahms Saal 600 *Policy:* rent, promote
Arts types: symphony, chamber music, lieder, recitals
Comments: see also Promoters

Österreichisches Kulturzentrum/Palais Palffy
Josefsplatz 6, 1010 **Wien**
Tel: 1-512 5681-0 Fax: 1-5125 68118
E-Mail: palaispalffy@netway.at
Direktorin Henriette Sztavjanik; Kulturreferent Mag. Chaim Beneven-Bothe
Venue type: 3 galleries, concert halls *Capacity:* Figarosaal 140, Beethovensaal 250, additional rooms for exhibitions *Policy:* rent, promote *Arts types:* concerts, classical, modern music, exhibitions

Radio Kulturhaus
Argentinierstr. 30a, 1040 **Wien**
Tel: 1-50101-18258/5017 0377 (box office)
Fax: 1-50101-18728
Internet: www.orf.at/orfon/kultur/oe1/kulturhaus
E-Mail: kulturhaus@orf.at
Geschäftsführerin Mag. Christiane Goller-Fischer
Capacity: Grosse Sendesaal 230, Radio-Cafe 70 *Policy:* present, rent *Arts types:* concerts, readings *Comments:* cultural venue of ORF (Österreichischer Rundfunk)

Ronacher Etablissement
Himmelpfortgasse 25, 1010 **Wien**
Tel: 1-514 110 Fax: 1-5141 1511
Internet: www.musicalvienna.at
E-Mail: info@vbw.telecom.at
Intendant Rudi Klausnitzer; Programmkoordination Peter Back-Vega (tel: 1-5883 0272); Verwaltung Dr Franz Schlosser; Betriebssekretariat Beatrix Pecha; techn. Direktor Peter Bouchier
Capacity: 820, 1000 *Policy:* rent, promote *Arts types:* musicals, variety, concerts *Comments:* the organisation behind this venue, Theater an der Wien (q.v.)and Raimund-Theater (q.v.) is Vereinigte Bühnen Wien GesmbH; see also Opera

Szene Wien
Hauffgasse 26, 1110 **Wien**
Tel: 1-749 3341 Fax: 1-749 2206
Internet: www.szenewien.com
E-Mail: office@szenewien.com
director Norbert Ehrlich; music programming Manfred Winter; organisation Gina Salis Soglio
Venue type: hall *Capacity:* up to 500 standing or 250 seating *Policy:* 80% company's own productions, 20% rent *Arts types:* mainly music (rock & ethnic), dance, dance-theatre, theatre

THEATER – Center – FORUM
Porzellangasse 50, 1090 **Wien**
Tel: 1-310 4646 Fax: 1-310 4647
Direktor u. Künstlerischer Leiter Stefan Mras; Sekretariat Birgit Fischer
Capacity: Theater-Forum I 120, Theater-Forum II 98, Theater-Forum III 40 *Policy:* rent, also own productions
Arts types: theatre, cabaret, comedy *Comments:* venue for alternative, free groups of all types

Theater m.b.H.
Zieglergasse 25, 1070 **Wien**
Tel: 1-523 1833 Fax: 1-5231 8332
Internet: www.theatermbh.ev.org
E-Mail: theatermbh@theatermbh.ev.org
directors Johanna Tomek, Werner Schönolt; production manager Andrea Braun-Steiner
Venue type: theatre *Capacity:* 100 *Policy:* present, rent (if suitable for other productions)
Arts types: drama, mainly premieres

Wiener Konzerthaus
Lothringerstrasse 20, 1030 **Wien**
Tel: 1-7124 6860 Fax: 1-713 1709
E-Mail: mail@konzerthaus.at
Generalsekretär Christoph Lieben-Seutter; Leiter des Pressebüros Peter Polansky
Venue type: multi purpose *Capacity:* Schubert Saal 330, Mozart Saal 750, Grosser Saal 1800 *Policy:* present, rent
Arts types: early to contemporary, conferences
Comments: offer subscription series, promote several festivals; see also Festivals and Promoters

WUK – Werkstätten und Kulturhaus
Währingerstrasse 59, 1090 **Wien**
Tel: 1-401 2135
Fax: 1-405 4944 (Programm)/1-408 4251 (PR)
Internet: www.wuk.at
E-Mail: info@wuk.at
Leitung Programm Vincent Abbrederis; Theaterprogramm Helmut Hartmann; Musikprogramm Jan Preuster; Galerieleitung Franziska Kasper; Public Relations und internationale Kontakte Sabine Schebrak; Generalsekretariat Barbara Bastirsch
Venue type: multi-media (cultural) centre *Capacity:* Großer Saal 200 (550), Foyer 60 (100), Museumssäale & Galerien *Policy:* rent, stage *Arts types:* concerts, theatres, dance, exhibitions + workshops, experimental film, festivals (dance), international projects, children's programme *Comments:* member of Trans Europe Halles (q.v.), IETM (q.v.), EFAH (q.v.) and Res Artis; see also Festivals (Tanzsprache)

Zur Kulisse
Verein zur Förderung kultureller Aktivitäten in den Aussenbezirken Wien, Rosensteingasse 39, 1170 **Wien**
Tel: 1-485 3870 Fax: 1-485 4402
Internet: www.kulisse.at
E-Mail: kulisse@onstage.at
Intendantin Doris Ringseis
Capacity: 216 *Policy:* promotes cultural activities on the outskirts of Vienna *Arts types:* cabaret, modern music concerts, readings *Comments:* promote 320 events a year, children's theatre on weekends

Stadttheater Wiener Neustadt
Herzog Leopold Strasse 17-21, 2700 **Wiener Neustadt**
Tel: 2622-373 ext. 334 Fax: 2622-65799
Intendant Peter Radmeyer
Venue type: theatre *Capacity:* 624
Policy: rent, co-produce
Arts types: theatre, musicals, opera, poetry readings

AZERBAIDZHAN (+994)

Azerbaidzhan State Philharmonia
Istiglaliyat St. 2, 370001 **Baku**
Tel: 12-931 651
director Melikov Akif Turan ogly

Chamber and Organ Music Hall
28 May St. 17, 370000 **Baku**
Tel: 12-937 537
director Meshadizade Yashar Agasi ogly

R Beybutov State Theatre
R Beybutov St. 12, 370000 **Baku**
Tel: 12-939 415
director Aslanov Niyazi Ingilab ogly

Republic Palace
Byul-Byul Avenue 35, 370014 **Baku**
Tel: 12-988 484
director Babayev Farhad Agasalim ogly

Shahriyar Baku Cultural Center
Beybutov St. 3, 370016 **Baku**
Tel: 12-932 583
director Kerimov Shirbala Dadashbala ogly

Gandja State Philharmonia
Atayevs St. 135, 374700 **Gandja**
director Gashimova Shahnaz Hasan Kizi

Nakchivan State Philarmony
Azadlyg Avenue 1, 363730 **Nakchivan**
director Abdullayev Abdulla Gasangulu ogly

BELARUS (+375)

Minsk Concert Hall
ul Oktiabrskaja 5, 220000 **Minsk**
Tel: 172-227 8726 Fax: 172-227 8726
director Aljexandr Gundar

BELGIUM (+32)

Cultureel Centrum de Werf
Molenstraat 51, 9300 **Aalst**
Tel: 53-732 812 Fax: 53-732 849
director Yvan Verhavert; ballet, dance, theatre, schools, concerts Kathleen Keymeulen; exhibitions Peter Bondewel; public relations, education Karin de Schutter; administration, accountancy Ludwig de Wael
Venue type: multi-purpose
Capacity: stage A 598, stage B 210, studio 80
Policy: present, rent *Arts types:* ballet, dance theatre, classical concerts, education, exhibitions, special projects *Comments:* publishes a free magazine with publicity and information once a year called Werfmagezien, and magazine MEMO (quarterly)

Cultureel Centrum Berchem
Driekoningenstraat 126, 2600 **Antwerp**
Tel: 3-286 8820 Fax: 3-286 8844
Internet: www.ccberchem.be
E-Mail: ccb@antwerpen.be
director & programming, dance Marc Goossens; communications Priscilla Peeters; music & production Gunter Lots; exhibitions & theatre Cathy Pelgrims; stand-up comedy Murat Can
Venue type: arts centre
Capacity: 400 *Policy:* rent, present, production
Arts types: dance, theatre, music, exhibitions, workshops, stand-up comedy
Comments: artists in residence

Fakkelteater
Reyndersstraat 7, 2000 **Antwerp**
Tel: 3-233 1588 Fax: 3-225 0244
general manager Walter Groener
Venue type: multi-purpose *Capacity:* Red House 268, Black House up to 150, Cellar 49 *Policy:* rent, produce
Arts types: all performing arts – theatre/dance/cabarets/small musicals
Comments: resident theatre company Educatief Theater Antwerp

International Arts Centre deSingel
Internationaal Kunstcentrum deSingel
Jan van Rijswijcklaan 155, 2018 **Antwerp**
Tel: 3-244 1920/248 2828 (box office)
Fax: 3-244 1959/248 2800 (box office)
Internet: www.desingel.be
E-Mail: info@desingel.be
general director Jerry Aerts; director administration Pierre Van Diest ; staff performing arts Myriam De Clopper, Katleen van Langendonck; staff music Tino Haenen; staff architecture Katrien Vandemarliere; staff communication Kristien Gerets
Venue type: arts centre
Capacity: Blauwe Zaal 940, Rode Zaal 800
Policy: present, rent, receiving house, co-produce
Arts types: symphony, chamber music, new music, lieder, recitals, theatre, dance, music theatre, architecture, non-western performing arts
Comments: subscription concerts; for tickets:
E-mail: tickets@desingel.be

Monty
Montignystraat 3-5, 2018 **Antwerp**
Tel: 3-238 6497 Fax: 3-238 0991
E-Mail: monty@village.uunet.be
executive director Anna Schoeters; artistic director Denis van Laeken
Venue type: theatre *Capacity:* 250, up to 600 for concerts *Policy:* produce, co-produce, present *Arts types:* avant-garde theatre, music, concerts, pop concerts, dance

Queen Elisabeth Hall
Elisabethzaal Flanders Congress & Concert Centre, Koningin Astridplein 26, 2018 **Antwerp**
Tel: 3-203 5600 Fax: 3-203 5601
E-Mail: luccleiren@flanderscongresszoo.com
sales manager Luc Cleiren; technical manager Stan Vancutsem
Venue type: congress center, concert hall *Capacity:* 2071 *Policy:* mainly rent *Arts types:* classical music, ballet, opera, chamber music, musicals, rock and pop concerts

Stadsschouwburg
Theaterplaen 1, 2000 **Antwerp**
Tel: 3-234 3302 Fax: 3-227 2658
director Marierose Vrejens
Venue type: concert hall and theatre
Capacity: small hall (performances for young audiences) 550, grande salle (music, theatre) up to 2000 *Policy:* present, rent; to support where possible the work of unknown artists and performers *Arts types:* concerts, classical, world music, theatre, ballet, musicals *Comments:* resident company: A.M.T. (Antwerp Musical Theatre)

Toneelhuis, Het
Jodenstraat 3, 2000 **Antwerp**
Tel: 3-224 8800 Fax: 3-224 8801
Internet: www.kns.be
E-Mail: info@kns.be
artistic director Luk Perceval; administrator Stefaan De Ruyck; public relations Johan van Steenkisté
Venue type: theatre (Bourla), cinema Tokio *Capacity:* 1100, 100 *Arts types:* drama, music
Comments: see also Drama

Maison de la culture d'Arlon
1 Parc des expositions, 6700 **Arlon**
Tel: 63-220 439 Fax: 63-219 789
directrice Marie-Claire Clausse
Venue type: multi-purpose *Capacity:* 613 *Policy:* rent, produce, co-produce, education, workshops, exhibitions, library *Arts types:* theatre, dance, music
Comments: see also Drama

Centre de musique Casino Beringen
Kioskplein 25, 3582 **Beringen**
Tel: 11-421 526 Fax: 11-434 787
Internet: www.limburg.be/casino
E-Mail: pcm@limburg.be
director Jan van Hamel; assistant Jos Biesmans
Venue type: concert hall *Capacity:* 731 *Policy:* present, co-produce, rent *Arts types:* music concerts, opera
Comments: alternative Internet: www.limburg.be/culturagenda

Cultuurcentrum Brugge
St. Jakobsstraat 20-26, 8000 **Brugge**
Tel: 50-443 040 Fax: 50-443 050
director Sonia Debal; programming assistant Peter Roose; programming assistant (plastic arts) Michel Dewilde; programming assistant (youth)
Sonja De Brouwer
Venue type: theatre *Capacity:* Stadsschouwburg 750, De Dijk 250, De Biekorf 254 *Policy:* present, rent *Arts types:* theatre, opera, operetta, musicals, ballet, classical concerts, dance, exhibitions *Comments:* also have 3 exhibition halls

Ancienne Belgique
Boulevard Anspach 110, 1000 **Brussels**
Tel: 2-548 2400 Fax: 2-548 2499
Internet: www.abconcerts.be
E-Mail: info@abconcerts.be
director Jari Demeulemeester; technical director Marc Vrebos; financial director Ignace de Breuck; commercial manager Peter Leyder
Venue type: theatre
Capacity: 2000, 2 stages linked with a professional recording studio
Policy: present, rent, produce, co-produce
Arts types: avant garde and mainline music

Beursschouwburg
August Ortsstraat 20-28, 1000 **Brussels**
Tel: 2-513 8290 Fax: 2-511 7315
Internet: beursschouwburg.vgc.be
E-Mail: beurs@innet.be
director Marijke Vandebuerie; programmer Dirk Seghers; promotion & press Patrick De Coster, Zoë De Smet
Venue type: theatre *Capacity:* 400
Policy: rent, co-present
Arts types: music, theatre, dance, visual arts, exhibitions, film *Comments:* July – organise music festival 'Klinkende Munt'

Botanique – Centre Culturel de la Communauté Française, Le
Rue Royale 236, 1210 **Brussels**
Tel: 2-226 1211 Fax: 2-219 6660
Internet: www.ais.be/botanique
E-Mail: botanique@arcadis.be
directeur général Georges Dumortier; directrice adjointe Annie Valentini; responsable presse et communcation Pascale Bertolini
Venue type: multi-purpose *Capacity:* L'Orangerie 359 (seated) 600 (standing), La Rotonde 125 (seated) 250 (standing), Le Cafe Théâtre 120-150, Le Musée, La Salle d'Animateurs, La Salle de Conférence, Salle de Cinéma 90 *Policy:* rent, produce, co-produce *Arts types:* concerts, ballet, exhibitions, film, theatre *Comments:* also museum, conference facilities, cinema, gallery and library

Centre Culturel J. Franck
94 chaussée de Waterloo, 1060 **Brussels**
Tel: 2-538 9020 Fax: 2-538 1648
E-Mail: ccjf@skynet.be
director Thierry Van Campenhout
Venue type: theatre/concert hall *Capacity:* 350 *Policy:* rent (at own risk) *Arts types:* dance, theatre, film, music, exhibitions *Comments:* theatre co-production; also residency to theatre groups

Cirque Royal
Galerie du Parlement 22, 1000 **Brussels**
Tel: 2-219 5149/218 2015 (bookings) Fax: 2-219 5958
director general Elizabeth t'Kindt
Venue type: multi-purpose *Capacity:* 1750 *Policy:* rent *Arts types:* all arts *Comments:* venue address: 81 Rue de l'Enseignement 1000 Brussels

Concert Noble
rue d'Arlon 82, 1040 **Brussels**
Tel: 2-237 0208 Fax: 2-237 0209
director Luce Anciaux
Venue type: multi-purpose (luxurious, palace like decor) *Capacity:* small palace 600 *Policy:* rent *Arts types:* classical concerts, theatre, dance, conferences

Conservatoire Royal de Musique de Bruxelles
rue de la Régence 30, 1000 **Brussels**
Tel: 2-511 0427 Fax: 2-513 9550/512 6979
director Jean Baily; booking Emile Wynants
Venue type: concert hall *Capacity:* 600 *Policy:* present, rent *Arts types:* classical music, occasional jazz concerts, conferences

Forest National
Avenue du Globe 36, 1190 **Brussels**
Tel: 2-340 2111 (administration)/2211 (booking)
Fax: 2-340 2299
Internet: www.forestnational.com
operational manager Peter Dobbels (2-340 2121); planning manager Nicole Demunter (2-340 2122); vip coordinator Mireille Dirix (2-340 2128)
Venue type: multipurpose *Capacity:* multi-purpose (concert) hall 7600 (seated) 8000 (standing) + 3 VIP spaces *Policy:* rent *Arts types:* all types (concert theatre, sport)

Halle de Schaerbeek
20 rue de la Constitution, 1030 **Brussels**
Tel: 2-227 5960/218 2107 (info) Fax: 2-219 4290
E-Mail: info@halles.be
directeur Philippe Grombeer; communication Philippe Kauffmann; jeune public Anne Kumps
Venue type: modern *Capacity:* grande salle 2200 (standing), 650-800 (seated); hall 450 (standing), 190 (seated); cave 300 (standing), 150 (seated) *Policy:* co-produce, produce, rent, present *Arts types:* theatre, dance, concerts, world music, new circus, youth theatre, expositions of cinema *Comments:* venue address: rue Royale St Marie n° 22A, 1030 Brussels

Halles de Schaerbeek – European Cultural Centre of the French-speaking community
Rue de la Constitution 20, 1030 **Brussels**
Tel: 2-227 5960 Fax: 2-219 4290
Internet: www.halles.be
E-Mail: info@halles.be
director Philippe Grombeer; circus programming Anne Kumps; financial manager Patrick Jonckheere; coordination of programme Philippe Kauffmann
Venue type: multi-purpose venue, renovated covered market *Capacity:* 2500 (for concerts), studio 200, basement 500 (but without equipment) *Policy:* co-present *Arts types:* world music, theatre, jazz, dance, circus, rock, animations, multi-media projects
Comments: member of Trans Europe Halles (q.v.); venue being fully equipped until end 1998; organises festival 'Couleur Café (Crossover Music)

L'Atelier
Rue du Commerce 51, 1040 **Brussels**
Tel: 2-511 2065
director Marcel Hastir
Venue type: concert hall *Capacity:* 100 *Policy:* rent *Arts types:* chamber music *Comments:* 30-35 concerts a year; also organise a few concerts in other venues, support young musicians by organising their concerts and promoting their work

Lunatheater 650
Quai des Péniches 2, 1000 **Brussels**
Tel: 2-201 5858 (admin)/5959 (bookings)
Fax: 2-201 5965
managing directors Agna Smisdom, Yohan Reyniers; dramaturge Marianne Van Kerkaoven
Venue type: theatre *Capacity:* 750 *Policy:* present, rent, produce *Arts types:* drama, music (classical and contemporary), dance

Palais des Beaux-Arts – Paleis Voor Schone Kunsten
rue Royale 10 Koningsstraat, 1000 **Brussels**
Tel: 2-507 8211/20 (rent)
Fax: 2-514 3044
E-Mail: pba.pskdir@skynet.be
general manager Marie-Madeleine Spehl-Robeyns; assistant general manager Ludo Willems
Venue type: concert hall *Capacity:* Grande salle Henry le Boeuf 2000, salle de musique de chambre 480, studio 210, Petit Théâtre 165 *Policy:* rent *Arts types:* concerts, music, theatre, chamber music, ballet, variety, films, conferences

Théâtre 140
Avenue Eugéne Plasky 140, 1030 **Brussels**
Tel: 2-734 4431 Fax: 2-734 4631
Internet: www.creativem.com/t140
E-Mail: t140@skynet.be
artistic director Jo Dekmine; assistant Renee Paduwat
Venue type: multi-purpose *Capacity:* 520 *Policy:* receiving, present, co-produce, rent *Arts types:* international work, theatre, dance, jazz, rock

Théâtre du Résidence Palace
155 rue de la Loi, Boite 4, 1040 **Brussels**
Tel: 2-231 0740 (admin)/0305 (booking)
Fax: 2-231 1222
direction et administration Anny Moureau
Venue type: Art Déco-theatre, built 1926 *Capacity:* 500 *Policy:* rent, present *Arts types:* theatre, dance, concerts (classical and modern), conferences, exhibitions, cinema, presentation of new products

Théâtre Saint Michel
Rue Père Eudore Devroy, 2, 1040 **Brussels**
Tel: 2-734 1665 Fax: 2-735 1225
directeur général & artistique Antonio Vilardi; responsable de la communication et de la programmation danse et Arts Plastiques Frédéric Tombelle; coordinateur général Pierre Paul Meur
Venue type: Grande salle de Theatre, Grand Hall
Capacity: Grande salle de Theatre 1400, Grand Hall 200
Policy: co-productions *Arts types:* orchestra music, chamber music, opera, choirs, contemporary & classical dance, unplugged rock & pop concerts, theatre, exhibitions (paintings & sculptures), cinema
Comments: interested in co-productions with other venues for music dance and theater (French speaking)

Palais des Beaux-Arts
Place du Manège, 6000 **Charleroi**
Tel: 71-314 420/205 645 Fax: 71-334 297
Internet: www.pba.be
E-Mail: resa@tba.be
director general Guy Rassel; president Christian Renard; communication Cécile Druart
Venue type: multi-purpose *Capacity:* Grande Salle 1800, Salle des Congrès 450 *Policy:* present, rent, co-produce, produce *Arts types:* opera, operetta, ballet, theatre, music, recitals, conferences, fashion-shows, exhibitions
Comments: alternative E-mail: info@tba.be

Centre Culturel de Dour
Grand'Place 1, 7370 **Dour**
Tel: 65-655 351 Fax: 65-652 958
administrateur Alain Audin; président-administrateur Huguette Carlier; directeur technique Freddy Dequevy
Venue type: multi-purpose *Capacity:* Salle de Spectacle 370, Salle d'Initiatives (200 sq. metres), foyer (100 sq. metres) *Policy:* present, rent *Arts types:* concerts, theatre, congresses, films, recitals, chamber music, opera, exhibitions, dance, pop and rock concerts, conferences, banquets, balls, cabaret, reunions

Media
Molenstraat 165, 9900 **Eeklo**
Tel: 93-779 394 Fax: 93-783 678
Internet: users.skynet.be/de.media
E-Mail: de.media@skynet.be
director Bernadette Vandercammen; programme Jan de Boever; technical Patrick Bastien
Venue type: multi-purpose *Capacity:* 200 *Policy:* presents *Arts types:* jazz, rock, contemporary music, world music

International Congress Centre (ICC)
Congres Centrum, 9000 **Gent**
Tel: 9-221 7497 Fax: 9-221 7498
Internet: come.to/congrescentrum
E-Mail: congrescentrum@skynet.be
director Mone Tielemous; manager Ann Rombaut
Venue type: congress centre *Capacity:* Congress Hall 1000, Orange Hall 280, Blue Hall 120, breakout rooms: 250, 250, 450, event & sports hall 5000 *Policy:* rent *Arts types:* mainly congresses and conferences, also concerts, dance

Nieuwpoorttheater
Nieuwpoort 31-35, 9000 **Gent**
Tel: 9-223 0000 Fax: 9-224 3361
E-Mail: nieuwpoorttheater@village.uunet.be
general manager Stef Ampe; artistic leaders Johan Dehollander, Arne Sierens
Venue type: theatre *Capacity:* 180 *Policy:* the aim is to make productions (without own company); Nieuwpoorttheater will be a 'productional arts centre'; there will also be time and space to invite productions, but especially (work of) people who are, in some way, related to the work of Dehollander & Sierens *Arts types:* dance, video, theatre *Comments:* Nieuwpoorttheater is an arts centre for innovative contempory art, esp. in the field of performing arts & media

Vooruit Arts Centre
Kunstencentrum VOORUIT/ Centre d'Arts
Sint Pietersnieuwstraat 23, 9000 **Gent**
Tel: 9-267 2820 Fax: 9-267 2830
Internet: www.vooruit.be
E-Mail: info@vooruit.be
director Erik Temmerman; dance Guy Cools; music Wim Wabbes; theatre Luc Dewaele; public relations Peter Van den Eede
Venue type: multi-purpose *Capacity:* theatre 880, concert hall (rock) 1200, Domzaal 200, Minard 220, Balzaal 300 (seated) 500 (standing), cafe, dance, music & theatre studios *Policy:* produce, present, rent *Arts types:* contemporary theatre and dance, new music, film, rock, VOORUIT Geluid music festival

Cultureel Centrum Hasselt
Kunstlaan 5, 3500 **Hasselt**
Tel: 11-229 931 Fax: 11-243 207
directeur René Geladé
Venue type: cultural centre *Capacity:* theatre I 803, theatre II 354 *Policy:* rent, present *Arts types:* theatre, orchestra, dance, opera, musical

Centre culturel régional de l'Arrondissement de Huy
Avenue Delchambre 7a, 4500 **Huy**
Tel: 85-235 309 Fax: 85-250 409
E-Mail: centre.culturel.huy@skynet.be
directeur Jean-Pierre Depaire; président du conseil d'administration Alexis Housiaux
Venue type: italian style theatre *Capacity:* 775 *Policy:* present, rent, co-production, education, production *Arts types:* dance, theatre, music *Comments:* also cultural centre promoting cultural activities in the region

De Kortrijkse Schouwburg
Schouwburgplein 14, 8500 **Kortrijk**
Tel: 56-239 850/855 (tickets)
Fax: 56-239 858
Internet: www.kortrijk.be
E-Mail: kortrij@innet.be
director Roos de Smet
Venue type: theatre *Policy:* present, rent *Arts types:* dance, theatre, ballet, classical music, opera

Limelight
Limelight vzw, Jan Persijnstraat 6, 8500 **Kortrijk**
Tel: 56-221 001 Fax: 56-200 493
E-Mail: limelight@kortijk.be
director & theatre programmation Willy Malysse; film programmation Lieve Vankeirsbulck; music & theme-projects Joost Fonteyne
Venue type: arts centre *Capacity:* three spaces: theatre for live-arts (music and theatre) 119, cinema and videotheatre 96, cinematheatre 50 *Policy:* present, produce *Arts types:* contemporary theatre, music, dance, film, video

Cultureel Centrum Leuven
Brusselsestraat 63, 3000 **Leuven**
Tel: 16-238 427 Fax: 16-291 215
Internet: www.cityleuven.be
directeur Yves Gasia
Venue type: multi-functional centre *Capacity:* Theatre 800, Concert Hall 503, Church 560, Chapel 203, Waaghuis 180 *Policy:* present, rent *Arts types:* orchestra, concerts, dance, theatre, recitals, musical

Stuc / Klapstuk
E van Evenstraat 2d, 3000 **Leuven**
Tel: 16-236 773 Fax: 16-224 676
Internet: www.stuc.kuleuven.ac.be
E-Mail: stuc@stuc.kuleuven.ac.be
business manager Kurt Lannoye; artistic directors theatre & film An-Marie Lambrechts, Karolien Derwael; artistic director dance An-Marie Lambrechts, Griet Van Laer; organisation Klapstuk (shares personnel & accomodation with Stuc)
Venue type: arts centre *Capacity:* 160, 120 and 100 *Policy:* present, co-produce, produce *Arts types:* contemporary theatre, dance, film, video, music, lectures *Comments:* alternative email: klapstuk@stuc.kuleuven.ac.be; see also Festivals

Musée d'Art Moderne et d'Art Contemporain
Parc de la Boverie 3, 4020 **Liège**
Tel: 4-343 0403 Fax: 4-344 1907
curators Francine Dawans, Françoise Safin; secretary Mrs Maisse
Venue type: museum room *Capacity:* 200 *Art types:* music and visual arts, chamber concerts, concerts, theatre, dance, essentially exhibitions *Comments:* Palais des Beaux Arts built for the Universal Exhibition of 1905

Palais des Congrès
Esplanade de l'Europe 2, 4020 **Liège**
Tel: 4-343 6424 Fax: 4-343 2085
E-Mail: palais.des.congres.liege@skynet.be
directeur général Stéphane Moreau; directeur de la communication Miguel Delrez; directeur marketing Philippe Bernimolin
Venue type: congress hall
Capacity: Salle Reine Elisabeth 500, Salle des Fêtes 800, Salle de l'Europe 1000, Salle Rogier 200, 10, 10 Salles de commission 2080, 5 multi-purpose rooms *Policy:* rent, organisation of events (creations – ready made events) *Arts types:* music, theatre, dance, exhibitions

Théâtre Royal de Liège
1 Rue des Dominicains, 4000 **Liège**
Tel: 4-221 4720 Fax: 4-221 0201
Internet: www.orw.be
E-Mail: direction@orw.be
directeur général Jean-Louis Grinda; secrétaire général André Dewez; directeur de la musique Friedrich Pleyer; directeur commercial Arnold Picard; directrice de la communication Martine van Zuylen; directeur financial Osean Defrére; directeur de la scéne Philippe Liesnard; diecteur technique Yvan Rossius
Venue type: theatre
Capacity: 1033
Policy: present, rent, produce and co-produce
Arts types: opera, concerts, theatre *Comments:* alternative Internet: www.eurolyrica.be

Adelberg, De
Adelberg Park 1, 3920 **Lommel**
Tel: 11-553 511 Fax: 11-553 514
director Veerle Ven Bun
Venue type: modern
Capacity: 470 *Policy:* present, rent
Arts types: all types

Centre Culturel, Théatre Royal de Mons
Grand Place 1, 7000 **Mons**
Tel: 65-395 939 Fax: 65-395 940
directeur Henri Camaratta; directeur général Roland Debodt
Venue type: theatre, cultural centre
Policy: present, rent, produce and co-produce
Arts types: opera, ballet, classical music, theatre, film, variety, avant-garde theatre and music
Comments: currently being refurbished

Centre Culturel Regional de Namur
Place du Théâtre 2, 5000 **Namur**
Tel: 81-256 161 (admin)/226 026 (bookings)
Fax: 81-256 160 (admin)/231 356 (bookings)
directeur Patrick Colté; programmation Alain Bombaert; technical director Marc Noël; communication Laurent Cools
Capacity: Théâtre Marlagne 474, Maison de Culture 450, Les Bateliers 100, La Grand Markèqe *Policy:* diffusion, produce, co-produce *Arts types:* classical concerts, theatre, dance, workshops for children, rock *Comments:* see also Drama

Théâtre Royal de Namur
Place du Théâtre, 2, 5000 **Namur**
Tel: 81-256 161 Fax: 81-256 160
E-Mail: theatre-de-namur@skynet.be
directeur Patrick Colté; conseiller artistique Pierre Debauche; responsables technique Vital van Kriekinge, Marc Noël; programmation théâtre, danse, variétés Alain Bombaert; programmation musique Marc Mazy; relations publiques et communication Laurent Cools; administration générale Françoise Pierlot
Capacity: Gande salle 950, Studio 130, Amphithéâtre 110, Foyer 250 *Policy:* rent, produce, co-produce *Arts types:* all performing arts *Comments:* artists in residence: Dominique Serron et l'Infini Théâtre, Etienne Rappe et l'Orchestre des Jeunes de Namur – Sinfonietta (39 musicians)

Casino Kursaal Oostende
Oosthelling, 8400 **Oostende**
Tel: 59-705 111 Fax: 59-708 586
Internet: www.flanderscoast.be/cko
E-Mail: casino.kursaal@flanderscoast.be
general managers Peter Verdonck, Willy Verdonck; entertainment manager Luc Verfaillie
Capacity: 1600 and 600
Policy: present, rent *Arts types:* opera, orchestra, dance, ballet, recitals, musicals

Centre Culturel Communal de Seraing
rue Renaud Strivay 44, 4100 **Seraing**
Tel: 4-337 5454 Fax: 4-337 1194
director Philippe Anciaux; public relations Therese Alba; stage manager Georges Van Dongen
Venue type: multi-purpose *Capacity:* up to 550 *Policy:* present, rent, produce and co-produce *Arts types:* all arts including classical concerts, dance, jazz, film, production workshops

Maison de la Culture
Esplanade Gesrge Grand, Avenue des Frizes Rimbaut, 7500 **Tournai**
Tel: 69-253 070 Fax: 69-210 692
Internet: www.maisonculturetournai.com
E-Mail: info@maisonculturetournai.com
director Philippe Deman
Capacity: theatre 880, other up to 450 *Policy:* present, rent, produce and co-produce *Arts types:* all kinds; dance, contemporary arts, theatre, ballet, concerts, workshops

De Warande
Warandestraat 42, 2300 **Turnhout**
Tel: 14-419 494 Fax: 14-420 821
Internet: www.warande.be
E-Mail: info@warande.be
director Staf Pelckmans; artistic director/head of drama Rebecca De Backer; artistic director/head of drama-theatre for children An Joseph; director exhibitions Jan Cools; director education Anja Geuns; coordination educational programme for schools Leen Thielemans
Venue type: theatre *Capacity:* 747
Policy: present, rent, produce, co-produce
Arts types: theatre, cabaret, music theatre, theatre for children, pantomime, drama, ballet, film, classical music, rock, folk dance, contemporary art, education programmes

Grand-Théâtre de Verviers
rue des Artistes 2, 4800 **Verviers**
Tel: 87-393 039 Fax: 87-393 038
Internet: www.ccrv.be
E-Mail: grandtheatre@skynet.be
artistic director Pierre Stembert
Venue type: theatre *Capacity:* 850 and 150 *Policy:* present, rent, produce and co-produce *Arts types:* opera, orchestra, recitals, ballet, dance theatre, variety

Cultuurcentrum De Schakel
Schakelstraat 8, 8790 **Waregem**
Tel: 56-621 340 Fax: 56-621 350
Internet: www.ccdeschakel.be
E-Mail: info@ccdeschakel.be
director Ria Merlier
Venue type: theatre *Capacity:* 546 *Policy:* present, rent
Arts types: plays, cabaret, theatre, music, film, exhibitions

BOSNIA & HERZEGOVINA (+387)

Academic Culture Centre of Sarajevo University
Mehmeda Spahe 20, 71000 **Sarajevo**
Tel: 71-442 958 Fax: 71-442 958

Bosnian Culture Centre
Branilaca grada 24, 71000 **Sarajevo**
Tel: 71-664 203/441 798
Fax: 71-664 203

Centar 'Skenderija'
Mice Sokolovica bb, 71000 **Sarajevo**
Tel: 71-215 970/213 222/33515 Fax: 71-31760
general manager Hasanbegovic Sadik; marketing manager Kravljaca Aleksandar; cultural programmes Enver Hadziomerspahie
Venue type: arts centre *Capacity:* 3600

BULGARIA (+359)

Concert Hall 'Bulgaria'
1 Benkovski str., 1000 **Sofia**
Tel: 2-987 7656
Venue type: concert hall *Capacity:* concert hall 1134, chamber hall 216 *Arts types:* classical and contemporary music

Festival Hall
kv. Geo Milev, 35 Manastirska str., 1111 **Sofia**
Tel: 2-723 882 Fax: 2-723 554
director Nikola Jekov
Venue type: sports hall
Capacity: up to 5000

National Palace of Culture
1 Bulgaria Square, 1414 **Sofia**
Tel: 2-543 121
director Hristo Droumev
Venue type: congress centre
Capacity: 16 halls up to 4000
Arts types: concerts, films, festival, drama

Universiada Hall
2 Shipchenski prohod Blvd., 1111 **Sofia**
Tel: 2-722 148 Fax: 2-973 3480
director Todor Bogdanov
Venue type: sports and concert hall
Capacity: up to 3500

Festival Complex – Varna
2 Slivnitza blvd., 9000 **Varna**
Tel: 52-21331 Fax: 52-236 123/608 446
director Ilia Raev
Capacity: up to 1000
Arts types: concerts, meetings

CROATIA (+385)

International Cultural Centre Groznjan
Medunarodni Kulturni Centar Hrvatske Groznjan
c/o Hrvatska glazbena mladez/Jeunesses Musicales of Croatia (JMC), Trg Stjepana Radica 4, 10000 **Zagreb**
Tel: 1-611 1579/611 1566/52-776 106 (Groznjan)
Fax: 1-611 1566
contact Dubravka Dujmovic; director Senka Janjanin Krkljes
Venue type: music centre *Capacity:* concert hall 120

Vatroslav Lisinski Concert Hall
Koncertna dvorana Vatroslava Lisinskog
Trg Stjepana Radicá 4, 10000 **Zagreb**
Tel: 1-612 1111/1163/1155
Fax: 1-535 283
director Lovro Lisicic
Venue type: concert hall, congress centre *Capacity:* 1850, small hall 300 *Arts types:* music, theatre, dance, exhibitions *Comments:* also congress and conference venue, rehearsal and concert venue for the Zagreb Philharmonic and Symphonic Orchestras

CYPRUS (+357)

Municipal Hall
Cultural Department, Larnaka Municipality, PO Box 40045, 6300 **Larnaka**
Tel: 4-657 745
Fax: 4-653 384/627 244
Venue type: multi-purpose hall *Capacity:* 230 *Policy:* rent *Arts types:* drama, music, dance, exhibitions, cinema *Comments:* venue address: Athinon Ave., Larnaka

Patticheion Municipal Amphitheatre
Cultural Department, Larnaka Municipality, PO Box 40045, 6300 **Larnaka**
Tel: 4-657 745 Fax: 4-653 384
Venue type: ancient style, open air *Capacity:* 2100 *Policy:* rent *Arts types:* drama, music, dance *Comments:* venue address: Salt Lake Park, Larnaka

Patticheion Municipal Theatre
Cultural Department, Limassol Municipality, PO Box 89, 3600 **Limassol**
Tel: 5-363 103 Fax: 5-365 497
Internet: www.limassolmunicipal.com.cy
E-Mail: limassol.municipal@cytanet.com.cy
Venue type: theatre hall *Capacity:* 760 *Policy:* rent *Arts types:* drama, music, dance *Comments:* venue address: Ayias Zonis 2, Limassol

Praxis Theatre
E.Th.A.L., PO Box 58096, 3730 **Limassol**
Tel: 5-357 570 Fax: 5-341 112
Venue type: theatre hall *Capacity:* 210 *Policy:* rent *Arts types:* drama, music, dance, cinema *Comments:* venue address: M. Michaelides & L. Akrita str., Limassol

Melina Mercouri Hall
Cultural Service, Nicosia Municipality, PO Box 21015, 1500 **Nicosia**
Tel: 2-665 006 Fax: 2-663 363
E-Mail: municipa@nicosia.com.org.cy
Venue type: multi-purpose hall *Capacity:* 190 *Arts types:* drama, music, dance, exhibitions *Comments:* venue address: King George II Square, Nicosia

Municipal Theatre
Cultural Service, Nicosia Municipality, PO Box 21015, 1500 **Nicosia**
Tel: 2-665 006/473 124
Fax: 2-663 363
E-Mail: municipa@nicosia.com.org.cy
Venue type: theatre and concert hall *Capacity:* 1200 *Policy:* rent *Arts types:* drama, music, dance *Comments:* venue address: Mouseion str., Nicosia

Markideion Theatre
Pafos Municipality, PO Box 60032, 8100 **Pafos**
Tel: 6-232 014 Fax: 6-247 964
contact Cultural Service of Pafos Municipality
Venue type: Italian stage theatre
Capacity: 385 *Arts types:* theatre, dance, symphonic and chamber music concerts
Comments: co-administered by Pafos Municipality and Theatre Organisation of Cyprus; venue address: 27 Andrea Geroudi Str., Pafos

Cultural Centre Vladimiros Kafkarides
Satirikon Theatre, Athinon & Serron 3, 2040 **Strovolos**
Tel: 2-312 940/421 609 Fax: 2-493 450
Venue type: theatre hall and open air stage *Capacity:* theatre hall 360, open air 260 *Policy:* rent *Arts types:* drama, music, dance, cinema

Makarios III Amphitheatre
c/o Theatre Organisation of Cyprus, Chalkanoros 2 & Liperti, 2000 **Strovolos**
Tel: 2-492 900 Fax: 2-492 923
Venue type: ancient style, open air *Capacity:* 1600 *Policy:* rent *Arts types:* drama, music, dance *Comments:* venue address: 28th October str., Strovolos

CZECH REPUBLIC (+420)

Bolek Polívka Theatre
Divadlo Bolka Polívky
Jakubské námestí 7, 602 00 **Brno**
Tel: 5-4221 4692 Fax: 5-4221 4692
director Boleslav Polívka; manager Petr Bílek
Venue type: theatre hall *Capacity:* 300 *Policy:* rent *Arts types:* drama, non-verbal theatre, pantomime, exhibitions

Cabinet of Muses
Kabinet Múz
Sukova 4/6, 602 00 **Brno**
Tel: 5-4221 6870
manager Alice Stuchlíková
Venue type: theatre and multi-purpose hall
Capacity: 100 *Policy:* rent *Arts types:* drama, music, jazz, exhibitions

Theatre below Cap
Divadlo pod cepicí
Trznice IGY – Prazská 1258/30,
370 00 **Ceské Budejovice**
Tel: 38-25829 Fax: 38-25829
manager Katerina Melenová
Venue type: theatre hall *Capacity:* 100 *Policy:* rent *Arts types:* drama, puppets, exhibitions

Theatre for 111
Divadlo pro 111
Mestsky kulturní dum,
370 01 **Ceské Budejovice**
Venue type: small theatre hall *Capacity:* 111 *Policy:* rent *Arts types:* drama

Petr Bezruc Theatre
Divadlo Petra Bezruce
tr. 28, rijna 120, 702 00 **Ostrava**
Tel: 69-612 4766
director Jarmila Hájková
Venue type: theatre hall *Capacity:* 150, Márnice (Morgue) 40 *Policy:* rent

Theatre Kruh – Cultural House
Divadlo Kruh – Kulturní dum
INVEST SHOP, Americká trída 49, 301 50 **Plzen**
Tel: 19-722 4742/4224/2568
manager Eva Willigová
Venue type: theatre hall and foyer *Capacity:* 286 *Policy:* rent *Arts types:* theatre, folk and chamber music, exhibitions

Black Light Theatre Image
Parízská 4, 110 00 **Praha** 1
Tel: 2-232 9191 Fax: 2-2481 1167
executive director Petr Ducik; producer Alexander Cihar
Venue type: multi-purpose hall *Capacity:* 200 to 250 *Policy:* rent *Arts types:* drama, black theatre, pantomime, dance

Central Hall of the Industry Palace
Stredni hala Prumyslového Paláce
Prague Exhibition Ground, Vystaviste,
170 00 **Praha** 7
Tel: 2-6679 8111
Venue type: large multi-purpose hall (stage 10 x 20m)
Capacity: 690 *Policy:* rent *Arts types:* theatre, dance, music, exhibitions *Comments:* part of Vystaviste (q.v.)

Foot Bridge Club
Klub Lávka
Novotného lávka 1, 110 00 **Praha** 1
Tel: 2-2421 4797 Fax: 2-2108 2288
director Boris Gajdecka
Venue type: chamber theatre and music hall, multi-purpose hall *Capacity:* 150 *Policy:* rent *Arts types:* drama, pantomime, black theatre, chamber concerts and opera

Gong – Theatre Stage
Gong – divadelní scéna
Sokolovská 191, 190 00 **Praha** 9
Tel: 2-6631 1629 Fax: 2-684 5460
manager Zuzana Pavlatová
Venue type: multi-purpose hall *Capacity:* 300, 100 to 200 (for dance performances) *Policy:* rent *Arts types:* drama, dance, music

Jirí Grossmann Theatre – DIF Centre
Divadlo Jirího Grossmanna – DIF Centrum
Václavské námestí 43, 110 00 **Praha** 1
Tel: 2-2421 1911 Fax: 2-2421 1911
manager Petr Tzc
Venue type: universal hall, cinema, great hall, cinema cafe *Capacity:* 460 *Policy:* rent *Arts types:* writers' theatre, entertaiment, music, cinema

Krizik Fountain
Krizikova Fontana
The Prague exhibition ground – Vystaviste,
170 00 **Praha** 7
Tel: 2-6679 8111
Venue type: multi-purpose *Capacity:* 2000 to 2500 *Arts types:* theatre, music, dance *Comments:* under the roof in the proximity of the fountain; part of Vystaviste (q.v.)

Labyrint – Art Centre on the Left Side of the River Vlatava
Labyrint – umelecké centrum na levém brehu Vltavy
Stefánikova 57, 150 43 **Praha** 5
Tel: 2-5732 1331 Fax: 2-548 062
director Karel Kríz
Venue type: theatre hall and multi-purpose studio stage
Capacity: 397 and 100 *Arts types:* drama, dance, non-verbal theatre, music, exhibitions, conferences
Comments: cafe, theatre club

Music Theatre – Stage of Czech Radio Prague
Divadlo hudby – scéna Ceského rozlasu Praha
Opletalova 5, 110 00 **Praha** 1
Tel: 2-2421 1690/0965 Fax: 2-2421 1697
Venue type: theatre and concert hall
Capacity: 220 *Policy:* rent, present at own risk *Arts types:* drama, concerts, exhibitions, press conferences
Comments: restaurant, bar, recording studio

Palace Akropolis
Palác Akropolis
Kubelíkova 27, 130 00 **Praha** 3
Tel: 2-697 6411 Fax: 2-2271 8212
Venue type: multi-purpose theatre hall *Capacity:* 250 *Policy:* rent *Arts types:* drama, nonverbal theatre, cabaret, jazz, exhibitions

Palace of Culture – Congress and Cultural Centre
Palác kultury – kongresové a kulturní centrum
Ulice 5. kvetna 65, 140 00 **Praha** 4
Tel: 2-6117 1111 Fax: 2-424 180
Venue type: 4 halls – Congress Hall, concert and theatre hall; Concert Hall, multi-purpose theatre and concert hall; Little Hall, multi-purpose hall; Chamber Hall, multi-purpose theatre hall type studio *Capacity:* Congress Hall 2839, Concert Hall 1200, Little Hall 350, Chamber Hall 190 *Policy:* rent *Arts types:* theatre, music, dance, congresses *Comments:* in the Congress Hall organ, translation section, TV productions, space for orchestra

Prague Exhibition Ground
Vystaviste
Vystaviste, 170 00 **Praha** 7
Tel: 2-6679 8111
Venue type: Summer Stages in the Exhibition space
Policy: rent *Arts types:* theatre performance, clown, music *Comments:* please see also: Strední hala Prumyslového paláce, Krizik fountain, Pyramid (q.v.), Central hall of the Industry palace (q.v.)

Puppets Empire
Ríse loutek
Zatecká 1, 110 00 **Praha** 1
Tel: 2-2481 9322 Fax: 2-2481 9324
manager Petr Vodicka
Venue type: theatre hall *Capacity:* 200 *Policy:* rent *Arts types:* puppet theatre only for string *Comments:* also a puppet's museum

Pyramid
Pyramida
Prague Exhibition Ground, Vystaviste,
170 00 **Praha** 7
Tel: 2-6679 8111 Fax: 2-371 355
Venue type: multi-purpose *Capacity:* 1000 *Policy:* rent *Arts types:* theatre, music, dance *Comments:* part of Vystaviste (q.v.)

Roxy – experimental space
Roxy – experimentální prostor
Dlouhá 33, 110 00 **Praha** 1
Tel: 2-2481 0951 Fax: 2-2482 8285
manager Anetta Riglová
Venue type: multi-purpose hall *Policy:* rent *Arts types:* drama, nonverbal theatre, cabaret, jazz, exhibitions

Rudolphinum Rudolfinum
c/o Ceská filharmonie, Alsovo nábr. 12,
110 00 **Praha** 1
Tel: 2-2489 3111 Fax: 2-231 9051/2489 3228
E-Mail: cforch@mbox.vol.cz
Venue type: 2 halls – Dvorák Hall, concert hall; Suk Room, concert room *Capacity:* Dvorák Hall 1100, Suk Room 200 *Arts types:* concerts *Comments:* alternative E-mail: cfmark@mbox.vol.cz

Smetana Hall
Smetanova sín
c/o Symfonicky orchestr hl.m.Prah FOK, nám. Republiky 5, 110 00 **Praha** 1
Tel: 2-231 5981/2048/1900 Fax: 2-231 0784
E-Mail: fok@login.cz
Venue type: multi-purpose room *Capacity:* 1150 *Arts types:* concerts, dance, conferences

Spiral
Spirála
Prague Exhibition Ground – Vystaviste, 170 00 **Praha** 7
Tel: 2-872 9380/1 Fax: 2-371 197
manager Stanislav Aubrecht
Venue type: circular partly variable theatre hall
Capacity: 488-860 *Policy:* rent
Arts types: theatre, multi-media, visual arts

Sti. Simenon and Juda's Church
Kostel sv....imona a Judy
c/o Symfonicky orchestr hl.m.Prahy FOK, nám. Republiky 5, 110 00 **Praha** 1
Tel: 2-231 5981/2048/1900 Fax: 2-231 0784
E-Mail: fok@login.cz
Venue type: concert room in a former church *Arts types:* concerts

Theatre Ark
Divadlo Archa
Na Porící 26, 110 00 **Praha** 1
Tel: 2-232 7570 Fax: 2-232 2089/2481 2468
Internet: www.archatheatre.cz
E-Mail: archa@archatheatre.cz
director Ondrej Hrab
Venue type: multi-purpose theatre hall *Capacity:* large auditorium (arena and proscenium) 300 up to 500, small auditorium up to 120 *Policy:* rent and present, commission new works *Arts types:* drama, dance, music, multi-media, visual arts *Comments:* see also Promoters and Drama

Theatre behind the fence
Divadlo za plotem
Ustavní 91, 180 00 **Praha** 8
Tel: 2-857 4515 Fax: 2-857 4515
director Vladimír Cerny
Venue type: universal, multi-purpose hall *Capacity:* 250 to 300 *Arts types:* theatre, concerts, dance, film *Comments:* semi-professional recording studio

Theatre in Celetná
Divadlo v Celetné
Celetná 17, 110 00 **Praha** 1
Tel: 2-2480 9168 Fax: 2-2481 09171
manager Robert Hron
Venue type: chamber theatre hall *Capacity:* 150 *Policy:* rent *Arts types:* theatre

Theatre in Reznická
Divadlo v Reznické
Reznická 17, 110 00 **Praha** 1
Tel: 2-2223 0996 Fax: 2-2223 0996
manager Yvetta Srbová
Venue type: multi-purpose theatre hall *Capacity:* 80 *Policy:* rent, present at own risk *Arts types:* theatre, exhibitions

Theatre of Dejvice
Dejvické divaldo
Zelená 15, 160 00 **Praha** 6
Tel: 2-311 2365/9108 Fax: 2-311 2359/9359
Internet: www.divadlo.cz/dd
E-Mail: dejvicke@vol.cz
director Eva Mericková; artistic chief Miroslav Krobot
Venue type: theatre hall *Capacity:* 150 *Policy:* rent *Arts types:* drama, puppets, jazz, exhibitions *Comments:* see also Puppetry

Viola
Viola
Národní trída 7, 110 00 **Praha** 1
Tel: 2-2422 0844 Fax: 2-2422 0844
director Miluse Viklická
Venue type: small theatre and concert hall *Capacity:* 82 *Policy:* rent *Arts types:* one-man show, poetry, jazz and classical music, conferences *Comments:* restaurant

Zizkov Theatre of Jára Cimrman
Zizkovské divadlo Járy Cimrmana
Stítného 5, 130 00 **Praha** 3
Tel: 2-628 4175 Fax: 2-627 8900
dirctor Jana Pazderníková
Venue type: theatre hall *Capacity:* 300 *Policy:* rent *Arts types:* theatre

Spanish Room
Spanelsky sál
Prague Castle Administration, 119 08 **Praha-Hrad**
Tel: 2-2437 2364 Fax: 2-2431 0896
E-Mail: pdn@hrad.cz
executive manager Martin Pechanec
Venue type: multi-purpose hall *Capacity:* 650 *Arts types:* concerts, conferences, official receptions

DENMARK (+45)

Sønderjyllandshallen
H P Hanssensgade 7, 6200 **Aabenraa**
Tel: 7462 3650 Fax: 7462 3309
director Ib Kragsfeldt; stage manager Peter Autzen
Venue type: cultural centre-multi purpose
Capacity: 1250 *Arts types:* theatre, concerts, opera, ballet, shows, exhibitions

Aalborg Kongres & Kultur Center
Box 149, 9100 **Aalborg**
Tel: 9935 5555 Fax: 9935 5533
E-Mail: akkc@akkc.dk
managing director Ernst Trillingsgaard; information chef Bettina Christensen
Venue type: multi-purpose *Capacity:* Hall A 2560, Hall B 700 *Arts types:* opera, ballet, theatre, shows, concerts, exhibitions, conferences

Symfonien
Kjellerupsgade 14, 9000 **Aalborg**
Tel: 9813 1955 Fax: 9813 0378
Internet: www.aalborgsymfoniorkester.dk
E-Mail: symfoni@pip.dknet.dk
Venue type: concert hall *Capacity:* 450 *Comments:* Symfonien is the name of the house where Aalborg Symfoniorkester (Aalborg Symphony Orchestra) resides

Aarhus Conference Hall
Aarhus Kongreshus
Amaliegade 23, 8000 **Aarhus** C
Tel: 8613 8844 Fax: 8613 9099
managing director Yrene Christensen
Venue type: multi-purpose *Capacity:* 1000 (max) *Policy:* rent *Arts types:* mainly conferences, also all types of performing arts

Helsingoer Theatre
Den Gamle By Danmarks Koebstadmuseum, Viborgvej 2, 8000 **Aarhus** C
Tel: 8612 1010 Fax: 8676 0687
E-Mail: DenGamleBy@DenGamleBy
director Elsebeth Aasted
Venue type: theatre *Capacity:* 235 *Policy:* the venue is available for rent *Arts types:* symphony orchestra, exhibitions, dance, opera, chamber music, recitals, drama

Musikhuset Aarhus
Aarhus Concert Hall
Thomas Jensens Allé, 8000 **Aarhus** C
Tel: 8931 8200 Fax: 8619 4386
Internet: www.musikhuset-aarhus.dk
E-Mail: musikhus@inet.uni-c.dk
managing director Hans N. Hansen; promoter Ilse Vestergaard; press & public relations manager Martin Lai
Venue type: multi-purpose *Capacity:* large auditorium 1500, small auditorium 300, foyer stage 600, amphistage 3000 *Policy:* rent, present events at own risk *Arts types:* symphony orchestra, pop, rock, exhibitions, dance, variety, opera, congress, theatre *Comments:* residence for: Aarhus Symphony Orchestra, National Opera, Danish Institute of Electro-Acoustic Music

VOX HALL
Vester Alle 15, 8000 **Aarhus** C
Tel: 8612 8044 ext 10 Fax: 8612 2889
E-Mail: slowgore@post4.tele.dk
director t.b.a.; music consultant Ib Valentin Ernst; director Thomas Fog; music consultant t.b.a.
Capacity: 500 *Policy:* promote, rent *Arts types:* rock, contemporary, jazz, world music, electronic

Dansescenen
Oester Faelled, Torv 34, 2100 **Copenhagen** Ø
Tel: 3543 8300 Fax: 3543 8110
E-Mail: dansescenen@image.dk
director Louise Seibæk; administrator/producer Anne Therese Rude
Venue type: open stage theatre *Capacity:* 350 *Policy:* rent, plus co-productions *Arts types:* contemporary dance

Den Anden Opera
Kronprinsensgade 7, 1114 **Copenhagen** K
Tel: 3332 3830/5556 (ticket office) Fax: 3332 3836
E-Mail: denandenopera@get2net.dk
manager Jesper Lützhøft
Capacity: up to 200 *Arts types:* contemporary opera, music, experimental music (not rock/jazz) *Comments:* see also Opera

Kanonhallen
Serridsslevvej 2, 2100 **Copenhagen**
Tel: 3543 2324 Fax: 3138 6611
Internet: www.kanonhallen.dk
E-Mail: kanon@post3.tele.dk
director Irene Møller; coordinator/pr Jens Frimann Hansen
Venue type: flexible *Capacity:* up to 600 *Policy:* present *Arts types:* performance, theatre, dance

Norresbros Teater
Ravnsborgsgade 3, 2200 **Copenhagen** N
Tel: 3535 2760 Fax: 3535 3730
director Leon Feder; dramaturg & pressechef Bina Hjorth; secretary Birgit Lassen; finance Lisa Meller
Capacity: 623 *Policy:* promote, rent *Arts types:* drama, musicals, music, dance

Privat Teatret
Nyropsgade 41, 1602 **Copenhagen** V
Tel: 3332 3333/3325 2517 Fax: 3321 5006
Internet: www.privatteatret.dk
manager Niels-Bo Valbro
Venue type: theatre, cinema *Capacity:* up to 650 *Policy:* rent *Comments:* see also Drama

Royal Danish Academy of Music
Det KGL Danske Musikkonservatorium
Niels Brocksgade 1, 1574 **Copenhagen** V
Tel: 3369 2269 Fax: 3369 2279
E-Mail: dkdm@dkdm.kum.dk
director Steen Pade
Capacity: 265 *Arts types:* mainly classical music

Rundetaarn
Købmagergade 52A, 1150 **Copenhagen** K
Tel: 3373 0373 Fax: 3373 0377
Internet: www.rundetaarn.dk
E-Mail: post@rundetaarn.dk
director Jesper Vang Hansen; musical director Tomas Krakowski
Venue type: exhibitions, concerts *Capacity:* max. 150 *Policy:* rent *Arts types:* exhibitions, concerts, observatory *Comments:* 80 concerts per season and 10 exhibitions per season

Tivolis Koncertsal
Vesterbrogade 3, 1630 **Copenhagen** V
Tel: 3315 1001 Fax: 3375 0378
Internet: www.tivoli.dk
E-Mail: lg@Tivoli.dk
director Lars Liebst; music director Lars Grunth
Capacity: 2000 *Policy:* rent, promote *Arts types:* chamber music, symphony, dance

Esbjerg Performing Arts Center
Musikhuset Esbjerg
Havnegade 18, 6700 **Esbjerg**
Tel: 7610 9000 Fax: 7610 9012
managing and artistic director Allan Xenius Grige; events manager Peter Dalsgaard; technical director Jens Kirkeby
Venue type: multi-purpose arts centre
Capacity: main auditorium: seated 1085, standing 2000; theatre/chamber music hall 250
Arts types: concerts, theatre, conferences, exhibitions
Comments: an open foyer stage, an amphitheatre, a lecture hall, as well as café, restaurant and meeting rooms

Multihus Tobaksfabrikken
Gasværksgade 2, 67000 **Esbjerg**
Tel: 7518 0222 Fax: 7545 9563
Internet: www.tobakken.dk
E-Mail: tobakken@email.dk
contact Jorgen Johansen
Venue type: multi-purpose
Capacity: varies
Comments: member of transEurope Halles, Tel: +33 1-4011 6414, Internet: www.teh.net

Danish National Radio Symphony Orchestra Hall
Radiohusets Koncertsal
Radiohuset, 1999 **Frederiksberg** C
Tel: 3520 6392/3040 Fax: 3520 6121
Internet: www.dr.dk/rso
E-Mail: dnrso@dr.dk
Capacity: 1050 *Arts types:* orchestra, opera, chamber music, recitals, choral concerts *Comments:* home to the Danish National Radio Symphony Orchestra, for concert entrance, address is : Julius Thomsens Gade 1, 1999 Frederiksberg C

Radisson S.A.S. Falconer Centret
Falkoner Allé 9, 2000 **Frederiksberg**
Tel: 3819 8001 Fax: 3815 8002
administrative director Per Kyed Jacobsen; administrator Henriette Hansen
Capacity: Falkoner Salen 2157, Falkoner Scenen 900
Policy: rent *Arts types:* theatre, dance, opera, concerts, conferences

Rialto Teatret
Smallegade 2, Box 723, 2000 **Frederiksberg**
Tel: 3888 0111 Fax: 3888 0100
Internet: www.mico.dk/rialto
E-Mail: info@rialtoteatret.dk
director Anders Ahnfelt-Rønne
Capacity: 200 *Arts types:* modern Danish drama and classical performances

Gjethuset
Gjethusgade 5, 3300 **Frederiksværk**
Tel: 4777 0607 Fax: 4777 0697
directir, booking/arranger Steen Jørgensen; communication, public relations Merete Bodenhoff; administration, economy Yvonne Johansen
Venue type: cultural centre *Capacity:* 450/1100 *Policy:* rent, present *Arts types:* concerts, exhibitions, theatre

Herning Kongrescenter
Østergade 37, 7400 **Herning**
Tel: 9721 0111 Fax: 9926 9909
E-Mail: hkc@kongrescenter.dk
director Gert Jepsen; marketing director Bent Mølgaard
Venue type: multi-purpose *Capacity:* Hall I 1800, Hall II 1700, Theatre 1032, Room 3 300, Room 4 400 *Policy:* rent, promote

Musikteatret Holstebro
Ved Hallen 4, 7500 **Holstebro**
Tel: 9611 7878/7979 Fax: 9611 7879
Internet: www.musikteatret.dk
E-Mail: musikteatret.holstebrohallen@holstebro.dk
arrangementschef Knud Kristensen; director Lars Sennels
Venue type: multi-purpose *Capacity:* 2500 *Policy:* present at own risk and shares risk with other promoters *Arts types:* orchestra, pop, rock, exhibitions, dance etc.

Trommen Concert and Theatre Hall
Bibliotekstorvet 1, 2970 **Hørsholm**
Tel: 4586 3235 Fax: 4576 6906
E-Mail: trommen@Hørsholm.dk
managing director Jerry Ritz; financial/sales manager Marianne Jensen; pr/information Annette Petersen; production manager Jesper Schulze; sales manager John Brauer
Venue type: multi-purpose *Capacity:* Main Room – seated 420, standing 840, Foyer stage 120 *Comments:* member of KND (Association of Danish Culture Houses)

Louisiana Museum of Modern Art
Gl. Strandvej 13, 3050 **Humlebaek**
Tel: 4919 0719/0791(aut info-line) Fax: 4919 3505
Internet: www.louisiana.dk
E-Mail: press@louisiana.dk
director Cristina Lage Hansen; deputy director Steingrim Laursen; curators Helle Crenzien, Kjeld Kjeldsen; press coordinator Susanne Hartz; music dept Lars Fenger; education Ida Brændholt
Venue type: museum with permanent international collection,exhibitions of modern art, concerts, children's wing, cinema, conference room, museum cafe and museum shop *Capacity:* concert hall 325, cinema 100 *Arts types:* international collection and changing exhibitions of modern art, concerts, cinema, children's wing

Brandts Klaedefabrik
5000 **Odense** C
Tel: 6613 7897 Fax: 6613 7310
Internet: www.brandts.dk
E-Mail: kunsthallen@brandts.dk
directors Finn Thrane, Karsten Ohrt, Ervin Nielsen; curators Lene Burkard, Andreas Jürgensen, Lis Steincke; head of press/public relations Eva S. Runge
Venue type: cultural centre *Capacity:* 400 *Arts types:* drama, exhibitions, seminars *Comments:* galleries, museums, libraries, concert hall, shops, cinemas, amphitheatre

Hotel H C Andersen
Claus Bergsgade 7, 5000 **Odense** C
Tel: 6614 7800 Fax: 6614 7890
Internet: www.radisson.com-odense.dk
general manager Jack Nielsen; marketing manager Lone Weidemann
Venue type: multi-purpose *Capacity:* Carl Nielsen 1200, Pro Musica Hall 360 *Policy:* rent *Arts types:* conferences and concerts *Comments:* has street level disable access and disabled toilets

Odense Konserthus
Claus Bertsh Gate 9, 5000 **Odense** C
Fax: 6591 0047
E-Mail: orchestra@odensesynfoni.dk
general manager Per Holst
Venue type: multi-purpose *Capacity:* 1200 *Policy:* rent, promote *Arts types:* mainly classical music *Comments:* home of Odense Symphony Orchestra (q.v.)

Kulturhus Viften
Rødovre Parkvej 130, 2610 **Rødovre**
Tel: 3670 4431 Fax: 3672 0803
E-Mail: Viften@rk.dk
directors John Frobøse, Inga Hansen
Venue type: multi-purpose *Capacity:* Auditorium 376, Koncerts (standing) 800, cinema 107, multi-purpose cafe 150 *Arts types:* dance, theatre and all types of music

Sankt Annæ Gymnasium, Sankt Annæ Salen
Sjælør Boulevard 135, 2500 **Valby**
Tel: 3646 6222 Fax: 3644 2112
E-Mail: sag@tic.dk
director Povl Markussen; secretary to choir & music dept Tove Joergensen
Venue type: auditorium *Capacity:* 800 *Arts types:* symphony concerts, jazz, classical concerts

ESTONIA (+372)

Culture Centre Mai
Kultuurikeskus Mai
Papiniidu 50, 80042 **Pärnu**
Tel: 44-24144 Fax: 44-44595
artistic manager Ludmilla Rein
Arts types: theatre, concerts

Brotherhood of Blackheads House
Mustpeade Maja
Pikk 26, 10133 **Tallinn**
Tel: 2-443 877
director Juta Taniel
Venue type: two concert halls *Arts types:* chamber concerts, exhibitions, choir concerts

Estonia Concert Hall
Eesti Kontserdi saal
Estonia pst. 4, 10148 **Tallinn**
Tel: 6-443 198 Fax: 6-314 171
administrator Sirje Piht
Capacity: 800 *Arts types:* symphony, chamber, organ, jazz concerts

Estonian Theatre Wintergarden
Estonia Teatri Talveaed
Estonia pst. 4, 10148 **Tallinn**
Tel: 6-260 247
director Viktoria Jagomägi
Capacity: 300 *Arts types:* soloists, chamber concerts

Salme Cultural Centre
Salme Kultuurikeskus
Salme 12, 10413 **Tallinn**
Tel: 2-602 158
director Aavo Lossmann; assistant Merike Purde
Venue type: theatre hall *Capacity:* 680 *Arts types:* theatre, dance, concerts

St Nicolas Museum Concert Hall
Niguliste Muuseum-Kontserdisaal
Rüütli 13, 10130 **Tallinn**
Tel: 2-449 911
director Marju Lagerküll
Arts types: organ, chamber and choir concerts

Tallinn City Hall
Tallinna Linnahall
Mere pst. 20, 10111 **Tallinn**
Tel: 2-601 893 Fax: 2-449 847
director Ago Kalde
Venue type: multi-purpose *Capacity:* 4200 *Arts types:* all art forms

Von Krahl Theatre
Rataskaevu 10, 10123 **Tallinn**
Tel: 6-269 090 Fax: 6-269 099
director Priit Raud
Venue type: production house *Capacity:* black box 150 *Policy:* rent and present *Arts types:* contemporary theatre, dance, musical theatre, jazz

Vanemuise Concert Hall
Vanemuise Kontserdimaja
Vanemuise 6, 51003 **Tartu**
Tel: 7-442 272 Fax: 7-442 253
director Laine Jänes
Capacity: 838 *Arts types:* classic, chamber, choir, music concerts

FINLAND (+358)

Espoo Cultural Centre
Espoon kulttuurikeskus
Kaupinkalliontie 10, 02100 **Espoo**
Tel: 9-816 5051 Fax: 9-8165 7220
Internet: www.espoo.fi/kuke/index.htm
E-Mail: espoo.kulttuurikeskus@espoo.fi
director Osmo Pylvänäinen; marketing manager Hilppa Sorjonen
Capacity: Tapiola Hall 787, Louhi Hall – stage A 178, stage B 241, stage C 304 *Policy:* present, rent *Arts types:* concerts, theatre, dance, opera, film, exhibitions
Comments: home of Tapiola Sinfonietta (Espoo City Orchestra); venue for piano, choir, jazz and film festivals

Hanasaari – The Swedish-Finnish Cultural Centre
Hanasaari – Ruotsalais-suomalainen kulttuurikeskus
02100 **Espoo**
Tel: 9-435 020 Fax: 9-467 291
E-Mail: hanasaari@hanaholmen.fi
director Anna-Maija Marttinen; conference manager Ari Vilkki
Venue type: multi-purpose and congress centre
Capacity: auditorium 240 *Policy:* rent *Arts types:* commercial, conferences & seminars *Comments:* hotel and restaurant section; wheelchair access and facilities; the centre is located on an island surrounded by the sea

Häme Castle
Kustaa III:n katu 6, 13100 **Hämeenlinna**
Tel: 3-675 6820 Fax: 3-616 6379
E-Mail: anne.parikka@nba.fi
director Anne Parikka
Comments: besides being a tourist attraction, the castle also offers exhibitions; facilities for weddings, concerts and other similar occasions, guided tours available in Finnish, Swedish, German and English

Finlandia Hall
Finlandia-talo
Mannerheimintie 13e, 00100 **Helsinki**
Tel: 9-40241 Fax: 9-402 4249
Internet: finlandia.hel.fi
E-Mail: finlandiahall@fin.hel.fi
director Auni Palo
Capacity: concert hall 1700, chamber music hall 350
Policy: rent *Arts types:* orchestra, chamber music, dance
Comments: home of Helsinki Philharmonic and Radio Symphony Orchestra

Helsinki Hall of Culture
Helsingin kulttuuritalo
Sturenkatu 4, 00510 **Helsinki**
Tel: 9-774 0270 Fax: 9-7740 2777
Internet: www.teak.fi/kulttuuritalo
E-Mail: marja.salo@teak.fi
managing director Kari Raina; sales manager Marja Salo
Venue type: concerts, exhibitions *Capacity:* Aalto hall 1403 *Policy:* rent *Arts types:* various-symphony,classical to rock *Comments:* building designed by Alvar Aalto

Kaapelitehdas
Tallberginkatu 1c/15, 00180 **Helsinki**
Tel: 9-4763 8300 Fax: 9-4763 8383
Internet: www.kaapeli.fi/~cable
E-Mail: jatta.raunila@kaapeli.fi
contact Marjatta Raunila
Venue type: multi-purpose *Capacity:* varies *Comments:* member of transEurope Halles, Tel: +33 1-4011 6414, Internet: www.teh.net

Kiasma Theatre
Kiasma Teatteri
Kiasma Museum of Contemporary Art, Mannerheiminaukio 2, 00100 **Helsinki**
Tel: 9-1733 6501 Fax: 9-1733 6503
Internet: www.kiasma.fi
E-Mail: info@kiasma.fi
producer Virve Sutinen (email: vsutinen@fng.fi); assistant producer Sanna Rekola (email: srekola@fng.fi); media curator Perttu Rastas (email: prastas@fng.fi)
Venue type: multi-purpose *Capacity:* auditorium theatre 217 *Policy:* present, produce, co-produce *Arts types:* contemporary & experimental, theatre, dance, video, film, multi-media, music, performance art, conferences (also on video)
Comments: Kiasma Theatre is part of Kiasma, Museum of Contemporary Art, Helsinki; exhibition rooms, mediatheque, seminar rooms, cafe, Kiasma shop etc.; museum director Tuula Arkio

Malmitalo, Cultural Centre of Northern Helsinki
Ala-Malmintori 1, 00700 **Helsinki**
Tel: 9-3108 0823 Fax: 9-3108 0830
Internet: www.kultuuri.hel.fi/malmitalo
E-Mail: risto.raty@hel.fi
Venue type: cultural centre, library, adult education and youth centres, music institute *Capacity:* two halls, exhibition area *Arts types:* wide range of cultural and artistic functions, courses, conferences, congresses, educational events

Old Student House
Vanha Ylioppilastalo
Mannerheimintie 3B, 00100 **Helsinki**
Tel: 9-1311 4371 Fax: 9-1311 4236
Internet: www.vanha.fi
director Antti Taavilalinen; manager Juva Vuorela
Venue type: festival hall/music hall, small music hall
Capacity: festival hall/music hall up to 1200, smaller spaces up to 100 *Policy:* rent *Arts types:* music, theatre, dance *Comments:* focus on new and avant-garde in Finnish and other cultures

Savoy Theatre
Savoy-teatteri
Kasarmikatu 46-48, 00130 **Helsinki**
Tel: 9-169 3705 Fax: 9-169 3810
Internet: www.kulttuuri.hel.fi/savoy
E-Mail: savoy@kulttuuri.hel.fi
director Tapani Närhi
Venue type: old cinema house from the early 19th century *Capacity:* 700 *Policy:* mainly rent *Arts types:* concerts, dance, theatre

Stoa, the Cultural Centre of Eastern Helsinki
Turunlinnantie 1, 00900 **Helsinki**
Tel: 9-3108 8410/09 Fax: 9-3108 8443
Internet: www.kulttuuri.hel.fi
E-Mail: stoa@kulttuuri.hel.fi
director Paula Lehto (9-3108 8410, email: paula.lehto@kulttuuri.hel.fi, internet: www.kulttuuri.hel.fi/stoa); cultural instructor Monika Silander (9-3108 8408); pr officer Karoliina Malmelin
Venue type: multi-purpose *Capacity:* theatre and dance hall 250, music hall 120 *Policy:* present, rent *Arts types:* dance, theatre, concerts, film *Comments:* many of the productions are sponsored by the Helsinki City Cultural Office; the venue is famous for presenting many international modern dance artists; one of Helsinki's best venues for modern dance

White Hall
Valkoinen Sali
Aleksanterinkatu 16-18, 00170 **Helsinki**
Tel: 9-169 3948 Fax: 9-169 3846
Internet: kulttuuri.hel.fi/valkoinen
E-Mail: valkoinen.sali@kulttuuri.nel.fi
director Tapani Närhi; coordinator Tomi Virtamen
Venue type: concert hall
Capacity: 450 *Policy:* rent *Arts types:* concerts, art exhibitions, seminars, conventions

Hyvinkää Hall
Hyvinkäässali
Kauppatori, 05800 **Hyvinkää**
Tel: 19-459 1358 Fax: 19-459 1361
Internet: www.hyvinkaa.fi
director Riitta Virtanen
Venue type: multi-purpose *Capacity:* up to 457
Policy: produce, rent
Arts types: concert, theatre, dance, conferences

Iisalmi Cultural Centre
Iisalmen kulttuurikeskus
Pl 5, Kirkkopuistonkatu 9, 74100 **Iisalmi**
Tel: 17-830 3361 Fax: 17-830 3390
E-Mail: kulttuurikeskus@iisalmi.fi
head at the centre Seppo Lyyra; cultural secretary Tuula Laatikainen
Venue type: multi-purpose *Capacity:* Eino Säisä hall 470, Karl Collan hall 208, 14 workrooms up to 40 *Policy:* rent *Arts types:* music, theatre *Comments:* also home to a music and art school,the natural history museum and two amateur theatre companies

Imatra Cultural Centre
Imatran kulttuurikeskus
Virastokatu 1, 55100 **Imatra**
Tel: 5-681 6641 Fax: 5-681 6628
Internet: www.Imatra.fi
cultural director Pentti Rossi; marketing secretary Sirpa Qvist (5-681 6698)
Venue type: concert & conference centre *Capacity:* Karelia Hall 536 *Arts types:* concerts, dance, conferences *Comments:* the centre also has an art gallery

Järvenpää Hall
Järvenpäätalo
PB 41, Hallintokatu 4, 04401 **Järvenpää**
Tel: 9-2719 2580 Fax: 9-271 1199
E-Mail: jarvenpaatalo@jarvenpaa.fi
manager Mikael Karikoski
Venue type: multi-purpose *Capacity:* Sibelius hall 579, Juhani Aho hall 170, theatre 100 *Policy:* produce, co-produce, rent *Arts types:* concerts, theatre, dance, exhibitions, conferences *Comments:* also own productions

Carelia Hall, Joensuu
Carelia-sali
Yliopistokatu 2, 80100 **Joensuu**
Tel: 13-267 5321 Fax: 13-267 5320
Internet: www.jns.fi
E-Mail: pirkko.ahola@jns.fi
artistic director & conductor of orchestra Atso Almila; director of orchestra Pirkko Ahola
Venue type: concert hall *Capacity:* Carelia Hall 605 *Policy:* rent and orchestra's own production *Arts types:* classical & contemporary music,orchestra and opera, popular and folk music *Comments:* home of Joensuu City Orchestra; the hall is jointly owned by the City and the University

Kaukametsä Congress and Concert Hall
Koskikatu 4A, PL 251, 87101 **Kajaani**
Tel: 8-615 5588 Fax: 8-615 5939
E-Mail: kaukametsa@kajaani.fi
director Aila Latipää; event secretary Raija-Leena Chorin
Venue type: concert hall *Capacity:* Kaukametsä hall up to 500 *Arts types:* concerts, meetings

Karkkila Hall
Karkkila-Sali
Anttilankatu 4, 03600 **Karkkila**
Tel: 9-2250 5251 Fax: 9-2250 5208
E-Mail: risto.hakomaki@karkkila.fi
director Risto Hakomäki
Venue type: concert hall *Capacity:* 400 *Policy:* rent *Arts types:* dance, theatre, concerts, film and video shows

Folk Arts Centre, Kaustinen
Volkskunst-Zentrum Kaustinen
Jyväskyläntie 3, PL 11, 69601 **Kaustinen**
Tel: 6-860 4111 Fax: 6-860 4222
Internet: www.lesti.kpnet.fi/kaustinen
E-Mail: folk.art@kaustinen.inet.fi
Venue type: congress venue, research and education centre for folk art and a modern folklore museum *Arts types:* folk music, conferences *Comments:* hosts the largest folk music festival in the Nordic countries

Kemi Cultural Centre
Kemin Taidemuseo/Kemin Kulttuurikeskus
Marina Takalon Katu 3, 94100 **Kemi**
Tel: 16-258 245 Fax: 16-258 243
E-Mail: unto.kayhko@kemi.fi
director Unto Käyhkö
Venue type: multi purpose *Capacity:* 300 *Arts types:* most

Kemijärvi Cultural Centre
Kemijärvi Kultuurikeskus
Hietaniemenkatu 3, PO Box 5, 98101 **Kemijärvi**
Tel: 16-878 310/274 Fax: 16-878 310/308
director Helena Junttila; cultural secretary Raila Haltynen (878 272)
Venue type: concert and theatre hall *Capacity:* main hall 200 *Policy:* rent , productions *Arts types:* theatre, music, dance, seminars

Kotka Concert House
Kotkan Konserttitalo
Keskuskatu 33, 48100 **Kotka**
Tel: 5-234 4714 Fax: 5-234 4274
E-Mail: jouko.koivukoski@kotka.fi
director Taina Rasi (234 4700)
Venue type: concert hall, congress *Capacity:* 456 *Policy:* rent, produce *Arts types:* music
Comments: home of Kotka City Orchestra

Kouvola Cultural Centre
Kouvola Kultuurikeskus
Varuskuntakatn 11, 45100 **Kouvola**
Tel: 5-829 6557 Fax: 5-375 1013
E-Mail: tourism@kouvola.fi
tourist secretary Raija Sierman
Capacity: Music Hall 332, Lecture Hall 70, five Meeting Rooms up to16 , Museum of Art, Entrance Hall and Foyer *Policy:* rent *Arts types:* concerts, operas, conferences, exhibitions *Comments:* restaurant and cafe services (seating for 80, buffet for 600); office address: Torikatu 10, 45100 Kouvola

Kuhmo Arts Centre
Kuhmo-talo, 88900 **Kuhmo**
Tel: 8-655 6750 Fax: 8-655 6758
Internet: www.kuhmotalo.fi
E-Mail: kuhmo.talo@kuhmo.fi
managing director Matti-Jussi Pollari; artistic director Seppo Kimanen
Venue type: cultural centre including concert hall *Capacity:* Lentua Hall 668, Pajakka Hall 99 *Policy:* rent, present at own risk *Arts types:* all arts types, congresses, conferences, chamber music, dance, exhibitions
Comments: designed by Uki Arkkitehdit Oy, Oulu; main venue for the annual Kuhmo Chamber Music Festival

Kuopio Music Centre
Kuopion Musiikkikeskus
Kuopionlahdenkatu 23, 70100 **Kuopio**
Tel: 17-182 111 Fax: 17-182 373
Internet: www.kulttuuri.kuopio.fi/musiikkikeskus
E-Mail: musiikkikeskus@kuopio.fi
general manager & intendant Michael Claussen; publicity manager Sari Kauhanen; sales managers Mervi Hänninen, Päivi Smeds-Oravainen
Venue type: multi-purpose *Capacity:* concert hall 1064, chamber music hall 240, auditorium 132, exhibition space, small meeting rooms *Policy:* available for rent, present *Arts types:* opera, dance, music festivals, concerts, conferences, meetings, exhibitions, banquests and balls *Comments:* home of Kuopio Symphony Orchestra (q.v.)

Kuusamo Hall
Kuusamohaus
Kaarlo Hännisen tie 2, 93600 **Kuusamo**
Tel: 8-850 6550 Fax: 8-850 6558
Internet: www.travel.fi/kuusamotalo
E-Mail: seija.vaisanen@kuusamo.fi
Venue type: main auditorium Oulanka Hall, a music institute with rooms for group work, a recording studio, art gallery *Arts types:* drama, music, congresses, meetings

Kuusankoski Hall
Kuusankoskitalo
Kymenlaaksonkatu 1, PL 55, 45701 **Kuusankoski**
Tel: 5-740 4256/4336 (tourist infomation)
Fax: 5-374 8937
E-Mail: tuijav@kuusankoski.fi
marketing secretary Tuija Vanhanen
Venue type: concert hall *Capacity:* Kuusaa hall 508, Voikkaa hall 206 *Policy:* own productions, rent *Arts types:* concerts, theatre, new productions, movies

Concert Hall of Lahti
Lahden konserttitalo
8 Sibelius Street, 15110 **Lahti**
Tel: 3-814 4453 Fax: 3-814 4451
E-Mail: ritvafrisk@lahti.fi
economic manager Ritva Frisk
Venue type: concert hall *Capacity:* 581 *Policy:* rent *Arts types:* symphony, chamber and other concerts, recitals, dance *Comments:* home of Lahti Symphony Orchestra; due to have changed address in 1999, no further details known at time of going to print ; see also Orchestras

SibeliusHall, Congress and Concert Centre
Sibeliustalo, Kongressi-ja Konserttikeskus
PL 202, 15101 **Lahti**
Tel: 3-814 2204 Fax: 3-814 2218
E-Mail: minna.jolkkonen@lahti.fi
programme manager Minna Jolkkonen

Lieksa Cultural Centre
Lieksan Kulttuurikeskus
Pielisentie 9-11, 81700 **Lieksa**
Tel: 13-520 2379 Fax: 13-520 2297
E-Mail: anneli.annqli@lieksa.fi
director Asko Saarelainen
Venue type: concert, conference hall *Capacity:* main hall 400, 4 conference rooms 50 *Arts types:* concerts, exhibitions, conferences

Lieska Cultural Centre
Lieksa-Kulturzentrum
Pielisentie 9-11, PL 31, 81701 **Lieksa**
Tel: 13-520 2370 Fax: 13-520 2393
Internet: www.lieksa.fi/lieksa
E-Mail: kirsi.nevalainen@lieksa.fi
Venue type: cultural centre *Capacity:* Brahe Hall 400, multipurpose hall 100, five meeting rooms *Comments:* the entrance hall is used for changing art exhibitions throughout the year

Concert Hall and Congress Hall Mikaeli in Mikkeli
Konsertti – ja kongressitalo Mikaeli
Sointukatu 1, 50100 **Mikkeli**
Tel: 15-194 2761 Fax: 15-362 757
Internet: www.mikkeli.fi/mikaeli
E-Mail: mikaeli@mikkeli.fi
director Matti Liukkonen
Venue type: concert, congress hall
Capacity: Martti Talvela Hall 694, Chamber Music Hall 166 *Policy:* rent
Arts types: concerts, opera
Comments: situated on the lake of the city

Muuramen kultuurikeskus
Muurame Cultural Centre
Nisulantie 1, 40950 **Muurame**
Tel: 14-659 611/733/770
Fax: 14-659 600
Internet: www.muurame.fi
director Ane Paprekaennen
Venue type: congress, concert hall
Capacity: auditorium 235 *Policy:* rent
Arts types: theatre, music

Kristoffer Hall
Kristoffer-Sali
Opintie 2, 21100 **Naantali**
Tel: 2-434 5231 Fax: 2-434 5433
director Kirsti Willberg
Venue type: concert hall *Capacity:* auditorium up to 238 *Policy:* rent, own productions *Arts types:* concert, theatre, dance

Oulu Music Centre
Oulun Musiikkikeskus
Lintulammentie 1-3, 90100 **Oulu**
Tel: 8-5584 7210 Fax: 8-5584 7299
general manager Riita Pulliainen
Venue type: concert, conference hall *Capacity:* Madetoja Hall 816, Tulindberg Hall 220 *Arts types:* concerts, conferences, exhibitions *Comments:* home of Oulu Symphony Orchestra (q.v.); see also Opera

Oulu City Theatre
Oulun kaupunginteatteri
Kaarlenvayla 2, 90015 **Oulu (Kaupunki)**
Tel: 8-5584 7000 Fax: 8-5584 7099
Internet: www.ouka.fi/teatteri
E-Mail: teatteri@ouka.fi
director Maarit Pyokäri
Venue type: theatre
Capacity: big stage 581, studio up to 180
Policy: rent (own risk) *Arts types:* theatre, congress

Pieksämäki Cultural Centre Poleeni
Pieksämäen kulttuurikeskus
Savontie 13, 76100 **Pieksämäki**
Tel: 15-781 1431 Fax: 15-481 301
E-Mail: mariella.haavisto@mail.pieksamaki.fi
managing director Mariella Haavisto
Venue type: concert hall
Capacity: 349 *Policy:* rent
Arts types: classical/contemporary music, theatre, cinema, conferences

Lappia Hall
Lappia-talo
Hallituskatu 11-13, 96100 **Rovaniemi**
Tel: 16-322 2510 Fax: 16-322 3232
Internet: www.rovaniemi.fi
E-Mail: teatteri@rovaniemi.fi
congress manager Heidi Torppa (tel: 16-322 2745, fax: 16-322 2992); theatre director/manager Ahti Ahonen (tel: 16-322 2500)
Venue type: theatre and congress hall
Capacity: congress and concert hall 560, theatre hall 427, congress hall up to 150
Arts types: music, theatre, films
Comments: designed by Alvaar Aalto; the Municipal Theatre/Lapland's Provincial Theatre, Lapland's Regional Radio of the Finnish Broadcasting Company, Lapland's Music College operate in this building; concert hall and theatre hall have 70 extra spaces for wheelchairs

Suolahti Hall
Suolahti-sali
Savontie 10, 44200 **Suolahti**
Tel: 14-549 611 Fax: 14-496 400
Internet: www.ksopisto.fi
E-Mail: gs.opistoc@goulud.suolahti.fi
secretary of culture Matti Virtanen (549 4241)
Venue type: auditorium, concert hall
Capacity: Suolahti hall 350, old hall 120
Policy: rent *Arts types:* music, theatre
Comments: hold two annual summer music courses

Cultural Centre of the Old Customs House
Tullikamarinaukio 2, 33100 **Tampere**
Tel: 3-3146 6391 Fax: 3-223 0121
Internet: www.tampere.fi/culture/tulli
E-Mail: tullikamari@tampere.fi
contact Tuula Pessa
Capacity: 600 (without seats 1200)
Arts types: music, theatre, dance, exhibitions

Tampere Hall
PO Box 16, 33101 **Tampere**
Tel: 3-243 4111 Fax: 3-243 4197
Internet: www.tampere.fi/TampereHall/
E-Mail: concert.department@tamperehall.tampere.fi
executive producer Jarmo Hakkarainen
Venue type: concert hall *Capacity:* main hall 2000, small hall 500, studio 170, banquet hall 1000 *Policy:* rent, own productions *Arts types:* opera, ballet, light music, classical music

Cultural Centre of Turku
Turun Kulttuurikeskus
Vanha Suurtori 7, 20500 **Turku**
Tel: 2-273 8300/8341 (information) Fax: 2-231 2808
Internet: www.turku.fi/kulttuurikeskus
E-Mail: kulttuurikeskus@turku.fi
director of cultural centre Helena Heikniemi-Pääkkönen
Venue type: cultural events *Capacity:* Old Town Hall 150 *Policy:* rent

Turku Concert Hall
Turun konserttitalo
Aninkaistenkatu 9, 20100 **Turku**
Tel: 2-233 6492 Fax: 2-233 6350
E-Mail: orchestra@turku.fi
contact Pertti Rastas
Venue type: concert hall *Capacity:* 1002 *Policy:* rent *Arts types:* music *Comments:* home of Turku Philharmonic Orchestral; postal address: Sibeliusenkatu 2B; 20110 Turku

Turkuhalli – Elysee Arena (formerly Typhoon)
Artukaistentie 8, PL 39, 20251 **Turku**
Tel: 2-21900 Fax: 2-219 0111
Internet: www.turkuhalli.fi
managing director Reijo Paksal; arena manager Kari Rantala; box office manager Tea Riekkinen
Venue type: multi-purpose *Capacity:* 10000-12000 *Policy:* rent, co-promote, promote
Arts types: opera, rock, classical concerts, circus, all kinds of show and sport events *Comments:* house video, sound, light and stage

Cultural Centre, Cruselli
Kultuurikeskus Cruselli
Culture Office, Rauhankatu 10, 23500 **Uusikaupunki**
Tel: 2-8451 5300 Fax: 2-8451 5442
cultural secretary Ilkka Rauvola
Venue type: concert hall *Capacity:* 260 *Policy:* rent, own productions *Arts types:* concerts, theatre, art exhibitions *Comments:* visiting address: Kullervontie 11 A, 23500 Uusikaupunki

Martinus Hall
Konserttitalo Martinus
Martinlaaksontie 36, 01620 **Vantaa**
Tel: 9-5045 5905 Fax: 9-5045 5954
operative director Kimmo Tammivaara (9-5045 5904)
Venue type: concert hall *Capacity:* 406 *Policy:* rent *Arts types:* concerts, dance, theatre, musical theatre *Comments:* home of the Vantaa Pops Orchestra

Myyrmäki Hall
Myyrmäki-Haus
Kilterinraitti 6, 01600 **Vantaa**
Tel: 9-5045 5456 Fax: 9-5045 5470
Internet: www.vantaa.fi
E-Mail: hannele.liljestrom@vantaa.fi
Comments: there are courses in art, music and information technology; the library provides versatile services and an efficient data network; the exhibition areas are used for art shows and performance-art events; the hall is also used for small-scale meetings and company functions

Congress and Cultural Center
Warkaus Hall, Kauppatori 6, 78250 **Varkaus**
Tel: 17-579 4944 Fax: 17-579 4949
Internet: www.varkaus.fi/kongressikeskus
E-Mail: kongressikeskus@vrk.varkaus.fi
Venue type: multi-purpose *Capacity:* 506 *Policy:* rent *Arts types:* congress centre, conferences, concerts, exhibitions

FRANCE (+33)

Centre Culturel de l'Albigeois
Place de l'Amitier entre les peuples, BP 49, 81002 **Albi** Cedex
Tel: 5-6354 1111 Fax: 5-6354 4647
directeur Ivan Morane; administrateur Lionel Schwartz; déléguée générale Joëlle Faroux
Venue type: multi-purpose *Capacity:* theatre 600, gymnasium 300 *Policy:* rent, produce, co-produce *Arts types:* drama, music, dance, classical art circus

Scène Nationale Théâtre d'Alençon
2 Av de Basingstoke, 61000 **Alençon**
Tel: 2-3329 1696 (booking)/0229 (administration)
Fax: 2-3329 6913
directeur Jean-Claude Collot; secrétaire général Franck Becker; régisseur Jean Pierre Legros
Venue type: modern theatre *Capacity:* 410 *Policy:* rent, present, co-produce *Arts types:* theatre, dance, music, variety, circus, puppetry for adults and children
Comments: also programme planners at other sites: Au Forum de Flers, Rue du Collège, 61100 Flers, Tel: 2-3364 2121, Fax: 2-3396 1298

Le Cratère – théâtre d'Alès
Le Cratère, Théâtre d'Alès, Scéne Nationale, BP 216, 30104 **Alès** Cedex
Tel: 4-6652 9000/5264 (booking) Fax: 4-6652 7680
directeur Denis Lafaurie; président Jean Bouet; administeur Marie-Claire Gelly; directeur technique Philippe Reginaud
Venue type: modern theatre *Capacity:* 850 *Policy:* produce, co-produce *Arts types:* live shows, theatre, dance, music, circus, shows for children *Comments:* Festival du Cinéma – April; Festival du Jeune Théâtre – July

Maison de la Culture d'Amiens
2 place Léon Gontier, BP 0631, 80006 **Amiens** Cedex 1
Tel: 3-2297 7979 Fax: 3-2297 7990
director Michel Orier; administrateur Brigitte Perin; programmateur théâtre Jean Michel Puiffe; programmateur danse Gilles Laprevotte
Venue type: multi-purpose *Capacity:* Grand Théâtre 1070, Petit Théâtre 300, Salle de Cinéma 180, two exhibition halls *Policy:* present, produce, co-produce *Arts types:* dance, theatre, music, jazz, variety

Nouveau Théâtre d'Angers
Centre Dramatique Nationnal, Maison de la Culture, 12 Place Louis Imbach, BP 2107, 49021 **Angers** Cedex 02
Tel: 2-4188 9008/9922 (bookings) Fax: 2-4188 3780
E-Mail: nouveau.theatre@wanadoo.fr
director (Maison de la Culture) François Dugoujon; director (Centre Dramatique, Nouveau Théâtre) Claude Yersin; administrateur François Dugoujon
Venue type: municipal theatre: theatre l'italienne, others: multipurpose *Capacity:* 2 halls: Salle Beaurepaire 500, Place Imbach 60, Atelier Jean Daste 80 *Policy:* present, produce, co-produce *Arts types:* theatre, dance, jazz, concerts, exhibitions *Comments:* see also Drama

Théâtre d'Angoulême, Scène Nationale
BP 287, 16007 **Angoulême** Cedex
Tel: 5-4538 6162 (booking)/6161 (admin) Fax: 5-4538 6151
directeur André Curmi; secretaire general & chargé jeune public Chantal Rocailleux; relations publiques Eliane Bonnin; communication Anne Marie Lalu; directeur technique Patrick Montion
Venue type: modern *Capacity:* 3 halls: hall A 730, hall B 120, hall C 70 *Policy:* rent, present, co-produce, produce *Arts types:* drama, dance, film, music *Comments:* visiting address: Avenue des Maréchaux, B287, 16007 Angoulême, Cedex; see also Drama and Promoters

Bonlieu Scène Nationale
BP 294, 74007 **Annecy** Cedex
Tel: 4-5033 4400 Fax: 4-5051 8209
E-Mail: bsn@cybercable.tm.fr
directeur Sawador Garcia; administrateur Françoise Turin; communication Pierre Brisebras; secrétariat général Edith Klein
Capacity: Théâtre d'Annecy 982, Espace up to 300
Policy: present, co-produce (theatre and dance), rent
Arts types: symphony concerts, theatre, dance
Comments: Festival du Cinéma Italien (Dec), Festival du Cinéma Espagnol (July); visiting address: 1 rue Jean-Jaurès, 74000 Annecy

Relais Culturel Château Rouge
BP 293, 74112 **Annemasse** Cedex
Tel: 4-5043 2425/2424 (bookings) Fax: 4-5043 2426
E-Mail: chateau.rouge@wanadoo.fr
directeur Jacques Maugein; président Pierre Goyard; relations scolaire Annie Viala; secrétaire artistique Marie-Claude Pochat; relations publiques Françoise Bonnaud
Venue type: theatre *Capacity:* Salle du Château Rouge up to 1200, auditorium 250 *Policy:* rent, present, produce, co-produce *Arts types:* opera, dance, theatre, variety, drama, shows for children

Centre Culturel Noroit
6-9 rue des Capucins, 62000 **Arras**
Tel: 3-2171 3012 Fax: 3-2171 0994
directeur Bernard Petitot
Venue type: multi-purpose *Capacity:* 110, and exhibition hall *Policy:* rent, present, co-produce *Arts types:* chamber music, jazz, theatre, classical and contemporary music, film, conferences, exhibitions

Fondation Royaumont
95270 **Asnières-sur-Oise**
Tel: 1-3035 5900 Fax: 1-3035 3945
Internet: royaumont.com
E-Mail: info@royaumont.com
directeur Francis Marechal; président Emmanuel Dandre; directeur administratif Franck Magloire; administratrice du centre de la voix Catherine Kollen; responsable de la communication Odile Brasset
Venue type: multi-purpose *Capacity:* 7 halls, including l'Ancien Réfectoire des Moines 600, Les Anciennes Cuisines des Moines 250, Salle des Charpente 230
Policy: rent, produce, co-produce *Arts types:* vocal music, contemporary poetry *Comments:* former abbey; seminars, congresses, early music; see also Festivals

Théâtre de la Commune
2 rue Edouard Poisson, BP 157, 93304 **Aubervilliers** Cedex
Tel: 1-4833 1616 (administration)/4834 6767 (locations)
Fax: 1-4834 3555
Internet: www.alegria.fr/theatre-commune
directeur Didier Bezace; administratrice Nathalie Lemaire; direction communication Catherine Dan; relations publiques t.b.a.
Venue type: theatre *Capacity:* Big Hall 530, Small Hall up to 230 *Policy:* produce, co-produce *Arts types:* drama
Comments: receiving house; see also Drama

Théâtre Jean Lurçat – Scène Nationale d'Aubusson
Avenue des Lissiers, BP 11, 23200 **Aubusson**
Tel: 5-5583 8687 Fax: 5-5566 2080
directeur, chargé de la programmation & jeune public Jean-François Hubert; communication Florent Guyot, Dorothée Bonnel
Venue type: modern *Capacity:* 260 *Policy:* present, co-produce *Arts types:* theatre, dance, music (jazz and classical)

Espace Jacques Prévert
134 rue Anatole France, 93600 **Aulnay-sous-Bois**
Tel: 1-4868 0818/0022/4866 4990 (bookings)
Fax: 1-4869 3522
directeur Christophe Ubelmann
Venue type: multi-purpose *Capacity:* 2 halls: Salle Molière 812, Salle Méliès 184 *Policy:* rent, present, produce, co-produce *Arts types:* all including film

Saison culturelle
4 rue de la Coste, 15000 **Aurillac** Cedex
Tel: 4-7145 4605 (administration)/4604 (theatre)
Fax: 4-7145 4644
E-Mail: culturelle@aurillac.fr
administrateur Jean-Paul Peuch; directeur des affaires culturelles Patrick Couvidoux
Venue type: theatre *Capacity:* 480 *Policy:* co-produce, rent *Arts types:* theatre, dance, shows for children, music

Théâtre Municipal d'Autun
4 av Charles de Gaulle, 71400 **Autun**
Tel: 3-8586 2000 (location)/8060 (administration)/8063 (regie théâtre) Fax: 3-8586 3483
responsable Claudine Demeusois-Laisis
Venue type: théâtre à l'Italienne (19th C) *Capacity:* 485 *Policy:* rent, produce, co-produce, mainly present *Arts types:* theatre, opera, music, jazz, variety

Théâtre de la Ville d'Auxerre
54 rue Joubert, 89000 **Auxerre**
Tel: 3-8672 2420 Fax: 3-8672 2425
directeur Jean Piret; communication Isabelle Thibaut
Capacity: Theatre 560, Atelier Théâtre 120 *Policy:* produce, present, diffuse, co-produce *Arts types:* drama, concerts, dance, jazz, opera lyrique, comedy

Action Culturelle du Barois Scène Nationale
7 rue Jeanne d'Arc, 55000 **Bar-Le-Duc**
Tel: 3-2979 4278 Fax: 3-2945 6027
directeur Françoise Houriet; comptable Catherine Taguel; directeur technique Michel Lombard
Capacity: Salle Dumas 600, Salle Theuriet 230
Policy: present, produce, co-produce
Arts types: theatre, dance, variety
Comments: 3 exhibition halls – contemporary art

Théâtre de Bayonne
Scène Nationale de Bayonne et du Sud-Aquitain, Théâtre de Bayonne, 18 ter blvd d'Alsace-Lorraine, 64100 **Bayonne**
Tel: 5-5955 8505 Fax: 5-5955 2170
E-Mail: snbayonne@aol.com
directeur Dominique Burucoa; administratrice Marie-Jeanne Mercapide; secrétaire général Jacques Guyard; directeur des animations Roger Goyheneche; régisseur general Richard Fano
Venue type: multi-purpose *Capacity:* 800 *Policy:* rent, produce, co-produce *Arts types:* theatre, orchestra, classical music, dance, mime, comedy, singing, jazz
Comments: Minitel: 3615 arts; see also Festivals

Théâtre Municipal de Beaune
64 rue de Lorraine, 21200 **Beaune** Cedex
Tel: 3-8024 5686 Fax: 3-8024 5620
directrice Agnès Galabert
Venue type: Théâtre à l'italienne
Capacity: 320 *Policy:* rent, co-produce
Arts types: contemporary & classical dance and theatre, puppet shows, concerts (classical & other), jazz, operetta

Théâtre de Beauvais
Place Georges Brassens, 60000 **Beauvais**
Tel: 3-4406 0820/22
Fax: 3-4406 0829
directeur Wilfrid Charles; administrateur Hervé Martin; secrétaire général Marie-Claude Noiran; directeur technique Philippe Tauleigne
Venue type: theatre *Capacity:* 738 and 132
Policy: present, co-produce, rent *Arts types:* theatre, dance, music, jazz, variety, cabaret, puppetry

Théâtre Granit – Scène Nationale Belfort
1 Faubourg de Montbéliard, BP 117,
90002 **Belfort** Cedex
Tel: 3-8458 6750 (administration)/8458 6767 (bookings)
Fax: 3-8457 0174
Internet: www.theatre-granit.asso.fr
E-Mail: granit-rp@hrnet.fr
directeur Henri Taquet; directeur adjoint Thierry Lesueur
Venue type: Théâtre à l'italienne *Capacity:* 2 halls: 603 and 50 *Policy:* present, produce, co-produce *Arts types:* theatre, dance, music/classical, music of the world, opera, jazz, youth theatre *Comments:* see also Festivals

Nouveau Théâtre de Besançon, Centre Dramatique National
Parc du Casino, Av Edouard Droz, 25000 **Besançon**
Tel: 3-8188 5511 Fax: 3-8150 0908
directeur Michel Dubois; conseillère artistique Christine Friedel; adminstrateur Pascale Vurpillot; relations publiques Jeanne-Antide Leque
Capacity: Théâtre du Casino 337 *Policy:* present, produce, co-produce *Arts types:* theatre *Comments:* see also Drama

Théâtre de l'Espace – Scène Nationale
Place de l'Europe, BP 2033, 25050 **Besançon** Cedex
Tel: 3-8151 0312 Fax: 3-8141 0061
direction t.b.a.; administrateur Daniel Boucon; programmation-cinéma Emmanuelle Prétot; communication Fabienne Chognard; relations publiques Marie-Hélène Créquy
Venue type: theatre *Capacity:* 2 halls: 434 and 80 *Policy:* present, produce, co-produce *Arts types:* contemporary: theatre, dance, cinema

Théâtre Municipal – Xavier Duchatelle
Bd. Victor Hugo, 62400 **Béthune** Cedex
Tel: 3-2157 2627 Fax: 3-2156 7156
directeur Xavier Duchatelle; relations publiques Laurent Rybarczyk; communication Anne Décobert; secrétariat Dominique Caron; accueil Lucile Peugnet; responsable technique Bertrand Cadart, Béryl Cochez
Venue type: multi-purpose *Capacity:* 921 *Policy:* rent, present, co-produce *Arts types:* music, dance, song, humour, opera

Barbacane – La Centre d'Action Culturelle Inter Communal
Place du 8 Mai 1945, 78650 **Beynes**
Tel: 1-3491 0658 Fax: 1-3489 9922
directeur Jean Feugere; régisseur responsable technique José Perucho; relations publiques Joël Dechanet
Venue type: multi-purpose *Capacity:* La Barbacane up to 420 *Policy:* produce, co-produce *Arts types:* theatre, music, symphony, opera, dance, film, shows for children

Théâtre Paul Eluard / Plateau pour la Dance
162 rue Maurice Berteaux, 95870 **Bezons**
Tel: 1-3410 2020 Fax: 1-3410 0163
directeur Dominique Ungar; pr Véronique Bellin; administ Paul Munuera; responsable jeune publiques Emmanuel Patrignani
Venue type: modern *Capacity:* 500 *Policy:* co-produce, diffusion *Arts types:* dance, children's events

Casino de Biarritz
c/o Biarritz Tourisme, 1, square d'Ixelles,
64200 **Biarritz**
Tel: 5-5922 3700 Fax: 5-5924 1419
Internet: www.tourisme.fr/biarritz/
directeur Olivier Lépine; sales manager Cordula Riedel; gestion des salles Marie-Hélène
Venue type: multi purpose theatre *Capacity:* 900 *Policy:* rent only *Arts types:* all types including congresses *Comments:* see also Palais des Festivals

Le Colisée, Biarritz culture
11 rue Sarasate, 64200 **Biarritz**
Tel: 5-5924 1307/5922 2021 (admin) Fax: 5-5922 4011
directeur Filgi Claverie; president Jakes Abeberry
Venue type: theatre *Capacity:* 189 *Policy:* rent *Arts types:* drama, classical concerts, cinema, jazz *Comments:* also 2 halls for exhibitions

Palais des Festivals
c/o Biarritz Tourisme, 1, square d'Ixelles, 64200 **Biarritz**
Tel: 5-5922 3700 Fax: 5-5924 1419
director Olivier Lépine; sales manager Cordula Riedel; gestion des salles Marie-Hélène
Venue type: multi-purpose *Capacity:* Salle Atalaya 1400, Salle Gamaritz 230, Casino Municipal *Policy:* rent only *Arts types:* all types including congresses *Comments:* see also Casino de Biarritz

Maison des Associations et de la Culture de Bischwiller
Espace Paul Kauss, BP 90, 67243 **Bischwiller** Cedex
Tel: 3-8863 0360 Fax: 3-8853 8810
directeur Christian Winterhalter; responsable technique Moritz Luc
Venue type: theatre *Capacity:* 900
Policy: present, produce, co-produce, rent
Arts types: concerts, dance, theatre, cinema, conferences, congresses, exhibitions, variety

Théâtre Missionne les Colonnes
4 rue du Docteur Castera, 33290 **Blanquefort**
Tel: 5-5695 4900 Fax: 5-5695 4909
directeur Alain Duchatel; régisseur Stéphane La Boucherie; chargée de communication Hélène Onnillon; animateur culturel Eric Andre
Venue type: 1 multi-purpose hall, 1 cinema *Capacity:* cinema 87, hall 300 *Policy:* present *Arts types:* all types of performing arts and art house films

Centre Culturel du Blesois – Halle aux Grains – Scène Nationale
Place de la République, 41000 **Blois**
Tel: 2-5490 4400 Fax: 2-5490 4401
directeur Gildas le Boterf
Capacity: auditorium 630, 1 exhibition hall *Policy:* present, produce, co-produce *Arts types:* theatre, dance, conferences, music, concerts, exhibitions

Théâtre des Provinces du Monde et Compagnie du Hasard
8 Rue du Lieutenant Godineau, 41000 **Blois**
Tel: 2-5457 0570 Fax: 2-5457 0579
E-Mail: compagnie.hasard@wanadoo.fr
administratrice Catherine Amilcar; directeur artistique Nicolas Peskine; relations publique Tania Horstmall, Catherine Rouillon
Venue type: theatre *Capacity:* 100 *Policy:* produce, co-produce *Arts types:* contemporary theatre, international performing arts *Comments:* also performances with a mobile theatre; see also Drama

MC93 – Centre International de Création et de Diffusion Artistiques, Bobigny
1 bd Lénine, B7 71 Centre Ville, 93002 **Bobigny** Cedex
Tel: 1-4160 7272 (bookings)/7260 (admin)
Fax: 1-4160 7261
E-Mail: mc93b@calvanet.calvacom.fr
directeur Ariel Goldenberg; secrétaire général et adminstrateur André Mondy; directeur technique Jacques Dubreuil; attachée de presse Viviane Got
Venue type: multi-purpose *Capacity:* 2 halls: 1000 and 400 *Policy:* new productions, co-produce, present *Arts types:* mainly theatre but also opera, music, dance *Comments:* co-productions with foreign companies; see also Promoters

Centre Dramatique National Bordeaux-Aquitaine
Square Jean-Vauthier, BP 7, 33031 **Bordeaux** Cedex
Tel: 5-5691 0181 (administration) Fax: 5-5692 8150
E-Mail: cdn.bordeaux@wanadoo.fr
directeur Jean-Louis Thamin; directeur technique Alain Pinel; directeur adjoint Gerard Lion; relations extérieures Corinne Reboud
Venue type: théâtre à l'italienne *Capacity:* Salle Jean Vauthier 484, Les Essais 50 *Policy:* rent, produce, co-produce *Arts types:* drama *Comments:* see also Drama

Conservatoire National de Région
22 quai Sainte Croix de Bordeaux, 33800 **Bordeaux**
Tel: 5-5692 9696 Fax: 5-5692 2230
directeur Michel Fusté-Lambezat; administrateur Philippe Riabokogne
Capacity: Salle Jacques Thibaut 1100 *Policy:* rent *Arts types:* theatre, opera, concerts, dance

Grand Orchestre de Bordeaux
BP 95, 33025 **Bordeaux** Cedex
Tel: 5-5600 8520 Fax: 5-5681 9366
directeur général Thierry Fouquet; directeur administratif François Vienne; chef d'orchestre Hans Graf
Venue type: theatre *Capacity:* 1114 *Policy:* produce, co-produce, rent *Arts types:* chamber music, opera, symphony, dance *Comments:* see also Orchestras, Opera and Dance

Palais des Sports
Place de la Ferme de Richemont,
33000 **Bordeaux**
Tel: 5-5679 3961 Fax: 5-5624 5120(Bordeaux townhall)
directeur Thierry Fouquet (5-5600 8520)
Venue type: concert hall *Capacity:* 1660 *Policy:* rent *Arts types:* orchestral music, variety, ballet *Comments:* it is administrated by the Grand Théâtre de Bordeaux

Théâtre Fémina – Opéra de Bordeaux
20 rue de Grassi, 33000 **Bordeaux**
Tel: 5-5679 0669 Fax: 5-5601 1330
directeur général Thierry Fouquet; directeur artistique Joël Brouche; directeur communcation t.b.a.
Venue type: theatre *Capacity:* 1200 *Policy:* rent, present, co-produce, produce (operetta) *Arts types:* theatre, dance, classical music, operetta, variety, jazz and ballet

Théâtre de Boulogne-Billancourt – TBB
60 rue de la Belle Feuille, 92100 **Boulogne-Billancourt**
Tel: 1-4603 6441 Fax: 1-4605 6519
directeur Bernard Sevège; responsable technique Jacques Nolais
Venue type: theatre *Capacity:* 587 *Policy:* present, produce, co-produce, rent *Arts types:* theatre, dance, varieties *Comments:* Festival de Jazz (May, annual); theatre closed for renovation; address for showing events: Salle des Fêtes Bernard Palissy, 1 Place Bernard Palissy, 92100 Boulogne

Théâtre de Bourg en Bresse
11 place de la Grenette, BP 146,
01004 **Bourg-en-Bresse** Cedex
Tel: 4-7450 4000 Fax: 4-7422 4966
E-Mail: theatre.Bourg-Bresse@wanadoo.fr
directeur Dominique Ferrier; administration Françoise Ridet; programmation musique Cyrille Mereu, Eric Chevalier; programmation danse et jeune public Nathalie Douillet
Venue type: Théâtre à l'italienne *Capacity:* Salon les Salles 114-500 *Policy:* present, produce, co-produce, rent *Arts types:* theatre, music, dance, young peoples theatre

Maison de la Culture de Bourges
Place André Malraux, BP 257,
18005 **Bourges** Cedex
Tel: 2-4867 0708 Fax: 2-4850 0749
E-Mail: maison.de.la.culutre.deux.bourges@wanadoo.fr
directeur Gilbert Fillinger; administratrice Simone Dumoux; secrétaire générale Françoise Roux; sécrétaire de direction Danielle Crochet; directeur technique Lucien Maillet
Venue type: theatre *Capacity:* Grand Théâtre 900, Salle Gilles Sandier 350, Cinema 110 *Policy:* rent, present, produce, co-produce *Arts types:* theatre, music (classical, jazz), dance, exhibitions, cinema

Théâtre Jacques Coeur
Rue Jacques Coeur, 18000 **Bourges**
Tel: 2-4870 5936 Fax: 2-4824 9673
directeur artistique Michel Pobeau;
régos généra Max Pace
Venue type: theatre *Capacity:* 338 *Policy:* rent, co-produce *Arts types:* classical and contemporary dance and drama, concerts, conferences, cinema

Théâtre de Caen
135 blvd Maréchal Leclerc, BP 71,
14007 **Caen** Cedex
Tel: 2-3130 7600 Fax: 2-3130 7629
E-Mail: theatre@ville-caen.fr
directrice Nadia Croquet; administrateur Patrick Foll; responsable de la communication Philippe Normand
Venue type: modern theatre *Capacity:* 1100 *Policy:* present, produce, co-produce, rent *Arts types:* opera, dance, theatre, classical music, jazz, traditional music
Comments: annexe venue: Eglise Notre Dame de la Gloriette-450 (ancient music)

Zénith de Caen
Rue Josèphe Philippon, BP 6069,
14062 **Caen** Cedex
Tel: 2-3129 1414 Fax: 2-3129 1415
Internet: www.ville-caen.fr/zenith
E-Mail: le.zenith@caramail.com
directeur Serge Langeois; directrice adjointe Sylvie Duchesne; directeur technique Eric Buisson; communication Elizabeth Alleaume
Venue type: multi-purpose
Capacity: 700-7000 *Policy:* rent
Arts types: concerts (classical, rock, jazz, etc.), meetings, conventions, conferences, theatre, circus, dance, sports events

Scène Nationale – Le Channel
BP 77, 62102 **Calais** Cedex
Tel: 3-2146 7710 Fax: 3-2146 7720
Internet: www.lechannel-calais.org
E-Mail: lechannel@lechannel-calais.org
directeur Francis Peduzzi; directeur technique Dominique Verbrugge; administratice Marianne Anselin; responsable de la galerie de l' ancienne poste Francis Peduzzi
Venue type: Théâtre à l'Italienne
Capacity: Théâtre de Calais 800, Cinéma Louis Daquin 360 *Policy:* mainly present, produce, co-produce
Arts types: theatre, contemporary dance, art house films, concert *Comments:* 1 exhibition hall (contemporary art) Galerie de l'ancienne poste

SEMEC – Palais des Festivals et des Congrès
Esplanade Président George Pompidou,
BP 272, 06403 **Cannes** Cedex
Tel: 4-9339 0101 Fax: 4-9399 3706
Internet: www.palais-festivals-cannes.fr
E-Mail: sempress@palais-festivals-cannes.fr
président Dario Perez; directeur général Philippe Villechaize; directeur général du tourisme et des congrès Henri Ceran; directeur des grands evénements Pierre Jean; relations presse Elisabeth Lara; directeur de l'évinementiel Bernard Oheix (e-mail: semcultu@palais-festival-cannes.fr)
Capacity: Auditorium Louis Lumière 2300, Théâtre Debussy 1000, exhibition hall (14,000 square meters)
Policy: rent *Arts types:* dance, opera, ballet, orchestra, theatre, exhibitions, film, conferences, congresses, variety; international shows
Comments: SEMEC organises festivals such as Festival International de Danse (December), Les Nuits Musicales du Suquet (July), Festival International d'Art Pyrotechique (July-August), Festival International des Marionnettes (Nov), Festival de Musique Classique (Febr), Festival International des Jeux (Feb-March), Festival International de Danse (Nov, biennal, 1999), Festival International du Film (May)

Théâtre de Cavaillon – Scène Nationale
BP 205, 84306 **Cavaillon** Cedex
Tel: 4-9078 6460 (adminstration) Fax: 4-9076 2267
directeur Bernard Montagne; directeur technique Marcel Abran; jeune public et secretaire générale Martine Petit
Venue type: multi-purpose *Capacity:* 400 *Policy:* present, produce, co-produce *Arts types:* mainly dance and theatre, music

Théâtre des Arts Cergy-Pontoise – Scène Nationale
Place des Arts, BP 307, 95027 **Cergy-Pontoise** Cedex
Tel: 1-3420 1425 Fax: 1-3038 2577
E-Mail: tda@apro.fr
directeur Jean-Joël Le Chapelin; administrateur t.b.a.; directrice des projets Michèle Tayon; directeur technique t.b.a.; relations publiques (+ jazz) André Bonneau
Venue type: theatre *Capacity:* Théâtre des Arts Cergy 200, Théâtre des Arts Les Louvrais Pontoise 560 *Policy:* present, produce, co-produce, rent *Arts types:* opera, theatre, jazz, dance, music, cinema, conferences, exhibitions, video *Comments:* each year: Fenetre au sud festival in June; see also Festivals and Promoters

Espace des Arts de Chalon sur Saône
5 bis av Nicéphore Nièpce, 71100 **Chalon-sur-Saone**
Tel: 3-8542 5200 Fax: 3-8542 5222
E-Mail: espace-des-arts@mairie-chalon-sur-saone.fr
directeur Jean-Marc Grangier; administratrice Bernadette Royot; régisseur général Bernard Gillet; communication, relations publiques Valérie Busseuil; conseiller arts plastiques Catherine Mottot; conseiller jeune public Bernadette Ronge; conseiller concerts – café théâtre Kenny Quaïo
Venue type: theatre *Capacity:* Grande salle 980, Petit Espace 300 + 3 exhibition halls *Policy:* produce, co-produce, rent *Arts types:* theatre, ballet, dance, orchestra, music, opera, singing, puppets, circus, variety, comedy, film, conferences, exhibitions (paintings and photos) *Comments:* Théâtre Municipal, rue auxfévres is also administrated by Espace des Arts

Espace Malraux Scène Nationale Maison de la Culture Chambéry et Savoie
67 Place François Mittérand, Carré Curial, BP 147, 73001 **Chambéry** Cedex
Tel: 4-7985 5543 Fax: 4-7985 2629
directeur Dominique Jambon; directeur administratif Thierry Vautherot; secretaire général Irène Basilis; directeur technique Christian Dalibert; artiste associé André Engel
Venue type: multi-purpose *Capacity:* Espace Malraux 947, Théâtre Charles Dullin 429, Le Curial 156 (cinema), 2 exhibition halls *Policy:* rent, present, co-produce *Arts types:* music, theatre, puppet, dance, cinema, conferences, exhibitions *Comments:* see also Promoters

Théâtre La Piscine
254 Av de la Division-Leclerc, 92290 **Chatenay-Malabry**
Tel: 1-4660 0564 Fax: 1-4661 5455
directrice Francoise Lletellier; administratrice Eveline Abdelkader
Venue type: theatre, concert hall *Capacity:* Salle Sandier 350, Salle Pediluve 80 *Policy:* produce, co-produce *Arts types:* theatre, musical comedy, youth theatre *Comments:* resident theatre company: 'Le Chapeau Rouge'

Théâtre de Châtillon
15, rue de la Gare, 92320 **Châtillon**
Tel: 1-4657 2211 Fax: 1-4657 2692
E-Mail: theatre.chatillon@wanadoo.fr
directeur et metteur en scene Serge Noyelle; co-directeur Pedro Garcia; communication Rachel Megissier; administrateur Frédéric Mazelly; responsable des relations avec le public Laurence Perez
Venue type: multi-purpose *Capacity:* La Chapelle des Sarments 100 *Policy:* present, co-produce and produce *Arts types:* theatre, dance, music, cinema, street theatre festival, modern, contemporary & experimental performances *Comments:* also organise a annual street theatre festival Les Arts dans la Rue; see also Drama

Théâtre de Cherbourg – Scène Nationale
Place du Général de Gaulle, BP 807, 50108 **Cherbourg** Cedex
Tel: 2-3388 5555 (bookings)/5550 (admin)
Fax: 2-3388 5559
E-Mail: theatre-cherbourg@wanadoo.fr
directrice Annette Breuil; secrétaire général Yannick Poignant; attachée de presse et communication Bernadette Clauss
Venue type: theatre *Capacity:* 600
Arts types: theatre, dance, singing, music, variety, jazz
Comments: see also Promoters

Comédie de Clermont-Ferrand – Scène Nationale
Rue Abbé de l'Epée, 63000 **Clermont Ferrand**
Tel: 4-7335 5010 Fax: 4-7334 2078
directeur Jean-Pierre Jourdain; directeur technique Daniel Fauriat; administratrice Colette Dumas-Fariney; régisseur général Julien Bruhnes
Venue type: multi-purpose *Capacity:* Salle Jean Cocteau 1422, Salle Boris Vian 340, Opera de Clermont-Ferrand 850 *Policy:* present, rent, produce *Arts types:* performing arts, also exhibitions, conferences, films, opera, theatre *Comments:* 1 exhibition hall: Salle Chavignier; see also Promoters and Opera

Maison des Allobroges
14 place des Allobroges, 74300 **Cluses**
Tel: 4-5098 0773 Fax: 4-5096 0487
directeur Joel Servigne; président Patrick Ribes; relations publiques Sophie Thibault
Venue type: Théâtre à l'italienne *Capacity:* from 567 to 607 (and 2 exhibition halls) *Policy:* present, produce, rent *Arts types:* theatre, dance, orchestra, opera, exhibitions, film *Comments:* also cultural centre

Atelier du Rhin – Centre Dramatique Regional d'Alsace
La Manufacture, 6 route d'Ingersheim, 68008 **Colmar**
Tel: 3-8941 7192 Fax: 3-8941 3326
directeur Matthew Jocelyn; administrateur Frèdéric de Beauvoir; directrice de la communication Michèle Gaujard
Capacity: 2 halls: 1st à l'italienne 340, 2nd variable up to 100 *Policy:* rent, produce, co-produce *Arts types:* theatre, musical theatre, opera *Comments:* see also Opera, Drama and Promoters

Coupole – Scène Nationale de Sénart, La
Rue Jean-François Millet, 77380 **Combs-la-Ville**
Tel: 1-6034 5370 Fax: 1-6034 5364
directeur Georges Buisson; président Jean-Charles Hohmann; directeur technique Gilles Roubault; administratrice Isabelle Duréault; relations publiques t.b.a.; relations presse Magalie Julien; comèdiens associés Flore Hofmann, Philippe Millat Carus; communication Marie Christine Menez
Venue type: multi-purpose *Capacity:* L'Arène up to 700, Le Théâtre 370, La Rotonde 370 *Policy:* present, produce, co-produce *Arts types:* theatre, dance, music, varieties, circus, cinema, congresses, exhibitions

Théâtre Français de la Musique
Théâtre impérial de Compiegne, 3 rue Othenin, 60200 **Compiègne**
Tel: 3-4440 1710/0800-031 346 (free booking number in France only) Fax: 3-4440 4404
Internet: www.cci-oise.fr/theatre
E-Mail: catherine.gravot@dlnet.inter.fr
directeur général et artistique Pierre Jourdan; président Claude Malatier; secrétaire générale Bettina Caignault; administrateur chargé de production Jean-Michel Barra; communication Catherine Gravot
Venue type: modern theatre l'italienne *Capacity:* 816
Policy: rent, produce, present *Arts types:* French music – opera, concert, ballet, theatre, cinema, congresses, recording music *Comments:* theatre built under Napoleon III, very large stage, very good sound quality; see also Opera

Théâtre Simone Signoret
12 Place Romagné, 78700 **Conflans-Sainte-Honorine**
Tel: 1-3972 5719/3490 9090 Fax: 1-3972 6177
E-Mail: Theatre.Signoret@wanadoo.fr
directeur Dominique Sautot; communication Lilias Benchabyles
Venue type: multi-purpose *Capacity:* 608 *Policy:* rent, produce, co-produce *Arts types:* theatre, song, music, circus, marionettes, dance *Comments:* see Festival de théâtre de rue

Théâtre Municipal
Les Unelles, BP 524, 50205 **Coutances** Cedex
Tel: 2-3376 7860 Fax: 2-3345 4836
Internet: www.oresia.com/jazzsouslespommier
E-Mail: JBLP@oresia.com
directeur Denis Lebas; directeur adjoint Jean-Paul Lecoutour; regisseur Gérard Marie; relations presses et administration Nicolas Jelansky; secretaire Corinne Leconte
Venue type: theatre *Capacity:* 650 *Policy:* present, co-produce, produce *Arts types:* theatre, dance, music, opera etc *Comments:* see also Festivals

Maison des Arts et de la Culture André Malraux Créteil-Val-de-Marne
Place Salvador Allende, 94000 **Créteil**
Tel: 1-4513 1919 Fax: 1-4399 4808
Internet: www.lemanege.com/mac.creteil
E-Mail: maison.arts@wanadoo.fr
directeur Didier Fusillier; conseille artistique Richard Castelli (4383 4953); directeur technique Michel Delort; administration Marie-Pierre de Surville; coordination Festival Exit Heidi Snitselaar; directrice de la communication Mireille Barucco
Venue type: multi-purpose *Capacity:* Hall A 1100, Hall B up to 350 *Policy:* rent, present, co-produce *Arts types:* theatre, dance, comedy, singing, spectacles jeune public, film, new technologies *Comments:* Festival International de Films de Femmes, Festival Exit (performing arts of the world), Les Fantaisies open-air event; see also Promoters

Salle de Spectacles L'Atrium de Dax
Cours Foch, 40100 **Dax**
Tel: 5-5890 1960/9909 (bookings) Fax: 5-5890 1960
administratrice Giselle Ruiz; maire adjoint, affaires culturelles Florence Defos du Rau; directeur technique Bernard Lasserre
Venue type: multi-purpose *Capacity:* up to 500
Policy: rent *Arts types:* all performing arts, exhibitions, congresses *Comments:* venue is listed building, Art Déco (built 1928); venue's administrative address: Hôtel de Ville, rue Saint-Pierre, BP 344, 40107 Dax Cedex

Tobboggan
BP 274, 69152 **Decines** Cedex
Tel: 4-7293 3000 Fax: 4-7293 3001
E-Mail: tobboggan@wanadoo.fr
directeur Jean-Paul Bouvet; responsable communcation Karine Dahan; assistant jeune publique Thierry Bergey
Venue type: cultural centre *Capacity:* 664 *Policy:* present
Arts types: all types *Comments:* venue address: 14 avenue Jean Macé, 69150 Decines Cedex

Dieppe Scène Nationale, Centre Jean Renoir
1 Quai Bérigny, 76374 **Dieppe** Cedex
Tel: 2-3582 0443 Fax: 2-3290 0034
Internet: www.normandnet.fr/dsn
E-Mail: dsn@club-internet.fr
directeur t.b.a.; directeurs techniques Pierre Hamon, Eric Aubisse; relations publiques Maryvone de Casanove, Sébastien Halley; administrateur Geneviève Hollemaert; programmation Olivier Bertrand
Venue type: theatre *Capacity:* 617 *Policy:* present, co-produce (mostly dance and theatre)
Arts types: dance, theatre, cinema, concerts, music (all kinds), world music

Atheneum – Centre Culturel de l'Université de Dijon
1 rue Edgar Faure, 21004 **Dijon** Cedex
Tel: 3-8039 5220 Fax: 3-8067 8934
E-Mail: atheneum@u-bourgogne.fr
directeur Claude Patriat
Venue type: centre culturel *Capacity:* 1 hall 200 + 2 exhibition rooms *Policy:* rent, produce, co-produce *Arts types:* theatre, dance, music, cinema, image diffusion

L'Auditorium
11 boulevard de Verdun, 21000 **Dijon**
Tel: 3-8060 4400 Fax: 3-8060 4440
Internet: www.auditorium-dijon.com
diecteur Jean-Claude Wambst; communication Evelyne Philippe
Venue type: modern *Capacity:* 1600 *Policy:* co-produce, present *Arts types:* classical music, contemporary and classical dance, congress

Palais des Congrès
3 Bld de Champagne, BP 108, 21003 **Dijon** Cedex
Tel: 3-8077 3900 Fax: 3-8077 3939
E-Mail: congresxpodijon@wanadoo.fr
directeur Christine le Guernic; attachés commercials Claude Gallay, Marie Louvot; responsable planning Françoise Gay
Venue type: exhibition halls & amphitheatres *Capacity:* 1 big amphitheatre 600, 20 rooms (multi-purpose) from 20-600, and 5 halls *Policy:* rent, present

Théâtre National Dijon/Bourgogne (TNDB)
BP 1230, 6 rue Rameau, 21029 **Dijon** Cedex
Tel: 3-8068 4747 Fax: 3-8068 4748
E-Mail: infotheatre@tndb.com
directeur Dominique Pitoiset; administrateur Régis Tison; relations publiques Alain Renault; secrétaire général Violette Belkadi
Venue type: theatre *Capacity:* 297 *Policy:* produce, co-produce *Arts types:* drama *Comments:* see also Drama and Festivals

Hippodrome de Douai, L'
Place du Barlet, BP 79, 59502 **Douai** Cedex
Tel: 3-2799 6660 (admin)/6666 (bookings)
Fax: 3-2799 6661
Internet: www.etnet.fr/hippo
E-Mail: hippo@etnet.fr
directeur Marie-Agnés Sevestre; directeur adjoint Jean Escher; règisseur général Stéphane Jagu; secrátoire général relations extérieures Stéphane Konopczynski
Venue type: multi-purpose *Capacity:* up to 1200 *Policy:* rent, produce, co-produce *Arts types:* circus, dance, theatre, mime, music, variety *Comments:* host Les Météores, see also Festivals

Théâtre de Douai – Théâtre Municipal
1 rue de la Comédie, 59500 **Douai**
Tel: 3-2788 8775 Fax: 3-2797 3977
directeur Claude Desmarets
Venue type: théâtre à l'Italienne *Capacity:* 500 *Policy:* rent *Arts types:* boulevard, lyric, dance, variety
Comments: historical listed building, open since 5th December 1785; same kind as the Comedie Française

Bateau Feu, Le
Scène Nationale de Durnkerque, Place du Général de Gaulle, BP 2064, 59376 **Dunkerque** Cedex 01
Tel: 3-2851 4030 Fax: 3-2851 4031
E-Mail: lebateaufeu@nordnet.fr
secrétaire général Christophe Potier; directeur Jean-Paul Noël
Capacity: 2 halls: 764 and 150-160
Policy: present, co-present
Arts types: music, dance, cabaret, concerts, theatre

Théâtre d' Evreux Scène Nationale
Place de Gaulle, 27000 **Evreux**
Tel: 2-3278 8520 Fax: 2-3278 8529
directeur Jacques Falguières; administrateur Emmanuel Placier; chargé de communication Nathalie Dionis; directeur technique Eric Valentin; responsable Ecole de la Forme Robert Llorca
Venue type: multi-purpose *Capacity:* 850, Théâtre à l'italienne 400, Salle de répétition 120 *Policy:* to promote contemporary theatre *Arts types:* theatre, dance, music, jazz – festival, world music *Comments:* responsible for programming theatre and dance events; Théâtre Municipal is rented; see also Drama

Théâtre de l'Agora – Scène Nationale Evry
Place de l'Agora, BP 46, 91002 **Evry** Cedex
Tel: 1-6091 6560 (administration)/6565 (bookings) Fax: 1-6091 6575
directeur Bernard Castéra; directeur technique Guy Varna; secrétaire génerale et administration Emmanuel Martinez
Venue type: multi-purpose *Capacity:* L'Hexagone 670, le Studio 240 *Policy:* produce, co-produce, present, rent *Arts types:* dance, theatre, music, variety, young people's theatre, circus and magic *Comments:* La Gallerie (photography exhibition hall); responsable – Patrick Drouaud

Centre Culturel d'Eysines
Rue de l'Hotel de Ville, 33320 **Eysines**
Tel: 5-5628 7777/5616 1810 (Mairie)
Fax: 5-5657 5264 (Mairie)
directrice Pascale Got
Venue type: multi-purpose *Capacity:* 2 halls: theatre 600, cinema Jean Renoir 160 *Policy:* present, produce, co-produce *Arts types:* theatre, dance, music, cinema, theatre and arts for young people

Salle Polyvalente du Vigean
rue Serge Mallet, 33320 **Eysines**
Tel: 5-5657 8001/5616 1800 (Mairie)
Fax: 5-5657 5264 (Mairie)
directrice Pascale Got
Venue type: multi-purpose *Capacity:* 900 *Policy:* present, rent *Arts types:* all kinds

Fecamp Scene Nationale
54 rue Jules Ferry, BP193, 76401 **Fécamp** Cedex
Tel: 2-3529 2281 Fax: 2-3528 5048
directrice & programmation Annick Bardol
Venue type: multi-purpose *Capacity:* 180 *Policy:* present, rent, produce, co-produce *Arts types:* all kinds including concerts, film *Comments:* organise Festival Déferlantes; see also Festivals

Centre Léonard de Vinci
Place René Lescot, BP9, 69551 **Feyzin** Cedex
Tel: 4-7867 6511 Fax: 4-7867 3150
directeurs Elizabeth Macocco, Dominique Lardenois; secrétaire général J.L. Sackur; relations publiques Brigitte Klépal; directeur technique Hervé Fontaine; communication Isabelle Guerrin
Venue type: multi-purpose *Capacity:* up to 700 *Policy:* rent, produce, present *Arts types:* performing arts, mainly theatre *Comments:* 1 exhibition hall

Espace Le Corbusier
rue de St Just Malmont, 42700 **Firminy**
Tel: 4-7710 0777 Fax: 4-7756 4737
Internet: www.ville-firminy.fr
directrice Danièle Best
Venue type: multi-purpose *Capacity:* Majestic Cinema up to 700 *Policy:* rent, present, co-produce *Arts types:* theatre, dance, music, exhibitions, conferences, film

Le Forum – Saison Culturelle de Flers
Rue du Collège, 61100 **Flers**
Tel: 2-3364 2121 Fax: 2-3329 6913 (Alençon)
directeur Jean-Claude Collot
Venue type: multi-purpose *Capacity:* 712 *Policy:* rent, present, co-produce *Arts types:* theatre, dance, classical music, world music, jazz, puppet theatre, circus *Comments:* linked with the Théâtre d'Alençon (administration), 2 Av. de Basingstoke, 61000 Alençon; Théâtre of Alençon, Flers, Tel: 2-3229 0229 (contact during summer when Le Forum is closed)

Abbaye Royale de Fontevraud – Centre culturel de l'Ouest
BP 24, 49590 **Fontevraud**
Tel: 2-4151 7352 Fax: 2-4138 1544
Internet: www.abbaye-fontevraud.asso.fr
directeur Jean-Paul Chaslus; président Olivier Guichard; directeur adjoint Marie Cécile Gaillard; vice-président Jean-Claude Groshens; directeur artistique René Martin
Venue type: cultural centre (abbey) *Capacity:* dortoire 400, grand réfectoire 600 *Policy:* present *Arts types:* concerts, music (mainly classical, medieval), theatre *Comments:* former abbey

Maison des Cultures Frontières
21 rue de la Croix, 57800 **Freyming-Merlebach**
Tel: 3-8781 6924 Fax: 3-8781 3912
directeur André Protin
Capacity: 500 *Policy:* present, rent *Arts types:* dance, theatre, concerts, exhibitions,conferences *Comments:* 2 exhibition halls; administered by the town hall

Théâtre la Passerelle
137 blvd Pompidou, 05000 **Gap**
Tel: 4-9252 5244/52 (bookings)
Fax: 4-9252 5242
direction Pierre-André Reiso; présidente Véronique Schreiber-Sabbian; directeur adjoint Dominique Chenet; administration gestion Evelyne Nicola; relations publiques Valérie Deulin
Capacity: 850 *Policy:* produce, rent *Arts types:* theatre, orchestra, rock music, jazz, contemporary dance, exhibitions, mainly theatre and children's theatre *Comments:* 1 exhibition hall (photography); conseillé artistique Bernard Descamps

Théâtre de Gennevilliers
41 Av des Grésillons, 92230 **Gennevilliers**
Tel: 1-4132 2610 (admin)/2626 (reservations)
Fax: 1-4086 1744
directeur Bernard Sobel; directeur adjointe Nicole Martin; administrateur Philippe Grimm; directeur technique Parick Yvernat; directrice communication & relations publiques Dominique Landré
Venue type: 2 flexible halls *Capacity:* from 250 to 350 (+ 400 or 450 with double stage) *Policy:* produce, co-produce, receive tours *Arts types:* theatre, all kinds *Comments:* publish theatre magazine Theatre/Public; see also Drama

Saisons du Théâtre du Givors, Les
2 rue Puits Ollier, 69700 **Givors**
Tel: 4-7224 2550 Fax: 4-7249 0499
directeur Antoine Conjard; secrétaire Frederico Maria; communication Hélène Fortin
Venue type: theatre *Capacity:* 180 *Policy:* rent, produce, co-produce *Arts types:* all performing arts: theatre, music, opera etc.

Auditorium du Musée de Grenoble
5, Place de Lavalette, BP 326,
38010 **Grenoble** Cedex 01
Tel: 4-7663 4444 Fax: 4-7663 4410
Internet: www.ville-grenoble.fr/musee-de-grenoble
E-Mail: serge-lemoine@ville-grenoble.fr
conservateur en chef du musée Serge Lemoine; responsable communication Oliver Tomasini (email: olivier.tomasini@ville-grenoble.fr)
Venue type: auditorium
Capacity: 250 *Policy:* also for rent
Arts types: music, congress, meetings *Comments:* alternative E-mail: musée-de-grenoble@ville-grenoble.fr

Auditorium Eric-Paul Stekel
6 Chemin de Gordes, 38100 **Grenoble**
Tel: 4-7646 4844 Fax: 4-7687 1120
directeur Michel Rotterdam; directeurs adjoint Jean-Claude Foulon, Catherine Baubin; directeur administratif Alain Clerc
Venue type: auditorium *Capacity:* 294 *Policy:* also for rent *Arts types:* music *Comments:* see also Promoters

Centre de Creation de Recherche et des Cultures (CREARC)
8 rue Pierre Duclot, 38000 **Grenoble**
Tel: 4-7601 0141 Fax: 4-7644 8483
directeur Fernand Garnier; relations publiques Alexandra Papayanni-Lambros; relations aux l'europe Christoph Tarade
Venue type: theatre *Capacity:* 80 *Arts types:* conferences, lectures, drama *Comments:* see also Drama

Compagnie Renata Scant
8 rue Pierre Duclos, 38000 **Grenoble**
Tel: 4-7644 6092 Fax: 4-7651 7427
Internet: www.neptune.fr/~scant/
directrice et metteur en scène Renata Scant; chargée de la communication Jean Repahette; directeur technique Pierre Auzas
Capacity: 250 *Policy:* produce, co-produce *Arts types:* drama *Comments:* organise the festival de théâtre Européen de Grenoble (last week June and first week July); see also Drama and Festivals

Le Cargo
Maison de la Culture de Grenoble, 4 rue Paul Claudel, BP 2448, 38034 **Grenoble** Cedex 2
Tel: 4-7625 9200 Fax: 4-7662 9869
directeur Roger Caracache; administrateur Michel Lemoine; directeur technique Dominique Guilbaud; secrétaire général Eliane Baracetti
Capacity: Grande Salle 1200, Théâtre mobile 500, Petite Salle 300 *Policy:* co-present, co-produce *Arts types:* all performing arts, modern (theatre, dance, music) *Comments:* planning to close for two years, contact for further information; see also Drama

Summum, Le
Rue Henri Barbusse, BP 2623, 38036 **Grenoble** Cedex 2
Tel: 4-7639 6300 Fax: 4-7639 6350
Internet: alpexpo.com
E-Mail: summum-grenoble@wanadoo.fr
directeur Dominique Mouraille; régisseur Franck Bucarie
Venue type: multi-purpose *Capacity:* 1000-5000 *Policy:* rent *Arts types:* classical dance, concerts (classical, rock, jazz, etc.), meetings, circus

Relais culturel de Haguenau/Théâtre Municipal
1 place Joseph Thierry, BP 249, 67504 **Haguenau** Cedex
Tel: 3-8873 3054 Fax: 3-8873 4404
directeur Daniel Chapelle; président Gérard Traband
Venue type: théâtre à l'italienne *Capacity:* 580 *Policy:* present, co-produce,rent *Arts types:* comedy, theatre, music *Comments:* organise a festival May, annual

Centre Dramatique National de Normandie
Théatre d'Herouville, BP 94,
14203 **Herouville Saint-Clair** Cedex
Tel: 2-3146 2727 Fax: 2-3146 2728
E-Mail: cdncacn@cybercable.tm.fr
directeur Eric Lacascade; directeur administratif Yvon Tranchant; conseiller artistique Philippe Lherbier; secrétaire générale Angelina Berforini
Venue type: theatre *Capacity:* Théâtre d'Hérouville-Saint-Clair 700, Théâtre des Cordes 300 *Policy:* present, produce, co-produce *Arts types:* theatre *Comments:* centre of contemporary art; see also Drama

Le Parvis, Scène Nationale Tarbes Pyrénées
Route de Pau, BP 20, 65421 **Ibos** Cedex
Tel: 5-6290 0855 Fax: 5-6290 6020
directeur Marc Bélit; administrateur t.b.a.; directeur technique Jean-Pierre Frin; chargé de communication Eric Defaix; relations publiques Valérie Tujagues
Venue type: multi-purpose *Capacity:* Grande Salle 750, Parvis Méridien (cinéma) 100 *Policy:* rent, present, produce, co-produce *Arts types:* opera, ballet, music, dance, theatre, film, young people's theatre, mime, circus, variety *Comments:* 2 exhibition halls; see also Promoters

Théâtre de l'Olivier
Blvd Léon Blum, 13800 **Istres**
Tel: 4-4255 2477 Fax: 4-4256 9536
direction Anne Renault; administration Yonick Lévy; direction de la communication et des relations publiques Claire Antognazza
Venue type: theatre *Capacity:* 574 *Policy:* rent *Arts types:* dance, theatre, opera, music

Théâtre d'Ivry Antoine Vitez
1 rue Simon Dereure, 94200 **Ivry-sur-Seine**
Tel: 1-4960 2696 Fax: 1-4670 2223
directice du théatre Leïla Cukierman; conseiller artistique musical Roland Lutz; directeur technique Patrick Molet; secrétariat-accueil Corinne Cottin; administration Nicoles Diot; relations publiques Stephanie La Capria; communication Marie-Agnès Boquien
Venue type: theatre *Capacity:* Room A 240, Room B 112 *Policy:* produce, present, co-produce *Arts types:* theatre, music, dance, singing, youth theatre

Centre Dramatique de La Courneuve
21 ave Gabriel Péri, 93120 **La Courneuve**
Tel: 1-4836 1144 Fax: 1-4836 2383
directeur Dominique Brodin; régisseur général Christian l'Habitant
Venue type: theatre *Capacity:* Centre Culturel Municipal 200, Room B 50 *Policy:* produce, co-produce *Arts types:* drama *Comments:* see also Drama

Centre pour le Création Théâtrale Européene – LE PLESSIS, théâtres...
Château de Plessis-lès-Tours, 37520 **La Riche**
Tel: 2-4738 2929 Fax: 2-4738 3565
directeur artistique José Manuel Cano Lopez; admin. Nathalie Zylbersztein; resp. formation Alain Papillon; resp. project, artistiques Françoise Canolopez; resp. diffusion et production Magali Berruet
Venue type: theatre, studio de répétition, résidence he'bergement, centre de documentation *Capacity:* 100 *Policy:* produce *Arts types:* theatre, dance, music, visual arts *Comments:* European theatre centre (Traditional and virtual Library-Residency-Workshops and Performances); see Festival: Acteurs-Acteurs; see Drama: Autruche Théâtre

La Coursive – Scène Nationale de La Rochelle
4 rue Saint-Jean-du-Pérot, 17025 **La Rochelle** Cedex
Tel: 5-4651 5400 Fax: 5-4651 5401
directeur M. Jackie Marchand; administrateur Francis Morin; secrétaire générale Florence Simonet; communication Monique Chabot, Dany Huc; directeur technique Alain Lafon; accueil des artistes Floraline Tison; cinéma Edith Perin; presse Monique Chabot
Venue type: multi-purpose *Capacity:* La Coursive grande salle 1003, Salle Bleue 284 *Policy:* present, rent, co-produce *Arts types:* theatre, dance, music, orchestra, recitals, classical concerts, jazz, cinema, conferences *Comments:* also collaborate on Festival International du Film de La Rochelle, Francofolies

LARC – Scène Nationale
Place de la Poste, BP 5, 71201 **Le Creusot** Cedex
Tel: 3-8555 3728 Fax: 3-8555 4894
directrice Claude Meiller; administratrice Marie-France Cottin; directeur technique Michel Olivier; relations publiques Virginie Boccard
Venue type: multi-purpose,theatre *Capacity:* Grand Theatre 941, Petit Theatre 235 *Policy:* produce, co-produce, present, rent *Arts types:* dance, music, theatre, film, visual arts *Comments:* 1 exhibition hall (la galerie du theatre), produce exhibitions

Le Volcan/Le Havre
Espace Oscar Niemeyer
BP 1106, 76063 **Le Havre** Cedex
Tel: 2-3519 1010 Fax: 2-3519 1000
Internet: www.infoceane.com/levolcan.html
directeur – metteur en scène Alain Milianti; directeur adjoint Roland Thomas; administratrice Christine Atienza; secrétaire général – direction de l'information t.b.a.; directeur des relations publiques Jean-Pierre Laurent; directeur de l'accueil Kassem Azimi; directeur technique Gérard Salamagnon; régisseur général Sylvain Ghiloni
Venue type: multi-purpose, dance, music, theatre *Capacity:* Le grand Volcan, salle de 1160 amphitheatre, exhibition hall & foyer bar; Le petit Volcan from 350 to 550; Cinéma l'Eden 300 *Policy:* rent (in particular circumstances), present, co-produce, produce *Arts types:* dance, music, theatre *Comments:* see also Promoters

Grand Bleu – Centre Dramatique National Jeunes Publics Lille Region Nord Pas de Calais, Le
36 Av Marx Dormoy, 59000 **Lille**
Tel: 3-2009 4550 Fax: 3-2009 2152
Internet: www.legrandbleu.com
E-Mail: grandbleu@nordnet.fr
directeur Bernard Allombert; communication Françoise Allombert; directeur technique Patrick Leroy; administration Ariane Braun
Capacity: Hall A 120, Hall B 323 *Arts types:* drama for young people *Comments:* organises the festival: Planetado, theatre and dance for european teenagers with professional performances and workshops presentations from teenagers (from Europe and other countries); see also Drama and Festivals

Lille Opera
Opéra de Lille
Maison de l' habitat, 2 rue Alexandre Desrousseaux, 59800 **Lille**
Tel: 3-2085 9537 (artistic direction) Fax: 3-2052 2258
Comments: the opera is closed for refurbishment for two years; see also Opera and Promoters

L'Aéronef
Av. Willy Brandt, 59777 **Lille-Euralille**
Tel: 3-2078 0000 Fax: 3-2078 0015
directeur Jean-François Driant; programmateur Delphine Debord, Thierry Six; relations publiques Eric Morange
Venue type: multi-purpose *Capacity:* salle A 2000, salle B 300, salle C 150 *Policy:* present, rent, co-produce, produce *Arts types:* rock, dance, opera,cinema, theatre, film (festival)

Lille Grand Palais
1 Boulevard des Cités Unies, 59777 **Lille-Euralille**
Tel: 3-2014 1516 Fax: 3-2014 1414
Internet: www.lillegp.com
E-Mail: lillegrandpalais@lillegp.com
directeur du zenith arena Arnaud Delbarre; commercial Eudes Desteract; communication Marie-Béatrice Mazuc
Venue type: multi-purpose *Capacity:* Arena (Zenith) seated 5000, plus standing 2000, 3 Amphitheatres-Vauban 1500, Pasteur 500, Eurotop 300 *Arts types:* music (congresses), concert, opera, dance, ballet, drama, circus *Comments:* simultaneous translations in various languages available

Centre Culturel Jean Moulin
76 rue des Sagnes, 87280 **Limoges**
Tel: 5-5535 0410 Fax: 5-5535 9826
directeur Hubert Bonnefond; responsable Daniel Fauchet
Venue type: multi-purpose *Capacity:* Centre Culturel Jean Moulin 800, salle de conf. n° 2 196, n°1 100 *Policy:* present, rent *Arts types:* music, theatre, dance

Centre Culturel John Lennon
41-Ter Rue de Feytiat, 87000 **Limoges**
Tel: 5-5506 2483 Fax: 5-5506 1514
directeur Hubert Bonnefond; responsable Christophe Guillot
Venue type: concert hall *Capacity:* 400 (seated) or 680 (standing) *Policy:* rental *Arts types:* concerts, cinema

Centres Culturels Municipaux de Limoges
7 Av Jean Gagnant, 87000 **Limoges**
Tel: 5-5534 4549/5545 6166 Fax: 5-5533 1144
directeur Hubert Bonnefond
Capacity: theatre 380, auditorium 110 *Policy:* own productions and rent *Arts types:* music, theatre, dance, comedy, cinema *Comments:* coordinate two other venues: Centre Culturel Jean Moulin and Centre Culturel John Lennon (see separate entries)

Théâtre de L'Union – Centre Dramatique National du Limousin
BP 206, 20 rue des Coopérateurs, 87006 **Limoges** Cedex
Tel: 5-5579 7479 Fax: 5-5577 3737
E-Mail: adm@theater.union.fr
directeur Silviu Purcarete; administrateur Denis Triclot; directeur technique Yvon Truffaut; conseiller artistique Alain Garlan
Venue type: theatre *Capacity:* 398 *Policy:* produce, co-produce, promote *Arts types:* drama
Comments: see also Drama

Théâtre de Lisieux
2 rue au Char, BP 7222, 14107 **Lisieux** Cedex
Tel: 2-3161 0440 Fax: 2-3132 3884
directeur Dominique Raulet; régisseure générale Christelle Rochet; relations publiques Emmanuelle Viel
Venue type: théâtre à l'italienne *Capacity:* 370 *Policy:* present, co-produce, rent *Arts types:* theatre, dance, variety, music, opera, young public theatre, exhibitions

Théâtre de Lorient – Centre Dramatique de Bretagne
11 rue Claire Droneau – BP 726, 56107 **Lorient** Cedex
Tel: 2-9783 5151 Fax: 2-9783 5917
direction Eric Vigner; administration Mona Guichard; relations publiques Marie Rose Hays, Philippe Arretez; secrétaire générale Benedicte Vigner; secrétariat direction Florence Noury; régisseur général Joseph Le Saint; régisseur plateau Didier Cadou; accueil Marianne Seveno
Venue type: theatre *Capacity:* 339 *Policy:* present, produce *Arts types:* drama

Auditorium de Lyon
82 rue de Bonnel, 69431 **Lyon** Cedex 03
Tel: 4-7895 9500 Fax: 4-7860 1308
Internet: www.mairie-lyon.fr
E-Mail: onl@Lyon.asi.fr
directeur général Patrice Armengau; directeur administratif Gilbert Blanc; chargé de communication Pierre Budimir
Venue type: concert hall
Capacity: 2045 *Policy:* present, co-produce, rent
Arts types: classical concerts, pop, cinema, variety, organ music
Comments: home of the National Orchestra of Lyon

GRAME
9 rue Garet, BP 1185, 69202 **Lyon** Cedex 1
Tel: 4-7207 3700 Fax: 4-7207 3701
Internet: www.grame.fr/
E-Mail: grame@rd.grame.fr
directeurs James Giroudon, Pierre Alain Jaffrennou; administratrice Florence Catrin; responsable recherche Yann Orlarey
Venue type: production centre *Capacity:* Salle Molière 600, Palais Bondy, Théâtre de la Renaissance 450, L'Embarcadère 100, Théâtre du parc 240, Opera de Lyon 400, Musée d'art contemporain de Lyon 500, auditorium Maurice Ravel *Policy:* produce *Arts types:* music, opera, incl. pyrotechnics, special effects, etc. *Comments:* Festival 'Musiques en Scène'- contemporary music and musical theatre (March/April); see also Promoters and Festivals

Halle Tony Garnier
20 place Antonin Perrin, 69007 **Lyon**
Tel: 4-7276 8585 Fax: 4-7872 3707
directeur exploitation Thierry Theodori; responsable administrative Sophie Iacconi
Capacity: 2000 & 17000 *Policy:* rent % of receipts according to audience capacity *Arts types:* music (classical, rock and pop) opera, cinema, exhibitions

La Maison de la Danse
Théatre du Huitième, 8 Av Jean Mermoz, 69008 **Lyon**
Tel: 4-7278 1818
Fax: 4-7278 7090 (communication)
Internet: www.maisondeladanse.com
E-Mail: maisondeladanse@wanadoo.fr
directeur Guy Darmet; secrétaire générale Michèle Luquet; directeur communication Jérôme Devèze; attaché de presse Jean-Paul Brunet
Venue type: theatre *Capacity:* 1100 *Policy:* rent, produce, co-produce *Arts types:* dance, exhibitions, cinema

Salle Albert Thomas
Ville de Lyon, Division du Domaine, 11 rue du Griffon, 69001 **Lyon**
Tel: 4-7210 3823 Fax: 4-7210 3820
Venue type: concert hall *Capacity:* 1960 *Arts types:* theatre, concerts, variety, conferences, dance
Comments: venue address: Bourse du Travàil, Place Guichard, 69003 Lyon

Salle Molière
Ville de Lyon, Division du Domaine, 11 rue du Griffon, 69001 **Lyon**
Tel: 4-7210 3030/3823 (bookings) Fax: 4-7210 3820
Internet: www.mairie-lyon.fr
Venue type: concert hall *Capacity:* 600 *Policy:* rent *Arts types:* classical music recitals *Comments:* venue address: 18 quai de Bondy, 69005 Lyon

Salle Rameau
Ville de Lyon, Division du Domaine, 11 rue du Griffon, 69001 **Lyon**
Tel: 4-7210 3823 Fax: 4-7210 3820
Venue type: concert hall *Capacity:* 865, theatre 670 *Policy:* rent *Arts types:* conferences, concert, variety, theatre, dance *Comments:* venue address: 29 rue de la Jaulimère, 69001 Lyon

Théâtre de la Tête d'Or
24 rue Dunoir, 69003 **Lyon**
Tel: 4-7895 4669 Fax: 4-7871 7708
directrice et metteur en scène Jacqueline Boeuf; communication Marie-Hélène Lépy; administratrice Françoise Guillermin; presse t.b.a.; relations publiques Antoinette Falcot; décorateur Christian Jaspard; costumiére Josyane Carron
Venue type: heatre *Capacity:* 240 *Arts types:* touring (in France), street theatre, comedy, children's shows, classical drama, exhibitions

Théâtre des Jeunes Années – Centre Dramatique National (TJA)
23 rue de Bourgogne, 69009 **Lyon**
Tel: 4-7253 1510 Fax: 4-7253 1519
directeurs artistiques Maurice Yendt, Michel Dieuaide; directeur technique Jean-Pierre Grosset
Venue type: theatre *Capacity:* Hall A 450, Hall B 100 *Policy:* produce, co-produce *Arts types:* contemporary drama for young audiences, classical *Comments:* see also Drama and Festivals

Théâtre les Ateliers
5 rue du Petit David, 69002 **Lyon**
Tel: 4-7837 4630 Fax: 4-7241 9302
directeur Gilles Chavassieux; secrétaire générale Nicole Lachaise; relations publiques Marie-Françoise Renouprez, Nathalie Teboul; administratrice Danièle Martigny; secrétaire générale Nicole Lachaise
Venue type: theatre *Capacity:* 230; 100 *Policy:* produce, co-produce, present *Arts types:* theatre, music, voice
Comments: see also Drama

Théâtre (Scène Nationale), Le
1511 Av Charles de Gaulle, 71000 **Mâcon**
Tel: 3-8533 5800 Fax: 3-8539 2163
E-Mail: theatre@club-internet.fr
directrice Gislaine Gouby; régisseur général Isabelle Senegre
Venue type: multi-purpose *Capacity:* Hall A 900, Hall B 300 *Policy:* rent, present, co-produce, produce *Arts types:* theatre, opera, contemporary music, concerts, variety, film, dance, congresses

Théâtre 71 – Scène Nationale
3 place du 11 Novembre, 92240 **Malakoff**
Tel: 1-4655 4345 Fax: 1-4655 1331
directeur Pierre Ascaride; secretaire générale Agnès Célérier; administratrice Ghyslaine Schueller; directrice technique Joëlle Payet
Venue type: multi-purpose,theatre *Capacity:* 516 *Policy:* present, co-produce,produce *Arts types:* theatre, dance, ballet, music *Comments:* see also Drama

Centre d'Art et de Culture de Marne-la-Vallée(Scéne Nationale)
La Ferme du Buisson, Allée de la Ferme, Noisiel, 77437 **Marne-la-Vallée** Cedex 2
Tel: 1-6462 7700 Fax: 1-6462 7799
président Jean Valentin; directeur administratif Vincent Eches; directeur artistique José-Manuel Gonçalvès; directeur technique t.b.a.; pr Evelyne Nedelec
Venue type: theatre *Capacity:* theatre 800, cinema I 300 , cinema II 200, art gallery *Policy:* present, co-produce *Arts types:* contemporary and music theatre, dance, music (classical), film, opera, shows for children, world music

Friche, La
23 rue Guidal, 13003 **Marseille**
Tel: 4-9111 4243 Fax: 4-9111 4244
Internet: www.lafriche.org
E-Mail: everges@lafriche.org
directeur Emmanuel Vergès

Théâtre Axel Toursky
16 passage Léo Ferré, 13003 **Marseille**
Tel: 4-9102 5835 Fax: 4-9167 9964
administrators Bernard Urbain, Corinne Vallalta; directeur artistique et comedien Richard Martin; directeur technique Daniel Tzicuris; responsable de la communication Françoise Tremlet
Venue type: theatre *Capacity:* 700 up to 800 *Arts types:* theatre, dance, jazz, variety, cinema, performances in foreign languages *Comments:* house company is Compagnie Richard Martin; see also Drama

Théâtre de Lenche
4 Place de Lenche, 13002 **Marseille**
Tel: 4-9191 5222/5556 (festival) Fax: 4-9190 9616
Internet: www.cartediem.com/lenche/
directeur Maurice Vinçon
Venue type: theatre *Capacity:* 80 *Policy:* co-produce, present, rent *Arts types:* drama *Comments:* organises the Festival des Iles; see also Festivals

Théâtre de Merlan – Scène Nationale
Avenue Raimu, 13014 **Marseille**
Tel: 4-9111 1930 Fax: 4-9111 1939
directeur Alain Liévaux; président Alain Vidal Naquet; secretaire générale Andrée Pascaud; directeur technique Pierre Andrac
Capacity: up to 540, Cinéma Merlan 90 *Policy:* co-produce, present *Arts types:* theatre, dance, exhibitions, variety, circus, live arts *Comments:* see also Promoters

Théâtre des Bernardines
17 bd Garibaldi, 13001 **Marseille**
Tel: 4-9124 3040 Fax: 4-9124 3041
directeur Alain Fourneau; administrateur Patrick Ranchain; directeur technique Xavier Sananas; secrétaire générale Suzanne Joubert
Venue type: 18th century chapel (listed building)
Capacity: 98 *Policy:* produce, co-produce *Arts types:* contemporary dance and theatre, contemporary music

Zénith de Marseille, Dome
48 avenue de St Just, 13004 **Marseille**
Tel: 4-9112 2121 Fax: 4-9112 2110
directeur Elie-Claude Argy; directeur technique Jacques Valente
Venue type: multi-purpose *Capacity:* 8500 *Policy:* rent *Arts types:* classical dance, concerts (classical, rock, jazz, etc.), meetings, conventions, conferences

Théâtre des Salins Scène Nationale
BP 75, 13692 **Martigues** Cedex
Tel: 4-4244 3601 Fax: 4-4244 3636
directeur Laurent Ghilini; chargée de mission et programmation de la salle au bout de la nuit(musique) Michel Antonelli; directeur technique Serge Boudin; administratrice Michelle Hettiger
Venue type: Amphitheatre *Capacity:* hall 615, Salle au bout de la nuit 180 *Policy:* present, produce and co-produce *Arts types:* jazz, rock, theatre, dance, exhibitions, theatre for young people *Comments:* visiting address: 19 Quai Paul Doumer, 13692 Martigues; see also Opera

Le Manège – Scène Nationale
Le Manège BP 105, 59600 **Maubeuge** Cedex
Tel: 3-2765 1500 Fax: 3-2765 9380
Internet: www.lemanege.com
E-Mail: manege1@worldnet.fr
président Jacques Montaron; directeur Didier Fusillier; administrateur Yves Vasseur; conseillers artistiques Gérard Hourbette, Richard Castelli; directeur technique Frédéric Platteau; relations publiques Corinne Solini, Fabien Lemaire, Florence Laly; directeur communications Gilles Bouckaert
Venue type: theatre *Capacity:* La Luna 2500, Salle Théophile Haut 2000, Centre Malraux 760, Théâtre du Manège 600, Salle Léo Ferré 600, Salles Sthrau-2 x 150, Chapelle des Soeurs Noires 90 *Policy:* present, produce, co-produce, rent *Arts types:* drama, music, dance, opera, music and dance theatre, new technologies *Comments:* working area: 3 towns: Mauberge, Jeumont, Aulnoye; see also Festivals

Zénith SA (France)
Zénith de Nancy (Zenith of Nancy), rue du Zénith, 54320 **Maxéville**
Tel: 3-8393 2700 Fax: 3-8397 0926
E-Mail: zenithnanc@aol.com
directeur Claude-Jean Antoine; directeur-adjoint Thierry Biscut; directeur technique Patrick Lamadon
Venue type: concert hall, multi-purpose *Capacity:* 6039 (indoor), up to 25000 (open-air amphitheatre) *Policy:* rent *Arts types:* music (concerts), dance, congresses, conferences, sport

Théâtre Luxembourg
4 rue Cornillon, BP 213, 77103 **Meaux** Cedex
Tel: 1-6436 4013 Fax: 1-6434 9051
directeurs Claudine Fievet, Jean-Luc Palies, Philipe Durand; responsable communications Miss Drouillat
Venue type: theatre *Capacity:* stage A 600, stage B 107
Policy: co-produce, produce, present *Arts types:* baroque-contemporary drama *Comments:* see also Drama – Influence Fievet-Palies, Champigny-sur-Marne

l'Arsenal
Avenue Ney, 57000 **Metz**
Tel: 3-8739 9200 Fax: 3-8775 2152
Internet: www.mairie-metz.fr:8080
E-Mail: arsenal@pub.mairie-metz.fr
directeur général Jean Larpenteur; programmation artistique Michèle Paradon; directeur technique Martial Roger; relations publiques Christine Raffin
Venue type: 2 concert halls and 1 exhibition hall
Capacity: 1350 + 352 *Policy:* present, rent, produce *Arts types:* classical music with philharmonic orchestras, chamber orchestras, contemporary dance, jazz, world music, ancient music (in Gallo-roman church)
Comments: the venue for ancient music is the oldest church in France – dating from the IV century

l'Héxagone – Scène Nationale
24 rue des Aiguinards, 38240 **Meylan**
Tel: 4-7690 0980 Fax: 4-7641 0449
Internet: www.hexagone-meylan.asso.fr
directeur Maurice Jondeau; pr Eliane Sausse
Venue type: 1 hall, theatre *Capacity:* 567 *Policy:* present, produce, co-produce, rent *Arts types:* theatre, operetta, music, french song, dance, comedy, jazz, circus

Théâtre de la Colonne
Rue Marcel Paul, 13140 **Miramas** Cedex
Tel: 4-9017 3080 Fax: 4-9058 2302
chargé de mission Jacques Bertrand; administration Marc Cohen; directeur technique Bernard Mabille; chargé de communication J P Quichner
Capacity: 800, amphithéâtre 1000, cinéma 250 *Policy:* present, rent, produce *Arts types:* theatre, orchestra, opera, dance, variety, congresses, exhibitions, film

Centre d'Art et de Plaisanterie Montbéliard
Hôtel de Sponeck, 54 rue Clemenceau, BP 236, 25204 **Montbéliard** Cedex
Tel: 3-8191 3711 Fax: 3-8191 1025
E-Mail: capsna@infrescom.fr
directeurs Jacques Livchine, Mme Hervée De LaFond; secteur diffusion Rosanna Locatelli
Venue type: multi-purpose, theatre *Capacity:* 450 *Policy:* produce, rent *Arts types:* theatre, street theatre
Comments: performances take place at: Théâtre de Montbéliard, Place St Martin, 25200 Montbéliard and Hôtel de Sponeck; see also Drama

Centre Animation et Rencontres
Quai Jules Chagot, 71300 **Montceau-les-Mines**
Tel: 3-8567 7810/11 (bookings) Fax: 3-8567 7819
directeur Patrick Lebossé
Venue type: theatre *Capacity:* 940 *Policy:* produce, co-produce, rent *Arts types:* music, theatre, dance, variety, exhibitions

Théâtre de Montelimar Centre Culturel
1 Place du Théâtre, BP 163, 26204 **Montelimar** Cedex
Tel: 4-7500 7900 Fax: 4-7500 7902
directrice Martine Denisé; jeune publique et relations publiques Jean- Marc Baudez; chargée de communication t.b.a.
Venue type: théâtre à la Italienne *Capacity:* Théâtre à la Italienne 250, Espace Mistral 1000, Auditorium 450, Cinema 118 *Policy:* present, produce, co-produce, rent *Arts types:* music, dance, drama, variety, cinema, youth theatre, opera

Athanor Centre des rencontres économiques et culturelles de Montluçon
BP 1144, Rue Pablo Picasso, 03103 **Montluçon** Cedex
Tel: 4-7008 1440 Fax: 4-7003 4700
E-Mail: athanor.montlucon@wanadoo.fr
directrice Brigitte Paulet; responsable de la programmation Marie-Claude Rochat; attachée à l'information t.b.a.; responsable technique Jean-Paul Chanal
Capacity: Omega 4000, Epsilon 400-600, Orangeraie 200 *Arts types:* music, opera, dance, visual arts, jazz
Comments: season from Oct to May

Les Fédérés – Centre Dramatique National de Création Région Auvergne
Espace Boris Vian, 03100 **Montluçon**
Tel: 4-7003 8618 Fax: 4-7005 8857
co-directeurs Olivier Perrier, Jean-Paul Wenzel; relations publiques Laurence Fleury
Capacity: 280 *Arts types:* contemporary theatre
Comments: see also Drama

Corum – Opera Berlioz et Palais des Congrès de Montpellier, Le
Esplanade Charles de Gaulle, BP 2200, 34027 **Montpellier** Cedex 1
Tel: 4-6761 6761 Fax: 4-6761 6759/6700
Internet: www.corum-montpellier.com
E-Mail: corum@corum-montpellier.com
directeur général François Barbance; directeur adjoint opéra Henri Maier; directeur de l´orchestre philharmonique de Montpellier Languedoc- Roussillon René Koering; directrice de la communication Marie-France Dewast
Venue type: opera, culture and conference hall *Capacity:* Hall A 2000 (Opera Berlioz), Hall B 745 (Salle Pasteur), Hall C (Einstein) 315, 2 exhibition halls, 21 salles de commission (30-40 each) *Policy:* produce, co-produce *Arts types:* contemporary, classical dance, theatre, opera, orchestra *Comments:* organise Festival International Montpellier Danse, Festival International de Radio France et Montpellier Languedoc- Roussillon; see also Orchestras

Théâtre Treize Vents
Domaine de Grammont, 34965 **Montpellier** Cedex 2
Tel: 4-6799 2529 (admin)/28/27
Fax: 4-6799 2529/8/7 (administration)
E-Mail: theatre.des.13.vents@wanadoo.fr
directeur Jean-Claude Fall; secrétaire général Blandine Verhaverbeke; administrateur Benoit Joessel; attachée de presse Claudine Arignon; directrice relations publiques Valérie Bousquet
Venue type: theatre *Capacity:* 591 *Policy:* produce, co-produce, rent *Arts types:* theatre, jazz

Zénith de Montpellier
Domaine de Gramont avenue Albert Einstein, 34000 **Montpellier**
Tel: 4-6764 6883 (admin)/5000 (audiophone)
Fax: 4-6765 3818
Internet: www.corum-montpellier.fr
E-Mail: zenith@corum-montpellier.fr
directeur J P Montanari; directeur technique Olivier Gleizes; communication Marie-France Dewast
Venue type: multi-purpose *Capacity:* 1900-6300 *Policy:* rent *Arts types:* concerts (classical, rock, jazz), meetings, conventions, conferences, theatre, circus, dance

Théâtre des Jeunes Spectateurs – Centre Dramatique National
26 place Jean Jaurès, 93100 **Montreuil**
Tel: 1-4870 4890 Fax: 1-4859 6044
directeur Daniel Bazilier; directeur adjointe Patricia Giros; administratrice Régine Guillotin; relations publiques Brigitte Bertin, Christelle Faure, Jeanne Garcia; régie général Pierre Hadef
Capacity: 340 *Policy:* produce, co-produce, present
Arts types: theatre for young audiences
Comments: see also Drama

La Filature – Scène Nationale
20 Allée Nathan Katz, 68090 **Mulhouse** Cedex
Tel: 3-8936 2829 Fax: 3-8936 2800
Internet: www.lafilature.asso.fr
E-Mail: mjl@lafilature.asso.fr
directeur général Christopher Crimes; attachée de direction Cécile Le Bomin; relations presse Marie-Josée Lagarde; délégué aux actions culturelles Francis Schaller; directeur technique Henri-François Monnier; secrétaire générale Denise Benabenq
Venue type: theatre
Capacity: Grande salle 1200, Salle 380, Cinema 100
Policy: rent, present, co-produce, produce
Arts types: theatre, dance, music (contemporary, classical and world music), video creations, opera, circus *Comments:* media resource centre, exhibition hall; alternative E-mails: chc@lafilature.asso.fr; see also Drama

Théâtre de la Sinne
39 rue de la Sinne, 68100 **Mulhouse**
Tel: 3-8945 2696 Fax: 3-8966 4017
administrateur Jean-Luc Castel
Venue type: théâtre à la Italienne *Capacity:* 823 *Policy:* rent, present *Arts types:* lyric, theatre, dance

Opéra de Nancy et de Lorraine
1 rue Sainte-Catherine, 54000 **Nancy**
Tel: 3-8385 3320/3060 (bookings)
Fax: 3-8385 3066
directeur général Jean-Marie Blanchard; administrateur Christophe Bezzone; directeur musical t.b.a.; directeur technique Serge Gachet; déléguée générale Liliane Martinez; directeur musicale de l'orchestre Sébastian Lang-Lessing
Venue type: 18th century italian style theatre *Capacity:* 950 *Policy:* produce, co-produce *Arts types:* opera, operetta, theatre, ballet, concerts *Comments:* see also Opera, Orchestras and Promoters

Salle Poirel (Nancy)
Service des affaires culturelles – C.O N° 1, Mairie de Nancy, Place Stanislas, 54035 **Nancy** Cedex
Tel: 3-8385 3080 Fax: 3-8332 9025
responsable Claude Hausermann
Venue type: concert hall, large gallery
Capacity: 912 *Policy:* rent
Arts types: concerts (orchestral, choral), variety, exhibitions, music
Comments: venue address: 3, rue Victor Poirel, 54000 Nancy, Tel: 3-8385 3085/8332 3125 (public)

Zénith de Nancy
rue du Zénith, 54320 **Nancy – Maxéville**
Tel: 3-8393 2727 Fax: 3-8397 0926
E-Mail: zenithnanc@aol.com
directeur Claude-Jean Antoine; directeur technique Patrick Lamadon; directeur general Thierry Biskup; communication Severine Ollivier
Venue type: concert hall
Capacity: 6000 (indoor), 25000 (open-air)
Policy: rent *Arts types:* concerts (music), meetings

Maison de la Musique
8 rue des Anciennes Mairies, 92000 **Nanterre**
Tel: 1-4137 9420/21 (bookings) Fax: 1-4137 0645
directeur Hugo Guffanti; administrator Laurence Terk; responsable j.p. Elissabeth Henry; communication Anne-Marie Goron; pr Nicole Kandel
Venue type: modern *Capacity:* 485-500 *Policy:* co-produce, present *Arts types:* music, lyrical, dance

Théâtre de Nanterre-Amandiers
7 Avenue Pablo Picasso, 92022 **Nanterre** Cedex
Tel: 1-4614 7070/7000 Fax: 1-4725 1775
directeurs Jean-Pierre Vincent, Marc Dondey; directeur technique Carlos Stavisky
Venue type: multi-purpose *Capacity:* up to 150, up to 500, up to 900 *Policy:* produce, co-produce, rent *Arts types:* modern, classical drama *Comments:* see also Drama and Promoters

CDRC
2, rue de la Biscuiterie, BP 21304, 44013 **Nantes** Cedex 1
Tel: 2-5182 1500 Fax: 2-4020 2012
E-Mail: crdc.lu@wanadoo.fr
directeur Jean Blaise; président Daniel Bridet
Capacity: salle 2000 *Policy:* produce, co-produce in various theatres and venues in Nantes *Arts types:* theatre, dance, festivals: Trafics (June), Fin de Siècle (October) *Comments:* from December 1999 will be linked to the theatre L' Usine; see also Festivals

Maison de la Culture de Loire Atlantique
Accueil et administration, 10, 12 Passage Pommeraye, BP 30111, 44001 **Nantes** Cedex 1
Tel: 2-5188 2525 Fax: 2-4047 9204
directeur Philippe Coutant; directeur administratif et financier Daniel Le Cars; directeur technique Laurent Copeaux; directeur des relations extérieures Benoît Martin; directeur animation Arnaud Cazaux
Capacity: Espace 879 *Policy:* rent, produce, co-produce, present *Arts types:* drama, classical music, ballet, variety, one man shows and concerts *Comments:* venue address: Théâtre, Espace 44, 84, rue du général Buat, 44000 Nantes

Maison de la Culture – Théâtre Municipal
2 bld Pierre De Courbertin, 58036 **Nevers** Cedex
Tel: 3-8636 1394 Fax: 3-8657 8570
programmation Olivier Peyronnaud; administration Philippe Jeanjean; direction technique Jean-Claude Dauphin; directeur de la vie culturelle Alain Keck; relations publiques Virginie Thiais; régisseur d'avance Philippe Jean Jean
Capacity: Salles Maison de la Culture 986, Salles Théâtre 300, Salles Auditorium 100, Salle Jean Lauberty 150 *Policy:* co-produce, rent *Comments:* festivals: theatre in May, Musique Ultine in June, lyric in July, rock in October and jazz in November; see also Festivals

Acropolis
1 Esplanade Kennedy, BP 4083, 06302 **Nice** Cedex 4
Tel: 4-9392 8300 Fax: 4-9392 8255
Internet: www.nice-acropolis.com
E-Mail: standard@nice-acropolis.com
président directeur général Jean Guillon
Venue type: multi-purpose *Capacity:* l'Apollon 2500, L'Athéna 750, L'Hermès 300, plus a further 30 rooms and conference rooms (35-250) *Policy:* present, rent *Arts types:* dance, opera, orchestra, variety

Théâtre de Nice – Centre Dramatique National Nice-Côte d'Azur
Promenade des Arts, 06300 **Nice**
Tel: 4-9313 9090 Fax: 4-9362 1946
directeur Jacques Weber; directeur administratif Yves Saussinan; directeur technique Yves Guérut; relations publiques Dany Montiglio; secrétaire générale Mady Léo; secrétaire de direction Simone Ginefri
Capacity: Salle Pierre Brasseur 1000, Salle Michel Simon 300 *Policy:* produce, co-produce *Arts types:* theatre, dance *Comments:* see also Drama

Moulin du Roc – Scène Nationale, Le
9 blvd Main, BP 405, 79004 **Niort** Cedex
Tel: 5-4977 3230 Fax: 5-4977 3231
Internet: www.moulinduroc.asso.fr
E-Mail: moulinduroc@moulinduroc.asso.fr
directeur Bernard Bonnet; directeur technique Bernard Canteaut; relations publiques Michèle Cassegrain; administrateur Bruno Denis; programmation danse Christian Vernadal
Venue type: multi-purpose *Capacity:* Hall A 936, Hall B 260, cinema Jacques Morel 300, video room *Policy:* present, co-produce, produce, rent *Arts types:* theatre, music, variety, dance, lyric, jazz, exhibitions, cinema, theatre for young people
Comments: see also Promoters

Centre Nationale de Creation et de Diffusion Culturelles
BP 118, 83190 **Ollioules** Cedex
Tel: 4-9422 7400 Fax: 4-9422 7419
information Nataly Bernard
Capacity: covered hall 500, amphithéâtre 1200, cinema 100 *Arts types:* contemporary dance, drama *Comments:* currently undergoing restructuring; see also Dance, Festivals and Promoters

Carré Saint-Vincent – Scéne Nationale
Carré Saint-Vincent, 45000 **Orléans**
Tel: 2-3862 4568 (admin)/7530 (public)
Fax: 2-3862 4730
E-Mail: ccnorleans@xernet.com
directeur Claude Malric; secrétaire général et direction de relations publiques Béatrice Cachin; administrateur Roger Fontanel; directeur technique Jean Guy Porché
Venue type: multi-purpose *Capacity:* Salle Pierre-Aimé Touchard 1000, Salle Antoine Vitez 220, Salle Jean-Louis Barrault 600 *Policy:* present, co-produce (occasionally), rent *Arts types:* orchestra, opera, theatre, dance, film *Comments:* see also Promoters, Drama and Dance

Centre National de la Danse
1, rue Victor Hugo, 93500 **Pantin**
Tel: 1-4274 4422 Fax: 1-4029 0646
Internet: www.centredanse.fr
E-Mail: cnd@wanadoo.fr
président Anne Chiffert; directeur Michel Sala; directeur de la maison des compagnies et des spectacles Daniel Gillet
Venue type: Maison des Compagnies et des Spectacles (q.v.) *Capacity:* 150 *Policy:* produce
Arts types: contemporary dance *Comments:* there is an information-orientation centre for dancers; see also National Organisations and Promoters

Athénée – Théâtre Louis Jouvet
4 Square de l'Opera-Louis Jouvet, 75009 **Paris**
Tel: 1-5305 1900 Fax: 1-5305 1901
Internet: www.theatreonline.com
E-Mail: info@athenee.com
directeur Patrice Martinet; directeur adjointe Hélène Icart; secrétaire générale Denis Bretin
Venue type: théatre á l'Italienne *Capacity:* Salle Christian Bérard 86, Salle Louis Jouvet 540 *Policy:* present, co-produce, produce *Arts types:* theatre, music *Comments:* 2nd address for administration:Courrier, 24 rue Caumartin,75009 Paris

Auditorium du Louvre
101 rue de Rivoli, 75058 **Paris** Cedex 01
Tel: 1-4020 5186 Fax: 1-4020 5430/5260 (auditorium)
Internet: www.louvre.fr
E-Mail: martinl@louvre.fr
chef du service Paul Salmona; chargée des concerts Monique Devaux; chargé de la musique filmée Christian Labrande; administratrice Delphine Samsoen; relations publiques Nelly Girault
Capacity: 420 *Policy:* co-produce *Arts types:* about 50 concerts a year, (chamber, baroque to C20th), films videos, conferences on arts, silent films with original music played live *Comments:* under the pyramid of the Louvre Museum; administrative address: auditorium du Louvre, 101 rue de Rivol, 75000 Paris

Auditorium du Musée d'Orsay
1 rue de Bellechasse, 75353 **Paris** Cedex 07
Tel: 1-4049 4757 Fax: 1-4284 0185
Internet: www.musée-orsay.fr
E-Mail: auditorium@musee-orsay.fr
directeur Henry Loyrette; programmateur musiques Pierre Korzilius (4049 4854); directeur du service culturel Nicole Savy(4049 4864); programmation cinéma t.b.a.; service presse Aggy Lerolle (4049 4920, fax: 4548 2123); responsable presse musicale Emmanuelle Duthu; responsable de l'auditorium Mark Gore (4049 4755)
Venue type: multi-purpose *Capacity:* 344 *Policy:* co-produce, produce *Arts types:* classical chamber music (1848-1914), silent cinema, workshops, cinema, drama, educational activities and conferences *Comments:* postal address: 62 rue de Lille, 75343 Paris Cédex 07 (administration); alternative E-mail: mgore@musee-orsay.fr

Auditorium Saint-Germain
4, rue Félibien, 75006 **Paris**
Tel: 1-4633 8703 Fax: 1-4634 1206
directrice Mdme. Quitterie, Leon Dufour; direction artistique François Bulteau
Venue type: concert hall *Capacity:* Auditorium 355 *Policy:* rent *Arts types:* classical, jazz, variety, dance, small opera, conferences, theatre *Comments:* also lecture facilities

Centre Georges Pompidou
75191 **Paris** Cedex 04
Tel: 1-4478 1233/1315 (locations/info. spectacles)
Fax: 1-4478 1300 (communication)
Internet: www.cnac-gp.fr
président Jean-Jacques Aillagon; directeur général Guillaume Cerutti; directeur musée national d'art modern/centre de création industrielle (MNAM/CCI) Werner Spies; directeur département du dévéloppment culturel (DDC) Daniel Soutif; directeur de la communication Jean-Pierre Biron; directeur des éditions Martin Bethenod; directrice de la production Sophie Aurand; directuer Institut de recherche et coordination acoustique/musique (IRCAM) Laurent Bayle; directeur artistique Institut de recherche et coordination acoustique/musique (IRCAM) Eric de Visscher
Capacity: 4 halls up to 400, Studio '5' 200, Salle Garance (cinema hall) 350, Petite Salle 160, Salle Polyralente 375 *Policy:* produce, co-produce *Arts types:* contemporary dance and theatre, exhibitions, cinema, conferences, festivals, music *Comments:* home of 2 festivals; the centre is undergoing a vast renovation but activities will carry on in and around the centre as well as in other locations in Paris

Centre International de Création Théâtrale
Théâtre des Bouffes du Nord, 37 bis Bld. de la Chapelle, 75010 **Paris**
Tel: 1-4607 3300 Fax: 1-4205 5483
E-Mail: cict@club-internet.fr
directeurs Peter Brook, Stephane Lissner; communication Anita Le Van, Valerie Guiter
Venue type: theatre *Capacity:* Théatre des Bouffes du Nord 510 *Policy:* produce (créations de Peter Brook), present *Arts types:* theatre, music, dance, song recitals
Comments: see also Drama

Cité de la Musique, La
221 Avenue Jean-Jaurés, 75019 **Paris**
Tel: 1-4484 4500/4565 (comm.)/4545
Fax: 1-4484 4536/4501 (main)
Internet: www.cite-musique.fr
E-Mail: scook@gwmail.cite-musique.fr
directeur général Brigitte Marger; directeur productions, salles Sophie Fournel-Barrat; directeur de la communication Marie-Françoise George; directeur des relations avec le public Annick Couapel; directeur du centre de resources musique et danses Caroline Rosoor; directeur musée Frédéric Dassas; president André Larquie
Venue type: concert hall *Capacity:* concert hall 800-1100, amphitheatre 230 *Policy:* production, co-production *Arts types:* all types of music *Comments:* information centre on music and dance; see also Services

Comédie de Paris, La
42 rue Fontaine, 75009 **Paris**
Tel: 1-4281 0011 Fax: 1-4526 3706
directeur Jean-Georges Tharaud; régisseur Pascal Perez; administratrice Chantal Fleury
Venue type: theatre *Capacity:* 200 *Policy:* rent, produce, co-produce *Arts types:* classical and mainly contemporary drama (based on humour)

Comédie des Champs-Elysées – Studio des Champs-Elysées
15 ave Montaigne, 75008 **Paris**
Tel: 1-5323 9910 Fax: 1-5323 9911
directeur Michel Fagadau; administratrice t.b.a.
Venue type: théâtre à l'italienne *Capacity:* comedie 630, studio 230 *Policy:* rent, produce, co-produce *Arts types:* contemporary French theatre

Espace Pierre Cardin
1-3 Avenue Gabriel, 75008 **Paris**
Tel: 1-4266 1730 Fax: 1-4266 1781
directeur Dominique Boitel; administration Audrey Absil, Marion Brenot
Capacity: theatre 720, multi-purpose hall 350, cinema 75 *Policy:* rent, produce, co-produce *Arts types:* theatre, dance, exhibition, congresses, concerts

Etablissement Public du Parc et de la Grande Halle de la Villette, L'
211 Av Jean Jaures, 75019 **Paris**
Tel: 1-4003 7575 (bookings)/7500 (administration) Fax: 1-4003 7599 (communication)
directeur général Monique Barbaroux; président Bernard Latarjet; directeur communication Vincent Poussou; responsable attaché de presse Bertrand Nogent
Venue type: multi-purpose *Capacity:* various halls of different sizes including: Espace Charlie Parker up to 2000, Salle Boris Vian 350, total capacity 2000 to 3000 *Policy:* rent, produce, co-produce *Arts types:* dance, theatre, exhibitions, cinema, music, events

L'étoile du nord
16 Rue Georgette-Agutte, 75018 **Paris**
Tel: 1-4226 4747 Fax: 1-4226 6398
E-Mail: etoilen@club-internet.fr
co-directeurs Jean Macqueron, Bernard Djaoui; equipe fondatrice Anne de Amezaga, Bernard Djaoui, Jérôme Franc, Jean Macqueron; programmation danse Christophe Martin; relations avec le public Virginie Fendler; directeur technique Boris Polinie; programmation jeune publique Bernard Djaoui
Venue type: modern theatre *Capacity:* 200 *Policy:* co-produce, co-create *Arts types:* contemporary drama, dance, theatre for young people
Comments: see also Drama

Lucernaire Forum – Centre National d'Art et d'Essai
53 rue Notre-Dame-Des-Champs, 75006 **Paris**
Tel: 1-4222 2650 Fax: 1-4544 8692
directeur Christian le Guillochet; secrétaire générale François Chaudier; attaché de presse Claire Giovanangeli; relations publique Sophie Guengau
Venue type: theatre *Capacity:* 2 halls: Théâtre Noir 140, Théâtre Rouge 140, 3 cinemas 60 *Arts types:* drama (6 plays per night, 3 in each theatre), film, exhibition gallery *Comments:* remains open throughout summer,restaurant and bar

Maison des Compagnies der Spectacles
9 rue Geoffroy L'Asnier, 75004 **Paris**
Tel: 1-4274 4422 Fax: 1-4029 0646
director Daniel Gillet
Capacity: 150 *Arts types:* dance *Comments:* part of the Centre National de le Danse (q.v.)

Maison des Cultures du Monde
101 Bld Raspail, 75006 **Paris**
Tel: 1-4544 7230/4142 (bookings) Fax: 1-4544 7660
Internet: www.mcm.asso.fr
E-Mail: mcmass@mcm.asso.fr
directeur Chérif Khaznadar; administratrice Martine Westphal; directeur technique Francis Comini; communication et presse Arwad Esber; programmation Pierre Bois, Arwad Esber
Venue type: théâtre à l'Italienne *Capacity:* 380 *Policy:* present, co-produce *Arts types:* theatre, traditional foreign songs and music, visual performances

Ménagerie de Verre
12-14, rue Léchevin, 75011 **Paris**
Tel: 1-4338 3344 Fax: 1-4338 7456
Internet: multimania.com/menageri
E-Mail: menageri@dub-internet.fr
directrice et directrice artistique Marie-Thérèse Allier
Capacity: 5 studios, including theatre 100 *Policy:* present, rent *Arts types:* contemporary dance, drama, exhibitions, performances
Comments: organise Les Inaccoutumés festival (Jan/Feb and May-June); see also Festivals and Promoters

Odéon – Théâtre de L'Europe
1 Place Paul Claudel, 75006 **Paris**
Tel: 1-4441 3636 Fax: 1-4441 3606
Internet: www.theatre-odean.fr
E-Mail: tno@clubinternet.fr
directeur Georges Lavaudant; administrateur Christopher Miles; directeur technique Alain Wendling; directeur programmation Borja Sitja; directeur production Rémy Jullien; directeur communication Alain Desrot
Venue type: theatre *Capacity:* 1017 *Policy:* rent *Arts types:* drama *Comments:* shows and performances in various foreign languages

Palais des Congrès de Paris, Le
2 Place de la Porte Maillot, 75017 **Paris**
Tel: 1-4068 2550 Fax: 1-4068 2740
Internet: www.palais-congres-paris.fr
E-Mail: dce@palais-congres-paris.fr
directeur général Dominique Fondacci; directrice des congrès-expositions Laure Mouton; communication Sibyle Giraud-Lavelle
Venue type: multi-purpose *Capacity:* concert hall 3723 (can be subdivided into one smaller hall of 1800), Salle Bleu 826, amphitheatre Bordeau 650, Havane 400 *Policy:* rental only *Arts types:* opera, ballet, dance, spectacles, concerts, congresses

Palais des Glaces
37 rue du Fbg du Temple, 75010 **Paris**
Tel: 1-4040 0994 (admin)/4202 2717 (bookings)/4803 1136 (room A) Fax: 1-4040 9512
directeur programmation Jimmy Levy; administrateur Jean Graziani
Venue type: multi-purpose
Capacity: Room A 500, Room B 100 *Policy:* co-produce, rent *Arts types:* comedy
Comments: closed during July and August

Palais Omnisports Paris-Bercy
8 Boulevard Bercy, 75012 **Paris**
Tel: 1-4002 6060 Fax: 1-4342 0950
Internet: www.bercy.com
directrice commercial, marketing, communication Anne Keim; directeur des relations publiques Alain Segurel
Venue type: multi-purpose *Capacity:* up to 17000 *Policy:* rent, produce, co-produce *Arts types:* music, dance, opera, sport, concerts (pop)

Regard du Cygne, Le
Association Musique Danse XXieme,
210 rue de Belleville, 75020 **Paris**
Tel: 1-4358 5593 Fax: 1-4636 7067
Internet: members.aol.com/redcygne
E-Mail: redcygne@aol.com
artistic directors Amy Swanson, Fabrice Dugied
Venue type: loft
Capacity: 80 *Policy:* production, co-production, co-réalisation, rent *Arts types:* contemporary dance, music, drama *Comments:* see also Promoters

Salle Gaveau
45 rue la Boétie, 75008 **Paris**
Tel: 1-4562 6971/4953 0507 (bookings)
Fax: 1-4225 9780
directeur général Jean-Marie Fournier; relations publiques Chantal Fournier
Venue type: concert hall *Capacity:* concert hall 1000, Salle Marguerite 145, Nostropovitch 350 *Policy:* rent, present, produce, co-produce *Arts types:* classical concerts, recitals

Salle Olivier Messiaen
Maison de Radio France, 116 avenue du President Kennedy, 75786 **Paris** Cedex 220
Tel: 1-4230 2380 Fax: 1-4230 4282
responsable du service accueil Yves Pacon; directeur de la music à Radio France Pascal Tumay; responsable de la promotion t.b.a.; responsable des relations publiques Laurence Laveau
Venue type: multi-purpose *Capacity:* 920 *Policy:* produce, co-produce, rent *Arts types:* classical music, variety, jazz, conferences

Salle Pleyel
252 rue du Faubourg St Honoré, 75008 **Paris**
Tel: 1-4561 5300 Fax: 1-4561 4687
président directeur général Hubert Martigny; responsable salles Philippe Cart; relations publiques Gabrielle Josso, Philippe Cart; directrice Madame Martigny
Capacity: Salle Pleyel 2300, Salle Chopin 470, Salle Debussy 110 *Policy:* rent *Arts types:* classical music, jazz *Comments:* home of Orchestre de Paris, Concerts Lamoureux, and the Ensemble Orchestral de Paris

Splendid Saint-Martin
48 rue du Faubourg St-Martin, 75010 **Paris**
Tel: 1-4208 2193 (booking)/1345(admin.)
Fax: 1-4241 2074
directeur Christian Spillemaeker; co-directeur Bruno Moynot
Venue type: theatre
Capacity: 300 *Policy:* present, produce, co-produce, rent *Arts types:* comedy, one-man show, music
Comments: facilities for the disabled

Théâtre Antoine- Simone Berriau
14 Bvd. de Strasbourg, 75010 **Paris**
Tel: 1-4208 4628 Fax: 1-4208 3840
E-Mail: theatre.antoine@wanadoo.fr
directeurs Héléna Bossis, Daniel Dares
Venue type: theatre (listed building) *Capacity:* 875 *Policy:* produce and co-produce *Arts types:* theatre *Comments:* admin address: 33 Fbg St. Martin, 75010 Paris

Théâtre de l'Atelier
43, rue d'Orsel, 75018 **Paris**
Tel: 1-4606 1989 Fax: 1-4264 5580
directeur Laura Pells
Venue type: théâtre à l'italienne *Capacity:* 566 *Policy:* produce, co-produce *Arts types:* drama

Théâtre de l'Est Parisien
159 Av Gambetta, 75020 **Paris**
Tel: 1-4031 2096 Fax: 1-4364 0750
directeur Guy Rétoré; administration Sébastien Angebault; relations publiques Marion Denizot; conseiller littéraire Philippe Ivernel
Venue type: theatre *Capacity:* 398 *Policy:* rent, present, produce, co-produce *Arts types:* classical & contemporary drama *Comments:* see also Festivals (Paroles d'Auteurs) and Competitions

Théâtre de l'Oeuvre
55 rue de Clichy, 75009 **Paris**
Tel: 1-4453 8880 (admin)/8888 (bookings)
Fax: 1-4453 8881
directeur et directeur artistique Gérard Maro; relations publiques Catherine Cléret; relations presse Isabelle Desgranges
Venue type: drama space, theatre *Capacity:* 325 *Policy:* present, co-produce, produce *Arts types:* drama

Théâtre de la Bastille
76 rue de la Roquette, 75011 **Paris**
Tel: 1-4357 4214 Fax: 1-4700 9787
E-Mail: theatre.bastille@wanadoo.fr
directeur général Jean-Marie Hordé; conseiller artistique Marc Sussi; programmation danse Jean Marc Adolphe; relations publiques Géraldine Clouard, Christophe Pineau; presse et communication Irène Gordon; directeur adjoint Marc Sussi
Capacity: Hall A 228, Hall B 150 *Policy:* present, co-produce *Arts types:* contemporary dance, theatre, music

Théâtre de la Bruyère
5 rue de la Bruyère, 75009 **Paris**
Tel: 1-4874 7699 Fax: 1-4023 9451
Internet: www.ddo.fr
directeur Stephan Meldegg; administratrice Ghislaine Sanguin
Venue type: theatre *Capacity:* 330 *Policy:* produce, co-produce, rent *Arts types:* contemporary theatre (sometimes classical)

Théâtre de la Huchette
23 rue de la Huchette, 75005 **Paris**
Tel: 1-4326 5162 (admin)/3899 (bookings)
Fax: 1-4051 7534
directeur Jacques Legré; administratrice Françoise Alessandri
Venue type: theatre *Capacity:* 90 *Policy:* produce, co-produce *Arts types:* modern writers *Comments:* La Cantatrice chauvë et la Lesson by Eugene Ionesco have been on stage for 43 years (13500 shows)

Théâtre de la Madeleine
19 rue de Surène, 75008 **Paris**
Tel: 1-4265 0628 Fax: 1-4266 2780
directeurs Simone Valère, Jean Desailly; administrateur Stephane Engelberg
Venue type: theatre a l`Italienne *Capacity:* 728 *Policy:* rent, present, produce, co-produce *Arts types:* theatre

Théâtre de la Michodière
4 bis rue de la Michodière, 75002 **Paris**
Tel: 1-4742 9677
directeur Jacques Crepineau; secrétaire général Stewart Vaughan
Venue type: théâtre à l'Italienne *Capacity:* 700 *Policy:* produce, co-produce, box-office share, rent *Arts types:* theatre – straight plays, comedies (including adaptations of English plays) *Comments:* available for hire for one-off events on Mondays

Théâtre de la Porte Saint Martin
17 rue René Boulanger, 75010 **Paris**
Tel: 1-4208 0001 (admin) Fax: 1-4240 1833
administratrice Nadine Thémines; directeurs Hélène et Bernard Régnier
Venue type: théâtre a l`Italienne *Capacity:* 1050 *Policy:* co-produce, rent, produce *Arts types:* drama, ballet, musicals *Comments:* theatre address: 16 Blvd. St. Martin, 75010 Paris

Théâtre de la Renaissance
20 bd St Martin, 75010 **Paris**
Tel: 1-4202 4735 Fax: 1-4203 1784
directeurs Christian Spillemaecker, Bruno Moynot
Venue type: Théâtre á l'Italienne *Capacity:* 630 *Policy:* rent, produce, co-produce *Arts types:* theatre, ballet, musicals

Théâtre de la Ville
2 Place du Chatelet, 75004 **Paris**
Tel: 1-4887 5442 (administration)/4274 2277 (bookings)
Fax: 1-4887 8115 (administration)/0981 (venue)
directeur Gérard Violette; secrétaire générale Anne-Marie Bigorne; administrateur Michael Chase; directeur adjoint à la programmation Serge Peyrat; conseiller artistique Thomas Erdos; conseiller chanson Jacques Erwan; conseiller musique classique Georges Gara; responsable relations avec le public Lydia Gaborit; responsable location, Marie Katz; directeur de production, responsable des services artistiques et techniques, Jean Sayous
Capacity: Théâtre de la Ville 1000 *Policy:* present, produce, co-produce *Arts types:* dance, theatre, traditional music, classical music, chanson (song), world music

Théâtre de Mogador
25 rue de Mogador, 75009 **Paris**
Tel: 1-5332 3200 (bookings)/3220 (admin)
Fax: 1-4878 9099 (bookings)/4874 7738
présidente directrice générale Denise Petididier
Venue type: theatre *Capacity:* 1792 *Policy:* co-produce, rent, present, produce *Arts types:* theatre, musicals, dance, songs *Comments:* Salles de Congrès 250-500 for rehearsals

Théâtre de Paris/Petit Théâtre de Paris
15 rue Blanche, 75009 **Paris**
Tel: 1-4874 1075 Fax: 1-4874 2809
directrice Christelle Durand
Venue type: théâtre à l'Italienne *Capacity:* Théâtre de Paris 1170, Petit Théâtre de Paris 300
Policy: rent, present, produce *Arts types:* contemporary + classical theatre

Théâtre de Poche – Montparnasse
75 bd Montparnasse, 75006 **Paris**
Tel: 1-4544 5021 Fax: 1-4284 1291
directrice – programmation Renée Delmas Bierry
Venue type: theatre *Capacity:* Hall A 130, Hall B 100
Policy: produce, co-produce *Arts types:* contemporary (especially) and classical theatre
Comments: see also Drama

Théâtre des Abbesses
31 rue des Abbesses, 75018 **Paris**
Tel: 1-4887 5442 (admin)/4274 2277 (bookings)
Fax: 1-4887 8115 (admin)
directeur Gérard Violette; secrétaire générale Anne-Marie Bigorne; administrateur Michael Chase; directeur adjoint à la programmation Serge Peyrat; conseiller artistique Thomas Erdos; conseiller chanson Jacques Erwan; conseiller musique classique Georges Gara; responsable relations avec le public Lydia Gaborit; responsable location Marie Katz; directeur de production, responsable des services artistiques et techniques Jean Sayous
Capacity: 420 *Policy:* present, produce, co-produce *Arts types:* dance, theatre, traditional music, classical music, chanson (song), world music

Théâtre des Bouffes Parisiens
4 rue Monsigny, 75002 **Paris**
Tel: 1-4296 9240 (admin)/9242 (bookings)
Fax: 1-4286 8873
programmation & directeur Jean Claude Brialy; administrateur Michel Le Brun; attaché de presse Bruno Finck
Venue type: Théâtre á l'Italienne *Capacity:* 660 *Policy:* rent, produce, co-produce *Arts types:* classical, comic theatre, musicals

Théâtre des Champs Elysées
15 ave Montaigne, 75008 **Paris**
Tel: 1-4952 5000 Fax: 1-4952 0741
E-Mail: theatre.champs.elysees@wanadoo.fr
directeur Dominique Meyer; directeur adjoint Francis Lepigeon; directeur technique Jacques Benyeta; secrétaire générale Catherine Lachaux
Venue type: Italian type *Capacity:* 1901 *Policy:* rent, produce, co-produce *Arts types:* opera, concerts, recitals, ballet *Comments:* see also Opera

Théâtre des Folies Bergere
32 Rue Richer, 75009 **Paris**
Tel: 1-4479 9860 (admin)/9898 (booking)
Fax: 1-4022 9447 (admin)/4770 9828 (booking)
Internet: www.foliesbergere.com
E-Mail: foliber@aol.com
directeur Helène Martini; administration Georges Terrey
Venue type: Théâtre l'Italienne *Capacity:* 1680 *Policy:* produce *Arts types:* musicals *Comments:* administrative address: 8 rue Saulnier, 75009 Paris

Théâtre des Mathurins
36 rue des Mathurins, 75008 **Paris**
Tel: 1-5305 2706 (admin)/4265 6246
Fax: 1-5305 2708
administration Michèle Jolly; directeur Julien Vartet; régisseur Pascal Vinet
Venue type: Theatre *Capacity:* Mathurins 500 *Policy:* produce, co-produce *Arts types:* plays by J.Vartet – Boulevard Theatre *Comments:* see also Drama

Théâtre des Nouveautés
24 bd Poissonnière, 75009 **Paris**
Tel: 1-4770 5277 Fax: 1-4523 3037
directeurs Denise Moreau Chantegris, Maurice Moreau-Chantegris; administratrice Geneviève Boyer
Venue type: Théâtre à l'Italienne *Capacity:* 585 *Policy:* rent, produce, co-produce *Arts types:* divertissement, comedy, théâtre de boulevard

Théâtre des Variétés
7 bd Montmartre, 75002 **Paris**
Tel: 1-4233 0992 (booking)/1141 (admin)
Fax: 1-4233 8362
directeur général Luc Tenard; PDG Jean-Paul Belmondo; administrateur Alain Belmondo
Venue type: Théâtre à l'Italienne *Capacity:* 924 *Policy:* rent, produce, co-produce *Arts types:* comedy
Comments: group and agencies booking: Tel: 1-4233 9955

Théâtre du Châtelet – Théâtre Musical de Paris
2 rue Edouard Colonne, 75001 **Paris**
Tel: 1-4028 2828 Fax: 1-4236 8975
directeur général Jean-Pierre Brossmann; directeur administratif Jacques Hedouin; secrétaire général Jean-François Brigy; directeur technique Jurgen Hoser
Venue type: Theatre a l'Italienne *Capacity:* Grande Salle 2010, Foyer 250 *Policy:* rent, present, produce, co-produce *Arts types:* opera, ballet, concerts, recitals, chamber music, theatre *Comments:* see also Opera

Théâtre du Chaudron
Cartoucherie, Route du Champ de Manoeuvres, 75012 **Paris**
Tel: 1-4328 9704 Fax: 1-4328 4015
directrice Anne-Marie Choisne; administratrice Marie Blanchez; relations publique Alexandra Acca
Capacity: 194 *Policy:* present
Arts types: drama, contemporary

Théâtre du Gymnase
38 bld Bonne Nouvelle, 75010 **Paris**
Tel: 1-4246 1511 Fax: 1-4801 0368
administrateur Hervé de Pazzis; programmation Jacques Bertin
Venue type: theatre *Capacity:* 800 *Policy:* rent, co-produce *Arts types:* theatre (classical & contemporary), variety, concerts

Théâtre du Palais Royal
38 rue de Montpensier, 75001 **Paris**
Tel: 1-4297 5976 Fax: 1-4261 4250
Internet: www.theatrepalaisroyale.com
E-Mail: tpr@theatrepalaisroyale.com
communication & relations publiques Isabelle Pilling; PDG Francis Nani
Venue type: á l'italienne *Capacity:* 792 *Arts types:* Boulevard theatre, comedy

Théâtre du Rond-Point/Cie Marcel Marechal
Rond-Point des Champs-Élysées 2 bis, Avenue Franklin Roosevelt, 75008 **Paris**
Tel: 1-4495 9800 Fax: 1-4075 0448
directeur Marcel Maréchal; directeur administratif François Collet; directeur artistique François Bourgeat; administrateur Jean-Luc Grandie
Capacity: Room A 754, Room B 176 *Policy:* produce, co-produce, rent *Arts types:* theatre
Comments: see also Drama

Théâtre Edouard VII – Sacha Guitry
10 place Edouard VII, 75009 **Paris**
Tel: 1-4742 3571(admin)/5992 (booking)
Fax: 1-4742 7768
directeur Julien Vartet
Venue type: Théâtre à l'Anglaise *Capacity:* 720 *Policy:* present, produce, co-produce *Arts types:* comedy
Comments: administration: 6 bis Impasse Sandrié, 75009 Paris

Théâtre Eldorado
4 bld de Strasbourg, 75010 **Paris**
Tel: 1-4238 0754 (bookings)/3460 (admin)
Fax: 1-4452 9195
directeur Maurice Molina
Venue type: theatre *Capacity:* 1080 *Policy:* rent, produce, co-produce *Arts types:* theatre, cinema, projections, conferences, seminars

Théâtre Essaion
6 rue Pierre au Lard, 75004 **Paris**
Tel: 1-4278 6173/4642 (booking) Fax: 1-4274 0454
directrice Alida Latessa; directeur artistique José Valverde
Capacity: Hall A 100, Hall B 80 *Arts types:* modern French writers *Comments:* see also Drama

Théâtre Fontaine
10 rue Fontaine, 75009 **Paris**
Tel: 1-4874 3068 (admin)/7440 (booking)
Fax: 1-4878 3744
directeur responsable de la programmation Dominique Deschamps
Venue type: theatre *Capacity:* 620 *Policy:* co-produce, rent, produce *Arts types:* comedy

Théâtre Hébertot
78 bis., Bd des Batignolles, 75017 **Paris**
Tel: 1-4387 2424/2323 (bookings)
Fax: 1-4293 9561
directeur Félix Ascot; co-directrice Simone Sobelman; administrateur Bernard Poussin
Venue type: théâtre à l'Italienne *Capacity:* 637 *Policy:* rent, present, co-produce *Arts types:* drama

Théâtre le Ranelagh
5 rue des Vignes, 75016 **Paris**
Tel: 1-4288 6444 Fax: 1-4230 8119
directrice Madona Bouglione
Venue type: théatre a'l'Italienne
Capacity: 338 *Policy:* rent, present, produce, co-produce
Arts types: theatre, film, dance, circus, classical music concerts, conventions
Comments: listed building

Théâtre Marigny/Salle Popesco
Carré Marigny, 75008 **Paris**
Tel: 1-4256 0506 Fax: 1-4359 0180
directeur général Jean Jacques Bricaire; PDG Christiane Porquerel; directeur technique Michel Andréassian
Capacity: Théâtre Marigny 1010, Salle Popesco 311
Policy: produce, co-produce, rent *Arts types:* classical and contemporary drama, musicals, cinema

Théâtre Michel
38 rue des Mathurins, 75008 **Paris**
Tel: 1-4265 4130 (admin)/3502 (booking)
Fax: 1-4007 0329
programmation Marc Camoletti; secretaire Monique Lami; régisseur général Vincent Bolognini
Venue type: Théâtre à l'Ítalienne *Capacity:* 350 *Policy:* produce, co-produce *Arts types:* comedy

Théâtre Montparnasse
31 rue de la Gaité, 75014 **Paris**
Tel: 1-4322 7730 Fax: 1-4320 0883
directeur Myriam de Colombi; directeur technique Georges Beilvaire; attachée de direction Marie-Françoise Morard; administrateur général Bertrand Thamin
Capacity: Montparnasse 715, Petit Montparnasse 150
Policy: produce, co-produce *Arts types:* contemporary drama *Comments:* Théâtre du Petit Montparnasse is closed

Théâtre National de la Colline
15 rue Malte Brun, 75020 **Paris**
Tel: 1-4462 5200 Fax: 1-4462 5290
directeur Alain Françon; adjointe à la direction artistique Myriam Desrumeaux; administrateur général Alain Herzog; directeur technique Francis Charles; conseiller littéraire Alain Satgé; relations publiques Armelle Slepien; presse Laure Hemain; secretaire générale Anne Goilard
Venue type: Théâtre
Capacity: Salle A 750, Salle B 214 *Policy:* produce, co-produce, present *Arts types:* theatre, music, film, concerts *Comments:* see also Drama

Théâtre Olympia
28 Boulevard des Capucines, 75009 **Paris**
Tel: 1-4742 2549 (box office)/5527 1000 (secrétariat)
Fax: 1-5527 1010
gèrantes associées Paulette Coquatrix, Patricia Coquatrix; directeur administratif Jean-Michel Boris
Venue type: music hall *Capacity:* 2000, 2574 (standing)
Policy: rent, produce, co-produce *Arts types:* concerts, theatre, dance *Comments:* second address: 18 rue Caumartin, 75009 Paris

Théâtre Ouvert – Centre Dramatique National de Création
Le Jardin d'Hiver, 4 bis Cité Véron, 75018 **Paris**
Tel: 1-4255 7440/4262 5949 (booking)
Fax: 1-4252 6776
directeurs Lucien Attoun, Micheline Attoun; relations publiques Marlène Daniel
Capacity: hall A 100, hall B 200 *Policy:* produce, co-produce *Arts types:* contemporary drama, performances by living, French authors *Comments:* see also Drama

Théâtre Paris Villette
211 ave Jean Jaurès, 75019 **Paris**
Tel: 1-4203 0255 (admin) Fax: 1-4202 4370
directeur Patrick Gufflet; attachée de l'administration Stephanie Jayet; directeur technique Julien Barbazin; secrétaire générale Stéphanie Jayet
Venue type: 19th century theatre
Capacity: Hall A 211, Hall B 70, Hall C 30
Policy: produce, co-produce, rent
Arts types: contemporary French work, theatre, French language theatre

Théâtre Rive Gauche
6 rue de la Gaité, 75014 **Paris**
Tel: 1-4322 1102 (admin)/4335 3231 (reservations)
Fax: 1-4320 3792
directeur Alain Mallet
Venue type: theatre
Capacity: 350 *Policy:* rent, produce, co-produce
Arts types: contemporary theatre

Théâtre Saint Georges
51 rue Saint Georges, 75009 **Paris**
Tel: 1-4878 7437/6347 (booking) Fax: 1-4526 9800
directrices France Delahalle, Marie France Mignal; administrateur Pascal Monge; directeur financier Jean Veltère
Venue type: theatre *Capacity:* 498 *Policy:* produce *Arts types:* théâtre contemporain de divertissement

Théâtre Silvia Monfort
106 rue Brancion, 75015 **Paris**
Tel: 1-4533 6670/4531 1096 (bookings) Fax: 1-4531 1571
directeur Régis Santon; administration t.b.a.; comptable Guy Cartier; relations publiques Christophe Cauchi
Venue type: Amphitheatre *Capacity:* 456 *Policy:* produce, co-produce, present *Arts types:* drama, dance, classical music *Comments:* see also Drama

Théâtre Tristan-Bernard
64 rue du Rocher, 75008 **Paris**
Tel: 1-4293 6536/4522 0840 (bookings) Fax: 1-4522 6486
admin. Béatrice Vignal; programmation Edy Saiovici
Venue type: theatre *Capacity:* 400 *Policy:* produce, co-produce *Arts types:* comedy, one man show, music, contemporary theatre, new productions

Tréteaux de France – Centre Dramatique National, Les
11 rue Yvon Villarceau, 75016 **Paris**
Tel: 1-4501 9132 Fax: 1-4501 6937
directeur Jean Danet; administrateur, pr Michel Clouet; directeur technique René Breton
Venue type: mobile tent *Capacity:* tent 540 *Policy:* produce, co-produce *Arts types:* music, theatre, dance, shows for children, classical music, festivals, variety
Comments: see also Drama

Vingtième Théâtre
7 rue des Platrières, 75020 **Paris**
Tel: 1-4366 0134/13 (bookings) Fax: 1-4636 7675
directeur Francis Sourbié; président Françoise Varenne
Capacity: 245 *Policy:* produce, co-produce *Arts types:* theatre, dance, music

Théâtre Saragosse
17 Av de Saragosse, 64000 **Pau**
Tel: 5-5984 1193 Fax: 5-5984 9124
Internet: perso.wanadoo.fr/theatre.saragosse
E-Mail: theatre.saragosse@wanadoo.fr
directeur Michel Vincenot
Venue type: theatre *Capacity:* 240 *Policy:* rent, produce, present *Arts types:* contemporary dance only
Comments: organise the Festival Plurielles (contemporary dance) (q.v.)

Zénith de Pau
Boulevard du Cami Salie, 64000 **Pau**
Tel: 5-5980 7750 Fax: 5-5980 7753
directeur Jacques Arcé
Venue type: multi-purpose *Capacity:* 600-7500 *Policy:* rent *Arts types:* concerts (classical, rock, jazz, etc.), meetings, conventions, conferences, theatre, circus, dance, sports events

Espace des Arts
144 Av Jean Jaurés, Place Charles De Gaulle, 93320 **Pavillons-sous Bois**
Tel: 1-4155 1280 Fax: 1-4802 1530
président Didier Blum
Capacity: up to 800 *Policy:* rent, present, co-produce
Arts types: music, dance, theatre, variety, cinema, jazz (all arts types), exhibitions

Palace, Le
du Nouveau Theatre de Perigueux, 1 avenue d'Aquitaine, 24000 **Périgueux**
Tel: 5-5353 1871/5302 8200 (service cultural mairie)
Fax: 5-5335 0857/5308 4500 (service cultural mairie)
directrice Chantal Achilli
Venue type: theatre *Capacity:* 209, theatre 850 *Policy:* present, produce, co-produce *Arts types:* contemporary theatre, music *Comments:* Le Nouveau Theate manage the rent of the hall Le Palace

Théâtre Maxime Gorki – Scène Nationale Petit Quevilly
rue Francas Mitterend, BP 14, 76141 **Petit-Quevilly** Cedex
Tel: 2-3572 6755/3503 2978 (bookins) Fax: 2-3503 3367
directeur Gèrard Marcon; responsable chansons et musiques actuelle Annie Coci; directeur technique Etienne Bisson; secrétaire général, responsable programmation Patrick Belaubre
Venue type: theatre *Capacity:* 600 *Policy:* present, produce, co-produce *Arts types:* contemporary theatre, music *Comments:* organise the festival Tranches d'Europe Express

Théâtre de Poissy
Hôtel de Ville, Place de la République, 78303 **Poissy** Cedex
Tel: 1-3979 0303/3922 5592 Fax: 1-3065 8018
directeur artistique Christian Chorier; administrative Miss Wiss
Venue type: theatre *Capacity:* 980-1028 *Policy:* co-production, rent *Arts types:* operas, recitals, concerts, drama *Comments:* see also Opera

Confort Moderne/L'Oreille est Hardie, Le
Faubourg du Pont Neuf 185, BP 502,
86012 **Poitiers** Cedex
Tel: 5-4946 0808 Fax: 5-4961 3034
Internet: www.confort-moderne.fr
E-Mail: box@confort-moderne.fr
directrice Isabelle Chaigne; président (L'Association l'Oreille est Hardie) Fazette Bordage; programmation musicale Philippe Levy, Angèle Pied; programmation arts plastiques Dominique Truco; communication, promotion Fabienne Ducros, Marie-Angèle Pied
Venue type: multi-purpose *Capacity:* seated 350, plus standing 700 *Policy:* rent, present, produce *Arts types:* music, rock, pop, exhibitions, experimental music *Comments:* organise with the Conservatoire of Poitiers, a festival called Musique Improvisée (3 days)

Théâtre-Scene Nationale de Poitiers, Le
1 place du Maréchal Leclerc, 86000 **Poitiers**
Tel: 5-4939 4000 Fax: 5-4955 1691
directeur Denis Garnier; administratrice Jocelyne Steffann; chef de projet Christian Chaignon; secrétaire générale Suzy Bély; responsable de l'information Monique Narciso; responsable des relations avec le public Sylvie Violan; coordinatrice de direction technique Valérie Bobin
Venue type: multi-purpose cultural centre *Capacity:* 890 *Policy:* present, rent *Arts types:* drama, music, film, dance *Comments:* organise film competition; see also Festivals

Théâtre Municipal de Privas
Place André Malraux, BP 623, 07006 **Privas** Cedex
Tel: 4-7564 6200 Fax: 4-7564 3510
direction t.b.a.; régisseur Yves Busson
Venue type: theatre *Capacity:* 800 *Policy:* rent, present, co-produce, produce *Arts types:* theatre, dance, music, opera, ballet

Centre National Art et Technologie – Scène Nationale de Reims
1 rue Eugène Wiet, BP 1183, 51057 **Reims** Cedex
Tel: 3-2682 4949 Fax: 3-2682 8832
E-Mail: CNAT@wanadoo.fr
directeur Jacques Darolles; directeur adjoint Serge Gaymard; responsable communication Sylvie Vincent
Venue type: Salle Frontale (le Manège), Salle en rond (le Cirque) *Capacity:* Le Manège 609, Le Cirque 1000 *Policy:* present, produce, co-produce *Arts types:* music, dance, exhibitions, art and technology

Comédie de Reims, La
3 Chaussée Bocquaine, 51100 **Reims**
Tel: 3-2648 4910 Fax: 3-2688 7695
directeur Christian Schiarétti; secrétaire général Christine Schmitt; administrateur Bernard Collet; chargée de production Vincent Marcoup; relations publiques Olivier Maby
Venue type: theatre *Capacity:* centre dramatique: salle A 1000, salle B 200, théâtre des Ateliers 50 *Policy:* present, produce, co-produce *Arts types:* modern, classical drama, comedy *Comments:* see also Drama

Grand Théâtre de Reims, Le
9, rue Chanzy, 51100 **Reims**
Tel: 3-2650 3100 Fax: 3-2684 9002
directeur Serge Gaymard; relations publiques Marie-Claire Legrand; directeur musical Gilles Nopre; directeur administratif Jilbert Henry; choregraphe Eric Margouet; directeur de scene Tony Amirati
Venue type: maison de la culture *Capacity:* 259 *Policy:* rent, present, co-produce *Arts types:* opera, theatre, orchestra, ballet, operetta, variety, musicals *Comments:* Le Grand Théâtre is closed until October 2000, currently using Comédie de Reims; see also Opera

Centre Culturel Triangle
Blvd de Yougoslavie, BP 2236, 35022 **Rennes** Cedex 2
Tel: 2-9922 2727 Fax: 2-9922 2733
E-Mail: trian_35@aol.com
directeur Christian Druart; administrateur Michel Gourlay
Capacity: Hall A 646, Hall B 300 *Policy:* rent, produce, co-produce *Arts types:* contemporary dance *Comments:* photographs, exhibitions

Théâtre National de Bretagne
1 rue Saint Hélier, BP 675, 35008 **Rennes** Cedex
Tel: 2-9931 5533 Fax: 2-9967 6619
directeur Francois Le Pillouërt; communication Bernadette Kessler; directeur administratif et financier Laurent Parigot; directrice adjointe Nathalie Solini
Venue type: multi-purpose, 3 halls *Capacity:* Vilar 1150, Ferrau 350, salle Louis Jouvet Cinema 400 *Policy:* present, co-produce, rent (for congresses) *Arts types:* theatre, dance, music, puppets *Comments:* includes Théâtre National de Bretagne; see also Drama and Festivals

Colisée, Le
Roubaix-Culture, Rue de l'Epeule, BP 4,
59051 **Roubaix** Cedex 1
Tel: 3-2024 5051 (bookings)/4656 (admin)
Fax: 3-2024 1918
directrice Marie-Cécile Laidebeur
Venue type: théâtre *Capacity:* Hall A 600, Hall B 1200, Hall C 1800 *Policy:* rent *Arts types:* theatre, music, dance, lyric, exhibitions, film, circus, championships, variety, opera, ballet, congresses, championships

Théâtre des Arts – Opéra de Normandie
Route du Docteur Rambert, 76000 **Rouen**
Tel: 2-3598 5098 Fax: 2-3515 3349
E-Mail: opera.2.rouen@wanadoo.fr
président Françoise Tron; directeur général Laurent Langlois; relations publiques Olivier Lefebvre; administrateur t.b.a.; chef d' orchestre Oswald Sallaberger
Capacity: Théâtre 1352 *Policy:* produce, co-produce, rent *Arts types:* new lyrical productions, ballet, symphonic music, reprises of other opera productions *Comments:* a choir, ballet and an orchestra(Orchestre Symphonique de Rouen) also belong to L'Opéra de Normandie; see also Dance and Opera

Théâtre des Deux Rives
48 rue Louis Ricard, 76000 **Rouen**
Tel: 2-3589 6341 Fax: 2-3570 5983
administrateur Jean-Marc Devaux; directeur artistique Alain Bézu; secrétaire générale Danièle le Bihan; attaché de presse Eric Talbot; responsable pédagogique Catherine Dewitt
Capacity: 215 *Policy:* mainly produce, co-produce, present *Arts types:* contemporary drama *Comments:* see also Drama

Théâtre Duchamp-Villon
Place de la Verrerie, Saint-Sever, BP 1033,
76171 **Rouen** Cedex
Tel: 2-3218 2828/10 (bookings) Fax: 2-3562 2166
directeur Ahmed Merghoub; administrateur Fabrice Manuel
Venue type: théâtre *Capacity:* seated 1460, standing 1000 *Policy:* rent, produce, co-produce *Arts types:* variety, dance, film, jazz, rock, pop concerts, world music, new music, contemporary dance, tales for children

Centre Culturel de la ville de Saint-Avold
1 rue de la Chapelle, 57500 **Saint-Avold**
Tel: 3-8791 0809 Fax: 3-8792 3396
directrice & programmation cinéma Annie Brosch; secretaire Valérie Saverweil
Capacity: Salle de Spectacle 1000, Salle de cinéma François Truffaut 164 *Policy:* rent, produce *Arts types:* theatre, dance, concerts *Comments:* it is also a documentation centre on arts

Passerelle, La
Scène Nationale de Saint-Brieuc, Place de la Resistance, BP 4133, 22041 **Saint-Brieuc** Cedex 2
Tel: 2-9668 1840 Fax: 2-9668 1841
Internet: www.artrock.org
directeur Jean Parthenay; administrator Jean-Michel Boinet; directrice de la communication Marie Lostys; régisseur général Pascal Le Montréer
Venue type: theatre *Capacity:* Grand Théâtre 1000, Petit Théâtre 300, Le Forum 1000 (standing) *Policy:* rent, present, produce, co-produce *Arts types:* music, theatre, dance, variety *Comments:* 2 exhibition halls; see also Festivals; organise Festival Art Rock

Théâtre Gérard Philipe – Centre Dramatique National
59 bd Jules Guesde, 93207 **Saint-Denis** Cedex 01
Tel: 1-4813 7010/7000 (bookings)
Fax: 1-4243 0337
E-Mail: tgp@club-internet.fr
directeur général Stanislas Nordey; administrateur Stéphane Gueirréro
Venue type: théâtre *Capacity:* Hall A 700, Hall B 80, Hall C 80 *Policy:* produce, co-produce, present *Arts types:* theatre, dance *Comments:* festival Enfantillages – May; festival AFRICOLOR – December

Comédie de St Etienne – Centre Dramatique National
7 Av Emile Loubet, 42000 **Saint-Étienne**
Tel: 4-7725 0124 Fax: 4-7741 9634
E-Mail: comédie.de.saint-etienne@wanadoo.fr
directeur Daniel Benoin; secrétaire général Christiane Raia; directeur technique Jean-Pierre Laporte; administrateur Rene Lévy; administrateur-adjoint Françoise Lecoq; régisseur général Daniel Cerisier
Capacity: Hall A 750, Hall B 370, Hall C 80, L'Usine 200-250 *Policy:* produce, co-produce, rent *Arts types:* theatre *Comments:* see also Drama

L'Esplanade Saint-Etienne
Jardin des Plantes, BP 237, 42013 **Saint-Étienne** Cedex 2
Tel: 4-7747 8347/8340 Fax: 4-7747 8369
directeur Jean-Louis Pichon; programmation danse Serge Horwath; programmation jazz, rock, variety Dominique Rouvier; administrateur Michel Fabre; directeur technique Gerard Plaideau; directeur de la communication Daniel Couriol; administrateur Michel Fabre
Capacity: Grand Théâtre 1260, Théâtre Copeau 330, Théâtre Ephémére 1100
Policy: produce, co-produce, present, rent
Arts types: opera, symphony, orchestra, vocal, dance, ballet, variety and shows for young audiences
Comments: see also Promoters, Dance and Opera

Théâtre Municipal Roger Ferdinand
Rue Saint-Thomas, BP 330, 50010 **Saint-Lo** Cedex
Tel: 2-3357 1149 Fax: 2-3357 7967
administration Annick Levilly; chargée de programmation Jean-Paul Mandon; régisseur général Sylvain Heleine; chargé de production Dominique Delaunay
Venue type: Théâtre à l'Italienne *Capacity:* 500 *Policy:* rent, present, produce, co-produce *Arts types:* drama, concerts, dance, one man show, variety

IDDAC (Institut départemental de développement Artistique et Culturel)
Place de la République, BP 90,
33166 **Saint-Médard-en-Jalles**
Tel: 5-5670 1313 Fax: 5-5670 1330
E-Mail: iddac.communication@cg33.fr
directeur Sylvain Gautier; administrateur Myriam Brun; regisseur général Yves Deniel; presse Françoise Houzelot; technique Didier Ponchon; communication Frédérique Andrivet
Venue type: Cultural centre *Capacity:* Salle de St Médiar 775, cinema municipal 90 *Policy:* co-produce, rent, present *Arts types:* theatre, dance, jazz, music, dance courses, cinema *Comments:* see also Festivals (Eté Girondin – Summer in Gironde))

Espace Marcel Carné
Place Marcel Carné, 91240 **Saint-Michel-sur-Orge**
Tel: 1-6904 9833 Fax: 1-6946 3080
directeur Loïc Lannou; secrétariat Marie-Claire Domecq; directeur technique Jean-Claude Dulieu; administratice Marie France Contesse
Capacity: 540 *Policy:* rent, present, produce, co-produce *Arts types:* symphony, theatre, dance, opera, jazz, variety, circus, world music, lyric

Centre Culturel le Fanal Scène Nationale de Saint Nazaire
33 blvd Victor-Hugo, BP 150, 44603 **Saint-Nazaire** Cedex
Tel: 2-4022 3938 Fax: 2-4022 9144
directeur Jean-Joël Le Chapelain; administration Maryvonne Bos; relations publiques Sylvette Magne; régié générale Patrick Balaud
Venue type: theatres *Capacity:* Théâtre Jean Bart 270, Théâtre Gerard Philipe 770, Salle Jacques Tati 150 , 2 exhibition halls *Policy:* rent, co-produce, present, produce *Arts types:* jazz, theatre, dance, music, song, cinema, world music *Comments:* organise 3 festivals; see also Festivals

Centre Culturel de Sarlat
Rue Gaubert, 24202 **Sarlat** Cedex
Tel: 5-5331 0949 Fax: 5-5331 0950
directeur Didier Pignon; directeur technique Jean-Marc Lajoinie
Venue type: multi purpose *Capacity:* seated 616, standing 1200 *Policy:* rent, produce, co-produce, present *Arts types:* dance, theatre, variety, orchestra, congresses, exhibitions, youth theatre, opera, circus

Théâtre de Sartrouville- Scène Nationale
Place Jacques-Brel, BP 93, 78505 **Sartrouville** Cedex
Tel: 1-3086 7777 Fax: 1-3914 8791
directeur Claude Sévénier; artistes associés Angélique Ionatos, Joël Jouanneau; directeur de production Guy d'Hardivillers
Venue type: theatre *Capacity:* 846, Espace Gérard Philipe 300 *Policy:* rent, present, produce, co-produce *Arts types:* dance, theatre, classical music, jazz, variety *Comments:* also Centre Dramatique National pour Enfants et Jeunes HEYOKA – children's entertainment; see also Drama

Les Gémeaux – Scène Nationale
49 Av Georges-Clemenceau, 92330 **Sceaux**
Tel: 1-4660 0564 (administration)/4661 3667 (bookings) Fax: 1-4661 5455
directrice Françoise Letellier; administratrice Evelyne Abdelkader; communication Nicolas Massadau
Capacity: Hall A 500, Hall B 180 *Policy:* present, produce, co-produce *Arts types:* theatre, opera, dance (contemporary), jazz, film, classical music, operatic music *Comments:* see also Festivals

Maison des Arts et Loisirs de Sochaux – MALS
Hôtel de Ville, BP 73089, 25603 **Sochaux** Cedex
Tel: 3-8194 1662 Fax: 3-8194 1193
directeur Albert Matocq-Gradot; président Libérot Cencig; chef de plateau Raimond Chuller; secrétaire général Jean-Paul Monnot
Venue type: multi-purpose *Capacity:* 1120 *Policy:* rent, co-produce, present, produce *Arts types:* theatre, dance, concerts, variety, jazz

Théâtre de St Quentin en Yvelines(Scéne Natonale)
Place Georges Pompidou, BP 317, Montigny Le Bretonnieux, 78054 **St Quentin-en-Yvelines** Cedex
Tel: 1-3096 9930 Fax: 1-3096 9929
direction Pierre Moutarde; secrétaire générale Gisèle Terrail; direction technique Daniel Hoye; directeur administratif Claude Drobinski; accueil des compagnies Marie Claude La Ronze
Venue type: theatre *Capacity:* Hall A 1100, Hall B 300 *Policy:* produce, co-produce, present *Arts types:* dance, music theatre, theatre, music, circus, opera, visual arts

Maillon, Le
13 place André Maurois, BP 10,
67033 **Strasbourg** Cedex 2
Tel: 3-8827 6171/6181/6191 (bookings) Fax: 3-8827 6182
Internet: www.le-maillon.com
E-Mail: info@le-maillon.com
directeur Nadia Derrar; responsable communication Angélique Regnier; presse Patricia Hanote
Venue type: modern *Capacity:* up to 550, theatre 380
Policy: co-produce, present *Arts types:* theatre, dance, world music

Palais de la Musique et des Congrès de Strasbourg
Place de Bordeaux, 67082 **Strasbourg** Cedex
Tel: 3-8837 6767 Fax: 3-8825 6196
membre du directoire, directeur commercial Jérôme Wagner; responsable de la communication et des relations publiques Alain Kuhn
Venue type: multi purpose *Capacity:* Erasme 2000, Schweitzer up to 1100, Salle Schuman 500 & 6 other halls *Policy:* rent, co-present *Arts types:* concerts, recitals, dance, opera, theatre, conferences *Comments:* home of The Philharmonic Orchestra of Strasbourg

Palais des Fêtes
5 rue Sellenick, 67000 **Strasbourg**
Tel: 3-8835 4907/8860 9717 (bookings)/12
Fax: 3-8860 9710
chef du service André Deppen; gestionnaire Daniel Kirsch
Venue type: multi purpose *Capacity:* Hall A 1100, Hall B: Salle de la Marseillaise 280 *Policy:* rent *Arts types:* concerts, classic music, ballet, ball, theatre

Pôle Sud
1 rue de Bourgogne, BP 65, 67024 **Strasbourg** Cedex 1
Tel: 3-8839 2340 Fax: 3-8840 0427
Internet: www.strasbourg.com/pole-sud
directeur Alain Py; attachée de presse Hydra Khelid; responsable de la programmation Joëlle Smadja, Alain Py; programmtion jazz Philippe Ochem
Venue type: théâtre *Capacity:* 330 *Policy:* produce, co-produce, present *Arts types:* contemporary dance, jazz, theatre, young peoples theatre

Centre Culturel de Terrasson
5 rue Marcel Michel, 24120 **Terrasson**
Tel: 5-5350 1380 Fax: 5-5350 4676
directeur Jean-Paul Dumas
Venue type: theatre *Capacity:* up to 250 *Policy:* present, co-produce *Arts types:* theatre, music, dance *Comments:* see also Festivals (Festival des chemins de l'imaginaire)

Maison des Arts Thonons-Evian
Avenue d'Evian, 74200 **Thonon**
Tel: 4-5071 3947 Fax: 4-5071 4171
Internet: www.mal.thonon.org
directeur Michel Chaboud; administrateur René Muller; relations publiques Alain Saillet
Venue type: theatre *Capacity:* 820, cinema 130 *Policy:* rent, co-produce, produce, present *Arts types:* all kind, cinema (art house films) *Comments:* exhibition hall

Opéra de Toulon
Boulevard de Strasbourg, 83000 **Toulon**
Tel: 4-9493 0376 Fax: 4-9409 3029
directeur général Guy Grinda; directeur administratif Serge Lopez; directeur de la scène Henry Murgue; régisseur général Philippe Pellier; directeur musical Christian Segarici; directrice de la danse Monique Andreoletti
Venue type: théâtre à l'Italienne *Capacity:* 1500 *Policy:* produce, co-produce, present, rent *Arts types:* opera, operette, theatre, dance *Comments:* see also Opera

Zénith Oméga
Boulevard du Commandant Nicolas, 83000 **Toulon**
Tel: 4-9422 6677 Fax: 4-9492 6688
directrice Annette Camus; directeur technique Edouard Leperlier
Venue type: multi-purpose *Capacity:* 1000-8500 *Policy:* rent, percentage *Arts types:* concerts (classical, rock, jazz), meetings, conventions, conferences, theatre, circus, dance

CDC / Structure de Diffusion
5 Avenue Etienne Billieres, 31300 **Toulouse**
Tel: 5-6159 9878 Fax: 5-6159 9904
E-Mail: cdc@com.unisoft.fr
directrice Annie Bozzini; trésorier Philippe Durand-Tonerre
Capacity: 90 *Policy:* co-produce, produce, present *Arts types:* contemporary dance
Comments: also offer training

Halle aux Grains
Place Dupuy, 31000 **Toulouse**
Tel: 5-6199 7800 Fax: 5-6162 1048
Internet: www.onct.mairie-toulouse.fr
director administration Robert Gouazé; director orchestra Michel Plasson; service presse Marie-Claire Rettig
Venue type: multi purpose *Capacity:* 2556 *Policy:* rent, produce, co-produce *Arts types:* opera, orchestra, theatre, concerts symphoniques, dance, variety
Comments: home of the National Orchestra of Toulouse

Théâtre du Capitole
Place du Capitole, BP 129, 31014 **Toulouse** Cedex 06
Tel: 5-6122 3131 Fax: 5-6272 2832
Internet: www.theatre-du-capitole.org
administrateur général Robert Gouazé; directeur artistique Nicolas Joël; relations publiques Jean-Paul Laffont; presse Marie-Claire Rettig
Venue type: Italian style *Capacity:* 1100 *Policy:* produce, co-produce, rent *Arts types:* opera, comic opera, ballet, operetta *Comments:* see also Dance and Opera

Centre Dramatique Regional de Tours
Direction Gilles Bouillon, 3 rue Léonard de Vinci, 37000 **Tours**
Tel: 2-4764 4864 Fax: 2-4720 1726
directeur Gilles Bouillon; administratrice Giovana Pacé; régisseur Xavier Carré; dramaturge Bernard Pico
Capacity: Théâtre Louis Jouvet 240 *Policy:* produce, diffuse *Arts types:* drama, animation
Comments: see also Drama

Grand Théâtre de Tours
34, rue de la Scellerie, 37000 **Tours**
Tel: 2-4705 3347/4720 3614 Fax: 2-4766 1192
directeur Michel Jarry; directeur technique Denis Baling; directeur musical Mr Talmont; responsable administratif Luc Cavalier
Venue type: théâtre à l'italienne (built in 1889) *Capacity:* 1010 *Policy:* produce, co-produce, rent, present *Arts types:* opera, operettas, recitals, ballet, classical concerts, theatre, boulevard *Comments:* see also Opera

Centre Culturel Aragon
24 bld de l'Hôtel de Ville,
93290 **Tremblay-en-France (Paris)**
Tel: 1-4963 7050/7058 (bookings) Fax: 1-4963 7067
directrice Josette Joubier; adjoint Benedick Picot; responsable jeune public Sylvie Delhoemmeau
Venue type: modern *Capacity:* 452 *Policy:* present, co-produce *Arts types:* mainly contemporary dance, theatre, music, children's events

Sept Collines-Centre Corrézien de Développement Culturel, Les
51 quai Aristide Brillant, BP 163, 19005 **Tulle** Cedex
Tel: 5-5526 8960 Fax: 5-5526 8874
directeur Solange Charlot; administrateur Claude Barrault; directeur technique Claude Hamel; responsable de l'information Frédérique Bernard-Sabliere; régisseur de scené Patrice Monzat
Venue type: theatre *Capacity:* 387 *Policy:* present, co-produce, produce *Arts types:* theatre, contemporary dance, music (classical, jazz) *Comments:* it's also Théâtre Municipal de Tulle

Centre de Recherche et d'Action Culturelle (CRAC)
Scéne Nationale de Valence, 36 Boulevard du Géneral de Gaulle, 26000 **Valence**
Tel: 4-7582 4411 Fax: 4-7582 4412
Internet: crac.asso.fr/image
E-Mail: crac@crac.asso.fr
directeur Françoise Calvez; président Christian Dewinter; administrateur Luc De Maesschalck; secretaire général Claude Labrue
Venue type: 2 cinema halls and 3 exhibition halls
Capacity: salle A 324, salle B 109 *Policy:* produce, co-produce *Arts types:* films (art et essai/rep), exhibitions, festivals, cinema, audiovisual arts theatre, music and research

Centre Culturel André Malraux
BP 126, 54504 **Vandoeuvre** Cedex
Tel: 3-8356 1500 Fax: 3-8353 2185
Internet: www.services.worldnet.fr/ccam
E-Mail: ccam@worldnet.fr
directeur Mr Finance
Venue type: modern *Capacity:* 250 *Policy:* co-produce, produce, present *Arts types:* all types *Comments:* venue address: Place de l'Hôtel de Ville, 54504 Vandoeuvre

Centre Culturel Charlie Chaplin
Place de la Nation, 69120 **Vaulx-en-Velin**
Tel: 4-7204 8118/9 Fax: 4-7204 3703
directeur Marc Masson; relations publiques auprès des comités d'enterprise et collectivités Josette Sala; relations publiques et communication Bernard Fontaine; directeur technique Gerard Teilhol
Capacity: 200-1000 *Policy:* present, produce, co-produce *Arts types:* theatre, dance, variety, young public theatre, jazz festival *Comments:* work with artists from Rhône-Alpes; see also Dance, Drama and Festivals

Théâtre Montansier de Versailles
13 rue des Réservoirs, 78035 **Versailles** Cedex
Tel: 1-3920 1600 Fax: 1-3953 4321
directeur Francis Perrin; administratrice Elisabeth Levasseur; directeur technique Michel La Porta
Venue type: theatre *Capacity:* 633 *Policy:* produce, co-produce, present, rent *Arts types:* theatre, concerts, conferences, recitals *Comments:* see also Drama

Thév'- Théâtre Edwige Feuillère Vesoul
2 Quai Pierre Rénet, 70000 **Vesoul**
Tel: 3-8475 4066 Fax: 3-8476 8928
directeur Jacky Castang
Venue type: frontal – modern *Capacity:* 715
Policy: rent, present, produce, co-produce
Arts types: theatre, dance, music

Palais des Congrés
5 rue du Casino, BP 2805, 03208 **Vichy** Cedex
Tel: 4-7030 5050 Fax: 4-7030 5010
directeur artistique Diane Polya; directeur général Jean-Philippe Gold
Venue type: théâtre à l'Italienne *Capacity:* 1400 *Policy:* rent, present, co-produce *Arts types:* opera, operetta, dance, recitals, variety, comedy, theatre, music, symphonic concerts *Comments:* see also Opera

Théâtre Antique de Vienne
rue du Cirque, 38200 **Vienne**
Tel: 4-7485 3923
directeur Etienne Paoli; communication Frédéric Ravel; régisseur général Michel Pradeil
Venue type: théâtre à l'ancienne *Capacity:* 8000 *Policy:* produce, co-produce *Arts types:* all types

Théâtre Municipal de Vienne
4 rue Chantelouve, 38200 **Vienne**
Tel: 4-7485 0005 Fax: 4-7485 4485
directeur Etienne Paoli; communication Frédéric Ravel; régisseur général Michel Pradell
Capacity: 200 *Policy:* produce, co-produce, rent *Arts types:* all kinds *Comments:* organisers of 'le festival de Vienne' first 2 weeks in July; see also Festivals

Théâtre Romain Rolland
18 rue Eugène Varlin, BP 11, 94801 **Villejuif** Cedex
Tel: 1-4958 1700 Fax: 1-4958 1710
directeur Henri Kochman
Capacity: 850 *Policy:* present, co-produce *Arts types:* all kinds and cinema *Comments:* see also Festivals (Rencontre Charles Dullin, Les Ices de Danse, Sons D'Hiver, Biennale Nationale de Danse du Val de Marne)

La Rose des Vents – Scène Nationale
Blvd Van Gogh, 59650 **Villeneuve-d'Ascq**
Tel: 3-2061 9690 Fax: 3-2061 9691
E-Mail: larosedesvents@infonie.fr
directeur Didier Thibaut; administrateur Veronique Alter; directeur technique Didier Torz; communication Hélène Laverge
Venue type: theatre *Capacity:* salle A 500, salle B 100
Policy: produce, co-produce, present *Arts types:* theatre, dance, youth theatre, music, concerts, variety

Centre Culturel Jacques Raphaël-Leygues
23 rue Etienne Marcel, 47300 **Villeneuve-sur-Lot**
Tel: 5-5370 1938 Fax: 5-5370 8654
directeur Joël Brouch
Venue type: theatre and multi purpose *Capacity:* Salle des Fontanelles 2000, théâtre Georges Leygues 800, Salle Jacques Raphaël-Leygues 300 *Policy:* present, co-produce, produce, rent *Arts types:* concerts, recitals, theatre, dance, jazz, young peoples theatre

Théâtre Gérard Philipe
46 cours de la République, 69100 **Villeurbanne**
Tel: 4-7885 7997 Fax: 4-7868 6244
directeur Françoise Maimone; administration Joelle Buffy-Lours; communication Laurence Bolliet, Chrystelle Jongit; conseillers jeunes publics Jacques Thomasson, Valérie Hiard; secretaire Simone Zagata; régisseur Alain Couvreur; assistant régisseur Eric Grosso
Venue type: theatre *Capacity:* 112-192 *Policy:* co-produce, present productions for young people
Arts types: theatre, dance

Gare Au Théâtre
13, rue Pierre-Sémard, 94400 **Vitry**
Tel: 1-4682 6190 Fax: 1-4681 2160
Internet: www.gare-au-web.com
E-Mail: contact@gare-au-web.com
directeurs Mustapha Aouar, Anne-Marie Simonin
Venue type: theatre *Capacity:* 220 *Policy:* co-produce, produce, diffuse-present *Arts types:* theatre, shadow theatre and image theatre, music *Comments:* organises meetings like PETIT, PETIT, PETIT between 10 theatre companies from Ile de France; see also Compagnie La Goutte d'eau (puppets)

GEORGIA (+995)

Great Concert Hall of the Ministry of Culture
1 Melikishvili St., 380009 **Tbilisi**
Tel: 32-983 227/987 681/815
manager Aleksandre Basilaia; artistic director Dorian Kitia; deputy manager Giorgi Koberidze; secretary Maia Jgenti
Venue type: concert hall *Capacity:* 2403 *Arts types:* symphonic, jazz, rock, concerts, mixed show programmes, films

Sport Complex Laguna Vere
34, Kostava (1st turning), 380009 **Tbilisi**
Tel: 32-998 231/360/179 Fax: 32-377 389
general director Vladimer Goiashvili; assistant Giorgi Kandelaki

Sport Palace
9, Kostava st., 380071 **Tbilisi**
Tel: 32-362 303/279
general director Lasha Lomidze; assistants Musali Melashvili, Kukuri Suriashvili; head of sport department Koba Lomtadze

Tbilisi Music Centre
125 Agmashenebeli Ave., 380064 **Tbilisi**
Tel: 32-960 620/957 899/961 243
president of centre Jansug Kakhidze; co-president Gogi Nijaradze; deputy director Laila Kikaaleishvili

Tbilisi State Conservatoire
8 Griboedov st., 380004 **Tbilisi**
Tel: 32-997 976/999 144 Fax: 32-942 447
rector Nodar Gabunia; director of big hall Manana Doijashvili; director of small hall Zurab Chekirashvili
Venue type: 2 conerts halls
Capacity: big hall 565, small hall 100
Arts types: symphonic and chamber music

GERMANY (+49)

Eurogress Aachen
Monheimsallee 48, 52062 **Aachen**
Tel: 241-91310 Fax: 241-913 1200
E-Mail: eurogress@t-online.de
Geschäftsführer Eugen Rinder
Venue type: congress centre *Capacity:* Großer Saal 1704 (maximum) *Policy:* rent *Arts types:* conferences, exhibitions, all types of music (40 concerts per season)

Stadthalle Ahlen
Westenmauer 10, 59227 **Ahlen**
Tel: 2382-2677 Fax: 2382-2658
Geschäftsführer Roland Schmidt
Venue type: Stadthalle, multi-purpose hall *Capacity:* 860 (seated), 1800 (standing) *Policy:* rent, promote *Arts types:* opera, operetta, drama, conferences, music, exhibitions

Stadthalle am Schloß
Schloßplatz 1, 63739 **Aschaffenburg**
Tel: 6021-395-6 Fax: 6021-395 777
E-Mail: contact@info.aschaffenburg.de
Geschäftsführerin Annette Frenz
Venue type: multi-purpose *Capacity:* 2 halls: Upper Saal 1170, Kleiner Saal 350 *Policy:* rent *Arts types:* music, dance, drama, varietè, opera, pantomime, jazz, conferences, congresses *Comments:* only for hiring through Festspieldirektion, Konzertagenturen, except conferences and congresses

Augsburg Kongreßhalle
Gögginger Strasse 10, 86159 **Augsburg**
Tel: 821-324 2348 Fax: 821-324 2363
Geschäftsführer Eckhard Schiweck
Venue type: congress hall, concert hall *Capacity:* Kongress Saal 1400, Mozartsaal 340 *Policy:* rent (contact: Gudrun Kapfer (Tel: 821-324 2348) *Arts types:* congresses, conferences, exhibitions, chamber music, drama, symphony, solo recitals, dance, banquet, company presentations

Backnanger Bürgerhaus
Bahnhofstraße 7, 71522 **Backnang**
Tel: 7191-32610 Fax: 7191-326 134
Internet: backnang.de
Geschäftsführer Markus P. Majev M.A.; Sekretariat Ursula Ebert, Christa Sauter, Ursula Fieder; Technische Leitung Uwe Hund
Capacity: main hall 760, small hall 165 *Policy:* rent, present *Arts types:* chamber music, drama, symphony, solo recitals, dance, theatre, opera

Historische Kuranlagen und Goethe-Theater Bad Lauchstädt GmbH
Parkstr. 18, 06246 **Bad Lauchstädt**
Tel: 34635-20244/20300 Fax: 34635-20083
Internet: member.aol.com/BadLauch
Geschäftsführer/Direktor Bernd Heimühle
Venue type: theatre *Capacity:* 454, Historischer Kursaal 240 *Policy:* rent, promote *Arts types:* theatre, symphony, chamber music, music theatre

Festspielhaus Baden-Baden
Beim Alten Bahnhof 2, 76530 **Baden-Baden**
Tel: 7221-301 3204 Fax: 7221-301 3206
Internet: www.festspielhaus.de
E-Mail: a.schmidt@festspielhaus.de
Intendant und Geschäftsführer Andreas Mölich-Zebhauser; Referent des Intendanten Dr. Johannes Bultmann; Kaufmännischer Leiter Michael Drautz; Leiter Künstlerisches Betriebsbüro Andreas Schmidt; Künstlerisches Betriebsbüro Tania Glawe; Produktionsbüro Markus Boss; Technischer Leiter Thomas Römer; Presse Uwe Jakobs; Ticketing Sabine Ludwig
Capacity: 2400 *Policy:* present
Arts types: opera, concerts, ballet, operetta
Comments: festivals held in Herbert von Karajan Pfingstfestspiele, Internationales Ballett-Festival, Internationale Opernfestspiele, Internationale Sommerfestspiele, Konzerte im Jahresprogramm

Kurhaus Baden-Baden
Kaiserallee 1, 76530 **Baden-Baden**
Tel: 7221-353 202/4 Fax: 7221-353 203
Internet: www.kurhaus-baden-baden.de
E-Mail: info@kurhaus-baden-baden.de
Geschäftsführender Vorstand Dr. Karlheinz Hillenbrand
Venue type: multi-purpose *Capacity:* 8 halls up to 1500 *Policy:* rent *Arts types:* all kinds of events

Stadthalle Balingen
Postfach 101051, Hirschbergstrasse 38, 72336 **Balingen**
Tel: 7433-2424 Fax: 7433-10482
Internet: www.stadthalle.balingen.de
E-Mail: info@stadthalle.balingen.de
Geschäftsführer Ulrich Klingler
Venue type: Stadthalle, culture and congress centre *Capacity:* 1100 *Policy:* also promote *Arts types:* chamber music, drama, symphony, solo recitals, dance, theatre, meetings and congresses, opera

Konzert-und Kongresshalle Bamberg
Mußstr. 1, 96047 **Bamberg**
Tel: 951-964 7200 Fax: 951-964 7222
Internet: www.bamberg.de/konzerthalle
E-Mail: konzerthalle@bamberg.de
Geschäftsführer Mathias Heurich
Venue type: multi-purpose *Capacity:* Großer Saal 1400, Kleiner Saal 665 *Policy:* rent *Arts types:* mainly classical music, congresses, conventions, meetings, fairs

Studiobühne Bayreuth
Röntgenstr. 2, 95447 **Bayreuth**
Tel: 921-76436-0 Fax: 921-764 3622
Internet: www.bayreuth-online.de/studiob
E-Mail: studiobuehne@bayreuth-online.de
Direktor Werner Hildenbrand
Capacity: Hauptbühne 99, Bühnenstudio 50 *Policy:* percentage *Arts types:* drama, music theatre, children's theatre, cabaret *Comments:* visiting address: Studiobühne Bayreuth, Röntgenstr. 2, 95447

Parktheater Bergstraße Bensheim
Kulturamt der Stadt Bensheim, Rathans, Kirchbergstraße 18, 64625 **Bensheim**
Tel: 6251-14261 Fax: 6251-142 655
Amtsleiter Berthold Mäuerer
Venue type: theatre *Capacity:* 500 *Policy:* rent and present *Arts types:* drama, music, ballet, musical
Comments: venue address: Promenadenstr, 64625 Bensheim; also promote (Bensheimer Musiktage, Woche Junger Schauspieler und Vergabe des Gestrud-Eysoldt-Pres); hire touring companies, also foreign language productions; Kinder-und Jugendtheater, special performances for seniors; performances in schools

Bürgerhaus Bergischer Löwe
Konrad-Adenauer-Platz, 51465 **Bergisch Gladbach**
Tel: 2202-34051 Fax: 2202-41627
E-Mail: theater@bergischgladbach.de
Geschäftsführer Volker Aurich
Venue type: multi-purpose
Capacity: 650 *Policy:* receiving venue
Arts types: all types

Akademie der Künste
Hanseatenweg 10, 10557 **Berlin**
Tel: 30-39076-0 Fax: 30-39076-175
Internet: www.adk.de
E-Mail: info@adk.de
Verwaltungsdirektor Dagobert Rohner; Präsidialsekretär Hans Gerhard Hannesen; Presse/Öffentlichkeitsarbeit Manfred Mayer
Capacity: Großes Parkett 507, Kleines Parkett 195 *Policy:* present and receive
Arts types: drama, dance, concerts, lit. readings, cinema, etc. *Comments:* second address: Pariser Platz 4, 10117 Berlin, closed until 2001

bat – Studiotheater der Hochschule für Schauspielkunst 'Ernst Busch' Berlin
Belforter Str. 15, 10405 **Berlin**
Tel: 30-442 7996 Fax: 30-442 6963
Director Prof. Peter Kleinert
Venue type: theatre
Capacity: 130 *Arts types:* drama
Comments: for student performances only

Dock 11 Studios
Kastanienallee 79, 10435 **Berlin**
Tel: 30-448 1222 Fax: 30-448 1185
Internet: www.dock11.de
E-Mail: dock11@berlin.contrib.net
contact Wibke Janssen, Kirsten Seeligmüller
Venue type: studios
Capacity: up to 100 *Policy:* present and receive
Arts types: dance, drama, music *Comments:* also workshops & lectures for all arts types

Friends of Italian Opera – The English-Language Theatre in Berlin
Fidicinstrasse 40, 10965 **Berlin**
Tel: 30-693 5692 (office)/691 1211 (box office)
Fax: 30-691 3937
Internet: www.thefriends.de
E-Mail: info@thefriends.de
managing director Bernd Hoffmeister; artistic director Günther Grosser; project coordinator Tara McGowan; pr officer Ulrike Dittrich
Venue type: level portal stage
Capacity: 75 *Policy:* present, rent
Arts types: any kind of theatre from classics to contemporary performance art (English-Language Theatre only)
Comments: see also Drama

Gustav-Böss-Freilichtbühne
c/o Kulturforum Villa Oppenheim, Schloßstr. 55, 14059 **Berlin**
Tel: 30-3430 4151 Fax: 30-3430 4160
Venue type: open air
Capacity: 999 *Policy:* promotes
Arts types: classical, folk, jazz etc., children's and youth theatre *Comments:* venue address: Volkspark Jungfernheide, Berlin; promotes the performances of Kuskus e.V., Tel: 30-381 6123

Haus der Kulturen der Welt
House of World Cultures
John-Foster-Dulles Allee 10, 10557 **Berlin**
Tel: 30-397 870/150 (public relations)
Fax: 30-394 8679
Internet: www.hkw.de
E-Mail: info@hkw.de
Geschäftsführer & Generalsekretär Dr Hans-Georg Knopp; PR Susanne Sporrer
Venue type: cultural centre; in the summer open-air venues *Capacity:* auditorium 1025, theatre 392, exhibition hall, conference rooms from 40 – 150)
Policy: present, rent
Arts types: music, dance, literature, fine arts, philosophy, lectures, media, performances, etc.
Comments: emphasis on the dialogue with non-Western cultures

Hebbel-Theater
Stresemannstrasse 29, 10963 **Berlin**
Tel: 30-259 0040 Fax: 30-2590 0449
Internet: www.hebbel-theater.de
E-Mail: pr@hebbel-theater.de
Direktorin u. künstlerische Leitung Nele Hertling; Stellv. künstlerische Leitung Maria Magdalena Schwaegermann; Verwaltungsleitung Martina Geßner; Öffentlichkeitsarbeit Wolfgang Kaldenhoff, Kirsten Herkenroth; technische Leitung Erich Stasch
Venue type: theatre
Capacity: 580 *Policy:* present
Arts types: dance, theatre, music
Comments: major venue for independent theatre companies

Konzerthaus Berlin
Schauspielhaus am Gendarmenmarkt, Gendarmenmarkt 2, 10117 **Berlin**
Tel: 30-20309-0 Fax: 30-2030 92209
Internet: www.konzerthaus.de
E-Mail: intendanz@konzerthaus.de
Intendant Prof. Dr Frank Schneider
Venue type: concert hall *Capacity:* Großer Saal 1700, Kleiner Saal 392, Musikclub 80
Policy: present, rent *Arts types:* classical and contemporary concerts in Großer Saal and Kleiner Saal, musical-literary events in Musikclub
Comments: home of Berliner Sinfonie-Orchester Berlin (q.v.); Konzerthaus closed every year from mid-July until end August, postal adress: 10106 Berlin

Künstlerhaus Bethanien
Mariannenplatz 2, 10997 **Berlin**
Tel: 30-6169 0316/5/4 Fax: 30-6169 0330
Internet: www.bethanien.de
E-Mail: kb@bethanien.de
Direktor Dr. Michael Haerdter; Atelierprogramm Heike Dander; Presse und Öffentlichkeitsarbeit Christina Sickert; Projektleiter Bildende Kunst Christoph Tannert; Projektleitung darstellende Kunst Ewa Strózczynska-Wille
Venue type: multi-purpose space
Capacity: 25 studios *Policy:* international artists programme, exclusively on invitation
Arts types: visual arts & theatre seminars; theatre, exhibitions, performances
Comments: also publish several art magazines, among them THEATERSCHRIFT (q.v.) and BE magazine

Philharmonie
Herbert Von Karajan Strasse 1, 10785 **Berlin**
Tel: 30-25488-0
Fax: 30-25488-105 (Intendanz)/261 4887 (Presse)
Internet: www.berlin-philharmonie.com
E-Mail: presseinfo@philharmonie.siveco.de
Intendant Dr Elmar Weingarten; Presse u. Öffentlichkeitsarbeit Dr Helge Grünewald
Venue type: concert hall
Capacity: Philharmonie: Großer Saal 2440, Kleiner Saal 1180 *Policy:* rent
Arts types: classical music
Comments: home of Berlin Philharmonic Orchestra (q.v.); to be rented by orchestras, soloists, ensembles etc.

Podewil
Klosterstrasse 68, 10179 **Berlin**
Tel: 30-247 496 Fax: 30-2474 9700
Internet: www.podewil.de
E-Mail: pr@podewil.de
Geschäftsführer/Programmdirector Wilhelm Großmann; Koordination Internationaler Kulturaustausch Alexandra Rückert; Öffentlichkeitsarbeit Gabriele Miketta; Verwaltungsleiterin Lilianna Russ; Musicprogramm Elke Moltrecht; Tanzprogramm Ulrike Becker, Andre Theriault; Theater und Performance Programm Aenne Quinones; Mediaprogramm Micky Kwella
Venue type: centre for contemporary arts *Capacity:* up to 240 *Policy:* present *Arts types:* music, dance, theatre/performance, new media, literature *Comments:* production house as well as a performance venue; internationally acclaimed centre for the promotion of contemporary art and culture; directed by a team of 4 curators; since 1997 Podewil has been offering an artist-in-residence programme

Statthaus Böcklerpark
Prinzenstr 1, 10969 **Berlin**
Tel: 30-615 8787 Fax: 30-6160 9574
Internet: www.bln.de/statthouseb
E-Mail: statthouseb@bln.de
Leiter Burkhard Wiesner; Presse t.b.a. (30-615 8164)
Venue type: socio-cultural centre *Capacity:* Saal 1 300, Clubraum 100, Wintergarten 100 *Policy:* rent, promotes *Arts types:* music performances, dance, drama; workshops, courses, seminars, exhibitions *Comments:* focus on foreign culture (Arabic, Brazilian, African etc) & multi-cultural youth centre

Tanzfabrik – Centrum für Zeitgenössischen Tanz
Möckernstrasse 68, 10965 **Berlin**
Tel: 30-786 6103 Fax: 30-786 1586
Internet: www.kulturbox.de/tanzfabrik
E-Mail: tanzfabrik@p-soft.de
administrator Eva-Maria Hoerster; artistic director Claudia Feest
Venue type: venue for dance groups, studio stage *Capacity:* 99 *Policy:* produce and present Berlin contemporary dance groups *Arts types:* modern, experimental, dance-theatre, dance-video *Comments:* organiation of workshops, master classes for professionals; amateur school with 50 classes and 500 students

Theater unterm Dach
Danzigerstraße 101, 10405 **Berlin**
Tel: 30-4240 1080 Fax: 30-4240 1086
Internet: www.kulturamtprenzlberg.de
E-Mail: info@kulturamt.prenzlberg.de
Leitung Liesel Dechant
Venue type: theatre *Capacity:* 80 *Policy:* co-produce *Arts types:* theatre, readings

ufaFabrik
Viktoriastrasse 10-18, 12105 **Berlin**
Tel: 30-755 030 Fax: 30-7550 3110
Internet: www.ufafabrik.de
E-Mail: info@ufafabrik.de
Verwaltungsdirektor Rudolf Brünger; Künstlerischer Direktoren Juppy Becher, Scotty Golumbeck; Communication Sigrid Niemer
Capacity: open-air stage 700, theatre 400, variety 200 *Policy:* venue and production *Arts types:* multi-media, alternative theatre, music, dance, cabaret, circus, children's theatre, children's circus festival, variety, world music *Comments:* member of Trans Europe Halles (q.v.); founded and managed by a resident community of 50 artists; workshop facilities, accommodation for artists can be provided; rehearsal space available

Stadthalle Betzdorf
Postfach 840, 57518 **Betzdorf**
Tel: 2741-29191 Fax: 2741-29119
Geschäftsführer Peter Dützer
Venue type: multi-purpose *Capacity:* 860 *Arts types:* drama, dance, music etc. *Comments:* visiting address: Hellerstr. 30

Stadthalle Biberach an der Riß
Postfach 1757, 88396 **Biberach**
Tel: 7351-51436 Fax: 7351-51511
Internet: www.biberach-riss.de
E-Mail: tourist-information@biberach-riss.de
Betriebsleiter Klaus Buchmann
Venue type: stadhalle with theater *Capacity:* Theater 567, Großer Saal 1400 *Policy:* rent, promote *Arts types:* classical, pop, exhibitions, dance, variety, opera, operetta, musicals, song evenings, theatre, pantomime, jazz *Comments:* visiting address: Theaterstraße 6, 88400 Biberach

Stadthalle Bielefeld Betriebs-GmbH
Postfach 102686, 33526 **Bielefeld**
Tel: 521-96360 Fax: 521-64933
Internet: shb.info24.de
E-Mail: shbielef@aol.com
Geschäftsführer Matthias Fuchs; Veranstaltungsleitung Barbara Stening; Technische Leitung Lutz Lessmann
Venue type: multi-purpose hall *Capacity:* Großer Saal up to 2300 seated (3860 standing), Kleiner Saal up to 700, 13 conference halls up to 200 *Policy:* rent *Arts types:* concerts of all types, congresses, meetings, exhibitions, etc *Comments:* Willy-Brandt-Platz 1, 33602 Bielefeld

Städtisches Bühnenhaus im Kulturzentrum Bocholt
Berliner Platz 1, 46395 **Bocholt**
Tel: 2871-953 340 Fax: 2871-953 342
Internet: www.bocholt.de
E-Mail: webmaster@mail.Bocholt.de
Vorsitzender und Geschäftsführer Bernd Hagmayer; Techn. Leiter Dieter Beckmann; Kulturamtsleiter Georg Ketteler
Venue type: theatre *Capacity:* 703 *Policy:* promote, rent *Arts types:* drama, musicals, opera, concerts

Ruhrlandhalle
Stadionring 20, 44791 **Bochum**
Tel: 234-959 180 Fax: 234-959 1810
Hallenleiter Wilfried Perner
Venue type: multi-purpose *Capacity:* 3000 *Policy:* rent *Arts types:* concerts, conferences, congresses, TV, balls, fashion shows

Schauspielhaus Bochum
Königsallee 15, 44789 **Bochum**
Tel: 234-3333-0 Fax: 234-333 3121 (Direktion)/3112 (kasse)
Internet: www.bochum.de/schauspielhaus
E-Mail: schauspielhaus@bochum.de
Intendant Leander Haußmann; Direktor Alexander von Maravic
Venue type: theatre *Capacity:* Schauspielhaus 836, Kammerspiele 410, ZadEck 99 *Policy:* present, rent *Arts types:* theatre, orchestras *Comments:* Spielstätte der Bochumer Symphoniker (Schauspielhaus)

Beethovenhalle
Wachsbleiche 16, 53111 **Bonn**
Tel: 228-722 2100 Fax: 228-722 2111
Internet: www.beethovenhalle.de
E-Mail: info@beethovenhalle.de
Direktor Günter Sick; Veranstaltungsleiter Michael Tänzer
Venue type: multi-purpose *Capacity:* großer Saal 2019, studio 487, Kammermusiksaal 220, Vortragssaal 200, rooms for semimars 300 *Policy:* rent *Arts types:* chamber music, drama, symphony, solo recitals, dance, theatre, conferences, congresses, social events, dance masterclasses

Contra-Kreis-Theater GmbH
Am Hof 3-5, 53113 **Bonn**
Tel: 228-632 307/635 517 Fax: 228-636 081
Internet: www.contra-kreis-theater.com
E-Mail: info@contra-kreis-theater.com
Intendanz u. Geschäftsführung Katinka Hoffmann, Horst Johanning; Verwaltungsleitung Hannelore Stauber-Berrisch, Ursula Annemarie Perzborn-Meisel; Öffentlichkeitsreferat Bettina Maretsch
Venue type: theatre *Capacity:* 261 *Policy:* produce *Arts types:* drama, comedy

Stadthalle Bad Godesberg
Koblenzer Straße 80, 53177 **Bonn**
Tel: 228-364 035 Fax: 228-357 681
Inhaber Thomas Weiermann
Venue type: multi-purpose hall *Capacity:* Großer Saal 900 *Arts types:* conferences, congresses

Brotfabrik
Kulturzentrum in Bonn/Beuel, Kreuzstraße 16, 53225 **Bonn-Beuel**
Tel: 228-421 310 Fax: 228-421 3129
Internet: www.beuel.de-brotfabrik
E-Mail: brotfabrik@aol.com
Programmleitung Gisela Mengelberg, Jürgen Becker; Bildunjswerk Mechthild Mays; PR Angela Vucko; Technik Frithjof Becker
Venue type: old factory *Capacity:* theatre 220, 3 dance spaces, cinema *Policy:* produce, promote, rent *Arts types:* theatre, dance, music, cinema *Comments:* Theatre Workshop for productions to rent; independent theatre groups from Bonn produce and perform here

Stadthalle Braunschweig
Leonhardplatz, 38102 **Braunschweig**
Tel: 531-70770 Fax: 531-707 7222
Internet: www.stadthalle-braunschweig.de
E-Mail: info@stadthalle-braunschweig.de
Geschäftsführer Uwe Birker
Venue type: multi-purpose *Capacity:* grosser Saal 2300, kleiner Saal 500 *Policy:* rent *Arts types:* concerts (various forms), family entertainment, congresses, sport *Comments:* concerts are arranged by agents; postal address: Postfach 4536, 38035 Braunschweig

Glocke, Die
c/o Glocke Veranstaltungs – GmbH, Postfach 10 54 20, 28054 **Bremen**
Tel: 421-3366-5 Fax: 421-320 298
Internet: www.glocke.de
E-Mail: Glocke@hvg-bremen.de
Geschäftsführerin Ilona Schmiel
Venue type: multi-purpose *Capacity:* Großer Konzertsaal 1400, Kleiner Konzertsaal 450 *Policy:* produce, promote, rent *Arts types:* concerts, musical, ballet, drama, workshops, exhibitions, presentations, TV and Radio productions, recordings *Comments:* visiting address: Domsheide 4/5, 28195 Bremen

Stadthalle Bremen
Postfach 101 349, 28013 **Bremen**
Tel: 421-3505-0 Fax: 421-350 5332
Internet: www.stadthalle-bremen.de
E-Mail: info@stadthalle-bremen.de
Geschäftsführer Claus Kleyboldt; Presse-/PR-Abt. Leiter Torsten Haar
Venue type: concert halls, multi-purpose *Capacity:* 6 halls: the biggest with a capacity of 10500 *Policy:* promote, rent *Arts types:* concerts (pop & rock), musicals, congresses, sport events, dance, fairs *Comments:* visiting address: Bürgerweide, 28209, Bremen

Stadthalle Bremerhaven
Wilhelm-Kaisen-Platz 1, 27576 **Bremerhaven**
Tel: 471-5917-0 Fax: 471-591 730
Internet: www.stadthalle-bremerhaven.de
E-Mail: info@stadthalle-bhv.de
Geschäftsführerin Kerstin Rogge-Mönchmeyer; Prokurist, Veranstaltungsleiter Ralf Türk; Kaufmännischer Leiter Rainer Müller; Technischer Leiter Günther Pirdszun
Venue type: stadhalle plus ice rink *Capacity:* up to 6000 *Policy:* rent, promote
Arts types: dance, shows, operettas, rock, pop, jazz concerts, exhibitions, conferences

Stadttheater Bremerhaven
Postfach 120 541, 27519 **Bremerhaven**
Tel: 471-482 060 Fax: 471-482 0682
Intendant Peter Grisebach; Verwaltungsdirektor Jürgen Ahlf; Oberspielleiter Wolfgang Hofmanni; Musikalischer Direktor Prof Leo Plettner
Venue type: theatre *Capacity:* Grosses Haus 722, Kleines Haus 122 *Policy:* promote, rent (2-3 times a year) *Arts types:* drama, opera, operetta, musicals, dance *Comments:* see also Drama

International Theatre Research Location Schloss Bröllin
Schloss Bröllin, 17309 **Bröllin**
Tel: 39747-50235 Fax: 39747-50302
E-Mail: schloss.broellin@t-online.de
contact Peter Legemann; information Ines Schulze (39747-50222)
Capacity: Große Halle up to 500, Probebühne 100, Studio II 50 *Policy:* produce, rent, promote *Arts types:* independent and experimental theatre, free theatre groups, workshops, dance, performance *Comments:* venue with rehearsal spaces, workshops and studios, production spaces for theatre, dance groups and artists etc; also have productions outside

Forum Castrop-Rauxel GmbH
Postfach 101345, 44543 **Castrop-Rauxel**
Tel: 2305-356 070 Fax: 2305-356 0777
Internet: www.forum-cr.de
E-Mail: info@forum-cr.de
Geschäftsführer Peter Bocklitz
Venue type: multi-purpose *Capacity:* Europahalle (standing) 3500, Stadthalle (standing) 1000 *Policy:* promote, rent *Arts types:* theatre, shows, concerts, events, fairs and balls, exhibitions, conferences, congresses, musicals *Comments:* visiting address: Europaplatz 6-10, 44575 Castrop-Rauxel

Schlosstheater Celle e.V.
Postfach 1333, 29203 **Celle**
Tel: 5141-905 080 Fax: 5141-905 0844
Internet: www.schlosstheater-celle.de
Intendant Karin H Veit; Geschäftsführer Klaus Tietje; Sekretariat Frau Mehling
Venue type: theatre *Capacity:* main auditorium 330, Malersaal 45 *Policy:* promote *Arts types:* theatre, concerts *Comments:* see also Promoters and Drama

Stadthalle Chemnitz – Kultur und Kongresszentrum GmbH
Postfach 928, 09009 **Chemnitz**
Tel: 371-45080 Fax: 371-4508-602
E-Mail: stadthalle.chemnitz@t-online.de
Geschäftsführer Roland Haase; Prokurist Rolf Pfaff; Technischer Leiter Michael Schubert
Venue type: Kultur u. Kongresszentrum, multi-purpose *Capacity:* Großer Saal 1780, Kleiner Saal 564, Salon am Tropenhaus 100-200, rooms for seminars 30 *Policy:* promote, rent *Arts types:* concerts, shows, congresses *Comments:* visiting address: Rathausstraße 1, 09111 Chemnitz

Congress-Centrum Luisenplatz
Luisenplatz 5, 64283 **Darmstadt**
Tel: 6151-132 072 Fax: 6151-132 075
E-Mail: furco@stadt.darmstadt.de
Direktor Rüdiger Hottenbacher
Venue type: multi-purpose hall, conference rooms *Capacity:* 12 rooms: up to 1100 *Policy:* rent *Arts types:* concerts, congresses, exhibitions *Comments:* also administer: Ernst Ludwig Saal, Goldener Löwe, Justus Liebig Haus, Bürgermeister Pohl Haus (venues for rent)

Deggendorfer Kultur- und Kongreßzentrum GmbH
Edlmairstraße 2, 94469 **Deggendorf**
Tel: 991-370 590 Fax: 991-370 5959
Internet: www.stadthalle-deggendorf.de
E-Mail: stadthalle-deggendorf@t-online.de
Prokurist Andreas Hille
Venue type: multi-purpose *Capacity:* main hall (standing) up to 2000 *Policy:* rent *Arts types:* drama, theatre, concerts of all types, cabaret, dance etc.

Stadthalle Dingolfing
Postfach 1340, 84124 **Dingolfing**
Tel: 8731-501 123 Fax: 8731-501 166
Internet: www.dingolfing.de
E-Mail: kultur@dingolfing.de
Hallenleiter Werner Müller
Venue type: multi-purpose *Capacity:* 902 *Policy:* rent, promote (x10 in a year) *Arts types:* all arts types

Westfalenhallen Dortmund GmbH
Postfach 10 44 44, 44044 **Dortmund**
Tel: 231-1204-0 Fax: 231-120 4444
Internet: www.westfalenhallen.de
E-Mail: info@westfalenhallen.de
general manager Dr. jur. Ludwig Jörder; managing director Jürgen Klocke; head of events department Jochen Meschke; head of public relations department Hans Ost; head of admin. department Artur Poppe
Venue type: 8 halls *Capacity:* Westfalenhalle1 13880
Policy: rent and promote *Arts types:* concerts, exhibitions, conventions, meetings *Comments:* visiting address: Rheinlanddamm 200, 44139 Dortmund

Theater im Bürgerhaus Sprendingen
Fichtestrasse 50, 63303 **Dreieich**
Tel: 6103-6000-0 Fax: 6103-600 077
E-Mail: buergerhaus@dreieich.de
Leiter Gustav Halberstadt
Venue type: theatre *Capacity:* 750 *Policy:* promote, rent *Arts types:* drama, concerts, social events, conferences, exhibitions, musicals, opera, operetta *Comments:* organise Festspiele in der Burg Dreieichenhain, festival Jazz in der Burg

Kulturpalast Dresden, Konzert- und Kongreßgesellschaft mbH
Schloßstraße 2, 01067 **Dresden**
Tel: 351-4866-0 Fax: 351-486 6239/6269
Internet: www.gcb.de/kulturpalast-dresden
E-Mail: kulturpalast@imedia.de
Geschäftsführer Rainer Wagner; Leiter Veranstaltungen/Verkauf Dietmar Kühnert; Technischer Leiter Steffen Meyer
Venue type: cultural and conference centre *Capacity:* Main Hall 2400, Studiotheatre 192 *Arts types:* conferences, seminars, concerts, festivals, shows *Comments:* venue of Dresdner Philharmonie; also congress centre; see also Orchestras

Duisburg Agentur GmbH, Mercatorhalle
Postfach 100402, 47004 **Duisburg**
Tel: 203-30505-0 Fax: 203-305 0571
Internet: www.duisburg.de/Hallen
Geschäftsführer Hans-Joachim Drozdek, Hans-Gerd Hirschfeld; Oberstadtdirektor Norbert Giersch; Oberbürgermeisterin Bärbel Zieling
Venue type: multi-purpose *Capacity:* Rheinhausen-Halle 897, Rhein-Ruhr-Halle 3500, Mercator Halle 1844 *Policy:* rent, promote *Arts types:* concerts, exhibitions, conferences *Comments:* masterconcerts series; visiting address: König-Heinrich-Platz, 47051 Duisburg

Musical Theater Duisburg
Plessingstr. 20, 47051 **Duisburg**
Tel: 203-282 5150 Fax: 203-285 110
Internet: www.musicalworld.compuserve.de
Venue type: musical theatre *Capacity:* 1550 *Comments:* the future of the venue was uncertain at time of going to print, please contact them for further information

European Dance Development Centre (EDDC)
tanzhaus nrw die WERKSTATT e.v.
Erkrather Staße 30, 40233 **Düsseldorf**
Tel: 211-17270-0 Fax: 211-17270-17
E-Mail: tanzhausnrw@t-online.de
künstlerischer Leiter Bertram Müller; Bühne Stefan Schwarz; Öffentlichkeitsarbeit t.b.a.; Tanz Werkstatt Dorothee Schackow
Capacity: Große Bühne 300, Kleine Bühne 100, Foyer 250 *Policy:* promote, produce (EDDC and CHO-Kol) *Arts types:* a variety of dance forms, music, drama

Philips-Halle
Siegburger Strasse 15, 40591 **Düsseldorf**
Tel: 211-899 3805 Fax: 211-892 9059
Leitung Manfred Kirschenstein
Venue type: multi-purpose *Capacity:* 7800 *Policy:* rent, promote (1-2 a year) *Arts types:* chamber music, drama, symphony, solo recitals, dance, theatre, rock, pop, sport

Tonhalle Düsseldorf
Ehrenhof 1, 40479 **Düsseldorf**
Tel: 211-899 2081 Fax: 211-892 9049
Internet: www.duesseldorf.de/tonhalle
E-Mail: tonhalle@compuserve.com
Intendantin Vera van Hazebrouck (tel: 211-899 6111, fax: 211-892 9143); Verwaltungsleiter Günther Bradtke; pr Udo Flaskamp (tel: 211-899 2884)
Venue type: concert hall *Capacity:* 1933 *Policy:* present, rent *Arts types:* symphonies, chamber, jazz, folklore, dance, exhibitions, workshops, contemporary music *Comments:* home of Düsseldorf Symphony Orchestra (q.v.); see also Promoters

zakk – Zentrum für Aktion, Kultur und Kommunikation
Kulturzentrum, Fichtenstr. 40, 40233 **Düsseldorf**
Tel: 211-973 0010 Fax: 211-973 0099
Internet: www.zakk.de
E-Mail: info@zakk.de
Geschäftsführer Reinhold Knopp; Aktuelle Musik Andrea Leonhard; Nutzungen Markus Unzen; Akuelles Zeitgeschehen Annette Loers; Presse und Öffentlichkeitsarbeit Jochen Molck
Venue type: concert hall, studio *Capacity:* concert hall 800, studio 300 *Policy:* promote, rent *Arts types:* concerts (no classical concerts), theatre, cabaret, jazz, exhibitions, political discussions, lectures *Comments:* bar and restaurant with beergarden

Schloß Elman
Schloß Elman, 82493 **Elman/Obb**
Tel: 8823-180 Fax: 8823-3719
Internet: www.schloss-elman.de
E-Mail: sarah.wilson@schloss-elman.de
Kulturbüro Alexandra Brecht; künstlerische Leitung Sarah Wilson
Venue type: multi-purpose *Policy:* present *Arts types:* classical music, jazz, dance, readings *Comments:* own magazine, library; organise own festivals; see also Promoters

Neues Theater Emden
Theaterstrasse, 26721 **Emden**
Tel: 4921-872 060/2051/2055
Fax: 4921-872 052 (Kulturamt)
Veranstaltungsleiter, Öffentlichkeitsreferat und Verwaltungsleitung Harm Janßen
Venue type: theatre *Capacity:* Schauspiel 681, Musiktheater 600, Nordseehalle 4500, Rathausfestsaal 250 *Policy:* promote, rent *Arts types:* musical, opera, operetta, music theatre, symphony concerts, master concerts *Comments:* administrated via the Kulturamt

Nordseehalle Emden
Früchteburger Weg 17-19, 26721 **Emden**
Tel: 4921-9400-0 Fax: 4921-940 011
Internet: www.emden.de
E-Mail: stadt-nordseehalle@t-online.de
Verwaltung u. Leiter des Öffentlichkeitsbüros Hans-Jürgen Janssen; technische Leitung Heinrich Weerts
Venue type: multi-purpose *Capacity:* seated 3500, standing 5500 *Policy:* promote, rent *Arts types:* concerts (pop, rock, musicals), shows, sport, conferences, TV productions

Stadttheater Emmerich
Grollscher Weg 20, 46446 **Emmerich**
Tel: 2822-939 911/12 Fax: 2822-939 922
Internet: www.emmerich.de
Theaterleitung Ludger Heyming; Stellv. Elfi Peters
Venue type: theatre *Capacity:* 564 *Policy:* promote, rent *Arts types:* drama, concerts (classical, rock, pop) *Comments:* joined to the theatre are the Photomuseum and the Plakatmuseum am Niederrhein

Kluterthöhle und Freizeit Verwaltungs – und Betriebs GmbH
Postfach 1239, 58256 **Ennepetal**
Tel: 2333-98800 Fax: 2333-73373
Geschäftsführer Wolfgang Kern
Venue type: multi-purpose *Capacity:* up to 640, seminar room up to 750, and cave *Policy:* rent *Arts types:* chamber music, drama, solo recitals, dance, rock, exhibitions, sales exhibitions, congresses *Comments:* visiting address: Gasstrasse 10, 58256 Ennepetal

Kongreßzentrum Erlangen
Heinrich Lades Halle, Rathausplatz, 91052 **Erlangen**
Tel: 9131-874-0 Fax: 9131-874 150
Geschäftsführer Jürgen Strobl
Venue type: multi-purpose, trade fairs *Capacity:* Großer Saal 1250, Kleiner Saal 270 *Policy:* rent *Arts types:* seminars, concerts (classical and modern), dance events, exhibitions, conferences, fashion shows, product presentations

Theater Erlangen
Wasserturmstr 16, 91054 **Erlangen**
Tel: 9131-862 369 Fax: 9131-862 104
Theaterleiter Hartmut Henne; Verwaltungsleiter Karl Heinz Lindner; Öffentlichkeitsarbeit Bodo Birk; Technischer Leiter Carsten Schmid; Künstlerische Betriebsdirektion Gerti Köhn; Dramaturgie Johannes Blum, Lissy Schmidt
Venue type: baroque theatre *Capacity:* Markgrafentheater 584, Garage 82 *Policy:* promote, rent *Arts types:* drama, dance, own productions and guest productions, annual International Festival of Figures *Comments:* oldest active baroque theatre in southern Germany; see also Drama

Colosseum
Altendorfer Str. 1, 45127 **Essen**
Tel: 201-2402-0 Fax: 201-2402-110
Internet: www.stella.de
E-Mail: stella@mail.stella.de
Vorstandsversitzender der Stella AG Hemjö Klein; Company Management Andrea Pier, Petra Hambückers; Künstl. Leitung Cornelius Baltus; Geschäftsführung Ingo Sturm
Venue type: Industriehalle, foyer
Capacity: 1550, foyer up to 2000
Policy: venue is available for rent for a variety of events
Arts types: foyer: shows, concerts, events; Industriehalle: exclusively for the production of Jesus Christ Superstar (until June)

Kulturzentrum Zeche Carl
Wilhelm Nieswandt Allee 100, 45326 **Essen**
Tel: 201-834 4410 Fax: 201-350 158
Internet: www.soziokultur.de//ZecheCarl
E-Mail: ZecheCarl@online.de
Verwaltungsleitung Udo Ruland; Künstlerische Leitung Bärbel König-Bargel; Musikalische Oberleitung Christoph Mews
Capacity: Hallen 350 *Arts types:* free theatre, pop & rock classes, political presentations, cabaret, comedy

Saalbau Essen
Huyssenallee 53, 45128 **Essen**
Tel: 201-247 040 Fax: 201-247 0499
Verwaltungsleiter Hans-Hubert Imhoff
Venue type: concert hall & conference centre
Capacity: 1458 *Policy:* present, rent, box-office split
Arts types: concerts of various kinds, including pop, conferences

Stadthalle Frankenthal Betriebs GmbH
Postfach 1928, 67209 **Frankenthal**
Tel: 6233-499-0 Fax: 6233-499 105
Geschäftsführer Hermann Buchloh; Management Beate Scholl; Aufsichtsratsvorsitzender Oberbürgermeister Peter Popitz
Venue type: multi-purpose *Capacity:* Großer Saal 1017, Kleiner Saal 307, Tagungsraum 110 (can be divided into 60 & 30) *Policy:* rent, promote *Arts types:* theatre, concerts, balls, exhibitions, conferences etc.
Comments: visiting address: Stephan-Cosacchi-Platz 5, 67227 Frankenthal

Alte Oper Frankfurt – Konzert u. Kongreßzentrum GmbH
Postfach 170151, 60075 **Frankfurt am Main**
Tel: 69-1340-0 Fax: 69-134 0284
Internet: www.eintrittskarte.de
E-Mail: info@alteoper.de
Geschäftsführer Michael Hocks
Venue type: concert hall and congress centre
Capacity: Großer Saal 2448, Mozart Saal 718, Hindemith Saal 313 *Policy:* present, rent
Arts types: chamber, symphony, recital, musical, ballet, cabaret, rock, pop *Comments:* visiting address: Opernplatz, 60313 Frankfurt am Main

Freies Theaterhaus Frankfurt
Schützenstraße 12, 60311 **Frankfurt am Main**
Tel: 69-299 8610 Fax: 69-2998 6112
Internet: www.theaterhaus-frankfurt.de
E-Mail: info@theaterhaus-frankfurt/de
Direktor Gordon Vajen; Verwaltung Goran Lakicevic; Öffentlichkeitsarbeit Henriette Leonhard; technische Leitung Susanne Freiling
Venue type: theatre *Capacity:* Freies Theaterhaus: Bühne 150, Keller 75 *Policy:* rent, promote *Arts types:* various including drama, puppetry, music-theatre, dance theatre, new-music, new jazz *Comments:* venue for free theatre groups

Kultur- und Kongresszentrum Jahrhunderthalle GmbH
Pfaffenwiese, 65929 **Frankfurt am Main**
Tel: 69-360 1211 Fax: 69-360 1222
Internet: www.jahrhunderthalle.de
E-Mail: FrichterHansen@jahrhunderthalle.com
Geschäftsführer Freimut Richter-Hansen
Venue type: multi-purpose *Capacity:* 2021 *Policy:* present, rent *Arts types:* chamber, symphony, ballet, dance, musicals

Künstlerhaus MOUSONTURM
Waldschmidtstrasse 4, 60316 **Frankfurt am Main**
Tel: 69-405 8950 Fax: 69-4058 9540
Internet: www.mousonturm.de
E-Mail: mousonturm.pr@t-online.de
Intendanz Dieter Buroch; Künstlerische Leitung Christine Peters; Betriebdirektion Karl Krause; Assistentin der künstl.Leitung Bettina Becht; Presse- und Öffentlichkeitsarbeit Martina Aschmies; Künstlerisches Betriebsbüro Dorothé Gebhart; Verwaltung Bernd Steuernagel
Venue type: multi-purpose
Capacity: Hall A 400, Hall B 100
Policy: present, produce, co-produce, seminars, workshops *Arts types:* dance, performance, theatre, cabaret, music, exhibitions
Comments: annual symposium Vision Zukunft; annual International Summer Academy for Performing Arts

Neues Theater Höchst
Emmerich-Josef-Str. 46a, 65929 **Frankfurt am Main**
Tel: 69-303 090 Fax: 69-301 321
Internet: www.neues-theater.de
E-Mail: neues-theater@t-online.de
Intendant u. Geschäftsführung Dusan Pintner; Öffentlichkeitsarbeit Ralf Ebert
Venue type: theatre *Capacity:* 250 *Policy:* promote, rent *Arts types:* cabaret, kleinkunst, theatre, cinema, childrens theatre, variety *Comments:* Post- und Büroadresse: Antoniterstr. 16-18, 65929 Frankfurt am Main, Tel: 69-303 016

Saalbau GmbH
Eschersheimer Landstr. 23, 60322 **Frankfurt am Main**
Tel: 69-15308-0 Fax: 69-1530 8499
Internet: www.saalbau.com
E-Mail: info@saalbau.com
Geschäftsführer Dr. A. Eichstaedt; Abteilungsleitung kulturelle Veranstaltungen K. Kletzka
Policy: rent, promote *Arts types:* events of all types (music, sport etc.) *Comments:* organisation administrating 30 venues in the Frankfurt area of different sizes

Städtische Bühnen Frankfurt
Das TAT (Theater Am Turm), Bockenheimer Depot, Bockenheimer Warte, 60325 **Frankfurt am Main**
Tel: 69-2123 7288 Fax: 69-2123 9541
Internet: www.frankfurt.de/theatre/theatre.htm
Intendant William Forsythe; Stellvertretende Direktoren Tom Kühnel, Robert Schuster; Ausstattungsleiter Jan Pappelbaum; Chefdramaturg Bernd Stegemann
Venue type: theatre *Capacity:* theater up to 450 *Policy:* produce, co-produce, present *Arts types:* modern and avant-garde theatre, performing arts, dance *Comments:* see also Drama and Dance (Balett Frankfurt)

Messe Freiburg und Co. KG
Postfach 505, 79005 **Freiburg**
Tel: 761-70370 Fax: 761-709 885
Geschäftsführer Klaus W Seilnacht; Prokurists Klaus Kiefer, Jürgen Friedmann
Venue type: Stadthalle, Exhibition Centre *Capacity:* Stadthalle 3000-5000, Exhibition Centre 5000-10000 *Policy:* rent only *Arts types:* concerts, exhibitions, conferences *Comments:* visiting address: Stadthalle, Schwarzwaldstrasse 80, 79102 Freiburg; Exhibition Centre, Hermann-Mitsch-Str. 3, 79108 Freiburg

Städtische Bühnen Freiburg
Bertholdstrasse 46, 79098 **Freiburg**
Tel: 761-201 2807/2950 Fax: 721-201 2999
Internet: www.uni-freiburg.de/theater/
contact Wolfgang Schröder; Intendant Hans J. Ammann; künstler. Betriebsdirektion Elke Hoch; Öffentlichkeitsarbeit Heike Neumann
Capacity: Grosses Haus 850, Schauspielhaus Kurbel 350, Theatercafe 150, Kamera 99 *Policy:* rent, promote, present *Arts types:* opera, dance, drama, orchestra *Comments:* see also Dance, Opera, Orchestras, Drama and Festivals

Stadthalle Friedberg
Am Seebach 2, 61169 **Friedberg**
Tel: 6031-88205/72460 Fax: 6031-61270
Geschäftsführer Otmar Stock
Venue type: Stadthalle *Capacity:* 1500 *Policy:* rent *Arts types:* concert, congresses, social events, conventions, drama

Graf-Zeppelin-Haus
Postfach 1525, 88005 **Friedrichshafen**
Tel: 7541-2880 Fax: 7541-288 150
Internet: www.gcb.de/gch-friedrichshafen
E-Mail: gch.friedrichshafen@t-online.de
Veranstaltungsleiter Ingeborg Rehm; Touristdirektor Dietmar Philipp
Venue type: cultural and congress centre *Capacity:* Hugo-Eckener-Saal 1080, Theodor-Kober-Saal 372, Ludwig-Dürr-Saal 430, Alfred-Colsman-Saal 333 *Policy:* rent *Arts types:* chamber music, drama, symphony, solo recitals, dance, theatre, opera, conferences, congresses, seminars, lectures and exhibitions *Comments:* visiting address: Olgastrasse 20, 88045 Friedrichshafen

Schloßtheater Fulda
Schloßstrasse 5, 36037 **Fulda**
Tel: 661-102 485 Fax: 661-102 489
E-Mail: angelika.lieder@fulda.de
Direktor Angelika Lieder
Venue type: theatre *Capacity:* 690 *Policy:* receiving company *Arts types:* opera, drama, concerts, operetta, musicals, ballet, children's theatre

Stadttheater Fürth
Königstrasse 116, 90762 **Fürth**
Tel: 911-974 2410 Fax: 911-974 2444
Intendant Werner Müller; Verwaltungsleiter Thomas Reher; Öffentlichkeitsarbeit Günter Pfaffenberger; Dramaturgie Barbara Bredow; Technische Leitung Manfred Dotter
Venue type: theatre *Capacity:* 740 *Policy:* receiving company, produce, co-produce *Arts types:* opera, drama, concerts, modern dance theatre, children's theatre, performances *Comments:* see also Drama

Kultur und Kongreßzentrum Gera
Schloßstraße, Postfach 208, 07502 **Gera**
Tel: 365-6190 Fax: 365-832 1429
Werksleiter Wolfgang Hogen
Venue type: culture and congress centre *Capacity:* Großer Saal 1800, seminar rooms up to 120 *Policy:* rent *Arts types:* concerts, congresses, shows, galas, dance, production presentations, fairs *Comments:* TV production presentations

Stadttheater Gießen
Berliner Platz, 35390 **Gießen**
Tel: 641-79570 Fax: 641-795 780
Intendant Guy Montavon; Verwaltungsdirektorin Ursula Wirtz-Knapstein; Chefdramaturg u. Stellvertreter des Intendanten Christian Marten-Molnar; Kommissarischer GMD Herbert Gietzen; Schauspieldirektoren Barbara und Jürgen Esser; Balletmeister Roberto Galvan
Venue type: Stadtheater *Capacity:* Stadttheater 574, Theaterstudio 199 *Arts types:* drama, opera, dance theater, symphony concerts, contemporary music *Comments:* see also Opera, Drama, Dance and Orchestra

Odeon Theater
Bismarckstrasse 1, 38640 **Goslar**
Tel: 5321-23038 Fax: 5321-41450
Direktor Wolf-Dieter Stelle; Technische Leitung Jürgen Witt
Venue type: theatre *Capacity:* 843 *Policy:* rent *Arts types:* drama, opera, ballet, musicals

Stadthalle Göttingen
Albaniplatz 2, 37073 **Göttingen**
Tel: 551-497 0033 Fax: 551-56396
Hallenleiter, Geschäftsführer Klaus Burckhardt
Venue type: Stadthalle *Capacity:* Großer Saal 1200, Kleiner Saal 170 *Policy:* rent *Arts types:* chamber music, symphony, solo recitals, dance, rock, pop, conferences (now and again), congresses, trade fairs *Comments:* 200 + events

Theater der Stadt Gummersbach
Reininghauser Strasse, 51643 **Gummersbach**
Tel: 2261-61265 Fax: 2261-87345
Kulturamtsleiter Gus Anton (2261-87542); Regieseur Siegfried Grote; Technische Leitung Peter Faust
Venue type: theatre *Capacity:* 800 *Policy:* rent, promote *Arts types:* theatre, opera, ballet, concerts

Stadthalle Gütersloh
Friedrichstrasse 10, 33330 **Gütersloh**
Tel: 5241-864 212/3 Fax: 5241-28234
Geschäftsführer Johann Nusser
Venue type: multi-purpose *Capacity:* Großer Saal 1150, Kleiner Saal 440 *Policy:* promote, rent *Arts types:* concerts, congresses, exhibitions, theatre

Theater der Stadt Gütersloh
Barkeystrasse 15, 33330 **Gütersloh**
Tel: 5241-822 707 (Kulturamt)/822 293 (Theater)
Fax: 5241-822 322 (Kulturamt)/421 (Theater)
Internet: www.guetersloh.de/gt/kultur
E-Mail: stadtguetersloh.fachbereichkultur@gt-net.de
Leiter Klaus Klein; Dramaturgie Joachim Martensmeier; Verwaltungsleiter Erhard Tarnowski
Venue type: theatre *Capacity:* main auditorium 518, Podium 99, Studio 80 *Policy:* promote *Arts types:* classical music, opera, drama, ballet *Comments:* do not rent theatre, although non-professionals (e.g. local drama groups of schools) are occasionally allowed to perform here

Stadthalle Hagen
Wasserloses Tal 2, 58093 **Hagen**
Tel: 2331-3450 Fax: 2331-345 1035
Internet: www.stadthalle-hagen.de
E-Mail: stadthalle-hagen@t-online.de
Geschäftsführerin Anna Maria Lieder
Venue type: Stadthalle
Capacity: Stadthalle 1775 *Policy:* rent
Arts types: concerts, exhibitions, conferences

Congress Centrum Hamburg
Postfach 30 2480, 20308 **Hamburg**
Tel: 40-3569-0 Fax: 40-3569 2182
Internet: www.cch.de
E-Mail: info@cch.de
Geschäftsführer Paul Busse
Venue type: international congress centre *Capacity:* 18 halls: up to 3000 *Policy:* rent *Arts types:* concerts (jazz, pop and classical), drama, ballet, dance festivals *Comments:* 250-300 concerts in a year; visiting address: Am Dammtor, 20355 Hamburg

Kampnagel Internationale Kulturfabrik
Jarrestrasse 20, 22303 **Hamburg**
Tel: 40-270 9490 Fax: 40-2709 4911
Internet: www.kampnagel.de
E-Mail: kampnagel@t-online.de
Kaufmännischer Direktor Jack Kurfess; Künstlerische Leitung Res Bosshart; Dramaturgie Sabine Gehm, Henning Fülle; Pressesprecherin Maiken Hagemeister; Marketing Matthias Forster
Venue type: former factory *Capacity:* 4 spaces: Space A 800, Space B 310, Space C 220, Space D 200
Policy: present, co-present, guest performances
Arts types: drama, music, performance art, dance-theatre, exhibitions

Musikhalle
Dammtorwall 46, 20355 **Hamburg**
Tel: 40-357 6660 (administration)/346 920 (tickets)
Fax: 40-348 0168
Geschäftsführer Benedikt Stampa; Booking Burkhard Lübke
Venue type: music hall *Capacity:* Großer Saal 2013, Kleiner Saal 630, Studio E 150 *Policy:* rent *Arts types:* mainly classical, some pop, rock and jazz

Neue Flora
Das Phanton der Oper Musical-Produktions GmbH, Stresemannstr. 159a, 22769 **Hamburg**
Tel: 40-431 650 Fax: 40-4316 5110
Vorstandvorsitzender Hemjö Klein; Geschäftsführung Uschi Neuß; Musikalischer Direktor Bernhard Volk
Venue type: music-theatre
Capacity: 1832 *Arts types:* music-theatre, musicals
Comments: the theatre was designed exclusively for the The Phantom of the Opera which is the only musical performed there

Operettenhaus Hamburg
Spielbudenplatz 1, 20359 **Hamburg**
Tel: 40-311 170 Fax: 40-3111 7252
Vorstandvorsitzender Stelle Musical AG Hemjö Klein
Venue type: musical theatre *Capacity:* 1125 *Comments:* exclusively for the production of CATS; managed by Stella AG, Stresemannstraße 161, 22769 Hamburg, Tel: 40-43176-0, Fax: 40-43176-610

St Pauli-Theater
Postfach 304140, 20324 **Hamburg**
Tel: 40-313 901 Fax: 40-319 1919
Internet: www.st-pauli-theater.de
Direktor Michael Collien; Verwaltungsleitung Thomas Collien; Buchhaltung Axel Schmidt; Öffenteichkeitsarbeit Anja Oeck; Technische Leitung Karsten Andersen
Venue type: theatre *Capacity:* 595
Policy: promote, rent *Arts types:* drama, comedy, musicals *Comments:* visiting address: Spielbudenplatz 29/30, 20359 Hamburg

Hanauer Stadthalle
Schloßplatz 1, 63450 **Hanau**
Tel: 6181-2775-0 Fax: 6181-24101
Geschäftsführer Karl-Heinz Trautmann
Venue type: Stadthalle *Capacity:* Großer Saal 600, + 6 conference rooms *Policy:* rent *Arts types:* drama, music, conferences etc.

Eisfabrik Hannover
Seilerstrasse 15-17, 30171 **Hannover**
Tel: 511-816 353 Fax: 511-816 353
Internet: www.foro-artistico.opus5.de
contact Wolfgang A. Piontek (Commedia Futura); contact Axel Bohse (Foro Artistico)
Venue type: former factory *Capacity:* Zentralhalle 100, Schwarzer Saal 99, Blaue Halle 80, Weisse Halle 200 *Policy:* promote, present *Arts types:* dance-, movement- and experimental theatre *Comments:* see also Commedia Futura (Dance and Drama sections); Foro Artistico – time based arts, light/sound/video performance

Theater am Aegi
Aegidientorplatz 2, 30159 **Hannover**
Tel: 511-989 3310 Fax: 511-989 3377
E-Mail: 051198933001-001@t-online.de
Intendant Gerd-Rainer Prothmann
Venue type: theatre *Capacity:* 1168 *Policy:* rent, promote *Arts types:* drama, opera, musicals, dance, rock, concerts, comedy shows

Theater im Künstlerhaus
c/o Tanz und Theaterbüro, Roscherstr. 12, 30161 **Hannover**
Tel: 511-343 919 Fax: 511-331 965
Programmleitung Christiane Winter; Mitarbeit Organisation Elke Weiler
Venue type: theatre *Capacity:* 200 *Policy:* receiving *Arts types:* Kleinkunst, cabaret, chanson, theatre
Comments: theatre address; Sophienstr. 2, 30159 Hannover; the promoter of the theatre is the 'Kulturamt der Stadt Hannover'

Kongreßhaus Stadthalle Heidelberg
Postfach 105 860, 69048 **Heidelberg**
Tel: 6221-583 093 Fax: 6221-142 266
Internet: www.heidelberg.de/verkehrsverein
E-Mail: cvbhd@info.hd.eunet.de
Geschäftsführer Thomas Jung; Stellv. Geschäftsführer Martin Waschner
Venue type: Stadthalle *Capacity:* Großer Saal 1300, Kammermusiksaal 220, Ballsaal 230 & 13 other conference rooms *Policy:* rent
Arts types: chamber, symphony, recitals, ballet, social events (e.g. balls), conferences *Comments:* visiting address: Neckarstaden 24, 69117 Heidelberg

Festhalle Harmonie
Allee 28, 74072 **Heilbronn**
Tel: 7131-562 265 (Amt für Marketing, Information und Tourismus) Fax: 7131-563 140 (Verkehrsamt)
Direktor Bernhard Winkler
Comments: closed until the end of 2001 due to renovation

Theater der Stadt Heilbronn
Berliner Platz 1, 74072 **Heilbronn**
Tel: 7131-563 000 Fax: 7131-563 139
E-Mail: TheaterHN@gmx.de
Intendant Klaus Wagner; Verwaltungsdirektor Jürgen Frahm; Chefdramaturg Dr. Günter Ballhausen; Chefdisponent und stellvertretender Intendant Andreas Oberbach
Venue type: theatre *Capacity:* main auditorium 705, Kammerspiele 110-140; Das Komödienhaus 380 (from end of 2000) *Policy:* present, receive
Arts types: drama; guest companies in dance, opera, operetta *Comments:* see also Drama and Festivals

Brunnentheater
Ortsteil Bad Helmstedt, Brunnenweg 7, 38350 **Helmstedt**
Tel: 5351-6313 Fax: 5351-17353
Internet: www.Stadt-Helmstedt.de
E-Mail: Ulbricht@Stadt-Helmstedt.de
Stadtverwaltung Fr. Döring (5351-17352), Herr Ammon (5351-17353)
Capacity: 615 *Policy:* rent

Kulturzentrum der Stadt Herne
Postfach 101820, 44621 **Herne**
Tel: 2323-162 316 Fax: 2323-162 977
Geschäftsführer Hubert Emmerich
Venue type: Stadthalle *Capacity:* 1200 *Policy:* rent, promote *Arts types:* concerts, theatre, conferences, exhibitions, seminars/conferences, balls *Comments:* concerts arranged by the 'Kulturamt'

Stadttheater Hildesheim
Stadttheater Hildesheim, Theaterstr. 6, 31141 **Hildesheim**
Tel: 5121-1693-0 Fax: 5121-169 393
Intendant Dr. Martin Kreutzberg
Venue type: theatre *Capacity:* Großes Haus 607, Theo/Studiobühne 68, Foyer 65
Arts types: theatre and musicals, opera, orchestra, dance

Freiheitshalle Hof
Postfach 1665, Kulmbacher Straße 4, 95015 **Hof**
Tel: 9281-815 268 Fax: 9281-815 499
E-Mail: stadt_hof@hof.baynet.de
Leitung Peter Nürmberger
Venue type: multi-purpose *Capacity:* Großes Haus 4500, Festsaal 800, Foyer 200, several smaller rooms *Arts types:* concerts of all types, exhibitions, conventions, meetings *Comments:* administrated by the 'Kulturamt'

Städtischer Saalbau Homburg
Zweibrückerstraße 22, 66424 **Homburg/Saar**
Tel: 6841-101 172 Fax: 6841-120 899
Internet: www.homburg.de
Direktor des Kultur und Verkehrsamtes Peter Emser
Venue type: Saalbau *Capacity:* 700 *Policy:* rent, promote
Arts types: chamber music, dance, recitals, drama, Meisterkonzerte *Comments:* administration: Kultur und Verkehrsamt, Rathaus am Forum 5, 66424 Homburg/Saar

Bürgerzentrum Hürth Betriebs GmbH
Friedrich-Ebert-Straße 40, 50354 **Hürth**
Tel: 2233-53710 Fax: 2233-53733
E-Mail: buergerhaus-huerth@t-online.de
Geschäftsführer Josefine Willems
Venue type: multi-purpose *Capacity:* 700 *Policy:* rent *Arts types:* music-theatre, cabaret, dance, theatre

Parktheater
Alexanderhöhe, Postfach 2462, 58634 **Iserlohn**
Tel: 2371-217 1910/1819 (box office)
Fax: 2371-217 1914
Internet: www.iserlohn.de
E-Mail: iserlohn@iserlohn.de
Kulturbüroleiter Herr Jostmann
Venue type: theatre *Capacity:* 817 *Policy:* rent, promote
Arts types: drama, concerts (classical), ballet, opera, musicals, jazz, rock, pop, symphony

Theaterhaus Jena GmbH
Schillergäßchen 1, 07745 **Jena**
Tel: 3641-8869-0 Fax: 3641-886 910
Internet: www.jenaonline.de/theaterhaus
E-Mail: theaterhausJena@t-online.de
Künstlerischer Geschäftsführer/Regie/Mitglied des Künstlerischen Stabes Claudia Bauer; Kaufmännischer Geschäftsführer Roman Rösener; Öffentlichkeitsarbeit Andrea Hesse
Venue type: theatre
Capacity: Hauptbühne 180 *Policy:* promote, guest performances *Arts types:* drama, dance theatre
Comments: mixture of own productions and touring groups (Gastspiele); see also Drama

Pfalztheater Kaiserslautern
Willy-Brandt-Platz 4-5, 67657 **Kaiserslautern**
Tel: 631-3675-0 Fax: 631-367 5235
Intendant Wolfgang Quetes; Künstl. Betriebsdirektor Peter Bachmaier; Chefdramaturg Stephan Kopf; Presse- und Werbeorganisation Günther Fingerle; Generalmusikdirektor Lior Shambadal; Ballettdirektor Eva Reinthaller
Venue type: theatre *Capacity:* Großes Haus 628, Werkstattbühne 100 *Policy:* promote, present *Arts types:* opera, operetta, musicals, ballet, drama *Comments:* own dance company – Pfalztheater-Ballett (q.v.), opera and theatre companies (q.v.); own ensemble

Bürgerzentrum Karben
Postfach 1107, 61174 **Karben**
Tel: 6039-48122 Fax: 6039-48130
Leiter Wolfgang Datz
Venue type: cultural centre *Capacity:* 721 *Policy:* rent, promote *Arts types:* drama, music, exhibitions, musicals, operetta *Comments:* visiting address: Rathausplatz 1, 61184 Karben

Karlsruher Kongress-und Ausstellungs GmbH
Festplatz, 76137 **Karlsruhe**
Tel: 721-3720-0 Fax: 721-3720 2106
Internet: www.kka.de
E-Mail: info@kka.de
Geschäftsführung Gerhard Hurst
Venue type: multi-purpose, exhibitions, congresses
Capacity: Hall A 5000, Hall B 3225, Hall C 1750, Hall D 1200, Hall E 1045 *Policy:* rent, promote
Arts types: dance, theatre, musicals, rock and pop concerts, cabaret, magicians, symphony, recitals, chamber music

Sandkorn Theater
Kaiserallee 11, 76133 **Karlsruhe**
Tel: 721-848 984 Fax: 721-853 321
Internet: www.sandkorn-theater.de
E-Mail: sandkorn-theater@t-online.de
Intendant Siegfried Kreiner; Verwaltungsleitung Ingrid Trinkl; Musikalische Leitung Wolfgang Wieland; Öffentlichkeitsarbeit Siegfried Kreiner, Stefanie Lackner; Dramaturgie Steffi Lackner
Venue type: theatre
Capacity: Fabriktheater 196, Studiotheater 120
Arts types: musicals, drama, cabaret, children's and youth theatre *Comments:* organise biennial international theatre festival, seminars, open rehearsals for schools, advisers to amateur groups

ZKM Institute for Visual Media
Lorenzstrasse 19, 79135 **Karlsruhe**
Tel: 721-8100 1500/02 Fax: 721-8100 1509
Internet: www.zkm.de
E-Mail: info@zkm.de
director Peter Weable; press department Sabylle Peine
Venue type: multi-purpose *Capacity:* media theatre 300
Policy: presents own programme, co-produce *Arts types:* theatre, dance, new media

Kassel Service GmbH Tagungs- und Veranstaltungszentrum Stadthalle
Friedrich-Ebert-Strasse 152, 34119 **Kassel**
Tel: 561-7882-0 Fax: 561-788 2218
Geschäftsführer Edgar Müller; Leiter Wolfgang Hanson
Venue type: congress centre and cultural centre
Capacity: Festsaal 2043, Blauer Saal 724, Garten Saal 486, Aschrott Flügel with 2 more halls cap. 200 each, plus 8 more conference rooms *Policy:* rent
Arts types: drama, dance, music, exhibitions, conferences, congresses

Kieler Schloß Veranstaltungshaus des Landes Schleswig-Holstein
Wall 74, 24103 **Kiel**
Tel: 431-906 7158 Fax: 431-906 7123/7358
Leiter Bernd Iwersen
Venue type: multi-purpose *Capacity:* Konzertsaal 1250
Policy: rent *Arts types:* chamber music, drama, symphony, solo recitals, dance, theatre

Pumpe, Die
Haßstr. 22, 24103 **Kiel**
Tel: 431-96161 Fax: 431-93548
Fremdveranstaltungen Bettina Jürgensen; Kino Gesa Rautenberg
Venue type: former industrial building *Capacity:* Hall A 800, Hall B 350 *Policy:* promote, rent *Arts types:* concerts, theatre, political events, seminars, cinema (Kommunales Kino in der Pumpe) *Comments:* funded by Stadt Kiel, but independent

KUFA Koblenz
Mayer-Albertistrasse 11, 56070 **Koblenz**
Tel: 261-85280 Fax: 261-802 869
Künstlerischer Leiter Ralf Lohr
Venue type: private theatre
Capacity: 350 *Policy:* rent and promote dance, drama and cabaret *Arts types:* cabaret, dance theatre, theatre, music *Comments:* member of Trans Europe Halles (q.v.), private theatre with own ballet company Tanztheater Regenbogen, also Theatre Company 'Koblenzer Jugendtheater'

Rhein-Mosel-Halle
Postfach 201551, Julius-Wegeler Strasse 4, 56015 **Koblenz**
Tel: 261-129 1651/52/53 Fax: 261-129 1694
Internet: www.Koblenz.de
E-Mail: touristik@koblenz.de
Geschäftsführer Engelbert Flöck
Venue type: multi-purpose *Capacity:* Großer Saal 1329, Kleiner Saal 420, combined 1700 *Policy:* only for rent and own productions *Arts types:* concerts, musicals, conferences, exhibitions

Alte Feuerwache
Melchiorstr 3, 50670 **Köln**
Tel: 221-973 155-0
Fax: 221-739 2030/9731 5526
Programmgestaltung Elisabeth Becker
Venue type: multi-purpose
Capacity: 200 *Policy:* rent, own productions
Arts types: contemporary dance, classical and experimental music and theatre, music theatre

Atelier-Theater
Roonstr. 78, 50674 **Köln**
Tel: 221-242 485 (info/tickets)/241 341 (theatre office)
Fax: 221-233 757
Direktor u. künstlerische Leitung Rosa K. Wirtz; Verwaltungsdirektorin und Öffentlichkeitsarbeit Sabine Heinrichs-Knab
Venue type: theatre
Capacity: 99 + Ateliercafe 80
Policy: promote *Arts types:* cabaret, variety theatre
Comments: daily performances; see also Drama and Festivals

Comedia Colonia Theater GmbH
Löwengasse 7-9, 50676 **Köln**
Tel: 221-247 650 Fax: 221-215 639
Internet: www.theaterszene-koeln.de
E-Mail: comedia@netcologne.de
Direktion u. Geschäftsführung Klaus Schweizer; Öffentlichkeitsarbeit Jürgen Pohl; Verwaltungsleiterin Ursula Siedler
Venue type: theatre *Capacity:* 312 *Policy:* promote, rent, guest performances *Arts types:* Sprechtheater, comedy, cabaret, children's and youth theatre *Comments:* venue for independent theatre groups – 150 performances per year, theatre workshops for professionals and amateurs, educational theatre, children's theatre; see also Drama

Kölner Philharmonie
Köln Musik GmbH, Bischofsgartenstrasse 1, 50667 **Köln**
Tel: 221-204 080 Fax: 221-2040 8222
Internet: www.koelner-philharmonie.de
E-Mail: koelnmusik@netcologne.de
Intendant Dr. Albin Hänseroth; Konzertplanung Dr. Annette Wolde; Betriebsdirektor Michael Kaufmann
Venue type: concert hall *Capacity:* 2171 *Policy:* present, rent *Arts types:* chamber and symphony, recitals, dance, pop, jazz, folk *Comments:* home of the Gürzenich – Kölner Philharmoniker and the WDR Sinfonieorchester Köln; alternative internets: www.koelnmusik.de or www.koelnticket.de

Senftöpfchen Theater
Alexandra Kassen Theater-Gesellschaft mbH, Große Neugasse 2-4, 50667 **Köln**
Tel: 221-258 1059 (office) Fax: 221-258 1283
Theaterleitung Alexandra Kassen jun. & sen.
Venue type: theatre
Capacity: 190 *Arts types:* theatre, music, cabaret and Kleinkunst

Konzilgebäude
Hafenstrasse 2, 78462 **Konstanz**
Tel: 7531-21221 Fax: 7531-17467
Geschäftsführer Hubert Hölzl
Venue type: multi-purpose historic building
Capacity: Großer Saal (bestuhlt) 800, Kleiner Saal (bestuhlt) 300
Policy: rent *Arts types:* chamber and symphony, recitals, dance, balls, seminars, fashion shows, fairs

Off-Off Theater (in der Tanzwerkstatt)
Kreuzlinger Str 54, 78462 **Konstanz**
Tel: 7531-26838 Fax: 7531-25716
Verwaltung und Künstlerische Leitung Inge Missmahl
Venue type: theatre
Capacity: 80 *Policy:* produce, rent
Arts types: dance, jazz concerts, dance theatre
Comments: International Performance Festival: Nov – application deadline: July

Seidenweberhaus
Theaterplatz 1, 47798 **Krefeld**
Tel: 2151-815-0 Fax: 2151-815 115
E-Mail: Seidenweberhaus-Krefeld@t-online.de
Geschäftsführer Horst Driever
Venue type: multi-purpose
Capacity: 1200 *Policy:* rent, present
Arts types: chamber and symphony, recitals, ballet, dance, entertainment shows and entertainment music, conferences

Stadthalle Kulmbach / Plassenburg
c/o Unternehmen Stadt Kulmbach, Sutte 2,
95326 **Kulmbach**
Tel: 9221-958 850 Fax: 9221-958 866
Internet: www.stadt-kulmbach.de
E-Mail: unternehmen@stadt-kulmbach.de
Betriebsleiter Wolfgang Klemenz; stellvertretende Betriebskeiterin Kerstin Hoppert; Tourist Information Petra Reuther
Venue type: concert hall *Capacity:* 800, Plassenburg 200, open-air 1700 *Arts types:* chamber music, drama, symphony, dance, theatre, congresses, conferences *Comments:* 275 events a year; 17000 qm open-air for festivals, exhibitions etc

Salzachhalle
Stadt Laufen, Rathausplatz 1, 83410 **Laufen**
Tel: 8682-898 726 Fax: 8682-898 731
Hallenleitung MA Stefan Feiler
Venue type: Stadthalle *Capacity:* 672 *Policy:* rent & promote *Arts types:* theatre, music, dance, art and culture events

Gewandhaus zu Leipzig
Postfach 100 853, 04008 **Leipzig**
Tel: 341-12700/280 Fax: 341-1270 200/22
Internet: www.gewandhaus.de
E-Mail: betriebsbuero@gewandhaus.de
Gewandhausdirektor Andreas Schulz; Gewandhauskapellmeister Herbert Blomstedt; Verwaltungsdirektor Volker Stiehler; Orchesterdirektor Dr. Siegfried Raschke
Venue type: concert hall *Capacity:* Großer Saal 1900, Mendelssohn-Saal 300 *Arts types:* classical music, jazz, conferences

Moritzbastei
Postfach 1027, 04109 **Leipzig**
Tel: 341-702 590 Fax: 341-702 5959
Internet: www.moritzbastei.de
E-Mail: moritz@mb.uni-leipzig.de
Programmdirektor Peter Matzke; Theater Lutz Hesse; Music Oliver Naumann
Venue type: varies in the remains of the old city wall (16th century) *Capacity:* concerts up to 400, theatre up to 200 *Policy:* rent, promote, produce *Arts types:* theatre, concerts (rock, pop, jazz), exhibitions (monthly comics exhibitions) *Comments:* venue address: Universitätsstr. 9, 04109 Leipzig; producing with free theatre groups

Stadthalle Leonberg
Postfach 1763, 71207 **Leonberg**
Tel: 7152-9755-0 Fax: 7152-975 597
Internet: Leonberg.de
E-Mail: stadthalle@Leonberg.de
Geschäftsführer Günther Philippi
Venue type: multi-purpose *Capacity:* 757 *Policy:* promote, rent *Arts types:* chamber music, drama, symphony, solo recitals, dance, theatre, ballet, operetta, musicals, opera, shows, light music *Comments:* visiting address: Römerstrasse 110, 71229 Leonberg

Forum Leverkusen
Postfach 101140, 51311 **Leverkusen**
Tel: 214-406 4118 Fax: 214-406 4103
Internet: www.leverkusen.de
E-Mail: 01.leverkusen@telef.net
Kultur fachliche Leitung Dr Erika Wegner; Verwaltungsleitung Gudrun Deuser; Veranstaltungen und Marketing Arthur Harvath; Dramaturgie Dr Michael Bilstein
Venue type: culture and congress centre *Capacity:* 5 spaces: 1200, 968, 320, 600, 160 *Policy:* promote, rent *Arts types:* chamber music, drama, symphony, solo recitals, dance, theatre, jazz, rock, conference, congresses, etc *Comments:* venue of Internationale Leverkusener Jazztage, Internationales Tanzfestival (biennial: next in 2000); see also Promoters (Stadt Leverkusen Kulturamt)

Stadthalle Limburg
Hospitalstrasse 4, 65549 **Limburg/Lahn**
Tel: 6431-98060 Fax: 6431-98614
E-Mail: stadthalle.limburg@t-online.de
Geschäftsführer Guido Lindeken
Venue type: Stadthalle *Capacity:* 1300-2200 (for rock & pop), Kleinkunstbühne up to 250 *Policy:* rent, promote *Arts types:* chamber music, drama, symphony, solo recitals, dance, theatre, musicals, rock & pop

Stadttheater Lindau
Fischergasse 37, 88131 **Lindau**
Tel: 8382-944 650 Fax: 8382-918 298
Leiter Dr Angela Heilmann
Venue type: theatre *Capacity:* Stadttheater 688, Konzertsaal 180 *Policy:* rent *Arts types:* drama, concerts *Comments:* pure 'Gastspielhaus' for German ensembles; one of the venues for Bodensee-Festival (q.v.)

Theater an der Wilhelmshöhe
Nordring 44, 49808 **Lingen (Ems)**
Tel: 591-91440 (Stadtverwaltung),64554 (theatre) Fax: 591-914 4416 (Stadtverwaltung)/966 0109 (theatre)
Verwaltung Rudolf Kruse; Theater und Beleuchtungsmeister Wolfgang Hardt
Venue type: theatre *Capacity:* up to 753 *Arts types:* drama, comedy, opera, operetta, ballet, orchestra, chamber concerts, recitals, musicals, children's theatre *Comments:* Stadtverwaltung: Stadt Lingen (Ems), PO Box 2060, 49803 Lingen (Ems)

Stadttheater Lippstadt
Cappeltor 3-5, 59555 **Lippstadt**
Tel: 2941-79861 Fax: 2941-3708
Internet: www.lippstadt.de/kwl
E-Mail: kwl.lippstadt@t-online.de
Geschäftsführer Carmen Harms; Verwaltung KWL-Kultur & Werbung, Lippstadt GmbH, Geiststr. 2, 59555 Lippstadt
Venue type: theatre *Capacity:* 787 *Policy:* rent *Arts types:* drama, dance, musicals, symphony concerts, choir, operetta, opera, youth theatre

Stadthalle Lübbecke
Postfach 1453, 32294 **Lübbecke**
Tel: 5741-276 178 Fax: 451-347 115
Leitung Bürgermeister Günter Steinmeyer
Venue type: stadthalle *Capacity:* 660 *Policy:* rent *Arts types:* chamber music, drama, symphony, solo recitals, dance, theatre *Comments:* visiting address: Bohlenstraße 29, 32312 Lübbecke

Lübecker Musik-und Kongreßhallen GmbH
Willy-Brandt-Allee 10, 23554 **Lübeck**
Tel: 451-7904-0 Fax: 451-790 4100
Internet: www.muk.de
E-Mail: muk@muk.de
Geschäftsführer Johann W. Wagner; Leiterin kulturelle Organisation Kristina Wulf; Marketingleitung Kerstin Freels; Technische Leitung Franz Münzebrock
Venue type: multi purpose *Capacity:* up to 2000 (1800 for conferences, concerts 3500) *Policy:* rent *Arts types:* music (classical, popular), conferences, exhibitions, fairs

Theater Combinale
Hüxstr. 115, 23552 **Lübeck**
Tel: 451-78817 Fax: 451-706 3078
Internet: www.combinale.de
E-Mail: info@combinale.de
contact Ulli Haussmann
Venue type: theatre *Capacity:* 130 *Policy:* promote, produce *Comments:* venue for free theatre groups; see also Drama

Forum am Schloßpark
Postfach 666, 71606 **Ludwigsburg**
Tel: 7141-91701 Fax: 7141-917 248
Internet: www.forum.ludwigsburg.de
E-Mail: info@forum.ludwigsburg.de
Geschäftsführer Wilfried Blickle
Venue type: cultural and congress centre *Capacity:* theatre 1248, hall 1100, 6 small rooms with 30 to 140 seats *Policy:* rent only *Arts types:* opera, musicals, drama, concerts, conferences, ballet

BASF-Feierabendhaus
BASF AG, 67056 **Ludwigshafen**
Tel: 621-604 3436 Fax: 621-602 0317
E-Mail: hans-peter.dott@basf.ag.de
Leiter Dr. Klaus Philipp Seif; Dramaturgie Hans-Peter Dott
Venue type: multi-purpose *Capacity:* 1370 *Policy:* promote *Arts types:* chamber, opera, operetta, symphony concerts, drama *Comments:* see also Promoters and Gesellschaftshaus BASF (Venues)

Friedrich-Ebert-Halle
LUBEGE Ludwigshafener Betriebsgesellschaft mbH, Erzbergerstraße 89, 67063 **Ludwigshafen**
Tel: 621-690 950 Fax: 621-690 9566
Internet: www.lubege.de
E-Mail: info@lubege.de
Geschäftsführer Ulrich Gaißmayer
Venue type: multi-purpose *Capacity:* 4452 or 3100 *Policy:* rent, promote *Comments:* adminstrated by LUBEGE Ludwigshafener Betriebsgesellschaft mbH, Pfalzbau q.v.

Gesellschaftshaus der BASF
Wöhlerstrasse 15, 67056 **Ludwigshafen**
Tel: 621-604 3436 Fax: 621-602 0317
E-Mail: hans-peter.dott@basf.ag.de
Leiter Dr. Klaus Philipp Seif; Dramaturgie Hans-Peter Dott
Venue type: concert hall *Capacity:* 300 *Policy:* promote *Arts types:* chamber music *Comments:* see also Promoters and BASF-Feierabendhaus (Venues)

Pfalzbau
LUBEGE Ludwigshafener Betriebsgesellschaft GmbH, Erzbergerstraße 89, 67063 **Ludwigshafen**
Tel: 621-690 950 Fax: 621-690 9566
Internet: www.lubege.de
E-Mail: info@lubege.de
Geschäftsführer Ulrich Gaißmayer
Venue type: multi-purpose *Capacity:* Pfalzbau: concert hall and multifunctional conference room 1412 *Policy:* rent, promote *Arts types:* concerts, balls *Comments:* Friedrich-Ebert-Halle q.v., both administrated by LUBEGE Ludwigshafener Betriebsgesellschaft GmbH

Heinz Hilpert Theater (Theater der Stadt Lünen)
Kurt-Schumacher-Strasse 39, 44532 **Lünen**
Tel: 2306-13604 Fax: 2306-25286
E-Mail: info@luenen.de
Verwaltungsleiterin Annette Borns; Theatre, Opera, Operetta, Ballet Werner Althoff; Symphony, Chamber, Rock & Jazz Uwe Wortmann
Venue type: theatre *Capacity:* 760 + 2 wheelchair spaces *Policy:* rent *Arts types:* opera, operetta, drama, symphony, chamber, ballet, rock, jazz *Comments:* jazz festival in November

Congress Centrum Mainz GmbH
Postfach 3468, 55024 **Mainz**
Tel: 6131-242 110 Fax: 6131-242 100
Internet: www.ccmainz.de
Geschäftsführung August Moderer; Marketing/Sales Antje Bothner, Katja Mailahn
Venue type: multi-purpose *Capacity:* Rheingoldhalle 2700, Eltzer Hof 1000, Kurf Schloß 1000, Frankfurter Hof 450 *Policy:* rent *Arts types:* chamber music, drama, symphony, solo recitals, dance, theatre, musicals, TV shows, conferences and congresses, exhibitions (art and industrial) *Comments:* responsible for the Mainz halls; visiting address: Rheinstrasse 66, 55116 Mainz

Kulturzentrum Mainz
Dagobertstr. 20B, 55116 **Mainz**
Tel: 6131-28686-0 Fax: 6131-28686-28
Geschäftsleitung Rüdiger Stephan, Norbert Munk, Joe Trautmann
Venue type: theatre (old workhouse) *Capacity:* up to 800 (standing) *Policy:* present, promote, rent, event cooperation *Arts types:* mainly concerts

Mainzer Kammerspiele im Fort Malakoff Park
Rheinstraße 4, 55116 **Mainz**
Tel: 6131-225 002 Fax: 6131-225 004
Internet: www.mainzer-kammerspiele.de
E-Mail: mail@mainzer-kammerspiele.de
Leitung Oliver Blank, Michael Heintz, Thomas Peifer, Claudia Wehner
Capacity: 365 *Policy:* rent, present, produce *Arts types:* drama, dance, cabaret *Comments:* occasional productions on tour; run as a 'cooperative'

Kulturzentrum Alte Feuerwache
Brückenstrasse 2, 68167 **Mannheim**
Tel: 621-293 9281 Fax: 621-293 9293
E-Mail: 410eff@mannheim.de
Leitung Eberhard Petri; Literature Ulrike Hacker; Photography Thomas Schirmböck; Musik Markus Sprengler (tel: 621-293 9281)
Venue type: multi-purpose *Capacity:* Großer Saal 850, Kleiner Saal 150 *Policy:* rent, promote *Arts types:* concerts (jazz, experimental, rock, pop), theatre, literature, photographic exhibitions *Comments:* venue formerly a fire station

Theater der Stadt Marl (TM)
Am Theater 1, 45765 **Marl**
Tel: 2365-992 621 (Theaterreferent)/91970 (i-Punkt)
Fax: 2365-992 603 (Theaterreferent)/919 718 (i-Punkt)
Theaterreferent Axel Schmidt-Scherer; Kulturamtsleiter Hermann Dorpmund
Venue type: theatre *Capacity:* 816 *Policy:* promote, rent *Arts types:* theatre, concerts, musicals *Comments:* home of the Philharmonia Hungarica; box office
Tel: 2365-57019

Stadthalle Meschede
Postfach 1665, 59870 **Meschede**
Tel: 291-1539 (Stadthalle)/171-533 4455 (mobile)
Fax: 291-1510
Leiter Ingo Becker
Venue type: Stadthalle *Capacity:* 622 *Policy:* rent, promote (very rarely) *Arts types:* opera, operetta, drama, concerts *Comments:* visiting address: Winziger Platz, 59872 Meschede

Stadttheater Minden
Tonhallenstrasse 3, 32423 **Minden (Westf.)**
Tel: 571-828 390 Fax: 571-828 3922
Theaterleiter Bertram Schulte
Venue type: theatre *Capacity:* 550 *Arts types:* concerts (opera, symphony, chamber, jazz), exhibitions, 'Liederabende', drama, pantomime, musicals, children's theatre, dance

Kaiser-Friedrich-Halle
Kongreßhallen u. Gäststätten GmbH, Hohenzollernstrasse 15, 41061 **Mönchengladbach**
Tel: 2161-10094 Fax: 2161-207 744
Geschäftsführerin Ingeborg Brüggen
Venue type: concert hall, congress centre *Capacity:* 950, seminar rooms *Policy:* rent *Arts types:* chamber, symphony, dance, drama, exhibitions, trade fairs, comedy

Stadthalle Mülheim an der Ruhr
Postfach 101953, Theodor-Heuss Platz 1,
45466 **Mülheim an der Ruhr**
Tel: 208-455 4110 Fax: 208-4555 84110
Internet: www.stucke.de
E-Mail: karin.fahrenbach@stadt-mh.de

Kulturbetriebsleiter Cornelia Schwabe; Technischer Leiter Peter Rey
Venue type: listed theatre building *Capacity:* 1085 (4wheelchair spaces) *Policy:* rent, present *Arts types:* theatre, dance, ballet, concerts, conferences, congress, cabaret *Comments:* see also Festivals

Das Schloss – Theaterzelt am Olympiaberg
Ackermannstr. 77, 80797 **München**
Tel: 89-300 3013 Fax: 89-300 8580
Organisation Veit Stöhr; Künstlerische Leitung Gunnar Petersen; Technische Leitung Gregor Hermens
Venue type: Theatre tent *Capacity:* 500 *Policy:* permanent circus tent available for rent, promote, produce *Arts types:* modern classics, literary theatre, fairs, congress and conferences *Comments:* see also Drama

Deutsches Theater München Betriebs – GmbH
Schwanthalerstrasse 13, 80336 **München**
Tel: 89-5523 1211 Fax: 89-5523 4234
Internet: www.deutsches-theater.de
E-Mail: info@deutsches-theater.de
Direktor Heiko Plapperer-Lüthgarth
Venue type: theatre *Capacity:* main hall 1660, small hall up to 240 *Policy:* produce, rent *Arts types:* musicals, operetta, ballet, entertainment, drama

Feierwerk
Hansastraße 39, 81373 **München**
Tel: 89-769 3600 Fax: 89-769 6032
contact Ulla Kart, Heiner Schmittner
Venue type: concert hall
Capacity: up to 400 *Policy:* rent *Arts types:* theatre, dance, performance, concerts, rock & pop concerts
Comments: emphasis on young artists; the old theatre has been demolished, a new one is being planned

FestSpielHaus
Quiddestr. 17, 81735 **München**
Tel: 89-672 020 Fax: 89-637 3450
Internet: www.bayern.com/festspielhaus
E-Mail: festspielhaus@bayern.com
Geschäftsführer Helmut von Ahnen
Capacity: 100 *Policy:* present, produce *Arts types:* theatre, photography, video

Gasteig (Münchens Kultur-, Bildungs- und Tagungszentrum)
Gasteig München GmbH, Rosenheimer Strasse 5, 81667 **München**
Tel: 89-48098-0 Fax: 89-48098-632
Internet: www.gasteig.de
E-Mail: zentral@gasteig.de
Geschäftsführerin Brigitte von Welser; Prokurist Ingomar Faull; Leiter Betriebsbüro Veranstaltungen Diedrich Klusmann; Leitung Kommunikation Dr. Hartmut Dedert; Leiter Technik Peter Fröhler; Leiter Veranstaltungstechnik Manfred Schwendinger; Leiter Haus- und Sachverwaltung Norbert Wienert
Venue type: cultural centre with theatre, concert hall
Capacity: Philharmonie 2400, Carl-Orff hall 600, Black Box 225, Kleiner Konzertsaal 190 *Policy:* rent, promote
Arts types: chamber music, drama, symphony, solo recitals, dance, theatre, exhibitions
Comments: 1800 events a year, home of the Munich Philharmonic Orchestra

Muffathalle
Zellstr. 4, 81667 **München**
Tel: 89-4587 5000 Fax: 89-4587 5050
Internet: www.muffathalle.de
E-Mail: info@muffathalle.de
Geschäftsführer Dietmar Lupfer, Christian Waggershauser
Venue type: multi purpose *Capacity:* 800, 1400-1500 standing *Policy:* rent, promote *Arts types:* concerts, drama, performance, dance and exhibitions
Comments: refurbished powerstation

NT – Neues Theater
Theaterverein Münche eV., Entenbachstaße 37, 81541 **München**
Tel: 89-650 000 Fax: 89-654 325
Vorstand Manfred Killer, Robert Hofmann
Venue type: theatre
Capacity: 120 & Foyer
Policy: present, rent *Arts types:* theatre, dance, performance, contemporary music

Pasinger Fabrik
August-Exter-Straße 1, 81245 **München**
Tel: 89-829 2900 Fax: 89-829 9099
Internet: www.pasinger-fabrik.com
E-Mail: info@pasinger-fabrik.com
Geschäftsführer Dr. Michael Stanic
Venue type: old factory *Capacity:* 8 spaces up to 200
Policy: rent, co-produce *Arts types:* mainly opera, theatre, dance, music (classical, jazz, contemporary)

Residenz München
Residenzstrasse 1, 80333 **München**
Tel: 89-290 671 Fax: 89-2906 7223
director Frau Reitberger
Venue type: rococo style *Capacity:* 500-600
Policy: rent *Arts types:* theatre, music

Halle Münsterland
Albersloherweg 32, 48155 **Münster**
Tel: 251-66000 Fax: 251-660 0109
Internet: www.halle-muensterland.de
E-Mail: info@halle-muensterland.de
Geschäftsführer Dr. Hans-Jürgen Gaida
Venue type: hall *Capacity:* up to 12000
Policy: rent, present *Arts types:* concerts, exhibitions, congresses etc. *Comments:* postal address: Postfach 3440, 48019 Münster

Kreativhaus
Diepenbrockstr. 28, 48145 **Münster**
Tel: 251-37054 Fax: 251-36997
Internet: www.muenster.de/kreativhaus
E-Mail: kreativhaus@muenster.de
Leitung Norbert Woestmeyer
Venue type: theatre *Capacity:* 130 *Policy:* rent, produce *Arts types:* dance, drama, music, cabaret *Comments:* also offers art classes; home of Jugendkunstschule (art school for children and young people)

Kulturschiene
Berliner Platz, 48143 **Münster**
Tel: 251-47849 Fax: 251-47841
E-Mail: rebel@muenster.net
Leitung Ingrid Heid; Inhaber David Rebel
Venue type: Freies Theater *Capacity:* 150 *Policy:* mainly rent *Arts types:* dance, music, cabaret, pantomime
Comments: visiting address: Im Hauptbahnhof

Städtische Bühnen Münster
Neubrückenstrasse 63, 48143 **Münster**
Tel: 251-5909-0 Fax: 251-590 9202
Internet: www.muenster.de/stb
E-Mail: staedt.buehnen@stadt-muenster.de
Generalintendant Herr Bockelmann; Oberspielleiter d. Schauspiels Sylvia Richter
Venue type: theatre *Capacity:* Großes Haus 956, Kleines Haus 321 *Policy:* produce, co-produce *Arts types:* music theatre, drama, dance theatre, children's and youth theatre, experimental and 'conventional' theatre, concerts

Hugenottenhalle
Frankfurter Str. 152, 63263 **Neu-Isenburg**
Tel: 6102-747 410 Fax: 6102-38177
Internet: www.neu-isenburg.de
Leiter Hugenottenhalle Thomas Leber; Leiter Kulturbüro Matthias Schubert; Technischer Leiter Manfred Möller
Venue type: multi-purpose hall with theatre *Capacity:* Großer Saal (standing) up to 2000 , Kleiner Saal *Policy:* promote and rent *Arts types:* ballet, balls, films shows, jazz, cabaret, concerts, musicals, opera, operetta, show, drama

Kammertheater Neubrandenburg im Schauspielhaus e.V.
Pfaffenstr. 22, 17033 **Neubrandenburg**
Tel: 395-544 2617/180-222 2617 (tickets & info)
Fax: 395-582 6179
E-Mail: kammertheater@t-online.de
Intendant Knut Hirche; Geschäftsführer Dieter Köplin
Capacity: up to 280 *Policy:* rent, produce, co-produce
Arts types: drama, puppetry *Comments:* home of Kammertheater Neubrandenburg- the oldest theatre venue in Northern Germany, built 1787

Markgrafenhalle
Postfach 1669,, 91406 **Neustadt a. d. Aisch**
Tel: 9161-66613 (city administration) Fax: 9161-66615
Internet: stadt-neustadt-aisch.de
E-Mail: stadt@stadt-neustadt-aisch.de
booking Mrs. Zerrath
Venue type: multi-purpose *Capacity:* 1420 *Policy:* rent, promote *Arts types:* drama, symphony, recitals, dance, theatre, concerts *Comments:* visiting address: Comeniusstr. 1, 91413 Neustadt a. d. Aisch

Rhein-Main Theater
c/o Hotel Micador, Zum grauen Stein 2, 65527 **Niederhausen**
Tel: 6127-9010 (Hotel Micador) Fax: 6127-901 641
E-Mail: micador.taunushotel@t-online.de
Leitung Dagmar Greis
Venue type: multi-purpose *Capacity:* 1500 *Policy:* rent
Arts types: concerts, theatre, dance, musicals, fairs, conferences, etc.

Meistersingerhalle
Münchener Strasse 21, 90478 **Nürnberg**
Tel: 911-492 011 Fax: 911-463 316
E-Mail: msh@mobile.stadt.nuernberg.de
Betriebsleiter Peter Frühwirth; Organisation Fritz Zander
Venue type: concert and multi-purpose hall *Capacity:* Großer Saal 2100, Kleiner Saal 500
Policy: rent *Arts types:* chamber and symphony, recitals, dance, opera, drama, ballet, trade fairs, congresses, conferences and balls *Comments:* 300 bedroom hotel in the building complex

Tafelhalle
Äußere Sulzbacher Str. 60-62, 90491 **Nürnberg**
Tel: 911-231 5297 Fax: 911-231 2310
E-Mail: kuf_veranstaltungen@kuf.nuernberg.de
Leiter Michael Bader; Verwaltung Martina Leykauf, Angelika von Drach; Öffentlichkeitsarbeit Ursula Diethe-Hollis; Technischer Leiter Gunnar Tippmann
Venue type: theatre
Capacity: Großer Theatersaal up to 500, Black Box 90
Policy: present *Arts types:* music, dance theatre, theatre, concerts, festivals
Comments: home of free theatre groups

Luise-Albertz-Halle
Düppelstraße 1, 46045 **Oberhausen**
Tel: 208-859 080 Fax: 208-859 0811
Internet: www.luise-albertz-halle.de
E-Mail: info@luise-albertz-halle.de
Geschäftsführer Jörn Raith; Kaufmännischer Leiter Rolf Kempelmann
Venue type: multi-purpose *Capacity:* Festsaal 1500, Mittelsaal 400, Auditorium 250, Wandelhalle 200, Konferenzraum 45 *Policy:* rent *Arts types:* chamber music, drama, symphony, solo recitals, dance, theatre, exhibitions, conferences

Capitol Entertainment Centre Rhein-Main
Goethestraße 1-5, 63067 **Offenbach**
Tel: 69-829 0020 Fax: 69-8290 0262
Internet: www.capitol-online.de
E-Mail: info@capitol-online.de
Geschäftsführer David Lieberberg; Technische Leitung Harald Ostermann
Venue type: multi-purpose *Capacity:* main auditorium 700-1800, Universum 120-200 *Policy:* rent *Arts types:* concerts, dance, musicals, theatre, conferences, congresses, etc.

Stadthalle Offenbach Veranstaltungs GmbH
Waldstr. 312, 63071 **Offenbach**
Tel: 69-857 0600 Fax: 69-8570 6060
Internet: www.stadthalle-offenbach.de
E-Mail: info@stadthalle-offenbach.de
Geschäftsführerin Brigitte Laufer; Veranstaltungsleitung Sibylle Harf
Venue type: Stadthalle, Mehrzweckhalle
Capacity: 3000 standing, 1734 seated
Policy: rent *Arts types:* musicals, conferences, trade fairs, balls, concerts, sport-championships
Comments: 2nd venue: Bürgerhaus Rumpenheim, 264 seated at tables, 350 seated in rows

Kulturetage Oldenburg
Bahnhofstraße 11, 26122 **Oldenburg**
Tel: 441-924 800 Fax: 441-924 8080
Internet: www.uni-oldenburg.de/kulturetage
E-Mail: ketage@uni-oldenburg.de
coordinator Honne Dohrmann; public relations Frank Mrozek; finance Irmtraud Strodtmann; director & ensemble Bernt Wach; technic Hartmut Lanje; central tickets Anne Plenge
Venue type: main theatre, 2 studios
Capacity: Ultra theatre 199, Studio 99 *Policy:* rent, co-produce *Arts types:* drama, dance, comedy, cabaret, music, entertainment – events
Comments: see Drama and Festivals

Osnabrücker Stadthallen GmbH
Schloßwall 1-9, 49074 **Osnabrück**
Tel: 541-34900 Fax: 541-349 018
E-Mail: stadthalle.osnabrueck@debitel.net
Geschäftsführer Günter Valjak
Venue type: multli-purpose *Capacity:* Europasaal 1900, Niedersachsensaal 450, Kongresshalle 700 up to 4050
Policy: rent only *Arts types:* music, drama, dance etc.

Wolf-Ferrari-Haus Kommunaler Eigenbetrieb Gemeinde Ottobrunn, Kultur und Veranstaltungszentrum
Rathausplatz 2, 85521 **Ottobrunn**
Tel: 89-60808-300/301 Fax: 89-6080 8303
Leitung Michael Dissing; Betriebsleiter Horst Frank; Künstlerischer Berater Bernd Seidel
Capacity: Festsaal 434, Ratssaal 264
Policy: rent, promote
Arts types: concerts, drama, conferences, congresses

PaderHalle
Heiersmauer 45-51, 33098 **Paderborn**
Tel: 5251-10394-0 Fax: 5251-10394-88
Internet: www.paderhalle.de
Geschäftsführerin Dr. Maria Rodehuth; Prokurist Jochen Möller; Public Relations Antje Ostermann
Venue type: Stadthalle *Capacity:* 954 *Policy:* rent, promote *Arts types:* theatre, concerts, exhibitions, conferences, musicals, opera, operettas, seminars

Fürstbischöfliches Opernhaus
Gottfried-Schäffer-Strasse 4, 94032 **Passau**
Tel: 851-929 1910 (administration)
Fax: 851-929 1920/1933 (KBB)
Internet: www.suedostbayerischesstaedtetheater.de/
E-Mail: stadttheater.passau@t-online.de
Verwaltungsleiter Ralf Schützenberger; Intendant Johannes Reitmeier; Musikdirektor Roger Boggasch; Oberspielleiter Norman Warmuth; Dramaturgie (Musikal. Abteilung) Andreas Frane
Venue type: opera house, Stadttheater Landshut
Capacity: 350 & 365
Arts types: opera, operetta, musical, concerts

Nibelungenhalle
Dr. Hans Kapfingerstr. 7, 94032 **Passau**
Tel: 851-396 340 Fax: 851-57604
Geschäftsführer Norbert Täuber
Venue type: multi-purpose *Capacity:* 5088 *Policy:* rent *Arts types:* music, drama, dance etc.

Stadthalle Pforzheim
Am Waisenhausplatz 1-3, 75172 **Pforzheim**
Tel: 7231-14545-0 Fax: 7231-14545-45
Geschäftsführer Günter Ihlenfeld; Techn. Leitung/Vermietung Andreas Aichele
Venue type: multi-purpose *Capacity:* 2000 *Policy:* rent *Arts types:* concerts, classical, rock, pop

Felsenbühne Rathen
c/o Landesbühnen Sachsen, Meißner Straße 152, 01445 **Radebeul**
Tel: 351-8954-0 Fax: 351-8954-201
Internet: www.dresden-theater.de
E-Mail: landesbuehnensachsen@dresden-theater.de
Intendant Christian Schmidt; Direktor der Felsenbühne Rathen Andreas Gärtner
Venue type: open-air theatre *Capacity:* 2000 *Policy:* mainly promote *Arts types:* opera, drama, music theatre (often German classical authors), concerts (orchestras, choirs and soloists) *Comments:* venue address: Kurort Rathen, 01824 Rathen

Haus des Bürgers
Am Neuen Markt 4, 66872 **Ramstein-Miesenbach**
Tel: 6371-592 222 Fax: 6371-592 218
Internet: www.Ramstein-Miesenbach.de
E-Mail: ramstein@t-online.de
Geschäftsführer Gerhard Denzer
Venue type: Stadthalle *Capacity:* 800 *Policy:* rent and promote *Arts types:* concerts (classical, pop etc.), theatre, operetta

Stadthalle Ransbach-Baumbach
Rheinstraße 103, 56235 **Ransbach-Baumbach**
Tel: 2623-9880-0 Fax: 2623-9880-20
E-Mail: ransbach-baumbach@t-online.de
Geschäftsführer Manfred Steinebach; Sekretariat Angelika Nobach-Hedtrich
Venue type: Stadthalle *Capacity:* Großer Saal, Kleiner Saal, combined 820, Kleinkunstbühne 130 *Policy:* rent and promote (about 10 in a year)
Arts types: all types of performances
Comments: seminars, exhibitions, conferences

Vestisches Cultur- & Congresszentrum Recklinghausen (Vcc)
Otto-Burrmeister-Allee 1, 45657 **Recklinghausen**
Tel: 2361-918 401 Fax: 2361-918 413
Internet: www.vccr.de
E-Mail: info@vccr.de
Geschäftsführer Achim Dionisius; Management Aida Kleinschmidt
Venue type: theatre and congress centre *Capacity:* Theatersaal 1024, Kasiopeia 500, Saalbau 832 *Policy:* mainly rent, promote *Arts types:* drama, opera, operetta, cabaret, dance, musicals, congresses

Kulturhalle Remchingen
Hauptstr. 115, 75196 **Remchingen**
Tel: 7232-3696-30 Fax: 7232-3696-80
Internet: www.netz-der-region.de/kulturhalle.htm
E-Mail: kulturhalle@t-online.de
Manager Roland Haag
Venue type: multi-purpose *Capacity:* 2 halls: 600 and 100 *Policy:* promote, rent *Arts types:* concerts (classical, jazz, pop, folk), drama, musicals, dance, filmshows etc.

Theater der Stadt Remscheid
Konrad-Adenauer-Str. 31-33, 42853 **Remscheid**
Tel: 2191-163 860 Fax: 2191-163 279
Internet: www.remscheid.de
Leiterin des Theaters und der städtischen Galerie Helga Müller-Serre
Venue type: Gastspieltheater *Capacity:* 619 *Policy:* co-produce, receive *Arts types:* all types

Kultur & Kongress Centrum Rosenheim
Kufsteiner Str 4, 83022 **Rosenheim**
Tel: 8031-3001-0 Fax: 8031-300 163/4
Internet: www.kuko.de
E-Mail: info@kuko.de
Geschäftsführer Heinz-W. Bleyl
Venue type: multi-purpose *Capacity:* 1000 to 1600, Congresszentrum 1-4 rooms: 60-450 *Policy:* rent, present *Arts types:* theatre, concerts, congresses etc.

Stadttheater Rüsselsheim
Am Treff 7, 65428 **Rüsselsheim**
Tel: 6142-832 620 (technische Leitung)
Fax: 6142-832 618
Internet: www.stadt-ruesselsheim.de/
Verwaltungsleitung Kurt Röder; Stellvertreter Ralf Keil
Venue type: theatre
Capacity: Stadttheater Rüsselsheim 865
Policy: rent, promote *Arts types:* opera, operetta, musicals, drama, concerts *Comments:* performances by groups in English & French, venue for festival Theatertage Rüsselsheimer Schulen

Congress-Centrum-Saar GmbH
Im Ludwigspark, 66113 **Saarbrücken**
Tel: 681-41800 Fax: 681-418 0131
Internet: www.ccsaar.de
E-Mail: ccsaar@t-online.de
Geschäftsführer Günther Junker, Elmar A. Peiffer; contact Florian M Korn
Capacity: congress hall 4500, Saarlandhalle 6500 *Arts types:* conferences, seminars, exhibitions, concerts, sports events

Kabarett im Ostviertel
Mainzer Str. 106, 66121 **Saarbrücken**
Tel: 681-62919 Fax: 681-583 816
Künstlerischer Leiter Jürgen Wönne (tel: 681-583 816)
Venue type: theatre *Capacity:* 75 *Policy:* rent *Arts types:* comedy, cabaret, literature, theatre

Saarländisches Staatstheater
Postfach 102735, 66027 **Saarbrücken**
Tel: 681-3092-0 Fax: 681-3092-325
Internet: www.saarland.de/staatstheater
E-Mail: ssto2@t-online.de
Generalintendant Kurt Josef Schildknecht; Kaufmännischer Direktor Helmut Beckamp; Generalmusikdirektor Olaf Henzold; Ballettleiter Bernd Roger Bienert; Oberspielleiter Musiktheater Philipp Himmelmann
Venue type: theatre *Capacity:* Staatstheater 875, Teater Arnual up to 99, Alte Feuerwache up to 300 *Policy:* produce, rent *Arts types:* drama, music theatre, dance, classical concerts *Comments:* visiting address: Schillerplatz 1, 66111 Saarbrücken; see also Opera, Drama and Dance

Theater im Viertel – Studio Theater
Nauwieser Str. 13, 66111 **Saarbrücken**
Tel: 681-390 4602 Fax: 681-63780
Vorsitzender Veronika Häfele-Zumbusch; 2. Vorsitzender Ralph Pierroth; Presse-Referentin Angelika Roth; Technik Hans-Jörg Ponath; künstlerische Leiterin Dieter Desgranges
Venue type: kleinbühne *Capacity:* 74 *Policy:* promote, rent, produce *Arts types:* theatre, children and youth theatre, music (classical, modern) *Comments:* organisation for touring companies; artists' agency

Uckermärkische Bühnen Schwedt
Berliner Straße 46-48, 16303 **Schwedt/Oder**
Tel: 3332-538-0 Fax: 3332-538 132
Intendant Reinhard Simon; Verwaltungsdirektor & 1. Stellvertreter des Intendanten Wilfried Peinke; Chefdramaturg & 2. Stellvertreter des Intendanten Wolfgang Bernert; Intendanzsekretärin & Personalbearbeiter Marga Lieder; Oberspielleiter Gösta Knothe; Direktor für künstlerische Produktion Peter Fabers; Leiterin Öffentlichkeitsarbeit Brigitte Hennig; Technischer Direktor Martin Feldner; Leiter Künstlerisches Betriebsbüro Dieter Wagner
Venue type: theatre *Capacity:* Große Bühne 832, Intimes Theater 100, Berlischky-Pavillon 100, Naturbühne Schloßpark-Theater 400, Studio F 240, Podium 80, Theaterklause 80, Theaterzelt 200 *Policy:* rent *Arts types:* drama, musical, opera, music, exhibitions, puppetry, cinema, seminars, conferences *Comments:* venue of Uckermärkische Bühnen (hired); give guest performances; see also Drama

Theater der Stadt Schweinfurt
Postfach, 97420 **Schweinfurt**
Tel: 9721-51741 Fax: 9721-51746
Direktor Rüdiger R. Nenzel; Verwaltung Zita Schneider-König
Venue type: theatre *Capacity:* 785 *Policy:* rent *Arts types:* drama, ballet, opera, symphony, chamber concert, operetta, musical, cabaret, children's theatre
Comments: visiting address: Roßbrunnstrasse 2, 97421 Schweinfurt

Bühne der Stadt Siegen
c/o Stadt Siegen, FB 4/2, 57003 **Siegen**
Tel: 271-404 1255 Fax: 271-404 2745
Internet: www.siegen.de
contact Petra Rosenthal
Venue type: theatre *Capacity:* 800 *Policy:* rent *Arts types:* theatre, film, concerts

Siegerlandhalle
Koblenzer Straße 151, 57072 **Siegen**
Tel: 271-33700 Fax: 271-339 233
Internet: www.siegerlandhalle.de
Geschäftsführer Dipl. Komm. Friedrich Schmidt
Venue type: multi-purpose *Capacity:* Großer Saal 2000, Leonhard-Gläser-Saal 810, Spandauer Saal 220, plus 8 rooms: up to 300 *Policy:* rent *Arts types:* drama, all types of concerts, opera, conferences, congress

Stadthalle Sindelfingen
Sindelfinger Veranstaltungs – GmbH, Postfach 406, 71046 **Sindelfingen**
Tel: 7031-690 827/94325 (box office) Fax: 7031-690 824
Internet: www.svg-sindelfingen.de
E-Mail: info@svg-sindelfingen.de
Geschäftsführer Hartmut Junker; Prokuristin Ursula Hermann
Venue type: multi-purpose *Capacity:* Stadthalle 1500, Bürgerhaus 600, Klosterseehalle 1200 *Policy:* rent *Arts types:* drama, concerts (classical, pop, jazz etc.), cabaret, ballet, dance *Comments:* visiting address: Schillerstraße 23, 71065 Sindelfingen

Stadthalle Soest
Daffelwall 1, 59494 **Soest**
Tel: 2921-36331 Fax: 2921-13492
Internet: www.stadthalle-soest.de
E-Mail: info@stadthalle-soest.de
Geschäftsführer Ferdinand Pollach
Venue type: multi purpose *Capacity:* 600 *Policy:* rent *Arts types:* theatre, music theatre, musicals, symphony, chamber music, poetry recitals, opera, rock concerts, congress, conferences, trade fairs

Theater und Konzerthaus
Postfach 100 165, 42648 **Solingen**
Tel: 212-290 2433 Fax: 212-290 2437
Leiter Kulturbüro Jürgen Ullmann; Generalmusikdirektor Romely Pfund
Venue type: multi-purpose *Capacity:* theatre 813, concert hall 1050 *Arts types:* concerts, exhibitions, dance, varietey, opera, 'Liederabende', drama, pantomime, jazz *Comments:* visiting address: Konrad-Adenauer-Strasse 71, 42651 Solingen

STADEUM Kultur- und Tagungszentrum Stade
Schiffertorsstraße 6, Postfach 2007, 21660 **Stade**
Tel: 4141-40910 Fax: 4141-409 110
E-Mail: stadeum@stade.de
Geschäftsführer Ernst Heinrich Abel
Venue type: multi-purpose centre with theatre, restaurant *Capacity:* 1 hall up to 1350, & 6 conference rooms *Policy:* rent and organise *Arts types:* drama, concerts, opera, musicals, ballet, jazz, rock, fashion shows, conferences, etc. *Comments:* cultural season from August-May

Theater am Hagen
Am Hagen 61, 94315 **Straubing**
Tel: 9421-944 255 Fax: 9421-944 113
Internet: www.straubing.baynet.de/stadt
E-Mail: stadt@straubing.baynet.de
Kulturamtsleiter Werner Wolff
Venue type: Gastspieltheater *Capacity:* 335 *Policy:* rent, present *Arts types:* theatre, Sprech -, music theatre, cabaret, opera, operettas, figurentheater *Comments:* works in conjuntion with the Südostbayerische Städtetheater

Altes Schauspielhaus
Kleine Königsstrasse 9, 70178 **Stuttgart**
Tel: 711-225 940 Fax: 711-225 9419
Internet: www.schauspielhaus-komoedie.de
E-Mail: schauspielhaus-komoedie@t-online.de
Intendant Elert Bode; Künstlerisches Betriebsbüro Christa Bode; Verwaltung Ines Pieper
Venue type: theatre *Capacity:* 486 *Policy:* own productions *Arts types:* drama *Comments:* see also Komödie im Marquardt

Komödie im Marquardt
Bolzstrasse 4-6, Postfach 100161, 70001 **Stuttgart**
Tel: 711-225 9421 Fax: 711-227 7050 (Verwaltung)/225 9419 (Intendanz)
Internet: www.schauspielhaus-komoedie.de
E-Mail: schauspielhaus-komoedie@t-online.de
Intendant Elert Bode; Künstlerisches Betriebsbüro Christa Bode; Dramaturgie Annette Weinmann; Verwaltung Ines Pieper
Venue type: theatre *Capacity:* 378 *Policy:* own productions *Arts types:* comedy only *Comments:* one children's play in Nov/Dec every year; see also Altes Schauspielhaus

Kultur-und Kongresszentrum Liederhalle
Postfach 103252, Berliner Platz 1-3, 70028 **Stuttgart**
Tel: 711-202 7710 Fax: 711-202 7760
Internet: www.congress-stuttgart.de
E-Mail: liederhalle@congress-stuttgart.de
Verwaltung Winfried Baum
Venue type: multi-purpose *Capacity:* Silcher-Saal 320, Mozart-Saal 752, Beethoven-Saal 2000, Hegel-Saal 1800, Schiller-Saal 406 *Policy:* rent, present *Arts types:* concerts, exhibitions, conferences, balls, etc *Comments:* venue for all important orchestras in the Stuttgart area (including Stuttgarter Philharmoniker)

Music Hall, Stuttgart
c/o Stella Music Management Gmbh, Plieninger Straße 100, 70567 **Stuttgart**
Tel: 711-7254-5 Fax: 711-7254-610
Geschäftsführer Jan Vervear
Capacity: 1800 *Policy:* exclusive venue for Miss Saigon
Arts types: musical

Theaterhaus Stuttgart
Ulmer Strasse 241, 70327 **Stuttgart**
Tel: 711-402 070 Fax: 711-427 363
Internet: www.theaterhaus.com
E-Mail: th@theaterhaus.com
Direktor Werner Schretzmeier; Public Relations Michael Fohler

Venue type: theatre *Capacity:* Hall I 620, Hall II 300, Hall III 150 *Policy:* rent, own productions, guest performances *Arts types:* music, theatre, dance, cabaret, comedy, political/scientific/literary readings, jazz *Comments:* theatre productions with own company; international invited companies showing theatre, music, comedy and satirical shows, dance, etc.; political-literary discussions; see also Drama

Bürgerhaus Troisdorf
Sekretariat, Wilhelm-Hamacher-Platz 24, 53840 **Troisdorf**
Tel: 2241-80050 Fax: 2241-800 550
Internet: www.buergerhaus-troisdorf.com
E-Mail: 0224180050@btx.gate.de
Venue type: town house cultural centre *Capacity:* 5 rooms: up to 1000 *Policy:* rent, promote *Arts types:* drama, concerts, pop, jazz, light music, cabaret, dance

Landestheater Württemberg-Hohenzollern Tübingen
Eberhardstr. 6, 72072 **Tübingen**
Tel: 7071-15920 Fax: 7071-159 270
Intendant Knut Weber; Verwaltungsdirektor Tilmann Pröllochs
Venue type: theatre *Capacity:* Großer Saal 400, Werkstatt 150, UI 100, Musikproberaum 50 *Policy:* produce *Arts types:* theatre *Comments:* see also Drama

ROXY – Kultur in Ulm
Postfach 4165, 89031 **Ulm**
Tel: 731-96862-0 Fax: 731-96862-29
Internet: www.roxy.ulm.de
E-Mail: mail@roxy.ulm.de
Leitung Peter Langer; Geschäftsführung und Verwaltung Brigitte Schirovsky; Programm Bernd Leitner, Peter Langer; Licht- und Ton-technik Micha Kast; Sekretariat Gabi Weber; Öffentlichkeitsarbeit Margit Wollner
Venue type: socio-cultural centre *Capacity:* stage A 1400, stage B 200, stage C 150 *Policy:* rent, present *Arts types:* music, theatre, dance, cinema, cabaret, concerts *Comments:* visiting address: Schillerstr. 1, 89077 Ulm

Erich Göpfert Stadthalle
Parkstraße 44, 59425 **Unna**
Tel: 2303-61004 Fax: 2303-68807
Geschäftsführer Horst Bresan; Techn. Leiter Gottfried Böcker
Venue type: multi-purpose *Capacity:* 1 hall + 2 rooms; 1100 (max) *Policy:* rent, produce, co-produce *Arts types:* classical concerts, rock, pop, drama, children's productions, dance, cabaret

FORUM NIEDERBERG VELBERT
Oststrasse 20, 42551 **Velbert**
Tel: 2051-9504-0 Fax: 2051-950 436
E-Mail: forum-velbert@t-online.de
Leiter des Forums Udo Kiethe
Venue type: theatre *Capacity:* Theatersaal 700, Kongressaal 690 *Policy:* rent, promote *Arts types:* drama, dance, music, exhibitions, conferences

Bühnen der Stadt Villingen-Schwenningen
Romäusring 2, 78050 **Villingen-Schwenningen**
Tel: 7721-822 310 Fax: 7721-822 317
Künstlerische Leitung Herbert Müller; Administrative Leitung Roland Besch; Leiter Neue Tonhalle Ralf Emig
Venue type: theatre, concerthall *Capacity:* Franziskaner Konzerthaus 965, Theater am Ring 828, Freilichtbühne im Komödiengarten 200, Beethovenhaus 546, small auditorium 250, Studiobühne 180, Scheuer 200, Neue Tonhalle 1000, Messegelände Eisstadion 5000 *Policy:* rent *Arts types:* theatre, concerts, recordings, conventions, congresses

Städtisches Bühnenhaus
Ritterstrasse 12-14, 46483 **Wesel**
Tel: 281-203 335 Fax: 281-203 617
Leiter Werner Arand (281-203 350); Verwaltung Jürgen Becks (281-203 340)
Venue type: theatre *Capacity:* up to 710

Landesbühne Niedersachsen Nord GmbH
Virchowstrasse 44, 26382 **Wilhelmshaven**
Tel: 4421-94010 Fax: 4421-940 145
künstlerischer Leiter Gerhard Hess
Venue type: theatre *Capacity:* up to 525 *Policy:* rent, own productions *Arts types:* theatre, drama, chamber music, opera, operetta, ballet

Wilhelmshaven Projekt GmbH
Postfach 1453, 26354 **Wilhelmshaven**
Tel: 4421-92790 Fax: 4421-12508
Geschäftsführer Rüdiger Kramp
Venue type: multi-purpose *Capacity:* 1600 *Policy:* rent *Arts types:* symphony, chamber, opera, musical, dance theatre, rock concerts, congresses, etc

Saalbau / Haus Witten
Kulturforum Witten, Bergerstraße 25, 58452 **Witten**
Tel: 2302-581 2424 Fax: 2302-581 2499
kaufmännischer Leiter Jürgen Küthe; techn. Leiter Uwe Greipel
Venue type: congress hall, Saalbau, Haus Witten *Capacity:* main hall 800, congress hall 800 *Policy:* rent *Arts types:* all types

Lessingtheater
Harztorwall 16, 38300 **Wolfenbüttel**
Tel: 5331-2350 Fax: 5331-86442
Venue type: theatre *Capacity:* 670 *Policy:* rent *Arts types:* drama, opera, symphony, cabaret *Comments:* for hire through Stadtverwaltung Wolfenbüttel: Tel: 5331-298 345

Theater Wolfsburg
Postfach 100930, 38409 **Wolfsburg**
Tel: 5361-26730 Fax: 5361-267 314
Intendant Hans Thoenies; Technischer Leiter Alex Kosnar; Disposition Marita Stolz
Venue type: theatre *Capacity:* up to 833 *Policy:* rent *Arts types:* opera, concerts, drama, ballet, etc. *Comments:* visiting address: Am Klieversberg, 38440 Wolfsburg

Städtisches Spiel und Festhaus
Bahnhofstrasse 4 1/10, 67547 **Worms**
Tel: 6241-88385 Fax: 6241-853 4008
Internet: www.worms-tickets.de
Amtsleitung Ulrich Mieland (Amtsrat); Abteilungsleitung Oliver Mang, Annemarie Neu
Venue type: theatre *Capacity:* up to 840 *Policy:* rent, produce *Arts types:* symphony, opera, operetta, recitals, musicals, cabaret

Historische Stadthalle am Johannisberg Wuppertal
Johannisberg 40, 42103 **Wuppertal**
Tel: 202-245 890 Fax: 202-455 198
Internet: www.stadthalle.de
E-Mail: info@stadthalle.de
Geschäftsführer Herr Wittersheim
Venue type: multi-purpose *Capacity:* Großer Saal 1500, Mendelssohn Saal 300, Offenbach Saal 300, Mahler Saal 150, Hindemith Saal 80, 4 conference rooms *Policy:* rent *Arts types:* music, dance, congresses, exhibitions, lectures

GIBRALTAR (+350)

Alameda Open Air Theatre
Gibraltar Botanic Gardens, Redsands Road, **Gibraltar**
Tel: 72639 Fax: 74022
E-Mail: wildlife_gib@compuserve.com
director John Cortes; theatre administrator Fabiola Offredi
Venue type: open air *Capacity:* 440 *Policy:* promote, rent *Arts types:* concerts, poetry readings, theatre, dance

Ince's Hall
310 Main Street, **Gibraltar**
Tel: 41687 Fax: 52589
E-Mail: minculture@gibnynex.gi
director of culture Manuel Galliano
Venue type: theatre *Capacity:* 320 *Policy:* rent *Arts types:* theatre, musical concerts, shows *Comments:* owned by the Ministry of Culture; organisers of annual drama festival (55th edition in Nov '99)

John Mackintosh Hall
308 Main Street, **Gibraltar**
Tel: 75669 Fax: 40843
E-Mail: gicl@gibnet.gi
director Geraldine Finlayson
Venue type: cultural centre, inc. library *Capacity:* theatre 480 *Arts types:* music, dance, theatre, musicals *Comments:* conference facilities including simultaneous translating equipment; also has three exhibition rooms; see also Drama

GREECE (+30)

Aplo Theatro
Charilaou Trikoupi 4, 17671 **Athens**
Tel: 1-922 9605 Fax: 1-923 3526
E-Mail: fasma@groovy.gr
director Antonis Andypas; technical director A. Synanos
Venue type: theatre *Capacity:* 2 stages; Central Stage 188, Nea Skene 125 *Policy:* own productions *Arts types:* drama, comedy

Athenaeum International Cultural Center
3, Adrianou St., 10555 **Athens**
Tel: 1-321 1949/55/87 Fax: 1-321 1196
Internet: athenaeum.ids.gr
E-Mail: athenm@ibm.net
general secretary Anna Koukouraki; president Louli Psychouli; executive secretary Michel Bichsel
Venue type: concert hall, recital room, stage *Capacity:* 180 *Policy:* present, rent *Arts types:* opera, oratorio, symphonic and chamber music *Comments:* also home of Maria Callas Foundation; member of the World Federation of International Music Competition; see also Promoters and Competitions

Megaron – Athens Concert Hall
Athens Concert Hall Organisation, Vass. Sofias & Kokkali, 11521 **Athens**
Tel: 1-728 2000/2333 (information) Fax: 1-729 0174
general manager Nikos Manolopoulos; chairman of OMA Christos D. Lambrakis; artistic director Nikos Tsouchlos; marketing director Eleni Spanopoulou; head of press office Yulie Papatheodorou
Venue type: concert hall and opera house, theatre, recital room *Capacity:* concert hall 1961, recital hall 484 *Policy:* promote, rent *Arts types:* classical music (opera, symphony, pre-classical), contemporary, jazz, performance, dance (ballet, modern), visual arts exhibitions, conferences

Theatre Elysee
Nymfaiou 12, Ilissia, 11528 **Athens**
Tel: 1-778 2354/2290 Fax: 1-777 1766
director Giorgos Lakoumentas; artistic director Jennie Fotiou
Venue type: italian stage *Capacity:* 250 *Policy:* home theatre of Paedagokike Skene theatre company *Arts types:* children's theatre, classical drama, modern drama

Theatre Minoa
91 Patission Str., 10434 **Athens**
Tel: 1-821 0048/823 2578 Fax: 1-821 0048
director G Giannakos
Venue type: Italian stage *Capacity:* 700 *Policy:* house production and co-productions, available to rent *Arts types:* drama, musical theatre, variety shows, concerts

Theatre Neo Rialto
Kypselis 54, Agiou Meletious Str., 11362 **Athens**
Tel: 1-882 7000/821 8973 Fax: 1-822 7921
artistic director Christo Kelandonis
Venue type: Italian stage *Capacity:* 500 *Policy:* resident company 'Thiasos 81', rented off season *Arts types:* mainly children's theatre

Theatro Embros
2 Riga Palamidi 2, Platia Ag. Anargyron, 10554 **Athens**
Tel: 1-323 8990
director Tassos Bantis
Venue type: ampitheatrical *Capacity:* 2 stages; Pano Orofos 88, Kato Orofos 155 *Arts types:* drama

Theatro Odou Kefallinias
18 Kefalinias St., 11361 **Athens**
Tel: 1-883 8727
producer Vassilis Paulaytzas
Venue type: Italian-stage theatre *Capacity:* main stage 180, second stage 50 *Arts types:* drama

Theatro Porta
Mesoghion 59, 11526 **Athens**
Tel: 1-724 0056 Fax: 1-771 3457/724 0056
E-Mail: mporta@otenet.gr
artistic director Xenia Kalogeropoulou
Venue type: classic stage theatre *Capacity:* 480 *Policy:* resident company 'Mikri Porta', commissioned by other companies for evening performances *Arts types:* drama, children's and youth theatre *Comments:* see also Drama

Theatro Stoa
55 Biskini St., 15771 **Athens**
Tel: 1-770 2830 Fax: 1-770 8828
E-Mail: thetstoa@otenet.gr
artistic director Thanasis Papageorgiou
Venue type: Italian-stage theatre *Arts types:* drama *Comments:* home of Stoa Theatre Company (q.v)

Kerkyra's Municipal Theatre
Dimotiko Theatro Kerkyras, 49100 **Corfu**
Tel: 661-33598/40676 Fax: 661-40676
administrative director George Lavranos
Venue type: Italian stage *Capacity:* 700 *Policy:* co-productions with Corfu's theatre companies & cultural organisations *Arts types:* theatre, opera, ballet, modern dance, symphonic concerts, jazz, street theatre *Comments:* open-air performances in Old Fort during summer

Theatre Logos
Garivaldi 26b, 45221 **Ioannina**
Tel: 1-36182/32642/36747 Fax: 1-32642/32642
artistic director Giorgos Nakos
Venue type: cyclical stage *Capacity:* 120 *Arts types:* contemporary, experimental theatre, performance art, theatre workshops, seminars *Comments:* home of Th. E. E.; see also Drama

Theatre Odou Ermou
106 Ermou Str., 10554 **Monastivaki (Athens)**
Tel: 1-321 4950
director Sotiriso Tsogas
Venue type: italian stage *Capacity:* 100 *Arts types:* theatre, drama

Theatro Technis-Karolos Koun
14 Frynichou Str., 10358 **Plaka (Athens)**
Tel: 1-323 6732 Fax: 1-322 9703
E-Mail: may@otenet.gr
artistic director Yorgos Lazanis
Venue type: Italian-stage theatre *Capacity:* 250 *Policy:* home of Theatro Technis T.C. *Arts types:* drama

Piramatiki Skini of Thessalonoki – Amalia Theatre
71 Amalia St, 54640 **Thessaloniki**
Tel: 31-821 483 Fax: 31-860 708
general manager Natasha Papadimitriou; artistic director Nikiforos Papandreou
Venue type: Italian stage *Capacity:* 240 *Arts types:* drama, Greek and world theatre *Comments:* international theatre festival every spring

GREENLAND (+299)

Katuaq – Greenland Cultural Centre
PO Box 1622, 3900 **Nuuk**
Tel: 323 300 Fax: 323 301
E-Mail: katuaq@greennet.gl
Venue type: cultural centre *Capacity:* concert hall 500, small hall 100 *Arts types:* drama, music (all types), film *Comments:* 2nd address: Nuuk Tourism, PO Box 199, 3900 Nuuk, Greenland, Tel: +229 322 700, Fax: +299 322 710

HUNGARY (+36)

Attila József Cultural Centre, Budapest
József Attila Müvelödési Központ, Budapest
PO Box 34, 1555 **Budapest**
Tel: 1-320 3824/44 Fax: 1-320 3843/349 8151
Internet: www.datanet.hu/~jamk/
E-Mail: jamk@mail.datanet.hu
director Kornél Fenyves
Venue type: municipal cultural centre *Capacity:* theatre hall 352, dance hall 120 *Policy:* rent *Comments:* alternative E-mail: jamk@satimex.tvnet.hu; visiting address: József Attila tér 4, 1131 Budapest XIII

Buda Park Stage, Budapest
Budai Parkszínpad, Budapest
Szabad Tér Színház Közhasznú Tár ság, Városmajor utca, 1122 **Budapest** XII
Tel: 1-466 9916 (theatre)/375 5922 (office) Fax: 1-356 0998
managing director Gábor Koltay (tel: 1-355 0175)
Venue type: open-air theatre *Comments:* operates between 25th May and 15th September every year; available for hire at other times; venue address: Kosztoláni Dezsö tér, 1011 Budapest I

Budapest Convention Centre
Budapest Kongresszusi Központ
PO Box 233, 1444 **Budapest**
Tel: 1-466 6756 Fax: 1-385 2127
Internet: www.hungary.com/pannonia/conventioncentre
E-Mail: conventioncentre@pannoniahotels.hu
director Achim Marowsky; director of art events Mate Lukacsi
Venue type: convention and concert halls, muslti-purpose congress centre *Capacity:* Patria Hall 1750, Bartók Hall 300, Chanson Hall 180, Palma Hall 120 *Policy:* rent, own presentation, cooperation with promoters *Arts types:* orchestra, chamber music, recital, jazz, variety, exhibitions, social events *Comments:* visiting address: Jagelló út 1-3, 1123 Budapest; see also Promoters

Budapest Cultural Centre (BMK)
Budapesti Müvelödési Központ (BMK)
Postafiók 145, 1518 **Budapest**
Tel: 1-203 4646 Fax: 1-203 4632
Internet: www.c3.hu/~muvhazak/bmk/angol.html
E-Mail: bmk@mail.matav.hu
director András Romhányi
Venue type: municipal cultural centre *Capacity:* BMK chamber hall 200 *Policy:* rent *Comments:* venue address: Etele út 55, 1119 Budapest XI; alternative E-mail: muvhazak@c3.hu

Ferenc Liszt Academy of Music
Liszt Ferenc Zeneművészeti Fóiskola
PO Box 206, 1391 **Budapest**
Tel: 1-341 4788 Fax: 1-342 0144
Internet: www.liszt.hu
E-Mail: zeneak@lib.liszt.hu
principal Istvan Lantos; events director Istvan Sörös; rector Prof Sándor Falvai
Venue type: concert halls *Capacity:* grand hall 1200, recital hall 800 *Policy:* available for rent, own presentation, cooperation with promoter *Arts types:* orchestra, chamber music, recital, jazz *Comments:* visiting address: Liszt Ferenc tér 8, 1061 Budapest

FONÓ Music Hall
FONÓ Budai Zeneház
Sztregova u. 3, 1116 **Budapest**
Tel: 1-206 5300 Fax: 1-206 1480/5300
director Zettwitz Sándorné; managing director Zoltán Krulik; international management Tibor Balogh
Venue type: concert hall, CD-shop, music studio, gallery *Capacity:* Music Hall 200, open air stage 200 *Arts types:* jazz, ethnic, contemporary and folk music

International Buda Stage (IBS)
Tárogató út 2-4, 1021 **Budapest**
Tel: 1-391 2525 Fax: 1-394 4974/2129
Internet: www.ibstage.hu
E-Mail: stage@tech.ibs-b.hu
executive dir. Bertalan Zsuzsanna; dir. Miklós Vámas
Venue type: theatre and cultural centre *Capacity:* cap. 265 *Arts types:* from large scale theatre productions to musical evenings, talk shows, student performances, concerts, community events and guest performances invited from all over the world *Comments:* theatre and cultural centre of the International Business School; only venue in the city to be dedicated to the English language and culture; provides a full season of cultural activities for English-speakers in Hungary

Marczibány Square Cultural Centre, Budapest
Marczibányi téri Müvelödéso Központ, Budapest
Postafiók 569, 1538 **Budapest**
Tel: 1-212 2820/0803/5789/5251 Fax: 1-212 4885
director Judit Szakall
Venue type: municipal cultural centre *Capacity:* theatre hall 350, chamber theatre 100 *Policy:* rent *Comments:* venue address: Marczibányi tér 5-9, 1022 Budapest

Margaret Island Open-Air Stage, Budapest
Margitszigeti Szabadtéri Színpad, Budapest
Postafiók 95, 1525 **Budapest**
Tel: 1-320 4866 (theatre)/375 5922 (office) Fax: 1-356 0998
managing director Gábor Koltay
Venue type: open-air venue *Capacity:* open-air stage 3200 *Comments:* located on Margaret Island, operates between 25 May and 15 September every year; available for hire at other times; venue address: Margitsziget utca, 1138 Budapest XIII; office address: Szabad Tér Színház Közhasznú, Városmajor utca, 1122 Budapest XII

Merlin Theatre
Merlin Színház
Gerloczy Utca 4, 1052 **Budapest**
Tel: 1-317 9338 Fax: 1-317 9338/206 0904
Internet: www.c3.hu/~merlin/english.htm#actual
E-Mail: merlin@c3.hu
co-founder & director Tamas Jordan; co-founder & consultant Don McGovern; co-ordinator of English-language season Laszlo Magacs
Venue type: theatre *Capacity:* 250 *Arts types:* English-language theatre, jazz club, occassional concerts

Mu Theatre
Körösy J u. 17, 1117 **Budapest**
Tel: 1-209 4014 Fax: 1-209 4014
E-Mail: mu@c3.hu
artistic director Gerzson Péter Kovács; admin. director Tibor Leszták
Venue type: theatre *Capacity:* 120 *Policy:* produce *Arts types:* contemporary dance, dance-theatre, theatre, performance art, concerts (jazz, contemporary, improvisation) *Comments:* venue for numerous festivals

Pesti Vigadó
Pesti Vigadó -Redoute
PO Box 329, 1369 **Budapest**
Tel: 1-318 9167 Fax: 1-318 9167/4127
Internet: www.vigado.hu
E-Mail: vigado@mail.elender.hu
director Andras Csonka; director of events Balazs Feledy; technical director János Boross
Venue type: concert halls, multi-purpose congress and arts centre *Capacity:* grand hall 700, chamber hall 210 *Policy:* rent, own presentation, cooperation with promoter *Arts types:* orchestra, pop, exhibitions, variety, chamber music, recitals, drama, jazz *Comments:* visiting address: Vörösmarty tér 1, 1051 Budapest

Petőfi Hall (Municipal Youth Entertainment Centre)
Petőfi Csarnok (Fővárosi Ifjúsági Szabadidó Központ)
POB 19, 1581 **Budapest**
Tel: 1-251 7266/7375 Fax: 1-343 3358
director Laszlo Lehel
Venue type: concert hall *Capacity:* (dance) 300, (pop concerts) 2000 *Policy:* own presentation, cooperation with promoter *Comments:* visiting address: Zichy Mihaly ut 14, 1146 Budapest

Scene, The
Szkéné Színház
Müegytem rkp. 3, 1111 **Budapest**
Tel: 1-463 2451/50 Fax: 1-463 2450
artistic & managing director János Regös
Venue type: studio theatre *Capacity:* 80 to 150 *Policy:* own presentations (ARVISURA University Theatre Group, Utolsó Vona/Last Line), promoting, co-productions *Arts types:* experimental theatre, contemporary dance *Comments:* IMMT/ Intern. Meeting of Moving Theatre (annual/Oct)

Trafó
Liliom utca 41, 1094 **Budapest**
Tel: 1-456 2040 Fax: 1-456 2050
Internet: www.c3.hu/trafo
E-Mail: trafo@trafo.c3.hu
contact Nora Molnar; director György Szabó; pr/press Kata Molnar, Adrienn Adanyi
Capacity: 300-500 *Policy:* rent *Arts types:* contemporary arts of all disciplines, emphasis on visual, non-visual theatre

Vígszínház, Budapest
Pannónia utca 1, 1136 **Budapest** XIII
Tel: 1-340 4059/4650/5057/8 (Vígszínház)/266 5245/5557/9932 (Pesti Színház) Fax: 1-329 2338/3919
Internet: www.vigszinhaz.hu
E-Mail: vigszinhaz@euroweb.hu
director László Marton (tel: 1-269 3916)
Venue type: theatre *Capacity:* Vígszínház 1102, Pesti Theatre 540 *Arts types:* drama, musicals
Comments: venue address: Vígszínház, Szent István körút 14, 1136 Budapest XIII; Pesti Színház, Váci utca 9, 1052 Budapest V

Ferenc Kölcsey Hajdú-Bihar Country Cultural Centre, Debrecen
Kölcsey Ferenc Megyei-Városi Müvelödési Lözpont, Debrecen
Hunyadi János utca 1-3, 4026 **Debrecen**
Tel: 52-326 288/413 977/895
Fax: 52-416 040
Internet: www.hbmo.hu/web1/muvhaz/muvhaz1.htm
E-Mail: kolcsey@c3.hu
director András Lukovics
Capacity: Bartók Concert Hall 650, Theatre Hall 408, conference room 120, multi-purpose dance hall 60, education room 60, open-air theatre 1500

József Katona Theatre, Kecskemét
Katona József Színház, Kecskemét
Postafiók 48, 6001 **Kecskemét**
Tel: 76-483 283/481 171 Fax: 76-481 417
Internet: www.kecskemet.szinhaz.hu
E-Mail: katonaj@mail.datanet.hu
director Géza Bodolay
Capacity: József Katona Theatre 581, László Kelemen Chamber Theatre 80 *Arts types:* festivals, lectures, other cultural events, drama

Kas Theater
Lackner K. út 22, 9400 **Sopron**
Tel: 99-317 341 Fax: 99-354 078
managing director Géza Demeter; artistic director Csaba Méhes
Venue type: theatre
Capacity: 80 *Arts types:* studio theatre, dance-theatre, concerts

ICELAND (+354)

Hafnarborg Institute of Culture and Fine Arts
Strandgata 34, 220 **Hafnarfjördur**
Tel: 555 0080 Fax: 565 4480
E-Mail: hafnaborg@centrum.is
managing director Pétrún Pétursdóttir
Venue type: art exhibitons hall *Capacity:* up to 260
Policy: promote, rent
Arts types: exhibitions, chamber music, recitals
Comments: guest atelier for visiting artists

Gerduberg Menningarmióstöd
Gerdubergi 3-5, 111 **Reykjavík**
Tel: 575 7700 Fax: 575 7701
E-Mail: gberg@skyrr.is
managing director Elisabet B. Thorisdottir
Venue type: multi-purpose
Capacity: 120 *Policy:* rent *Arts types:* theatre, dance, concerts, opera, exhibitions

Icelandic Opera
Islenska Operan
PO Box 1416, 121 **Reykjavík**
Tel: 552 7033 Fax: 552 7384
E-Mail: opera@opera.is
general manager Bjarni Danielsson; artistic director Gerrit Schuil
Venue type: theatre and concert hall
Capacity: 473 *Policy:* produce, rent
Arts types: opera, chamber music, classical, musicals
Comments: visiting address: Islenska Operan, Ingolfsstraeti, 101 Reykjavík

National Theatre of Iceland
Thjódleikhúsid, Hverfisgata 19, 101 **Reykjavík**
Tel: 551 1204 Fax: 561 1200
Internet: www.theatre.is
E-Mail: stefbald@centrum.is
artistic director Stefán Baldursson; dramaturg Melkorka Tekla Olafsdottir; production manager Sigmundur Örn Arngrímsson; administrative director Gudrún Gudmundsdóttir; marketing manager Gudrún Bachmann
Venue type: theatre *Capacity:* main stage 530, studio 150, small stage 100 *Arts types:* new writing, modern and classical plays, musicals, opera *Comments:* offices at Lindargata 7, 101 Reykjavík; see also Drama

Nordic House
Norraena Húsid / Nordens Hus / Pohjolan Talo
Hríngbraut, 101 **Reykjavík**
Tel: 551 7030 Fax: 552 6476
Internet: nordice.is
E-Mail: nh@nordice.is
director Riitta Heinämaa; programme secretary Ingibjörg Björnsdóttir
Venue type: exhibition hall, auditorium, concert hall
Capacity: 100 *Policy:* rent or arrange own productions
Arts types: concerts, lectures, conferences, seminars, film shows, exhibitions
Comments: focus on Nordic music and culture; the centre has a library and a cafeteria

Reykjavik City Theatre
Borgarleikhúsid – City Theatre
Listabraut 3, 103 **Reykjavík**
Tel: 568 8000 Fax: 568 0383
Venue type: theatre *Capacity:* theatre 536, studio 200
Arts types: theatre, opera, ballet
Comments: home of Reykjavik Theatre Company

Sigurjón Ólafsson Museum
Listasafn Sigurjóns Olafssonar,
Laugarnestanga 70, 105 **Reykjavík**
Tel: 553 2906 Fax: 581 4553
director Brigitta Spur
Venue type: gallery, the main exhibition room is also used as a concert hall *Capacity:* 100 *Policy:* rent, presents *Arts types:* solo and chamber music concerts *Comments:* presents events at its own risk and shares the risk with another promoter as the summer concerts cycle (June-July and August); gallery of sculptures by Sigurjón Ólafsson

IRELAND Republic of (+353)

Institute of Technology Carlow
Kilkenny Road, **Carlow**
Tel: 503-70423 Fax: 503-41349
E-Mail: mcenteej@itcarlow.ie
head of external affairs Jim McEntee
Venue type: multi-purpose
Capacity: Barrow Centre 700
Policy: rent only *Arts types:* concerts, exhibitions etc.
Comments: availability limited to weekends and non-term times ie. Christmas, Easter, Summer holidays

City Hall Conference & Exhibition Centre
City Hall, **Cork**
Tel: 21-966 222 Fax: 21-314 238
E-Mail: norrenmulcahy@cork.corp/ie
administrator G O'Sullivan
Venue type: concert hall
Capacity: 1000 *Policy:* rent
Arts types: pop, orchestral concerts, exhibitions

Cork Opera House
Emmet Place, **Cork**
Tel: 21-274 308/270 022 (box office)/271 168 (marketing) Fax: 21-276 357
E-Mail: operahousecork@tinet.ie
executive director Gerry Barnes; marketing manager Miriam Hurley
Venue type: national touring house *Capacity:* 1000
Policy: rent *Arts types:* drama, dance, opera, comedy, music, classical concerts

Everyman Palace
15 Mac Curtain Street, **Cork**
Tel: 21-503 077 (administration) Fax: 21-502 820
technical manager Tim Fehilly; artistic director Geoff Gould
Venue type: theatre
Capacity: 628 + wheelchair spaces
Policy: rent, promote, co-produce *Arts types:* drama, dance, concerts, ballet, exhibitions etc

Granary Theatre, The
The Mardyke, **Cork**
Tel: 21-904 275 Fax: 21-904 272
artistic director Alli Robertson; administrator Maeve Lewis; technial manager Ivan Tilkington
Venue type: student theatre in the round
Capacity: 150 *Policy:* receive, present, produce
Arts types: all types

Triskel Arts Centre
Tobin Street off South Main Street, **Cork**
Tel: 21-272 022 Fax: 21-272 592
E-Mail: triskel@iol.ie
executive director Deirdrie Enright
Venue type: multi-purpose gallery x 2, smaller ground floor gallery *Capacity:* auditorium 100, gallery 40 *Policy:* present, co-produce, rent *Arts types:* film & video, music, drama, emerging performers, exhibitions, literature *Comments:* Triskel has recently opened phase II, giving all the new spaces as outlined above; offers education workshop and two artists studios; also has facilities for film/projection

Andrews Lane Theatre
9-17 Andrews Lane, **Dublin** 2
Tel: 1-679 5720 Fax: 1-679 7552
E-Mail: condon1@indigo.ie
general manager Patricia Moylan; administrator Laura Condon
Venue type: theatre *Capacity:* 220, studio 76 *Policy:* mainly for rent *Comments:* home of Theatre O Company, Andrews Lane Productions

Bank of Ireland Arts Centre
Foster Place, **Dublin** 2
Tel: 1-671 1488/670 7555 Fax: 1-670 7556
social and cultural activities co-ordinator Barry O'Kelly
Venue type: arts centre
Capacity: up to 200 *Policy:* produce
Arts types: lunch-time and evening recitals, theatre, films
Comments: rehearsal venue, exhibitions, audio-visual and reception facilities; re-opened after extensive refurbishment

City Arts Centre
23/25 Moss Street, **Dublin** 2
Tel: 1-677 0643 Fax: 1-677 0131
Internet: homepage.tinet.ie/~cityarts/
E-Mail: cityartscentre@tinet.ie
executive director Sandy Fitzgerald; general manager Audrey Behan; programming manager Collette Farrell; communications director Kathrin Laffey
Venue type: multi-purpose, theatre and gallery *Capacity:* up to 130 *Arts types:* multi-disciplinary community arts centre exploring issues of equality & social justice through artistic processes & celebrations; incorporates theatre, gallery, music, dance & education *Comments:* studios available for rehearsals for music (bands)

Crypt Arts Centre
Dame Street, Dublin Castle, **Dublin** 2
Tel: 1-671 3387 Fax: 1-671 3370
E-Mail: crypt@clubi.ie
general manager David Pearse; artistic director John O'Brien; technical manager Paul Winters; executive director Niall Ó Sioradáin
Venue type: performance and exhibition space *Capacity:* 100 *Policy:* in-house productions, rent, promote *Arts types:* performance, exhibition, multimedia *Comments:* home of Iomhá Ildánach Theatre Company; springboard for emerging new and experimental companies and artists; see also Drama

Focus Theatre
6 Pembroke Place, **Dublin** 2
Tel: 1-676 3071/660 7109 Fax: 1-660 7109
E-Mail: weakley@indigo.ie
administrator Etàin Winder; artistic director Deidre O'Connell; assistant manager Kevin O'Brien
Venue type: theatre *Capacity:* 77 *Policy:* rent, produce
Arts types: drama, jazz *Comments:* see also Drama

Gaiety Theatre
South King Street, **Dublin** 2
Tel: 1-679 5622 (admin)/677 1717 (box office)/456 9569 (ticketmaster) Fax: 1-677 1921
Internet: www.gaietytheatre.com
E-Mail: prgaiety@indigo.ie
executive director John Costigan; assistant to executive director Rebecca McCauley
Venue type: theatre *Capacity:* 1165 *Policy:* receiving house
Arts types: theatre, musicals, opera, concerts, pantomime

House of Lords
Bank of Ireland, 2 College Green, **Dublin** 2
Tel: 1-661 5933 ext 2265 Fax: 1-661 5675
head of public affairs David Holden
Venue type: historical chamber *Policy:* produce, present
Comments: lectures every Tuesday, admission free

Hugh Lane Municipal Gallery of Modern Art
Charlemont House, Parnell Square, **Dublin** 1
Tel: 1-874 1903 Fax: 1-872 2182
E-Mail: hughlane@siol.ie
director Barbara Dawson; music organiser Gavin o'Sullivan
Venue type: art gallery *Capacity:* 300 *Policy:* produce, present *Arts types:* instrumental, choral, recital and chamber concerts with emphasis on contemporary music, exhibitions and lectures *Comments:* largest collection of contemporary Irish art

Irish Museum of Modern Art – Royal Hospital Kilmainham
Military Road, Kilmainham, **Dublin** 8
Tel: 1-612 9900 Fax: 1-612 9999
Internet: www.modernart.ie
E-Mail: info@modernart.ie
director Declan McGonagle; head of public affairs Philomena Byrne
Venue type: multi-purpose *Capacity:* Great Hall 550, Chapel 250 *Policy:* rent, produce
Arts types: concerts, wide range of events, exhibitions, conferences in Museum

National Concert Hall
An Ceoláras Náisiunta
Earlsfort Terrace, **Dublin** 2
Tel: 1-475 1666 (admin)/1572 (box office)
Fax: 1-478 3797 (admin)/475 1507 (box office)
director Judith Woodworth; chairman of board Dermot Egan
Venue type: concert hall *Capacity:* 1200 *Policy:* present, rent in accordance with seat prices *Arts types:* concerts
Comments: home of National Symphony Orchestra, concert pipe organ installed Sept '91

Olympia Theatre
72 Dame Street, **Dublin** 2
Tel: 1-677 7744 (box ofice)/478 2153 (production & pr)
Fax: 1-679 9576/9474 (box office)/478 2176 (production & pr)
managing director Gerry Sinnott; general manager Brian Whitehead; theatre manager/pa to md Tara Sinnott; stage manager John Brogan; box office manager Veronica Hearst
Venue type: theatre
Capacity: 1272 (stalls 507, circle 421, boxes 44, gallery 300) the seats in the stalls can be removed to allow for 900 standing *Policy:* rent, produce, present
Arts types: drama, concerts (late night music concerts – folk, jazz, rock), plays, dance
Comments: oldest theatre in Dublin

Peacock Theatre
26 Lower Abbey Street, **Dublin** 1
Tel: 1-874 8741 Fax: 1-872 9177
general manager Martin Fahy; artistic director Patrick Mason; director of PR and marketing Magdalene Boughton; managing director Richard Wakely
Venue type: theatre
Capacity: 157 *Policy:* rent, present
Arts types: experimental theatre of all kinds; plays in the Irish language
Comments: aims to showcase new Irish writers, further experimental theatre, encourage Irish language productions; see also Drama

Point Theatre
East Link Bridge, **Dublin** 1
Tel: 1-836 6777 Fax: 1-836 6422
chief executive Mike Adamson; general manager Cormac Rennick; assistant manager Philip Rogers
Venue type: theatre
Capacity: up to 8500
Policy: rent *Arts types:* classical, pop, opera, ballet, major musicals

Project Arts Centre
39 East Essex Street, Temple Bar, **Dublin** 2
Tel: 1-679 6622 Fax: 1-636 9151
Internet: www.project.ie
E-Mail: info@project.ie
general manager Tom Coghlan; artistic director Kathy McArdle; director of public affairs Janice McAdam; visual arts director Valerie Connor
Venue type: multi-purpose arts centre
Capacity: main auditorium 250, studio space 100
Policy: own productions, rent
Arts types: varies – springboard for emerging new and experimental companies and artists
Comments: strong visual arts policy (gallery space), strong dance programme; new custom-built venue opening March 2000 with three multi-configurable spaces

RHA Gallagher Gallery
15 Ely Place, **Dublin** 2
Tel: 1-661 2558 Fax: 1-661 0762
E-Mail: gallagher@tinet.ie
director Patrick Murphy;
administrator Patricia Moriarty
Venue type: 4 galleries *Capacity:* Hall A 300, Hall B 700, Hall C 100, Hall D 150
Policy: rent, produce, co-produce
Arts types: functions, exhibitions, ballet, conferences, concerts, recitals, opera

Royal Dublin Society Concert Hall
c/o Royal Dublin Society, Ballsbridge, **Dublin** 4
Tel: 1-668 0866 Fax: 1-660 4014
Internet: www.rds.ie
E-Mail: marketing@rds.ie
arts development executive Adriane Dunne
Venue type: concert and conference hall *Capacity:* 900
Policy: rent *Arts types:* classical music, drama, banquets, lectures, fashion shows, conferences, orchestral concerts, recitals, exhibitions

Tivoli Theatre
135/138 Francis Street, **Dublin** 8
Tel: 1-454 4472 Fax: 1-453 3167
director and artistic director Tony Byrne
Venue type: theatre *Capacity:* up to 500, Tivoli 2 (theatre, concert hall) up to 900 *Policy:* rental, in house productions, takes touring companies
Arts types: mixed programme

Vicar Street
59 Thomas Street, **Dublin** 8
Tel: 1-454 5533 Fax: 1-454 6787
contact Bren Berry
Venue type: cabaret style *Capacity:* 650 *Policy:* rent, own programming *Arts types:* musical theatre

Táin Theatre – Town Hall Dundalk
Crowe Street, **Dundalk**
Tel: 42-32276 Fax: 42-46761
E-Mail: dundarts@indigo.ie
arts officer Brian Harten
Venue type: concert hall
Capacity: Hall A 649, Hall B 80
Policy: rent, produce (by council)
Arts types: chamber orchestral, choral, traditional, world, country, folk, dance, drama, concerts, readings, exhibitions, ballet, opera

An Taibhdhearc Theatre
Middle Street, **Galway**
Tel: 91-562 024/563 600 (box office)
Fax: 91-563 195
Internet: www.iol.ie/~taibh/
E-Mail: taibh@iol.ie
administrator Aoife Ní Scolaí; artistic director Éamonn Draper
Venue type: theatre *Capacity:* 180 *Policy:* rent, present, produce *Arts types:* drama, concerts, film, workshops
Comments: national theatre for Irish language; particular emphasis on Irish language productions

Nun's Island
Galway Arts Centre
23 Nun's Island, **Galway**
Tel: 91-565 886 Fax: 91-568 642
E-Mail: gac@indigo.ie
director of visual arts/education/development Paul Fahy; director/administrator Trish Fitzpatrick; Galway Youth Theatre artistic director Niamh Dillon, Maeve Murray; finance manager John Kelly
Venue type: theatre *Capacity:* 100
Policy: rent, produce *Arts types:* drama, concerts, poetry readings, exhibitions, dance, lectures, education programmes *Comments:* also – Galway Arts Centre Galleries, 47 Dominick Street, Galway; 2 years part-time acting course; 1 year part-time production course; produces Irelands foremost literary event, the Cuirt International Festival of Literature

Belltable Arts Centre
69 O'Connell Street, **Limerick**
Tel: 61-319 709 (administration)/61-319 866 (box office)
Fax: 61-418 552
E-Mail: belltable@iol.ie
director Mary Coll; admininstrator Oonagh O'Shea; press & publicity officer Cecilia O'Dongonhue; production manager Gerry Meagher
Venue type: theatre, gallery
Capacity: 315 *Policy:* rent, receiving venue, split *Arts types:* drama, music, dance, opera, children's productions, exhibitions, film, poetry recitals

University Concert Hall
University Concert Hall, **Limerick**
Tel: 61-331 549 Fax: 61-331 585
director Michael Murphy
Venue type: concert hall *Capacity:* 1037 *Policy:* rent, co-produce, events at own risk, share risk with promoters
Arts types: classical, symphony, variety, opera, country, pop, chamber music, recitals, dance, exhibitions, product launches, conferences, fashion shows
Comments: 2 smaller theatres which seat 250 and 150 respectively; both of these theatres can be linked by sound and vision to the main concert hall or can be used independently; also hard of hearing and wheelchair facilities

Hawk's Well Theatre
Temple Street, **Sligo**
Tel: 71-62167/61526 Fax: 71-71737
E-Mail: hawkswell@tinet.ie
director Denis Clifford; assistant director Averyl Dooher; stage manager Barry McKinney; box office manager Caroline Pilkington
Venue type: theatre *Capacity:* 350
Policy: rent, presents events at own risk *Arts types:* drama, music, dance, comedy

Premier Hall
O'Donovan Rossel St., **Thurles (Co. Tipperary)**
Tel: 504-21938
manager Father James Walton
Venue type: multi-purpose
Capacity: standing 900 *Policy:* rent
Arts types: opera, concerts, drama, dance, musicals
Comments: Thurles Musical Society

Tipperary Excel Heritage Company Ltd.
Station House, Station Road, **Tipperary Town**
Tel: 62-52011 Fax: 62-31067
E-Mail: wted@tinet.ie
general manager Paul Grisewood
Venue type: multipurpose
Capacity: 350 *Policy:* present, rent, co-produce
Arts types: music, theatre, film, fine arts
Comments: due to have re-opened by December 1999; open for bookings; the centre will include 2 small cinemas (cap 140 & 90), an art gallery, workroom and exhibition centre

Siamsa Tire Theatre
Town Park, **Tralee (Co. Kerry)**
Tel: 66-23055 Fax: 66-27276
general manager Martin Whelan; artistic director John Sheeghan; technical director Jimmy McDonnell
Venue type: theatre
Capacity: 355 *Policy:* rent, produce, co-produce
Arts types: drama, dance, recitals, music series, exhibitions *Comments:* brings in other touring companies; adjoining artists exhibition arena; residence of the National Folk Theatre of Ireland; see also Drama

Garter Lane Arts Centre
22A O'Connell Street, **Waterford**
Tel: 51-855 038 (box office)/877 153 (admin)
Fax: 51-871 570
Internet: www.io.ie/~glac
E-Mail: admin@garterlane.ie
artistic director Caroline Senior; general manager Lilly O'Reilly; finance manager Jim Sammon; box office manager Margaret O'Neill; technical manager Michael Oates; front of house manager Liam Fitzpatrick
Venue type: gallery, theatre *Capacity:* theatre 200, gallery 150 *Policy:* rent, produce *Arts types:* drama, dance, music, literature, comedy, film, children and young peoples events, exhibitions and workshops

Theatre Royal Waterford
The Mall, **Waterford**
Tel: 51-874 402 Fax: 51-856 900
chairman Laurence Fanning
Venue type: theatre *Capacity:* 645 *Policy:* rent, produce
Arts types: opera, concerts, drama, dance, musicals, variety, festivals

Theatre Royal
27 High Street, **Wexford**
Tel: 53-22400 (administration)/22144 (box office)
Fax: 53-24289 (administration)/47438 (box office)
Internet: www.wexfordopera.com
E-Mail: wexfordopera@iol.ie
chief executive Jerome Hynes; artistic director Luigi Ferrari
Venue type: theatre *Capacity:* 550 *Policy:* rent, organise
Arts types: classical & pop concerts, drama, opera, dance *Comments:* organise Wexford Opera Festival Oct-Nov in theatre; see also Festivals

Wexford Arts Centre
Cornmarket, **Wexford**
Tel: 53-23764 Fax: 53-24544
artistic director Denis Collins; community artist Anne Heffernan; publicity officer Johanna Murphy
Venue type: community arts centre, multi-purpose hall, theatre *Capacity:* up to 135 *Policy:* produce, rent *Arts types:* exhibitions, dance, drama, music, workshops, community arts, readings

ITALY (+39)

Teatro Comunale
Via Savona N.1, 15100 **Alessandria**
Tel: 0131-234 266 Fax: 0131-253 200
direttore t.b.a.; presidente Maria Grazia Bandirola; uff. stampa Maria Grazia Robotti
Venue type: theatre & multi-screen cinema *Capacity:* 1173 *Policy:* rent *Arts types:* drama, ballet, cinema, concerts, lyric *Comments:* Sala Adelio Ferrero 236 for cineforum, also another room for talks and seminars

Teatro de I Rinnovati
Via Browning 192, 31011 **Asolo (TV)**
Tel: 0423-952 115 Fax: 0423-520 567
direttore Anna Pieroni; direttore artistico Roberto Zarpellon
Venue type: theatre *Capacity:* 250 *Policy:* rent *Arts types:* drama, cinema, concerts, congresses

Teatro Eleonora Duse
Via Regina Cornaro, 31011 **Asolo (TV)**
Tel: 0423-5245 (switchboard comune) Fax: 0423-950 130
Internet: www.comune.asolo.tv.it
Comments: the theatre is partially open; contact Assessorato alla Cultura del Comune di Asolo

Teatro Comunale di Atri
Piazza del Duomo, 64032 **Atri (TE)**
Tel: 085-879 1223 Fax: 085-879 1217
assessore alla cultura Dott.ssa Gabriella Liberatore
Venue type: theatre *Capacity:* 350 *Policy:* rent *Arts types:* operetta, lyric, dance, drama, concerts *Comments:* administration: Comune di Atri – Assessorato alla Cultura, Palazzo Ducale, 64032 Atri (TE)

Kursaal Santalucia
Largo Adua, 5/9, 70121 **Bari**
Tel: 080-524 6070 Fax: 080-524 6214
Internet: www.kursaal.it
E-Mail: kursaal@igsnet.it
direttore artistico Gigi Proietti (teatro), Rino Marrone (musica), Angelo Ceglie (cinema)
Venue type: cinema – theatre *Capacity:* 512 *Policy:* rent
Arts types: drama, music, cinema, conferences with simultaneous translated in 5 languages *Comments:* built in 1927 it was refurbished in the 80's

Teatro Abeliano
Via della Costituente 84/A, 70125 **Bari**
Tel: 080-542 7678 Fax: 080-542 5924
E-Mail: abeliano@iqsnet.it
presidente Anna Sciannimanico; direttore artistico Tina Tempesta
Venue type: theatre *Capacity:* 210 *Policy:* own productions, rent, residencies *Arts types:* drama

Teatro Casa di Pulcinella
Arena della Vittoria 4A, 70123 **Bari**
Tel: 080-521 9974/534 4660 Fax: 080-572 0658
Internet: www.aziendeonline.it/casadipulcinella/
E-Mail: casadipulcinella@mail.clio.it
organizzazione Maria Laterza; direttore artistico Paolo Comentale; ufficio stampa Emilia Brunetti, Patrizia Fatuzzo
Capacity: 120 *Arts types:* theatre for children and adolescents, exhibitions, workshops *Comments:* see also Puppetry and Festivals

Teatro Kismet Opera
Strada San Giorgio Martire 22/F, 70123 **Bari**
Tel: 080-574 9254 Fax: 080-574 9228
E-Mail: kismet@pangeanet.it
presidente Augusto Masiello; direttore artistico Carlo Bruni; direttore artistico della programmazione musicale Antonio Princigalli; responsabile distribuzione Diane Guerrier; press office Marcella Chiummo
Venue type: fully refurbished old industrial factory
Capacity: 220 + 100 *Policy:* the theatre is given free to companies that have similar projects to those of the Company Kismet *Arts types:* drama, experimental theatre, concerts, children's theatre, exhibitions of visual arts, European projects *Comments:* also have an open-air space

Teatro Comunale Vittorio Emmanuele II
Corso Garibaldi, 82100 **Benevento**
Tel: 0824-21848/42711 Fax: 0824-42711
Venue type: theatre *Capacity:* 400 *Policy:* rent *Arts types:* ballet, concerts, opera, drama *Comments:* tthe Comune of Benevento also manages Auditorium di Via Calandra-750; Auditorium di S. Nicola-220; Teatro de Simone-252

Sala Piatti
c/o Istituto Musicale G. Donizetti, Via San Salvatore 6, 24129 **Bergamo**
Tel: 035-237 374/816 Fax: 035-237 374/816
director Marco Giovanetti
Capacity: 300 *Policy:* rent *Arts types:* classical music, jazz, drama *Comments:* at time of going to print the venue was temporarily closed for refurbishment

Teatro Donizetti
Piazza Cavour 15, 24121 **Bergamo**
Tel: 035-399 320/208 Fax: 035-233 488/234 110
Internet: teatro.gaetano-donizetti.com
E-Mail: teatro@gaetano-donizetti.com
direttore artistico Alessio Vlad
Venue type: 3 stages, 2 galleries *Capacity:* 1154 *Arts types:* opera, operetta, Festival Donizettiano, symphony, concerts, theatre, jazz, dance, drama *Comments:* the theatre is managed by the city council department of culture: Assessorato alla Cultura, Tel: 035-416 0604/605, Fax: 035-233 488

Teatro Tascabile di Bergamo
Via Colleoni 2, 24129 **Bergamo**
Tel: 035-235 350/210 281/231 191 Fax: 035-242 095
E-Mail: titibi@spm.it
artistic director Renzo Vescovi; organisation Antonella Baldi; administration Elena Donda
Venue type: theatre *Capacity:* 60 *Policy:* resident company and touring companies *Arts types:* chamber theatre, contemporary theatre *Comments:* organises international festival of music and dance 'Sonavan....Le Vie Dintorno'; part of Accademia della Forme Sceniche

Arena del Sole – Nuova Scena – Teatro Stabile di Bologna
Via Indipendenza 44, 40121 **Bologna**
Tel: 051-270 789 Fax: 051-239 588
Internet: www.arenadelsole.it
E-Mail: info@arenadelsole.it
direttore artistico e organizzativo Paolo Cacchioli; presidente Massimo Terranova; vice presidente e direttore amministrativo Carla Magri; direttore della comunicazione Bruno Damini; co-direttore organizzativo Natalino Mingrone
Venue type: Italian theatre *Capacity:* Sala Grande 900, Sala Interaction (studio theatre) 180-250, Sala Degli Archi 64 *Policy:* rent *Arts types:* drama, dance, music
Comments: home of the Teatro Stabile di Bologna (q.v.)

Link Project
Via Fioravanti N. 14, 40129 **Bologna**
Tel: 051-370 971 Fax: 051-370 972
Internet: www.comune.bologna.it/iperbole/link
E-Mail: link@iperbole.bologna.it
musica elettronica Mauro Boris Borella; music contemporanea Denrico Croci; teatro e performances Silvia Fanti; settore visivo Daniele Gasparinetti
Venue type: multi-purpose *Capacity:* Room Blue 300, Room White 800, Sublink 400, Infoshop 100, Deviant Dark Room 400 *Policy:* residencies, own productions, also rent *Arts types:* theatre, media arts, electronic music, poetry *Comments:* alternative E-mail: info@linkproject.org; alternative Internet: www.linkproject.org; see also Agents & Producers, Promoters and Festivals

Teatri di Vita
via del Pratello 90/92, 40122 **Bologna**
Tel: 051-522 032 Fax: 051-523 113
Internet: www.comune.bologna.it/bologna/teatvita
E-Mail: teatvita@iperbole.bologna.it
artistic director Stefano Casi; organisation director Barbara Pulliero
Venue type: multi-purpose *Capacity:* 90 *Policy:* present, produce, rent *Arts types:* contemporary dance and theatre *Comments:* since October 1999 have opened a new theatre in Bologna: Parco dei Pini, Via E. Ponente 485, 40132 Bologna, with 2 rooms (one has cap. 300); the new venue will be used for international programmes, productions and workshops, also the PIERCE project which aims to highlight the multiplicity of various arts types of new artists and groups in Bologna and Emilia Romagna; Teatri di Vita info-point: Parco dei Pini, Via Emilia Ponente 485, 40132 Bologna; see also Promoters

Teatro Comunale
Largo Respighi 1, 40126 **Bologna**
Tel: 051-529 011 Fax: 051-529 934/905/945
Internet: www.nettuno.it/bo/teatro-comunale
E-Mail: teatro.comunale@bo.nettuno.it
sovrintendente Prof. Arch. Felicia Bottino; ufficio sponsorizzazioni Pier Paolo Sabbatini; ufficio stampa e pubbliche relazioni Michele D'Agostino; vice presidente Federico Stame; direttore artistico Gianni Tangucci; segretario artistico Aldo Sisillo; segretario generale Sandra Dal Pan; direttore allestimenti scenici Italo Grassi
Venue type: 17th C. theatre *Capacity:* 960 *Arts types:* symphonic, chamber, opera, morning and lunch time concerts *Comments:* see also Orchestras and Opera

Teatro Dehon
Via Libia 59, 40138 **Bologna**
Tel: 051-342 934 (box office)/238 592 (admin)
Fax: 051-238 592
amministrazione Renata Fiorentini; direttore artistico Guido Ferrarini; direttore dell'organizzazione e ufficio stampa Tiziano Tommesani
Venue type: theatre *Capacity:* 500 *Arts types:* drama, exhibitions, visual art performances and installations in the foyer once a month, prosa *Comments:* organises festival La Scrittura Incantata, also poetry readings and book launches; see also Drama & Festivals

Teatro delle Moline
Via delle Moline 1, 40126 **Bologna**
Tel: 051-235 288 Fax: 051-226 767
E-Mail: tnuove@iperbole.bologna.it
direttore Luigi Gozzi; direzione artistica Marinella Manicardi
Venue type: theatre *Capacity:* 60 *Policy:* rent *Arts types:* contemporary drama, music, theatre, dance *Comments:* managed by: Teatro Nuova Edizione; see also Drama

Teatro Testoni
via Matteotti 16, 40129 **Bologna**
Tel: 051-379 000 Fax: 051-377 851
E-Mail: testrag@iperbole.bologna.it
administrative director & legal representative Lucio d'Amelio; artistic director Valeria Frabetti; press officer Paolo Rubini; vice-presidente Roberto Frabetti
Venue type: theatre *Capacity:* Sala A 500, Sala B 120 *Policy:* rent *Arts types:* children's theatre
Comments: see also Drama

Auditorium Provinciale
Via Dante, 39100 **Bolzano**
Tel: 0471-992 111 (Dr Lampis)/991 200
Fax: 0471-991 209
contact Dr Lampis
Venue type: auditorium *Capacity:* 742 *Comments:* previously known as Cinema Augusteo; now the refurbished auditorium is the home of Orchestra Sinfonica Haydn and Societa dei Concerti di Bolzano

Nuovo Teatro Comunale / Neues Stadtheater Bozen
Piazza Verdi, 39100 **Bolzano**
Tel: 0471-304 100/111 (switchboard)/113 (admin)
Fax: 0471-304 114
interim director Dr Renzo Caramaschi (tel: 0471-997 373, fax: 0471-997 387)
Venue type: theatre *Capacity:* sala grande 810, sala polirunzionale 240 *Policy:* rent *Arts types:* drama, opera, ballet, concerts, recitals
Comments: opened Sept 1999; the theatre houses Teatro Stabile di Bolzano and Vereinigte Bühnen Bozen; see also Drama

Sala Concerti del Conservatorio Claudio Monteverdi
Piazza Domenicani N. 19, 39100 **Bolzano**
Tel: 0471-978 764/089 Fax: 0471-975 891
director Prof. ssa Vea Carpi
Venue type: concert hall *Capacity:* 470 *Policy:* rent *Arts types:* classic

Teatro Comunale di Gries
Galleria Telser N. 13, 39100 **Bolzano**
Tel: 0471-262 320 Fax: 0471-997 387
Venue type: theatre *Capacity:* 370 *Policy:* rent
Comments: the theatre belongs to the Comune di Bolzano; to rent it contact: Ufficio Attività Culturali, Tel: 0471-997 373/392 388/292

Teatro Grande
via Paganora 19/a, 25121 **Brescia**
Tel: 030-297 9311/33 (box office)
Fax: 030-297 9342
artistic director & responsabile artistico per la stagione lirica Giovanni Andreoli; amministratore Giuseppe Morandi
Venue type: theatre *Capacity:* 1147 *Policy:* rent *Arts types:* opera, symphony, concerts, drama, ballet

Teatro Santa Chiara
Associazione Centro Teatrale Bresciano, contrada S. Chiara 50/A, 25122 **Brescia**
Tel: 030-377 1111/2134 Fax: 030-293 181/377 0784
direttore artistico Cesare Lievi; ufficio stampa Bianca Simoni
Capacity: 154 *Arts types:* drama

Teatro Accademico
Via Garibaldi, 31033 **Castelfranco Veneto**
Tel: 0423-494 500 Fax: 0423-735 580 (municipio)
assessore alla cultura del comune di castelfranco veneto Maria Gomierato
Venue type: theatre *Capacity:* 286
Arts types: drama, concerts

Ente Autonomo Regionale Teatro Massimo Bellini
Via Perrotta 12, 95131 **Catania**
Tel: 095-730 6111(switchboard)/715 0200 (press office)
Fax: 095-321 830 (press)
presidente Avv. Vincenzo Bianco; sovrintendente Alberto Bombace; direttore artistico Piero Rattalino; responsabile delle comunicazioni dott. Nino Milozzo; segretario artistico Mauro Trombetta; direttore del coro Tiziana Carlini; direttore amministrativo Antonio Ferro
Venue type: theatre
Capacity: 1200 *Arts types:* opera, symphony, ballet, concerts, choral, dance
Comments: seasons run from Sept/Oct to June; in July the activities take place in Villa Bellini, an open space (gardens); see also Opera and Orchestras

Piccolo Teatro di Catania
Via F. Ciccaglione 29, 95125 **Catania**
Tel: 095-447 603/552 083 Fax: 095-552 083
artistic/administrative director Giovanni Salvo; technical director/press officer Luisa Fiorello
Venue type: amphitheatre *Capacity:* 242 *Policy:* own productions also rent *Arts types:* music, dance, theatre
Comments: see also Drama

Teatro Metropolitan
Via S Euplio 21, 95124 **Catania**
Tel: 095-322 323 Fax: 095-316 596
gestore del teatro Antonino Mazza
Capacity: 1700, with boxes 1780 *Policy:* rent *Arts types:* drama, concerts, ballet, cinema, operetta *Comments:* also organise festivals

Teatro Stabile de Catania – Teatro Angelo Musco
Via Umberto, 312, 90100 **Catania**
Tel: 095-535 514/354 466 Fax: 095-365 135/351 919
director Prof Filippo Amoroso; president Prof Giuseppe Giarrizzo
Venue type: drama theatre
Capacity: 290 *Arts types:* drama
Comments: managed by Teatro Stabile di Catania

Teatro Stabile di Catania – Sala Teatro Verga
Via Giuseppe Fava 39, 95123 **Catania**
Tel: 095-354 466 Fax: 095-365 135/351 919
director Prof Filippo Amoroso
Capacity: 672 *Arts types:* drama *Comments:* managed by Teatro Stabile di Catania

Teatro Comunale Degli Illuminati
Via dei Fucci, 06012 **Città di Castello (PG)**
Tel: 075-855 5687/5901 Fax: 075-855 4639
Internet: www.comune.cittá-di-castello.perugia.it
E-Mail: biblioteca@comune.cittá-di-castello.perugia.it
director Anna Maria Traversini
(director Biblioteca Comunale)
Venue type: theatre (17th century)
Capacity: 350 *Arts types:* drama, concerts, ballet
Comments: technical management: SOGEPU (Tel: 075-852 0808, Fax: 075-852 0786); artistic and administrative managed by the Biblioteca Comunale (council library)

Teatro Sociale
via Bellini 3, 22100 **Como**
Tel: 031-270 170 Fax: 031-271 472
presidente Maestro Enrico Collina; vice-presidente Enrico Cantoni; consiglieri Francesco Peronese, Giorgio Carcano, Marco Molteni, Lodovico Alfieri
Venue type: theatre
Capacity: 999 *Policy:* rent
Arts types: opera, drama, concerts, dance

Teatro Comunale Alfonso Rendano
Piazza XV Marzo, 87100 **Cosenza**
Tel: 0984-74165/813 220 Fax: 0984-74165
Internet: www.comune.consenza.it/rendano
E-Mail: rendano@comune.cosenza.it
administrative director Dott. Aldo Dolce; direttore artistico Maestro Italo Nunziata; ufficio stampa Annarita Callari; sovrintendente Giuseppe di Donna
Venue type: theatre
Capacity: 800 & Sala Ridotto 250 *Policy:* rent
Arts types: opera, symphony, ballet, concerts, drama

Teatro dell'Acquario
Via Galluppi 15/19, 87100 **Cosenza**
Tel: 0984-73125 Fax: 0984-73125
Internet: www.linkey.net/acquario
E-Mail: cratcs@tin.it
direzione generale Antonello Antonante, Massimo Costabile
Venue type: theatre
Capacity: 200 *Policy:* co-promote music and dance season; also rent to other promoters
Arts types: research theatre, music, dance *Comments:* home of 'Centro R.A.T.' drama company (q.v.)

Teatro Comunale Amilcare Ponchielli
Corso Vittorio Emanuele 52, 26100 **Cremona**
Tel: 0372-407 274/5 (segreteria)/273 (box office)/802
Fax: 0372-460 180
Internet:
www.rccr.cremona.it/doc_comu/tea/tea_index.htm
E-Mail: ponchielli@rccr.cremona.it
presidente Prof. Paolo Bodini; direttore artistico Dott. Angela Cauzzi
Venue type: theatre *Capacity:* 1246 *Policy:* rent *Arts types:* lyric, concerts, drama, jazz, dance, youth theatre
Comments: host Festival di Cremona Claudio Monteverdi

Teatro Gentile da Fabriano
Via Gentile 3, 60044 **Fabriano (AN)**
Tel: 0732-709 259 (theatre)/7091 (townhall switchboard) Fax: 0732-709 320
Internet: www.retecivica.janet.it
E-Mail: pellegrini@cadnet.marche.it
assessore Mr Aladini (tel: 0732-709 230)
Venue type: theatre *Capacity:* 915, Sala Montini 250, il Ridotto del Teatro 200 *Arts types:* drama, lyrical theatre, dance, symphony *Comments:* the theatre is now managed by Assessorato alla Cultura del Comune di Fabriano

Teatro Comunale di Ferrara
Corso Martiri della Libertà 5, 44100 **Ferrara**
Tel: 0532-202 675 (box office)/312/218 311
Fax: 0532-247 353
E-Mail: teatro.comfe@fe.nettuno.it
direttore Dott. Gisberto Morselli; president Dott.ssa Alessandra Zagatti; ufficio stampa e pr Dott.ssa Federica Tassinari; coordinatrice progetto bicentenario Dott. ssa Bruna Grasso
Venue type: theatre *Capacity:* 990 *Arts types:* concerts, drama, dance, opera *Comments:* the theatre is often used for recordings; also have another space in the theatre – Ridotto del Teatro 150, which is used for conferences, concerts and different types of events

Teatro Romano
Via Portigiani 1, 50014 **Fiesole (FI)**
Tel: 055-59477/59118 Fax: 055-59118
direttore Marcello Lotti
Venue type: theatre/archeological site *Capacity:* 1950
Policy: rent *Arts types:* dance, music, opera, theatre, cinema (only during summer), drama *Comments:* contact: Coumune di Fiesole, Piazza Mino 1, 50014 Fiesole (FI), Tel: 055-59611, Fax: 055-59045

Teatro Comunale Garibaldi
Piazza Serristori, 50063 **Figline Valdarno**
Tel: 055-952 433/91251 (comune switchboard)
responsabile ufficio cultura Cosimo Adamo (tel: 055-912 5247, fax: 055-953 654))
Venue type: theatre *Capacity:* 490 *Policy:* also for rent
Arts types: drama, concerts, opera, operetta, musicals, ballet *Comments:* see also Promoters: Associazione Musicale Schumann

Teatro del Maggio Musicale Fiorentino
Via Solferino 15, 50123 **Firenze**
Tel: 055-27791/211 258 (box office)/277 9281 (press)
Fax: 055-239 6954/277 9410 (box office)
Internet: www.maggiofiorentino.com
E-Mail: tickets@maggiofiorentino.com
sovrintendente t.b.a.; direttore artistico Cesare Mazzonis; direttore amministrativo Fabrizio Bini; ufficio stampa Susanna Colombo
Capacity: 2004 *Arts types:* concerts, opera, recitals, ballet *Comments:* see also Opera, Dance, Orchestras and Festivals

Teatro della Pergola
Via della Pergola 18, 50121 **Firenze**
Tel: 055-247 9651/2 Fax: 055-247 7969
Internet: www.pergola.firenze.it
E-Mail: teatro@pergola.firenze.it
direttore responsabile Ilaria Fabbri
Capacity: 999 *Arts types:* drama, concerts, 'maggio musicale fiorentino', opera and ballet, conferences, lectures, seminars, etc.

Teatro di Rifredi
Via Vittorio Emanuele 303, 50134 **Firenze**
Tel: 055-422 0361/2 Fax: 055-422 1453
Internet: www.toscanateatro.it
E-Mail: staff@toscanateatro.it
organisation director Francesco de Biasi; artistic director Angelo Savelli; legal representative Giancarlo Mordini
Venue type: theatre *Capacity:* 284 *Policy:* also rent
Arts types: dance, theatre

Teatro Puccini
Via delle Cascine 41, 50144 **Firenze**
Tel: 055-362 067 (box office)/331 666 Fax: 055-331 108
Internet: www.dada.it/bit
artistic director Claudio Bisio; press Emilia Paternostro; organisation Lorenzo Luzzetti
Venue type: theatre, cinema *Capacity:* 700 *Policy:* rent
Arts types: prosa, cabaret, cinema, comedy, jazz
Comments: also known as Teatro Stabile della Satira e della Contaminazione dei Generi

Teatro Verdi
Via Ghibellina 99, 50122 **Firenze**
Tel: 055-212 320 (box office)/239 6242
Fax: 055-281 640/288 417
Internet: www.teatroverdifirenze.it
E-Mail: ort@dada.it
director Marco Parri; press Laura Reali
Venue type: theatre *Capacity:* 1538 *Policy:* rent *Arts types:* prosa, ballet, cinema, operetta, world music, classical, jazz *Comments:* managed by Fondazione Orchestra Regionale Toscana, Tel: 055-280 670/281 993, Fax: 055-281 640, Internet: www.dada.it/ort

Teatro Comunale U. Giordano
Piazza C. Battisti 21, 71100 **Foggia**
Tel: 0881-774 640 Fax: 0881-773 883
cordinatore attività teatro (settore cultura comune di Foggia) Gloria Fazia; responsabile organizzativo Angela Ribezzo
Venue type: theatre *Policy:* rent *Arts types:* drama, music, opera *Comments:* theatre under refurbishment; have use of amphitheatre Teatro Mediterraneo 3100, Foggia

Teatro Giovanni Testori
Via Vespucci, 13, 47100 **Forlì**
Tel: 0543-722 456 Fax: 0543-725 651
Internet: www.office.it
E-Mail: teatroarca@office.it
administrative & artistic director Franco Palmieri; technical director Sergio Cangini
Venue type: theatre *Capacity:* 287 *Policy:* rent *Arts types:* prose, children/youth theatre, concerts, experimental *Comments:* host the Drama Season of Forlì; see also Drama

Fondazione Carlo Felice
Passo Eugenio Montale 4, 16121 **Genova**
Tel: 010-53811/254-223 (uff stampa) Fax: 010-538 1222
Internet: www.carlofelice.it
E-Mail: cfstampa@tin.it (press office)
sovrintendente dott. Nicola Costa; direttore artistico Alessio Vlad; direttore degli allestimenti scenici Gianfranco Padovani; direttore del personale Luigi Molari
Venue type: theatre *Capacity:* 2005 *Policy:* also rent *Arts types:* operas, concerts, ballets, jazz, exhibitions *Comments:* host to the 'N. Paganini' competition, Festival Internazionale del Balleto di Nerv; own orchestra Orchestra e Coro del Teatro Comunale dell' Opera Carlo Felice; alternative E-mail: staff@carlofelice.it (theatre); see also Festivals, Orchestras and Promoters

Teatro della Corte
Via E. F. Duca d'Aosta, 16129 **Genova**
Tel: 010-53421 (switchboard)/534 2200
Fax: 010-534 2510
Internet: www.teatro-di-genova.it.net
E-Mail: teatro-di-genova@it.net
artistic/administrative director Ivo Chiesa; secretary general Carla Cannone; president Giovanni Salvarezza; press Rosanna Figliomeni
Capacity: 1014 *Policy:* own productions by Teatro Stabile di Genova, and rent *Arts types:* prosa *Comments:* managed by Teatro Stabile di Genova, see Drama

Teatro di Sant'Agostino
Piazza Negri, 4, 16123 **Genova**
Tel: 010-248 7011 (switchboard)
Fax: 010-251 1275/261 488
Internet: www.teatrodellatosse.it
E-Mail: tdtosse@money.it
presidente & direttore artistico Tonino Conte; direttore artistico Emanuele Luzzati; organizzazione Antonello Pischedda; ufficio stampa Maria de Barbieri, Laura Grendanin
Venue type: theatre *Capacity:* Sala Aldo Trionfo 500, Sala Dino Campana 250, Sala Agora 150 *Policy:* own productions, rent, residencies *Arts types:* visual and experimental theatre, dance, concerts, exhibitions *Comments:* the theatre is run by the association Teatro della Tosse; see also Drama

Teatro Duse
Via Bacigalupo 6, 16122 **Genova**
Tel: 010-53421 (switchboard)/534 2200
Fax: 010-534 2510
Internet: www.teatro-di-genova.it.net
E-Mail: teatro-di-genova@it.net
artistic/administrative director Ivo Chiesa; secretary general Carla Cannone; president Giovanni Salvarezza; press Rosanna Figliomeni
Capacity: 500 *Policy:* own productions by Teatro Stabile di Genova, and rent *Arts types:* prosa *Comments:* managed by Teatro Stabile di Genova, see Drama

Teatro Genovese
via Bacigalupo 2, 16122 **Genova**
Tel: 010-831 1456 Fax: 010-846 1053
Internet: www.politeama.genova.it
E-Mail: politeama@cis.it
director Danilo Staiti; artistic director Massimo Chiesa; president Savina Savini
Venue type: theatre *Capacity:* 1068 *Policy:* rent *Arts types:* drama, musical, cabaret

Teatro Gustavo Modena
Piazza Gustavo Modena n° 3, 16149 **Genova**
Tel: 010-65921 Fax: 010-659 2224
Internet: www.archivolto.it
E-Mail: info@archivolto.it
organizzatrice Giuseppina Rando; direttore artistico Giorgio Gallione; ufficio stampa Fulvia Bardelli
Venue type: Italian theatre *Capacity:* 557 *Policy:* own productions, also rent *Arts types:* dance, music, drama *Comments:* run by: Teatro dell'Archivolto; see also Drama

Teatro Comunale Ruggero Ruggeri di Guastalla
Via Verdi 7, 42016 **Guastalla (RE)**
Tel: 0522-839 757 Fax: 0522-839 756
Internet: www.pobassareggiana.com/guastalla
E-Mail: servizicultural i@comunediguastalla.com
direttore Fiorello Tagliavini
Venue type: baroque theatre
Capacity: 430 *Policy:* produces baroque music
Arts types: drama, symphonic and chamber music, baroque opera, ballet
Comments: contact: Centro Culturale (mornings only), Tel: 0522-839 755; see also Early Music

Teatro Comunale di Gubbio
Via del Popolo17, 06024 **Gubbio**
Tel: 075-927 5551 (box office)/923 7529 (office)
Fax: 075-923 7530
direttore Mauro Tomarelli
Venue type: theatre *Capacity:* 414
Policy: promote, rent, co-produce
Arts types: dance, ballet, operetta, drama
Comments: work in collaboration with Teatro Stabile dell' Umbria

Teatro Comunale 'Ebe Stignani'
Via Verdi 1-3, 40026 **Imola (BO)**
Tel: 0542-602 600 Fax: 0542-602 626
Internet: www.teatroimola.com
E-Mail: stignani@mbox.queen.it
istruttore direttivo Anna Bandini; direttore artistico e organizzativo Luca Rebeggiani
Venue type: Italian style 17th C. theatre
Capacity: 499 *Policy:* rent *Arts types:* ballet, chamber and symphonic, drama, opera, operetta
Comments: also venue for conventions; box office: Via Verdi, 3; theatre entrance: Piazza Abate Ferri

Teatro Comunale G B Pergolesi
Piazza della Repubblica 9, 60035 **Jesi (AN)**
Tel: 0731-538 350/351/348/355 (box office)
Fax: 0731-538 356
Internet: www.teatropergolesi.org
E-Mail: teatro.pergolesi@comune.jesi.an.it
direttore artistico lirica e sinfonica Angelo Cavallaro; administrative director Simonetta Bianchelli; organisation director Franco Cecchini
Venue type: theatre a l'Itallienne
Capacity: 700 *Arts types:* lyric, concerts, drama
Comments: theatre dates from 1798

Teatro Comunale de l'Aquila
Piazza del Teatro 1, 67100 **L'Aquila**
Tel: 0862-62946/413 200/25584 (box office)
Fax: 0862-414 269
Internet: www.webaq.it/tsa
E-Mail: tsa@webaq.it
commissario straordinario Arch. Renato Nicolini; direttore Federico Fiorenza; ufficio stampa Roberta Gargano
Venue type: theatre
Capacity: 600 *Policy:* rent *Arts types:* drama, concerts, ballet, exhibitions *Comments:* Ridotto del Teatro Comunale cap. 220 is also for rent, contact: Via Roma 54, 67100 L'Aquila, Tel: 0862-62946/413 200, Fax: 0862-414 269; see also Drama

Teatro Civico de La Spezia
Piazza Mentana 1, 19100 **La Spezia**
Tel: 0187-733 098 Fax: 0187-734 298
responsabile amministrativo Patrizia Zanzucchi; direzione artistica Antonello Pischedda
Venue type: theatre *Capacity:* 926
Policy: rent *Arts types:* drama, dance, classical music, opera, concerts, children's theatre

Teatro Comunale Fedele Fenaroli
Via dei Frentani, 66034 **Lanciano (CH)**
Tel: 0872-717 148
Fax: 0872-726 221 (comune)
Internet: www.cmns.mnegri.t/comune
E-Mail: comune@www.teknet.rgn.it
Venue type: theatre
Capacity: 336 *Arts types:* drama, concerts, ballet, opera
Comments: run by Comune di Lanciano, Assessorato alla Cultura (tel: 872-7261)

Teatro Politeama Greco
Via XXV Luglio 30, 73100 **Lecce**
Tel: 0832-241 468 Fax: 0832-241 468
proprietario avv. Alberto Greco; allestimento scenico dott. Giuseppe Greco
Venue type: theatre, cinema
Capacity: 988 *Policy:* also for rent *Arts types:* concerts, opera, ballet, congresses, cinema, prosa

Teatro Goldoni – C.E.L Teatro di Livorno
Via Goldoni 83, 57125 **Livorno**
Tel: 0586-889 111 Fax: 0586-899 920
Internet: www.comune.livorno.it/txt/cel/home.htm
E-Mail: cel@comune-livorno.it
presidente Marco Bertini; consulente artistico (lirica) Alberto Paloscia; amministrazione e produzioni Isabella Bartolini; affari generali e programmazione Paolo Demi; comunicazione-immagine Antonella Peruffo; responsabile ufficio stampa Antonella Peruffo
Venue type: theatre *Comments:* the theatre is closed for refurbishment; it is due to reopen in 2000; alternative E-mail: cel@mclink.it; see also Opera, Drama and Promoters

Teatro Comunale Giuseppe Verdi
Piazza Matteotti 1, 36045 **Lonigo (VI)**
Tel: 0444-835 010/513 Fax: 0444-835 010
Internet: www.enti.keycomm.it/lonigo
E-Mail: comune.lonigo@keycomm.it
president Manlio Onorato; administrative director dott. Francesco Merle
Venue type: theatre *Capacity:* 613 *Policy:* rent *Arts types:* opera, operetta, ballet, concerts, drama, art exhibitions

Azienda Teatro del Giglio – A.T.G.
Piazza del Giglio 13/15, 55100 **Lucca**
Tel: 0583-46531/467 521 Fax: 0583-490 317
Internet: www.comune.lucca.it/GIGLIO
E-Mail: teatro.giglio@comune.lucca.it
direttore Luigi Angelini; consiglio di amministrazione presidente Luigi Della Santa; consiglieri Gabriella Biagi Ravenni, Maria Francesca Pardini, Angelo Fanucchi, Laura Bruna Innocenti
Venue type: teatro all'italiana *Capacity:* 750 *Arts types:* lyric, concerts, drama, cabaret, ballet

Arena Sferisterio
Piazza Nazario Sauro 2, 62100 **Macerata**
Tel: 0733-261 335/334/230 735 (box office)
Fax: 0733-261 499
Internet: www.macerataopera.org
E-Mail: macerataopera@mercurio.it
sovrintendente Claudio Orazi; tecnico organizzativo Bruno Carletti; direttore tecnico t.b.a.
Venue type: arena *Capacity:* 2400-2500 *Arts types:* opera, symphony, concerts *Comments:* Other venue: Teatro Lauro Rossi 400 – Tel: 033-256 306; contact: Arena Sferisterio, Via S. Maria della Porta 65, 62100 Macerata; see also Agents & Producers

Teatro Sociale
Piazza Cavallotti, 46100 **Mantova**
Tel: 0376-362 739 Fax: 0376-362 739
direttore organizzativo artistico e amministrativo Ezio Ricci; presidente e legale rappresentante Riccardo Rivaberni
Venue type: theatre *Capacity:* 1000 *Policy:* rent *Arts types:* opera, symphony, ballet, theatre, drama, films

Teatro Comunale
Piazza Roma, 46045 **Marmirolo**
Tel: 0376-294 180 (comune)
Fax: 0376-294 045 (comune)
administrative & cultural advisor Silvia Terzioli; assessore alla cultura Francesco Lanfredi
Venue type: theatre *Capacity:* 335 *Policy:* also for rent *Arts types:* drama – lyrical season, cinema *Comments:* the theatre is managed by Assessorato alla Cultura (City Council of Marmirolo – Department of Culture)

Ente Autonomo Regionale Teatro di Messina
Via Pozzoleone, 98122 **Messina**
Tel: 090-345 233/572 2111 Fax: 090-343 629/572 2240
presidente avv. Pompeo Oliva; direttore musica t.b.a.; direttore prosa Nimni Bruschetta
Venue type: lyrical & drama theatre *Capacity:* Teatro Vittorio Emanuele 1000, Sala Laudamo 140
Arts types: drama, music, ballet, lyric, exhibitions, conferences and seminars

BLOOM
Via Curiel 39, 20050 **Mezzago (MI)**
Tel: 039-623 853 Fax: 039-602 2742
Internet: www.rete039.it/bloom
E-Mail: bloom@rete.039.it
theatre coordinator Alessandra Anzaghi; exhibitions coordinator Maria Mesch; music programming Francesco Pitillo
Venue type: cultural centre, on 2 floors with 4 different rooms *Policy:* rent *Arts types:* films, theatre, underground rock concerts, art exhibitions, meetings, video makers, research on art in general *Comments:* organise different courses in music, language, dance, cinema

Auditorium di Milano
C.so San Gottardo, Angolo via Torricelli, 20136 **Milano**
Tel: 02-8901 3121 Fax: 02-7209 9819
Internet: www.orchestrasinfonica.milano.it
E-Mail: info@orchestrasinfonica.milano.it
direttore musicale Riccardo Chailly; direttore emerito Carlo Maria Giulini; direttore generale Luigi Corbani; ufficio stampae relazioni esterne Gianni Testa
Venue type: auditorium *Capacity:* 1400 *Arts types:* music

Centro Culturale
Piazza San Fedele 4, 20121 **Milano**
Tel: 02-8635 2231 Fax: 02-8635 2233
artistic director Maria Pia Pagliarecci
Venue type: theatre *Capacity:* 300 plus 3 exhibition spaces *Policy:* produce, present and rent *Arts types:* drama, cinema, visual arts, conferences *Comments:* home of Compagnia Picciola; see also Drama

Piccolo Teatro Grassi
via Rovello 2, 20121 **Milano**
Tel: 02-723 331 (switchboard)/7233 3222 Fax: 02-874 836
Internet: www.piccoloteatro.it
E-Mail: info@piccoloteatro.org
director Sergio Escobar; artistic director Luca Ronconi; general secretary Gianmario Maggi; production & organisation Rosanna Purchia; press office Giovanni Soresi
Venue type: Italian theatre *Capacity:* 600 *Policy:* own productions, rent, residencies *Arts types:* drama, recitals, ballet, musicals, concerts, foreign guest productions *Comments:* see also Drama

Piccolo Teatro Studio
Via Rivoli N. 6, 20122 **Milano**
Tel: 02-723 331 Fax: 02-874 836
Internet: www.piccoloteatro.it
E-Mail: info@piccoloteatro.org
director Sergio Escobar; artistic director Luca Ronconi; general secretary Gianmario Maggi; production & organisation Rosanna Porchia; press office Giovanni Soresi
Venue type: theatre *Capacity:* 420 *Policy:* own productions, rent *Arts types:* drama, music, recitals, dance, experimental theatre *Comments:* home of the drama school: Scuola di Teatro Fondata da Giorgio Strehler Diretta da Luca Ronconi, Via Degli Angioli N.3, 20121 Milano (same building as Piccolo Teatro Studio), Tel: 02-7233 3414; see also Drama

Teatro alla Scala Fondazione di Diritto Privato
Via Filodrammatici 2, 20121 **Milano**
Tel: 02-88791 Fax: 02-887 9331
Internet: www.LaScala.milano.it
sovrintendente Carlo Fontana; direttore artistico Paolo Arcá; uff. stampa Luciana Fusi (tel: 02-887 9412); relazioni esterne Donatella Brunazzi (tel: 877 9264)
Venue type: theatre *Capacity:* 2000 *Policy:* also co-productions *Arts types:* opera, concerts, ballet
Comments: it hosts the Museo Teatrale alla Scale, Piazza della Scala, Tel: 02-805 3418, Direttore Matteo Sartorio; see also Dance, Orchestras and Opera

Teatro Carcano
Corso di Porta Romana 63, 20122 **Milano**
Tel: 02-5518 1377/1362 Fax: 02-5518 1355
Internet: www.teatrocarcano.com
direttore artistico Giulio Rosetti; amministratore unico Nicoletta Rizzato; press office Brunella Portoghese
Venue type: theatre *Capacity:* 990 *Arts types:* drama, occasionally ballet and music
Comments: see also Drama

Teatro dell' Elfo
Via Ciro Menotti 11, 20129 **Milano**
Tel: 02-7611 0007 Fax: 02-7012 3851
Internet: www.elfo.org
E-Mail: info@elfo.org
organizzazione Fiorenzo Grassi, Rino de Pace; direttore artistico Ferdinando Bruni, Elio De Capitani; ufficio stampa Barbara Caldarini; responsabile amministrativo Carmelita Scordamaglia; segretario generale Marina Gualandi
Venue type: theatre *Capacity:* up to 580
Policy: own productions, residencies *Arts types:* mainly drama, some dance and music *Comments:* see also Drama and Festivals

Teatro Dell'Arte
Viale Alemagna, 6, 20121 **Milano**
Tel: 02-861 901 Fax: 02-863 813
E-Mail: teatrocrt@iol.it
direttore Massimo Mancini; presidente e direttore artistico Sisto Dalla Palma; ufficio stampa Maria Chiara Bachetti
Venue type: theatre *Capacity:* 700 *Policy:* rent *Arts types:* prosa, dance, exhibitions, concerts, conferences, workshops *Comments:* also run Salone CRT 100, Via Ulisse Dini 7, 20142 Milano, for theatre research

Teatro Franco Parenti
Via Pier Lombardo 14, 20135 **Milano**
Tel: 02-5518 4075/545 7174 Fax: 02-545 5929
administrative director Giovanni Valle; artistic director Andree Ruth Shammah; press officer Andrea Bisicchia
Venue type: theatre *Capacity:* 500 *Policy:* rent *Arts types:* theatre, dance, concerts *Comments:* see also Drama

Teatro Giorgio Strehler
Largo Paolo Grassi N.2, 20121 **Milano**
Tel: 02-723 331 Fax: 02-874 836/8901 4202
Internet: www.piccoloteatro.it
E-Mail: info@piccoloteatro.org
director Sergio Escobar; artistic director Luca Ronconi; general secretary Gianmario Maggi; head of production & organisation Rosanna Purchia; press office Giovanni Soresi
Venue type: Italian theatre *Capacity:* 940 *Policy:* own productions, rent, residencies *Arts types:* drama, opera, dance, music, cinema *Comments:* see also Drama

Teatro Lirico
via Larga 14, 20121 **Milano**
Tel: 02-809 665 Fax: 02-805 2737
Internet: www.orchestrasinfonica.milano.it
E-Mail: info@orchestrasinfonica.milano.it
direttore teatro Giorgio Casellato; press officer Gianni Testa
Venue type: theatre *Capacity:* 1750
Arts types: symphony orchestra

Teatro Litta
Corso Magenta 24, 20123 **Milano**
Tel: 02-805 5882/5891/8645 4546 Fax: 02-7201 0640
E-Mail: teatro.litta@galactica.it
organisation director Nicoletta Cardone Johnson; artistic & producer director Gaetano Gallegaro; press office Giulia Tatulli; administrative director Giuliana Cidri
Venue type: Italian theatre *Capacity:* 250 *Policy:* rent *Arts types:* drama, dance *Comments:* oldest theatre in Milan; see also Drama

Teatro Manzoni
Via Manzoni 42, 20121 **Milano**
Tel: 02-7602 0543/4 Fax: 02-7600 5471
Internet: www.teatromanzoni.it
E-Mail: teatromanzoni@athena2000.it
direttore Luigi Foscale
Venue type: theatre *Capacity:* 850 *Policy:* rent *Arts types:* drama, comedy, concerts

Teatro Nazionale
Piazza Piemonte 12, 20145 **Milano**
Tel: 02-4800 7700/6415 Fax: 02-4800 5495
Internet: www.teatronazionale.com
E-Mail: info@teatronazionale.com
gestione kosmos srl, amministratore unico Geppy Glejeses; direttore artistico Massimo Chiesa; uffico stampa Marco Guerini
Venue type: theatre *Capacity:* 1589 *Policy:* rent *Arts types:* drama, musical, dance

Teatro Officina
Via S. Elembardo 2, 20126 **Milano**
Tel: 02-255 3200 Fax: 02-2700 0858
Venue type: theatre *Policy:* produce *Arts types:* concerts, classical and popular music, drama, variety

Teatro Portaromana
Corso di Porta Romana 124, 20122 **Milano**
Tel: 02-5831 5896 Fax: 02-5831 4881
Internet: www.elfo.org
E-Mail: info@elfo.org
organizzazione Fiorenzo Grassi, Rino Pace; direttore artistico Ferdinando Bruni, Elio de Capitani; ufficio stampa Barbara Caldarini; responsabile amministrativo Carmelita Scordamaglia
Venue type: formerly cinema *Capacity:* 500 *Policy:* own productions, rent, residencies *Arts types:* mainly drama, some dance and music
Comments: see also Drama and Festivals

Teatro Smeraldo
Piazza XXV Aprile 10, 20121 **Milano**
Tel: 02-2900 6767/657 5203 (press office)
Fax: 02-2900 2406
Internet: www.smeraldo.it
E-Mail: stampa@smeraldo.it
direttore Paolo Duranti; amministratore unico, proprietario e direttore artistico GianMario Longoni; capo uffico stampa Marco Guerini
Venue type: theatre *Capacity:* 2000 *Policy:* rent *Arts types:* musicals, concerts, dance, comedy *Comments:* legal address: Gestioni Teatrali srl, Bastioni di Porta Nuova 10, 20121 Milano; newly refurbished; a marquee (Teatro Tenda cap 2000) has been erected nearby and is managed by the same team

Teatro Comunale di Modena
Via del Teatro 8, 41100 **Modena**
Tel: 059-200 020 (switchboard) Fax: 059-200 021
Internet: www.comune.modena.it/teatrocomunale
E-Mail: teatro.comunale@comune.modena.it
direttore dott. Pietro Valenti; consulente artistico Maestro Aldo Sisillo
Venue type: theatre *Capacity:* 900 *Policy:* rent *Arts types:* opera, ballet, dance, concerts *Comments:* the theatre was built in 1841; refurbishment took place in 1999; they also rent scenery

Teatro Storchi
Largo Garibaldi 15, 41100 **Modena**
Tel: 059-223 783/230 094/223 244 (bigliettera)
Fax: 059-234 979
Internet: www.emiliaromagnateatro.com
E-Mail: info@emiliaromagnateatro.com
direttore Pietro Valenti
Venue type: theatre *Capacity:* 962 *Policy:* produce, rent
Arts types: mainly drama

Teatro Comunale
Corso del Popolo 20, 34074 **Monfalcone (GO)**
Tel: 0481-494 366/8/790 470
Fax: 0481-44480
Internet: www.comune.monfalcone.go.it
E-Mail: culturasport@comune.monfalcone.go.it
dirigente Dott. ssa Giovanna D'Agostini; direttore artistico (musica) Carlo de Incontrera; curatore settore prosa e cinema Dott. ssa Mariacarla Comelli
Venue type: multi-purpose *Capacity:* 603 *Arts types:* concerts, drama, music festivals, films

Teatro Sociale
Via Teatro 67, 38065 **Mori (Trento)**
Tel: 0464-916 200 Fax: 0464-916 300
responsabile Marco Nardelli (servizio cultura comune), Dott. ssa Angela Colella
Venue type: theatre *Capacity:* 285 *Policy:* rent *Arts types:* comedy, drama, cabaret

Teatro Bellini – Teatro stabile di Napoli
via Conte di Ruvo 14, 80135 **Napoli**
Tel: 081-549 9723/1266 Fax: 081-549 9656
Internet: www.netgroup.it/teatrobellini
artistic director Tato Russo; press officer Roberta Russo
Venue type: Italian theatre *Capacity:* 850 *Policy:* rent *Arts types:* operetta, musical, concerts, drama, dance
Comments: the theatre hosts the Cooperativa Teatrale Nuova Commedia (an organisation of different drama companies); see also Drama

Teatro di San Carlo
Via San Carlo 98F, 80132 **Napoli**
Tel: 081-797 2111 Fax: 081-797 2306/9
Internet: www.teatrosancarlo.it
E-Mail: infoteatro@teatrosancarlo.it
sovrintendente Francesco Canessa; direttore artistico Carlo Mayer; capo ufficio stampa Filippo Arriva (tel: 081-797 2202, fax: 081-797 2306)
Venue type: theatre *Capacity:* 1400 *Policy:* own productions, rent *Arts types:* symphony, chamber concerts, opera, ballet *Comments:* see also Opera, Dance,Orchestras and Festivals

Teatro Diana
Via Luca Giordano 64, 80127 **Napoli**
Tel: 081-556 7527/0107/578 1905 (office)
Fax: 081-556 0151
Internet: www.teatrodiana.it
E-Mail: teatro@teatrodiana.it
president Maria Caterina de Gaudio; press office Claudia Mirra
Venue type: Italian theatre *Capacity:* 1000 *Policy:* rent *Arts types:* drama, concerts, opera, dance *Comments:* they very often host a drama school, and organise workshops; see also Drama

Teatro Coccia
via Fratelli Rosselli 47, 28100 **Novara**
Tel: 0321-620 400/234 Fax: 0321-640 962
responsible Giovanni Cardone; assessore alla cultura Prof. Dorino Tuniz
Capacity: 925 *Arts types:* theatre, dance, operetta, musical, concerts, cabaret *Comments:* cooperates with different Italian theatres (incl. children's) depending on type of event

Auditorium Cesare Pollini
Via Eremitani 18, 35121 **Padova**
Tel: 049-875 0648 Fax: 049-661 174
direttore Claudio Scimone
Capacity: 544

Sala dei Giganti – Palazzo Liviano
Piazza Capitaniato 7, 35139 **Padova**
Tel: 049-827 4693 Fax: 049-827 4690
E-Mail: plettere@ux1.unipd.it
president Prof. ssa Silvana Collodo
Capacity: 200 *Comments:* owned by literature and philosophy faculty of Padova University: preside Prof. ssa Silvana Collodo, rettore Prof. Giovanni Marchesini (via VIII Febbraio 2, Palazzo BO); currently being restored

Teatro Verdi
Via del Livello 32, 35139 **Padova**
Tel: 049-875 2260/876 0339 (box office)
Fax: 049-661 053
direttore Mauro Carbenoli; presidente Francesco Raimondo Donà; coordinatrice Marina Valenta
Venue type: theatre *Capacity:* 800 *Policy:* host to theatre companies *Arts types:* drama, operetta, musicals, comedy *Comments:* see also Ass. Teatro Stabile del Veneto Carlo Goldoni in Venice; see also Drama

Teatro Golden
Via Terra Santa, 60, 90141 **Palermo**
Tel: 091-300 609 (administration)/300 745
Fax: 091-300 155 (administration)/818 (artistic director)
Internet: www.eaoss.it
theatre director Giuseppe Di Liberto; artistic director Maestro Giuseppe Cataldo
Venue type: sala *Capacity:* 1031 *Policy:* rent *Arts types:* concerts *Comments:* administration address: Via G. La Farina, 29, 90141 Palermo; see also Orchestras

Teatro Massimo di Palermo
Piazza Giuseppe Verdi, 90139 **Palermo**
Tel: 091-605 3111/3224/3253 (press office)
Fax: 091-605 3325/3330 (press office)
Internet: teatromassimo.it
E-Mail: infotm@teatromassimo.it
presidente Leoluca Orlando; sovrintendente Francesco Giambrone; direttore operativo Antonio Cognata; direttore artistico Marco Betta; direttore di produzione Giovanni Mazzara; consiglio d'amministrazione Agostino Ziino, Sebastiano Giacobello, Eugenio Derosa, Giovanni Maniscalco Basile; capa uff. stampa Laura Oddo
Venue type: theatre *Capacity:* 1320 *Arts types:* opera, dance, concerts *Comments:* owned by the City Council of Palermo which lends it to the Fondazione Teatro Massimo di Palermo; alternative E-mail: stampatm@teatromassimo.it (press office)

Teatro Due
viale Basetti 12A, 43100 **Parma**
Tel: 0521-230 242 (info)/208 088 Fax: 0521-231 232
Internet: www.teatrostabileparma.com
E-Mail: info@teatrostabileparma.com
presidente Paola Donati; artistic director Walter Le Moli; uffinio stampa Laura De Stefano, Carlotta Varge
Venue type: theatre *Capacity:* Spazio Grande 500, Spazio Bignardi 150, Spazio minimo 100, piccola sala 80 *Policy:* for rent *Arts types:* theatre, music, dance *Comments:* see also Festivals and Drama

Teatro Lenz
Via Pasubio, 3/D, 43100 **Parma**
Tel: 0521-270 141 Fax: 0521-272 641
E-Mail: lenzteat@tin.it
administator Marisa Bertolotti; artistic directors Maria Federica Maestri, Francesco Pititto; organiser & press officer Viviana Colla
Venue type: theatre *Capacity:* 100 seats: 2 rooms Sala Majakowskij and Sala Est *Arts types:* drama, dance, exhibitions, contemporary theatre
Comments: see also Drama

Teatro Regio
via Garibaldi 16/a, 43100 **Parma**
Tel: 0521-218 678 (box office)/912 (prod. office)/692 (press office) Fax: 0521-206 156
Internet: www.comune.parma.it
E-Mail: tregio@provincia.parma.it
artistic & organisation director Prof. Gian Piero Rubiconi; president Mayor Elvio Ubaldi
Venue type: historical theatre (built 1829) *Capacity:* 1380 *Arts types:* opera, symphonic and chamber concerts, theatre, ballet

Teatro Comunale di Pegognaga
Via Verdi 16, 46020 **Pegognaga (MN)**
Tel: 0376-554 6207/550 213 (theatre)
Fax: 0376-550 071 (comune)
Internet: www.polirone.mn.it
E-Mail: urp.pegognaga@polirone.mn.it
responsabile Marco Frignani; organizzazione Riccarda Pini; consulenza artistica Normanno Gobbi
Venue type: theatre *Capacity:* 400 *Policy:* rent *Arts types:* drama, concerts, operetta, cabaret

Teatro Comunale Francesco Morlacchi
Piazza Morlacchi 13, 06123 **Perugia**
Tel: 075-573 0105/572 2555 (box office) Fax: 075-572 9039
Internet: www.teatrostabile.umbria.it
E-Mail: tsu@krenet.it
direttore Aldo Lorenzi; ufficio stampa Francesca Torcolini
Venue type: 18th C. Italian theatre *Capacity:* 850 *Policy:* own production, rent, residencies *Arts types:* drama, concerts, Umbria jazz, ballet, dance, pop music, meetings *Comments:* run by: Fondazione Teatro Stabile dell'Umbria, Via del Verzaro 20, 06123 Perugia

Teatro Comunale G. Rossini
Piazzale Albani, 12, 61100 **Pesaro**
Tel: 0721-69359/33184 (box office) Fax: 0721-32962
Internet: www.comune.pesaro.ps.it
E-Mail: g.castellani@comune.pesaro.ps.it
direttore & responsabile della programmazione Giorgio Castellani
Venue type: theatre *Capacity:* 800 *Arts types:* concerts, dance, opera, theatre *Comments:* co-produce the Rossini Opera Festival (q.v.); alternative E-mail: u.sampa@comune.pesaro.ps.it

Teatro Municipale di Piacenza
Via Verdi 41, 29100 **Piacenza**
Tel: 0523-492 252/251 (box office) Fax: 0523-492 253
Internet: www.comune.piacenza.it/teatro
direttore Dott. Stefano Pronti; ufficio stampa Roberto Mori
Venue type: theatre *Capacity:* 1100 *Policy:* rent *Arts types:* opera, symphony, concerts, school theatre, drama, rent to privates, lyric, ballet

Teatro Comunale di Pietrasanta
Piazza Duomo, 55045 **Pietrasanta (LU)**
Tel: 0584-24348 (comune)/795 311 (teatro)/265 (winter season) Fax: 0584-795 310 (comune)
direttore artistico Franco Martini
Venue type: theatre *Capacity:* 563 *Policy:* rent *Arts types:* drama, dance, cinema *Comments:* administration by: Comune di Pietrasanta, Uffició Cultura

Teatro Comunale Giuseppe Verdi
Via Palestro 40, 56127 **Pisa**
Tel: 050-941 111/141 (press office)
Fax: 050-543 555 (press)
Internet: www.teatrodipisa.pi.it
E-Mail: pressoff@teatrodipisa.pi.it
direttore Riccardo Bozzi; presidente Ilario Luperini; direttore attivita formative Claudio Proietti; ufficio stampa Valeria Della Mea, Maria Beatrice Meucci
Capacity: 800 *Policy:* rent *Arts types:* lyric, dance, concerts, drama, didactics *Comments:* home of 'Teatro di Pisa' lyric company; home of Ensemble of Micha van Hoecke and Città Lirica Orchestra; alternative E-mail: mencci@teatrodipisa.pi.it; see also Opera, Dance and Orchestras

Teatro Comunale A Manzoni
Corso Gramsci 127, 51100 **Pistoia**
Tel: 0573-27112/99161 Fax: 0573-34789/507 042
Internet: www.sionline.it/scena_italiana/CRTD
E-Mail: teatromanzoni@comune.pistoia.it
presidente Renzo Berti; coordinatrice Rossella Biagini
Venue type: theatre *Capacity:* 800 *Policy:* rent *Arts types:* mainly drama but also music, dance and opera
Comments: Associazione Teatrale Pistoiese is a cultural association composed of public institutions; it manages the Teatro Comunale A. Manzoni and also the Teatro Comunale Pacini of Pescia (PT) cap. 490 and the Teatro Mascagni of Popiglio (PT) cap. 100; it is also co-producing the season of the Teatro Nazionale di Quarrata, cap. 250 and organises various summer cultural events and programmes; alternative E-mail: crtd@sionline.it

Teatro Era
Via Manzoni 22, 56025 **Pontedera**
Tel: 0587-55720/57034 Fax: 0587-213 631
Internet: www.pontederateatro.it
E-Mail: teatro@pontederateatro.it
president Enrico Forte; co-directors Luca Dini, Carla Pollastrelli; artistic direction Roberto Bacci; press office Nicola Pasquinucci
Capacity: 800 + 1000 *Arts types:* experimental theatre
Comments: due to open at the beginning of 2000

Teatro Metastasio
Via Cairoli 59, 59100 **Prato**
Tel: 0574-6084 (switchboard)/60854 (press office)
Fax: 0574-608 520
Internet: www.metastasio.net
E-Mail: info@metastasio.net
direttore Massimo Castri; organizzazione Maria Teresa Bettarini; press office Franca Mezzani
Venue type: Italian theatre *Capacity:* 630 *Policy:* own productions, present, rent *Arts types:* drama

Ravenna Teatro
c/o Teatro Rasi, Via di Roma 39, 48100 **Ravenna**
Tel: 0544-36239/30227 Fax: 0544- 33303
Internet: www.netgate.it/ra/teatro
E-Mail: ra.teatro@netgate.it
presidente Luigi Dadina; direttore organizzativo Marcella Nonni; stampa Barbara Fusconi; promozione Monica Randi; amministrazione Stefania Nanni
Venue type: theatre *Capacity:* 500 *Arts types:* children & youth theatre, contemporary, research, animated, theatre, jazz, rock and blues concerts, theatre workshops *Comments:* gestione: Ravenna Teatro, Via di Roma 39, 48100 Ravenna, Tel: 0544-36239, Fax: 0544-33303

Teatro Alighieri
Via Mariani 2, 48100 **Ravenna**
Tel: 0544-249 211 (direzione)/249 237 (uff. stampa)
Fax: 0544-36303
Internet: www.ravennafestival.org
E-Mail: info@ravennafestival.org
direttore t.b.a.
Venue type: theatre *Capacity:* 800 *Arts types:* opera, symphony, ballet, concerts, theatre *Comments:* gestione: Fondazione Ravenna Manifestazioni, Via Dante Alighieri 1, 48100 Ravenna, Tel: 0544-249 211

Teatro Comunale F. Cilea
Corso Garibaldi, 89100 **Reggio Calabria**
Tel: 0965-362 202 Fax: 0965-811 657
Comments: the theatre is under refurbishment

Consorzio i Teatri
Piazza Martiri 7 Luglio, 42100 **Reggio Emilia**
Tel: 0522-458 811/167-554 222 (Numero Verde)
Fax: 0522-458 922
Internet: www.i-teatri.re.it
E-Mail: uffstampa@i-teatri.re.it
direttore Bruno Borghi; presidente Elio Canova; segreteria artistica Lorella Govi, Costanza Casula; dirigente amministrativo Daniela Spallanzani; ufficio stampa Mario Vighi
Venue type: theatre *Capacity:* Teatro Municipale Romolo Valli 1200, Teatro Ariosto 700, Cavallerizza 400 *Policy:* rent *Arts types:* drama, classical and jazz concerts, opera, ballet *Comments:* Consorzio i Teatri manage the three different places, and also organise a festival of contemporary music

Teatro Municipale R. Valli
Piazza Martiri del VII Luglio 7, 42100 **Reggio Emilia**
Tel: 0522-458 811 Fax: 0522-458 822
Internet: www.i-teatri.re.it
E-Mail: direzione@i-teatri.re.it
director Bruno Borghi; president Elio Canova
Venue type: theatre *Capacity:* 1130 *Policy:* rent *Arts types:* concert, opera, ballet, lyrical, operetta *Comments:* the theatre has recently be refurbished; alternative E-mail: uffstampa@i-teatri.re.it

Teatro San Prospero (S.c.r.l)
Via Guidelli 5, 42100 **Reggio Emilia**
Tel: 0522-439 346 Fax: 0522-452 455
presidente Roberto Leoni
Venue type: theatre *Capacity:* 192 *Policy:* rent
Arts types: drama, youth theatre, dialect drama
Comments: run by a cooperative

Teatro Comunale
Via Dante 2, 46036 **Revere (MN)**
Tel: 0386-46502 (theatre)/46001/2 (townhall)
Fax: 0386-467 274
president (Pro Loco) Rag.Gazzi Gianni (0386-846 092)
Venue type: cinema-theatre *Arts types:* theatre, films, conferences *Comments:* managed by Pro-Loco, c/o Comune-Palazzo Ducale, Revere; the venue is closed for major refurbishment and is due to re-open at the end of 2000

Auditorium S Leone Magno
Via Bolzano 38, 00198 **Roma**
Tel: 06-8632 0534 Fax: 06-8530 1484
direttore Prof. Santino Amici
Venue type: auditorium *Capacity:* 820 *Policy:* for rent *Arts types:* film, theatre, dance, concerts

Centro Petralata
Associazione Culturale Metropolis Europa, Via di Pietralata N. 159/A, 00158 **Roma**
Tel: 06-451 5756/0347-713 2220 (mobile)
Internet: www.geocities.com/vienna/strasse/7392
E-Mail: petra01@global-italianet.it
rappresentante legale Antonino Catalano; procuratore speciale Francesca Mandará; direzione artistica Anna Catalano, Luciano Meldolesi
Venue type: cultural centre *Capacity:* two theatres: 400-500, 100 *Policy:* production, promotion *Arts types:* dance, theatre, music, interdisceplinary *Comments:* has 3-4 rehearsal, work shop and class spaces; also has a video place and music room; is funded by the Italian government, the Municipality of Rome and Regione Lazio; it is especially dedicated to contemporary productions and promotion of young Italian and international authors; residence of Danzacompagnia Anna Catalano; see also Dance

Nuova Teatro Eliseo spa
Via Della Consulta 1, 00184 **Roma**
Tel: 06-488 721 Fax: 06-485 600
E-Mail: teliseo@tin.it
rappresentante legale Giampaolo Vianello; direzione artistica Maurizio Scaparro
Venue type: theatre *Capacity:* Sala Eliseo 950, Sala Piccolo Eliseo 250 *Policy:* own productions, rent *Arts types:* prosa, jazz, children's theatre *Comments:* 2 venues: Sala Eliseo, Sala Piccolo Eliseo; see also Drama (Nuova Eliseo S.P.A.)

Palazzo della Cancelleria
Piazza Cancelleria 1, 00186 **Roma**
Tel: 06-6988 7566 (portineria)/4816 (inform.)
Fax: 06-6988 3141
Capacity: 2 venues: Aula Magna 400 + 50 on side bankets, Sala dei 100 Giorni (or Sala del Vasari) 250
Policy: rent *Arts types:* concerts, conventions *Comments:* management of venues: Amministrazione del Patrimonio della Sede Apostolica (A.P.S.A.)tours are accepted following telephone booking

Sala Casella
c/o Accademia Filarmonica Romana, Via Flaminia 118, 00196 **Roma**
Tel: 06-320 1752 Fax: 06-321 0410
Internet: www.nexus.it./filarmonica
E-Mail: filarmonica@mail.nexus.it
presidente M° Roman Vlad; direttore artistico Matteo D'Amico
Venue type: small concert hall *Capacity:* 176 *Policy:* present *Arts types:* concerts, rehearsals, puppetry, modern ballet, new music recitals, jazz, conferences
Comments: Sala Casella is a pavillion in the garden of Accademia Filarmonica Romana

Teatro Anfitrione
Via san Saba 24, 00153 **Roma**
Tel: 06-575 0827 Fax: 06-578 3116
legal representative Sergio Ammirata; artistic director & press office Patricia Parisi
Capacity: 20 *Policy:* rent *Arts types:* classical & contemporary comedy *Comments:* see also Drama

Teatro Argentina
Largo di Torre Argentina, **Roma**
Tel: 06-6840 0001 Fax: 06-8768 77396
Internet: www.teatro.roma.it
E-Mail: teatrodiroma@mail.nexus.it
director Mario Martone; president Watter Pedulla; press office Roberta Rem
Venue type: theatre *Capacity:* 750 *Arts types:* drama *Comments:* see also Promoters and Agents & Producers

Teatro Brancaccio
Via Merulana, 244, 00184 **Roma**
Tel: 06-487 4563 Fax: 06-487 0568
sovrintendente Paolo Donat Cattin
Venue type: theatre *Capacity:* 1500 *Arts types:* dance, opera, drama, music

Teatro dei Satiri
c/o Compagnia del Teatro dei Satiri s.a.s., Via di Grotta Pinta 19, 00186 **Roma**
Tel: 06-687 1639 Fax: 06-687 1578
E-Mail: satiri@pronet.it
direttore artistico Benedetto Margiotta; direttore amministrativo Marco Riccobono; ufficio stampa Diego Ruiz de Ballesteros
Venue type: theatre *Capacity:* Sala Grande 250, Sala Cabaret 80 *Arts types:* drama, cabaret, comedy *Comments:* ancient theatre awarded the title of Teatro di Tradizione; built on the remains of the Roman Theatre of Pompeius

Teatro dell'Angelo
Via Simone De Saint-Bon, 17, 00195 **Roma**
Tel: 06-372 0958/3600 2640 (press office)/372 0933
Fax: 06-3751 6055
E-Mail: immobilgen@iol.it
ufficio stampa Laura del Vecchio; direttore tecnico Danilo Facco; direttore artistico Bedi Moratti
Venue type: theatre *Capacity:* 150 *Policy:* rent

Teatro dell'Opera di Roma – Fondazione
P.zza Beniamino Gigli 8, 00184 **Roma**
Tel: 06-481 601 Fax: 06-488 1253/481 8847 (press office)
Internet: themix.it
E-Mail: sovrintendenza@opera.roma.it
sovrintendente Franceso Ernani; direttore artistico e musicale Giuseppe Sinopoli; uff. stampa Renato Bossa
Venue type: theatre *Capacity:* 1604 *Policy:* also rent *Arts types:* opera, concerts, ballet *Comments:* see also Opera, Dance, Festival and Orchestras

Teatro dell'Orologio
Via dei Filippini 17a, 00186 **Roma**
Tel: 06-6830 8735/8330 (sala orfeo) Fax: 06-683 2764
direttore artistico Mario Moretti,
Valentino Orfeo (sala orfeo)
Venue type: several halls *Capacity:* sala grande 100, sala Orfeo 100, sala Caffé Teatro 50, sala Artaud 40 *Arts types:* drama – contemporary, experimental, concerts *Comments:* theatre is managed by two different drama groups: I.T and Ass. Culturale Orfeo; see also Drama

Teatro Furio Camillo
Via Camilla N.44, 00181 **Roma**
Tel: 06-7834 7348 Fax: 06-7834 7348
artistic & adminstrative director Gianluca Riggi
Andrea Felici
Venue type: theatre *Capacity:* 99 *Policy:* own productions, present, rent *Arts types:* drama, dance *Comments:* managed by Association l'Archimandrita; resident company Dark Camera (q.v.)

Teatro Ghione
Via delle Fornaci 37, 00165 **Roma**
Tel: 06-637 2294 Fax: 06-639 0578
Internet: www.ghione.it
E-Mail: ghione@pronet.it
direttore (teatro) Ileana Ghione; direttore (musica) Christopher Axworthy
Capacity: 628 *Policy:* present, rent, produce *Arts types:* classical recitals, contemporary music, theatre, Euromusica (Euromusica-master concert series), master concert series

Teatro Greco
Via Ruggero Leoncavallo 16, 00199 **Roma**
Tel: 06-860 7513 Fax: 06-860 7740
general manager Palma Marzilli; artistic director Maria Teresa Dal Medico
Venue type: theatre, is also a TV studio *Capacity:* 392 *Policy:* private venue, presents, produces *Arts types:* dance, music, musical, prosa

Teatro Olimpico
Piazza Gentile da Fabriano 17, 00196 **Roma**
Tel: 06-326 5991 Fax: 06-323 4908
Internet: www.teatroolimpico.com
E-Mail: olimpico@tiscalinet.it
amministratore delegato Lucia Bocca; presidente Avv. Edoardo Pugliese
Venue type: theatre *Capacity:* 1300 *Policy:* rent *Arts types:* concerts, ballet, drama, opera

Teatro Parioli
Via G. Borsi 20, 00197 **Roma**
Tel: 06-808 5303/807 2139 Fax: 06-807 4951
director Luciano Samero
Venue type: theatre *Capacity:* 600 *Policy:* produce, present, rent *Arts types:* music, drama, dance, comedy *Comments:* the theatre is managed by the agency Fascino s.r.l. (q.v.)

Teatro Tordinona
Via Degli Acquasparta 16, 00186 **Roma**
Tel: 06-6880 5890 Fax: 06-6880 4982
E-Mail: tordinona@tin.it
direttore tecnico Gerardo Galdi; direttore artistico Renato Giordano
Venue type: sala *Capacity:* 96 *Policy:* rent *Arts types:* contemporary theatre *Comments:* home of 'Compagnia Stabile del Teatro Tordinona'; also organises theatre courses

Teatro Vascello
Via Giacinto Carini 72/78, 00152 **Roma**
Tel: 06-589 8031/588 1021 Fax: 06-581 6623
Internet: www.vascello.it
E-Mail: teatrovascello@xwnet.com
presidente e direttore artistico Giancarlo Nanni; ufficio stampa e pr t.b.a.; amministrazione Marco Ciuti
Venue type: multi-purpose *Capacity:* 400 *Policy:* rent, present *Arts types:* drama, dance, concerts, films *Comments:* home of 'Cooperativa La Fabbrica Dell'Attore'

Teatro Vittoria
piazza S. Maria Liberatrice 8/11, 00153 **Roma**
Tel: 06-578 1960/578 2314/574 0170 (box office)
Fax: 06-575 9935
direttore artistico e organizzativo Attilio Corsini; direttore tecnico Stefano Valle
Venue type: theatre *Capacity:* 585 *Policy:* have guest companies and share the profits (percentage) *Arts types:* drama, concert, dance theatre & figure theatre *Comments:* home to Coop. Attori e Tecnici, drama company; see also Drama

Teatro Comunale R Zandonai
Corso Bettini 82, 38068 **Rovereto**
Tel: 0464-452 159/198 Fax: 0464-436 127
Internet: www.comune.rovereto.tn.it
E-Mail: cultura@comune.rovereto.tn.it
direttore, ufficio cultura Dott ssa Simonetta Festa
Venue type: Italian-stage theatre *Capacity:* 549 *Policy:* rent *Arts types:* drama, contemporary dance, classical music concerts, operetta

Teatro Sociale
Piazza Garibaldi 14, 45100 **Rovigo**
Tel: 0425-25614/27853 (office)/21734 Fax: 0425-29212
Internet: www.comune.rovigo.it/teatrosociale
E-Mail: teatrosociale@comune.rovigo.it
assessore delegato ass. Gabbris Ferrari; consulente Massimo Contiero
Venue type: theatre *Capacity:* 750 *Policy:* rent *Arts types:* opera, ballet, symphony, concerts, theatre *Comments:* Teatro Don Bosco 400, used for performances for children; administrative office: Via Casalini 2, 45100 Rovigo

Teatro Civico
Corso Vittorio Emanuele, 35, 07100 **Sassari**
Tel: 079-232 182 Fax: 079-280 714 (assessorato)
dirigente servizi culturali Francesca Chessa; funzionario servizi culturali Dott. Mariangela Valentini; collaboratrice settore cultura Maria Fiori
Venue type: theatre *Capacity:* 290 *Policy:* rent *Arts types:* drama, dance, concerts, exhibitions, conferences *Comments:* the theatre is managed by the Assessorato alla Pubblica Istruzione, Cultura, Sport, Politiche Giovanili e Turismo, Viale Dante, 1, 07100 Sassari, Tel: 079-283 0900/904, Fax: 079-283 0905

Teatro-Cinema Politeama Verdi
Via Politeama, 2, 07100 **Sassari**
Tel: 079-239 479 Fax: 079-294 376
direttore Rag. Gavino Guarino; collaboratore Bruno Desogus
Venue type: theatre *Capacity:* 950 *Policy:* rent *Arts types:* drama, opera, concerts, dance, cinema *Comments:* the theatre is run by: Ditta E.C.R. Esercizi Cinema Riuniti, registered address: Viale Trento, 5, 07100 Sassari, Tel: 079-291 273, Fax: 079-239 479

Teatro Comunale Chiabrera
Piazza Diaz 2, 17100 **Savona**
Tel: 019-820 409/838 6995 Fax: 019-838 6995
direttore dott.Roberto Bosi
Venue type: theatre *Capacity:* 700 *Policy:* present, rent *Arts types:* theatre, classical concerts, opera

Teatro Studio di Scandicci
Via Donizetti 58, 50018 **Scandicci (FI)**
Tel: 055-757 348 Fax: 055-757 348
Internet: www.firenze.net/teatrostudio
E-Mail: teatrostudio@firenze.net
direttore artistico t.b.a.; uff. stampa t.b.a.
Capacity: 350 *Arts types:* experimental theatre, jazz and contemporary music *Comments:* part of cultural institution Istituzione Servizi Culturali Comune di Scandicci with music school and library

Teatro Della Limonaia
Via Gramsci 426, 50019 **Sesto Fiorentino (FI)**
Tel: 055-440 852 Fax: 055-440 852
Internet: www.teatro-limonaia.fi.it
E-Mail: info@teatro-limonaia.fi.it
artistic director Barbara Nativi
Capacity: 100 *Arts types:* small shows, monologues *Comments:* also houses a theatre school; also organise the Festival Intercity Berlin; see also Festivals

Teatro dei Rinnovati
Piazza del Campo 1, 53100 **Siena**
Tel: 0577-292 225 (ufficio attivita' teatrali)/266 (portiniera)/265 (box office) Fax: 0577-292 296
performing arts & theatre officer Donatella Pollini
Venue type: theatre *Capacity:* 570 *Policy:* rent *Arts types:* drama, ballet, concerts, conferences *Comments:* they also manage Teatro dei Rozzi (q.v.)

Teatro dei Rozzi
Piazza Indipendenza, 53100 **Siena**
Tel: 0577-46960 (theatre)/292 225 (culture office)
Fax: 0577-292 296
performing arts & theatres officer Donatella Pollini
Venue type: theatre *Capacity:* 499 *Policy:* rent *Arts types:* drama, ballet, concerts, conferences *Comments:* an historical theatre built in 1817 by the Accademia dei Rozzi; see also Teatro dei Rinnovati

Teatro Comunale di Sulmona
Via A.De Nino, 67039 **Sulmona (AQ)**
Tel: 0864-52224/242 249/283 Fax: 0864-32199
direttore Dott. Franco Del Monte
Venue type: theatre *Capacity:* 700 *Policy:* rent *Arts types:* drama, concerts, ballets, opera

Centro Teatro CREST
Via Duomo 273, 74100 **Taranto**
Tel: 099-471 4520 Fax: 099-470 4792
E-Mail: c.r.e.s.t@iol.it
amministrator Clara Cottino; direttore artistico Mauro Maggioni
Venue type: sala *Capacity:* 90 *Arts types:* youth theatre *Comments:* home of CREST

Teatro Vaccai
P.zza Vaccaj, 62029 **Tolentino (MC)**
Tel: 0733-968 460/960 059 Fax: 0733-973 844
Internet: www.musical.it
E-Mail: rancia@musical.it
direttore organizzativo Bruno Borracini; direttore artistico Saverio Marconi; responsabile relazioni esterne, ufficio stampa e promozione Massimo Zenobi; segreteria organizzativa e amministrativa Anna Grottesi, Elisabetta Foresi
Venue type: theatre *Capacity:* 450 *Arts types:* drama, music, dance *Comments:* run by 'Compagnia Della Rancia'; see also Drama and Agents & Producers

Alfa Teatro
c/o A.G.S. Augusto Grilli Spettacoli,
Via Casalborgone 16, 10132 **Torino**
Tel: 011-819 3529/5803 Fax: 011-819 3529
Internet: www.alfateatro.it
E-Mail: info@alfateatro.it
artistic director & administrator/legal representative Augusto Grilli; pr & press officer Claudio Bertoni
Venue type: theatre *Capacity:* 300 *Policy:* rent *Arts types:* musical, operetta, drama, youth theatre, puppetry, opera, conventions, prosa *Comments:* puppets museum in the theatre; workshops: operetta, theatre and puppetry; casting for new artist; have two theatrical seasons; see also Opera, Puppets and Agents & Producers

Auditorium RAI
Piazza Rossaro, 10124 **Torino**
Tel: 011-817 3872 (press office) Fax: 011-888 300
E-Mail: robotti@rai.it
general manager Dott. Cesare Dapino; artistic director Daniele Spini
Venue type: concert hall *Policy:* rent *Arts types:* symphony, chamber *Comments:* under refurbishment; see also Orchestras

Teatro Adua
Corso Giulio Cesare 67, 10152 **Torino**
Tel: 011-856 521 (theatre)/817 0680 Fax: 011-889 711
administrator & co-proprietor dott. Lorenzo Ventavoli
Venue type: cinema/theatre *Capacity:* Adua 200: 149; Adua 400: 384; Sala Mariani: 60 *Policy:* rent *Arts types:* cinema, theatre, conferences *Comments:* theatre is available for rent anytime through Ventavoli offices

Teatro Alfieri
c/o Torino Spettacoli, Piazza Solferino 4, 10121 **Torino**
Tel: 011-562 3800 Fax: 011-562 3435
Internet: www.torinospettacoli.it
E-Mail: tospett@tin.it
direzione artistica Germana Erba
Venue type: theatre *Capacity:* 1512 *Policy:* present, rent, co-promote *Arts types:* concerts, musical comedy, plays, revues, pop concerts, operetta, cinema
Comments: Torino Spettacoli also run the Teatro Erba in Torino (q.v.), see also Drama, Promoters and Agents & Producers

Teatro Araldo
Via Chiomonte 3, 10141 **Torino**
Tel: 011-331 764 (theatre)/489 676 (office)
Fax: 011-473 3102
Internet: www.arpnet.it/~angolo
E-Mail: angolo@arpnet.it
direttore Massimo Calì; direttore tecnico Carlo Pregno
Venue type: sala *Capacity:* 214 *Policy:* main venue of Teatro dell'Angolo (q.v.), occasionally rent to other organisations *Arts types:* drama for young people

Teatro Carignano
Piazza Carignano 6, 10123 **Torino**
Tel: 011-547 048/562 2791 Fax: 011-544 889
Internet: www.teatrostabile.torino.it
E-Mail: info@teatrostabile.torino.it
direttore artistico Gabriele Lavia; presidente Agostino Rebaudengo
Venue type: Italian theatre *Capacity:* 700 *Policy:* own production, rent, residencies *Arts types:* drama
Comments: see also Drama

Teatro Colosseo
Via Madama Cristina 71, 10125 **Torino**
Tel: 011-669 8034 Fax: 011-658 919
Internet: www.ipsnet.it/teatrocolosseo
segretaria Patrizia Arico; direttore artistico Claudia Spoto
Venue type: theatre *Capacity:* 1600 *Policy:* rent *Arts types:* drama, comedy, musicals, concerts, cabaret

Teatro Erba
c/o Torino Spettacoli, Corso Moncalieri 241, 10133 **Torino**
Tel: 011-661 5447/5415 Fax: 011-661 5415
Internet: www.torinospettacoli.it
E-Mail: tospett@tin.it
direzione artistica Germana Erba
Venue type: theatre, cinema
Capacity: 360 *Arts types:* plays, concerts, revues, cinema
Comments: Torino Spettacoli also runs the Teatro Alfieri in Torino (q.v.), see also Drama, Promoters and Agents & Producers

Teatro Juvarra
Via Juvarra 15, 10122 **Torino**
Tel: 011-540 675 Fax: 011-517 5084
Internet: www.quiaffari.it/juvarra
E-Mail: multiteatro@tin.it
direttore Sergio Martin; consultant Giovanna Franco; ufficio stampa Maura Sesia
Venue type: theatre *Capacity:* Teatro Juvarra 222, Café Procope 149 *Arts types:* drama, dance, concerts, cabaret, exhibitions *Comments:* home of M.A.S. Juvarra (Multimedia Arte Spettcolo)

Teatro Nuovo
c/o Fondazione Teatro Nuovo, Corso Massimo d'Azeglio 17, 10126 **Torino**
Tel: 011-650 0211 Fax: 011-650 0265
Internet: www.tnt.nuovo.it
E-Mail: nuovotnt@tin.it
direzione artistica Gian Mesturino; direzione attivitá formative Germana Erba
Venue type: theatre
Capacity: 3 halls: Sala Grande 1000, Sala Valentino I 300, Sala Valentino II 300
Policy: present, rent, co-promote *Arts types:* international dance, musical, prose, concerts, cinema *Comments:* also run Accademia regionale di Danza, Liceo Artistico Coreutico, Liceo per l'Arte e lo Spettacolo; see also Dance, Festivals and Promoters

Teatro Regio
Piazza Castello 215, 10124 **Torino**
Tel: 011-88151 (switchboard)
Fax: 011-881 5214
Internet: www.regio-torino.org
direttore artistico Claudio Desderi; responsabile servizi promozionali e pr Piero Robba (tel: 011-881 5212); responsabile servizi amministrativi Carlo Carrà; responsabile servizi personale e scritture Fabrizio Pugliese; responsabile servizi stampa, comunicazione e marketing Ugo Sandroni; sovrintendente Walter Vergnand; progetti di comunicazione Paola Giunti (tel: 011-881 5233)
Venue type: theatre
Capacity: 2 venues: Teatro Regio 1592, Piccolo Regio 388, Sala Pavone (for press meetings) 90 *Policy:* produce, rent, co-productions
Arts types: opera, ballet, concerts
Comments: home of orchestra and choir of Teatro Regio; see also Opera, Orchestras and Festivals

Sala dei Concerti della Società Filarmonica
Via Verdi 30, 38100 **Trento**
Tel: 0461-985 244 Fax: 0461-985 244
E-Mail: filartn@tin.it
presidente Marco de Battaglia; vice presidente avv. Antonio Divan; direttore amministrativo Dott. Lorenzo Arnoldi; segretario artistico Antonia Carlini
Venue type: chamber music hall
Capacity: 250 *Policy:* also for rent
Arts types: chamber music
Comments: see also Promoters

Teatro Auditorium Santa Chiara
Via S. Croce 67, 38100 **Trento**
Tel: 0461-986 488 Fax: 0461-231 044
E-Mail: cscsctn@tin.it
presidente Claudio Visintainer; director Franco Oss-Noser
Venue type: multi-purpose *Capacity:* 838, Teatro Sperimentale 252 *Policy:* rent *Arts types:* cinema, concerts, ballet, operetta and lyric theatre, drama, congresses etc.

Teatro Comunale – Treviso
Via Diaz 7, 31100 **Treviso**
Tel: 0422-410 130 Fax: 0422-582 285
Comments: theatre under refurbishment until 2004, administration folded; no further details known at time of going to print

Kulturni Dom
Via Petronio 4, 34138 **Trieste**
Tel: 040-632 664 Fax: 040-368 547
presidente Filiberto Benedetic; direttore artistico Marco Sossi
Venue type: theatre *Capacity:* 550 *Policy:* own production, rent *Arts types:* classical drama, concerts, youth theatre

Teatro Comunale Giuseppe Verdi
Riva 3 Novembre 1, 34121 **Trieste**
Tel: 040-672 2111 Fax: 040-672 2249
Internet: www.teatroverdi-trieste.com
E-Mail: info@teatroverdi-trieste.com
sovrintendente dott. Lorenzo Jorio; segretario artistico Maestro Giovanni Pacor; direttore amministrazione Alessandra Delfin; direttore affari generali Antonio Quadrelli; responsabile uffico stampa e relazioni Esterne Nicoletta Cavalieri (040-672 2209); direttore artistico Giandomenico Vaccari; direttore di produzione Gianni Gori
Venue type: theatre *Capacity:* 1324 *Policy:* also rent *Arts types:* opera, concerts, operetta, ballet *Comments:* see also Festivals, Orchestras, Dance and Opera

Teatro Cristallo
Via del Ghirlandaio 12, 34138 **Trieste**
Tel: 040-948 471/390 613 Fax: 040-946 460
E-Mail: contrada@spin.it
direttore organizzativo Ivaldo Vernelli; presidente Orazio Bobbio; direttore artistico Francesco Macedonio
Venue type: theatre *Capacity:* 752 *Arts types:* drama, children's theatre *Comments:* home of La Contrada Teatro Stabile; see also Drama

Teatro Politeama Rossetti
Viale XX Settembre 45, casella postale 590, 34126 **Trieste**
Tel: 040-567 201 Fax: 040-52447
E-Mail: ts.rossetti@spin.it
direttore unico Antonio Calenda; presidente Prof. Roberto Damiani; ufficio stampa Mario Brandolin, Marinella Chirico
Venue type: theatre *Capacity:* 1450 *Arts types:* drama, occasional symphonic concerts, recitals *Comments:* home of Teatro Stabile di Prosa del Friuli Venezia Giulia; gestione: Teatro Stabile del Friuli-Venezia Giulia; will be under refurbishment in the year 2000; all the performances will take place at the Sala Tripcovich 950

Gran Teatro La Fenice
c/o Palafenice Isola Nuova del Tronchetto, 30135 **Venezia**
Tel: 041-786 511 Fax: 041-786 580
Internet: www.tin.it/fenice
E-Mail: fenice@interbusiness.it
sovrintendente Mario Messinis; direttore di produzione Dino Squizzato; capo ufficio stampa e relazioni esterne Cristiano Chiarot; coordinatore della produzione artistica Paolo Pinamonti; direttore stabile dell' orchestra M° Isaac Karabtchevsky
Venue type: tent (Palafenice) *Capacity:* Palafenice 1400
Comments: the Gran Teatro La Fenice is currently under reconstruction; mean while the activities are held at the Palafenice; see also Opera and Orchestras

Teatro Goldoni
Teatro Goldoni, San Marco 4650/B, 30124 **Venezia**
Tel: 041-520 5422/7583 (box office) Fax: 041-520 5241
E-Mail: teatrogo@tin.it
direttore Mauro Carbonoli; presidente Francesco Raimondo Donà; coordinatrice Cristiana Csermeliy; ufficio stampa Jacqueline Gallo
Venue type: theatre *Capacity:* 800 *Arts types:* drama, lyric, operetta, musicals, comedy *Comments:* see also Teatro Verdi in Padova; see also Drama

Arena Di Verona – Ente Autonomo
Piazza Bra 28, 37121 **Verona**
Tel: 045-805 1811 (switchboard)/1891 (press office)/1832
Fax: 045-803 1443 (press office)
Internet: www.arena.it
sovrintendente Gianfranco de Bosio; direttore artistico Gabriele Gandini
Venue type: arena/open air amphitheatre (Roman Amphitheatre) *Capacity:* 1600 *Arts types:* opera, recitals, ballet *Comments:* the physical space is owned by the City Council of Verona which hire it to Ente Autonomo

Teatro Filarmonico
Via Mutilati 4/K, 37121 **Verona**
Tel: 045-805 1811/1838 (switchboard)/800 5151 (box office) Fax: 045-803 1443 (press office)
Internet: www.arena.it
Venue type: theatre *Capacity:* 1200 *Arts types:* concerts, ballet, opera *Comments:* the theatre is owned by Accademia Filarmonica; it is closed during the summer season (approx May-October) when all activities are moved to Arena di Verona

Teatro Laboratorio
Piazza Fontanelle Santo Stefano 12, 37129 **Verona**
Tel: 045-803 1321/913 261 Fax: 045-803 1321
E-Mail: mscdc@tin.it
direttore Jana Balkan; ufficio stampa e segreteria Cecilia Filippin
Venue type: multipurpose *Capacity:* 150 *Arts types:* pantomime, concerts, ballets, conferences, drama
Comments: home of Cooperativa del Teatro Scientifico; see also Drama and Festivals

Teatro Nuovo
Piazza Viviani 10, 37121 **Verona**
Tel: 045-800 6100 Fax: 045-803 0815
E-Mail: berardi@mbox.vol.it
direttore e gestore Dott. Paolo Valerio; organizzazione Lucia Rubini; direzione tecnica Enrico Berardi
Venue type: theatre *Capacity:* 844 *Policy:* produce, also for rent *Arts types:* drama, concerts, ballet, symphony
Comments: Shakespeare's plays throughout the year; some educational work; the theatre has a foyer (150) overlooking Juliet's balcony and courtyard; they also manage Cinema-Teatro Alcione (500) used mainly for research and young people's theatre

Teatro Olimpico
c/o Assessorato di Servizi Culturali, Levà degli Angeli 11, 36100 **Vicenza**
Tel: 0444-323 781/222 101 (assessorato)
Fax: 0444-222 155
Internet: www.comune.vicenza.it
E-Mail: stampcultura@comune.vicenza.it
ufficio stampa Riccardo Brazzale (444-222 121), Loretta Simoni
Venue type: theatre *Capacity:* 470 *Policy:* rent *Arts types:* ballet, chamber music, classical drama performances, jazz *Comments:* theatre address: Piazza Matteotti, 11, 36100 Vicenza; the theatre is open for tours every day except Monday from 10am-7pm (summer) & 9am-5pm (winter); the theatre season is from April-October

Teatro San Marco
Via San Francesco 76, 36100 **Vicenza**
Tel: 0444-921 560/323 837 Fax: 0444-324 907
direttore Don Giuseppo Ruaro; organisation Geom. Aldo Zordan
Venue type: theatre, cinema *Capacity:* 449 *Arts types:* drama, cabaret, folk concerts, dance, cinema

LATVIA (+371)

Big Hall of Latvian University
Latvijas Universitâtes Lielâ aula
Raiòa bulv. 19, 1586 **Riga**
Tel: 7-228 928
Capacity: 800
Arts types: symphonic music, choirs, organ

Concert Hall Ave Sol
Ave Sol koncertzâle
Citadeles 7, 1010 **Riga**
Tel: 7-027 547 Fax: 7-027 570
Capacity: 320
Arts types: chamber music, choirs, drama

Concert Hall The Big Gild
Koncertzale Liela Ìilde
6 Amatu, 1664 **Riga**
Tel: 7-213 798 Fax: 7-224 850
E-Mail: lnso@mail.bkc.lv
Capacity: 750 *Arts types:* symphonic and chamber music, choirs, dance, pop, rock music, jazz

J Vîtols Academy of Music of Latvia
J Vîtola Mûzikas akademijas Lielâ zâle
K. Barona 1, 1050 **Riga**
Tel: 7-228 684 Fax: 7-280 271
E-Mail: karlsons@muza.lv
Capacity: 345 *Arts types:* symphonic and chamber music, choirs

Meßaparks Open-air Stage
Meßaparka Lielâ estrâde
Meßaparka Lielâ estrâde, 1014 **Riga**
Tel: 7-557 490 Fax: 7-557 490
Capacity: 2700, stage cap. 17000 *Arts types:* song and dance festivals, pop, rock music

National Opera House
Nacionâlâs operas nams
Latvian National Opera, Aspazijas bulv. 3, 1050 **Riga**
Tel: 7-223 297/225 747 Fax: 7-228 930
Capacity: 950 *Arts types:* opera, ballet, symphonic music, drama *Comments:* see also Opera

Reformed Church Concert Hall
Reformâtu baznîcas koncertzâle
Riga Recording Company, Alksnâju 3, 1050 **Riga**
Tel: 7-225 725 Fax: 7-226 407
Capacity: 150
Arts types: symphonic and chamber music, choirs

Riga Congress House
Rîgas Kongresu nama Lielâ zâle
Kr. Valdemâra 5, 1010 **Riga**
Tel: 7-323 370 Fax: 7-830 244
Capacity: big hall 1200, small hall 285 *Arts types:* congress events, films, symphonic music, choirs, dance, ballet, pop, rock music, jazz, festivals, entertainment, drama, multimedia performances

Riga Dome Concert Hall
Doma Koncertzâle
Kaïíu 11a, 1664 **Riga**
Tel: 7-224 432 Fax: 7-213 497
E-Mail: S.zake@bkc.lv
Capacity: 2000 *Arts types:* organ music, choirs, symphonic and chamber music

Riga Latvian Society House
Rîgas Latviesu Biedrîbas
Meríeïa 13, 1050 **Riga**
Tel: 7-222 932 Fax: 7-226 924
Capacity: big hall 670, gilded hall
Arts types: symphonic and chamber music, choirs, congress events, entertainment

Riga St Jon's Church Concert Hall
Rîgas Sv. Jâòa Baznîcas koncertzâle
Kaïíu 11a, 1664 **Riga**
Tel: 7-213 426 Fax: 7-213 497
Capacity: 628
Arts types: chamber music, choirs, organ music

Wagner Chamber Music Hall
Vâgnera Koncertzâle
Vagnera ielâ 4, 1664 **Riga**
Tel: 7-210 817 Fax: 7-213 426
Capacity: 260 *Arts types:* chamber music, jazz, conferences, seminars

LIECHTENSTEIN (+423)

Theater am Kirchplatz
Reberastrasse 12, Postfach, 9494 **Schaan**
Tel: 237 5960 Fax: 237 5961
Internet: www.lol.li/tak
E-Mail: tak@theater.lol.li
Direktor Georg Rootering; Persönliche Mitarbeiterin des Intendanten Anita Kaiser-Panzer; Dramaturgic/Öffentlichkeitsarbeit Ingo-Yves Kleinheisterkamp
Venue type: theatre
Capacity: Tak 344, Takino 204
Policy: present, rent, co-produce
Arts types: classical concerts, theatre, jazz, dance, cabaret *Comments:* when promoting also use 707-seat house in Vaduz

LITHUANIA (+370)

Joint-Stock Company Alytaus Tekstile Culture Centre
Akcines Bendroves Alytaus Tekstile kulturos centras
Pramones 1a, 4580 **Alytus**
Tel: 35-57754 (director)
Venue type: cultural centre

Kaunas Artificial Fibre Factory's Palace of Culture and Healthiness
Kauno Dirbtinio Pluosto Gamyklos Kulturos Ir Sveikatingumo Rümai
Kovo 11-osios 26, 3031 **Kaunas**
Tel: 7-756 490 (director)

Kaunas Artists' Centre
Kauno Menininku Rümai
V. Putvinskio 56, 3000 **Kaunas**
Tel: 7-224 475 (director)

Kaunas Culture Centre
Kauno Kulturos Rümai
Vytauto pr. 79, 3000 **Kaunas**
Tel: 7-228 579 (director)
Venue type: cultural centre

Kaunas Philharmonic Hall
Kauno filharmonijos sale
Spaiegos St. 5, 3000 **Kaunas**
Tel: 7-222 558 Fax: 7-229 208
Venue type: concert hall *Capacity:* 500 (seated)

Sport Complex Azuolynas
Azuolyno Sporto Kompleksas
Perkuno 5, 3005 **Kaunas**
Tel: 7-200 514 (director)

Klaipeda Artist's Centre
Klaipedos Menininku Rümai
Baznyciu 4/Darzu 10, 5800 **Klaipeda**
Tel: 61-52948 (director)

Klaipeda Fishermen's Centre of Culture and Sport
Klaipedos Zveju Kulturos Ir Sporto Rümai
Taikos pr. 70, 5799 **Klaipeda**
Tel: 61-73421 (vice-director)

Culture Centre of Mazeikiai State Entreprise Nafta
Mazeikiu Valstybinès Imonès Nafta Kulturos Ir Technikos Rümai
Naftininku g., 5500 **Mazeikiai**
Tel: 93-79654/93-79754 Fax: 93-79754

Palanga Summer Season Concert Hall
Palangos Vasaros Koncertu Sale
Vytauto 45, 5720 **Palanga**
Tel: 36-13959 (director)

Panevezys Centre of Culture Ekranas
Panevezio Ekrano Kulturos Rümai
Kranto 28, 5319 **Panevezys**
Tel: 54-61216 (director)

Siauliai Entertainment Centre
Siauliu Miesto Kulturos Centras
Ausros al. 31, 5400 **Siauliai**
Tel: 14-24700 (director)

Centre of Culture and Sport of the Ministry of Internal Affairs
Vidaus Reikalu Ministerijos Kulturos Ir Sporto Rümai
Sporto 21, 2051 **Vilnius**
Tel: 2-733 578 (director)

Lithuanian Artists' Centre
Lietuvos Menininku Rümai
Didzioyi 31, 2001 **Vilnius**
Tel: 2-618 179 Fax: 2-224 167

Lithuanian Opera and Ballet Theatre
Lietuvos operos ir baleto teatras
A. Vienuolio St. 1, 2000 **Vilnius**
Tel: 2-620 636 Fax: 2-623 503
Venue type: opera house *Capacity:* 1200

Lithuanian Trade Unions' Communities' Centre of Culture
Lietuvos Profesiniu Sajungu Bendrijos Kulturos Rümai
V. Mykolaicio-Putino 5, 2009 **Vilnius**
Tel: 2-635 620 (manager)

National Philharmonic Hall Vilnius
Lietuvos nacionalines filharmonijos sale
Ausros Vartu St. 5, 2001 **Vilnius**
Tel: 2-626 802 Fax: 2-622 859
Venue type: 2 concert halls
Capacity: 650 and 150 (seated)

Vilnius Palace of Concerts and Sport
Vilniaus Koncertu ir Sporto Rümai
Rinktines 1, 2051 **Vilnius**
Tel: 2-352 321 (director) Fax: 2-354 534
director E. Romanovas; department of press/information N. Ruzgiene (357 161)

Vilnius Teachers' House
Vilniaus Mokytoju Namai
Vilniaus 39/6, 2600 **Vilnius**
Tel: 2-623 514 (director)

Vingio Parko Estrada
Odminiu 3, 2001 **Vilnius**
Tel: 2-611 037/615 575 Fax: 2-628 494
manager A. Nomeika; business manager V. Liaudankus (615 575)
Comments: an open venue for folk festivals

Youth Centre of Art Meno Lyga
Jaunimo Meno Centras Meno Lyga
Kauno 5, 2006 **Vilnius**
Tel: 2-692 771 (director) Fax: 2-222 423

LUXEMBOURG (+352)

Kulturfabrik – Esch – Alzette
BP 370, 4004 **Esch-sur-Alzette**
Tel: 554 4931 Fax: 550 403
Internet: www.kulturfabrik.lu
E-Mail: mail@kulturfabrik.lu
artistic director Karin Kremer
Venue type: old slaughterhouse with various spaces
Capacity: concert hall 1000, theatre 400 + workshops
Policy: produce, present
Arts types: drama, music, dance, cinema, visual arts
Comments: performance spaces, workshops, cinema, gallery, cafe and rehearsal space for musicians; resident theatre company is Théatre GmbH; member of Trans Europe Halles

Théâtre Municipal de la Ville d'Esch-sur-Alzette
BP 44, 4001 **Esch-sur-Alzette**
Tel: 540 387/540 916 (booking) Fax: 542 896
directeur Philippe Noesen; administratrice Marie-Josée Herber
Venue type: theatre *Capacity:* 517 *Policy:* present, rent, produce, co-produce *Arts types:* orchestra, dance, ballet, theatre, exhibitions, operettas

Théâtre des Capucins
Rue des Capucins, 2613 **Luxembourg**
Tel: 4796 2433 Fax: 465 065
directeur Marc Olinger; directeur technique Remy Theisen
Venue type: theatre *Capacity:* 269 *Policy:* rent, produce, co-produce *Arts types:* ballet, concerts (small ensembles), theatre, spoken theatre (French and German)
Comments: see also Drama

Théâtre des Casemates
BP 452, 2014 **Luxembourg**
Tel: 291 281
président Pierre Capesius (291 281); directrice artistique Christine Reinhold; directeur technique Patrick Colling
Venue type: theatre *Capacity:* 100 *Policy:* produce, co-produce, rent *Arts types:* avant garde and classic theatre performances in German and Luxembourgeois
Comments: see also Drama

Théâtre Municipal
110 avenue Gaston Diedrich, 1420 **Luxembourg**
Tel: 4796 2710/11/13/470 895 (booking) Fax: 465 777
directeur/manager Jeannot Commes
Venue type: theatre and concert hall *Capacity:* Grande Salle 941, Studio 446 *Policy:* rent, produce, co-produce (for 2001) *Arts types:* orchestras, dance, opera, films, operetta, drama, recitals, chamber music *Comments:* closed for renovation until April 2001; see also Opera and Drama

MACEDONIA (+389)

Culture and Information Centre
Kulturno-Informativen Centre
Mose Pijade 1, Postfah 589, 91000 **Skopje**
Tel: 91-236 724/230 206/233 510
director Olga Popovska; music programming Violeta Lazova; theatre programming Katarina Mihajlova
Capacity: hal '1919' 150

MALTA (+356)

Manoel Theatre
Old Theatre Street, **Valetta** VLT 07
Tel: 222 618/237 397 Fax: 247 251/250 436
E-Mail: mtadmin@teatrumanoel.com.mt
artistic director Tony Cassar Darien; chairman John Lowell
Venue type: theatre *Capacity:* 600 *Policy:* rent, produce, co-produce *Arts types:* musical concerts, recitals, opera, drama and dance

Astra Theatre
9 Republic Street, **Victoria, Gozo** VCT 103
Tel: 556 256 Fax: 559 366
president Dilindu Cassar; secretary Tony Velli
Venue type: theatre *Capacity:* 1200 *Policy:* rent, present
Arts types: drama, opera, variety, recitals, films
Comments: produce 1 opera; the Astra Theatre Complex includes exhibition halls and the Planet Discotheque

Aurora Opera House
c/o Leone Philarmonic Society, 100, Triq ir-Repubblika, **Victoria, Gozo**
Tel: 562 974 Fax: 562 559
president Dr. Michael Caruana L.L.D.; secretary Patrick Camilleri; resident musical director Colin Attard
Venue type: social club and theatre *Capacity:* 1900 *Arts types:* music, opera, drama *Comments:* see also Promoters

MOLDOVA (+373)

National Palace
Puskin str. 21, 2012 **Chisinau**
Tel: 2-238 258 Fax: 2-238 257
director Valentin Goga

National Philharmonic
Filarmonica Nationala
78 Mitropolit Vaarlam, 2012 **Chisinau**
Tel: 2-238 258 Fax: 2-238 257
director Ion Josanu

Organ Hall
Sala cu Orga
81 Stefan cel Mare bld., 2012 **Chisinau**
Tel: 2-237 262 Fax: 2-238 257
director Mihai Coretchi

Republican Palace
16, Maria Cebotari str., 2012 **Chisinau**
Tel: 2-232 613 Fax: 2-232 242
manager Vasile Chirica

MONACO (+377)

Opera de Monte Carlo – Salle Garnier
Place du Casino, BP 139, 98007 **Monaco**
Tel: 9216 6473 Fax: 9330 0757
Internet: www.opera.mc
E-Mail: opera@sbm.mc
directeurs John M Mordler (opera), Jean-Christophe Maillot (ballet), Marek Janowski (orchestra)
Venue type: opera *Capacity:* 520 *Policy:* produce *Arts types:* classical music, ballet, opera, conferences

Théâtre Princesse Grace
12 avenue d'Ostende, 98000 **Monaco**
Tel: 9350 0345 Fax: 9330 2439
directeur Patrick Hourdequin
Venue type: theatre *Capacity:* 400 *Policy:* present, produce, co-produce *Arts types:* theatre, variety, jazz, comedy, magic shows

NETHERLANDS (+31)

Provadja, Stichting
Theater Provadja, Verdronkenoord 12, 1811 BE **Alkmaar**
Tel: 72-511 0136 Fax: 72-515 9793
Internet: org.nhkanaal.nl/provadja/.
E-Mail: provadja@multiweb.nl
interim artistic director & planning L. Bankersen; planning Nick V. der Hain (cinema); public relations Jaap-Wim V. D. Horst
Venue type: studio theatre *Capacity:* 80
Policy: present *Arts types:* dance, experimental groups, music, mime, movies

Theatre Hotel
Postbus 465, 7600 AL **Almelo**
Tel: 546-810 061 Fax: 546-821 665
Internet: www.theatrehotel.nl
E-Mail: info@theatrehotel.nl
directors Han & Marianne Hammink; theatre manager Miriam Gerretsan
Venue type: theatre *Capacity:* Procenieum Arch 750
Policy: rent, present, produce, co-produce *Arts types:* covers everything

Almeers Theaters
Metropolestraat 11, 1315 KK **Almere**
Tel: 36-548 8222 (administration) Fax: 36-548 8223
acting assistant director Peter Voorbraak; publicity and PR Lunetta van de Plas
Venue type: 2 theatres, multi-purpose *Capacity:* 610 + 180 *Policy:* rent, produce, non-profit organisation *Arts types:* theatre, dance, concerts, ballet, opera, musicals, children's theatre

De Flint Amersfoort Theater en Congrescentrum
Coninckstraat 60, 3811 WK **Amersfoort**
Tel: 33-422 9222 (admin)/9 (box office) Fax: 33-475 7280
E-Mail: de.flint@wxs.nl
director Peter Erkelens
Venue type: theatre, concert hall *Capacity:* theatre 900, concert hall up to 1200 standing and up to 800 seated, church 200 *Policy:* present, rent *Arts types:* dance, experimental groups, music, theatre, youth theatre, puppets, music (pop, jazz, classical), musicals, conferences

Beurs van Berlage
Damrak 213, 1012 ZH **Amsterdam**
Tel: 20-627 1161 Fax: 20-622 9939
E-Mail: roboverman@nedpho.nl
general manager Rob Overman; head of marketing and management Willam Leopold
Venue type: concert hall *Capacity:* Yakult Zaal 655, Aga Zaal 200 *Policy:* present, rent *Arts types:* music
Comments: owned by Nederlands Philharmonisch Orkest and Chamber Orchestra

Bimhuis
Oude Schans 73-77, 1011 KW **Amsterdam**
Tel: 20-623 3373 Fax: 20-620 7759
Internet: www.bimhuis.nl
E-Mail: bimhuis@bimhuis.nl
publicity Karin Klooster; artistic director Huub van Riel
Venue type: concert hall *Capacity:* up to 400 *Arts types:* concerts *Comments:* 150 concerts a year offer an overall view of the Dutch and international jazz and improvised music scene in all its varieties, emphasizing recent developments; see also Promoters

Centre for Culture and Politics De Balie
Kleine-Gartmanplantsoen 10, 1017 RR **Amsterdam**
Tel: 20-553 5151 (admin)/5100 (box office)
Fax: 20-553 5155
Internet: www.balie.nl
E-Mail: balie@balie.nl
director C. Keulemans; administrator H. Thijssen; head technician H. Ellenbroek; producer Mrs. E. Ludenhoff; PR J. Hazelhoff
Venue type: cultural centre *Capacity:* Hall A 180, Hall B 80, Hall C 35 *Policy:* co-produce (most of the time), present, rent (sometimes)
Arts types: experimental groups, theatre, debates, lectures, new media (Digital City)

Flemish Cultural Institute Brakkegrond
Nes 45, 1012 KD **Amsterdam**
Tel: 20-622 9014 Fax: 20-625 3279
Internet: www.brakkegrond.nl
E-Mail: info@brakkegrond.nl
director Guido Vereecke
Venue type: cultural centre *Capacity:* space A 200, space B 180, space C 50 *Policy:* produce, present, rent *Arts types:* drama, modern dance, mime, music theatre, music *Comments:* also organise exhibitions, debates, and literary activities; promote and support Flemish culture in the Netherlands

Het Concertgebouw N.V
Concertgebouwplein 2-6, 1071 LN **Amsterdam**
Tel: 20-573 0573 Fax: 20-573 0570
Internet: www.concertgebouw.nl
E-Mail: gbnv1@euromail.nl
managing director Martijn Sanders
Venue type: concert hall
Capacity: main hall 2037, recital hall 470
Policy: present events at own risk, rent, co-production
Arts types: orchestra, chamber music, recitals, popular music *Comments:* present own concert series; see also Promoters

IJsbreker, De
Weesperzijde 23, 1091 EC **Amsterdam**
Tel: 20-668 1805 Fax: 20-694 6607
Internet: www.ijsbreker.nl
E-Mail: post@ijsbreker.nl
director & programming Jan Wolff
Venue type: concert hall
Capacity: 120 *Policy:* present, rent
Arts types: contemporary music *Comments:* also Tropeninstitute, Rode Hoed; 200 concerts of 20th century music a year; other venues to accommodate larger audiences; see also Promoters

Koninklijk Theater Carré
Amstel 115-125, 1018 EM **Amsterdam**
Tel: 20-622 6177 (admin)/5225 (box office)
Fax: 20-624 1991(admin)/8499 (box office)
Internet: www.aub.nl
E-Mail: theater.carre@wxs.nl
general manager Hein Vens; deputy general manager Hubert Atjak; deputy executive manager Charles Droste; box office manager Tessa Oostergetel; marketing manager Benien van Berkel
Venue type: multi-purpose
Capacity: 1997 *Policy:* rent, co-present
Arts types: dance, music, theatre, concerts, rock, circus, musicals and one-man shows, film
Comments: former circus venue; built in 1887 by circus director Oscar Carré

Meervaart, De
Meer en Vaant 300, 1068 LE **Amsterdam**
Tel: 20-410 7713 Fax: 20-410 7789
Internet: www.meervaart.nl
E-Mail: info@meervaart.nl
director Pieter Erkelens; programmer Sophie Lambo; pr Willemiem Van Lith; acting manager Bert Liebregs; administration Elly Bontjes
Venue type: multi-purpose
Capacity: total 2000 *Policy:* rent, produce
Arts types: dance, experimental groups, music, theatre, youth theatre, puppets, opera, operette, festivals
Comments: see also Festivals

Melkweg
Lijnbaansgracht 234a, 1017 PH **Amsterdam**
Tel: 20-624 1777 Fax: 20-620 1209
Internet: www.melkweg.nl
E-Mail: melkweg@melkweg.nl
director Cor Schlösser; adjunct director Erik Backee; music programmer pop & dance John van Luyn; music programmer world music Feans Goossens; theatre & gallery programmer Suzanne Dechert; cinema programmer Is Hoogland
Venue type: multi-purpose *Capacity:* 2 concert halls: The Max 1000, Oude Zaal 750 *Policy:* own programme, rent occasionally *Arts types:* dance, experimental groups, music, cinema, theatre, video, photo-exhibitions
Comments: multi media and arts centre including cinema, video room, dance studio and gallery; member of Trans Europe Halles (q.v.)

Muziektheater, Het
Postbus 16822, Waterlooplein 22, 1001 PG **Amsterdam**
Tel: 20-551 8911/625 5455 (box office)
Fax: 20-551 8068
E-Mail: info@het-muziektheater.nl
board of directors Jaap Mulders, Truze Lodder, Wayne Eagling, Pierre Audi; director of guest programming Pieter Hofman; director of theatre organisation Marieke Schoenmakers
Venue type: opera and dance house *Capacity:* 1600
Policy: present, rent, produce, co-produce *Arts types:* opera, ballet, dance, music theatre *Comments:* home of The Netherlands Opera and The Dutch National Ballet; lunch concerts at the Boekmanzaal (cap 180); bookings Miriam van Marken, City Hall Tel: 20- 552 3458

Stadsschouwburg Amsterdam
Leidseplein 26, 1017 PT **Amsterdam**
Tel: 20-523 7700/624 2311 (box office)
Fax: 20-623 8685 (box office)
E-Mail: ssba@xs4.all.nl
director Henk Van Der Wolf
Venue type: theatre *Capacity:* 900, studio 100, small hall (for lunch time performances) 60 *Policy:* rent, present, co-present *Arts types:* dance, experimental groups, theatre, ballet, opera, musicals *Comments:* home of Toneelgroep Amsterdam for part of year; open throughout the summer; promotes international summer programmes (July-Aug)

Stichting NES Theaters / De Brakke Grond
Oz Voorburgwal 304, 1012 GL **Amsterdam**
Tel: 20-622 7860 (Nes)/626 6866 (De Brakke Grond)
Fax: 20-638 3349
E-Mail: post@nestheaters.nl
managing director Florian Diepenbrock; manager Maryke Giesbers; artistic director Nan Van Houte; marketing/publicity Lizzy Ondaatje
Venue type: theatre *Capacity:* 3 spaces: Theatre 150, Theatre 120, Studio 50 *Policy:* co-produce, rent, present
Arts types: drama, modern dance, mime, music theatre, youth theatre *Comments:* see also Frascati; theatre address: Nes 45, 1012 KD Amsterdam; see also Promoters

Stichting NES Theaters / Frascati
Oz Voorburgwal 304, 1012 GL **Amsterdam**
Tel: 20-622 7860 (Nes)/7461 (Frascati)
Fax: 20-638 3349
E-Mail: post@nestheaters.nl
managing director Florian Diepenbrock; manager Anne Marie Kalkman; artistic director Nan van Houte; marketing/publicity Lizzy Ondaatje
Venue type: theatre
Capacity: 3 spaces: theatre 190, theatre 90, studio 45
Policy: co-produce, present, rent
Arts types: drama, modern dance, mime, music theatre, contemporary music *Comments:* see also Stichting NEW Theaters / De Brakke Grond; theatre address: Nes 63, 1012 KD Amsterdam

Theater Bellevue
Leidsekade 90, 1017 PN **Amsterdam**
Tel: 20-530 5300 (admin)/5301 (box office)
Fax: 20-530 5303
Internet: www.xs4all.nl/~bellevue/
E-Mail: bellevue@xs4all.nl
director H. Rudelsheim; manager technical affairs H. Bruyn; producer lunchtime shows H. de Zwart
Venue type: theatre *Capacity:* space A 250, space B 100, space C 75 *Policy:* present, rent *Arts types:* dance, experimental groups, music, theatre, cabaret *Comments:* produces lunchtime shows; see also Nieuwe de La Mer

Theater Nieuwe de la Mer
Marnixstraat 404, 1017 PL **Amsterdam**
Tel: 20-530 5300 (admin)/5302 (box office)
Fax: 20-530 5303
Internet: www.xs4all.nl/~bellevue/
E-Mail: bellevue@xs4all.nl
director H. Rudelsheim; manager technical affairs H. Bruyn; producer lunchtime shows H. de Zwart
Venue type: theatre
Capacity: 580 *Policy:* produce, present
Arts types: music, classic theatre, cabaret
Comments: see also Theater Bellevue

Theater Tropen Institute/Royal Tropical Institute
Linnaeusstraat 2, 1092 CK **Amsterdam**
Tel: 20-568 8451 Fax: 20-568 8384
E-Mail: theater@ket.nl
director Otto Romyn; performing arts co-ordinator H. Haringhuizen
Venue type: cultural centre
Capacity: auditorium 454, small theatre 185
Policy: present *Arts types:* non-western cultural activity (music, dance, theatre, film, exhibitions)

Theater Zuider Amstelkanaal
Fred. Roeskestraat 84, PO Box 74144, 1070 BC **Amsterdam**
Tel: 20-675 0613 Fax: 20-675 6316
director t.b.a.; contact Co van Dieben
Venue type: theatre, concert hall *Capacity:* NOG Zaal 450 *Policy:* present, rent *Arts types:* opera, dance, music, drama, workshops *Comments:* see also Promoters

Schouwburg Orpheus
Churchillplein 1, 7314 BZ **Apeldoorn**
Tel: 55-521 2474 Fax: 55-521 7702
director G. Kroeze (Mrs); head of press and PR Leonoor Mees; head technician Leo Krullaars
Venue type: multi-purpose
Capacity: Rabobank Zaal 820, Wegener Arcade Zaal 300
Policy: present, rent *Arts types:* dance, theatre, music, opera, musicals, cabaret

Musis Sacrum / Schouwburg Arnhem
PO Box 1103, 6801 BC **Arnhem**
Tel: 26-372 0720 Fax: 26-443 4396
director Freek van Duÿn; pr & marketing Lineke Kortekaas
Venue type: theatre with 2 auditoria
Capacity: Room A 750, Room B 200 *Policy:* rent, present
Arts types: dance, experimental groups, music (symphony, chamber, recitals), theatre, youth theatre, puppets *Comments:* venues for Images; see also Festivals and Promoters

Stadsschouwburg de Maagd
Postbus 300, 4600 AH **Bergen Op Zoom**
Tel: 164-280 500 Fax: 164-266 227
director & programmer A. L. J. Heck
Venue type: Auditorium *Capacity:* 648 *Policy:* present, rent *Arts types:* performing arts

Chassé Theater
Claudius Prinsenlaan 8, 4811 DJ **Breda**
Tel: 76-530 3100 Fax: 76-530 3190
E-Mail: chasse@tref.nl
director Cees Langeveld; managing director/programme director Joy Arpots
Venue type: concert hall, theatre, cinema *Capacity:* Holland Casino Zaal up to 1300, VSB Zaal 700, ABN Amro 200, Cinema 1: 112, Cinema 2: 72 *Policy:* present *Arts types:* dance, music, theatre, films

Theatre 't Spant
Dr A Kuyperlaan 3, 1402 SB **Bussum**
Tel: 35-693 3254 Fax: 35-693 2854
E-Mail: spantbussum@wxs.nl
director and artistic director W P M Voorman; head of administration M Zwanenburg
Venue type: theatre, multi-purpose *Capacity:* Hall A 800, Hall B 225 *Policy:* present, rent *Arts types:* theatre, musicals, cabaret, jazz, mime, popular music, opera, performances, ballet, big band, plays etc. *Comments:* see also Promoters

Diligentia
Lange Voorhout 5, 2514 EA **Den Haag**
Tel: 70-365 7552 (admin)/1859 (box office) Fax: 70-361 7528
Internet: www.diligentia.nl
E-Mail: diligentia@wxs.nl
director Mr. H. Boerendomk; financial manager Mr. A. Volebregt; arts programming Mrs. E. Olofsen
Venue type: concert hall and theatre *Capacity:* 500 *Policy:* present, co-present, rent *Arts types:* chamber music, cabaret, theatre, recitals, concerts, world music *Comments:* see also Promoters

Dr Anton Philips Zaal
Postbus 11543, 2505 AM **Den Haag**
Tel: 70-360 7927 Fax: 70-362 2773
director Gabriel Oostvogel
Venue type: concert hall *Capacity:* 1890 *Policy:* present, rent *Arts types:* symphony, chamber music recitals, some jazz/pop, world music *Comments:* venue address: Spuiplein 150, 2511 DG Den Haag

Koninklijke Schouwburg
Korte Voorhout 3, 2511 CW **Den Haag**
Tel: 70-356 5356 Fax: 70-361 7455
E-Mail: info@ks.nl
general manager Hans van Westreenen; deputy general manager (programming) Oscar Wibaut; technical manager Henk Derek; head of finance/controller Andrew van den Bosch; head of communication department Beleke Bagchus
Venue type: theatre *Capacity:* 680 *Policy:* promote, rent *Arts types:* classical repertory, modern drama, opera, youth theatre, cabaret *Comments:* home of Het Nationale Toneel Theatre company

Lucent Danstheater
Postbus 333, 2501 CH **Den Haag**
Tel: 70-360 9931 Fax: 70-361 7156
managing director Jaap Hülsmann; business manager Willem van der Voort
Venue type: dance theatre; also suitable for operas, concerts & musicals *Capacity:* 1001 *Arts types:* dance, music, opera, classical ballet, musicals *Comments:* home of the Nederlands Dans Theater (q.v.)

Stichting Grote Kerk Den Haag
PO Box 555, 2501 CN **Den Haag**
Tel: 70-302 7630 Fax: 70-361 7486
director Michiel de Ligt
Venue type: multi-purpose 15th century church *Capacity:* 1000-1600 *Policy:* rent *Arts types:* all kind of cultural events

Theater aan het Spui
PO Box 109, 2501 CC **Den Haag**
Tel: 70-346 5280 Fax: 70-365 0313
director and artistic director John Reinders; general administrator t.b.a.; assistant director Hillie Fokkena
Venue type: theatre *Capacity:* Hall A 390, Hall B 180 *Policy:* co-present, rent
Arts types: dance, festivals, theatre

VSB Circustheater
PO Box 87899, 2508 DG **Den Haag**
Tel: 70-416 7611 Fax: 70-358 4551
E-Mail: info@vsbcircustheater.nl
technical manager Tom Goudswaard; marketing manager Tanja Dek
Venue type: theatre *Capacity:* up to 1750 *Policy:* present, rent *Arts types:* mainly musical, concerts, theatre, conferences,etc.
Comments: musicals are from Tuesday-Sunday

Schouwburg de Leeuwenbrug
PO Box 555, 7400 AN **Deventer**
Tel: 570-683 555 Fax: 570-683 525
Internet: www.schouwburgdeventer.nl
director Yolanda Mergler
Venue type: theatre *Capacity:* Hall A 750, Hall B 240 *Policy:* present, rent *Arts types:* dance, music, theatre, opera (amateurs and professionals) *Comments:* venue address: Leeuwenbrug 2, 7411 TJ Deventer

Schouwburg Kunstmin
Sint Jorisweg 76, Pb 1114, 3300 BC **Dordrecht**
Tel: 78-639 7979 Fax: 78-639 7971
Internet: www.kunstmin.nl
director Dick Wolf; pr & marketing Diana van der Klooster
Venue type: concert hall *Capacity:* Room A 750, Room B 180 *Policy:* present, rent *Arts types:* dance, experimental groups, music, theatre, youth theatre, puppets

De Lawei, Theater en Concertzaal
PO Box 31, 9200 AA **Drachten**
Tel: 512-513 344 Fax: 512-514 545
E-Mail: gootthom@euronet.nl
director Rund van Zuilen; administrator Patrick Hankel; marketing manager & pr Jos Jutte; technical manager Henk Bergsma; events manager Henri Hogenhuis
Venue type: concert hall/theatre, theatre and 2 studio theatres *Capacity:* Room A 850, Room B 500, Room C 150, Room D 50 *Policy:* co-present, rent *Arts types:* theatre, music, opera, musicals, cabaret, variety, dance, ballet, chamber music, artistic film, exhibitions *Comments:* venue address: Burgemeester Wuiteweg 24, 9203 KL Drachten

Muziekcentrum Frits Philips
Jan Van Lieshoutstraat 3, PO Box 930, 5600 AX **Eindhoven**
Tel: 40-265 5600 Fax: 40-246 4020
Internet: www.philipshall.nl
E-Mail: algemeen@philipshall.nl
general manager Margreet Teunissen; programming coordinator Maaike van den Hoek
Venue type: concert hall *Capacity:* Grote Zaal 1250, (for pop concerts) 1800, Kleine Zaal 400 *Policy:* rent, produce *Arts types:* symphony concerts, chamber music, recitals, pop, jazz, blues, folk, world music

Plaza Futura
Leenderweg 65, 5614 HL **Eindhoven**
Tel: 40-294 6840 (office)/6849 Fax: 40-294 6841
Internet: www.dse.nl/plazafutura
E-Mail: internet@plazafutura.nl
director Geert Colsen; programmer film Mau Stappers; programmer theatre Mark Timmer; marketing Gert van Vliet
Venue type: theatre & cinema *Capacity:* 2 cinemas 91 & 48, theatre 118 *Policy:* to develop the film & theatre climate in the region and Eindhoven; rent, produce *Arts types:* films (new releases, classics & alternative arts movies), theatre *Comments:* own productions: Plaza werkplaats productions; film & theatre courses available; also have a restaurant

Stadsschouwburg Eindhoven
Postbus 90156, 5600 RJ **Eindhoven**
Tel: 40-238 9680/4851 (pr) Fax: 40-238 4810
E-Mail: info@schouwburgeindhoven.nl
director Alfonsis Bruins; head of promotions Erika Goudsmit
Venue type: theatre *Capacity:* Room A 946, Room B 450 *Policy:* present, rent *Arts types:* dance, experimental groups, music, theatre, youth theatre, puppets, ballet, musicals, opera, mime, cabaret, jazz, circus *Comments:* venue address: Elzentlaan 50, 5615 CN Eindhoven

Theater de Muzeval
Boermarkeweg 43, 7822 HM **Emmen**
Tel: 591-619 200/617 000 (box office) Fax: 591-643 135
business director G. Nijhuis; artistic director W.J.M.L. Kluivers
Venue type: theatre *Capacity:* Room A 650, Room B 260, Room C 130, Room D 130 *Policy:* rent, present *Arts types:* dance, music, theatre, children's theatre, opera, operetta, musicals, etc.

Twentse Schouwburg/Muziekcentrum Enschede
Langestraat 49, 7511 HB **Enschede**
Tel: 53-485 8585
Fax: 53-485 8595 (music centre)/8590 (theatre)
E-Mail: info@twentseschouwburg.nl
managing director Lex Kater; commercial manager Jetty Postma
Venue type: theatre, music hall *Capacity:* theatre: Kleine Zaal 300, Grote Zaal 898, Music Hall 1050: Arke Zaal 200, Church 400 *Policy:* rent, present *Arts types:* presentation of wide variety of theatre, opera, dance, musical & music *Comments:* second address: Noorderhagen 27, Enschede 7511 AK; see also Promoters

Schouwburg de Nieuwe Doelen
Haarstraat 64, 4201 JD **Gorinchem**
Tel: 183-692 220 Fax: 183-637 046
E-Mail: info@doeltargett.nl
director Roy Grünewald; public relations Anne de Vey; financial administrator Guus van de Craats; sales Anna van Kuÿk; senior producer Marc van Laere
Venue type: theatre *Capacity:* 560 *Policy:* rent, present events at own risk, also risk-sharing with other promoters *Arts types:* dance, drama, music, musicals, operetta, shows, cabaret, comedy

Schouwburg Gouda
Boelekade 67, 2806 AE **Gouda**
Tel: 182-513 353/750 (box office) Fax: 182-580 881
theatre director Nel Oskam
Venue type: theatre, studio theatre *Capacity:* Room A 798, Room B 220 *Policy:* present, rent (by negotiation) *Arts types:* dance, theatre, musicals, opera (including amateur performances)

De Oosterpoort/Stadsschouwburg
Postbus 775, 9700 AT **Groningen**
Tel: 50-368 0102 (De Oosterpoort)/313 1044 (box office)/314 2555 (Stadsschouwburg)/312 5645 (box office) Fax: 50-313 8507 (Stadsschouwburg)/368 0280 (De Oosterpoort)
Internet: www.cultuur.groningen.nl
E-Mail: info@kenc.groningen.nl
general manager Seerp Leistra; music & theatre director Thom Vander Goot
Venue type: concert hall (big and small), arts centre, theatre, studio theatre *Capacity:* big concert hall up to 2000, small concert hall up to 750, theatre 770, studio theatre 100 *Policy:* present, co-present, rent *Arts types:* symphony orchestras, pop, rock, exhibitions, variety, opera, chamber music, recitals, dance, experimental groups, theatre, youth theatre, puppets, world music, blues, jazz, cabaret, entertainment *Comments:* home of Noord Netherlands OrKest and a variety of music festivals ranging from Noorderslag to the Rhythm & Blues Night; venue addresses: De Oosterpoort, Trompsingel 27, 9724 DA Groningen; Stadsschouwburg, Turfsingel 86, 9711 VX Groningen; see also entry under Stadsschouwburg (listed below)

Stadsschouwburg, De
Groningen
Comments: see entry under De Oosterpoort/Stadsschouwburg

Concertgebouw
2 A Klokhuistplein, 2011 HK **Haarlem**
Tel: 23-512 1212 Fax: 23-512 1211
director Marc den Hertog
Venue type: concert hall *Capacity:* Hall A 1250, Hall B 250 *Policy:* present, rent *Arts types:* symphony, chamber music, recitals, popular music *Comments:* see also Promoters

Stadsschouwburg Haarlem
Wilsonplein 23, 2011 VG **Haarlem**
Tel: 23-512 1212 Fax: 23-512 1211
E-mail: ssh@worldonline.nl
Internet: www.theater-haarlem
director Neil Wallace; manager Bas Schoonderwoerd
Venue type: theatre *Capacity:* 750 *Policy:* present, rent *Arts types:* theatre, cabaret, musicals, dance, ballet, popular

Toneelschuur
Smedestraat 23, 2011 RE **Haarlem**
Tel: 23-532 8450 Fax: 23-534 1016
Internet: www.toneelschuur.nl
E-Mail: info@toneelschuur.nl
director Frans Lommerse
Venue type: theatre, studio, cinema *Capacity:* Room A 178, Room B 80, Room C 90 *Policy:* produce, present *Arts types:* drama, dance, music theatre, film

Parkstad Limburg Theaters – Stadsschouwburg Heerlen
Postbus 300, 6400 AH **Heerlen**
Tel: 45-576 8576 Fax: 45-571 8794
director B.M Schoonderwoerd
Venue type: theatre *Capacity:* 894 and 151 *Policy:* present, rent *Arts types:* symphony, ballet, theatre, cabaret, mime, opera, concerts, dance, classical & modern music *Comments:* has merged with Wijngrachttheater, Kerkrade (q.v.); visiting address: Burgemeester van Grunsvenplein 145, 6411 AS Heerlen;
see also Promoters

Wijngrachttheater – Parkstad Limburg Theaters
Postbus 300, 6400 AH **Heerlen**
Tel: 45-576 8576 (admin)/571 6607 Fax: 45-571 8794
manager Bas Schoonderwoerd
Venue type: theatre *Capacity:* 625 *Policy:* present, rent *Arts types:* dance, experimental groups, music, theatre, youth theatre, puppets, film *Comments:* has merged with Stadsschouwburg Heerlen (q.v.); visiting address: Theaterpassage 2, Kerkrade

Schouwburg Hengelo
Beursstraat 5, 7551 HP **Hengelo**
Tel: 74-291 1866 Fax: 74-250 1023
Comments: planning to open a new 800 seater theatre in April 2001

Stichting Witte Theater
PO Box 260, 1970 AG **Ijmuiden**
Tel: 25-552 1972 Fax: 25-553 7564
artistic director Dirk van Zonderen
Venue type: theatre *Capacity:* up to 150 *Policy:* rent (90%), sometimes produce *Arts types:* film, theatre, music, dance *Comments:* visiting address: Kanaalstr 257

Stadsgehoorzaal Kampen
Burgwal 84, PO Box 1026, 8260 BA **Kampen**
Tel: 38-331 7343/7373 Fax: 38-332 8878
director B. Koolstra
Venue type: theatre *Capacity:* Room A 520, Room B 100 *Policy:* present, rent *Arts types:* all performing arts

Rodahal
Postbox 34, 6460 AA **Kerkrade**
Tel: 45-567 9230 (admin)/33 (bookings)
Fax: 45-567 9243
E-Mail: rodahal@wxxs.nl
managing director Paul J. J. Priem
Venue type: concert hall *Capacity:* standing 3500, seated 2400 *Policy:* present, rent

Schouwburg de Harmonie
Postbus 323, Ruiterskwartier 4,
8901 BC **Leeuwarden**
Tel: 58-233 0230 Fax: 58-233 0220
Internet: www.harmonie.nl
director Gerard Tonen
Venue type: Great Hall (theatre or concert hall), multi-functional hall, studio theatre *Capacity:* Stages A 920, standing 800, Satge B 450, Stage C 250
Policy: present, rent *Arts types:* dance, music, theatre, opera, classical, pop music

LAKtheater, Het
Postbus 9515, 2300 RA **Leiden**
Tel: 71-512 4890 Fax: 71-527 2361
director R Helmer
Venue type: theatre *Capacity:* 170 *Policy:* rent *Arts types:* music, theatre, dance *Comments:* visiting address: Cleveringaplaats 1, 2311 BD Leiden

Theater aan het Vrijthof
Postbus 882, 6200 AW **Maastricht**
Tel: 43-350 5555 Fax: 43-350 5522
Internet: www.theateraanhetvrijthof.nl
director Piet K.J. van Hest
Venue type: multi-purpose theatre *Capacity:* 900 *Arts types:* dance, experimental groups, music, theatre, youth theatre, puppets, exhibitions *Comments:* visiting address: Vrijthof 47, 6211 LE Maastricht

Naald Theatre & Film Evanemanten, De
Stokdijkade 3, 2671 GW **Naaldwijk**
Tel: 174-637 564/636 900 (vesv)
Fax: 174-625 914
Internet: www.westnet.nl/nald
director Marc von Kaam
Venue type: theatre and film centre *Capacity:* Hall A 450, Hall B 110 *Policy:* rent *Arts types:* all performing arts

Concertgebouw De Vereeniging
Oranjesingel 1, Postbus 364, 6500 AJ **Nijmegen**
Tel: 24-322 8344 Fax: 24-322 2465
Internet: www.dunamis.nl/schouwburg
E-Mail: schouwburg.nijmegen@inter.nl.net
interim director Ed Burgers
Venue type: concert hall, multi-purpose
Capacity: Hall A 1500, Hall C 100 *Policy:* rent
Arts types: symphony orchestras, chamber music, song recitals, chorus, jazz, pop, rock, music-shows, new music, old music, guitar concerts, etc.

Doornroosje
Groenewoudseweg 322, 6525 EL **Nijmegen**
Tel: 24-355 4243 Fax: 24-356 8015
Internet: www.doornroosje.nl
E-Mail: roosje@molyvos.net
general director Narda Eerdmans; artistical directors Gert Gering, Ger Laning; head of press & public relations Titus Meeuwesen
Venue type: 2 halls, multi-purpose cultural centre
Capacity: Hall A 500, Hall B 150
Policy: rent, present *Arts types:* dance, experimental groups, music, theatre, pop concerts, performance, film

O 42
Oranjesingel 42, 6511 NW **Nijmegen**
Tel: 24-322 2045 (office) Fax: 24-360 0806
director D. de Ruijter; music programming, theatre and dance programming Maarten Rovers
Venue type: theatre, multi-purpose
Capacity: Blue hall 115 (seated) 300 (standing), Upper hall 80 *Policy:* present, rent
Arts types: dance, experimental groups, music, world music, pop, theatre, jazz

Stadsschouwburg Nijmegen
Keizer Karelplein 42 H, Postbus 364,
6500 AJ **Nijmegen**
Tel: 24-322 8344/1100 (box office) Fax: 24-322 2465
Internet: www.dunamis.nl/schouwburg
E-Mail: schouwburg.nijmegen@inter.nl.net
interim director Ed Burgers
Venue type: theatre, multi-purpose *Capacity:* Hall A 850, Nederrinjzaal 250 *Policy:* present, rent *Arts types:* drama, dance, ballet, experimental groups, puppets, opera, operetta, musicals, shows, revues, mime, cabaret, concerts, children's and family theatre, exhibitions, specials, various personalities

Theater de Willem
Postbus 11, 3350 AA **Papendrecht**
Tel: 78-615 8226/641 1421 Fax: 78-641 1316
E-Mail: willem@traf.nl
director R Wolters
Venue type: theatre *Capacity:* 479 *Policy:* rent
Arts types: theatre, ballet, cabaret, dance

Theatre Hotel de Oranjerie
Kloosterwandplein 12-16, 6041 JA **Roermond**
Tel: 475-391 491 Fax: 475-317 188
director C. Polman
Venue type: multi-purpose
Capacity: 818 *Policy:* present, rent *Arts types:* dance, music, theatre, opera, etc.

Schouwburg de Kring
Kerkstraat 1, 4701 HT **Roosendaal**
Tel: 165-555 555 Fax: 165-548 214
Internet: www.tref.nl/roosendaal/dekring
E-Mail: schouwbrgdekring@tref.nl
managing director Leo Kievit; pr Hedi Egelmeers
Venue type: theatre, multi-functional hall
Capacity: HAll A 841, Hall B 220
Policy: rent, present at own risk
Arts types: dance, theatre, music, all types

Concert and Congress Centre De Doelen
PO Box 972, 3000 AZ **Rotterdam**
Tel: 10-217 1700 Fax: 10-433 2237/213 0913
E-Mail: intdoel1@xs4all.nl
general manager and artistic director Huub van Dael; manager, communications dept. Ton de Langen; assistant manager Anton Vliegenthart
Venue type: concert hall, multi purpose
Capacity: Hall A 2250, Hall B 620, other halls up to 250
Policy: present, co-present, rent *Arts types:* chamber music, recitals, symphony, musicals, concerts, jazz, world music *Comments:* visiting address: Kruisstraat 2, 3012 CT Rotterdam; alternative email: intdoel2@xs4all.nl; building new congress hall; see also Promoters

Hal 4
Watertorenweg 200, 3063 HA **Rotterdam**
Tel: 10-412 6031 Fax: 10-453 1817
Internet: www.hal4.nl
E-Mail: hal4@hal4.nl
director G.E.van der Most
Venue type: multi-purpose
Capacity: 550 *Policy:* rent *Arts types:* theatre, jazz, film, concerts, dance

Luxor Theatre
Kruiskade 10, 3012 EH **Rotterdam**
Tel: 10-414 1116 Fax: 10-411 6009
administration Déssirée Elens; press M. Dumas (tel: 10-233 1952)
Arts types: musical, music, dance *Comments:* moving to a new venue spring 2001

Rotterdamse Schouwburg
Schouwburgplein 25, 3012 CL **Rotterdam**
Tel: 10-404 4111 Fax: 10-413 2404
E-Mail: kassa@schouwburg.rotterdam.nl
managing & artistic director Jan Zoet
Venue type: theatre
Capacity: Room A 900, Room B 170 *Policy:* present, produce *Arts types:* drama, dance, opera, experimental groups, music, theatre, youth theatre, puppets

Theater Lantaren/Venster
PO Box 25278, 3001 HG **Rotterdam**
Tel: 10-277 2266 (office)/77/88 (box office)/1331 (info. line) Fax: 10-277 2286
Internet: www.lantaren-venster.nl
E-Mail: mail@lantaren-venster.nl
managing director Theo Ruyter; theatre programming Anne-Rienke Hendrikse; programming film & cinematheque Leo Hannewijk; front of house manager Pim Seinen; workshop Sanne Hilhorst; programming contemporary music Theo Muller
Venue type: theatre and cinema and contemporary music *Capacity:* Lantaren 1 (theatre) 184, Lantaren 2 (theatre) 93, Venster 1 (cinema) 186, Venster 2 (cinema) 103, Venster 3 (cinema) 85, Venster 4 (cinema) 69 *Policy:* present, produce *Arts types:* theatre, film, dance, cultural events, festivals, contemporary music *Comments:* visiting address: Gouvernestraat 133, 3014 PM Rotterdam

Theater Zuidplein
Zuidplein 60-64, 3083 CW **Rotterdam**
Tel: 10-203 0207 (office)/481 6500 (box office)
Fax: 10-480 3340
Internet: www.theater.nl/zuidplein
director C. Langeveld
Venue type: theatre *Capacity:* main auditorium 614, Arlecchino 199 (black box)
Policy: rent and shared risk *Arts types:* plays, dance, music theatre, variety, youth theatre

V2_Organisation – Institute for the Unstable Media
Eendrachtsstraat 10, 3012 XL **Rotterdam**
Tel: 10-206 7272 Fax: 10-206 7271
Internet: www.v2.nl
E-Mail: v2@v2.nl
director Alex Adriaanses (email: alex@v2.nl); programming & publications Joke Brouwer (email: jb@v2.nl); manager Anne Nigten (email: anne@v2.nl); programme coordinator, theory Andreas Broeckmann (email: abroeck@v2.nl); production coordinator Marc Thelosen (email: marc@v2.nl)
Venue type: interdisciplenary centre for art, technology and society *Capacity:* main hall 400, medialab 30 *Policy:* present, produce and research of media-art, rental for non-profit organisations *Arts types:* exhibitions, workshops, concerts and performances, symposia, online events; visual arts *Comments:* includes V2_Lab, V2_Shop and DEAF (Dutch Electronic Art Festival); distribute books, magazines, CD's, CD Roms; publications: thematical book, catalogues; also available to rent for digital video-editing and has a digital audio-studio

Youth Theatre Hofplein
Jeugdtheater Hofplein
Benthemstraat 13, 3032 AA **Rotterdam**
Tel: 10-466 0311 Fax: 10-243 5059
artistic director Louis Lemaire; manager M. Keeveen
Venue type: theatre *Capacity:* 500 *Policy:* produce, present *Arts types:* drama *Comments:* theatre school produces own productions

Theater aan de Parade
Postbus 12345, 5200 GZ **s'-Hertogenbosch**
Tel: 73-680 9809 Fax: 73-612 4235
Internet: www.tref.nl/s'Hertogenbosch/theater-parade
E-Mail: theater.parade@tref.nl
general manager Tom Odems;
deputy manager F. Bekker
Venue type: theatre, arts centre, cinema *Capacity:* Room A 900, Room B up to 450 *Policy:* present, co-present, rent *Arts types:* dance, music, theatre, congresses, film

Theatre de Teerstoof
Stadserf 1, 3100 AG **Schiedam**
Tel: 10-246 7467 Fax: 10-426 0513
Internet: www.schiedam.nl/theatre
E-Mail: theatre@schiedam.nl
director Paul van Oord
Venue type: theatre *Capacity:* 104 *Policy:* present, rent
Arts types: cabaret and music theatre, children's theatre
Comments: no wheelchair access

VSB Theater a.d. Schie
PO Box 414, 3100 AK **Schiedam**
Tel: 10-246 7467 Fax: 10-426 0513
Internet: www.schiedam.nl/theater
E-Mail: theater@schiedam.nl
diector Paul Vanoort; press officer Inge Muef
Venue type: theatre *Capacity:* 704 *Policy:* rent *Arts types:* music, musical theatre, drama, cabaret *Comments:* visiting address: Theatre VSB, Stadserf 1, Schiedam

Cultureel Centrum de Stadsschouwburg
Postbus 247, Wilhelminastraat 18, 6130 AE **Sittard**
Tel: 46-420 5699 Fax: 46-420 5690
E-Mail: theatsit@wxs.nl
director Pierre Gorissen
Venue type: cultural centre, theatre *Capacity:* 791 *Policy:* present at own risk, shared risk, rent *Arts types:* dance, music, theatre, youth theatre, puppets, orchestra, variety, opera, operetta, musicals, shows, circus cabaret
Comments: see also Drama and Puppets

Sirkel Theater
Postbus 214, 6130 AE **Sittard**
Tel: 46-452 5574 Fax: 46-452 6432
artistic directors Frans Malschaert, Anandi Teeuw; technicians Dik Beets, Marc Claessens; office Marÿle van Hout
Venue type: Black Box *Capacity:* 100 *Policy:* poduce, present young directors *Arts types:* theatre, dance, music, children's theatre *Comments:* 60 performances in a season; second address: Putstraat 22, 6131 HL Sittard; see also Drama, Venues and Puppets

Cultureel Centrum de Stoep
Uitstraat 43, 3201 EN **Spijkenisse**
Tel: 181-696 100/101 Fax: 181-696 122
director Mr. R. P. C. Barra; marketing Mrs. M van Halen
Venue type: cultural centre *Capacity:* 412 *Policy:* present, rent *Arts types:* dance, music, theatre, drama, sculpture
Comments: part of Centre for Arts and Education School of Music, Arts and Drama

013
PO Box 9022, 5000 HA **Tilburg**
Tel: 13-460 9500 Fax: 13-460 9501
Internet: www.013web.nl
E-Mail: fons@013web.nl
contact Fons van Iersel
Venue type: multi-purpose *Capacity:* varies *Comments:* venue address: Veemarktstraat 44, 5000 HA Tilburg; member of Trans Europe Halles, Tel: +33 1-4011 6414, Internet: www.teh.net

Schouwburg & Concertzaal Tilburg
Louis Bouwmeesterplein 1, Postbus 3035,
5003 DA **Tilburg**
Tel: 13-549 0390/543 2220 (box office) Fax: 13-543 0957
E-Mail: sct@worldonline.nl
director Leo Pot; marketing manager Maurice Schmitz
Venue type: theatre/concert hall *Capacity:* Room A (Schouwburg) 870, Room B 175, Concertzaal 800
Arts types: dance, music, theatre, concerts, cabaret, ballet, opera, musicals, jazz, mime, pop concerts, classical concerts, world music

Muziekcentrum Vredenburg
Postbus 550, Vredenburgpassage 77,
3500 AN **Utrecht**
Tel: 30-286 2286 Fax: 30-231 6522
Internet: www.vredenburg.nl
E-Mail: info@vredenburg.nl
general manager Peter Smids; programme manager (classical music) Jessica De Hiir; programme manager (other music) Anna van Dyk; head of marketing, press & pr Mathieu Heinrichs
Venue type: concert hall *Capacity:* Hall A 1800, Hall B 300 *Policy:* present, rent *Arts types:* all kinds of music
Comments: see also Promoters

Stadsschouwburg Utrecht
Lucas Bolwerk 24, 3512 EJ **Utrecht**
Tel: 30-232 4125 Fax: 30-231 4499
managing director Henk Scholten; programming and marketing Gerrit Reus; publicity Ab Hooÿer
Venue type: theatre *Capacity:* Douwe Egbertszaal 1000, Blauwe Zaal 250 *Policy:* present, co-present, rent *Arts types:* opera, musicals, theatre, dance, ballet, cabaret, circus, childrens & youth theatre, international theatre productions from all over the world

Cultureel Centrum de Maaspoort
Postbus 333, 5900 AH **Venlo**
Tel: 77-320 7222 Fax: 77-354 4220
Internet: www.maaspoort.nl
E-Mail: maaspoort@maaspoort.nl
director Math Schmeitz
Venue type: theatre, concert hall *Capacity:* Hall A 760, Hall B 175 *Policy:* present, rent
Arts types: all arts types *Comments:* venue address: Oude Markt 30, 5911 HH Venlo

Stadsgehoorzaal/Harmonie
Schiedamseweg 51, 3134 BB **Vlaardingen**
Tel: 10-434 0399 (admin)/0500 (box office)
Fax: 10-460 4225
E-Mail: stadsgehoorzaal@vlaardingen.nl
director Sándor Góra; marketing Maurice de Jong
Venue type: theatre *Capacity:* 649 *Policy:* rent, present
Arts types: theatre, cabaret, dance, musicals, music (modern & classical)

Cultureel centrum De Klinker
Stikkerlaan 41, 9675 AA **Winschoten**
Tel: 59-741 5555 Fax: 59-741 5192
programming & marketing Wubbe Koning;
manager H. van der Wal
Venue type: theatre *Capacity:* 650 *Policy:* rent, present
Arts types: theatre, dance, music, shows, musical
Comments: also wholesale and conference spaces

Nieuwe Buitensociëteit, De
Postbus 530, 8000 AM **Zwolle**
Tel: 38-426 0260 Fax: 38-426 0210
director Ger Vanes
Venue type: theatre *Capacity:* 820
Policy: present, rent *Arts types:* dance, experimental groups, music, theatre, youth theatre, puppets, musicals, cinema *Comments:* visiting address: Stationsplein 1, 8011 CW Zwolle

NORWAY (+47)

Bergen International Theatre
Bergen Internasjonale Teater
Nostegaten 54, 5013 **Bergen**
Tel: 5523 2235 Fax: 5523 1815
Internet: www.bgnett.no/bit/
E-Mail: bit@bgnett.no
artistic director Sven Åge Birkeland; admin. director Mette Helgesen; production director Lars Ove Toft
Venue type: theatre/multi-purpose *Capacity:* 400 seated, 1200 standing *Policy:* rent *Arts types:* theatre, dance, music, literature, art exhibitions
Comments: producers/co-producers of international theatre and dance

Grieghallen AS
Edward Griegs Plass 1, 5015 **Bergen**
Tel: 5521 6100 Fax: 5521 6199 (admin)
E-Mail: grieghallen@grieghallen.no
director Gert Atle Gundersen; arrangement director Rolf Skogstrand
Venue type: multi-purpose *Capacity:* 1500 *Arts types:* concerts, ballet, opera, theatre, exhibitions, congresses
Comments: home of the Bergen Philharmonic

Logen, Bergen
Ole Bulls plass 14, 5012 **Bergen**
Tel: 5523 2015 Fax: 5532 5785
director Trond Lohne (mobile: 94-686 866); technical manager Godthard Larsen (mobile: 95-059 376)
Capacity: 403 *Arts types:* various performances and concerts *Comments:* available for hire

USF Arts Centre, Bergen
Kulturhuset USF, Bergen
Georgernes Verft 3, 5011 **Bergen**
Tel: 5531 5570 Fax: 5523 2006
Internet: www.kulturhuset-usf.no
E-Mail: sti-kult@online.no
director Kari Patricia Kleppe; chairperson Martin Smith-Sivertsen (tel: 5531 5410/mobile:93-038 766)
Venue type: multi-purpose *Capacity:* Scene USF 144, Sardinen USF 850, Røkeriet 720 *Arts types:* theatre, dance, film, music

Nøtterøy Art Centre, Borgheim
Nøtterøy kulturhus, Borgheim
Tinghaug, 3162 **Borgheim**
Tel: 3334 6165 Fax: 3338 4530
Internet: www.notteroey.kommune.no
E-Mail: notteroy.kommune@vf.telia.no
director Knut Alfsen (tel: 3334 6164, email: kalfsen@c2i.net); venue manager Åse Unni; technial manager Jan Egel (tel: 3334 6163)
Venue type: arts centre *Capacity:* theatre 409, black box theatre 150 *Policy:* presents *Arts types:* theatre performances, concerts, art exhibition and conferences
Comments: available for hire

Hordaland Teater
Stend Hovedgard, 5244 **Fana**
Tel: 5591 6020 Fax: 5591 5945
Internet: www.hordaland-teater.no
E-Mail: vera.rostin.wexelsen@hordaland-teater.no
director Vera Rostin Wexelsen; chief administrator Arne Thomassen; production manager John Stavland
Venue type: theatre *Capacity:* 200 *Policy:* produce, rent, present *Arts types:* puppet theatre, ordinary theatre, theatre for young people *Comments:* both touring company and permanent stages (2)

Festiviteten Theatre and Concert Hall
Festiviteten teater og konserthus
Postboks 145, 5501 **Haugesund**
Tel: 5273 4430 Fax: 5273 4420
Internet: www.prosag.no/festiviteten
E-Mail: festiviteten@haugesund.kommune.no
director Bjarne Dankel Jr (tel: 5273 4451, email: bjarne.dankel@haugesund.kommune.no)
Venue type: theatre and concert hall *Capacity:* 429 *Arts types:* theatre, ballet, concert and conferences
Comments: home to Sildajazz, Norway's international tradjazz festival (q.v.); every second year co-produces opera performances in collaboration with the Norwegian Opera; visiting address: Knut Knutsen OAS gate 4, 5501 Haugesund

Henie-Onstad Artcenter
Sonja Heniesvei 31, 1311 **Hövikodden**
Tel: 6780 4880 Fax: 6754 3270
E-Mail: jenny.tuhus.@hok.no
director Stein Slyngstad; artistic director Gavin Jantjes
Venue type: cultural centre/museum *Capacity:* Kultursentret up to 1500 *Arts types:* all arts types, speciality: international contemporary modern art
Comments: new wing houses an art collection with around 7000 art pieces

Sonja Henie Niels Onstad Foundation
Sonja Heniesvei 31, 1311 **Hövikodden**
Tel: 6780 4880 Fax: 6754 3270
E-Mail: jenny.tuhus.@hok.no
director Stein Slyngstad; artistic director Gavin Jantjes
Venue type: concert hall *Capacity:* outside auditorium 500, concert hall 300 *Arts types:* concerts, theatre, dance
Comments: arts centre with largest museum of international modern art in Norway

Inderøy Art Centre
Inderøy kulturhus
Kulturhuset, 7670 **Inderøy**
Tel: 7415 3800 Fax: 7415 3905
Internet: www.inderoy.kulturhus.no
E-Mail: inderoy.kulturhus@inderoy.online.no
director Lugie O Skrove (email: lugie.skrove@inderoy.online.no); technical & venue bookings manager Egil Kvam (email: egil.kvam@inderoy.online.no)
Capacity: 430 *Comments:* hosts various touring performances; available for hire

Kautokeino Arts Centre
Kautokeino kulturhus
Bredbuktnesveien 50, 9520 **Kautokeino**
Tel: 7848 8500 Fax: 7848 5895
director Reidar Erke; technical manager Leif Isak E Nilut (tel: 7848 6811, email: leif.isak.nilut@beaivvas.com)
Venue type: municipal venue *Capacity:* auditorium 150
Policy: availability in partnership with the theatre *Arts types:* performing arts

Town Hall Theatre, Kongsvinger
Rådhusteatret, Kongsvinger
Skolegata 1, 2226 **Kongsvinger**
Tel: 6282 0240 Fax: 6282 0293
Internet: web.nexttel.no/Kongsvinge
E-Mail: kongsv@online.no
head of culture Nstig Fonås (tel: 6282 0239)
Capacity: 538 *Arts types:* theatre, concerts *Comments:* also receives touring shows; available for hire

Agder Teater
PO Box 582, 4665 **Kristiansand**
Tel: 3812 2888/3802 4300 Fax: 3812 2880
Internet: www.agderteater.va.no/
E-Mail: teateras@online.no
programme director Grunnar Grimstad; head of press and information Nina Hammersmark
Venue type: modern style *Capacity:* 460 *Policy:* rent, own programming *Arts types:* theatre, dance, music, opera
Comments: visiting address: Kongensgate 2, 4601 Kristiansand

Kulturhuset Banken
Kirkegata 41, 2609 **Lillehammer**
Tel: 6126 6810 Fax: 6125 9220
E-Mail: banken@lillehammer.kommune.no
general manager Trond Johnsnen; secretary Inger Helene Hosar; technical Per Anderson; marketing Frode Fossbakken
Venue type: multi-purpose *Capacity:* main house 250, 2 small halls each 100 *Policy:* rent *Arts types:* drama, classical concerts, symphony, chamber, jazz, dance, conferences *Comments:* also private functions

Black Box Theatre
Stranden 3, 0250 **Oslo**
Tel: 2201 4020 Fax: 2283 7347/2201 4021
Internet: www.blackbox.no
E-Mail: blackbox@blackbox.no
artistic & managing director Inger Buresund; administrative director Sven Erik Dahl; technical manager Jean Vincent Kerebel; production manager Saskia Wieringa; marketing manager Erik Meling; publicity & press IvHeidi Grande; project manager Shanti Brahmachari
Venue type: theatre *Capacity:* large stage 200, small stage 100 *Policy:* rent, co-produce, programming national & international performances *Arts types:* contemporary dance & theatre *Comments:* present 50 productions and 250-260 performances per year

Chateau Neuf
Slemdalsveien 7, 0369 **Oslo**
Tel: 2269 3794 Fax: 2269 1139
Internet: www.thalia.no
managing director Bjørn Heisedal (email: bjorn.heisedal@thalia.no); technical manager Ola A Neergaard (email: ola.neergaard@thalia.no)
Venue type: theatre *Capacity:* 1005 *Arts types:* musicals, shows, dance, new concerts *Comments:* also a popular venue for large-scale TV productions, eg awards ceremonies; available for hire

Mars AS
Storgata 22, 0184 **Oslo**
Tel: 2316 3280 Fax: 2316 3281
Internet: www.marsclub.no
E-Mail: info@marsclub.no
promotion Torse Noren; booking Jan-Martin Jensen; production Pål Johnsen
Venue type: rock club/concert hall *Capacity:* 800 *Policy:* rent, co-produce, present *Arts types:* all types

Old Masonic Hall
Den gamle logen
Grev Wedels plass 2, 0151 **Oslo**
Tel: 2233 4470 Fax: 2233 3521
director Heidi Wear; sales manager Tore Sørhøy; hall manager Kjell Andre Røttervold
Venue type: Oslo's oldest cultural building *Capacity:* 508
Arts types: mainly concerts *Comments:* available for hire

Oslo Konserthus
Oslo Concert Hall
Munkedamsveien 14, PO Box 1437 Vika, 0115 **Oslo**
Tel: 2311 3100 Fax: 2311 3110
E-Mail: knutvhan@online.no
general manager Knut Vigar Hansen; concert manager Svein Eriksen
Venue type: multi-purpose halls *Capacity:* large hall 1404, small hall 266 *Policy:* rent, present *Arts types:* orchestra, jazz, pop, rock, ballet, chamber music, recitals, musicals, folklore, exhibitions, congresses
Comments: home of Oslo Philharmonic Orchestra

Oslo Spektrum
Sonja Henies plass 2, 0185 **Oslo**
Tel: 2205 2900 Fax: 2205 2905
Internet: www.oslospektrum.no
E-Mail: spektrum@oslospektrum.no
managing director Jan Beckmann; director of marketing/sales Knut Aga; director of finance Bente Ottesen
Venue type: muli-purpose *Capacity:* up to 10000
Policy: rent *Arts types:* concerts, classical and pop events, conferences, exhibitions, sporting events

Storsalen
PO Box 6830, 0166 **Oslo**
Tel: 2298 6250 Fax: 2233 5520
managing director Andreas Eidsaa
Venue type: multi-purpose
Capacity: 508 *Policy:* rent, produce, co-produce
Arts types: chamber music, recitals, banqueting, music concerts, conferences
Comments: special arrangements and performances; there is a stage, but limited theatre facilities, leading Norwegian recital room; venue address: Staffeldtsgate 4, 0166 Oslo

Troldhaugen – Nina og Edvard Griegs hjem
Troldhaugveien 65, 5232 **Paradis**
Tel: 5591 0710 Fax: 5591 1395
Internet: bergen.by.com/museum/troldhaugen
E-Mail: trold@online.no
director Erling Dahl jr.
Venue type: Grieg's home, now a museum including a concert hall *Capacity:* 200
Arts types: classical/chamber music

Bjergsted Music Centre
Bjergsted, 4007 **Stavanger**
Tel: 5183 4000 Fax: 5183 4050
Internet: www.his.no/
E-Mail: postmottak@his.no
head of administration Tore Bjoern Hotleskog
Venue type: multi-purpose *Capacity:* 4 halls: Stavanger Concert Hall 1100, 2 auditoriums each 250 , Organ hall 125 *Arts types:* chamber, classical, pop, rock, jazz, folk, symphonic *Comments:* consists of/or houses: Stavanger Concert Hall (q.v.), Stavanger Symphony Orchestra (q.v.), Stavanger School of Arts Education, Stavanger School of Music, Rogaland Music Society, Stavanger Concert Association (q.v.), Speculum (q.v.); Stavanger International Chamber Music Festival takes place in August each year

Stavanger Konserthus
Bjergsted, 4007 **Stavanger**
Tel: 5150 8810 Fax: 5150 8822
Internet: www.stavanger-konserthus.no
E-Mail: grete@stavanger-konserthus.no
managing director Anna-Marie Antonius (tel: 5150 8812); hall manager Joar Saether; marketing manager Grete Straume
Venue type: multi-purpose auditorium
Capacity: 1178 *Policy:* present, rent
Arts types: orchestra, ballet, musicals, folkloric, theatre and modern dance *Comments:* main venue for Stavanger Symphony Orchestra

Stord Arts Centre
Kulturhuset på Stord
Postboks 414, 5403 **Stord**
Tel: 5349 6951 Fax: 5349 6967
E-Mail: stordkk@online.no
director Herdis Elin Belsvik (tel: 5349 6958)
Venue type: multi-purpose auditorium *Capacity:* 427
Policy: available for hire *Arts types:* concerts, films, art exhibitions, rehearsals, meetings, conferences
Comments: there is also a library; visiting address: Kulturhuset, 5403 Stord

KulturHuset
Postboks 1208, 9262 **Tromsø**
Tel: 7766 3810 Fax: 7766 3811
Internet: www.kulturhuset.tr.no
E-Mail: kulturhuset@trollnet.no
managing director Kjell Magne Mælen; assistant managing director Kari Levang
Venue type: multi-purpose *Capacity:* Main hall 661, Small hall 200 *Policy:* co-produce, produce *Arts types:* classical concerts, ballet/dance, theatre, opera, musicals, jazz, pop, rock, folklore, conferences (inc. meals and banqueting) *Comments:* houses Hålogaland Teater (q.v.) and a restaurant (Teaterkafeen)

OlavsHallen
Kjøpmannsgaten 44, PO Box 611, 7406 **Trondheim**
Tel: 7399 4000 Fax: 7399 4099
Internet: www.aksess.no/olavshallen/
general manager Grete Komissar; marketing secretary Tone M. Strickert; financial manager Elin Jegerstedt; technical/production manager Sten Mosand; administration secretary Inger M. Finseraas
Venue type: multi-purpose
Capacity: Hall A 1265, Hall B 300, Hall C 120
Policy: rent *Arts types:* symphony orchestra, ballet, theatre, conferences, shows, concerts
Comments: Trondheim Music School, Music Conservatory also housed in the same building

Teaterhuset Avantgarden
Olav Trggvassonsgate 5, 7011 **Trondheim**
Tel: 7353 0890/5592 Fax: 7352 4732
E-Mail: tav-g@online.no
director Kristian Seltun
Venue type: multi-purpose centre *Capacity:* black box theatre 100 *Arts types:* fringe theatre, strong focus on experimental and children's theatre
Comments: available for hire

POLAND (+48)

Sala Filharmonia
ul Podlesna 2, 15-227 **Bialystok**
Tel: 85-732 2331/1786 Fax: 85-741 6709
Venue type: concert hall *Capacity:* 300

Sala Filharmonia Pomorska
ul Libelta 16, 85-080 **Bydgoszcz**
Tel: 52-210 920 Fax: 52-210 752
E-Mail: fp@psi.com.pl
Venue type: concert hall
Capacity: concert hall 925, chamber hall 180

Sala Filharmonia
pl. Wilsona 16, 42-200 **Czestochowa**
Tel: 34-244 230 Fax: 34-243 437
Venue type: concert hall *Capacity:* concert hall 900, chamber hall 200

Sala Filharmonia Baltycka
ul.Olowianka 1, 80-751 **Gdansk**
Tel: 58-305 2040/2041/3960 Fax: 58-305 2040/2041/3960
Venue type: concert hall, opera house *Capacity:* 550

Sala Filharmonia Slaska
ul Sokolska 2, 40-084 **Katowice**
Tel: 32-586 261 Fax: 32-589 885
Venue type: concert hall *Capacity:* 500

Sala Filharmonia
Pl. Moniuszki 2, 25-334 **Kielce**
Tel: 41-681 191 Fax: 41-681 191
Venue type: concert hall *Capacity:* 350

Sala Filharmonia
Zwyciestwa 105, 75-001 **Koszalin**
Tel: 94-423 696 Fax: 94-342 6220
Venue type: concert hall *Capacity:* 320

Sala Filharmonia Krakowska
ul Zwierzyniecka 1, 31-103 **Krakow**
Tel: 12-422 4312 Fax: 12-422 4312
Venue type: concert hall *Capacity:* 900

Sala Filharmonia
ul Piotrkowska 243, 90-125 **Lodz**
Tel: 42-637 2652 Fax: 42-636 8232
Venue type: concert hall *Capacity:* 350

Centrum Kultury Lublin
Ul. Peowiaków, 20-007 **Lublin**
Tel: 81-538 700/532 7583 Fax: 81-532 8700/7583
E-Mail: ck@ck.lublin.pl
director Alexander Szpechk; festivals Beata Michalkiewicz
Venue type: 5 theatres *Policy:* own programme, presents, rent *Arts types:* drama, dance *Comments:* see also Promoters and Festivals (International Festival Theatre Confrontations)

Sala Filharmonia
ul. Kapucynska 7, 20-009 **Lublin**
Tel: 81-743 7821 Fax: 81-532 4421
Venue type: concert hall *Capacity:* 250

Sala Filharmonia
ul Kosciuszki 39, 10-503 **Olsztyn**
Tel: 89-527 2302/5175 Fax: 89-527 2302
Venue type: concert hall *Capacity:* 400

Sala Filharmonia
ul Krakowska 24, 45-075 **Opole**
Tel: 77-454 3371/3736
Venue type: concert hall *Capacity:* 380

Sala Filharmonia
ul Sw. Marcin 81, 61-808 **Poznan**
Tel: 61-852 3451 Fax: 61-852 3451
Venue type: concert hall *Capacity:* 800

Sala Filharmonia
ul Chopina 30, 35-055 **Rzeszow**
Tel: 17-628 408/622 333 Fax: 17-622 333
Venue type: concert hall *Capacity:* 800

Sala Filharmonia
Pl. Armii Krajowej 1, 70-455 **Szczecin**
Tel: 91-422 0589 Fax: 91-422 0079
Venue type: concert hall *Capacity:* 500

Sala Filharmonia Sudecka
ul Slowackiego 4, 58-300 **Walbrzych**
Tel: 74-24180 Fax: 74-22893
Venue type: concert hall *Capacity:* 500

Centre of Contemporary Art Zamek Ujazdowski
Centrum Sztuki Wspolizesnej
Al. Ujazdowskie 6, 00-461 **Warszawa**
Tel: 22-628 1271/7683 Fax: 22-628 9550
E-Mail: csw@ikp.atm.com.pl
director Wojciech Krukowski
Policy: present *Arts types:* theatre, dance, music theatre
Comments: about 90 projects a year, about a third international; see also National Organisations

Centrum Sztuki Studio
Palac Kultury, Pl. Defilad 1, 00-695 **Warszawa**
Tel: 22-620 4770/4369 Fax: 22-620 0138
Capacity: main stage 342, small stage 200 *Policy:* present *Arts types:* theatre, chamber orchestra, art gallery, documentation video centre

Concert Hall of the Royal Castle
Sala Koncertowa Zamku Królewskiego
Pl Zamkowy 4, 00-277 **Warszawa**
Tel: 22-635 4195 Fax: 22-657 2306
managing director Anna Kociecka
Venue type: concert hall *Capacity:* 198 *Policy:* rent for chamber concerts *Arts types:* chamber music, small ensembles, recitals

Congress Hall of Palace of Culture and Science
Sala Kongresowa PKiN
00-901 **Warszawa**
Tel: 22-826 9478 Fax: 22-826 6887
Venue type: multi-purpose *Capacity:* 2893 *Policy:* rent (mainly for pop rock concerts)

'Fryderyk Chopin' Society
Towarzystwo im Fryderyka Chopina
ul Okólnik 1, 00-368 **Warszawa**
Tel: 22-827 5471/9589 Fax: 22-827 9599
director Albert Grudzinski; president Prof. Tadeusz Chmielewski
Venue type: concert hall in the society's building
Capacity: 165 *Policy:* present, rent *Comments:* concerts at the park in Zelazowa Wola, May-Oct; see also National Organisations

S-1 Studio-Radio Hall
ul Woronicza 17, 00-999 **Warszawa**
Tel: 22-645 5051 Fax: 22-843 4462
director Jolanta Bilinska
Capacity: 380 *Arts types:* orchestra and chamber concerts, recitals

Sala Filharmonia Narodowa
ul. Jasna 5, 00-950 **Warszawa**
Tel: 22-826 8311/267 281 Fax: 22-826 5617
Capacity: concert hall 1050, chamber music hall 500
Comments: home of National Philharmonic Orchestra (q.v.)

Sala Filharmonia
ul J. Pilsudskiego 19, 50-044 **Wroclaw**
Tel: 71-344 2001 Fax: 71-344 8980
Venue type: concert hall *Capacity:* 500

Sala Filharmonia
Pl. Powstanców 10, 65-075 **Zielona Gora**
Tel: 68-325 5946 Fax: 68-325 6513
Venue type: concert hall *Capacity:* 240

PORTUGAL (+351)

Ginjal Space
Espaço Ginjal
Apartado 285, Cova da Piedade,
2801-997 **Almada**
Tel: 1-273 1532/33 Fax: 1-273 1532
E-Mail: olho@mail.telepac.pt
artistic director João Garcia Miguel
Venue type: warehouse multi-purpose informal space
Capacity: up to 300 *Policy:* rent, present, produce *Arts types:* contemporary & new exhibitions performance
Comments: venue address: Rua do Cais do Ginjal 53-54, Cacilhas, 2800-285 Almada; administration: Olho Associação Teatral (q.v.); also workshop and rehearsal facilities; see also Festivals and Drama

Teatro Municipal de Almada
Rua Conde Ferreira, 2804-523 **Almada**
Tel: 1-275 2175/6567 Fax: 1-274 4856
director Joaquim Benite; administrator Maria Laita
Venue type: concert hall/theatre *Capacity:* main hall 119, studio 40 *Policy:* produce, co-produce *Arts types:* drama, music, dance *Comments:* financed by State Secretary for Culture and the Municipal Chamber of Almada; see also Drama and Festivals

Teatro Circo
Av da Liberdade 697, 4700 **Braga**
Tel: 53-217 167/262 403 Fax: 53-612 174
manager Rui Madeira
Venue type: theatre *Capacity:* Sala A 1200, Sala B 100
Arts types: music, theatre, dance, cinema, concerts
Comments: own professional theatre company 'Companhia de Teatro do Braga'; Sala C is under construction; see also Drama

Teatro Académico de Gil Vicente
Praça da República, Av Sá da Bandeira, 3000 **Coimbra**
Tel: 39-827 837/829 372/823 820
Fax: 39-820 513
Internet: www.uc.pt/tagv
E-Mail: tagvart@ci.uc.pt
director Prof. Dr. Abílio Hernandez Cardoso; assistant director Francisco Paz
Venue type: théâtre à l'italienne *Capacity:* 784 *Policy:* co-production *Arts types:* music, opera, drama, dance, cinema, photography exhibitions, poetry *Comments:* owned by Coimbra University

Teatro Experimental de Cascais
Av. Fausto Fiqueiredo, Monte Estoril, 2765 **Estoril**
Tel: 1-467 0320/486 7933 Fax: 1-483 2186
director João Vasco
Venue type: theatre *Capacity:* Stage A 150, Stage B 120
Arts types: theatre
Comments: independent company subsidized by State Secretary for Culture; administration address: Av. Marchal Carmona 6B, 2750 Cascais; see also Drama

Centro Cultural de Évora/Teatro Garcia de Resende
Praça Joaquim António de Aguiar, 7000-510 **Évora**
Tel: 66-705 533/703 112 Fax: 66-741 181
Internet: www.evora.net/cendrev
E-Mail: cendrev@mail.evora.net
directors José Russo, Mário Barradas
Venue type: cultural centre, théâtre à l'italienne *Capacity:* 300 *Policy:* produce, co-produce *Arts types:* theatre, concerts, recitals, dance, opera *Comments:* see also Festivals, Drama and Puppets

Centro Pastoral Paulo VI
Santuário de Fátima, 2496 **Fátima** Codex
Tel: 49-539 6000 Fax: 49-539 6075
contact Teresa Miranda
Venue type: amphitheatre, conference rooms, concert hall *Capacity:* Amphitheatre 2124 (divisible by 3), hall 'Bom Pastor' (Salao Menor) 800, 8 meeting rooms: 2 rooms 90 each, 1 room 60, 5 rooms 40 each *Arts types:* conferences, exhibitons, concerts-only of religious or cultural nature *Comments:* organise all activities

Auditório da Exponor
Feira Internacional do Porto, 4450-618 **Leça da Palmeira**
Tel: 2-998 1400 Fax: 2-995 7499/998 1482
Internet: www.exponor.pt
E-Mail: pmbg@exponor.mailpac.pt
producer Oriana Noronha
Venue type: conference rooms, theatre, concert hall, auditorium *Capacity:* 1000, 3 small rooms 30-40, 4 medium rooms 90-100, 3 large rooms 200 (in total 2500 seats) *Arts types:* theatre, music, dance, seminars, conferences *Comments:* equiped with modern audio-translation facilities

Associação Zé Dos Bois
Trav. do Arco de Jesus, 24 r/c Esq., 1200 **Lisboa**
Tel: 21-397 0048/343 0205 Fax: 21-347 6892
E-Mail: zedosbois@ip.pt
directors Francisca Bagulho, Claudia Castela
Policy: promote *Arts types:* theatre, performing art
Comments: promotes performing art; provides space for theatre companies; runs biennial performing arts festival – Atlântico; see also Festivals

Aula Magna
Reitoria da Universidade de Lisboa,
Alameda da Universidade, 1649-004 **Lisboa**
Tel: 21-796 7624/793 2579 Fax: 21-793 3624
Internet: www.ul.pt
E-Mail: gae@reitoria.ul.pt
coordinator Dra Isabel Maçana Bruxo; technical supervisors Dra Isabel M. Tadeu, Dra Gabriela Bragansa, Dra Tània Peneina; apoio Ane Neues
Venue type: multi-purpose *Capacity:* Salão Nobre da Reitoria da Universidade 200, Aula Magna 1653, Sala de Conferéncias 50 *Arts types:* classical music, jazz, traditional music, Fado, theatre, dance, conferences, congress

Centro Cultural de Belém
Praça do Império, 1449-003 **Lisboa**
Tel: 21-361 2400 Fax: 21-361 2500
Internet: www.ccb.pt
E-Mail: ccb@ccb.pt
manager Adelaide Rocha; president Prof. Frausto da Silva; managers Miguel Lobo Antunes, Adelaide Rocha; performing arts director Miguel Leal Coecho; exhibition centre director Margarida Veiga
Venue type: cultural centre *Capacity:* large auditorium 1500, small auditorium 450 *Arts types:* classical and modern dance, jazz, theatre, art exhibitions, cinema *Comments:* shopping centre, art galleries all year round; see also National Organisations

Culturgest
Edifício-Sede da Caixa Geral de Depósitos,
Portario da Rua Arco do Cego, 1000 **Lisboa**
Tel: 21-790 5454/795 3000 Fax: 21-848 3903
Internet: www.cgd.pt/cultgest/index/htm
E-Mail: culturgest@cgd.pt
president Manuel José Vaz; vice-president Fátima Ramos; artistic director António Pinto Ribeiro; technical director Eugénio Sena; producer Margarida Mota da Costa; promotion Leonor Barata; front of the house Joana Aurelio
Venue type: theatre, exhibition centre *Capacity:* large auditorium 652, small auditorium 149 *Policy:* rent, present *Arts types:* theatre, music, dance, exhibitions, seminars, conferences, colloquia
Comments: see also Promoters

Fundação Calouste Gulbenkian/Calouste Gulbenkian Foundation
Ave. de Berna 45-A, 1067 **Lisboa** Codex
Tel: 21-782 3000 Fax: 21-793 7296
Internet: www.ip.pt/musica-
E-Mail: musica@gulbenkian.pt
directors Gulbenkian Foundation music department Dr. Luis Pereira Leal
Venue type: multi-purpose *Capacity:* grand auditorium 1200, Auditorio Dois 344 *Arts types:* music, dance, theatre, visual arts, exhibitions, concerts-music
Comments: see also Ministries, Choirs, Orchestras, Dance, Festivals (2) and Promoters

Institute for Theatrical Formation, Research and Creation – IFICT
IFICT – Instituto de Formação, Investigação e Criação Teatral
Rua de Santiago 19, 1100 **Lisboa**
Tel: 21-888 4503 Fax: 21-886 8917
president Adolfo Gutkin; teaching director Carmen Prast; assistant director Paula Freitas
Venue type: former factory with 1 performance hall and 1 exhibition hall *Capacity:* performance hall 100 *Arts types:* theatre, concerts, conferences, exhibitions *Comments:* size of exhibition hall: 250 sq.metres; see also Festivals

Teatro da Trindade/Inatel
Largo da Trindade, 7-A, 1200 **Lisboa**
Tel: 21-342 3200 Fax: 21-343 2955/342 9835
principal director Dr. Carlos Fragateiro; vice-director Dr. Rui Sergio; technical director José Carlos Barros
Venue type: theatre, stadium, theatre bar *Capacity:* 641, Stadium 60, Theatre bar 60 *Policy:* presentation directed to the worker's leisure time *Arts types:* music, opera, dance, theatre, conferences *Comments:* the theatre is owned by Inatel, a national association for the enhancement of the worker's free time

Teatro Municipal de S. Luiz
Rua António Maria Cardoso, 40, 1200 **Lisboa**
Tel: 21-342 7172/346 1260 Fax: 21-347 6858
director Cezar Gomes
Venue type: classic Italian-style theatre *Capacity:* 1027 *Policy:* rent, produce *Arts types:* drama, classical and popular music, dance, cinema *Comments:* owned by Câmara Municipal de Lisboa and managed by Pelouro da Cultura

Teatro Municipal Maria Matos
Av. Frei Miguel Contreiras, 52, 1700 **Lisboa**
Tel: 21-849 7007/08 Fax: 21-847 0972
director Dr. Luis Pires
Venue type: theatre *Capacity:* 680 *Policy:* assist small independent groups with free theatre space *Arts types:* theatre, music, dance, children's theatre *Comments:* emphasis on theatre

Teatro Nacional D. Maria II
Praça D. Pedro IV, 1100-201 **Lisboa**
Tel: 21-325 0800 Fax: 21-325 0938
director Carlos Avilez; assistant director Man Riçio; producer Antonino Folmer; public relations Cristina Martins; director of scenes Alberto Ullar; artistic director Manuel Coelho
Venue type: theatre *Capacity:* Sala Garrett 550, Amélia Rey Colaço/Robles Monteiro Studio 80 *Policy:* present, produce *Arts types:* classical and modern theatre repertoire, musicals *Comments:* government funded (national); see also Drama

Auditório Nacional de Carlos Alberto
Rua das Oliveiras 43, 4050-449 **Porto**
Tel: 2-339 5050 Fax: 2-339 5060
director Nuno Cardoso; technical director Jorge Costa
Venue type: multi-purpose *Capacity:* 549 *Arts types:* music, theatre, dance, cinema *Comments:* financed by Portuguese Institute for Performing Arts (Instituto Português das artes do espectaculo)

Balleteatro Auditorio
Praça 9 de Abril 70/76, 4200 **Porto**
Tel: 2-550 8918/9 Fax: 2-550 8919
director Isabel Barros
Venue type: auditiorium *Capacity:* 200 *Policy:* creates, co-produce, produce and present *Arts types:* dance (modern & contemporary), theatre, music *Comments:* funded by the Ministry of Culture; organises workshops and debates; see also Dance and Promoters

Empresa Artística, SA (Coliseu do Porto)
Rua Passos Manuel 137, 4000 **Porto**
Tel: 2-200 5196 Fax: 2-201 1386
administrator Dr. J. José Antonio-Varres
Venue type: multi-purpose *Capacity:* 3000 *Policy:* rent, co-produce *Arts types:* all performing arts

House of the Arts
Casa das Artes
Rua Ruben A. 210, 4150 **Porto**
Tel: 2-600 6153 Fax: 2-600 6152
E-Mail: cartesb@mail.telepac.pt
manager Manuel Matos Fernandes
Venue type: cultural centre *Capacity:* 2 x 195 *Policy:* produce, co-produce, rent *Arts types:* cinema, multimedia, video, chamber music, conferences, theatre, exhibitions *Comments:* Casa des Artes is an art unit extension of the Ministry of Culture's IPAE (Portuguese Institute for the Performing Arts)

Casino da Póvoa
Apartado 29, Avenida Braga, 4490 **Póvoa do Varzim**
Tel: 52-690 888 Fax: 52-690 871
Internet: www.casinos-estorilpovoa.com
E-Mail: casino.povoa3@mail.telepac.pt
vice-president (working committee) Eng. Joaquim Reis; artistic director Jorge Castro Guedes; responsible marketing & public relations Maria Joá Torsé; responsible sales La Solete Corrcia
Venue type: dinning room show *Capacity:* 450 + 200 *Arts types:* music, theatre, dance
Comments: see also Festivals

Teatro Municipal sá da Bandeira
Rua João Afonso 7, 2000 **Santarem**
Tel: 43-391 510 (Câmara de Santarem)
Fax: 43-333 643
E-Mail: cmsantcultsocia@mail.telepac.pt
artistic director José Manuel
Venue type: theatre *Capacity:* 280 *Arts types:* theatre
Comments: run by the Santarem regional council (Câmara de Santarem)

Teatro Municipal Sá de Miranda
Rua de Sá Miranda, 4900-529 **Viana do Castelo**
Tel: 58-823 259 (teatro do Noroeste) Fax: 58-825 957
director João Alpuim
Venue type: theatre *Capacity:* 490 *Arts types:* theatre, orchestra, ballet, cinema *Comments:* own professional company 'Teatro do Noroeste'

RUSSIA (+7)

Central House of Painters
10 Krymsky Val, **Moscow**
Tel: 095-238 1955/9634 Fax: 095-238 9810

Central State Concert Hall ROSSIA
Varvarka 6, 103495 **Moscow**
Tel: 095-298 3946

Concert Hall of Central Tourist's House
Leninski prosp. 146, **Moscow**
Tel: 095-434 9492

Concert Hall of Russian Academy named by Gnessinykh
M. Rjevski per. 1, 121069 **Moscow**
Tel: 095-290 2422

Concert Hall on Prechistinka
Prechistinka 32, DMSH #11, 119034 **Moscow**
Tel: 095-201 3783

Conservatory
13 Bolshaya Nikitskaya, 103871 **Moscow**
Tel: 095-229 0225/7246/7446/2060
Venue type: concert hall *Capacity:* Great Hall, Small Hall

Glinka Museum Hall
4 Ul. Fadeeva, 125047 **Moscow**
Tel: 095-972 3237

Izmailovo Concert Hall
Izmailovskoe Shosse 71-E, **Moscow**
Tel: 095-166 7844

Kolonny Zal
1 B. Dimitrovka, 103009 **Moscow**
Tel: 095-292 0736/0956 Fax: 095-292 7131

Kremlin Palace
Trinity Gate, **Moscow**
Tel: 095-929 7901

National Academy of Music
Maluy Rzhevsky per 1, **Moscow**
Tel: 095-290 6737/2422

Olympic Village Concert Hall
1 Michurinski prosp., 117602 **Moscow**
Tel: 095-437 5650

Rakhmaninov Hall of the Conservatory
11 Bolshaya Nikitskaya, **Moscow**
Tel: 095-229 0294

Russia Concert Hall
Ul Varavarka 6, **Moscow**
Tel: 095-281 5550/3779

Russian Army House
2 Suvorovskaya sq., **Moscow**
Tel: 095-281 5550/6759

Scientist's House Hall
Prechistenka 16, **Moscow**
Tel: 095-201 4555

Scriabin Museum Hall
Tverskaya ul. 31, **Moscow**
Tel: 095-299 4981/1192

Shuvalova House
30/1 Povarskaya, **Moscow**
Tel: 095-290 2422

Tchaikovsky Concert Hall
4/31 Triumfalnaya Ploshchad, **Moscow**
Tel: 095-299 0378/3681

Tchakhovskaya House
Sadovaya-Kudrinskaya ul 6, **Moscow**
Tel: 095-291 6345

Children's Philharmonic Society
ul Mokhovaya 15, 191028 **St Petersburg**
Tel: 812-279 7531/273 0370
general director Evgeny Tugovikov; artistic director Natalia Entelis

D Shostakovich Hall of St Petersburg Philharmonic Society
ul Mikhailovskaya 2, 191011 **St Petersburg**
Tel: 812-110 4291/311 7331 Fax: 812-311 2126
director Dmitry Sollertinsky

Glinka Academic Kapella – Great Hall
Moika 20, 191186 **St Petersburg**
Tel: 812-110 6873/314 1073 Fax: 812-110 6913
general director Vitaly Lavrov; artistic director Vladislav Chernishenko

Glinka Academic Kapella – Small Hall
VO 4 linia 15, 199053 **St Petersburg**
Tel: 812-213 6170/106 873
director Agnessa Urchak

Glinka Hall of St Petersburg Philharmonic Society
Ul. Mikhailovskaya 2, 191011 **St Petersburg**
Tel: 812-311 1531/7331 Fax: 812-311 2126
director Valentina Azovskaya; artistic director Natalya Eremina

Jazz Philharmonic Society
Zagorodny pr 27, 191180 **St Petersburg**
Tel: 812-113 5331 Fax: 812-164 9843
administrative director German Vasinsky; artistic director David Goloschekin

Municipal Cultural Centre Beloselski – Belozerski
Nevsky 41, 191011 **St Petersburg**
Tel: 812-315 4076 Fax: 812-311 3690
general director Albert Magalashvili

Mussorgsky Opera and Ballet Theatre
Akademicheskiy teatr opery i baleta imeni M P Mussorgskogo
1 Art Square, 191011 **St Petersburg**
Tel: 812-219 1943 Fax: 812-314 3653
administrative director Victor Kusch; artistic general director Stanislav Gaudasinsk (tel: 812-219 1798, fax: 812-312 2774); deputy artistic director Victoria Gordievskaya (tel: 812-219 1989); chief conductor Andrey Anikhanov (tel: 812-219 1946/314 7248); artistic director of ballet NIkolay Bojartchikov (tel: 812-219 1986)
Venue type: theatre

Octiabrsky Concert Hall
Ligovsky pr 6, 193060 **St Petersburg**
Tel: 812-272 4220
general director Emma Lavrinovitch

Opera and Music Theatre
St Petersburg State Marinsky Theatre (Kirov), 1 Theatre Square, 190000 **St Petersburg**
Tel: 812-114 4110/4164/4441 Fax: 812-314 1744
executive director Jury Shvartsbopff; general artistic director Valery Gergiev; director Anatoly Malkov
Venue type: theatre

Petersburg Concert Philharmonic Society
Fontanka 41, 191011 **St Petersburg**
Tel: 812-110 4043 Fax: 812-311 2066
general director Alexander Yablonsky

Saint Petersburg State Musical Theatre Music Hall
Alexandrovsky park 4, 197198 **St Petersburg**
Tel: 812-232 9466 (director) Fax: 812-232 5329
artistic director Ilya Rakhlin (tel: 812-232 6165)

Smolny Sobor Concert Hall
Rastrelli pl 3/1, 191011 **St Petersburg**
Tel: 812-271 7632 Fax: 812-311 3690
general director Victor Gribanov

Yussupov Palace
Moika 94, 190000 **St Petersburg**
Tel: 812-314 3066
director's assistant Zhanna Makovieva
Venue type: concert hall and theatre

SAN MARINO (+378)

Cinema Teatro Concordia
Via della Concordia, 47893 **Borgo Maggiore**
Tel: 902 466/962 Fax: 903 562
responsabile Dott.ssa Gemma Cavalleri, Manlio Gozi (ufficio attivita sociali e culturali)
Venue type: cinema-theatre-auditorium *Capacity:* 386-414 *Policy:* rent *Arts types:* drama, concerts, cinema

Teatro Titano
Piazza Sant'Agata 5, 47890 **Città di San Marino**
Tel: 882 416 Fax: 882 300
responsabile D.ssa Gemma Cavalleri (ufficio attivita' sociali e culturali) tel. 882 452
Venue type: theatre and concert hall *Capacity:* 320 *Policy:* rent *Arts types:* classical music concerts, congresses, small theatre productions, cabaret

Cinema – Teatro Nuovo
Piazza Marino Tini 7, 47891 **Dogana**
Tel: 885 515 Fax: 882 300
responsabile D.ssa Gemma Cavalleri (tel. 882 452)
Venue type: cinema, theatre, concert hall
Capacity: 872 *Policy:* rent *Arts types:* film, theatre, classical music, pop, rock

Sala Polivalente
Via Ezio Balducci, 47899 **Serravalle**
Tel: 549-901 775 Fax: 882 300
contact Gemma Cavalleri (882 452)
Venue type: concert hall, theatre *Capacity:* 267 *Arts types:* classical music, congresses, recitals, cabaret

SLOVAKIA (+421)

Many telephone and fax numbers in Slovakia are in the process of being changed. We have included all new numbers known at the time of going to print.

Cultural Park
Park kultúry a oddychu
nábr. L. Svobodu 3, 815 15 **Bratislava**
Tel: 7-5441 5801/6608/5102 Fax: 7-5441 5348
director Jarmila Mikusová
Venue type: multi-purpose *Capacity:* 800 *Arts types:* theatre, dance, music, visual arts

CULTUS – Centre for Culture and Arts
CULTUS – centrum pre kultúru a umenie
Ruzinovská 28, 820 09 **Bratislava**
Tel: 7-4333 0260/0446 Fax: 7-4333 2246
director MA Ján Hiznay
Venue type: multi-purpose *Capacity:* Hall 1 400, Hall 2 200 *Arts types:* music, theatre, dance, visual arts, classical, pop, folk, jazz concerts

Studio L + S
Námestie 1 mája 5, 816 06 **Bratislava**
Tel: 7-5292 1584/5296 3691 Fax: 7-5292 5082
director Milan Lasica
Capacity: 200 *Arts types:* theatre, concerts

SLOVENIA (+386)

Festival Hall Bled
Festivalna Dvorana Bled
Cesta svobode 11, 4260 **Bled**
Tel: 64-744 079/743 640/741 831 Fax: 64-744 776
E-Mail: marjana.bajt@congress.bled.si
manager Matjaz Zavrsnik; prod. manager Marjana Bajt

Venue type: multi-purpose centre *Capacity:* main hall 514, 3 meeting rooms up to 150 *Policy:* rent, share risk *Arts types:* dance, orchestra, rock, fashion shows, chamber music, recitals, drama *Comments:* international music festival held every summer

Cankarjev Dom – Cultural and Congress Centre
Cankarjev Dom – Kulturni in kongresni center
Presernova 10, 1000 **Ljubljana**
Tel: 61-176 7100 (switchboard)
Fax: 61-224 279 (arts & culture)/217 431 (congress)
Internet: www.cd-cc.si
E-Mail: stanekoblar@cd-cc.si
director general Mitja Rotovnik (tel: 61-212 508, fax: 61-176 7119, email: mitja.rotovnik@cd-cc.si); congress director Srecko Peterlic (tel: 61-224 133, fax: 61-217 431, e-mail: srecko.peterlic@cd-cc.si); technical director Saso Kranjc (tel: 61-212 584, fax: 61-223 896, email: saso.kranjc@cd-cc.si); head of music & ballet Monika Kartin (ext 160, email: monika.kartin@cd-cc.si); managing director Jana Kramberger (tel: 61-176 7106, email: jana.kramberger@cd-cc.si); head of theatre projects Ursula Cetinski (ext. 154, email: ursula.cetinski@cd-cc.si); head of Arts Agency Natasa Kelhar (ext 166, email: natasa-kelhar@cd-cc.si); head of public relations Stane Koblar (ext 168, email: stane-koblar@cd-cc.si); head of jazz, rock, pop and entertainment music Bogdan Benigar (ext 157, email: bogdan.benigar@cd-cc.si); head of film & video Jelka Stergel (ext 150, email: jekla.stergel@cd-cc.si); head of humanistic & general cultural education programme Peter Savli (ext 161, email: peter.savli@cd-cc.si); head of box office Breda Pecovnik (ext 300, email: breda.pecovnik@cd-cc.si)
Venue type: multi-purpose *Capacity:* Gallus Hall up to 1600, Linhart Hall 616, Kosovel Hall 187, Stih Hall 245, Club 250, conference rooms 10 to 300, gallery, foyers, Lily Novy Literary Club, cd gallery, small gallery *Policy:* production and co-production , presentation of international programme, promotion of the arts, Slovene and international artists, education programmes for children and adults, Ljubljana International Jazz Festival, Ljubljana International Film Festival *Arts types:* symphony, opera, ballet, chamber music, choral music, recitals, variety, jazz, rock, pop, world music, folk music, drama, dance, pantomime, exhibitions, feature and documentary film *Comments:* see also Competitions

Cultural and Art Club France Preseren
KUD France Preseren
Karunova 14, 1000 **Ljubljana**
Tel: 61-332 288/210 491 Fax: 61-210 338
E-Mail: kud@kud-fp.si
president Jani Kovacic; secretary Zelko Pelicon; programme coordinator Tone Skrjanec
Venue type: cultural and art centre
Capacity: hall 200 (100 seats), gallery 150, patio 500, club 25 *Policy:* KFP is a non-profit making, civil institution which promotes young, independent culture with productions of its own and co-productions; venues sometimes also available for rent to similar institutions and individuals
Arts types: theatre and cabaret, artistic and experimental film/video, exhibitions, concert (rock, jazz, ethno-, chamber music), lectures, puppets for adults and children, recitals, fashion performances, fine arts, poetry readings, multi-media shows

Cultural Centre Nova Gorica
Kulturni dom Nova Gorica
Bevkov Trg 4, 5000 **Nova Gorica**
Tel: 65-135 4010/13 Fax: 65-135 4020
Internet: www.kulturnidom-ng.si
E-Mail: kult-dom.ng@guest.arnes.si
director Tanja Kustrin; assistant director Vesna Mariatti; pr Mirka Kriznic
Arts types: music
Comments: participate in organisation of Slovene and international festivals: Slovene Days of Music, Kogoj Days, International Festival Alpe-Adria, International Festival ALLFRONTIERS; represent and manage Slovene musicians

Auditorium Portoroz – Arts and Convention Centre
Avditorij Portoroz – Kulturni, kongresni in promocijski center
Sencna pot 10, 6320 **Portoroz**
Tel: 66-476 700 Fax: 66-476 718
director Jana Tolja; convention manager Stefanija Pierucci; arts events manager Matjaz Ukmar
Venue type: multi-purpose
Capacity: summer amphitheatre 1800, 4 conference rooms 700 *Policy:* promote: own risk & shared risk *Arts types:* orchestra, theatre, classical & modern music, opera, children's programmes, film, exhibitions

SPAIN (+34)

Auditorio Municipal de Albacete
Plaza de la Catedral s/n, 02071 **Albacete**
Tel: 967-596 100 Fax: 967-596 116
jefe activades culturales Gines Orpuño
Capacity: 570
Arts types: theatre, cinema, music

Teatro Salón Cervantes
Fundación Colegio del Rey, c/Cervantes, s/n, 28801 **Alcalá de Henares (Madrid)**
Tel: 91-882 2497 Fax: 91-881 3906
E-Mail: fcolrey@mx2.redestb.es
director y jefe de actividades y programación Pablo Nogales (10-2pm: 1-881 3934; 5-8pm and weekends: 1-882 2497); secretaria Josefa Peñaranda
Venue type: theatre *Capacity:* 489 *Policy:* own programme for the season; own small productions *Arts types:* music, theatre, dance *Comments:* managed by Ayuntamiento de Alcalá de Henares

Teatro Municipal
Calle del Teatro 1, 44600 **Alcañiz (Teruel)**
Tel: 978-870 565 ext. 233 Fax: 978-870 033
Internet: www.aragon.net/alcaniz.htm
E-Mail: alcaniz@correu.aragon.net
técnico responsable Area de cultura Ignacio Micolau
Venue type: theatre *Capacity:* 332
Arts types: drama, puppets, classical music
Comments: administrated by Ayuntamiento de Alcañiz, Plaza de España 1, 44600 Alcañiz

Centre Cultural d'Alcoi
Avda País Valenciano N° 1, 03801 **Alcoi (Alicante)**
Tel: 96-554 4122 Fax: 96-554 4425
director Jordi Botella i Miró
Venue type: arts centre *Capacity:* 212 *Arts types:* chamber concerts, dance, drama, puppets, pantomime, cinema
Comments: funded by Ayuntamiento d'Alcoi; see also Competitions

Sala Arniches
Av. Aguilera 1, 03007 **Alicante**
Tel: 96-593 4794 Fax: 965-934 771
gerente Germán Marco Ponce; director artístico Juan Alfonso Gil-Albors; administrador Ignacio Ferrando de la Cuadra; responsable de Sala Juan Alberti; director Rafael Hernandez
Venue type: theatre *Capacity:* 271 *Arts types:* concerts, dance, lectures, theatre
Comments: managed by: Teatres de la Generalitat Valenciana; they organise cultural promotion throughout the year – free cultural events (theatre, dance, music); see also National Organisations

Teatro Principal de Alicante
Plaza Ruperto Chapi s/n, 03001 **Alicante**
Tel: 96-521 9157 Fax: 96-520 9723
jefe administracion Mª Dolores Padilla; secretario Milagros García Casarrubios; delegado consejero Manuel Sanchez Monllor
Venue type: theatre *Capacity:* 1024 *Arts types:* theatre, ballet, opera, zarzuela, concerts, comedy *Comments:* co-owners: Ayuntamiento de Alicante, Caja de Ahorros del Mediterráneo and Sociedad de Conciertos

Corral de Comedias de Almagro
Plaza Mayor 17, 13270 **Almagro (Ciudad Real)**
Tel: 926-860 046 (town hall)/861 539 (theatre)
Fax: 926-860 717
Internet: www.telematica.es/aytoalmagro.es
concejal de cultura y turismo Angel Gómez Malagón
Venue type: theatre – open-air, built end of 16th C.
Capacity: 293 *Policy:* rent
Arts types: classical theatre *Comments:* managed by Ayuntamiento de Almagro; home of Festival International de Teatro Clásico de Almagro; no representation from Dec-Feb; see also Festivals

Teatro Municipal de Almagro
San Agustín 20, 13270 **Almagro (Ciudad Real)**
Tel: 926-861 361 Fax: 926-882 202
concejal del teatro Angel Gómez Malagón
Venue type: theatre *Capacity:* 530 *Arts types:* all types (concerts, theatres, opera etc.) *Comments:* management: Ayuntamiento de Almagro, Plaza Mayor 1, 13270 Almagro, Tel: 926-860 035

Auditorio Municipal Maestro Padilla
Avda. del Mediterráneo s/n, 04007 **Almería**
Tel: 950-273 002 (auditorio)/620 585 (cultura)
Fax: 950-276 923 (auditorio)/270 302 (management)/269 122 (cultura)
coordinación Jose Luis Cantón
Venue type: theatre *Capacity:* 956 *Arts types:* music, theatre, dance *Comments:* management: Area de Cultura del Ayuntamiento de Almería; home of The International Jazz Festival and Jornadas de Teatro del Sigio de Oro; see also Festivals

Teatro Apolo
Rambla Obispo Olberá 25, 04001 **Almería**
Tel: 950-269 268 Fax: 950-276 923
coordinacion José Luis Cantón
Venue type: Italian style theatre
Capacity: 300 *Policy:* own programme & presents *Arts types:* music, theatre, dance

Gran Teatro de Alzira
Plaza Alborxi s/n, 46600 **Alzira (Valencia)**
Tel: 96-241 1244 (theatre)/240 0450 (ayuntamiento)
Fax: 96-240 1391 (ayuntamiento)
responsable de programación Enrique Aranda Gallardo
Venue type: theatre *Capacity:* 896
Policy: presents own cultural programme *Arts types:* theatre, concerts – classical, jazz, contemporary, folk, dance, opera *Comments:* management: Ayuntamiento de Alzira, San Roque 6, 46600 Alzira (Valencia)

Nave de Cambaleo, La
Av. de Loyola 8, 28300 **Aranjuez (Madrid)**
Tel: 91-892 1793 Fax: 91-892 1877
Internet: www.arrakis.es/~/cambaleo/index.htm
E-Mail: cambaleo@arrakis.es
director Carlos Sarrió; manager David Ruiz; production Antonio Sarró
Venue type: flexible space
Capacity: 120 *Policy:* own company productions, co-produce, present
Arts types: theatre, visual arts, concerts *Comments:* visiing address: Avenida del Matadero s/n, 28300 Aranjuez (Madrid); member of Coordinadora de Salas Alternativas; see also National Organisations

Auditorio de la Casa Municipal de Cultura de Avilés
Plaza de Álvarez Acebal 2, 33401 **Avilés**
Tel: 98-551 0439/0452 Fax: 98-551 1352
director Antonio Rípoll
Venue type: modern style *Capacity:* 667 *Policy:* rent, programming *Arts types:* all types *Comments:* Fundación Municipal de Cultura de Avilés

Teatro Palacio Valdés
Armando Palacio Valdés s/n, 33401 **Avilés**
Tel: 98-554 9658 Fax: 98-551 1352
director Antonio Ripoll
Venue type: Italian style *Capacity:* 747 *Comments:* Fundación Municipal de Cultura de Avilés, Casa Municipal de Cultura (Avilés)

Teatro Baztartxo de Azkoitia
Aingeru kalea 30, 20720 **Azkoitia (Gipuzkoa)**
Tel: 943-857 170 Fax: 943-852 140
Internet: www.azkoitia.net
E-Mail: azkoitia@net
concejal de cultura t.b.a.; animador sociocultural Jesus Arrizabalaga
Venue type: theatre *Capacity:* 600
Policy: rent *Arts types:* music, drama, dance, cinema
Comments: administrated by Ayuntamiento de Azkoitia, Mayor 47, 20720 Azkoitia

Consorcio Teatro Lope de Ayala
Paseo San Francisco n°1, 06002 **Badajoz**
Tel: 924-220 934 Fax: 924-254 702
Internet: www.iponet.es/ldayala
E-Mail: ldeayala@iponet.es
director Miguel Murillo Gómez; prensa Ana González
Capacity: 750 *Policy:* present, produce *Arts types:* music, theatre, dance *Comments:* visiting address: Plaza de Minayos s/n, 06002 Badajoz

Sala Tragaluz
c/ Muñoz Torrero n° 22B, 06001 **Badajoz**
Tel: 924-245 493 Fax: 924-245 497
Internet: www.tragaluz.com
E-Mail: tragaluz@ctv.es
director Paco Espada; director de programación José Manuel Silvestre; director de produción Manuel Durán
Capacity: 100 *Policy:* rent, produce, co-produce, present
Arts types: theatre, music, visual arts *Comments:* member of Coordinadora de Salas Alternativas, see also National Organisations

Teatro Zorrilla
c/ Canonge Baranera 17, 08911 **Badalona**
Tel: 93-384 4022 Fax: 93-389 3528
director Andreu Solsona; cap tecnic Antonio Martinez
Venue type: Italian style *Capacity:* 452 *Policy:* own programming *Arts types:* theatre, music, dance
Comments: offices: Sant Miquel 54, 08911 Badalona; refurbished theatre built 1868; owned by Ajuntament de Badalóna

Teatro Barakaldo – Barakaldo Antzokia
c/ Juan Sebastián Elcano 4,
48901 **Barakaldo (Bizkaia)**
Tel: 94-478 0600 Fax: 94-478 0461
E-Mail: ctencenoa@nexo.es
director ejecutivo Gonzalo Centeno Anta;
director de comunicacion y relaciones publicas Edilberto Fernandez
Venue type: theatre *Capacity:* teatro 697, sala polivalente 152 *Policy:* present, produce, co-produce *Arts types:* theatre, symphony, music concerts, flamenco, recitals, dance, exhibitions, conferences, opera

Ateneu Popular nou Barris
c/ Portlligat s/n, 08042 **Barcelona**
Tel: 93-353 9516 Fax: 93-350 3000
Internet: www.bcnet.upc.es/9bnet/ateneu
E-Mail: ateneu@redestb.es
artistic director Xavi Perez; administration Rosa Torrecillas
Venue type: theatre
Capacity: 325 *Policy:* rent, present, produce
Arts types: all types *Comments:* member of Trans Europe Halles, Tel: +33 1-4011 6414, Internet: www.teh.net

Centre Cultural de la Fundación La Caixa
Passeig de Sant Joan 108, 08037 **Barcelona**
Tel: 93-458 8907 Fax: 93-458 1308
Internet: www.fundacio.lacaixa.es
E-Mail: ccbn.fundacio@lacaixa.es
director Jordi Ardit; programación musical/directora artística Maricarmen Palma
Venue type: cultural centre *Capacity:* 450
Arts types: chamber, classical, early music, ethnic music
Comments: temporada musical Jan to Dec; see also Promoters

El Arca
c/ Llagostera 8, 08026 **Barcelona**
Tel: 93-455 1952 Fax: 93-311 0210
directora Avelina Arguelles
Venue type: refurbished industrial warehouse
Capacity: 180 *Policy:* rent, possibly own programming
Arts types: special contemporary dance, theatre
Comments: collaboration with ICUB, Tel: 93-301 7775, Fax: 93-301 6100

Espai Escenic Joan Brossa
c/ Allada Vermell 10 (Final Calle Princesa), 08003 **Barcelona**
Tel: 93-310 1364/315 1596 Fax: 93-315 1596
director Hermann Bonnin; administration Jesús Júlve
Venue type: alternative *Capacity:* 60 *Policy:* own programming, co-productions *Arts types:* theatre, magic
Comments: venue address: Allada Vermell 13, 08003 Barcelona

Fundació Joan Miró
Parc de Montjuic, 08038 **Barcelona**
Tel: 93-329 1908 Fax: 93-329 8609
Internet: www.bcn.fjmiro.es
E-Mail: fjmiro@bcn.fjmiro.es
director Rosa María Malet; presidente Eduard Castellet; relaciones públicas Ana Noelle; sub-directora Dolors Ricart
Venue type: multi-purpose *Capacity:* 212 *Policy:* rent *Arts types:* dance, concerts, drama, exhibitions, puppets, theatre for children *Comments:* the foundation is dedicated to the study of Miro's work, Pedagogic Department, contemporary art library; temporary exhibitions; see also Promoters

Gran Teatre del Liceu
La Rambla 51-59, 08002 **Barcelona**
Tel: 93-485 9900 Fax: 93-485 9918
Internet: www.liceubarcelona.com
E-Mail: info@liceubarcelona.com
director general Josep Caminal i Badia; director artistico Joan Matabosch; gerente Gemma Sendra
Arts types: concerts, operas, recitals, ballet *Comments:* due to have reopened October 99; management: Fundació del Gran Teatre del Liceu

Jove Teatre Regina
Seneca 22, 08006 **Barcelona**
Tel: 93-218 1512/1474 Fax: 93-415 0098
directora María Agustina Solé i Riumalló
Venue type: theatre *Capacity:* 435 *Policy:* own productions and programming
Arts types: children's and adults theatre
Comments: own company La Trepa; see also Drama

L'Auditori
Calle Lepant 150, 08013 **Barcelona**
Tel: 93-247 9300 Fax: 93-247 9301
Internet: www.obc.es
E-Mail: informacio@obc.es
director OBC Laurent Foster; gerente Miquel Lumbierres; presnsa Marta Muntada; admin director Andreu Puig
Venue type: modern style auditorium *Capacity:* sala sinfonica 2200, sala polivalent 400-700 *Policy:* rent, own programme *Arts types:* music, conferences, theatre, dance *Comments:* home of the OBC (Orquestra Simfonica de Barcelona i Nacional de Catalunya) (q.v.)

L'Espai de Dansa i Música de la Generalitat de Catalunya
Travessera de Gràcia 63, 08021 **Barcelona**
Tel: 93-414 3133 Fax: 93-200 8548
Internet: gencat/cultura/espai
E-Mail: espai@qiz.net
coordinador Josep Andraga Escola; director de dansa Marta Garcia; director de música Carlos Sala
Venue type: theatre *Capacity:* 370 *Policy:* present *Arts types:* contemporary dance, music *Comments:* from Oct-Jun; managed by Generalitat de Catalunya; see also National & Regional Ministries Cultural & Funding Agencies and Promoters

Mercat de les Flors
Calle Lérida 59, 08004 **Barcelona**
Tel: 93-426 1875 Fax: 93-426 0106
E-Mail: tmercatf@intercom.es
director del teatro Joan M. Gual; director gerente del Instituto de Cultura de Barcelona Ferran Mascarell
Venue type: multi-purpose *Capacity:* Sala Maria Aurelia Capmany: modular space 711-1000, Sala Sebastia Gasch 80 *Policy:* presents, produce and co-produce
Arts types: theatre, music, dance
Comments: owned by Ayuntamiento de Barcelona; managed by Instituto de Cultura de Barcelona, Palacio de la Virreina, La Rambla 99, Tel: 93-301 4198, Fax: 93-301 6100; see also National Organisations

Nou Teatro Tantarantana
c/ Les Flors nº 22, 08001 **Barcelona**
Tel: 93-441 7022 Fax: 93-441 7094
directors Julio Álvarez, Victor Suañez
Capacity: 145 *Comments:* member of Coordinadora de Salas Alternativas and ADETCA (q.v.) (Tel: 93-909 7900); also theatre producers for children's and adult theatre

Palau de la Música Catalana
San Fransisco de Paula 2, 08003 **Barcelona**
Tel: 93-268 1000 Fax: 93-268 4824
managing director Felix Millet i Tusell
Capacity: Palau de la Música 2000 *Policy:* produce, rent
Arts types: music *Comments:* management: Orfeó Catalá, home of Orfeó Catala; the most important venue in Catalonia; see also Publications, Promoters and Choirs

Sala Artenbrut
c/ Perill nº 9-11, 08012 **Barcelona**
Tel: 93-457 6516
directora Mercé Anglés
Capacity: 100 *Policy:* present, produce, rent *Comments:* member of Coordinadora de Salas Alternativas, see also National Organisations

Sala Beckett
Alegre de Dalt 55 bis, 08024 **Barcelona**
Tel: 93-284 5312 Fax: 93-219 7927
E-Mail: salabeckett@ctv.es
directors Tony Casares, Pep Far; secretaría Mercé García
Venue type: small scale experimental space *Capacity:* 75
Policy: present own productions and programmes *Arts types:* theatre: avant garde, modern, experimental etc; dance, music
Comments: lectures, exhibitions, courses; library; own company: El Teatro Fronterizo, see also Drama

Teatre Adrià Gual
Institut del Teatre de la Diputació de Barcelona, c/ Sant Pere més baix 7, 08003 **Barcelona**
Tel: 93-268 2078 Fax: 93-268 1070
E-Mail: i.teatre@diba.es
director Pau Monterde; sub-director Agusti Humet; gerente Francesc Colomé
Capacity: Sala Adria Gual (A) 288, Sala La Cuina (B) 140
Policy: 50% teaching activities, 50% public performances

Teatre Condal
Avenida del Paralelo 91, 08004 **Barcelona**
Tel: 93-442 3132 Fax: 93-442 9556
responsable Daniel Martinez
Venue type: theatre *Capacity:* 699 *Policy:* present, produce *Arts types:* theatre, music *Comments:* agents: Focus, Tel: 93-309 7538; publicity agent: Publiespec, Tel: 93-485 1377

Teatre Grec
Paseo de Santamadrona 36, 08004 **Barcelona**
Tel: 93-301 7775 (cultura) Fax: 93-301 6100
Internet: www.grecbcn.com
E-Mail: smillet@mail.bca.es
gerente del institut de cultura de Barcelona Ferran Mascarell; director festival D'estiu de Barcelona, Grec Xavier Albertí
Capacity: 1900 *Arts types:* music, theatre, dance
Comments: management: Instituto de Cultura de Barcelona, Palacio de la Virreina, Rambla 99, 08002 Barcelona, Tel: 93-301 7775, Fax: 93-317 1240; home of the Festival d'Estiu de Barcelona Grec; alternative E-mail: infoicup@mail.bcn.es

Teatre Lliure
Montseny 47, 08012 **Barcelona**
Tel: 93-218 9251 Fax: 93-237 1243
directors Lluís Pasqual, Guillem-Jordí Graells; prensa Marc Gall
Venue type: polivalent theatre *Capacity:* 300 *Policy:* produce and present own productions *Arts types:* theatre, chamber concerts, dance *Comments:* home of the Orquestra de Cambra Teatre Lliure (Lliure Theatre Chamber Orchestra); also home of Compañia Teatre Lliure; collaboration with El Grec Festival of Barcelona; organsie workshops for directors and actors; produce own scenery, lighting and props; building new venue in Palau de la Agricultura Montjuic Barcelona; see also Drama and Orchestras

Teatre Malic
Compañia de Marionetas la Fanfarra, c/ Fusina 3, 08003 **Barcelona**
Tel: 93-310 7035 Fax: 93-319 5647
Internet: www.daucom.es/malic/
E-Mail: malic@pangea.org
director of theatre for adults Antoni Rumbau; puppets director Eugenio Navarro
Venue type: Italian-style theatre, seats removable
Capacity: 50 *Policy:* own productions *Arts types:* puppets, opera, flamenco, lectures, drama, dance, music
Comments: home of puppet company La Fanfarra; see also Puppets

Teatre Nacional de Catalunya
Plaça de les Arts 1, 08013 **Barcelona**
Tel: 93-306 5700 Fax: 93-306 5701
Internet: www.cultura.gencat.es/tnc
E-Mail: info@tnc.es
director Domenec Reixach; general administrator Josep Maria Busquets; coordinador Antoni Tarrida
Venue type: theatre (designed by Ricardo Bofill)
Capacity: Sala Gran 896, Sala Petita 500, Sala Taller 500
Policy: produce, co-produce *Arts types:* theatre, dance, children's & youth theatre *Comments:* opened 11 Sept. 1997; committed to raise theatrical standards through various educational schemes and activities; owned by the Generalitat de Catalunya; funded by The Department of Culture of the Generalitat de Catalunya; see also Drama

Teatre Polioràma
La Rambla 115, 08002 **Barcelona**
Tel: 93-317 7599 Fax: 93-412 2239
E-Mail: poliorama@compuserve.com
gerente Jaume Colomer; administracion Guillerno Moreso; jefa de sala Pepa Ferruz
Venue type: theatre *Capacity:* 654 *Policy:* rent *Arts types:* classical, contemporary, international drama, music, dance *Comments:* managed by Tres per 3, S.A.

Teatre Romea
c/Hospital 51, 08001 **Barcelona**
Tel: 93-301 5504 Fax: 93-485 1512/412 3032
E-Mail: focus@mail.cinet.es
director Calixto Bieito
Capacity: 578 *Policy:* presents own programmes *Arts types:* theatre (Catalonian – international) *Comments:* managed by Focus, S.A., Passatge Trullat 10, 08005 Barcelona, Tel: 93-309 7538

Teatre Victoria
Avenida Paralelo 67, 08004 **Barcelona**
Tel: 93-329 9189 Fax: 93-441 3948
E-Mail: tresper3@compuserve.com
gerente Jaume Colomer; administración Guillermo Moreso; jefa de sala Montserrat Pardo
Venue type: theatre *Capacity:* 1224 *Policy:* rent, present
Arts types: all types of theatre, some dance, some music and opera *Comments:* home of Dagoll Dagom and El Tricicle; managed by Tres per 3, S.A.; see also Drama and Agents

Teatreneu
c/ Terol 26-28, 08012 **Barcelona**
Tel: 93-284 7733 Fax: 93-213 0340
managing director Josep Salvatella
Venue type: Italian-style theatre *Capacity:* main hall 375, amphitheatre 100 *Policy:* own productions, also hire the theatre to groups *Arts types:* theatre, dance and music
Comments: own company 'Teatreneu' which contracts actors for each production; 'Theatre in English for Students'; newly refurbished building

Villarroel Teatre
c/ Villarroel 87, 08011 **Barcelona**
Tel: 93-451 1234 Fax: 93-451 6566
Internet: www.barcelonet.com/villarroel
E-Mail: villarroel.teatre@teleline.es
gerente Adolfo Bras; directores artístico Angel Alonso; press Begoña Calabrés
Venue type: Italian style theatre *Capacity:* 520 *Policy:* present, produce *Arts types:* theatre, dance, small musicals

Euskalduna Jaurejia – Palacio de Congresos y de la Música de Bilbao
Abandoibarra Etorbidea 4, 48009 **Bilbao**
Tel: 94-403 5000 Fax: 94-403 5001
Internet: www.bizkaia.net/pcongresos
E-Mail: pcongresos@bizkaia.net
director general Jon Ortuzar
Venue type: music and congresses centre, comprising several halls *Capacity:* Auditorium 2200, sala A1 600, sala A2 300, sala A3 150, 3 halls of 100 each, 5 halls of 50 each, 3 press halls, exhibition space, full service areas *Policy:* rent *Arts types:* music, conferences, visual arts, congresses
Comments: owned and managed by Diputación Foral de Vizcaya; funded by Basque Government and European Community; due to have opened Dec 1998; telephone and fax numbers may change, no further details available at time of going to print

La Fundición
c/ Francisco Macía nº 1-3, 48014 **Bilbao**
Tel: 94-475 3327 Fax: 94-475 9115
E-Mail: lafundicion.aretoa@jet.es
directora Laura Etxebarría
Venue type: Italian style theatre *Capacity:* 100
Policy: present *Arts types:* mainly contemporary dance
Comments: member of Coordinadora de Salas Alternativas; season runs Oct-June; see also National Organisations

Teatro Arriaga
Plaza Arriaga s/n, 48005 **Bilbao**
Tel: 94-416 3533/3244/3333 Fax: 94-416 3185/6112
director general t.b.a.; relaciones públicas Xabier Landaburu; producciones José María Viteri
Capacity: (including 369 with restricted visibility) 1628
Arts types: theatre, opera, zarzuela, ballet, concerts
Comments: coproductions

Teatro Ayala
Manuel Allende 18, 48010 **Bilbao**
Tel: 94-421 2260 Fax: 94-410 4454
empresario Antonio Ochoa González-Echávarri
Venue type: Italian-style theatre *Capacity:* 924 *Arts types:* comedy, cinema, symphonic music, theatre, dance

Teatro Coliseo Albia
Alameda de Orquijo 13, 48008 **Bilbao**
Tel: 94-423 2148/415 3954 Fax: 94-423 1001
director Alesandro Beitia
Venue type: Italian style theatre *Capacity:* 1975 *Policy:* rent *Arts types:* theatre, dance, ballet, music

Teatro Los Gigantillos
c/ Asunción de Ntra. Sra 3 bajo, **Burgos**
Tel: 947-218 653 Fax: 947-202 200
director José Luis Karraskedo Heras; presidente José María Costa Acha; gerente-administrador Asunción Garnica Rodríguez
Venue type: theatre *Capacity:* 100 *Arts types:* puppets and children's theatre *Comments:* museum, workshop and theatre for glove and rod puppets

Gran Teatro
c/ San Antón s/n, 10003 **Cáceres**
Tel: 927-212 949/215 651 Fax: 927-212 949
Internet: www.bme.es/granteatro
E-Mail: granteatro@bme.es
gerente Roberto Garcia del Rio; director en funciones Marceliano Solís Romero
Venue type: theatre *Capacity:* 675 *Policy:* present *Arts types:* drama, theatre, dance, music, opera, video
Comments: belongs to: Junta de Extremadura, Ayuntamiento de Caceres, Diputacion Provincial, Caja de Extremadura; presents 'WOMAD' and organises Festival de Teatro Clásico de Cáceres; see also Festivals

Gran Teatro Falla
Plaza de Falla, s/n, 11003 **Cádiz**
Tel: 956-220 828/34/94 Fax: 956-220 354
gerente Vicente Ferrer
Capacity: 1214 *Policy:* present *Arts types:* theatre, music, opera, cinema *Comments:* management: Fundación Municipal de Cultura, Isabel la Católica 12, 11004 Cadiz
Tel: 956-221 680/211 123, Fax: 956-222 051

Teatro Principal
Avda Esponceda nº 10, 12004 **Castellón**
Tel: 964-212 600 Fax: 964-251 785
director Armando Alegre Gomez
Venue type: multi-purpose auditorium *Capacity:* 1000
Arts types: theatre, zarzuela, opera, ballet, classical music, concerts, jazz

Teatro Lope de Vega de Chinchón
Plaza del Palacio s/n, 28370 **Chinchón (Madrid)**
Tel: 91-893 5444 Fax: 91-894 0887
Internet: www.ayuntamientochinchon.com
Venue type: Italian-style theatre *Capacity:* 420 *Policy:* rent
Arts types: drama, cinema *Comments:* management Comunidad de Madrid and administrated by Ayuntamiento de Chinchón, Plaza Mayor 3, 28370 Chinchón, Tel: 91-894 0084

Teatro Municipal Quijano de Ciudad Real
Ciruela 9, 13001 **Ciudad Real**
Tel: 926-223 855/252 291 Fax: 926-252 291 (cultura)
tecnica de cultura Pilar Cascante
Venue type: theatre *Capacity:* 966 *Arts types:* theatre, cinema, music, dance *Comments:* management: Ayto de Ciudad Real, Plaza Mayor 1, 13001 Ciudad Real, Tel: 926-211 044/196; responsible: Concejalia Municipal de Cultura, c/Prado 4, 13001 Ciudad Real

Teatro Municipal Diéguez de Colmenar de Oreja
Convento 5, 28380 **Colmenar de Oreja (Madrid)**
Tel: 91-894 3030 Fax: 91-894 3198
Venue type: theatre *Capacity:* 555 *Arts types:* drama, all types *Comments:* administrated by Comunidad de Madrid y Ayuntamiento de Colmenar de Oreja, Plaza Mayor 1, 28380 Colmenar de Oreja

Gran Teatro de Córdoba
Avenida Gran Capitan 3, 14008 **Córdoba**
Tel: 957-480 237/479 238 Fax: 957-487 494
director del teatro Manuel Angel Jiménez Arévalo; jefe de producción Ana Linares; prensa Carmen Ruiz; relaciones públicas Pablo Domíneuez; imagen Jose Luis Priego; jefe tecnico José Antonio Figuerola
Venue type: theatro a la Italiana *Capacity:* 946 *Policy:* rent *Arts types:* theatre, music, including opera, dance, cinema *Comments:* management: Fundacion Publica municipal del Gran Teatro, Avenida Gran Capitan 3, 14008 Córdoba; home of Festival de Guitarra International (July)

Palacio Revillagigedo – International Art Centre
Palacio Revillagigedo – Centro Internacional de Arte
Plaza del Marqués 2, 33201 **Gijón**
Tel: 98-534 6921 Fax: 98-535 8123
director Regina Rubio Martinez; co-ordination Adelaida Bermudez
Venue type: 18th C. Palace
Capacity: Colegiata de San Juan Bautista 200 *Arts types:* theatre, music, dance, exhibitions *Comments:* owned by Caja de Asturias, Plaza de la Escandalera 2, 33003 Oviedo, Tel: 98-510 2222

Sala Quiquilimón
Pedro Duro, 13 bajo, 33206 **Gijón**
Tel: 98-535 7318 Fax: 98-517 1013
gerente/administradors/distribución Rosa Garnacho; director de programación y espectaculos Jesús Sánchez; coordinadora pedagógica Margarita Rodríguez, José Luis García; director técnico Carmelo Jesús Plágaro
Capacity: 200
Policy: rent and own productions & programmes
Arts types: theatre, cinema, music, recitals
Comments: management: 'Producciones Quiquilimón'; home of theatre company: 'Quiquilimón'

Teatro Jovellanos
Paseo de Begoña, 11, 33201 **Gijón**
Tel: 98-517 2409 Fax: 98-534 9309
Internet: www.teatrojovellanos.com
E-Mail: info@teatrojovellanos.com
presidente Daniel Gutierrez Granda; director/gerente Miguel Rodríguez Acevedo; coordinador técnico Luis Cascallana Ruiz; jefe de prensa Carmen Fernández
Venue type: theatre *Capacity:* 1200
Arts types: theatre, concerts, dance, pop, rock
Comments: office: c/ Casimiro Velasco 23, 33201 Gijón (Asturias); management: Entidad Mercantil Artístico Musical Teatro Municipal Jovellanos de Gijón S.A.

Centro Cultural Manuel de Falla
Paseo de los Martires s/n, Alhambra, 18009 **Granada**
Tel: 958-222 188/228 289
Fax: 958-228 289
director Jose Antionio Cantón García
Venue type: auditorium *Capacity:* 2 halls totalling 1275
Arts types: concerts, Oct-May: classical music
Comments: also organise 'Archivo Manuel de Falla' and own programme; Curso Int 'Manuel de Falla', Orquesta Giudad de Granada, Casa Museo Manuel de Falla; see also Orchestras

Palacio de Exposiciones y Congresos
Paseo del Violón s/n, 18006 **Granada**
Tel: 958-246 700 Fax: 958-246 702
Internet: www.siapi.es/palacio
E-Mail: palacio@pcgr.org
director J. Luis G. Candal
Venue type: multi-purpose
Capacity: Sala Garcia Lorca 2000, Sala Falla 580
Policy: rent, present *Arts types:* concerts, dance, conferences, music, opera, theatre

Gran Teatro de Huelva
Vazquez Lopez 13, 21001 **Huelva**
Tel: 959-245 703/282 813 Fax: 959-282 820
jefe tecnico José Antonio Melo
Venue type: theatre *Capacity:* 644 *Policy:* present, produce *Arts types:* theatre, jazz, dance (including ballet), music etc, new age, zarzuela, cinema
Comments: closed from June 30th – Sept 30th; summer venues: Foro Iberoamericano de la Rabida 3000 (open-air); management: Ayuntamiento de Huelva, Gran Via s/n, 21001 Huelva

Centro Cutural Amaia
Plaza Pio XII, s/n, 20300 **Irún**
Tel: 943-614 022 (theatre)/649 200 (ayuntamiento)
Fax: 943-626 007
jefe del area de educación, cultura Yokin Ormazabal; animador cultural Javier Garcia
Venue type: multi-purpose venue, plus dance hall and conference hall 70 *Capacity:* 600 *Policy:* rent, present, co-produce *Arts types:* music, drama, dance *Comments:* administrated by Ayuntamiento de Irún: Ayuntamiento de Irun, Plaza San Juan, 1, 20303 Irun, Tel: 943-629 200

Teatro Villamarta
Plaza Romero Martínez s/n, 11402 **Jerez de la Frontera**
Tel: 956-329 313 Fax: 956-329 508
director Francisco López; director de comunicación Jose Ángel Bermejo
Venue type: Italian style theatre *Capacity:* 1300
Policy: programme, rent *Arts types:* opera, concerts, theatre, music *Comments:* season from Sept-July; see also Opera

Coliseum de la Cornña
Av. Alfonso Molina s/n, 15008 **La Coruña**
Tel: 981-133 190 Fax: 981-136 001
presidente IMCE J. L. Méndez Romeu; coord. prensa IMCE Ramon García Barros
Venue type: multi-purpose *Capacity:* 7000 *Policy:* own programme, rent *Arts types:* all types *Comments:* IMCE: Instituto Municipal Coruña Espectáculos

Palacio de Congresos Teatro Nacional de la Opera
Glorieta de América s/n, 15004 **La Coruña**
Tel: 981-140 404 Fax: 981-261 284
Internet: www.palacongres.com
E-Mail: recepcion@palacongres.com
director Enrique Pena
Venue type: modern *Capacity:* 11 halls: large 1800, small 200 *Policy:* rent, own programming *Arts types:* all types

Teatro Colón La Coruña
Avenida de la Marina s/n, 15003 **La Coruña**
Tel: 981-229 213 Fax: 981-229 357
manager Luis Seoane Seijás
Venue type: theatre *Capacity:* 1338 *Policy:* rent *Arts types:* film, opera, dance, ballet, drama *Comments:* management: Empresa Fraga de Espectáculos S.A., c/o Jorge Juan 51, 3 izq, 28001 Madrid, Tel: 91-435 7005

Teatro Rosalía de Castro
Riego de Agua 37, 15003 **La Coruña**
Tel: 981-203 286/133 190 (coliseum) Fax: 981-224 775
presidente IMCE J. L. Méndez Romeu; coord. prensa IMCE Ramon García Barros
Venue type: Italian style theatre *Capacity:* 700 *Policy:* own programme, rent *Arts types:* theatre, dance, musical, opera *Comments:* recently refurbished; IMCE: Instituto Municipal Coruña Espectáculos

Auditorio Alfredo Kraus
Playa de Las Canteras, s/n,
35010 **Las Palmas de Gran Canaria**
Tel: 928-491 770 Fax: 928-491 853
Internet: www.auditorio-alfredokraus.com
E-Mail: info@auditorio-alfredokraus.com
director general D. Antonio Castellano Auyanet; director de programación D. Fausto Bethencourt Morell; jefe de los servicios técnicos D. Juan Carlos Ramallo Ramos
Venue type: modern style theatre *Capacity:* sala sinfónica 1664, sala de cámara 322 *Policy:* own programme, rent *Arts types:* music, theatre, opera

Centro Insular de Cultura
Pérez Galdós 53, 35002 **Las Palmas de Gran Canaria**
Tel: 928-371 912 Fax: 928-364 239
coordinator dance & theatre Oscar Millares
Capacity: 250 *Arts types:* theatre, music, contemporary ballet *Comments:* funded by Cabildo Insular

Teatro Pérez Galdós
Plaza de Estagno 1, 35002 **Las Palmas de Gran Canaria**
Tel: 928-361 509/368 993 Fax: 928-368 993
administrador Juan Molero Suárez
Capacity: 1400 *Policy:* rent *Arts types:* theatre, music, opera, dance *Comments:* management: Dept de Cultura, Ayto de Las Palmas, Leon y Castillo 270, 30005 Las Palma, Tel:928-446 000; Festival de Musica, April 10th-June 10th – Festival de Opera, Nov 15th-Dec 15th – Festival de Zarzuela; see also Festivals and Promoters

Auditorium Municipal
Avda. de la Paz 11, 26071 **Logroño**
Tel: 941-277 023 Fax: 941-231 397
E-Mail: aytoalc@eniac.eniac.es
concejal de festejos Eugenio de la Riva Ibañez
Capacity: 798 *Arts types:* theatre, music, dance, cinema, lectures *Comments:* belongs to Area de Cultura del Ayuntamiento de Logroño; space for regional companies

Sala de Cultura Gonzalo de Berceo
Calvo Sotelo 11, 26003 **Logroño**
Tel: 941-291 280/100 Fax: 941-291 261
director t.b.a.
Venue type: Italian theatre *Capacity:* 215 *Policy:* present
Arts types: theatre, cinema, concerts, conferences
Comments: administrated by Consejería de Cultura de la C.C.A.A. de la Rioja, Portales 2, 26071 Logroño, portales-2; all events in the theatre are free, except the charity events; colaborate in Festival Actual (January)

Teatro Bretón de los Herreros
Ayuntamiento de Logroño, Avda. de la Paz 11,
26004 **Logroño**
Tel: 941-243 222 (town hall, ext 133)/207 231 (theatre)
Fax: 941-234 932/231 394 (theatre)
director general Jorge Quirante Sánchez; secretario administrativo José Luis Rubio; jefe de prensa y relaciones públicas Ana Bengoa
Venue type: traditional Italian-style theatre *Capacity:* 988
Arts types: theatre, music (incl. opera and zarzuela), dance, film, exhibitions *Comments:* venue address: Bretón de los Herreros 11, 26001 Logroño; owned and managed by: Town Hall (Ayuntamiento de Logroño)

Teatro Guerra de Lorca
Plaza de Calderon de la Barca s/n, 30800 **Lorca (Murcia)**
Tel: 968-460 212 Fax: 968-460 212
Internet: www.zoom.es/~beraldo/
E-Mail: beraldo@zoom.es
director Ginés Bayones Pérez-Muelas
Venue type: theatre *Capacity:* 518 *Policy:* own production, present *Arts types:* theatre, music, dance *Comments:* 2 own theatre companies: one adults' (Compañía Estable Teatro Guerra de Lorca) and one children's; built in 1861; horse-shoe shape; management: Ayuntamiento de Lorca (Murcia); see also Drama

Auditorio Nacional de Música
c/ Principe de Vergara 146, 28002 **Madrid**
Tel: 91-337 0140 Fax: 91-337 0300
Internet: www.auditorionacional.mcu.es
E-Mail: auditorio.nacional@inaem.mcu.es
managing director Isabel Vázquez; public relations officer Laura Garcia Ruiz
Venue type: 2 concert halls *Capacity:* sympophonic hall 2293, chamber hall 692 *Arts types:* symphony, chamber music *Comments:* home of Orquesta y Coro Nacionales de España (OCNE) and Joven Orquesta Nacional de España (JONDE); see also Orchestras, Promoters & Festivals

Casa de América
Paseo de Recoletos 2, 28001 **Madrid**
Tel: 91-595 4800/24 (prensa)
Fax: 91-595 4828 (prensa)
Internet: www.casamerica.es
E-Mail: prensa@casamerica.es
director general Tomas Rodriguez Pantoja; director de ateneo americano Iñigo Ramírez del Haro; director de tribuna americana Manuel Piñeiro; jefe departamento de comunicación Laureano Suárez del Canto
Venue type: multi-purpose *Capacity:* Amphitheatre 175-375, Miguel de Cervantes 60, Sala Bolivar 80, Cinema 80, Ambassador's Hall (standing only) *Policy:* own production *Arts types:* music, theatre, cinema and other events related to Iberoamerican culture *Comments:* promoters of Latin American culture in Spain; see also Promoters

Centro Cultural de la Villa
Plaza Colón s/n, Jardines del Descubrimiento, 28001 **Madrid**
Tel: 91-576 6080 (centralita)/4551 (prensa)
Fax: 91-576 1438
director Antonio Guirau Sena; coordinador de promoción e imagen Eugenio Cano
Venue type: theatre, conference hall *Capacity:* Sala I 776, Sala II 288 *Policy:* presents own cultural programme *Arts types:* Sala 1: theatre, opera, zarzuela, chamber recitals, Spanish dance and ballet; Sala 2: lectures, theatre, music, seminars *Comments:* management: Ayuntamiento de Madrid, Area de Cultura Educación, Juventud y Deporte, Pza de la Villa 4, 28005 Madrid

Centro Cultural del Conde Duque
Conde Duque 9-11, 28015 **Madrid**
Tel: 91-588 5285/86 Fax: 91-588 5800
press & pr Paula Criado
Capacity: Salón de actos 270, Auditorio 286, two courtyards for open air performances *Policy:* present, programme *Arts types:* music, theatre, dance, visual arts, home of festivals: San Isidro, Veranos de la Villa, Festival de Jazz de Otoño *Comments:* owned and managed by Municipal Government: Ayuntamiento de Madrid; has permanent collection of contemporary art

Centro Cultural Galileo
Fernando el Católico 35, 28015 **Madrid**
Tel: 91-593 2230/00/85 Fax: 91-593 4213
Venue type: flexible space *Capacity:* 320, smaller space for chamber music 147 *Policy:* programme, present *Arts types:* theatre, classical music, jazz, rock, contemporary and classical dance *Comments:* owned and managed by Municipal Government: Ayuntamiento de Madrid

Círculo de Bellas Artes
c/ Alcalá 42, 28014 **Madrid**
Tel: 91-360 5400/08 Fax: 91-531 0552/523 2812
E-Mail: areas@c-bellasartes
director general César Antonio Molina; relaciones públicas Javier Lanza; sub-director de gestion cultural Claude Bussac
Capacity: various salas including main hall 500, small hall 250 *Arts types:* contemporary music, theatre, workshops, exhibitions, lectures *Comments:* funded by Ayuntamiento, Comunidad de Madrid, Iberia

El Canto de la Cabra
c/ San Gregorio 8, 28004 **Madrid**
Tel: 91-310 4222 Fax: 91-308 3868
E-Mail: elcantodelacabra@keltia-wss.net
directors Elisa Gálvez, Juan Úbeda
Capacity: 60 (winter), 120 (summer) *Policy:* present, produce, co-produce *Arts types:* theatre, dance *Comments:* member of Coordinadora de Salas Alternativas; also organise courses and workshops; see also National Organisations

El Montacargas
Antillón 19, 28011 **Madrid**
Tel: 91-526 1173 Fax: 91-463 2207
direccion Manuel Fernández, Aurora Navarro
Capacity: 60 *Policy:* present, produce, co-produce *Arts types:* theatre, poetry, story-telling *Comments:* member of Coordinadora de Salas Alternativas, see also National Organisations

Espada de Madera
c/ Calvario 21, 28012 **Madrid**
Tel: 91-528 0435 Fax: 91-420 0672/539 5080
director artistico Antonio Diaz-Florian; gerente Ana Gomez
Venue type: converted old garage *Capacity:* 64 *Arts types:* theatre – baroque acting *Comments:* bilingual group promoting Spanish & French plays; managed by Espada de Madera Ltd along with another theatre in Paris called Teatre de L'Epée de Bois, Tel: +33 1-4808 3974

Fundación Teatro de la Abadía – Centro de Estudios y Creación Escénicos de la Comunidad de Madrid
Miembro de la Unión de los Teatros de Europa (U.T.E.), c/ Fernández de los Ríos 42, 28015 **Madrid**
Tel: 91-448 1181/1338 Fax: 91-448 1449
E-Mail: abadia@ctv.es
director artistico José Luis Gómez; gerente Isabel Navarro; director técnico Josep Solbes; jefe de producción Miguel Ojea; jefa de prensa Isabel Juanco
Venue type: sala Juan de la Cruz (performances in a reformed church); sala José Luis Alonso – performances in an italian space *Capacity:* sala Juan de la Cruz 300, sala José Luis Alonso 206 *Policy:* own performances and also invite other companies and festivals, and rent *Arts types:* theatre, dance, music, opera, puppets, poetry *Comments:* see also Drama

Marquina Theatre
Teatro Marquina
c/ Prim 11, 28004 **Madrid**
Tel: 91-532 8554/3186/531 6535 Fax: 91-522 5711
E-Mail: adeima@navta.es
director Alejandro Colubi (91-532 3186); director artistico Jose Francisco Tamarit
Venue type: Italian-style theatre *Capacity:* 500 *Policy:* present at own risk, share risk with other promoters *Arts types:* drama, theatre, comedy *Comments:* wheelchair-access; reopened Oct. 1997 after extensive refurbishment; season runs from Sept-June

Nuevo Apolo – Teatro Musical de Madrid
Plaza Tirso de Molina 1, 28012 **Madrid**
Tel: 91-369 0637 Fax: 91-369 0637
gerente Emilio Rodriguez
Venue type: Italian style theatre *Capacity:* 1300 *Policy:* produce, co-produce, occasionally rent *Arts types:* theatre, dance, music, including opera and ballet *Comments:* co-managed by Focus (q.v.)

Real Academia de Bellas Artes de San Fernando
Alcalá 13, 28014 **Madrid**
Tel: 91-532 1546/1549/522 1491 Fax: 91-523 1599
director de la academia Ramón González de Amezua; director del museo Antonio Bonet Correa; manager of exhibitions & cultural acts Ascension Circuelos Gonzalo
Venue type: concert hall *Capacity:* 220 *Arts types:* music, conferences, concerts *Comments:* weekly concerts of all sorts, though less frequently at some times of year; funded by Ministerio Educacion y Cultura

Sala Cuarta Pared
Ercilla 17, 28005 **Madrid**
Tel: 91-517 2317/473 9666 Fax: 91-517 1144
direccion y programación Javier García Yagüe; gerencia Francisco García; promoción Amador González, Eva Gómez; secretaria Cristina García; coordinación técnica Richard Vázquez
Capacity: 172 *Policy:* present, rent *Arts types:* theatre, dance *Comments:* runs courses; resident company Cuarta Pared; see also Drama

Sala del Mirador
c/ Doctor Fourquet 31, 28012 **Madrid**
Tel: 91-539 5767/528 9504 (escuela) Fax: 91-539 5767
director Cristina Rota
Venue type: multi-purpose theatre *Capacity:* 160 *Policy:* productions with own company, co-productions *Arts types:* independent theatre *Comments:* home of Grupo de Representaciones Teatrales: Nuevo Repertorio, and theatre school Estudio Cristina Rota; engaged in a project to develop productions with theatre professionals from Estudio Cristina Rota; see also Drama

Sala Ensayo 100
Raimundo Lulio 20, 28010 **Madrid**
Tel: 91-447 9486 Fax: 91-447 9486
Internet: www.usuarios.iponet.es/ensayo
E-Mail: ensayo100@iponet.es
director artístico Jorge Eines
Venue type: flexible space *Capacity:* 90 (varies) *Policy:* produce, co-produce, present *Arts types:* theatre, poetry *Comments:* member of Coordinadora de Salas Alternativas, see also National Organisations; resident company Ensayo 100, see also Drama

Sala Triángulo
c/ Zurita 20, 28012 **Madrid**
Tel: 91-530 6891 Fax: 91-539 2518
Internet: www.salatriangulo.com
E-Mail: salatriangulo@salatriangulo.com
gerente y director artístico Alfonso Pindado; secretario administrativo Melanie Pindado, Natalia Ortega
Capacity: Hall A 177, Hall B 45, Hall C 60 *Policy:* present, own productions *Arts types:* experimental theatre, dance, theatre for children, café teatro *Comments:* own company Triángulo Teatro (7 actor)s and La Banda de Crisofilas; productions and coproductions with European companies; organises: Muestra Alternativa Internacional de Teatro; see also Festivals & Drama

Teatro Albéniz
Paz 11, 28012 **Madrid**
Tel: 91-521 9998/522 0200
Fax: 91-522 7584
directora Teresa Vico
Capacity: 1040 *Arts types:* theatre, dance, opera, music *Comments:* management: Comunidad Autonoma de Madrid, Consejeria de Educación y Cultura, Plaza de España 8, 28008 Madrid, Tel: 91-580 2500

Teatro Alcázar
Alcalá 20, 28014 **Madrid**
Tel: 91-532 0616/522 7742
Fax: 91-523 3298
gerente Isabel G. Cuadra; director Juan José Arteche
Venue type: Italian-style theatre *Capacity:* 803 *Policy:* rent *Arts types:* drama, zarzuela, musicals

Teatro Alfil
Pez 10, 28004 **Madrid**
Tel: 91-521 4541(admin)/5827 (box office)
Fax: 91-521 6879
management/artistic direction Yllana Producciones
Venue type: theatre *Capacity:* 250 *Policy:* own production, present, present with split box-office *Arts types:* focused on comic theatre *Comments:* home of Yllana (drama), and the International Festival of Comic Theatre; managed by: Producciones Yllana, c/Jesus 20, 4° A, 07003 Palma de Mallorca, Tel: 971-207 410, Fax: 971-202 157; see also Drama and Festivals

Teatro Bellas Artes
Marqués de Casa Riera 2, 28014 **Madrid**
Tel: 91-532 4438 Fax: 91-522 3181
representante Antonio Diaz Martinez; director artístico José Tamayo
Venue type: theatre *Capacity:* 455 *Policy:* present & own production *Arts types:* classical drama *Comments:* home of Compañia Titular Lopez de Vega, theatre company: Lopez de Vega Producciones S.L.; see also Drama

Teatro Calderón
Atocha 18, 28012 **Madrid**
Tel: 91-402 3601
Comments: venue closed awaiting announcement of when re-opening; no further details known at time of going to print

Teatro de la Comedia
Compañía Nacional de Teatro Clásico, Príncipe 14, 28012 **Madrid**
Tel: 91-532 7928 Fax: 91-522 4690
director Rafael Perez Sierra
Venue type: Italian-style theatre *Capacity:* Teatro de la Comedia 600 *Policy:* own productions *Arts types:* classic Spanish theatre *Comments:* owned & managed by INAEM, home of the Compañía Nacional de Teatro Clásico; see also Drama

Teatro de la Zarzuela
Jovellanos 4, 28014 **Madrid**
Tel: 91-524 5400 Fax: 91-429 7157/523 3059 (press)
director artistico Emilio Sagi; secretaría de dirección Lola San Juan/Esther López; director técnico Victor Naranjo; jefe de prensa y relaciones públicas Angel Barreda; secretaría de prensa Pilar Albizu; coordinador artístico Manuel Guijar; director gerente José Luis Morata; directora de producción Isabel Gonzàlez; jefa de abonos y taquillas Paloma Vázquez
Capacity: (including 108 with restricted visibility) 1250 *Arts types:* Madrid's main zarzuela, ballet *Comments:* founded 1856, titular of the Teatro de la Zarzuela: Orquesta de la Comunidad de Madrid (q.v)

Teatro de Madrid
Avda de la Ilustración s/n, 28029 **Madrid**
Tel: 91-740 5274/5292 Fax: 91-740 5512
director José Tamayo; dirección artística y administración general José Manuel Garrido; producción James Bartek; comunicación Manuel Lagos; gerencia Mercedes Serrano
Venues type: Italian style *Capacity:* 700 *Policy:* present *Arts types:* dance *Comments:* now managed by Artibus

Teatro Español
Spanish Theatre
c/ Principe 25, 28012 **Madrid**
Tel: 91-429 6293/0318 Fax: 91-429 6250
director Gustavo Perez Puig; director adjunto Mara Recateo
Venue type: Italian style theatre *Capacity:* 733 *Policy:* comedy – of mainly Spanish authors *Arts types:* theatre, comedy *Comments:* property of Ayuntamiento de Madrid; it is the oldest theatre in Spain, dating from the 16th century

Teatro Estudio de Madrid
Cabeza 14, 28012 **Madrid**
Tel: 91-539 6447 Fax: 91-539 6447/530 9178
Internet: wainer.hypernet.net
directora artística Marina Wainer
Capacity: 50 *Arts types:* theatre, courses
Comments: theatre library; member of Coordinadora de Salas Alternativas; rehearsal space for hire; see also National Organisations

Teatro Fígaro
Doctor Cortezo 5, 28012 **Madrid**
Tel: 91-369 4953/4916 Fax: 91-369 4916
director Angel García Moreno
Venue type: Italian style theatre *Capacity:* 649 *Policy:* produce and co-produce *Arts types:* contemporary theatre

Teatro La Latina
Plaza de la Cebada 2, 28005 **Madrid**
Tel: 91-365 0671/2835(ticket office)
Fax: 91-366 6208
gerente Angel Gutierrez Hervas
Venue type: Italian-style theatre
Capacity: 1060 *Policy:* rent, own productions
Arts types: comedy music revues

Teatro Lara
c/o Pigmalión, Gran Vía 61, 8ª, 28013 **Madrid**
Tel: 91-548 4000 (admin)/531 2166 (theatre)
Fax: 91-541 2199 (admin)/521 0552 (theatre)
E-Mail: pigmalion@retemail.es
director Luis Ramírez
Capacity: 448 *Policy:* produce, present *Arts types:* music, theatre, dance *Comments:* venue address: Corredera Baja de San Pablo 15, 28004 Madrid; managed by: Pigmalión – Productora de Espectáculos; see also Agents & Producers

Teatro Lope de Vega
c/o Pigmalión, Gran Vía 61, 8ª, 28013 **Madrid**
Tel: 91-548 4000 (admin)/7091 (theatre)
Fax: 91-541 2199 (admin)/547 2011 (theatre)
E-Mail: pigmalion@retemail.es
director Luis Ramírez
Capacity: 1465 *Policy:* produce, present
Arts types: music, theatre, dance
Comments: venue address: Gran vía 57, 28013 Madrid; managed by: Pigmalión – Productora de Espectáculos; see also Agents & Producers

Teatro Maravillas
Manuela Malasaña 6, 28004 **Madrid**
Tel: 91-446 7194 Fax: 91-447 0032
director Enrique Cornejo
Venue type: theatre *Capacity:* 875
Policy: rent, own production
Arts types: theatre, music, dance
Comments: theatre closed for refurbishment

Teatro María Guerrero
Tamayo y Baus 4, 28004 **Madrid**
Tel: 91-310 2949 Fax: 91-319 3836
director Juan Carlos Perez de la Fuente; director de produccion Julio Alvarez; jefe de prensa Jose Ramon Fernandez
Venue type: theatre (Italian style) *Capacity:* 700 *Arts types:* drama *Comments:* home of Centro Dramático Nacional, who also co-produce with other companies; see also Drama

Teatro Olimpia
Pl. de Lavapiés s/n, 28012 **Madrid**
Tel: 91-467 7662/527 4622
Fax: 91-467 0666
director Juan Carlos Perez de la Fuente; producción Julio Alvarez; directora adjunta Rosario Calleja
Venue type: Italian-stlye theatre, converted cinema
Capacity: 500 *Arts types:* contemporary art forms: theatre, dance, modern dance *Comments:* home of Centro Dramatico Nacional (CDN) with Teatro Maria Guerrero; temporarily closed for refurbishment

Teatro Permanente de Títeres del Retiro
Parque del Retiro, (entrada Plaza de la Independencia), 28013 **Madrid**
Tel: 91-577 1581/813 2533/2099/559 7540
Fax: 91-577 1581/813 2533/2099/559 7540
presidente Asociación Cultural Rayuela Luis Ghiringhelli (91-577 1581)
Venue type: open-air theatre *Capacity:* 300 *Policy:* present, produce *Arts types:* all types puppets
Comments: home of the Fiesta del Títere de Los Veranos de la Villa (puppet festival); managed by Asociación Cultural Rayuela; formed by 4 puppet companies: Teatro La Gaviota, Marimba Marionetas, La Mar de Marionetas & Hilando Títeres; address: c/ Jerez 476 – Urb. Calypo Fado, 28600 Navalcarnero (Madrid); see also Festivals, Puppets and Promoters

Teatro Pradillo
c/Pradillo 12, 28002 **Madrid**
Tel: 91-416 9011 Fax: 91-416 9968
programador y director Juan Muñóz Rebollo; administración Javier Roríguez
Venue type: theatre *Capacity:* 120 *Policy:* rent, own productions *Arts types:* contemporary dance, children's theatre, alternative theatre
Comments: home of La Tartana – Teatro de Títeres; see also Drama and Puppets

Teatro Real
Plaza de Oriente s/n, 28013 **Madrid**
Tel: 91-516 0600 Fax: 91-516 0651/72
Internet: www.teatro-real.com
E-Mail: info@teatro-real.com
director Juan Cambreleng; director artístico y musical Luis Antonio García Navarro; jefe de prensa Juan Marchán
Venue type: Italian-style theatre *Capacity:* 1742 *Policy:* produce, co-produce, present *Arts types:* opera, ballet, concerts *Comments:* managed by: Fundación del Teatro Lírico; see also Opera

Teatro Reina Victoria
Carrera de San Jerónimo 24, 28014 **Madrid**
Tel: 91-429 5890/1
director Delfina Muñoz Lusarreta
Venue type: theatre *Capacity:* 988 *Policy:* rent *Arts types:* comedy, drama

Teatro San Pol
Pl. San Pol de Mar 1, 28008 **Madrid**
Tel: 91-541 9089/547 9422 Fax: 91-547 9946
E-Mail: jfischtelsanpol@compuserve.com
director gerente y artístico Julio Jaime Fischtel; jefe de prensa Ana María Boudeguer, Natasha Fischtel
Venue type: theatre *Capacity:* 500 *Arts types:* children's theatre, musical theatre, drama

Teatro Municipal Miguel de Cervantes
C/ Ramos Marin s/n, 29012 **Málaga**
Tel: 95-222 4109/00/0237
Fax: 95-221 2993/222 4545
Internet: www.teatrocervantes.com
E-Mail: info@teatrocervantes.net
director Salomón Castiel; producción Francisco Rodríguez; comunicación Andrés Merodio
Venue type: theatre *Capacity:* 1171
Policy: own opera and zarzuela productions, rent *Arts types:* theatre, dance, music, opera, zarzuela *Comments:* organize several festivals

Sala Trajano
Muza 60, 06800 **Mérida**
Tel: 924-381 222/300 162 (junta de extremadura)/313 955 (theatre) Fax: 924-381 313
director centro dramático y musical Carmelo Sayago Hernández; director gral Onorio Blasco Puerto; consejero Francisco Muñoz Ramirez
Capacity: 300 *Arts types:* dance, music, theatre
Comments: owned by Junta de Extremadura; managed by Dirección General de Promoción Cultural, Junta de Extremandura (Almendralejo 14, 06800 Mérida); see also National & Regional Ministry

Teatro de Mérida
c/ Jose Ramon Melida s/n, 06800 **Mérida**
Tel: 924-312 530 Fax: 924-313 363
E-Mail: cmerida@redestb.es
gerente Jose Maria Soriano Llamazares; director Mº Del Mar Lozano Bartolozzi
Capacity: 7000 *Policy:* rent *Arts types:* theatre, dance, music (classical) *Comments:* managed by: Consorcio Ciudat Monumental de Merida, c/ Reyes Huertas, Entre Nº 5, 06800 Merida (Badajoz), Tel: 924-312 024

Auditorio y Centro de Congresos Región de Murcia
Avda. 1º de Mayo s/n, 30006 **Murcia**
Tel: 968-341 060 Fax: 968-342 968
Internet: www.auditoriomurcia.org
producción Antonio Bautísta; jefa de sala Ma. Isabel Fernández-Serrano; prog. musica José F. Burgos, Francisco Martín; especial prog. Mª José Marín
Venue type: 11 halls *Capacity:* 469, 1800, 150 *Comments:* also exhibitions hall

Aula de Cultura del Centro Cultural Caja de Ahorros del Mediterraneo
c/ Salzillo 7, 30001 **Murcia**
Tel: 968-228 565 Fax: 968-228 528
director centro Mariano Sanchez Gil; jefe territorial de obra social Manuel González-Sicilia Llamas
Venue type: multi-purpose *Capacity:* 396 *Policy:* own programmes, present *Arts types:* theatre, other arts

Teatro Romea
Plaza Julián Romea s/n, 30001 **Murcia**
Tel: 968-355 390 Fax: 968-211 638
Internet: www.forodigital.es/romea
E-Mail: romea@forodigital.es
director general Lorenzo Piriz Carbonell; relacions publicas Ricardo Garcia
Venue type: theatre *Capacity:* 1179 *Policy:* present, rent *Arts types:* dance, theatre *Comments:* belongs to ayuntamiento de Murcia, Glorieta de España, 30001 Murcia, Tel: 968-221 933

Teatro Centro de Navalcarnero
Plaza del Teatro s/n, 28600 **Navalcarnero (Madrid)**
Tel: 91-811 0271/0065/0212
Fax: 91-811 3161
director de patronato Carlos Navarro
Venue type: Italian-style theatre *Capacity:* 385 *Policy:* present *Arts types:* theatre, dance, music
Comments: administrated by Ayuntamiento de Navalcarnero, Plaza de Segovia 1, 28600 Navalcarnero; presents in colaboration with Comunidad de Madrid; home of Festival de Teatro Aficionado de Navalcarnero (organised by Azabache)

Teatro Campoamor
c/ 19 de Julio s/n, 33002 **Oviedo**
Tel: 985-207 355 Fax: 985-200 646
E-Mail: tcampoamor@ayto-oviedo.es
director Carmen Granda Rodriguez
Venue type: Italian-style theatre
Capacity: 1490 *Arts types:* opera festival Sept/Oct, concert cycles all year, Festival de Música, Teatro y Danza de Asturias (May), cinema cycles
Comments: see also Festivals

Auditorium de Palma de Mallorca
Centro para las Artes y Convenciones, Paseo Marítimo 18, 07014 **Palma de Mallorca**
Tel: 971-735 328/730 423 Fax: 971-289 681
Internet: www.auditorium-pm.com
E-Mail: auditorium@auditorium-pm.com
proprieter and director Rafael Ferragut Bonafé
Venue type: 8 halls
Capacity: Sala Magna 1739, Sala Mozart 331, Sala Albéniz 200, Sala Falla 100, Sala Bach 70, Sala Granados 40, Sala Turina 100, Sala Victoria 100
Policy: present, rent *Arts types:* theatre, music, dance, symphony, chamber music, opera, ballet, conventions, conferences *Comments:* management: Rafael Ferragut Bonafé, Federico Garcia Lorca 1, 07014 Palma de Mallorca, Tel: 971-735 328/730 423; Orquesta Sinfónica Ciutat de Balears

Centre de Cultura Sa Nostra
c/ Concepció 12, 07012 **Palma de Mallorca**
Tel: 971-725 210/392 Fax: 971-713 757
E-Mail: Cultura.Palma@osic.sanostra.es
director Albert Ribas Juan; subdirectora Magdalena Aguiló Victory
Venue type: multi-purpose auditorium *Capacity:* 244
Policy: presents own cultural programme *Arts types:* symphony, chamber music, jazz, etc., theatre, dance
Comments: managed by: Departament D'Obra Social i Cultural Caixa de Balears Sa Nostra; see also Promoters

Sa Nau Centro de Arte y Movimiento
c/ dr. Andres Feliu Nº 23, 07010 **Palma de Mallorca**
Tel: 971-201 408 Fax: 971-201 408
director Marga Llobera Luis; director programacion y director area de cine Miguel Ramon Valent; director arte dramatico Adolfo Diez; directora area danza Marga Llobera Luis
Capacity: 2 halls: sala danza 14-16 (rehearsal), sala multimedia 120 *Policy:* open to negotiation, private owned venue *Arts types:* contemporary dance, cinematography, dramatic art, circus, performance
Comments: Sa Nau is a totally private enterprise combining teaching and production

Teatre del Mar
Capità Ramonell y Boix nº 90,
07006 **Palma de Mallorca**
Tel: 971-248 400 Fax: 971-256 110
Internet: www.mallorcaweb.com/teatredelmar
E-Mail: iguanateatre@balearkom.es
director Carles Molinet; presidente Joan Mas
Venue type: flexible *Capacity:* 200 *Policy:* own programme & own productions *Arts types:* drama, music *Comments:* summer drama courses; home of Iguana Teatre; see also Drama

Teatre Sans
Estudi Zero, Sans 5, 07001 **Palma de Mallorca**
Tel: 971-727 166 Fax: 971-723 597
director del teatro Pere Mestre; conseso rector de la escuela Mona Belizan, Pepa Ramon, Pere Mestre
Venue type: theatre, (café-theatre) *Capacity:* Cafè-teatre 90, Sala Negra 45 *Arts types:* independent, contemporary theatre *Comments:* founding member of Coordinadora de salas alternativas; see also Drama

Teatro Municipal de Palma
Paseo Mallorca 9, 07011 **Palma de Mallorca**
Tel: 971-714 745/727 744 (Ayuntamiento)/739 148 (Teatre) Fax: 971-716 474/738 901
E-Mail: cultura@a.palma.es
encargado del teatro Rafael Perello; coordinador Jose Gabriel Pomar Ordinas
Venue type: theatre *Capacity:* 224 *Arts types:* theatre, classical music, cinema, dance *Comments:* owned by Ayuntamiento de Palma de Mallorca

Teatro Principal de Palma de Mallorca
c/ La Riera 2-A, 07003 **Palma de Mallorca**
Tel: 971-713 346/725 548 Fax: 971-725 542
Internet: www.teatreprincipal.com
E-Mail: teatreprincipal@cim.net
director Pedro Noguera; asesora artistico musical Sylvia Corbacho; coordinador de la temporadas de opera y zarzuela Encarnita Grizon; director de los cors dei teatre principal Francesc Bonnin; coordinador de la escola de musica del teatre principal Guillem Grimalt
Venue type: Italian-style theatre
Capacity: 1100 *Arts types:* performing arts *Comments:* funded by Consell Insular de Mallorca, Palau Real 1, 07001 Palma de Mallorca, Tel: 971-173 500; Coro del Teatre Principal 80 voice choir; negotiating coproductions with other theatres; season: March-July; season runs Sept-July; see also Opera

Sala E.N.T. (Escuela Navarra de Teatro)
c/ San Agustín nº5, 31001 **Pamplona**
Tel: 948-229 239 Fax: 948-229 239
E-Mail: escuela@can.es
director Javier Pérez Eguaras; coordinator Patxi Larrea
Venue type: theatre *Capacity:* 300 *Policy:* present, own productions, rent *Arts types:* contemporary theatre *Comments:* member of Coordinadora de Salas Alternativas; alternative theatre programming in Autumn, rent the rest of the time; see also National Organisations

Teatro Gayarre
c/o Fundación Municipal Teatro Gayarre,
Av. Carlos III, 3, 31002 **Pamplona**
Tel: 948-220 139(12-2 pm and 5pm onwards)/212 350
Fax: 948-220 139/212 350
gerente Valentín Redín
Capacity: 786 *Policy:* rent, programme, produce *Arts types:* opera, concerts, theatre, zarzuela, ballet *Comments:* managed by Fundación Municipal Teatro Gayarre, owned by Ayuntamiento de Pamplona

Teatro de Petrer
C/ Gabriel Paya, 03610 **Petrer (Alicante)**
Tel: 96-537 1050 (entralita) Fax: 96-537 6968
E-Mail: adlpetreadip-alicante.es
programador Juan R García Azorin
Venue type: Italian-style theatre *Capacity:* 690 *Policy:* rent *Arts types:* symphony, chamber music, theatre, dance, cinema *Comments:* ayuntamiento address: Plaça de Baix 1, Petrer

Teatro Principal de Puerto Real
c/ Amargura 59, 11510 **Puerto Real (Cádiz)**
Tel: 956-834 205

Teatro Principal
c/ Cruces s/n, 46340 **Requena (Valencia)**
Tel: 96-230 1400 (town hall)
Fax: 96-230 3553 (town hall)
E-Mail: cultura.requena@ayuntamiento.m400.gva.es
programador José Angel Jesús-María Romero
Venue type: Italian-style theatre *Capacity:* 1500 *Policy:* present, rent *Arts types:* drama, dance, jazz, folk music *Comments:* belongs to Ajuntament de Requena

Teatre Municipal La Farándula
c/ d'Alfons XIII, 33, 08202 **Sabadell (Barcelona)**
Tel: 93-725 8122 (teatro)/745 3150(ayuntamiento)
Fax: 93-725 8455
Internet: www.sabadellciutat.org
E-Mail: partistica@ajsabadell.org
director general Ignacio Riu
Venue type: Italian style theatre *Capacity:* 1103 *Policy:* rent, presents own programmes *Arts types:* symphonic music, opera, theatre, dance, *Comments:* belongs to Ajuntament de Sabadell, who rent theatre and present at own risk and risk of other promoters

Teatro Romano de Sagunto
c/ Castillo s/n, 46500 **Sagunto (Valencia)**
Tel: 96-266 5581/265 0746 Fax: 96-266 5581
E-Mail: MOD149@centres.cult.gva.es
directora Emilia Hernandez
Venue type: theatre *Capacity:* 1171 *Arts types:* theatre, music; presents 'Sagunt A Escena' festival every summer (collaborates with ayuntamiento de Sagunto) *Comments:* management: Generalitat Valenciana; owned by Ministerio de Cultura

Teatre de Salt
Centre de Creació Teatral, Plaça Sant Jaume 9,
17190 **Salt (Girona)**
Tel: 972-402 004 Fax: 972-400 019
E-Mail: bitoteatre@arquired.es
gerente Joaquim Masó
Capacity: 320-450 *Arts types:* theatre, dance and music, performing arts *Comments:* centre for creation, production and exhibition of drama, contemporary dance and music; home of Bitó Produccions; see also Agents

Real Coliseo de Carlos III, de San Lorenzo de El Escorial
Floridablanca 18,
28200 **San Lorenzo de El Escorial (Madrid)**
Tel: 91-890 4411/4544 Fax: 91-890 4411
director Luis Abella
Venue type: Italian-style theatre *Capacity:* up to 365 *Policy:* present, rent *Arts types:* theatre, music, lectures, dance *Comments:* management: Comunidad de Madrid, Plaza España 8, 3°, 28008 Madrid, Tel: 91-580 2739

Teatro Victoria Eugenia
Republica Argentina 2, 20004 **San Sebastián**
Tel: 943-481 155/158 Fax: 943-481 162
Internet: www.donostiakultura.com
E-Mail: komunikazioa@donostiakultura.com
responsable programación t.b.a.; director patronato Antón Azpitarte; responsable teatro Javier Sabadie
Venue type: Italian-style theatre *Capacity:* 1200 *Policy:* rent, presents own programme *Arts types:* theatre, music, opera, ballet, symphony, chamber music, concerts (musical, orchestra) *Comments:* management: Patronato Municipal de Cultura, Paseo de la Republica Argentina s/n, 20004 San Sebastian Tel: 943-481 150

Palacio de Festivales de Cantabria
c/ Gamazo s/n, 39004 **Santander**
Tel: 942-361 606/311 150 Fax: 942-364 061
E-Mail: palacio.cantabria@redteatros.inaem.es
director Juan Calzada; coordinador Roman Calleja; secretario administrativo Alfonso de la Mora
Venue type: multi-purpose venue *Capacity:* Sala Argenta 1648, Sala J. M. Pereda 570 *Policy:* rent, own productions *Arts types:* music, drama, dance

Palacio de Festivales de Cantabria
Calle Gamazo s/n, 39004 **Santander**
Tel: 942-361 606 Fax: 942-364 061
director Juan Calzada Aspiunza; coordinador Roman Calleja; prensa Gema Agudo
Venue type: modern style *Capacity:* big 1650, small 550 *Policy:* rent *Arts types:* all types

Auditorio de Galicia
Avda. Burgo das Nacions s/n,
15705 **Santiago de Compostela (La Coruña)**
Tel: 981-573 855/574 153/571 026 (ticket office)
Fax: 981-574 250
Internet: www.audigal.es
E-Mail: info@audigal.es
director José Denis Hombre
Venue type: concert and exhibition halls *Capacity:* Sala Angel Brage 1000, Sala Mozart 320, Sala Circular 100, Sala de Exposiciones Isaal Diaz Pardo *Arts types:* classical music, ballet, opera *Comments:* resident orchestra: Real Filarmonia de Galicia, principal conductor: Helmut Rilling, second conductor: Maximino Zumalave; see also Orchestras

Nave de Servicios Artísticos (NASA)
Rúa San Lourenzo 51-53,
15705 **Santiago de Compostela (La Coruña)**
Tel: 981-573 998 Fax: 981-573 998
E-Mail: salanasa@interbook.net
director de operaciones XRON; director tecnico Oscar Alvarez; xefe de propaganda Miguel de Lira; producción artistica John Eastham
Venue type: multi-purpose
Capacity: seated 200, standing 500 *Arts types:* theatre, concerts, performances, film, exhibitions, workshops *Comments:* home of the theatre company Chevere

Teatro Galán
Rúa Gómez Ulla nº 7,
15702 **Santiago de Compostela (La Coruña)**
Tel: 981-585 166 Fax: 891-585 121
E-Mail: t-galan@teleline.es
director Baltasar Patiño; dirección artística Ana Vallés; gestión Eugenia Iglesias
Capacity: 101 *Policy:* produce, co-produce, rents, present *Arts types:* theatre, contemporary dance, music, visual art *Comments:* member of Coordinadora de Salas Alternativas, see also National Organisations

Teatro Principal
Rúa Nova 21,
15705 **Santiago de Compostela (La Coruña)**
Tel: 981-586 555/521 Fax: 981-588 987
concejal de cultura t.b.a.; programador Montserrat Cillero
Venue type: theatre *Capacity:* 459 *Policy:* rent, organises own theatre season and cinema festival: Cine Europa *Arts types:* drama, music, cinema *Comments:* owned by Ayuntamiento de Santiago de Compostela, Plaza del Obradoiro, 15705 Santiago de Compostela, Tel: 921-542 300; see also Festivals

Teatro Juan Bravo
Plaza Mayor Nº 6, 40001 **Segovia**
Tel: 921-460 039 Fax: 921-460 040
director gerente Antonia Arranz; ayudante dirección Encarnacion Martín
Capacity: 489 *Policy:* rent, own programming *Arts types:* theatre including puppets, dance, music *Comments:* owned by: Diputacion Provincial

Auditorium de Sevilla – La Cartuja
Plaza de Los Descubrimientos s/n, Isla de la Cartuja,
41092 **Sevilla**
Tel: 95-446 1513 Fax: 95-446 0748
gerente Angel del Cerro; director técnico Pablo Sotillos
Venue type: open-air auditorium *Capacity:* 10000 (6600 + 3500 on stage if required)
Policy: present, produce, rent
Arts types: zarzuela, musical comedy, music (jazz, world music, opera, rock, etc), recitals, dance *Comments:* for bookings contact Tel: 95-518 6229

El Palenque
Isla de la Cartuja, Parque Tecnológico,
41092 **Sevilla**
Tel: 95-446 3110/1992/629-106 944 (mobile)
Fax: 95-446 0206/3440
director Rafael Candau; coordinator Guillermo Aguado
Venue type: flexible space
Capacity: 1500 (seated), up to 4000 (restricted view), total 10000 *Policy:* rent, co-produce *Arts types:* music, theatre, dance, ballet, conferences, fairs, symposia *Comments:* management: AGESA, Auda Americo Vespucio 25, Edificio s-3, 41092 Sevilla

Sala la Imperdible
Plaza S. Antonio de Padua Nº 9, 41002 **Sevilla**
Tel: 95-438 8219 Fax: 95-490 5380
E-Mail: imperdible@arrakis.es
director artistico Jose Maria Roca Gonzalez; director programas Gema Lopez; jefe tecnico Jose Osorno
Venue type: multi-purpose
Capacity: 200 *Policy:* centre for artistic creation
Arts types: theatre, dance, music, multi-media
Comments: contemporary cultural centre funded by Consejeria de Cultura de la Junta de Andalucia & INAEM; see also Festivals & Drama

Teatro Alameda
Crédito 13, 41002 **Sevilla**
Tel: 95-438 8312/490 0164/0165
Fax: 95-490 5632
director Guadalupe Tempestini
Venue type: theatre *Capacity:* 480 *Arts types:* theatre, exhibitions, pantomime *Comments:* international puppet festival Festival Internacional del Títere de Sevilla (q.v.); special hall for children's and youth theatre; see also Festivals

Teatro Central
c/ José de Galvez s/n, Isla de la Cartuja,
41092 **Sevilla**
Tel: 95-446 0780 Fax: 95-446 0880
Internet: www.teatrocentral.com
E-Mail: oficinatecnica@teatrocentral.com
public relations Neri Miranda; director técnico José Helguera; coordinador de programación Manuel Llanes; jefe prensa Raquel Fuentes
Venue type: multi-purpose modern theatre *Capacity:* standing 900, otherwise up to 450 *Policy:* rent, share own risk, risk with other promoters *Arts types:* new theatre, dance theatre, music, jazz, new age, flamenco *Comments:* management: Junta de Andalucia Consejeria de Cultura and Empresa Publica de Gestion de Programas Culturales

Teatro de la Maestranza
Paseo de Colón 22, 41001 **Sevilla**
Tel: 95-422 3344 (centralita) Fax: 95-422 5995
Internet: www.maestranza.com
E-Mail: rrpp@arrakis.es
director José Luis Castro; director economico-administrativo Francisco Santamaría; director de produccion Giuseppe Cuccia; director tecnico Antonio Moreno; jefe de prensa y rrpp Rocío Castro
Venue type: Italian-style theatre, opera theatre, auditorium *Capacity:* 1800 *Policy:* present *Arts types:* opera, ballet, symphony, recitals, dance *Comments:* largest theatre stage in Spain

Teatro Municipal de Lope de Vega
Avenida Maria Luisa s/n, 41013 **Sevilla**
Tel: 95-459 0853/4 Fax: 95-459 1827
director Juan Victor Rodriguez Yagüe; relaciones publicas Soledad Vazquez Jaramillo
Venue type: Italian-style theatre
Capacity: 730 *Arts types:* theatre, opera, music, dance *Comments:* belongs to Sevillas City Hall, Plaza Nueva 1, Sevilla, Tel: 95-459 0100; built 1929; see also National Ministries

Teatro Bellas Artes
Av Navarra 10, 50500 **Tarazona (Zaragoza)**
Tel: 976-644 011 (theatre)/199 110 (ayuntamiento)
Fax: 976-199 054 (ayuntamiento)
Internet: www.aytotarazona.es
E-Mail: tarazona@redestb.es
concejal delegado de cultura t.b.a.
Venue type: Italian style theatre *Capacity:* 570 *Policy:* mainly own programmes, occassionally rent *Arts types:* concerts, musical revues, cinema, theatre, dance *Comments:* resident companies: 1 choir, 3 chamber orchestras and municipal band; owned and managed by Ayuntamiento de Tarazona, Plaza de España 2, 50500 Tarazona (Zaragoza), Tel: 976-199 110

Centro Cultural de la Caixa de Tarrassa
Rambla d'Egara 340, 08221 **Terrassa (Barcelona)**
Tel: 93-780 4144 Fax: 93-733 1393
Internet: www.c-cultural-terrassa.es
E-Mail: info@c-cultural-terrassa.es
director Eduard Vives; responsable programación Toni Aliaga
Venue type: multi-purpose auditorium *Capacity:* Auditorium 733, Sala de Actos 310 *Policy:* presents own program *Arts types:* dance, music, theatre *Comments:* also has 5 exhibition halls for art shows; owned and managed by: Fundació Cultural Caixa de Tarrassa; see also Promoters

Teatro de Rojas
Plaza Mayor s/n, 45001 **Toledo**
Tel: 925-223 970/215 708 Fax: 925-254 778
director Francisco Plaza; coordinador/ayte dirección/relaciones publicas Adolfo Cano Montero
Venue type: Italian-style theatre *Capacity:* 478 *Policy:* rent *Arts types:* theatre, dance, music, cinema *Comments:* management: Patronato Municipal (Ayuntamiento de Toledo), Plaza del Consistorio 1, 45071 Toledo, Tel: 925-269 700

Teatro José María Rodero de Torrejón de Ardoz
Londres 3, 28850 **Torrejón de Ardoz (Madrid)**
Tel: 91-677 2234 (teatro)/656 3411
Fax: 91-677 3463
programdora Remedios Nuñez
Venue type: Italian-style theatre *Capacity:* 619 *Policy:* rent and programmes *Arts types:* drama, music, dance *Comments:* administrated by Patronato de Cultura del Ayuntamiento, Londres 5, 28850 Torrejón de Ardoz, Tel:91-677 2234

Teatro Municipal de Valdemoro
Estrella Elola 27, 28340 **Valdemoro (Madrid)**
Tel: 91-895 5613/5681 Fax: 91-895 3838
concejal de cultura t.b.a.; directora Isabel Mesa
Capacity: 388 *Policy:* rent, programme, present *Arts types:* music, theatre, dance *Comments:* owned and managed by Ayuntamiento de Valdemoro

OAM – Palau de la Música, Congresos y Orquesta de Valencia
Paseo de la Alameda 30, 46023 **Valencia**
Tel: 96-337 5020 Fax: 96-337 1521/337 0988 (dirección)
Internet: www.palauvalencia.com
E-Mail: palaudelamusica@resone.es
president of OAM Maria Irene Beneyto
Venue type: 5 multi-purpose halls, 1 purpose built concert hall *Capacity:* A:symphonic concerts 1793, B:chamber music 420, C,D:lectures and meetings 100 each, E:exhibition hall 395 *Arts types:* concerts, symphony, opera, chamber music, exhibitions, young dance, jazz, world music- flamenco, African music etc. *Comments:* home of the Orquesta de Valencia (Valencia Orchestra), 'Collegium Instrumentale' (Chamber Orchestra of the Palau), 'Taller de Opera' (opera workshop), 'Coro de Valencia'; see also Promoters, Orchestra and Choirs

Sala Escalante
c/ Landerer 5, 46003 **Valencia**
Tel: 96-391 2442 Fax: 96-391 4678
E-Mail: araceli.gras@diputacion.m400.gva.es
director Vicent Vila Berenguer; relaciones públicas Araceli Gras
Venue type: theatre *Capacity:* 350 *Arts types:* puppets, children's theatre *Comments:* management: Diputacion de Valencia, Plaza Manises 4, Tel: 96-388 2739

Teatre Principal
c/ Barcas 15, 46002 **Valencia**
Tel: 96-351 0051/353 6746 Fax: 96-394 2184
gerente German Marco Ponce; director artistico Juan Alfonso Gil-Albors; administrador Ignacio Ferrando de la Cuadra; jefe de sala Amparo Colon; jefe de administración Elías Falomí
Venue type: Italian-style theatre *Capacity:* 1072 *Policy:* own productions and colaborations with other public and private institutions *Arts types:* all types: opera, zarzuela, music, theatre, jazz, singers, ballet, contemporary dance etc. *Comments:* owned by: Diputación Provincial de Valencia; managed by: Teatres de la Generalitat Valenciana; see also National Organisations and Festivals

Teatre Talía
Cavallers 31, 46001 **Valencia**
Tel: 96-391 2920 Fax: 96-391 5080
gerente Germán Marco Ponce; director artístico Juan Alfonso Gil-Albors; administrador Ignacio Ferrando de la Cuadra; responsable de Sala Jose Luis Muñoz
Venue type: theatre *Capacity:* 400 *Arts types:* all types *Comments:* owned by: Junta de la Casa de los Obreros de San Vicente Ferrer; rented and managed by: Teatres de la Generalitat Valenciana; see also National Organisations

Teatro Rialto
Placa de l'Ajuntament 17, 46002 **Valencia**
Tel: 96-351 2336 Fax: 96-394 2099
Internet: www.cult.gva.es/tgv
E-Mail: fmedina@cult.gva.es
gerente Germán Marco Ponce; director artistico Juan Alfonso Gil-Albors; administrador Ignacio Ferrando de la Cuadra; jefe de sala javier Gallart
Venue type: theatre
Capacity: 394 *Policy:* theatre and dance: own productions and collaboration with other public and private productions; main venue for annual festival Dansa Valencia *Arts types:* dance, theatre
Comments: owned by: Generalitat Valenciana; managed by: Teatres de la Generalitat Valenciana; see also National Organisations and Festivals

Teatre Principal de Vilanova i la Geltrú
Rambla Principal 4,
08800 **Vilanova i la Geltrú (Barcelona)**
Tel: 93-814 1952 Fax: 93-893 6302
E-Mail: cultura@vilanova.org
director Noemi Cusine; adminstrador Angels Daviu
Venue type: Italian-style theatre
Capacity: 460 *Policy:* rent *Arts types:* all types: theatre, music, concerts etc. *Comments:* management: Ajuntament de Vilanova i la Geltru, Plaça de la Vila 8, 08800 Vilanova i la Geltru, Tel: 93-814 0000, Fax: 93-814 2425 – hire at promoter's risk

Teatro Principal Anzokia
San Prudencio 29, 01005 **Vitoria-Gasteiz**
Tel: 945-161 264 (admin)/045/046 (theatre)
Fax: 945-161 276 (admin)/547(theatre)
Internet: www.vitoria-gasteiz.org
E-Mail: ayuntio5@sarenet.es
director de cultura Enrique Ruiz de Gordoa; concejala t.b.a.
Capacity: 1000 *Policy:* rent, present, own programmes *Arts types:* drama, concerts, comedy, folk, dance *Comments:* organised by Ayuntamiento de Vitoria, Departamento de Cultura, Palacio de Villasuso, Plaza del Machete s/n, 01001 Vitoria

Teatro Principal
Calle San Vicente 2, 49004 **Zamora**
Tel: 980-534 719/530 751 (box office)
Fax: 980-530 785
E-Mail: zd16350@autovia.com
director-gerente Daniel Pérez Fernandez; jefe de produccion Cesar Ramos Blanco; secretaria direccion Belen Montero Martin
Venue type: Italian-style theatre
Capacity: 362 *Policy:* present at own risk, share own risk with other promoters
Arts types: all types of music, dance and theatre
Comments: owned by Ayuntamiento de Zamora, Tel: 980-548 700

Auditorio del Palacio de Congresos de Zaragoza
c/ Eduardo Ibarra 3, 50009 **Zaragoza**
Tel: 976-721 300 Fax: 976-350 514
E-Mail: auditorio.zaz@sendanet.es
director Miguel Angel Tapie
Venue type: multi-purpose auditorium *Capacity:* Sala Mozart 1992, Sala Luis Galve 429, Sala Mariano Gracia 200, Sala Multiusos 6500 (standing) 2500 (sitting), 10 salas at 100 each *Policy:* produce, rent *Arts types:* music, theatre, dance *Comments:* home of Coro Amici Musicae; see also Choirs

Teatro de la Estación
Teniente Coronel Pueyo 8-10, 50004 **Zaragoza**
Tel: 976-445 011 Fax: 976-445 127
E-Mail: rafat@redestb.es
director Rafael Campos; gerente Cristina Yañez
Capacity: 135 *Policy:* present, produce *Arts types:* theatre *Comments:* resident company Tranvía Teatro (q.v.)

Teatro de Marionetas Arbolé
c/ Francisco Ferrer 7, 50015 **Zaragoza**
Tel: 976-734 466/62-962 2687 (mobile)
Fax: 976-510 689
E-Mail: arbolea@ctv.es
director José Ignacio, Juárez Montolío
Capacity: 140 children or 90 adults *Policy:* mainly own production and programmes *Arts types:* puppets, pocket theatre; café theatre (for adults) *Comments:* home of 'Arbolé Company'; also have a publication for puppets; see also Puppets

Teatro del Mercado
Plaza Santo Domingo s/n, 50003 **Zaragoza**
Tel: 976-437 662 Fax: 976-280 879
gerente Angel Anadón Torres; director Jesús Baselga Colás; prensa Pilar Ariza Castillo
Venue type: multi media centre *Capacity:* 208 *Policy:* rent, produce *Arts types:* theatre, recitals, jazz *Comments:* management: Patronato Municipal de Artes Escenicas y de la Imagen; season 15 Sept – 15 June

Teatro Principal
Plaza José Sinues, 2, 50001 **Zaragoza**
Tel: 976-296 099 Fax: 976-200 403
director D. Angel Anadón Torres; concejeal t.b.a.
Venue type: Italian-style theatre *Capacity:* 1100 *Arts types:* theatre, opera; season 15 September to 15 June, dance *Comments:* visiting address: c/ Coso 57, 50001 Zaragoza; see also National Ministries

SWEDEN (+46)

Hagegården, Stiftelsten Hagegården
Gunnarsbyn, 671 94 **Brunskog**
Tel: 570-58500 Fax: 570-58585
E-Mail: hage@hagegarden.se
director Håkan Hagegard
Venue type: music centre
Comments: education, rehearsal and recreation venue, recordings, no performance facilities, accommodation facilities for 23

Atalante
Övre Husargatan 1, 411 22 **Göteborg**
Tel: 31-711 8200 Fax: 31-136 317
Internet: www.atalante.org
managing director Mika Becker; artistic directors Eva Ingemarsson (choreographer), Gunilla Witt (poet/choreographer), Niklas Rydén (composer/journalist); light designer Anna Wemmert
Venue type: theatre *Capacity:* 120
Policy: produce, guest playing dance performance, rent
Arts types: contemporary dance and music, art, literature, theatre, opera, performance, video, multimedia
Comments: theatre especially built for dance

Göteborg Operan
Christina Nilssons Gata, 411 04 **Göteborg**
Tel: 31-108 000 Fax: 31-108 030
Internet: www.opera.se
E-Mail: info@opera.se
general director Dag Hallberg; artistic director Kjell Ingebretsen; finance manager Mikael Milocco; marketing manager Pernilla Warberg-Andersson; programme editors Astrid Pernille-Hartmann, Ulla Dahlbäck-Hägglund; ballet director Anders Hellström; technical manager Maths G. Nyström
Venue type: opera house
Capacity: main auditorium 1300, experimental stage up to 300 *Arts types:* opera, operettas, musicals and ballets from classical and modern repertoire

Göteborgs Konserthus
Götaplatsen, 412 56 **Göteborg**
Tel: 31-615 300 Fax: 31-203 502
Internet: www.goteborgs-konsert.se
E-Mail: info@goteborgs-konsert.se
general manager Sture Carlsson; house manager Johan Bjorkman; contact for rent Marie-Louise Jung; marketing manager Ulf Olsson; tour & project manager Lars Nyström; administrative manager Maj Ahlqvist; artistic planning manager Karin Tufvession-Hjöme; orchestra manager Josef Rhedin
Venue type: multi-purpose
Capacity: Stora salen (big hall) 1286, Stenhammarsalen 402 *Policy:* rent, organise events for Göteborg Symfoniker *Arts types:* concerts – symphony, chamber, jazz, pop, theatre, conferences
Comments: home of the Göteborgs Symfoniker

Göteborgs Stadsteater
Box 5094, 402 22 **Göteborg**
Tel: 31-615 100 Fax: 31-615 114
E-Mail: info@stadsteatern.goteborg.se
general manager Gunwy Silander; artistic director Jasenko Selimovic; technical manager Björn Lengstrand; marketing manager Malin Johansson
Venue type: all purpose *Policy:* present, rent *Arts types:* drama *Comments:* see also Drama

Pusterviksteatern
Jarntorgsg. 12-14, 413 01 **Göteborg**
Tel: 31-136 610/132 091/139 337
Fax: 31-132 633
Internet: www.goteborg.se/kultur/teater/pustervik/
E-Mail: puster@netg.se
manager Anders Öhrn
Venue type: theatre *Capacity:* up to 250 *Policy:* rent (percentage of box office) *Arts types:* mainly independent, professional theatre, also dance, music, performance theatre

Helsingegarden
820 40 **Järvso**
Tel: 651-40084 Fax: 651-40362
Internet: www.helsingegarden.x.se
director Peter Osaarson
Venue type: small theatre *Capacity:* 50 *Policy:* rehearsal space *Arts types:* theatre

Jønkøping Concert Hall
Programbolaget
PO Box 6095, 550 06 **Jønkøping**
Tel: 36-129 210 Fax: 36-129 410
Internet: www.programbolaget.se
E-Mail: perolof@programbolaget.se
director Perolof Kallings
Venue type: multi-purpose *Capacity:* Room A 1100, Room B 300, Room C for rock/pop concerts 8000 standing, Room D 3000 *Policy:* rent, produce *Arts types:* symphony and chamber concerts, ballet, theatre, pop, rock concerts, musicals

Mejeriet
Stora Södergatan 64, 222 23 **Lund**
Tel: 46-211 4474/3611 Fax: 46-211 0175
Internet: www.kulturmejeriet.se
administrator & jazz, world etc. bookings Paul Eriksson; rock, club etc. bookings Lotta Wahldén; projects administrator Birgitta Persson; theatre group Månteatern Anders Widell
Venue type: arts centre
Capacity: concert hall – seated 450, standing 925, cafe theatre 150, cinema 50 *Policy:* present, rent
Arts types: mainly music (including folk, rock, jazz), drama, multi-art, film *Comments:* email: (name of person)@kulturmejeriet.se

Dansstationen – Dance Station
N. Vallg 28, 211 25 **Malmö**
Tel: 40-611 1730 Fax: 40-306 116
Internet: www.dansstationen-nova.se
E-Mail: dansstationen@mailbox.swipnet.se
general manager and producers Torsten Schenlaer, Lars Eidevall
Venue type: theatre
Capacity: up to 120 *Policy:* produce, rent, present
Arts types: new experimental stage, dance, theatre
Comments: Dansdagar, annual modern dance festival in April and Salto! annual festival modern dance for children in October

Malmö Dramatiska Teater
Box 175 20, 200 10 **Malmö**
Tel: 40-208 600 Fax: 40-208 638
Internet: www.malmo-dramatiska-teater.se
E-Mail: dramatiska.teatern@malmo.se
general director Nicolai Vemming
Venue type: theatre *Capacity:* Hipp 450, Intiman 200, Odromen 40 *Arts types:* drama

Malmö Konserthus
205 80 **Malmö**
Tel: 40-343 510 Fax: 40-611 7505
Internet: www.mso.se
E-Mail: office@mso.se
director Anders Franzen
Venue type: concert hall *Capacity:* 1208 *Policy:* rent *Arts types:* orchestral and chamber concerts *Comments:* home of the Malmö Symphonie Orkester (q.v.)

Louis De Geer Conserthall & Congress Centre
Dalsgatan 15, 601 81 **Norrköping**
Tel: 11-155 030 Fax: 11-155 075
Internet: www.louisdegeer.com
E-Mail: camilla.nilsson@ldg.norrkoping.se
managing director Kaj Krantz; manager Camilla Nilsson; technical chief Dan Valberg; conference/congress administration Inger Löfgren, Christina Falk
Venue type: proscenium arch *Capacity:* 1300 *Policy:* rent, present, co-produce *Arts types:* concerts, dance, lectures, conferences, congresses, exhibitions, trade fairs *Comments:* home of Norrköping Symphony Orchestra; concerts national and international artists

Dalhalla
Box 1, 795 21 **Rättvik**
Tel: 248-797 950 Fax: 248-797 960
Internet: www.dalhalla.se
contact Ulla Gudmundson; artistic director Margareta Dellefors (8-333 673); managing director Hakan Ivarson
Venue type: multi-purpose *Capacity:* 3800 *Arts types:* opera, concerts *Comments:* opened 1995; second address: M. Dellefors, Sveaarägen 119, 11349 Stockholm

Berwaldhallen
Sveriges Radio, Strandvägen 69, 105 10 **Stockholm**
Tel: 8-784 5108/708-944 512 Fax: 8-662 5845
Internet: www.sr.se/berwaldhallen
E-Mail: gunilla.streijffert@bwh.sr.se
director Christina Mattsson
Venue type: concert hall *Capacity:* 1300 *Arts types:* Swedish Radio Symphony Orchestra, Swedish Radio Choir, chamber music, recitals *Comments:* the Swedish Radio's big music studio

Cirkus Kungl
Kungl Djurgärden, Box 27821, 115 93 **Stockholm**
Tel: 8-5879 8700/55 Fax: 8-5879 8749
E-Mail: p.gustavsson@cirkus.se
general manager Peter Gustavsson
Venue type: theatre *Capacity:* 1600 *Arts types:* musicals, theatre, opera, festival, rock concerts, exhibitions, conferences *Comments:* see also EMA – Telstar promoters

House of Dance Foundation
Dansens Hus
Wallingatan 21, 111 24 **Stockholm**
Tel: 8-676 9600/796 0081/4910 (box office)
Fax: 8-796 7040
Internet: www.dansenshus.se
E-Mail: marknad@dansenshus.se
artistic and general director Jan Zetterberg; administrator Ulrika Johanson; international relations/communications Christina Molander; project leader Anita Brundahl; technical director Peter Lindström; international relations/communications Pia Bise
Venue type: dance house *Capacity:* Stora Teatern 850, Black Box 150 *Policy:* present, co-produce *Arts types:* contemporary and most other kinds of dance *Comments:* film and video; national and international touring groups; foremost presenter of contemporary dance in Nordic countries, 20-30 projects a year, Aug-June

Kulturhuset
Box 164 14, 103 27 **Stockholm**
Tel: 8-5083 1400 Fax: 8-5083 1409
director Christina Björk; head of theatre, music, dance dept. Claes Karlsson; producer: jazz, folk music, literature Monica Jakobson-Dikanski
Venue type: multi-purpose, concert hall, theatre *Capacity:* Hall A 450, Hall B 150 *Arts types:* modern art exhibitions, theatre, music, mostly new and modern *Comments:* programme department produces about 300 events a year; emphasis on contemporary, experimental

Moderna Dansteatern
Slupskjuisvägen 32, 111 49 **Stockholm**
Tel: 8-611 1456/3233 Fax: 8-611 9087
Internet: www.mdt.a.se
E-Mail: office@mdt.a.se
chairman Lena Hammergren; artistic director Margaretha Åsberg; manager Ann Larsson; producer Håkan Jelk
Venue type: 1 stage *Capacity:* 130
Arts types: modern and post-modern dance

Orion Teatern
Katarina Bangata 77, 116 42 **Stockholm**
Tel: 8-640 2960/2970 Fax: 8-643 3004
Internet: www.orionteatern.se
E-Mail: info@orionteatern.se
general manager Lena Lindahl; artistic director Peter Oskarson; press & public relations Tina Karnéus
Venue type: flexible space (formerly old mechanical workshop) *Capacity:* up to 320 *Policy:* present, produce, co-produce, rent *Arts types:* experimental theatre, music, poetry, children's theatre, dance

Stockholm Concert Hall
Stockholms Konserthus
PO Box 7083, 103 87 **Stockholm**
Tel: 8-786 0200 Fax: 8-791 7330
Internet: www.konserthuset.se
E-Mail: info@konserthuset.se
executive and artistic director Åse Hedstrom; marketing Peter Schele
Venue type: multi-purpose *Capacity:* Main Hall 1800, Grünewald Hall 480, Aulin Hall 140 *Arts types:* concerts (symphony, chamber, jazz, pop, musical), conferences *Comments:* residence of the Royal Stockholm Philharmonic Orchestra

Stockholm Globe Arena
Box 10055, 121 27 **Stockholm-Globen**
Tel: 8-725 1000 Fax: 8-725 1280
Internet: www.globen.se
E-Mail: info@globen.se
managing director Stefan Holmgren; marketing director Anders Ullson
Venue type: multi-purpose arena *Capacity:* Arena up to 17000, Annexet up to 3400 *Policy:* rent, produce *Arts types:* opera, theatre, concerts, sports, conferences *Comments:* largest indoor arena in Sweden

Bohusläns Teater
Strömstradsvägen 41, 451 50 **Uddevalla**
Tel: 522-91990 Fax: 522-91991
E-Mail: ida@sbt.se
director Ronnae Hallgrem
Venue type: modern style theatre *Capacity:* 2 halls: 225, 150 *Policy:* own programme, rent *Arts types:* theatre, dance

Teater Halland
Nia Vägen 27, 432 40 **Varberg**
Tel: 340-88925 Fax: 340-88995

Frölunda Kulturhus
Box 63, 421 21 **Västra Frölunda (Göteborg)**
Tel: 31-851 665 Fax: 31-851 667
Internet: www.frolunda-kulturhus.goteborg.se
E-Mail: lena.holmquist@frolunda.goteborg.se
culture director Kerstin Holmqvist; information officer Annika Pertjell; performing arts director Lena Holmquist
Venue type: multi-purpose *Capacity:* main room 260 *Policy:* rent *Arts types:* theatre, concerts, dance, exhibitions *Comments:* meeting place for professionals and amateurs

SWITZERLAND (+41)

Casino Baden
Haselstrasse 2, 5400 **Baden**
Tel: 56-221 2733 Fax: 56-221 2705
Internet: www.casinobaden.ch
E-Mail: casinoadm@casinobaden.ch
director Roberto Scheuer
Venue type: concert hall / multipurpose *Capacity:* 800 *Policy:* rent, own risk *Arts types:* theatre, concerts, conferences, special parties

forumclaque
Kronengasse 4, 5400 **Baden**
Tel: 56-222 9988 Fax: 56-221 8052
E-Mail: forumclaque@bluewin.ch
Künstlerische Leitung Heinz Gubler, Michel Mettler; Geschäftsleitung Küde Meier
Venue type: theatre, performance space, gallery *Policy:* produce *Arts types:* contemporary art, literature and music projects

Kurtheater Baden Gastspielbetrieb
Postfach, 5401 **Baden**
Tel: 56-426 1252 Fax: 56-426 6717
Internet: www.kurtheater.ch
Verwaltungsleiterin Berthe Zehnder; Technischer Leiter Othmar Zehnder
Venue type: theatre *Capacity:* 611 *Policy:* rent to visiting companies *Arts types:* drama, classical concerts, operas, operettas, ballet *Comments:* visiting address: Kurtheater, Parkstr. 20, 5400 Baden, Tel: 56-222 2245

Stadt-Casino Basel
Steinenberg 14, 4001 **Basel**
Tel: 61-272 6658 Fax: 61-272 5822
direktor Markus Hasler
Venue type: concert halls *Capacity:* Musiksaal 1512, Großer Festsaal 700, Hans-Huber Saal 540 *Policy:* rent *Arts types:* symphony, chamber, recitals, folklore, dance, musicals, exhibitions, banquets

Vorstadt Theater
St. Alban-Vorstadt 12, Postfach 124, 4009 **Basel**
Tel: 61-272 2320 Fax: 61-272 2308
künstlerischer Leiter Gerd Imbsweiler
Venue type: theater *Capacity:* 100 *Policy:* own productions, co-productions, for rent *Comments:* diverse guest artists, German-speaking and foreign

Kultur Casino Bern
Herrengasse 25, 3011 **Bern**
Tel: 31-328 0228 Fax: 31-328 0222
verwaltungsleiter Herr Berthoud
Venue type: concert & congress hall
Capacity: 1350 *Policy:* rent
Arts types: symphony, chamber, recitals

Kulturhallen Dampfzentrale Bern
Marzilistrasse 47, 3005 **Bern**
Tel: 31-311 6337 Fax: 31-312 5105
Internet: www.dampfzentrale.ch
E-Mail: kultur@dampfzentrale.ch
management Christoph Balmer; music Pascal Dussex; dance Johanna Mahler; pr Reto Clavadetscher; finance Maurice Berger; theatre Stephan H. Kraft; president Hans Burgener
Venue type: multi-purpose cultural centre *Capacity:* Hall A 500, Hall B 450, Hall C 150 *Policy:* rent *Arts types:* dance, theatre, exhibitions, visual art, sounds, new media *Comments:* sometimes promotes

Kongresshaus Biel
CTS sa, 2501 **Biel**
Tel: 32-323 3311 Fax: 32-323 1972
E-Mail: info@ctssa.ch
director Daniel Suter
Venue type: concert and congress hall *Capacity:* 1200, small hall 250 *Policy:* rent *Arts types:* classical, pop, rock, jazz, dance

Stadttheater Biel
Burggasse 13/19, 2500 **Biel** 3
Tel: 32-328 8969 Fax: 32-328 8967
director Peter Theiler
Venue type: theatre *Capacity:* 280 *Policy:* produce, co-produce and rent *Arts types:* theatre, opera, music concerts (classical to jazz) *Comments:* see also Orchestras, Opera and Promoters

Tourismus-center Simplon
Postfach 688, 3900 **Brig**
Tel: 27-921 6030 Fax: 27-921 6031
Internet: www.brig-tourismus.ch
E-Mail: info@brig-tourismus.ch
Verkehrsdirektor Beat Pfammatter
Venue type: multi purpose *Capacity:* 1500 *Policy:* rent and organise *Arts types:* music, theatre, dance, opera

Stadttheater Chur
Zeughausstr. 6, 7000 **Chur**
Tel: 81-252 2503 Fax: 81-252 7686
director and administration Hans-Heinrich Rüegg
Venue type: theatre *Capacity:* 480
Policy: rent *Arts types:* drama, opera, modern music, concerts, ballet

Cite bleue
46 ave de Miremont, 1206 **Genève** 25
Tel: 22-839 2101 Fax: 22-839 2223
Internet: www.unige.ch/cite-uni
directeur Jean-Jacques Monney; location Suzanna Benghone; programmation artistique M. Philippe Cohen
Venue type: multi-purpose inc. exhibition room *Capacity:* 327 *Policy:* produce, co-produce *Arts types:* music, dance, theatre

L'Usine
4 Place des Volontaires, 1204 **Genève**
Tel: 22-781 3490 Fax: 22-781 4138
Internet: www.usine.ch
secrétariat général Renaud Christin; théâtre Yann Marussich, Florence Chappuis, Karine Decorne; cabaret Manual Minazio, Damien Schmocker, Yannick Lamm; cinéma Abel Davaine; art comtemporain Constantin Sguridis, Sény Waner; association PTR Julien Amey
Venue type: modular concert hall
Capacity: modular concert hall 200/800 (seated)
Policy: present *Arts types:* film, contemporary art, concerts (mainly rock), theatre, discos

St Gervais, Genève, Fondation pour les arts de la scène et de L'image
5 rue du Temple, 1201 **Genève**
Tel: 22-908 2000 Fax: 22-908 2001
Internet: www.sgg.ch
E-Mail: sgg@sgg.ch
administration Brigitte Chapuis; directeur artistique Centre par l'image contemporain (C.I.C.) André Iten; directeur artistique théâtre Phillipe Macasdar
Venue type: theatre – Image (photos, video, production, creation, multi-media)
Capacity: 200 *Policy:* produce, co-produce *Arts types:* contemporary drama, contemporary arts (video,etc)
Comments: for young artistes; performances in foreign languages

Victoria Hall
rue Général-Dufour, 1204 **Genève**
Tel: 22-328 3573 (administration)/8121 (bookings)
Fax: 22-781 4740
chef de service J-C Poulin, Service de l'art musical, 19 route de Malagnou, 1211 Geneva 17, Case Postale 10
Venue type: concert hall *Capacity:* 1834 *Policy:* rent, produce
Arts types: orchestras, chamber music, recitals, variety

Stadttheater Langenthal
Aarwangenstrasse 8, 4900 **Langenthal**
Tel: 62-916 2111 (sekretariat) Fax: 62-923 0330
Sekretär der Theaterkommission Bernhard Moor
Venue type: theatre *Capacity:* 446 *Policy:* rent *Arts types:* theatre, opera, operetta

Casino de Montbenon
Allée Ernest Ansermet 3, 1003 **Lausanne**
Tel: 21-323 8251 Fax: 21-315 2013
E-Mail: mjehouda.sni@bluewin.ch
Intendant Claude Dettly
Venue type: concert hall (and festival hall – salle des fêtes) *Capacity:* Paderewski 495, ballroom *Policy:* rent
Arts types: chamber music, recitals, conferences, exhibitions, jazz, cinema

Fondation Metropole – Lausanne
Case Postale 2735, 1002 **Lausanne**
Tel: 21-312 8965 Fax: 21-312 4589
Administrateurs Jean Daniel Cattaneo, Jean-Claude Steiner
Capacity: 1116 *Policy:* rent *Arts types:* dance, classical music, jazz, variety, concerts

Théâtre Arsenic
57, rue de Genéve, 1004 **Lausanne**
Tel: 21-625 1122 Fax: 21-625 1124
Internet: www.cyberlab.ch/arsenic
E-Mail: arsenic@cyberlab.ch
direction Thiery Spicher; administration Chantal Albrecht; relations avec le public Rita Freda; service de presse Adriana Mazza
Venue type: theatre *Capacity:* 3 halls: hall 1: 150, hall 2: 90, hall 3: 60 *Policy:* present only *Arts types:* dance, dance theatre, theatre and live arts

Théâtre de Beaulieu
Palais de Beaulieu, CP 89, 1000 **Lausanne** 22
Tel: 21-643 2111 Fax: 21-643 3711
E-Mail: Brouze@comptoir.ch
responsable Brouze René
Venue type: theatre *Capacity:* 1870 *Policy:* rent
Arts types: ballet, dance, music, opera, theatre, concerts
Comments: home of Orchestre de la Suisse Romande (q.v.)

Théâtre Municipal de Lausanne
Case Postale 3972, 1002 **Lausanne**
Tel: 21-310 1616 Fax: 21-310 1690
directeur Dominique Meyer; directeur technique Bruno Boyer; press & communication Laurence Authier
Venue type: theatre *Capacity:* 993 *Policy:* produce, co-produce and rent *Arts types:* opera, ballet, concerts, recitals, conferences

Theatre Sévelin 36
Case Postale 110, 1000 **Lausanne** 20
Tel: 21-626 1398 Fax: 21-626 3814
E-Mail: cie.saire@bluewin.ch
artistic director Philippe Saire; programmateur Michel Beltex; administrators Juan Pittalis
Venue type: dance only *Capacity:* 180 *Arts types:* dance
Comments: stage fully technically equipped, rehearsal studio; visiting address: Av. Sévelin 36, 1000 Lausanne 20; annual Festival de Danse Contemporerine

Théâtre Vidy-Lausanne
Av. E. Jaques-Dalcroze 5, 1007 **Lausanne**
Tel: 21-619 4544/5 Fax: 21-619 4510
E-Mail: s.turin@theatrevidy.ch
directeur René Gonzalez; directeur adjoint René Zahnd; directeur technique Rémy Monachon
Venue type: receiving and creating house *Capacity:* Hall A 400, Hall B 140, chapiteau 200 *Policy:* rent, produce, co-produce *Arts types:* theatre, puppets, dance, exhibitions, conference, circus

Kleintheater am Bundesplatz
Bundesplatz 10/14, 6003 **Luzern**
Tel: 41-210 1219 Fax: 41-210 2873
Internet: www.centralnet.ch/kultur/kleintheater
E-Mail: kleintheater@centralnet.ch
Leitung Andrej Togni
Capacity: Kleintheater 250 *Policy:* present, promote *Arts types:* drama, concerts, pantomime etc., international guests, comedy

Kultur-und Kongreßzentrum Luzern Management AG
Europaplatz 1, Postfach, 6005 **Luzern**
Tel: 41-226 7070 Fax: 41-226 7071
Internet: www.kkluzern.ch
E-Mail: info@kkluzern.ch
general manager Michael Wittwer; f & b manager Claude Rossé; Technischer Leiter Michael Lipphardl; assistant to general manager Kurt Koch
Venue type: multi-purpose *Capacity:* Konzertsaal 1840, Mittlerer Saal 890, Auditorium 274, Kunstmuseum
Policy: rent only *Arts types:* music, opera, dance, conferences, exhibitions, visual arts *Comments:* Konzertssal is completed; other parts of Kultur- und Kongreßzentrum will open in March 2000

Théâtre de Beausobre
Avenue Vertou 2, 1110 **Morges**
Tel: 21-803 0917 Fax: 21-803 0910
directeur Jean-Marc Desponds
Venue type: theatre (amphitheatre)
Capacity: 850 *Policy:* diffuse, co-produce, sometimes produce *Arts types:* variety, comedy, classical theatre, world music, special shows for children, humour
Comments: see also Agents (SDS Lausanne)

Théâtre de la Poudrière
Quai Godet 18, 2000 **Neuchâtel**
Tel: 32-724 6519 Fax: 32-724 6517
Directeur Yves Baudin; Administratrice Corinne Grandjean
Venue type: multi-purpose
Capacity: 120 *Policy:* produce, co-produce, present
Arts types: puppet, drama
Comments: see also Puppets and Festivals

L'Octogone
41, av. de Lavaux, 1009 **Pully/Lausanne**
Tel: 21-721 3647 Fax: 21-721 3616
director Jean-Pierre Althaus; administration Yasmine Wegmuller
Venue type: theatre
Capacity: 455 *Policy:* produce, co-produce, present
Arts types: dance, modern and classical music, theatre
Comments: home of Linga Danse Project; see also Dance and Festivals

Stadttheater Schaffhausen
Herrenacker 23, 8201 **Schaffhausen**
Tel: 52-632 5111/5288 Fax: 52-632 5432
Internet: www.stadt-schaffhausen.ch
E-Mail: rolfmuller@stsh.ch
director Rolf C. Müller; technician Peter Surbeck
Venue type: theatre
Capacity: 687 seated, 80 standing
Policy: rent, present *Arts types:* ballet, theatre, opera, operetta, music theatre, comedy, children's and youth theatre

Kellerbühne am Müllertor
St. Georgenstr. 3, 9000 **St Gallen**
Tel: 71-223 3959 Fax: 71-222 8009
Leitung Kurt Schwarz; Sekretariat Vreni Wagner
Capacity: 160 *Policy:* present, rent
Comments: welcome performers from national and internatinal cabaret scene, c/o Kurt Schwarz, St. Georgenstr. 3, 9000 St Gallen

Tonhalle St. Gallen
Postfach, Museumstrasse 1/25, 9004 **St Gallen**
Tel: 71-242 0632 Fax: 71-242 0708
E-Mail: sg@bluewin.ch
Leiter Tonhalle t.b.a.
Venue type: concert hall *Capacity:* 915 *Policy:* rent *Arts types:* concerts – classical, jazz, pop, folk *Comments:* concert series by Symphony Orchestra St Gallen

Théâtre de Vevey
rue du Théâtre 4, 1800 **Vevey**
Tel: 21-923 5396 Fax: 21-923 5540
E-Mail: theatre-vevey@bluewin.ch
directeur artistique Philippe de Bros; administration Jean Pierre Candaux; Adjointe Jose Zenger-Carasso
Venue type: theatre *Capacity:* 750 *Policy:* present, rent
Arts types: theatre, opera, dance, classical concerts, spectacles for youth *Comments:* organise own season with 50 performances

Tonhalle
Tonhallestr. 29, 9500 **Wil**
Tel: 71-913 8920 Fax: 71-913 8931
Leiter Suzanne Witf
Capacity: 500 *Policy:* rent
Arts types: performances by drama companies, orchestra, opera, operette, choirs etc.

Theater am Stadtgarten
Theaterstrasse 4, 8402 **Winterthur**
Tel: 52-267 5020 Fax: 52-267 5030
Künstlerische Beratung Alex Freihard; general director peter Wehrli
Venue type: receiving venue (Gastspiel Theater)
Capacity: 800 *Policy:* mainly present, but some rent
Arts types: ballet, dance, musicals, opera, operetta, theatre, cabaret
Comments: stage 150 performances per season

Théâtre Benno Besson
Case Postale 65, 1401 **Yverdon-les-Bains**
Tel: 24-423 6580 Fax: 24-426 1959
Directeur Pierre Bauer
Venue type: theatre *Capacity:* 460
Policy: present, co-produce
Arts types: drama, dance

Théâtre de l'Echandole
Case Postale 65, 1401 **Yverdon-les-Bains**
Tel: 24-423 6580 Fax: 24-426 1959
directrice Annedominique Chevalley
Capacity: 150 *Policy:* present *Arts types:* jazz, French chanson, multimedia

Theater Casino Zug
Postfach 50, 6301 **Zug**
Tel: 41-729 1050 Fax: 41-729 1051
director August P. Villiger
Venue type: theatre *Capacity:* 630 *Policy:* rent *Arts types:* ballet, dance, chamber and symphony concerts, opera, operetta, shows, theatre, conferences, meetings
Comments: Operating management: Artherstr. 2-4, 6300 Zug, Tel: 41-729 0550, Fax : 41-729 0551

AG Hallenstadion
Wallisellenstrasse 45, 8050 **Zürich**
Tel: 1-316 7777 Fax: 1-316 2700
E-Mail: hallenstadion@hallenstadion.ch
director André Béchir
Venue type: multi-purpose *Capacity:* up to 12000 *Policy:* rent *Arts types:* mainly pop but also classical, folk, jazz concerts, opera

Rote Fabrik
Seestrasse 395, 8038 **Zürich**
Tel: 1-482 4212 (theatre office)/481 9811 (music office)
Fax: 1-481 9145
Internet: www.rotefabrik.ch
E-Mail: rotefabrik@hugo.ch
contacts Catja Loepfe (theatre), Nadya Khelili (music), Holger Klüpfel (music)
Venue type: cultural centre *Capacity:* Hall A 1300 (250 seated), Hall B 600, Hall C 100 (seated) *Policy:* present
Arts types: dance, concerts, theatre, children's & youth theatre, reading, etc. *Comments:* member of Trans Europe Halles (q.v.); member of EU net art

Theaterhaus Gessnerallee
Gessnerallee 8, 8001 **Zürich**
Tel: 1-212 1220 Fax: 1-212 1228
E-Mail: theaterhaus@gessnerallee.ch
artistic directors Armin Kerber, Jean Grädel; technical director Stefan Keller
Venue type: theatre *Capacity:* up to 600 *Policy:* rent *Arts types:* drama, international and national contemporary theatre, music theatre, dance theatre, dance

Tonhalle und Kongresshaus Zürich
Gotthardstrasse 5, Postfach 4779, 8022 **Zürich**
Tel: 1-206 3636 Fax: 1-206 3659
Internet: www.kongresshaus.ch
E-Mail: info@kongresshaus.ch
director Norbert Bolinger; marketing Ruth Wunderlin Jud
Venue type: concert hall *Capacity:* Großer Tonhalle Saal 1435, Kleiner Tonhalle Saal 636, Kongresshaus 1750
Policy: rent *Arts types:* opera, operetta, concerts, classical and easy listening
Comments: see also Promoters

TURKEY (+90)

Atatürk Culture Centre
Atatürk Kültür Merkezi
Hipodrom Mevkii, **Ankara**
Tel: 312-341 1416/342 1010 Fax: 312-341 1416
director Mümtaz Kaya
Capacity: 236

CSO Concert Hall
Cumhurbaskanligi Senfoni Orkestrasi Konser Salonu
Talatpasa Bulvari No. 38, 06330 **Ankara**
Tel: 312-310 7290/311 0991/309 1343 Fax: 312-311 7548
director Nedim Tanrikulu
Capacity: 800 *Arts types:* orchestras, recitals

Opera House
Opera Binasi
Atatürk Bulvari, Opera Meydani, Ulus, 06050 **Ankara**
Tel: 312-311 2430/324 1476 Fax: 312-311 9731
director Mete Önal
Capacity: 723 *Arts types:* opera, theatre, musicals, ballet

Ataturk Culture Centre
Atatürk Kültür Merkezi
Taksim, **Istanbul**
Tel: 212-251 5600 Fax: 212-243 3261
director Ülker Yegin
Venue type: 4 performance areas *Capacity:* Grand Hall 1300, Chamber Theatre 290, concert hall 500
Comments: home for dance and opera company, symphony orchestra, drama company, Turkish classic music choir

Cemal Resit Rey Concert Hall
80200 Harbiye, **Istanbul**
Tel: 212-246 0695/231 5103/232 9830 Fax: 212-248 5451
program co-ordinator Murat Gürol; general music director Arda Aydogan
Venue type: multi-purpose *Capacity:* 1000 *Arts types:* concerts, recitals, jazz, ballet, dance
Comments: season from October until May

Hagia Eireni Museum
Aya Irini Muzesi
Sultanahmet Meydani, Sultanahmet, **Istanbul**
Tel: 212-522 1750 Fax: 212-512 5474
director Ali Kilinçkaya
Capacity: 1123 *Comments:* open only for the festivals, between May-September

Istanbul Convention & Exhibition Centre
Lütfi Kirdar Uluslararasi Kongre ve Sergi Sarayi
Harbiye, 80230 **Istanbul**
Tel: 212-296 3055 Fax: 212-224 0878
general manager Sinan Bilsel
Capacity: 1750 *Arts types:* concerts, performances, congress, exhibitions, etc.

Istanbul Open-Air Theatre
Harbiye, **Istanbul**
Tel: 212-240 2244 Fax: 212-248 2667
director Muharrem Ergül
Capacity: 3900 *Arts types:* dance, music, drama, jazz, ballet, recital and pop music

Performing Arts Centre
Ozel Amerikan Robert Lisesi, Arnavutköy, **Istanbul**
Tel: 212-265 9480
Capacity: 500 *Arts types:* dance, music, drama

UKRAINE (+380)

Kyiv (Kiev) Philharmonic
Volodymyrskyi Uzviz 2, 252001 **Kiev (Kyiv)**
Tel: 44-228 0330

Organ and Chamber Music Hall
Krasnoarmiyska St. 77, 252150 **Kiev (Kyiv)**
Tel: 44-269 8617
director Volodymyr Lebedev

UNITED KINGDOM (+44)

Café Graffiti
Tel: 131-557 8003 Fax: 131-557 8003
Internet: www.cafegraffitti.com
E-Mail: cafegr@ffitti.abel.co.uk
director Peter Simpson
Arts types: music *Comments:* moving to a new address in January 2000; no further details known at time of going to print

His Majesty's Theatre
Rosemount Viaduct, **Aberdeen (Scotland)** AB25 1GL
Tel: 1224-637 788/641 122 (box office)
Fax: 1224-632 519
operations manager Martin Milne; sales & marketing manager Alison Lubek; technical manager Lena Dowell; stage manager Graeme Shepherd
Venue type: theatre *Capacity:* 1445 *Policy:* rent, co-present *Arts types:* opera, ballet, plays, musicals, children's shows

Music Hall Aberdeen
Union Street, **Aberdeen (Scotland)** AB10 1QS
Tel: 1224-632 080 Fax: 1224-632 400
E-Mail: abzmusichall@dial.pipex.com
operations managers Duncan Hendry, Julie Sinclair
Venue type: concert, multi-purpose hall *Capacity:* seated 1280, standing 1507 *Policy:* rent, co-present, present *Arts types:* orchestra, pop, rock, exhibitions, dance, variety, jazz, world music, conferences

Canolfan Y Celfyddydau
Aberystwyth Arts Centre
Penglais, **Aberystwyth (Wales)** SY23 3DE
Tel: 1970-622 882 Fax: 1970-622 883
Internet: www.aber.ac.uk/~arcwww/index.htm
E-Mail: lla@aber.ac.uk
director Alan Hewson; administrator Maris Davies; marketing Louise Amery
Venue type: theatre and concert hall, exhibitions
Capacity: concert hall 900, theatre 321; extra performance studio 120, cinema theatre 120, conference facilities *Policy:* rent, produce, co-produce, receiving venue, festivals *Arts types:* drama, opera, light entertainment, ballet, classical music, children's entertainment, contemporary dance, local amateur companies, pantomime *Comments:* £4 million redevelopment project completed October 1999

Jubilee Hall Aldeburgh
Crabbe Street, **Aldeburgh** IP15 5BN
Tel: 1728-454 212
chairwoman Mrs M. Steen
Venue type: theatre *Capacity:* 240
Policy: rent *Arts types:* drama, music, concerts, dance
Comments: venue available to lease for private functions/meetings

Snape Maltings Concert Hall
Aldeburgh Productions, High Street, **Aldeburgh** IP15 5AX
Tel: 1728-452 935 Fax: 1728-452 715
Internet: www.adleburgh.co.uk
E-Mail: enquiries@aldeburghfestivals.org
chief executive Jonathan Reekie;
general administrator Clare Lovell
Venue type: concert hall *Capacity:* 832 *Policy:* present, rent *Arts types:* music, education projects, dance
Comments: see also Festivals

Tameside Hippodrome
Oldham Road, **Ashton under Lyne** OL6 7SE
Tel: 161-330 2095 Fax: 161-343 5839
theatre manager Karen Jones; assistant manager Matthew Beesley
Venue type: theatre
Capacity: 1262 *Policy:* rent *Arts types:* ballet, opera, music, theatre, comedy acts, children's shows
Comments: national touring house; contact Nicky Monk-tel. 1865-782 900 for hire of the theatre

Civic Centre Aylesbury
Market Square, **Aylesbury** HP20 1UF
Tel: 1296-585 541 Fax: 1296-392 091
head of leisure services Paul Tonks; programming manager Sam McCaffrey; centre manager Phil Barker
Venue type: multi-purpose *Capacity:* Maxwell Hall (standing) 1150 *Policy:* rent, co-present *Arts types:* varied programme

Civic Theatre
Contant Avenue, Craigie, **Ayr (Scotland)** KA8 0EF
Tel: 1292-617 400/611 222 (box office)
Fax: 1292-880 044
theatre manager Gordon Taylor
Venue type: theatre *Capacity:* 345
Policy: rent, co-present, produce
Arts types: drama, small music performances
Comments: venue for touring theatres; managed from Gaiety Theatre, Ayr (q.v.)

Gaiety Theatre
Carrick Street, **Ayr (Scotland)** KA7 1NU
Tel: 1292-617 400/611 222 (box office)
Fax: 1292-880 044
theatre manager Gordon Taylor
Venue type: theatre *Capacity:* 582 *Policy:* rent, co-present, produce *Arts types:* mid scale touring ballet, opera, drama *Comments:* touring theatre

Theatr Gwynedd
Ffordd Deiniol, **Bangor (Wales)** LL57 2TL
Tel: 1248-351 707/708 (box office)
Fax: 1248-351 915
Internet: www.users.golbalnet.co.uk/~theatr/
E-Mail: theatr@globalnet.co.uk
administrative director Dafydd Thomas; artistic director Sian Summers; marketing officer Fiona Otting; production manager Dylan Rowlands
Venue type: theatre *Capacity:* 348
Policy: rent, buy-in, own company, produce, receiving theatre *Arts types:* English and Welsh drama, dance, children's theatre, pantomime, opera, concerts
Comments: resident company Cwmni Theatr Gwynedd

Queen's Theatre
Boutport Street, **Barnstaple** EX31 1SY
Tel: 1271-327 357 Fax: 1271-326 412
Internet: www.northdevontheatres.org.uk
E-Mail: northdevon.theatres@sosi.net
programming director Karen Turner; financial controller Chris Sawle; theatre manager Darren Regan; marketing Debbie Cooke
Venue type: theatre, concert hall
Capacity: 688 *Policy:* mainly split or guarantee, hire *Arts types:* theatre, musicals, opera, comedy, dance, live music (classical, jazz, folk, contemporary, rock), children's shows *Comments:* receiving venue; see also The Landmark (q.v.)

Anvil, The
Churchill Way, **Basingstoke** RG21 7QR
Tel: 1256-819 797 Fax: 1256-331 733
Internet: www.winterthur-life.co.uk/anvil.html
E-Mail: christine.bradwell@dial.pipex.com
chief executive Christine Bradwell; marketing director Matthew Cleaver; operations director Ian Trow
Venue type: concert hall and entertainment venue
Capacity: main auditorium: 1400 in concert format, 1000 with proscenium arch; small auditorium up to 100
Policy: present events at own risk, co-present and rent out; c. 300 performances a year, including 20-25 classical orchestral concerts
Arts types: music from classical to rock, opera, ballet, musicals, pantomime, arthouse/quality film in small auditorium
Comments: 12 wheelchair spaces, induction loop and infra-red hearing enhancement; the venue was designed by Renton Howard Wood Levin

Haymarket Theatre
Wote Street, **Basingstoke** RG21 7NW
Tel: 1256-323 073 Fax: 1256-357 130
Internet: www.haymarket.org
E-Mail: info@haymarket.org.uk
theatre director Alasdair Ramsay;
theatre manager Tim Wills
Venue type: repertory theatre *Capacity:* 426 *Policy:* produce, rent *Arts types:* drama, musicals, concerts, dance *Comments:* base for Haymarket Theatre Company; see also Drama

Theatre Royal Bath
Sawclose, **Bath** BA1 1ET
Tel: 1225-448 815/844 (box office) Fax: 1225-444 080
director Danny Moar; marketing manager Anna Farr; development director Robert Pitts
Venue type: theatre *Capacity:* 904 *Policy:* terms by negotiation, occasionally rent *Arts types:* drama, comedy, musicals, opera, dance *Comments:* national touring house; 140 seater studio – The Ustinov Studio; welcomes premieres

Bedford Corn Exchange
Harp Street Offices, Harp Street, **Bedford** NK40 1SL
Tel: 1234-344 813 Fax: 1234-325 358
E-Mail: cornexch@bedford.btinternet.com
general manager Ian Morrison; pr Andrew Jacques
Venue type: multi-purpose *Capacity:* 800 *Policy:* rent, own programming *Arts types:* dance, theatre, music

Belfast Waterfront Hall, The
Conference & Concerts Centre, 2 Lanyon Place,
Belfast (Northern Ireland) BT1 3WH
Tel: 28-9033 4400 Fax: 28-9024 9862
Internet: www.waterfront.co.uk
general manager Tim Husbands; sales & marketing manager Andrew Kyle; finance & administration manager Mark McBride
Venue type: conference & concert centre *Capacity:* main auditorium 2235 (seated), 2700 (standing/seated), studio 500 *Arts types:* concerts, conferences, exhibitions, dance, gallery, all types of performances and sporting use

Crescent Arts Centre
2-4 University Road,
Belfast (Northern Ireland) BT7 1NH
Tel: 28-9024 2338 Fax: 28-9024 6748
Internet: www.crescentarts.org
manager Louise Emerson (email: louise@crescentarts.org); technical officer Bill Smith (email: bill@crescentarts.org); accounts officer Elizabeth Donnan (email: elizabeth@crescentarts.org); arts outreach officer t.b.a.; administrator Hazel McAnally (email: hazel@crescentsarts.org); receptionist Eileen McNally (eileen@crescentarts.org)
Venue type: multi-purpose incl. workshops, studio, performance and dance space, Fenderesky Gallery
Capacity: Gym (Black Box) 200, Dance Studio 110
Policy: promote (emphasis on local companies) *Arts types:* dance, performing arts, entertainment, visual arts, jazz, new genre music, childrens activities, writers festival, community arts *Comments:* funded by Arts Council, Belfast City Council and Baring Foundation

Golden Thread Theatre
Brookfield Business Centre, 333 Crumlin Road,
Belfast (Northern Ireland) BT14 7EA
Tel: 28-9074 5241/0122 Fax: 28-9074 8025
promotions officer Paula McGrogan
Venue type: modern style theatre *Capacity:* 200 *Policy:* rent, own programming *Arts types:* all types *Comments:* rehearsal space available

Grand Opera House
Great Victoria Street,
Belfast (Northern Ireland) BT2 7HR
Tel: 28-9024 0411/1919 (ticket shop) Fax: 28-9023 6842
Internet: www.gohbelfast.com
director Derek Nicholls; marketing manager Mary Trainor; public relations manager Ian Wilson
Venue type: theatre *Capacity:* 1001 *Policy:* present, rent
Arts types: drama, opera, ballet, concerts, musicals, pantomime, children's shows *Comments:* national touring house

Kings Hall Exhibition & Conference Centre
Balmoral, **Belfast (Northern Ireland)** BT9 6GW
Tel: 28-9066 5225 Fax: 28-9066 1264
Internet: www.kingshall.co.uk
E-Mail: press@kingshall.co.uk
chief executive (RUAS) William Warr; commerical director Philip Rees; sales & marketing manager Lucy Moore
Venue type: multi-purpose *Capacity:* Kings Hall 7000, Conference Centre 600 *Policy:* mainly rent *Arts types:* exhibitions, concerts, dance *Comments:* disabled facilities throughout; restaurant in exhibition hall; rehearsal space and sound and lighting equipment available for hire; owned by the Royal Ulster Agricultural Society (RUAS)

Old Museum Arts Centre
7 College Square North,
Belfast (Northern Ireland) BT1 6AR
Tel: 28-9023 5053/3332 (box office) Fax: 28-9032 2912
director Anne McReynolds; technical manager Roger Nicolson; marketing & fundraising officer Gillian Mitchell; admin. assistant John Stewart; outreach coordinator Lizzie Devlin
Venue type: arts centre *Capacity:* 2 spaces: theatre 90 seats, other space 120 *Policy:* present, commission, co-produce *Arts types:* Irish and international theatre, dance, photography, music, all visual art forms catered for *Comments:* I.E.T.M. member; BSL signer available, please telephone for details

Ulster Hall
Bedford Street, **Belfast (Northern Ireland)** BT2 7FF
Tel: 28-9032 3900 Fax: 28-9024 7199
manager Pat Falls
Venue type: concert, multi-purpose hall *Capacity:* up to 1800 *Policy:* rent *Arts types:* all types concerts, exhibitions, boxing, conferences, religous meetings, rallies, amateur music events

Maltings, The
Eastern Lane, **Berwick-upon-Tweed** TD15 1DT
Tel: 1289-330 661 (admin)/999 (box office)
Fax: 1289-330 448
business manager Maureen McLeod; director Celia Frisby; marketing manager Beverley Briggs
Venue type: arts centre *Capacity:* theatre 327, hall 200 *Policy:* present, produce *Arts types:* dance, drama, music, opera, children's shows, cinema *Comments:* fully accessible for disabled patrons

Forum Theatre
Town Centre, **Billingham** TS23 2LJ
Tel: 1642-551 389/552 663 (box office)
Fax: 1642-360 656
general manager Derek Cooper; technical manager Terry Gleaver; marketing manager Liz Cooper; duty manager John Hall
Venue type: theatre *Capacity:* 619 *Policy:* guarantee, rent, percentage split *Arts types:* drama, concerts, ballet *Comments:* touring house

Alexandra Theatre
Station Street, **Birmingham** B5 4DS
Tel: 121-643 5536/1231 (box office) Fax: 121-632 6841
general manager James Haworth; deputy manager Stephen Levine; assistant manager Sarah Bleasdale; marketing manager Samantha Knight
Venue type: theatre *Capacity:* 1372 *Policy:* rent *Arts types:* plays, musicals, concerts *Comments:* national touring house; part of Apollo Leisure Group – head office is in Oxford

Birmingham Hippodrome
Hurst Street, **Birmingham** B5 4TB
Tel: 121-689 3030/622 7486 Fax: 121-622 5518
Internet: www.birmingham-hippodrome.co.uk
E-Mail: admin@birmingham-hippodrome.co.uk
theatre director Peter Tod; head of sales Paul Steeples; technical & operations director Tony Guest
Venue type: theatre *Capacity:* 1887 *Policy:* rent, sharing terms *Arts types:* opera, ballet, theatre, musicals, mixed programme *Comments:* national touring theatre, home of the Birmingham Royal Ballet; will close for refurbishment at the end of January 2000, will re-open at the end of 2000

Birmingham Repertory Theatre
Centenary Square, Broad Street, **Birmingham** B1 2EP
Tel: 121-236 6771 (administration)/4455 (box office)
Fax: 121-236 7883
Internet: www.birmingham/rep.co.uk
E-Mail: info@birmingham/rep.co.uk
executive producer John Stalker; artistic director Bill Alexander; head of sales & marketing Amie Smart; press officer Jane Spence (121-237 1525)
Venue type: theatre *Capacity:* main house 882, studio 120 *Policy:* both auditoria available for rent (contact Gary Stewart, tel: 121-236 6771) *Arts types:* classical, modern & new plays *Comments:* alternative Internet: www.the/door.co.uk; see also Drama

Birmingham Town Hall
Victoria Square, **Birmingham** B3 3DQ
Comments: undergoing extensive refurbishment, due to re-open Dec 2000

MAC, The Centre for Birmingham
Cannon Hill Park, **Birmingham** B12 9QH
Tel: 121-440 4221/3838 (box office)
Fax: 121-446 4372
director Dorothy Wilson; finance manager Michael Price; marketing manager Shirley Kirk; general manager Jaki Booth; new work & productions Paul Herbert; cinema programmer Taz Bashir; exhibitions programmer Judy Danes; education & outreach Gabrielle Oliver
Venue type: arts centre *Capacity:* The Theatre 201, The Arena Theatre – stage A 350, stage B 470, The Hexagon 86 *Policy:* buy-in, co-present, rent, produce *Arts types:* theatre, concerts, dance, comedy, film, visual and performance arts *Comments:* home of: Chitraleka and Dancers, Sampad (South Asian Arts Development Agency), Caliche, GEESE Theatre Company, Stan's Cafe

NEC, The
Birmingham B40 1NT
Tel: 121-780 4141/4133 (box office) Fax: 121-780 3856
Internet: www.necgroup.co.uk
chief executive Barry Cleverdon; managing director Bob Prattey; arenas director Linda Barrow
Venue type: exhibition centre, concert hall, multi-purpose hall *Capacity:* NEC Arena 12500, National Indoor Arena 13000, Symphony Hall 2200 *Policy:* present, rent by negotiation *Arts types:* concerts, family shows, spectator sport

Old Rep Theatre
Station Street, **Birmingham** B5 4DY
Tel: 121-605 5116 Fax: 121-605 5121
manager Teresa Jansson
Venue type: Italian style *Capacity:* 378 *Policy:* rent, own productions *Comments:* resident company Birmingham Stage Company

Symphony Hall, Birmingham
International Convention Centre, Broad Street, **Birmingham** B1 2EA
Tel: 121-200 2000 Fax: 121-212 1982
E-Mail: symphony-hall@necgroup.co.uk
director Andrew Jowett; operations manager Chris Baldock; development manager Philippa Sherwood; marketing manager Mary Coles; press & pr manager Fiona Fraser
Venue type: concert hall
Capacity: 2200 *Policy:* present, rent
Arts types: orchestra, recitals, all types of music

King George's Hall (incorporating The Windsor Suite)
Northgate, **Blackburn** BB2 1AA
Tel: 1254-582 579 (administration)/1254-582 582 (box office) Fax: 1254-667 277
E-Mail: geoff.peake@blackburn.gov.uk
general manager Geoff Peake; production manager Howard Alderson-Perkins; promotions manager Steve Burch
Venue type: multi-purpose halls *Capacity:* Hall A 2000, Hall B 750 *Policy:* rent, co-present *Arts types:* orchestra, opera, ballet, pop, rock, musicals, exhibitions, conferences etc., ice-shows

Blackpool Grand Theatre
Church Street, **Blackpool** FY1 1HT
Tel: 1253-290 111/190 (box office)
Fax: 1253-751 767
Internet: ww.blackpoolgrand.co.uk
E-Mail: admin@blackpoolgrand.co.uk
general manager Stephanie Sirr; deputy general manager Neil Thomson; administration/personnel manager Catherine Gibson
Venue type: theatre *Capacity:* 1211 *Policy:* rent, co-present *Arts types:* varied range of productions from national and international companies presenting everything from contemporary dance to serious drama *Comments:* national touring house; also education department, education office: Celine Wyatt tel: 1253-299 797, and youth theatre

Opera House & Winter Gardens
Church Street, **Blackpool** FY1 1HW
Tel: 1253-625 252 Fax: 1253-751 204
general manager Steve Marshall; front of house manager Linda Baker
Venue type: opera house *Capacity:* 2960 *Policy:* rent *Arts types:* all forms including musicals, comedy, opera, ballet, pop concerts, etc. *Comments:* open all year round with broad range Christmas season

Octagon Theatre
Howell Croft South, **Bolton** BL1 1SB
Tel: 1204-529 407/520 661 (box office)
Fax: 1204-380 110
head of marketing and sales Lynn Melville; press & marketing officer Rachel Bartholomew
Venue type: theatre *Capacity:* main house 420, Bill Naughton Theatre up to 100 *Policy:* produce *Arts types:* drama *Comments:* offers loop induction system and wheelchair access (lift, ramps & seating arrangements); see also Drama

Bournemouth International Centre
Exeter Road, **Bournemouth** BH2 5BH
Tel: 1202-456 400 Fax: 1202-456 500
Internet: www.bournemouth.gov.uk/bic
director Kevin Sheehan; entertainments and events manager Rob Zuradzki; operations manager Barry Wilson; publicity officer Anthony Hardman; technical manager (stage) Roger Stares
Capacity: Windsor Hall up to 4000, Tregonwell Hall 1220, Purbeck Hall 3000 *Policy:* percentage, rent *Arts types:* multi-functional, conferences, exhibitions, entertainment *Comments:* main season: May-Sept; one nights and other attractions throughout the year

Pavilion Theatre
Exeter Road, **Bournemouth** BH2 5BH
Tel: 1202-456 456 Fax: 1202-456 500
director Kevin J. Sheehan; entertainments and events manager Rob Zuradzki; publicity officer Anthony Hardman
Venue type: pavilion theatre
Capacity: 1072 stalls, circle 446 *Policy:* rent, percentage
Arts types: ballet, drama, concerts, pantomime, ice shows *Comments:* administrated by Bournemouth International Centre

Pier Theatre
Bournemouth Pier, **Bournemouth** BH1 5AD
Tel: 1202-456 456 Fax: 1202-456 500
director of Bournemouth International Centre Pavilion Kevin Sheehan; entertainments manager Rob Zuradzki; publiciy officer Anthony Hardman
Venue type: theatre *Capacity:* 837 *Policy:* percentage, rent *Arts types:* summer season farce & musical, pantomime, plays, one-nighters *Comments:* national touring house, newly refurbished auditorium; administrated by Bournemouth International Centre

South Hill Park Arts Centre
Bracknell RG12 7PA
Tel: 1344-427 272/484 123 (box office) Fax: 1344-411 427
E-Mail: marketing@southhillpark.org.uk
director Tim Brinkman; director of programming David Fry; director of sales & marketing Emma Cooper-Hammond
Venue type: arts centre *Capacity:* theatre 330, recital room 100, cellar bar 120, cinema 60, dance studio 50 *Policy:* co-present, rent *Arts types:* concerts, theatre, ballet, opera, alternative cabaret, rock jazz, dance, folk, world music *Comments:* also workshops and courses for all age ranges; educational & community programmes available

Alhambra Theatre
Morley Street, **Bradford** BD7 1AJ
Tel: 1274-752 375/000 (box office) Fax: 1274-752 185
general manager John Botteley; administrator Laura Wood; marketing manager Kathryn Mawre; technical manager Neil Bohanna; head of marketing & sales David Warren
Venue type: theatre, studio
Capacity: theatre 1482, studio 250
Policy: present, rent *Arts types:* drama, ballet, musicals, opera, concerts, pantomine
Comments: part of Bradford Theatres, includes St. George's Concert Hall; owned by Bradford Council

St George's Concert Hall
Bridge Street, **Bradford** BD1 1JS
Tel: 1274-752 186/000 (box office)
Fax: 1274-720 736
general manager John Botteley (1274-752 375); head of customer services Gerry Clifford; marketing manager Katherine Mawer (1274-752 375)
Venue type: concert hall *Capacity:* up to 2000 *Policy:* rent, own risk and shared risk *Arts types:* Asian arts, dance, rock & pop concerts, orchestral *Comments:* part of Bradford Theatres; owned by Bradford Council

Watermans Arts Centre
40 High Street, **Brentford** TW8 0DS
Tel: 20-8847 5651/8568 1176 (box office)
Fax: 20-8569 8592
Internet: waterman.org.uk
E-Mail: watermans@compuserve.com
executive director Lesley Wake; programme director t.b.a.; cultural development Hardial Rai; centre manager Lovna O'Leary; press & publicity officer Natasha Bucknor; production manager Alan Hibbs; marketing manager t.b.a.; cinema director John Morgan-Tamosuras
Venue type: multiple arts centre
Capacity: theatre 239, cinema 125, music 500, gallery
Policy: rent, co-produce, box office split, produce
Arts types: theatre, popular and world music, film, Asian arts, workshops, some mixed media and professional and community based exhibition programmes, an education programme covers all areas of work, visual arts *Comments:* restaurant/bar available

Brighton Centre
King's Road, **Brighton** BN1 2GR
Tel: 1273-290 131 Fax: 1273-779 980
Internet: www.brightoncentre.co.uk
E-Mail: b-centre@pavilion.co.uk
general manager Steve Piper; marketing & programme manager Wendy Walton
Venue type: multi-purpose civic venue with three spaces
Capacity: main hall 5100, Hewison Hall 600, east wing 600 *Policy:* available for rent and/or shared promotion
Arts types: rock, pop, exhibitions, ballet, orchestra, jazz world music, sporting events, ice shows & conferences

Gardner Arts Centre
University of Sussex, Falmer, **Brighton** BN1 9RA
Tel: 1273-685 447 (administration)/861 (box office)
Fax: 1273-678 551
E-Mail: gardner-arts@pavilion.co.uk
director Sue Webster; technical manager Phil Webb; theatre manager Tony Loveless; administrator Cheryl Pierce; marketing officer Lisa O'Connor
Venue type: arts centre, gallery
Capacity: 482 auditorium, gallery 100, studio gallery 30
Policy: present, rent *Arts types:* theatre, dance, mime, music, exhibitions, physical theatre, puppetry, film
Comments: provide infra-red hearing enhancement; free parking after 6.00pm

Theatre Royal Brighton
New Road, **Brighton** BN1 1SD
Tel: 1273-327 480 Fax: 1273-777 156
general manager Roger Neil; house manager Tim Slater
Venue type: theatre
Capacity: 952 *Policy:* rent, percentage deals
Arts types: drama, opera, ballet, musicals, pantomime, occasional one nighters
Comments: national touring – pre and post London

Arnolfini
16 Narrow Quay, **Bristol** BS1 4QA
Tel: 117-929 9191 Fax: 117-925 3876
Internet: www.channel.org.uk/arnolfini
E-Mail: arnolfini@arnolfini.demon.co.uk
director Caroline Collier; deputy director Helen Pearson; dance and live art programmer Helen Cole; publicity and marketing Catriona Henderson; operations manager Polly Cole
Venue type: art gallery, theatre, cinema, cafe bar, bookshop *Capacity:* 231 *Policy:* presents its own programme of work with a national/international reputation; for conferencing facilities – contact deputy director *Arts types:* contemporary visual arts, dance, theatre, live art, performance, film, music, bookshop readings, lectures and talks *Comments:* runs educational projects in conjunction with exhibitions and performances

Bristol Hippodrome
St Augustine's Parade, **Bristol** BS1 4UZ
Tel: 117-926 5524/870-607 7500 (box office)
Fax: 117-925 1661
general manager John Wood; deputy general manager Julian Withers; press officer Sarah Bennett-Milne; pa to general manager David Dunn
Venue type: theatre *Capacity:* 1977 *Policy:* rent, co-present *Arts types:* opera, ballet, concerts, musicals, comedy *Comments:* national touring theatre

Bristol Old Vic
Theatre Royal, King Street, **Bristol** BS1 4ED
Tel: 117-949 3993 (admin)/987 7877 (box office)
Fax: 117-949 3996
Internet: www.bristol-old-vic.co.uk
E-Mail: bristol.old.vic@cableinet.co.uk
general manager Sarah Smith; artistic director Andrew Hay; production manager Derek Simpson; assistant general manager James Taljaard; education director Heather Williams; press officer Phil Gibby; marketing officer Andrew Smaje
Venue type: theatre and small theatre *Capacity:* Theatre Royal 656, New Vic up to 200, New Vic basement 80 *Policy:* produce, rent *Arts types:* drama, musicals, comedy, opera *Comments:* national touring house; offers hearing loops, signed performances, ground floor disabled access & facilities (ramps, stair-lift, toilets); see also Drama

Colston Hall
Colston Street, **Bristol** BS1 5AR
Tel: 117-922 3693/3673 Fax: 117-922 3681
E-Mail: ken_lovell@bristol-city.gov.uk
general manager Ken Lovell; concert planning and promotions manager Paul Preager; management officer Carole Lumber
Venue type: concert hall *Capacity:* 2121/1886 *Policy:* rent, co-promote *Arts types:* all types of music

St George's Brandon Hill
Bristol BS1 5PZ
Tel: 117-929 4929 Fax: 117-927 6537
director Jonathan Stracey; administrator Catherine Freda; head of marketing & development Suzanne Clatworthy
Venue type: concert hall & recording studio *Capacity:* 500 *Policy:* present, co-present, rent for concerts and classical music, recordings *Arts types:* classical music, jazz, world music *Comments:* BBC lunchtime concerts for Radio 3; disabled access, restaurant and bar

Churchill Theatre
High Street, **Bromley** BR1 1HA
Tel: 20-8464 7131 (admin)/8460 6677 (box office) Fax: 20-8290 6968
administrator Dominic Adams; head of marketing & publicity Colin Hilton; production manager Digby Robinson; producer Ian Ross; theatre manager John Short
Venue type: theatre *Capacity:* 785 *Policy:* rent, co-present, produce *Arts types:* dance, drama, musicals, children's shows, comedies, concerts, opera
Comments: see also Drama

Theatre Royal Bury St Edmunds
Westgate Street, **Bury St Edmunds** IP33 1QR
Tel: 1284-769 505 (box office)/755 127 (admin)
Fax: 1284-706 035
Internet: www.theatreroyal.org
theatre director Colin Blumenau; head of marketing Matthew Sanders; marketing assistant Sarah Croker; box office manager Louise Money; technical manager Mark Passey; chief electrician Trudi Ninnim; front of house manager Ian Laidlaw; education & community co-ordinator Helen Dilley
Venue type: theatre *Capacity:* 360 *Policy:* receiving theatre that takes mainly professional touring companies; also available for rent to amateur companies *Arts types:* drama, dance, opera, jazz, film, children's theatre, pantomime, mime, music, ballet

Buxton Opera House
Water Street, **Buxton** SK17 6XN
Tel: 1298-72050 Fax: 1298-27563
Internet: www.buxton-opera.co.uk
E-Mail: boxoffice@buxton-opera.co.uk
theatre director Andrew Aughton; marketing manager Helen Dunnett; sponsorship director Pam Wright; box office manager Chris Nelson; technical manager Guy Dunk; house manager Martin Robinson
Venue type: theatre *Capacity:* 937 *Policy:* rent, co-present, receiving venue *Arts types:* ballet, opera, drama, concerts, children's theatre, comedy, music, dance, pantomime *Comments:* July: Buxton Festival (opera); August: International Gilbert & Sullivan Festival

ADC Theatre
Park Street, **Cambridge** CB5 8AS
Tel: 1223-359 547 (admin)/503 333 (box office)
Fax: 1223-300 085 (admin)
Internet: www.adc-theatre.cam.ac.uk
E-Mail: info@adc-theatre.cam.ac.uk
manager Zoë Curnow; production & publicity Alex Godden, Tom Steer
Venue type: theatre *Capacity:* 227 *Policy:* rent *Arts types:* musicals, opera, dance, drama *Comments:* managed by the University of Cambridge; rent theatrical equipment; box office is at Cambridge Arts Centre

Cambridge Arts Theatre
6 St Edwards Passage, **Cambridge** CB2 3PJ
Tel: 1223-578 933 (admin) Fax: 1223-578 929 (admin)
E-Mail: theatre@cambarts.demon.co.uk
artistic director Ian Ross; marketing manager Nicola Upson
Venue type: theatre *Capacity:* 666 *Policy:* receive *Arts types:* all types *Comments:* receiving venue

Cambridge Corn Exchange
Wheeler Street, **Cambridge** CB2 3QB
Tel: 1223-457 555 (admin)/357 851 (box office)
Fax: 1223-457 559 (admin)/329 074 (box office)
Internet: www.cambridge.gov.uk/cornex.htm
E-Mail: boxoffice@cambridge.gov.uk
director Robert Sanderson; business manager Graham Saxby; entertainment and events manager Mick Gray; marketing manager Neil Jones; box office manager Roberta Gates; front of house manager Jeff Charnock
Venue type: multi-purpose *Capacity:* seated 1411, standing 1837 *Policy:* emphasis on rent, by negotiation *Arts types:* music, dance, opera, theatre, exhibitions, conferences *Comments:* venue funded by Cambridge City Council

Junction, The
Clifton Road, **Cambridge** CB1 7GX
Tel: 1223-578 000 Fax: 1223-565 600
Internet: www.junction.co.uk
E-Mail: vito@junction.co.uk
artistic director Paul Bogen; general manager Gary Woolley
Venue type: performing arts venue *Capacity:* 850 standing, 200 seated *Policy:* rent, produce, present *Arts types:* live music, peformance theatre, etc.

Mumford Theatre
APU, East Road, **Cambridge** CB1 1PT
Tel: 1223-352 932 (admin & box office) Fax: 1223-352 973
E-Mail: mumford@bridge.anglia.ac.uk
theatre manager Richard Purkiss; production coordinator Leigh Stephenson; box office/clerical assistant Sally Buckingham
Venue type: theatre *Capacity:* 250 *Policy:* rent, present *Arts types:* drama, musicals, dance, festivals, concerts, opera, ballet, conferences, lectures
Comments: disabled facilities (access, toilet, space for up to 5 wheelchairs); induction loop system; occassional signed performances

Marlowe Theatre, The
The Friars, **Canterbury** CT1 2AS
Tel: 1227-763 262 Fax: 1227-781 802
theatre director Mark Everett; head of marketing & development Karen Adams; theatre manager Peter Walker
Venue type: theatre *Capacity:* 997 *Policy:* present *Arts types:* drama, opera, dance, classical music, comedy, popular music, children's shows *Comments:* national touring house plus active Education and Outreach programme

Chapter Arts Centre
Market Road, Canton, **Cardiff (Wales)** CF5 1QE
Tel: 29-2031 1050/3430 (minicom) Fax: 29-2031 3431
Internet: www.chapter.org
E-Mail: enquiry@chapter.org
director Janek Alexander; theatre director Gordana Vnuk; marketing & media Carol Jones
Venue type: arts centre *Capacity:* 120, 100, 60 *Policy:* present, co-production, commission *Arts types:* contemporary performing arts from Britain and the world, specialising in theatre, visual arts and cinema
Comments: member of IETM

New Theatre
Park Place, **Cardiff (Wales)** CF10 3LN
Tel: 29-2087 8787 Fax: 29-2087 8880
head of arts & cultural services, Cardiff County Council Judi Richards; strategic planning manager Susan Lewis; development manager Jane Sorotos; head of marketing, arts & cultural services Michael Grensted; general manager Giles Ballisat; marketing manager Matt Smith; senior house manager Jeff Burns
Venue type: theatre *Capacity:* 1156 *Policy:* split box office, guarantee, receiving house *Arts types:* opera, theatre, dance, musicals, drama, pantomime, children's shows *Comments:* tours; performing home of Welsh National Opera; owned, managed and funded by the City & County of Cardiff

Sherman Theatre
Senghennydd Road, off Park Place,
Cardiff (Wales) CF24 4YE
Tel: 29-2064 6901 (stagedoor)/6900 (box office)
Fax: 29-2064 6902
general manager Margaret Jones; artistic director Philip Clark
Venue type: theatre *Capacity:* main 474, studio theatre 180 *Policy:* rent, producing young people theatre, takes touring companies *Arts types:* mainstream, new and experimental drama, dance, music, Welsh language productions, comedy *Comments:* home for the Sherman Theatre Company; see also Drama

St David's Hall
The Hayes, **Cardiff (Wales)** CF1 2SH
Tel: 29-2087 8500/8444(box office) Fax: 29-2087 8599
head of arts & cultural services, Cardiff City & County Council Judi Richards
Venue type: concert and conference hall *Capacity:* 2000 *Policy:* mainly present *Arts types:* classical concert recitals, jazz, pop & rock, comedy, roots & world music, light entertainment *Comments:* receiving venue; workshops for all age ranges; educational programmes

Wales Millenium Centre
Canolfan Mileniwm Cymru
PO Box 2001, **Cardiff (Wales)** CF1 6YS
Tel: 29-2040 2000 Fax: 29-2040 2001
E-Mail: wales.millenium.centre@wmc.org.uk
chairman Sir Alan Cox; chief executive Kathryn McDowell
Venue type: modern *Capacity:* 1800 + other spaces *Comments:* due to open 2001; houses 7 residents among which: Diversions Dance Company and Welsh National Opera

Everyman Theatre
Regent Street, **Cheltenham** GL50 1HQ
Tel: 1242-512 515(admin)/572 573 (box office)
Fax: 1242-224 305/236 700 (press)
Internet: www.everyman.u-net.com
E-Mail: admin@everyman.u-net.com
chief executive Philip Bernays; administrative coordinator Michelle Draine
Venue type: theatre and studio theatre *Capacity:* 658, studio 60 *Policy:* presenting and producing theatre with active reachout department *Arts types:* wide range of theatre, modern, classical, dance, musicals, concerts, comedy, conferences *Comments:* see also Drama

Town Hall
Imperial Square, **Cheltenham** GL50 1QA
Tel: 1242-521 621/227 979 (box office) Fax: 1242-573 902
chief officer for festivals and entertainments Jeremy Tyndall; entertainments and marketing manager Tim Hulse
Venue type: concert hall *Capacity:* main room 1000, pillar room 320 *Policy:* rent, self-promotion *Arts types:* classical, jazz, pop, folk concerts, dance, festivals, recitals, comedy *Comments:* connected venues: The Pittville Pump Room cap 400

Gateway Theatre Company
Hamilton Place, **Chester** CH1 2BH
Tel: 1244-344 238 Fax: 1244-317 277
Internet: www.gateway/theatre.org
administrative director Shea Connolly; artistic director Deborah Shaw; head of marketing Judith Edwards
Venue type: theatre *Capacity:* 440 *Policy:* mainly produce, some rent, co-presentations *Arts types:* drama, concerts, musicals, dance, community projects
Comments: see also Drama

Chichester Festival Theatre
Oaklands Park, **Chichester** PO19 4AP
Tel: 1243-784 437/781 312 (box office) Fax: 1243-787 288
E-Mail: admin@cft.org.uk
director Andrew Welch; theatre manager Janet Burton
Venue type: theatre & studio *Capacity:* Main House 1374, Minerva Studio 280 *Policy:* present, rent, produce *Arts types:* drama, musicals, concerts
Comments: rent and hire from October-April; from May-October venue is used by Chichester Festival Theatre Company; extending own productions in autumn, also take in touring companies; also used as a cinema; see also Drama

West Cliff Theatre
Tower Road, **Clacton-on-Sea** CO15 1LE
Tel: 1255-474 000 Fax: 1255-475 730
acting administrator Alan King
Venue type: theatre *Capacity:* 590
Policy: rent or shared risk *Arts types:* concerts, drama, dance, variety, childrens' shows

Festival Halls & Theatre Complex
George Street, **Corby** NN17 1QB
Tel: 1536-402 551(admin)/233(box office)
Fax: 1536-403 748
general manager Ted Blair; technical manager Richard Glen; catering manager Mike Green
Venue type: multi-purpose
Capacity: Festival hall – cabaret style 550, theatrical 690, 700 standing, 274 balcony seats *Policy:* produce, rent, present *Arts types:* all arts types except the visual arts and crafts *Comments:* theatre has been recently refurbished and has disabled access

Belgrade Theatre
Belgrade Square, **Coventry** CV1 1GS
Tel: 24-7625 6431 Fax: 24-7655 0680
Internet: www.belgrade.co.uk
director Bob Eaton; general manager David Beidas; head of marketing Simon Daykin; associate producer Jane Hytch
Venue type: Studio Theatre, Main House
Capacity: Studio 60, Main House 866 *Policy:* mixture of home-produced shows and touring productions and one night events *Arts types:* new writing: work for young people, classics, comedy, musicals
Comments: hold 'Coventry Arts Alive Festival'; see also Drama and Festivals

Warwick Arts Centre
University of Warwick, Gibbet Hill Road, **Coventry** CV4 7AL
Tel: 24-7652 3734(admin)/4524 (box office)
Fax: 24-7652 3883
Internet: www.warwick.ac.uk/artscentre
E-Mail: p.m.king@warwick.ac.uk
director Stella Hall; deputy director Alan Rivett; technical director Howard Potts; marketing director Robert McPherson; press officer Paula King
Venue type: arts centre: theatre, studio, concert hall, film theatre, gallery, lecture theatre
Capacity: Butterworth Hall 1471, other spaces 150-540
Policy: promotes, co-produces, rent
Arts types: all aspects of performing, visual & media arts
Comments: all areas of the Arts Centre are accessible for wheelchair users

The Hawth
Hawth Avenue, **Crawley** RH10 6YZ
Tel: 1293-552 941 Fax: 1293-533 362
Internet: www.hawth.co.uk
E-Mail: hawth@enterprise.net
theatre and arts manager Kevin Eason; promotions & entertainments manager Dave Watmore; arts officer Cathy Westbrook; assistant arts officer Liz Hart; publicity officer Steve Crane
Venue type: theatre and arts centre
Capacity: main house 850, studio 147, amphitheatre 300
Policy: present *Arts types:* wide range of theatre, music, dance

Fairfield Halls
Park Lane, **Croydon** CR9 1DG
Tel: 20-8681 0821/8688 9291(box office)
Fax: 20-8760 0835
Internet: www.croydon.gov.uk/fairfield
E-Mail: dbarr@fairfield.co.uk
chief executive Derek Barr; head of artistic planning Nick Leigh; head of marketing & development Vicky Nicholls
Venue type: concert hall, theatre
Capacity: concert hall 1600, Ashcroft Theatre 750 *Policy:* rent, co-present *Arts types:* ballet, dance, concerts, drama, opera, films, pantomime *Comments:* home of the London Mozart Players

Arts Centre
Vane Terrace, **Darlington** DL3 7AX
Tel: 1325-483 271 (admin)/486 555 (box office)
Fax: 1325-365 794
head of theatre and arts Peter Cutchie; performing arts programmer Lynda Winstanley
Venue type: arts centre and Myles Meehan Gallery
Capacity: up to 350 *Policy:* rent, present, co-productions
Arts types: music, theatre, exhibitions, installations, workshops, dance, film, education initiatives
Comments: resident company: Cleveland Theatre Company

Darlington Civic Theatre
Parkgate, **Darlington** DL1 1RR
Tel: 1325-468 006 (administration)/486 555 (box office)
Fax: 1325-368 278
Internet: www.darlington-arts.co.uk
E-Mail: admin@darlington-arts.co.uk
head of theatre and the arts Peter Cutchie; theatre manager Sarah Richards; front of house manager Stephen Sandford; technical manager Adam Nix; chief electrician Stephen Sanderson; stage manager Bill Cunningham; box office manager Pat Fawcett; secretary Betty MacFall
Venue type: theatre
Capacity: 900 *Policy:* present
Arts types: major touring of plays, ballet, opera, musicals, variety, concerts and major pantomime season *Comments:* national touring house

Orchard, The
The Home Gardens, **Dartford** DA1 1ED
Tel: 1322-220 099 (administration)/220 000 (box office) Fax: 1322-227 122
theatre manager Vanessa Hart
Venue type: multi-purpose *Capacity:* 960 *Policy:* rent, present, co-productions, split percentage *Arts types:* opera, ballet, concerts, musicals, comedy *Comments:* touring theatre

Assembly Rooms
Market Place, **Derby** DE1 3AH
Tel: 1332-255 443 (management)/255 800 (box office)
Fax: 1332-255 788
general manager Chris Ward-Brown; administrator Harriet Spalding; marketing manager Suzanne Sharris
Venue type: multi-purpose *Capacity:* 3 halls plus suites: Hall I – seated 1742, standing 2000, Hall II – seated 330, standing 500, Hall III – seated 246 *Policy:* mainly rental and risk share, some self promote *Arts types:* full range of live acts presented, also exhibitions, conferences etc.

Derby Playhouse
Eagle Centre, **Derby** DE1 2NF
Tel: 1332-363 271 Fax: 1332-294 412
Internet: www.derbyplayhouse.demon.co.uk
E-Mail: admin@derbyplayhouse.demon.co.uk
executive director David W. Edwards; artistic director Mark Clements; press & marketing manager Jonathan Saville; associate director, education Pete Meakin
Venue type: Main House, Studio Theatre *Capacity:* Main House 535, Studio 110 (max.) *Policy:* produce, rent *Arts types:* various including plays, musicals, dance, concerts
Comments: subsidised regional theatre; own productions 40 weeks a year; sunday concerts; occasional touring productions; see also Drama

Gaiety Theatre
Harris Promenade, **Douglas (Isle of Man)** IM1 2HH
Tel: 1624-624 006 (admin)/625 001 (box office)
Fax: 1624-629 028
artistic director Mervin Russell Stokes; production manager Seamus Shea; front of house manager Annette Christian
Venue type: proscenium theatre *Capacity:* 869 *Policy:* guarantees, percentage deals & box office splits *Arts types:* musicals, concerts, opera, ballet, plays, pantomime and summer season *Comments:* national touring house; venue newly restored; Victorian stage; disabled access

Dudley Town Hall
St James's Road, **Dudley** DY1 1HP
Tel: 1384-815 544/577 (admin)/812 812 (box office)
Fax: 1384-815 534
venue manager Andrew Grimshaw; principal arts officer Rosemary Amos; senior arts officer Stephanie Donaldson (tel: 815 540)
Venue type: multi-purpose concert hall
Capacity: concert hall 1060 *Policy:* present, rent, box office split *Arts types:* orchestra, chamber music, folk music, jazz, rock, pop

Caird Hall
City Square, **Dundee (Scotland)** DD1 3BB
Tel: 1382-434 451/940 (box office) Fax: 1382-434 451
Caird Hall manager Susan Pasfield
Venue type: multi-purpose *Capacity:* 2400, 1300, 400
Policy: rent, percentage deals *Arts types:* dance, concerts, exhibitions, conferences

Dundee Repertory Theatre
Tay Square, **Dundee (Scotland)** DD1 1PB
Tel: 1382-227 684 Fax: 1382-228 609
chief executive, artistic director Hamish Glen; administrative director Joanna Reid; artistic director – Scottish Dance Theatre Janet Smith; associate director – community Stephen Stenning
Venue type: repertory theatre and national touring dance co. *Capacity:* 455 *Arts types:* drama (classical repertoire from throughout the world translated and adapted by contemporary playwrights mixed with new plays by local writers), jazz and folk musical evenings, stand-up comedy *Comments:* venue for Scottish and international groups; home of Scottish Dance Theatre; see also Drama and Dance

Whitehall Theatre
Bellfield Street, **Dundee (Scotland)** DD1 5JA
Tel: 1382-322 684 Fax: 1382-226 926
chairman t.b.a.; general manager Brian Wyles; administration Mike Paterson
Venue type: theatre *Capacity:* 742 *Policy:* hire/percentage
Arts types: ballet, drama, opera, concerts, touring groups *Comments:* venue is self-financing

Congress Theatre
Carlisle Road, **Eastbourne** BN21 4BP
Tel: 1323-412 000/415 500 Fax: 1323-727 369
general manager Ian Alexander; director of tourism and community services Ronald G Cussons
Venue type: theatre *Capacity:* 1689 *Policy:* present, rent
Arts types: opera, ballet, concerts, musicals, conferences
Comments: national touring house

Point Dance & Arts Centre, The
Leigh Road, **Eastleigh** SO50 9DE
Tel: 1703-629 226 (admin)/652 333 (box office)
Fax: 1703-651 123
Internet: www.eastleigh.gov.uk
E-Mail: thepoint@eastleigh.gov.uk
director Mary Dawson; marketing manager Katie Campbell; technical manager Colin Monk; dance development manager Clare Purnell; front of house manager April Orlawski
Venue type: multi-media arts centre & cinema
Capacity: theatre 300, dance studio 30
Policy: promote, rent
Arts types: dance, drama, music, opera, visual arts, literature, film, workshops, classes, festivals, conference
Comments: performances, workshops, outreach & education work in all media, for all ages

Assembly Rooms
54 George Street, **Edinburgh (Scotland)** EH2 2LR
Tel: 131-220 4348/4349 (box office)
Fax: 131-220 6812
Internet: dialspace.dial.pipex.com/assemblyrooms/
E-Mail: assemblyrooms@dial.pipex.com
manager Simon Robson; assistant managers Jackie Skinner, Dave Meah; lettings officer Yvonne Elliot
Venue type: multi-purpose *Capacity:* music hall 700, assembly room 400, supper room 150, drawing room A 100, drawing room B 80, smoke rooms 20 *Policy:* building available for rent and co-promotions *Arts types:* music, dance, theatre, comedy

Edinburgh Festival Theatre
13/29 Nicolson Street, **Edinburgh (Scotland)** EH8 9FT
Tel: 131-662 1112/529 6000 (box office)
Fax: 131-667 0744
Internet: www.eft.co.uk
E-Mail: empire@edfestth.demon.co.uk
general manager Stephen Barry; marketing manager Anne McCluskey; press officer Julie McSkimming; education officer Jo Pink
Venue type: opera house, dance house, Grand Palace of Varieties *Capacity:* Milburn auditorium 1900
Policy: share, rent, by negotiation *Arts types:* opera, dance, drama, musicals and mixed programme
Comments: 'a diversity of extremes'; largest stage in Britain; educational programmes; workshops for all age ranges

King's Theatre
2 Leven Street, **Edinburgh (Scotland)** EH3 9LQ
Tel: 131-662 1112 (admin)/529 6000 (box office)
Fax: 131-667 0744
E-Mail: empire@eft.co.uk
technical manager Alan Campbell; marketing and development manager Anne McCluskey
Venue type: Proscenium Arch theatre *Capacity:* 1340
Policy: rent, share
Arts types: wide range of programmes, mainly drama, musicals, comedy & pantomimes
Comments: national touring house; major Scottish venue; disabled access; wheelchair spaces; sennheiser sound system; usually one signed & audio described performance per production; working in conjunction with Edinburgh Festival Theatre

Playhouse Theatre
18-22 Greenside Place, **Edinburgh (Scotland)** EH1 3AA
Tel: 131-557 2692 Fax: 131-557 6520
chairman Paul Gregg; general manager Andy Lyst; marketing manager Sarah Heney; press officer Pam Blyth
Venue type: multi-purpose hall
Capacity: 3056 *Policy:* rent by negotiation, receiving house *Arts types:* musicals, comedy, rock, pop
Comments: disabled access

Queen's Hall
Clerk Street, **Edinburgh (Scotland)** EH8 9JG
Tel: 131-668 3456/667 7776 (box office)
Fax: 131-668 2656
E-Mail: queenshall@cablesnet.com.uk
general manager Beth Cavanagh; hall manager Gwen Orr
Venue type: concert hall
Capacity: 850 *Policy:* rent, co-present *Arts types:* classical, but also jazz, rock, pop, folk, comedy
Comments: home of: Scottish Chamber Orchestra, B.T. Scottish Ensemble

Theatre Workshop
34 Hamilton Place, **Edinburgh (Scotland)** EH3 5AX
Tel: 131-225 7942 Fax: 131-220 0112
E-Mail: theatreworkshop@ednet.co.uk
general manager Paula Van Hagen; artistic director Robert Rae; technical director Allan Woolfe; marketing manager Jane Molyneux
Venue type: theatre and arts centre
Capacity: auditorium 155, small studio 55
Policy: in-house producing company, occassional touring companies with strong educational bias
Arts types: emphasis on theatre, but also music, exhibitions, dance *Comments:* disabled access to all areas; text phone and induction loop for deaf patrons

Traverse Theatre
Cambridge Street, **Edinburgh (Scotland)** EH1 2ED
Tel: 131-228 3223 (admin)/1404 (box office)
Fax: 131-229 8443
administrative producer Lucy Mason; artistic director Philip Howard
Venue type: theatre and studio theatre space *Capacity:* Traverse I 250, Traverse II 100 *Policy:* produce *Arts types:* new writing, foreign plays in translation, European coproductions *Comments:* Britain's first purpose built theatre for new writing; see also Drama

Usher Hall
Lothian Road, **Edinburgh (Scotland)** EH1 2EA
Tel: 131-228 8616 (manager's office)/228 1155 (box office) Fax: 131-228 8848
manager Moira McKenzie; events coordinator Fiona Easton
Venue type: concert hall
Capacity: 2231 *Policy:* rent *Arts types:* classical music, pop, light entertainment, conferences
Comments: touring; the hall will be closed for refurbishment, re-opening in Dec 2000

Ardhowen – The Theatre By The Lakes
Dublin Road,
Enniskillen (Northern Ireland) BT74 6BR
Tel: 1365-323 233 (administration)/325 440 (box office)
Fax: 1365-327 102
manager and artistic director Eamonn Bradley; assistant manager Pamela Scrayfield; administrative assistant Jackie Owens
Venue type: theatre, arts centre *Capacity:* 290, studio 60 *Policy:* present, co-present, rent *Arts types:* theatre, opera, dance, classical music, variety, jazz, blues, folk
Comments: theatre can also be accessed by boat

Fermanagh Lakeland Forum
Broadmeadow,
Enniskillen (Northern Ireland) BT74 7EH
Tel: 1365-324 121 Fax: 1365-328 622
manager Iain Kennedy
Venue type: main hall, multipurpose *Capacity:* 1000 *Policy:* £5M public liability, rent if possible *Arts types:* pop concerts, Ulster orchestra *Comments:* stage can be constructed if required; workshops for all ages; educational and community programmes

Northcott Devon Theatre and Arts Centre
Northcott Theatre, Stocker Road, **Exeter** EX4 4QB
Tel: 1392-256 182/493 493 (box office)
Fax: 1392-499 641
Internet: www.ex.ac.uk/northcott
administrator John W Clarke; artistic director Ben Crocker; marketing director Sarah Dance; front of house & box office manager Liz Romer
Venue type: self-producing rep theatre *Capacity:* Northcott Theatre 433, Studio Theatre 80 *Policy:* produce, co-produce, incoming companies, rent, receive *Arts types:* drama, opera, dance, jazz *Comments:* see also Drama

Riverside Leisure Centre
Cowick Street, **Exeter** EX4 1AF
Tel: 1392-221 771 Fax: 1392-499 676
general manager Phil Roebuck; events manager Caroline Dodd
Venue type: multi-purpose *Capacity:* 1200 *Policy:* present, rent, split *Arts types:* concerts, exhibitions, conferences

St George's Hall
George Street, **Exeter** EX1 1BU
Tel: 1392-265 866 Fax: 1392-422 137
E-Mail: markets.halls@exeter.gov.uk
manager, halls & events David Lewis
Venue type: multi-purpose hall, concert hall, theatre *Capacity:* 500 *Policy:* rent by negotiation, sole & joint promotions *Arts types:* concerts, stage shows, films, conferences

Falkirk Town Hall
Municipal Building, Bridge Street,
Falkirk (Scotland) SK1 5RA
Tel: 1324-506 070/620 110 (box office)
Fax: 1324-506 001
entertainments officer A Craig Murray; communications manager Caroline Binnie
Venue type: multi-purpose *Capacity:* up to 900 *Policy:* rent, co-promote, promote *Arts types:* all performing arts *Comments:* disabled access (including ramps & lifts) and toilets

Farnham Maltings
Bridge Square, **Farnham** GU9 7QR
Tel: 1252-726 234 Fax: 1252-718 177
Internet: www.farnmaltings.com
E-Mail: farnmalt@aol.com
director Paul James; venue manager John Heath; visual arts officer Tozzy Bridger; marketing t.b.a.
Venue type: arts centre *Capacity:* Great Hall 456, Barley Room 150, Godwins & Tannery Room 200, Long Kiln Room 100, South West Kiln 25 *Policy:* present, rent *Arts types:* classical, contemporary, concerts, recitals, dance, folk music, conferences, exhibitions, jazz

Spa Pavilion Theatre
Undercliff Road West, **Felixstowe** IP11 8AQ
Tel: 1394-283 303/282 126 (box office) Fax: 1394-278 978
general manager Miles Cowburn; assistant manager Justine Clayton
Venue type: theatre (& restaurant)
Capacity: 919 *Policy:* available for rent, shared risk *Arts types:* rock, pop, variety, Irish, comedians, country & western, blues, drama, musicals, dance *Comments:* undergoing 5 year extensive refurbishment plan; seven wheelchair spaces and one wheelchair toilet; managed by Apollo Leisure Group in partnership with Suffolk Coastal District Council

Leas Cliff Hall
The Leas, **Folkstone** CT20 2DZ
Tel: 1303-254 695/253 193 (box office)
Fax: 1303-221 175
E-Mail: jobarnes@leascliffhall.freeserve.co.uk
general manager Jo Barnes; deputy manager Karen Thompson
Venue type: multi-purpose *Capacity:* seated 825, standing 1400 *Policy:* mainly hire *Arts types:* concert, dance, variety, comedy, jazz *Comments:* wheelchair access (lift); loop induction system; managed by Apollo Leisure UK, Ltd, Oxford

Gateshead Music Centre
Civic Centre, Regent Street, **Gateshead** NE8 1HH
Tel: 191-477 1011 Fax: 191-477 5154/478 2755
Internet: www.gatesheadmbc.gov.uk
E-Mail: 106074.677@compuserve.com
special projects Peter Starck (ext 2986, fax: 191-477 9136)
Venue type: modern style theatre *Capacity:* 1650, 400 + rehearsal rooms *Policy:* rent, own programming *Arts types:* music *Comments:* due to open 2002

CCA (Centre for Contemporary Arts)
McLellan Galleries, 270 Sauchiehall Street,
Glasgow (Scotland) G2 3EH
Tel: 141-332 7521 (admin)/0522 (box office)
Fax: 141-332 3226
E-Mail: gen@cca-glasgow.com
director Graham McKenzie; general manager Michael Jones; head of programme Francis McKee; head of marketing & development Morag Hendry
Venue type: flexible space for performance and exhibitions *Capacity:* flexible up to 250 *Policy:* producing, receiving, rent, present *Arts types:* new works, specialises in new developments in visual & performing arts, live arts, literature *Comments:* committed to presenting an innovative and challenging programme of exhibitions, performances, events and activities exploring new developments in the arts, and providing opportunities for artists and audiences in a local, national and international context; licensed cafe and arts bookshop at venue

Citizens' Theatre
Gorbals, **Glasgow (Scotland)** G5 9DS
Tel: 141-429 5561 (admin)/0022 (box office)
Fax: 141-429 7374
Internet: www.citz.co.uk/boxoffice/
E-Mail: boxoffice@citz.co.uk
general manager Sharman Weir; artistic directors Giles Havergal, Philip Prowse, Robert David MacDonald
Venue type: theatre
Capacity: Citizens' Theatre 600, Circle Studio 120, Stalls Studio 60 *Arts types:* British and foreign classics, Christmas shows, some visiting companies
Comments: home of Citizens' Company; established 1943; free previews of all Citizens' Company productions; see also Drama

City Halls & Old Fruit Market
Candleriggs, **Glasgow (Scotland)** G1 1NQ
Tel: 141-287 5511 (box office) Fax: 141-287 5533
Internet: www.glasgow.gov.uk/jav
E-Mail: city.live@glasgow.gov.uk
director, Glasgow City Council department of culture and leisure Bridget McConnell; programmer Maggie MacDonald (tel: 141-287 5023); media & pr Lesley Booth
Venue type: concert hall/city halls: contemporary music venue/exhibition space/theatre productions at the Old Fruit Market *Capacity:* Grand Hall 1216, Fruitmarket 1000 *Policy:* rent by negotiation *Arts types:* classical, jazz, folk and rock music events, conferences and exhibitions *Comments:* wheelchair access; disabled toilet & loop induction system (if required)

Glasgow Royal Concert Hall
2 Sauchihall Street, **Glasgow (Scotland)** G2 3NY
Tel: 141-332 6633/353 4137 (info.line)
Fax: 141-333 9123/353 4134 (box office)
Internet: www.grch.com
E-Mail: grch@grch.scotnet.co.uk
director Louise Mitchell; finance and administrator controller Arthur Laird; senior events administrator Karen Taylor; stage and events production manager Phil Smith; box office manager Jo Campbell; marketing manager Simon Drysdale
Venue type: multi-purpose with dedicated concert hall
Capacity: 2481, Strathclyde Suite 500 *Policy:* rent, present *Arts types:* symphony, chamber, light music, jazz, pop, country and western, folk
Comments: wheelchair access, induction loop system, free copies of monthly programme available on disc and in braille; guide dogs welcome

King's Theatre
294 Bath Street, **Glasgow (Scotland)** G2 4JN
Tel: 141-287 3651 Fax: 141-287 5533
Internet: www.king-glasgow.co.uk
E-Mail: city.lwe@glasgow.gov.uk
director, Glasgow City Council department of culture and leisure Bridget McConnell; senior programming officer Pauline Murphy; technical manager Peter Green; theatre operations manager Stephen Kelly; media & PR Lesley Booth; head of marketing & commercial development Julie Tait
Venue type: theatre *Capacity:* 1785 *Arts types:* performance, drama, opera, dance, variety
Comments: touring house

Mitchell Theatre & James Moir Hall Complex
Granville Street, **Glasgow (Scotland)** G3 7DR
Tel: 141-282 5033/287 4855 Fax: 141-221 0695
Internet: www.glasgow.gov.uk/pav
E-Mail: city.lwe@glasgow.gov.uk
director, Glasgow City Council department of culture and leisure Bridget McConnell; head of programming Susan Deighan; technical manager t.b.a.; theatre operations manager Stephen Kelly; media & PR Lesley Booth; marketing manager Julie Tait
Venue type: multi-use theatre and conference complex
Capacity: Mitchell Theatre 418, James Moir Hall 400
Policy: rent *Arts types:* drama, music, dance, exhibitions, conferences

Royal Scottish Academy of Music and Drama
100 Renfrew Street, **Glasgow (Scotland)** G2 3DB
Tel: 141-332 4101/5057 (box office) Fax: 141-332 8901
Internet: www.rsamd.ac.uk
E-Mail: registry@rsamd.ac.uk
business manager Kevin Kelly; publications & publicity officer Gillian Bruce; principal Dr Philip Ledger; diector of school of drama Vladimir Mirodan; director of school of music Rita McAllister; director finance & administration Isobel Fowler
Venue type: multi-purpose *Capacity:* Stevenson Hall 364, Guinness Room 108, New Athenaeum Theatre 360, Chandler Studio Theatre up to 130, Opera Studio up to 130 *Policy:* rent, present *Arts types:* drama, conferences, classical and jazz concerts, exhibitions
Comments: disabled access (incl. ramps & lift); also loop induction system

Theatre Royal Glasgow
282 Hope Street, **Glasgow (Scotland)** G2 3QA
Tel: 141-332 3321/9000 (box office) Fax: 141-332 4477
Internet: www.arts.gla.ac.uk/tfts/scotop/scotop.html
E-Mail: 101776.3173@compuserve.com
managing director Ruth Mackenzie; technical director Julian Sleath; head of marketing & press Roberta Doyle; theatre manager Diane Long
Venue type: theatre *Capacity:* 1541 *Policy:* present, rent *Arts types:* opera, ballet, drama, dance, concerts, musicals, comedy *Comments:* national touring house: Scottish Opera, Scottish Ballet and other national touring theatre companies, ballet companies, commercial tours

Tramway
25 Albert Drive, **Glasgow (Scotland)** G41 2PE
Tel: 141-422 2023 (stage door)/287 3921 (admin)
Fax: 141-422 2021/287 5533 (admin)
Internet: www.tramway.org
E-Mail: amanda.brown@cls.gla.gov.uk
director, Glasgow City Council Department of Culture & Leisure Bridget McConnell; head of programming Susan Deighan; marketing manager Julie Tait; Media & PR Lesley Booth; theatre operations manager Stephen Kelly; programmer Stephen Slater
Venue type: multi-purpose arts venue
Capacity: Tramway 1 475, Tramway 2 (gallery) 1400, Tramway 4 (studio) 115 *Policy:* policy for production of contemporary performing and visual arts in four large refurbished industrial spaces. Commission, produce and co-produce
Arts types: exhibitions, installations, dance, performance, music theatre, opera, informal musics
Comments: wheelchair access; Tramway is undergoing major refurbishment, no further details available at time of going to print; due to re-open in early 2000

Tron Theatre Company
63 Trongate, **Glasgow (Scotland)** G1 5HB
Tel: 141-552 3748 Fax: 141-552 6657
Internet: www.tron.co.uk
E-Mail: neil@tron.co.uk
admin. director Neil Murray; artistic director Irina Brown; head of marketing & sales Damon Scott
Venue type: converted church – small scale touring
Capacity: 272 *Policy:* produce, rent, splits and guarantees *Arts types:* theatre, dance, music, comedy
Comments: newly upgraded auditorium;
currently large scale building redevelopment being undertaken (due to lottery funding) – completion date Feb 99; see also Drama

Guildford Civic
London Road, **Guildford** GU1 2AA
Tel: 1483-444 721 (administration)/555 (box office)
Fax: 1483-301 982
Internet: www.guildford-civic.co.com
E-Mail: info@guildford-civic.co.uk
manager John Holmes; deputy manager Kerry Whelan *Venue type:* concert hall, multi-purpose *Capacity:* 1500 *Policy:* rent, co-present *Arts types:* mixed *Comments:* wheelchair access; each show restricted to 16 wheelchairs; loop induction system

Victoria Theatre
Wards End, **Halifax** HX1 1BU
Tel: 1422-351 156/158 (box office) Fax: 1422-320 552
E-Mail: postbox@victoria-theatre.yorks.com
principal theatre & entertainment manager George Candler; marketing manager Helen Moran; assistant theatre manager Alison Metcalfe; technical manager Tim Fagan
Venue type: multi-purpose *Capacity:* 1585 *Policy:* rent, guarantee, receive, box office split *Arts types:* major symphony orchestras, light entertainment, dance, opera, drama, conferences, exhibitions, seminars, comedy, rock/pop, pantomime, musicals *Comments:* wheelchair access; loop induction system; signed performances

Hamilton Arts Centre
154 Montrose House, Montrose Crescent, **Hamilton (Scotland)** ML3 6LL
Tel: 1698-455 931 Fax: 1698-455 952
project coordinator Ken Meek; arts manager Sandy McBain
Venue type: multi-purpose *Capacity:* 300-500 *Comments:* at present still in planning stage, due to open in 2000

Playhouse
Playhouse Square, **Harlow** CM20 1LS
Tel: 1279-446 760(admin)/431 945 (box office)
Fax: 1279-424 391
Internet: www.harlow.gov.uk/arts.htm
E-Mail: nicola.bowland@harlow.gov.uk
general manager Laurence Sach; marketing manager Nicky Bowland; box office manager Sami Ballington; technical manager John Mann; stage manager Anthony Osbourne
Venue type: theatre *Capacity:* 400, studio 120 *Policy:* mainly receiving house *Arts types:* dance, drama, music, opera, conferences, jazz *Comments:* national touring house; restaurant and cafe bar

Harrogate International Conference and Exhibition Centre
Kings Road, **Harrogate** HG1 5LA
Tel: 1423-500 500 Fax: 1423-537 210
Internet: www.harrogateinternationalcentre.co.uk
E-Mail: sale@harrogateinternationalcentre.co.uk
director P. Lewis; administrator Christine Williams; technical division D. Wilmore
Venue type: entertainment venue *Capacity:* Harrogate Centre Auditorium 2000, Royal Hall 1260 *Policy:* rent *Arts types:* all types incl concerts, opera, dance, ballet, musicals, comedy, conferences, exhibitions, trade-fairs

Harrogate Theatre
Oxford Street, **Harrogate** HG1 1QF
Tel: 1423-502 710 Fax: 1423-563 205
Internet: www.harrogate.com/theatre
E-Mail: hgte-theatre@pop3.poptel.co.uk
executive director Sheena Wrigley; artistic director Rob Swain; marketing manager Rita Mulvey; production manager Phil Day
Venue type: theatre *Capacity:* main theatre 500, studio theatre 50 *Policy:* rent, producing repertory theatre, touring *Arts types:* full range of arts *Comments:* home of Harrogate Theatre Company; alternative Internet: www.harrogatetheatre.co.uk; see also Drama

White Rock Theatre
White Rock, **Hastings** TN34 1JX
Tel: 1424-781 010/000 (box office)
Fax: 1424-781 170
theatre manager Andy Mould; deputy manager Andrea Pulford; head of leisure services Michael Marsh
Venue type: civic centre *Capacity:* 1165 (1470 seated & standing) *Policy:* rent, first call, guarantee, percentage *Arts types:* plays, musicals, pantomime, one-nighters, classical orchestras, wrestling

Beck Theatre
Grange Road, **Hayes** UB3 2UE
Tel: 20-8561 7506 (admin)/8371 (box office)
Fax: 20-8569 1072
general manager Graham P Bradbury
Venue type: theatre *Capacity:* 600 *Policy:* rent *Arts types:* theatre, cinema, music, concerts *Comments:* national touring house; disabled facilities – toilets, ramps and loop induction system

Dacorum Pavilion
Marlowes, **Hemel Hempstead** HP1 1HA
Tel: 1442-228 707 (enquiries)/700 (box office)
Fax: 1442-228 735
E-Mail:
dacorumpavilion@hemelhempsted.freeserve.co.uk
general manager Nick Mowat; marketing manager Karen Winrow; programmes manager Louise Cecil; box office/administration manager Eve White
Venue type: multi-purpose *Capacity:* 1055 (seated), 1500 (standing) *Policy:* present, rent, share risk with other promoters *Arts types:* orchestra, pop, rock, exhibitions, dance, variety, pantomime, jazz, world music, conferences *Comments:* wheelchair access; infrared hearing system; disabled toilet & parking spaces; for What's On guide Tel: 1442-228 717 (available on audio tape & large print)

Queen's Hall Arts Centre
Beaumont Street, **Hexham** NE46 3LS
Tel: 1434-606 787/8/607 272 (box office)
Fax: 1434-606 043
marketing & press officer Mylee Hall; arts administrator Annette Dickson; arts manager Geof Keys; technical supervisor Andrew Biscoe; visual arts officer t.b.a.; outreach & education Sean Burn
Venue type: arts centre *Capacity:* 400
Policy: present, rent *Arts types:* music, drama, dance, visual arts *Comments:* also suite of photographic darkrooms; disabled access (ramp) to theatre, library & Queen's Cafe

Wycombe Swan
St Mary Street, **High Wycombe** HP11 2XE
Tel: 1494-514 444 Fax: 1494-538 080
Internet: www.wycombeswan.co.uk
E-Mail: enquiries@wycombeswan.co.uk
general manager Stuart Griffiths; assistant general manager Roger Keele; head of marketing Kirstie Higgins; house manager Joy Campbell; technical manager Carlos Queiroz
Venue type: theatre *Capacity:* theatre 1076, town hall 400, Oak Room 130 *Policy:* by negotiation *Arts types:* concerts, opera, ballet, plays, contemporary dance, musicals, pantomime, exhibitions, conferences
Comments: Town Hall and Oak Room also for hire; full access and facilities for wheelchairs in theatre

Broxbourne Civic Hall
High Street, **Hoddesdon** EN11 8BE
Tel: 1992-441 931 (admin)/946 (box office)
Fax: 1992-451 132
public hall manager David Cooper
Venue type: civic hall *Capacity:* 564 *Policy:* rent, receive, present *Arts types:* drama, opera, concerts, classical, jazz, musicals, pantomime, films *Comments:* wheelchair access; induction loop system can be provided

Queen's Theatre
Billet Lane, **Hornchurch** RM11 1QT
Tel: 1708-456 118/443 333 (box office) Fax: 1708-452 348
E-Mail: queens@globalnet.co.uk
administrative director Tony Hill; artistic director Bob Carlton; production manager Brod Mason; house managers Dave Ross, John Kliber
Venue type: theatre *Capacity:* 506 *Policy:* rent, present, produce *Arts types:* drama, concerts, children's shows, music and dance *Comments:* run by Havering Theatre Trust Ltd.; disabled access: induction loop system; signed and audio described performances;
see also Drama

Huddersfield Town Hall
Ramsden Street, **Huddersfield** HD1 2TA
Tel: 1484-221 900 Fax: 1484-221 541
E-Mail: cultural-hq@geo2.poptel.org.uk
town halls manager Julia Robinson; principal arts officer Glenis Burgess; arts officers Andrew Eastwood, Marcia Layne; multicultural arts officer Asif Khan
Venue type: multi-purpose concert hall *Capacity:* 1100, reception rooms available for smaller recitals *Policy:* rent, joint-promotion *Arts types:* symphony concerts, drama, light entertainment, conferences *Comments:* in-house catering available; also runs the following town halls as venues: Dewsbury (cap. 650), Cleckheaton (cap. 400), Batley (cap. 350) contact Julia Robinson

Lawrence Batley Theatre/Cellar Theatre
Queen's Square, Queen Street, **Huddersfield** HD1 2SP
Tel: 1484-425 282 Fax: 1484-425 336
artistic director Ron McAllister
Capacity: Lawrence Batley Theatre 477, Cellar Theatre 150, Attic Theatre 100 *Policy:* rent, co-produce *Arts types:* classic and contemporary drama, opera, dance, folk, jazz, comedy and film *Comments:* home of the Huddersfield Contemporary Music Festival (q.v)

Hull City Hall
Victoria Square, **Hull** HU1 3RQ
Tel: 1482-320 3880/613 808 (marketing)/226 655 (box office) Fax: 1482-613 961 (marketing)
theatre & hall director Russel E Hills; operations manager Tony Ridley; programme & development manager Michael J Lister; marketing officer Marie Burkitt; administrative assistant Claire Elsdon; press officer Alison Duncan
Venue type: concert hall, multi-purpose hall *Capacity:* 1648 *Policy:* present, rent *Arts types:* music, organ recitals, dance, pop, rock, conferences, exhibitions
Comments: promotes own orchestral music services, dance festivals; disabled access

Hull New Theatre
Kingston Square, **Hull** HU1 3HF
Tel: 1482-320 244/613 808 (marketing)/226 655 (box office) Fax: 1482-587 233/613 961 (marketing)
theatre & hall director Russell E Hills; programme & development manager Michael J Lister; marketing officer Marie Burkitt; administrative assistant Claire Elsdon; press officer Alison Duncan; stage manager Allan Green; chief electrician Allan Edwards; operations manager Tony Ridley
Venue type: theatre *Capacity:* 1189 *Policy:* hire, guarantee, first call *Arts types:* drama, opera, ballet, musicals, pantomimes *Comments:* touring theatre; owned and funded by Kingston upon Hull City Council; disabled access

Hull Truck Theatre
Spring Street, **Hull** HU2 8RW
Tel: 1482-224 800/323 638 (box office)
Fax: 1482-581 182
E-Mail: admin@hulltruck.co.uk
executive director Simon Stallworthy; artistic director John Godber; general manager Joanne Gower
Venue type: theatre *Capacity:* 300 *Policy:* produce, rent *Arts types:* theatre, comedy, drama, music *Comments:* home of the Hull Truck Theatre Company; main producer of works by John Godber; see also Drama

Landmark, The
Wilder Road, **Ilfracombe** EX34 9BZ
Tel: 1271-865 655 Fax: 1271-867 707
Internet: www.northdevontheatres.org.uk
E-Mail: northdevon.theatres@sosi.net
programming director Karen Turner; financial controller Chris Sawle; theatre manager Erick Muzard; marketig Jo Lock
Venue type: theate, concert hall *Capacity:* 483 *Policy:* mainly split or guarantee, hire *Arts types:* theatre, musicals, opera, comedy, dance, live music (classical, jazz, folk, contemporary, rock), children's shows
Comments: receiving venue; see also Queen's Theatre

Eden Court Theatre
Bishop's Road, **Inverness (Scotland)** IV3 5SA
Tel: 1463-239 841 ext. 149 (publicity)/234 234 (box office) Fax: 1463-713 810
Internet: www.edencourt.uk.com
E-Mail: ecmail@cali.co.uk
theatre director Colin Marr; marketing manager Kirsty McDougall
Venue type: all purpose *Capacity:* theatre 825, cinema 84 *Arts types:* all including visual arts *Comments:* only theatre in the Highlands; thriving educational outreach programme working with 14-19 year olds throughout Highlands, contact Sonia Rose

Corn Exchange
King Street, **Ipswich** IP1 1DH
Tel: 1473-255 851/215 544(box office)
Fax: 1473-250 951
Internet: www.ipswich-ents.co.uk
E-Mail: boxoffice@ipswich-ents.co.uk
general manager Billy Brennan; operations manager Craig Oldfield; publicity officer Hazel Clover
Venue type: multi-purpose hiring venue *Capacity:* up to 1000 *Policy:* rent, co-present *Arts types:* concerts, conferences, exhibitions *Comments:* wheelchair access, induction loop system

Brewery Arts Centre
Highgate, **Kendal** LA9 4HE
Tel: 1539-725 133 Fax: 1539-730 257
Internet: www.lakesnet.co.uk
E-Mail: brewery@lakesnet.co.uk
artistic director Anne Pierson
Venue type: arts centre, 2 galleries *Capacity:* Malt Room 300, theatre 250, studio 50 *Policy:* present, rent *Arts types:* concerts, theatre, jazz, folk and blues music, film *Comments:* 4 arts and crafts workshops, photography and exhibition space, visual arts and exhibition space; full disabled access (lifts); induction loop system

Kendal Leisure Centre
Burton Road, **Kendal** LA9 7HX
Tel: 1539-729 511/702 (theatre bookings)
Fax: 1539-731 135
manager P Stewart; recreation officer, special events D. Garnett; council entertainments officer Imelda Winter-Lewis(1539-733 333)
Venue type: leisure centre, multi-purpose *Capacity:* 1000 *Policy:* rent, manage *Arts types:* concerts (light & classical), opera, jazz, pop, rock, exhibitions, dance, chamber music, pantomime, conferences *Comments:* located between Morecambe and Carlisle; ideal for Lakes with many seasonal visitors, free car park, wheelchair access

Kings Lynn Arts Centre
27-29 King Street, **Kings Lynn** PE30 1HA
Tel: 1553-765 565 Fax: 1553-762 141
Internet: www.west-norfolk.gov.uk
general manager Howard Barnes
Venue type: arts centre and galleries *Arts types:* alternative theatre, classical music, comedy, contemporary dance, contemporary visual arts

Kings Lynn Corn Exchange
Tuesday Market Place, **Kings Lynn** PE30 1JW
Tel: 1553-765 565 Fax: 1553-762 141
Internet: www.west-norfolk.gov.uk
general manager Howard Barnes
Venue type: multipurpose concert venue *Capacity:* 733 seated, 1200 flatfloor *Arts types:* classical music, ballet, rock, pop, comedy

City Varieties Music Hall
Swan Street, **Leeds** LS1 6LW
Tel: 113-242 5045/243 0808 (box office) Fax: 113-234 1800
general manager Peter Sandeman
Venue type: music hall *Capacity:* 531 *Policy:* present, rent, co-produce *Arts types:* drama, music, variety, revue, pantomime *Comments:* national touring house

Corn Exchange, The
Call Lane, **Leeds** LS1 7BR
Tel: 113-234 0363 Fax: 113-234 1745
centre manager Annie Connolly; assistant centre manager Lisa Chadderton
Venue type: shopping centre with large space for performing arts *Capacity:* 1150 *Policy:* rent, present, may offer free performing arts space depending on negotiation *Arts types:* all types *Comments:* provides space for performing arts groups, artists etc; member of Trans Europe Halles, Tel: +33 1-4011 6414, Internet: www.teh.net

Leeds Grand Theatre and Opera House
46 New Briggate, **Leeds** LS1 6NZ
Tel: 113-222 6222 (box office) Fax: 113-246 5906
Internet: www.leeds.gov.uk/GrandTheatre
general manager Warren Smith; house manager Anne Baxendale; marketing manager Margaret Ashbee
Venue type: theatre *Capacity:* 1550 *Policy:* rent, co-present, shared risk *Arts types:* ballet, drama, opera, pantomime, variety, musicals, concerts *Comments:* national touring house; home of Opera North

Riley Theatre, The
Northern School of Contemporary Dance,
98 Chapeltown Road, **Leeds** LS7 4BH
Tel: 113-219 3000 Fax: 113-219 3030
Internet: www.nscd.ac.uk
senior administrator Sue Logan
Venue type: dance venue *Capacity:* 270 *Arts types:* dance *Comments:* former Synagogue

West Yorkshire Playhouse
Playhouse Square, **Leeds** LS2 7UP
Tel: 113-213 7800 Fax: 113-213 7250
Internet: www.wyp.co.uk
artistic director (chief executive) Jude Kelly; managing director Maggie Saxon; community & educational director Maureen Rooksby; black arts co-ordinator Jackie Cristie; international co-ordinator Jude Kelly; press officer Philip Meeks; catering/commerical manager Sue Chappelow
Venue type: theatre *Capacity:* Quarry Theatre 750, Courtyard Theatre 356 (collapsable rostrum) *Policy:* produce, present *Arts types:* plays, comedy, music, dance, poetry, readings *Comments:* conference facilities available for hire; wide educational programme: theatre-base workshops and outreach – contact Lisa Parrot (113-213 7290); see also Drama

De Montfort Hall
Granville Road, **Leicester** LE1 7RU
Tel: 116-233 3113 (admin)/3111 (box office)
Fax: 116-233 3182
E-Mail: haswr001@leicester.gov.uk
manager Richard Haswell; marketing manager Nick Hallan; finance manager t.b.a.; technical manager John E Sippitt; house manager Pete Cooper; operations manager Alvin Hargreaves
Venue type: concert, multi-purpose hall *Capacity:* Hall A 1973, Hall B 1600-2000 *Policy:* rent, co-present *Arts types:* classical, pop, rock, jazz, opera, ballet, musicals *Comments:* newly refurbished

Haymarket Theatre
Belgrave Gate, **Leicester** LE1 3YQ
Tel: 116-253 0021/9797 (box office) Fax: 1162-513 310
Internet: www.netpresence.co.uk/leicesterhaymarkettheatre/
E-Mail: enquiry@haymarkettheatre.demon.co.uk
artistic director Paul Kerryson; artistic associate Vayu Naidu; executive director Kathleen Hamilton; public relations manager Alison Chapman
Venue type: Thrust Stage theatre *Capacity:* main house 752, studio theatre 120 *Policy:* present, rent, produce *Arts types:* theatre, dance, musical theatre *Comments:* disabled access; induction loop system; signed performances; programmes available in large print and audio tapes; see also Drama

Phoenix Arts
21 Upper Brown Street, **Leicester** LE1 5TE
Tel: 116-224 7700 Fax: 116-224 7701
Internet: www.phoenix.org.uk
director Rachael Collinge; live programmer Judi Hughes; head of marketing Jennie Jordan; film programmer Alan Alderson Smith
Venue type: arts centre *Capacity:* 262 *Policy:* present, rent *Arts types:* contemporary theatre, music, dance, world cinema, silent films, contemporary, independent cultural film

Theatre Royal Lincoln
Clasketgate, **Lincoln** LN2 1JJ
Tel: 1522-523 303/525 555/534 570 (box office)
Fax: 1522-545 490
director Christopher Moreno; theatre manager Keith Richards; marketing manager Richard Kort
Venue type: theatre *Capacity:* 482 *Policy:* co-present, produce *Arts types:* musicals, concerts *Comments:* national touring house

Everyman Theatre
5-9 Hope Street, **Liverpool** L1 9BH
Tel: 151-708 0338/709 4776 (box office)
Fax: 151-709 0398
Internet: www.everymantheatre.com
E-Mail: info@everyman.org.uk
chief executive Rose Guthbertson; general manager Chris Ricketts; head of marketing Mike James; education officer Lisa Stam; press officer Paul Bell
Venue type: theatre *Capacity:* 402 *Policy:* present, rent *Arts types:* drama, comedy, music, dance *Comments:* producing venue and receiving venue for touring companies; minicom 151-709 0534; loop induction system in the auditorium; signed and audio described performances; street level wheelchair access to auditorium, (fire & lift), access to bar, cafe & foyer; home of new company (merger of Liverpool Rep. Theatre and Everyman Theatre); see also Drama

Liverpool Empire Theatre
Lime Street, **Liverpool** L1 1JE
Tel: 151-709 3200 Fax: 151-709 6757
general manager Rachel Miller
Venue type: concert hall and theatre *Capacity:* 2347 *Policy:* rent *Arts types:* orchestra, pop, rock, dance, variety, opera, drama, pantomime, jazz, world music *Comments:* touring theatre, for booking details contact Nicky Monk on 1865-782 900

Philharmonic Hall
Hope Street, **Liverpool** L1 9BP
Tel: 151-210 2895/709 3789 (box office)
Fax: 151-210 2902
Internet: www.rlps.co.uk
E-Mail: RLPSociety@aol.com
chief executive Antony Lewis Crosby; orchestral director Sandra Parr; orchestra manager Marian McGrath; principal conductor Petr Altrichter; director of marketing Ian Archer; hall director Alex Medhurst
Venue type: concert hall *Capacity:* 1803 *Policy:* present all types of concerts and other activities *Arts types:* all *Comments:* home of the Royal Liverpool Philharmonic Orchestra (see Orchestras); recently refurbished hall

Royal Court
Roe Street, **Liverpool** L1 1HL
Tel: 151-709 1808 (administration)/4321 (box office)
Fax: 151-709 2678
general managers Simon Geddes, Richard Maides; box office manager T. Griggs
Venue type: concert hall/theatre *Capacity:* seated 1525, 1796 half standing *Policy:* rent *Arts types:* theatre, concerts, comedy, music theatre *Comments:* rennovation work ongoing but still open; limited disabled access; signed performance available upon request

North Wales Theatre and Conference Centre
Promenade, **Llandudno (Wales)** LL30 1BB
Tel: 1492-879 771/872 000 (box office)
Fax: 1492-860 790
Internet: www.nwtheatre.co.uk
E-Mail: info@nwtheatre.co.uk
general manager, theatre & conference centre Nick Reed; operations manager Bridget Jones; marketing manager Huw Roberts; technical manager John Owen; stage manager Keith Guy; box office manager Andrew Carruthers
Venue type: multi-purpose *Capacity:* theatre auditorium 1500, main hall standing 1100 *Policy:* rent, percentage, guarantee, 1st call *Arts types:* opera, ballet, orchestral music, No 1 touring shows, popular music, comedy, variety *Comments:* large scale receiving theatre, Wales' largest centre for live arts & entertainment incorporating North Wales Theatre, North Wales Conference Centre and Theatr Colwyn; disabled access; infrared hearing loop; occassional signed performance

Adelphi Theatre Co. Ltd
411-412 The Strand, **London** WC2R 0NS
Tel: 20-7836 1166 (enquiries/theatre manager)
Fax: 20-7379 5709 (theatre manager)
theatre co-ordinator (The Really Useful Group) Fiona Magill; theatre manager Thomas Baxter
Venue type: theatre *Capacity:* 1500
Policy: rent by negotiation with theatre manager
Arts types: musicals, west end productions
Comments: large scale musical house offering a well equiped stage; good disabled access; administration address: The Really Useful Group,
22 Tower Street, London WC2H 9NS

Albery Theatre (Associated Capital Theatres Ltd)
St Martin's Lane, **London** WC2N 4AH
Tel: 20-7867 1125 (stage door)/304 7922 (ACT head office) Fax: 20-7240 3478
human resources manager Hugh Hales; theatre manager Peter Faldon; operations manager Vince Jervis
Venue type: Proc Arch *Capacity:* 859 + 21 standing *Policy:* rent by negotiation *Arts types:* playhouse theatre

Aldwych Theatre
Aldwych, **London** WC2B 4DF
Tel: 20-7416 6000 (box office)/7379 6736 (theatre manager) Fax: 20-7379 6736
general manager Peter Wilcox; administration Michael Codron Plays Ltd.; theatre manager Stephen Thrussen; assistant manager Bryan Lewis; box office manger David Smith
Venue type: theatre *Capacity:* 1200 *Policy:* commercial theatre productions *Arts types:* plays, musicals
Comments: access for one wheelchair – check with box office Tel: 20-7379 3367

Alexandra Palace
Alexandra Palace Way, Wood Green, **London** N22 7AY
Tel: 20-8365 2121 Fax: 20-8883 3999
Internet: www.alexandrapalace.com
E-Mail: alexandrapalace@dial.pipex.com
contact The Sales Dept.
Venue type: multi-purpose halls *Capacity:* West Hall 2500, Great Hall 7250 *Policy:* rent *Arts types:* concerts, dance *Comments:* disabled access

Almeida Theatre
Almeida Street, Islington, **London** N1 1TA
Tel: 20-7226 7432(admin)/7359 4404 (box office)
Fax: 20-7704 9581
Internet: www.almeida.co.uk
E-Mail: almeidatheatre@demon.co.uk
executive director Nick Starr; head of production Paul Clay; administrative assistant to director Anne Hudson; production co-ordinator Kevin Fitzmaurice; education officer Jo Godwin
Venue type: theatre *Capacity:* 300 *Policy:* produce, hire (4-6 weeks outside season) *Arts types:* drama, opera, cabaret *Comments:* Almeida Theatre Company, Almeida Opera based here; international theatre season; disabled access & facilities (lift, ramps, toilet); see also Drama

Ambassadors Theatre
West Street, **London** WC2H 5ND
Tel: 20-7565 5050/5000 (box office)/7494 0333 (ATG)
Fax: 20-7565 5001 (admin)/5002 (artists)
Internet: www.royal-court.org.uk
E-Mail: royal-court@cityscape.co.uk
executive director Vikki Heywood; artistic director Ian Rickson; press manager Anne Mayer
Venue type: theatre *Capacity:* stage 66, circle 140 *Policy:* produce new plays *Arts types:* drama *Comments:* under Royal Court's Theatre Management

Apollo Theatre
Shaftesbury Avenue, **London** W1V 7HD
Tel: 20-7437 3435/1872/7494 5070 (box office)
theatre manager Martin Floyd
Venue type: West End Theatre – playhouse theatre *Capacity:* 776 *Policy:* West End runs *Arts types:* drama, comedy *Comments:* Stoll Moss Theatres Ltd, Tel: 20-7494 5200 (administration), Fax: 20-7434 1217

Apollo Victoria Theatre
17 Wilton Road, **London** SW1V 1LG
Tel: 20-7834 6318/7416 6059 (box office)
Fax: 20-7630 7716
general manager Jamie Baskeyfield; deputy general manager Stefan Gilson; assistant manager Nicola Taylor
Venue type: theatre *Capacity:* (including 40 standing for Starlight Express) 1574 *Policy:* rent *Arts types:* Starlight Express since 1984 *Comments:* Apollo Leisure have hired theatre to The Really Useful Theatre Company, Starlight Express; disabled access (if notified in advance); signed performances

BAC
Lavender Hill, **London** SW11 5TF
Tel: 20-7223 6557/7326 8222 (press) Fax: 20-7978 5207
director Tom Morris; administrative director Caroline Routh; press & marketing Ben Chamberlain
Venue type: arts centre, theatre *Capacity:* theatre 180, Studio I 48, Studio II 60 *Policy:* box office split *Arts types:* music, jazz, drama, cabaret, comedy, art gallery *Comments:* promotions include festivals, plays, home of following festivals: British Fest of Visual Theatre, London Int. Mime Fest, Short Back and Sides Fest; home of following companies: Heavy Pencil, Puppet Centre, Shape; cafe, bar

Barbican Centre
Silk Street, **London** EC2Y 8DS
Tel: 20-7638 4141 Fax: 20-7920 9648
Internet: www.barbican.org.uk
E-Mail: press@barbican.org.uk
managing director John Tusa; artistic director Graham Sheffield; director of public affairs Ruth Hasnip;

commercial director Mark Taylor; head of music Robert van Leer; head of marketing Chris Travers; head of press & public relations Amanda Jones; educational manager Jillian Barker; head of theatre Louise Jeffreys
Venue type: arts centre
Capacity: Barbican Hall 1989, Theatre 1168, The Pit 200
Policy: present, rent; available as film location
Arts types: theatre, classical & non-classical music, dance, film, comedy, visual and applied arts, musicals, talks *Comments:* London Symphony Orchestra, Royal Shakespeare Company (q.v.) are resident companies for part of the year; conference and exhibition facilities, conservatory, lending library, shops, restaurants, cafés and bars

Blackheath Halls
23 Lee Road, **London** SE3 9RQ
Tel: 20-8318 9758/8463 0100 (box office)
Fax: 20-8852 5154
Internet: www.blackheathhalls.com
E-Mail: mail@blackheathhalls.com
artistic director Peter Conway
Venue type: flexible concert halls purpose built in 1885
Capacity: Recital Room 220, Great Hall – seated 700, standing 1000 *Policy:* rent, presents own events and co-presents *Arts types:* classical, jazz, folk, opera, musicals, recordings, exhibitions, rehearsals, rock, pop
Comments: recording venue

Bloomsbury Theatre
15 Gordon Street, **London** WC1H 0AH
Tel: 20-7504 2777 (admin)/7388 8822 (box office)
Fax: 20-7383 4080
Internet: www.ucl.ac.uk/BloomsburyTheatre/
E-Mail: blooms.theatre@ucl.ac.uk
general manager Michael Freeman; marketing manager Marcus J Wilson; administrator Mark Feakins
Venue type: theatre
Capacity: 558 *Policy:* rent
Arts types: comedy, drama, contemporary dance, opera, music

Brick Lane Music Hall
134-146 Curtain Road, **London** EC2A 3AR
Tel: 20-7739 9996/9997 Fax: 20-7739 9998
Internet: www.Brick-Lane-Music-Hall co.uk
E-Mail: fun@bricklanemusichall.freeserve.co.uk
theatre director Vincent Hayes; theatre manager Hilary Philpott
Venue type: theatre, music hall
Capacity: up to 250 seated,up to 400 standig *Policy:* rent, present own music hall shows
Arts types: music hall, comedy, revue, Sunday concerts, pantomimes, variety, film, pop video location, corporate, product launches, conferences *Comments:* the music hall has full catering facilities

Bush Theatre, The
Shepherds Bush Green, **London** W12 8QD
Tel: 20-7602 3703 Fax: 20-7602 7614
E-Mail: thebush@dircon.co.uk
executive producer Fiona Clark; artistic director Mike Bradwell
Venue type: pub theatre, producing theatre
Capacity: 105 *Policy:* produce and host two touring productions a year *Arts types:* drama, new plays
Comments: specialise in new British writing and contemporary theatre; see also Drama

Cambridge Theatre
Earlham Street, Seven Dials, **London** WC2H 9HU
Tel: 20-7240 7664/7379 0075 (stage door)
Fax: 20-7836 9076
theatre manager Pauline Lorraine; house manager Maureen Hooper
Venue type: West End Theatre *Capacity:* 1237
Policy: West End runs Mon-Sat. and Sunday concerts
Arts types: mainly musicals *Comments:* Stoll Moss Theatres Ltd, Tel: 20-7494 5200 (administration), Fax: 20-7434 1217

Chisenhale Dance Space
64-84 Chisenhale Road, **London** E3 5QZ
Tel: 20-8981 6617 Fax: 20-8980 9323
Internet: www.chisenhale.demon.co.uk
E-Mail: mail@chisenhale.demon.co.uk
centre co-ordinator Kristina Leonnet
Venue type: dance space *Capacity:* 75 *Policy:* by negotiation, rent rehearsal space, work on community and education-based projects *Arts types:* independent/experimental dance, movement-based and cross-media/cross-cultural work *Comments:* basic stage lighting & sound system; fully sprung maple dance floor; offers performances, workshops, residencies, discussions and rehearsal spaces

Comedy Theatre (Associated Capital Theatres Ltd)
Panton Street, **London** SW1Y 4DN
Tel: 20-7973 0018 (stage door)/7304 7922 (ACT Head Office) Fax: 20-7839 3663
theatre manager Simon Francis; head of sales & marketing (ACT) Alec Jessel; artistic advisor responsible for programming Nick Salmon
Venue type: theatre *Capacity:* 795 *Policy:* rent
Arts types: plays, small scale musicals

Commonwealth Institute
Kensington High Street, **London** W8 6NQ
Tel: 20-7603 4535 Fax: 20-7602 7374
Internet: www.commonwealth.org.uk//
E-Mail: info@commonwealth.org.uk
commercial director Paul Kennedy; director general David French; director of education Steve Brace; director of public affairs Graeme Carter
Venue type: multi-purpose – performance and conference venue *Capacity:* 460 *Policy:* rent + VAT *Arts types:* theatrical performances, concerts and musical events
Comments: brochure available Fax: 20-7603 3412

Criterion Theatre Trust
2 Jermyn Street, **London** SW1Y 4XA
Tel: 20-7839 8811 (stage door)
Fax: 20-7925 0596
director Sally Greene; theatre manager Fiona Callaghan; assistant manager Vicki Clark; chief electrician Simon Thomas Colquhoun; master carpenter Simon Renton
Venue type: Playhouse *Capacity:* 583 *Policy:* transfers of small innovative plays from outer London theatres *Arts types:* theatre *Comments:* facilities for disabled; the Criterion Theatre Trust, a registered charity, is managed by Associated Capital Theatres Ltd

Dominion Theatre
269 Tottenham Court Road, **London** W1P 0AQ
Tel: 20-7580 1889 Fax: 20-7580 0246
managing director Sam Shrouder; general manager theatre bookings Nicky Monk (1865-782 900); general manager S. P. Murtagh; deputy manager J. Rainsford
Venue type: West End venue *Capacity:* 2082 *Policy:* by negotiation *Arts types:* musicals, drama, music theatre, concerts *Comments:* at present home to: Disney's Beauty and The Beast

Donmar Warehouse (Associated Capital Theatres Ltd)
Thomas Neal's, 41 Earlham Street,
London WC2H 9LD
Tel: 20-7836 3939/7304 7922 (ACT Head Office)
Fax: 20-7836 4099/7867 1131 (head office)
general manager Nick Frankfart; executive producer Caro Newling; artistic director Sam Mendes; casting director Anne McNulty; theatre manager Julia Christie; general manager Nick Frankfort; marketing co-ordinator Lucy Ryan
Venue type: studio theatre *Capacity:* 252 *Policy:* produce
Arts types: varied programme in-house productions
Comments: see also Drama

Duchess Theatre
Catherine Street, **London** WC2B 5LA
Tel: 20-7379 0495/7377 0495 (stage door)
manager Chris Isherman
Venue type: West End Theatre, commercial West End venue *Capacity:* 470 *Policy:* West End runs *Arts types:* all
Comments: Stoll Moss Theatres Ltd, Tel: 711-494 5200 (administration), Fax: 171-434 1217

Duke of Yorks
St Martin's Lane, **London** WC2N 4BG
Tel: 20-7565 5050/5000 (box office)/7494 0333 (ATG)
Fax: 20-7565 5001(admin)/5002(artistic)
Internet: www.royal-court.org.uk
E-Mail: royal-court@cityscape.co.uk
executive director Vikki Heywood; artistic director Ian Rickson; press manager Anne Mayer
Venue type: West End theatre *Capacity:* 586 *Policy:* produce new plays *Arts types:* drama *Comments:* under Royal Court's Theatre Management

Earl's Court Exhibition Centre
Warwick Road, **London** SW5 9TA
Tel: 20-7370 8009 (sales department)/8144
Fax: 20-7370 8144
Internet: www.eco.co.uk
E-Mail: marketing@eco.co.uk
sales director Chris Vaughan; hall director Karen Taylor; box office manager Zahir Jaffer; marketing director Alison Berends; catering marketing manager Yvette Bradley; car parks manager Sarah Hemsley
Venue type: arena, exhibition centre, conference centre
Capacity: up to 22000 *Policy:* rent, co-produce *Arts types:* used for large-scale opera productions and concerts
Comments: negotiable rates on application

Fortune Theatre
Russell Street, Covent Garden, **London** WC2B 5HH
Tel: 20-7836 6260/2238 (box office)
Fax: 20-7379 7493
artistic director Paul Gane; director Keith Dainton; manager Andrew Jenkins
Venue type: West End venue *Capacity:* 440 *Policy:* co-present, receiving theatre *Arts types:* plays, musicals

Garrick Theatre
Charing Cross Road, **London** WC2H 0HH
Tel: 20-7836 9396/8271 (stage door)
manager Philip Hawkeswood
Venue type: West End Theatre, West End venue
Capacity: 678 *Policy:* West End runs *Arts types:* comedies, plays, musicals *Comments:* Stoll Moss Theatres Ltd, Tel: 20-7494 5200 (administration), Fax: 20-7434 1217

Gielgud Theatre
Shaftesbury Avenue, **London** W1V 8AR
Tel: 20-7439 1912 Fax: 20-7437 0784
manager John Fitzsimmons
Venue type: West End Theatre *Capacity:* 889 *Policy:* West End runs *Arts types:* commercial drama *Comments:* Stoll Moss Theatres Ltd, Tel: 20-7494 5200 (administration), Fax: 20-7434 1217

Greenwich Theatre
Crooms Hill, **London** SE10 8ES
Tel: 20-8858 4447(admin)/7755 (box office)
Fax: 20-8858 8042
executive director Hilary Strong
Venue type: theatre *Capacity:* 423 *Policy:* recieving house
Comments: the theatre has been closed and was due to re-open in Nov1999; disabled access; induction loop system; see also Drama

Hackney Empire
291 Mare Street, Hackney, **London** E8 1EJ
Tel: 20-8986 0171(admin)/8985 2424 (box office)
Fax: 20-8985 4781
Internet: www.hackneyempire.co.uk
E-Mail: press@hackemp.demon.co.uk
director Roland Muldoon; general manager Simon Thomsett; programmer Clarie Muldoon
Venue type: theatre & concert hall *Capacity:* 1300, plus standing 200, studio theatre 50 *Policy:* present, rent, share risk *Arts types:* music, theatre, dance, opera, comedy,variety *Comments:* national touring house

Hackney Empire Studio Theatre (at the Samuel Pepys)
289 Mare Street, **London** E8 1EJ
Tel: 20-8986 0171(admin)/8985 2424 (box office)
Fax: 20-8985 4781
Internet: www.hackneyempire.co.uk
E-Mail: press@hackemp.demon.co.uk
director Roland Muldoon; programmer Claire Muldoon
Venue type: end of stage studio theatre *Capacity:* 48
Policy: limited runs *Arts types:* small scale plays, comedy/cabaret, poetry, workshops, acoustic music
Comments: administrated by Hackney Empire Ltd

Hampstead Theatre
Swiss Cottage Centre, **London** NW3 3EX
Tel: 20-7722 9224/1189 (production office)
Fax: 20-7722 3860
Internet: www.hampstead-theatre.co.uk
E-Mail: hampstead_theatre@atlas.co.uk
general manager James Williams; artistic director Jenny Topper; production manager John Titcombe; technical manager Philip Gladwell; sales & marketing Vicky Biles; technical director Alison Buchanan
Venue type: theatre (studio) *Capacity:* 174 *Policy:* produce (occasionally receive), present new work *Arts types:* drama, new writing *Comments:* disabled access; wheelchair spaces; induction loop system; signed performance for each production; membership club; see also Drama

Hellenic Centre, The
16-18 Paddington Street, **London** W1M 4AS
Tel: 20-7487 5060 Fax: 20-7486 4254
director Agatha Kalisperas
Venue type: cultural centre *Capacity:* seated 180, standing 300 *Policy:* rent *Arts types:* concerts, exhibitions, lectures, conferences

Her Majesty's Theatre
Haymarket, **London** SW1Y 4QL
Tel: 20-7930 5337 Fax: 20-7930 8467
theatre manager Rupert Bielby; house manager Lucy Williams
Venue type: West End Theatre *Capacity:* 1100 *Policy:* West End runs *Arts types:* musicals, drama, concerts
Comments: Stoll Moss Theatres Ltd, Tel: 20-7494 5200 (administration), Fax: 20-7434 1217

Hoxton Hall
130 Hoxton Street, **London** N1 6SH
Tel: 20-7684 0060/7739 5431(box office) Fax: 20-7729 3815
Internet: www.hoxtonhall.dabsol.co.uk
E-Mail: office@hoxtonhall.dabsol.co.uk
director Chris Bowler
Venue type: theatre; Grade II listed building *Capacity:* 100 *Arts types:* innovatory and experimental theatre and performing arts events, music events, visual and physical theatre, puppet and circus shows *Comments:* charitable organisation; the theatre is available for hire, contact Franck Bordese

Institute of Contemporary Arts - ICA
The Mall, **London** SW1Y 5AH
Tel: 20-7930 0493 (admin)/3647 (box office)
Fax: 20-7873 0051
Internet: www.ica.org.uk
E-Mail: info@ica.org.uk
director Philip Dodd; centre manager James Van Werven; live arts officer Vivien Gaskin
Venue type: multi-media arts centre *Capacity:* seated 164, standing 350 *Policy:* present, rent *Arts types:* experimental dance, avant-garde theatre, music, film, exhibitions, talks *Comments:* limited disabled access; induction loop system; occassional signed performance

King's Head Theatre
115 Upper Street, Islington, **London** N1 1QN
Tel: 20-7226 8561/1916 (box office)
Fax: 20-7226 8507
administrator Pam Mears; artistic director Dan Crawford
Venue type: fringe theatre, pub theatre *Capacity:* 125 *Policy:* produce, rent *Arts types:* theatre-contemporary, classical & comedy, musicals *Comments:* lunch-time and dinner theatre; see also Drama

Lewisham Theatre
Rushey Green, Catford, **London** SE6 4RU
Tel: 20-8690 2317 (admin)/0002 (box office)
Fax: 20-8314 3144
E-Mail: 100316.1453@compuserve.com
management Chris Hare, Martin Costello
Venue type: civic theatre *Capacity:* Theatre 845, Studio 100 *Policy:* rent, percentage deals, promotions *Arts types:* all types including one-nighters, week runs, pantomime (5 week season) *Comments:* number 1 venue for West Indian Comedy, specialise in light entertainment; disabled access; induction loop system; occasional signed pantomime

London Coliseum
St Martin's Lane, **London** WC2N 4ES
Tel: 20-7836 0111 (admin)/7632 8300 (box office)
Fax: 20-7836 8379
Internet: www.eno.org
general director Nicholas Payne; music director Paul Daniel; director artistic administration & dramaturgy Terri Jayne Griffin; director public relations Maggie Sedwards
Venue type: opera house *Capacity:* 2358 *Policy:* produce, present, co-produce, rent in the summer by negotiation *Arts types:* opera, dance *Comments:* home of English National Opera; dance companies July-Aug

London Palladium
Argyll Street, **London** W1A 3AB
Tel: 20-7734 6846 Fax: 20-7437 4010
theatre manager Gareth Parnell
Venue type: West End Theatre *Capacity:* 2280 *Policy:* West End runs *Arts types:* large scale musicals, concerts, conferences *Comments:* Stoll Moss Theatres Ltd, Tel: 20-7494 5200 (administration), Fax: 20-7434 1217

Lyric Theatre
Shaftesbury Avenue, **London** W1V 7HA
Tel: 20-7437 5443
manager Alison Heys
Venue type: West End Theatre
Capacity: 916 *Policy:* West End runs *Arts types:* drama *Comments:* Stoll Moss Theatres Ltd, Manor House, 21 Soho Square, London W1V 5FD, Tel: 20-7494 5200 (administration), Fax: 20-7434 1217

Lyric Theatre Hammersmith
King Street, **London** W6 0QL
Tel: 20-8741 0824 Fax: 20-8741 7694
chief executive Sue Storr; artistic director Neil Bartlett; administrative producer Simon Mellor; finance director Pam Cooper
Venue type: theatre *Capacity:* Main House 537, Studio 110 *Policy:* present, co-produce, rent *Arts types:* musicals, drama *Comments:* see also Drama

New London Theatre
Drury Lane, **London** WC2B 5PW
Tel: 20-7242 9802 (stage door)
Fax: 20-7405 5827
theatre manager Calum Cunningham; administration Kim Robbins; general manager Billy Differ
Venue type: bricks and mortar *Capacity:* 1106 *Policy:* rent *Arts types:* commercial presentations *Comments:* part of Really Useful Group, Tel: 20-7240 0880

Ocean Music Trust
Ocean, 270 Mare Street, **London** E8 1HE
Tel: 20-8986 5336 Fax: 20-8533 1991
Internet: www.ocean.org.uk
E-Mail: omt@oceanmusicvenue.co.uk
development manager Simon Delf; project director Mark Higham; administrator Greg Williams
Venue type: music venue & music training & resource centre *Capacity:* main auditorium 1880, studio 1 300, studio 2 70 *Arts types:* all types of music representing the ethnic & cultural diversity of the local region *Comments:* Ocean Music will integrate performance, residency, rehearsal and an extensive education & training programme; planned to open in September 2000

Ocean Music Venue
270 Mare Street, Hackney, **London** E8 1HE
Tel: 20-8986 5336 Fax: 20-8533 1991
Internet: www.ocean.org.uk
E-Mail: omt@oceanmusicvenue.co.uk
project director Mark Higham; development manager Simon Delf
Venue type: purpose built music venue
Capacity: main auditorium 1900, studio I 300, studio II 70 *Policy:* mainly in-house productions and partnership productions, also rent
Arts types: diverse range of popular, contemporary and classical music, reflect the range of ethnic and cultural traditions in London *Comments:* also has fully equipt training and resource centre; facilities for live recording and outside broadcast; disabled access to all performance areas and backstage; due to open September 2000

Old Vic, The
Waterloo Road, **London** SE1 8NB
Tel: 20-7928 2651/7616 (box office) Fax: 20-7261 9161
general manager Michael Morris
Venue type: theatre *Capacity:* 1077 *Policy:* rent, produce, receiving venue *Arts types:* drama, musicals *Comments:* now charitably run by The Old Vic Theatre Trust (chair Alex Bernstein); see also Drama

Oval House
52-54 Kennington Oval, **London** SE11 5SW
Tel: 20-7582 0080 (admin)/7680 (box office)
Fax: 20-7820 0990
E-Mail: ovalhouse@dircon.co.uk
theatre programmer Paul Everitt; director Deborah Bestwick; marketing Debbie Vannozzi; education co-ordinator Melanie Sharp; general manager Mark Allen
Venue type: theatre *Capacity:* 100, 50 *Policy:* rent, box office split *Arts types:* drama, poetry, comedy, performance art, programmed new & experimental theatre, carnival *Comments:* also offer a variety of workshops; rehearsal facilities (2 x dance studios, sprung floors/mirror, workshop rooms

Palace Theatre
Shaftesbury Avenue, **London** W1V 8AY
Tel: 20-7434 0088 Fax: 20-7734 6157
theatre manager Mark Hone; assistant theatre manager Stephen Bush; administration Kim Robbins
Venue type: West End venue *Capacity:* 1404 *Policy:* rent *Arts types:* West End productions (Les Miserables) *Comments:* part of Really Useful Group

Peacock Theatre, The
Portugal Street, off Kingsway, **London** WC2A 2HT
Tel: 20-7863 8268 (admin)/8222 (box office)
Fax: 20-7314 9004
chief executive Ian Albery; marketing manager David Hopper; chief technician Mark Dawson; press officer Peter Leone; general manager Paula Gillespie
Venue type: Proc Arch *Capacity:* 1000 *Policy:* present, rent, co-present, receiving theatre *Arts types:* ballet, dance, opera, lyric theatre, drama, children's shows, music *Comments:* The Peacock Theatre (formerly the Royalty Theatre) will continue to be managed by Sadler's Wells (q.v.), presenting a diverse and distinctive programme of international dance, opera and musical theatre

Phoenix Theatre (Associated Capital Theatres Ltd)
110 Charing Cross Road, **London** WC2N 0JP
Tel: 20-7465 0211 (stage door)/7304 7922 (ACT Head Office) Fax: 20-7465 0212
general manager David Lyness; operations manager (ACT) Vincent Jervis
Venue type: theatre *Capacity:* 1016 + 56 standing *Policy:* rent *Arts types:* musicals, diverse range of drama

Piccadilly Theatre (Associated Capital Theatres Ltd)
Denman Street, **London** W1V 8DY
Tel: 20-7867 1128/7304 7922 (ACT Head Office)
Fax: 20-7437 5336/7867 1131 (head office)
theatre manager Keith Honhold; general manager (ACT) Hugh Hales
Venue type: theatre *Capacity:* large theatre: 1214 + 32 standing, small theatre: 783 + 32 standing *Policy:* rent *Arts types:* playhouse theatre, ballet, musicals

Place Theatre, The
17 Dukes Road, **London** WC1H 9AB
Tel: 20-7380 1268/7387 0031 Fax: 20-7383 2003
Internet: www.theplace.org.uk
E-Mail: placetheatre@easynet.co.uk
director John Ashford; administration Colette Mansford; technical manager Ian Richards; marketing & press officer Nicole Matthews; associate director Emma Gladstone; projects coordinator Anna Scott
Venue type: large studio theatre *Capacity:* 300 *Policy:* present, rent (dance series)
Arts types: dance, contemporary dance
Comments: The Place is a national dance agency with studio space to rent; also has disabled access

Playhouse Theatre
Northumberland Avenue, **London** WC2N 5DE
Tel: 20-7839 4292/4401(box office) Fax: 20-7839 1195
proprietor/producer t.b.a.
Venue type: West End theatre *Capacity:* 780
Policy: present, rent *Arts types:* all

Polka Theatre for Children
240 The Broadway, **London** SW19 1SB
Tel: 20-8543 3741/4888 (box office) Fax: 20-8542 7723
Internet: www.polkatheatre.com
E-Mail: polkabox@hotmail.com
administrative director Stephen Midlane; artistic director Vicky Ireland;
director of development Judy Vereker
Venue type: theatre (2 spaces)
Capacity: auditorium 300, adventure theatre 80 *Policy:* hire, present (5 main house productions) *Arts types:* theatre for children *Comments:* air-conditioned auditoria, wheelchair access to most parts of the building; induction loop system; signed performances by arrangement, seasonal brochures available on cassette and in large print; scripts available in advance; special needs workshops available; range of exhibitions to complement productions; small unusual playground; range of workshops and cafe; see also Drama

Prince Edward Theatre
Old Compton Street, **London** W1V 6HS
Tel: 20-7437 2024/7447 5400 (box office)
Fax: 20-7734 1454
chairman and chief executive George Biggs; general manager Peter Austin; box office manager Neil Franklin
Venue type: theatre *Capacity:* 1614
Policy: rent *Arts types:* musicals
Comments: 4 bars; limited disabled access; occassional signed performances

Prince of Wales Theatre
31 Coventry Street, **London** W1V 8AS
Tel: 20-7930 9901(admin)/7839 5972 (box office)
Fax: 20-7930 8970
managing director George Biggs; general manager Mike Churchill; box office manager Martin Clark
Venue type: theatre *Capacity:* 1133 *Policy:* rent *Arts types:* light entertainment, comedy, musicals *Comments:* disabled facilities are limited

Queen's Theatre
Shaftesbury Avenue, **London** W1V 8BA
Tel: 20-7734 1348
manager Hugh McLeod
Venue type: West End Theatre
Capacity: 990 *Policy:* West End runs
Arts types: drama, musicals, comedy *Comments:* Stoll Moss Theatres Ltd, Tel: 171-494 5200 (administration), Fax: 171-434 1217

Riverside Studios
Crisp Road, Hammersmith, **London** W6 9RL
Tel: 20-8237 1000 (admin)/1111 (box office)
Fax: 20-8277 1001
E-Mail: richard@riversidestudios.demon.co.uk
director William Burdett-Coutts; general manager Shona Clelland; programme manager Jon Fawcett
Venue type: arts centre *Capacity:* Studio One 500, Studio Two 400, Studio Three 100
Policy: present, rent *Arts types:* new performance work in dance and drama, comedy
Comments: gallery space, repertory cinema, community education, children's department, rehearsal space, television studios, conference facilities

Roundhouse, The
Chalk Farm Road, **London** NW1 8BG
Tel: 20-7424 9991 (admin)/9800 (box office)
Fax: 20-7414 9992
E-Mail: theroundhouse@msn.com
chief executive Marcus Davey; administration Olivia Robinson; development director Sarah Coop
Venue type: multi-purpose; grade II listed building used for a variety of performing arts
Capacity: varies depending on event: up to 1300 seated, 1000 standing *Policy:* rent
Arts types: all types including music, dance, theatre, circus *Comments:* offers workshops and educational outreach programme

Royal Albert Hall
Kensington Gore, **London** SW7 2AP
Tel: 20-7589 3203 Fax: 20-7823 7725
E-Mail: royalalberthall.com
chief executive David Elliot; director of sales & marketing Eve Hewitt; front of house manager Brian Gray; sales managers Donna Malcolm, Simone Pomerance; show dept manager Rob Flower; box office manager Sarah Howarth
Venue type: multi-purpose *Capacity:* 5100 *Policy:* rent
Arts types: music, galas, sporting events, exhibitions, banquets, pop concerts, dance, ballet, comedy, presentations *Comments:* BBC Henry Wood Promenade Concerts based here; over 350 shows in 1998, from BATFA Awards to tennis and Ocean Colour Scene

Royal Court Theatre (English Stage Company)
Sloane Square, **London** SW1W 8AS
Tel: 20-7565 5050/5000 (box office)
Fax: 20-7565 5001 (admin)/5002 (artists)
Internet: www.royalcourt.com
E-Mail: marketing@royal-court.demon.co.uk
artistic director Ian Rickson; executive director Vikki Heywood; finance director Donna Munday; literary manager Graham Whybrow; production manager Paul Handlay; head of marketing Stuart Buchanan
Venue type: Proc Arch and 2 Studios *Capacity:* Theatre 586, Studios 135 & 60 *Policy:* produce *Arts types:* drama, new work *Comments:* rebuilt and refurbished Royal Court opened in aumtum 1999 following a three year lottery project; alternative E-mail: info@royalcourttheatre.com; see also Drama

Royal Festival Hall & Hayward Gallery on the South Bank
Belvedere Road, **London** SE1 8XX
Tel: 20-7921 0600/7960 4242 (box office)
Fax: 20-7928 0063
Internet: www.sbc.org.uk
chairman Elliott Bernerd; chief executive Karsten Witt; commercial director Mike McCart; performing arts director Jodi Myers; planning director Malcolm Young; Hayward Gallery director Susan Ferleger Brades; finance director Paul Mason; head of classical music Amelia Freedman
Venue type: music, dance, literature & art venues
Capacity: Royal Festival Hall 2909, Queen Elizabeth Hall 911, Purcell Room 373, Voice Box 77 *Policy:* own promotions and rent *Arts types:* all types of music including world music, jazz & pop, classical music and dance, visual arts and literature, crossover art forms
Comments: Arts Council's poetry collection housed in Saison Poetry Library; poetry read in the Voice Box; exhibitions at the Hayward Gallery and a wide range of free foyer entertainment, exhibitions in the foyer; disabled access; induction loop system in Royal Festival Hall and Queen Elizabeth Hall

Royal National Theatre
Royal National Theatre, South Bank, **London** SE1 9PX
Tel: 20-7452 3333/3000 (box office)/3400 (ticket info)
Fax: 20-7452 3030
Internet: www.nt-online.org
director Trevor Nunn; executive director Genista McIntosh; general manager Maggie Whitlum; head of finance Lew Hodges; theatre manager John Langley; head of public affairs Vivien Wallace; director of development Brenda Daly; head of press Fiona Walsh; marketing manager David Hamilton-Peters
Venue type: theatre complex *Capacity:* Olivier 1160, Lyttelton 890, Cottesloe 400 *Policy:* building-based producing company, occasional receiving venue for major international companies; foyers have a regular programme of live music and exhibitions, daily backstage tours and wide range of education activities, events and activities front of house *Arts types:* repertoire drawn from a wide range of world drama; classics, new plays, musical theatre, shows for young people
Comments: disabled access and facilities; induction loop system; signed performances; programmes available on cassette and in large print; restaurants and bars; see also Drama

Sadler's Wells
Rosebery Avenue, **London** EC1R 4TN
Tel: 20-7863 8198/8000 (ticket office) Fax: 20-7863 8199
arts programming director Nigel Hinds; chief executive Ian Albery; theatre administrator Nadia Stern; senior press officer Peter Leone
Venue type: theatre *Capcity:* main theatre 1600, Lilian Baylis 180 *Policy:* present, hire, co-present, receiving theatre *Arts types:* dance, lyric theatre, opera, visual arts
Comments: re-opened after two year redevelopment; stage has doubled in size; now offers world class facilities

Savoy Theatre
Strand, **London** WC2R 0ET
Tel: 20-7836 8888 Fax: 20-7379 7322
general manager Thomas Bohdanetzky (tel: 20-7828 0600); theatre manager Niklaus Head
Venue type: theatre *Capacity:* 1144 *Policy:* present,rent
Arts types: drama, music, ballet, opera, concerts, conferences *Comments:* recently renovated, art deco interior

Shaftesbury Theatre
210 Shaftesbury Avenue, **London** WC2H 8DP
Tel: 20-7379 3345 Fax: 20-7497 0208
chief executive Andrew Leigh; founder Ray Cooney; theatre manager Chris Fletman
Venue type: theatre *Capacity:* 1433 *Policy:* rent, produce
Arts types: comedies, musicals, plays *Comments:* Theatre of Comedy Company based here

Shakespears's Globe
The International Shakespeare's Globe Centre Ltd, 21 New Globe Walk, Bankside, **London** SE1 9DT
Tel: 20-7401 9919 (box office)/7902 1401 (admin)
Fax: 20-7902 1475 (box office)/7902 1401 (admin)
Internet: www.shakespeares-globe.org
E-Mail: 100741.1611@compuserve.com
chief executive Peter Kyle; artistic director Mark Rylance
Venue type: historical theatre – theatre, exhibition and education centre *Capacity:* 1500 (1000 seated, 700 standing) *Policy:* own resident company *Arts types:* Shakespeare and his contemporaries, new plays
Comments: exhibiton open 7 days a week (10am-5pm Oct-April, 9.30am-12.30pm May-Sept, phone before for details), entrance fee includes guided tour of theatre; education centre open 7 days a week

Southwark Playhouse
62 Southwark Bridge Road, **London** SE1 0AS
Tel: 20-7652 2224/7620 3494 (box office)
Fax: 20-7261 1271
E-Mail: skplay@globalnet.co.uk
artistic director t.b.a.; chief executive Juliet Alderdice
Venue type: fringe theatre *Capacity:* 90 *Policy:* receive, produce *Arts types:* drama, fringe productions

St John's
Smith Square, **London** SW1P 3HA
Tel: 20-7222 2168 Fax: 20-7233 1618
general manager Paul Davies; assistant manager Laura Curtis
Venue type: concert hall (Baroque Church)
Capacity: 780 *Policy:* rent
Arts types: classical music, recitals
Comments: concerts most evenings, recitals, recitals alternate Thursday lunchtimes

St Martin's Theatre
West Street, **London** WC2H 9NG
Tel: 20-7497 0578/7836 1443 (box office)
Fax: 20-7379 8699
general manager Thomas Bohdanetzky; theatre manager Tracey John; artistic director David Turner
Venue type: theatre *Capacity:* 553 *Policy:* rent
Comments: has been the home of Agatha Christie's "The Mousetrap" for 23 years

Strand Theatre
Aldwych, **London** WC2B 5LD
Tel: 20-7836 4144/7930 8800 (box office)
Fax: 20-7836 4992
general manager Nigel Everett; theatre manager Gloria Louis; chairman Arnold Crook
Venue type: West End theatre
Capacity: 1067 *Policy:* negotiable terms depending on the production *Arts types:* plays, musicals, variety

Tara Arts Centre
356 Garratt Lane, **London** SW18 4ES
Tel: 20-8333 4457 Fax: 20-8870 9540
Internet: www.tara-arts.com
E-Mail: tara@tara-arts.com
administrator t.b.a.; artistic director Jatinder Verma
Venue type: small scale studio theatre
Capacity: 50 *Policy:* company base for Tara Arts Group, venue also for rent with preference given to Asian work
Arts types: storytelling, theatre performance, summer school, predominantly Asian theatre
Comments: wheelchair access; signed performances only when touring; see also Drama

Theatre Royal Drury Lane
Catherine Street, **London** WC2B 5JF
Tel: 20-7836 3687 Fax: 20-7379 6836
manager Rupert Bielby; house manager Emma Cleaves; assistant manager Louise Guedalla
Venue type: West End theatre
Capacity: 2184 *Policy:* West End runs Mon-Sat. and Sunday concerts *Arts types:* large musical plays, concerts, conferences
Comments: Stoll Moss Theatres Ltd, Tel: 20-7494 5200 (administration), Fax: 20-7434 1217; guided tours and restaurant facilities

Theatre Royal Haymarket
Haymarket, **London** SW1Y 4HT
Tel: 20-7930 8890 (management)/8800 (box office)
Fax: 20-7839 6473 (theatre manager)
general manager Nigel P Everett; president Enid Chanelle; chairman Arnold M Crook; theatre manager Mark Stradling; marketing director Damien Crook
Venue type: theatre *Capacity:* 888 *Policy:* rent *Arts types:* revivals, new plays *Comments:* grade I listed drama theatre, backstage tours available; film/event hire

Toynbee Studios
28 Commercial St, **London** E1 6LS
Tel: 20-7247 5102 Fax: 20-7247 5103
Internet: www.artsadmin.co.uk
E-Mail: space@artsadmin.co.uk
booking managers Gill Lloyd, Helen Ugwu
Venue type: arts resource centre *Capacity:* 288 seat theatre + 4 other rehearsal spaces *Policy:* rehearsal spaces are to rent + a video resource facility
Comments: rehearsal facilities, workshops, studios, cafe/restaurant

Tristan Bates Theatre
1a Tower Street, Covent Garden, **London** WC2H
Tel: 20-7240 3940/6283 Fax: 20-7240 3896
E-Mail: TBTrental@actorscentre.demon.co.uk
art director Mark Wing-Davey; contact Emy Ball
Venue type: small theatre *Capacity:* 75 *Policy:* rent, present *Arts types:* theatre, poetry

Vaudeville Theatre
404 Strand, **London** WC2R 0NH
Tel: 20-7828 0600 Fax: 20-7836 1820
directors Richard Q Hoare (chairman), Sir Stephen Walet-Cohen (managing); theatre manager Alistair D Sutherland
Venue type: theatre *Capacity:* 694 *Policy:* rent *Arts types:* plays, comedy, musicals, revue

Victoria Palace
Victoria Street, **London** SW1E 5EA
Tel: 20-7834 2781/1317 (box office)
Fax: 20-7931 7163
general manager Thomas Bohdanetzky
Venue type: theatre *Capacity:* 1517 *Policy:* rent
Arts types: plays, musicals

Warehouse, The
13 Theed Street, **London** SE1 8ST
Tel: 20-7928 9251 Fax: 20-7928 9252
Internet: www.lfo.co.uk
E-Mail: orchestra@lfo.co.uk
artistic director Ross Pople
Venue type: multi-purpose renovated warehouse
Capacity: 200 *Policy:* produce, hire
Arts types: orchestras, dance, ballet, choirs, photo-shoots, conferences, lectures *Comments:* the Warehouse is the rehearseal, recording and concerts venue for London Festival Orchestra; renovated Victorian warehouse with sprung wooden floors and designated recording room; available for hire by other organisations and has become, in the first two years of existence, one of the preferred venues for recording and rehearsal in the country; Warehouse Two renovated with further facilities (adjacent to the Warehouse-see also Services; also workshops, classes and community projects

Westminster Central Hall
Storey's Gate, Westminster, **London** SW1H 9NH
Tel: 20-7222 8010 Fax: 20-7222 6883
Internet: www.wch.co.uk
E-Mail: events@wch.co.uk
general manager t.b.a.; events officers Moira Langston, Nicholas Graham, Cathy Williamson
Venue type: multi-purpose hall
Capacity: Great Hall 2350, Lecture Hall 500, Library 500
Policy: rent *Arts types:* orchestra, choral music, pops, visual arts exhibitions
Comments: recently refurbished; some disabled access: catering and coffee shop, a.v. facilities

Whitehall Theatre (Associated Capital Theatres Ltd)
14 Whitehall, **London** SW1A 2DY
Tel: 20-7867 1129 (stage door)
Fax: 20-7839 3462 (theatre)
theatre manager Craig Prentice
Venue type: theatre
Capacity: 630 *Policy:* rent by negotiation
Arts types: playhouse theatre

Wigmore Hall
36 Wigmore Street, **London** W1H 0BP
Tel: 20-7486 1907 Fax: 20-7224 3800
Internet: www.wigmorehall.org.uk
E-Mail: info@wigmorehall.org.uk
director William Lyne; general administrator Marion Friend
Venue type: concert hall
Capacity: 539 *Policy:* rent
Arts types: chamber, vocal, early music, classical, romantic, contemporary repertoire, jazz
Comments: 11-month season, 9 concerts a week; restaurant and bar; 1 rehearsal room and Bechstein room (for receptions/talks); see also Services

Wilton's Music Hall
1 Graces Alley, **London** E1 8HY
Tel: 20-7702 9555 Fax: 20-7702 9555
producer Flora Smith
Arts types: opera *Comments:* resident company: Broomhill Opera; see also Opera

Wyndham's Theatre (Associated Capital Theatres Ltd)
Charing Cross Road, **London** WC2H 0DA
Tel: 20-7867 1125 (stage door)/7304 7922 (ACT Head Office) Fax: 20-7240 3492
operations manager Vince Jervis; theatre manager William Ingrey
Venue type: Proc Arch
Capacity: 757, plus standing 41 *Policy:* rent
Arts types: playhouse theatre

Young Vic Theatre, The
66 The Cut, **London** SE1 8LZ
Tel: 20-7633 0133 Fax: 20-7928 1585
E-Mail: info@youngvic.org
administrative producer Caroline Maude; artistic director Tim Supple; director of communications Alex McGowan; finance director Elaine Lavelle; production manager Paul Russell; development director John Nicolls; artistic associate Sue Emmas
Venue type: theatre
Capacity: main house theatre 330-450, The Cut studio 85 *Policy:* produce, rent *Arts types:* classics, new work
Comments: see also Drama

Hazlitt Theatre
Earl Street, **Maidstone** ME14 1PL
Tel: 1622-753 922 (administration)/602 178 (management) Fax: 1622-602 194
commercial manager Mandy Hare; operations manager Eric Lund; pr Alison Eames (1622-602 193)
Venue type: multi-functional Proc Arch Theatre exchange (multi-purpose open stage)
Capacity: theatre 383, exchange 400
Policy: guarantees, rent by negotiation, percentage packages and first call
Arts types: drama, variety, dance, cabaret, jazz, rock concerts, exhibitions, opera, pantomimes
Comments: disabled access (incl toilets); induction loop system; occasional signed performances

Malvern Theatres
Grange Road, **Malvern** WR14 3HB
Tel: 1684-569 256 (admin)/892 277 (box office)
Fax: 1684-893 300
E-Mail: post@malvern-theatres.co.uk
chief executive Nicolas Lloyd; assistant manager Melanie Matthews; development manager Dorothy Warner; technical manager Stuart Davis; education officer Emma Jane Benning
Venue type: national touring venue/concert hall
Capacity: Festival Theatre 830, New Space 850, Malvern Cinema 400 *Policy:* present, rent by negotiation, co-production, guarantee, guarantee & split *Arts types:* concerts, opera, drama, variety, youth and children's theatre, dance *Comments:* full disabled access

Contact Theatre
Oxford Road, **Manchester** M15 6JA
Tel: 161-274 3434 Fax: 161-273 6286
Internet: www.contact-theatre.org.uk
E-Mail: info@contact-theatre.org.uk
artistic director John E McGrath; executive producer Fiona Gasper; head of marketing & pr Lesa Drybrugh
Venue type: theatre and studio *Capacity:* theatre 360, studio 100 *Policy:* produce, rent *Arts types:* modern drama, classical and new work *Comments:* Manchester's Young People's Theatre expected to have re-open in Oct 1999 on the same site with enlarged capacity; see also Drama

G-Mex (The Greater Manchester Exhibition and Event Centre)
G-Mex Centre, **Manchester** M2 3GX
Tel: 161-834 2700 Fax: 161-833 3168
Internet: www.g-mex.co.uk
E-Mail: email@g-mex.co.uk
chief executive Terry McCreery; general man. David Mallard
Venue type: multi-purpose *Capacity:* fully seated 8726, part standing 9880, seminar centre 500, all standing 12000 *Policy:* rent *Arts types:* exhibitions, concerts, sporting events *Comments:* restaurant/bar; disabled access (incl. parking)

Green Room
54-56 Whitworth Street West, **Manchester** M1 5WW
Tel: 161-950 5777/5900 (box office) Fax: 161-950 5776
Internet: www.u-net.com/set/greenroom
E-Mail: greenroom@easynet.com.uk
director Garfield Allen; marketing manager Christopher Hodgson
Venue type: performance space cafe-bar *Capacity:* 166
Policy: present, produce *Arts types:* new and innovative local, national and international, dance theatre and live art *Comments:* rececently redeveloped, the Green Room now houses performance space, workspaces and meeting room (all available for private hire)

Lowry Centre Trust, The
West Pavilion, Harbour City, Salford Quays,
Manchester M5 2BH
Tel: 161-955 2020 Fax: 161-955 2021
Internet: www.thelowry.org.uk
E-Mail: info@thelowry.org.uk
chief executive Stephen Hetherington; company secretary Chris Hulme; theatres director Robert Robson; galleries director David Alston; head of marketing Sarah Lugg
Venue type: multi-purpose visual and performing arts centre with receiving theatres and 3 major galleries
Capacity: Lyric Theatre 1650/1730, adaptable theatre 400/450/466 *Policy:* major tours of music, opera, drama, ballet & dance, periods of residences with major national & international companies invited *Arts types:* opera, drama, music, ballet, dance, comedy, light entertainment *Comments:* opening 28 April 2000; the National Landmark Millennium Project for the Arts

Opera House
Quay Street, **Manchester** M3 3HP
Tel: 161-228 6255 (admin)/834 1787(venue)
Fax: 161-834 5243 (venue)/237 5746 (administration)
Internet: www.manchestertheatres.co.uk
general manager Ian Sime; marketing manager Sue Hibbert; technical manager Pat O'Leary; corporate entertainment manager Heather Foster
Venue type: theatre *Capacity:* 1909 *Policy:* rent, split deals, occasionally produce *Arts types:* ballet, dance, musicals, drama, concerts *Comments:* all booking enquiries to Nicky Monk at Apollo Leisure (UK) Ltd., Tel: 1865-782 900; administration and marketing based at Palace Theatre; corporate facilities available for hire

Palace Theatre
Oxford Street, **Manchester** M1 6FT
Tel: 161-228 6255 Fax: 161-237 5746
Internet: www.manchestertheatres.co.uk
E-Mail: palace@manchestertheatres.co.uk
general manager Peter Evans; marketing manager Sue Hibbert; technical manager Pat O'Leary; corporate entertainment manager Heather Foster
Venue type: theatre *Capacity:* 2029 *Policy:* rent, split deals, occasionally produce *Arts types:* musicals, comedy, opera, ballet, drama, dance, concerts
Comments: national touring house; all booking enquiries: Nicky Monk at Apollo Leisure (UK) Limited, Tel: 1865-782 900; corporate facilities available for hire

Royal Exchange Theatre
St Ann's Square, **Manchester** M2 7DH
Tel: 161-833 9333 Fax: 161-832 0881
Internet: www.royalexchange.co.uk
E-Mail: administration@royalexchange.co.uk
general manager Patricia Weller; artistic directors Braham Murray, Gregory Hersov, Matthew Lloyd; marketing director Ivan Wadesun
Venue type: theatre-in-the-round
Capacity: theatre-in-the-round 740, replica mobile theatre 400 *Policy:* produce *Arts types:* drama, concerts, play-readings, childrens events, jazz, music, comedy
Comments: the main theatre has moved back to its original site after being badly damaged in the Manchester bombing; it has been fully re-furbished and has full disabled access; see also Drama

Royal Northern College of Music
124 Oxford Road, **Manchester** M13 9RD
Tel: 161-907 5200 Fax: 161-273 7611
E-Mail: info@rncm.ac.uk
promotions co-ordinator Philip Jones; events and front-house manager Allan Taylor; press & publicity officer Marian Blaikley
Venue type: theatre *Capacity:* Lord Rhodes Room 150, The Siemens Theatre 626, Sema Group Concert Hall 620 *Arts types:* music, theatre, dance, master classes, exhibitions *Comments:* see also Promoters

The Bridgewater Hall
Manchester M2 3WS
Tel: 161-950 0000 Fax: 161-950 0001
Internet: www.bridgewater-hall.co.uk
E-Mail: admin@bridgewater-hall.co.uk
chief executive Howard Raynor; chairman John Glester; technical manager Chris Wright; director of marketing Maria Bota
Venue type: concert hall *Capacity:* fixed seating of 2400 over 4 levels incl 24 Wheelchair seats *Arts types:* classical music to light entertainment *Comments:* home of the Hallé Orchestra, Manchester Camerata (chamber orchestra) and the BBC Philharmonic. The Bridgewater Hall is managed by Hallogen Ltd

Town Hall
Albert Road, **Middlesbrough** TS1 1EL
Tel: 1642-263 848/242 561 (box office)
Fax: 1642-221 866
venue manager Jean Hewitt
Venue type: concert hall
Capacity: (inc. standing) 1350, Town Hall crypt 600
Policy: rent, co-present, occasionally present *Arts types:* rock, pop, jazz, classical, variety, comedy, exhibitions, conferences, also rehearsals

Torch Theatre
St Peter's Road, **Milford Haven (Wales)** SA73 2BU
Tel: 1646-694 192
Fax: 1646-698 919/693 605 (marketing)
publicity & marketing manager Lesley Jones; artistic director Peter Doran; financial director Roland Williams
Venue type: theatre *Capacity:* 297 *Policy:* produce, rent, bought-in *Arts types:* repertory, dance, music, cinema, art exhibitions *Comments:* see also Drama

Clwyd Theatr Cymru
Mold (Wales) CH7 1YA
Tel: 1352-756 331 Fax: 1352-758 323
E-Mail: drama@celtic.co.uk
general manager Sarah Holmes; artistic director Terry Hands; marketing manager Ann Williams
Venue type: arts centre *Capacity:* main theatre 582, Clwyd Room 350, Emlyn Williams Theatre 200 *Policy:* produce, present *Arts types:* drama plus general mixed programme *Comments:* have own company based here, repertory and repertoire seasons; disabled access; induction loop system; audio described performances; see also Drama

Longborough Festival Opera
New Banks Fee, Longborough,
Moreton-in-Marsh GL56 0QF
Tel: 1451-830 292 Fax: 1451-830 605
E-Mail: longboroughfestivalopera@btinternet.com
directors Martin & Lizzie Graham; pr & marketing Tei Williams (tel: 1865-883 139, fax: 1865-884 011, e-mail: tei@artsmarketing.demon.co.uk); sponsorship manager Susan Foster (tel: 1865-735 201)
Venue type: converted barn with palladian frontage
Capacity: 470 (370 in stalls, 100 in boxes) *Policy:* to produce a top class opera experience at affordable prices *Arts types:* opera *Comments:* annual festival in summer, with own formed Festival Company; see also Festivals and Opera

Corn Exchange, The
Market Place, **Newbury** RG14 5BD
Tel: 1635-582 666/522 733 (box office)
Fax: 1635-582 223
E-Mail: cornexchange@compuserve.com
general manager Jane Morgan; technical manager Guy Dickens; conference manager Ann Parsonson
Venue type: multi-purpose middle scale touring theatre
Capacity: 400 *Policy:* rent, co-promote
Arts types: all art forms

New Vic Theatre
Etruria Road, **Newcastle-under-Lyme** ST5 0JG
Tel: 1782-717 954 (administration)/539 (marketing)/962 (box office) Fax: 1782-712 885
Internet: www.uktw.co.uk
artistic director Gwenda Hughes; general manager Ludo Keston; head of marketing & business development John Morton; production manager David Martin; theatre manager Judy Bowker
Venue type: theatre-in-the-round *Capacity:* New Vic theatre-in-the-round 605, Stephen Joseph Studio 100
Policy: rent, produce *Arts types:* plays, concerts, musicals, comedy, classical, jazz, opera *Comments:* wheelchair access; induction loop system available; guide dogs accepted with prior notice; minicom; see also Drama

Newcastle City Hall
Northumberland Road, **Newcastle-upon-Tyne** NE1 8SF
Tel: 191-222 1778/261 2606 (box office)
Fax: 191-261 8102
general manager Peter J. Brennan
Venue type: concert hall *Capacity:* 2133 *Policy:* rent by negotiation *Arts types:* orchestra, pop concerts, conferences, meetings

Newcastle Playhouse and Gulbenkian Studio
Haymarket, **Newcastle-upon-Tyne** NE1 7RH
Tel: 191-232 3366/230 5151 (box office) Fax: 191-261 8093
E-Mail: northern.stage@ncl.ac.uk
artistic director Alan Lyddiard; associate directors Neil Murray, Ed Robson; executive director Mandy Stewart; head of education & outreach Tony Harrington; director customer relations Mark Dobson
Venue type: theatre, concert hall *Capacity:* theatre 512, studio 160 *Policy:* produce, receive, co-produce *Arts types:* music, theatre, dance, comedy *Comments:* Northern Stage is the resident company, also touring venue; 20+ weeks a year devoted to touring theatre, dance, festivals; signed performances

Theatre Royal Newcastle upon Tyne
Grey Street, **Newcastle-upon-Tyne** NE1 6BR
Tel: 191-232 0997 (admin)/2061 (box office)
Fax: 191-261 1906
general manager Peter Sarah; finance & administration Graham Armstrong
Venue type: theatre *Capacity:* 1294 (4 levels) *Policy:* present, rent by negotiation *Arts types:* opera, drama, ballet, musicals, concerts, RSC, pantomine, comedy
Comments: national touring house; disabled access; wheelchair spaces; occassional signed performances

Tyne Theatre & Opera House
111 Westgate Road, **Newcastle-upon-Tyne** NE1 4AG
Tel: 191-232 1551/0899 Fax: 191-230 1407
manager Ann Palmer; front of house manager Alison McGarrigal; administration manager Regan Old
Venue type: theatre *Capacity:* 1130 *Policy:* rent *Arts types:* opera, musicals, plays, dance, comedy, children's theatre *Comments:* disabled access; infra-red system for the hard of hearing

Newport Centre
Kingsway, **Newport (Wales)** NP20 1UH
Tel: 1633-662 662/666 (box office) Fax: 1633-670 748
events manager Roger Broome; box office manager Glenys Hawkes
Venue type: multi-purpose hall *Capacity:* main hall 2024, Riverside Suite 400 *Policy:* rent, co-present, guarantees considered *Arts types:* classical, major rock and pop concerts, dance, drama, musicals, opera

Newry & Mourne Arts Centre
1A Bank Parade, **Newry (Northern Ireland)** BT35 6HP
Tel: 1693-66232 Fax: 1693-66839
arts & museum officer Mark Hughes; assistant administrator Jacqueline Turley; museum officer Norine Cunningham
Venue type: multi-purpose *Capacity:* Theatre 150 *Policy:* rent and present *Arts types:* drama, dance, music, arts
Comments: amphitheatre

Ards Arts Centre
Town Hall, Conway Square,
Newtownards (Northern Ireland) BT23 4DB
Tel: 1247-810 803 Fax: 1247-823 131
E-Mail: angelahaley@leisureservices-council.gov.uk
arts officer Eilis O'Baoill; secretary Jill Graham; arts centre co-ordinator Angela Haley; caretaker Thelma Bell; community arts development officer Kate Wimpress
Venue type: arts centre *Capacity:* main recital room 70
Policy: rent, presents a broad cross-discipline programme in 2 seasons *Arts types:* music, dance, drama, exhibitions, educational outreach schemes, story telling, poetry, readings

Princess Theatre Hunstanton
The Green, Hunstanton, **Norfolk** PE36 5AH
Tel: 1553-765 565 Fax: 1553-762 141
Internet: www.west-norfolk.gov.uk
general manager Howard Barnes
Venue type: variety theatre *Capacity:* 64
Arts types: pantomime, comedy, country music

Derngate
19-21 Guildhall Road, **Northampton** NN1 1DP
Tel: 1604-626 222 Fax: 1604-250 901
Internet: www.derngate.org
E-Mail: postbox@derngate.demon.co.uk
general manager Roger Hopwood; company secretary Neil Smith ACMA; programming manager Rosemary Jones
Venue type: multi-entertainment format *Capacity:* concert 1550, Lyric 1198 *Policy:* present, rent *Arts types:* dance, classical music, drama, opera, comedy, pop music *Comments:* owned by Northampton Borough Council, operated by The Derngate Trust

Norwich Arts Centre
St Benedict's Street, **Norwich** NR2 4PG
Tel: 1603-660 387 (admin)/352 (box office)
Fax: 1603-664 806
programme director Pam Reekie; publicity Robert Lockwood; financial manager Alison Schofield; technical manager John Hartwell; visual arts Ian Hutchinson
Venue type: arts centre – converted medieval church
Capacity: seated 120, standing 300 *Policy:* rent by negotiation, guarantee, box office split, receive *Arts types:* concerts – jazz, pop, folk, indie, mime, comedy, drama, classical concerts
Comments: runs an outreach programme for community; photographic gallery, café-bar

St Andrew's & Blackfriars' Hall
St Andrew's Plain, **Norwich** NR3 1AU
Tel: 1603-628 477 Fax: 1603-762 182
Internet: www.norwich.gov.uk
E-Mail: taldous.ncc.sah@gtnet.gov.uk
general manager Timothy Aldous
Venue type: multi-purpose *Capacity:* St Andrew's 850, Blackfriars 370 *Policy:* rent only *Arts types:* symphony, conference, exhibitions, some opera

Theatre Royal Norwich
Theatre Street, **Norwich** NR2 1RL
Tel: 1603-623 562/630 000 (box office)
Fax: 1603-762 904/622 777 (box office)
Internet: www.theatreroyalnorwich.co.uk
E-Mail: marketing@theatreroyalnorwich.co.uk
chief executive and theatre manager Peter Wilson; marketing manager Mark Hazell; press officer Jane Walsh; technical coordinator Arthur Hoare; programming director Roger Richardson; finance manager Norman Cullingford; box office manager Jane Anthony; front of house manager Marney Meakin
Venue type: Proc Arch
Capacity: 1300 *Policy:* receive, produce
Arts types: dance, musicals, opera, concerts, theatre, comedy, pantomime *Comments:* East Anglia's premier touring house

Nottingham Playhouse
Wellington Circus, **Nottingham** NG1 5AF
Tel: 115-947 4361 Fax: 115-947 5759
Internet: www.nottinghamplayhouse.co.uk/playhouse
executive director Venu Dhupa; artistic director Giles Croft; administrative director Jim Robertson; head of marketing William Jones
Venue type: theatre *Capacity:* 750-808 *Policy:* produce, rent *Arts types:* plays, comedy, contemporary, classic, dance *Comments:* wheelchair access, enhanced hearing system, sign language interpretated and audio described performances; see also Drama

Royal Centre
Theatre Square, **Nottingham** NG1 5ND
Tel: 115-989 5500 Fax: 115-947 4218
Internet: www.netpresence.co.uk/royalcentre/
E-Mail: enquiry@royalcentre.co.uk
director J. Michael Grayson; operations director James Ashworth
Venue type: hall & theatre
Capacity: Theatre Royal 1199, Royal Concert Hall 2499
Policy: present by contractual negotiation
Arts types: Royal Concert Hall: classical dance, pop, classical, comedy, jazz; Theatre Royal: drama, ballet, opera, musicals, yearly pantomime

Theatre Royal Nottingham
Royal Centre, Theatre Square,
Nottingham NG1 5ND
Tel: 115-989 5500 Fax: 115-947 4218
Internet: www.netpresence.co.uk/royalcentre/
E-Mail: enquiry@royalcentre.co.uk
managing director J. Michael Grayson; operations director James Ashworth
Venue type: theatre *Capacity:* 1199 *Policy:* terms negotiable *Arts types:* musicals, plays, opera, recitals
Comments: touring venue

Oswestry Leisure Centre
College Road, **Oswestry** SY11 2SA
Tel: 1691-659 349 Fax: 1691-671 007
leisure services manager M Bamber
Venue type: leisure centre – flexible stage – seating
Capacity: 850 *Policy:* private rent or shared (negotiable only) *Arts types:* comedy, dance, concerts (classical, jazz), pantomime

Jacqueline du Pré Music Building
St. Hilda's College, **Oxford** OX4 1DY
Tel: 1865-276 821 Fax: 1865-286 174
E-Mail: jdp@St-hildas.ox.ac.uk
manager Marie-Alice Frappat
Venue type: concert hall, practice rooms, recording facilities *Capacity:* 200 *Policy:* mainly receiving venue
Arts types: concerts, recitals
Comments: excellent accoustics; disabled access

Oxford Apollo Theatre
George Street, **Oxford** OX1 2AG
Tel: 1865-243 041 Fax: 1865-791 976
general manager Louise Clifford; pr Samantha Barlett
Venue type: buildt 1933
Capacity: 1850 *Policy:* rent
Arts types: opera, ballet, theatre

Oxford Playhouse
11-12 Beaumont Street, **Oxford** OX1 2LW
Tel: 1865-247 134 (administration)/798 600 (box office)/792 055 (marketing)/721 091 (PR)/792 758 (stage door) Fax: 1865-793 748
Internet: www.oxfordplayhouse.demon.co.uk
E-Mail: admin@oxfordplayhouse.demon.co.uk
joint theatre directors Tish Francis, Hedda Beeby; front of house manager Jonathan Nash; adminstration Catherine Mallyon; technical manager Tim Boyd; marketing manager Katie Anderson
Venue type: Proc Arch/Pit theatre
Capacity: 600 *Policy:* receive, co-produce, rent by negotiation *Arts types:* drama, dance, opera, music, concerts
Comments: other activities: conferences, conducted tours, workshops, lectures; national touring house; catering service for up to 600; licensed cafe & bar; disabled access to stalls

Sheldonian Theatre
Broad Street, **Oxford** OX1 3AZ
Tel: 1865-277 299 Fax: 1865-277 299
custodian Mrs. S. E. Waldman
Venue type: university ceremony hall
Capacity: 1000 *Policy:* rent by negotiation only
Arts types: recitals, classical music

Perth City Hall
King Edward Street, **Perth (Scotland)** PH1 5UG
Tel: 1738-624 055
Fax: 1738-441 690 (sales)/630 566 (management)
manager Drew Scott; booking/sales Nikky Ananand
Venue type: civic hall
Capacity: main hall 1600, lesser hall 300, smaller meeting rooms also available *Policy:* rent *Arts types:* concerts, opera, dance, conferences, exhibitions
Comments: annual Perth festival of arts, annual schools music festival; see also Festivals

Perth Repertory Theatre
185 High Street, **Perth (Scotland)** PH1 5UW
Tel: 1738-472 700 Fax: 1738-624 576
Internet: www.perth.org.uk/perth/theatre.htm
E-Mail: theatre@perth.org.uk
general manager Paul Hackett; artistic director Michael Winter
Venue type: theatre
Capacity: theatre 490, studio 120
Policy: rent, produce *Arts types:* drama, musicals, comedy *Comments:* home of Perth Repertory Theatre Company, season runs Aug- May, audio described and sign language interpreted performances of each play available; see also Drama

Key Theatre
Embankment Road, **Peterborough** PE1 1EF
Tel: 1733-552 437 Fax: 1733-567 025
director and administrator Derek Killeen
Venue type: studio type theatre – Thrust Stage *Capacity:* 399 *Policy:* produce, receive, rent by negotation; mainly touring – in-house productions *Arts types:* drama, musicals, concerts, pantomime, ballet, opera
Comments: touring theatre and season

Pitlochry Festival Theatre
Port-Na-Craig, **Pitlochry (Scotland)** PH16 5DR
Tel: 1796-484 600/626 (box office) Fax: 1796-484 616
Internet: www.pitlochry.org.uk
E-Mail: admin@pitlochry.org.uk
artistic director Clive Perry; administrator Sheila Harborth; production manager Elaine Kyle; theatre & box office manager Margaret Pirnie
Venue type: theatre *Capacity:* 540 *Policy:* producing house *Arts types:* theatre, concerts, visual arts
Comments: 6 productions in rolling repertoire each season

Plymouth Pavilion
Millbay Road, **Plymouth** PL1 3LF
Tel: 1752-222 200 Fax: 1752-263 505
chief executive Adrian Vinken; events & marketing manager Liam Smith
Venue type: concert arena *Capacity:* seated 2500, standing 3500 *Policy:* rent, box office split deals *Arts types:* orchestra, pop, rock, exhibition, dance, variety, conferences, sporting events
Comments: full access for the disabled

Theatre Royal Plymouth
Royal Parade, **Plymouth** PL1 2TR
Tel: 1752-668 282/267 222 (box office)
Fax: 1752-671 179/221 267
E-Mail: information@theatreroyal.demon.co.uk
chief executive Adrian Vinken; head of operations Margaret Garcia; head of production Alan Finch; artistic director Simon Stokes
Venue type: theatre, Drum Theatre
Capacity: Proc Arch 1296, Drum 200 *Policy:* produce, receive, box office split, rent *Arts types:* drama, musicals, opera, ballet, dance, pantomime, children's shows
Comments: multi-cultural festival; national touring house, houses Royal Shakespeare Company season from Spring 2000; disabled access (level to both auditoria); signed and audio described performances; see also Drama

Poole Arts Centre
Kingland Road, **Poole** BH15 1UG
Tel: 1202-665 334 (management)/685 222 (box office)
Fax: 1202-670 016
Internet: pooleartcentre.co.uk
chief executive Ruth Eastwood; marketing & publicity manager Sarah Chapman; programme director Alistair Wilkinson
Venue type: arts centre *Capacity:* Wessex Hall (theatre style) 1473, 2459 (flat floor), Towngate Theatre 670
Policy: present, rent *Arts types:* concerts (classical, rock, jazz), drama, ballet, dance, opera, light entertainment, children's productions & workshops *Comments:* also have cinema (cap. 109) concentrating mainly on Art films; induction loop system; full access for disabled patrons and performers

New Theatre Royal
Guildhall Walk, **Portsmouth** PO1 2DD
Tel: 23-9264 6477 (admin)/9000 (box office)
Fax: 23-9264 6488
administrator Gareth Vaughan; technical director Mark Ebden; assistant to administrator Fiona Cole; marketing officer Karen Gregory-Reader
Venue type: Victorian theatre *Capacity:* 320 *Policy:* own risk and/or share basis; also available for rent *Arts types:* classical, folk, jazz, world music, music theatre/opera, small scale theatre/one man shows, foreign language productions, dance
Comments: venue undergoing extensive restoration and rebuilding of entire backstage area; events presented on a temporary stage; available for conferences, trade shows etc.

Portsmouth Guildhall
Guildhall Walk, **Portsmouth** PO1 2AB
Tel: 23-9283 4146/9282 4355 (box office)
Fax: 23-9283 4177
general manager Martin Dodd; deputy general manager Danny Green
Venue type: multi-purpose concert venue
Capacity: 2228 *Policy:* co-promote, hire, guarantee
Arts types: ballet, concerts, comedy, shows, exhibitions
Comments: full wheelchair access, induction loop system

Theatr Hafren
Llanidloes Road, Newtown, **Powys (Wales)** SY16 4HU
Tel: 1686-625 447/007 (box office)
Fax: 1686-625 446
E-Mail: boxoffice@coleg-powys.ac.uk
administrator Sara Clutton; marketing manager Iain Kempton; technical manager Peter Whitehead; front of house manager Barbara Jones
Venue type: Proc Arch *Capacity:* 568 *Policy:* receive, guarantee, box office split, rent *Arts types:* drama, dance, opera, concerts (classical, comedy, jazz, rock, folk), productions for children, workshops *Comments:* national touring house

Guild Hall Centre
Lancaster Road, **Preston** PR1 1HT
Tel: 1772-203 456/258 858 (box office)
Fax: 1772-881 716
general manager John Shedwick; marketing manager Bill Jones; arts & education officer Megan Elliot
Venue type: multi-purpose
Capacity: Guild Hall 2020, Charter Theatre 780 *Policy:* present, rent by negotiation *Arts types:* complete range of entertainment, conferences

Hexagon, The
Queens Walk, **Reading** RG1 7UA
Tel: 118-939 0123/960 6060 (box office)
Fax: 118-939 0028
Internet: www.public.reading.gov.uk/hexagon
E-Mail: the.hexagon@reading.gov.uk
director Andrew Ormston; business manager Shirley Britton; marketing manager Andrew Jones; technical manager Paul Kennedy
Venue type: multi-purpose
Capacity: theatre 1000, concert 1484 *Policy:* by negotiation *Arts types:* drama, orchestra, variety, popular music, opera, dance, film, comedy, children's shows
Comments: touring house; full access for disabled, infrared system for the hard of hearing, special seats for the blind and partically sighted

Palace Theatre
Alcester Street, **Redditch** B98 8AE
Tel: 1527-61544 Fax: 1527-60243
theatre manager and artistic director Michael Dyer; theatre administrator Sandra Phipps; production manager Andrew Sheriff; press & publicity officer Paul Hughes
Venue type: Proc Arch *Capacity:* 399 *Policy:* present, rent, produce *Arts types:* theatre, dance, opera, concerts, pantomime, comedy, musicals, variety *Comments:* national touring house; Palace Theatre Company is based here

Harlequin Theatre & Cinema
Warwick Quadrant, **Redhill** RH1 1NN
Tel: 1737-773 721/765 547 (box office) Fax: 1737-765 549
manager Tom Kealey; technical manager John Hewitt; administration manager Bobbie Weekes; marketing manager Audrey Ryan; house manager Janet Franklin
Venue type: multi-purpose arts centre *Capacity:* 494, cinema 100 *Policy:* rent, percentage, guarantees, receiving house *Arts types:* drama, dance, ballet, musicals, comedy, pantomime, concerts (jazz, rock, classical, opera)

Carn Brea Leisure Centre
Station Road, Pool, **Redruth** TR15 3QS
Tel: 1209-714 766 Fax: 1209-610 888
manager Gary Adamson
Venue type: leisure centre *Capacity:* 1250 *Policy:* present, rent by negotiation *Arts types:* various including opera, drama, ballet, folk dance, concerts *Comments:* restaurant and bar facilities available (with possibilities for special licensing); disabled access

Pavilion Theatre
Promenade, **Rhyl (Wales)** LL18 3AQ
Tel: 1745-332 414 (admin)/330 000 (box office)
Fax: 1745-339 819
Internet: www.rhylpavilion.co.uk
E-Mail: gareth.owen@denbighshire.gov.uk
theatre manager Gareth Owen; theatre administrator Valerie Simmons; technical manager Andrew Hughes; marketing officer Jenny Brownless
Venue type: theatre *Capacity:* 1030 *Policy:* rent and own, share risk *Arts types:* drama, opera, ballet, musicals, concerts, conferences, rock, panto *Comments:* young people's theatre – members aged 5-21 years

Georgian Theatre Royal
Victoria Road, **Richmond** DL10 4DW
Tel: 1748-823 710/021 (box office) Fax: 1748-823 710
manager Bill Sellars
Venue type: theatre *Capacity:* 214 *Policy:* rent, book *Arts types:* various including concerts, plays, ballet, opera *Comments:* museum attached to theatre; also guided tours of theatre (the oldest in England in its original form – built in 1788)

Richmond Theatre
The Green, **Richmond** TW9 1QJ
Tel: 181-940 0220/0088 Fax: 181-948 3601
E-Mail: theatre@dircon.co.uk
acting chief executive Karin Gartzke; marketing manager Sally-Anne Lowe; theatre manager Simon Pearce; technical manager Neil Keane
Venue type: Proscenium Theatre *Capacity:* 840 *Policy:* receive, box office split, guarantee by negotiation *Arts types:* drama, comedy, opera, dance, musicals, pantomime
Comments: middle to large scale touring venue

Assembly Hall Theatre
Crescent Road, **Royal Tunbridge Wells** TN1 2LU
Tel: 1892-530 613/532 072 Fax: 1892-525 203
Internet: www.tunbridgewells.gov.uk/ah
E-Mail: info@tunbridgewells.gov.uk
theatre manager Pat Casey; marketing manager Sheila Ryall; business manager Brian McAteer; operations manager John Sumner; catering manager Les Woolgar
Venue type: multi-purpose *Capacity:* seated 933, standing 1200 *Policy:* rent, co-present, percentage terms only *Arts types:* opera, ballet, dance, drama, comedy, pantomime, young people's and children's shows, craft fair, exhibitions

City Hall Salisbury
Malthouse Lane, **Salisbury** SP2 7TU
Tel: 1722-334 432 (admin)/327 676 (box office)
Fax: 1722-337 059
administrator Denise Maidment; city hall manager Phillip Smith; marketing officer t.b.a.
Venue type: multi-purpose hall *Capacity:* 953 *Policy:* rent, box office split *Arts types:* dance, comedy, concerts (all types), musicals, opera

Salisbury Arts Centre
Bedwin Street, **Salisbury** SP1 3UT
Tel: 1722-321 744 Fax: 1722-331 742
Internet: www.sac.dircon.co.uk
E-Mail: info@sac.dircon.co.uk
director Jill Low; publicity officer Steve Kellow; centre manager Catherine Sandbrook
Venue type: arts centre, 2 galleries *Capacity:* seated 140, standing 400 *Policy:* present at own risk, rent *Arts types:* complete range of contemporary performing arts, all types of music, dance, theatre *Comments:* almost exclusively a touring venue, small scale dance; 'large percentage' voluntary staff; also community arts centre which liases with other local community groups; 1999: emphasis on world music, dance and arts

Salisbury Playhouse
Malthouse Lane, **Salisbury** SP2 7RA
Tel: 1722-320 117/333 (box office)
Fax: 1722-421 991
executive director Rebecca Morland; artistic director Joanna Read; marketing manager James Gough; head of education Trevelyan Wright
Venue type: theatre *Capacity:* main auditorium 517, studio theatre 140 *Policy:* produce, rent *Arts types:* pantomime, plays, comedy, dance, children's shows *Comments:* induction loop in the main auditorium, facilities for the disabled, guide dogs are welcome; see also Drama

Spa Complex
South Bay, **Scarborough** YO11 2HD
Tel: 1723-376 774 Fax: 1723-355 821
general manager Keith Norton; assistant managers Brendan Sheerin, Carole Mills
Venue type: multi-purpose *Capacity:* Spa Grand Hall 1825, Spa theatre 620, Spa ocean ballroom 850, Suncourt Enclosure 260 *Policy:* present, co-present, rent *Arts types:* orchestral concerts, theatre, dance, variety *Comments:* summer season of resident orchestra and gala concerts; annual drama festival (Easter), traditional summer season

Stephen Joseph Theatre
Westborough, **Scarborough** YO11 1JW
Tel: 1723-370 540 (administration)/541 (box office)
Fax: 1723-360 506
Internet: www.sjt.uk.com
E-Mail: response@sjt.onyxnet.co.uk
theatre manager Elizabeth Brown; artistic director Alan Ayckbourn; financial administrator Keith McFarlane; general administrator Stephen Wood; production manager Alison Fowler; press & marketing manager Andie Hawkes
Venue type: theatre, cinema *Capacity:* in-the-round auditorium 404, McCarthy auditorium 165 *Policy:* produce; mainly new writing *Arts types:* new works by Alan Ayckbourn, new works by other writers, new adaptations, classics, modern and classical music *Comments:* access by wheelchairs; infra-red system in theatre, induction loop in cinema; signed performances

STAG Theatre
London Road, **Sevenoaks** TN13 1ZZ
Tel: 1732-451 548/450 175 (box office)
Fax: 1732-743 306
general manager Terry Shaw; publicity officer Francis Price; administration manager Jans Grater
Venue type: theatre, cinema, banqueting/function room *Capacity:* main auditorium 453, Cormack Stage 139, Theatre-In-The-Round 650, cinema I 130, cinema II 103 *Policy:* rent and present *Arts types:* varied programme

Crucible Theatre
55 Norfolk Street, **Sheffield** S1 1DA
Tel: 114-249 5999/6000 (box office)
Fax: 114-249 6003
chief executive Graham Morris; artistic director Deborah Paige; production manager Rob McKinney; marketing director Angela Galvin
Venue type: theatre *Capacity:* Thrust Stage 1000, Studio 400 *Policy:* mainly produce, also rent, receive *Arts types:* mainly drama, some dance, opera, concerts, musicals *Comments:* the studio is the home of the Sheffield Chamber Music Festival, main part in May, plus events throughout the year; managed by Sheffield Theatres; see also Drama

National Centre for Popular Music, The
Paternoster Row, **Sheffield** S1 2QQ
Tel: 114-249 8885 (admin)/296 2626 (box office)
Fax: 114-249 8886
Internet: www.ncpm.co.uk
E-Mail: info@ncpm.co.uk
chief executive Stuart Rogers; creative director Tim Strickland
Venue type: arts and exhibitions centre with performance space *Capacity:* 200
Policy: receive *Arts types:* popular music
Comments: receiving venue

Sheffield Arena
Broughton Lane, **Sheffield** S9 2DF
Tel: 1142-562 002 Fax: 1142-565 520
Internet: www.sheffield-arena.co.uk
general manager David Vickers; box office manager Sharon Doran-Thorp; director of marketing Jo Crutchley
Venue type: entertainment centre
Capacity: up to 12241 *Policy:* fixed rental, percentage deals, co-promotions *Arts types:* pop, rock, opera, classical, exhibitions, conferences, jazz, product launches, ice hockey, ice shows, spectator sports, equestrial events
Comments: managed by Apollo Leisure UK

Sheffield City Hall
Barker's Pool, **Sheffield** S1 2JA
Tel: 1142-734 550 (admin)/789 789 (box office)
Fax: 1142-769 866
E-Mail: info@sheffhall.demon.co.uk
general manager Maire McCarthy; marketing manager Donna Linehan; operations manager Richard Hunter; box office manager Joanne Chapple; publicity officer Dominic Russell Price
Venue type: multi-purpose *Capacity:* Oval Hall 2346, Memorial Hall 522, Central Suite (standing) 850 *Policy:* percentage deals, joint promotions, rent *Arts types:* pop, rock concerts, classical music, ballet, drama, dance, comedy, conferences, musical, ballroom dancing

Sheffield Lyceum
55 Norfolk Street, **Sheffield** S1 1DA
Tel: 114-249 5999/6000 (box office)
ax: 114-249 6003
chief executive Graham Morris; artistic director Deborah Paige; production manager Rob McKinney; marketing director Angela Galvin
Venue type: proc arch *Capacity:* lyceum 1000 *Policy:* guarantee split by negotiation, rent, receive *Arts types:* all artforms, drama, opera, musicals, pantomime, dance, ballet, concerts *Comments:* national touring house, managed by Sheffield Theatres

Music Hall
The Square, **Shrewsbury** SY1 1LH
Tel: 1743-352 019 Fax: 1743-358 780
Internet: www.musichall.co.uk
E-Mail: mail@musichall.demon.co.uk
general manager Lezley Picton; house manager David Jack; marketing manager Lynette Adji; technical manager Grant Wilson; admin & finance officer Val Philips
Venue type: multi-purpose main hall, film theatre, function suites, photographic gallery *Capacity:* main hall 400, film theatre 100 *Policy:* own promotions and rent *Arts types:* theatre, contemporary dance, popular music, chamber music, comedy, film, photographic touring exhibitions, family events, pantomime *Comments:* restaurants and bar

Customs House, The
Mill Dam, **South Shields (Tyne & Wear)** NE33 1ES
Tel: 191-454 1234 Fax: 191-456 5979
Internet: www.customshouse.co.uk
E-Mail: mail@customshouse.demon.co.uk
director Gordon Bates; administrator Sue Wright; arts development Pauline Moger; marketing manager Robin Byers; theatre manager Richard Flood; technical manager Paul Tague
Venue type: Theatre, cinema, gallery
Capacity: 400 and 180 *Policy:* available to local and national groups *Arts types:* theatre, comedy, opera, rock, local amateur performances, film
Comments: funding support for local community, workshops and participation events

Mayflower, The
Commercial Road, **Southampton** SO15 1GE
Tel: 23-8071 1800 Fax: 23-8071 1801
director Dennis L J Hall; head of marketing and operations Paul Lewis; financial controller Wycliffe Musuku
Venue type: theatre *Capacity:* 2289 *Policy:* rent, box office splits *Arts types:* opera, ballet, musicals, concerts, large-scale drama *Comments:* national touring house; facilities for the disabled

Nuffield Theatre, Southampton
University Road, **Southampton** SO17 1TR
Tel: 23-8031 5500 Fax: 23-8031 5511
E-Mail: nuffieldt@all.com
administrative director Mark Courtice; artistic director Patrick Sandford; production manager Julien Boast; marketing manager James Woods
Venue type: building-based
Capacity: 481 *Policy:* produce, occasionally receive, available for rent to local amateur groups and occasional touring productions; also present events at own risk or sometimes have a co-production *Arts types:* theatre, comedy, dance, music
Comments: the venue has recently been refurbished; full disabled access (ramps and lifts – access for all); see also Drama

Southampton Guildhall
West Marlands Road, **Southampton** SO14 7LP
Tel: 23-8083 2070 Fax: 23-8033 7802
Internet: www.southampton.gov.uk
E-Mail: h.richardson@southampton.gov.uk
general manager Sue Cheriton; operations manager Nigel Greene; assistant operations managers Nicky Kelso, Les Turner; sales & marketing manager Heather Richardson
Venue type: multi-purpose hall, lecture theatre
Capacity: Guildhall 1749, lecture theatre 118, 6 meeting rooms including syndicate room
Policy: rent *Arts types:* orchestra, pop, folk, jazz, world music, conferences, dinners, dance, exhibitions, concerts, variety, wrestling, films, workshops, lectures
Comments: 2 bars and catering facilities; middle scale touring house; disabled access and toilets

Turner Sims Concert Hall
University of Southampton, **Southampton** SO17 1BJ
Tel: 23-8059 2223/5151 (box office) Fax: 23-8059 2505
E-Mail: turnsims@soton.ac.uk
concert hall manager Peter Bolton;
publicity/marketing Jan Ward
Venue type: concert hall *Capacity:* 460 *Policy:* present, rent, share *Arts types:* concerts (classical, jazz, world music, chamber music, contemporary music), music theatre, dance, childrens events *Comments:* Foyer used for small scale performances and offers facilities for disabled participants

Cliffs Pavilion
Station Road, **Southend-on-Sea** SS0 7RA
Tel: 1702-331 852 (general manager)/390 657 (administration and management)/391 573 (gen. office)/351 135 (box office) Fax: 1702-433 015
general manager Charles Mumford; stage and events officer David Bunting; marketing officer Paul Driscoll; building operations officer Mark Homer; finance officer Chris Clark; administration officer Anne Kentuck
Venue type: multi-purpose hall
Capacity: seated 1630, standing 2000
Policy: present, rent by negotiation *Arts types:* one-nighters, shows, all types of music, dance, drama, comedy, West-End musicals, rock concerts, ice shows
Comments: national touring house

Kings Theatre
Albert Road, **Southsea** PO5 2QJ
Tel: 1705-811 394 Fax: 1705-735 242
general manager Mrs V M Dowling; administrator and co-lessee I S Barnes; co-lessee Mrs J N Cooper
Venue type: theatre *Capacity:* 1450 *Policy:* rent, split, co-production *Comments:* national touring house

Alban Centre
Civic Centre, **St Albans** AL1 3LD
Tel: 1727-861 078 (admin)/844 488 (box office)
Fax: 1727-865 755
Internet: www.stalbans.gov.uk/arena
E-Mail: arena@relaxion.co.uk
manager Roger Cramer; catering mananger Nicola Cork
Venue type: multi-purpose entertainment centre
Capacity: seated 850, standing 1100
Policy: present, rent *Arts types:* mainly one-nighters, drama, music, dance, variety, cinema, annual pantomine, conferences, exhibitions
Comments: disabled access; disabled toilets, infra red system for the hard of hearing

Theatre Royal St Helens
Corporation Street, **St Helens** WA10 1LQ
Tel: 1744-756 333 (admin)/000 (box office)
Fax: 1744-756 777
theatre manager Basil Soper; technical/stage manager Mike Littlewood
Venue type: bricks and mortar
Capacity: 701 *Policy:* rent, percentage
Arts types: various including concerts, variety, ballet, music *Comments:* soley operated by The Independent Methodist Association Incorporated

Stafford Gatehouse
Eastgate Street, **Stafford** ST16 2LT
Tel: 1785-253 595 Fax: 1785-225 622
manager Gatehouse Daniel Shaw; arts development officer Nick Mowat
Venue type: multi-purpose *Capacity:* Gatehouse Theatre 564, Studio Theatre 120 *Policy:* present, rent
Arts types: ballet, drama, opera, variety *Comments:* disabled access and facilities

Gordon Craig Theatre
Stevenage Arts & Leisure Centre, Lytton Way, **Stevenage** SG1 1LZ
Tel: 1438-242 642 (admin)/242 866(box office)
Fax: 1438-242 342
arts & entertainments manager Bob Bustance; marketing manager Ann Dopson; technical manager Nigel Howlett
Venue type: Proc Arc theatre, concert hall, exhibition hall, conference facilities *Capacity:* theatre 506, concert hall – seated 1150, standing 1800, conference rooms 20-120 *Policy:* co-produce, receive, rent by negotiation *Arts types:* plays, opera, dance, orchestral concerts, music rock concerts
Comments: national touring house

MacRobert Arts Centre
University of Stirling, **Stirling (Scotland)** FK9 4LA
Tel: 1786-467 155/461 081 (box office)
Fax: 1786-451 369
Internet: www.stir.ac.uk/mcrobert/
E-Mail: macrobert-arts@stir.ac.uk
director Liz Moran; marketing manager Charlotte Halliday; general manager Bill Armitage; technical manager Colin Proudfoot
Venue type: arts centre, theatre *Capacity:* main theatre 500, studio theatre 140 *Policy:* rent, present, co-produce and commission *Arts types:* film, drama, music, dance, childrens theatre, opera, exhibitions *Comments:* Sennheiser infra-red system, level access for wheelchairs, 2 wheelchair spaces in main auditorium

ARC
Dovecot Street, **Stockton-on-Tees** TS18 1LL
Tel: 1642-611 625 Fax: 1642-666 668
Internet: www.arts-centre.co.uk
E-Mail: arc@tremens.co.uk
director Frank Wilson (email: frank@tremons.demon.co.uk); marketing & customer services manager Clare Frolley
Venue type: theatre – multimedia *Capacity:* cinema 130, theatre 275, theatre space + cabaret etc. 300 *Policy:* rent, own risk *Comments:* conference facilities; digital art suite; organise Stockton International Riverside Festival; see also Festivals

Victoria Hall
Bagnall Street, Hanley, **Stoke on Trent** ST1 3AD
Tel: 1782-213 808 Fax: 1782-214 738
executive director Richard Wingate; operation manager Andrew Macduff; marketing manager David Brownlee; stage manager Martin Lund
Venue type: multi-purpose concert hall *Capacity:* 1350 seated, 1700 standing
Policy: co-present *Arts types:* various including classical concerts, trade fairs, children's productions
Comments: re-opened Nov 1998 after extensive refurbishment; disabled access

Stratford Theatres
RSC at Stratford upon Avon, Waterside, **Stratford upon Avon** CV37 6BB
Tel: 1789-296 655/403 403 (box office)
Fax: 1789-294 810
Internet: www.rsc.org.uk
artistic director Adrian Noble; executive producer Lynda Farran; general manager William Weston; head of press & pr Ian Rawley
Venue type: 3 different style venues *Capacity:* Royal Shakespeare Theatre 1412, Swan Theatre-Thrust 464, The Other Place studio theatre 175 *Policy:* booking terms by negotiation, produce
Arts types: when RSC not resident: opera, musicals, touring drama, concerts *Comments:* Royal Shakespeare Company (q.v.) resident all year; some opportunities for visiting companies in autumn

Empire Theatre
High Street West, **Sunderland** SR1 3EX
Tel: 191-514 2517/510 0545 (admin)
Fax: 191-553 7427
managing director Symon Easton; finance director Stuart Anderson; technical manager Melvyn P. James; operations manager Christabel Brett; head of marketing & sales Katy Raines
Venue type: theatre *Capacity:* 1900 *Policy:* present, rent by negotiation *Arts types:* opera, ballet, concerts, variety, pantomime, mixed programme *Comments:* national touring house

Brangwyn Hall
City & County of Swansea, Leisure Department, The Guildhall, **Swansea (Wales)** SA1 4PE
Tel: 1792-635 489 Fax: 1792-635 489
manager Sean Keir; director of leisure services David Evans
Venue type: concert hall *Policy:* rent *Arts types:* concerts, exhibitions *Comments:* Swansea Festival of Music and the Arts, Brangwyn International Concerts; available for recordings, conferences, dinners etc.; capacity was due to have changed during 1999, new capacity not known at time of going to print

Swansea Grand Theatre
Singleton Street, **Swansea (Wales)** SA1 3QJ
Tel: 1792-475 242 (admin)/715 (box office)
Fax: 1792-475 379
general manager Gary Iles; assistant general manager Gerald Morris; marketing officer (arts) Paul Hopkins; assistant marketing officer (arts) Nicola Beake
Venue type: theatre *Capacity:* 1020 *Policy:* split box office, rent *Arts types:* dance, ballet, plays, opera, one night concerts, conferences, community & youth involvement
Comments: national touring house, own fully refurbished youth theatre, Grand Theatre Dance School

Wyvern Theatre
Theatre Square, **Swindon** SN1 1QN
Tel: 1793-535 534 (admin)/524 481(box office)
Fax: 1793-480 278
general manager Ted Doan; manager Apollo Leisure (UK) Ltd. (Nicky Monk 1865-782 900)
Venue type: Proc Arch *Capacity:* 617 *Policy:* rent *Arts types:* opera, dance, ballet, variety, pantomime, drama
Comments: national touring house

Princess Theatre
Torbay Road, **Torquay** TQ2 5EZ
Tel: 1803-290 288/290 (box office)
Fax: 1803-290 170
general manager Wendy Bennett; deputy manager Sarah Griffiths; assistant manager Russell Miller
Venue type: Proc Arch *Capacity:* 1495 *Policy:* present, rent *Arts types:* drama, musicals, variety, concerts, pantomime, comedy, pop *Comments:* management: Apollo Leisure Group, Tel: 1865-782 900

Hall for Cornwall
Back Quay, **Truro** TR1 2LL
Tel: 1872-262 465 Fax: 1872-260 246
E-Mail: Hallforcornwall@enterprise.net
general manager Tim German; artistic & operations director Chris Warner; marketing manager Trevor Gardiner; catering manager Ian Mathieson; accounts manager Peter Stokes; technical manager Andrew Oram; box office manager Debbie McRory
Venue type: multi-purpose hall with stage/Proc Arch theatre, concert hall *Capacity:* theatre style 950, standing 1700 *Policy:* rent, split, guarantee *Arts types:* musicals, drama, variety, music, dance, touring companies, pop concerts *Comments:* re-opened in Nov '97 after major refurbishment; Cornwall's only professional middle scale venue

Theatre Royal and Opera House
Drury Lane, **Wakefield** WF1 2TE
Tel: 1924-215 531(admin)/211 311 (box office)
Fax: 1924-215 525
general manager Murray Edwards; operations manager Marie Dalton
Venue type: theatre *Capacity:* 509 *Policy:* hire by negotiation, guarantees, box office splits, 1st calls *Arts types:* dance, mime, music events, comedy, musicals, drama, opera *Comments:* medium scale presenting house; Matcham Theatre

Parr Hall
Palmyra Square South, **Warrington** WA1 1BL
Tel: 1925-634 958/651 178 Fax: 1925-234 144
E-Mail: parrhall@warrington.gov.uk
administration manager Delphine Corcoran; entertainment manager John Perry; marketing & promotions manager Nick Shaw
Venue type: multi-purpose concert hall *Capacity:* up to 1100
Policy: rent, co-present *Arts types:* dance, drama, pantomime, opera, comedy, concerts (jazz, classical, rock)

Palace Theatre Watford
Clarendon Road, **Watford** WD1 1JZ
Tel: 1923-235 455 (admin)/225 671 (box office)
Fax: 1923-819 664
E-Mail: info@watfordtheatre.co.uk
administrative director Alastair Moir; artistic director Lawrence Till
Venue type: Proc Arch *Capacity:* 663 *Policy:* produce, rent by negotiation *Arts types:* drama, dance, comedy, pantomime *Comments:* middle scale touring venue; see also Drama

Wembley Conference and Exhibition Centre and Wembley Arena
c/o Wembley (London) Ltd., Elvin House, Stadium Way, **Wembley** HA9 0DW
Tel: 20-8902 8833 (switchboard)/0902 (box office)
Fax: 20-8585 3879
Internet: www.wembley.co.uk
E-Mail: Venues@wembley.co.uk
managing director Janet Garner; sales and marketing manager Peter Tudor; operations manager David Thomson
Venue type: multi-purpose entertainment, conference and exhibition venue *Capacity:* Arena 12000, Grand Hall 2700 (DMX lighting and turbo sound system) *Policy:* rent & shared risk basis *Arts types:* rock and pop concerts, contemporary music, recitals, dance, pantomime, filming, conferences, product launches, exhibitions, lectures, sporting events *Comments:* Exhibition Halls may be used for dance productions, gymnastics, stand up pop shows, major banquets

Palace Theatre Centre
430 London Road, **Westcliff on Sea** SS0 9LA
Tel: 1702-347 816 Fax: 1702-435 031
artistic director Roy Marsden; marketing manager Marion Orchard
Capacity: mainhouse 603, studio 100 *Policy:* rent, produce *Arts types:* concerts, drama, comedy *Comments:* provide signed performances and audio described performances for sight/hearing impaired audiences; wheelchair spaces; see also Drama

Playhouse Theatre
High Street, **Weston super Mare** BS23 1HP
Tel: 1934-627 457/645 544 (box offfice)
Fax: 1934-612 182
E-Mail: playhouse@n-somerset.gov.uk
general manager Vivian Thomson; marketing manager Ruth Staple; technical manager Peter Magor
Venue type: theatre *Capacity:* 658 *Policy:* rent, co-present, percentage deals *Arts types:* theatre, musicals, opera, ballet, star attractions *Comments:* national touring house; disabled access

Winter Gardens Pavilion
Royal Parade, **Weston super Mare** BS23 1AQ
Tel: 1934-417 117/645 544 (box office) Fax: 1934-612 323
venue manager Vivienne Thomson; technical manager David Gentle; business manager Peter Undery; customer services manager Flannon Ball
Venue type: multi-purpose *Capacity:* ballroom 650, hall 600 *Policy:* present, rent *Arts types:* music, dance, drama, children's entertainment, festivals

Pavilion Theatre (Pavilion Complex)
Leisure & Entertainments Dept, Pavillion Complex, The Esplanade, **Weymouth** DT4 8ED
Tel: 1305-765 218 Fax: 1305-761 654
Internet: www.weymouth.gov.uk
E-Mail: tourism@weymouth.gov.uk
director of tourism & corporate services Ian Locke; theatre manager Stephen Young
Venue type: entertainments and conference centre *Capacity:* theatre 1012, Ocean room 720 *Policy:* present, buy-in, rent by negotiation *Arts types:* classical and pop concerts, amateur use also
Comments: summer season, tours

Theatre Royal Winchester
Jewry Street, **Winchester** SO23 8SB
Tel: 1962-842 226
Comments: closed for redevelopment, due to re-open early 2000, no further details available at time of going to print; contact Campaign Office for further details

New Victoria Theatre
The Ambassadors, Peacocks Centre, **Woking** GU21 1GQ
Tel: 1483-747 422/761 144 (box office) Fax: 1483-770 477
E-Mail: howardpanter@theambassadors.com
managing director Howard Panter; executive director Rosemary Squire; chief executive David Blyth
Venue type: Proc Arch *Capacity:* 1300 *Policy:* rent by negotiation *Arts types:* drama, musicals, touring opera and ballet, West End shows, comedy, pantomime, concerts, classical *Comments:* management: Woking Turnstyle Ltd; subsidiary of Ambassadors Theatre Group (ATG)

Rhoda McGaw Theatre
The Ambassadors, Peacocks Centre, **Woking** GU21 1GQ
Tel: 1483-747 422 Fax: 1483-770 477
managing director Howard Panter; chief executive, Woking Turnstyle David Blyth
Venue type: Proc Arch *Capacity:* 230 *Policy:* rent by negotiation *Arts types:* most art forms *Comments:* management: Woking Turnstyle Ltd.

Civic Hall/Wulfrun Hall
North Street, **Wolverhampton** WV1 1RQ
Tel: 1902-552 122/121 (box office) Fax: 1902-552 123
E-Mail: wolvescivicwulfrun@dial.pipex.com.
civic halls manager Mark Blackstock; deputy manager Joe Hilton; music development officer Simon Pugh; technical manager Wayne Larner; marketing officer Ruth Hickinbotham
Venue type: multi-purpose halls *Capacity:* Wulfrun – seated 672, standing 756, Civic – seated 2039, standing 2126 *Policy:* present, rent, available for rent percentage etc. *Arts types:* pop, rock, jazz, folk, variety, comedy, dance, conferences

Wolverhampton Grand Theatre
Lichfield Street, **Wolverhampton** WV1 1DE
Tel: 1902-573 300 (admin)/429 212 (box office)/573 311 (marketing) Fax: 1902-21447
Internet: www.grandtheatre.co.uk
E-Mail: marketing@grandtheatre.co.uk
chief executive Brian Goddard; general manager Tony Pugh; financial controller Gary Postins; technical manager Ian Griffiths; commercial manager Steve Collins; marketing manager Joseph Hocking
Venue type: victorian theatre *Capacity:* 1200 *Policy:* receiving theatre *Arts types:* musicals, plays, children's shows, concerts, variety, opera, ballet, pantomime
Comments: national touring lyric theatre; recently refurbished; currently base for D'Oyly Carte Opera Company

Assembly Hall
Stoke Abbott Road, **Worthing** BN11 1HQ
Tel: 1903-239 999 (administration)/820 500 (box office)
Fax: 1903-821 124
theatre manager Peter Bailey; business development manager Trevor Gray; marketing manager Louise Sommerstein; administrative officer Rosie Gray
Venue type: multi-purpose *Capacity:* seated 930, standing 1100 *Policy:* rent *Arts types:* music, dance, conferences, exhibitions
Comments: full access for the disabled

Connaught Theatre
Union Place, **Worthing** BN11 1LG
Tel: 1903-231 799 Fax: 1903-215 337
theatre administrator/arts development officer David Smith
Venue type: proc. arch *Capacity:* main house 514 *Policy:* middle scale touring house; willing to premier work *Arts types:* mixed programme including drama, dance, ballet, opera, pantomime, children's shows, films, concerts, studio drama, mime *Comments:* medium scale touring house; managed by Worthing Borough Council from late 1999; also has cinema

Pavilion Theatre
Marine Parade, **Worthing** BN11 3PX
Tel: 1903-239 999 ext.2530 (admin)/820 500 (box office) Fax: 1903-821 124
theatre manager Peter Bailey; business development manager Trevor Gray; house manager Paul Gordon; marketing manager Louise Sommerstein
Venue type: multi-purpose theatre, exhibition venue *Capacity:* seated 850, standing 1100 *Policy:* rent venue, present, co-present *Arts types:* mixed programme throughout the year including popular music, comedians, opera, ballet, conferences, concerts
Comments: full disabled access and toilets, full Proscenium Arch theatre

Octagon Theatre
Hendford, **Yeovil** BA20 1UX
Tel: 1935-422 836/884 (box office) Fax: 1935-475 281
general manager John G White; marketing officer Dianne Wynn
Venue type: theatre *Capacity:* 625 *Policy:* rent, co-present *Arts types:* drama, opera, ballet, musicals, concerts
Comments: national touring house

Arts Centre
Micklegate, **York** YO1 1JG
Tel: 1904-642 582 (admin)/627 129 (info)
Fax: 1904-642 582
Internet: www.lds-ltd.com/yac
E-Mail: yorkartscentre@pop3.poptel.org
director Peter Lennox; programme manager Kenny Lieske; venue manager Tony Clarke
Venue type: arts centre *Capacity:* seated 160, standing 200 *Policy:* present, rent by negotiation *Arts types:* theatre, music, comedy, multi media events *Comments:* developing Arts for 21st centry, multi-media and technology led events for local groups

Theatre Royal York
St. Leonard's Place, **York** YO1 7HD
Tel: 1904-658 162 (admin)/623 568 (box office)
Fax: 1904-611 534
executive director Elizabeth Jones; artistic director Damian Cruden; marketing manager t.b.a.; production manager Matt Noddings; education & outreach officer Brian Higginson
Venue type: theatre *Capacity:* 863 *Policy:* mainly producing, some tours *Arts types:* contemporary dance, opera, drama, pantomime, musicals, comedy
Comments: disabled access (level to stalls, lift to bar & toilet); loop induction systems; signed & audio described performances; see also Drama

York Barbican Centre
Barbican Road, **York** YO10 4NT
Tel: 1904-628 991 Fax: 1904-628 227
E-Mail: 100530.1026@compuserve.com
entertainments programme coordinator Craig Smart
Venue type: flexible performance space *Capacity:* seated 1500, standing 1800 *Policy:* own promotions, rent, joint arrangements *Arts types:* orchestra, pop, rock, variety, opera, spectator sports, comedy, children's shows
Comments: Other activities: exhibitions, conferences, seminars; owned and managed by City of York Council

YUGOSLAVIA (+381)

Due to the war in Kosovo we have been unable to update the following entries for Yugoslavia

Cultural Centre Bar
Kulturnu centar Bar
Jovana Tomasevica 57, 85000 **Bar**
Tel: 85-12431 Fax: 85-13818
director Dragica Milic

Cultural Centre Vuk Karadzic
Kulturni centar Vuk Karadzic
Marsala Tita 14, 21220 **Becej**
Tel: 21-815 336
director Jelena Brankov; music editor Miroslav Silacki

Belgrade Cultural Centre
Kulturni Centar Beograda
Knez Mihajlova 6, 11000 **Belgrade**
Tel: 11-621 134/622 058 Fax: 11-623 853
director Danica Jovovic; music editor Nena Mihajlovic
Venue type: multi-purpose *Capacity:* 200 *Arts types:* music

Belgrade Youth Arts Centre
Dom omladine
Makedonska 22, 11000 **Belgrade**
Tel: 11-324 8202/322 0133 Fax: 11-324 1187
director Ninoslav Randelovic; music director Jasna Dimitrijevic
Venue type: multi-purpose *Capacity:* total 1280 *Arts types:* shows, theatre, dance, music, etc.

Cultural Foundation of Ilija Kolarac
Zaduzbina Ilije Kolarca
Studentski trg 5, 11000 **Belgrade**
Tel: 11-635 037 Fax: 11-636 319
director Olga Milutinovic; head of music department Vera Stojanovic
Venue type: 3 concert halls *Capacity:* 340 *Arts types:* music

Russian Cultural Centre
Ruski dom – kulturni centar
Narodnog fronta 33, 11000 **Belgrade**
Tel: 11-642 178/682 162 Fax: 11-641 351
director Vladimir Vasiljevic Kuterin; music editor Vladimir Meljnik

Student Cultural Centre
Studentski kulturni centar
Srpskih vladara 48, 11000 **Belgrade**
Tel: 11-682 726/659 277 Fax: 11-659 376
director Slavoljub Veselinovic
Venue type: multi-purpose *Capacity:* 340 *Policy:* produce *Arts types:* theatre

Trade Union Centre
Dom sindikata
Trg Nikole Pasica 5, 11000 **Belgrade**
Tel: 11-323 4894 Fax: 11-323 4224
director Dragoslav Agatonovic; art programme director Miroslav Vasic
Venue type: concert hall *Capacity:* large hall 1750, small hall 300

Students Cultural Centre
Studentski kulturni centar
Radoja Domanovica 12, 34000 **Kragujevac**
Tel: 34-336 122 Fax: 34-335 050
director Zivomir Rankovic; art editor Radisa Radovanovic

Cultural Centre Nis
Kulturni centar Nis
Stanoja Bunusevca bb, 18000 **Nis**
Tel: 18-45394/354 364 Fax: 18-47995
director Predrag Jelenkovic; art editor Nenad Cveticanin

Students Cultural Centre Nis
Studentski kulturni centar Nis
Sumatovacka bb, 18000 **Nis**
Tel: 18-523 364 Fax: 18-523 120
director Nebojsa Randelovic; editor for theatre Sasa Stepanovic

Sava Arts and Congress Centre
Sava centar
Milentija Popovica 9, 11070 **Novi Beograd**
Tel: 11-222 4323 Fax: 11-222 1156
Venue type: multi-purpose *Capacity:* main concert hall 3672 *Arts types:* performing arts, concerts, congresses
Comments: 15 performing areas

Student Arts Centre
Dom kulture Studentski grad
Bulevar AVNOJa 179, 11070 **Novi Beograd**
Tel: 11-691 442 Fax: 11-673 623
director Miro Maksimovic; art editor Jelena Oljaca
Venue type: multi-purpose *Capacity:* 400
Arts types: theatre

Novi Sad Cultural Centre
Kulturni centar Novog Sada
Katolicka porta 5, 21000 **Novi Sad**
Tel: 21-28972 Fax: 21-25168
director Dragan Sreckov

Sport and Business Centre Vojvodina
Spsortski poslovni centar Vojvodina
Sutjeska 2, 21000 **Novi Sad**
Tel: 21-613 849/622 222 Fax: 21-611 581
Venue type: 7 halls *Capacity:* 250 to 6000
Arts types: music and theatre

Students Cultural Centre
Studentski kulturni centar
Dr Sime Milosevica 1, 21000 **Novi Sad**
Tel: 21-350 744 Fax: 21-350 579
director Maja Tesic

Moraca Cultural Centre
Moraca kulturni centar
Dure Salaja bb, 81000 **Podgorica**
Tel: 81-51831/51366

Republic Cultural Centre
Republicki kulturni centar
Njegoseva 2, 81000 **Podgorica**
Tel: 81-23408/24145

Youth Arts Centre Budo Tomovic
Dom omladine Budo Tomovic
Vaka Durovica 12, 81000 **Podgorica**
Tel: 81-45682/45345 Fax: 81-44563
director Ranko Vukovic

Cultural Centre Boro i Ramiz
Kulturni centar Boro i Ramiz
Kragejevacka bb, 38000 **Pristina**
Tel: 38-27850/51 Fax: 38-27852
director Ljubomir Vujovic

Students Cultural Centre
Studentski kulturni centar
Desanke Mksimovic bb, 38000 **Pristina**
Tel: 38-27671 Fax: 38-27671
director Drasko Dosljak; art editors Milijana Nedeljkovic, Aleksandar Maskovic

Youth Cultural Centre
Dom mladosti
Narodne omladine 1, 23000 **Zrenjanin**
Tel: 23-66712 Fax: 23-62931
editor in chief Nada Panic; music editor Misa Kozarev

Promoters

Promoters
Essentially this list comprises impresarios, 'programmateurs' or producing houses. The nature of the arts business means that companies seeking engagements should look not only at this section, but also the sections on Festivals, Venues, Agents and, for example, some of the theatres in the Drama section.
Within country the promoters are ordered by city, and alphabetically within city. When the promoter is an individual's name, the ordering is done by christian name.

Promoteurs
Dans son ensemble cette rubrique englobe des impresari, programmateurs ou maisons de production. La nature même du monde des Arts Vivants fait que les compagnies qui cherchent des engagements devraient se reporter également aux sections 'Festivals', 'Salles de Spectacle', 'Agents' et certaines parution dans la section 'Théâtre'.
Pour chaque pays les promoteurs sont classés dans l'ordre des villes et par ordre alphabétique. Dans le cas où le nom du promoteur est celui d'une personne, le prénom figure en premier.

Veranstalter
In diesem Kapitel werden Veranstalter, 'programmateurs' und Organisationen, die u.a. als Veranstaltungsträger tätig sind, aufgeführt. Wegen der Unterschiede innerhalb des Bereichs der darstellenden Kunst sollten Ensembles, die Engagements suchen, nicht nur in diesem Kapitel sondern auch in den Kapiteln 'Festivals', 'Venues', 'Agents & Producers' sowie innerhalb der Theatereintragungen im Kapitel 'Drama' nachschlagen.
Die Einträge werden innerhalb aller Staaten alphabetisch nach Stadtnamen und innerhalb der Stadt alphabetisch nach Namen geordnet. Organisationen, die den Namen eines Individuums tragen, werden nach dem Vornamen geordnet.

Organizzatori di Spettacoli e Concerti
Essenzialmente questa sezione include gli organizzatori, gli impresari e le case di produzione. Ad esempio una compagnia in cerca di scrittura non deve limitarsi a consultare questa sezione ma fare riferimento alle sezioni Festival,Venues, Agents ed anche ad alcuni teatri inclusi nella sezione Drama.
Ogni Paese racchiude al suo interno le cittá ordinate alfabeticamente ed all'interno di esse anche gli organizzatori seguono lo stesso criterio. Quelle associazioni che hanno lo stesso nome del titolare o il cui nome é un nome di persona, vengono ordinate a seconda del nome di battesimo.

Promotores
Esencialmente esta lista incluye empresarios, coordinadores de programación o casas de producción. Compañías en búsqueda de contactos o contratos deberían mirar no sólo en esta sección, sino también en Festivals, Venues, Agents y por ejemplo alguno de los teatros de la sección de Drama.
Dentro del país, los promotores están ordenados por ciudades y siguen un orden alfabético dentro de cada ciudad. Cuando la denominación de una organización está bajo un nombre propio (por ejemplo Frank Smith) se sigue el orden alfabético del nombre de pila. Si el nombre de la organización fuera Künstlersekretariat Frank Smith, la clasficación se haría de acuerdo con el primer vocablo.

Promoters (후원자)
이 리스트는 근본적으로 단장(흥행주), '프로 편성자', 제작소 등으로 구성되었다. 예술 비지니스의 성격상, 공연을 원하는 단체들은 이 부문뿐만 아니라, 페스티발 부문, 공연장소 부문, 에이전시 부문 그리고 연극부문에 있는 극장단체 등을 포괄적으로 참조해야 할 것이다. **리스트는 국가별, 도시별, 그리고 다시 알파벳순으로 기재되었다. 후원자가 개인의 이름일 경우는, 이름 (christian name)에 따른 순서로 기재되었다.**

赞助机构
基本上本名单包括了主办者或制作公司。艺术事业的本质意味着寻找演出节目的公司不但应该阅本章节，而且也应阅关于艺术、场所、中间商以及如戏剧章节中一些剧院等章节。**在每个国家里促进组织是按城市顺序来排列的，而在每一城市里促进组织又是按字母顺序排列的。当一促进组织为一某个人的名字时，就按名的字母顺序来排列。**

プロモーター
このリストには興業主、興業会社等を掲載しました。芸術、芸能ビジネスの構造を考え、売り込み中の個人、グループはこの章だけではなく、フェスティバル、会場、エージェント等の章も参考にして下さい。例えば、劇団のいくつかは演劇の章に掲載されています。**リストは国、都市別で、都市内ではアルファベット順に記載されています。興行主が個人名だった場合、名、姓の順になっています。**

ALBANIA (+355)

Alb-Art Artistic Society
P.O. Box 2896, **Tirana**
Tel: 42-26093/29089
Fax: 42-26093/29089

Albanian Civil Society Foundation
Rr Asim Vokshi, Vila 137, **Tirana**
Tel: 42-33067
Fax: 42-33067
E-Mail: rolanda@acsf.tirana.al
executive director Rolanda Dhimitri

Fondacioni Fan Noli
Tirana
executive director Dhimiter Anagnosti

Music Foundation Dhora Leka
Rr Durresit, Pallati 240,
shkalla 8 ap.66, **Tirana**
Tel: 42-30715 Fax: 42-30715
president Dhora Leka

New Albanian Music, The
Academy of Arts,
Nene Tereza Street, **Tirana**
Tel: 42-62899
president Aleksander Peci
Policy: promotors of new music *Comments:* member of the European conference

Pan-Albanian Union of Music Professionals
L. 9, Rr. Muhamet Gjollesha,
P. 54/11/22, **Tirana**
Tel: 42-37012 Fax: 42-25488

ARMENIA (+374)

N.A.B. Artists Management Ltd
4-4 Azatoutian Street, 375037 **Yerevan**
Tel: 2-254 493 Fax: 2-151 431 (AT&T)
Internet: www.arminco.com/homepages/nab
E-Mail: nbart@arminco.com
manager Nika Babaian

AUSTRIA (+43)

Amt der Landeshauptstadt Bregenz – Abteilung für Kultur
Belruptstr. 1, 6901 **Bregenz**
Tel: 5574-410 1510 Fax: 5574-410 550
E-Mail: bkv@bkv.vol.at
Leiter der Kulturabteilung Dr. Wolfgang Fetz
Events: 40 *Arts type:* classical concerts, opera, ballet, theatre, exhibitions *Venues:* Festspielhaus, Kongresshaus, Theater Kornmarkt, Palais Thurn und Taxis *Comments:* promotes Bregenzer Meisterkonzerte, Bregenzer Frühling, Kunst in der Stadt

Kulturreferat Dornbirn
Rathausplatz 2, 6850 **Dornbirn**
Tel: 5572-306 4200
Fax: 5572-306 408
E-Mail: kultur@dornbirn.at
Kulturreferat Helmut Fussenegger
Events: 24 *Perfs:* 24 *Arts type:* classical theatre, music theatre, chamber concerts, dance, Kleinkunst
Venues: Kulturhaus Dornbirn 730 *Comments:* 6 symphony concerts between Oct and May

Amt der Burgenländischen Landesregierung
Abteilung 7 Kultur, Wissenschaft und Archiv,
Europaplatz 1, 7000 **Eisenstadt**
Tel: 2682-600 2089 Fax: 2682-600 2058
E-Mail: josef.tiefenbachbgld.gv.at
Leiter der Abteilung Kultur und Wissenschaft und Archiv Dr. Josef Diefenbach
Arts type: opera, operetta, chamber, symphonic music, piano concerts, jazz, visual art exhibitions *Venues:* Freilichtbühne Mörbisch/See 4500, Haydnsaal 600
Comments: subsidises Haydnfestspiele March-Oct, Seefestspiele Mörbisch July-Aug, St Magareten – Festspiel July-Aug, Jazzfestival in Wiesen May-Aug, children's theatre Forchtenstein Phantastisch July-Aug, other events throughout the year; see also Ministries

Gesellschaft der Musikfreunde Feldkirch
Amt der Stadt Feldkirch, Schlossergasse 8,
6800 **Feldkirch**
Tel: 5522-304 272 Fax: 5522-304 279
E-Mail: kultur@rathaus.feldkirch.com
Vorstandsvorsitzender Michael Buchrainer
Events: 14 (8 chamber concerts – July/Aug, 6 orchestra concerts – spring/autumn) *Perfs:* 14 *Arts type:* chamber orch, choral music, chamber music, early music, inst recitals, sacred music, symphony music, classical ballet
Venues: Montforthaus 1200, Festsaal d. Landeskonservatoriums 350, Schattenburg 150, Pförtnerhaus 300 *Comments:* organise Feldkircher Schloss und Palais konzerte: summer season; share administration with Musikkreis Feldkirch (Prof. Walfried Kraher); strives to further the careers of international composers; has published CD with works by 20th C. composers; international cultural exchange programme

Musikverein für Steiermark
Landhausgasse 12, 8010 **Graz**
Tel: 316-829 924 Fax: 316-8299 2423
Generalsekretärin Mag. Uta Werner
Events: 53 *Arts type:* symphony, chamber, recital, liederabend, children's concerts *Venues:* Grazer Congress: Stephaniensaal 1073 *Comments:* season runs from September to June

Steirische Gesellschaft der Musikfreunde – Grazer Symphonisches Orchester
Albrechtgasse 1, 8010 **Graz**
Tel: 316-822 184 Fax: 316-837 418
Internet: www.sime.com/musikfreunde-stmk
E-Mail: musikfreunde.stmk@sime.com
Präsident Dr. Günther Ziesel; Künstlerischer Leiter Ulrike Danhofer; Chefdirigent Milan Horvat
Perfs: 11 *Arts type:* classical *Venues:* Stefaniensaal 1100
Comments: see also Orchestras

Galerie St. Barbara
Herzog-Otto-Strasse 4, 6060 **Hall in Tirol**
Tel: 5223-56706 Fax: 5223-45926
Internet: www.tirolkultur.at/g.st.barbara
E-Mail: g.st.barbara@tirolkultur.at
Geschäftsführerin Maria Crepaz;
Künstlerischer Leiter Gerhard Crepaz
Events: 60 (including: Oster-Festival Musik der Religionen) *Arts type:* music early and new, non-european music, dance theatre, physical theatre *Venues:* up to 1500 *Comments:* marketing & advertising dealt with by: CMM Agency, Tel: 5223-452 220, email: cmm@magnet.at

Amt der Landeshauptstadt Innsbruck
Konsertbüro Kulturamt, Stiftgasse 16,
6020 **Innsbruck**
Tel: 512-536 0652 Fax: 512-536 0649
Senatrat Dr. Frenzel
Events: 36-40 *Arts type:* symphony concerts, 'Meister' concerts, chamber music concerts *Venues:* Congress Innsbruck, Saal Tirol 1500, Konservatorium Saal 317
Comments: season runs from September to May

Utopia
Tschamlerstrasse 3, 6020 **Innsbruck**
Tel: 512-588 587 Fax: 512-563 427
Internet: www.utopia.or.at
E-Mail: office@utopia.or.at
Kaufmännische Leitung Dr Reinhard Prinz;
Musikalische Programmleitung Marco Gambacorta;
Konzertmanagement Karin Säser
Events: 180 (15 per month) *Arts type:* all kinds of contemporary music, concerts *Venues:* most events in Utopia's Celler 300 *Comments:* Voices – Stimmenfestival, Internet-Cafe

Christlicher Kulturverband
10 Oktoberstr. 25/III,
9020 **Klagenfurt**
Tel: 463-516 243 Fax: 463-502 379
Internet: www.kkz.at
E-Mail: office@kkz.at
sekretar Nuzej Tolmajer
Events: 30-40 *Arts type:* drama – mainly children's theatre, puppets, literature, choirs *Comments:* central cultural organisation (40 member organisations) for Slovene population in Kärnten

KUNSTHALLE KREMS Betriebsges m.b.h.
Steiner Landstraße 8,
3500 **Krems – Stein**
Tel: 2732-82669 Fax: 2732-826 6916
Internet: www.kunsthalle.krems.at
E-Mail: office@krems.kunsthalle.at
Direktor Magister Carl Aigner;
techn. und musikalischer Leiter Jo Aichinger
Arts type: chamber orchestra, choral music, chamber music, early music, electronic music, folk music, instrumental recitals, jazz, new music, sacred music, song recitals, symphony music, multi media, opera, world music, visual art exhibitions, photography exhibitions, artists presentations, new media, design, global art; choir, instrumental music, classical, sound performances, installations, art exhibitions *Venues:* Kunsthalle, Minoritenkirche Stein (Minoritenplatz 4), Kunsthalle, Hauptgebäude (Steiner Landstr. 8)
Comments: program for pupils; books and catalogues

Linzer Veranstaltungsgesellschaft
Untere Donaulände 7, 4010 **Linz**
Tel: 732-7612
Fax: 732-783 745
Internet: www.liva.linz.at
Vorstandsdirektoren Wolfgang Winkler,
Ing. Mag. Wolfgang Lehner
Events: 11 series with 5-12 concerts each (Brucknerhaus), Linzer Klangwolke, Brucknerfest *Perfs:* 300 + *Arts type:* symphony, chamber music, soloists, recitals, jazz, big band, pop, cabaret, exhibitions, puppets, children's theatre *Venues:* Brucknerhaus (q.v.), Posthof Linz, Kinderkulturzentrum, Linzer Stadium *Policy:* cultural events *Comments:* Posthof Linz is used for cabaret, theatre, dance and popular music concerts; alternative internet: www.brucknerhaus.linz.at

Magistrat der Landeshauptstadt Linz
Kulturdirektion, Neues Rathaus,
Haupstr. 1-5, 4041 **Linz**
Tel: 732-7070/2930/31 Fax: 732-7070 2955
Internet: www.linz.at
E-Mail: info@kua.mag.linz.at
Leiter der Kulturdirektion Mag Siegbert Janko; Kunst-,Kultur-u. Projektförderung Dr Peter Leisch; Kultur, Organisation und Service Karl-Heinz Höllersberger; Städtische Kulturentwicklung Mag. Christian Denkmaier
Events: 200 *Arts type:* chamber orchestra, choral music, chamber music, early music, electronic music, folk music, instrumental recitals, jazz, new music, music theatre, operetta, sacred music, song recitals, symphony music, multi media, opera, world music, classical ballet, folk dance, modern ballet, modern dance, classical theatre, mime, modern theatre, puppet, street theatre, visual arts exhibitions, large festivals, music, street festivals

Kulturforum Saalfelden
Brandstättengasse 1, 5760 **Saalfelden**
Tel: 6582-72770 Fax: 6582-727 7702
E-Mail: Vermembacher@aon.at
Leiter d. Kulturforums Dipl. Ing. Gottfried Embacher
Events: 12-15 *Arts type:* chamber music, classical, jazz, modern, theatre, cabaret *Venues:* various, including Pfarrsaal 100-150, Schloß Ritzen 100-150, largest is Festsaal up to 800, Htl Saalfelden 100-200 *Policy:* balance between contemporary and classical art forms

Internationale Stiftung Mozarteum Salzburg
Schwarzstrasse 26, 5020 **Salzburg**
Tel: 662-889 4021 Fax: 662-872 996
Leiter des Künstlerischen Betriebsbüros Dr Josef Tichy;
Präsident Dr. Friedrich Gehmacher;
Geschäftsführer Wieland Lafferentz
Arts type: chamber orchestra, choral music, chamber music, sacred music, song recitals, symphony music
Venues: Großer Saal 800, Wiener Saal 200
Comments: see also Venues and Festivals

Konzertagentur Steinschaden & Hiller
Nonntaler Hauptstraße 59/8, 5020 **Salzburg**
Tel: 662-828 695 Fax: 662-8286 9514
Internet: www.salzburg-concerts.com
E-Mail: office@salzburg-concerts.com
Leiter Georg Steinschaden, Konstantin Hiller
Events: Sonntagsmatineen Im Schloss Mirabell, Abendkonzerte, Sonderkonzerte, Opernproduktionen
Perfs: 400 *Arts type:* all types of music: early to contemporary, but mainly classical music including chamber music and opera *Venues:* Großer Saal/Mozarteum 800, Große Aula 700, Schloß Mirabell/Marmorsaal, Residenz, Schloß Hellbrunn
Comments: see also Festivals

Konzertdirektion Nerat Mozart Serenaden
Lieferinger Hauptstr. 136, 5013 **Salzburg**
Tel: 662-436 870 Fax: 662-436 970
Internet: www.austria./at/mozartserenaden/
E-Mail: mozart@salzburg.co.at
Veranstaltung Elisabeth Nerat;
Künstlerischer Leiter Harald Nerat
Events: annual January *Perfs:* 120 *Arts type:* chamber orch, chamber music *Venues:* Gotischer Saal 250, Mozarteum Saal 800 *Policy:* promoting Mozart's chamber music *Comments:* see also under Festivals, Agents and Producers

Salzburger Bachgesellschaft
Augustinergasse 4/1, 5020 **Salzburg**
Tel: 662-435 3710 Fax: 662-435 3714
Künstlerischer Leiter Dr Albert Hartinger
Events: 12 concerts, Oct-June *Arts type:* baroque music – chamber, choir, vocal, youth concerts *Venues:* Salzburger Dom 800 *Comments:* concentrate on works by Bach and his contemporaries and works by composers from Salzburg

Salzburger Festungskonzerte
Konzertdirektion Papousek,
Anton Adlgasser-Weg 22,
5020 **Salzburg**
Tel: 662-825 858
Fax: 662-825 859
Internet: www.salzburg.co.at.festungskonzerte
E-Mail: festungskonz@salzburg.co.at
Veranstalter Gerhard Papousek;
Geschäftsführer Dr. Erich Berer
Events: all year *Perfs:* 300 *Arts type:* chamber music, works of great composers with emphasis on W. A. Mozart; Easter, Christmas, Advent and New Year concerts *Venues:* Festung Hohensalzburg 180, Salzburger Residenz 800

Salzburger Kulturvereinigung
Waagplatz 1a, 5020 **Salzburg**
Tel: 662-845 346
Fax: 662-842 665
Generalsekretär Dr. Heinz Klier
Perfs: 32 + 30 street theatre *Arts type:* symphony music, classical ballet, street theatre *Venues:* Großes Festspielhaus 2100 *Policy:* concerts with symphony music *Comments:* concerts main activity

Salzburger Schlosskonzerte
Griesgasse 6 , 5020 **Salzburg**
Tel: 662-848 586
Fax: 662-844 747
Internet: www.esp.at/schlosskonzerte
E-Mail: schlosskonzerte@esp.at
Inhaber Lanz Eskowitz; Presse-und Öffentlichkeitsarbeit Mag. Silvia Spam; Kartenbestellungen Brita Pohl; Buchhaltungen Annemarie Göttlich
Events: daily concerts from May-September (October-April 2-4 times a week) *Arts type:* classical chamber music *Venues:* Marble Hall of Mirabelle Palace
Comments: second E-mail: schlosskonzerte@EUnet.at; see also Agents & Producers

Schlägler Musikseminare – Schlägler Orgelkonzerte
Schlägler Hauptstr. 2, 4160 **Schlägl**
Tel: 7281-6464
Fax: 7281-6260
Stiftskapellmeister Dr Rupert Gottfried Frieberger
Events: 13 (May/Nov) *Arts type:* oratoria, chamber music, organ, sacred *Venues:* Pfarrkirche Aigen 900, Stiftskirche Schlägl 450 *Comments:* seminars for gregorianics, baroque chants

Avantgarde Schwaz
c/o Marianne Penz – van Stappershoef,
Wopfnerstrasse 16,
6130 **Schwaz/Tirol**
Tel: 5242-65737
Fax: 5242-61199
Internet: www.tirol.com/avantgarde-schwaz
E-Mail: avantgarde.schwaz@tirol.com
Comments: organises annual International Academy for New Composition, 14 days at the end of August/beginning of September, with composition courses and instrumental workshops, exhibitions, concerts, installations; cooperates with the Polish Art Society Muzyka Centrum in Krakow

Stift Seitenstetten
am Klosterberg 1, 3353 **Seitenstetten**
Tel: 7477-4230-0
Fax: 7477-423 0050
Internet: www.stift-seitenstetten.at
E-Mail: stift@stift-seitenstetten.at
Direktion der Musikveranstaltungen Pater Franz Hörmann, Abt Magister Berthold Heigl
Events: 20 concerts *Arts type:*
chamber music, lied, choral, organ, orchestra, early music, inst. recitals, sacred music, song recitals, drama, exhibitions *Comments:* daily tours incl visits to historic court-garden

Musik Kultur St. Johann
Oberhofenweg 57, 6380 **St Johann (Tirol)**
Tel: 5352-61284 Fax: 5352-61284
Internet: www.muku-stjohann.at
E-Mail: info@muku-stjohann.at
contact Hans Oberlechner
Events: throughout the year *Arts type:* contemporary jazz
Venues: various in St. Johann

Kulturverwaltung / Magistrat der Landeshauptstadt
Prandtauerstraße 2, 3100 **St Pölten**
Tel: 2742-333 2600 Fax: 2742-333 2609
Leiter der Kulturabteilung Dr.Thomas Karl
Events: 100 *Arts type:* symphony, chamber, modern/classical theatre, jazz, modern dance, rock festival (open-air) *Venues:* Stadtsaal 600, Synagoge 300, Stadtheater St Pölten 383, Bühne im Hof 400, Veranstaltungszentrum up to 2200, Festspielhaus 1031

Culturcentrum Wolkenstein
Bahnhofstraße 110, 8950 **Stainach**
Tel: 3682-23250
Fax: 3682-23251
E-Mail: ccw@telecom.at
contact Reinhard E H Gosch
Events: 50 *Arts type:* classical music, jazz, new music, music theatre, multi-media, opera, world music, modern dance, modern theatre, puppet, visual arts exhibitions *Venues:* up to 250 *Comments:* highlight of the year Hörfest Stainach (every October)

Villa Schindler
Obermarktstrasse 45, 6410 **Telfs**
Tel: 5262-66208
Fax: 5262-67566
artistic director Michel Sogny
Events: 5 concerts (Oct-April) *Arts types:* concerts, piano recitals, young talent *Venues:* Villa Schindler 100
Policy: organises concerts, piano recitals, discovery of young talents and support of their international careers; young artists management; piano masterclasses and preparation for international competition

Festival-Management Wien – Osterklang & Klangbogen
Rathausstr. 4, 1010 **Wien**
Tel: 1-4000 84720 Fax: 1-40009 98400
Internet: www.festival-management.at
E-Mail: wlerner@yahoo.com
Musikintendant Roland Geyer;
Marketing/PR Wolfgang Lerner
Arts type: opera, operetta, concerts, festivals

Gesellschaft der Musikfreunde in Wien
Musikverein, Bösendorferstrasse 12, 1010 **Wien**
Tel: 1-505 8681 Fax: 1-505 9409
Internet: www.musikverein.at
E-Mail: office@musikverein.at
Generalsekretär Dr Thomas Angyan
Events: 350 *Arts type:* symphony music, chamber orch, choral music, chamber music, early music, new music, song recitals, sacred music *Venues:* Musikverein, Grosser Saal 1750 + 300 (standing), Brahms Saal 600
Comments: see also Venues

Internationale Chopin-Gesellschaft in Wien
Biberstr.4, 1010 **Wien**
Tel: 1-512 2374/6463 Fax: 1-512 646 375
Internet: www.brh-gov-pl.or.at/ICG
E-Mail: ICG@netway.at
Präsident Dr. Theodor Kanitzer
Arts type: chamber orch, choral music, chamber music, early music, fok music, inst. recitals, sacred music, song recitals, symphony music, world music, classical ballet, folk dance *Venues:* Chopin festival in the Charterhouse Gaming Niederösterreich; concerts in Festsaal der Bank Austria Renngasse 2 *Comments:* has own publication 'Wiener Chopin Blätter'

Jeunesse Österreich Musikalische Jugend (Österreichs)
PO Box 45, Lothringerstraße 20, 1037 **Wien**
Tel: 1-710 3616 (admin)/505 6356 (box office)
Fax: 1-710 3616/17 (admin)/8277 (box office)
Internet: www.jeunesse.at
E-Mail: mail@jeunesse.at
general secretary Matthias Naske (e-mail: m.naske@jeunesse.at); concerts administration Alexandra Tscheitschonig (e-mail: a.tscheitschonig@jeunesse.at), Antonia Schmidt-Chiari (e-mail: a.schmidt-chiari@jeunesse.at); marketing Catharina Jues (e-mail: cjues@jeunesse.at); dramaturgy Dr. Astrid Schramek (e-mail: a.schramek@jeunesse.at); press Albert Seitlinger (e-mail: a.seitlinger@jeunesse.at)
Arts type: chamber orch, choral music, chamber music, early music, electronic music, inst recitals, jazz, new music, music theatre, symphony music, opera *Venues:* predominantly Musikverein and Konzerthaus in Vienna + about 30 other venues throughout Austria (e.g Mozarteum Salzburg, Stefaniensaal Graz, Musikverein Klagenfurt) *Comments:* promoting classical music for a youth audience; box office: Bösendorferstraße 12, 1010 Wien, E-mail: tickets@jeunesse.at;
see also National Organisations

MA 7 Kulturabteilung der Stadt Wien
Friedrich Schmidt-Platz 5, 1082 **Wien**
Tel: 1-4000 81174
Fax: 1-4000 7216
E-Mail: vic@gku.magwien.gu.at
Leiter der Kulturabteilung Dr. Bernhard Denscher;
Amtsführender Stadtrat für Kultur von Wien
Peter Marboe
Events: 2 per annum *Arts type:* theatre, music, literature, fine arts, dance, film *Comments:* organise festival: Blasmusikfestival, Adventsinger; financial support of events

Stadtinitiative Wien
Burggasse 28-32/2, 1070 **Wien**
Tel: 1-523 1729/20 Fax: 1-523 1729/90
contact Ingrid Hraba; theatre contact Suzanne Veres; Stadtinitiative contact Monika Bangert
Events: 200 *Perfs:* from Sept-June *Arts type:* jazz, avant-garde, contemporary music, exhibitions, theatre, children's theatre, classical concerts *Venues:* Das Theater der Stadtinitiative 100
Policy: coordination of events

Wiener Konzerthaus Society
Lothringerstrasse 20, 1030 **Wien**
Tel: 1-7124 6860
Fax: 1-713 1709
E-Mail: mail@konzerthaus.at
Generalsekretär Christoph Lieben-Seutter;
Marketing & Werbung Peter Polansky
Events: 600 *Arts type:* from early music to contemporary
Venues: Schubert Saal 330, Mozart Saal 750, Großer Saal 1800 *Comments:* organiser of Festival Wien Modern (see Festivals) and other concerts, Film & Musik Live!, Hörgänge (q.v.), Frühlingsfestival, Resonanzen, Internationales Musikfest, see also Venues and Festivals

Verein der Freunde der Claviermusik Stift Altenburger Musik Akademie (AMA)
Penknergasse 21, 3150 **Wilhelmsburg**
Tel: 1-586 1900
Fax: 1-586 1900
E-Mail: freunde.der.claviermusik@vienna.at
Künstlerische Leitung Robert Lehrbaumer
Events: 10 (July) *Arts type:* mastercourses for piano, organ, harpsichord, piano recitals, chamber orch concerts, chamber music, music rarities, music humour, inst recitals, new music, sacred music, symphony music
Venues: Stift Altenburg up to 600, Bibliothek 600, Kaisersaal 200, Marmorsaal 200 *Comments:* also organise lectures, seminars and workshops

BELARUS (+375)

Belarussian State Philharmonic Society
Bjelaruskoe Gosudarstvjennoe
Filarmonichjeskoe Obshchjestvo
pr Franciska Skoryny 50, 220005 **Minsk**
Tel: 172-334 974 Fax: 172-319 050
director Vladimir Ratobylski

BELGIUM (+32)

City of Antwerp
Department of Culture,
Kipdorp 48,
2000 **Antwerp**
Tel: 3-201 3167 Fax: 3-201 3180
director of the department for sport and culture Joris Sels

Metropolitain Entertainments
Driekoningenstraat 82, 2600 **Berchen**
Tel: 3-239 2872
Fax: 3-239 2872
Internet: www.metro-world.com
E-Mail: metro.world@skynet.be
director Alan Reghero
Arts type: classical, rock 'n roll, jazz
Venues: venues in Belgium *Comments:* see also Agents

Alias / Pierre Beauvois
14 Rue Kessels, 1030 **Brussels**
Tel: 2-242 9137 Fax: 2-242 4046
E-Mail: alias.mumo@skynet.be
directeur Pierre Beauvois
Events: 60-90 *Arts type:* musical sculptures
Venues: Centre Culturel, festivals, schools, in public areas also *Policy:* travel to places to meet children and introduce them to music *Comments:* promotion of the Musical Gardens (water instruments)

Association des Arts et de la Culture (ADAC)
Rue Royale No. 10, 1000 **Brussels**
Tel: 2-507 8520 Fax: 2-507 8533
director Alain Leempoel;
public relations Sophie du Parc
Events: 20 + 1 festival *Arts type:* dance, music, opera, circus, ballet, comedy, theatre *Venues:* l' Auditorium du passage 44: 880, Palais des Beaux Arts: Salle A 2000, Salle B 480, Salle C 220, Cirque Royal 1500, Théâtre des Galleries 890, Centre Culturel d'Uccle *Comments:* see also Francophonies Théâtrales (Festival)

Concerts Astoria
rue Royale 103, 1000 **Brussels**
Tel: 2-216 1437/513 0965 (boîte à musique)
Fax: 2-216 1437
managing director Philippe van Heurck;
musical director Jerrold Rubenstein
Events: 40 *Arts type:* chamber music *Venues:* Waldorf Room Hotel Astoria 220 *Comments:* second address: La Boîte à Musique, rue Ravenstein 17, 1000 Brussels

Concerts de Midi
Rue aux Laines 20, 1000 **Brussels**
Tel: 2-512 8247
Fax: 2-512 8247
president Ludo De Bie; vice-presidents Jacques Lievens; treasurer Clément Beckers; music director Jozef De Beenhouwer; general secretary Berthe Ingber
Events: 30 concerts per year, Sept-end of May
Arts type: chamber orchestra, chamber music, instrumental recitals *Venues:* lunchtime concerts every Wednesday at Musée d'Art Ancien 650 seats
Comments: venue address: Musée d'Art Ancien, Rue de la Régence 3, 1000 Brussels

Jeugd en Muzick België
(jeuneses musicales de Belgique)
Rue Royale 10, 1000 **Brussels**
Tel: 2-507 8435
Fax: 2-507 8437
E-Mail: jeugd.en.muziek@skynet.be
secrétaire général Luc Leytens, Hubert van Aschen
Events: 2500 *Perfs:* 8500 (concerts, workshops) *Arts type:* music: classical, folk, contemporary etc. *Venues:* schools *Comments:* see also National Organisations

Jeunesses Musicales de Belgique/
Jeugd en Muziek België
Rue Royale 10, 1000 **Brussels**
Tel: 2-507 8540 (French Community)
Fax: 2-507 8541 (French Community)
E-Mail: jmb@arcadis.be (French Community)
French president Marc Herduet; secrétaire général t.b.a.
Events: 2500 *Perfs:* 8500 (concerts, workshops) *Arts type:* music: classical, folk, contemporary, etc *Venues:* schools *Comments:* see also National Organisations and Promoters (Flemish Community)

Live Music Now – Belgium
Chaussée de Boondael 6, 1050 **Brussels**
Tel: 2-647 3838
Fax: 2-647 9926
Internet: users.skynet.be/lmn
E-Mail: lmn@skynet.be
directrice Valerie Jacob

Perfs: 50 *Arts type:* chamber orch, choral music, chamber music, early music, folk music, jazz, new music theatre, operetta, sacred music, song recitals, symphony music, opera, world music *Venues:* various from hospital wards to theatres/concert halls up to 400 *Policy:* to promote young professional musicians & to take music to a wide variety of people, especially the underpriviledged *Comments:* concerts are given for the elderly, sick and disabled, as well as for private and company events; founded by Yehudi Menuhin; original projects, training, dance, drama, exhibitions

Music Management F.E.W.
c/o Francois-Emmanuel de Wasseige,
Rue Grisar 21, 1070 **Brussels**
Tel: 2-520 2009 Fax: 2-520 7150
Internet: www.cyclone.be/Wasseige
E-Mail: F.E.de.Wasseige@cyclone.be
Comments: see also Agents & Producers

Paleis VZW
Palais des Beaux Arts, Rue Royale 10, 1000 **Brussels**
Tel: 2-507 8510/15 Fax: 2-507 8517
dance, theatre Ingrid De Ketelaere; music, jazz Paul Buekenhout; secretary Cristine Thielemens
Events: 5-10 music/12 theatre/5 dance *Arts type:* modern dance, theatre, avant-garde and traditional music, ethnic music *Venues:* Palais de Beaux Arts, Grande Salle 2000, Salle de Musique de Chambre 470, Studio 210

Société Philharmonique de Bruxelles
rue Baron Horta 11, 1000 **Brussels**
Tel: 2-507 8410 Fax: 2-511 7977
Internet: www.sofil.be
E-Mail: sofil@ibm.net
director general Paul Dujardin;
production manager Christian Renard
Events: 250 (September-June) *Arts type:* classical music, chamber orchestra, choral music, chamber music, early music, inst recitals, jazz, new music, sacred music, song recitals, symphony music, world music *Venues:* Palais des Beaux-Arts 2000, Le conservatoire 600, L'Eglise des Minimes 500 *Comments:* work with all the major orchestras in Belgium and many foreign orchestras

Stella Rossa
PO Box 26, 8500 **Kortrijk**
Tel: 56-358 201 Fax: 56-358 101
promoter, organiser- music Lieven Masschelein;
promoter, organiser- dance Gloria Carlier
Arts type: new music, world music, modern dance, street theatre *Comments:* organises events mainly for cultural centres throughout Flanders; Netherlands for street theatre

Service Provincial des Arts de la Scène
rue paul Pastur 33, 7100 **La Louvière**
Tel: 64-226 340 Fax: 64-281 509
chef de secteur Michel Tanner
Events: 90 *Arts type:* mainly theatre, also music & dance
Comments: promote events in the region of Hainaut

Les Amis Des Concerts Du Dimanche Matin ASBL
c/o Jean Duchesne, 41 rue des Guillemins, 4000 **Liège**
Tel: 4-252 0701 Fax: 4-252 0701
directeur Jean Duchesne
Events: 10 *Arts type:* chamber music
Venues: Salle du Musée 200

Service Jeunesse de la Province de Liège
Rue Belvaux 123, 4030 **Liège (Grivegnee)**
Tel: 4-344 9110
Fax: 4-341 5386
chief organiser Jean Pierre Burton
Events: 3 *Arts type:* theatre for young people, non-professional theatre *Comments:* promotes concerts and shows in schools and theatres in Belgium and Liège in particular; main festival in August; other events throughout the year

Centre of International Cultural Relations
c/o Association for Public Benefit,
Torenstraat 13, 9160 **Lokeren**
Tel: 9-348 8000/9010/4993 Fax: 9-348 9974
E-Mail: j-p.vanavermaet@skynet.be
managing director Jean Pierre Van Avermaet;
staff member Vessela Dyakova
Policy: dedicated to international cultural exchanges
Comments: organise concert tours in co-operation with cultural societies and small towns; concerts of Belgium and European artists and festivals all over Europe

Promotion des Arts Forains
rue des Brasseurs 156, 5000 **Namur**
Tel: 81-222 042 Fax: 81-222 042
Internet: www.namur.be
directeur Jean-Félix Tirtiaux
Events: 1 festival: The Festival International des Arts Forains *Arts type:* street theatre, spectacles in tents, dance, comedy, visual arts and crafts *Policy:* promotes all contemporary artistic expressions including fairgrounds, fairs and mime through organising, producing and promoting shows, exhibtions, seminars, conferences and events; also producing, publishing and distributing merchandising
Comments: see also Festivals

Koninklÿke Turnhoutse Concertvereniging
Corn. Mertenslaan 2,
2360 **Oud-Turnhout**
Tel: 14-410 407 Fax: 14-410 416
president Louis Kruyfhooft
Events: Sept-March *Perfs:* 6 *Arts type:* chamber orchestra, choral music, chamber music, early music, sacred music, symphony music, recitals piano-violin
Venues: Cultureel Centrum de Warande, Turnhout 700

Promotion des Arts de la Scène – A.M. Lomba
Rue Monseigneur Cerfaux 1, 6250 **Presles**
Tel: 71-404 656
Fax: 71-404 657
directeur André-Marie Lomba
Arts type: contemporary/classical theatre, dance
Comments: world tours; see also Agents and Producers

BOSNIA & HERZEGOVINA (+387)

Centre for Culture
Gorazde
Tel: 73-221 344 Fax: 73-221 344
director Elvedin Hrelja

Concert Agency of the Music Academy
c/o Music Academy,
Josip Stadler Str 1, 71000 **Sarajevo**
Tel: 71-200 299 Fax: 71-444 896

Concert Agency Sarajevo Art
Dalmatinska 2, 71000 **Sarajevo**
Tel: 71-207 972/207 971 Fax: 71-207 972/207 971
director Halid Kuburovic
Arts type: organise different events but mainly concerts
Comments: see also Agents and Producers

JazzFest
P.O. Box 600, 71000 **Sarajevo**
director Edin Zubcevic
Arts type: mainly jazz *Comments:* organises jazz festival in Sarajevo in November

Music Youth Sarajevo
Jeunesse Musicales de Sarajevo
Mis Irbina 10, 71000 **Sarajevo**
Tel: 71-665 713 Fax: 71-665 713
E-Mail: muzomlsa@soros.org.ba
secretary Slavica Spoljaric
Comments: organizes concerts of students and young artists

BULGARIA (+359)

International Foundation Humour of People – Gabrovo
PO Box 104, Dom na Humora & Satirata,
5300 **Gabrovo**
Tel: 66-27228 Fax: 66-26989
director Tatiana Tzankova

Agency Music – Festival Concert Society
14 Naiden Gerov St., PO Box 545, 4000 **Plovdiv**
Tel: 32-222 897/864 Fax: 32-262 626/266 343
director Yanko Yanev
Events: min. 200 in a year *Venues:* Antique Theatre 2000, Summer Theatre 3000, Concert Hall A 700, Concert Hall B 600, Chamber Hall A 150, Chamber Hall B 200, Chamber Hall C 400

Apollonia Art Foundation
11 Slaveykov Sq., 1000 **Sofia**
Tel: 2-980 5642/7833 Fax: 2-980 7833
E-Mail: apolonia@techno-link.com
president Prof. Dimo Dimov; artistic director Margarita Dimitrova; international relations Ana Rousseva
Comments: produce and carry out educational arts programmes; Apollonia Summer Festival in Sozopol; Christmas and Spring festivals

Foundation Idea for Theatre
12 Narodno sabranie Square, 1000 **Sofia**
Tel: 2-881 760 Fax: 2-883 301
president Vesselina Giuleva
Arts type: drama

International Foundation St. Cyril and Methodius
19 Oborishte Str., 1504 **Sofia**
Tel: 2-464 131/430 163/001 Fax: 2-446 027
president Petar Kenderov

Multiart – Art Agency
1 Angel Kantchev Str., 1000 **Sofia**
Tel: 2-888 051 Fax: 2-802 401
director George Petkov
Arts type: choirs, orchestras

Soros Center for the Arts
19 Angel Kantchev Str., 1000 **Sofia**
Tel: 2-980 0244 Fax: 2-980 0244
Internet: www.sca.bg
E-Mail: tzviossifova@sca.osf.acad.bg
performing arts programme coordinator
Tzvetelina Iossifova
Comments: funding agency, initiate and manage arts projects; founded by Opera Society Foundation, Sofia; see also Agents & Producers

CROATIA (+385)

RIMI CO CONCERTS
Rimi Co koncertno – priredivacko poduzece
Villa Frappart, V.C. Emina 5, 51415 **Lovran**
Tel: 51-291 001 Fax: 51-292 313
director Ino Mirkovic; contact Silvana Sepic

Zadar Concert Office
Koncertni ured Zadar
Trg Petra Zoranica 1, 23000 **Zadar**
Tel: 23-315 807 Fax: 23-315 807
contact Branka Dolicki

Zagreb Concert Management
Koncertna Direkcija Zagreb
Kneza Mislava 18, 10000 **Zagreb**
Tel: 1-461 1709 Fax: 1-461 1807
director Erika Krpan
Arts type: artists agency, concert promoter *Comments:* publishes and protects scores by Croatian composers; organises large-scale musical events

CYPRUS (+357)

Papadopoulos & Schinis Productions
PO Box 51651, 3507 **Limassol**
Tel: 5-372 855 Fax: 5-361 290
E-Mail: schinis@cytanet.com.cy
directors P. Schinis, M. Papadopoulos
Arts type: dance, drama, classical music, concerts, operas, festivals *Comments:* promote throughout the year

Methexis Art Services
Stassinou Ave. 10, 1060 **Nicosia**
Tel: 2-761 923 Fax: 2-760 676
director Natasa Ierides
Arts type: organisation of cultural events (theatre, dance, music, performing arts), cultural services, publications

CZECH REPUBLIC (+420)

Bohuslav Martinu Institute
Besednî 3, 118 00 **Praha** 1
Tel: 2-5731 3104 Fax: 2-5731 3104
Internet: www.vol.cz/SDMUSIC/MARTINU
E-Mail: martinu@martinu.cz
president Viktor Kalabis; director PhDr. Ales Brezina
Comments: includes also Bohuslav Martinu Study Centrum; see also National Organisations

Theatre Ark
Divadlo Archa
Na Porici 26, 110 00 **Praha** 1
Tel: 2-232 7570 Fax: 2-232 2089/2481/2468
Internet: www.archatheatre.cz
E-Mail: archa@archatheatre.cz
director Ondrej Hrab
Arts type: theatre and dance performances, concerts (rock, pop and classical), festivals, exhibitions *Venues:* Archa Theatre: large auditorium (arena and proscenium) – up to 500, small auditorium 120 *Comments:* member of IETM (q.v.); see also Venues and Drama

DENMARK (+45)

Foreningen Ny Musik
Kirkegårdsgade 3, 9000 **Aalborg**
Tel: 9816 6462 Fax: 9816 4536
director Birgitte Rode
Events: February-December *Perfs:* 8-10 *Arts type:* experimental, electronic music, new rock music, classical rock, modern ballet, new music, world music *Venues:* Student House 500, open-air concerts 2000 *Comments:* promotes musicians and groups from abroad; non-profit making organisation

Aarhus Concert Hall
Musikhuset Århus
Thomas Jensens Allé, 8000 **Aarhus** C
Tel: 8931 8200 Fax: 8619 4386
Internet: www.musikhuset-aarhus.dk
E-Mail: info@mus.aarhus.dk
managing director Hans Hansen; programme manager Ilse Vestergaard; press and publicity officer Martin Lai
Events: 300-550 *Perfs:* 300-550 *Arts type:* music, theatre, ballet *Venues:* Musikhuset Aarhus, large hall 1600, small hall 316 *Comments:* Numus Festival- April, showcases modern classical music composers, Arhus International Jazz Festival in July

KIT – Copenhagen International Theatre
Vestergade 5, 3rd Floor, 1456 **Copenhagen** K
Tel: 3315 1564 Fax: 3332 8182
Internet: www.kit.dk/
E-Mail: info@kit.dk
director Trevor Davis, art programmer Katherine Varwilt
Events: June-August *Perfs:* 60+ *Arts type:* worldwide contact for other festival organisers and professional non-established dance, theatre and performance groups; presenter of international guest performances and festivals of dance, theatre, music and new circus
Comments: it is funded by The Danish Theatre Council, The City of Copenhagen, The Ministry of Culture and The County of Copenhagen

Skræp Experimental Music Forum
Kronprinsengade 7, 1114 **Copenhagen** K
Tel: 3332 7222/4798 2763 Fax: 3332 7234/4798 2764
Internet: skraep.dk
E-Mail: skraep@skraep.dk
director Niels Winther (e-mail: otis.winther@getznet.dk
Events: 5 concerts in Spring, 8 in Autumn + 1 annual festival C.I.E.F. *Perfs:* 78 *Arts type:* experimental music *Venues:* Den Anden Opera, Statens Museum for Kunst, Teater Styhr & Kjaer and outdoor events around Copenhagen *Policy:* development of experimental music *Comments:* concerts featuring acoustic and electronic instruments playing new scored and/or improvised music in solo, group or even multi-media presentations often including the musicians/ composers themselves; see also Festivals (C.I.E.F)

Women in Music
Kvinder i Musik
The Royal Danish Academy of Music, The Library, Niels Brocksgade 1, 1574 **Copenhagen** V
Tel: 3369 2246 Fax: 3369 2279
director Tove Krag
Events: 8-10 concerts annually *Arts type:* choral music, chamber music, early music, electronic music, inst recitals, jazz, new music, light orch music, sacred music, song recitals, multi-media, world music, modern dance *Comments:* archive information centre on women composers; organise concerts where music composed by women is performed

Århus Musikforening
Lindevangsvej 15, 8240 **Risskov**
Tel: 8617 7141 Fax: 8619 6128
E-Mail: kilian@microbiology.au.dk
director Mogens Kilian
Events: 8 (October-April) *Perfs:* 8 *Arts type:* chamber music series *Venues:* Musikhuset Aarhus 350 *Policy:* to promote a high calibre of chamber music

Franz Schubert Selskabet Danmark
Postbox 283, 4000 **Roskilde**
Tel: 4635 2434 Fax: 4635 0338
Internet: www.schubertselskabet.dk
E-Mail: franz@schubertselskabet.dk
president Møller Rasmussen;
general secretary Roma Engmann
Events: 20 *Perfs:* 100+ *Arts type:* classical music, specialising in Schubert and Danish composers *Policy:* to promote Schubert in Denmark and Danish composers

ESTONIA (+372)

Foundation of Pärnu Opera and Ballet
Pärnu Ooperi ja Balleti Fond
Kuninga 24, 80011 **Pärnu**
Tel: 4-444 993
intendant Andrus Kallastu
Arts type: classical music, opera and dance *Comments:* produceing music and dance events and performances in Pärnu city and county; see also Opera

2.tants – Independent Dance Organisation
Rataskaevu 10, 10123 **Tallinn**
Tel: 6-269 094 Fax: 6-269 099
director Priit Raud
Events: 50 *Arts type:* all kinds of dance *Comments:* organise contemporary dance festival Evolutsioon (q.v.)

Eesti Kontsert
Estonian Concert, The State Concert Organisation
Estonia pst. 4, 10148 **Tallinn**
Tel: 6-443 670 Fax: 6-443 198
Internet: www.concert.ee
E-Mail: eesti.kontsert@concert.ee
director Enno Mattiesen; producers Madis Kolk, Peeter Vähi, Lauri Aav, Andres Uibo
Events: 800 concerts in a year *Arts type:* classical music, chamber music, soloists, orchestra, choirs *Venues:* Estonia Concert Hall 810 *Comments:* organisers of NYYD Festival, see also Festivals

Estonian Stage Productions – ESP
Rataskaevu 10, 10123 **Tallinn**
Tel: 6-269 098 Fax: 6-269 099
director Valdo Kask; assistant Katrin Vingel
Arts type: theatre and mixed art forms

Lendmuusik
Lend Music Ltd
Köömne 33, 10617 **Tallinn**
Tel: 6-565 304
director Toivo Lend
Events: 50 *Arts type:* classical music
Comments: organising concerts in churches

National Song Festival Managing Board
Üldlaulupeo Direktsioon
Suur-Karja 23, 10140 **Tallinn**
Tel: 6-449 262
Fax: 6-449 147
manager Ilmar Moss
Arts type: folk dance and song *Comments:* organise all-Estonian Song and Dance Festivals and Youth Song and Dance Festivals (q.v.)

FINLAND (+358)

Helsinki Early Music Society
Helsingen vanhan musiikin seura r.y.
c/o Markku Åberg, Sammalkalliontie 6 E 111, 02210 **Espoo**
Tel: 9-804 4328 Fax: 9-456 6619
E-Mail: markku.aberg@vtt.fi
chairman Markku Åberg; secretary Leena-Maija Åberg; treasurer Anders Stenberg
Arts type: early music, early dance *Comments:* courses and seminars, supports student and amateur ensembles, and arranges concerts, mainly for student ensembles; keeps a performer-orientated library for its members

Konserttikeskus r.y./konsertcentralen
Malmgatan 24D38, 00100 **Helsinki**
Tel: 9-694 3348 Fax: 9-694 3427
Internet: www.konserttikeskus.fi
E-Mail: konserttikeskus@konserttikeskus.fi
managing director Kari Leasi
Comments: concert promotion mainly for schools

Kuhmo Music Society
Torikatu 39, 88900 **Kukmo**
Tel: 8-652 0936 Fax: 8-652 1961
E-Mail: kuhmo.festival@kajak.fi
artistic director Seppo Kinanen
Comments: organisers of the Kuhmo Chamber Music Fest and Kuhmo Chamber Music Competition; see also Festivals and competitions

FRANCE (+33)

Direction Régionale des Affaires Culturelles de Provence-Alpes-Côte d'Azur
23 Bld du Roi René, 13617 **Aix-en-Provence** Cédex 1
Tel: 4-4216 1900 Fax: 4-4238 0322
E-Mail: Ledoux@Provence.culture.fr
directeur François de Banes Gardonne; théâtre et action culturelle Yves Olivier; musique et danse André Santelli; communication Alain Bez;
chargé de documentation M. Ledoux
Arts types: all types *Comments:* see also National & Regional Ministries

Direction Régionale des Affaires Culturelles de Corse (Corsica)
19 Cours Napoléon, BP 301, 20181 **Ajaccio** Cedex 1
Tel: 4-9551 5213/15 Fax: 4-9521 2069
directeur Pierre Berthier; action culturelle et spectacles vivants Marie-Jeanne Nicoli; communication Matthieu Coti
Arts types: all types *Comments:* see also National & Regional Ministries

Direction Régionale des Affaires Culturelles de Picardie
5, rue Henry Daussy, 80044 **Amiens** Cedex 1
Tel: 3-2297 3300 Fax: 3-2297 3356
E-Mail: maunier@picardie.culture.fr
directeur Yves Martial; musique et danse Christine Dogny; théâtre et action culturelle Fabrice Morio; communication Michel Maunier; arts plastiques Corine Le Neun; service livres et lecture t.b.a.
Arts types: all types *Comments:* see also National & Regional Ministries

Scène Nationale, Théâtre d' Angoulême
BP 287, 16007 **Angoulême** Cedex
Tel: 5-4538 6161 Fax: 5-4538 6151
directeur André Curmi; secrétaire génerale Chantal Rocailleux; relations publiques Eliane Bonnin; communications Anne-Marie LaLu
Events: 70 *Perfs:* 90 *Arts type:* theatre, dance, music *Venues:* Théâtre 730, Hall B 120, Hall C 70 *Policy:* rent, present, produce, co-produce *Comments:* the theatre has recently moved; formerly known as 'Les Plateaux'; new visiting address: Avenue des Maréchaux, 16007 Angoulême; see also Venues and Drama

Direction Régionale des Affaires Culturelles de Franche-Comté
7 rue Charles Nodier, 25043 **Besançon** Cedex
Tel: 3-8165 7200 Fax: 3-8165 7272
directrice Madame De Boisjolly; théâtre et action culturelle Dominique Daeschler; musique et danse Jean-Marc Vernier; communication Françoise Josseron
Arts type: all types *Comments:* see also National & Regional Ministries

Biarritz Culture
Javalquinto, 64200 **Biarritz**
Tel: 5-5922 2021 Fax: 5-5922 4011
E-Mail: btzculture@aol.com
director Filgi Claverie; directrice adjointe Laurence Pekar; ress. humain/finances Mariann Vincent; diffusion Veronique Noblia, Yvonne Pochelu; communication Marie Hélène Labasse
Events: 40 *Perfs:* 80 *Arts type:* classical music, opera, theatre, dance, visual arts exhibitions *Venues:* Gare du Midi (danse classique) 1400, Théâtre du Casino Municipal (dance contemporaine, opera, orchestres) 700, Théâtre le Colisee 189 *Comments:* organises 2 festivals; Le Temps d'Aimer (ballet) and Les Fetes Musicales (classical music); see also Festivals (Les fêtes musicales et Le temps d'aimer)

Odyssud – Espace pour la Culture et la Communication
4 avenue du Parc,
31706 **Blagnac** Cedex
Tel: 5-6171 7515 Fax: 5-6171 7545
E-Mail: corbier.odyssud@wanadoo.fr
directeur Thierry Carlier; responsable de l'accueil Michel Savignac; directeur technique Daniel Alayrac; adjoint du directeur, chargé du la communication et des relation esclecieuces Alban Corbier-Labasse
Events: 50 (Oct-June) *Perfs:* 120
Arts type: jazz, multi-media, opera, classical ballet, modern dance, classical theatre, modern theatre, visual arts exhibitions, theatre, contemporary dance, music, young people's theatre *Venues:* grand théâtre 950, Chapelle Saint Exupèrie 140

Centre National de Création et de Diffusion Artistiques – MC93
1 Boulevard Lénine, BP 71, Centre Ville,
93002 **Bobigny** Cedex
Tel: 1-4160 7272 (bookings) 1-4160 7260 (admin)
Fax: 1-4160 7261
E-Mail: mc_93@calvanel.calvacom.fr
directeur Ariel Goldenberg; secrétaire général et administrateur André Mondy; presse & relations publiques Viviane Got; directeur technique Jacques Dubreuil
Events: 18 *Arts type:* contemporary theatre, dance
Venues: Hall A 1000, Hall B 400
Comments: see also Venues

Direction Régionale des Affaires Culturelles Aquitaine
54 Rue Magendie,
33074 **Bordeaux** Cedex
Tel: 5-5795 0202 Fax: 5-5795 0125
E-Mail: m.parisot@culture.fr
directeur Jean-Michel Perthod; théâtre et action culturelle Jean René Girard; musique et danse Patrick le Dauphin-Dubourg; documentation Martine Parisot
Comments: see also National & Regional Ministries

Quartz, Centre National Dramatique et Chorégraphique, Le
BP 411, 2 et 4 Avenue Clemenceau, 29275 **Brest** Cedex
Tel: 2-9844 0807 (admin)/2-9844 1010 (public)
Fax: 2-9844 0066
E-Mail: dsalaun.lequartz@wanadoo.fr
directeur artistique Jacques Blanc; directeur de la communication Yves Leroy; directeur technique Nicolas Minssen; administrateur Claude Becker; assistante artistique Nadège Loir
Events: 10 productions, creations *Perfs:* 150 *Arts type:* choral music, chamber music, folk music, jazz, song recitals, symphony music, opera, world music, classical ballet, modern dance, classical & modern theatre
Venues: centre Culturel Stage A: 1560, Stage B: 314
Comments: new productions; visiting address: 2-4 Boulevard Clémenceau, 29200 Brest; see also Drama

Direction Régionale des Affaires Culturelles de Basse-Normandie
13, Bis rue St Ouen, 14052 **Caen** Cedex 4
Tel: 2-3138 3940 Fax: 2-3123 8465
E-Mail: girot@bnormand.culture.fr
directrice générale Elisabeth Gauthier-Desvaux; théâtre et action culturelle Gérard Brision; musique et danse Gérard Baille (3138 3976); communication Jocelyne Girot
Arts type: all types *Comments:* see also National & Regional Ministries

Théâtre des Arts Cergy-Pontoise, Scène Nationale
Place des arts, BP 307, 95027 **Cergy-Pontoise** Cédex
Tel: 1-3420 1425 Fax: 1-3038 2577
E-Mail: tda@apro.fr
directeur Jean-Joël Le Chapelin;
directrice des projets Michèle Tayon;
relations publiques André Bonneau (+ jazz)
Arts type: opera, theatre, dance, music, jazz, cinema, conferences, exhibitions *Venues:* Théâtre des arts Cergy 200, Théâtre des arts les Louvrais Pontoise 672
Comments: see also Venues and Festivals

Direction Régionale des Affaires Culturelles de Champagne-Ardenne
3 rue du Faubourg Saint-Antoine,
51037 **Chalons-en-Champagne** Cedex
Tel: 3-2670 3650 Fax: 3-2670 4371
E-Mail: rollet@culture.fr
directeur Richard Lagrange; théâtre et action culturelle Marie-Claire Riou;
musique et danse Michel Louis Richard
Arts type: all types *Comments:* see also National & Regional Ministries

Espace Malraux – Scène Nationale – Maison de la Culture Chambéry et Savoie
67 Place François Mittérand, Carré Curial, BP 147,
73001 **Chambéry** Cédex
Tel: 4-7985 5543 Fax: 4-7985 2629
directeur Dominique Jambon; administrateur Thierry Vautherot; secrétaire général Irene Basilis;
directeur technique Christian Dalibert;
artiste associé Andre Engel
Events: 75 *Venues:* Espace Malraux 947, Théâtre Charles Dullin 429 *Comments:* see also Venues

Théâtre de Cherbourg – Scène Nationale
Place du Général de Gaulle, BP 807,
50108 **Cherbourg** Cedex
Tel: 2-3388 5550 Fax: 2-3388 5559
E-Mail: theatre-cherbourg@wanadoo.fr
directrice Annette Breuil;
secrétaire général Yannick Poignant; attachée de presse et communications Bernadette Clauss
Perfs: 120 *Arts type:* theatre, dance, music, variety, jazz *Venues:* theatre 600 *Comments:* see also Venues

Direction Régionale des Affaires Culturelles d'Auvergne
4 rue Pascal, BP 378, 63001 **Clermont-Ferrand**
Tel: 4-7341 2700 Fax: 4-7341 2769
E-Mail: ricard@culture.fr
directeur Dommique Paillarse; affaires générales et financières Patrice Ducher; communication presse Marie-Claire Ricard; théâtre et action culturelle Daniel Poignant; musique et danse Philippe Bucherer
Arts type: all types *Comments:* see also National & Regional Ministries

Atelier du Rhin – Centre Dramatique Régional d'Alsace
La Manufacture, 6 route d'Ingersheim,
68008 **Colmar** Cédex
Tel: 3-8941 7192 Fax: 3-8941 3326
directeur Matthew Jocelyn;
directrice de la communication Michèle Gaujard;
administrateur Frèdèric de Beauvoir
Events: 2 *Perfs:* 100 *Arts type:* music theatre, modern theatre, puppet, musical theatre, contemporary creations, drama, opera *Venues:* La Manufacture 340 *Policy:* rent, co-produce, produce *Comments:* see also Drama, Opera and Venues

Maison des Arts et de la Culture André Malraux Créteil du Val de Marne
Place Salvador-Alliende, 94000 **Créteil**
Tel: 1-4513 1919 Fax: 1-4399 4808
Internet: www.lemanege.com/mac.creteil
E-Mail: maison.arts@wanadoo.fr
directeur Didier Fusillier; directeur technique Michel Delort; conseiller artistique Richard Castelli (4383 4953); administration Marie-Pierre de Surville; directrice de la communications Mireille Barucco
Events: 3 festivals *Perfs:* 350 *Arts type:* theatre, dance, comedy, singing, puppets, films, new technologies *Venues:* Hall A 1100, Hall B 350 *Policy:* rent, present, co-produce *Comments:* organise 3 festivals – Festival Exit (performance arts of the world), Festival International de Films de Femmes, and Les Fantaisies (an open-air event); see also Venues

Direction Régionale des Affaires Culturelles de Bourgogne
Hôtel Chartraire de Montigny, 41 rue Vannerie,
21000 **Dijon**
Tel: 3-8068 5050 Fax: 3-8068 5099/8031 6862
E-Mail: bourgogne@bourgogn.culture.fr
théâtre et action culturelle Ghislain Mille; musique et danse Mireille Pic; communication Brigitte Hautier-Mansat; attachée principale adjointe au directeur Marie-Josèphe Gaillard
Arts type: all types *Comments:* see also National & Regional Ministries

Allumés du Plat Pays, Les
Fargou, 46250 **Goujounac**
Tel: 5-6536 6947 Fax: 5-6536 6948
contact Mime Rutlen
Arts type: theatre for young people *Comments:* they have no activities planned for this year due to their move

Auditorium Eric-Paul Stekel
6, Chemin de Gordes, 38100 **Grenoble**
Tel: 4-7646 4844 Fax: 4-7687 1120
directeur Michel Rotterdam;
directeurs adjoints Jean-Claude Foulon, Catherine Baubin;
directeur administratif Alain Clerc
Events: 40 *Arts type:* mainly music, also theatre *Venues:* Auditorium Eric-Paul Stekel 350
Comments: see also Venues

L'Oreille en Fête – Musée en Musique
50 Quai de France, 38000 **Grenoble**
Tel: 4-7687 7731 Fax: 4-7687 7761
Internet: www.alpesweb.com/musee-musique
president Pascale Galliard; administration général – communication Françoise Duchene
Events: 30 *Arts type:* classical music, chamber music, piano recitals, contemporary music, jazz *Venues:* Auditorium du Musée de Grenoble 275 *Policy:* organises concerts, journeys to the Operas de Lyon

Le Parvis – Scène Nationale de Tarbes-Pyrénées
Route de Pau, BP 20, 65421 **Ibos Tarbes** Cedex
Tel: 5-6290 0855
Fax: 5-6290 6020
directeur Marc Bélit; chargé de communication Olivier Defaiy; relations publiques Eric Defaix, Valérie Tujagues; directeur technique Jean-Pierre Frin
Events: 64 *Arts type:* all kinds including: classical and contemporary theatre, music and dance, mime, circus varieties *Venues:* grande salle 750, Parvis Méridien (salle de cinéma) 100 *Comments:* see also Venues

Le Volcan / Le Havre
BP 1106, 76063 **Le Havre** Cédex
Tel: 2-3519 1010
Fax: 2-3519 1000
Internet: www.infoceane.com/levolcan.html
directeur Alain Milianti; directeur adjoint Roland Thomas; directeur technique Gérard Salamagnon; directeur de l'accueil Kassem Azimi; directeur de la communication Jean-Pierre Laurent; administratrive Christine Atienza; regisseur général Sylvain Ghiloni
Events: 29 + 10 (during the festival)
Perfs: 70 *Arts type:* dance, music, theatre *Venues:* Le Grand Volcan 1160, Le petit Volcan 350-550, Cinéma l'Eden 300, Exhibition hall, 2 bars *Policy:* rent (occassionally), present, co-produce, produce
Comments: see also Venues & Festival le Printemps

Association Musiques-Echanges
680, chemin de la Tubasse,
13540 **Lignane-Puyricard**
Tel: 4-4292 6542/3662
Fax: 4-4292 6542
directeur artistique Michel Bourdoncle
Events: spring (Mar/April), annual *Perfs:* 7
Arts type: classical music: chamber, symphony, instrumental recitals *Venues:* capacity 650

Danse à Lille
Opéra de Lille, Maison de l'habitat,
2 rue Alexandre Desrousseaux, 59800 **Lille**
Tel: 3-2085 9537 (artistic direction)
Fax: 3-2052 2258
Comments: closed for two years

Direction Régionale des Affaires Culturelles de Nord-Pas de Calais
Hôtel Scrive, 1 rue du Lombard,
59800 **Lille**
Tel: 3-2006 8758
Fax: 3-2074 0720
E-Mail: yvesledun@nord.culture.fr
directeur Richard Martineau;
musique et danse Marc Le Bourhis;
théâtre et action culturelle Denis Decelerck;
documentation Nicole Moussarie;
information Yves Ledun
Arts type: all types *Comments:* see also National & Regional Ministries

Direction Régionale des Affaires Culturelles du Limousin
6 rue Haute de la Comédie,
87036 **Limoges** Cédex
Tel: 5-5545 6645
Fax: 5-5545 6644
directeur Jean-Luc Massy; théâtre et action culturelle Richard Madjarev; musique et danse Fabrice Linon; centre d'information et de documentation, communication, accueil Catherine Catinus;
arts plastiques Anne Martinet
Arts type: all types *Comments:* see also National & Regional Ministries

Direction Régionale des Affaires Culturelles de Rhône-Alpes
Le Grenier d'Abondance
6 quai Saint-Vincent, 69283 **Lyon** Cédex 01
Tel: 4-7200 4400/4449 Fax: 4-7200 4330
E-Mail: kneubuhler@culture.fr
directeur Abraham Bengio; théâtre Mr Roussel; musique et danse Laure Marcel-Berlioz, Laurent Van Kote; communication Michel Kneubühler;
adjoint au directeur Pierre Sigaud
Arts type: all types *Comments:* see also National & Regional Ministries

Grame
Centre National de Création Musicale, 9,
rue du Garet, BP 1185, 69202 **Lyon** Cédex 1
Tel: 4-7207 3700 Fax: 4-7207 3701
Internet: www.grame.fr
E-Mail: grame@rd.grame.fr
directeurs James Giroudon, Pierre Alain Jaffrennou;
administrateur Florence Catrin;
responsable recherche Yann Orlarey
Arts type: chamber orch, chamber music, electronic music, new music, music theatre, multi-media, opera, visual arts exhibitions, contemporary music, research, conferences, festivals *Venues:* Musée d'Art Contemporain, Salle Varése CNSM Lyon *Comments:* see also Venues & Festivals

Mairie de Marseille
Direction Général des Affaires Culturelles,
38, rue Saint-Ferréol, 13001 **Marseille**
Tel: 4-9114 5340 Fax: 4-9114 5341
Internet: www.mairie-marseille.fr
directeur Jean Mangion;
musiques et danses René Murat;
théâtre Marie-Laure Salvarelli;
arts contemporains Jaqueline Nardini
Arts type: all types: dance theatre, music, cinema, plastic arts *Policy:* coordination of 7 cultural services
Comments: see also National and Regional Ministries of Culture and Funding Agencies

Marseille Objectif Danse
3rue St Ferréol, 13001 **Marseille**
Tel: 4-9155 5884
Fax: 4-9155 5920
E-Mail: mod@dial.oléane.com
déléguée général Josette Pisani
Events: 12 *Arts type:* contemporary dance, film, video, exhibitions *Venues:* 48 Marseille theatres: Les Bernardines 100, La Minoterie 200, Le Toursky 600, La Fricha 200 *Policy:* produce, present
Comments: programme videos and films all year; organise contemporary dance courses in Marseille, spectacles de danse contemporaine,
vidéos et films, stages

Théâtre du Merlan Scène Nationale
Avenue Raimu, 13014 **Marseille** Cédex 14
Tel: 4-9111 1930
Fax: 4-9111 1939
directeur Alain Liévaux;
secrétaire générale Andrée Pascaud;
président Alain Vidal-Naquet;
directeur technique Pierre Andrac
Events: 15 *Perfs:* 24 *Arts type:* dance, theatre, music, variety, exhibitions, circus & all kinds of performing arts *Venues:* Cinéma Merlan 90, others up to 540 *Policy:* co-produce, present *Comments:* see also Venues

Direction Régionale des Affaires Culturelles de Lorraine
6 place de Chambre, 57045 **Metz** Cédex 1
Tel: 3-8756 4100
Fax: 3-8775 2828
E-Mail: silistrini@culture.fr
directeur Jacques Charlot; théâtre, cinèma, audiovisuel Yvette Masson; communication Isabelle Wagner; documentation t.b.a.; musique et danse François Derudder; arts plastiques Jacques Bayle; livre et lecture Françoise Vincent; audiovisual René Peilloux
Arts type: all types *Comments:* see also National & Regional Ministries

District de L'Agglomération Montargoise
2 rue Franklin Roosevelt,
BP 317, 45203 **Montargis** Cédex
Tel: 2-3895 0202 Fax: 2-3895 0229
secrétaire général Maurice Grandcoin;
chargée de l'action culturelle Claudine Clairay;
président Max Nublat;
vice-président François Bonneau;
communication Céline Hebert
Events: 20 *Arts type:* baroque music, theatre, variety for adults and young people, dance *Venues:* Salle de Spectacle du Tivoli 300, Salle des Fêtes de Montargis up to 300, Espace Jean Villars à Amilly 700, Salle du Chateau Blanc 2700

Direction Régionale des Affaires Culturelles de Languedoc-Roussillon
Hôtel de Grave, 5 rue Salle l'Evêque,
BP 2051, 34024 **Montpellier** Cédex 1
Tel: 4-6702 3200
Fax: 4-6702 3204
E-Mail: eid@languedo.culture.fr
director Michel Fontes; théâtre Jean-Claude Loubière; musique et danse François-Victor Lepargneur; communication Jakline Eid; action culturelle Isabel Martinez
Arts type: all types *Comments:* see also National & Regional Ministries

Opera de Nancy et de Lorraine
1 rue Sainte-Catherine, 54000 **Nancy**
Tel: 3-8385 3320/3060
Fax: 3-8385 3066
E-Mail: opera@mairie-nancy.fr
directeur Jean-Marie Blanchard;
administrateur Christophe Bezzone tel. 8385 3061;
relations publiques Liliane Martinez
Perfs: 10 (opera) *Arts type:* choral music, opera, operetta, symphony music, classical ballet, modern ballet, classical theatre, modern theatre *Venues:* Opéra (950), Salle Poirel (980)
Policy: produce, co-produce, present *Comments:* see also Venues, Opera, Orchestra and Dance

Théâtre de Nanterre-Amandiers
7 Avenue Pablo Picasso,
92022 **Nanterre** Cédex
Tel: 1-4614 7070 (admin)/ 4614 7000 (pub)
Fax: 1-4725 1775
directeur Jean-Pierre Vincent; directeur administratif Marc Dondey; directeur technique Carlos Stavisky; secrétaire général Marc Dondey
Events: 200-250 *Arts type:* modern, classical, drama *Venues:* Théâtre de Nanterre, Hall A up t 150, Hall B up to 500, Hall C up to 900
Comments: see also Venues and Drama

CREA/ Centre de réalisations et d'etudes artistiques
14 rue M-A de Bollage, 44000 **Nantes**
Tel: 2-4069 1597
Fax: 2-4073 6470
president Jacques Dagault; director René Martin
Events: 3 (1festival + 2 musical series)
Arts type: chamber music, spiritual concerts *Comments:* creators of festival La Folle Journeé; see also Festivals

Direction Régionale des Affaires Culturelles des Pays de la Loire
BP 63518, 1, rue Stanislas Baudry,
44035 **Nantes** Cédex 1
Tel: 2-4014 2300/23 (info & doc. centre)
Fax: 2-4014 2301
E-Mail: ecormier@culture.fr (theatre)
directeur régional Michel Clement; adjointe au directeur chargée de l'aménagement culturel du territoire et service de coordination Chantal Dagault; service des affaires financières et générales Loïc Brosseau; servico communication Elisabeth Hodebourg de Verbois; responsable du centre d'information et de documentation générale Anne de Chanterac; conseiller pour l'action culturelle, le théâtre et le cinéma Elysabeth Cormier; conseiller pour la musique et la danse Gerard Cieslik; conseiller pour les arts plastiques Norbert Duffort
Arts type: all types *Comments:* E-mail musique et danse: gerard.cieslik@culture.fr; see also National & Regional Ministries

Centre International de Recherche Musicale, Centre National de Création Musicale
Musique Actuelle-Nice, Côte d'Azur,
33, av Jean Médecin, 06000 **Nice**
Tel: 4-9388 7468
Fax: 4-9316 0766
Internet: www.nom.fr/manca
E-Mail: cirm_studio@compuserve.fr
attachée de presse Martine Danguy d'Alessandro; administration Olivier Enguehard
Events: 6 *Perfs:* 30 *Arts type:* concerts and festivals of contemporary music *Venues:* throughout Nice; mainly in the auditorium Musée D' Art Moderne et Contemporain 225 *Comments:* organises concerts and festivals in France (Nice mainly) and around the world; see also Festivals (MANCA)

Scène Nationale le Moulin du Roc
9 boulevard Main,
BP 405, 79004 **Niort** Cédex
Tel: 5-4977 3230
Fax: 5-4977 3231
Internet: moulinduroc.asso.fr
E-Mail: moulinduroc@moulinduroc.asso.fr
directeur Bernard Bonnet; administrateur Bruno Denis; programmation danse Christian Vernadal; relations extérieures Michèle Cassegrain; relations publiques Jacques Morel
Events: 45 *Arts type:* theatre, dance, music, lyric, jazz, exhibitions, cinema, variety, youth theatre *Venues:* Le Théatre 936, Le Studio up to 260 *Policy:* rent, present, produce, co-produce *Comments:* see also Venues

Centre National de Creations et de Diffusions Culturelles
BP 118, 83190 **Ollioules** Cédex
Tel: 4-9422 7400
Fax: 4-9422 7419
information Nataly Bernard
Venues: Amphithéâtre 1200, indoor hall 500, cinéma 100 *Comments:* see also Festivals, Dance and Venues

Centre Chorégraphique National d'Orléans
Carré Saint-Vincent, 45000 **Orléans**
Tel: 2-3862 4100 Fax: 2-3877 0855
E-Mail: ccnorleans@xernet.com
directeur Josef Nadj (tel: 1-4289 6102, fax: 1-4289 4466); diffusion & production Martine Dionisio (tel: 1-4289 6102, fax: 1-4289 4466); secrétaire générale et direction des relations publiques Béatrice Cachin (tel: 1-4289 6102, fax: 1-4289 4466)
Arts type: contemporary dance, drama, dance theatre *Venues:* Salle Jean Guy Aimé Touchard 1000, Salle Antoine Vitez 220, Salle Jean-Louis Barrault 600 *Policy:* present, produce, rent, occassionally co-produce *Comments:* see also Drama, Venues and Dance

Direction Régionale des Affaires Culturelles de la région Centre
6 rue de la Manufacture,
45043 **Orléans** Cedex 1
Tel: 2-3878 8500
Fax: 2-3878 8599
E-Mail: Drac.centre@wanadoo.fr
directeur Alain Marais; action culturelle Mr Nordmand; théâtre Kattel Pouessen; musique et danse Joël Forgues; communication Jean-Louis Gauthier; documentation générale Jean-Pierre Bouguier
Arts type: all types *Comments:* see also National & Regional Ministries

Théâtre de la Renaissance
7 rue Orsel, 69600 **Oullins**
Tel: 4-7239 7491
Fax: 4-7850 7651
directeur Michel Thion; relations publiques Anne Daynes; communication Nicole Levy; directeur technique Christian Reat
Events: 23 *Arts type:* theatre, music, cinema, conferences, new music, folk music, music theatre, song recitals, world music, modern dance, classical theatre, modern theatre, visual arts exhibitions *Venues:* 493

Centre National de la Danse
Rue Victor Hugo, 93507 **Pantin** Cedex
Tel: 1-4183 2727 Fax: 1-4840 3366
Internet: www.centredanse.fr
E-Mail: cnd.pantin@wanadoo.fr
présidente Anne Chiffert; directeur général Michel Sala; directeur administratif et financier Bruno Lobé; directeur technique Jean-Pierre Belet; directeur maison des compagnies et des specticles Daniel Gillet; directrice institut de pédagogie et de recherche chorégraphiques Anne-Marie Reynaud; directrice adjointe institut de pédagogie et de recherche chorégraphiques Bernadette Leguil; directeur département des métiers Thierry Jopeck; directrice département du développement de la culture chorégraphique Claire Rousier; communication Vergine Dupray
Arts type: contemporary dance, and information centre for dancers, jazz, classical ballet, modern ballet, modern dance, visual art exhibitions *V enues:* 120 *Policy:* produce *Comments:* see also Venues and National Organisations

Académie des Arts Baroques
150 rue Saint Maur, 75011 **Paris**
Tel: 1-4357 0884
Fax: 1-4357 0787
E-Mail: diderot@imaginet.fr
chargée de production Aude Leriche; président Jean-Paul Combet; communication Marc Bayard
Events: 15-20 *Arts type:* baroque music, theatre, conferences, travel *Policy:* production, present

Centre d'Études Beethovéniennes de France
21 rue de Cloÿs, 75018 **Paris**
Tel: 6-6222 3310 Fax: 1-4257 3310
Internet: perso.libertysurf.fr/hodie
E-Mail: c.e.b.f@libertysurf.fr/
honary president Prof. Serge Gut; chief executive Prof. Katarzyna Le Fé; research and artistic director Dr. Maximianno Cobra
Comments: musicology research centre devoted to Ludig van Beethoven's works and life as well as 18th-19th century musicology studies; publications: thematic catalogue, scholarly editions amd critical score editions

Cie Herve-Gil
14 Rue du Moulinet, 75013 **Paris**
Tel: 1-4580 5333 Fax: 1-4580 5333
artistic director Miriam Herve-Gil
Arts type: contemporary dance and theatre

Direction Régionale des Affaires Culturelles de l'Ile de France
98 rue de Charonne, 75011 **Paris**
Tel: 1-5606 5000
Fax: 1-5606 5248
directeur Alain Van Der Malière; directrice adjointe Anne-Marie Le Guérel; théâtre Yves Chevallier, Edithe Rappoport, Brigitte Perrault; action culturelle Yvette Masson; musique et danse Pierre Costes, Catherine Reflé
Arts type: all types *Comments:* see also National & Regional Ministries

Encore Productions
6 rue du Mont Thabor, 75001 **Paris**
Tel: 1-4260 6125 Fax: 1-4260 6940
directeur Pascal Bernardin
Perfs: 50-100 *Arts type:* rock, variety, circus *Venues:* all venues throughout France *Policy:* organise concerts of pop stars throughout France *Comments:* organises concerts for artists such as Sting

Gruber Ballet Opéra
70 rue Amelot, 75011 **Paris**
Tel: 1-4357 3060
Fax: 1-4357 7365
director Béatrice Gruber; administratrice Brigitte Gruber
Events: 150 *Arts type:* ballet, music, opera
Policy: organise tours

Inter Concerts
59 Av. Victor Hugo, 75016 **Paris**
Tel: 1-4504 7120 Fax: 1-4504 0092
directrice Jackie Lombard
Arts type: music

IRCAM – Institute de Recherche et de Coordination Acoustique/Musique
1 Place Igor Stravinsky, 75004 **Paris**
Tel: 1-4478 4843/4880
Fax: 1-4478 1540/4478 4806
Internet: www.ircam.fr
directeur Laurent Bayle; directeur artistique Eric De Visscher; directeur honoraire Pierre Boulez; communications Madame Manceau
Arts type: contemporary music, choral music, chamber music, early music, electronic music, inst recitals, new music, light orchestral music, music theatre, song recitals, symphony music, multi-media, opera, modern ballet, modern dance, modern theatre, visual arts exhibitions *Venues:* IRCAM, Centre Georges Pompidou, Théatre du Chatelet, Cité de la Musique
Comments: research, commissions and productions of new work, concerts, tours, summer workshops; see also Competitions

Istvan's Performing Arts Agency
24, rue la Condamine, 75017 **Paris**
Tel: 1-4293 0727/6-8235 7969
Fax: 1-4387 6408
director Istvan van Heuvzerzwyn
Arts type: theatre *Comments:* specialise in European tours; second address: 194 Filips van Cleefaan, 9000 Gent, Belgium, Tel: 9-224 1460; see also Agents

Jeanine Roze Production
17 rue du Colisée, 75008 **Paris**
Tel: 1-4256 9010 Fax: 1-4359 5437
E-Mail: rozeprod@aol.com
producteur de concerts Jeanine Roze; directeur Michel Franck
Perfs: 150 *Arts type:* classical, chamber music, opera, symphony, baroque music *Venues:* Salle Pleyel 2300, Théâtre des Champs-Elysées 1900, Comèdie des Champs Elysèes 650, Chatelet 2000 *Policy:* production company *Comments:* for children on Sundays – free (while parents are at the theatre): Atelier d'eveil et d'Initiation à la musique

Jeunesses Musicales de France
20 rue Geoffroy l'Asnier, 75004 **Paris**
Tel: 1-4461 8686 Fax: 1-4461 8688
E-Mail: jmf_jbf@club-internet.fr
directeur Robert Berthier; administration Didier Gobillot; président Jean Loup Tournier
Arts type: music (young artists)
Comments: second E-mail: info@j-musi-fr.org; see also National Organisations

Ladanse
92 rue Myrha, 75018 **Paris**
Tel: 6-1305 2925
Internet: www.ladanse.com/
E-Mail: info@ladanse.com
contact Philippe Madala (head), Nicolas Lauchy, Sylvie Martin, Pascale Fauverge
Arts type: dance

Ménagerie de Verre
12/14 rue Léchevin, 75011 **Paris**
Tel: 1-4338 3344 Fax: 1-4338 7456
Internet: www.multimania.com/menageri
E-Mail: menageri@club-internet.fr
directrice artistique Marie-Therése Allier
Arts type: contemporary dance, drama *Venues:* La Salle Off 100 & 5 studios *Policy:* present, rent
Comments: organise the festival Les Inacoutumés; see also Venues and Festivals

MPM International
21 rue du Grand Prieuré, 75011 **Paris**
Tel: 1-4923 8360 Fax: 1-4338 4314
directeur artistique Philippe Genty; direction Marie-Pierre Paillard
Perfs: 100-110 *Arts type:* contemporary dance, drama
Comments: see also Drama, Puppet, Dance and Agents and Producers

Proquartet
20 rue Geoffroy l'asnier, 75004 **Paris**
Tel: 1-4461 8350 Fax: 1-4461 8353
E-Mail: proquartet@wanadoo.fr
directeur Georges Zeisel; organiser masterclasses Patricia Nydegger
Events: 20 *Arts type:* string quartet, chamber music
Policy: promotes and presents *Comments:* mandated by the Ministry of Culture; also organise masterclasses

Regard du Cygne, Le
Association Musique Danse xxéme,
210 rue de Belleville, 75020 **Paris**
Tel: 1-4358 5593 Fax: 1-4636 7067
Internet: members.aol.com/redcygne
E-Mail: redcygne@aol.com
artistic directors Amy Swanson, Fabrice Dugied
Events: 60 (contemporary dance) 20 (concerts) *Arts type:* contemporary dance and music *Venues:* capacity 80 *Policy:* produce, co-produce, rent
Comments: see also Venues

Société Internationale Franz Schreker
24, rue des Petites Ecuries, 75010 **Paris**
Tel: 1-4824 2197 Fax: 1-4824 2199
E-Mail: jorge.zulueta@wanadoo.fr
président Jorge Zulueta; vice président Jacobo Romano; présidents d'honneur Haidy Schreker-Burés, Prof. Eugenio Burès; communication Franck Hargeres Uthenow
Events: 6 (big events) *Prefs:* 7 *Arts type:* opera, Schreker music *Policy:* to promote the music and works of Franz Schreker everywhere in the world

Théâtre Musique et Danse dans la Ville Association
15, rue Jean Lantier, 75001 **Paris**
Tel: 1-4508 5561 Fax: 1-4508 5528
responsable Emmanuel Dechartre; administrateur Laëtitia Versini-Campinchi
Events: 5-6 *Arts type:* theatre, jazz, music, dance *Venues:* theatre 14 200, others in Paris *Comments:* organises events, performances, concerts everywhere in Paris; fireworks; also organise a festival last week of June

Direction Régionale des Affaires Culturelles de Poitou-Charentes
Hôtel de Rochefort, 102 Grand-Rue,
BP 553, 86020 **Poitiers** Cedex
Tel: 5-4936 3030
Fax: 5-4988 3202
E-Mail: duvigneau@culture.fr
directeur Jean-Pierre Pottier; théâtre et action culturelle Jean Claude Senechal; musique et danse Pierre Blanc; adjointe au directeur Claudine Trougnou; chargée de communication Madame Duvigneau
Arts type: all types *Comments:* see also National & Regional Ministries

Direction Régionale des Affaires Culturelles de Bretagne
Hôtel de Blossac,
6 rue du Chapitre
35044 **Rennes** Cedex
Tel: 2-9929 6767
Fax: 2-9929 6799
E-Mail: pichon@bretagne.culture.fr
directeur Raymond Lachat; théâtre et spectacles Bernadette Rousseaux; musique et danse Anne-Christine Micheu; communication et documentation Hervé Musse
Arts type: all types *Comments:* see also National & Regional Ministries

Direction Régionale des Affaires Culturelles de Haute-Normandie
2 rue Saint-Sever,
76032 **Rouen** Cedex
Tel: 2-3563 6160
Fax: 2-3572 8460
E-Mail: xerri@hnormand.culture.fr
directeur Sylvane Tarst-Gillery; adjointe du directeur Thiery Delamare; secretaire générale Isabelle Revol; conseillère pour le théâtre Françoise Bauer; conseillère pour l'action culturelle Sophie Bardet; conseiller pour le musique et la danse Jérôme Alexandre; chargée de la communication Natacha Xerri
Arts type: all types *Comments:* see also National & Regional Ministries

L'Esplanade-Saint Étienne
Jardin des Plantes, BP 237,
42013 **Saint-Étienne** Cedex 2
Tel: 4-7747 8347 Fax: 4-7747 8369
directeur Jean-Louis Pichon; programmation danse Serge Horwath; programmation jazz, rock, variety Dominique Rouvier; directeur de la communication Daniel Couriol; administrateur Michel Fabre
Events: 21 représentations lyrique, 12 musical et 11 de danse *Perfs:* 200 (140 young audiences, 10 drama, 20 variety/jazz/rock, 12 dance, 26 lyric)
Arts type: opera, ballet, choir music, orchestra, symphony, variety, pop-rock, modern & contemporary dance, shows for young audiences *Venues:* Hall A 1260, Hall B 330, Théatre Ephemère 1100, Théatre Massenay 2001 *Policy:* produce, co-produce, rent, present
Comments: Grand Théâtre had burnt down; see also Venues and Opera

Thélème Contemporain
Grises, 26740 **Savasse**
Tel: 4-7546 0349
Fax: 4-7546 0349
secrétaire Danielle Quet; artistic director Bertrand Merlier; présidente Hélène Planel; trésorière Marie-Claude Planel
Arts type: electronic music, multi-media, electro acoustic music

Direction Régionale des Affaires Culturelles d'Alsace
Palais du Rhin, 2 place de la République,
67082 **Strasbourg** Cedex
Tel: 3-8815 5700/5771
Fax: 3-8875 6095
E-Mail: catherine.marco@culture.fr
directeur Jean-Luc Bredel; conseiller technique théâtre et action culturelle Pia Jung; conseiller technique musique et danse Sophie Mège; information et documentation Catherine Marco; communication Hoeckel
Arts type: all types *Comments:* attached to the minister de la culture; see also National & Regional Ministries

Théâtre National de Strasbourg
Avenue de la Marseillaise,
BP 184/R5, 67005 **Strasbourg** Cedex
Tel: 3-8824 8800
Fax: 3-8837 3771
Internet: www.strasbourg.com/tns
directeur Jean Louis Martinelli; administrateur Philippe Buquet; directeur des relations publiques Jean-Claude Champesme; press Anne-Laure Vesperini; directeur technique Jean-Michel Du Bois; directrice des études de l'ecole superieure d'art dramatique Dominique Le Coyer; communication Fabienne Meyer
Arts type: theatre *Venues:* Salle Bernard – Marie Koltès 600, Salle Hubert Gignoux 200
Comments: see also Drama

Centre de Développement Chorégraphique – Toulouse Midi-Pyrénées
5, Avenue Etienne Billières, 31300 **Toulouse**
Tel: 5-6159 9878 Fax: 5-6159 9904
E-Mail: cdc@com.unisoft.fr
président Francis Balagna; directrice Annie Bozzini
Events: 21 *Perfs:* 42 *Arts type:* contemporary dance
Comments: documentation centre

Direction Régionale des Affaires Culturelles de Midi-Pyrénées
56 rue du Taur, BP 811, Place Alphonse Jourdain,
31080 **Toulouse** Cédex 06
Tel: 5-6230 3100 Fax: 5-6123 1271
E-Mail: kowalewski@culture.fr
directeur Didier Deschamps; adjoint Pierre-Jean Dupuy; action culturelle Francis Luttiau; musique et la danse Francis Barascou; communication et information Anne-Françoise Kowalewski; théâtre Jean-Michel Treguer
Arts type: all types *Comments:* see also National & Regional Ministries

Les Arts Renaissants
24 rue Croix Baragnon, 31000 **Toulouse**
Tel: 5-6125 2732
Fax: 5-6132 1463
président Jean-Pierre Decavele
Events: 10 concerts *Arts type:* concerts, international organ competition, annual masterclass
Venues: various up to 600

Centre de Musique Baroque de Versailles
22, Avenue de Paris, BP 353,
78003 **Versailles** Cédex
Tel: 1-3920 7810/7800 (bookings)
Fax: 1-3920 7801
E-Mail: accueil@cmbv.com
directeur Vincent Berthier de Lioncourt; relations publiques Catherine Thepot
Events: 35 *Arts type:* baroque music, chamber orch, choral music, chamber music, early music, music theatre, sacred music, opera *Venues:* Chateau de Versailles: Chapelle Royale 700, Opera Royal 618, Salon d' Hércule 300, Le Grand Triasoni 250-300
Comments: see also Festival: Automne Musical du Château de Versailles

Musiques Vivantes
3 rue Jean-Jaurès, 03200 **Vichy**
Tel: 4-7031 1500 Fax: 4-7031 5766
president Jean-Michel Guerre; communication Ginette Coste
Events: 106 *Perfs:* 21 *Arts type:* chamber orch, choral music, chamber music, inst recitals, sacred music
Venues: Eté. departement de l'allier; Vichy + historic monuments of Allier *Policy:* enhancing architectural heritage with music *Comments:* organise festival Nuits Musicales en Bourbonnais in summer, and Opus concert series in winter; ORFEO: musical activities in schools; FUGUES: cultural travels to opera or theatres in the region

Atelier de Musique de Ville d'Avray
Chateau de Ville D'Avray,
10 rue de Marnes, 92410 **Ville D'Avray**
Tel: 1-4750 4428
Fax: 1-4750 5390
contact Jean Louis Petit
Comments: see also Orchestras

GEORGIA (+995)

International Bureau for Caucasian Cultural Programmes
45 Chavchavadze av., 380062 **Tbilisi**
Tel: 32-294 306
Fax: 32-294 306/231 196
E-Mail: IBCCP@lingua.edu.ge
director IBCCP Georgia Levan Dadiani; director IBCCP Azerbaijan Jahangir Selimkhanov (e-mail:jselimkhanov@OSI-AZ-org); director IBCCP Armenia Arthur Gukasyan (e-mail: aghukasyan@hotmail.com)
Arts type: all types *Comments:* coordinates educational programmes, management training centre, information centre, festival centre, publishing house etc.; see also National Organisations

Stichting Caucasus Foundation
45 I. Chavchavadze Av., 380062 **Tbilisi**
Tel: 32-294 306/250 089
Fax: 32-294 306/231 196
E-Mail: SCF@lingua.edu.ge
president Levan Khetaguri; chairman Steve Austen; programme coordinator Iuri Mgebrishvili
Arts type: all types *Policy:* supports Caucasian countries in the process of cultural integration with European countries, sets up and implements programmes and events in art and culture for professional artists
Comments: regional programmes coordinated by IBCCP (International Bureau for Caucasian Cultural Programmes), educational programmes, management training centre, information centre; office in the Netherlands: secretary Henk van Silfhout, Koxhorn 32-3, 1082 EW Amsterdam; see also National Organisations

GERMANY (+49)

Amt für Kultur und Touristik
Postfach 607, Stadthaus, 91511 **Ansbach**
Tel: 981-51243/51323 Fax: 981-51365
Internet: www.ansbach.de
E-Mail: akut@ansbach.de
Direktor Siegfried Blank
Events: 4-6 event series *Arts type:* chamber orch, choral music, chamber music, early music, folk music, inst recitals, jazz, music theatre, operetta, sacred music, song recitals, symphony music, opera, folk dance, modern dance, classical theatre, mime, modern theatre, puppet, street theatre, visual arts exhibitions
Venues: Orangerie, Haus der Volksbildung, Kulturzentrum Karlsplatz, Castle Yard, Tagungszentrum
Comments: Bach Week, biennial; Rokoko Festival, annual; International Guitar Concerts, annual

Haus der Volksbildung EG Kultur am Schloss
Promenade 29, 91522 **Ansbach**
Tel: 981-97040-0
Fax: 981-2476
E-Mail: kultur.am.schloss@t-online.de
Geschäftsführerin Irene Pachur
Events: 39 *Arts type:* orchestra, choral, chamber music, lied, theatre, ballet, cabaret *Venues:* St Gumbertuskirche, Orangerie im Hofgarten, Onoldiasaal, Kultur am Schloss

Stadt Arnsberg Kulturbüro
Alter Markt 19, 59821 **Arnsberg**
Tel: 2931-893 1120 Fax: 2931-893 1115
Leiter Peter Kleine
Events: 50-60 *Arts type:* music theatre, operetta, song recitals, symphony music, opera, classical ballet, modern ballet, modern dance, classical theatre, mime, modern theatre, visual arts exhibitions, concerts, kindertheater (children's theatre) *Venues:* Sauerland Theater 586, Rittersaal 150, Studio 100 & various other small scale venues

Augsburger Konzertdirektion Georg Hörtnagel
Josef Priller Straße 10, 86159 **Augsburg**
Tel: 821-593 835/731-33426
Fax: 731-33425
Inhaber Georg Hörtnagel
Events: 8 *Arts type:* symphony music, classical concerts, soloists *Venues:* Kongresshalle Augsburg 1395
Comments: see also Agents & Producers; Konzertbüro Heide Salzmann (q.v.)

Deutsche Mozartgesellschaft
Mozarthaus, Frauentorstraße 30, 86152 **Augsburg**
Tel: 821-518 588 Fax: 821-157 228
Internet: www.deutsche-mozart-gesellschaft.de
E-Mail: Deutsche-Mozart-Gesellschaft@t-online.de
Geschäftsführer Brigitte Löder
Events: 3 *Perfs:* 36 (18 each season) *Arts type:* chamber orch, symphony music, music theatre, opera: the music of Mozart *Venues:* Sept. 2000 – Hildesheim, 2001 Augsburg *Policy:* research is main focus *Comments:* Mozart Musizierwoche is for amateurs who play under the instruction of professionals

Konzertbüro Heide Salzmann
Josef Priller Straße 10, 86159 **Augsburg**
Tel: 821-593 835/731-33426
Fax: 731-33425
Direktion Heide Salzmann
Events: 10 *Arts type:* classical concerts, operetta, ballet, soloists *Venues:* various venues in Augsburg, Kempten, Oberstaufen, Obersdorf, Immenstadt *Comments:* also organises coach trips to opera festivals (worldwide); second address: Galgenbergweg 36, 89077 Ulm; see also Augsburger Konzertdirektion Georg Hörtnagel (q.v.)

Konzertbüro Uebelherr
Neidhartstr 2, 86159 **Augsburg**
Tel: 821-586 028 Fax: 821-584 072
Inhaber Sigfried Uebelherr
Arts type: Augsburger Puppenkiste
Venues: touring in Germany

Stadt Augsburg Kulturbüro
Bahnhofstr. 18 1/3A, 86150 **Augsburg**
Tel: 821-324 3250 Fax: 821-324 3252
Leiterin Irmgard Baur
Events: 4 *Perfs:* approx. 100 *Arts type:* classical and jazz concerts, puppetry, literature
Venues: Kulturhaus Abraxas/Theater 150 *Comments:* organises annual events: Mozart-Sommer, Jazz-Sommer im Botanischen Garden, Augsburger Puppenspieltage and literature series

Arbeitskreis für Musik eV
Nachtigallenstrasse 7, 36251 **Bad Hersfeld**
Tel: 6621-5067-0
Fax: 6621-64355
Vorstand Dr Krug (6621-50670); Information Herta Hildebrandt (6621-2635); Press Marlis Fey (6622-3726)
Arts type: opera, recitals, concerts, symphony music
Venues: Stiftsruine Bad Hersfeld 1000, Ev. Stadtkirche Bad Hersfeld 300 *Policy:* opera and concerts *Comments:* organises festivals over Summer and also one at Easter

Brahmsgesellschaft Baden-Baden eV
Brahmshaus, Maximilianstraße 85,
76534 **Baden-Baden**
Tel: 7221-99872 Fax: 7221-71104
Präsident Dr. Werner Hoppe;
Geschäftsführung Ilka Hecker
Events: May, biennial (2001) *Perfs:* 7
Arts type: concerts: chamber music, symphony music
Venues: Kurhaus, Baden-Baden, Festspielhaus Baden-Baden *Comments:* biennial Brahms festival

Festival Baden-Baden Veranstaltungs GmbH
Schloß Solms, Solmsstr. 1, 76530 **Baden-Baden**
Tel: 7221-275 275
Fax: 7221-275 222
E-Mail: festivalBB@aol.com
Geschäftsführender Gesellschafter (Programmdirektion) Joachim Heiermann
Events: 200 *Arts type:* classical music, musicals, special events *Venues:* Kurhaus Baden up to 1200

Hotel Römerbad
Schloßplatz 1, 79410 **Badenweiler**
Tel: 7632-700 Fax: 7632-70200
Internet: www.hotel-roemerbad.de
E-Mail: info@hotel-roemerbad.de
Direktor Klaus Lauer
Events: 14 *Arts type:* chamber music, recitals, colloquia
Venues: Hofsaal im Hotel Römerbad 260 *Comments:* emphasis on new music

Musica Canterey Bamberg e.V.
Obere Dorotheen Str. 3, 96049 **Bamberg**
Tel: 951-519 0041
Fax: 951-519 0041
Direktor Gerhard Weinzierl
Events: 5 (2000) *Arts type:* baroque, early music, renaissance, choral *Venues:* historical venues and churches in the area *Comments:* promote 'Tage Alter Musik' every two years; next event June 2000; the theme is English music of the 17th C.

Musikverein Bamberg
Frutholfstr. 17, 96049 **Bamberg**
Tel: 951-601 312 Fax: 951-601 312
Internet: musikverein.bamberg.baynet.de
E-Mail: musikverein@bamberg.baynet.de
1.Vorsitzender Andrea Paletta;
2. Vorsitzender Wilhelm Kauffler
Events: 7 *Arts type:* soloists, chamber ensembles
Venues: Konzert u. Kongreßhalle, Josef Kalberth Saal 1400

Gesellschaft der Kulturfreunde
Steigerwaldstr. 5, 95448 **Bayreuth**
Tel: 921-92193
Fax: 921-970 107
Vorsitzender des Vorstandes Wilfried Laudel (Dipl. Ing.); finance manager Diethelm Petermann
Events: 15 *Arts type:* chamber orch, choral music, chamber music, early music, inst recitals, light orch music, song recitals, symphony music *Venues:* Grosses Haus der Stadthalle, Bayreuth 1000, Markgräfliches Opernhaus 500

Berlin Konzertchor eV
Starnberger Straße 3, 10781 **Berlin**
Tel: 30-218 5001 Fax: 30-213 8703
Geschäftsstelle Doris Rohrschneider;
künstlerischer Leiter Mathias Elger
Events: 6 *Arts type:* choral, symphonic concerts
Venues: Berliner Philharmonie 2400; Kammermusiksaal d. Philharmonie 1500 *Comments:* subscription series; see also Choirs

Konzert-Direktion Hans Adler
Auguste-Viktoria-Strasse 64 (1. Etage), 14199 **Berlin**
Tel: 30-895 9920 Fax: 30-826 3520
Internet: www.musikadler.de
E-Mail: info@musikadler.de
Inhaber Witiko Adler
Events: 80 *Arts type:* classical music
Venues: Philharmonie 2400, Konzerthaus
Comments: see also Agents

Konzertbüro Thomas Voigt
Mindener Strasse 11, 10589 **Berlin**
Tel: 30-3490 2199 Fax: 30-3490 2145
Internet: www.voigtmanagement.de
E-Mail: voigt@voigtmanagement.de
Inhaber Thomas Voigt
Arts type: chamber orchestra, choral music, chamber music, early music, symphony music, opera, world music *Comments:* see also Agents

Kulturbureau Berlin Marthen Maasen Meyer Gbr
Olivaer Platz 16, 10707 **Berlin**
Tel: 30-8855 0716/0642 Fax: 30-8855 0756
Internet: www.kulturbureau-berlin.de
E-Mail: mmmkultur@aol.com
Geschäftsführer Peter Maassen; contact Silke Marthen
Events: 300 *Arts type:* mostly comedy, also music theatre, mime *Comments:* for cabaret: Kulturbureau Klaus Meier; Freiburg office: Scheffelstr. 42, 79102 Freiburg, Tel: 761-709 867

Otfried Laur Veranstaltungs-Management
Hardenbergstrasse 6, 10623 **Berlin**
Tel: 30-313 7007 Fax: 30-312 6553
Inhaber Otfried Laur; Mitarbeiter Björdis Mell
Events: 100-150 *Arts type:* classical, jazz, pop, cabaret, ballet, theatre, musicals *Venues:* Berliner Philharmonie, Kammermusiksaal, Hochschule d. Künste, Urania – Theater, ICC, Konzerthaus am Gendarmenmarkt

Piranha
Carmerstrasse 11, 10623 **Berlin**
Tel: 30-318 6140 Fax: 30-3186 1410
Internet: www.piranha.de
E-Mail: womex@piranha.de
Geschäftsführer Brigitte Bieg,
Christoph Borkowsky-Akbar
Arts type: world music *Comments:* see also Festivals (Heimatklänge)

TanzKontakt e.V.
Weisestrasse 46, 12049 **Berlin**
Tel: 30-6270 5136 Fax: 30-6270 5136
directors Philippe Rives, Sigrid Westenfelder, Nicole Hartmann
Arts type: arts of the body (dance, performance, mime)
Comments: non-profit international association, aid to artists, promotion, networks, events creation and development

TanzWerkstatt Berlin
Klosterstr 68-70, 10179 **Berlin**
Tel: 30-2474 9756 Fax: 30-2474 9757
Internet: www.tanzwerkstatt.bkv.org
E-Mail: twb@bkv.org
artistic directors Ulrike Becker, André Thériault
Events: 3 *Perfs:* 20 *Arts type:* contemporary dance and performance *Venues:* various up to 1000 *Policy:* special foucs on works that cross over into the areas of theatre, dance, music and the visual arts *Comments:* main event: Internationales Tanzfest Berlin – Tanz im August

Veranstaltungs – Management GmbH
Hardenbergstr. 6, 10623 **Berlin**
Tel: 30-3173 7007 Fax: 30-312 7083
business manager Volker Schmidt-Gertenbach
Arts type: classical concerts, musicals, contemporary, some popular

Gabriel Concerts
Am Markt 24, 53111 **Bonn**
Tel: 228-696 991 Fax: 228-694 835
E-Mail: Gabriel_Concerts@t-online
Inhaberin Dorothea Gabriel
Events: 200 *Arts type:* opera, entertainment, operetta, light music, pop, musicals *Venues:* Beethoven Halle 2000, Stadthalle 2000, Kölner Sporthalle 8000, Phillips – Halle Düsseldorf 5000 *Comments:* do touring world wide with 4 own productions; see also Agents and Producers

Konzert Rabofsky Bonn
Postfach 1867, 53008 **Bonn**
Tel: 228-662 001 Fax: 228-662 002
Inhaber Gerda Rabofsky
Arts type: classical concerts *Venues:* Beethoven Halle 1700 *Comments:* also act as agents and producers

Kulturgemeinde der Stadt Borken eV
Silberschmiedweg 3, 46325 **Borken**
Tel: 2861-2538 Fax: 2861-67143
Vorsitzender Wilm Wülfing;
Geschäftsführerin Ursula Groskopff
Events: 33 *Arts type:* theatre, classical, rock and pop concerts, cabaret, children's theatre *Venues:* Stadthalle Vennehof, Borken 700, Orangerie des Schlosses Velen 200

Schlosskonzerte Ahaus
Fachbereich 40 (Kultur, Schule, Sport),
Burloer Straße 93, 46325 **Borken**
Tel: 2861-821 348 Fax: 2861-821 365
Internet: www.kreis-borken.de
E-Mail: t.wigger@kreis-borken.de
Events: 6 subscription concerts per season, Oct-March
Perfs: 6 *Arts type:* chamber orch, chamber music, early music *Venues:* Schloss Ahaus, Fürstensaal 300

Braunschweiger Konzertdirektion
Am Fallersleber Tore 6, 38100 **Braunschweig**
Tel: 531-44115 Fax: 531-46873
Direktoren Hans Ulrich Schmid, Bernd Vorhamme
Arts type: philharmonic concerts *Venues:* Stadthalle up to 2300 *Comments:* see also Agents

Braunschweigische Musikgesellschaft e.V.
Lessingplatz 12, Haus Salve Hospes,
38100 **Braunschweig**
Tel: 531-41021 Fax: 5304-3578
E-Mail: salbert@online.de
Vorsitzender Wolf Horenburg; Schatzmeisterin Hilma Abraham; Stellv. Vorsitzender Prof. Dr. Dieter Salbert
Events: 8-10 *Arts type:* chamber orch, chamber music, early music, new music *Venues:* Städtisches Museum 250, Altstadt Rathaus 250 *Comments:* see also Neue Akademie Braunschweig e.V. (q.v.), competitions (Kompositionswettbewerb)

Kammermusikverein aus Mitgliedern des Staatsorchesters Braunschweig e.V.
Am Theater, 38100 **Braunschweig**
Tel: 531-236 1650
Fax: 531-236 1651
Vorsitzender Günther Westenberger; Stellv. Vorsitzender Martin Baumgarte
Events: 6-8 per season (Oct -May)
Arts type: classical chamber music *Venues:* Weißer Saal des Staatstheaters Braunschweig 150, and special concerts in various other venues in Braunschweig

Kirchenmusik im Braunschweiger Dom
Domplatz 5, 38100 **Braunschweig**
Tel: 531-46473 Fax: 531-125 065
Kirchenmusikdirektor Gerd Peter Münden;
Assistenz Hannah Wolf
Events: 30-40 *Arts type:* oratorios, organ concerts in cathedral, chamber music, chamber orchestra, early music, song recitals, sacred music, symphony music
Venues: Braunschweiger Dom 950

Stadt Braunschweig Kulturinstitut
Steintorwall 3, 38100 **Braunschweig**
Tel: 531-470 4840
Fax: 531-470 4809
Internet: www.braunschweig .de
Leitung Dr Anja Hesse; Music,
Literature Dr Annette Boldt-Stülzebach;
Theatre, Cabaret Wolfgang Hartwig
Arts type: folk theatre, cabaret, mime, puppets, literature, chamber orch, choral music, chamber music, electronic music, folk music, inst recitals, jazz, new music, light orch music, song recitals, multi-media, world music, folk dance, modern dance, classical theatre, modern theatre, puppet, street theatre, visual arts exhibitions *Venues:* open air venues (parks, town squares, buildings and other places of historical and modern day interest) *:* Festival Orient trifft Okzident

Praeger & Meier GmbH
Schnoor 15, 28195 **Bremen**
Tel: 421-336 870
Fax: 421-336 8710
Internet: www.praeger-meier.de
Managing Director Hermann Pölking-Eiken
Events: 20-30 *Arts type:* classical concerts
Comments: see also Agents & Producers

Shaksfin & Company GmbH
Torgauer Straße 27, 28215 **Bremen**
Tel: 421-375 507
Fax: 421-375 508
E-Mail: shaksfin@ibm.net
managing directors Hannes Nimpuno, Michael Driemler
Events: 30-40 *Arts type:* classical music, jazz, world music, dance, theatre
Comments: arts producer and marketing team, arts consultancy; see also Agents and Producers

Norddeutsche Konzertdirektion Melsine Grevesmühl
Postfach 310265,
Triftstrasse 11, 27538 **Bremerhaven**
Tel: 471-88068 Fax: 471-88060
Internet: www.grevesmühl.de
E-Mail: grevesmühl@t-online.de
ballet, dance Melsine Grevesmühl;
music Wolfgang Grevesmühl
Events: 400 *Arts type:* chamber music, early music, music theatre, sacred music, opera, world music, classical ballet, folk dance, modern ballet, modern dance, classical theatre, mime, modern theatre
Comments: see also Agents and Producers

Celler Schlosstheater e.V.
Postfach 1333, 29203 **Celle**
Tel: 5141-905 080 Fax: 5141-905 0844
Internet: www.schlosstheater-celle.de
Intendant Karin H. Veit;
Geschäftsführer Klaus Tietje;
Sekretariat Frau Mehling
Events: 16 *Arts type:* chamber music, recitals, classical theatre, modern theatre, musical
Venues: Hauptbühne 330, Malersaal 45
Comments: see also Drama and Venues

Gesellschaft der Musikfreunde Coburg eV
Nordlehne 3, 96450 **Coburg**
Tel: 9561-75041 Fax: 9561-94887
Vorsitzender Oberstudiendirektor J Schaschek
Events: 7 *Arts type:* recitals, classical music, chamber music *Venues:* Kongresshaus 900

Chopin-Gesellschaft in der Bundesrepublik Deutschland eV
Kasinostrasse 3 (John F Kennedy Haus),
64293 **Darmstadt**
Tel: 6151-25957/55897 Fax: 6151-25957/955 974
Präsident Maciej Lukaszczyk; Vorstand Dr. Helmut Kelleter, Frau Irmgard Hörl, Frau Erna Weitzel
Events: 20 *Arts type:* piano music *Venues:* Darmstadt
Comments: main area of activity: Chopin piano competition, Europäischer Chopin-Klavierwettbewerb 2002; also master courses

KulturTeam der Stadt Detmold
c/o Herr Seeg, Wittekindstr. 7, 32758 **Detmold**
Tel: 5231-977 920 Fax: 5231-977 916
Manager Reinhold Seeg
Events: 80 (all year) *Perfs:* 100 *Arts type:* electronic music, folk music, jazz, new music, music theatre, sacred music, song recitals, multi-media, world music, folk dance, modern dance, modern theatre, puppet, street theatre, visual arts exhibitions *Venues:* Stadthalle up to 900, Studiobühne up to 200, Alte Schule am Wall up to 300 *Comments:* alternative kultur open-air events, 1 summer open air concert series, 1 autumn concert series, International Jazznight, International Bluesnight, Straßentheaterfestival, Palaisgartenfest

Konzertdirektion Richard Berg
Messler Weg 21, 64807 **Dieburg**
Tel: 6071-23134
Fax: 6071-81254
E-Mail: konzertdirektionberg@t-online.de
Geschäftsführer Richard Berg
Events: 40 *Arts type:* classical concerts
Venues: various in the region of Südhessen *Comments:* see also Agents and Producers

Dresden Centre of Contemporary Music
Dresdner Zentrum für zeitgenössiche Musik (DZzM)
Schevenstrasse 17, 01326 **Dresden**
Tel: 351-26462-0
Fax: 351-264 6223
Internet: www.zeitmusik.de
E-Mail: wirrmann@zeitmusik.de
Direktor Prof. Udo Zimmermann; Verwaltungsleiterin Heike Höfer, MD Jürgen Wirrmann; Leiter der PR + Öffentlichkeitsarbeit Marc Ernesti; Archivarin Brigitte Schwäbe; Sekretariat Brigitte Uhlmann; Leiterin des Bereiches Musik Wissenschaft Marion Demuth
Venues: capacity 100 *Comments:* organises concerts, symposiums and conferences on music; organises competition Blaue Brücke and festival Dresdner Tage der Zeitgenössiche Musik; has own venue and library (including archieve open to the public); see also Orchestras, Festivals and Competitions

Projekttheater Dresden e.V.
Louisenstrasse 47, 01099 **Dresden**
Tel: 351-804 3041
Fax: 351-803 3547
E-Mail: projekttheater@add-on.de
Geschäftsführer Detlef-Gerhard Skowronek;
Technische Leitung Maik Blaum;
Organisation Vivian Richter
Arts type: dance, music, installations, theatre
Venues: Projekttheater 80 *Comments:* member of IETM (q.v.); promote events in own venue – Projekttheater – see also Venues

Konzert Theater Kontor René Heinersdorff
Wallstr. 10, 40213 **Düsseldorf**
Tel: 211-130 030 Fax: 211-130 0399
E-Mail: heinersdorff@t-online.de
Inhaber René Heinersdorff jr
Events: 130 concerts in Düsseldorf and Köln
Arts type: chamber music, symphony, jazz, pop, folk music, new music, light orchestral music, inst recitals, world music *Venues:* various big venues in Cologne (i.e. Philharmonie) and Düsseldorf (i.e. Tonhalle)
Policy: subscribtion series for classical music

Tonhalle Düsseldorf
Ehrenhof 1, Tonhalle, 40479 **Düsseldorf**
Tel: 211-899 6111 Fax: 211-892 9143
Internet: www.duesseldorf.de/tonhalle
E-Mail: tonhalle@compuserve.com
Intendantin Vera van Hazebrouck
Arts type: symphonic and chamber music, jazz, folklore, dance, exhibitions, workshops
Venues: Tonhalle, Robert Schumann Saal, H. Hentrich Saal *Comments:* see also Venues

Schloß Elmau
Schloß Elmau, 82493 **Elmau/Obb.**
Tel: 8823-180 Fax: 8823-3719
Internet: www.schloss-elmau.de
E-Mail: sarah.wilson@schloss-elmau.de
Kulturbüro Alexandra Brecht;
Künstlerische Leitung Sarah Wilson
Events: several musical and literature events *Perfs:* 50+ *Arts type:* classical music, jazz, dance, also readings, symposiums (history, politics, philosophy) *Venues:* Großer Konzertsaal, Literatursaal, Kaminsaal *Policy:* promotes national and international culture
Comments: own magazine, library; organises own festival; offers scholarships; the cultural commitment of Schloß Elmau is supported by Stifterverein Elmau gemeinnützige GmbH und e.V.; see also Venues

Choreographic Centre NRW
Zollverein Bullmannaue 20, 45327 **Essen**
Tel: 201-302 523 Fax: 201-302 528
Internet: www.cznrw.de
E-Mail: cznrw@t-online.de
Arts type: dance *Venues:* currently under construction
Comments: further educational training courses for professionals

Franz Siebenlist Konzertdirektion
Aiblinger Str. 9, 83620 **Feldkirchen-Westerham**
Tel: 8063-83700 Fax: 8063-83703
E-Mail: classic_reisen@t-online.de
Inhaber Franz Siebenlist
Events: 5-10 *Arts type:* opera, ensembles worldwide
Comments: see also Agents and Producers

Konzertdirektion Fritz Dietrich GmbH
Eckenheimer Landstrasse 483,
60435 **Frankfurt am Main**
Tel: 69-544 504 Fax: 69-548 4107
Inhaber Fritz Dietrich; Geschäftsführer Susanne Volz
Arts type: chamber orch, choral music, chamber music, early music, inst recitals, light orch music, music theatre, operetta, sacred music, song recitals, symphony music, opera, world music, classical ballet, classical theatre, conductors, soloists, organise theatre tours, choirs *Policy:* act solely as Vermittlungs (negotiating) agency *Comments:* 2nd office:
Büro Gießen/Marburg/Wetzlar, An der Sonnseite 7, 35096 Niederwalgern (Tel: 6426-7742, fax: 6426-6058, Ursula Leeder); see also Agents and Producers

Kultur in der Brotfabrik e.V.
Kulturzentrum, Bachmannstraße 2-4,
60488 **Frankfurt am Main**
Tel: 69-978 4550/13
Fax: 69-9788 0092
Internet: www.brotfabrik.de
1. Vorsitzender Peter Schneckmann;
Technische Leitung Andy Abel
Events: 150 *Arts type:* mainly world music, jazz, dance (Salsa) *Venues:* Großer Saal 200 (seated), 400 (standing) *Policy:* present but also rent

Kultur-und Kongresszentrum Jahrhunderthalle
Pfaffenwiese, 65929 **Frankfurt am Main**
Tel: 69-360 1211 Fax: 69-360 1222
Internet: www.jahrhunderthalle.de
E-Mail: FRichterHensen@jahrhunderthalle.com
Intendant Freimut Richter-Hansen
Events: 47 *Arts type:* symphony, recitals, ballet, opera, organ recitals, musical, and operetta *Venues:* capacity 2021 *Comments:* see also Venues

Pro Arte Frankfurter Konzertdirektion GmbH & CoKg
Staufenstr. 4, 60323 **Frankfurt am Main**
Tel: 69-971 2400
Fax: 69-9712 4040
E-Mail: fed-proarte@t-online.de
Geschäftsführer Gerd Reul
Events: 30 *Arts type:* chamber music, orchestra and soloist *Venues:* Alte Oper Frankfurt 2448 *Comments:* concerts in Frankfurt; see also Agents and Producers

Asia Network
c/o Constanze Schliebs,
Bachmannstr. 2-4, 60488 **Frankfurt/Main**
Tel: 69-9788 4152 Fax: 69-9788 84154
Internet: www.asianetwork.de
E-Mail: cschliebs@asianetwork.de
Arts type: modern jazz, world music

AAK Freiburg – Arbeitskreis Alternative Kultur
Im E-Werk, Eschholzstr. 77, 79106 **Freiburg**
Tel: 761-207 570 Fax: 761-207 5748
Geschäftsführende Leitung Atai Keller,
Wolfgang Herbert
Events: 130-150 *Arts type:* all types of performing arts
Venues: E-Werk 300-1000 *Comments:* organise Internationales Freiburger Theaterfestival (q.v.) and Festival Neuer Tanz (q.v.)

Albert-Konzerte
Postfach 1349, 79013 **Freiburg**
Tel: 761-289 442 Fax: 761-289 742
Künstlerische Leitung Dirk Nabering
Events: 20 *Arts type:* chamber music, symphony concerts, piano evenings *Venues:* Konzerthaus 1700, Hochschule f. Musik 700

Raddatz Concerts
Burgunderstrasse 4, 79104 **Freiburg**
Tel: 761-23380
Fax: 761-554 862
Inhaber Theresa Raddatz
Arts type: instrumentalists, ensembles and orchestras
Comments: organise competitions including Internationaler Violinwettbewerb Ludwig Spohr, the Festival Wolfgang Marschner Hinterzarten; International Max Reger competition for chamber music; see also Agents & Producers; annual masterclasses in Sondershausen/ Weimer in cooperation with the Loh-Orchestra Sondershausen; emphasis on promotion of young artists; see also Competitions

Forum Artium
Am Kasinopark 1-3, 49124 **Georgsmarienhütte**
Tel: 5401-35077
Fax: 5401-34223
Geschäftsführer Herbert Vieth
Perfs: 25-30 *Arts type:* classical music *Venues:* various venues around Osnabrück (always historical buildings)
Comments: see also Agents and Producers

Göttinger Händel-Gesellschaft e.V.
Hainholzweg 3/5, 37085 **Göttingen**
Tel: 551-56700 Fax: 551-45395
Internet: www.haendel.org
E-Mail: info@haendel.org
Leitung der Geschäftsstelle Benedikt Poensgen
Events: 15 (during the festival) *Perfs:* 20 *Arts type:* chamber orch, chamber music, early music, music theatre, sacred music, song recitals, symphony music, scenic opera, oratories and concerts by Händel and his contemporaries *Venues:* various in Göttingen up to 18000 *Policy:* festival organisation *Comments:* Göttinger Händelfestspiele are the only ones in the world who present historic productions of Handel's operas; see also Festivals

Konzertdirektion Weichert
Langegeismarstrasse 79, 37073 **Göttingen**
Tel: 551-46029 Fax: 551-46089
contact Frau Perl
Arts type: classical music *Venues:* Stadthalle Göttingen 1158

Karsten Jahnke Konzertdirektion GmbH
Hallerstrasse 72, 20146 **Hamburg**
Tel: 40-414 7880 Fax: 40-443 597
Internet: www.karsten-jahnke.de
E-Mail: karsten-jahnke@t-online.de
managing directors Karsten Jahnke, Hauke Tedsen
Arts type: jazz, folk music, music theatre, world music, classical ballet, folk dance, modern dance, puppets
Venues: Kongreßzentrum 3000 & 1500, Musikhalle 1600, Sporthalle 6000, Stadtpark (open air) 4000
Comments: see also Agents and Producers

Konzertdirektion Hans Werner Funke
Brahmsallee 6, 20144 **Hamburg**
Tel: 40-4501 1010 Fax: 40-4501 1020
E-Mail: info@funkemedia.de
Geschäftsführers Hans-Werner Funke, Pascal Funke
Arts type: all types of concerts (from classical to rock)
Venues: various venues in Hamburg *Comments:* see also Agents and Producers

Konzertdirektion Hans Ulrich Schmid
Postfach 1667, 30016 **Hannover**
Tel: 511-366 0760/27 Fax: 511-366 0734
Internet: www.kdschmid.de
E-Mail: RT@kdschmid.de
managing directors Cornelia Schmid, Harold Clarkson; chairperson Hans Ulrich Schmid
Arts type: classical music *Comments:* visiting address: Schmiedestrasse 8, 30159 Hannover; see also Agents and Producers

Künstlersekretariat Stefan Trhal
Waldstr. 36, 30163 **Hannover**
Tel: 511-669 277 Fax: 511-669 200
Inhaber Stefan Trhal
Events: 6-8 *Arts type:* solo instrumentalists, orchestras
Venues: Congress Union Celle 1000 *Comments:* organise orchestra tours; see also Agents and Producers

Show Tops
Osterstrasse 26, 30159 **Hannover**
Tel: 511-301 856-0 Fax: 511-3018 5630
Inhaber Klaus Ritgen
Events: 60 *Arts type:* ballet, classical music, rock, pop, techno, events *Venues:* all major venues within a 100km radius of Hannover, including: the Music hall, Niedersachsenstadion Sportpark Hannover/Garbsen 25000, Insel im Salzgittersee, Eilenrudehalle, Stadionsporthalle *Comments:* local concert season; see also Agents and Producers

Konzertdirektion Werner Laube
Hauffstrasse 17, 76199 **Karlsruhe**
Tel: 721-883 498 Fax: 721-885 527
Inhaber Werner Laube
Events: 8 *Arts type:* classic concerts *Venues:* Brahmssaal in der Stadthalle Karlsruhe 1746, Konzerthaus 1000

Bach-Verein Köln e.V.
Bahnstraße 39, 50858 **Köln**
Tel: 2234-942 723 Fax: 2234-942 7235
E-Mail: riedel@netcologne.de
Vorsitzender Uwe Riedel; Künstlerische Leitung des Chores Winfried Toll; Schriftführer Walter Bässler
Arts type: mainly orchestral choral music, J. S. Bach to contemporary *Venues:* Kölner Philharmonie 2200, Basilika St. Maria im Kapitol 1000

Köln Musik GmbH
Bischofsgartenstrasse 1, 50667 **Köln**
Tel: 221-20408-0 Fax: 221-2040 8222
Internet: www.koelnmusik.de
E-Mail: koelnmusik@netcologne.de
Intendant der Kölner Philharmonie u. Geschäftsführer d. Köln Musik GmbH Dr. Albin Hänseroth;
Konzertplanung Dr. Annette Wolde;
Arts type: classical music, symphony, chamber orch, choral music, chamber music, early music, dance, jazz, folk and pop, inst recitals, new music, light orch music, operetta, sacred music, song recitals, symphony music, modern ballet, modern dance *Venues:* Kölner Philharmonie 2171 *Comments:* alternative internet: www.koelner-philharmonie.de or koelnticket.de

Kontrapunkt-Konzerte
Minoritenstrasse 7, 50667 **Köln**
Tel: 221-257 8468 Fax: 221-257 8468
E-Mail: Kontrapunkt@t-online.de
Inhaber Martin Blankenburg
Events: 12 *Arts type:* classical music, chamber orchestra, choral music, symphony music *Venues:* Kölner Philharmonie 2096 *Comments:* concentrate on promotion of the former East German state orchestras; contact address Martin Blankenburg: Lohnskotter Weg 18, 51069 Köln Tel/Fax: 221-601 798

La Gala – Internationale Kulturprojekte
PF 300808, 50778 **Köln**
Tel: 221-550 4315
Fax: 221-955 3508
Internet: www.lagala.de
E-Mail: lagalaint@aol.com
Manager Annette Meisl
Events: 100 *Arts type:* street theatre & music groups from Africa, Italy, Spain, Latin America and Turkey, world music, ballet and dance *Comments:* see also Agents and Producers

SK Stiftung Kultur der Stadtsparkasse Köln
Im Mediapark 7, 50670 **Köln**
Tel: 221-226 2433
Fax: 221-226 3410
Internet: www.sk-kultur.de
Executive Director Hans-Georg Bögner;
Director Photographic Collection Dr. Susanne Lange;
Director Deutsches Tanzarchiv Frank-Manuel Peter
Events: 100 *Perfs:* 52 *Arts types:* street theatre, visual arts exhibitions, literature *Venues:* 10 open air, 3 exhibition rooms, Videotheque

Tanz Performance Köln
Melchoirstr. 3, 50670 **Köln**
Tel: 221-722 133
Fax: 221-739 2030
E-Mail: tpkoeln@pironet.de
Directors Madeline Ritter, Heike Lehmke
Arts type: contemporary dance, new media, film and video, organises festivals and events (e.g. Pictures of (e)motion), international networks for young choreographers: Dance Roads *Venues:* Alte Feuerwache Köln, Kunst-und Ausstellunghalle der Bundesrepublik Deutschland, Bonn *Comments:* collaboration with several organisations in Germany, Europe and abroad

Westdeutsche Konzertdirektion Köln
Obenmarspforten 7-11, 50667 **Köln**
Tel: 221-258 1017
Fax: 221-257 8949
E-Mail: WDKK@netcologne.de
Inhaber Witiko Adler
Events: 30 *Arts type:* classical music
Venues: Philharmonie 2196 *Comments:* Meisterkonzerte in der Kölner Philharmonie

Kronberg Academy (International Kammermusik-Akademie Kronberg)
Königsteiner Strasse 5,
61476 **Kronberg**
Tel: 6173-950 085
Fax: 6173-950 086
Internet: members.aol.com/ikacello
E-Mail: IKACello@aol.com
Vorsitzender Edmund Knapp;
Künstlerischer Leiter Raimund Trenkler
Events: 4 *Arts type:* chamber music, cello
Venues: Stadthalle Kronberg 440 and other venues (e.g. churches) in Kronberg *Comments:* see also Festivals and Competitions

Bach-Archiv Leipzig
Thomaskirchhof 16, 04109 **Leipzig**
Tel: 341-96441-0
Fax: 341-964 4196
Internet: www.uni-leipzig.de/bach/
E-Mail: jsbach@rzaix530.rz.uni-leipzig.de
Direktor Prof. Dr. Hans-Joachim Schulze;
Geschäftsführer Bernhard Heß; Leiterin Veranstaltungen Sabine Martin (341-96441-65);
Leiterin Museum Cornelia Krumbiegel (341-96441-35)
Arts type: chamber orch., choral music, chamber music, Early music, instr. recitals, new music, music theatre, sacred music, jazz, song recitals, symphony music, opera, classical ballet, modern ballet *Venues:* Sommersaal 60, Thomaskirche 1500, Nikolaikirche 1500, Gewandhaus 1900, Altes Rathaus 200
Policy: not only promote events, also run museum, research institute and International Johann-Sebastian-Bach-Competition (q.v.)
Comments: Bach-Fest Leipzig 2000, Int. Wiss Konferenz, Int. Johann Sebastian Bach Wettbewerb

Neue Bachgesellschaft e.V. (NBG)
Postfach 100727, 04007 **Leipzig**
Tel: 341-960 1463
Fax: 341-960 1463
Vorsitzender Prof. Dr. habil. Martin Petzoldt
Events: organisers of the annual Bachfest
Comments: visiting address: Geschäftsstelle Leipzig, Thomaskirchhof 16, 04109 Leipzig; see also Festivals

Artists International
Postfach 310154, 51328 **Leverkusen**
Tel: 2171-42663 Fax: 2171-43981
managing director Linda Abberton
Events: 75 *Arts type:* classical music *Comments:* international music management promotes thematic festivals, touring and project management, recording and media enterprises + sponsorship; visiting address: Humboldtstraße 17, 51379 Leverkusen; see also Agents & Producers and Orchestras (Westdeutsche Sinfonia)

Kulturabteilung der Bayer AG
Gebäude 4815, 51368 **Leverkusen**
Tel: 214-307 1410 Fax: 214-306 2973
E-Mail: Jutta.Drews.JD1@bayer-ag.de
Leitung Nikolas Kerkenrath; Theater/Dramaturgie Roland Lillie; Projekte/Jazz Reiner Ernst Ohle; Kunst Elisabeth Bott; Musik Carolin Sturm; Ballett/Tanz Wanda Puvogel; Verwaltung Jutta Drews
Events: 86 *Perfs:* 117 *Arts type:* chamber music, piano recitals, inst. recitals, jazz, new music, light orch music, music theatre, symphony music, classical ballet, modern ballet, modern dance, classical theatre, modern theatre, puppet, visual arts exhibitions, theatre for children *Venues:* Erholungshaus 780, Forum 980

Stadt Leverkusen Kulturamt
Postfach 101140, 51311 **Leverkusen**
Tel: 214-406 4118
Fax: 214-406 4103
Internet: www.leverkusen.de
E-Mail: 01.leverkusen@tele.net
kulturfachliche Leitung Dr. Erika Wegner;
Verwaltungsleitung Gudrun Deuser;
Veranstaltungen und Marketing Arthur Horvath
Perfs: 120 *Arts type:* classic rock and pop, theatre, opera, operetta, cabaret, children's theatre, kleinkunst, drama, musical, dance etc. *Venues:* Forum Leverkusen (5 spaces), Festhalle Opladen 630
Comments: see also Venues (Forum Leverkusen)

Salten Gastspiele
Beuthener Str. 5, 67117 **Limburgerhof**
Tel: 6236-67811
Fax: 6236-8731
Inhaberin Lilo Salten
Events: 350 *Arts type:* theatre *Venues:* Stadttheater Rüsselsheim 850, and other venues *Comments:* alternative address: Postfach 90, 67114 Limburgerhof; see also Agents & Producers

Kreis Coesfeld
Burg Vischering, 59348 **Lüdinghausen**
Tel: 2591-79900
Fax: 2591-799 029
E-Mail: kreis-coesfeld@kreis-coesfeld.de
contact & music Frau Dr. Sarrazin
Arts type: chamber orch, early music, folk music, jazz
Venues: Schloß Nordkirchen in Nordkirchen 300, Burg Vischering, Lüdinghausen 100, Kolvenburg, Billerbeck 80

Kulturamt Ludwigsburg
PF 249, 71602 **Ludwigsburg**
Tel: 7141-910 2533 Fax: 7141-910 2539
Internet: stadt.ludwigsburg.de
E-Mail: kultur@stadt.ludwigsburg.de
contact Christoph Peichl
Events: 30 *Arts type:* dance, ballet, opera, chamber orchestra, theatre, opera, classical ballet, folk dance, modern ballet, modern dance, classical theatre, modern theatre *Venues:* Forum am Schloßpark 1200

BASF AG Ludwigshafen
67056 **Ludwigshafen**
Tel: 621-604 8244 Fax: 621-602 0317
Internet: www.basf.de
E-Mail: BASF.Konzerte@BASF-AG.de
Kulturelle Veranstaltungen Klaus Philipp Seif
Events: 67 between September and May *Arts type:* symphony concerts, chamber music, shows, electronic music, folk music, jazz, new music, operetta, sacred music, classical ballet, modern dance, pop and rock
Venues: Festsaal 1370, Kammermusiksaal 280
Comments: see also Venues

Fortbildungszentrum für Neue Musik Lüneburg
c/o Prof. H. W. Erdmann,
An der Münze 7, 21335 **Lüneburg**
Tel: 4131-309 390 Fax: 4131-309 390
E-Mail: erdmann@uni-lueneburg.de
Arts Types: contemporary music *Comments:* organises lectures and workshops on contemporary music; two international weeks in May; Week of Studies of Contemporary Music in October,
Festival Meeting with Composers

Hanseatische Konzertdirektion GmbH
In der süßen Heide 4, 21335 **Lüneburg**
Tel: 4131-46321 Fax: 4131-46366
Geschäftsleitung Klaus Wollny, Anke Hennig;
Prokuristin Anke Henning
Arts type: classical music – soloists, orchestras, open-air concerts in Kiel, Lübeck, Hamburg, Hannover, Bremen
Venues: Musikhalle Hamburg 2000 and other venues
Comments: see also Agents and Producers

BB Promotion GmbH – The Art of Entertainment
L7, 7a, 68161 **Mannheim**
Tel: 621-107 920
Fax: 621-13314
Internet: www.bb-promotion.com
E-Mail: zentrale@bb-promotion.com
producer Michael Brenner;
general mamagers Matthias Mantel, Ralf Kokemüller
Events: 1000-2000 *Arts type:* contemporary dance, gospel singers, musicals, shows
Comments: amongst others represent in Europe: Hubbard Street Dance, Alvin Ailey American Dance Theatre, The Harlem Gospel Singers (worldwide); see also Agents and Producers

Hoffmann Music & Events
N3, 10, 68161 **Mannheim**
Tel: 621-42620
Fax: 621-426 2222
E-Mail: hoffmannmusic@t-online.de
Geschäftsführer Desi Hoffmann
Events: 50 *Arts type:* classical music
Comments: represents Montserrat Caballé

Evangelisches Seminar
Klosterhof 12-17, 75433 **Maulbronn**
Tel: 7043-7734
Fax: 7043-5702
Internet: www.maulbronn.de/klosterkonzerte
E-Mail: klosterkon@aol.com
Künstlerischer Leiter KMD & StD Jürgen Budday
Events: 25 *Arts type:* orchestral and chamber concerts, oratoria, early music, sacred music, Liederabende
Venues: Klosterkirche 900, Laienrefektorium 550, Kreuzganggarten 800

Neue Akademie Braunschweig e.V.
c/o Prof Dr. Dieter Salbert,
Reiherweg 3, 38527 **Meine**
Tel: 5304-3578
Fax: 5304-3578
Internet: www.kulturserver.de/home/nab
E-Mail: nab@kulturserver.de
1.Vorsitzender Prof.Dr. Dieter Salbert;
2.Vorsitzender Hans-Peter Schier;
Schatzmeister Alrun Salbert-Zahoransky
Events: synthesizer music festival (media night)
Perfs: 1-3 concerts *Arts type:* electronic music, computer music, new music in combinations with traditional instruments, multi-media, visual arts, modern dance, mime *Venues:* LOT Theater Braunschweig, Braunschweigisches Landesmuseum/Burgplatz
Comments: see also Competitions, Braunschweigische Musikgesellschaft e.V. (q.v.)

Jo Schmidt Theaterorganisation
Am Buchwald 6, 64367 **Mühltal**
Tel: 6154-630 751
Fax: 6154-630 753
E-Mail: jo.schmidt1212@t-online.de
contact Jo Schmidt
Events: 20 *Perfs:* 30 *Arts type:* mime, modern theatre, puppet, street theatre, modern dance, classical theatre, world music, modern ballet
enues: Wacker Fabrik/Mühltal 250 & 99, Stadt Mainz (for street theatre)

Art-Concerts GmbH
Widenmayerstr 41, 80538 **München**
Tel: 89-290 749-0
Fax: 89-2907 4999
E-Mail: mail@art-concerts.de
Geschäftsführer Franz Abraham;
Leiterin der Presseabteilung Jasmine Harde;
Technische Leitung Andy Kuhn
Events: 10 *Arts type:* pop, rock, avantgarde, classical, electronic music, opera, world music, jazz
Comments: Art-Concerts works in all branches of music; apart from organising and promoting concerts, tours and festivals it also produces own projects; see also Agents and Producers

Bayerische Konzertdirektion Paul Kreye
Marienplatz 1, 80331 **München**
Tel: 89-227 488
Fax: 89-225 311
E-Mail: B.Pkreye@t-online.de
Inhaber Paul Kreye
Perfs: 60-80 *Arts type:* chamber orch, choral music, chamber music, early music, sacred music, song recitals, symphony music *Venues:* Philharmonie, Herkulessaal; cloisters, castles, churches
Comments: see also Agents and Producers

Concerto C W Winderstein GmbH
Postfach 440446,
Leopoldstraße 25, 80753 **München**
Tel: 89-383846-0
Fax: 89-337 938
Internet: www.winderstein.de
E-Mail: artists@winderstein.de
Geschäftsführer Dr Hans-Dieter Göhre
Perfs: 24 *Arts type:* orchestra, piano
Venues: Philharmonie, Herkulessaal
Comments: see also Agents & Producers

ELYSIUM – Between Two Continents
Bonner Platz 1/IV, 80803 **München**
Tel: 89-3072 9519 Fax: 89-3077 9138
artistic director Gregorij H. von Lëitis;
managing director Michael Lahr;
music director Hartmut Kretzschmann
Arts type: all types *Venues:* Goethe-Institute, New York; Kloster Bernried (summer academy for music theatre) *Policy:* foster cultural exchange between Europe and America through theatre plays, operas, concerts and exhibitions; to build bridges between different nations, ethnic and religious groups with the means of art in order to heal historic rifts and foster a better understanding of each other *Comments:* also present the annual Erwin Piscator Award; USA address: PO Box 1553, New York, NY 10011-1553,
Tel: +1 212-242 0134, Fax: +1 212-242 4939

Joint Adventures
Emil-Geis-Str. 21, 81379 **München**
Tel: 89-724 2515 Fax: 89-723 7782
Internet: www.tanznetz.de
E-Mail: jointadventures@t-online.de
Direktor Walter Heun; Administration Ingrid Kalka;
Press Stephanie Thiersch, Sarah Bergh
Arts type: contemporary dance *Venues:* various venues up to 1200 *Policy:* internationally active production company which applies itself above all to cultivating structures which promote contemporary dance and movement theatre *Comments:* promoting Tanzwerkstatt Europa and co-produces other dance events; artistic advice to several festivals; organises Tanzplattform Deutschland

Konzertdirektion Wolf Siegel
Gotthelfstraße 49, 81677 **München**
Tel: 89-9107 5941 Fax: 89-9107 5941
concert manager Wolf Siegel
Events: 10 *Arts type:* piano recitals, guitar recitals between Oct and May, gospel concerts *Venues:* Herkulessaal München 1270, Musichochschule 600
Comments: in '99/2000 season mainly guitar recitals

Konzertveranstaltungen Andreas Schessl GmbH & Co KG
Postfach 810952, 81909 **München**
Tel: 89-936 093 Fax: 89-930 6494
E-Mail: schessl.konzerte@t-online.de
managing director Andreas Schessl;
ticket management Carola Pils;
event manager Andrea F. Zycheinski-Schessl
Events: 80-90 *Arts type:* chamber music, chamber orchestra, choral music, folk music, inst recitals, song recitals, symphony music, world music, gospel *Venues:* various in München (including: Residenz, Philharmonie, Prinzregententheater, St Lukas Kirche)
Comments: also manages Vocalissimo

MamaConcerts & Rau GmbH
Rosenheimer Str. 145e, 81671 **München**
Tel: 89-992 922-0 Fax: 89-9929 2222
Internet: www.mamaconcerts.de
E-Mail: mcr@websale.de
Geschäftsführer Marcel Avram, Mario M. Mendrzycki
Arts type: mainly rock, pop, jazz, singer-songwriter
Policy: promoter of international pop-rock, dance & classical concerts *Comments:*
see also Agents & Producers

Münchener Bach Konzerte e.V., Münchener Mozart Konzerte eV
Brienner Str. 55, 80333 **München**
Tel: 89-545 8950/55 (box office) Fax: 89-5458 9599
Internet: www.muenchen-tourist.de/german/konzerte/service.htm
E-Mail: MBK@real-net.de
kaufmännischer Geschäftsführer Helmut Pauli; künstlerischer Geschäftsführer Dr Irmgard Schmid;
Öffentlichkeitsarbeit und Marketing Angelika Vitzthum
Events: 50 *Perfs:* 50 *Arts type:* chamber orch, choral music, chamber music, early music, inst recitals, jazz, new music, song recitals, symphony music *Venues:* Philharmonie im Gasteig 2400; Herkulessaal der Residenz 1260; Prinzregententheater 1000 *Comments:* alternative E-mail: MMK@real-net.de; see also Agents & Producers (hp-Musik Management)

Münchner Konzertdirektion Hörtnagel GmbH
Neufahrner Straße 23, 81679 **München**
Tel: 89-982 928-0 Fax: 89-9829 2833
E-Mail: konzert@hoertnagel.de
Geschäftsführer Georg Hörtnagel
Events: 100 *Venues:* Philharmonie am Gasteig 2400, Herkulessaal in der Residenz 1260, Prinzregententheater 1000 *Comments:* organise classical music tours in Europe;
see also Agents and Producers

Siemens AG BDL Kulturprogramm
80312 **München**
Tel: 89-6363 3594 Fax: 89-6363 3615
E-Mail: karolin.timm@mchw.siemens.de
Leitung Michael Roßnagl
Arts type: all performing and visual arts, art of media, dance music *Comments:* visting address: Wittelsbacher Plaz 2, 80333 München

Theaterbühne Kreativ-haus eV
Diepenbrockstr. 28, 48145 **Münster**
Tel: 251-37054/36997 Fax: 251-36997
Internet: www.kreativ-haus.de
E-Mail: theater@kreativ-haus.de
contact Norbert Woestmeyer
Events: 150 *Arts type:* contemporary dance, theatre, music *Venues:* own theater 130

Konzertagentur Wachsmann & Beniashvili
Beethovenweg 1, 73655 **Plünderhausen**
Tel: 7181-998 6014/ 171-722 0808 (mobile)
Fax: 7181-998 6060
E-Mail: shalvabeniashvili@t-online.de
contact Fr. Wachsmann, Hr. Beniashvili
Arts type: classical music, ballet; event and project management *Comments:* see also Agents & Producers

Concertino GmbH
Berliner Strasse 40, 14467 **Potsdam**
Tel: 331-270 9888 Fax: 331-270 9891
Geschäftsführerin Jutta Jochimsen
Events: 20 *Arts type:* chamber music, choral
Venues: Berliner Philharmonie 2200, Konzerthaus, Kloster Zinna 600, and several churches

Odeon Concertagentur Reinhard Söll
Schenkendorfstr. 9, 93049 **Regensburg**
Tel: 941-296 000 Fax: 941-296 0019
Internet: members.aol.com/odeonrgbg/homepage.htm
E-Mail: odenrgbg@aol.com
Inhaber Reinhard Söll; Mitarbeiterin Kerstin Katz
Events: 50 *Arts type:* classical concerts – chamber orchestra, choral music, chamber music, inst recitals, music theatre, sacred music, song recitals, symphony music, opera *Venues:* University Regensburg: Auditorium Maximum 1500, open air concerts
Comments: see also Agents and Producers

Perspective GmbH
Intermarionett-Theater,
Passagestraße 2-4, 66111 **Saarbrücken**
Tel: 681-936 490 Fax: 681-32921
Internet: saarbruecken.de/sbnet/perspect.htm
E-Mail: ccaimacan@aol.com
Künstlerischer Leiter Christian Caimacan
Perfs: approx. 50 *Arts type:* puppetry
Venues: new venue for Intermarionett-Theater in the Ratskeller *Policy:* Figurentheater

Internationale Bachakademie Stuttgart
Johann-Sebastian-Bach-Platz, 70178 **Stuttgart**
Tel: 711-619 21-0 Fax: 711-619 2123
Internet: www.bachakademie.de
E-Mail: office@bachakademie.de
Künstlerische Leitung KMD Prof. D. Dr. h.c. Helmuth Rilling; Geschäftsführung Andreas Keller; Planung und Realisation Dr. Christian Eisert; PR Rita Püpcke
Events: two weeks in Aug/Sept *Perfs:* ca. 60 (Aug/Sept)
Arts type: choral music, chamber orchestra, chamber music, sacred music, new music, courses, seminars, lectures etc *Venues:* Kultur und Kongreßzentrum Liederhalle, churches in Stuttgart *Comments:* international guests; Europäisches Musikfest Stuttgart, 27 Aug-10 Sept 2000, theme: PASSION 2000

Internationale Hugo-Wolf-Akademie
Jägerstraße 40, 70174 **Stuttgart**
Tel: 711-221 177 Fax: 711-227 9919
Internet: www.hugo-wolf-akademie.de
E-Mail: hugowolf@t-online.de
Vorsitzender Georg Büchner; Künstlerischer Leiter Prof. Hartmut Höll; Geschäftführerin Brigitte Kurz
Arts type: chamber music, instrumental recitals, song recitals, lectures, readings
Venues: mainly Stuttgarter Liederhalle

Südwestdeutsche Konzertdirektion Stuttgart Erwin Russ GmbH
Postfach 104262, 70037 **Stuttgart**
Tel: 711-163 5311 Fax: 711-163 5330
Internet: www.sksruss.de
E-Mail: info@sksruss.de
Inhaber Michael Russ
Events: 150 *Arts type:* all arts types from classical to pop
Venues: Hanns-Martin-Schleyer-Halle, Kultur- und Kongreßzentrum Liederhalle
Comments: regional promoter; visiting address-Charlottenplatz 17, 70173 Stuttgart

Euro-Studio, Konzertdirektion Landgraf GmbH & Co KG
Lärchenweg 1, 79822 **Titisee-Neustadt**
Tel: 7651-2070
Fax: 7651-20799
Internet: www.landgraf.de
E-Mail: pfeifer@landgraf.de
Leitung Joachim u. Birgit Landgraf; Dramaturgie Birgit Landgraf; Verwaltungsleiter Rudi Schuderer;
Disposition Christian Kreppel
Perfs: 1500 *Arts type:* drama, opera, operetta, musical, ballet, dance, pantomime, symphony music, chamber orch, choral music *Venues:* Theater im Rathaus (Essen), Parktheater (Augsburg) *Comments:* organise tours throughout Europe; emphasis on own theatre productions; see also Agents

WiV Promotion
Frauenstr. 47, 89073 **Ulm**
Tel: 731-967 64-0 Fax: 731-967 6420
Internet: wiventertainment.com
E-Mail: wivulm@aol.com
director Winfried Völklein;
promotion Marina Spitzenberg
Events: Jan-Dec 100 *Perfs:* 200 *Arts type:* jazz, classical, choral and world music, theatre, musicals, Ice shows, gospel, light orch music, pop/rock & entertainment, modern theatre *Venues:* various from 500-10000
Policy: agency, promoter *Comments:* tours, concerts, agency; see also Agents

Württemberg-Bayerische Konzertdirektion
Münsterplatz 51, 89073 **Ulm**
Tel: 731-967 070 Fax: 731-967 0744
Inhaber Michael Russ;
Geschäftsführerin Anuschka Russ
Events: 30-60 *Arts type:* all arts types (from classical to pop) *Venues:* various in Ulm

Konzertdirektion Hans G Jaax
Falkenring 48, 49134 **Wallenhorst**
Tel: 5407-7386 Fax: 5407-7322
Inhaber Hans G. Jaax
Arts types: mainly chamber music *Venues:* various in the Wallenhorst region *Comments:* see also Agents

Jeunesses Musicales Deutschland
Marktplatz 12, 97990 **Weikersheim**
Tel: 7934-280 Fax: 7934-8526
Internet: www.JeunessesMusicales.de
E-Mail: weikersheim@JeunessesMusicales.de
Präsident Prof. Martin Christoph Redel;
Generalsekretär Thomas Rietschel
Perfs: 70 *Arts type:* chamber orch, choral music, chamber music, early music, electronic music, jazz, new music, music theatre, operetta, symphony music
Venues: Gewehrhaus 200, Gartenhaus 150, Schloßhof 1500, Rittersaal 600
Policy: promotion of young musicians

Konzertdirektion Kempf
Schöne Aussicht 34, 65193 **Wiesbaden**
Tel: 611-525 091/2 Fax: 611-525 093
E-Mail: konzert-kempf@t-online.de
Inhaber Wilfried Strohmeier
Events: 50 *Arts type:* chamber music, orchestra concerts, tours, singer *Comments:* organise 'Meister' concert tours in Aachen, Wiesbaden and Würzburg; see also Agents and Producers

Z-Concerts & Music GmbH
Postfach 6220, 65052 **Wiesbaden**
Tel: 611-520 037 Fax: 611-520 039
Geschäftsführer Rainer Zosel
Events: 80-100 *Arts type:* rock to classical music
Comments: national promoter

Kulturbüro der Stadt Worms
Abtlg. Städt. Spiel-und Festhaus,
Bahnhofstr. 4,1/10, 67547 **Worms**
Tel: 6241-88385 Fax: 6241-853 4070
Internet: www.worms.de
Leiter Amtsrat Ulrich Mieland;
Abteilungsleiter Oliver Mang, Annemarie Neu
Perfs: 70 (season Oct-June) *Arts type:* jazz, music theatre, operetta, symphony music, classical ballet, classical theatre, modern theatre, recitals, puppet, modern ballet, opera *Venues:* Städt. Spiel – und Festhaus Worms 844 *Policy:* theatre – produce and rent
Comments: jazz festival in July,
open air concerts during summertime

Konzertgesellschaft Wuppertal GmbH
Robertstr. 3, 42107 **Wuppertal**
Tel: 202-245 850 Fax: 202-245 8540
E-Mail: konzertgesellschaft@wtal.de
contact Meike Bolte
Events: 15 *Perfs:* 15 *Arts type:* chamber music, singing
Venues: Stadthalle Wuppertal (Grosser Saal 1400, Kammermusiksaal 418), Immanuelskirche 650
Policy: classical music

Argo Konzerte GmbH
Schweinfurterstr. 44, 97076 **Würzburg**
Tel: 931-23021 Fax: 931-26935
E-Mail: kw@argo.konzerte.de
Inhaber Peter Pracht
Events: 220 a year *Arts type:* wide range of music types, mostly mainstream music *Comments:* Argo Konzerte GmbH (Filiale) Bayernstrasse 100, 90471 Nürnberg,
Tel: 911-471 9301, Fax: 911 471-9302;
see also Agents & Producers

Konzertagentur Fahrenholtz
Winterleitenweg 17 B, 97082 **Würzburg**
Tel: 931-784 7230
Fax: 931-784 7230
Direktor Wolfgang Fahrenholtz
Arts type: classical and modern music *Comments:* an agency that negotiates between instrumentalists, chamber music ensembles and promoters; see also Agents and Producers

GREECE (+30)

Cultural Organization of the Municipality of Athens, The
50, Akademias ave, 10679 **Athens**
Tel: 1-364 2067/360 7867
Fax: 1-360 2102
Internet: www.athens-culture.ids.gr
manager, vice-president Elli Evagelidou
Arts type: performing arts (chamber & symphonic music, opera, traditional music, jazz, ethnic music, theatre, puppetry, poetry etc) and fine arts
Comments: the Cultural Centre is the main body producing and promoting the arts for the cultural activities of the City of Athens and the greater regions of Athens; it organises amongst others festivals, workshops, competitions, symposia, publications

Maria Callas Foundation
International Cultural Centre Athenaeum,
3, Adrianou St., 10555 **Athens**
Tel: 1-321 1949/55/87
Fax: 1-321 1196
Internet: www.athenaeum.ids.gr
E-Mail: athenm@ibm.net
secretary general Anna Koukouraki;
president Louli Psychouli
Events: 40-80 *Arts type:* chamber orchestra, choral music, chamber music, early music, inst. recitals, jazz, song recitals, symphony music, opera, oratorio-lied
Venues: International Cultural Centre Athenaeum (2 concert halls, 1 stage) *Comments:* administration of the Maria Callas Grand Prix and the Alexandra Trianti Grand Prix; member of the World Federation of International Music Competitions;
see also Competitions

Greek Section of Jeunesses Musicales
Stratigou Kallari 52, 15452 **Athens-Psychico**
Tel: 1-671 2332
Fax: 1-231 4888
president Domini Sarri;
vice-president Marilena Kerameus
Arts type: symphonic & chamber, classical music concerts, recitals, ballet
Venues: college of Athens Theatre

Center for the Art of Dance
78, M Botsari Str & Matinias str,
54644 **Thessaloniki**
Tel: 31-822 200
Fax: 31-862 827
general manager Papadopoulos Athanasios;
artistic director Dimitra Koronaiou
Events: 1 *Arts type:* dance *Venues:* Kipos Theatre
Comments: dance school for children 4-12 years and 12-18 years old; professional preparation classes; also traditional & jazz dance

HUNGARY (+36)

Mandel Productions Ltd
Mandel Produkciós Kft
Fodros utca 7/b, 2040 **Budaörs**
Tel: 23-417 007
Fax: 23-417 007
Internet: www.mandel.hu
E-Mail: mandel@mail.datanet.hu
director Róbert Mandel
Arts type: concerts and major events promoter

Bacchus Arts
Vörösmarty ter 1, Room 623, 1051 **Budapest**
Tel: 1-317 7031
Fax: 1-318 7223
director Istvan Nyikos
Comments: promoter of annual International Wine and Arts Festival in Budapest and wine-growing areas in Hungary

Budapest Convention Centre
Budapesti Kongresszusi Központ
PO Box 233, 1444 **Budapest**
Tel: 1-466 6756
Fax: 1-385 2127
Internet:
www.hungary.com/pannonia/conventioncentre
E-Mail: conventioncentre@pannoniahotels.hu
director Achim Marowsky;
director of art events Mate Lukacsi
Events: 30 throughout the year *Arts type:* symphony orchestra, chamber music, recitals *Venues:* own venue (q.v.) *Comments:* visiting address: Jagelló út 1-3, 1123 Budapest

Budapest Open Air Theatres
Szabad Tér Színház
POB 95, 1525 **Budapest**
Tel: 1-355 0175 Fax: 1-356 0998
director Ivan Gal; artistic director Gábor Koltay
Events: 60-65 July-Aug *Arts type:* opera, dance, music
Venues: Margaret Island Open Air Theatre 3000, Budai Park Theatre 2300, Dominican Courtyard at Hilton Hotel 370 *Comments:* visiting address: Varosmajor park 1, 1122 Budapest

Clemens Concerts Ltd
Clemens Koncertiroda Kft
Attila 61, 1014 **Budapest**
Tel: 1-212 2045 Fax: 1-212 2045/375 8162
E-Mail: ClemensConcerts@compuserve.com
director Pal Kelemen
Comments: see also Promoters

Concert Masters International Ltd CMI
Koncertszervezö és Kulturalis Szolgáltató Kft
Szabó József ut. 14/c, 1145 **Budapest**
Tel: 1-341 3988 Fax: 1-341 3988
managing director Laszlo Varga
Comments: see also Promoters

Hungarian Dance Art Media Centre
Magyar Táncmüvészeti Média Központ
PF 160, 1734 **Budapest**
Tel: 1-217 0795/2095 12308(mobile) Fax: 1-217 0795
E-Mail: camddamc@hotmail.com
director Miklós Kékesi
Arts type: dance *Comments:* Ráday U 37, 1734 Budapest; see also Agents & Producers

Hungarian Music Society
Magyar Zenemüvészeti Társaság
Bertalan 15, 1111 **Budapest**
Tel: 1-466 0543 Fax: 1-466 0543
president János Devich; secretary Eszter Judik
Events: organises 30-40 concerts each year
Comments: see also Festivals

Institut Francais
Fö 17, 1011 **Budapest**
Tel: 1-202 1133 Fax: 1-202 1323
E-Mail: inst-france@inst-france.hu
music programmer Agnes Havas;
director Henri Lebreton

Jakobi Concert Ltd
Jakobi Koncert Kft
Gyenes 3, 1032 **Budapest**
Tel: 1-335 0378/368 4334
Fax: 1-368 4334/335 0378
director Laszlo Jakobi
Events: Forras Balaton Festival (July-August) 20 concerts, Godollo Harp Festival (October) 5 concerts, Forras Concerts throughout the year 15 concerts
Venues: Ferenc Liszt Academy of Music

Musica Hermina
Filler 1, 1024 **Budapest**
Tel: 1-212 5416 Fax: 1-212 5416

Musica Sacra Mu Sa
Kende 12, 1114 **Budapest**
Tel: 1-365 2293
Fax: 1-365 2293
director Laszlo Rigo

Óbuda Society
Óbudai Társaskör
Kiskorona utca 7, 1036 **Budapest** 111
Tel: 1-250 0288/250 4937
Fax: 1-250 0288/387 8376
E-Mail: gandrasi@c3.hu
director Dr Judit Merényi
Events: organises 180 activities throughout the year
Arts type: various including classical concerts, chamber music, literature and art exhibitions

Philharmonia Budapest Kht
Filharmónia Budapest Kht
PO Box 49, 1364 **Budapest**
Tel: 1-302 4961/331 2521
Fax: 1-331 2521/302 4962
E-Mail: philharm@mail.elender.hu
director Gyorgy Igric;
deputy director Endre Kovács;
manager of international dept Donatella Failoni
Events: 400, season and summer
Arts type: symphony orchestra, chamber music, recitals, lieder-abende, classical *Venues:* different venues in cities Gyor, Pécs, Szeged, Miskolc, Debrecen (major cities) (q.v.) *Comments:* visiting address: Jokai 6, 1066 Budapest; non-profit organisation

Strém Concert agency
Strém Kulturális Szolgáltató
Bimbo 75, 1022 **Budapest**
Tel: 1-326 6152
Fax: 1-326 6152
director Kalman Strem
Events: 70 activities every year
incl. concerts and festivals

Strém Concert Agency
Strém Kulturális Szolgáltató Bt
Bimbó út 75, 1022 **Budapest** II
Tel: 1-326 6152
Fax: 1-326 6152
director Kálmán Strém
Events: 70 activities each year
Comments: organises concerts and festivals;
see also Agents & Producers

Vigado Redoute
PO Box 329, 1369 **Budapest**
Tel: 1-318 9167
Fax: 1-318 9167
director Andras Csonka;
director of events Balazs Feledy
Events: 50-60 throughout the year *Arts type:* symphony orchestra, chamber music, recitals *Venues:* own venue (q.v.) *Comments:* visiting address: Vörösmarty tér 1, 1051 Budapest

VIP Arts Management
Postafiók 447, 1537 **Budapest**
Tel: 1-302 4290/332 4816
Fax: 1-332 4816
director Teodóra Bán
Comments: visiting address: Hajós utca 13-15, II/3, 1061, Budapest VI, Hungary; based at the State Opera House , organises the Budapest Summer Opera and Ballet Festival; see also Agents & Producers

Workshop Foundation
Mühely Alapítvány
Liliom u. 41, 1094 **Budapest**
Tel: 1-456 2045
Fax: 1-456 2050
E-Mail: workshop@c3.hu
director & interim relations György Szabó (tel: 343-8044); secretary Adrienn Szabó; training coordinator Zsuzsa Gasparice; program manager/coordination Beatrice Rossi
Arts type: dance & interdisciplinary work
Comments: interdisciplinary work between dance and other art forms; also one of the centers of the Gulliver Clearing House; Hungarian partner for MAPA (Moving Academy for Performing Arts); IETM member

**MASZK Association/
Centre for Hungarian Alternative Theaters**
P.O. Box 905, 6701 **Szeged**
Tel: 62-312 303
Fax: 62-312 303
Policy: aim to establish the Centre for Contemporary Performing Arts under the name ALTERRA
Comments: see also Agents & Producers

ICELAND (+354)

Reykjavik Chamber Music Society
Kammermusikklubburinn
Espilundi 11, 210 **Gardabaer**
Tel: 565 6028
chairman Gudmundur W Vilhjálmsson
Events: 5 (per season: Sept to March)
Arts type: chamber music *Venues:* Bústada Church 350

Musica Antiqua
Mjóstraeti 10, 101 **Reykjavík**
Tel: 551 0033
Fax: 551 0033
contact Snorri Örn Snorrason
Arts type: events/concerts on early music only
Comments: organises Northern Lights; see also Festivals and Early Music

IRELAND Republic of (+353)

Ballina Arts Events
Markievicz House, Pearse Street,
Ballina (Co. Mayo)
Tel: 96-73593
Fax: 96-73593
secretary Liam Clarke; chairman t.b.a.
Arts type: choral music, chamber music, inst recitals, song recitals, modern dance, classical theatre, mime, modern theatre, puppet, visual arts exhibitions
Comments: voluntary organisation which promotes various arts events especially through workshops/painting and drawing classes

Music for Galway
9 Lakeview, **Claregalway (Galway)**
Tel: 91-798 140
Fax: 91-798 140
E-Mail: mfg@iol.ie
programme director Dr Jane O'Leary;
administrator Madeleine Flanagan
Events: Sept-May *Perfs:* 25-30
Arts type: chamber orch, chamber music, jazz, song recitals, symphony music *Venues:* Aula Maxima, National University of Ireland, Galway 250 , Leisureland 800, Town Hall Theatre 400, St. Nicholas Collegiate Church 350 *Policy:* a variety of concerts throughout the season, with emphasis on international chamber music
Comments: Galway Arts Festival (July); series of concerts throughout the year

Cork Orchestral Society
1 Audley Place, Patrichs Hill, **Cork**
Tel: 21-502 163
Fax: 21-502 163
secretary Maire Fleischmann; chairman Geoffrey Spratt
Events: 25 (Sept-June throughout Cork and Dublin)
Arts type: chamber music *Venues:* Cork School of Music 300, Aula Maxima 250

Firkin Crane
Dance Development Agency, Shandon, **Cork**
Tel: 21-507 487 Fax: 21-501 124
E-Mail: firkin@iol.ie
artistic director Mary Brady;
marketing manager Ger O'Riordan;
dance administrator Sharon Sheehan;
box office Marie Lynch
Arts type: dance, classical ballet, folk dance, modern ballet, modern dance, choreographic research and development, dance commissions, dance workshops *Venues:* presenting venue and rehearsal spaces, Smukfit Auditorium 250 seats (can be moved to create working space), Musgrave Theatre 75 seats (in the round) *Policy:* produce new dance theatre, centre for choreographic research and development, dance education and community dance *Comments:* the centre also provides a public information and advice service on dance training programmes and funding opportunities, currently creating a library and dance archive, and a national database for dance

Limerick Music Association
48 Ulverton Road, **Dalkey (Co. Dublin)**
Tel: 1-282 6918
Fax: 1-287 2296
hon. secretary John A. Ruddock
Events: 15 *Arts type:* chamber orch, chamber music, inst recitals, song recitals *Venues:* University of Limerick – Jean Monnet Theatre 330, University Concert Hall 1000

Irish Museum of Modern Art
Royal Hospital, Military Road, Kilmainham, **Dublin** 8
Tel: 1-612 9900 Fax: 1-612 9999
Internet: www.modernart.ie
E-Mail: info@modernart.ie
director Declan McGonagle; head of public affairs Philomena Byrne; senior curator: exhibitions Brenda McParland; senior curator: collection Catherine Marshall
Events: 2 (Spring and Autumn) *Perfs:* 8 *Arts type:* chamber music, visual arts exhibitions, chamber orchestra, song recitals *Venues:* Great Hall 550, Chapel 250 *Comments:* themed classical music series e.g. Chopin Plus, Schubert & Beethoven; venues available for private rental

Music Network
The Coach House, Dublin Castle, **Dublin** 2
Tel: 1-671 9429/30
Fax: 1-671 9430
E-Mail: info@musicnetwork.ie
chief executive John O'Kane;
performance programme manager Ms Catherine Carey;
regional development manager Ms Orla Moloney;
research & resourcing manager Peter Mangan
Events: 12-14 *Perfs:* 150 *Arts type:* chamber music, jazz, traditional Irish music, new music *Venues:* various venues North and South of Ireland cap. 50-300 *Comments:* classical, jazz and traditional music tours in Ireland and International; patron: President of Ireland, Mary McAleese; see also National Organisations

Rathmines & Rathgar Musical Society
67/69 Upper Rathmines Road, **Dublin** 6
Tel: 1-4971 577
Events: 2 (1 Gaiety Theatre Oct/Nov, 1 National Concert Hall March) *Perfs:* 2 *Arts type:* musicals, concerts *Venues:* Gaiety Theatre 1200, National Concert Hall 1200

Robert Nolan Concerts Promoter
36 Castleknock Way, Laurel Lodge, Castleknock, **Dublin** 15
Tel: 1-836 5629/820 4559

Waterford Music Club
14 Grange Park Avenue, **Waterford**
Tel: 51-874 405
president Pat Grogan
Events: 8 (Oct-April) *Perfs:* 8 *Arts type:* chamber orch, chamber music, inst recitals, song recitals *Venues:* City Hall, Waterford 260 *Policy:* the provision of live music in the categories listed *Comments:* founded in 1942, this is Ireland's longest established music club; venue address: City Hall, The Mall, Waterford, Tel: 51-873 501, Fax: 51-879 124

ITALY (+39)

Clamat – Associazione Club Amici Della Musica Abano Terme
Via A. Stella N. 6,
35031 **Abano Terme (PD)**
Tel: 049-860 1342
Fax: 049-860 1120
E-Mail: clamat@excite.com
presidente Dr. Günter Kirschner;
dir. artistic Prof. Emanuele Pasqualin
Events: 40 *Arts type:* chamber orch, choral music, chamber music, sacred music, classical, contemporary *Venues:* Sala A 200 Posti, Kursaal (Abano Terme) Sala A 650 Posti, Palazzo Congressi (Abano Terme)
Policy: not-for-profit association
Comments: music school

Associazione La Fenice
L.Go Leopardi 4, 63021 **Amandola (AP)**
Tel: 0736-848 323/845 500 Fax: 0736-848 323
Internet: www.softland.it/fenice
E-Mail: fenice@softland.it
president & director Vincenzo Pasquali (736-847 577)
Events: 10/15 *Arts type:* chamber orch, chamber music, new music, pop and contemporary music, choral music, electronic music, jazz, multi media, symphony music *Venues:* Chiostro San Francesco, Parco Nazionale dei Monti Sibillini (in-door and out-door) *Comments:* various music courses and a musical competition; publish a quarterly magazine, Musicultura on Line address: www.softland.it/Musicultura; also have language courses (English & French) with mother-tongue teachers; organise a festival Muscia nel Parco Festival with competition Intermusic (cash prize), own orchestra Orchestra Intermusic; music therapy courses and an annual seminar (October) on music therapy and language globalization; operate in collaboration with Centro di Pedagogia Musicale with financial support from provincal government

AMAT – Associazione Marchigiana Attività Teatrali
Corso Mazzini 148, 60121 **Ancona**
Tel: 071-207 5880/326
Fax: 071-54813
Internet: www.amat.marche.it
E-Mail: info@amat.marche.it
presidente Prof. Aldo Amati
Events: 700 per year *Arts type:* drama, dance
Policy: organise and promote drama acitivity in the Marche region *Comments:* financed by the state and the Marche region

Associazione L'incontro musicale
Via Goito 4, 60121 **Ancona**
Tel: 071-889 625/200 646/0348-335 2683 (mobile)
Fax: 071-200 646
Internet: www.musica.it
E-Mail: d.vico@musica.it
direttore artistico e organizzativo Deborah Vico; ufficio stampa Roberto Farroni
Arts type: concerts, festival, competition
Comments: see also Concorso Musicale Internazionale Riviera Del Conero

Società Filarmonica Marchigiana
Via Degli Aranci No.2, 60121 **Ancona**
Tel: 071-206 168 Fax: 071-206 730
presidente Giuliano Gasparini; direttore artistico Gustav Kuhn; responsabile ufficio stampa e pr Margherita Rinaldi
Events: 100 *Arts type:* classical, contemporary, chamber *Venues:* Aula Magna D'Ateneo-Ancona 630, Teatro Pergolesi-Iesi 850 *Comments:* also conventions, conferences, didactic activities for children

Fondazione Guido D'Arezzo
Corso Italia 102, 52100 **Arezzo**
Tel: 0575-356 203/23835
Fax: 0575-324 735
E-Mail: fondguid@nots.it
commissario straordinario t.b.a.
Arts type: festivals, competitions, courses, choral music, folk choral music, gregorian chant *Venues:* Teatro Petrarca, Chiesa Sta Maria della Pieve, P.zza S. Domenico *Comments:* organise mainly festival (q.v.) and polifonic composition competitions (q.v.); see also Competitions

Asolo Musica – Veneto Musica
Casa Pase – Via Browning 141, 31011 **Asolo**
Tel: 0423-950 150 Fax: 0423-529 890
presidente Dr. Battista Parolin; vice presidente Ing. Carlo Tortato; direttore Artistico Maestro Federico Pupo; produzione Anna Lydia Dallarosa; amministrazione Maria Rosa Florian
Events: 100 concerts and 10 master classes *Arts type:* chamber orchestra, choral music, chamber music, inst recitals, jazz, light orch music, music theatre, operetta, sacred music, song recitals, symphony music, multimedia, world music, classical ballet, master classes *Venues:* Chiesa di San Gottardo and Teatro dei Rinnovati in Asolo, Teatro Eleonora Duse in Asolo, Conservatorio A. Steffani in Castelfranco Veneto (TV), Palazzo Auditorium Belluno, Conservatorio di Vicenza Arrigo Pedroko *Comments:* organise Festival Internazionale di Musica da Camera (Aug/Sept); organise master classes Da Fromgennto in December

Accademia Perduta – Romagna Teatri
c/o Teatro Goldoni,
Piazza Libertà, 21, 48012 **Bagnacavallo (RA)**
Tel: 0545-64330/667 294 (box office)
Fax: 0545-64320
E-Mail: aprteatri@mail.avianet.it
direzione artistica e amministrativa Claudio Casadio, Ruggero Sintoni
Arts type: drama, dance, research and youth theatre *Venues:* Teatro Goldoni di Bagnacavallo 370, Teatro di Faenza 490, Teatro di Cervia 250, Teatro 'il Piccolo di Forlì 300, Teatro Dragoni di Meldola (FO) 320, Teatro Comunale di Conselice (RA) 450, Teatro Comunale di Riolo Terme (RA) 500, Teatro Conunale di Galeata (FO) 200 *Comments:* manage and produce theatre companies and festivals; registered address: Via Maggiore, 65, 48100 Ravenna; offices address: Teatro Il Piccolo, Via Cerchia 98, 47100 Forlí, Tel: 0543-64300, Fax: 0543-64025, and also in Teatro Masini di Faenza, Piazza Nenni 3, 48018 Faenza (RA), Fax: 0546-680 121, press office Tel: 0546-667 294

Associazione Musicale Il Coretto
Via Argiro no.8, 70122 **Bari**
Tel: 080-521 9302/8411 Fax: 080-521 9302
presidente Elena Vigliano
Events: Oct-May *Perfs:* 40-50 *Arts type:* chamber music, new music, classical and contemporary music *Venues:* Auditorium la Vallisa 200 *Comments:* masterclasses, competition on music research and music classes

Camerata Musicale Barese
via Sparano 141, 70121 **Bari**
Tel: 080-521 1908 Fax: 080-523 7154
direttore organizzativo dr. Rocco De Venuto; direttore artistico M° Giovanni Antonioni; presidente prof. Francesco Antonioni; ufficio stampa Dr. Gustavo Delgado; presidente onorario On. le Avv. Nicola Vernola
Events: 25 *Arts type:* symphonic, chamber, recitals, ballet, jazz *Venues:* Teatro Piccinni 750, Teatro Team 2200, Sala Europa, Villa Romanazzi 600

Circolo Culturale Bellunese
Via De Stefani 7, 32100 **Belluno**
Tel: 0437-25233 Fax: 0437-944 805
presidente onorario Maurizio Fistarol;
presidente Luisa Coin
Events: 25 including summer events *Arts type:* recitals, chamber, jazz, some symphonic, ballet *Venues:* Auditorium Comunale 180, Teatro Comunale 650, churches in town

Cooperativa Artservice
Via Valeriano 6, 32100 **Belluno**
Tel: 0437-940 288 Fax: 0437-940 775
artistic director Bepi Santuzzo;
president Aurelio Roberto Rota
Events: 60 *Arts type:* festivals, theatre, carnivals and other performing arts, and educational activities

Associazione Musica Aperta
Via Borgo Palazzo N. 31, 24125 **Bergamo**
Tel: 035-242 287 Fax: 035-242 287
Internet: mabguniv.unibg.it/~MABG
E-Mail: mabg@unibg.it
direttore artistico Pieralberto Cattaneo, Vittorio Fellegara
Events: 50 *Arts types:* chamber orchestra, choral music, chamber music, early music, electronic music, inst recitals, jazz, new music, music theatre, sacred music, song recitals, symphony music, opera *Venues:* Sala Piatti 300, Teatro Donizetti 1200, Teatro del Borgo 400 *Comments:* see also Festival: Incontri Europei con la Musica; Comporre Oggi; compleni: Gruppo Fiati Musica Aperta Orchestra degli Incontri Europei

Societa' del Quartetto
Viale Vittorio Emanuele 65, 24100 **Bergamo**
Tel: 035-232 612/236 293/528 497/249 680
Fax: 035-235 835
E-Mail: bgp560@uninet.com.it
presidente avv. Arbace Mazzoleni; vice presidente t.b.a.; segretario generale Sergio Fornoni
Events: 10 *Arts type:* chamber, symphonic *Venues:* Sala Auditorium Casa della Libertà

Associazione Clavicembalistica Bolognese
via Saragozza 86, 40123 **Bologna**
Tel: 051-330 228 Fax: 051-583 364
presidente Maria Pia Jacoboni; vice presidente Giorgio Tabacco; segretario Carlo Jacoboni; membri Giuseppina La Face Bianconi, Tito Gotti
Events: 14 in spring and autumn season *Perfs:* 10 *Arts type:* chamber music, early music, recitals, music theatre, sacred music *Venues:* Convento dell'Osservanza, Bologna *Comments:* organise a national harpsichord competition and publish manuscripts of antique harpsichord music

Associazione Musicale Giuseppe Torelli
Via Brigata Bolero 23, 40132 **Bologna**
Tel: 051-564 200 Fax: 051-575 120
presidente Dott.ssa Graziella Taglioli; direttore artistico Carlo Mazzoli; segreteria Cristina Bernardi
Events: 40 *Arts type:* concerts, opera, jazz *Comments:* organise the festival Primavera e Autunno Musicale (q.v.)

Link Project
Via Fioravanti N. 14, 40129 **Bologna**
Tel: 051-370 971 Fax: 051-370 972
Internet: www.linkproject.org
E-Mail: info@linkproject.org
musica elettronica Mauro Boris Borella; musica contemporanea Enrico Croci; teatro e performances Silvia Fanti; settore visivo Daniele Gasparinetti
Events: 200 (Oct-May) *Arts type:* performance, media arts, electronic music, visual arts, modern dance, multi media *Venues:* Sala Blu 300, Sala Blanca 800, Sublink 400, Infoshop 100, Deviant Dark Room 400
Comments: see also Agents & Producers and Venues

Musica Insieme
Galleria Cavour 3, 40124 **Bologna**
Tel: 051-271 932
Fax: 051-271 668
Internet: www.ritram.it/musicainsieme
E-Mail: musicainsieme@ritram.it
direttore generale Bruno Borsari;
presidente ing. Marco Fier;
segretaria generale Susanna Migli
Events: 3, Oct-May *Perfs:* 30 *Arts type:* chamber music, chamber orchestra *Venues:* Teatro Comunale 900, Palazzo dei Congressi 1100, Arena del sole 800, Museo Morandi, Aula Absidale S. Lucia

Teatri di Vita
International Center for Performing Arts,
via del Pratello 90/92, 40122 **Bologna**
Internet: www.teatridivita.it
E-Mail: info@teatridivita.it
artistic director Stefano Lasi
Venues: studio *Comments:* new PIERCE project in order to highlight the multiplicity of new artists and groups of various arts types in Bologna and Emilia Romagna; info-point address: Teatri diVita, Info-Point, Parco dei Pini, Via Emilia Ponente 485, 40132 Bologna;
see also Venues

Konzertverein Bozen/Società dei Concerti di Bolzano
piazza Domenicani 19, 39100 **Bolzano**
Tel: 0471-976 568
Fax: 0471-973 579
E-Mail: socconbz@tin.it
presidente Franz von Walther; vice presidente M.C. Mohovich; direttore artistico Dr. Josef Lanz
Arts type: chamber, recitals, soloists
Venues: Sala del Conservatorio 430

Associazione Musicale Anton Diabelli
Via dei Mille 12, 35030 **Bosco di Rubano (PD)**
Tel: 049-631 334
Fax: 049-631 334
presidente Prof. Ugo Armano; vice-presidente Ivano Paterno; secretary Maurizio Righi; coordinator for courses Patrizia Ravasio
Events: 5/6 *Arts type:* chamber orch, choral music, chamber music, early music, electronic music, inst recitals, new music, classical music, contemporary
Comments: organising a competition on "Musica Consonante" for junior musicians; it also takes part in an international competition in Poland and Belgium; organised the Italian section of New Music for New Pianist, international competition for junior musicians; organises piano seminars for teachers; summer full-immersion training for children and young people; education programme for all activities

Fondazione Romano Romanini
Via Elia Capriolo 48, 25122 **Brescia**
Tel: 030-280 188
Fax: 030-375 0602
manager/conductor Mario Conter
Venues: Sala San Carlino 160 *Comments:* provide specialization courses for string instruments, piano and composition; also organise an international competition for violin: Città di Brescia, which is held every two years; also have Accademia del Canto and Accademia Europea di Interpretazione Pianistica

Accademia Internazionale di Perfezionamento Musicale – Sol Oriens
Via Koch 1, 09121 **Cagliari**
Tel: 070-505 984 Fax: 070-522 108
president Anna Maria Punzo;
vice president Valentina Savona;
Tesoriere Vincenzo Tuveri
Events: 5 *Arts type:* festivals, concerts, competitions, seminars, courses in classical music *Venues:* Sala Concerti dell Accademia Sol Oriens 50
Comments: non-profit organisation

Associazione Serate Musicali in Sardegna
Via Carducci 16, 09128 **Cagliari**
Tel: 070-43621/0336-776 858
Fax: 070-43621
presidente e direttore artistico Franco Maggio Ormezowski; segretaria Barbara Lunetta Maggio
Events: 25 Estate musicale internazionale Alghero (July-Sept), Concerti d'Autunno (Oct/Dec) *Perfs:* 30
Arts type: chamber music, concerts for schools *Venues:* Il Chiostro di S. Francesco – Alghero, EXMA and various places in Cagliari

Ce.D.A.C. – Sardegna
Via Mameli 153, 09123 **Cagliari**
Tel: 070-270 577
Fax: 070-270 932
presidente Mario Pinna;
vice presidente e amministratore Antonio Caviddu
Events: 45 *Perfs:* 245 *Arts type:* drama, dance, music
Venues: Teatro Alfieri (Cagliari) 704, Teatro Verdi (Sassari) 900, Teatro Civico (Alghero), Teatro Giordo (Tempio Pausania), Teatro Comunale (S. Gavino), Teatro Longobardo (La Maddalena), Teatro Olbia, Teatro Garau (Oristano) etc. *Comments:* summer festial of poetry and theatre

Amici della Musica di Campobasso-Onlus
Viale Elena 54, 86100 **Campobasso**
Tel: 0874-416 374/413 333
Fax: 0874-416 374
presidente avv. Renato Rizzi;
vice presidente Angelina Weidmann;
consiglieri Ciotoli Pasquale, Sabatino Del Sordo;
consigliere uscente Niro Piero;
direttore artistico Walter De Angelis
Events: 24, Oct-March *Arts type:* chamber orch, choral music, chamber music, early music, folk music, inst recitals, jazz, new music, sacred music, symphony music *Venues:* Auditoriun del Liceo Classico 400
Policy: music promotion

Amici della Musica
Via Soranza 135, 31033 **Castelfranco Veneto (TV)**
Tel: 0423-494 943 Fax: 0423-736 220
presidente ing. Umberto Fraccaro Genovese;
direttore artistico prof.ssa Gabriella Pasut;
direttore amministrativo dott. Giancarlo Manzonetto prof.ssa Gabriella Pasut;
segretario artistico Maria Teresa Anselmi Guizzon
Events: 10 *Arts type:* chamber *Venues:* Teatro Accademico 280

Amici della Musica di Castellana Grotte
via Fato 3, 70013 **Castellana Grotte (BA)**
Tel: 080-496 5207 Fax: 080-496 5207
direttore amministrativo Mariella Losavio; segretario generale Enrico Cavaleri; presidente e direttore artistico Grazia Salvatori
Events: 20 *Arts type:* chamber, recitals *Venues:* Sala Fato 100 *Comments:* an organ festival for the region; seminars on organ music in June and September; jazz course, conference on futurism in arts

Associazione Musicale Etnea
via Museo Biscari 10, 95131 **Catania**
Tel: 095-321 252
Fax: 095-320 424
consiglio direttivo, presidente Salvatore Toscano; vice presidente Vittoria Napoli; tesoriere Marcello Iakomin, Maria Rosa de Luca, Giuseppe Montemagno; Collegio dei Revisori dei conti Giuseppa Moncada (presidente), Guido Consoli, Giorgio Costanzo; direttore artistico Salvatore Enrico Failla; segretario generale Isabella Guillot; segretario organizzativo Antonella Coco
Events: 3 per season (Nov-April) *Perfs:* 36 *Arts type:* chamber orch, choral music, chamber music, folk music, inst recitals, music theatre, sacred music, symphony music, multi-media, world music, folk dance, modern ballet, modern dance, contemporary symphony, recitals, contemporary dance
Venues: Piccolo Teatro di Catania 300, Teatro Metropolitan 1800 *Comments:* 11 morning and 25 evening concerts as part of the season

Centro Teatrale Siciliano (CTS)
Piazza dei Martiri, 8, 95131 **Catania**
Tel: 095-535 453 Fax: 095-538 364
president Graziana Maniscalco;
artistic director Nino Romeo;
organization Giuseppe Maniscalco
Events: 150/200 *Arts type:* drama *Venues:* various *Policy:* organise and promote theatre shows in Sicily
Comments: registered address: Via Gramignani, 46, 95121 Catania; see also Drama

Società Italiana della Musica e del Teatro
Via L. Colazilli 5, 66100 **Chieti**
Tel: 0871-401 373/898 191/0360-618 035
Fax: 0871-401373
president Antonello Pellegrini;
press agent Stanislao Liberatore
Perfs: 100 *Arts type:* classical music, festival 'Majellarte', theatre, concert series *Venues:* Teatro Marrucino 500

Associazione Autunno Musicale a Como
Villa Olmo, via Cantoni 1, 22100 **Como**
Tel: 031-571 150 Fax: 031-570 540
Internet: www.camtam.it
E-Mail: camtam@galactica.it
presidente e direttore artistico M° Italo Gomez
Perfs: 40 *Arts type:* symphonic, chamber, recitals, sacred, ballet, contemporary music and pop *Venues:* Teatro Sociale 1000, Villa Olmo 220, Teatro Sociale di Canzo 120, churches of Como, Civic Museums of Como
Comments: period: Sept-December run Festival Internazionale Autunno Musicale a Como;
see also Festivals

Società Concerti di Cremona
c/o Teatro A. Ponchielli,
corso Vittorio Emanuele 52, 26100 **Cremona**
Tel: 0372-407 274/5 Fax: 0372-460 180
Internet:
www.rccr.cremona.it/doc_comu/tea/tea-index.htm
E-Mail: ponchielli@rccr.cremona.it
presidente ing. Gianfranco Carutti; ufficio stampa e promozione Teatro A. Ponchielli Arnaldo Bassini
Events: concerts season Dec-April *Arts type:* symphonic, chamber, recitals, jazz, choral *Venues:* Teatro Ponchielli 1246 *Comments:* box office: Tel: 0372-407 273/802;
see also Venues

Società Beethoven ACAM
Largo Umberto I N. 58, 88074 **Crotone**
Tel: 0962-900 848/25539/961 248 Fax: 0962-900 848
presidente Mariarosa Romano; vice-presidente Rocco Calarco; direttore artistico Fernando Romano;
secretario Maria Milano
Events: 54-60 *Arts type:* classical music, dance, recitals
Venues: Teatro Apollo 800, Auditorium Liceo Musicale 'O Stillo' 250 *Comments:* also organise events in other venues outside Crotone

Associazione Ferrara Musica
Corso Giovecca 38, 44100 **Ferrara**
Tel: 0532-202 400/220 Fax: 0532-212 006
E-Mail: femusic@tin.it
responsabile organizzativo Alessandra Abbado;
direttore artistico Lorenzo Fasolo;
presidente onorario Maestro Claudio Abbado
Events: 20 *Arts type:* chamber orchestra, choral music, chamber music, early music, music theatre, symphony music, opera *Venues:* Teatro Comunale – Ferrara 990
Comments: season from Oct-May,
also produce Lyric Operas; Italian residence of the Mahler Chamber Orchestra (q.v)

Associazione Musicale Schumann
c/o Teatro Garibaldi, P.zza Serristori,
50063 **Figline Valdarno**
Tel: 055-915 5655/91251 (comune switchboard)
presidente Nocentini Patrizio;
direttore artistico Lorenzo Parigi
Events: 20 *Arts type:* chamber concerts, opera, master-classes *Venues:* Ridotto of Teatro Comunale 100
Comments: see also Venues

Associazione Amici della Musica di Firenze
via G Sirtori 49, 50137 **Firenze**
Tel: 055-608 420/607 440/609 012 Fax: 055-610 141
Internet: www.amicimusica.fi.it
E-Mail: info@amicimusica.fi.it
amministrazione Daniela Agresti; presidente Stefano Passigli; vice presidenti Paolo Barile, Paolo Bonami;
programmazione artistica Domitilla Baldeschi
Events: 75 + 20 music master classes *Arts type:* chamber music *Venues:* various Florence venues, usually Teatro della Pergola 1000, Istituto degli innocenti 400, Teatro Goldoni 600, Teatro Comunalle 1600; also in Figline Valdarno *Comments:* also run the annual festival 'Settembre Musica'

Fondazione Toscana Spettacolo
Via Alamanni 41, 50123 **Firenze**
Tel: 055-219 851 Fax: 055-219 853
Internet: www.fts.toscana.it
E-Mail: fts@fts.toscana.it
direttore Manrico Ferrucci; ufficio stampa Daniele Stortoni
Events: 350 *Perfs:* 300 *Arts type:* drama, music, dance
Venues: Teatri Toscani
Comments: organise theatre courses

Musicus Concentus
piazza del Carmine 19, 50124 **Firenze**
Tel: 055-287 347 Fax: 055-287 347
E-Mail: musicus@dada.it
presidente Fernando Fanutti; vice presidente Alessandro Tarchiani; press officer Giuseppe Vigna
Events: 35 concerts throughout the year *Arts type:* jazz & new music *Venues:* Sala Vanni 200, Teatro Verdi 1500, Teatro Puccini 800

Amici della Musica di Foggia
Piazza Marconi 11, 71100 **Foggia**
Tel: 0881-772 914/774 640 Fax: 0881-709 194
presidente Vittorio Fabbrini; vice presidente Annamaria Attianese; direttore artistico Maestro Domenico Losavio
Events: Jan-Dec *Arts type:* classical music & ballet *Policy:* promoters of international artistis and young winners of competitions : see also Festivals, Orchestras

Associazione i Solisti Dauni
Piazza Marconi 11, 71100 **Foggia**
Tel: 0881-772 914/774 640/709 194 Fax: 0881-709 194
direttore e direttore artistico Domenico Losavio;
consulente musicale Giulio D'Angelo;
direttor organizzativo Lilly Carfagno
Events: 1 *Perfs:* 4 *Arts type:* from classical to contemporary music *Comments:* see also Orchestras, Festivals: Teatri Possibili

Foundazione Carlo Felice
Passo Eugenio Montale 4, 16121 **Genova**
Tel: 010-53811 Fax: 010-538 1233
Internet: www.carlofelice.it
E-Mail: ctstampa@tin.it (press office)
sovrintendente Dott. Nicola Costa; direttore artistico Alessio Vlad; direttore del personale Luigi Molari; capo ufficio stampa Andrea Fasano; responsabile servizio relazioni esterne Graziella Rapallo Sincich
Events: Sept-July *Arts type:* chamber, choral music, electronic music, jazz, sacred music, song recitals, symphony music, opera, classical ballet, modern ballet, modern dance, visual arts exhibitions *Venues:* Grande Sala 2000, Auditorium 200, Teatro di Parchi di Nervi 1206 *Policy:* promotional activity for youth : E-mail for theatre: staff@carlofelice.it

Giovine Orchestra Genovese
Via di Canneto il Lungo. 37/11, 16123 **Genova**
Tel: 010-251 0078 Fax: 010-254 2786
Internet: www.gog.it
E-Mail: info@gog.it
segretaria artistica Carola De Mari; responsabile amministrativo Monica Puppo; responsabile organizzativo Floriana Muri; ufficio stampa A.A.R.T.S. Pierluigi Togni; progetti speciali Roberta Argento; presidente Mirella Rocco
Events: 40 *Arts type:* mainly chamber music *Venues:* Teatro Carlo Felice 2007 *Comments:* 1 season Oct/June; also organise a musical theatre for children, plus two competitions: one for young musicians and one for composers; non for profit society

Spazio Musica
Via Parini 10, 16145 **Genova**
Tel: 010-317 192/338-723 2815 Fax: 010-317 192
Internet: internet.village.it/cli/spaziomusica
E-Mail: spmusica@tn.village.it
president Manlio Palumo Mosca; direttore artistico Gabriella Ravazzi
Arts type: classical, jazz and lyric *Venues:* Teatro Mancinelli di Orvieto 800, Palazzo dei Sette 300, Chiostro del Museo Faina 300 *Comments:* they organize instrumental and vocal master classes, opera workshops for conductors, singers, repetiteurs, directors, orchestra and opera and concert season (every July and August); annual academy for conductors, singers, repetiteurs

Associazione Culturale M° Rodolfo Lipizer
via Don Giovanni Bosco 91, 34170 **Gorizia (GO)**
Tel: 0481-34775/532 551/533 264 Fax: 0481-536 710
Internet: www.seta.it/lipizer/
E-Mail: lipizer@mail.seta.it
presidente prof. Lorenzo Qualli; vice presidente e direttore artistico prof. Elena Lipizer; direttore amministrativo Luciano Milani; segretario generale Gianni Drascek
Events: concert season: Oct – May *Perfs:* 32 concerts *Arts type:* symphony music, chamber music, recitals *Venues:* Auditorium di Gorizia 372 *Policy:* international divulgation of Rudolfo Lipizers works and promotion of young talents *Comments:* international violin competition; see also competitons

Accademia Jaufré Rudel di Studi Medievali
Calle Dei Macellai 2, 34172 **Gradisca D'Isonzo (GO)**
Tel: 0481-531 326 Fax: 0481-531 326
Internet: www.accademia.it
E-Mail: dramsam@mail.seta.it
direttore artistico Giuseppe Paolo Cecere; presidente dott. Fabio Cavalli
Arts type: medieval cultural events (music, art, dance, literature and life, cuisine) *Venues:* Castello di Torre Chiara Langhirano (PA) 500, Castello Medioevale di Gorizia 200 *Comments:* the academy organises courses, seminars and events in connection with the medieval world; see also Choirs and Early Music

Associazione Culturale Claudio Monteverdi
P.za Garibaldi 1, 42016 **Guastalla (RE)**
Tel: 0522-839 758/839 765 Fax: 0522-839 756
Internet: www.comguastalla.it
E-Mail: cultural@pragmanet.it
presidente Maurizio Barazzoni; direttore artistico Sandro Volta
Events: 10 *Perfs:* 35 *Arts type:* music, mainly baroque, oratory, opera *Venues:* Teatro Ruggeri 450, Teatro all' Antica di Sabbioneta (MN) 150, Chiesa di San Francesco, Piazza Martini *Comments:* specialises in staging baroque music; works closely with the local cultural centre; also record concerts on CD; also work in collaboration with Opera Youth Europe, based in Arezzo for the organisation of seasons of baroque opera and lyric opera music

Accademia Pianistica Internazionale Incontri col Maestro
P.le G. Dalle Bande Nere 12, 40026 **Imola (BO)**
Tel: 0542-30802
Fax: 0542-30858
E-Mail: accademia.pian@imola.queen.it
direttore Franco Scala; presidenti Paolo Casadio Pirazzoli, Marcello Abbado; presidente onorario Vladimir Ashkenazy
Events: 4 *Arts type:* classical piano music *Venues:* Rocca Sforzesca 1000, Palazetto 180 *Comments:* courses for piano, chamber music and flute for concert performers – in October/May every year

Il Circolo della Musica di Imola
Via Francucci 4, 40026 **Imola (BO)**
Tel: 0542-22762/35248
Fax: 0542-22762/35248
direttore artistico e organizzativo prof.ssa Lora Gallotti Montanari; presidente prof. Leopoldo Montanari; vice presidente ing. Domenico Mirri; direttore artistico prof. Massimo Montanari
Events: 13 (Oct-April) *Arts type:* chamber orch, chamber music, early music, inst recitals, new music, music theatre, sacred music, song recitals, symphony music *Venues:* Teatro Comunale 499, Ebe Stignani

Associazione Rovere d'Oro
Via Aurelia no.139, S. Bartolomeo al Mare, 18016 **Imperia**
Tel: 0183-400 967/400 888 Fax: 0183-403 050
E-Mail: roveredoro@hotmail.com
direttore organizzativo Carla Brun; direttore operativo Rita Romani Arimondo; direttore artistico Maestro Luciano Lanfranchi
Arts type: chamber music *Comments:* organise competitions; see also Competitions

Ente Musicale Società Aquilana dei Concerti B. Barattelli
Castello Cinquecentesco, 67100 **L'Aquila**
Tel: 0862-24262/414 161 Fax: 0862-61666
Internet: www.barattelli.org
E-Mail: barattelliconcerti@barattelli.org
presidente Lucio Barattelli; direttore artistico Fabrizio Pezzopane
Events: 70 *Perfs:* 80 *Arts type:* chamber orch, choral music, chamber music, early music, electronic music, folk music, jazz, new music, sacred music, song recitals, symphony music, world music, classical ballet, modern ballet, modern dance *Venues:* Teatro Comunale 600, Auditorium del Castello 300, Auditorium guardia di Finanza 1200, Del Castello N. Carloni 300, churches in town *Comments:* winter and summer season: Oct/May, July/Aug

Società dei Concerti ONLUS
Viale Italia 320, 19126 **La Spezia**
Tel: 0187-520 470 Fax: 0187-510 481
presidente Prof. Ernesto Di Marino; vicepresidente Prof. Sergio Cozzani; consigliere coordinatore Bruno Fiorentini; segretario generale Maestro Piero Barbareschi; direttore artistieo Massiliamo Damerini
Events: 40 *Arts type:* symphony, chamber orch, choral music, chamber music, solo recitals, early music, folk music, jazz, new music, sacred music, song recitals, world music *Venues:* Teatro Civico 900, Anfiteatro di Viale Alpi 1500, Sala Dante 200 *Comments:* winter and summer season, jazz festival, organ concert; see also Festivals

AMA Calabria
via P. Celli 23, 88046 **Lamezia Terme (CZ)**
Tel: 0968-24580/453 090 Fax: 0968-201 005
Internet: www.infoline.it/amacalabria
E-Mail: amacalabria@infoline.it
presidente Dott.. Gennaro Pollice; direttore amministrativo Prof.ssa Vittoria Sonni; direttore artistico Francescantonio Pollice; segretario generale Dott.ssa Laura Gambardella; presidente del Collegio dei Revisori Rag. Maria Antonietta Pianini
Perfs: 25 *Arts type:* chamber music concerts, recitals, symphonic, sacred music, contemporary *Venues:* Teatro Grandinetti 900, Auditorium 400, Teatro Umberto 150 *Comments:* also organise the National Competition AMA Calabria in May; premio internazionale di esecuzione pianistica; non-profit organisation; publication of books and CD's

Associazione Amici della Musica Fedele Fenaroli
Via F. Filzi 7, 66034 **Lanciano (CH)**
Tel: 0872-710 241 Fax: 0872-710 518
presidente arch. Filomena Di Renzo; ufficio stampa Antonietta Centofanti; direttore artistico Walter Tortoreto
Events: 40 *Arts type:* jazz, ethnic, classical music, modern and contemporary music *Venues:* Torri Montanare, Auditorium Diocleziano, Sala Mazzini, Torri Montanare 600, Auditorium Diocleziano 200, Sala Mazzini 200, Teatro Comunale Fenaroli *Comments:* also organises a festival (May-Dec) and seminars (July/Aug); see also Festivals

Campus Internazionale di Musica
c/o Universitá Pontina, Viale Le Corbusier 379, 04100 **Latina**
Tel: 0773-605 551 Fax: 0773-605 548
Internet: www.panservice.it/campusmusica
E-Mail: campus.musica@panservice.it
presidente Riccardo Cerocchi; presidente onorario Festival Pontino Goffredo Petrassi; direttore artistico Incontri int. li musica contemporanea Prof. Raffaele Pozzi; direttore artistico Stagione invernale dei concerti Maestro Bruno Canino; direttore corsi di perfezionamento musicale Maestro Francesco Petracchi
Events: contemporary music & courses in June/July, winter concerts from Oct/Dec *Arts type:* symphony, chamber music, solo recitals, contemporary music *Venues:* Castello Caetani di Sermoneta 1000, Infermeria Abbazia di Fossanova 200, winter concerts: Teatro Ri dotto 400, Grande di Latina 700 *Comments:* run Festival Pontino di Musica

Camerata Musicale Salentina
Via XXV Luglio 29, int.4, 73100 **Lecce**
Tel: 0832-309 901 Fax: 0832-309 901
presidente Maria Teresa Russo; direttore artistico Maria De Bellis-Vitale; segretario Mario Muja
Events: 40 *Arts type:* symphonic, chamber, recitals, jazz *Venues:* Teatro Politeama and other venues in the province of Lecce

Associazione Musicale Jubilate
PO Box 160, 20025 **Legnano (MI)**
Tel: 0331-594 504/454 707 Fax: 0331-597 433
Internet: www.nemo.it/guests/jubilate/default.htm
E-Mail: amj@mail.nemo.it
presidente onorario Bruno Bettinelli; presidente Claudio Martino
Arts type: choral music *Comments:* see also Choirs and Festivals: La Fabbrica del Canto; music course and music therapy course

Associazione Culturale Habanera
PO Box 144, 57100 **Livorno (LI)**
Tel: 050-32693 Fax: 050-30469
Internet: www.habanera.it
E-Mail: info@habanera.it
general manager Patrizia Ascione; president Stefano Cavallini
Events: 5 *Perfs:* 40-60 *Arts type:* contemporary (jazz, ethnic, folk) music *Comments:* production of international projects and secretariate of single international artists

C.E.L. – Teatro di Livorno
Via Goldoni 83, 57125 **Livorno (LI)**
Tel: 0586-889 111 Fax: 0586-899 920
Internet: www.comune.livorno.it/txt/cel/home.htm
E-Mail: cel@mclink.it
presidente Marco Bertini; consulente artistico lirica Alberto Paloscia; amministrazione e produzioni Isabella Bartolini; affari generali e programmazione Paolo Demi; comunicazione-immagine e responsabile ufficio stampa Antonella Peruffo
Events: drama Oct-Apr, classical concerts Jan-May, lyric Sept-Dec *Arts type:* chamber orch, chamber music, jazz, pop music, musical, operetta, classical and contemporary dance, classical and contemporary theatre *Venues:* Teatro La Gran Guardia 1600; Teatro i Quattro Mori 650; Teatro Mascagni di Villa Corridi 200 *Policy:* own productions and other external productions *Comments:* see also Opera, Drama and Venues

Associazione Musicale Lucchese
Via San Micheletto 3, 55100 **Lucca**
Tel: 0583-469 960 Fax: 0583-469 960
segretario generale Fabrizio Giovannelli; presidente ing. Guido Veronesi; presidente onorario Carol MacAndrew; vice presidente Marcello Parducci Ravenni; tesoriere Stefano Ragghianti; direttore artistico Herbert Handt
Events: 16 *Arts type:* chamber orch, choral music, chamber music, music theatre, sacred music
Venues: various

Associazione Musicale Massese
P.za San Martino 1, 54100 **Massa**
Tel: 0585-43732/791 625 Fax: 0585-791 625
presidente e direttore artistico Paolo Biancalana
Events: 15 *Arts type:* classical music *Venues:* Palazzo Ducale 400, Teatro Guglielmi di Massa 500, Teatro Animosi di Carrara 400 *Comments:* the association organises courses and a summer festival; see Festivals

ARTEria Associazone d'Arte e Cultura – Matera
vico XX Settembre 2, 75100 **Matera**
Tel: 0835-337 363 Fax: 0835-337 363
Internet: www.space.tin.it/associazioni/arteria
E-Mail: arteeria@tin.it
Events: 3 concert seasons June-Dec. *Arts type:* classical, symphonic, chamber music *Venues:* Cine Teatro Duni 1000 *Comments:* legal address: via F. lli Cervi 11, 75100, Matera Tel: 0835-383 330 Tel/Fax: 0835 337 363; second E-mail: vivaverdi@lycosmail.com

Accademia Filarmonica di Messina
Via della Munizione 3, 98123 **Messina**
presidente e direttore artistico Giuseppe Uccello; vice president Giuseppe Signorino; secretary M. G. Patanè
Events: 30 *Arts type:* classical, contemporary, ethnic music, jazz and ballet, symphonic *Venues:* Theatre Vittorio Emanuele 1100, Sala Laudamo 200, Theatre Domenico Savio 580, Tempio di San Francesco (XV century church) *Comments:* collaborate with Associazione Musicale V. Bellini

Associazione Musicale V. Bellini
Via S. Barbara 5, 98123 **Messina**
Tel: 090-717 127/336-926 614 (mobile – president)
presidene e direttore artistico Antonio Alí; vice presidente Giuseppe Ramirez; segreteria Fortunata Pirrotta
Events: 30 *Arts type:* symphony, chamber music, recitals, ballet, classical and contemporary music *Venues:* Teatro Vittorio Emanuele 1100, Sala Laudamo 200, Teatro Savio 580, Teatro Apollo 400 *Comments:* they organise concert with Accademia Filarmonica

Filarmonica Laudamo
Via Peculio Frumentario 3, 98122 **Messina**
Tel: 090-710 929 Fax: 090-672 974
presidente avv. Manlio Nicosia; vice presidente ing. Aldo D'Amore; direttore artistico Prof.ssa Alba Crea
Events: 32 *Arts type:* symphonic, chamber, recitals, ballet, choral music, early music, music theatre, folk *Venues:* Teatro Vittorio Emanuele, Sala Laudamo, Teatro Savio, Auditorium della Gazzetta del Sud 170 *Comments:* also runs a public music library; with video-library, disco-library and early musical manuscripts

Associazione Amici della Musica di Mezzago
Via G. Matteotti 66, 20050 **Mezzago (MI)**
Tel: 039-602 2656/606 7098 Fax: 039-602 2656
presidente Angelo Sala; direttore dell'Accademia Pianistica 'Alberto Mozzati' Alberto Baldrighi
Events: 20 *Arts type:* classical music, chamber music, inst recitals *Venues:* Palazzo Archinti 100 *Comments:* association promotes concerts by young musicians; administers L'Accademia Pianistica Alberto Mozzati; courses & master classes

Centro Culturale Rosetum
via Pisanello 1, 20146 **Milano**
Tel: 02-4870 7203/4009 2195 Fax: 02-4009 2195
Internet: www.rosetum.it
E-Mail: info@rosetum.it
presidente Padre Demetrio Carlo Patrini; segretario generale Rodolfo Rota
Events: 100 *Arts type:* choral, symphony, dance, chamber, recitals, theatre, cinema, opera *Venues:* Teatro Rosetum 400 *Comments:* also do Cine Forum

Gioventù Musicale D'Italia
via S. Croce 4, 20122 **Milano**
Tel: 02-8940 0840/8940 0848 Fax: 02-5810 3697
Internet: www.jeunesse.it
E-Mail: jeunesse@tin.it
presidente Lando Lanni Della Quara; consigliere delegato Maria Luisa Vanin Tarantino
Events: 300 *Arts type:* chamber, recitals, jazz, folk
Comments: work throughout Italy

Serate Musicali
Galleria Buenos Aires 7, 20124 **Milano**
Tel: 02-2940 9724/8039 Fax: 02-2940 6961
presidente Giovanni Fazzari; direttore amministrativo Stefania Milan; segretario artistico M.Luisa Longhi
Events: 50-60 Oct-June *Perfs:* 50-60 *Arts type:* symphonic, chamber, recitals *Venues:* Conservatorio G.Verdi 1500, Societa' del Giardino 200, La Scala 1800, other theatres in Lombardy *Comments:* registered address: Via Settala, 72, 20124 Milano

Società dei Concerti
Via V.Pisani 31, 20124 **Milano**
Tel: 02-6698 6956/4134 Fax: 02-6698 5700
E-Mail: socconmi@tin.it
presidente Gabriele Zosi;
direttore artistico Antonio Mormone
Events: 80 *Arts type:* chamber orch, choral music, chamber music, inst recitals, song recitals, symphony music *Venues:* Conservatorio G.Verdi 1550, Teatro delle Erbe 350, Sala Puccini 450

Società del Quartetto
Via Durini 24, 20122 **Milano**
Tel: 02-795 393/600 5500 Fax: 02-7601 4281
E-Mail: quartetto.milano@iol.it
presidente Guido Rossi;
vicepresidente esecutivo Avv. Antonio Magnocavallo; consigliere delegato Dott. Maria Majno
Events: 1 season a year *Perfs:* 23 *Arts type:* chamber, recitals, symphonic *Venues:* Sala Verdi del Conservatorio 1600 *Comments:* subscription series only

Associazione Amici della Musica 'Mario Pedrazzi'
c/o Fondazione San Carlo – Via San Carlo 5, 41100 **Modena**
Tel: 059-366 410 Fax: 059-224 411 (Giulia Zanfrognini)
E-Mail: md4824@mclink.it
segretario generale Giuseppe Tarzia; presidente Mariella Stagi; vice presidente Giulia Zanfrognini; direttore artistico Mirko Caffagni
Events: 12 *Arts type:* all types of classical chamber music *Venues:* Auditorium S Carlo 450, Chiesa S. Carlo

ATER – Associazione Teatrale Emilia Romagna
Via Giardini 466/G, 41100 **Modena**
Tel: 059-340 221 Fax: 059-342 802
Internet: www.regione.emilia-romagna.it/ater
E-Mail: rer3@nettuno.it
president Maurizio Roi; direttore Roberto Giovanardi
Arts type: mainly dance and music *Comments:* also organizes tours and shows in Italy and abroad; courses and consultancy; see Agents & Producers, Courses and Festivals

Associazione Arcadia
Via Colombo 26, 70042 **Mola di Bari (BA)**
Tel: 080-473 5703
presidente Rita Guastamacchia;
coordinatori Maria Antonietta Lamanna, Maria Roca
Arts type: early music (courses)
Venues: Masseria Serra dell'Isola 100

Associazione A.Scarlatti
Piazza dei Martiri 58, 80121 **Napoli**
Tel: 081-406 011/405 637
Fax: 081-405 637
Internet: www.technapoli.it/musica/
E-Mail: ascarlat@technapoli.it
presidente onorario Dott. Raffaele Minicucci; presidente Lucio Sicca; vice president Bruno Calamare
Events: 45 concerts a year *Arts type:* chamber, recitals, jazz, folk *Venues:* Teatro delle Palme 1000

Associazione Amici della Musica Vittorio Cocito
via Ravizza 6A, 28100 **Novara**
Tel: 0321-626 344 Fax: 0321-626 344
presidente e direttore artistico M° Folco Perrino; direttore artistico prof. Elena Bollatto
Events: 36 *Arts type:* chamber orch, choral music, chamber music, early music, sacred music, song recitals, symphony music *Venues:* Salone dei Congressi Palazzo Borsa 400, Teatro Coccia 950 *Comments:* run 3 festivals in Novara Festival G Cantelli in Orta San Giulio, Festival Cusiano and Festival I Concerti dei Fiori; see also Festivals

Amici della Musica di Padova
via San Massimo 37, 35128 **Padova**
Tel: 049-875 6763 Fax: 049-875 6763
direttore amministrativo Paolo Bettella; direttore prof.Francesco Dalla Libera; presidente prof. Nicolò Dalla Porta; direttore artistico M° Filippo Juvarra
Events: 36 *Arts type:* chamber music *Venues:* Auditorio Pollini, Chiesa di s.Sofia, Chiesa Degli Eremitani, Chiesa do Ognissanti

Associazione Siciliana Amici della Musica
Piazza Marina 19, 90133 **Palermo**
Tel: 091-584 679/665 Fax: 091-611 1727
segretario generale dr. Agostino Messina; presidente barone Francesco Agnello;
vice presidente Ruggiero Paderni, Raffaello Rubino; direttore artistico Dott. Dario Oliveri
Events: 80, Oct-May *Arts type:* chamber, recitals, ensemble *Venues:* Teatro Golden *Comments:* they organise concerts in Agrigento, Castelvetrano, Sciacca

Fondazione Arturo Toscanini
Via G. Tartini 13, 43100 **Parma**
Tel: 0521-274 421
Fax: 0521-272 134
Internet: www.fondazione-toscanini.it
E-Mail: fondazione@toscanini.dsnet.it
head of international relations branch Fulvio Zannoni
Arts type: music *Comments:* own symphonic orchestra Orch. Sinfonica dell' Emilia Romagna; organises competitions and festivals – Concorso Internazionale di Composizione, Arturo Toscanini Intern. Competition for Conductors, Festival Mozartiano; see also Festivals, Competitions and Orchestras

Associazione Amici della Musica di Perugia
corso Vannucci 63, 06123 **Perugia**
Tel: 075-572 5264/2271
Fax: 075-572 5264
presidente dr. Franco Buitoni; vice presidente M° Massimo Bogianchino, avv. Stelio Zaganelli; direttore artistico Andrew Starling
Events: 40 *Arts type:* symphony, chamber music, solo recitals, vocal, choral, jazz *Venues:* Teatro Morlacchi 850, Sala dei Notari 500, Teatro Pavone 500

Associazione Musica Libera
Via Ciro Menotti 147, 61100 **Pesaro**
Tel: 0721-414 341 Fax: 0721-414 341
Internet: www.efn.it/mus/giazo.Rtm
E-Mail: musicalibera@abanet.it
general manager Antonio Cioffi;
artistic director Paolo Giaro
Comments: programme annual international music festival Pesaro Spring Festival in Pesaro; promote seminars and conferences and promote the Paolo Giaró Ensemble

Hangart- Associazione Culturale
Via A. Sciesa 13, 61100 **Pesaro**
Tel: 0721-414 618
Fax: 0721-414 618
organiser Antonio Cioffi; president and director of education Rosanna Gorgolini
Arts type: teaching of all forms of dance; presentation of performances of contemporary dance and experimental theatre, concerts, lectures and visual art exhibitions

Ente Manifestazioni Pescaresi
Via Liguria 6, Int. 14, 65122 **Pescara**
Tel: 085-374 198/421 0112
Fax: 085-421 0757
Internet: www.pescarajazz.com
presidente Lucio Fumo
Arts type: drama, ballet, operetta, concerts, jazz, opera *Venues:* Teatro G.D'Annunzio 1800, Teatro S.Andrea 322 *Comments:* in July-August they run the Pescara Jazz Festival (q.v.)

Societa' del Teatro e della Musica L.Barbara
via Liguria 6, 65122 **Pescara**
Tel: 085-422 1463
Fax: 085-422 1463
E-Mail: Socteatromusicape@iolpro.it
direttore amministrativo rag. Pasquale Fattibene; segretario generale rag. Stefano Renzetti; presidente dott. Lucio Fumo; vice presidenti avv. Alfonso Vasile – avv. Francesco Barbara; secretary Stefano Renzetti
Events: drama 15, music 30 (Oct-May and July/Aug) *Perfs`:* drama 15, music 30 (Oct-May) *Arts type:* drama, symphonic, chamber, recitals, ballet, jazz *Venues:* Teatro Michetti 600, TeatroCircus 800

Associazione Farandola
Via Caboto 1, 33170 **Pordenone**
Tel: 0434-21367 Fax: 0434-21367
Internet: www.farandola.it
E-Mail: serivi@farandola.it
direttore artistico Francesco Carone; presidente Gabriella Bassignano
Events: 50 *Arts type:* chamber orch, choral music, chamber music, early music, folk music, inst recitals, music theatre, song recitals, multi-meida, opera, folk dance, modern dance, classical theatre, mime, modern theatre, street theatre *Comments:* the association organises a festival and courses

Musicando Insieme
Via Eleonora d'Arborea 34, 07046 **Porto Torres (SS)**
Tel: 079-514 324/515 012/368-379 9612 (mobile)
Fax: 079-515 012
presidente Tina Parodi
Arts type: classical, jazz *Venues:* Basilica di San Gavino 600, Teatro Olimpia in Porto Torres 800 *Comments:* also run instrumental and music courses; see also Orchestras

Societa dei Concerti di Ravello
Via Trinita 3, 84010 **Ravello**
Tel: 089-858 149/335 Fax: 089-858 249
Internet: www.rcs.amalficoast.it
E-Mail: info@rcs.amalficoast.it
presidente Palumbo Pasquale; direttore artistico Antonio Porpora Anastasio; segretario Dr. Paola Amato
Events: 60 *Arts type:* chamber concerts *Venues:* Villa Rufolo Auditorium and Gardens

Associazione Musicale Angelo Mariani
Circonvallazione Piazza D'Armi 130, 48100 **Ravenna**
Tel: 0544-482 441 Fax: 0544-248 764
Internet: www.netgate.it/aziende/mariani.html
E-Mail: ass.mariani@netgate.it
presidente Maria Cristina Busi;
direttore amministrativo Carlo Fabbri
Events: 20 *Arts type:* symphonic, chamber, recitals *Venues:* Teatro Alighieri 800 *Comments:* also organises adult educational programme; second address: artistic director, Via Gordini 27, 48100 Ravenna

Ravenna Teatro
Via Di Roma 39, 48100 **Ravenna**
Tel: 0544-36239 Fax: 0544-33303
Internet: www.netgate.it/ra.teatro
E-Mail: ra.teatro@netgate.it
direttore artistico Marco Martinelli; presidente Luigi Dadina; direttore organizzativo Marcella Nonnis; administrazione Stefania Nanni; resp. promozione Monica Randi; officio stampa Barbara Fusconi; venoita spettacoli eatro delle albe Francesca Venturi
Events: 10 contemporary theatre Jan-May, 8 prose Nov-March/Jan-May *Arts type:* drama, theatre in general, classical theatre, modern theatre *Venues:* Teatro Rasi 500, Teatro Alighieri 800 *Comments:* manage and programme for Teatro Alighieri and Teatro Rasi, and produce theatre shows for adults and young people; in their drama companies they have Senegalese actors: 1st example of inter-ethnic theatre in Italy;
see also Drama and Venues

Artè
Via San Carlo 1, 42100 **Reggio Emilia**
Tel: 0522-437 443 Fax: 0522-437 443
E-Mail: sidenar@tin.it
contact Silvana Denaro
Arts type: drama *Policy:* organise and produce children & youth shows; proposes and distributes drama shows; assists and promotes the development of drama and cultural projects of both private organisations and institutions *Comments:* the organisation looks after the interests of various drama companies

Associazione Culturale 5T
Via de Gasperi N. 4, 42100 **Reggio Emilia**
Tel: 0522-383 178 Fax: 0522-383 176
Internet: space.tin.it/spettacolo/tinonari
E-Mail: cinqueti@tin.it
presidente e coordinatore attività Tiziana Monari; responsabile progetti didattici e rapporti scuole Linda Eroli
Events: 5 *Perfs:* 280 *Arts type:* drama, dance, ethnic music *Comments:* the activities are promoted jointly with Comune di Reggio Emilia and Consorzio I Teatri; Associazione 5T run the theatre Piccolo Orologio 100 with varied activities concerning theatre for young people and courses; they also work on a series of projects in the province

Academia Musicae Pro Mundo Uno
Via Villa Maggiorani 20, 00168 **Roma**
Tel: 06-305 4141 Fax: 06-305 0117
presidente M° Giuseppe Juhar;
direttore artistico D.ssa Monika Ryba
Events: 30 concerts *Arts type:* every type of classical music *Comments:* organise courses and the festival Festa Musica Pro Mundo Uno; International masterclasses: annual (Rome); International choir meeting ('Mundus Cantat') in different Italian cities and opera studio; they offer scholarships to orchestra directors for three years in Hungary and Germany; see also Festivals

Accademia Filarmonica Romana
via Flaminia 118, 00196 **Roma**
Tel: 06-320 1752 Fax: 06-321 0410
Internet: www.nexus.it/filarmonica
E-Mail: filarmonica@mail.nexus.it
presidente M° Roman Vlad; vice presidenti Luisa Pavolini, Ing Paolo Baratta, Avv. Luigi Mazzella; direttore artistico M° Matteo d'Amico; presidente onorario Goffredo Petrassi
Events: Oct-June *Perfs:* 70 *Arts type:* chamber orch, choral music, chamber music, early music, inst recitals, music theatre, classical ballet, modern ballet, modern dance *Venues:* Teatro Olimpico 1300 , Sala Casella 200, Giardini della Filavmo-niea 250 *Comments:* is the oldest private accademia musicale in Italy (c:1821) organising public concerts and children's music courses; the Accademia also has three choirs

AIDA – Accademia Internazionale delle Arti
Via Crescenzio 58, 00193 **Roma**
Tel: 06-6880 4620 Fax: 06-6880 4620
Internet: www.aidarte.org
E-Mail: aida@rmnet.it
president Doris Andrews; vice president Roberto Paris; promotion V. Fernando Reynoso
Events: concerts winter & summer *Perfs:* 50 *Arts type:* all types, master classes in music, cinema, art exhibitions *Comments:* Aida chamber and symphony orchestra & Aida International Soloist Group; seminars, masterclasses, electronic music laboratory

Arte della Commedia s.r.l
Via del Viminale 51, 00184 **Roma**
Tel: 06-485 498/487 0630 Fax: 06-487 0568
direttore generale Paolo Donat-Cattin
Arts type: drama *Comments:* moving in the year 2000

Arte Spettacolo International
Via di Pallacorda 11/a, 00186 **Roma**
Tel: 06-687 4982 Fax: 06-687 4982
presidente e direttore artistico Daniele Valmaggi; organizzazione e coordinatore Sabine Frantellizzi
Arts type: theatre (especially international visual/avant-garde), show events, concerts (early, chamber, opera, new age, world), lectures *Comments:* organise various festivals (international theatre, music); produce own theatre performances and site-specific, large-scale events, also involving local artistic groups; see also Drama

Associazione Coro Polifonico Romano Oratorio del Gonfalone 'Gastone Tosato'
vicolo della Scimia 1/b, 00186 **Roma**
Tel: 06-687 5952 Fax: 06-687 5952
presidente Antonio Triglia; vicepresidenti Emilio Acerna; direttore artistico Maestro Angelo Persichilli; ufficio stampa Marco Mauceri; segretario Marco De Totis
Events: 20 October- June *Arts type:* chamber, polifonic concerts, choral *Venues:* Oratorio Caravita 400, Palazzo della Cancelleria Apostolica 500 *:* Oratorio del Gonfalone under refurbishment; opening possibly in spring 2000

Associazione Culturale Concerti dell'Arcadia
via dei Maffei 60, 00165 **Roma**
Tel: 06-6641 1649 Fax: 06-6641 1649
presidente Loreto Bianco;
direttore artistico Francesco Vignanelli
Arts type: baroque, chamber, harpsichord, organ concerts, courses

Associazione Giovanile Musicale (AGIMUS)
via dei Greci 18, 00187 **Roma**
Tel: 06-3600 1902/3081 0714 Fax: 06-3081 1587
Internet: www.webeco.it/agimu
E-Mail: agimus@uni.net
presidente Raffaele Bevilacqua; vicepresidente Giuseppe Basile; direttore artistico M° Sergio Perticaroli; segretario generale Anna Maria Brancati Guzzoni; coordinatore nazionale Sig.Ra Fiammetta Mazzoleni
Events: 600 *Arts type:* symphonic, chamber recitals, dance, ballet, musicals, folk music, choral music, competitions, seminars, courses, conferences
Comments: about 70 offices all over Italy, each organising in their own region or area, L' Agimus é Riconosciuta dal Ministero della Pubblica Istruzione e dal Consiglio dei Ministri – Dipartimento dello Spettacolo; alternative E-mails: info.agimos@uni.net and agimus.roma@uni.net

Associazione Nuova Consonanza
Via Simone de Saint Bon 61, 00195 **Roma**
Tel: 06-370 0323
Fax: 06-372 0026
Internet: users.iol.it/nuovaconsonanza
E-Mail: nuovaconsonanza@iol.it
presidente e direttore artistico Mauro Cardi ; vice presidente Michele Dall'Ongaro; segretario Enrico Marocchini; consiglieri Alessandro Sbordoni, Piero Niro
Events: 20 (May/June) (Oct-Dec) *Arts type:* contemporary and chamber music, symphony, recitals, seminars, conferences, new music, electronic music *Venues:* Goethe Institut 300, Acquario Romano 300

Associazione Teatro di Roma – Teatro Argentina
Via dei Barbieri 21, 00186 **Roma**
Tel: 06-6840 0008/ 687 5445 (promotion)
Fax: 06-8768 77396
Internet: www.teatro.roma.it
E-Mail: teatrodiroma@mail.nexus.it
direttore Mario Martone; presidente Walter Pedulla; amministrazione Filippo Vacca; produzione Antonietta Rame; attività culturalie progetti special Miriam Tassi; promozione Sandro Piccioni; responsabile tecnico Gino Potini; ufficio stampa Roberta Rem
Events: 40 *Arts type:* drama *Venues:* Teatro Argentina 650, Teatro India *Policy:* own productions and hosts other Italian and foreign companies *Comments:* the Teatro Argentina, Largo di Torre Argentina (tel: 6-684 001) belongs to the city of Rome; it organises laboratories of integration for young people with or without handicaps through the language of theatre; courses for young actors; see also Venues and Agents & Producers

Atlantide Entertainment s.r.l.
Lungotevere Flaminio 62, 00196 **Roma**
Tel: 06-320 1532 Fax: 06-320 1425
administrative director Francesco Bellomo;
artistic director Michele Placido;
technical director Paolo Fortini
Events: 3 *Perfs:* 250 *Arts type:* drama
Comments: see also Agents & Producers

Future Music
Via Federico Patetta 79, 00167 **Roma**
Tel: 06-662 1973 Fax: 06-6601 3730
Internet: www.timcompetition.org
E-Mail: info@timcompetition.org
presidente Federico Fait; direttore artistico Luigi Fait
Arts type: chamber orch, choral music, chamber music, folk music, jazz, operetta, sacred music, song recitals, symphony music, multi-media *Comments:* artist management, CD production, festivals and competitions organisation; see also Competitions and Agents & Producers

Istituzione Universitaria dei Concerti
Lungotevere Flaminio 50, 00196 **Roma**
Tel: 06-361 0051/2 Fax: 06-3600 1511
Internet: www.concertiiuc.it
E-Mail: segreteria.iuc@concertiiuc.it
presidente Arcangela Bucci Fortuna; consielio artistico Antonio Ballista, Ennio Morricone, Franco Piperno
Events: 40 (from Oct-April) *Arts type:* chamber orch, choral music, chamber music, early music, electronic music, folk music,inst recitals, jazz, new music, sacred music, symphony music,song recitals *Venues:* Aula Magna dell'Università 'La Sapienza'
Policy: diffusion of music amongst young people and university environment

Kybalion
Via Antonio Serra 82, 00191 **Roma**
Tel: 06-334 0198 Fax: 06-334 0198
president Alberto Zanmatti; artistic director Gisella Johnson; vice president Marisella Mazzaroli; technical and practical music provisioner Rojo
Arts type: theatre, dance, music, visual arts *Venues:* Trevi Teatro, Teatro Vascello Rome, Teatro Caio Melisso di Spoleto, Teatro Torti, Teatro Subasio di Spello *Policy:* promotion and production of events especially in the dance world *Comments:* see also Dance and Competitions

Pentagono Produzioni Associate
Via Salaria 72, 00198 **Roma**
Tel: 06-854 9851 Fax: 06-841 6174
direttore artistico Renata Orso Ambrosoli; legale rappresentante Roberto Carnielli
Events: 6 *Perfs:* 60 *Arts type:* ballet, contemporary and experimental dance

Semar Publishers srl
Via di Torre Argentina 47, 00186 **Roma**
Tel: 06-687 6523/9333 Fax: 06-6830 8601
Internet: www.semarweb.com
E-Mail: semarpublishers@altavista.net
president and artistic director Sahlan Momo
Events: 3 on average *Perfs:* 5 on average *Arts type:* classic contemporary *Policy:* promotion of new talents
Comments: see also Recorded Media

Associazione Filarmonica
C.so Rosmini 78/c , 38068 **Rovereto (TN)**
Tel: 0464-435 255 Fax: 0464-435 255
presidente onorario M° Silvio De Florian; presidente Andrea Condihi; vice presidente Oliviero Defloriah; direttore artistico Mariano Andreolli
Events: 20, Oct-May *Arts type:* symphonic, chamber, recitals *Venues:* Teatro Comunale Zandonai, Sala Filarmonica

Associazione Culturale Centro d'Arte La Pescaiola
Via Erbosa 1, **S. Andrea in Pescaiola (PI)**
Tel: 050-864 550
Fax: 050-864 550
presidente Renato Baldasserini;
segretario Francesco Boaghini
Arts type: music, theatre, opera, visual arts exhibitions

Accademia Musicale Valdarnese
Viale Gramsci, 11, 52027 **S. Giovanni Valdarno (AR)**
Tel: 055-942 845 Fax: 055-942 845
presidente onorario Roman Vlad; presidente Geom. Sergio Passerotti; vice presidente Prof. Franco Sabatini; direttore artistico GianLuca Passerotti
Events: 15 *Arts type:* chamber concerts, classical *Venues:* Teatro Masaccio 500 (S. Giovanni Valdarno), Teatro Comunale 200 (Cavriglia), various *Comments:* courses

Associazione Musicale 'Ars Antiqua'
via Vittorio Veneto 16/7, Casella Postale 79, 16039 **Sestri Levante (GE)**
Tel: 0185-485 169 Fax: 0185-485 169
direttore amministrativo Camilla Pigati; segretario generale Franca Campodonico; presidente Giulio Costa; vice presidente Francesco Gardella;
direttore artistico Vittorio Costa
Arts type: classical and chamber music *Venues:* auditorium 200, Grand Hotel dei Castelli 200, Chiesa di S. Nicolò 500 *Comments:* organise festival Estivo di Musica da Camera, concerts and competition; see Festival Piano Competition

Accademia Musicale Chigiana
via di Città 89, 53100 **Siena**
Tel: 0577-46152 Fax: 0577-288 124
Internet: www.chigiana.it
E-Mail: accademia.chigiana@chigiana.it
direttore amministrativo Mario Naldini;
presidente Prof. Giovanni Grottanelli De'Santi;
direttore artistico Mffl Aldo Bennici
Events: Luglio-agosto – Nov/May *Arts type:* chamber orch, choral music, chamber music, early music, inst recitals,new music, music theatre, sacred music, song recitals, symphony music, world music *Venues:* Palazzo Chigi Saracini, Chiese di Sant 'Agostino, Teatro dei Rinnovati, Palazzo Pubblico, Teatro dei Rozzi
Comments: also organise masterclasses, festivals

Foundazione INDA – Istituto Nazionale Dramma Antico
C.so Matteotti 29, 96100 **Siracusa**
Tel: 0931-67415 Fax: 0931-21424
presidente Walter le Moli; direttore organizzativo t.b.a.
Arts type: classical drama *Venues:* Teatro Greco di Siracusa 10000 (national monument) *Comments:* also organise the festival Internazionale Teatro dei Giovani, the congresso Internazionale Dramma Antico, courses, conferences and edit magazine Dioniso;
see also Festivals

Associazione culturale L'Orfeo di Spoleto
casella postale 62, 06049 **Spoleto (PG)**
Tel: 0743-260 337 Fax: 0743-260 337
Internet: orfeo.ezb.net
E-Mail: ass.orfeo@bigfoot.com
presidente e direttore artistico Mffl Fabrizio Ammetto
Events: 30 *Perfs:* Jan-Dec *Arts type:* concerts (chamber orch, choral music, chamber music, early music, inst recitals, sacred music, classical and contemporary music, music courses, seminars, musicological conferences *Venues:* Teatro Caio Melisso, Sala Pegasus, Chiesa Cattedrale, Chiesa S. Gregorio Maggiore, Chiesa S. Sabino *Policy:* diffusion of music *Comments:* organise concerts-seasons (Jan/Dec); possession library; visiting address: piazza G. Bovio 1, 06049 Spoleto (PG)

Teatro Lirico Sperimentale di Spoleto 'Adriano Belli'
Piazza Bovio n.1, 06049 **Spoleto (PG)**
Tel: 0743-221 645/220 440 Fax: 0743-222 930
Internet: www.caribusiness.it/lirico
E-Mail: teatrolirico@mail.caribusiness.it
presidente avv. Carlo Belli; direttore artistico M° Michelangelo Zurletti; segretario generale Claudio Lepore; presidente onorario Goffredo Petrassi; artistic assitant Nadia Nigris; administration Adele Capone; public relations Andrea Penna
Perfs: 4 opera productions every year and concerts *Arts type:* concerts, opera, lieder concerts, chamber operas *Venues:* Teatro Nuovo, Caio Melisso – Spoleto
Comments: organisation of a young opera singers competition, winners will attend a course and then play in their opera season; organisation of a new chamber opera competition called "Orpheus", biennial; professional training course for orchestral players; see also Festivals and Competitions

Associazione Musicale Maria Caniglia
Vico dei Sardi 9, 67039 **Sulmona (AQ)**
Tel: 0864-212 207 Fax: 0864-260 668
direttore artistico Dott. Filippo Tella
Events: 10 *Arts type:* lyric concerts *Venues:* Teatro Comunale di Sulmona 980 *Comments:* organises concorso internazionale di canto Maria Caniglia; see also Competitions

Camerata Musicale Sulmonese
Vico dei Sardi 9, 67039 **Sulmona (AQ)**
Tel: 0864-212 207
Fax: 0864-260 668
presidente Avv. Vincenzo Masei;
direttore artistico Dott. Filippo Tella
Events: 30 *Arts type:* symphonic, chamber, recitals, ballets, jazz *Venues:* Teatro Comunale 980, Auditorium dell'Annunziata 300 *Comments:* season Oct to May

Associazione Culturale Iniziativa Camt Monferrato
Via Ovada n° 13, 15070 **Tagliolo Monferrato (AL)**
Tel: 0143-89327/0338-667 1562
Fax: 0143-89327
Internet: web.tin.it/nhfede/camt/
E-Mail: nhbors@tin.it
president Maurizio Barboro;
vice-president Federico Borsari;
artistic director Luigi Dominici
Events: 4 *Perfs:* 50 *Venues:* Castello Reale di Racconigi (300), Oratorio di S. Giovanni Battista (Ovada) 200

Accademia Corale Stefano Tempia
via del Carmine 28, 10122 **Torino**
Tel: 011-521 4266
Fax: 011-521 4266
presidente dott. Guido Pignocchino; vicepresidente ing. Camillo Montanaro; direttore artistico Alberto Peyretti
Events: 13 *Arts type:* symphonic, choral , chamber concerts

Associazione Musicale Antidogma Musica
Via Cernaia, 38, 10122 **Torino**
Tel: 011-542 936
Fax: 011-542 936
Internet: arpnet.it/~amusica
E-Mail: ecorreg@tin.it
president Dora Filippone;
artistic director Enrico Correggia
Events: 12-15 *Arts type:* classical & contemporay music *Venues:* Conservatorio G. Verdi *Comments:* Ensemble Antidogma which tours abroad; Antidogma Musica festival of ancient and contemporary music – June-July and Sept/Oct, see also Festivals

Associazione Piemonte Danza Musica Teatro
via Petrarca 37, 10126 **Torino**
Tel: 011-650 0211 Fax: 011-650 0265
Internet: www.tnt.nuovo.it
E-Mail: nuovo@mail.tin.it
presidente Girolamo Angione;
consultente artistico Secondo Villata
Events: 1 *Perfs:* 30 *Arts type:* classical concerts
Venues: Teatro Alfieri 1500

Camerata Strumentale Alfredo Casella
Via Cernaia 38, 10122 **Torino**
Tel: 011-542 936 Fax: 011-542 936
Internet: arpnet.it/~casella
E-Mail: ecorreg@tin.it
presidente Enrico Correggia;
direttore artistico Alberto Peyretti
Events: 10 *Arts type:* classical music, contemporary
Venues: Conservatorio G Verdi,
churches and castles in Piedmont

Fondazione Teatro Nuovo per la Danza
Cso Massimo d'Azeglio 17, 10126 **Torino**
Tel: 011-650 0211
Fax: 011-650 0265
direttore artistico Eian Mesturino; responsabile attività didattiche Germon Erbe; ufficio promozione Roberto Angi; direttore organizzativo Lino Bongiovanni
Venues: Teatro Nuovo Torino, sale teatrali: Sala grande 1000, Sala Valentino 1 300, Sala Valentino 2 300 *Policy:* production, promotion, distribution and training
Comments: see also Dance and Festivals

Torino Spettacoli
P.za Solferino 4, 10121 **Torino**
Tel: 011-562 3800
Fax: 011-562 3435
direzione artistica Germana Erba
Arts type: musical comedy, plays, classical and pop concerts, revues, operetta, cinema *Venues:* Teatro Alfieri 1500, Teatro Erbo 360 *Comments:*
Teatro Stabile Privato di interesse pubblico; see also Venues and Agents & Producers

Unione Musicale
Piazza Castello 29, 10123 **Torino**
Tel: 011-544 523/517 5188
Fax: 011-533 544
Internet: www.inrete.it/classica/um/um.html
E-Mail: um@inrete.it
presidente Alberto Papuzzi;
direttore artistico Giorgio Pugliaro;
amministratore Fausta Civati;
ufficio stampa Paola Mohzolon
Events: 50 in Torino, 550 in Piemonte *Arts type:* chamber music, recitals *Venues:* Conservatorio G. Verdi, Auditorium del Lingotto, Teatro Regio

Associazione Amici della Musica di Trapani
Piazza Umberto I, 5, 91100 **Trapani**
Tel: 0923-569 213/871 312
Fax: 0923-569 211
direttore artistico Paolo Nicolosi;
presidente Prof. Alessandro de Santis;
vice presidente avv. Vittorio Cangemi;
direttore amministrativo geom. Natale Augugliaro
Events: 30 *Perfs:* 30 *Arts type:* chamber orch, chamber music, soloists, contemporary dance *Venues:* Astoria Park Hotel 350, Auditorium Polo Univeritario Trapani 1000 *Comments:* summer concerts and seminars Trapani

Associazione Culturale Antonio Pedrotti
P.zza Mostra 19, 38100 **Trento**
Tel: 0461-231 223
Fax: 0461-232 592
Internet: www.ishost.net/concorsopedrotti
E-Mail: a.pedrotti.competition@tn.nettuno.it
secretary Lorenza Mascagni;
presidente Mauro Pedrotti;
direttore artistico Maurizio Dini Ciacci
Comments: organiser of Antonio Pedrotti, Concorso Internazionale per Direttori D'Orchestra;
see also Competitions

Società Filarmonica
Via Verdi 30, 38100 **Trento**
Tel: 0461-985 244
Fax: 0461-985 244
E-Mail: filartn@tin.it
presidente Marco de Battaglia; vice presidente Avv. Antonio Divan; direttore amministrativo Avv. Lorenzo Arnoldi; segretario artistico Antonio Carlini
Events: Oct-May *Arts type:* symphonic, chamber, recitals
Venues: Sala Filarmonica 250
Comments: see also Venues

Associazione Promusica
Via Catraro 6, Via Imbriani 5, 34124 **Trieste**
Tel: 040-636 263 Fax: 040-636 263
E-Mail: cappciv@tin.it
direttore artistico Marco Sofianopulo
Events: 20 *Arts type:* choral music, chamber music, sacred music, song recitals, inst recitals *Venues:* Cattedrale di S. Giusto, Auditorium del Museo Revoltella, Tempio Anglicano *Comments:* organises concerts music courses and seminars;
see also Festivals

Cappella Civica del Comune di Trieste
Via Imbriani 5, 34122 **Trieste**
Tel: 040-636 263 Fax: 040-636 263
E-Mail: cappciv@tin.it
director Marco Sofianopulo;
organist of the Cathedral Mauro Macri
Perfs: 120 *Arts type:* sacred music, Gregorian chants, chamber vocal, historical research *Venues:* Cappella, San Giusto Cathedral *Comments:* Laie Institution founded and supports by Comune di Trieste since 1538; they have different types of courses

Società dei Concerti
Via C. Beccaria 4, 34133 **Trieste**
Tel: 040-362 408
Fax: 040-362 409
direttore amministrativo prof. Tullio Corzani; segretario artistico ing. Nello Gonzini; presidente dott. Federico Morway; vice presidenti dott. Tullio Corzani, M° Raffaello de Banfield; ufficio stampa M° Emilio Curiel
Events: Oct-May *Perfs:* ooni concerto replicato 2 volte (22 in total) *Arts type:* chamber, recitals
Venues: Sala Tripcovich 2030

Associazione Mittelfest
Stretta San Martino 4, Cividale del Friuli, 33043 **Udine**
Tel: 0432-730 793 Fax: 0432-701 099
Internet: www.regione.fvg.it/mittelfest
E-Mail: mittelfest@regione.fvg.it
presidente Avv. Giovanni Pelizzo
Perfs: 40 *Arts type:* drama, music, dance, cinema, puppetry, poetry, visual arts *Venues:* Teatro Comunale A.Ristori 499, theatre and open air spaces in the town *Comments:* member of the CEI – Central European Initiative (with 16 central European countries); organisers of Mittelfest (q.v.); see also Festivals

Fondazione Giorgio Cini
Isola San Giorgio Maggiore, 30124 **Venezia**
Tel: 041-528 9900 Fax: 041-523 8540
Internet: www.cini.it
E-Mail: fondacini@cini.it
presidente Feliciano Benvenuti; vice presidente Marino Cortese, Francesco Valcanover; addetto stampa Giusi Conti; segretario generale Renzo Zorzi
Events: 20-22 *Arts type:* early music (vocal & instrumental), chamber ensemble, seminars, exhibitions
Venues: Fondazaione Cini: Sala degli Arazzi 500, Refettorio Palladiano 450 *Comments:* summer music courses in July and August

Associazione Amici della Musica
Via Camozzini 4, 37126 **Verona**
Tel: 045-914 729 Fax: 045-913 108
presidente e direttore artistico Maestro Guido Begal; vice presidente dott. Bartolomeo Costantini e rag. Mario Trotto
Events: 16 Oct-Apr *Arts type:* chamber, recitals *Venues:* Teatro Nuovo 800, Teatro Filarmonico 1100 *Comments:* non-profit association

Foundazione A.I.D.A./Centro Teatro Ragazzi
Vicolo Dietro Campanile Filippini 6, 37121 **Verona**
Tel: 045-800 1471/595 284 Fax: 045-800 9850
E-Mail: fondazione@f-aida.it
general management and administration Roberto Terribile; artistic production Gianni Franceschini; press office, public relations Flaminia Scanu, Meri Malaguti
Arts type: children's theatre, puppets, musical theatre *Policy:* operates mainly as a centre for production and promotion of theatre and theatrical events, dedicated to children and teenagers *Comments:* Vicolo Dietro Campanile Filippini 16, 37121, Verona Tel:045-592 709; second E-mail: f-aida@f-aida.it; A.I.D.A. provides an advisory service for schools, providing them with the help of the centre's specialists to produce their end of year plays

Associazione Amici della Musica di Vicenza
via Arzignano, 1, 36100 **Vicenza**
Tel: 0444-511 799 Fax: 0444-511 721
Internet: www.amicidellamusica.vi.it
E-Mail: info@amicidellamusica.vi.it
direttori amministrativi Federico Caprin, Adriana Cristini; segreteria Carla Bordin; direttore artistico Piergiorgio Meneghini; presidente Gian Nico Rodighiero; vicepresidente Paolo Portinari
Events: 25 *Arts type:* chamber orch, choral music, chamber music, early music, electronic music, folk music, jazz, song recitals, symphony music, classical ballet *Venues:* Auditorium Canneti 300, Teatro Olimpico 500, Auditorium della Fiera di Vicenza 750, Basiliea dei Santi Felice e Fortunato 800 *Comments:* also organise masterclasses, and other cultural activities

Associazione Amici della Musica 'Rosario Lucchesi'
via Garibaldi 179, 97019 **Vittoria (RG)**
Tel: 0932-862 785/868 006 Fax: 0932-862 785
presidente dr. Salvatore Spatola; dir art Maestro Enrico Lancia; direttore amministrativo Prof.ssa Dora Giacchi; segretario generale Prof.ssa Rosamaria Alescio
Events: 16 *Arts type:* symphony, chamber music, solo recitals *Venues:* Golden Hall 420, Teatro Comunale di Vittoria 320

Luca Pellizzaroli
V. Porcia 25, 31029 **Vittoria Veneto (TV)**
Tel: 0438-59552 Fax: 0438-59552
E-Mail: lukesp@libero.it
Arts type: classical recitals

LATVIA (+371)

Agency Riga 800
Torna 4 IB-103, 1050 **Riga**
Tel: 7-320 550 Fax: 7-320 609
Internet: www.riga800.lv
E-Mail: riga800@rcc.lv
director general Mrs. Inguna Ribena

Culture Capital Foundation
Latvijas Kultûrkapitâla Fonds
Pils iela 20, 1050 **Riga**
Tel: 7-503 177 Fax: 7-503 176
E-Mail: kkf@parks.lv
director Mâris Berzins
Comments: support and promote development of creative activity in all branches of culture and art, aquiring of education, and preserving of cultural heritage; see also National Organisations

Culture Department of Riga City
Rîgas pilsetas Kultûras Pârvalde
Kr. Valdemâra 5, 1010 **Riga**
Tel: 7-320 941/320 398 Fax: 7-320 635
Internet: www.rcc.lv
E-Mail: rdkp@latnet.lv
head of department Rolands Jurasevskis
Comments: second E-mail: viktors@rcc.lv; municiple institution that manages and supervises, supports and promotes cultural activities (amateur and professional art); see also Ministries and Festivals

E Melngailis Folk Art Centre
E. Melngaiïa Tautas Mâkslas centrs
4 Pils laukums, 1364 **Riga**
Tel: 7-228 985 Fax: 7-227 405
E-Mail: festival@latnet.lv
director Janis Kurpnieks
Arts type: folk music and art

International New Music Centre
Starptautiskais Jaunfas Muzikas centrs
Jelgavas 25, 1004 **Riga**
Tel: 7-82 8538 Fax: 7-82 8538
director Egils Straume
Arts type: management of concerts, workshops and festivals of contemporary and jazz music

Latvian Concert Agency
Latvijas Koncertdirekcija
11a Kaïîu, 1664 **Riga**
Tel: 7-213 426 Fax: 7-213 497
E-Mail: koncdir@mail.bkc.lv
director Gints Kârkliòs

Riga Early Music Centre
Riga Senas Muzikas Centrs
Brivibas iela 85, 1001 **Riga**
Tel: 7-275 575 Fax: 7-275 060
managing director Solvita Sejane;
director Boriss Avramecs
Arts type: early music

LITHUANIA (+370)

Concert Agency Litart
Koncertine agentura Litart
Laisvės al. 51a, 3000 **Kaunas**
Tel: 7-203 261 Fax: 7-706 642

Kaunas Philharmonic Society
Kauno Filharmonija
Sapiegos 5, 3000 **Kaunas**
Tel: 7-222 558 (director)
Fax: 7-706 642
director Justinas Krepsta

Music Company Combo
Muzikine firma Combo
Mickeviciaus 8a, 3000 **Kaunas**
Tel: 7-209 419

Klaipeda Philharmonic Society
Klaipedos Filharmonija
Danes 19, 5800 **Klaipeda**
Tel: 6-113 959 (director)

Siauliai Philharmonic Society
Siauliu Filharmonija
Ausros al. 15, 5400 **Siauliai**
Tel: 41-35743 (director)

Club Jauna Muzika
Klubas Jauna Muzika
PO Box 980, 2000 **Vilnius**
Tel: 2-227 784 Fax: 2-226 679
president Algis Gurevicius

Lithuanian Concert Promoters' Association
Zemaitijos 8/11-222, 2001 **Vilnius**
Tel: 2-628 503 Fax: 2-220 966
contact E. Zalpys
Comments: see also National Organisations and Agents & Producers

National Philharmonic Society of Lithuania
Lietuvos Nacionaline Filharmonija
Ausros Vartu 5, 2001 **Vilnius**
Tel: 2-626 802 Fax: 2-622 859
E-Mail: info@filharmonija.lt
general director Gintautas Kevisas

Open Society Foundation Lithuania
Atviros Lietuvos Fondas
c/o Open Society House, J. Jaksto 9, 2600 **Vilnius**
Tel: 2-223 695 Fax: 2-223 691
Internet: www.osf.lt
performing arts programme coordinator
Elona Bundzaitė-Bajorinienė
Comments: see also National Organisations

State Concert Organisation Tonas
Valstybine Koncertine Organizacija Tonas
Ausros Vartu 5, 2001 **Vilnius**
Tel: 2-615 704 (director) Fax: 2-622 859
director J. Ereminas

LUXEMBOURG (+352)

Soirées de Luxembourg/Jeunesses Musicales du Luxembourg
Youth & Music
129 Mühlenweg, 2155 **Luxembourg**
Tel: 492 924 Fax: 492 884
E-Mail: rfranck@pt.lu
secrétaire général Rémy Franck;
président Jean Wenandy
Events: 30 concerts for young audiences, 12 concerts 'Les Soirees de Luxembourg' for all age groups *Perfs:* 38 *Arts type:* chamber orch, chamber music, folk music, inst recitals, symphony music, choral music, song recitals *Venues:* Conservatoire du Luxembourg 700

MACEDONIA (+389)

Association of Macedonian Composers
Sojuz na kompozitorite ná Makedonija
Maksim Gorki 18, 91000 **Skopje**
Tel: 91-220 567/234 953
Fax: 91-235 854
president Vlastimir Nikolovski;
secretary Marko Kolovski

Youth Cultural Center – Skopje
Kej Dimitar Vlahov bb, 91000 **Skopje**
Tel: 91-111 508/225/233 401 Fax: 91-115 906

MALTA (+356)

Concert Europe Festival Incentive Tours
Nazju Falzon Street, **Birkirkara**
Tel: 491 610/441 157
Fax: 491 598
Internet: dream.vol.net.mt/com/concerteurope
E-Mail: conceuro@dream.vol.net.mt
managing director Francis Pullicino
Arts type: festivals, concerts, shows, events
Comments: see also Competitions

Leone Philarmonic Society
Aurora Opera House, 100 Republic, **Victoria, Gozo**
Tel: 562 974 Fax: 562 559
president Dr. Michael Caruano L.L.D.;
secretary Patrick Camilleri
Arts type: annual: 2 symphonic band concerts by the Leone Band and 1 opera *Venues:* capacity 1000 *Policy:* to spread the art of music and culture in the Maltese Islands *Comments:* the Leone Philarmonic Society organises the feast of St. Mary on the 15th August from the Gozo Cathedral

MOLDOVA (+373)

Interarta – Republican Association of Artistic Impressariat
Puskin Str. 21, 2012 **Chisinau**
Tel: 2-238 258 Fax: 2-238 257
director Victor Bublitchi
Coments: see also National Organisations

National Philharmonic Society
Filarmonica Nationala
78 Mitropolitul Vaarlam, 2012 **Chisinau**
Tel: 2-238 258 Fax: 2-238 257
director Ion Josanu

O.C.I. Moldova-Concert
21, Puskin str., 2012 **Chisinau**
Tel: 2-233 005 Fax: 2-238 257
director Valentin Goga

NETHERLANDS (+31)

Groene Kerkje, Het
Kapershof 23, 1657 LM **Abbekerk**
Tel: 229-582 162
artistic director and chairman Paula Doesburg-Langer
Events: 9 *Perfs:* 9 *Arts type:* chamber music *Venues:* Het Groene Kerkje 150 *Comments:* events are held once a month

Kulturele Stichting Abcoude-Baambrugge
Doude van Troostwijkstraat 51, 1391 ER **Abcoude**
Tel: 294-281 724
secretary Annie Pabon-Bos
Events: 6 *Arts type:* chamber music, choral, orchestras + small ensembles *Venues:* De Dorpskerk 400

Stichting Alkmaarse Kamermuziek
Emmastraat 232, 1814 DV **Alkmaar**
Tel: 72-512 3115
secretary M G Vermooten
Events: 6 concerts yearly *Arts type:* chamber music, song recitals (choral music), solo recitals *Venues:* De Vest Theatre, Alkmaar 700

Stichting ACHK-De Paviljoens
De Roestbak/De Metropole/Dienst Kunstzaken
Odeonstraat 3, 1325 AL **Almere**
Tel: 36-545 0400 Fax: 36-545 0800
Internet: www.achk-depaviljoens.nl
E-Mail: info@achk-depaviljoens.nl
director Lia Gieling;
public relations Antoinette Andriese
Events: 130 *Arts type:* art exhibitions, performances
Venues: De Metropole 600, De Roestbak 180

Culturele Stichting Cornelis de Vlaming
Ahornstraat 4, 2404 VP **Alphen a/d Rijn**
Tel: 172-475 597
secretary Mrs M.A.R. Van Harten; chairman H. Smid
Events: 4 *Arts type:* chamber music *Venues:* Oudshoornse Kerk, Alphen aan den Rijn 350

Stichting Vrienden Kasteel Amerongen
Drostestraat 20, 3958 BK **Amerongen**
Tel: 454 212 (Amerongen Castle)
administrator N Hangelbroek
Events: 3 *Arts type:* chamber music
Venues: Amerongen Castle

Theater and Congress Centrum de Flint
Postbus 246, 3800 AE **Amersfoort**
Tel: 33-422 9229/9222 Fax: 33-475 7280
E-Mail: de.flint@wss.nl
director P. Erkelens; head of publicity Nrndr Dekaus
Events: 210 *Arts type:* music, theatre, dance, mime, puppets, childrens theatre, cabaret
Venues: Stadshal 1000, De Flint 800

Dienst Onderwijs en Cultuur
Postbus 4, 1180 BA **Amstelveen**
Tel: 20-540 4475 Fax: 20-540 4461
director Rein Vos
Events: 230 *Arts type:* classical, pop music, theatre, cabaret, lectures, art exhibitions *Venues:* Schouwburg Amstelveen 640, Museum of Modern Art of Amstelveen

Begijnhofconcerten Engelse Kerk
Begijnhof 48, 1012 WV **Amsterdam**
Tel: 20-624 9665
artistic directors Leo van Doeselaar, Marten Root
Events: 70 *Arts type:* chamber music
Venues: Engelse Kerk 225

Bimhuis
Oude Schans 73-77, 1011 KW **Amsterdam**
Tel: 20-623 3373 Fax: 20-620 7759
Internet: www.bimhuis.nl
E-Mail: bimhuis@bimhuis.nl
artistic director Huub van Riel;
production & public relations Karin Klooster
Events: 150 *Arts type:* jazz and improvised music *Venues:* concert series 'Music Now' (10 annual concerts): Stedelijk Museum, Amsterdam; Bimhuis Amsterdam 400 *Comments:* organisation: Stichting Jazz Amsterdam/Bimhuis; see also Venues

Bureau Berbee Culturele affairs
Karte Leidsedwassraat 12, 1017 RC **Amsterdam**
Tel: 20-627 0455 Fax: 20-625 0616
director Inke Berbee
Arts type: mime, dance *Comments:* see also Agents & Producers, Dance and Drama (Karina Holla)

Concertgebouw NV, Het
Concertgebouwplein 2-6, 1071 LN **Amsterdam**
Tel: 20-573 0573/671 8345 (box office) Fax: 20-573 0570
Internet: www.concertgebouw.nl
E-Mail: cgbnvl@euronet.nl
managing director Martijn Sanders;
head of marketing department Ms Doele
Events: 700 *Arts type:* chamber orchestra, choral music, chamber music, early music, electronic music, folk music, instrumental recitals, jazz, new music, light orchestral music, music theatre, operetta, sacred music, song recitals, symphony music, multi media, opera, world music *Venues:* main hall 2037, recital hall 470 *Policy:* rent + own risk *Comments:* see also Venues

De IJsbreker
Weesperzijde 23, 1091 EC **Amsterdam**
Tel: 20-668 1805 Fax: 20-694 6607
Internet: www.ijsbreker.nl
E-Mail: post@ijsbreker.nl
director & programming Jan Wolff;
publicity and marketing Menno Tummers
Events: 200 concerts of 20th century music a year *Arts type:* chamber music, electronic music, new music, music theatre, song recitals, multi media, world music *Venues:* 1 concert hall 120, Tropeninstitutute, Rode Hoed *Comments:* artistic staff organises own programme; hire if space in programme

Jeunesses Musicales Nederland
PO Box 424, 1000 AK **Amsterdam**
Tel: 20-420 6027 Fax: 20-420 8130
Internet: www.jmnl.demon.nl
E-Mail: secr@jmnl.demon.nl
secretary general Löis de Jong
Arts type: chamber orch, choral music, chamber music, new music, light orch music, music theatre, song recitals, symphony music, early music, electronic music, folk music, inst recitals, jazz, operetta, sacred music *Comments:* Jeunesses Musicales Nederland is a federation of organisations; organisations for national youth music projects; local offices, National symphonic orchestra, summer music academy; Jeunesses Musicales Nederland is a member of the 'Fédération Internationale des Jeunesses Musicales

Reizend Muziek Gezelschap, Het
Postbox 15566, 1001 NB **Amsterdam**
Tel: 20-427 7772 Fax: 20-427 7774
E-Mail: rmg@ezh.nl
director Christiaan Bor
Perfs: 40-50 *Arts type:* chamber music *Venues:* Concertgebouw, Amsterdam, + throughout the Netherlands : organises concert series in May and November as well as annual
Zomer Muziekfestival in August

Stichting Caucasus Foundation
Koxhorn 32-3, 1082 EW **Amsterdam**
secretary Henk Van Silfhout;
president Levan Khetaguri (Georgia)
Arts type: all types *Policy:* supports Caucasian countries in the process of cultural integration with European countries, sets up and implements programmes and events in art and culture for professional artists
Comments: regional programmes coordinated by IBCCP (International Bureau for Caucasian Cultural Programmes), educational programmes, management training centre, information centre, publishing programme; principal office in Georgia
– see separate entry

Stichting Nes Theaters/De Brakke Grond & Frascati
oz voorburgwal 304, 1012 GL **Amsterdam**
Tel: 20-622 7860 Fax: 20-638 3349
E-Mail: post@nestheaters.nl
managing director Florian Diepenbrock; artistic director Nan van Houte; managers Marijke Giesbers, Anne Marie Kalkman; marketing/publicity Lizzy Ondaatje
Perfs: 800 *Arts type:* drama, modern dance, mime, music theatre *Venues:* De Brakke Grond – 3 spaces: Theatre 150, Theatre 120, Studio 50; Frascati – 3 spaces: Theatre 190, Theatre 90, Studio 50 *Comments:* produce, present; carries out programming for two Amsterdam theatres: Frascati, De Brakke Grond; see also Venues

Theater Zuider Amstelkanaal
Fred. Roeskestraat 84, PO Box 74144, 070 BC **Amsterdam**
Tel: 20-675 0613Fax: 20-675 6316
director t.b.a.; contact Co van Dieben
Perfs: 25 *Arts type:* opera, classical ballet, classical theatre, modern theatre, dance, workshops
Venues: own theatre 450 *Comments:* see also Venues

Theaterzaken Via Rudolphi
Korte Leidsedwarsstraat 12, 1017 RC **Amsterdam**
Tel: 20-627 7555 Fax: 20-627 8541
E-Mail: info@viaRudolphi.nl
contact Marie Anne Rudolphi
Events: 6 *Perfs:* 200-300
Arts type: modern dance, mime, modern theatre
Comments: represent Suver Nuver-physical theatre, Carver-physical theatre, Hussaarts & Van Lohuizen, children's theatre; see also Drama and Agents & Producers

Musis Sacrum / Schouwburg Arnhem
PO Box 1103, 6801 BC **Arnhem**
Tel: 26-372 0720Fax: 26-443 4396
director F. W. van Duÿn
Arts type: all arts types *Venues:* Musis Sacrum 955, Schouwburg 750 & 200 *Comments:* see also Venues

Stichting De Baarnse Muziekkring
Prof Fockema Andreaelaan 35, 3741 EJ **Baarn**
Tel: 35-541 4562
Fax: 35-541 4562
chairman & secretary Anton A Hooijdonk
Events: 16 *Arts type:* classical chamber music
Venues: Hasselaerzaal, Baarn *Comments:* venue address: Hasselaerzaal, Kasteel Groeneveld, Groeneveld 2, 3744 ML Baarn 150

Holland Music Sessions
Postbus 250, 1860 AG **Bergen**
Tel: 72-582 1300
Fax: 72-582 1299
E-Mail: hmsinfo@haaf.nl
general manager Perry Reitsma;
artistic director Frans Wolfkamp;
artistic manager Jaco Mijnheer
Events: 120 classical music concerts, 80 masterclasses
Perfs: 200 *Arts type:* chamber orch., classical music concerts, masterclasses, chamber music *Venues:* Concertgebouw Amsterdam, Beurs van Berlage Amsterdam, Ruïnekerk Bergen, Grote Sint Laurenskerk, Alkmaar, De Haaf International Centre for Music Bergen, Conservatory Alkmaar *Policy:* stimulate young, international musicians *Comments:* visiting address: Natteweg 9, Bergen

Stedelijke Muziekschool Breda
Molenstraat 6, 4811 GS **Breda**
Tel: 76-522 6400
Fax: 76-521 3099
director Jatti Ratteng
Events: 10 *Arts type:* chamber music, pop, theatre, fine art *Venues:* concert hall 200, theatre hall 200
Comments: also have studios and working space, workshops etc., promote the pop festival Bredabarst

Theatre 't Spant
Dr A Kuyperlaan 3, 1402 SB **Bussum**
Tel: 35-693 3254 Fax: 35-693 2854
E-Mail: spantbussum@wxs.nl
head of administration M. Zwanenburg; director and artistic director William P M Voorman
Events: 53 *Arts type:* all types including theatre, dance, recorded TV shows in the theatre
Comments: see also Venues

Mojo Concerts B.V.
POB 3121, 2601 DC **Delft**
Tel: 15-212 1980 Fax: 15-214 4445
Internet: www.mojo.nl
managing director Leon Ramakers
Events: 120 concerts + 9 festivals *Arts type:* pop music, jazz, dance music *Venues:* Ahoi, Rotterdam 10000 + others *Comments:* organises North Sea Jazz Festival and Lowlands Festival

Diligentia
Lange Voorhout 5, 2514 EA **Den Haag**
Tel: 70-365 7552
Fax: 70-361 7528
Internet: www.diligentia.nl
E-Mail: diligentia@wxs.nl
director H. Boerendomk; financial manager A. Volebregt; arts programming E. Olofsen
Events: 260 *Arts type:* chamber music, theatre, cabaret
Venues: Diligentia 500 *Comments:* see also Venues

Stichting Promotie Den Haag
Gevers Deynootweg 1134, 2586 BX **Den Haag**
Tel: 70-306 9911 Fax: 70-355 4953
E-Mail: info@scheveninhan.nl
manager Ben Vermijs
Events: 35 (incl sport) *Arts type:* classical and jazz concerts *Venues:* VSB circus theatre (at Scheveningen) 1700, Kurhaul Hotel, Scheveningen

Stichting Kamermuziek Deventer
Laan van Borgele 8, 7415 DJ **Deventer**
Tel: 570-629 988 Fax: 570-629 988
director W. J. Feikema
Events: 7 *Perfs:* 6-7 *Arts type:* chamber music, classical song recitals, piano recitals *Venues:* Schouwburg, Deventer: Cultureel Centrum Leeuwenbrug

Stichting Muziek in de Maartenskerk
Berkenweg 18, 3941 JB **Doorn**
Tel: 343-415 747 Fax: 343-415 747
artistic director Mrs. E. Frÿlink
Events: 5-7 (series) + Sept festival Vladimir Mendelssohn *Arts type:* international chamber music
Venues: Maartenskerk 500 *Comments:* prestigious series of chamber music concerts

Muziekcentrum
Langestraat 49, 7511 HB **Enschede**
Tel: 53-485 8585 Fax: 53-485 8595
E-Mail: info@twentseschouwburg.nl
director Lex Kater
Events: 200 *Arts type:* symphony, chamber music, recitals, jazz, swing, pop concerts *Venues:* Hall A 1050, Hall B 200 *Comments:* venue address: Noorderhagen 27, 7511 AK Enschede; see also Venues

American Voices Association – Netherlands
Graaf Florisweg 22, 2805 AL **Gouda**
Tel: 182-678 683 Fax: 182-678 683
Internet: www.americanvoices.org
E-Mail: americanvoices@wxs.nl
artistic director John Ferguson
Perfs: 100 *Arts type:* concerts, musicals, cabaret, jazz, orchestra, special projects, chamber music, inst recitals, jazz, new music, music theatre, sacred music, song recitals, choral music *Venues:* throughout Europe
Policy: American music *Comments:* Copland Centennial 2000; Centennial Kurt Weill; artist-in-residence programs; music library development programs for Eastern Europe; consulting for American Music programs and cultural projects

Groningse Muziekvereniging
Helper Esweg 17, 9722 RP **Groningen**
Tel: 50-527 2377 Fax: 50-527 2677
contact Mrs K A Volten
Events: 7, Oct-May *Arts type:* chamber music, vocal and instrumental soloists *Venues:* Oosterpoort 450
Comments: see also Venues

Concertgebouw
2A Klokhuisplein, 2011 HK **Haarlem**
Tel: 23-512 1212 Fax: 23-512 1211
director Mark den Hertog
Events: 40-50 *Arts type:* symphonic, chamber orch & music, inst recitals, popular music *Venues:* Concertgebouw 1250, Recital Hall 250 *Policy:* present, rent *Comments:* see also Venues

Muzenforum
Zandvoorter Allee 6, 2106 BW **Heemstede**
Tel: 23-529 0045 Fax: 23-529 5816
E-Mail: olt_bijl@compuserve.com
secretary J Bijl;
programmer Mr van Eechen (70-353 2309)
Events: 8-12 *Perfs:* 8 *Arts type:* chamber orch, chamber music, choral music, early music, electronic music, folk music, inst recitals, jazz, new music, light orchestral music, music theatre, operetta, sacred music, song recitals, symphony music, multimedia, opera, world music, classical theatre, modern theatre *Venues:* Bloemendaal Town hall 300

Parkstad Limburg Theaters
Postbus 300, 6400 AH **Heerlen**
Tel: 45-576 8576 Fax: 45-571 8794
director B.M. Schoonderwoerd
Events: 250 *Perfs:* 350 *Arts type:* classical music, concerts opera, musicals, ballet, dance, pop, jazz, cabaret, drama *Venues:* Stadsschouwburg Heerlen 894 and 151, Wijngrachttheater Kerkrade 600
Comments: see also Venues

CNM Centrum Nederlandse Muziek
P.O. Box 1634, 1200 BP **Hilversum**
Tel: 35-624 0957 Fax: 35-621 0570
Internet: www.cnm.nl
E-Mail: info@cnm.nl
managing director JW ten Broeke;
label manager Gabriëla Börger
Events: 25 concerts a year, 12 CD releases on own label nm classical *Policy:* promote Dutch composers

Fred Luiten Concert Series
PO Box 2277, 2301 CG **Leiden**
Tel: 71-514 0235/364 0066 (information)
Fax: 71-566 3066
contact Fred Luiten
Arts type: baroque music, solo recitals, choir, orchestras, chamber music, opera, oratorio *Venues:* Concertgebouw 2000, Beurs van Berlage 650, Westerkerk 1000, Engelse Kerk 350 *Comments:* also organises the International Baroque Festival Amsterdam (q.v.)

Stichting Intro
St Maartenspoort 2, 6221 BA **Maastricht**
Tel: 43-325 0511/3453 Fax: 43-325 7488
director Paul Coenjaarts
Events: 30 concerts between Oct-May *Arts type:* choral music, chamber music, new music, music theatre, song recitals, multi media, new music ensambles *Venues:* theatres in Maastricht *Comments:* see also Festivals (New Music Festival Maastricht)

St Nieuwe Muziek Zeeland Kloveniersdoelen
Postbus 15, 4330 AA **Middelburg**
Tel: 118-623 650 Fax: 118-624 754
Internet: www.zeelandnet.nl/cunzld
E-Mail: cunzld@zeelandnet.nl
director Ad vant Veer
Events: 90 *Arts type:* contemporary, classical, avantgarde and improvised music *Venues:* Centre for New Music 120 *Comments:* new year festival (1 & 2 Jan) with contemporary music; annual festival in October

International Music Management
PO Box 1498, 3430 BL **Nieuwegein**
Tel: 30-280 2330 Fax: 30-280 3331/280 5326
E-Mail: immgroap@immgroap.com
managing director Ruud de Graaf
Events: 30 *Arts type:* classical music, pop music, theatre
Comments: see also Agents & Producers

Koninklijke Liedertafel – Souvenirs des Montagnards
Gemullehoekenweg 29B, 5061 MB **Oisterwijk**
Tel: 13-528 4286 Fax: 13-528 7596
president Dr Loevendie; secretary Mrs J. Dÿkstra
Events: 12-15 (June) *Arts type:* chamber music *Venues:* University of Tilburg *Comments:* aim to promote high quality chamber music in local area, invite international professional performers (organisation is run by volunteers)

Concert- en congresgebouw De Doelen
Postbus 972, 3000 AZ **Rotterdam**
Tel: 10-217 1750 Fax: 10-213 0913/433 2237
E-Mail: intdoell@xs4all.nl
general manager and artistic director Huub van Dael;
assistant manager Anton Vliegenthart;
publicity manager Ton de Langen
Events: 1600 *Perfs:* 700 *Arts type:* chamber orch, choral music, chamber music, early music, electronic music, folk music, jazz, new music, symphony music, opera, world music, pop concerts *Venues:* concert hall: main hall 2250, recital hall 620, other multi-purpose halls up to 250 *Comments:* street address- Kruisstraat 2, 3012 CT Rotterdam; see also Venues

Stichting Kamermuziekvereeniging Rotterdam
Burd. de Villeneuvesingel 18, 3055 AN **Rotterdam**
Tel: 10-418 2608 Fax: 10-422 0144
secretary Boks Keller; chairman t.b.a.;
treasurer B. H Boks
Events: 8 *Arts type:* chamber music, mainly string quartet *Venues:* small hall, De Doelen, Rotterdam 604
Comments: normal period of events Oct. to April

Zaal de Unie
Postbus 2800, 3000 CV **Rotterdam**
Tel: 10-414 1666 Fax: 10-413 5195
Internet: www.rks.nl
E-Mail: unie@rks.nl
contact Elizabeth Leve
Events: 100 *Arts type:* avant-garde films, debates & discussions on literature, visual arts, design, architecture, other arts form cross-over projects *Venues:* capacity 80+ *Comments:* part of Rotterdam Arts Council; visiting address:
Mauritsweg 34, 3012 JT Rotterdam

Concert-Stichting Hillegondakerk
Terbregseweg 73, 3056 JT **Rotterdam/Hillegersberg**
Tel: 10-420 0397 Fax: 10-420 0397
secretary C C van Hoft; bookings Mrs C. Wynbergen
Events: 9 *Arts type:* classical music, Easter and Christmas mainly choir and organ music *Venues:* Hillegondakerk 450 *Comments:* every 3rd Saturday of the month between Sept. and May

Theatre aan de Parade
PO Box 12345, 5200 GZ **s-Hertogenbosch**
Tel: 73-680 9809 Fax: 73-612 4235
Internet: www.tref.nl/s'Hertogenbosch/theater-parade
E-Mail: theater.parade@tref.nl
director Tom Odems; press and public relations Kirsten Sinke; deputy manager F. Bekker
Events: 300 *Arts type:* large-scale productions of drama, opera, music and ballet, conferences *Venues:* Room A 900, Room B up to 450, cinema 184, 3 breakout rooms
Policy: present, co-present, rent *Comments:* street address: Parade 23, 's-Hertogenbosch, Netherlands

Konings Loo
Koningin Wilhelminaweg 1, 7391 ER **Twello**
Tel: 571-270 028 Fax: 571-270 026
programme advisor A Kuiper
Events: 12-14 *Arts type:* chamber orch, choral music, chamber music, early music, folk music, inst recitals, sacred music, song recitals *Venues:* de Koninklÿk Paleis Het Loo 220

Holland Festival Early Music Utrecht & Early Music Network
Organisation for Early Music Holland,
PO Box 734, 3500 AS **Utrecht**
Tel: 30-236 2236 Fax: 30-232 2798
Internet: www.oudemuziek.nl
E-Mail: oom@oudemuziek-nl
executive producer Tineke de Ruiter van der Wal; artistic adviser Jan Nuchelmans; executive director Casper Vogel
Events: 150 (HFEMU), 120 (EM Network) *Arts type:* chamber orch, choral music, early music, music theatre, sacred music, song recitals, opera, world music *Comments:* the organisation Early Music runs both the HFEMU and the EMNetwork, both annual; HFEMU Aug-Sept, EMNetwork Oct-June nationwide; see also Festivals

Muziekcentrum Vredenburg
Postbus 550, Vredenburgpassage 77, 3500 AN **Utrecht**
Tel: 30-286 2286 Fax: 30-231 6522
Internet: vredenburg.nl
E-Mail: info@vredenburg.nl
general manager Peter Smids; programme manager (classical music) Jessica Hiir; programme manager (other music) Anna van Dyk; head of marketing/ press and PR Mathieu Heinrichs
Perfs: 450 *Arts type:* all kinds of music *Venues:* main hall 1800, small hall 300 *Comments:* see also Venues

Stichting Kunstkring Duivenvoorde
Papelaan West 168, 2254 AJ **Voorschoten**
Tel: 71-561 7633
artistic manager Peter Hansen; contact Mr Dekkers
Arts type: chamber concerts *Venues:* Castle Duivenvoorde 150

NORWAY (+47)

Bergens Kammermusikkforening
Post Box 935, 5002 **Bergen**
Tel: 5597 2026
chairman Finn Totland; vice-chairman Michael Farstad
Events: 8-12 *Perfs:* 8-12 *Arts type:* chamber orch, chamber music, instr recitals, new music *Venues:* Troldsalen 200, Bergen Billedgaleri 100, Bergen Music Conservatory 150, Hakonshallen 400, Grand Selskepslokaler up to 300, Logen 300, Grieghallen up to 450 *Comments:* chairman's address: Edvard-Grieg vei 12, 5037 Solheimsviken; non-profit organisation, member of Bergen 2000 (q.v.)

Norwegian Sound and Pictures Ltd
Norsk lyd & bilde A/S
Øverbu, Rute 598, 2760 **Brandbu**
Tel: 6133 4374/9203 6359 (mobile) Fax: 6133 4274
administrative director Odd Erik Hagen; project director Eli Kristin Hovdsveen Hagen
Arts type: classical, folk songs, popular music

Johan Halvorsen Foundation
Johan Halvorsen Stiftelsen
Rådhusgt 18, 3015 **Drammen**
Tel: 2244 0182 Fax: 2244 0182
chairman of the board Knut Strøm Andersen

Association for Music in Schools
Landslaget Musikk i Skolen
Tollbugata 28, 0157 **Oslo**
Tel: 2241 9380 Fax: 2241 9383
E-Mail: jowangen@iskolen.nl
président Signe Kalsnes; pedagogical offices Jo Wangen
Policy: promote musical education *Comments:* also publish Arabesk – 8 times a year

Gunnar Eide Concerts
Sonya Henies pl 2, 0185 **Oslo**
Tel: 2217 4070 Fax: 2217 4075
E-Mail: christin@gec.no
promoters Rune Lem, Christian Schøven, Robin Goddier
Events: 150 *Arts type:* mainly rock but occasional classical and jazz events *Venues:* Oslo Spectrum 10,000, Valle Hovin Stadium (open-air) 40000 : alternative E-mail: robin@gec.no

Impresario A/S
Tollbugaten 3, 0152 **Oslo**
Tel: 2242 6379 Fax: 2233 2238
directors Elsa-Mai Gottschalk and Vibeke Gottschalk
Events: 15 *Arts type:* jazz, ballet, orchestra tours, chamber music, operetta, song recitals, symphony music, opera, classical ballet, modern ballet *Comments:* see also Agents and Producers

Norwegian Tape Fund
Norsk kassettavgiftsfond
Øvre Sllottsgate 2b, 0157 **Oslo**
Tel: 2233 5250 Fax: 2233 5250
director Ole Richenberg; consultant Karin Krok
Policy: supports production and promotion of Norwegian phonograms (gramophone records or cassettes) and various other projects of high artistic quality *Comments:* financial support for Norwegian recording artists

Ny Musikk- Norwegian Section of the International Society for Contemporary Music
Ny Musikk
Tollbugaten 28, 0157 **Oslo**Tel: 2233 7090
Fax: 2233 7095
Internet: www.notam.uio.no/ny_musikk
E-Mail: ny-musikk-adm@notam.uio.no
executive director Janne Stangdahl; president Peter Tornquist; Cikado manager Sten Cranner
Events: approximately 100 concerts a year in eight Norwegian cities *Arts type:* contemporary music series, new music *Comments:* administer Cikada (group performing contemporary music), New Musics Composers Group, Albedo Record label; see also National Organisations

Oslo Arts Management
Brennerveien 11, 0182 **Oslo**
Tel: 2220 6307 Fax: 2220 6312
E-Mail: ad@osloarts.no
managing director Per Boye Hansen; managers Anita Dahlström, Elisabeth Quarré
Events: 12 *Arts type:* annual concert series orchestra and recitals (chamber orch, early music, inst recitals, song recitals, symphony music) *Venues:* Oslo Konserthus 1400 *Comments:* artist representation, general management and Scandanavian representation; see also Agents & Producers

Oslo Konsertdireksjon
Bjerkebakken 1, 0756 **Oslo**
Tel: 2252 2546
Fax: 2273 0103
contact Ruth Klungsøyr
Comments: see also Agents and Producers

Rikskonsertene – Norwegian Concert Institute
PO Box 2835 Solli, 0204 **Oslo**
Tel: 2283 8350
Fax: 2283 1610
Internet: www.rikskonsertene.no
E-Mail: post.rikskonsertene.no
exectutive director Einar Solbu
Arts type: choral music, early music, electronic music, instrumental music, jazz, new music, music theatre, sacred music, song recitals, symphony music, chamber music, world music, rock music, contemporary music *Venues:* different venues all over Norway *Comments:* Norway's largest producer and distributor of live music (approx. 10000 concerts annually); strives towards an overall artistic vision; public concerts, concerts for children, projects, multicultural music; see also National Organisations

Sirkus Management A/S
Cort Adelersgate 2, 0254 **Oslo**
Tel: 2243 1700
Fax: 2244 6640
director Peter Sandberg
Comments: company's activities focus on revues, concerts, musical theatre tours and individual artists management; also consultancy on artists' legal rights; see also Agents & Promotors and Services

Stand-in Arrangement
Bogstadveien 43, 0366 **Oslo**
Tel: 2246 4536 Fax: 2269 5411
E-Mail: kjbanjam@sn.no
administrative director Grethe-Laila Fjelberg
Arts type: classical music, popular music, children's music

Trond and Trond
Trond og Trond
Oscarsgate 30, 0352 **Oslo**
Tel: 2269 8010
Fax: 2269 5011
E-Mail: trondogtrond@online.no
administrative director Trond Myhre
Arts type: various kinds of music
Comments: see also Agents & Producers

Stavanger Concert Association
c/o Kirsten Bernhardt,
Tennisveien 22, 4021 **Stavanger**
Tel: 5155 8530
Fax: 5155 8530
manager Kirsten Bernhardt
Events: 10 (Sept to May) *Perfs:* 10-12 *Arts type:* chamber music, sacred music, inst recitals *Venues:* Bjergsted Music Centre, small auditorium 250, an organ hall 150, Rogaland Museum of Fine Arts 200, Stavanger Museum of Fine Arts 150

POLAND (+48)

Art Society Muzyka Centrum
ul. Starowislna 3, 31-038 **Kraków**
Tel: 12-167 6195 Fax: 12-167 6195
Internet: www.cyf-kr.edu.pl/-zbcholon/mch
E-Mail: zbcholon@cyf-kr.edu.pl
Comments: organises concerts and annual festivals of Audio Art Festival, Cracow; studio for electroacoustic music; see also Festivals

International Cultural Centre Cracow
Rynek Glówny 25, 31-008 **Kraków**
Tel: 12-421 8601/421 8400
Fax: 12-421 8571/421 7844
Internet: www.mck.kracow.pl
E-Mail: sekret@mck.kracow.pl
director Jacek Purchla
Policy: heritage management, research

Centrum Kultury Lubin
U. Peowiaków, 20-007 **Lublin**
Tel: 81-532 8700/532 7583 Fax: 81-532 8700/532 7583
E-Mail: ck@ck.lublin.pl
director Alexander Szpechk; festival organiser Beata Michalkiewicz
Arts type: theatre, dance *Venues:* 5 halls *Comments:* see also Venues, Festivals (International Festival Theatre Contratations)

IMPRESARIAT Inter Art
ul Narutowicza 15/45, 33-110 **Tarnow** 2
Tel: 14-217 267 Fax: 14-217 267
artistic directors Teresa Kaban, Henryk Blazej
Arts type: music, festivals, concerts

Centre of Cultural Animation
Centrum Animacji Kulturalnej
ul. Krakowskie Przedmiescie 21/23,
00-071 **Warszawa**
Tel: 22-826 2117
Fax: 22-826 0662
director Stanislaw Kolbusz
Comments: acting as cultural promotion office of the Ministry of Culture

Cultural Promotion Centre
ul. Krakowskie Przedmiescie 21/23,
00-071 **Warszawa**
Tel: 22-826 5982 Fax: 22-826 0262
Internet: www.kultura-polska.biz.pl/biuletynmkis.htm
E-Mail: cak@kultura-polska.biz.pl

Institute of Culture
ul. Swietojariska 2, 00-288 **Warszawa**
Tel: 22-635 4564

Polish Section of Jeunesses Musicales
Hoza 50/51, 00-660 **Warszawa**
Tel: 22-625 1937
Fax: 22-625 5810
president Stanislaw Skoczynski; director Danuta Kaniewska

PORTUGAL (+351)

Associação de Artes Performativas de Beja
Apartado 10, 7800 **Beja**
Tel: 284-327 153 Fax: 284-327 153
E-Mail: azinho.falante@ip.pt
producer José Barbieri
Arts type: theatre *Venues:* theatre Arte Pública
Policy: promotes theatre and arts in Alentejo Region of Portugal *Comments:* runs international meeting called Criativas; has own theatre Arte Pública; see also Drama and Festivals

Etnia – Cooperativa Cultural
Rua Direita 156, 4910 **Caminha**
Tel: 258-722 557/721 218
Fax: 258-922 590
Internet: www.terravista.pt/anseada/1465
E-Mail: etnia@esoterica.pt
director Mario Alves
Events: concerts *Arts type:* all types, focus on ethnic & folk arts *Policy:* creation and co-production of cultural events relating to traditional and folk artistic manifestations *Comments:* second address (branch): Calçada do Marquês de Abrantes 10, 3° esq, 1200-719 Lisboa, Tel: 1-395 1415, Fax: 1-396 1355; member of European Forum of Worldwide Music Festivals

Instituto Paulo Quintela
Faculdade de Letras da Universidade de Coimbra, Largo de Porta Ferrea, 3049 **Coimbra Codex**
Tel: 239-484 865
Fax: 239-484 853/836 733
contact Faculdade de Letras da Universidade de Coimbra (Combria University)
Events: 4 or 5 plus festival *Arts type:* music, theatre *Venues:* university theatre Gil Vicente 946, monasteries, churches, open-air venues *Policy:* do not organise but inform and present *Comments:* occasional concerts, theatre and dance performances, and Bienal Universitario de Coimbra festival; documentation centre

Calouste Gulbenkian Foundation
Fundação Calouste Gulbenkian
Avenida de Berna 45-A, 1067 **Lisboa** Codex
Tel: 21-782 3000 Fax: 21-793 7296
Internet: www.telepac.pt/earte/gulbenkian
E-Mail: musica@gulbenkian.pt
president Prof. António Ferrer Correia; director, Acarte (Department of Animation, Artistic Creation and Education through Art) Yvette Centeno

Arts type: chamber orch, choral music, chamber music, early music, electronic music, jazz, new music, sacred music, song recital, symphony music, multi media, modern ballet, modern dance, modern theatre, puppet, street theatre, visual arts exhibitions *Venues:* Grand Auditorium 1200, Auditorio Dois 344, Auditorio tres 72, and other venues throughout Portugal *Policy:* decentralisaiton programme – brings Portuguese culture to people everywhere; 25% of arts funding in Portugal *Comments:* promotes throughout Portugal; see also Ministries, Orchestras, Dance, Choirs, Festivals (2) and Venues

Clube Português de Artes e Ideias
Rua do Sol ao Rato, 73 – 1°, 1250-262 **Lisboa**
Tel: 21-387 8121/2 Fax: 21-387 6667
E-Mail: artes.ideias@mail.telepac.pt
president Jorge Barreto Xavier
Events: productions all over Portugal, annual arts festival, programs in arts education, international exchanges *Perfs:* more than 60 programs per year *Arts type:* electronic music, folk music, inst recitals, jazz, new music, music theatre, multi-media, modern dance, modern theatre, visual arts exhibitions *Policy:* promotion of contemporary arts, promotion of new Portuguese artists *Comments:* promote young artists in all areas of the arts; organise national contests, prizes and exchanges; help members to produce their art projects; provide information about young Portuguese artists; national not-for-profit arts association funded by the government; member of IETM and Network of Cultural Centres of the Council of Europe; see also National Organisations

Culturgest – Gestâo de Espaços Culturais s/a
Edifício-Sede da Caixa Geral de Depósitos,
Rua Arco do Cego, 1000 **Lisboa**
Tel: 21-790 5454/795 3000 Fax: 21-848 3903
Internet: www.cgd.telepac.pt/culdgeft/index.htm
E-Mail: culturgest@cgd.pt
presidente Manuel José Vaz; vice-presidente Fátima Ramos; board member Luis dos Santos Ferro; assessor artístico António Pinto Ribeiro; assessor técnico Eugénio Sena
Arts type: theatre, cinema, opera, jazz *Venues:* large auditorium 652, small auditorium 149 *Comments:* 2 galleries with temporary exhibitions; see also Venues

Decima Colina, Organização de Espectáculos, Lda.
Rua Academia de Ciencias 9 2ª esq., 1200 **Lisboa**
Tel: 21-322 5909 Fax: 21-322 5911
production Antonio Lobo, Alexandra Mauricio; marketing and public relations Vera Salles
Events: several during the year *Arts type:* music, classical music, dance, contemporary dance, folk music, symphony orch, soloists, opera, chamber music, recitals, jazz *Venues:* CCB 1600, Coliseu dos Recreios 2500, Teatro da Trinidade 641, other venues 600-800, Pavilmão Atlântico (Atlantic Pavilion on the Lisbon expo site) capacity 16,000 (note this is a covered venue)

Juventude Musical Portuguesa
Section des Jeunesses Musicales Portugaise
Rua Rosa Araújo 6,3°, 1250-195 **Lisboa**
Tel: 21-357 3131 Fax: 21-354 3330
E-Mail: juv@telepac.pt
secretary general Antonio Jorge Alpendre; president Emanuel Frazão Pereira
Arts type: classical, choral, string orchestra *Comments:* season Sept.-July; see also National Organisations

Vo'Arte Associaçao
Rua Presidente Arriaga 29 – 1ª-ESQ, 1200 **Lisboa**
Tel: 21-397 0204 Fax: 21-397 0204
E-Mail: vo.arte@mail.teleweb.pt
artistic director Ana Rita Barata; assistant producer Laura Alvelos; Producer Sofia Campos; architecture/collaborator Wilson Galvao
Events: 1 Festival – Lugar à Danca – Festival Internacional de Danca em Paisagens Urbanas – III edition 2000 June *Perfs:* 27 companies, 130 artists, 40 performances *Arts type:* architecture/site specific work, dance, theatre, music, video, photography : Network Citjdades que Danzan collaboration with Barcelona Associació Marató d'el Espectacle – Dies de Dansa *Policy:* support and promote performing art projects that can develop new language in dance and other art forms/ co-productions with other cities *Comments:* organises exhibitions of dance photography

Associação Visões Úteis
Av. Vímara Peres 46 4° Dta., Sala 33, 4000-544 **Porta**
Tel: 22-200 6144 Fax: 22-200 6144
E-Mail: visoesuteis@mail.telepac.pt
contact Carlos Costa
Arts type: theatre
Policy: promotes theatre and theatre festivals

Prestissimo
Rua Vasco Santana N° 1 – 8° Dto,
2685-246 **Portela-LRS**
Tel: 21-945 7077 Fax: 21-945 7078
manager Sebastião Ribeiro
Arts type: classical music, soloists
Comments: see also Agents & Producers

Ballet Teatro
Praça 9 De Abril 76, 4200 **Porto**
Tel: 22-550 8918 Fax: 22-550 8919
directors Jorge Levi, Né Barros, Isabel Barros
Events: 1 festival (Festival International de Teatro)
Perfs: 30 *Arts type:* theatre, dance *Venues:* capacity 200
Comments: promote workshops, intensive courses, seminars; in ballet teatro audiovisu (an audiovisual enterprise); see also Dance and Venues

ROMANIA (+40)

JMR – Impresariat Inter Art
CP 13 – 53, **Bucharest** 13
Tel: 1-230 3205 Fax: 1-230 3205
president Luigi Gageos;
director programs Hortensia Orcula

Academia de Musica Gheorghe Dima
str. I.C. Bratianu 25,
3400 **Cluj-Napoca**
Tel: 64-193 879
Comments: see also Festivals (Nicolae Bretan Festival) and Competitions (The Nicolae Bretan International Competition for Vocal Interpretation)

RUSSIA (+7)

Andrey Korobeinikov
26 Bakinsky Komissarov St, 12-3-245, 117526 **Moscow**
Tel: 095-433 7035
Fax: 095-433 7035
Events: national & international concerts, festivals, courses *Arts type:* opera, music, dance, drama

Artistic Association
Vivaldi House, Ul. Herzena 46 Office 4,
121069 **Moscow**
Tel: 095-290 0032/0283
Fax: 095-290 0356
general director Yuri Maslennikov;
deputy director Nikolai Filipchenko;
executive manager Vladimir Yuriev;
arts manager Marina Klimenko
Comments: represents ensembles and instrumentalists; Organise masterclasses, festivals, exhibitions, sales of instruments, paintings, folk-production, fashion shows

Firebird
Maly Kislovsky 3, Office 304, 103009 **Moscow**
Tel: 095-290 0268
Fax: 095-290 0268
general manager Igor Belyaev
Arts type: chamber, symphony, contemporary, vocal music

International Confederation of Theatre Unions
Leontyevsky per. 21/1, 103009 **Moscow**
Tel: 095-229 3785
Fax: 095-742 0933
president Kirill Lavrov;
executive secretary Valery Shadrin

Moscow City Council (Department of Culture)
Neglinnaya 8/10, 103031 **Moscow**
Tel: 095-921 9864
Fax: 095-928 9915
director Igor Bugayev

Moscow Concert Organisation SADKO
Gasheka 12-6, 125047 **Moscow**
Tel: 095-250 9832
Comments: see also Agents & Producers

Moscow Conservatory
Bolshaya Nikitskaya 13, 103871 **Moscow**
Tel: 095-229 9436
manager Vladimir Zakharov
Arts type: classical music concerts *Venues:* Great Hall

Moscow Music Society
ul. Tverskaya 31, 103050 **Moscow**
Tel: 095-229 4981 Fax: 095-200 2216/7
vice-chairman Ilya Belkin

Music Guest-room of Shuvalov's House
Povarskaya 30, 121069 **Moscow**
Tel: 095-290 2422
Comments: see also Agents & Producers

Philharmonic Moscow Concert Organisation
Leningradski prosp. 30, build 2, room 208,
125040 **Moscow**
Tel: 095-213 1950

Romans-Salon of Natalia Pavlova
Academica Anokhina 26-3-395, 117602 **Moscow**
Tel: 095-112 0688
Comments: see also Agents & Producers

Russian National Federation of International Festivals Rosinterfest
Sadovaya Triumfalnaya ul. 12/14, 103006 **Moscow**
Tel: 095-209 2261/200 6585 Fax: 095-209 9709
general director Igor Gurevich

Russian State House of Folk Arts
Rossiiski Gosudarstvenny Dom
Narodnogo Tvorchestva
Sverchkov per. 8 , bldg 3, **Moscow**
Tel: 095-921 9284 Fax: 095-921 7917
director Elvira Kunina
Comments: nation-wide organisation working with folk music, dance and song groups, amateur theatre, amateur painting, embroidery and other handicraft artists, organises exhibitions, festivals and competitions, Russian professional and amateur folk group tour abroad; see also National Organisations

State Moscow Organisation Moskontsert
Leningradski prosp. 30, build. 2, 125040 **Moscow**
Tel: 095-212 2101
Comments: see also Agents & Producers

State Theatre of Nations
Petrovsky pereulok 3, 103031 **Moscow**
Tel: 095-229 7777/229 5672
Fax: 095-229 5672/6033
director Mikhail Chiguir
Comments: produces theatre productions, organises foreign theatre tours and Festivals in Russia, Russian theatre tours abroad (drama, ballet, music theatre, opera, pantomine, etc.); see also Agents & Producers

Theatre Centre Kremlin Ballet
Kremlin, **Moscow**
Tel: 095-248 0153
Fax: 095-230 2427
president Alexey Tobachnikov

Theatre-Concert Agency
Rodchelskaya 11/5, 123100 **Moscow**
Tel: 095-205 2496
Comments: see also Agents & Producers

Tour-Concert Fund RUSKONTSERT
B.Polyanka 2/10, 109180 **Moscow**
Tel: 095-230 0875
Comments: see also Agents & Producers

Jazz Philharmonic Society
Zagorodny pr 27, 191180 **St Petersburg**
Tel: 812-113 5331 Fax: 812-164 9843
artistic director David Goloschekin;
administrative director German Vasinsky

Petersburg Concert Philharmonic Society
Fontanka 41, 191011 **St Petersburg**
Tel: 812-110 4043 Fax: 812-311 2066
general director Alexander Yablonsky

St Petersburg City Council (Department of Culture)
Nevskii 40, 191011 **St Petersburg**
Tel: 812-312 2471
Fax: 812-110 5515

St Petersburg Philharmonic
Mikhailovskaya ul. 2, 191011 **St Petersburg**
Tel: 812-311 7331
Fax: 812-311 2126
director Anton Getam

Starlet – Stage Business Agency
ap.#9, Tchaikovskogo st., 191123 **St Petersburg**
Tel: 812-275 4831 Fax: 812-275 4831
E-Mail: Starlet@email.convey.ru
artistic director Vladimir Mischuk;
general director Inga Kytyianskaya;
art manager Denis Leonov
Arts type: mainly classical music, some drama, folk and dance *Comments:* aim to support young artists; organise festivals, music and art contests in St Petersburg; separate theatre department; member of the Association of European Artist Agents; production of celebration events: release of classical LP records and CD; see also Agents & Producers and Competitions

SAN MARINO (+378)

Istituto Musicale Sammarinese
Via O. Scarito 33, Borgo Maggiore, 47893 **San Marino**
Tel: 903 002/902 002
Fax: 907 089
E-Mail: ims@omniway.sm
presidente Orazio Pignatta;
direttore artistico Italo Capicchioni
Events: 20 *Arts type:* chamber and symphonic music
Comments: collaborate with the local "Ufficio Attivita Culturali"

Repubblica di San Marino – Ufficio Attivitá Sociali e Culturali
Contrada Omagnano 20, 47890 **San Marino**
Tel: 882 452
Fax: 882 300
responsabile D.SSa Gemma Cavalleri (tel. 882 452); capo sezione Manlio Gozi
Arts type: performing arts *Venues:* Teatro Nuovo, Cinema Teatro Concordia di Borgomaggiore, Sala Polivalente Serravalle
(half way between Rimini & S. Marino)

SLOVAKIA (+421)

Many telephone and fax numbers in Slovakia are in the process of being changed. We have included all new numbers known at the time of going to print.

City Cultural Centre
Mestské kultúrne stredisko
Ursulínska 11, 812 93 **Bratislava**
Tel: 7-5441 6548
Fax: 7-5441 2234
E-Mail: mksba@netlab.sk
director Pavol Schwarz

Cultus-Centre for Culture and Art
Cultus-Centrum pre kultùru a umenie
Ruzinovskà 28, 820 09 **Bratislava**
Tel: 7-4333 0260/0466 Fax: 7-4333 2246
director MA Ján Hiznay
Arts type: theatre, dance, music, visual arts, classical pop, folk, jazz concerts *Venues:* multi purpose, Capacity Hall 1-400, Hall 2-200

Intermedia
Jakubovo nam 12, 811 09 **Bratislava**
Tel: 7-363 700/363 707 Fax: 7-363 296
general manager Peter Horak

Slovak Philharmonic
Slovenská filharmónia
Medená 3, 816 01 **Bratislava**
Tel: 7-5443 3351 Fax: 7-5443 5956
director Ing. Jozef Tkácik; music director Ondrej Lenárd

State Philharmonic Kosice
Státna filharmónica Kosice
Dom umenia, Moyzesova 66, 041 23 **Kosice**
Tel: 95-622 4514/09
Fax: 95-622 4509
Internet: www.sfk.sk
director Július Klein

House of Art Piestany
Dom umenia Správy kultúrnych zariadení MK SR
Nábrezie Ivana Krasku No. 1, 921 01 **Piestany**
Tel: 838-762 5571/5365 Fax: 838-772 5626
director Edita Bjelosevicová

Slovak Sinfonietta – State Chamber Orchestra Zilina
Státny komorny orchester Zilina
Dolny val 47, 011 28 **Zilina**
Tel: 89-620 952
Fax: 89-626 972
director Jozef Buda

SLOVENIA (+386)

BUNKER
Zavod za organizacijo in izvedbo kulturnih prireditev
Rimska 2, 1000 **Ljubljana**
Tel: 61-224 563
Fax: 61-224 563
E-Mail: nevenka.koprivesk@guest.arnes.si
Arts type: dance theatre *Comments:* production centre: production, presentation, promotion; dance theatre; Festival Mladi Levi; member of networks Junge Hunde, IETM, DBM; see also National Organisations

Jeunesses Musicales of Slovenia
Glasbena Mladina Slovenije
Kersnikova 4, 1000 **Ljubljana**
Tel: 61-1317 039 Fax: 61-322 570
Internet: www.gms.drustvo.si
secretary general Kaja Sivic;
president Silvester Mihelcic;
programme manager Roman Ravnic;
manager of public affairs Branka Novak
Comments: registered as a union of 10 local associations throughout Slovenia;
see also National Organisations

KUD France Preseren
Karunova 14, 1000 **Ljubljana**
Tel: 61-332 288/210
Fax: 61-210 338
E-Mail: kud@kud-fp.si
president Jani Kovacic; secretary Zelko Pelicon;
programme coordinator Tone Skrjanec
Arts type: theatre (comedy, puppets, performance), fine art exhibitions, concerts, video and film, shows and lectures *Venues:* hall 100 (seated) to 240 (standing), gallery 150, patio 2500, club room 25 *Comments:* small cultural centre for performing and fine arts mostly presenting at own risk but also prepared to share risk

Concert Office Maribor
Koncertna Poslovalnica Maribor
Rotovski trg 1, 2000 **Maribor**
Tel: 62-225 375
Fax: 62-225 376
director Metka Curman; deputy Andrej Borko
Arts type: concerts of classical music, Oct-June
Venues: Union Hall 650, Casino Hall, Theatre 200, Stolnica church 350, Viteska Hall 200, Cankarjek Dom and others

SPAIN (+34)

Caja de Ahorros del Mediterráneo Obra Social
San Fernando 40, 03001 **Alicante**
Tel: 96-590 6363/5505
Fax: 96-590 5820
director Obras Sociales Francisco Monllor Fuster
Events: 1 festival of music, 1 literature competition
Arts type: exhibitions, courses, music, theatre
Venues: Auditorio del Aula de Cultura 250, Auditorio 250, Aula de Cultura 406 *Policy:* promotes different activities related to culture, environment and social cooperation *Comments:* co-organise Festival Internacional de Música Contemporánea de Alicante; organise Muestra de
Teatro de Autores Contemporaneos

Amics de la Música de Barcelona
Ortigosa 14-16, 08003 **Barcelona**
Tel: 93-268 0122
Fax: 93-310 1147
presidente de la junta Germa Vidal
Events: 6 concerts (spring), 1 concert (autum)
Arts type: music *Policy:* mainly to promote musical activities through the dissemination of information
Comments: 6000 members; also publishes Information Musical, monthly bulletin about
musical activities in Cataluna

Associació Marató de L'Espectacles
Trafalgar 78, 1-1, 08010 **Barcelona**
Tel: 93-268 1868
Fax: 93-268 2424
Internet: www.marato.espect/marato.com
E-Mail: marato.espect@marato.com
directores Arnau Vilardebó, Juan Eduardo López;
producción Julia Martinez, Elena Cebres,
Montserrat Gausachs, Elena Molins
Events: 10 *Perfs:* 200 *Arts type:* scenic art, plastic art, visual art, story telling *Policy:* producers of theatre events (plays, festivals) *Comments:* organisers of Dies de Dansa (international festival of dance in urban landscapes), and Marató de L'Espectacles and Des de la Paraula; see also Festivals

Associació Musical Tempus
c/ Valencia 35 1°),
La Roca Del Valles,
08430 **Barcelona**
Tel: 93-879 5097
contact Josep Maria Sauret
Events: 20 *Arts type:* classical music, festivals organiser, management of orchestras

En Dansa
Travesera de Grácia 63, 08021 **Barcelona**
Tel: 93-414 3133
Fax: 93-200 8548
Internet: gencat/cuttura/spai
E-Mail: spai@qrz.net
director Josep Andrada Escola; programador danza Marta Garcia; programador musica Carlos Sala
Events: 15 *Arts type:* dance *Venues:* L'Espai, Barcelona 370, other venues in Cataluña *Policy:* programmers of dance and music
Comments: programmers of venues owned by Generalitat de Catalunya (regional government) responsible for the programming of dance at L'Espai; see also National & Regional Ministries and Venues

Fundació Joan Miró
Parc de Montjuic, 08038 **Barcelona**
Tel: 93-329 1908
Fax: 93-329 8609
Internet: www.bcn.fjmiro.es
E-Mail: fjmiro@bcn.fjmiro.es
directora Rosa María Malet; presidente fundación Eduard Castellet; subdirectora Dolors Ricart
Events: 11 *Arts type:* exhibitions, electronic music, multi media, world music, puppets, visual arts, new music, concerts, conferences *Venues:* multi-purpose auditorium 212 *Comments:* a small part of the foundation dedicated to study of Miro's work; awards grants; see also Venues

Fundació la Caixa Departamento Musical
Paseo de San Juan 108,
08037 **Barcelona**
Tel: 93-458 8905/06/07 (music dept)
Fax: 93-459 0662
Internet: www.fundacio.lacaixa.es
E-Mail: info.fundacio@lacaixa.es
programación musical Maricarmen Palma
Events: 75 concerts, 2 courses, 2 festivals
Arts type: chamber orchestra, choral music, chamber music, early music, electronic music, folk music, instrumental recitals, jazz, new music, light orchestral music, music theatre, sacred music, song recitals, multi media, opera, world music, puppet, visual arts exhibitions
Venues: Centre Cultural de la Caixa 450 *Policy:* runs courses (early music and chamber) for young musicians; also organises a musical season for the family *Comments:* organises two festivals: Festival de Música Antigua (Apr-May) and Festival de Música Étnica (Oct); see also Venues and Festivals

Fundació Orfeo Catalàn – Palacio de la Música Catalana
Sant Francesc de Paula 2, 08003 **Barcelona**
Tel: 93-268 1000 Fax: 93-268 4824/0995
director Rosa Garicano; president Fèlix Millet i Tussell
Events: 'Palau 100' concert cycle (17 concerts Oct-June); Escolas del Palau music for schools (54 concert); Domingos del Palau Sunday concerts (6 concerts); symphonic concerts (8 concerts); Primer Palau cycle with young musicians (4 concerts); Conciertos Sinfonicos symphonic concerts (5 concerts) *Arts type:* classical music, especially Catalan composers *Venues:* Palau de la Música Catalana 2060 *Policy:* promote classical music through a programme of public concerts *Comments:* promotes, sponsors; own choirs Orfeo Català (adults, children, youth); see also Choirs and Venues

Fusic (Fundació Societat i Cultura)
Concell de Cent 347, Sobreatic, 08007 **Barcelona**
Tel: 93-215 7411 Fax: 93-215 7932
Internet: personal.redestb.es/fusic
E-Mail: fusic@mx2.redestb.es
international manager Argi Ibañez;
director Victor Cucurull
Arts type: music, theatre, conferences, publications
Policy: management & promotion of cultural activities
Comments: member of network Live Music Now; promoters of classical music by young musicians for disadvantaged social groups

Ressons
Travesera de Gracia 63, 08021 **Barcelona**
Tel: 93-414 3133 Fax: 93-200 8548
Internet: cultura.gencat.s/espai
E-Mail: espai@qrz.net
director Carles Sala
Events: 20 *Perfs:* 60 *Arts type:* alternative music, pop, jazz, Catalonian music *Venues:* L'Espai 370 *Comments:* responsible for the music programming at L'Espai owned by Generalitat de Catalunya (regional government) and the dance programmes run by En Dansa; see also Venues

Sanzkonzert
c/ Pau Claris 113 1° 2, 08009 **Barcelona**
Tel: 93-487 3833 Fax: 93-487 7892
Internet: www.sanzkonzert.es
E-Mail: sanz@sanzkonzert.es
gerente firector Alfonso Sanz López;
adjunta dirección Kueta Sanzova
Arts type: chamber ensembles, philharmonis and symphonic orchestras, opera, soloists, ballet
Comments: present their own concert season; see also Agents & Producers

Spanish Section of Jeunesses Musicales
Juventudes Musicales de España
Marina 164, Pral 3°, 08013 **Barcelona**
Tel: 93-265 2371 Fax: 93-265 9080
Internet: www.clubjm.org
E-Mail: jmspain@opensl.es
dirección ejecutiva Esther Vargas; secretario general Joaquim Cardellach; presidente Jordi Roch
Events: 3000 *Arts type:* classical music, jazz, folk music
Comments: member of (JMI), (EMCY) and (CIM UNESCO), concerts within Spain; international exchanges of young artists; courses and competitions; quarterly newsletter; give grants, great variety of cultural activities; see also National Organisations and Competitions

Sociedad Filarmónica de Bilbao
Marqués del Puerto 2, 48009 **Bilbao**
Tel: 94-423 2621 Fax: 94-423 9092
administrador Fernando Bravo;
secretario Jorge Barandiarán e Ibáñez de Betolaza;
presidente Asís de Aznar e Ybarra
Events: 35 concerts, Oct-May *Arts type:* chamber orch, chamber music, recitals, occasionally symphony music in the theatres below *Venues:* Sala de Conciertos de la Sociedad Filarmónica 1000, Teatro Arriaga 1685, Teatro Coliseo Albia 2100, Teatro Campos Eliseos 1260

Fundació ACA Area Creació Acústica
Son Bieli, 07311 **Búger (Mallorca)**
Tel: 971-516 501 Fax: 971-516 502
E-Mail: fundacioaca@new-ton.com
general coordinadora Beatriz Florit;
presidente Antonio Caimari Alomar
Events: 40-50 concerts, 20-25 lectures, 2 courses, 1 annual festival 'Encontre de Compositors'October, recordings *Arts type:* music, especially contemporary, poetry, multi-media performances (dance, theatre, moving image, film), courses, symposiums, lectures, music theatre, visual arts exhibitions, symphony music *Venues:* Sala de Piano up to 90 (Son Bielf) *Policy:* offers the possibility to work and record for composers; promotes all type of activities related to contemporary music *Comments:* building a residence for composers, an electronic studio and auditorium (500), has a documentation centre on historical music and mallorquin composers; runs courses for composers, organises a week of organ music, works in common projects with 'Fundació Miró'; organises yearly 'Encontre de Compositors' and has its own recording studio 'Unió Music';
see also Festivals and Recorded Media

Sociedad Filarmónica de Burgos
Avda. Reyes Católicos 1, 09005 **Burgos**
Tel: 947-288 200 Fax: 947-288 210
director José Manuel Alegría de Rioja
Events: 30 *Arts type:* classical music, chamber music *Venues:* Auditorio de la Caja de Ahorros del Circulo Católico 500 *Policy:* organises and produce concerts *Comments:* 750 members

Obra Social y Cultural Cajasur
Ronda de Los Tejares 22, 6°, 14001 **Cordoba**
Tel: 957-214 421/24 Fax: 957-214 420
E-Mail: admin@cajasur.es
sub-director José Eduardo Hertas Muñoz
Events: 91 concerts, 800 publications, 73 conferences, 39 conventions, 102 exhibitions, 9 competitions, 6 cinema series *Arts type:* music, cinema, art *Venues:* Centro de Congresos Santo Angel 500, Salón de Actos Museo Obispado Cajasur de Bellas Artes 250, Auditorium Cajasur-Gran Capitán 225, Auditorium Cajasur-Reyes Católicos 200 and 15 exhibition venues *Policy:* organises programmes for all its venues; to promote culture from the Andalucia area *Comments:* own choirs: Orfeón Cajasur and Coro de Opera Cajasur; new exhibition gallery; see also Choirs

Fundación Orquesta Filarmónica de Gran Canarias
Bravo Murillo 21-23, 35003 **Las Palmas de Gran Canaria**
Tel: 928-320 513/321 747 Fax: 928-314 747
Internet: www.orfigc.com
E-Mail: orfigc@orfigc.com
gerente Juan Antonio Gonzalez Ojellón; director titular Adrian Leaper; coordinador artistico Manuel Benitez
Events: 94 concerts, 1 competition *Arts type:* music (classical, symphonic, vocal) *Venues:* Teatro Perez Galdós 1500, Auditorio Alfredo Kraus 1700 *Policy:* organises concerts, competition and other activities related to the promotion of classical music *Comments:* organises Concurso Internacional de Canto Alfredo Kraus; own orchestra; see also Competitions and Orchestras

Sociedad Filarmónica de Las Palmas de Gran Canaria
Pza de Estagno 1, Teatro Pérez Galdós,
35002 **Las Palmas de Gran Canaria**
Tel: 928-369 737 Fax: 928-369 737
Internet: www.socfilarmlp.es
E-Mail: socfilarmlp@socfilarmlp.es
presidente Juan Estany Cabrera; vice presidente Margarita Guerra Caballero;
secretario Vincente Gonzáles Rosales
Events: 20 concerts, Oct-June *Perfs:* 20 concerts, Oct-June *Arts type:* classical music, chamber orch., chamber music, song recitals *Venues:* Teatro Pérez Galdós 1409, Auditorio Alfredo Kraus 1500 *Policy:* organise concerts and has a program to promote young musicians from the conservatorio, organising performances in concerts *Comments:* some concerts in collaboration with Orquesta Filarmónica de Gran Canaria

Casa de América
Paseo de Recoletos, 2, 28001 **Madrid**
Tel: 91-595 4800/24 (prensa) Fax: 91-595 4828 (prensa)
Internet: www.casamerica.es
E-Mail: prensa@casamerica.es
director general Tomas Rodriguez Pantoja; director del ateneo americano Iñigo Ramirez del Haro; direcotr de tribuna americana Manuel Piñeiro; jefe departamento de comunicación Laureano Suárez del Canto
Events: 20 concerts, 20 exhibitions, 6 theatre *Perfs:* 25 *Arts type:* music, theatre, lectures, exhibitions, seminars, modern theatre, visual arts exhibitions *Venues:* Amphiteatre 175-375, Sala Miguel de Cervantes 60, Sala Bolivar 80, Cinema 80, Ambassador's Hall (standing only) *Policy:* cultural & diplomatic institution aiming to increase awareness of art, literature, cinema & theatre from the Americas in Spain *Comments:* see also Venues

Centro para la Difusión de la Música Contemporánea – C.D.M.C.
Museo Nacional, Centro de Arte Reina Sofía,
c/ Santa Isabel 52, 28012 **Madrid**
Tel: 91-468 2310/2931 Fax: 91-530 8321
E-Mail: consuelo.diez@cdmc.inaem.es
directora Consuelo Diez Fernandez; coordinadora Ajuncion Tirado
Events: 100 concerts, 12 courses, 10 lectures, 46 comissions *Arts type:* contemporary music: young composers, electroacustic music, Latin American music, European music, chamber orch, choral music, chamber music, electronic music, new music, music theatre, song recitals, symphony music, multi-media *Venues:* Centro de Arte Reina Sofía 150, Auditorio Nacional 700, Casa de América 250, Instituto Francés 400, courses in Conservatorio de Música, lectures in Residencia de Estudiantes and Sgae (Sala Manuel de Falla 100) *Policy:* producers of events related to the promotion and difussion of contemporary music; organises concerts & lectures; comission works from composers *Comments:* co-productions with European and Latin American countries; owns an archive with 3750 scores of contemporary composers and a electroacustic music laboratory (musical production studio); produce international contemporary music festival in Alicante;
see also Festivals

Fundación Autor
c/Barbara de Traganza 7, 28004 **Madrid**
Tel: 91-503 6800
Fax: 91-503 6819
Internet: www.sgae.es
E-Mail: sgae@tsai.es
secretario general Francisco Galindo Villoria
Arts type: music, theatre, cinema *Policy:* promtes cultural and social activities related to authors of music, theatre and cinema *Comments:* cultural branch of the Spanish Society for Authors and Publishers; gives bursaries for artists and interpreter help for productions and tours; see also National Organisations

Fundación Caja de Madrid
Plaza de Celenque nº 2, 28013 **Madrid**
Tel: 91-379 1083/2852 Fax: 91-379 2020
Internet: www.cajamadrid.es
E-Mail: fundacioncajamadrid@madcervicom.es
gerente Alfredo Perez de Armiñan;
president Miguel Blesa
Events: 150 concerts, 5 scholarships *Arts type:* music, cultural tours round Madrid, courses, art exhibitions, classical music *Policy:* promote culture in Comunidad de Madrid, especially enhancing the cultural tradition of the province *Comments:* scholarships for young musicians (study bursaries); Fundación is an autonomous body that works with funding from Caja de Madrid

Fundación Cultural – Arte Tripharia
c/Montera 25, 2° 2ª, 28013 **Madrid**
Tel: 91-522 1715
Fax: 91-521 4742
Internet: www.intercultur.com
E-Mail: arte@mail.com
presidente Rudesindo Soutelo
Events: publications *Arts type:* chamber orchestra, choral music, chamber music, early music, electronic music, inst. recitals, sacred music, symphony music, opera, classical ballet, modern ballet *Venues:* Auditorio del Museo Thyssen Bornemisa 200 *Policy:* promote young musicians and artists, organising concerts, performances; help them with management; funding for assistance to festivals; recordings

Fundación Jacinto e Inocencio Guerrero
Gran Vía 78, 1°, 28013 **Madrid**
Tel: 91-547 6618 Fax: 91-548 3493/547 6618
E-Mail: jeig@adenle.es
directora Rosa Mº Garcia Castehanos;
presidente Lorenzo Lopez Sancho
Events: competitions: piano 4 April 2001, singers 3 April 2000, guitar 6 November 2000 *Arts type:* classical music *Venues:* Real Conservatorio Superior de Música de Madrid 400 *Policy:* private foundation, aims to promote classical music with prizes and engagements *Comments:* organize competitions, gives prizes, organizes concerts to promote the work of Jacinto Guerrero; give prizes for graduate students from the Real Conservatorio Superior de Musica; arrange engagements for young musicians; application deadlines: piano 22 April 2001, singers 22 April 2000, guitar 6 November 2000

Fundación Juan March
Castelló 77, 28006 **Madrid**
Tel: 91-435 4240
Fax: 91-576 3420
Internet: www.march.es
E-Mail: webmast@mail.march.es
director gerente José Luis Yuste Grijalba; director actividades culturales Antonio Gallego Gallego; director de exposiciones José Capa Eiriz; director administrativo Tomás Villanueva Iribas; director de comunicación Andrés Berlanga Agudo
Events: Genente de proyectors socioculturales Mº Dolores Borreguero Lorenzo *Arts type:* chamber music, new music, song recitals, symphony music, exhibitions, recitals, conferences *Venues:* sala A 380, sala B 150 *Policy:* promotion and patronage of culture and science *Comments:* lunchtime youth concerts (Sept-June); houses a library of contemporary Spanish music and theatre

Obra Social Caja de Ahorros y Monte de Piedad de Madrid – Programas Socioculturales
Plaza de Celenque Nº2 2° Planta, 28013 **Madrid**
Tel: 91-379 2216
Fax: 91-379 2138
Internet: www.cajamadrid.es
director gerente Obra Social Antonio Herrero Alcón (1-379 2648); directora de programacion & coordinacion educativa y cultural Mª Fernanda Ayan San Jose; gerente de proyectos socioculturales Mª Dolores Borreguero Lorenzo
Events: 916 music, 30 dance, 280 theatre, 62 visual arts *Arts type:* 7 fine art competitions *Venues:* 4 Areas de Cultura with multi-purpose Auditorium 200 in cities throughout Spain, 11 art exhibition venues *Policy:* reinvests interest from customers deposits in social and cultural programmes; emphasis on the educational activities in schools and programmes of sports information *Comments:* Social and Cultural Department, part of Caja de Madrid

Pro Música
Capitán haya 22 2° C, 28020 **Madrid**
Tel: 91-597 1554 Fax: 91-556 9887
directores artísticos Xavier Güell,
Ricardo E. de Quesada
Events: 10 symphonic concerts, 12 contemporary music concerts, 10 conferences *Arts type:* chamber orch, chamber music, early music, symphony music, contemporary music *Venues:* Auditorio Nacional (concerts), Museo Thyssen Bornemisa (conferences) *Policy:* non profit organisation which presents various performing arts programmes, including concert series and conferences in Madrid, Palma de Mallorca, Seville and Barcelona *Comments:* aims to promote the importance and globalisation of classical music

Mestizo Asociación Cultural
c/ Vinadel 6, Bajo, 30004 **Murcia**
Tel: 968-217 651 Fax: 968-217 651
Internet: www.mestizo.org
E-Mail: mestizo@mestizo.org
directors Joaquin Canovas, Francisco Martin,
Paco Salinas, Maria Jose Turralba
Events: 1-5 *Perfs:* 30 *Arts type:* folk music, new music, world music, visual arts exhibitions, book publishing *Venues:* 1 exhibition hall for visual arts, Sala Mestizo 150 *Policy:* promote unofficial/non-commercial artistic projects *Comments:* works as a collective and in collaboration with other cultural organisations throughout Spain; receives funding from national and regional government; non-profit organisation

Asociación Cultural Rayuela
c/ Jerez 476, Urb. Calypo Fado,
28600 **Navalcarnero (Madrid)**
Tel: 91-577 1581/813 2099/2533/559 7540
Fax: 91-577 1581/813 2099/2533/559 7540
presidente Luis Ghringhelli
Events: 1 festival, 1 educational programme
Perfs: 160 in theatre + own companies performing *Arts type:* puppetry *Venues:* Teatro de Títeres del Retiro 300 *Comments:* an association of 4 puppet companies (Teatro la Gaviota, La Mar de Marionetas, Marimba Marionetas and Hilando Títeres); runs puppetry venue and organises puppet festival;
see also Festivals and Puppetry

Caja de Asturias-Obra Social y Cultural
c/o Argüelles 27, 33003 **Oviedo**
Tel: 98-510 2222/46
Fax: 98-510 2268
jefatura de la Obra social y cultural
Regina Rubio Martínez
Events: 100 concerts, 35 theatre (plays), 12 dance, 25 lectures, 2 cinema seasons *Arts type:* classical, modern music, dance, theatre, exhibitions, lectures *Venues:* Monte de Piedad Gijón 250, Salón de Actos de Oviedo 180 (multi-purpose venues
Comments: also runs a social programme with cultural activities for elderly people

Sociedad Filarmónica de Oviedo
Mendizábal 3, 2°, 33003 **Oviedo**
Tel: 98-521 2237 Fax: 98-521 2237
administrador Angel Luis Alvarez Menendez;
presidente Jaime Alvarez-Buylla;
secretario Jose Ramon Fernandez Cuevas
Events: 17-20 (Oct-May) concerts *Arts type:* classical music *Venues:* own venue: Teatro Filarmónica 1200

Departament d'Obra Social i Cultural Caixa de Balears 'Sa Nostra'
Carrer Ter, Núm. 16, Poligon Son Fuster,
07009 **Palma de Mallorca**
Tel: 971-171 925 Fax: 971-171 795
E-Mail: cultura.Palma@sanostro.es
sub-director Fernando Márquez Tous; director de la obra social Miguel Alenyá i Fuster;
prensa Coloma Borrás Cerdá
Events: 52 concerts, 12 theatre plays, 1 festival, 1 competition *Arts type:* chamber music, small-scale theatre, exhibitions *Venues:* Centro de Cultura 'Sa Nostra' 244 *Comments:* cultural branch of Caja de Ahorros y Monte de Piedad de las Baleares; organises Setmana Internacional D'Orgue de Menorca, Mallorca i Eivissa; see also Venue, Festivals and Competitions

Sociedad Filarmónica de Pamplona
Avda. San Ignacio 12, 2° dcha, 31002 **Pamplona**
Tel: 948-221 966/705
Fax: 948-211 876
secretario general Manuel Flandes Muñoz; presidente José María de Andrés Solaluce
Events: 9-11(Oct-June) *Arts type:* symphony, chamber music *Venues:* Teatro Gayarre 1100 *Policy:* promote classical music in the area of Navarra

Asociación de Cultura Musical de San Sebastián
c/ San Marcial 21, 20005 **San Sebastián**
Tel: 943-430 080/431 472
Fax: 943-423 417
E-Mail: clausen@jet.es
presidente Eduardo Clausen Zubiría
Events: 30 (Oct to June) concerts *Arts type:* classical music *Venues:* Teatro Victoria Eugenia 1300

Fundación Kutxa Caja Gipuzkoa San Sebastián
Garibai 20, 20004 **San Sebastián**
Tel: 943-411 182 Fax: 943-432 054
Internet: www.kutxa.es
E-Mail: infokutxa@kutxa.es
jefe de la Obra Cultural Alberto Martínez Aranberri; jefe de la Obra Social Francisco Esquiroz Fernandino
Events: 1 scholarship for young interpreters, 1 literary prize, exhibitions, publications *Arts type:* choral music, chamber music, early music, electronic music, folk music, inst recitals, jazz, new music, light orch music, sacred music, song recitals, multi-media, world music, mime, street theatre, visual arts exhibitions *Venues:* Sala Andía (Auditorium) 250, Sala Arrasate 220 *Comments:* organises with Diputación de Guipzcoa scholarhsip Nicanor Zabalet, funds the activities of Quincena Musical, Orquesta de Euskadi and lots of other cultural activities/organisations

Fundación Marcelino Botín
c/ Pedrueca 1, 39003 **Santander**
Tel: 942-226 072 Fax: 942-226 045
E-Mail: fmabotin@fundacionmbotin.org
director Enrique Martínez Berro;
administrador Luis Herrero Pellón;
secretaria general técnica Esperanza Botella Pombo
Events: 20 concerts, 43 lectures, 8 exhibitions *Arts type:* chamber orch, choral music, chamber music, folk music, inst. recitals, new music, light orch music, operetta, sacred music, song recitals, multi media, opera, jazz, world music, visual arts exhibitions, grants, publications and lectures, research/conservation of historic heritage *Venues:* Salón de Actos 250, Sala polivalente 100, Sala de Seminarios 71, Sala de Exposiciones, Library *Policy:* education, support and information *Comments:* fortnightly youth concerts; organise Manuel Valcárel International Piano Composition Competition; also runs a music documentation centre

Obra Cultural Caja de Ahorros de Santander y Cantabria
Centro Cultural Modesto Tapia, Tantín 25,
39001 **Santander**
Tel: 942-204 300 Fax: 942-361 160
Internet: www.cajacantabria.com
jefe centro cultural Gregorio Barriuso Carazo;
coordinador de espectaclos Javier Ontañon;
director Guillermo Rubio Haro
Events: 300 *Arts type:* theatre, ballet, music (popular, jazz, opera, folk) *Venues:* Sala Centro Cultural Modesto Tapia 500, Teatro Residencia Cazoña 250, other exhibition venues in Cantabria *Policy:* organises cultural activities throughout Cantabria, promoting local artists

Fundación Max AUB
AP. Correos 111, 12400 **Segorbe (Castelión)**
Tel: 96-471 3866 Fax: 96-471 3877
Internet: www.maxaub.org
E-Mail: fundacion@maxaub.org
director Miguel González Sanchez; presidenta Elena Aub; archivo Maria José Calpe
Events: 3 *Perfs:* 2 *Arts type:* theatre, story-telling, edition of works, documentation centre *Comments:* c/ Cronista Faus S/N, 12400, Segorbe (Castelión)

Fundación Don Juan De Borbón
Juan Bravo 7, 1°, 40001 **Segovia**
Tel: 921-461 400/416 Fax: 921-462 249
Internet: www.fundac-juandeborbon.com
E-Mail: f-d-j-b-sj@mx3-redestb.es
coordinador general Rodrigo Peñalosa Izuzquiza;
presidente Ramon Escobar
Events: 60 concerts, 10 theatres, 10 lectures, 3 dance, 4 exhibitions, courses *Arts type:* music, theatre, dance, exhibitions *Venues:* various including cathedral, churches and other historical buildings *Policy:* promote culture on a national and international level *Comments:* organises Verano Musical de Segovia, which includes Festival Joven, Semana de Camara, Festival Folk, Semana de Musicas y Festival International; has an educational arm, Escolanía de Segovia, that runs courses in choral singing and interpretation for professionals; see also Festivals

Obra Social y Cultural de la Caja de Ahorros de Segovia
Plaza de San Facundo 3, 40001 **Segovia**
Tel: 921-463 036/921-463 035 Fax: 921-463 042
Internet: www.cajasegovia.es
E-Mail: jtomas@cajasegovia.es
director de obra social y cultural Malakias del Pozo
Policy: help with funding other promoters to organise cultural activities, especially Fundación Don Juan de Borbón; all the performing arts events funded are organised by Fundación Don Juan de Borbón
Comments: collaboration with funding in Verano Musical of Segovia, a season of music festivals, concerts and events; also promote cultural activities throughout the province of Segovia

Fundacio Cultural Caixa de Terrassa
Rambla d'Egara 340, 08221 **Terrassa (Barcelona)**
Tel: 93-780 4144 Fax: 93-733 1393
Internet: www.c-cultural-terrasa.es
E-Mail: info@c-cultural-terrasa.es
director Eduard Vives;
responsable programacion Toni Aliaga
Events: 9 music, 12 dance, 8 theatre *Arts type:* theatre, dance, music, jazz, cinema, art exhibitions *Venues:* Multi-purpose Auditorium 733, Sala de Actos 310 *Policy:* promoters of all cultural activities; programme its own activities *Comments:* the dance season (ballet)is one of the most important in Catalunya; see also Venues

Fundación Bancaja
Plaza de Tetuan 23, 46003 **Valencia**
Tel: 96-387 5864 Fax: 96-352 3303/387 5578
Internet: www.bancaja.es
gerente Miguel Ángel Utrillas
Arts type: theatre, ethnic music, jazz *Venues:* Salón de Actos 291 *Policy:* promote and fund cultural activities
Comments: organise cultural activities programme called Red de Bancaja throughout Valencia; regional

OAM Palau de la Música i Congresos de Valencia
Paseo de la Alameda 30, 46023 **Valencia**
Tel: 96-337 5020 Fax: 96-337 1521
Internet: www.palauvalencia.com
E-Mail: palaudelamusica@resone.es
sub-dir Alfredo Pascual;
president of OAM María Irene Beneyto
Events: 250 *Arts type:* concerts, symphony, jazz, chamber music, choral music, early music, visual arts exhibitions, opera in concert, lectures, flamenco *Venues:* multi-purpose hall 420, purpose built concert hall 1774, + 2 venues, each for conferences, exhibitions and gallery 100, concert hall Jose Iturbi 1793 *Policy:* programmers of a wide range of cultural activities to promote the performing arts in Valencia; publishes Preludio (information music bulletin) *Comments:* major subscription series; home of the Orquesta de Valencia and Coro de Valencia; organises festivals of modern music Otras Musicas; home of the chamber orchestra Collegium Instrumentale; see also Venues, Orchestras and Choirs

Real Music Productions, The
Peris Brell, 13, 46022 **Valencia**
Tel: 96-168 7341 Fax: 96-168 7342
Internet: www.ctv.es/USERS/trm
E-Mail: trm@ctv.es
director Joaquin Martinez; co-ordinator y administración Aranzazu Alcañiz
Events: 80 *Perfs:* 100 *Arts type:* jazz music *Policy:* manage own groups and artists as well as organising tours of international artists *Comments:* organise Festival de Jazz Universidad de Valencia; exclusive promotion of artist Ximo Tebar

Sociedad Filarmónica de Valencia
Plaza Alfonso el Magnánimo 11 Bajo, 46003 **Valencia**
Tel: 96-351 6106 Fax: 96-351 6106
secretario general Jose Lapiedra Martinez; presidente M° Cruz Cabeza Sanchez-Albornoz
Events: 22-23 (Oct-May) *Arts type:* classical, chamber music, recitals *Venues:* Palau de la Música – Sala Iturri 1793 *Policy:* organises concerts for members to promote classical music *Comments:* has 1300 members

Asociación Cultural Salzburgo
Apdo 3160, c/ Recoletas 4, 47006 **Valladolid**
Tel: 983-339 542 Fax: 983-222 469
representante José Antonio Nieto de Miguel; secretaria Marina Pilar Gutiérrez Lozano; vice presidente Antonio Medina Cabrerizo
Events: 5-6 *Arts type:* classical music, opera, ballet
Venues: Teatro Calderón, Auditorio de la Feria Internacional de Muestras 625 *Comments:* see also Opera

Obra Social y Cultural de Caja España
Plaza de Fuente Dorada n° 6-7, 47001 **Valladolid**
Tel: 983-425 500/535 Fax: 983-425 546
Internet: www.cajaespana.es
E-Mail: mcalleja@cajaespana.es
head of cultural department María Calleja
Arts type: seminars, environmental issues, publications, art exhibitions, classical music, jazz, theatre, dance, cinema *Venues:* different venues in Valladolid (Sala de Actos Caja Espana), Palencia, Zamora and Léon *Policy:* organises concerts, performances, lectures, cinema season, own cultural programmes *Comments:* coordinates cultural activities for the provinces of Valladolid, Zamora, Palencia and Léon; organises Premio Caja España de Teatro Breve; see also Competitions

Ibercaja (Caja de Ahorros y Monte de Piedad de Zaragoza, Aragón y Rioja)
Departamento de Obra Cultural
Plaza de Basilio Paraíso n° 2, 50008 **Zaragoza**
Tel: 976-767 842 Fax: 976-232 811
jefe de la obra cultural de Ibercaja Javier Pomer; responsable de exposiciones Gonzalo de Diégo; responsables de música Gonzalo de Diégo, Magdalena Lasala; responsable de teatro infantil Magdalena Lasala; director del patronato Jose Luis Lasala Morer
Events: theatre 110, music 320, courses 20, cinema 185, lectures 235, congress 9 *Arts type:* theatre, music, dance, art exhibitions, seminars *Venues:* Centro de Exposiciones y Congresos 400, Zaragoza, venues in 14 other cities in Spain *Policy:* promote cultural activities in different cities in Spain *Comments:* Social and Cultural Department, part of (and dependent on) Ibercaja

SWEDEN (+46)

Hans Edler AB
Gökholmsbacken 21, 124 74 **Bandhagen**
Tel: 8-647 5104 Fax: 8-993 939
managing director Hans Edler
Events: 5 *Arts type:* dance and rock events, TV programmes, annual songwriters competition (Sweden) *Comments:* also own a record label 'GFO'; see also Recorded Media

Dalasinfoniettan
Nybrogaton 12, Box 275, 791 26 **Falun**
Tel: 23-18250 Fax: 23-13540
Internet: www.musikidalarna.se
E-Mail: dalassinfoniettan@musikidalarn.se
manager Hakan Ivarson
Events: 50 concerts; incl sinfonietta concerts
Arts type: symphony orchestra, chamber music *Venues:* venue in Falun 500, and around the county
Comments: see also Orchestras

Musik Gävleborg – Landstinget Gävleborg
Slottet, 802 66 **Gävle**
Tel: 26-155 976 Fax: 26-605 879
E-Mail: kenneth.johansson@lg.se
music director Kenneth Johnansson
Events: 600 concerts + 200 for schools
Comments: non-profit organisation

Stiftelsen Musik i Väst
Head office, Box 3066, 400 10 **Göteborg**
Tel: 31-102 100 Fax: 31-102 101
Internet: www.miv.se
E-Mail: info@miv.se
director Monika Ejserholm
Events: 1500 (Aug-May) *Perfs:* 1500 *Arts type:* festivals, concerts, educational events *Policy:* produce

Stiftelsen Musik i Halland
Box 378, 301 09 **Halmstad**
Tel: 35-177 979 Fax: 35-177 989
E-Mail: p.a.hubner@musikin.se
director of music Paul Stempel (tel. 35-1177 970); intendent Anita Johansson
Perfs: 200 + min. 2 festivals *Arts type:* most kinds of music including classical, folk and jazz, specifically aimed at young people *Comments:* alternative email: paul.stempel@musikin.se

Musik i Västernorrland
Head Office, Köpmangatan 1, 871 30 **Härnösand**
Tel: 611-80323 Fax: 611-23545
director of music Eva Potter
Events: approx 700 concerts/year *Arts type:* music *Policy:* to promote high quality public concerts with priority on school concerts for children *Comments:* also at: Sollefteå Musikavdelning, Storgaten 136, 881 40 Sollefteå, Tel: 620-19695, Fax: 620-10479, manager: Kennet Lindholm

Musik i Blekinge
Box 4045, 271 81 **Karlskrona**
Tel: 455-81777
Fax: 455-18011
E-Mail: hp@sweipnet.se
executive director Olle Lind; producer Roland Ekwall; information Claes Göran Bjerding
Events: 1400 *Arts type:* music *Comments:* organises all kinds of music for community activities

Musikteatern i Värmland (Värmlands Teater-och Musikstiftelse)
Ålvgatan 49, 652 30 **Karlstad**
Tel: 54-140 840 Fax: 54-100 533
Internet: www.musikteaternivarmland.se
E-Mail: musikteatern@alfascop.net
managing director Hans Hiort;
director of finance Christina Nilsson;
opera producer Pernilla Bergland-Eduard;
orchestra producer Ole Wiggo Bang;
marketing manager Kristina Bergh
Events: 200 concerts a year *Perfs:* 130 musicals & opera
Arts type: chamber orchestra, choral music, chamber music, early music, electronic music, folk music, instrumental recitals, jazz, new music, light orchestral music, music theatre, operetta, sacred music, song recitals, symphony music, opera *Venues:* Karlstad Teater 381
Comments: organises tours, has own orchestra and own soloists; all kinds of music; see also Opera

Musik i Skåne
Kanalgatan 30, 291 34 **Kristianstad**
Tel: 44-205 880
Fax: 44-211 925
Internet: www.musikiskane.se
E-Mail: tutti@musikiskane.se
director of music Birger Ericson
Arts type: concerts, most kinds of music, including classical jazz and rock, chamber orch, choral music, chamber music, early music, electronic music, folk music, inst recitals, jazz, new music, light orch music, music theatre, sacred music, song recitals, symphony music, multi-media, world music, folk dance, modern ballet, modern dance

Stiftelsen Östgötamusiken
Box 140, 581 02 **Linköping**
Tel: 13-312 950 Fax: 13-122 640
Internet: 193.14.174.105
E-Mail: wind.music@ostgotamusiken.se
manager Perlow Pell
Events: 1244 *Arts type:* wind chamber repertoire, wind symphonic repertoire, new music *Venues:* Linköping Concert Hall 1200 *Policy:* contemporary Nordic/Swedish music for winds *Comments:* see also Östgöta Winds Symphony

Norrbottensmusiken
Box 972, 971 29 **Luleå**
Tel: 920-236 666 Fax: 920-236 667
E-Mail: norrbottensmusiken@NLL.SE
director of music Gunnal Karben
Arts type: most music including jazz, big band, music theatre, dance theatre, music concerts, chamber orchestra, children's concerts

Music and Theatre in Sörmland
Kultur & Utbildning Sörmland, Box 314, 611 26 **Nyköping**
Tel: 155-247 090 Fax: 155-285 542
E-Mail: diariet.kuf@kuf.d11.se
director Ingela Malmberg; producers Agneta Bertilsson, Jonas Burman; coordinator Anita Hedlund; information officer Ulf Thörn
Events: theatre performances mainly for children and young people 400, concerts for children and young people 400, public concerts 100 *Perfs:* 1500 *Arts type:* promotes most genres *Comments:* employs 18 musicians and many freelance musicians and ensembles; trying to enlarge the interest in cultural events within the region of Sörmland and to make it possible for more inhabitants to attend concerts, theatreplays, exhibitions etc.

Kalmar Läns Musikstiftelse
Box 14, 572 21 **Oskarshamn**
Tel: 491-10696 Fax: 491-77915
E-Mail: kl@lamsmusipen.h.se
director of music Skjell Lindström
Events: 450 annually *Arts type:* chamber orch, choral music, chamber music, early music, electronic music, folk music, inst recitals, jazz, new music, song recitals, symphony music, multi media, world music *Touring:* Europe *Policy:* tours in Sweden (Kalmar County) and Europe *Comments:* Camerata Roman of Sweden; see also Orchestras

Länsmusiken i Jämtlands Län
Box 377, 831 25 **Östersund**
Tel: 63-147 250 Fax: 63-147 265
Internet: www.gll.se/verksam/lansmusik/musik.htm
E-Mail: lansmusiken@hotell.itz.se
director of music Thomas Florentin
Events: 500 (per year) *Arts type:* wide variety of music (e.g. jazz, chamber, new music)

Contemporary Chamber Music Society
Samtida Musik
c/o Lindgren, Vikingagatan 20, 113 42 **Stockholm**
Tel: 8-310 521/309 505 Fax: 8-310 521
chairman Ingrid Lindgren; vice chairman Stig Gustav Schönberg; secretary Henrik Löwenmark
Events: 6-7 concerts/year *Arts type:* chamber music, new music *Venues:* Musikaliska Akademien 400, Musikmuséef 300, Radiohuset 250 *Comments:* participates in ISCM Festival, Nordic Music days, Swedish Music Spring, Stockholm New Music, a commission a year to a composer

Danscentrum
Jungfrugatan 7B, 114 44 **Stockholm**
Tel: 8-660 7216 Fax: 8-660 2981
Internet: www.danscentrum.se
E-Mail: danscentrum@danscentrum.se
Art types: dance, modern dance *Comments:* promotes dance as an art form; coordinator and organiser of dance festivals, courses, etc.

Dansens Hus
Wallingatan 21, 111 24 **Stockholm**
Tel: 8-676 9600 Fax: 8-796 7040
Internet: www.dansenshus.se
E-Mail: info@dansenshus.se
artistic and general director Jan Zetterberg; marketing director Pia Bisi
Events: 20-30 *Perfs:* 30-40 *Arts type:* contemporary and ethnic dance *Venues:* Stora Scenen 830, Black Box 150, Big Theatre 850, Blue Box 150 *Comments:* national and international touring groups; foremost presenter of contemporary dance in Nordic countries, season from Aug-June and Jan-Dec; see also Venues

EMA – Telstar
Box 24151, 104 51 **Stockholm**
Tel: 8-665 0100
Fax: 8-665 1791
Internet: www.ema.se
E-Mail: mail@ema.se
director Thomas Johannsen; promoters Jans Gílle, David Maloney
Perfs: 300 *Arts type:* folk music, jazz, new music, music theatre, symphony music, world music, classical ballet, modern ballet, modern dance, rock and pop *Venues:* Circus Theatre, Stockholm (standing) 1800, seated 1500, the Concert House (Stockholm & Gottenburg), the Globe Arena (Stockholm), the Ice Stadium (Stockholm), the Annex (Stockholm) *Comments:* promote throughout Scandinavia + venues in Denmark and Norway

Folkparkerna
PO Box 17194, 104 62 **Stockholm**
Tel: 8-452 2500 Fax: 8-452 2505
Internet: www.folkparkerna.se
E-Mail: info@folkparkerna.se
executive director John Brattmyhr; cultural director Gunno Sandahl; information officer Peter Axelsson
Arts type: dance, music, solo artists, theatre and others *Comments:* unites 180 Folkparks (amusement and leisure parks) whose activities are supported by non-governmental and governmental organisations; see also National Organisations

Fylkingen
Box 17044, 104 62 **Stockholm**
Tel: 8-845 443/844 289 Fax: 8-669 3868
Internet: www.fylkingen.se
E-Mail: intermedia@fylkingen.se
producer Tomas Bokstad; chairman Mats Lindström
Perfs: 60 *Arts type:* electronic music, new music and intermedia art, multi-media, modern dance, visual arts exhibition, performance, video, improvised music *Venues:* capacity 140 *Comments:* concert hall, promoting body; have prof-PA, multi slide projection (computer controlled) large-screen video projector, 16mm film projector, limited stage lighting. Other equipment hired or borrowed as requested

Intercult
Nytorgsgatan 15, 116 22 **Stockholm**
Tel: 8-644 1023 Fax: 8-643 9676
Internet: www.intercult.se
E-Mail: info@intercult.se
artistic director Chris Torch; producer Ida Burén; audience development and network coordinator Rani Sukhia
Events: 15-20 *Perfs:* 40-50 *Arts type:* world music, folk music, modern theatre, street theatre, folk dance, modern dance, international artists and ensembles, festivals, small events, visual arts exhibitions *Venues:* various spaces in Stockholm; also cooperation with major cultural festivals in Scandinavia *Policy:* international and intercultural exchange in the performing arts *Comments:* international cultural exchange through guest performances in Scandinavia; projects and co-productions across national and artistic boundaries; bring together non-European and European artforms by use of co-productions between Sweden and non-European countries; see also Agents & Producers

Jeunesses Musicales (Sweden)
Rikskonserter, Nybrokajen 11, 111 48 **Stockholm**
Tel: 8-407 1600 Fax: 8-407 1645
E-Mail: annetteliljefars@srk.se
president Martin Martinsson; vice-president Kerstin Fondberg; general secretary Annette Liljefors
Comments: JM organises cooperation between educational organisations, communal music schools and Svenska Rikskonserter

Nordic Artist AB
Box 17779, 118 93 **Stockholm**
Tel: 8-5626 2050 Fax: 8-5626 2060
Internet: www.nordicartist.se
E-Mail: info@nordicartist.se
impresario Johan Englund; marketing director t.b.a.; production manager Patrick Froom
Arts type: chamber orch, choral music, early music, light orch music, symphony music, opera, subscribed concert series Mästarkonserter comprising 35 concerts and large events in Scandinavian arenas *Venues:* Berwaldhallen and other venues in Stockholm and other Swedish cities, Arenas + Europe: Stockholm Globe, Oslo Spectrum, Scandinavium Gothenburg, Elysée Hall Turku, Forum Copenhagen *Comments:* production of television, radio and gramophone recordings and CD recordings; visiting address:
Söder Mälarsterand 21, 118 93 Stockholm

Re: Orient
Box 4215, 102 65 **Stockholm**
Tel: 8-640 0828 Fax: 8-702 1599
Internet: www.reorient.se
E-Mail: info@reorient.se
artistic director Ozan Sunar; general manager Anders Lindblom; producer Anna Ljungqvist; programming coordinator Jonas Elvestig; marketing manager Anneli Gunnar; marketing Maria Malmqvist
Events: 3-5 throughout the year *Arts type:* music: both modern and traditional, dance, seminars & debates, poetry-literature, focusing on the Orient *Venues:* festival area at Sjöhistoriska museet: 2-3 tents cap. from 500 up to 1500 + different venues in Stockholm *Comments:* arrange concerts and seminars, lectures and debates; see also Festivals

Stockholm Concert Hall Foundation
Box 7083, 103 87 **Stockholm**
Tel: 8-786 0200 Fax: 8-791 7330
Internet: konserthuset.se
E-Mail: karinasvensson@konserthuset.se
executive and artistic director Arthur Hedström; planning manager Mats Engström
Arts type: classical music, symphony and chamber music concerts, recitals *Venues:* Main Hall 1800, Grünewald Hall 480, Aulin Hall 140 *Comments:* 1-2 international music festivals annually

Swedish Concert Institute
Svenska Rikskonserter
Nybrokajen 11, 111 48 **Stockholm**
Tel: 8-407 1600 Fax: 8-407 1645/47 (Martin Martinsson)
Internet: www.srk.se/
E-Mail: marianne.beskow@srk.se
director Martin Martinsson;
head of production department t.b.a.
Comments: a State foundation for the nationwide promotion of musical activity by various methods; activities are adapted to regional and local needs; since the reorganisation on Jan 1 1988, the county councils have taken on the responsibility for the regional activities and for 21 of Sweden's 22 Regional Music Depts (Länsmusikstiftelser)

Norrlandsoperan
Box 360, 901 08 **Umeå**
Tel: 90-154 300 Fax: 90-126 845
Internet: www.vbm.se
E-Mail: info@vbm.se
general and artistic director Lars Tibell; deputy general director & finance minister Helen Sundström-Hetta; assistant to director Tomas Kerslow; press officer Björn Björklund; technical administrator Anders Andersson; production manager t.b.a.; orchestra manager Lena Byström
Perfs: 100 *Arts type:* opera, symphony & chamber music *Venues:* Norrlandsoperan 300, The Sagatheatre 380, Iduntheatre 580 *Policy:* touring mostly in Scandinavian countries, also world wide *Comments:* see also Opera

Stiftelsen Musik i Uppland
PO Box 3106, 750 03 **Uppsala**
Tel: 18-171 920
Fax: 18-171 930
Internet: www.miu.se
E-Mail: info@miu.se
general manager Göran Kåver;
orchestral manager Nils Olof Sondell;
managers other groups Bengt Hilding, Gabriel Lindborg
Events: 600 public and school concerts a year *Arts type:* all types of music *Comments:* ensembles include Uppsala Kammarsolister, Linnékvintetten, Trio Con X, Uppsala Kammarorkester

Hässelby Castle – Nordic Cultural Centre
Hässelby Slott – nordiskt kulturcentrum
Box 520, 162 15 **Vällingby**
Tel: 8-620 3440
Fax: 8-620 3449
Internet: www.hasselbyslott.a.se
E-Mail: info@hasselbyslott.a.se
director Torbjörn Forsell (fax: 8-620 3449); information officer Ingrid Stenmark
Perfs: 20 *Arts type:* music from Nordic countries and Baltic states, chamber music, folk music, visual arts exhibitions, song recitals *Venues:* concert hall 150 *Comments:* organise concert series, literature performances, art exhibitions

Vätmanlandsmusiken
Hässlö, 721 31 **Västerås**
Tel: 21-800 800
Fax: 21-800 801
director of music Lars Knutson;
information officer Helena Wessman
Events: 680 *Arts type:* mostly classical music but also jazz, etc. *Venues:* Västerås Concert Hall 1000, Hässlö Salen Concert Hall 250 (own venue), & others in the region of Västerås

Stiftelsen Musik i Kronoberg
Villan, Kungsgatan 29, 352 33 **Växjö**
Tel: 470-18418
Fax: 470-48822
E-Mail: villan@mik.g.se
director of music Nils Wallnäs (470-18410); orchestral manager Thomas Liljeholm (470-18413)
Events: 540 *Arts type:* chamber orch, choral music, chamber music, early music, electronic music, folk music, jazz, new music *Comments:* Musica Vitae Chamber Orchestra (q.v.)

Stiftelsen Gotlandsmusiken
Kneippbygatan 2, 621 48 **Visby**
Tel: 498-264 450
Fax: 498-264 032
chairman of the board Lilian Edvards; managing director Gunnela Frumbirie
Events: 400, including 375 ensemble concerts and 25 freelance productions *Arts type:* classical music, school concerts *Policy:* produce, promote

SWITZERLAND (+41)

Orchesterverein Aarau
Scheibenschachenstrasse 1, 5000 **Aarau**
Tel: 62-824 3889
E-Mail: hrdietrich@bluewin.ch
Sekretärin Helene Dietrich
Events: 5 (Sept-June) *Arts type:* chamber concerts and inst. recitals, own productions with guest soloists *Venues:* Saalbau, Aarau 450

Allgemeine Musikgesellschaft (AMG)
Konzertgesellschaft, Hochstrasse 51, Postfach, 4002 **Basel**
Tel: 61-366 9166 Fax: 61-366 9169
E-Mail: amg-basee@datacomm.ch
president Dr. Thomas Staehelin; art dir Mario Venzago
Events: 22 concerts (Sept-June) *Perfs:* 21 *Arts type:* symphonic music *Venues:* Stadt Casino Basel 1512 *Comments:* see also Baseler Musik Forum (BMF) and Konzertgesellschaft

Basler Kulturgemeinschaft
Postfach 145, 4005 **Basel**
Tel: 61-681 2266 Fax: 61-681 3311
president Vera Gerwig; artistic director Erich Holliger
Events: 5 *Arts type:* classical concerts *Venues:* Stadt Casino, Basel up to 1527

Basler Musik Forum (BMF)
Postfach 1209, 4002 **Basel**
Tel: 61-366 9166 Fax: 61-366 9169
Programmausschuss Heinz Holliger, Klaus Schweizer, Jürg Wyttenbach
Events: 6 concerts *Arts type:* new music, symphony music *Venues:* Stadt Casino Basel 1512 *Comments:* see also Konzertgesellschaft and Allgemeine Musikgesellschaft

Basler Solistenabende
Burgunderstrasse 42, Postfach, 4002 **Basel**
Tel: 61-272 2902 Fax: 61-272 2902
directors Hans Rudolf Fuog
Events: 10 (Oct-May) *Arts type:* chamber and concert music, recitals *Venues:* Musik Saal, Stadt Casino 1500 *Policy:* recitals by soloists *Comments:* see also Konzertgesellschaft und Allgemeine Musik Gesellschaft (q.v.)

Gesellschaft für Kammermusik Basel
Postfach 1437, 4001 **Basel**
Tel: 61-4617 788 Fax: 61-4617 788
Internet: ourworld.compuserve.com/homepages/kammermusik
E-Mail: kammermusik@compuserve.com
president Bruno W. Häuptli; artistic direction Jans
Events: 10-11 (Oct-May) *Arts type:* chamber music *Venues:* Stadt Casino-Festsaal 700, Hans Huber Saal 550, Martinskirche 600 *Policy:* string quartet

Konzertgesellschaft
Hochstrasse 51, Postfach, 4002 **Basel**
Tel: 61-366 9166 Fax: 61-366 9169
director Kathrin Klingler
Arts types: orchestra, recitals *Venues:* Stadtkasino Basel, Tonhalle Zürich, Kasino Bern *Comments:* also promote individual artists; see also Baseler Musik Forum (BMF) and Allgemeine Musikgesellschaft

Konzertdirektion Bern
Rolf Hamberger, Münzgraben 2, 3011 **Bern**
Tel: 31-311 2515 Fax: 31-311 8531
E-Mail: hambergerbern@suissonline.ch
Leitung Rolf Hamberger
Perfs: 10-20 *Arts type:* chamber orch, chamber music, symphony music *Venues:* chamber orchestra and chamber music concerts in the most important concert halls in Switzerland

Stiftung Berner Symphonieorchester (BSO)
Münzgraben 2, Postfach, 3000 **Bern** 7
Tel: 31-328 2424 Fax: 31-328 2425
Internet: www.stub.unibe.ch/kultur/bmg.index.html
president t.b.a.; orchestra manager t.b.a.; chief-conductor Dmitrij Kitajenko
Events: 16 symphonic concerts *Perfs:* 3 each for elderly/young people; summer, family, open air; new year concerts etc. *Arts type:* symphony, chamber music, opera *Venues:* Konservatorium Bern 350, Konzerthaus Casino 1300

atp – artists theatre promotion (KTV)
Obergasse 1, Postbox 3350, 2500 **Biel** 3
Tel: 32-323 5085 Fax: 32-323 5072
Internet: www.ktv.ch
E-Mail: ktv-atp@bluewin.ch
Direktor Denis Alber; Sekret Marianne Gschwind, Martine Clémence, Ursula Lehmann; Präsident Peter Bissegger
Arts type: theatre, dance, jazz, pantomime, classical music etc, cabaret, café theatre *Policy:* to promote the arts across all language and cultural barriers *Comments:* publish atp Gazette four times a year in French, German and Italian; see also National Organisations: Vereinigung für Künstler/innen, Theater und Veranstalter/innen (KTV/ATP); runs Schweizer Künstlerbörse (every last week of April); see also Festivals: KTV/ATP-Künstler börse (artists exchange)

Konservatoriums – u Musikgesellschaft Biel KMB
c/o Frau Jeannine Botteron, Orchestergesellschaft Biel, Burggasse 31 / Postfach, 2500 **Biel** 3
Tel: 32-328 8979 Fax: 32-328 8977
Events: 11 *Perfs:* 5 symphony, 6 chamber concerts *Arts type:* symphony, chamber, recital, soloists *Venues:* Kongresshaus Biel 1200, Farel Saal 200, Saal der Loge 100, Kirche Pasquart 200 *Policy:* promotion of young artistis

Concerts de la Ville de Genève
Service de l'art musical, 19, route de Malagnou, Case postale 10, 1211 **Genève** 17
Tel: 22-418 6530/32 Fax: 22-418 6501
E-Mail: dac@ville-ge.ch
chef de service Jean-Claude Poulin;
assistant Beatrice Mawjee
Events: 25 jazz, 20 variety, 5 symphonic, 10 chamber music *Arts type:* classical, symphonic, chamber music, jazz, variety, folk music, song recitals *Venues:* Victoria Hall 1760, Cour de l'Hôtel de Ville 440, Théâtre de Verdure 1200, Cour du Collége Voltaire *Comments:* organise La Fête de la Musique; see also Festivals

International Cultural Exchange (ICE)
15 Chemin de la Rochette, 1202 **Genève**
Tel: 22-733 2222 Fax: 22-733 4400
E-Mail: ktice@bluewin.ch
impresario Kazuma Tomisawa
Arts type: classical music, opera, various, overseas tour, festival and artist promotion *Comments:* find and coordinate sponsorship for major promotions; stage technical and theatre consultancy;
see also Agents and Producers

Jeunesses Musicales de Suisse (Youth & Music)
Maison de la Radio, Case Postale 233, 1211 **Genève** 8
Tel: 22-328 7064 Fax: 22-328 5193
E-Mail: jmusicales@bluewin.ch
secrétaire générale Christiane Buntschu;
président Jean-Louis Juvet
Events: 50 *Arts type:* mostly classical
Comments: competition every 2 years

Société de Musique de La Chaux-de-Fonds
Case postale 1342, 2301 **La Chaux-de-Fonds**
Tel: 32-968 4866 Fax: 32-926 0023
administrator Raymond Oppliger (32-926 4638);
president Prof. Luc Humair
Events: 12 concerts + 1 free concert *Perfs:* 13 *Arts type:* chamber orch, choral music, chamber music, symphony music *Venues:* Salle de Musique 1200
Comments: season: Oct – May

Concerts de Montbenon
Case postale 306, 1000 **Lausanne** 17
Tel: 21-647 9281 (administration)/323 8251 (bookings)
Fax: 21-647 9281
president Pierre Hugli
Events: 10 concerts *Arts type:* chamber, recitals *Venues:* Salle Paderewski 600 (in the Casino de Montbenon)

Trägerverein Luzerner Sinfonieorchester
Zentralstrasse 44, 6003 **Luzern**
Tel: 41-210 5050/3487/3060 Fax: 41-210 2693
Internet: www.sinfonieorchester.ch
E-Mail: info@sinfonieorchester.ch
managing director Peter Keller
Events: 50 *Arts type:* choral music, chamber music, light orch music, music theatre, operetta, sacred music, symphony music, classical ballet *Venues:* Kultur- und Kongresshaus Luzern 1800, Luzerner Theater 500

Fondation pour la Diffusion de la Musique
Case postale 198, 2006 **Neuchâtel** 6
Tel: 32-730 5318 Fax: 32-730 5318
directrice Denise Perret
Arts type: first performances, avant garde repertoire performed by chamber and symphony orchestras from all over Europe *Comments:* produce CDs of the performances and scores in modern writing with the CD

Société de Musique de Neuchâtel
PO Box 1192, 2000 **Neuchâtel** 1
Tel: 32-725 6773 Fax: 32-725 6773
secretary general Jean-Pierre Mauler;
président Claude Delley
Events: 9 (6 symphony, 3 chamber) *Arts type:* symphony, chamber, recitals *Venues:* Salle de Musique du Temple-du-Bas 900

Born Theater & Konzert
Postfach 82, Gentenwisstr. 15, 8332 **Russikon**
Tel: 1-955 0747 Fax: 1-955 0751
Direction Peter-Matthias, Regula Born
Arts type: theatre, concert and show *Comments:* only operate in Switzerland, Austria and Germany

Schauwerk (formerly Theater im Fass)
Postfach 1532, 8201 **Schaffhausen**
Tel: 52-620 0586
Fax: 52-620 2475
Theaterbüro Schauwerk Katharina Furrer
Arts types: drama, musical theatre, cabaret, modern theatre *Venues:* capacity 100-300 *Comments:* welcomes foreign independent theatre groups

Konzertverein St Gallen
Museumstrasse 1, 9004 **St Gallen**
Tel: 71-242 0707 Fax: 71-242 0708
E-Mail: konzertverein.sy@beuewin.ch
Sinfonieorchester St. Gallen – Chefdirigent Jiri Kout; Geschäftsführer Marc Walter Haefelin
Events: 35 *Perfs:* 30 *Arts type:* chamber orch, chamber music, serenades, inst recitals, symphony music, new music, sacred music *Venues:* Tonhalle 950

Société des Concerts de Fribourg
Cormanon 5, 1752 **Villars-sur-Glâne**
Tel: 26-402 0637 Fax: 26-402 0650
président Dr. Joseph von der Weid
Events: 10 (Oct-May) *Arts type:* chamber orch, chamber music, inst recitals, song recitals, symphony music
Venues: Aula de l'Université 800

Musikkollegium Winterthur
Rychenbergstrasse 94, 8400 **Winterthur**
Tel: 52-268 1560 Fax: 52-268 1570
E-Mail: musikkollegium@musikkollegium.ch
director Karl Bossert; music director Heinrich Schiff
Events: 60 *Arts type:* chamber orch, choral music, chamber music, early music, inst recitals, new music, sacred music, song recitals, symphony music *Venues:* Stadthaus 800 *Comments:* see also Orchestras

Federation of Migros Cooperatives- Cultural Commitment/Performing Arts
Migros Genossenschafts Bund-Kulturprozent/Performing Arts
Limmatstrasse 152,
PO Box, 8031 **Zürich**
Tel: 1-277 2084 Fax: 1-277 2274
Internet: www.culturprozent.ch
E-Mail: christopher.haering@mgw.ch
dance Isabella Spirig (tel: 1-277 2049); theatre Dr Veronika Sellier; Kleinkunst/cabaret Christoph Haering, Margrit Bayer; music Dr. René Karlen
Events: 100-150 *Arts type:* dance, theatre, Kleinkunst organise tours *Comments:* sponsored by a 1% cultural levy of the turnover of the Migros Cooperatives; organise tours, organise STEPS (q.v.), an international contemporary dance festival

Good News Productions AG
Postfach, 8065 **Zürich**
Tel: 1-809 6666 Fax: 1-809 6600
Internet: www.ticketcorner.ch
E-Mail: promotions@email.ch
director André Béchir
Events: 80 *Arts type:* rock, pop, classical
Venues: Hallenstadium, Kongreßhaus, Volkshaus, St. Jakobhalle *Comments:* see also Agents and Producers

Klubhaus-Konzerte
Federation of Migros Cooperatives,
Postfach, 8031 **Zürich**
Tel: 1-277 2040 Fax: 1-277 2335
director Dr. René Karlen
Events: 50-60 *Arts type:* symphony concerts, new music
Venues: Basle, Berne, Geneva, Lausanne, Montreux, St Gallen, Zurich and others *Comments:* sponsored by Cultural Levy of the Migros Cooperatives

Tonhalle Gesellschaft
Gotthardstrasse 5, 8002 **Zürich**
Tel: 1-206 3440
Fax: 1-206 3436
executive director Trygve Nordwall; music director David Zinman; artistic administrator Etienne Raymond; managing director Jürg Keller
Events: 140 *Arts type:* chamber orch, choral music, chamber music, early music, sacred music, symphony music, new music *Venues:* Tonhalle – Großer Saal 1466, Kleiner Saal 636 *Comments:* see also Venues

UBS – Arena Konzerte
Postfach, 8098 **Zürich**
Tel: 1-236 5719 Fax: 1-236 8525
Internet: www.ubs.com
E-Mail: martinerpen@ubs.com
Leiter und Kultursponsor für Film, Klassische- und Jazz Musik Martin Erpen
Events: 15-20 per year *Perfs:* 20 *Arts type:* chamber music, jazz *Venues:* Zürich Kaufleuten 400

TURKEY (+90)

Promotion Foundation of Turkey
Turk Tanitma Vakfi
Köroglu Cad, Kavli Sok, No 24, Gaziosmanpasa, **Ankara**
Tel: 312-437 5166/4576
Fax: 312-436 4511
president Kemal Baytas

Sevda-Cenap and Music Foundation
Sevda-Cenap and Müsik Vakfi
Tunali Hilmi Caddesi 114/43, 06700 **Ankara**
Tel: 312-427 0855 Fax: 312-467 3159
E-Mail: scavakfi@ada.com.tr
coordinator Elif Basman; president Mehmet Basman
Comments: organisers of International Ankara Music Festival, see also Festivals

Istanbul Foundation for Culture and Arts
Yildiz Kültür ve Sanat Merkezi
istiklal caddesi 146, **Beyoglu (Istanbul)**
Tel: 212-249 6610 Fax: 212-249 5667
Internet: www.istfest.org
E-Mail: press.pr@istfest-tr.org
general director Melih Fereli; president Sakir Eczacibasi

Izmir State Turkish Classical Music
Izmir Devlet Klasik Türk Müzigi
Gazi Bulvari, Serbölük Ishani No 81, Kat-4, **Izmir**
Tel: 232-483 0960 Fax: 232-425 6691
director Teoman Önaldi

UKRAINE (+380)

Kievconcert
Richna St. 4, 252135 **Kiev (Kyiv)**
Tel: 44-216 5015
director Vyacheslav Stratienko

UNITED KINGDOM (+44)

Centre for Performance Research
8 Science Park, **Aberystwyth (Wales)** SY23 3AH
Tel: 1970-622 133 Fax: 1970-622 132
Internet: www.aber.ac.uk/~cprwww
E-Mail: cprwww@aber.ac.uk
administrator Claire Swatherage; artistic director Richard Gough; producer Judie Christie
Events: approx 80 (in any year, including workshops and conferences) *Arts type:* folk music, sacred music, multimedia; traditional music and performance forms alongside avant garde and experimental music and performance forms *Venues:* range from studios theatres 100+ to main stage/concert halls 2000+, also non-conventional theatre spaces and sites *Policy:* to offer opportunities for public and professional practitioners *Comments:* promotes traditional dance, theatre and music from around the world and visual, avant garde and experimental theatre from Europe and the Americas; see also Services

Manchester Chamber Concerts Society
c/o Greta Stanley, Preston Cottage, Brook Lane, **Alderley Edge** SK9 7QQ
Tel: 1625-582 349 Fax: 1625-582 308
E-Mail: margaret_m.stanley@virgin.net
publicity officer Alison Reade-Jahn (tel: 1663-745 003, fax: 1663-745 223)
Events: 6-7 (Oct-Mar) *Perfs:* 6 *Arts type:* chamber music, string quartets etc *Venues:* Concert Hall of the Royal Northern College of Music, Manchester 463 *Comments:* 300 subscribers, international artists

Stockport Symphony Orchestra
27 Ollerbarrow Road, Hale, **Altrincham** WA15 9PP
Tel: 161-926 9633 Fax: 161-926 9634
secretary Peter Austin
Events: 8 (Oct-June) *Perfs:* 10-12 *Arts type:* symphony music *Venues:* Stockport Town Hall 700

Seaton & District Music Club
Stoney House, Stoney Lane, **Axminster** EX13 5BU
Tel: 1297-33416 Fax: 1297-631 165
programme secretary Hilary Juster
Events: 6 Oct-March *Arts type:* chamber orch, chamber music, choral music, early music, inst recitals, song recitals *Venues:* Seaton Town Hall 280

Bedford Music Club
2 Keats Close, **Bedford** MK40 2AR
Tel: 1234-354 082
E-Mail: xy055@dial.pipex.com
secretary Roy Hoskins; treasurer Joe Pinnock
Events: 7 *Arts type:* chamber music, early music, singers & choirs, inst recitals *Policy:* chamber music by established groups and new combinations *Comments:* enocuragement and promoting artists at the beginning of their career always form part of the concert season

Aiken Promotions
Marlborough House, 348 Lisburn Road, **Belfast (Northern Ireland)** BT9 6GH
Tel: 28-9038 1047 Fax: 28-9068 2091
E-Mail: cathy@aiken.co.uk
promoter Jim Aiken; producer Peter Aiken
Events: 30 (all year: mainly summer) *Perfs:* 100 *Arts type:* rock to popular classics *Venues:* indoor, outdoor large scale

Belfast Music Society
147a Kings Road, **Belfast (Northern Ireland)** BT5 7EG
Tel: 28-9048 3459
chairman Leonard Pugh
Comments: promotes an annual series of celebrity concerts consisting of all forms of chamber music, also presents recitals by international artists throughout the year

Bournemouth Chamber Music Society
91 East Avenue, **Bournemouth** BH3 7BU
Tel: 1202-764 255 Fax: 1202-762 703
secretary Michael Read; concerts director Sandrey Date
Events: 6 *Perfs:* 6 *Arts type:* chamber music, early music, inst recitals, new music, song recitals
Venues: Talbot Heath School 249

WOMAD
c/o World in the Park Ltd., Mill Lane, **Box Corsham** SN13 8PN
Tel: 1225-744 188/744 494
Fax: 1225-743 481
Internet: www.womad.org
E-Mail: womad@realworld.on.net
artistic director Thomas Brooman; financial administrator Karen Coghlan; WOMAD music Annie Reed; events coordinator Geraldine Roule; production director Steve Haddrell; education & WOMAD Foundation Mandy Macfarlane; production coordinator Lesley Kingsley; marketing & media manager Mandy Craine; Friends of WOMAD coordinator Annie Menter
Events: 10 festivals pa *Arts type:* world music, arts and dance *Venues:* touring organisation working in Australia, Japan, Spain, UK, USA, Austria, Portugal, Italy, Canary Islands, South Africa
Comments: producing around 10 festivals a year internationally, working with a wide variety of performing musicians from around the globe; presenting festivals in Australia, Japan, Spain, UK, USA, Austria; see also Festivals

Bradford Theatres Classical Music Season
St. George's Concert Hall, Bridge Street, **Bradford** BD1 1JS
Tel: 1274-752 375 (administration)/752 000 (box office)
Fax: 1274-754 128
general manager John Botteley (1274-752 375); music planning officer Laura Wood
Events: 12 (Oct-May) *Perfs:* 10-12 *Arts type:* chamber orch, chamber music, choral music, symphony music *Venues:* St George's Concert Hall 1700, and other venues in Bradford *Comments:* see also Venues

Classical Management Services
Opera Box Ltd, Rhydyberi Cottages, Merthr Cynog, **Brecon (Wales)** LD3 9SA
Tel: 1874-690 339
Fax: 1874-690 254
Internet: www.operabox.freeuk.com
E-Mail: opera-box@international.freeserve.co.uk
directors Bredan Wheatley, Bridget Gill
Events: 30 *Perfs:* 30 *Arts type:* opera, concerts *Venues:* The Cannizaro Park Festival 633 (month long festival) *Comments:* see also Festivals (The Cannizaro Park Festival) and Agents & Producers (Opera Box)

Rostrum Promotions
4 Ferniebank Brae, **Bridge of Allen (Scotland)** FK9 4PJ
Tel: 1786-834 449
Fax: 1786-833 949
E-Mail: rostrum@compuserve.com
director Fiona Paterson
Arts type: primarily instrumental soloists
Policy: promotes soloist professional musicians
Comments: organises arts conference and festival coordination, provides musicians for private events, parties and corporate events

Cambridge City Council
Leisure Service, The Guildhall, **Cambridge** CB2 3QJ
Tel: 1223-457 521
Fax: 1223-457 519
Internet: www.cambridge.gov.uk/leisure
E-Mail: marketing@cambridge.gov.uk
director of leisure services Ian Cooper; marketing & promotions manager Pauline Haughey; director Cambridge Corn Exchange Robert Sanderson; marketing manager Tim Holt
Events: 100 (Corn Exchange 300) *Arts type:* folk, children's events, fairs, fireworks, senior citizen's events, shows, concerts, festivals
Venues: Cambridge Corn Exchange 1800 *Policy:* to ensure an extensive programme of events to meet a wide cross-section of tastes *Comments:* events year round include Children's Festival, Cambridge Folk Festival, 'Summer in the City'; open air concerts; see also Venues (Cambridge Corn Exchange)

Canterbury Music Club
130 Salisbury Road, **Canterbury** CT2 7SE
Tel: 1227-462 029
secretary Jill Waters; treasurer Mayling Stone; chairman Tony Hickson
Events: 6 professional, 1 young local virtuosi *Perfs:* 6 *Arts type:* chamber music, inst recitals etc. *Venues:* mainly school halls and churches ranging from 350 up to 700 *Policy:* concerts of classical music by professional musicians

Acorn Entertainments Ltd.
PO Box 64, **Cirencester** GL7 5YD
Tel: 1285-644 622
Fax: 1285-642 291
Internet: www.hrpl.u-net.com
E-Mail: acornents@btconnect.com
contact Dudley Russell
Perfs: 150 *Arts type:* folk music, music theatre, modern theatre, light orch music, comedy, solo theatre shows
Comments: theatre producers and concert promoters

Dorking Halls Concertgoers Society
Hythe Lodge, Knoll Road, **Dorking** RH4 3EP
Tel: 1306-887 390 Fax: 1306-884 766
contact Gordon Coton
Events: 10 *Perfs:* 10 (Oct-April) *Arts type:* chamber orch, choral music, chamber music, early music, inst recitals, sacred music, song recitals, symphony music *Venues:* Dorking Halls 750 *Policy:* to bring first rate professional performances of fine music to audiences

Evesham & District Music Club
The Hayes, Drakesbridge Road, **Eckington** WR10 3BN
Tel: 1386-750 416 Fax: 1386-750 392
secretary Miss L. Goodwin
Events: 6 *Arts type:* chamber music, inst recitals, song recitals *Venues:* Evesham Arts Centre 300, All Saints Church

Assembly Direct
89 Giles Street, **Edinburgh (Scotland)** EH6 6BZ
Tel: 131-553 4000 Fax: 131-554 0454
Internet: www.jazzmusic.co.uk
E-Mail: info@assemblydirect.ednet.co.uk
directors Fiona Alexander, Roger Spence; programming Fiona Alexander
Perfs: 120 per year *Arts type:* jazz and blues
Venues: major stages throughout UK including Royal Festival Hall, Queen's Hall, Edinburgh; Glasgow City Hall; Aberdeen Music Hall *Comments:* UK wide jazz and blues promoters; independent, non-profit making company; expanding into Europe with concerts in Germany, France, Netherlands and Czech Republic

City of Edinburgh Council
Department of Recreation, Usher Hall, **Edinburgh (Scotland)** EH1 3BG
Tel: 131-529 7844 Fax: 131-529 7472
director Herbert Coutts
Arts type: Arts Development dept supports organisations involved in: symphony orchestra, dance, theatre, mime, recitals, drama, jazz, pantomime, folk, ethnic music & dance, pop, rock, minority & ethnic *Venues:* Arts & Heritage dept manages these venues: Usher Hall 2215, Assembly Rooms – 4 rooms up to 800, Churchill Theatre 361, Portobello Town Hall 771, Hall 250, Thomas Morton Hall 420 *Comments:* events promoted all year

Georgian Concert Society
3 East Castle Rd., **Edinburgh (Scotland)** EH10 5AP
Tel: 131-229 8018
administrator Stephen Strugnell
Events: 6 (from October-March) *Perfs:* 6 *Arts type:* early music *Venues:* St. Cecilia's Hall 250 *Comments:* the ensembles play on original and reproduction nstruments; emphasis on authenticity

Unique Events
17-23 Calton Road, **Edinburgh (Scotland)** EH8 8DL
Tel: 131-557 3990 Fax: 131-557 8566
E-Mail: unique@ednet.co.uk
managing director Pete Irvine; assitant to director Georgia Macleod; admin assistant Louise Kidd
Events: 3-5 (throughout the year) *Arts type:* festivals & large scale events including street theatre, all types music (chamber orch, folk music, jazz, world music), multi-media, children's events (puppets), visual arts exhibitions, sports *Venues:* various indoor/outdoor small-large scale venues *Comments:* organisers of biggest New Years Party in the world – Edinburgh's Hogmanay

Glasgow City Council Department of Culture and Leisure
16 Albion Street, **Glasgow (Scotland)** G1
Tel: 141-287 5429 Fax: 141-287 5533
Internet: www.glasgow.gov.uk/cls
E-Mail: city.lwe@glasgow.gov.uk
director Bridget McConnell
Events: 100+ *Perfs:* 1000+ *Arts type:* contemporary and classical theatre, dance and music, opera, jazz, folk and rock music, visual arts exhibitions and installations, multi-media events, children's workshops and activities, street theatre *Venues:* King's Theatre, Tramway, City Hall, Old Fruitmarket, Mitchell Theatre (all q.v.); 6 community venues throughout the city, also museums, libraries, sports centres *Policy:* developing policies and programmes for culture and leisure in Glasgow; sustaining and extending cultural initiatives across the city; promoting events and activities to further enhance Glasgow's reputation as a cultural centre

Sonata
11 North Park Street, **Glasgow (Scotland)** G20 7AA
Tel: 141-946 7034/945 3553 Fax: 141-946 7034
Internet: www.sonata.freeserve.co.uk
E-Mail: gtassie@sonata.freeserve.co.uk
managing director Gregor Tassie
Events: 20 *Perfs:* 100-150 *Arts type:* chamber orch, choral music, chamber music, inst recitals, new music, music theatre, sacred music, song recitals, symphony music, opera; primarily European choirs, opera and soloists
Venues: South Bank Centre; St. John's, Smith Square; and nationwide *Policy:* to promote both popular and little known music by artists of the highest calibre
Comments: arrange major tours and recording projects; also work in assisting UK artists tour the C.I.S (Russia, Ukraine, Belarus etc.)

Victoria Theatre
Metropolitan Borough of Calderdale, Wards End, **Halifax** HX1 1BU
Tel: 1422-351 156/158 (box office) Fax: 1422-320 552
E-Mail: postbox@victoria-theatre.york.com
principal entertainments manager George Candler
Events: 180 (March-March) *Arts type:* major symphony orchestras, light entertainments, conferences, musicals, drama, children's product; dance, opera *Venues:* 7 halls up to 500 (contact Piece Hall tel: 1422-358 087, Hebden Bridge Cinema/Theatre 500, Victoria Theatre 1585

Huddersfield Music Society, The
Moisy Cottage, 23 Smithy Place, Brockholes, **Huddersfield** HD7 7AG
Tel: 1484-663 474 Fax: 1484-667 988
E-Mail: gordon.sykes@virgin.net
president Stephen Smith; hon. secretary Gordon Sykes; treasurer P. Micheal Lord
Events: 7 (Oct-April) *Perfs:* 7 *Arts type:* chamber music, inst recitals, song recitals *Venues:* St Paul's Hall, University, Queensgate, Huddersfield 250, plus behind artists 100 *Policy:* 18th, 19th & 20th century chamber music

Ilkley Concert Club
22 Sunset Drive, **Ilkley** LS29 8LS
Tel: 194-360 9744 Fax: 194-360 9744
chairman & artistic director David Pyett; secretary Rebecca Metcalfe
Events: 8-12 (Sept-May) *Perfs:* 12 *Arts type:* chamber orch, chamber music, early music, inst recitals, song recitals, jazz *Venues:* Kings Hall 480 *Policy:* subscription series of chamber music

Blue Snow
20 Downs View, **Isleworth** TW7 5HS
Tel: 467-810 560
Internet: easyweb.easynet.co.uk/~bluesnow
E-Mail: bluesnow@easynet.co.uk
director Philip Sheppard
Arts type: contemporary jazz and ambience music
Comments: CD Label and promoter of events; see also Recorded Media

Keele Concerts Society
c/o Department of Music, Keele University, **Keele** ST5 5BG
Tel: 1782-714 897 (Mondays) Fax: 1782-583 295
E-Mail: keele.concerts.society@afsoc.keele.ac.uk
artistic director Alexandra Scott
Events: 14 (Oct-March) *Perfs:* 14 *Arts type:* chamber orchestra, choral music, chamber music, early music, jazz, new music, light orch music, song recitals, symphony music, world music *Venues:* University Chapel 400, Westminster Theatre 400 *Policy:* to increase the amount of classical concerts presented by professional musicians in the region

Music in Country Churches
Hall House, Boughton, **Kings Lynn** PE33 9AG
Tel: 1366-501 129 Fax: 1366-501 129
trustee & honorary music director Alan Wilkinson
Events: 3 *Arts type:* chamber orch, choral music, chamber music, early music *Comments:* charity; patron: HRH The Prince of Wales

Leeds City Council Leisure Services
Leeds Town Hall, The Headrow, **Leeds** LS1 3AD
Tel: 113-247 8336 Fax: 113-247 8397
leisure services director Denise Preston; principal music officer Matthew Sims
Events: c.200 (Sept-July) *Arts type:* chamber orchestral, choral music, chamber music, early music, inst recitals (organ), jazz, light orch music, brass bands, sacred music, song recitals, symphony music, opera *Venues:* Leeds Town Hall 1700, West Yorkshire Playhouse 750, Civic Theatre 550, Yeadon Town Hall 550, Garforth Community College 300, City Art Gallery 220, Morley Town Hall 700, Civic Hall 250 *Comments:* young musician series, family concerts, summer music

De Montfort Hall
De Montfort Hall, Granville Road, **Leicester** LE1 7RU
Tel: 116-233 3113 Fax: 116-233 3182
Internet: www.demontforthall.co.uk
E-Mail: hasrw001@leicester.gov.uk
manager Richard Haswell; operations manager Alvin Hargreaves; marketing manager Nick Hallam; technical manager John Sippet; house manager Pete Cooper
Events: 270 *Arts type:* classical, rock, pop and popular concerts; asian dance/music; also chamber orch, choral music, electronic music, folk music and dance, jazz, music theatre, operetta, symphony music, opera, world music, classical and modern ballet, modern dance, classical theatre *Venues:* De Montfort Hall 1600-2000

Abbotsholme Arts Society
c/o Lichfield Festival Office, 7 The Close, **Lichfield** WS13 7LD
Tel: 1543-257 298
Fax: 1543-415 137
E-Mail: paul.spicer@lichfield-arts.co.uk
artistic director Paul Spicer; administrator Ruth Hardingham; secretary Claire Tetley; treasurer Carol Kersey Bemment
Events: 14 *Arts type:* chamber music, choral music, early music, inst recitals, jazz, new music, sacred music, song recitals, classical ballet, visual arts exhibitions, modern dance *Venues:* Abbotsholme School 200 seated *Policy:* to provide high quality arts for North Staffordshire/ South Derbyshire UK

Lincoln Choral Society
Clariden, 21 Daniel Crescent, **Lincoln** LN4 1QT
Tel: 1522-790 422 Fax: 1522-584 915
secretary Geoffrey Brown; principal conductor Neville Turner
Events: 3-4 *Perfs:* 3-4 *Arts type:* choral
Venues: Lincoln Cathedral 1500

Brouhaha International
4th Floor Gostins Bgd., 32-36 Hanover St., **Liverpool** L1 4LN
Tel: 151-709 3334 Fax: 151-709 4994
Internet: www.brouhaha.demon.co.uk
E-Mail: admin@brouhaha.demon.co.uk
director Francisco Carrasco; chair Ms. Penny Feeny
Events: 3 arts festivals *Arts type:* all performing and visual arts *Comments:* research into arts in the economy; teaching in local universities and art training; European arts database; see also National Organisations and Services

Alternative Arts
47a Brushfields Street, **London** E1 6AA
Tel: 20-7375 0441 Fax: 20-7375 0484
directors Maggie Pinhorn, Liz Weston
Events: 20+ *Arts type:* street theatre, dance, mime, music, opera, performing poetry, drama, circus, jazz, etc. *Venues:* various in London *Policy:* to invest in new artists and new ideas and present a programme of open-air events throughout the year *Comments:* see also Festivals, National Organisation

Apples & Snakes
BAC, Lavender Hill, **London** SW11 5TF
Tel: 20-8692 0393 (programming)/8347 (educaiton)
Fax: 20-8692 4551
E-Mail: apples@snakes.demon.co.uk
admin. director Geraldine Collinge; programmer Roger Robinson; education co-ordinator Malika Booker
Events: a series of own special events, tours & festivals through the year, regular events at Battersea Arts Centre every fortnight *Arts type:* poets: incld – cabaret/comic/political poets, rap/dub poets, jazz poets, storytellers, sound poets & a range of musicians *Venues:* Battersea Arts Centre 80 *Policy:* promote; to give a platform to voices traditionally excluded from the cultural mainstream *Comments:* aims to establish the most progressive & best known promotional organisation for poetry & poets working in the UK today; represents poets from a range of artistic & cultural backgrounds; operate a Poets in Education Scheme (PIES)

Arts Connect
EMC EuroPR, 22-24 Worple Road, **London** SW19 4DD
Tel: 20-8944 5800 (direct)/20-8879 3033 (main office)
Fax: 20-8944 5800 (direct)/8947 9042 (main office)
E-Mail: artscoemc@aol.com
contact Robert Moffat
Arts types: music, mainly vocal *Comments:* linking the arts, business and the consumer

Artsfusion Ltd
74 Mortimar Street, **London** W1N 7DF
Tel: 20-7637 7088 Fax: 20-7636 4822
E-Mail: admin@artsfusion.co.uk
contacts Tricia Murray-Bett, Tony Barlow
Arts type: predominantly ballet and opera *Comments:* see also Agents & Producers and Opera (Wroclaw Opera)

Asian Music Circuit
Ground Floor, Unit E, West Point, 33/34 Warple Way, **London** W3 0RG
Tel: 20-8742 9911 Fax: 20-8749 3948
chairman Viram Jasani; assistant admin coordinator Kuldeep Jalf; programme co-ordinator Penny King; education officer Alistair Will
Events: 8-10 tours; 3-10 artists per tour; 6 concerts per artist; touring UK, Europe; all Asian artists *Perfs:* 50 *Arts type:* folk music, inst recitals, new music, music theatre, sacred music, world music, traditional music *Venues:* South Bank Centre up to 1000 *Comments:* promotes Asian and UK Asian music in the UK; also educational programme

Chinese Cultural Centre
27 Old Gloucester Street, **London** WC1N
Tel: 20-7633 9878 Fax: 20-7405 1656
administrator Susie Wong; artistic director Dai Ailian
Events: 10+ *Perfs:* 25+ *Arts type:* chamber orch, folk music, song recitals, world music, classical theatre, puppet, visual arts exhibitions, modern dance, mime theatre, folk dance, new music, classical theatre, puppets, street theatre *Venues:* concert halls and theatres in London & major cities *Policy:* national organisation for Chinese arts; promotes Chinese arts in the UK *Comments:* venue base for London Chinese Orchestra, Chinese Dance and MIme theatre

Classical Opera Company, The
2 Arundel Street, **London** WC2R 3LT
Tel: 20-7844 4440 Fax: 20-7844 9564
Internet: www.classicalopera.co.uk
E-Mail: info@classicalopera.demon.co.uk
artistic director Ian Page; administrator Nicholas Morrison; chairman Vernon Ellis
Arts type: opera, classical music, education *Comments:* company's new fund raising board: Amadeus Society

Contemporary Music Network
Arts Council of England, 14 Great Peter Street, **London** SW1P 3NQ
Tel: 20-7973 6504 Fax: 20-7973 6590
Internet: www.cmntours.org.uk
E-Mail: beverley.crew@artscouncil.org.uk
producer Beverly Crew; CMN assistant Marcel Jenkins
Events: 10 tours per season *Perfs:* 60-70 per season *Arts type:* music: contemporary, classical, jazz, world, electronic, new, multi-media *Venues:* small-large scale concert halls, clubs *Policy:* funds and co-ordinates tours of new music throughout the country *Comments:* the Contemporary Music Network is a subsidised touring scheme for new music set up by the Arts Council in 1971; the scheme is designed to increase, through concert tours and related educational events, the range and availability of new and experimental music to audiences around the country

Early Music Network
31 Abdale Road, **London** W12 7ER
Tel: 20-8743 0302 Fax: 20-8743 0996
Internet: www.earlymusic.org.uk
E-Mail: glyn@earlymusicnet.demon.co.uk
administrator Glyn Russ
Events: 120 *Arts type:* early music,vocal & instrumental ensembles *Venues:* venues around the country
Comments: plus directory of recommended projects circulated nationwide; see also National Organisations

Edward Snape Ltd
22-24 Torrington Place, **London** WC1E 7HF
Tel: 20-7580 6792 Fax: 20-7580 6652
director Edward Snape
Events: 10-30 *Arts type:* music theatre, opera, classical theatre, modern theatre, comedy *Venues:* west end theatres & regional theatre *Comments:* tour and production management for producers, promoters and repertory companies; see also Agents

Foundation for Education and Arts
1 Carriage Hall, 29 Floral Street, **London** WC2E 9DP
Tel: 20-7483 3383 Fax: 20-7483 3353
E-Mail: gamma.london@dial.pipex.com
contact Marc Waterman ACA
Events: 1-10 *Arts type:* all types *Comments:* see also Dance, Festivals

Joseph Seelig Ltd.
35 Little Russell Street, **London** WC1A 2HH
Tel: 20-7637 5661 Fax: 20-7323 1151
E-Mail: joseph.seelig@easynet.co.uk
contacts Joseph Seelig, Helen Lannaghan
Comments: international arts festival and theatre management; see also New Zealand International Festival of the Arts (MOD) and The London International Mime Festival

Kirckman Concert Society
110 Gloucester Avenue, **London** NW1 8HX
Tel: 20-7483 2681 Fax: 20-7586 5343
E-Mail: sarah.gordon@easynet.co.uk
artistic director Neil Black; administrator Sarah Gordon
Perfs: 12 *Arts type:* classical/chamber concerts and recitals *Venues:* Wigmore Hall, Purcell Room (South Bank) *Comments:* organisation designed to help young musicians at the early stages of their career

Latin American & Caribbean Cultural Society (LACCS)
c/o J R Monroy Management, PO Box 30, **London** N12 0PR
Tel: 20-8446 6416 Fax: 20-8446 5547
director John R Monroy; project manager J L Sylvester
Events: 20-25 projects each year *Perfs:* 35 *Arts type:* chamber orchestra, chamber music, folk music, song recitals, symphony music, world music, folk dance, visual arts exhibitions *Venues:* Barbican, South Bank Centre, Wigmore Hall, St. John's, Smith Square and overseas venues (Asia, Latin America, Africa and Europe) and other venues in London & provinces in UK *Policy:* promotes the music (composers and performers, especially guitarists) of artists from Latin America, Antillas and other continents; promoter of popular Latin American music in classical style

Marshall Arts
Leeder House, 6 Erskine Road, **London** NW3 3AJ
Tel: 20-7586 3831
Fax: 20-7586 1422
E-Mail: info@marshall-arts.co.uk
managing director Barrie Marshall; director Jenny Marshall; financial director Doris Dixon
Arts type: most music (R&B, jazz, rock, classical, opera, world music) *Comments:* international concert promoters & tour co-ordinators

Music by the Commons
31 Gilbey Rd, **London** SW17 0QQ
Tel: 20-8767 7201
E-Mail: anthony.penny@which.net
chairman Anthony Penny; treasurer John Waller
Events: 8-9 *Perfs:* 8-9 *Arts type:* early music performed on period instruments *Venues:* mostly at St Mary's Church, Putney Bridge, London SW 15 *Comments:* concerts begin at 8 pm, admission £6, concessions £3

Polish Cultural Institute
34 Great Portland Place, **London** W1N 4HG
Tel: 20-7636 6032/3/4 Fax: 20-7637 2190
E-Mail: PCI-LOND@pcidir.demon.co.uk

Royal Choral Society
Unit 9, 92 Lots Road, **London** SW10 0QD
Tel: 20-7376 3718 Fax: 20-7376 3719
Internet: goourworld.nu/royalchoralsociety
E-Mail: royalchoralsociety@compuserve.com
administrator Graeme Tonge; music director Richard Cooke; choir secretary Helen Boby
Events: 2 *Perfs:* 20 *Arts type:* wide repertoire including choral music, opera and popular classics *Venues:* Royal Festival Hall, Royal Albert Hall, Barbican Hall, etc. *Comments:* 200 singers; Royal Choral Society increasing in demand for orchestras and entrepeneurs; see also National Organisations and Choirs

Royal Philharmonic Society, The
10 Stratford Place, **London** W1N 9AE
Tel: 20-7491 8110 Fax: 20-7493 7463
E-Mail: admin@rps-uk.demon.co.uk
general administrator Rosemary Johnson
Arts type: chamber orch, chamber music, inst recitals, new music, song recitals, symphony music *Policy:* recitals, lectures and awards *Comments:* commisions new music; organises annual RPS Music Awards for outstanding achievement (12 categories); administers RPS Composition Prize, Julius Isserlis Scholarship (awarded by competition), Emily Anderson Prize for Violin, Society's Gold Medal, instituted 1870, awarded internationally for services to music

Serious Ltd
Chapel House, 18 Hatton Place, **London** EC1N 8RU
Tel: 20-7405 9900 Fax: 20-7405 9911
E-Mail: david@seriousltd.demon.co.uk
directors David Jones, John Cumming, Claire Whitaker
Arts type: new music, jazz, world music *Venues:* Royal Festival Hall, Queen Elizabeth Hall (q.v.), the Barbican and other major London venues, some touring *Comments:* concert producers, with a strong interest in international cooperation; producers of London International Jazz Festival in November

Sonic Arts Network
The Jerwood Space, 171 Union Street, **London** SE1 0LN
Tel: 20-7928 7337 Fax: 20-7928 7338
Internet: www.sonicartsnetwork.org
E-Mail: phil@sonicartsnetwork.org
senior administrator Phil Hallett;
education director Paul Wright
Arts type: electro-accoustic music *Venues:* nation-wide *Comments:* National association of composers, performers, teachers and others interested in the application of technology to the composition and performance of music; membership organisation

Huddersfield Choral Society, The
Jennie Blythe Artists Management, Sunnyside,
Lower Swell GL54 1LG
Tel: 1451-830 059 Fax: 1451-832 357
secretary Stephen Brook; principal conductor Martyn Brabbins; principal guest conductor Jane Glover; chorus master Joseph Cullen;
agent Jennie Blythe Artists' Management
Events: 6 (Sept-June) + 1 tv & 3 radio recordings *Perfs:* 15 *Arts type:* choral music, new music, sacred music, opera, world music *Venues:* Huddersfield Town Hall 1200 *Policy:* to further the enjoyment of choral music of performer and listener by the promotion of choral concerts *Comments:* 200 singers

Malvern Concert Club
5 North Hill Court, Newtown Road, **Malvern** WR14 1PD
Tel: 1684-565 996
secretary Catherine Freeman; treasurer Maureen McCulloch; chairman Prof. Peter Evans
Events: concerts Sept-May *Perfs:* 6 *Arts type:* chamber music, early music, inst recitals, song recitals *Venues:* Malvern Theatre 800 *Comments:* for Malvern Theatres – Tel: 1684-892 277

Royal Northern College of Music
124 Oxford Road, **Manchester** M13 9RD
Tel: 161-907 5200 Fax: 161-273 7611
E-Mail: info@rncm.ac.uk
promotions coordinator Philip Jones;
events and front-of-house manager Allan Taylor;
press & publicity officer Marian Blaikley
Events: 200 *Arts type:* all arts types *Venues:* Lord Rhodes Room 150, The Siemens Theatre 626, Sema Group Concert Hall 463 *Comments:* the seating cap of the Sema Group Concert Hall can be extended to 620, see also venues

Wavendon Allmusic Plan
The Stables, Wavendon, **Milton Keynes** MK17 8LT
Tel: 1908-582 522 Fax: 1908-281 024
Internet: www.stables.org
general manager Jacky Scott; joint presidents John Dankworth, Cleo Laine; programmer Rachel Fleet; marketing officer Joanna Wardle
Events: 200 *Arts type:* chamber music, early music, electronic music, folk music, inst recitals, jazz, new music, world music, light orch music *Venues:* capacity 300 *Policy:* programming all styles of music

Raymond Gubbay Ltd
Knight House, 29-31 East Barnet Road,
New Barnet EN4 8RN
Tel: 20-8216 3000 Fax: 20-8216 3001
Internet: www.raymond-gubbay.co.uk
E-Mail: info@raymond-gubbay.co.uk
managing director Raymond Gubbay; deputy managing director Robert Jolley; events director Anthony Findlay; financial controller Ade Aderogba
Events: 250-350 *Arts type:* classical concerts
Venues: major concert halls and arenas in UK, Europe and worldwide

Chester Music Society
2 Greenfield Way, Cuddington, **Northwich** CW8 2YH
Tel: 1606-882 007
secretary David Parks-Smith; treasurer Dr. E. B. Ranby (1244-381 995); chairman J. Herson (1244-340 029)
Events: 16 (Sept-June) *Perfs:* 16 *Arts type:* classical, jazz, chamber orch, choral music, chamber music, early music, sacred music, song recitals, symphony music, youth choirs, inst recitals *Venues:* Cathedral 950, Chester Town Hall 400 *Comments:* chorus – 150 singers, musical evenings once a week from Sept-March, winter chamber concert series, a junior chorus with 70 singers (aged 11-17 yrs); also the preludes for children aged 6-10yrs

Nottingham City Council
55 Castlegate, **Nottingham** NG1 6AF
Tel: 115-915 5555 Fax: 115-915 3599
performing arts officers Andrew Chetty,
June Whitesides
Arts type: symphony orchestras, festivals, jazz, exhibitions, dance, comedy, chamber music, drama, theatre, world music *Venues:* Royal Concert Hall 2500, Albert Hall 900, Nottingham Playhouse 750, Congregational Hall 450, various pubs and clubs *Comments:* events promoted throughout the year, indoors and outdoors

London Bach Society
Bach House, 73 High Street, **Old Oxted** RH8 9LN
Tel: 1883-717 372 Fax: 1883-715 851
contact Margaret Steinitz
Perfs: up to 12 *Arts type:* baroque music, the music of JS Bach, in particular the Cantatas, early music, chamber orch, choral music, chamber music *Venues:* various, mostly historic buildings *Policy:* mainly promotional activity: London Bach Festival, annually in autumn *Comments:* professional performers only

Music at Oxford
Elms Court, Botley, **Oxford** OX2 9LP
Tel: 1865-242 865 Fax: 1865-242 867
Internet: www.musicatoxford.demon.co.uk
E-Mail: info@musicatoxford.demon.co.uk
general manager Melinda Jordan; artistic administrator Jennifer Johns; marketing manager Georgia Rivers; development officer Lindsey Glen
Events: 30 (in Oxford) *Perfs:* 30 *Arts type:* classical concerts including chamber orch, choral music, chamber music, early music, inst recitals, sacred music, symphony music; also jazz, song recitals and new music, light orch music, music theatre, opera *Venues:* Sheldonian Theatre 900, Christ Church Cathedral 1800, University Church St Mary the Virgin 450, Oxford Townhall 650, Holywell Music Room 250, Harnabus Oxford 300 *Comments:* independent charity which promotes about 30 classical concerts per year in and around Oxford

Oxford Chamber Music Society
19 Essex Street, **Oxford** OX4 3AW
Tel: 1865-722 991
Fax: 1865-722 991
chairman Dr Woodgate; secretary Joan Fraser
Events: 6 (Oct-June) *Perfs:* 6 *Arts type:* chamber music, inst recitals *Venues:* Holywell Music Room 200

Barnes Music Society
28 Denehurst Gardens, **Richmond** TW10 5DL
Tel: 20-8876 3919
president Stephen Dodgson;
chairman Peter Brown; recitals secretary Sheila Kearvell; administrative secretary Kathy Avdiev
Events: 8 (Oct-May) + 4 children's, 1 youth, 2 local young musicans *Perfs:* 16 *Arts type:* chamber orch, chamber music, early music, inst recitals, new music, sacred music, song recitals, ensembles, solo artists, youth orchestras, children's concerts *Venues:* local churches, school halls up to 250 *Comments:* series of first class chamber recitals with special encouragement to young and local musicians

Uppingham Concerts
Uppingham School, **Rutland** LE15 9QU
Tel: 1572-822 267
Fax: 1572-822 792
secretary & director of music Neil Page;
administrator Carol Hopkins;
joint secretary Alex Tester
Events: 8 *Perfs:* 8 *Arts type:* chamber music, orchestra, vocal, jazz, early music, inst recitals, light orch music, sacred music, symphony music
Venues: School Hall 650, School Chapel 700 *Comments:* subscription concert series

Performing and Community Arts
Central Library, Surrey Street, **Sheffield** S1 1XZ
Tel: 114-273 4427
Fax: 114-273 5009
performing and community arts manager Bill Paton; community arts officers Marie de Souza,
Su Walker (tel: 114-273 4716);
administrator Ann Bradley
Events: over 100 events during literature festival – workshops, author visits, exhibitions, children's activities *Perfs:* 100 *Arts type:* theatre, literature, visual arts *Venues:* Library Theatre 260 (available for hire) *Policy:* small-scale direct promotions *Comments:* also facilitates other art forms through grants; award approx. 80 grants per year

Sheffield Philharmonic Concerts Department
City Hall, **Sheffield** S1 2JA
Tel: 114-273 4249
Fax: 114-275 8437
music officer Sara Unwin
Events: up to 20; October-May main season, but also events outside this period *Arts type:* chamber orchestra, choral music, symphony music *Venues:* City Hall 2300

Dartington Arts
The Gallery, Dartington Hall, **Totnes** TQ9 6DE
Tel: 1803-865 864
Fax: 1803-868 108
Internet: www.dissorg.unet.com
E-Mail: paul@dissorg.unet.com
office manager Jenny Pink;
theatre & art development manager Paul Goddard;
marketing manager Kamya O'Keeffe;
administrator (summer school) Lisa Warren;
box office manager Nikki Lewis;
film programmer John Gridley;
music programmer Lewis Riley
Events: over 250 plus 100+ concerts during July-Aug for the International Summer School and Festival of Music
Perfs: 350 (including summer school)
Arts type: film, opera, inst recitals, drama, music theatre, jazz, world music, Asian music, Japanese music, choral work, mime, dance, workshops, masterclasses, environmental music, chanting, community plays, African drumming, gamelan *Venues:* Great Hall 400, Barn Theatre 200, two studio spaces at 120, open air venues in summer *Comments:* emphasis on contemporary performance artists and also on participation and developing work in South Devon

Three Spires Arts Foundation
23 Lemon Street, **Truro** TR1 2LS
Tel: 1872-264 440
Fax: 1872-264 450
chair Valerie Blake
Events: periodically throughout the year
Arts type: classical music, orchestral concerts, oratorio, chamber music, recitals, also dance, poetry, drama, art exhibitions *Venues:* Truro Cathedral 1200, Truro College 300, Chapterhouse of the cathedral 180, Hall for Cornwall 1200

MCP Promotions Limited
16 Birmingham Road, **Walsall** WS1 2NA
Tel: 1922-620 123
Fax: 1922-725 654
Internet: www.live-music.com/uk
E-Mail: press@mcp.promotions.co.uk
directors Tim Parsons, Stuart Galbraith, Steve Moxham
Events: 600+ *Arts type:* pop & rock shows, electronic music, folk music, jazz, new music *Venues:* every major UK venue from Club to green field site

Welwyn Garden Concert Club
11 Roundwood Drive,
Welwyn Garden City AL8 7JZ
Tel: 1707-323 840
secretary Dr. Margaret Wood;
chairman Dr. Mary Anstey; treasurer Adrian de Baat
Events: 5 (Oct-March) *Perfs:* 5
Arts type: chamber music, song recitals *Venues:* Campus West Theatre, Welwyn Garden City 301 *Policy:* promotion of first-class chamber recitals

Whitstable Music Club
6 West Cliff, **Whitstable** CT5 1DN
Tel: 1227-261 153
secretary Sara Wheeler; chairman J. V. Walker
Events: 9 (6 in winter, 3 in summer) *Perfs:* 9 *Arts type:* chamber music, early music, inst recitals, song recitals *Venues:* Methodist Church, Whitstable 250

Edward Aldwell

Sergei Babayan

* Michel Block

Esther Budiardjo

Gwhyneth Chen

Anton Kuerti

Jerome Lowenthal

* Chitose Okashiro

* Vardo Rumessen

Katia Skanavi

Ju-Ying Song

* Vladimir Viardo

Oxana Yablonskaya

* The Chamber Ensemble of New York

Chitose Okashiro, pianist

Vladimir Viardo, pianist

Michel Block, pianist

Vardo Rumessen, pianist

**Personal Representation Worldwide*

Pro Piano Management

Ricard de La Rosa

85 Jane Street, New York, NY 10014

Tel: (01) 212/206-8794

Fax: (01) 212/633-1207

E-mail: ricard@propiano.com

http://www.propiano.com

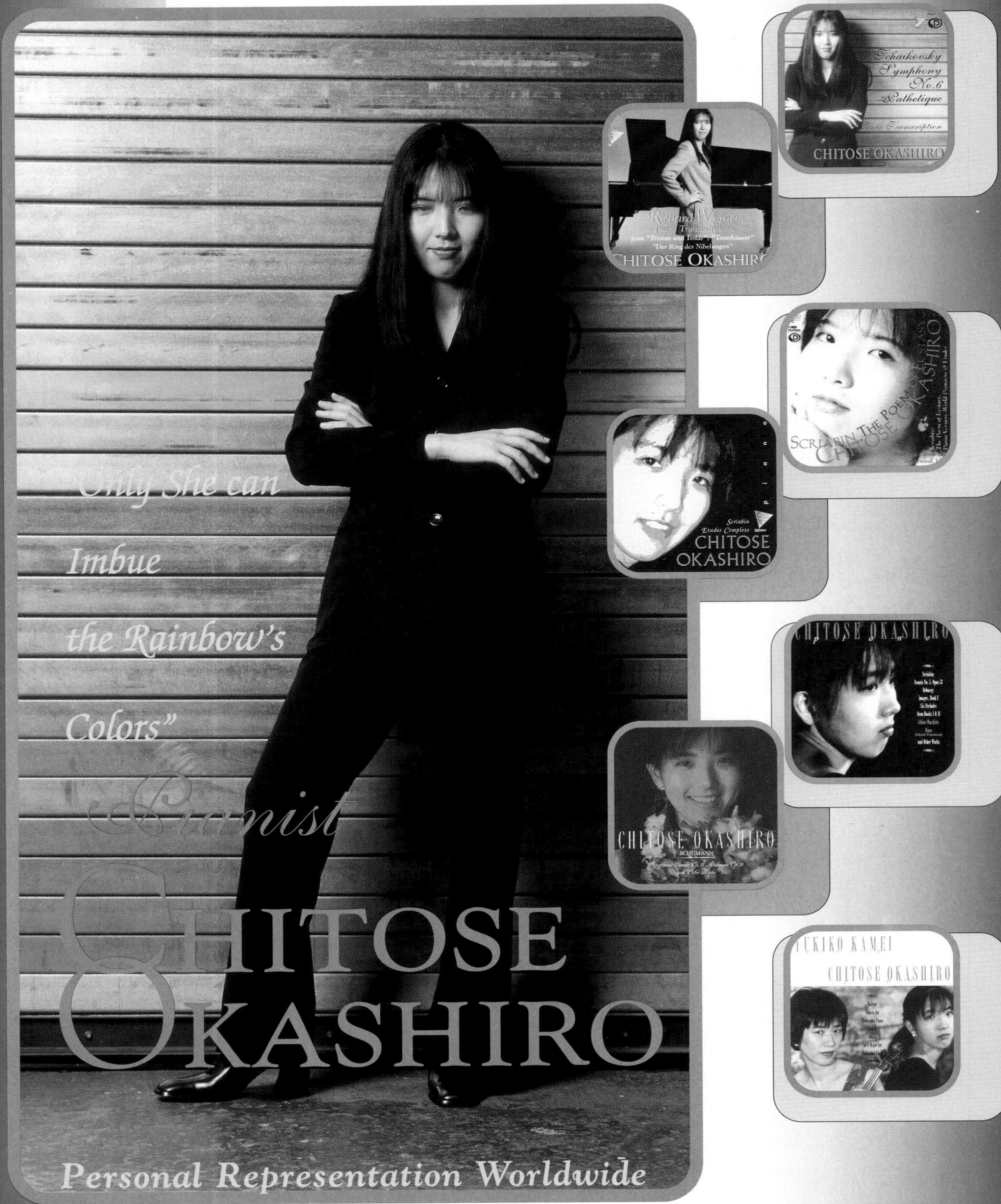

ProPiano
RECORDS

Pianist's
Perspective
Recording
5D 24bit

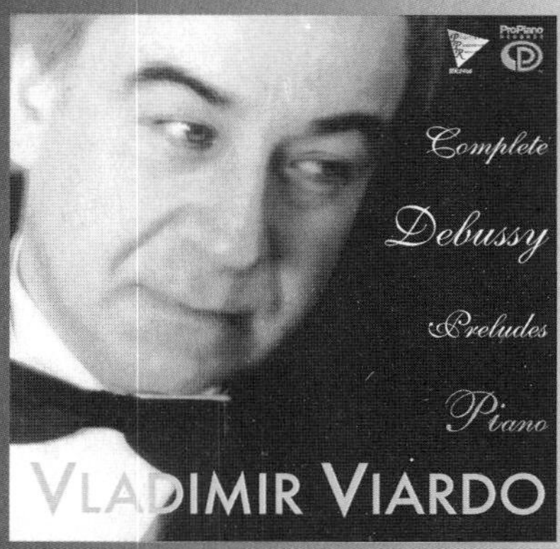

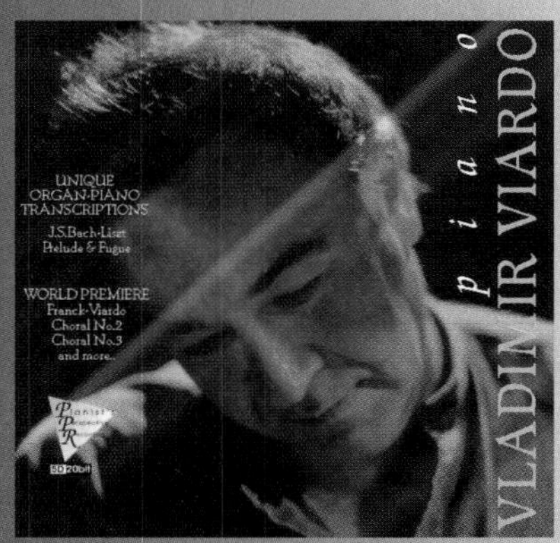

Vladimir Viardo

"The only "Russian" still primed for lift-off"

CAMERATA ACADEMICA SALZBURG

welcomes in 2000:

Franz Welser-Möst

Augustin Dumay

Yuri Bashmet

Joshua Bell

Pierre Boulez

Vadim Repin

Sir Roger Norrington,
chief conductor

Murray Perahia

Zoltan Kocsis

as well as Alexander Janiczeck, Leonidas Kavacos, Nikolai Demidenko, Alexander Lonquich, Peter Schreier, Melvyn Tan, Stefan Vladar, Ian Bostridge, Christopher Maltmann and others.
Touring 2000: Europe, North America, Japan

CAMERATA ACADEMICA SALZBURG

Bergstraße 22 • 5020 Salzburg • Austria
Phone: 0043 662 87 31 04 • Fax: 0043 662 87 31 04 5
E-Mail: camerata@net4you.co.at
www.camerata.at

lok

PRAGUE SYMPHONY ORCHESTRA
65.th SEASON 1999-2000

ELISABETH LEONSKAYA CHRISTIAN LINDBERG JIŘÍ BĚLOHLÁVEK GAETANO DELOGU

TASMIN LITTLE SALVATORE ACCARDO TADEUSZ STRUGALA EMMA KIRKBY

MAXIM SHOSTAKOVICH PETR ALTRICHTER ZDENĚK MÁCAL IMOGEN COOPER

LEILA JOSEFOWICZ LIBOR PEŠEK SERGE BAUDO ISABELLE van KEULEN

TRAWICK ARTISTS MANAGEMENT

Trawick Artists is a diversified organization focusing on management, concert presentation and the development of exciting new projects for today's arts and entertainment world. In addition to the wide array of artists and attractions mentioned herein, Trawick Artists has recently acquired Community Concerts, further expanding its diverse roster.

Trawick Artists Management, Inc. looks forward to a dynamic season of continued growth and artistic excellence as it brings artists and audiences together throughout the world.

Brenda Trawick
Chairman & CEO

Jon Aaron (ja)
Bill Fegan (bf)
David W. Middleton (dwm)
Elly Miller (em)
Eleanor Oldham (eo)
John Schimmelman (js)
Brenda Trawick (bt)
Diane Zola (dz)

2000/2001

Artist Roster

Instrumental Ensembles

Absolute Ensemble, Kristjan Jaarvi, Director (eo)
Arden Trio (dwm)
Boston Brass (dwm)
Hesperion XX, Jordi Savall, Director (ja)
Los Angeles Guitar Quartet (ja)
Lydian String Quartet (dwm)
Musica Antiqua Köln, Reinhard Goebel, Director (ja)*
Philharmonia Quartett Berlin (dwm)*
Proteus 7 (js)
Carol Wincenc & Nancy Allen, flute and harp (dwm)

Chamber Orchestras

Israel Kibbutz Orchestra (dwm)*
Avi Ostrowsky, Director / Aviram Reichert, piano soloist
Le Concert des Nations, Jordi Savall, Director (ja)*
Manhattan Chamber Orchestra (js)
Richard Auldon Clark, Artistic Director
Orchestra of the 18th Century, Frans Brüggen, Director (ja)*
Philadelphia Virtuosi Chamber Orchestra (js)
Daniel Spalding, Director / Gabriela Imreh, piano soloist

Vocal Ensembles

Black Mountain Male Chorus of Wales (js)
Gabrieli Consort, Paul McCreesh, Director (ja)*
Orlando Consort (ja)*
Sequentia, Benjamin Bagby, Director (ja)
Tallis Scholars, Peter Philips, Director (ja)*

World Music & Dance

Klezmer Conservatory Band (United States) (ja)
Mísia (Portugal) (eo)*
Noche Flamenca (Spain) (ja)
Yair Dalal and Al Ol (Israel) (ja)*

Special Residency Program

Joe Burgstaller, trumpet (js)
"The Rafael Méndez Project"

Special Attractions

Benjamin Bagby's "Beowulf" (ja)
Birth of the Beat (js)
Chinese Golden Dragon Acrobats (js)
Dale Gonyea, "Gonyea with the Wind" (js)
I Love New York &
the Lights of Broadway! (js)
Jurys Irish Cabaret (dwm)*
Julia Migenes, "Diva on the Verge" (eo)
The Ossipov Balalaika Orchestra (js)

Pop & Jazz

The Galaxy Trio, "Silk, Satin & Swing" (js)
Pasadena Roof Orchestra,
"Swing That Music!" (dwm)
Side Street Strutters (js)

Instrumentalists

Michael Barrett, piano (dz)
Steven Blier, piano (dz)
Nikolai Lugansky, piano (dwm)*
Haesun Paik, piano (ja)
Aviram Reichert, piano (ja)
Andrew Rengell, piano (ja)
Grigory Sokolov, piano (ja)*
Dubravka Tomsic, piano (ja)
John Musto, piano/composer (dz)
Augustin Dumay, violin (ja)*
Paul O'Dette, lute/guitar (ja)
Jordi Savall, viola da gamba (ja)*
Ransom Wilson, flute (dwm)
Carol Wincenc, flute (ja)

Sopranos

Diane Alexander (em)
Jennifer Aylmer (dz)
Darlene Bennett (dz)
Theresa Cincione (em)
Janice Dixon (dz)
Gail Dobish (em)
Lauren Flanigan (bt/eo)
Dana Hanchard (dz)
Amy Johnson (dz)
Judith Lovat (dz)
Cheryl Parrish (em)
Pamela South (em)

Mezzo-sopranos

Elaine Bonazzi (em)
Nelly Boschkowa (dz)
Luretta Bybee (dz)
Kathleen Hegierski (em)
Susan Nicely (em)
Stephanie Novacek (dz)
Kitt Reuter-Foss (em)
Melanie Sonnenberg (em)
Jean Stilwell (dz)
Tichina Vaughn (dz)
Julia Anne Wolf (em)

Tenors

Dean Anthony (dz)
Ravil Atlas (em)
Michael Rees Davis (dz)
John McVeigh (dz)
Marc Molomot (em)
Jay Hunter Morris (dz)
Beau Palmer (em)
Douglas Perry (em)
Curt Peterson (dz)
Chad Shelton (dz)
Mark Thomsen (em)
Bradley Williams (em)
Gran Wilson (em)
Thomas Young (eo)

Baritones

Daniel Belcher (dz)
Victor Benedetti (em)
Don Davis (em)
Gordon Hawkins (dz)
Scott Hendricks (dz)
Kimm Julian (em)
Robert Orth (em)
Mark Pedrotti (em)
Carlos Serrano (em)
Chris Pedro Trakas (dz)

Bass-baritones

Stephen Bryant (dz)
Eduardo Chama (dz)
Steven Condy (em)
Kristopher Irmiter (em)
François Loup (dz)
Herbert Perry (dz)

Basses

Ryan Allen (em)
Stephen Milling (dz)
Wilbur Pauley (em)

Conductors

Michael Barrett (dz)
Frans Brüggen (ja)*
Reinhard Goebel (ja)
Reinbert de Leeuw (ja)*
Diego Masson (eo)*
Paul McCreesh (ja)*
Brent McMunn (dz)
Paul Nadler (dz)
Ted Taylor (dz)
Yaron Traub (eo)
Andreas S. Weiser (eo)*
Ransom Wilson (ja)
Rachael Worby (eo)

Stage Directors

Joshua Major (dz)
Christopher Mattaliano (em)

* North America only

Trawick Artists Management, Inc.

250 West 57th Street, Suite 901
New York, NY 10107 USA
Tel: 1 212 581 6181
Fax: 1 212 581 4002
E-mail: info@trawickartists.net

Visit our Web site at
www.trawickartists.net

Agents

Agents and Producers
The majority of the agents listed are involved with music, opera and dance/ballet. There are few actor's agents or personal managers. **Within country the agents/producers are ordered alphabetically by organisation name. When the organisation name is that of an individual (e.g. Frank Smith) the ordering is done by christian name. When the organisation name is, for example, Künstlersekretariat Frank Smith, the indexing is done on the first word.**

Agents et producteurs
La plupart des agents qui apparaissent dans cette rubrique s'occupent de musique, de'opéra et de danse/du ballet. Il y a peu d'agents d'acteur ou de managers. **Pour chaque pays, les agents/producteurs sont classés par ordre alphabétique suivant le nom de leur organisation. Dans le cas ou le nom de l'organisation est celui d'un individu, le prénom figure en premier. Dans le cas ou une organisation se nomme par exemple 'Kunstlersekretariat Frank Smith', le premier mot figure en premier.**

Vermittler und Produzenten
Die meisten der in diesem Kapitel verzeichneten Vermittler befassen sich mit Musik, Oper und Tanz/Ballett. Ebenfalls aufgeführt sind eine kleine Anzahl von Schauspielvermittlern und privaten Künstlermanagern. **Die Einträge werden innerhalb aller Staaten alphabetisch nach dem Namen der Organisation geordnet. Organisationen, die nach einer Person benannt sind, (z.B. Frank Smith) werden nach dem Vornamen geordnet. Organisationen, die z.B. Künstlersekretariat Frank Smith heißen, sind nach dem ersten Buchstaben des Firmennamens alphabetisch geordnet.**

Agenti e Produttori
La maggior parte degli agenti da noi elencati sono connessi con il mondo della musica, l'opera, il balletto e la danza. In numero minore sono gli agenti o personal managers. **All'interno di ogni Nazione gli agenti/produttori sono ordinati alfabeticamente a seconda del nome dell'organizzazione. Quando l'organizzazione prende il nome dal titolare viene inserita alfabeticamente a seconda del nome di battesimo (es Frank Smith). Dove il nome dell'organizzazione é Kunstlersekretariat Frank Smith si elenca seguendo l'iniziale della prima parola.**

Agencias y Productores
La mayoría de los espectáculos listados están involucrados en el mundo de la música, ópera y danza/ballet. También se encuentran listados algunos representantes de actores o managers. **Dentro de cada país las agencias están ordenados por ciudades y siguen un orden alfabético dentro de cada ciudad. Cuando la denominación de una organización está bajo un nombre propio (por ejemplo Frank Smith), se sigue el orden alfabético del nombre de pila. Si el nombre de la organización fuera Künstlersekretariat Frank Smith, la clasificación se haría de acuerdo con el primer vocablo.**

Agents and Producers (에이전트 및 프로듀서)
이 리스트에 오른 대부분의 에이전시들은 음악, 오페라 무용/발레 등에 관계한다. 배우들을 고용하는 에이전시나 개인적인 매니저들은 거의 기재되지 않았다. **에이전시/프로듀서들은 조직명칭에 따라 알파벳순으로 기재되었다. 조직명칭이 개인의 이름일 경우는** (예: Frank Smith), **이름** (christian name)**에 따른 순서로 기재되었다. 조직명칭이 예를 들어** Künstlersekretariat Frank Smith**일 경우는, 첫 단어에 따른 순서로 기재되었다.**

代理商和制作商
在这列出的代理商大多从事音乐、戏剧和舞蹈或芭蕾. 演员的代理或个人经纪为数不多。在每个国家里代理商或制作商是按机构名称的字母顺序来排列的。**当机构名称是某一个人（如Frank Smith）时，则按名来排列。例如，**Künstlersekretariat Frank Smith，**是按第一个字排列的.**

エージェントとプロデューサー
リストの大半が音楽、オペラ、ダンス／バレーを扱うエージェントです。俳優エージェント、パーソナル・マネージャーも多少掲載されています。**リストは国別で、エージェント／プロデューサーの組織名はアルファベット順になっています。組織名が個人名である場合（例：Frank Smith）は、姓ではなく名（SではなくF）で探して下さい。例えば、Künstlersekretariat Frank Smithのような場合は最初に来る文字で探します。**

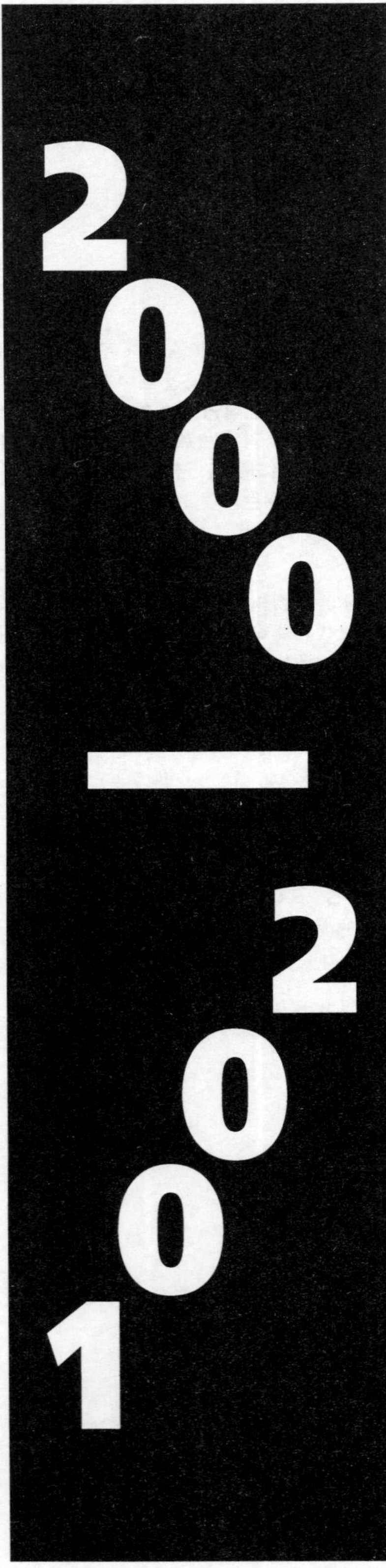

Arthur Shafman International, Ltd.

Special Attractions

Sandra ReAves-Phillips *in*
- A. *The Late Great Ladies of Blues & Jazz* **(Farewell Tour)**
- B. *"Glory Hallelujah" Gospel*

★ **The Shirelles**
★ **Shields & Yarnell**
● **Heather MacRae**
"Songs For My Father" The film songs of Gordon MacRae
●★ **Judy Glen** *"Spaghetti Opera"*
Anna Russell ....
"Still in Retirement"
and
Avner The Eccentric
in "Exceptions To Gravity"

Dance

Kibbutz Contemporary Dance Company
production of "Aide Memoire"
Ballet Contemporaneo De Caracas
- A. *John Butler's "Carmina Burana"*
- B. *"Diary of Anne Frank" The Ballet*
- C. *"Amadeus" The Ballet*

● **Inbal Dance Theatre of Israel**
- A. *The Story Of Ruth*
- B. *Sajarra (North American Premiere)*

✔ **Rhapsody in Taps**

Visual Theatre

Imago *production of "Frogs, Lizards, Orbs and Slinkys"*
● **Umo Ensemble**
- A. *"Expressions Of The Spirit: Tales of The Brothers Grimm"*
- B. *"El Dorado"*

✔ **The Chameleons**
KEITH BERGER / SHARON DISKIN
● **Tom Murphy** *in "MetaMURPHosis"*
● **Clipa** *The untraditional Visual Theatre from Israel*

Theatre

● **No Exit**
by Jean Paul Sartre
An IMAGO Theatre Production
Joseph Mydell
"OLIVIER AWARD" Winner as PAUL LAURENCE DUNBAR
Geoff Hoyle *in CONCERT*

● New to ASIL Roster
★ Symphony Pops
✔ Calif. Arts Council Touring Roster

NAPAMA

163 Amsterdam Ave., #121 • New York, NY 10023-5001
Tel: (212) 799-4814 • Fax: (212) 874-3613 • E-Mail: AShafman@aol.com
Web Address: http://www.PerformingArts.net//Shafman

ALBANIA (+355)

Ministry of Culture, Youth and Sport
Bulevardi 'Dëshmorët e Kombit', **Tirana**
Tel: 42-23236/50387 Fax: 42-32488
director of performing arts Marieta Ljarja; minister of culture Ms Arta Dade; director of foreign relations department Ylljet Alicka
Comments: acts as agent for artists in Albania; see also National Ministries

Miqte e Artit
PO Box 8188, **Tirana**
Tel: 42-72198
artistic director Pjeter Guralumi

Tirana 2000
PO Box 113, **Tirana**
Tel: 42-30953/42217 Fax: 42-30953/42217
artistic director Besim Petrela
Comments: artistic agency; visiting address: Rr Barrikadave, nr. 69

ANDORRA (+376)

RIAL Andorra Ltd
24 Av de Tarragona, **Andorra la Vella**
Tel: 8-60686 Fax: 8-60992
E-Mail: r.i.a.l@andorra.ad
managing director Pascal Lair
Artforms: classical and jazz *Comments:* artist management and tour promotion

ARMENIA (+374)

N.A.B. Productions Ltd
4-4 Azatoutian Street, 375037 **Yerevan**
Tel: 2-254 493/525 840 Fax: 2-151 431 (AT & T)
Internet: www.arminco.com/homepages/nab
E-Mail: nbart@arminco.com
manager Nika Babaian
Artforms: symphonic & chamber orchestras, ensembles, vocalists, instrumentalists

Phaeton Producers Company
Abovian Str. 16, 375001 **Yerevan**
Tel: 2-569 244/420 989
president Tigran Mkhoyan

AUSTRIA (+43)

Agentur Ingo Kleinheisterkamp
Rechte Lände 10, 6820 **Frastanz**
Tel: 664-252 9790 (mobile)
E-Mail: ingoyves@hotmail.com
Inhaber Mag. Ingo Kleinheisterkamp
Artforms: stage, classical music, theatre

Andreas Zadeyan
Herzg. 92/17, 1100 **Wien**
Tel: 1-602 4770/664-141 2707 (mobile)
Fax: 1-602 4770
E-Mail: AZRNC@a-topmail.at
contact Andreas Zadeyan
Artforms: composers, conductors, orchestras, jazz, classical ensembles, music management, musical projects, concert management, opera productions, CD productions, tour guide, dance groups, vocalists
Comments: see also Recorded Media (Re Nova Classics)

Ars Media Konzertservice GmbH
Bergstr 22/38, 5020 **Salzburg**
Tel: 662-873 335 Fax: 662-874 752
director Freimuth Teufel
Comments: cultural programme organisation for galas, conventions, events, etc.

artsprojects
Meytensgasse 14, 1130 **Wien**
Tel: 1-876 6728 Fax: 1-876 0755
E-Mail: k.josel@artsprojects.com
Geschäftsführung Kristel Josel
Comments: personal management of soloists and organisation-consulting for music festivals

Associazione Italia Musica
Pramergasse 8/2, 1090 **Wien**
Tel: 1-319 8631 Fax: 1-319 8631
president Odile Taliani; artistic director Mario Pasquariello, Guiseppe Mariotti; general secretary Pada Bono
Artforms: season of chamber music concerts of Italian repertory, by Italian artists, in Vienna

Austroconcert International
Gluckgasse 1, 1010 **Wien**
Tel: 1-513 2657 Fax: 1-512 6154
E-Mail: aconcert@magnet.at
Inhaber Prof Wolfgang Hartl; Mitarbeiter Mag. Erich Arthold, Dr. Ulrike Seifert, Eveline Hartl, DIng. Dagmar Plskova, Elisabetta Hartl; Leiter der Konzertabteilung Mag. Erich Arthold; Leiterin der Opernabteilung Elisabetta Hartl
Artforms: theatre, concerts, opera

B-project
Kranzpasse 18, 1150 **Wien**
Tel: 1-897 2371 Fax: 1-897 2371/77
E-Mail: Gerald.Buchas@blackbox.at
Künstlerischer Leiter Gerald Buchas; Kaufmännische Leiterin Andrea Kellner; Dramaturgie Dr. Robert Streibel
Artforms: theatre productions, installations, memory activities, room-directions *Comments:* European co-productions

Cadenza Concert
Franz-Josef-Kai 3, 5020 **Salzburg**
Tel: 662-840 505 Fax: 662-847 728
director Alja Batthany-Végh; assistant Dr. Barbara Heuberger
Artforms: chamber music ensembles (wind and strings), soloists, conductors *Comments:* orchestral tours, concert management, festival planning & direction, among others: Cervo-Festival di Musica da Camera (Italy), Açores Festival (Portugal)

Columbia Artists Management International GmbH
Linzer Gasse 21, 5020 **Salzburg**
Tel: 662-874 733/009 Fax: 662-886 804
E-Mail: cami_a@csi.com
managing director Till Janczukowicz
Artforms: instrumentalists, ensembles, orchestras, special attractions

crepaz music management
Straubstraße 1, 6060 **Hall in Tirol**
Tel: 5223-45222 Fax: 5223-452 2220
Internet: www.crepaz-music.com
E-Mail: info@crepaz-music.com
director Christoph Crepaz
Artforms: instrumental soloists, ensembles, chamber music, orchestras, conductors, composers

Esther Schollum Artists Management
Guntramsdorferstr 12/2, 2340 **Mödling bei Wien**
Tel: 2236-41004/676-545 4654 (mobile)
Fax: 2236-410 044
Internet: www.art-mgmt.com
E-Mail: es@art-mgmt.com
director Esther Schollum
Artforms: orchestra touring, personal management, conductors, singers, soloists, chamber music, actors

EUROMUSE – ART PROMOTION
Atelier n. 353, 9640 **Kötschach**
Tel: 4715-8942 Fax: 4715-2984
director Silvano Piovesan; coordination in Austria & Germany Nanine Burkart, Evelyne Csybulka
Artforms: musicals, promote concerts, orchestras, ballet, recital

FRAMES
Kranzgasse 18, 1150 **Wien**
Tel: 1-897 2371 Fax: 1-897 2371/77
kfm. Leitung Gergely Téglásy
Artforms: concerts, events, film, cultural events
Comments: European co-productions

Gerhild Baron Internationale Künstleragentur
Dornbacher Straße 41/3/2, 1170 **Wien**
Tel: 1-489 6154 Fax: 1-485 6711
E-Mail: baron@via.at
Inhaberin Gerhild Baron; management assistant Daniela Wacha; organisation Laura Borsi
Artforms: concerts, opera, orchestra tours, general management, local representations

Goodmusic – Artists' Management and Consulting Künstlervermittlung KEG
Dopschstraße 20/3, 1210 **Wien**
Tel: 1-259 2027 Fax: 1-259 6124
Internet: www.goodman.at
E-Mail: johngoodman@goodman.at
Inhaber John Goodman
Artforms: music theatre (opera, operetta, musical), festivals, concerts, contemporary music *Comments:* personal international management for singers, conductors, stage directors, instrumentalists, chamber music ensembles and orchestras, as well as theatrical and concert events

H2 – arts & acts
Taubstummengasse 5/4, 1040 **Wien**
Tel: 1-504 3645 Fax: 1-5043 64513
E-Mail: h2@magnet.at
contacts Peter Hauptmann, Isabella Heugl
Artforms: touring theatre companies, experimental theatre, street theatre, puppet theatre *Comments:* organisation of events, projects, international exchange; promotes mostly Austrian companies with national and international tours, but also promotes some foreign companies nationally

Kammermusik-Vereinigung Wien
Ganglbauergasse 38-6, 1160 **Wien**
Tel: 1-492 3684 Fax: 1-493 3927
music director Yossi Gutman; manager Anna Vonneman
Artforms: artist representation specialising in chamber music

Konzertagentur Image Hosek & Petrovic OEG
Orangerie im Schloß Schönbrunn, Schönbrunner Schloßstraße 47, 1130 **Wien**
Tel: 1-812 5004/5000 Fax: 1-812 5424
Internet: www.imagevienna.com
E-Mail: office@imagevienna.com
contact & president Peter Hosek; executive director Sascha Petrovic
Artforms: chamber music, classical concerts *Comments:* represent original Wiener Johann Strauss Kapelle (in historical costumes) and Schönbunner Schlosskonzerte

Konzertdirektion Gerhard Schröder
Am Steinbruch 20, 4040 **Linz-Puchenau**
Tel: 732-221 523 Fax: 732-221 952
Internet: www.netway.at/kdschroeder
E-Mail: kdschroeder@netway.at
Inhaber Gerhard Schröder
Artforms: concerts, light music shows, tv productions
Comments: 200 concerts a year

Konzertdirektion Nerat 'Mozart Serenaden'
Lieferinger Hauptstr 136, 5013 **Salzburg**
Tel: 662-436 870 Fax: 662-436 970
Internet: www.austria.at/mozartserenaden/
E-Mail: mozart@salzburg.co.at
Veranstaltung Elisabeth Nerat; Künstlerische Leitung Harald Nerat
Artforms: chamber music *Comments:* ca. 120 concerts a year; see also Festivals & Promoters

Konzertdirektion Schlote GmbH
Danreitergasse 4, 5020 **Salzburg**
Tel: 662-622 174 Fax: 662-629 9645
Geschäftsführer Michael Schlote, Joachim Schlote
Artforms: symphony, soloists, dance, opera, operetta, musicals, drama *Comments:* 600 performances, 250 cities in 10 European countries and elsewhere; also personal management and touring management

Künstleragentur Dr Rudolf Raab und Dr Horst Böhm GmbH
Plankengasse 7, 1010 **Wien**
Tel: 1-512 0501 Fax: 1-512 7743
E-Mail: raab.boehm@magnet.at
concert division Dr. Horst Böhm; opera division t.b.a.
Artforms: opera, operetta, classical music *Comments:* international and limited personal management of distinguished singers (concert, opera, operetta), instrumentalists, chamber ensembles & orchestras, conductors, extensive orchestra touring and special projects

Künstleragentur Hollaender-Calix Konzessionierte Bühnenvermittlung
Grinzinger Allee 46/2, 1190 **Wien**
Tel: 1-320 5317/328 4733 Fax: 1-320 5317
Inhaber Ariane Hollaender-Calix
Artforms: opera, concerts, musicals *Comments:* international artists agency

Künstlermanagement Till Dönch
Weimarer Strasse 48, 1180 **Wien**
Tel: 1-470 8083 Fax: 1-479 6971
E-Mail: tdoench@ins.at
Inhaber Till Dönch
Artforms: orchestras, soloists, conductors, chamber ensembles, chamber orchestras, ballet, singers

Künstlersekretariat Buchmann GmbH
Schachnerstrasse 27, 1220 **Wien**
Tel: 1-203 6357 Fax: 1-203 7483
E-Mail: buchmann@xpoint.at
director Prof. Rudolf Buchmann
Artforms: orchestras, soloists, conductors, chamber orchestras, singers, ballet, operetta, opera *Comments:* also agent for major festivals in Europe

Künstlervermittlung Klaus Eisenberger
PO Box 3, 1183 **Wien**
Tel: 1-368 1363 Fax: 1-369 2323
Internet: www.classic-music.at/eisenberger
E-Mail: eisenberger@classic-music.at
Inhaber Klaus Eisenberger
Artforms: chamber music, vocal and instrumental soloists, early music, contemporary &Viennese music *Comments:* visiting address: Peter-Jordan-Strasse 8, 1190 Wien

M.A.M Management (Mayler Artist Management)
Längenfeldgasse 26/7/33, 1120 **Wien**
Tel: 1-815 3733 Fax: 1-812 7167
E-Mail: mam-vienna@netway.at
Inhaber Keith Hoare-Mayler
Artforms: ensembles, instrumental soloists, chamber orchestras, early music *Comments:* personal management, including concert management and PR for a select list of artists

Martin C Turba Arts Management
Franz-Josef-Kai 7, 5020 **Salzburg**
Tel: 662-846 578 Fax: 662-847 556
Internet: www.turba.at
E-Mail: turba@netway.at
Inhaber Martin C. Turba
Artforms: artist agency, concert management, orchestral tours

Melos Konzerte
Postfach 71, Salesianergasse 12/11, 1037 **Wien**
Tel: 1-714 9196 Fax: 1-714 9191
chairman Christian May; artist management Eleonore Schmidt, Martha Maluk
Artforms: instrumentalists, conductors, orchestras, singers *Comments:* foreign office in Munich; orchestra tours throughout Europe

Mersich & Kiess OEG
Tivoligasse 3, 12 , Bezirk, 1120 **Wien**
Tel: 1-817 8773 Fax: 1-817 8773
contact Mag. Thomas Mersich
Artforms: classical, jazz *Comments:* concert/artist management agency; also publish musical works

MMM–Watzek KEG – Music Mangement Rudolf Morawitz
Nussdorferstrasse 38/19, 7000 **Eisenstadt**
Tel: 1-317 1871 Fax: 1-317 1872
Internet: www.mmmagency.com
E-Mail: m.m.m@appleservice.com
director Rudolf Morawitz
Artforms: classical music, orchestra and chamber music for instrumental soloists, orchestra tours, festival consulting *Comments:* management services; also office in Wien: Nußdorferstraße 38/19, 1090 Wien

Morawitz Music Management
Pramergasse 6, 1090 **Wien**
Tel: 1-317 1871 Fax: 1-317 1872
E-Mail: mmm@appleservice.com
director Rudolf Morawitz; artists dept Christa Redik
Artforms: artist representation and concert promotion especially for orchestras, chamber music, instrumental soloists and conductors; festival consulting

Opera Vladarski
Reithlegasse 12, 1190 **Wien**
Tel: 1-368 6960/1 Fax: 1-368 6962
E-Mail: opera.vladarski@netway.at
Inhaberin Lotte Vladarski
Artforms: opera singers, instrumentalists

part of art – cultural management
Sigmund-Haffner-Gasse 5, 5020 **Salzburg**
Tel: 662-842 484 Fax: 662-842 484
E-Mail: e.knorr.art@salzburg.co.at
Director Mag. Edmund Knorr
Artforms: classical music, soloists, chamber orchestras, operas, personal management
Comments: specialises in medieval and renaissance music; production of operas and opera galas

Primusic – Internationale Künstlervermittlung
Herrengasse 6-8, 1010 **Wien**
Tel: 1-5327 1240 Fax: 1-532 7140
Internet: primusic.at
E-Mail: Primusic@magnet.at
manging director Thomas Wolfram
Artforms: orchestra tours, conductors, solists, attractions

Riezouw Associates GmbH
Dorfstrasse 5, 6384 **Waidring**
Tel: 5353-6311 Fax: 5353-5708
Internet: www.riezouw.com
E-Mail: info@riezouw.com
director Robert Riezouw
Artforms: dance theatre, show management and production *Comments:* European management of Momix, Sydney Dance Company and Salzburger Dance Companies

Salzburger Schlosskonzerte
Griesgasse 6, 5020 **Salzburg**
Tel: 662-848 586 Fax: 662-844 747
Internet: www.esp.at/schlosskonzerte
E-Mail: schlosskonzerte@esp.at
Inhaber Luz Leskowitz; Presse und Öffentlichkeitsarbeit Mag. Silvia Span; Kartenbestellungen Brita Pohl; Buchhaltung Annemarie Göttlich
Artforms: classical chamber music throughout Europe
Comments: concerts in the Marblehall of the castle Mirabelle; very often Mozart; daily concerts from May-September (October-April 2-4 times a week); aternative E-mail: schlosskonzerte@EUnet.at; see also Promoters

Seitter Erich Bühnen- und Konzertvermittlung
Opernring 8/13, 1010 **Wien**
Tel: 1-513 7592 Fax: 1-512 9351
E-Mail: agentur.seitter@aon.at
Inhaber Erich Seitter, Mag. Kurt-Walther Schober
Artforms: opera, concerts, operetta, musicals
Comments: worldwide

Showservice à la carte
Pontlatzerstr 46, 6020 **Innsbruck**
Tel: 512-206 377/664-200 1265(mobile)
Fax: 512-206 377
Inhaberin Rita Amoser
Artforms: light entertainment, shows, serious variety, film, musicals, orchestra music, jazz, country music
Comments: music and artist management, promoter for musicals

Stein Music Vienna
R. Steinmetz & COKEG, Bernardgasse 39/33, 1070 **Wien**
Tel: 1-526 7871 Fax: 1-523 9891
E-Mail: Stein.Music@techno.at
directors Regine Steinmetz, Brigitte Puhr
Artforms: music theatre, cabaret

Verde Publishing – Musikverlag und Künstleragentur
Kwizda Str. 11 Top 9, 2100 **Koneuburg**
Tel: 2262-64828/664-300 1118 (mobile) Fax: 2262-648 2810
Internet: www.eventpartner.at
E-Mail: office@eventpartner.at
Inhaber Michael Kremnitzer
Artforms: chamber music, jazz, pop, entertainment

Victoria Concerts
Postfach 123, 5024 **Salzburg**
Tel: 662-660 024 Fax: 662-664 943
Direktor Dr. Helene Kamensky
Artforms: opera, concert and tour management *Comments:* visiting address: Föhrenweg 11, 5300 Salzburg-Hallwang

Vladimir und Estragon
Agentur für Theater und Publikum, Khunngasse 17/4, 1030 **Wien**
Tel: 1-799 5091 Fax: 1-799 5092
E-Mail: v.est@magnet.at
Management Thomas Licek
Artforms: national and international management of contemporary dance, music theatre, modern theatre

AZERBAIDZHAN (+994)

Tour-Concert Union 'Azconcert'
Azerbaidzhan Avenue 59, 370010 **Baku**
Tel: 12-938 100
general director Kasimov Ildrim Alinazir ogly

BELARUS (+375)

Belkoncert State Company
Gosudarstvjennoe Objedinjenije Bjelkoncjert
pr. Franciska Skoryny 50, 220005 **Minsk**
Tel: 172-134 251 Fax: 172-310 758
director Alexandr A Litvinovich

National & International Festivals & Competitions Office
Bjiuro Nacionalnykh i Mjezhdunarodnykh Fjestivaljej i Konkursov
pr Franciska Skoryny 50, 220005 **Minsk**
Tel: 172-310 553
director Galina Wagner

BELGIUM (+32)

Aden Arts Management
Rue Gachard 72 – boîte 4, 1050 **Brussels**
Tel: 2-647 4630 Fax: 2-647 4630
Internet: users.skynet.be/aden
E-Mail: aden@skynet.be
administrateur Antoine Panier
Artforms: classical music, jazz, contemporary dance, classical dance, tapdance, musicals

Argonote
23 Avenue Général Eisenhower, 1030 **Brussels**
Tel: 2-242 9703 Fax: 2-245 3885
Internet: www.netbeat.com/carbon7
E-Mail: 100257.214@compuserve.com
contact Muriel D'Archabau; director Guy Segers
Artforms: jazz, new music, world music, rock *Comments:* also distribute CDs on own label

Ariën International Concert & Theater Bureau
De Boeystraat 6, 2018 **Antwerp**
Tel: 3-218 6975 Fax: 3-230 3523
managers Albrecht Klora, Pascale Montauban
Artforms: opera singers, instrumentalists, conductors, orchestras

Artists' Management Liliane Weinstadt
Rue Langeveld 69, 1180 **Brussels**
Tel: 2-374 2138/375 2251 Fax: 2-375 7382
E-Mail: concerts.weinstadt@euronet.be
executive director Liliane Weinstadt; managing director Luc Van Loocke
Artforms: classical music *Comments:* artist agent

Azymuth Governmental Foundation
Association for Public Benefit, Torenstraat 13, 9160 **Lokeren**
Tel: 9-348 8000 Fax: 9-348 9974
E-Mail: j-p.vanavermaet@skynet.be
managing director Jean-Pierre Van Avermaet
Artforms: soloists, orchestras, chamber groups, choirs, classical music only *Comments:* organise tours in Europe and abroad, coordinate different choir festivals in Eastern Europe; staff correspondents: English, French, Dutch, German, Russian; see also Promoters

Brussels International Artists Management
7, Avenue du Feuillage, 1180 **Brussels**
Tel: 2-374 5315 Fax: 2-375 2631
E-Mail: mazy.marc.biam@skynet.be
general manager Marc Mazy; assistant manager Patricia Debeche
Artforms: opera & concert singers *Comments:* concert office, artists management; international artists on request

Bureau de Concerts Jacques Mauroy s.a. r. l.
508 avenue Molière, 1050 **Brussels**
Tel: 2-345 3935 Fax: 2-347 5928
E-Mail: marianne.gerard@skynet.be
directors Marianne Gérard, Jacques Mauroy
Artforms: local management of conductors, instrumentalists, chamber ensembles, chamber and symphonic orchestras *Comments:* second office: 19 rue de Primevère, 2351 Luxembourg; see also entry in Luxembourg

Centre Dramatique Hainuyer
c/o Carré des Arts, Rue des Sœurs Noires 4a, 7000 **Mons**
Tel: 65-328 700 Fax: 65-328 709
E-Mail: cdhainuyer@skynet.be
administrateur Anne André; président Pierre Bolle; directeur Daniel Cordova
Artforms: theatre: directors, stage designers
Comments: see also Promoters

European Artists Management
2, Av. de la Jonction, BP 10, 1060 **Brussels**
Tel: 2-343 2612 Fax: 2-344 1335
directrice Michaela Ganea Tache
Artforms: classical music, concerts

Fa Artists Management
101, rue Alexandre Markelbach, 1030 **Brussels**
Tel: 2-242 5921 Fax: 2-241 3885
director Françoise Emmanuelle Denis
Artforms: exclusively guitarists and ensembles
Comments: they also promote guitar label: E-mail for label: info@gha.be, Internet for label: www.gha.be

Frans Brood Productions
Muinklaan 10, 9000 **Gent**
Tel: 9-234 1212 Fax: 9-265 9650
Internet: www.fransbrood.com
E-Mail: info@fransbrood.com
director Gie Baguet; managers Lisbet Van de Sype, Bieke Vandecaveye, Greta Depaepe
Artforms: street theatre, dance theatre companies, visual theatre, installation

International Artist Representation Marleen Coppens
BP 18, 6720 **Habay**
Tel: 63-422 942 Fax: 63-424 050
E-Mail: Intart.M.Coppens@village.uunet.be
director Marleen Coppens
Artforms: instrumental soloists, chamber music

Joy Mebus Artists' Management NV
Waterstraat 43, 3770 **Zussen-Riemst**
Tel: 12-457 236 Fax: 12-457 234
E-Mail: mebus.artists@ping.be
director Joy Mebus
Artforms: conductors, pianists, instrumentalists

Maestro Music Productions
Leeuwerikstraat 20, 3680 **Maaseik**
Tel: 89-567 557 Fax: 89-561 117
Internet: maestro-brosse.be
E-Mail: info@maestro-brosse.be
manager Eric R G Langie; compositeur, chef d'orchestre Dirk Brossé
Artforms: combination of ethnic music and symphonic music; film music for large orchestras (60-100)
Comments: large scale international production

Metropolitan Entertainments
Driekoningenstraat 82, 2600 **Berchen**
Tel: 3-239 2872 Fax: 3-239 2872
Internet: www.metro-world.com
E-Mail: metro.world@skynet.be
director Alan Raghero
Artforms: classical (worked with Yehudi Menuhin Foundation), rock, jazz
Comments: see also Promoters

Musargentine, La
69 Av. Terlinden, 1310 **La Hulpe**
Tel: 2-653 0331 Fax: 2-653 0331
directrice Anne Van Hollebeke
Artforms: classical music: soloists, piano recitals, chamber music, singers, personal management

Music Management F.E. de Wasseige
c/o Francois-Emmanuel de Wasseige, Rue Grisar, 21, 1070 **Brussels**
Tel: 2-520 2009 Fax: 2-520 7150
Internet: www.cyclone.be/Wasseige
E-Mail: F.E.de.Wasseige@cyclone.be
director F. E. de Wasseige
Artforms: instrumental chamber music, soloists (no singers), concert organisation *Comments:* see also Festivals – Festival des Midis-Minimes

Promorga S.A.
Villalaan 26, 1630 **Linkebeek**
Tel: 2-380 9860 Fax: 2-380 8876
E-Mail: mhe@euronet.be
manager Michel Hellawell
Artforms: concert promotion – international management for Brazilian production, among others 'Brasil Tropical' carnaval show

Promotion des Arts de la Scène A.M. Lomba
Rue Monseigneur Cerfaux 1, 6250 **Presles**
Tel: 71-404 656 Fax: 71-404 657
administrateur-délégué André-Marie Lomba; directeur p.p. David Lomba
Artforms: 20 freelance companies working in theatre, dance and mime *Comments:* see also Promoters

Promotions s.c.
4 rue de la Vénerie, 1170 **Brussels**
Tel: 2-647 1950 Fax: 2-647 9926
founder/manager promotions Valerie Jacob
Artforms: classical, jazz, folk music and dance for all types of events *Comments:* specialises in music and events "made-to-measure"

ProSpectrum
Pleinstraat 62, 3001 **Heverlee**
Tel: 16-230 629 Fax: 16-230 629
manager Patrick Suttels
Artforms: classical ensembles *Comments:* consultancy (promotion, recordings, sponsorship)

Sight of an Ignored Landscape (SOIL)
Avenue Stalingrad 8, 1000 **Brussels**
Tel: 2-502 2808 Fax: 2-502 7558
E-Mail: s.o.i.l@ping.be
general manager Linda Sterckx; artistic director Geert Van Goethem
Artforms: opera, music theatre, animated film, video, visual arts, new media

Square Music
Persoonstraat 29, 3454 **Rummen**
Tel: 11-583 030 Fax: 11-583 033
E-Mail: squaremusic@ibm.net
managing director Geert Lavrysen
Artforms: classical music *Comments:* creative project management for ensembles and soloists, also acting as local agent for special projects

T L P Productions
309 Chaussée De Tongres, 4540 **Amay**
Tel: 85-312 235 Fax: 85-312 000
director Jean Stasse; secretary Claudine Landureau
Artforms: opera, operetta, musicals, orchestra tours
Comments: co-produces with Théâtre Musical Européen (see Opera) and Opéra Magna; tours – Belgium, Switzerland, France, Germany – see Drama; also produces CDs – see also Recorded Media

Variations
rue de la Forière, 75, 4100 **Seraing**
Tel: 43-376 353 Fax: 43-376 353
director Cécile Petit
Artforms: musicians, soloists

Walrus Productions
Rue des Ecriniers 5, 7800 **Ath**
Tel: 68-840 470 Fax: 68-840 721
E-Mail: walrus@online.be
directeur Luc de Groeve
Artforms: street theatre *Comments:* organise festival of street theatre in Ath; see also Festivals

Yves Rosseel
Brusselsesteenweg 324, 9050 **Gent**
Tel: 9-232 1926 Fax: 9-232 0999
E-Mail: yves.rosseel@skynet.be
artists manager Yves Rosseel
Artforms: classical instrumentalists, singers *Comments:* also CD production

BOSNIA & HERZEGOVINA (+387)

Concert Agency Sarajevo Art
Dalmatinska 2, 71000 **Sarajevo**
Tel: 71-207 972/971 Fax: 71-207 972/971
director Halid Kuburovic
Comments: organises different events, but mainly concerts

BULGARIA (+359)

Apollonia Art Foundation
11 Slaveykov Sq., 1000 **Sofia**
Tel: 2-980 5642/7833 Fax: 2-980 7833
E-Mail: apolonia@techno-link.com
president Prof. Dimo Dimov
Artforms: concert tours, master classes, impresario activities *Comments:* produce and carry out educational arts programmes, Apollonia Summer Festival in Sozopol, Christmas and Spring Festivals

Bulgarian Chamber Music Agency
1 Aksakov Street, 1000 **Sofia**
Tel: 2-801 189/876 522
director Alexander Kouyumdziev
Artforms: chamber music, soloists, ensembles and choirs

Musica Agency
10a Gr. Ignatiev Str., 1000 **Sofia**
Tel: 2-986 1390/1691
director Zafir Nikolov
Artforms: impresario activities

Nelly Lalova Management
Udovo 10, bx 2, 1463 **Sofia**
Tel: 2-292 8076 Fax: 2-292 8076
managing director Nelly Lalova
Artforms: concert tours of Bulgarian artists, choirs, orchestras and ensembles, dance groups etc

Sofiaconcert
P. Volov Street 3, 1527 **Sofia**
Tel: 2-442 914 Fax: 2-445 136
director Jeanna Mollova
Artforms: choirs, orchestras, singers and instrumentalists

CROATIA (+385)

Art Agent
Marulicev Trg. 13, 10000 **Zagreb**
Tel: 1-420 383/423 374 Fax: 1-420 383
general manager Miroslav Poljanec
Comments: concert management productio tour service

RIMI CO CONCERTS
RIMI CO koncerto – priredivacko poduzece
Villa Frappart, V.C. Emina, 51415 **Lovran**
Tel: 51-291 001 Fax: 51-292 313
director Ino Mirkovic; contact Silvana Sepic
Artforms: instrumentalists

Vatroslav Lisinski Concert Hall
Koncertna Dvorana Vatroslava Lisinskog
Trg. Stjepana Radica 4, 10000 **Zagreb**
Tel: 1-612 1111/163/155 Fax: 1-535 283
director Lovro Lisicic

Zadar Concert Office
Koncertni ured Zadar
Trg Petra Zoranica 1, 23000 **Zadar**
Tel: 23-315 807
contact Branka Dolicki

Zagreb Concert Management
Koncertna Direkcija Zagreb
Kneza Mislava 18, 10000 **Zagreb**
Tel: 1-461 1709 Fax: 1-461 1807
director Erika Krpan
Artforms: artists agency, concert promoter *Comments:* publishes and protects scores by Croatian composers; organises large-scale musical events

CYPRUS (+357)

GN Transeuropean Artists Ltd
Julia House, 3 Themistoklis Dervis Street, 1066 **Nicosia**
Tel: 2-475 194 Fax: 2-475 194
contact John Yriart
Artforms: gospel singers & spiritual groups

CZECH REPUBLIC (+420)

Amadeus Mozart Interfest
Borivojova 50, 130 00 **Praha** 3
Tel: 2-2271 1558 Fax: 2-2271 1558
E-Mail: monoszon@mbox.cz
director Boris Monoszon

ARS koncert s.r.o.
Úvoz 39, 602 00 **Brno**
Tel: 5-4323 3116 Fax: 5-4323 3358
E-Mail: ars@arskoncert.cz
director Miroslav Stehlík
Artforms: classical music
Comments: 2nd address: Masnà 10, 702 00 Ostrava 1, Tel: 69- 612 2300, Fax: 69-611 4016; artists management, festivals, see also Festivals

Arstour Praha s.r.o.
Ulice 28, října 14, 110 00 **Praha** 1
Tel: 2-2421 8973 Fax: 2-2421 8805
E-Mail: arstour@login.cz
Artforms: serious music
Comments: also acts as travel agency

Art 38 – West Bohemian Art Agency
Art 38 – Západoceská umelecká agentura
Západní 63, 360 01 **Karlovy Vary**
Tel: 17-322 4598/4827/6607 Fax: 17-322 4827
Artforms: theatre, classic music, pop, rock and folk
Comments: second address: Sedláckova 7, 30000 Plzen, tel: 19-220 724, fax: 19-227 182; national and international productions, radio

Art Production K./2
Malá Stépánská 3, 120 00 **Praha** 2
Tel: 2-2491 8489/2492 0467 Fax: 2-2491 9532
Internet: www.apk2.cz
E-Mail: sekretariat@apk2.cz
director Miloslav Zapletal
Artforms: production & publicity agent

ARTAMA – Information and Consultancy Centre for Regional Culture
ARTAMA – Informacní a poradenské stredisko pro místní kulturu
Kresomyslova 7, 140 00 **Praha** 4
Tel: 2-6121 5684/7 Fax: 2-6121 5688
Internet: www.ipos-mk.cz
E-Mail: artama@ipos-mk.cz
Comments: co-organisers of festivals, competitions and exhibitions; centre of amateur arts

Aura Pont s.r.o.
Radlická 99, 150 00 **Praha** 5
Tel: 2-539 909/536 351/531 257 Fax: 2-539 909
Internet: www.aura-pont.cz
E-Mail: aurapont@login.cz
director Zuzana Jezková
Artforms: theatre and literary agency

B-Arts Agency s.r.o
Moravská 35, 120 00 **Praha** 2
Tel: 2-258 540/2523 2407
Fax: 2-258 540/2523 2407
director Ing. Olga Kokosková
Artforms: classical music

Bohemia Euroservice
Ukrajinská 7, 625 00 **Brno**
Tel: 5-4724 1437 Fax: 5-4724 1437
E-Mail: ormston@mbox.vol.cz
contact Ing. Barbara Ormston
Artforms: chamber music *Comments:* represent Brno Chamber Orchestra

BTI – Bohemia Tickets International
nám Míru 15, 120 00 **Praha** 2
Tel: 2-627 6940/0411/0427
Fax: 2-627 6926/254 078
director Ing. Bedrich Plechác
Artforms: serious, brass and folklore music and festivals

Concert Agency Lupulus Prague
Korunní 60, 120 00 **Praha** 2
Tel: 2-2251 1752 Fax: 2-2251 3782
E-Mail: lupulus@comp.cz
general manager Oldrich Vlcek

Cultural Centre ALBIS – Art Agency
Kulturní stredisko ALBIS – umelecká agentura
Hrbovická 182, 400 21 **Ústí nad Labem**
Tel: 47-560 1505 Fax: 47-560 1505
Internet: www.hippoware.vol.cz/albis/
E-Mail: albis@mbox.vol.cz
Artforms: theatre, music, entertainment
Comments: national and international productions

Czech Artists Agency JU Dr. Bechyne
V olsinách 114, 100 00 **Praha** 10
Tel: 2-781 3801/782 0633 Fax: 2-781 3801
E-Mail: bechyne@terminal.cz
director JUDr Václav Bechyne
Artforms: classical music and opera

Dance Prague
Tanec Praha
Jirsíkova 4, 186 00 **Praha** 8
Tel: 2-2481 3899/7886/602-368 979 (mobile)
Fax: 2-231 9576
Internet: www.tanecpha.cz
E-Mail: office@tanecpha.cz
director Yvonna Kreuzmannová-Danková
Artforms: contemporary dance *Comments:* international festival and conference for critics and theoreticians; also manages independent dance group and seminars and creates its own performances; see also Festivals

Dilia
Krátkého 1, 190 03 **Praha** 9
Tel: 2-826 841/848/444/348 (music dept)
Fax: 2-824 009
Internet: www.dilia.cz
E-Mail: info@dilia.cz
director Ladislav Simon
Artforms: theatre and literary agency

Echo Theatre Agency Ltd.
Divadelní agentura ECHO s.r.o
Rehorova 5, 130 00 **Praha** 3
Tel: 2-2271 1515 Fax: 2-2423 1368
contact Václav Kotek
Artforms: theatre, entertainment *Comments:* national and international productions; also creates own productions; see also Drama (Jara Cimrman Theatre)

Festa s.r.o.
Londynská 8, 120 00 **Praha** 2
Tel: 2-258 335 Fax: 2-258 335
director Bohumir Gemrot
Artforms: serious music and festivals

FOIBOS art agency
Ume lecká agentura FOIBOS
Atelier Trmalova vila, Vilová 11, 100 00 **Praha** 10
Tel: 2-7210 1121 Fax: 2-7210 1120
Internet: www.foibos.cz
E-Mail: foibos@login.cz
director Marek Vesely; manager Oldrich Janota
Artforms: theatre
Comments: national and international productions

Hafan Studio
Studio Hafan
Wuchterlova 16, 160 00 **Praha** 6
Tel: 2-2431 3151 Fax: 2-2431 3151
manager Blanka Boruvková
Artforms: theatre
Comments: national productions; also creates its own performances; see also Puppets (Continuo)

Milan Oliverius Art & Recording Production
Italská 27, 120 00 **Praha** 2
Tel: 2-2225 0718/603-460 283 (mobile) Fax: 2-2225 0718
Internet: www.oliverius.cz
E-Mail: agency@oliverius.cz
director Milan Oliverius
Artforms: classical concerts including chamber orch, choral music, chamber music, early music, inst recitals, sacred music, symphony music, festivals

Moravian Art Agency
Moravská umelecká agentura
Anenská 10, 657 41 **Brno**
Tel: 5-4321 1593/1721/1715 Fax: 5-4321 1266
E-Mail: jsajtar@iol.cz
manager PhDr. Jirí Sajtar (serious music), Marta Seitlová, Zuzana Majnosová
Artforms: pop music, serious music *Comments:* national and international productions, import and export national and foreign groups

Musart Prag
Kaplická 35, 140 00 **Praha** 4
Tel: 2-438 774 Fax: 2-437 081
director Zinaida Hortková
Comments: artists management

Orfeus Agency
Agentura Orfeus
Vystaviste, LDS 1/20, 170 05 **Praha** 7
Tel: 2-2010 3280/95 Fax: 2-373 474
director Miroslav Janícek
Artforms: theatre, music, dance *Comments:* program of Krizíkova fontána (see also Venues); also creates its own performances

Peitho Artists Agency Ltd.
Ronkova 1831/6, 180 00 **Praha** 8
Tel: 2-684 5819 Fax: 2-684 5820
Internet: www.vol.cz/peitho
E-Mail: peitho@mbox.vol.cz
president Dr. Petr Hosna

Posh Co. Art
Lublaòská 13, 120 00 **Praha** 2
Tel: 2-9000 4206 Fax: 2-9000 4206
Internet: www.mujweb.cz/www/part
E-Mail: poshp@telecom.cz
director Bohumil Pospiech; assistant artistic director Hana Capková
Artforms: opera, operetta, orchestras, chamber ensembles, choirs, composers, conductors, intrumental soloists, singers, ballet, show

Prago Art Concerts
Orlická 9, 130 00 **Praha** 3
Tel: 2-651 3977 Fax: 2-227 2281
director Tomás Sousedik

Pragokoncert Bohemia a.s.
Peckova 13, 180 00 **Praha** 8
Tel: 2-2481 7272/7259/8277 Fax: 2-2481 8272
director Ivo Letov (prom phil.)
Artforms: theatre, music (classical, jazz, pop)
Comments: national and international production, export and import; also organise: Nostic salon – classical music and Jazz Club Reduta

Prague Theatre Agency
Prazská divadelní agentura
Jarníkova 1875, 148 00 **Praha** 4
Tel: 2-792 9860 Fax: 2-792 9860
contact Václav Hanzlícek
Artforms: theatre *Comments:* produces out of Prague; also creates its own performances, advance ticket sales

Sonata Arts Agency
Dykova 16, 101 00 **Praha** 10
Tel: 2-2425 1531 Fax: 2-2251 6514
E-Mail: sonata@praha.czcom.cz
general manager David Stranofsky
Artforms: chamber music, chamber opera, ensembles, chamber and symphony orchestras, soloists, singers, jazz, entertainment *Comments:* alternative E-mail: sonata@atlas.cz

VIA Praga Ltd. – Festival Mozart Open
Zatecká 1, 110 00 **Praha** 1
Tel: 2-232 3429/2536 Fax: 2-232 3429/4198
Internet: www.mozart.cz
E-Mail: via@gts.cz
director Jan Dvorák; contact Daniel Dvorák, Jirí Herold, Viktor Meska
Artforms: theatre, opera, puppet theatre opera
Comments: national and international productions, see also Festivals (Mozart Open); alternative E-mail: festival@mozart.cz

Zizkov Theatre and Music Agency Ltd.
Zizkovská divadelní a hudební agentura s.r.o.
Kubelíkova 27, 130 00 **Praha** 3
Tel: 2-2271 0147 Fax: 2-2272 1180
Internet: www.radio.cz/akropolis/
E-Mail: akropol@jk.anet.cz
contact Jaroslav Rauser, Radvan Pácl
Artforms: theatre (including puppet theatre), jazz, rock music, exhibitions, film *Comments:* national and international productions; also creates its own performances; see also Venues (Palác Akropolis)

DENMARK (+45)

Alteration
Niels Ebbesensvej 29, 1911 **Copenhagen** FC
Tel: 3379 8788
Internet: www.alteration.dk
E-Mail: delete@compuserve.com
artistic director Jørgen Teller
Artforms: new music productions for events, releases, commissions and collaborations including songs, rock, ambient, dance, operatorium, electroacoustics and poetry

Arte Booking
Hvidkildevej 64, 1st floor, 2400 **Copenhagen** NV
Tel: 3888 5555/7014 (foreign dept) Fax: 3833 2083
Internet: www.arte.eon.dk
E-Mail: arte@arte.dk
general manager Mogens Hjorth
Artforms: most types of music inc. jazz, rock, classical and entertainment for children, also authors and writers

Danish Music Agency A.P.S.
Sankt Hans Torv 26, 1, 2200 **Copenhagen** N
Tel: 3536 7565 Fax: 3536 8565
Internet: www.dmamusic.dk
E-Mail: dma@dmamusic.dk
director Jørgen H Jangmark
Artforms: classical music, rock, jazz, drama, dance, shows, entertainment *Comments:* intermediary between Danish artists and organisers of events worldwide

Gøsta Schwarck
48 Dalgas Boulevard, 2000 **Copenhagen** F
Tel: 3887 7010 Fax: 3887 7011
managing director Gøsta Schwarck
Artforms: singers, instrumentalists, opera, theatre, concerts *Comments:* promotes events at own risk; organises opera tours

Greiff Musik
Gammeltoftsgade 16, 1355 **Copenhagen** K
Tel: 3315 5570 Fax: 3313 5540
Internet: www.greiff.dk
E-Mail: info@greiff.dk
production manager Anja Reiff; administrative manager Nicolai Gjessing; artistic director Lars Henriksson
Artforms: classical and early music, ensemble and festival management

International Personal Management
St. Kongensgade 46, 1264 **Copenhagen** K
Tel: 3311 5225 Fax: 3313 1950
managing director Steen Wittrock
Comments: artist management, concert manager and tour operator

Rohr Artists Management
Grøndalsvej 47, 2000 **Copenhagen** F
Tel: 3887 3223 Fax: 3887 3223
E-Mail: rohr.voss@get2net.dk
director Joyce Rohr
Artforms: orchestral soloists, instrumentalists, chamber ensembles, composers, singers, jazz guitar *Comments:* USA address for Joyce Rohr: 775 Pleasant Street, Boulder, CO 80302, Tel/Fax: +1 303-443 0710

Tivoli Artists Management
Vesterbrogade 3, 1630 **Copenhagen** V
Tel: 3375 0400 Fax: 3375 0375
Internet: www.tam.dk
E-Mail: artistsmanagement@tivoli.dk
director Tom Kristensen (Email: tk@tivoli.dk)
Artforms: conductors, singers, instrumentalists, ballet projects and event management *Comments:* concert, opera, ballet management; personal artists' management

Wilhelm Hansen Concert and Theatre Management
Gothersgade 11, 4th floor, 1123 **Copenhagen** K
Tel: 3314 3710 Fax: 3314 4428
managing directors Hanne Wilhelm Hansen
Artforms: singers, instrumentalists, directors, set-designers etc.

ESTONIA (+372)

2.tants – Independent Dance Organisation
Rataskaevu 10, 10123 **Tallinn**
Tel: 6-269 094 Fax: 6-269 099
director Priit Raud
Artforms: dance *Comments:* personal tour management for Estonian and Russian contemporary dance groups worldwide

Concerto Grosso
Rävala pst. 12, 10143 **Tallinn**
Tel: 6-466 655 Fax: 6-466 656
director Egmont Välja
Artforms: classical music, choirs, ensembles

Estonian Concert
Eesti Kontsert
Estonia pst. 4, 10148 **Tallinn**
Tel: 6-443 670 Fax: 6-443 198
Internet: www.concert.ee/
E-Mail: eesti.kontsert@concert.ee
director Enno Mattiesen
Artforms: classical music (soloists, chamber groups, orchestras, choirs)
Comments: State Concert Organisation

Lend Music Ltd.
Lendmuusik
Köömne 33, 10617 **Tallinn**
Tel: 6-565 304
director Toivo Lend
Artforms: classical music

FINLAND (+358)

Allegro Artist Management
TAP House, Tapiolan Keskustorni 11 Floor, 02100 **Espoo**
Tel: 9-462 007/40-512 1230 (mobile) Fax: 9-5259 4200
E-Mail: allegro.artist@dlc.fi
director Pekka K Pohjola; assistant Vilja Valkeinen
Artforms: classical music (mainly opera singers)

Drama Corner Näytelmäkulma
Meritullinkatu 33, 00170 **Helsinki**
Tel: 9-135 7098/7093/7591 Fax: 9-135 7061
chief dramaturg Riitta Pohjola (on leave until 28.2.99); dramaturgs Hanna Jääskinen (135 7591), Aino Piirola (135 7093); drama assistant Merja Tuominen (135 7098)
Artforms: drama *Comments:* the major drama agency in Finland; supplies foreign plays for all Finnish theatres, both professional and amateur

Fazer Artists' Management Inc
Nervanderinkatu 5 E 46, 00100 **Helsinki**
Tel: 9-454 2470 Fax: 9-446 841
E-Mail: tuula.sarotie@fazerartists.fi
director Tuula Sarotie
Artforms: classical music *Comments:* biggest and oldest classical management in Finland

Festium Oy
Partiotie 34, 00370 **Helsinki**
Tel: 9-556 024 Fax: 9-557 020
contact Mirja Salomaa
Artforms: classical music, symphony, chamber orchestra, recitals, folk, singers, instrumental
Comments: concert management

FinnConcert
Päivöläntie 12, 73770 **Säyneinen**
Tel: 400-279 455 (mobile) Fax: 17-610 285
Internet: www.nettilinja.fi/~someroj/
E-Mail: someroj@nettilinja.fi
director Helena Raija; general manager t.b.a.
Artforms: soloists, chamber orchestras

JMP Music Ltd
Nöykkiöntie 18, 02320 **Espoo**
Tel: 9-262 8109 Fax: 9-262 8113
Internet: www.jmpmusic.fi
E-Mail: jmp@jmpmusic.fi
director Lassi Marttala
Artforms: orchestral and other tours, concerts and festival productions, Finland and abroad *Comments:* agency, concert management

Orfeo Oy Ltd. Singers Agency
Rauhankatu 7, 00170 **Helsinki**
Tel: 9-135 8993 Fax: 9-6227 3400
E-Mail: orfeo@pp.kolumbus.fi
managing director Erkki Alste; assistant Maarit Mattala
Artforms: personel and concert management of singers
Comments: represents singers only

poloARTico Oy
Ruonasalmentie 17A 2, 00830 **Helsinki**
Tel: 9-759 3189 Fax: 9-755 6801
E-Mail: polo@poloartico.fi
managing director Kari Varpio; chief executive officer Veijo Varpio
Artforms: conductors, instrumentalists and singers, chamber music, recitals, orchestral concerts, orchestra tours and promotes jazz music

PPM Artists Management
PO Box 46, 00511 **Helsinki**
Tel: 9-738 473 Fax: 9-730 367
E-Mail: ppm@ppm.pp.fi
director Tuomas Pulakka
Artforms: soloists, chamber orchestras

Sibelius Academy Concert Agency
PO Box 86, 00251 **Helsinki**
Tel: 9-405 4662/4645 Fax: 9-405 4603
Internet: www.siba.fi
E-Mail: anna.krohn@siba.fi
managers Anja Frösen, Anna Krohn
Artforms: mostly classical music, also jazz and folk
Comments: concerts usually in connection with master courses

FRANCE (+33)

Agence Artistique Air' Show
BP 27, 2 rue Jean-Jaures, 59880 **Saint Saulve**
Tel: 3-2730 9002 Fax: 3-2730 0528
director Michèle François
Artforms: all performing arts *Comments:* also production

Agence Artistique Catherine Petit
26 rue de la Libération, 92210 **Saint-Cloud**
Tel: 1-4602 3336 Fax: 1-4602 2725
E-Mail: aacp@wanadoo.fr
director Catherine Petit
Artforms: classical music (soloists, conductors, orchestras, chamber music)
Comments: see also Festivals (Vladimir Krainev invites) and Competitions (International Vladimir Krainev's Young Pianists Competition)

Agence Artistique Eliane Ribet
9 rue Ledion, 75014 **Paris**
Tel: 1-4543 2607 Fax: 1-4543 5825
director Eliane Ribet
Artforms: soloists, duos, trios, quartets, orchestras, chamber music

Agence Artistique Krystyna de Obaldia
109 av Ledru Rollin, 75011 **Paris**
Tel: 1-4806 8371 Fax: 1-4021 9882
Krystyna de Obaldia
Artforms: contemporary music

Agence Artistique Marie-Claude Godon
47 ter boulevard St Germain, 75005 **Paris**
Tel: 1-4407 2900 Fax: 1-4407 2909
director Marie-Claude Godon
Artforms: actors, authors, directors, producer

Agence Artistique Michèle Cerou
3 Chemin des Oliviers, 34430 **Saint Jean de Vedas**
Tel: 4-6742 5577 Fax: 4-6742 2647
director Mme. Michèle Cerou
Artforms: variety performers, children's

Agence Artistique Monique Cazeneuve
5-7 av Mac-Mahon, 75017 **Paris**
Tel: 1-4380 1586 Fax: 1-4622 5876
Monique Cazeneuve
Artforms: classical music

Agence Artistique Myriam Bru
80 Avenue Charles de Gaulle, 92200 **Neuilly-sur-Seine**
Tel: 1-4624 9730 Fax: 1-4624 1832
contact Mme. Myriam Bru
Artforms: mainly comedians, also authors, directors, costume designers

Agence Artistique Nicole Cann
1 rue Alfred de Vigny, 75008 **Paris**
Tel: 1-4415 1420 Fax: 1-4415 1421
directrice générale Nicole Cann
Artforms: actors, directors, scriptwriters

Agence Artistique Pablo Guzmán
16 Ave. Galliéni, 77590 **Bois-le-Roi**
Tel: 1-6481 1070 Fax: 1-6481 1070
E-Mail: Pabguzman@aol.com
director Pablo Guzmán
Artforms: classical and contemporary dance
Comments: representation of dancers and choreographers; international tour management for dance companies

Agence Artistique Simone Kornmeyer
9 rue de la Heid, BP 6, 67490 **Dettwiler**
Tel: 3-8871 9175 Fax: 3-8871 9175
director Simone Kornmeyer
Artforms: variety shows

Agence Artistique Thérèse Cedelle
78 blvd Malesherbes, 75008 **Paris**
Tel: 1-4953 0002 Fax: 1-4563 7023
directeur Thérèse Cedelle; collaborateurs Xavier Tamalet, Frédéric Demarquet
Artforms: opera singers

Agence Artistique Vincent Bréget
BP 14, 53800 **Renazé**
Tel: 2-4194 2567 Fax: 2-4194 2165
Internet: www.perso.wanadoo.fr/spectacles.breget
E-Mail: spectacles.breget@wanadoo.fr
directeur artistique Vincent Bréget
Artforms: shows, spectacles, musicals, variety artists

Agence JFPM Representation
11 rue Chanez, 75016 **Paris**
Tel: 1-4743 1314 Fax: 1-4743 1165
Internet: www.jfpm.fr
E-Mail: jfpm@jfpm.fr
directeur Jean-François Pignard de Marthod
Artforms: performing arts, mainly actors

Agence Léz Ards Vivants
56, bd Jeanne d'Arc, 93100 **Montreuil**
Tel: 1-4287 6013 Fax: 1-4287 9613
E-Mail: lezaviva@club-internet.fr
directeur Pierre Hivernat
Artforms: contemporary dance and theatre
Comments: see also Services

Agence M. F. Huisman
11 rue La Boétie, 75008 **Paris**
Tel: 1-4017 0220 Fax: 1-4268 0393
directrice Marie Françoise Huisman; collaboratrice Mirabel Auria
Artforms: comedians, authors, film directors

Agence Villeminot
Lamourio, 46230 **Montdoumerc**
Tel: 5-6524 7027 Fax: 5-6524 7485
Internet: www.Art6.com
E-Mail: Agence.Villeminot@wanadoo.fr
directeur Philippe Villeminot
Artforms: orchestras, ensembles, soloists, early music

André Gintzburger Conseiller en Organisation de Spectacle Vivant
47 rue de Richelieu, 75001 **Paris**
Tel: 1-4297 4536 Fax: 1-4296 4299
E-Mail: gintzburger@wanadoo.fr
administrateur Edith Santistèbe
Artforms: theatre, street theatre, new circus *Comments:* contact for Royal de Luxe, Plasticiens Volants, Delices Dada (France), Teatro del Silencio (Chile), Théâtre Frances (St Petersburg), Que-Cie-Que (France, Switzerland), Pesce Crudo (France, Spain), etc.

Artis Diffusion
68 rue de Vincennes, 93100 **Montreuil**
Tel: 1-5586 9231 Fax: 1-5586 9231
Internet: www.artis-diffusion.com
E-Mail: courrier@artis-diffusion.com
director Daniel Sultan
Artforms: artistic management, especially contemporary music and composition; artistic production, administration and conception; collaboration with musicians, composers, conductors *Comments:* represent 60 French and international artists (19 countries)

IMG *Artists Paris*

Conductors
Gisèle Ben-Dor *Gen*
Jean-Claude Casadesus *Gen*
Stéphane Denève *Gen*
Lawrence Foster *F (opera only)*
Patrick Fournillier *Gen*
Patrick Gallois *Gen*
John Eliot Gardiner *F*
Marco Guidarini *F + sundry*
Michiyoshi Inoue *F + sundry*
Mariss Jansons *F*
Philippe Jordan *Gen*
Djansug Kakhidze *Gen*
Jiri Kout *Gen*
Sebastian Lang-Lessing *F*
Friedemann Layer *F (opera only)*
Shao-Chia Lü *Gen*
Ion Marin *F*
Antonio Pappano *Gen*
Marco Parisotto *Gen*
Libor Pesek *F*
Fabrice Pierre *Gen*
Carlo Rizzi *F*
Dmitry Sitkovetsky *F*
Andreas Stoehr *Eur*
Yuri Temirkanov *F*

Pianists
Leif Ove Andsnes *F*
Jonathan Gilad *F*
Eric le Sage *Gen*
Mikhail Rudy *F*
Aleksandar Serdar *Gen*
Jean-Yves Thibaudet *F*

Harpsichordists
Elisabeth Chojnacka *Gen*

Violinists
Augustin Dumay *F*
Hilary Hahn *F*
Leila Josefowicz *F*
Misha Keylin *Gen*
Dmitry Sitkovetsky *F*

Cellists
Alban Gerhardt *F*
Lynn Harrell *F*
Jian Wang *F*

Flutist
Patrick Gallois *Gen*

Harpist
Fabrice Pierre *Gen*

Chamber Music
Trio Pires-Dumay-Wang* *F*
Emerson String Quartet *F*
Philharmonia Quartett Berlin *F + UK*
Quintette Gallois *Gen*

Vocal ensembles
Accentus Chamber Choir *Gen*
The King's Singers *F*

Sopranos
Laura Aikin *F*
Susan Anthony *F + sundry*
Tatiana Anisimova *Gen*
Lisbeth Balslev *F*
Patrizia Biccirè *Gen*
Barbara Bonney *Eur*
Elizabeth Connell *F*
Renée Fleming *Eur*
Tamar Javakishvili *Gen*
Eva Kirchner *F*
Cynthia Lawrence *F*
Georgina Lukacs *F*
Emily Magee *F*
Marie McLaughlin *F*
Alwyn Mellor *F*
Mary Mills *F*
Maureen O'Flynn *F*
Deborah Riedel *F*
Cyndia Sieden *F*
Sharon Sweet *F*
Veronica Villarroel *F*
Mariana Zvetkova *Eur+sundry*

Mezzo-Sopranos
Larissa Diadkova *F*
Kathryn Harries *F*
Kristine Jepson *Eur*
Kathleen Kuhlmann *Gen*
Doris Lamprecht *Gen*
Susanna Poretsky *F*
Florence Quivar *F*
Hanna Schaer *Gen*
Randi Stene *F*
Frederica Von Stade *F + sundry*
Kerstin Witt *F*

Tenors
Mark Baker *F*
Marco Berti *Gen*
Yann Beuron *Gen*
Rockwell Blake *F + sundry*
Ian Caley *F*
Richard Croft *F*
Franco Farina *F*
Vladimir Galouzine *Gen*
Andreas Jaeggi *F+*
Richard Leech *Eur*
Richard Margison *F*
William Matteuzzi *F + sundry*
Thomas Moser *Gen*
Roberto Sacca *F*
Robert Tear *F*
Jacque Trussel *Eur*

Baritones
Stéphane Degout *Gen*
Philippe Georges *Gen*
Rodney Gilfry *F*
Thomas Hampson *F*
Francois Harismendy *Gen*
Monte Pederson *F*
Roberto Scaltriti *Gen*
Wolfgang Schoene *F*
William Shimell *F*
Michael Volle *F + sundry*

Bass
Till Fechner *Gen*
Aage Haugland *F*
Cornelius Hauptmann *F+*
Victor Matorine *F*
René Pape *F*
Franz-Josef Selig *F*
John Tomlinson *F*

Our tours departement has organised or is organising tours and appearences for the following orchestras and ensembles in France :

Academy of Saint Martin in the Fields
BBC Philharmonic Orchestra
Camerata Academica de Salzbourg
Chicago Sinfonietta
Dresdner Staatskapelle
The English Concert
Ensemble Orchestral de Paris
Freiburger Barockorchester
Gustav Mahler Jugendorchester
I Salonisti
I Solisti Veneti
Leipziger Gewandhausorchester
Les Eléments
Monteverdi Choir / English Baroque Soloists
NDR Sinfonie-Orchester (Hambourg)
Kirov / Théâtre Mariinsky de St-Petersbourg
Orchestre de Paris
Orchestre National de France
Orchestre National du Capitole de Toulouse
Orchestre Philharmonique d'Oslo
Orchestre Philharmonique de Géorgie
Orchestre Philharmonique de St-Petersbourg
Orchestre Philharmonique Hongrois
Orchestre Révolutionnaire et Romantique
Orchestre de la Radio de Moscou
Orchestre Symphonique de Vienne
Philadelphia Orchestra
Pittsburgh Symphony Orchestra
Royal Concertgebouw Orchestra
Royal Opera House Covent Garden
Royal Scottish National Symphony Orchestra
Sinfonia Varsovia
Ulster Orchestra
Wiener Sangerknaben

Gen = Worldwide management
Eur = Europe
F = France
*** = in agreement with Askonas Holt Ltd**

Artists International Management Ltd
10 rue des acacias, 75017 **Paris**
Tel: 1-4574 1624 Fax: 1-4574 3320
E-Mail: aim-music@wanadoo.fr
contact Claude-Franck Boisson
Artforms: promotion of international artists, specialised in musicians and conductors, orchestral touring and projects management *Comments:* personal management

Association Bourguignonne Culturelle
BP 1002, 4 Place Darcy, 21024 **Dijon**
Tel: 3-8030 5978 Fax: 3-8050 1808
directeur Thierry Macia; administrateur Patrick Vuiton
Artforms: theatre, music, dance, jazz, variety, activities
Comments: 50 shows a year; venue: le theâtre des Feuillants 500

B.A. Musique
37 rue de Vilmorin, BP 14, 45290 **Nogent-sur-Vernisson**
Tel: 2-3897 6004 Fax: 2-3897 6406
director Julien Azaïs; co-director Marie-José Azaïs
Artforms: classical music

Bel Air Media
15 rue du Louvre, 75001 **Paris**
Tel: 1-4488 2818 Fax: 1-4488 2814
E-Mail: bel.air.media@wanadoo.fr
directors François Duplat, Xavier Dubois
Artforms: music, opera, ballet, also documentation
Comments: see also Recorded Media

Briant Spectacle
27 rue de l'Echiquier, 75010 **Paris**
Tel: 1-4770 4401 Fax: 1-4523 4136
director Arnaud Briant
Artforms: organise and manage spectacles for private performances

Bureau de Concerts de Valmalete
7, rue Hoche, 92300 **Levallois Perret**
Tel: 1-4759 8759 Fax: 1-4759 8750
Internet: www.valmalete.com
E-Mail: valmalete@dial.deane.com
director Marie-Anne de Valmalete; co-directeur Hervé Corre de Valmalete
Artforms: classical music

Bureau de Concerts Isoard Sola
22 rue Ernest Révillon, 77630 **Barbizon**
Tel: 1-6066 4488 Fax: 1-6066 2999
director Christiane Isoard Sola
Artforms: jazz

Bureau de Concerts Maurice Werner
7 rue Richepance, 75008 **Paris**
Tel: 1-4703 1360 Fax: 1-4926 0507
director Maurice Werner
Artforms: classical music (soloists, conductors, chamber groups)

Bureau George Lambert
13 bis av. de la Motte-Picquet, 75007 **Paris**
Tel: 1-4555 4352 Fax: 1-4753 8951
E-Mail: lambertgeo@aol.com
director George Lambert
Artforms: actors, directors, authors

Bureau International de Concerts et Conferences – (BICC)
252 rue du Faubourg Saint-Honoré, 75008 **Paris**
Tel: 1-4563 7955 Fax: 1-4562 2417
directeur conférences /connaissance du monde Jean-Michel Berrier ; gérant Camille Kiesgen
Artforms: classical music (soloists), conferences of films

Camus and Camus Productions
6 rue Daubigny, 75017 **Paris**
Tel: 1-4440 3333 Fax: 1-4622 6724
director Jean-Claude Camus
Artforms: music only (singers, musicians, etc)

CIM – Classics International Management
54 Avenue d'Iéna, 75116 **Paris**
Tel: 1-4720 5553 Fax: 1-4720 3751
director Jacqueline Guélis
Artforms: classical music soloists, conductors, chamber musicians, orchestras *Comments:* producer of orchestras tours, produces recitals

Cindy Brace Agency (CBA)
31 rue Milton, 75009 **Paris**
Tel: 1-4526 3342/49 Fax: 1-4874 5142
E-Mail: c_b_a@club-internet.fr
director Cindy Brace
Artforms: bilingual actors and actresses only *Comments:* second office: CBA International, Teddington Studios, Broom Road, Teddington, TW11 9NT, Director Cindy Brace, Tel: +44 20-8614 2168, Fax: +44 20-8755 0076

Classical Artist Management
16 rue du Regard, 75006 **Paris**
Tel: 1-4544 4945 Fax: 1-4544 4882
director Eliza Jamin
Artforms: classical music – soloists, singers, orchestras, opera production *Comments:* concert organiser

Coccinelle
28 rue de Trévise, 75009 **Paris**
Tel: 1-4246 5500 Fax: 1-4246 0794
directrice Maryse Gagnieux
Artforms: adverts, cinema, children, comedians

Conseiller Artistique Thomas Erdos
11 av Delcassé, 75008 **Paris**
Tel: 1-4563 3341 Fax: 1-4289 4466
directeur Thomas Erdos
Artforms: dance, music, traditional music

Consortium Artistique International
27 rue Marignan, 75008 **Paris**
Tel: 1-4359 0200 Fax: 1-4225 4157
director Bernard Hilda
Artforms: variety performers

Contagion
29 rue des Petites-Ecuries, 75010 **Paris**
Tel: 1-4523 4343 Fax: 1-4523 4340
Internet: www.contagion.fr
contact Hervé Boissiere, Vincent Nayrolles
Artforms: classical music, electronic music *Comments:* an independent agency for artist development; guide artists through all their projects whatever the form: live, audiovisual or multimedia

DLB Spectacles Performing Arts
8 Cité du Midi, 75018 **Paris**
Tel: 1-4251 7363 Fax: 1-4223 7776
E-Mail: 106145.1130@compuserve.com
directeur Didier Le Besque
Artforms: dance, ballet, modern and contemporary
Comments: alternative E-mail: didier.le-besque@wanadoo.fr

Epidemic
15, allée Massenet, 93270 **Sevran**
Tel: 1-4383 4953 Fax: 1-4936 0439
Internet: www.cicv.fr/epidemic
E-Mail: epidemic@compuserve.com
directeur Richard Castelli
Artforms: contemporary theatre and music, new technologies, contemporary dance *Comments:* works with Art Zoyd, Jean-Michel Bruyère, Dumb Type, Granula Synthesists, Robert Lepage, Lalala Human Steps; see also Orchestras

Fondation Jacques Toja pour le Théâtre
93 Boulevard Haussmann, 75008 **Paris**
Fax: 1-4266 8500
Artforms: contemporary theatre
Comments: co-productions of plays

Georges Gara – Conseiller artistique
20 rue Le Sueur, 75116 **Paris**
Tel: 1-4500 7576 Fax: 1-4500 9912
E-Mail: gara@cybercable.fr
Artforms: classical music, opera

Graph'théâtre
3 Rue Francis de Pressensé, 75014 **Paris**
Tel: 1-4545 4409/607-625 370 (mobile) Fax: 1-4545 4459
promoter Janie Bel
Artforms: visual theatre, circus, new circus, comedians
Comments: fax (provinces) 7576 0415

Harry Lapp Organisation
9 av de la Liberté, 67000 **Strasbourg**
Tel: 3-8815 2929 Fax: 3-8824 0316
E-Mail: Harry.LAPP@wanadoo.fr
directeur Harry Lapp; directeur de production Dominique Leiterer
Artforms: symphonic concerts, recitals, chamber music, opera, theatre, dance, jazz *Comments:* Venues: Palais de la Musique et des Congrès – Salle Erasme, Salle Schweitzer; organise 100+events in Strasbourg and on tour

IMG Artists
54 Avenue Marceau, 75008 **Paris**
Tel: 1-4431 4431 Fax: 1-4431 4432
artist management Philippe Etourneau; production and touring Gilles Demonet; vocal division Peter Wiggins
Artforms: orchestras, piano, violin (soloists), classical

Instant Pluriel
51 Rue de Chabrol, 75010 **Paris**
Tel: 1-4800 8100 Fax: 1-4800 8111
E-Mail: instant.pluriel@wanadoo.fr
Artforms: classical music

International Spectacle 2000
BP 4066, 31029 **Toulouse** Cedex 4
Tel: 5-6155 1918 Fax: 5-6155 1918
director Daniel Lacombe
Artforms: variety, theatre, concerts, speciality: orchestral balls *Comments:* main activity in Spain, Portugal, Italy

Istvan's Performing Arts Agency
24, rue la Condamine, 75017 **Paris**
Tel: 6-8235 7969 Fax: 1-4387 6408 (director)
director Istvan van Heuverzwyn
Artforms: theatre *Comments:* specialise in European tours; second address: 194 Filips van Cleeflaan, 9000 Gent, Belgium, Tel: +32 9-224 1460; see also Promoters

Jacques Thelen
15 Avenue Montaigue, 75008 **Paris**
Tel: 1-5689 3200 Fax: 1-5689 3201
E-Mail: jthelen@wanadoo.fr
directeur Jacques Thelen
Artforms: classical music

Jardin des Délices
2 Rue de la Banque, 75002 **Paris**
Tel: 1-4419 7676 Fax: 1-4419 7664
E-Mail: lejardindesdelices@lemet.fr
director Didier Vuillecot
Artforms: classical music, jazz, soloists, theatre, dance

Jazz diffusion
26 rue des ponts de Comines, 59800 **Lille**
Tel: 3-2031 0524 Fax: 3-2031 0746
E-Mail: jazzdiffusion@nordnet.fr
chargé de production, coordination artistique Robert Petkowski; administrateur Alain Nguyen; relations public Hélène Fontaine
Artforms: jazz, organisation of concerts, artists' management *Comments:* provides information and promotes jazz; organises Improvisibles festival of jazz music

Jean-Marie Fournier Productions
Salle Gaveau, 45 rue la Boetie, 75008 **Paris**
Tel: 1-4562 6971 Fax: 1-4225 9780
directeur Jean-Marie Fournier; attachée de presse Chantal Fournier
Artforms: classical music *Comments:* organise 100 concerts a year; venue: Salle Gaveau; see also Competitions

L'Officina
29, rue Neuve St Catherine, 13007 **Marseille**
Tel: 4-9155 6806 Fax: 4-9155 6713
director Cristiano Carpanini; secretaire générale Fanny Du Pasquier
Artforms: dance *Comments:* also organise festivals, produce and distribute

Living Art Impresariat
9 blvd Montmartre, 75002 **Paris**
Tel: 1-4236 4944/3632 Fax: 1-4233 6491
director Angelika Belamaric
Artforms: opera singers, conductors, lyric artists

Lorentz Concerts
3 rue la Boëtie, 75008 **Paris**
Tel: 1-4266 1232 Fax: 1-4268 0887
E-Mail: lorentz@club_internet.fr
director Marie-Andrée Benhamou
Artforms: classical music (soloists, chamber groups)

Ludmila Lincy Artist's Management
35 avenue des Champs Elysées, 75008 **Paris**
Tel: 1-5353 9710 Fax: 1-5353 9711
E-Mail: llincy@aall-paris.com
artists manager Ludmila Lincy; assistant Marie-Annick Talhouarn
Artforms: classical music: instrumentalists, lyric singers, chorus, orchestras, conductors, jazz, variety, world music, shows, stage directors, costume designers

Mi Fa Agency
Agence Mi Fa
20 Rue du Télégraphe, 75020 **Paris**
Tel: 607-515 716 Fax: 1-4358 7231
director Michel Faussurier
Artforms: singers, conductors, gospel-jazz, pop-rock, classical music

Mondial Musique
17 rue Brey, 75017 **Paris**
Tel: 1-5537 9350 Fax: 1-5537 9351
contact Robert Alfonsi
Artforms: classical: singers, conductors, instrumentalists

Monique Baudouin Opéra
3 rue Volta, 75003 **Paris**
Tel: 1-4271 2008 Fax: 1-4271 1050
director Monique Baudouin
Artforms: opera

Monita Derrieux Agencea
34 rue Vivienne, 75002 **Paris**
Tel: 1-4501 2431 Fax: 1-4501 2432
E-Mail: derrieux@aol.com
associate director Jean Lue Darier, Monita Derrieux
Artforms: actors, authors, directors

MPM International
21 rue du Grand Prieure, 75011 **Paris**
Tel: 1-4923 8360 Fax: 1-4338 4314
E-Mail: mpm.international@wanadoo.fr
direction Marie-Pierre Paillard
Artforms: contemporary dance, drama *Comments:* see also Dance, Puppets, Promoters, Drama

Music Consulting Productions
69 rue des Rigoles, 75020 **Paris**
Tel: 1-4358 0603 Fax: 1-4358 0803
manager Maria Rosa Cusma
Artforms: symphony orchestras, chamber orchestras, chamber music, classical music and concert producers

conductors

Michael Butterman
Opera Southwest, (Music Director)/Louisiana Philharmonic. A 1999 Tanglewood conducting Fellow,/ recording contract with the Centaur label.

Ermanno Florio
American Ballet Theatre (Music Director) Houston Ballet (Music Director) / Birmingham Royal Ballet / Covent Garden / Teatro alla Scala / Opera Lyra / Grand Theatre de Genevre / Paris Opera Ballet / Orchestra London /Gala Opera Programs, Opera Lyra. Teatro dell' Opera Rome/Toronto Symphony / Bordeaux Orchestra / Edinburgh Festival

Paul Nadler (It)
Metropolitan Opera / Chicago Grant Park / Minnesota Opera / Utah / Memphis Operas / Southwest Florida Symphony (Music Director) Orchestras Bucharest / Hongkong / Bangkok / Jerusalem / Baltimore / Calgary Opera

stage director

Franco Gentilesca
Verdi Project, New York Grand Opera in Central Park, Edinburgh Festival, Spoleto Festival, Philidelphia, New Jersey State, Tulsa, Florentine, Connecticut Grand Opera companies, Opera Metropolitan, Caracus

chamber music

Cuarteto Latinoamericano, string quartet
specializing in the classical repertoire of Latin America and the composers of the Americas

4-concert series/residency at Carnegie Mellon University Pittsburgh, and Centro Nacional de las Artes, Mexico City.

"..a wonderful concert..I want to have them back...It was especially nice to hear so many works that we have never had before, and their Shostakovich was as good as any of the other performances we have had to date. The audience left very happy." Vincent Wagner, Maverick Concerts

'..WORLD CLASS PERFORMANCE...Cuarteto Latinoamericano is a musical gem Pittsburgh shares with the world...' Pittsburgh Tribune. October 99.

Recordings:

3 Elan CDs - **"one of the best five in 1989"** New York Times.

3 New Albion CDs - **"... some of the greatest music in captivity ...details come through with stinging clarity and the playing claims a unanimity of thought and approach that few ensembles could match."** Cleveland Plain Dealer.

2 Dorian Records - Orbon Concerto for Quartet Orchestra, plus 5 CDs released of the complete quartets of Villalobos

jazz

Giorgio Gaslini, pianist and the Gaslini Quartet
Italy's Internationally recognized Jazz Musician with more than 3000 concerts and 80 plus recordings available. Mr. Gaslini has appeared with Max Roach, Eddie Gomez, Roswell Rudd, Anthony Braxton and Steve Lacy. He was featured with his Quartet at the Houston International Festival.

singers

Millicent Scarlett, soprano
1995 Pavarotti winner/1996 performances with Pavarotti Philadelphia/1998 Faure Requiem,National Symphony Washington/Italian tour Orchestra Internazionale d'Italia/ 1999 Winnipeg Youth Orchestra, Oakville and York Symphonies, Washington Chorus/2000 "Porgy and Bess" Illinois Opera.

Juan Navarro, tenor
97/98 US debut "La Traviata" Fort Worth Opera/ 98/99 "Don Giovanni" Fort Worth Opera/Italian debut tour Orchestra Internazionale d'Italia.

Alvy Powell, bass/baritone
Internationally recognized as a great interpreter of Gershwin's "Porgy", makes New York Opera debut in 2000. 2001 will see Powell move to Verdi repertoire in Italy/Orchestra appearances include Hollywood Bowl, San Antonio, Colorado Springs, Honolulu, and Cleveland Orchestras.

George Shirley, tenor/narrator
One of America's most versatile tenors, has given Narrations at Aspen Festival, the Rundfunksinfonierorchester, Recorded by Capriccio, and Chicago Symphony. Role of Sportin' Life in Bregenz Festival "Porgy and Bess". Received 1999 Annual Award from Voice Foundation.

The New Bel Canto Trio
Performing together in Italy, Scarlett/ Navarro/ Powell thrilled audiences and critics. Now following in the tradition of Frances Yeend, Mario Lanza, and George London, their programs include opera excerpts of Gershwin, Bernstein, Verdi, and Puccini.

instrumentalists

*Christina Petrowska, pianist**
One of Canada's most important pianists, noted for her enormous repertoire that reflects her work with Europeans Boulez, Ligeti, Americans, Copland, Cowell, Cage, Liebermann and del Tredici. Her latest CD, "Northern Sirens" features works by Ann Southam, Alexina Louie, Larysa Kuzmenko, Heather Schmidt, and Diana McIntosh. Recordings with CBC, Welspring, True North, York Fine Arts.

*Santiago Rodriguez, pianist**
A Rachmaninoff specialist, with 9 solo recordings available on the Elan label. Described as "among the finest pianists in the world" by the Baltimore Sun.

*Available also as guest artist with Cuarteto Latinoamerican

Ann Summers International, Box 188, Station A, Toronto M5W 1B2
Tel. (416) 362-1422 • Fax (416) 359-0043 • Email: sumintl@sympatico.ca
Casella Postale 232, Roma Centro • 00187 Italia • Tel. (06) 3751 4433 • www.sumarts.com

ann summers international

Musicaglotz
11 rue le Verrier, 75006 **Paris**
Tel: 1-4234 5340 Fax: 1-4046 9377
Internet: www.musicaglotz.com
E-Mail: general@musicaglotz.com
directors Michel Glotz, Thérèse Darras
Artforms: classical: singers, conductors, instrumentalists

Musilyre
1, Square de Châtillon, 75014 **Paris**
Tel: 1-4542 6500 Fax: 1-4542 6501
E-Mail: musilyre@club_internet.fr
directrice Véronique Réaud; assistante artistique Dianne de Monteynard
Artforms: classical and baroque music (singers, conductors, baroque ensembles), concert organisation
Comments: lyrical productions

Olivier Gluzman – Les Visiteurs du Soir
40 rue de la Folie Régnault, 75011 **Paris**
Tel: 1-4493 0202 Fax: 1-4493 0440
E-Mail: ogluzman@aol.com
directeur Olivier Gluzman
Artforms: variety, singers, cinema, theatre

Organisation Internationale Artistique
16 av Franklin Roosevelt, 75008 **Paris**
Tel: 1-4225 5834 Fax: 1-4225 6497
E-Mail: oia@oia_poilve.com
directeur Jean-Marie Poilvé
Artforms: lyrics

Organisation Internationale Opera et Concert
1 rue Volney, 75002 **Paris**
Tel: 1-4296 1818 Fax: 1-4296 1800
administrators Paule Fabre, Jacqueline Chollet; artists managers Charles Fabius, Dominique Riber, Christophe Delhoume, Diane du Saillant; assistants Carla Gaussman, Corinne Guitou, Corine Verset
Artforms: classical music, opera, conductors, instrumentalists, singers *Comments:* represent more than 250 artists; acting internationally for opera and classical music

PIAS – Productions Internationales Albert Sarfati
21 rue le Peletier, 75009 **Paris**
Tel: 1-4770 8927 Fax: 1-4247 1501
E-Mail: PrdSarfati@aol.com
directrices Lily Sarfati, Cathy & Vony Sarfati
Artforms: classical music, opera, ballet, drama, tour and concert management *Comments:* about 10 events a year; international orchestra series 'Les Symphoniques' at the Théâtre des Champs Elysées in Paris

Production 2 M
7 place Sithieu, 62500 **Saint Omer**
Tel: 3-2198 1226 Fax: 3-2198 1226
E-Mail: malinsplaisirs@wanadoo.fr
administrateur Alain Nguyen; secrétariat général Tanette Lyoen; directeur artistique Vincent Tavernier
Artforms: theatre, opera *Comments:* creator, producer and touring; see also Festivals

Sarah Turner – Bureau de Concerts, Communication
24 rue du Buisson Richard, 78600 **Le Mesnil Le Roi (Paris)**
Tel: 1-3912 1191/3962 2966 Fax: 1-3962 0722
director Sarah Turner
Artforms: classical concerts, from medieval music to contemporary, vocal (professional English choir), instrumental and baroque music, chamber music, also oratorio, opera and concerts, tango, world music
Comments: liaison for arts enterprises and events, leading English, Dutch and Austrian soloists, ensembles and orchestras, between 40 and 60 concerts a year

Satirino Sarl
118 rue Haxo, 75019 **Paris**
Tel: 1-4208 6814 Fax: 1-4003 8770
E-Mail: satirino@compuserve.com
contact Ian Malkin, Christine Menguy
Artforms: classical music, early music

Tigressa
6 rue Gustave Courbet, 75116 **Paris**
Tel: 1-4755 4707 Fax: 1-4755 1632
managing director Helena Alexander
Artforms: personal management of instrumentalists, writers and visual artists *Comments:* also has an office in America: Tigressa, 1305 NE 63rd Street, Seattle WA 98115, USA, Tel: +1 206-523 6869, Fax: +1 206-523 3030

V.M.A. (Voyez Mon Agent)
10 Avenue Georges V, 75008 **Paris**
Tel: 1-5367 4757 Fax: 1-4720 1586
E-Mail: vma@starnet.fr
director Rose Léandri
Artforms: actors, variety shows

GERMANY (+49)

Agentur ECCO
Luisenstr. 108, 42103 **Wuppertal**
Tel: 202-370 3404/172-605 4714(mobile) Fax: 202-370 3406
Internet: www.ecco-projects.de
E-Mail: ecco.Hesseling@t-online.de
director Sabine Hesseling
Artforms: music (especially free improvised new music), contemporary dance, performances, workshops with and for professional musicians and dancers *Comments:* production of arts projects, personal management, tour-management, festival and congress organization

Agentur Faasch
Faasch Agency
Seilerstraße 36, 20359 **Hamburg**
Tel: 40-3179 1874 Fax: 40-3179 1875
E-Mail: Alfaah@hanse-net.de
Inhaber Albrecht Faasch
Artforms: soloists, conductors, directors, scene & costume designers *Comments:* also literary agency (dramatic works and advertising)

Allegro Konzertagentur
Laplacestr. 1, 81679 **München**
Tel: 89-981 665/171-313 1188 (mobile) Fax: 89-982 8348
Internet: www.allegrokonzert.de
E-Mail: allegroMch@de
contact Susanna Uszkurat
Artforms: represents singers, conductors, musicians, choirs & orchestras for classical concerts and music theatres, chamber music ensembles

Argo Konzerte GmbH
Schweinfurter Str. 44, 97076 **Würzburg**
Tel: 931-23021 Fax: 931-26935
E-Mail: kw@argo.konzerte.de
Inhaber Peter Pracht
Artforms: classical and pop music events *Comments:* 220 concerts a year; Argo Konzerte GmbH (Filiale), Bayernstrasse 100, 90471 Nürnberg tel: 911-471 9301, fax: 911-471 9302; see also Promoters

Aries Entertainment GmbH
Postfach 102607, 34026 **Kassel**
Tel: 561-709 550 Fax: 561-103 046
Geschäftsführer Christian Schaeling
Artforms: mainstream music concerts: rock, pop, folk, jazz; events *Comments:* concert agency and local promoter

Art-Concerts GmbH
Widenmayerstr. 41, 80538 **München**
Tel: 89-290 749-0 Fax: 89-2907 4999
E-Mail: mail@art-concerts.de
Geschäftsführer Franz Abraham
Artforms: mainly opera and musical productions
Comments: see also Promoters

Art-Productions
Bertelestr. 30, 81479 **München**
Tel: 89-791 6562 Fax: 89-791 6582
E-Mail: art.productions@t-online.de
contact Irena Nemecek
Artforms: classical music, jazz *Comments:* management and orchestra touring worldwide; also promotes concerts

Arte Music Konzertagentur
Gabelsbergerstr. 48/b, 80333 **München**
Tel: 89-523 3461 Fax: 89-523 1259
contact Bettina Braun-Angott
Comments: artists representation

Artists International
Postfach 310154, 51328 **Leverkusen**
Tel: 2171-42663 Fax: 2171-43981
managing director Linda Abberton
Artforms: classical music *Comments:* international music management, thematic festivals, concert series, media and recording enterprises, recording and project management, sponsorship,150 concerts; visiting address: Humboldtstraße 17, 51379 Leverkusen; see also Orchestras (Westdeutsche Sinfonia) and Promoters

Artists Management Hartmut Haase
Aalgrund 8, 31275 **Lehrte**
Tel: 5175-953 232 Fax: 5175-953 233
E-Mail: artists@t-online.de
Inhaber Hartmut Haase
Artforms: only represent soloist singers (classical music) & conductors

artists & projects
Gierather Mühlenweg 15, 51469 **Bergisch Gladbach**
Tel: 221-968 9390 Fax: 221-968 9391
Inhaberin Claudia Nitsche
Artforms: classical music (baroque to modern), international soloists and chamber music ensembles

Augsburger Konzertdirektion Georg Hörtnagel
Josef Priller Straße 10, 86159 **Augsburg**
Tel: 821-593 835/731-33426 Fax: 731-33425
Inhaber Georg Hörtnagel
Artforms: chamber, symphony, soloists *Comments:* 8 concerts; use Kongresshalle in Augsburg; see also Promoters

Baillie Music Management International
Marterburg 55-58,, Apt. No 3, 28195 **Bremen**
Tel: 421-336 5432 Fax: 421-336 5432
E-Mail: alexander-baillie@t-online.de
general manager and president Alexander Baillie
Artforms: classical music (recitals, chamber music) *Comments:* own productions, tours and festivals; UK address: 8 Bristol Gardens, London W9 2JG, Tel: +44 20-7286 7526, Fax: +44 20-7266 2687

Bayerische Konzertdirektion Paul Kreye
Marienplatz 1, 80331 **München**
Tel: 89-227 488 Fax: 89-225 311
E-Mail: B.PKreye@t-online.de
Inhaber Paul Kreye
Artforms: chamber music, oratorio, choir *Comments:* personal management; see also Promoters

BB Promotion GmbH – The Art of Entertainment
L7, 7a, 68161 **Mannheim**
Tel: 621-107 920 Fax: 621-13314
Internet: www.bb-promotion.com
E-Mail: zentrale@bb-promotion.com
Geschäftsführer Matthias Mantel, Ralf Kokemüller; producer Michael Brenner
Artforms: dance, musical, gospel, concert, theatre, performance entertainment *Comments:* Die Schöne und das Biest (German original version); The Harlem Gospel Singers; Queen Esther Marrow; Alvin Ailey American Dance Theatre, Hubbard Street Dance Chicago, The Harlem Gospel Singers; Tap Dogs; STOMP; Les Ballets Troekadero de Monte Carlo; see also Promoters

Bellegato Artists' Management
Freiburgerstraße 1-2, 69126 **Heidelberg**
Tel: 6221-374 302 Fax: 6221-372 690
E-Mail: bellegato@hotmail.com
manager Sofia Simmons
Artforms: opera, concerts, singers, conductors, pianists, stage directors, personal management

Berliner Konzertagentur 3-Klang
Raoul-Wallenberg Str. 44, 12679 **Berlin**
Tel: 30-933 2014 Fax: 30-933 1821
E-Mail: agentur3-klang@t-online.de
managing director Horst Gutteck
Artforms: classical music- orchestral, instrumental soloists, conductors, chamber music and chamber orchestras *Comments:* no singers

Berliner Konzertagentur Monika Ott
Dramburger Straße 46, 12683 **Berlin**
Tel: 30-514 4858 Fax: 30-514 2659
E-Mail: BerlinKonzert.ott@t-online.de
managing director Monika Ott
artist manager Simone Ott
Artforms: conductors and instrumental soloists

Bielefelder Konzertdirektion Werner Vollmer
Vormbaumstrasse 9a, 33604 **Bielefeld**
Tel: 521-285 565 Fax: 521-270 3524
Inhaber Werner Vollmer
Artforms: orchestral (Europe wide), soloists *Comments:* manage the Bielefelder Meisterkonzerte in the Oetkerhalle

Boris Orlob Management
Jägerstraße 70, 10117 **Berlin**
Tel: 30-2045 0839/172-851 5514 (mobile)
Fax: 30-2045 0849
E-Mail: BORIS_ORLOB@csi.com
Inhaber Boris Orlob; artist manager Natascha van Rondenborgh
Artforms: singers, conductors

Born & Born Konzertagentur
Parkstr 73, 28209 **Bremen**
Tel: 421-349 065 Fax: 421-345 631
Internet: www.born-born.de
E-Mail: info@born-born.de
Inhaber Charly Born
Artforms: concerts, operetta, musical, rock, pop

Braunschweiger Konzertdirektion
Am Fallersleber Tore 6, 38100 **Braunschweig**
Tel: 531-44115 Fax: 531-46873
Direktor Hans Ulrich Schmid, Bernd Vorhamme
Artforms: philharmonic concerts *Comments:* venues: Stadthalle 2300; see also Promoters

Bühnen- und Konzertagentur Marianne Böttger
Dahlmannstr 9, 10629 **Berlin**
Tel: 30-324 8527 Fax: 30-323 1193
Inhaberin Marianne Böttger
Artforms: classical *Comments:* does not promote

Büro für Internationale Kulturprojekte GmbH
Schwarzwaldstr. 298a, 79117 **Freiburg/Breisgau**
Tel: 761-612 238 Fax: 761-62229
E-Mail: Bik@fmf.notes-net.de
Geschäftsführerin Karin Paeffgen

Catago Entertainment Medienproduktions GmbH
Prinzregentenstrasse 79, 81675 **München**
Tel: 89-417 760-0 Fax: 89-4177 6077
E-Mail: CATAGO@t-online.de
Geschäftsführer Dieter Weilert, Abel Höhler
Artforms: TV shows/programme, music
Comments: media and music production; artist management (TV and music); media advice; partner company: Gregor Prächt SMC Management

Nijinsky Speaks

Mr. Crofoot moves with compelling lyricism. "Nijinsky Speaks" is a *tour de force.*

New York Times

onald Byrd/The Group

Byrd's fierce inventiveness doesn't falter and his performers never fail him. This is why people sweat and strain for years to become dancers – for the chance to appear in such a work, It is also why some of us spend four nights a week in the theatre; in hopes of seeing, maybe once or twice a year, a piece so rewarding.

New York Daily News

Joe Goode Performance Group

Here is an American dancemaker working at the top of his form. Here also is the promise of a profoundly moving millenial epic where irony yields to emotion, movement to ecstasy, nostalgia to hope.

San Franciso Chronicle

Diavolo

An evening crammed with tableaux ranging from Brando-esque "Apocalypse Now". horrors to fun-house frippery, Jacques Heim's Diavolo Dance Theatre again proved that its brand of iconoclastic movement might very well be the dance bridge to the 21st century. Los Angeles Times

Watts Prophets

Before rap, before hip-hop, there were the Watts Prophets with their message of peace, courage and strength for those of us hip enough to hear it.

Los Angeles Times

American Chamber Theater Ensemble

This company must be seen to be believed. The performances are quite stupendous. The show is an absolute "must".

South China Morning Post

ONTIUS AVENUE LOS ANGELES CA 90064 PHONE 310.312.1648 FAX 310.479.3388 SHOE 213.792.0600 liebermand@aol.cor

Drastic Cuts leaves no doubt about Byrd's trenchant imagination, his richly varied craft, or his soulful intensity.
The Washington Post
Donald Byrd/The Group
...The Power of an unstoppable dream
Dance Magazine
Diavolo
See this show!
John Simon, New York Magazine
Leonard Crofoot in Nijinsky Speaks
Joe Goode Performance Group
...Fresh, touching and wickedly funny.
New York Times
Watts Prophets Talk Up/Not Down
Building Community through knowledge
American Chamber Theater Ensemble
A hush of reverence and discovery
lingers on stage.
Seattle Times

Cecilia Music Concept GmbH
Am Eichenwäldchen 23, 50996 **Köln**
Tel: 2236-62329 Fax: 2236-62391
director Franz-Georg Stähling
Artforms: instrumentalists (piano, cello, chanson), chamber ensembles, orchestras, singers, composers, conductors

Christian Lange Personal Artist Management
Ludwig-Behr-Str. 7, 82327 **Tutzing**
Tel: 8158-1832 Fax: 8158-8521
director Christian Lange
Artforms: personal management of singers *Comments:* audio and video producer; Christian Lange is also the artistic director of Herbstliche Musiktage Bad Urach and Richard-Strauss-Festspiele Garmisch-Partenkirchen

Christine Sauer-Intveen International Music Management
Poststraße 22, 78315 **Radolfzell/Bodensee**
Tel: 7732-58837 Fax: 7732-58836
Inhaberin Christine Sauer-Intveen
Artforms: chamber music, orchestral touring, personal management, conductors, pianists, soloists, recitals *Comments:* emphasis on working with young musicians, organising master-classes at Radolfzell/Bodensee

COCOMICO Theater-und Medienprojekte Köln
Postfach 190211, 50672 **Köln**
Tel: 221-921 2360 Fax: 221-9212 3625/26
Internet: www.cocomico.de
E-Mail: cocomico@t-online.de
Geschäftsführer Karl-Heinz March; Theaterleitung Marcell Gödde
Artforms: production of music theatre, musicals

Compact Artists Management – Volker Schmidt-Gertenbach
Rudower Chaussee 3, 12489 **Berlin**
Tel: 30-6704 4884 Fax: 30-6704 4880
Inhaber Volker Schmidt-Gertenbach
Artforms: classical music *Comments:* concert management

con musica konzerte
Konferenzhaus, Festplatz 9, 76137 **Karlsruhe**
Tel: 721-933 5511 Fax: 721-933 5566
Internet: www.conmusica.de
E-Mail: info@tickets-s.de
Geschäftsführer Harmut Raupp
Artforms: agency for classical music, cabaret, music theatre, world music, flamenco; management of musicians, presenting international orchestras and soloists

Concert Management Classic 2000
Hans-Bredow-Str. 42B, 65189 **Wiesbaden**
Tel: 611-464 619/461 941 Fax: 611-464 755
Inhaber Rista Savic
Artforms: solo musicians, chamber ensemble, conductor

Concertino Agentur Rita de la Chevallerie
Nerotal 24, 65193 **Wiesbaden**
Tel: 611-180 5656 Fax: 611-180 5657
Internet: www.t-online.de/home/concwies
E-Mail: concwies@t-online.de
Inhaberin Rita de la Chevallerie
Artforms: serious music, soloists, ensembles, chamber orchestras

Concerto C W Winderstein
Leopoldstrasse 25, Postfach 440446, 80753 **München**
Tel: 89-383 846-0 Fax: 89-337 938
Internet: www.concerto.de
E-Mail: artists@winderstein.de
Geschäftsführer Dr Hans-Dieter Göhre
Artforms: whole sphere of classical music *Comments:* see also Promoters

Concertservice Hilmar Schunke
Tempelhofer Weg 9, 61348 **Bad Homburg**
Tel: 6172-303 397 Fax: 6172-304 566
E-Mail: medicals@aol.com
Inhaber Hilmar Schunke
Artforms: singers, choirs, chamber orchestras, symphony orchestras *Comments:* organises concert tours in Germany and Europe; personal and concert management

CONTOUR, Büro für Concert- und Gastspieltourneen GmbH
Postfach 250152, 40093 **Düsseldorf**
Tel: 211-934 8486/8529 Fax: 211-345 235
E-Mail: contour@online-club.de
Geschäftsführer Klaus Winkes
Artforms: symphony orchestras, boys' choirs, chamber music, music theatre, dance *Comments:* visiting address: Hildebrandtstr. 7, 40215 Düsseldorf; alternative E-mail: contour@rp-plus.de

Crescendo Artists Management
Eckberg Str. 27, 76534 **Baden-Baden**
Tel: 7221-99801/171-670 9345 (mobile)
Fax: 7221-99802
E-Mail: creartman@compuserve.com
president Alec Band
Artforms: chamber ensembles, orchestras, soloists, conductors, orchestra tours *Comments:* can also be contacted in New York: +1 212-504 7985; or Paris: +33 1-5301 3297

Dagmar von Vietinghoff-Scheel – Personal Artists Management
Lange Furche 44, 72072 **Tübingen**
Tel: 7071-73566 Fax: 7071-76612
Inhaberin Dagmar von Vietinghoff-Scheel
Artforms: chamber music, soloists

Daniela Wiehen Artists Management
Falkenried 7, 20251 **Hamburg**
Tel: 40-4231 3121 Fax: 40-4231 3120
Internet: www.wiehen.de
E-Mail: daniela@wiehen.de
Inhaberin Daniela Wiehen
Artforms: chamber music, soloists, conductors

Der weisse Wal, Büro für Kultur und Kommunikation
Ketzerbach 14, 35037 **Marburg**
Tel: 6421-66308/177-660 9548 (mobile) Fax: 6421-66536
contact Raine Eble
Artforms: out-door production (especially from the Pacific area, dance productions, classical guitar

Dirk Lotze Musikmanagement
Rheinallee 119, 40545 **Düsseldorf**
Tel: 211-570 701/177-317 4664 (mobile) Fax: 211-557 0156
Internet: www.DLmusik.nvo.com/
E-Mail: service@DLmusik.nvo.com
Artforms: contemporary music (ensembles, soloists, composers) *Comments:* also PR services

ecotopia dance productions
Bunzstr. 3, 71638 **Ludwigsburg**
Tel: 7141-903 383/84 Fax: 7141-903 385
E-Mail: ecotopia@t-online.de
Inhaberin Claudia Bauer
Artforms: dance, dance theatre *Comments:* international management of dance companies and performance arts

Edith Roschlau – Agentur für Musiktheater und Konzerte
Samuel-Schmidt-Strasse 7, 96450 **Coburg**
Tel: 9561-32549 Fax: 9561-420 792
Inhaberin Edith Roschlau
Artforms: chamber music, folk music, instrumental recitals, light orchestra music, music theatre, operetta, song recitals, symphony music, opera *Comments:* agency for ensembles, soloists, composers

Elisabeth Meister
Mallertshofener Str. 8, 85716 **Unterschleißheim**
Tel: 89-3177 0924 Fax: 89-3177 0925
E-Mail: elisabeth.meister@t-online.de
Inhaberin Elisabeth Meister
Artforms: orchestral touring, conductors

EUCREA-Agentur
Friedensallee 45, 22765 **Hamburg**
Tel: 40-3990 2212 Fax: 40-390 8895
contact Jutta Schubert
Artforms: music, theatre, cabaret, literature and fine arts
Comments: special mediating agency for handicapped artists; see also Supranational and National Organisations: EUCREA-Deutschland

Euro-Studio – Konzertdirektion Landgraf GmbH & CoKg
Lärchenweg 1, 79822 **Titisee-Neustadt**
Tel: 7651-2070 Fax: 7651-20799
Internet: www.landgraf.de
E-Mail: postbox@landgraf.de
Leitung Joachim u. Birgit Landgraf; Disposition Christian Kreppel
Artforms: theatre, opera, operetta, musicals, concerts, ballet, dance, worldwide artists management
Comments: visiting address: Lärchenweg 1,79822 Titisee-Neustadt; also run two playhouses in Germany: Theater im Rathaus in Essen and Parktheater in Augsburg; alternative E-mail: pfeifer@landgraf.de; see also Promoters

Evelyn Wenzel
Waldowstrasse 3a, 13156 **Berlin**
Tel: 30-4747 5835 Fax: 30-4747 5846
E-Mail: ewe@snafu.de
director Evelyn Wenzel
Artforms: contemporary dance, theatre, film *Comments:* management, production, tour planning, promotion, pr/press for special projects; worldwide and local representation of artists and companies

Faces & Voices
Hierlangerweg 9, 81369 **München**
Tel: 89-782 572 Fax: 89-782 509
Internet: filmemacher.de
E-Mail: joachimdsb@aol.com
contact Joachim Schmahl
Artforms: castings, demo-videos, video production, internet database for performing arts, film & TV

festival arts – Büro für Konzert und Theater
Postfach 580248, 10412 **Berlin**
Tel: 30-449 1671/440 7117 Fax: 30-449 1671
E-Mail: annerose.schroeder@germanyweb.com
Geschäftsführung Annerose Schröder
Artforms: music, dance

Florian Kadner Sekretariat Joaquín Clerch
Schraudolphstr. 13 B, 80799 **München**
Tel: 89-272 3338 Fax: 89-272 3338
director Florian Kadner
Artforms: classical and contemporary music
Comments: representation of guitarist and composer Joaquín Clerch

Forum Artium
Am Kasinopark 1-3, 49124 **Georgsmarienhütte**
Tel: 5401-35077 Fax: 5401-34223
Geschäftsführer Herbert Vieth
Artforms: early music, classical music
Comments: see also Promoters

Forum kunstvereint eV
Bismarckstraße 260, 45889 **Gelsenkirchen**
Tel: 209-988 2282 Fax: 209-988 2362
E-Mail: forumkunstvereint@t-online.de
director Michael Gees
Artforms: pianist(s), dance theatre, theatre, children, youth theatre *Comments:* producers aiming to further contact between artist and audience; see also Recorded Media (Kunstvereint)

Franz Siebenlist Konzertdirektion
Aiblinger Str. 9, 83620 **Feldkirchen-Westerham**
Tel: 8063-83700 Fax: 8063-83703
E-Mail: classic_reisen@t-online.de
Inhaber Franz Siebenlist
Artforms: singers, conductors, pianists, music theatre, instrumental soloists *Comments:* worldwide personal – concert management; see also Promoters

Franz-Georg Schulze
Königsallee 14e, 14193 **Berlin**
Tel: 30-8909 2061 Fax: 30-8909 2062
Inhaber F.G. Schulze
Artforms: actors *Comments:* personal management (agency/pr) of up to 5 artists

Gabriel Concerts
Am Markt 24, 53111 **Bonn**
Tel: 228-696 991 Fax: 228-694 835
E-Mail: Gabriel_Concerts@t-online.de
Inhaberin Dorothea Gabriel
Comments: concert and touring agency; see also Promoters

Georg A. Weth
Geyer-zu-Lauf-Str. 26, 79312 **Emmendingen**
Tel: 7641-4071 Fax: 7641-43519
E-Mail: weth-dks@t-online.de
Artforms: special events (Erlebnisgastronomie), lectures
Comments: see also Drama (Deutsche Kammerschauspiele)

Gerhard Kehren
Am Bongert 3, 41804 **Erkelenz**
Tel: 2431-3541 Fax: 2431-3375
E-Mail: teddymusic@t-online.de
Comments: personal management of different artists and groups (especially 60s and 70s music); TV research

Gosh Artistic in Concert e.V.
Bureau Berlin, Mariannenplatz 23, 10997 **Berlin**
Tel: 30-611 3243 Fax: 30-611 8134
Internet: www.gosh.de
E-Mail: info@gosh.de
contact Thomas Schobert

Gregor Prächt SMC Management
Theodorstraße 7, 90489 **Nürnberg**
Tel: 911-396 450 Fax: 911-396 404
E-Mail: CATAGO@t-online.de
managing director Sara Valentino; owner Gregor Prächt
Artforms: artist development, cross-over/tour promoter, record company; management, project development
Comments: exclusive management for Gregor Prächt; partner company: Catago Entertainment Medienproduktions GmbH (q.v.)

Günter Ocklenburg
Hartungstrasse 15, 20146 **Hamburg**
Tel: 40-418 656/410 1494 Fax: 40-410 4668
managing directors Günter Ocklenburg, Wolfgang Schmitt
Artforms: opera *Comments:* worldwide

Hahn Produktion
Hess-Straße 132, 80797 **München**
Tel: 8171-21541/89-1216 2370
Fax: 8171-76331/89-1216 2369
E-Mail: Reithalle1@aol.com
managing director Jochen Hahn; artistic director Dagmar Hahn
Artforms: theatre and festival producers *Comments:* organisers of international cultural exchange, main emphasis- the Ukraine, Russia, and China; new venue – Reithalle, Munich

Hannagret Bueker
Fuhsestr. 2, 30419 **Hannover**
Tel: 511-271 6910 Fax: 511-271 7873
Inhaber Hannagret Bueker
Artforms: opera, concert singers *Comments:* worldwide

Hans Otto Musikmanagement
Boisseréestr. 3, 50674 **Köln**
Tel: 221-240 8980 Fax: 221-240 8982
E-Mail: hansotto.mak@t-online.de
Inhaber Hans Otto
Artforms: early music, soloists, chamber ensembles, music projects, opera productions

Hanseatische Konzertdirektion GmbH
In der süßen Heide 4, 21335 **Lüneburg**
Tel: 4131-46321 Fax: 4131-46366
Prokuristin Anke Hennig
Artforms: orchestras, soloists, open-air concerts
Comments: concert management; operates in Northern Germany; see also Promoters

Herwald Artists' Management
Strasse des Roten Kreuzes 64, 76228 **Karlsruhe**
Tel: 721-947 3939 Fax: 721-947 3937
E-Mail: HerwaldArtists@t-online.de
Direktor Thomas Herwald
Artforms: classical

hp – Musik Management
Brienner Str. 55, 80333 **München**
Tel: 89-545 9140 Fax: 89-5459 1499
E-Mail: hpmusikmanagement@realnet.de
Inhaber Helmut Pauli
Artforms: soloists, chamber orchestras, symphony orchestras, choirs, singers *Comments:* see also Promoters (Münchener Bach Konzerte e.V. and Münchener Mozart Konzerte e.V.)

Image Concert GmbH
Heidestr. 1, 37412 **Herzberg am Harz**
Tel: 5521-5610 Fax: 5521-72972
E-Mail: Image.Concert@t-online.de
leader Thomas Krause; bureau Ilse Fischer
Artforms: classical chamber orchestras, soloists
Comments: organise Walkenrieder Kreuzgangkonzerte (Zisterzienser Cloister)

Impresariat Simmenauer GmbH
Falkenried 7, 20251 **Hamburg**
Tel: 40-4231 3111 Fax: 40-4231 3113
E-Mail: sonia.simmenauer@t-online.de
Inhaberin Sonia Simmenauer
Artforms: chamber music, soloists, conductors

International Festival Management – Thomas Hummel
Sophienterrasse 6, 20149 **Hamburg**
Tel: 40-4135 0490/171-410 8554 (mobile)
Fax: 40-4135 0492
E-Mail: ifmhummel@aol.com
Geschäftsführer Thomas Hummel
Artforms: classical, early music
Comments: organiser of 'Usedomer – Musik Festival', 'Cello Festival in Kronberg' , 'Dollart-Organ-Festival'

JA/NEIN Musikverlag GmbH
Hallerstr. 72, 20146 **Hamburg**
Tel: 40-410 2161 Fax: 40-448 850
E-Mail: JaNeinMV@aol.com
general manager Mary Dostal; admin. manager Heino Müller
Artforms: jazz, rock, blues, pop, klezmer

Jaro Medien GmbH
Bismarckstr 43, 28203 **Bremen**
Tel: 421-78080/705 771 Fax: 421-74066
Internet: www.jaro.de
E-Mail: jaro@fuego.de
director Ulli Balss; agent Piet Mau; distribution Jorg Werner
Artforms: choral and instrumental ensembles
Comments: worldwide exlusive management of the Bulgarian Voices-Angelite, Luis Di Matteo, Sarband, Trinovox, Moscow Art Trio

Joe Carusa Music
Prinzregentenstr. 110, 81677 **München**
Tel: 89-470 3257 Fax: 89-470 4324
contact Gottfried Seidl, Joe Carusa
Artforms: personal management *Comments:* management of up to 5 artists or groups

Josch Arts & Concepts
Dudenstr. 7, 45239 **Essen**
Tel: 201-405 399/177-326 6389 (mobile)
Fax: 201-405 399
E-Mail: joscharts@01019freenet.de
Direktor Joachim Goldschmidt
Artforms: choreographers, singer, dancers

Karsten Jahnke Konzertdirektion GmbH
Hallerstrasse 72, 20146 **Hamburg**
Tel: 40-414 7880 Fax: 40-443 597
Internet: www.karsten-jahnke.de
E-Mail: Karsten-Jahnke@t-online.de
managing directors Karsten Jahnke, Hauke Tedsen
Artforms: jazz, rock, entertainment, show *Comments:* 500-800 concerts; see also Promoters

KIR – Resonanz
Mockenhübel 25, 66117 **Saarbrücken**
Tel: 681-583 816/171-530 2809(mobile) Fax: 681-583 816
Organisation Jürgen Wönne
Artforms: drama, cabaret, Kleinkunst, comedy, children's theatre workshops
Comments: artists management; touring, productions, theatre festival Pro. Drama

KoKo Entertainment
Bruderturmgasse 4a, Postfach 101063, 78410 **Konstanz**
Tel: 7531-90880 Fax: 7531-908 888
Internet: www.koko.de
E-Mail: koko-kn@t-online.de
Geschäftsführer Dieter Bös, Armin Nissel, Clemens Zipse
Artforms: symphony orchestras, all sorts of concerts including open-air *Comments:* concert management; also promotes locally

Kölner Tanzagentur
Kunstzentrum Wachsfabrik, Industriestr. 170, 50999 **Köln**
Tel: 2236-963 589 Fax: 2236-963 590
Geschäftsführerin Kim vom Kothen
Artforms: dance theatre, (companies and soloists)
Comments: dance agency concerned with the training and other requirements of independent dancers in the local area; also serves as a production venue; houses two dance companies: 'Mind The Gap' and 'Maja Lex'; database of dance artists/groups available

Konzert- & Gastspieldirektion Hubert Geulen
Von-Coels-Strasse 181-183, 52080 **Aachen-Eilendorf**
Tel: 241-551 250 Fax: 241-558 156
E-Mail: saaltheater-geulen@t-online.de
Inhaber Hubert Geulen
Artforms: orchestras, soloists, opera, easy listening
Comments: operate in Aachen, Netherlands, Belgium

Konzert- & Künstleragentur Jens Gunnar Becker
Grünstr. 13, 58313 **Herdecke**
Tel: 2330-70389 Fax: 2330-7507
Internet: www.beckerkonzert.de
E-Mail: becker@beckerkonzert.de
Inhaber Jens Gunnar Becker;
Mitarbeiter Evelyn Dürwald
Artforms: represents singers, conductors, soloists & orchestras for classical concerts and music theatres

CMC

Cecilia Music Concept GmbH

Franz-Georg Stähling
Am Eichenwäldchen 23, D-50996 Köln
fon +49 (0) 2236/62329 fax 62391 / mobile 0172-9207248
Mitglied im Verband der Deutschen Konzertdirektionen

Piano
SILKE AVENHAUS*
see:www.silke-avenhaus.de
ECKHARD RADMACHER*

Cello
FRANÇOISE GROBEN*

Conductor
MARCUS BOSCH

Chamber Ensemble
bach, blech & blues*
(brassgroup: quintet up to 12 musicians)
see:www.bachblechblues.de
BLÄSERSOLISTEN DER DEUTSCHEN KAMMERPHILHARMONIE

Singers
ANGELA RUDOLF, Soprano
KAROLINA RÜEGG, Soprano
BARBARA SPIEß, Soprano
ANNA MARIA DUR, Mezzosoprano
KATJA BOOST, Contralto
PEER ABILGAARD, Countertenor
GARY BENNETT, Tenor
CARSTON LAU, Tenor
IVAN MOUTAFTCHIEV, Tenor
RAPHAEL PAUSS, Tenor
YOO-CHANG NAH, Baritone
MARTIN BLASIUS, Bass
ARND GOTHE, Bass

Chanson
GISELA MAY*
(2000: Kurt-Weill-Programme)

Composer/Arranger
ANDREAS N.TARKMANN*
1999/2000 new works for Scharoun Ensemble, hr-brass, Staatstheatre Hannover, etc.

BERLINER KONZERTAGENTUR
MONIKA OTT
Dramburger Str. 46, 12683 Berlin
Tel.: (49) 30- 5 14 48 58 Fax: (49) 30- 5 14 26 59
e-mail: BerlinKonzert.ott@t-online.de
http://www.berlinkonzert-ott.de

CONDUCTORS
Kurt Sanderling **
Heinz Rögner *
Rolf Reuter *
Andrey Boreyko ***
Christian Kluttig *
Jac van Steen G
Christian Ehwald *
Arvo Volmer G
Georg Fritzsch *
Stefan Malzew *
Victor Puhl G

VIOLIN
Torsten Janicke *
Sergej Krylov G
Elisabeth Glass *
Oleh Krysa G
Denis Goldfeld G
Michael Erxleben G

VIOLA
Daniel Raiskin ***

VIOLONCELLO
Anne Gastinel G
Torleif Thedéen G
Ramon Jaffé G

PIANO
Susanne Grützmann *
Gülsin Onay ***
Paulo Alvares ***
Gilead Mishory * *
Boris Bermann G

TRUMPET
Joachim Pliquett *
Uwe Komischke

* Generamanagement
** Generalmanagement exept G/A
G Germany
*** Sundry Territories

---

boris orlob management

Boris Orlob
Jägerstraße 70
D-10117 Berlin

Tel +49-30-204 508 39
Fax +49-30-204 508 49
Mobil +49-172-851 551 4
E-mail BORIS_ORLOB@csi.com

ARTISTS LIST

Soprano
LIVIA AGH ◆
LUCIA ALIBERTI ▼
MALIN HARTELIUS ★
BRIDGETT HOOKS ● ▮
SOILE ISOKOSKI ▼ ✿ ✔
SUMI JO ●
ANNA KORONDI ★

Mezzo
GAIL GILMORE ▮ ▼
ULRIKE HELZEL ▼
URSULA HESSE ★
BEATRICE URIA-MONZON ●
DALIA SCHAECHTER ★
MARIETTA SIMPSON ◆

Tenor
DANIEL GALVEZ-VALLEJO ●
NICOLAI GEDDA ▼ ✿
DONALD GEORGE ▼
DANIEL KIRCH ● ▼
DENNIS O`NEILL ● ✿

Baritone
FRANÇOIS LE ROUX ●
DAVID PITTMAN-JENNINGS ●

Bass
MANFRED HEMM ●
JAAKKO RYHAENEN ● ✔
DANIEL LEWIS WILLIAMS ▼

Conductor
ROGER EPPLE ●
DERRICK INOUYE ◆
IVO LIPANOVIC ● ▼
JOHN MAUCERI ● ▼

Special Attractions
UTE LEMPER
HANNA SCHYGULLA

Collaborator
NATASCHA VAN RANDENBORGH

✔ in agreement with Allegro Artist Management

For artist representation in North America: in cooperation with Matthias Vogt Artist's Management

✿ concerts and recitals
★ World
◆ Europe
▼ various
● Germany
▮ France

Konzert- & Künstleragentur Johanna von Mikusch-Buchberg
Max-Weber Platz 8a, 81675 **München**
Tel: 89-470 5686/171-456 2123(mobile)
Fax: 89-470 6152
E-Mail: mikuschjv@aol.com
Inhaberin Johanna von Mikusch-Buchberg
Artforms: classical concerts and music, singers, conductors, musicians, choirs and orchestras
Comments: advice on recorded media, international representation, PR management

Konzert- & Künstleragentur Michael Herrmann
Thorwaldsenanlage 74, 65195 **Wiesbaden**
Tel: 611-599 998 Fax: 611-599 895
Inhaber Michael Herrmann
Artforms: conductors, pianists, chamber orchestras
Comments: also the artistic director of the Rheingau Musik Festival; see also Promoters

Konzert- & Theaterdirektion Delmenhorst
Kleines Haus, Max-Planck-Str., 27749 **Delmenhorst**
Tel: 4221-16565 Fax: 4221-129 212
Direktion Ulrike Thümmel
Artforms: drama and music theatre in different languages (German, English, French, etc.)

Konzertagentur Dagmar Körner
Bergstrasse 15, 85120 **Hepberg bei Ingolstadt**
Tel: 8456-1530 Fax: 8456-2109
E-Mail: koerner.konzerte@t-online.de
Inhaberin Dagmar Körner
Artforms: soloists, chamber orchestras, chamber music, symphony orchestras *Comments:* worldwide concert management

Konzertagentur Erika Esslinger
Spittlerstrasse 6, 70190 **Stuttgart**
Tel: 711-283 276 Fax: 711-261 421
Internet: www.konzertagentur.de
E-Mail: esslinger@konzertagentur.de
Inhaberin Erika Esslinger
Artforms: early music (vocal and instrumental), orchestras, chamber ensembles and soloists (vocal and instrumental)

Konzertagentur Eva Maria Kaufmann
Pillnitzer Landstraße 7, 01326 **Dresden**
Tel: 351-268 7212/172-991 1639 (mobile)
Fax: 351-264 0585
Internet: www.mon.de/del/kaufmann.243382
E-Mail: konzertagenturkaufmann.dd@t-online.de
contact drama, musical, event technology, bookings Thomas Kaufmann
Artforms: galas, represent artists of all types, event management

Konzertagentur Fahrenholtz
Winterleitenweg 17 B, 97082 **Würzburg**
Tel: 931-784 7230 Fax: 931-784 7230
director Wolfgang Fahrenholtz
Artforms: classical, modern music *Comments:* negotiates between instrumentalists, chamber music ensembles and promoters; see also Promoters

Konzertagentur Heide Stock
Ferdinand-Wallbrecht-Str. 13, 30163 **Hannover**
Tel: 511-394 3114 Fax: 511-394 3115
E-Mail: heide.stock@gmx.de
Inhaber Heide Stock
Artforms: early music, instrumentalists, chamber ensembles *Comments:* personal management

Konzertagentur Ingrid Hellmann
Birnenweg 12, 06112 **Halle/Saale**
Tel: 345-560 3041 Fax: 345-560 3654
E-Mail: KAHellmann@aol.com
Inhaberin Ingrid Hellmann
Comments: represents singers, conductors, musicians, choirs & orchestras for classical concerts and music theatres

Konzertagentur Jörg Hannemann
Haynstraße 15, 20249 **Hamburg**
Tel: 40-480 7575 Fax: 40-486 281
Inhaber Jörg Hannemann
Artforms: chamber music, symphony, ensembles, conductors, soloists *Comments:* concert tours

Konzertagentur Strad
Konzert Europaplatz 20/7, 70565 **Stuttgart**
Tel: 711-715 6603 Fax: 711-715 7599
E-Mail: mgvoicu@aol.com
contact Gabriel Voicu
Artforms: singers, instrumentalists

Konzertagentur Thüringen
Freiligrathstraße 8, 99096 **Erfurt**
Tel: 361-346 5875 Fax: 361-346 5875
Inhaber Dr. Jürgen Kupfer
Artforms: represent singers, conductors, musicians, choirs and orchestras for classical concerts and music theatres *Comments:* medieval music projects, e.g. early music concerts in original costume; chamber music projects; also various projects in showbiz

Konzertagentur Trude Kleinheisterkamp
Welzheimer Strasse 28A, 70188 **Stuttgart**
Tel: 711-483 247 Fax: 711-485 796
Inhaberin Trude Kleinheisterkamp; Mitarbeiter Hans Kleinheisterkamp
Artforms: international soloists, chamber music, orchestras

Konzertagentur Wachsmann & Beniashvili
Beethovenweg 1, 73655 **Plüderhausen**
Tel: 7181-998 6014/171-722 0808/671 9288 (mobiles)
Fax: 7181-998 6060
E-Mail: shalvabeniashvili@t-online.de
contact Fr. Wachsmann, Hr. Beniashvili
Artforms: classical music, ballet; event and project management *Comments:* see also Promoters

Konzertbüro Andreas Braun
Sülzgürtel 86, 50937 **Köln**
Tel: 221-942 0430 Fax: 221-9420 4319
Internet: Konzertbuero-Braun.de
E-Mail: braun@angel.de
Inhaber Andreas Braun
Artforms: orchestras, chamber orchestras, chamber music, soloists, conductors, singers, vocal ensembles, choirs (worldwide)

Konzertbüro Richard Weber
Hauptstr. 66, 77652 **Offenburg**
Tel: 781-72041 Fax: 781-23406
Internet: www.ivan-rebroff.de
E-Mail: konzertbuero.weber@baden-online.de
Inhaber Irma Weber; Prokura Ursula Juncker
Artforms: singers and classical *Comments:* own record label- Elisar Records; visiting address: Hauptstraße 66, 77652 Offenburg

Konzertbüro Thomas Voigt
Mindener Str. 11, 10589 **Berlin**
Tel: 30-3490 2499 Fax: 30-3490 2145
Internet: www.voigtmanagement.de
E-Mail: voigt@voigtmanagement.de
Inhaber Thomas Voigt
Artforms: artists, orchestras, chamber ensembles
Comments: concerts and tours; see also Promoters

Konzertdirektion Andrea Hampl
Prenzlauer Promenade 189, 13189 **Berlin**
Tel: 30-478 2699/172-380 5645 (mobile)
Fax: 30-478 3792
E-Mail: hampl@konzertdirektion.de
director Andrea Hampl
Artforms: soloists, chamber music ensembles, orchestras, touring

Konzertdirektion Collien
Spielbudenplatz 29-30 (St Pauli-Theater), 20359 **Hamburg**
Tel: 40-313 901/902 Fax: 40-319 1919
E-Mail: collien@t-online.de
Direktor Michael Collien
Artforms: easy listening

Konzertdirektion Dr Rudolf Goette
Brahmsallee 6, 20144 **Hamburg**
Tel: 40-4501 1850 Fax: 40-4501 1860
E-Mail: info@goette.de
directors Hans-Werne Funke, Bernd Voorhamme
Artforms: orchestras, soloists, conductors, chamber music ensemble – worldwide

Konzertdirektion Fischer GmbH
Joh. Phil-Palm-Str. 21, 73614 **Schorndorf**
Tel: 718-160 000 Fax: 718-610 0050
director Dieter Fischer
Artforms: artist representation for soloist pianists

Konzertdirektion Franz Günther Büscher
Postfach 101424, 69004 **Heidelberg**
Tel: 6223-40695 Fax: 6223-47135
Inhaber Franz Günther Büscher; director Tiana Büscher-Wigle
Artforms: mainly chamber music, symphony, soloists, conductors *Comments:* arranges chamber orchestra concerts, chamber recitals and symphony concerts

Konzertdirektion Fritz Dietrich GmbH
Eckenheimer Landstrasse 483, 60435 **Frankfurt am Main**
Tel: 69-544 504/545 658 Fax: 69-548 4107
Inhaber Fritz Dietrich; Geschäftsführerin Susanne Volz
Artforms: chamber music, symphony, opera, singers, conductors, ensembles, instrumentalists, theatre, choirs *Comments:* 2nd office: Büro Gießen/Marburg/Wetzlar, An der Sonnseite 7, 35096 Niederwalgern, Tel: 6426-7742, Fax: 6426-6058, contact: Ursula Leeder; see also Promoters

Konzertdirektion Georg Hörtnagel
Postfach 210220, 90120 **Nürnberg**
Tel: 911-558 003 Fax: 911-550 422
Geschäftsführer Georg Hörtnagel
Artforms: chamber music, symphony
Comments: promote up to 50 concerts in Nürnberg; visiting address: Äußere-Cramer-Klett-Straße 5, 90489 Nürnberg

Konzertdirektion Hans Adler
Auguste-Viktoria Strasse 64, (1. Etage), 14199 **Berlin**
Tel: 30-895 9920 Fax: 30-826 3520
Internet: www.musikadler.de
E-Mail: info@musikadler.de
Inhaber Witiko Adler
Artforms: conductors, instrumentalists, singers, chamber ensembles, orchestras, choirs
Comments: 80 concerts; see also Promoters

Konzertdirektion Hans G Jaax
Falkenring 48, 49134 **Wallenhorst**
Tel: 5407-7386 Fax: 5407-7322
Inhaber Hans G. Jaax
Comments: agent to predominantly young classical instrumentalists

Konzertdirektion Hans Ulrich Schmid
Postfach 1667, 30016 **Hannover**
Tel: 511-366 0760/27 Fax: 511-366 0734
Internet: www.kdschmid.de
E-Mail: RT@KDSchmid.de
managing directors Cornelia Schmid, Harold Clarkson; chairperson Hans Ulrich Schmid
Artforms: conductors, instrumentalists, ensembles, chamber orchestras, choirs, orchestras, singers
Comments: organise concerts in Hannover, mediates worldwide for artists; visiting address: Schmiedestrasse 8, 30159 Hannover; for UK-office see separate entry

Konzertdirektion Hans-Werner Funke
Brahmsallee 6, 20144 **Hamburg**
Tel: 40-4501 1010 Fax: 40-4501 1020
E-Mail: info@funkemedia.de
Geschäftsführer Hans Werner Funke, Pascal Funke
Artforms: classical music to rock *Comments:* organise and manage artist tours – Germany, Austria, Switzerland; see also Promoters

Konzertdirektion Hörtnagel
Oranienburger Str. 50, 10117 **Berlin**
Tel: 30-308 8770 Fax: 30-3088 7733
Internet: www.hoertnagel.com
E-Mail: agentur@hoertnagel.com
director Beatrice Hörtnagel
Artforms: classical music, artists management

Konzertdirektion Kempf
Schöne Aussicht 34, 65193 **Wiesbaden**
Tel: 611-525 091/2 Fax: 611-525 093
E-Mail: konzert-kempf@t-online.de
Inhaber Wilfried Strohmeier
Artforms: chamber music, orchestras *Comments:* concert tour organiser; 50 concerts; see also Promoters

Konzertdirektion Martin Müller
Vintrup 4, 59320 **Ennigerloh-Ostenfelde**
Tel: 2522-960 200 Fax: 2522-960 201
E-Mail: MuellerKD@aol.com
Inhaber Martin Müller
Artforms: conductors, soloists, chamber music, chamber orchestras, orchestras, special projects
Comments: see also Festivals (Europäisches Musikfest Münsterland)

Konzertdirektion Meuer
Geislinger Weg 28, 89522 **Heidenheim**
Tel: 7321-55381 Fax: 7321-55381
Inhaberin Martha Munz
Artforms: orchestras, soloists, theatre

Konzertdirektion Rainer Haas
Postfach 1240, 69247 **Schönau b. Heidelberg**
Tel: 6228-1375 Fax: 6228-8455
Inhaber Rainer Haas
Artforms: soloists, chamber ensembles
Comments: artists management; concert management; visiting address: Fuchslochweg 18, 69250 Schönau bei Heidelberg

Konzertdirektion Richard Berg
Messler Weg 21, 64807 **Dieburg**
Tel: 6071-23134 Fax: 6071-81254
E-Mail: konzertdirektionberg@t-online.de
Geschäftsführer Richard Berg
Artforms: classical music
Comments: personal management for soloists and ensembles; see also Promoters

Koordination Kunst und Kultur
Vera Christ, Postfach 410243, 50862 **Köln**
Tel: 221-442 400/173-938 8921 Fax: 221-442 400
Internet: www.koor-k-vc.com
E-Mail: coart@koor-k-vc.com
director Vera Christ; co-worker Siberian music Eugen Wagner; co-worker classical music Jutta Freiwald
Artforms: dance theatre, mime, theatre, personal artists management, tango musicians, cabaret, choirs, classical music ensembles, chamber orchestra & emsembles, classical folkloric ensembles (dance & music) : visiting address: Hollarstrass 2, 50931 Köln; international emsembles, project coordination on advice, special contact for Siberian opera and philharmonic society, diverse contacts to free working artists

ARTISTS

CONDUCTORS

- • Marc Andreae
- • Peter Gülke
- • Gerhard Markson
  Principal Guest Conductor RTÉ National Symphony Orchestra of Ireland
- ▲ Lior Shambadal
  Chief Conductor Berliner Symphoniker
  Music Director designated Slovenian Radio & Television Symphony Orch.
- ◆ Neal Stulberg

INSTRUMENTALISTS

Piano
- ◆ Ronald Brautigam
- ▲ Konstanze Eickhorst
- • Mi-Joo Lee
- • Anna Malikova
- • Michael Roll
- • Janis Vakarelis

Fortepiano
- ◆ Ronald Brautigam

Violin
- ▲ Christian Altenburger
- • Rachel Elena Schettmann

Viola
- • Lars Anders Tomter

Violoncello
- • Maria Kliegel
- ◆ Raphael Wallfisch

Clarinet
- ◆ Martin Fröst

Horn
- • Ab Koster

Guitar
- ▲ Ernesto Bitetti

CHAMBER MUSIC

Duo
- ◆ Isabelle van Keulen (vl./va.) - Ronald Brautigam (piano)
  (in collaboration with Konzertdirektion Goette)
- ▲ Maria Kliegel (vc.) and Elsbeth Moser (bayan)

Trio
- ◆ Haydn Trio Vienna (piano trio)
- • Grieg Trio (piano trio)

Quartet
- ◆ Sine Nomine Quartet Lausanne

Ensemble
- ▲ Esbjerg Ensemble

Chamber Orchestra
- ◆ Czech Chamber Soloists (artistic leader: Ivan Matyáš)
- ▲ Wiener Concert-Verein
  (Chamber Orchestra of Vienna Symphony)

PROJECTS

TOURING PROJECTS

- ◆ STAVANGER SYMPHONY ORCHESTRA
  29th September – 5th October 2000
  Alexander Dmitriev, conductor

- ◆ NORWEGIAN RADIO ORCHESTRA
  19th - 31st March 2001
  Ari Rasilainen (conductor)
  Lars Anders Tomter (viola)

- • General Management
- ◆ Germany
- ▲ Germany and various countries

We present to the musical world

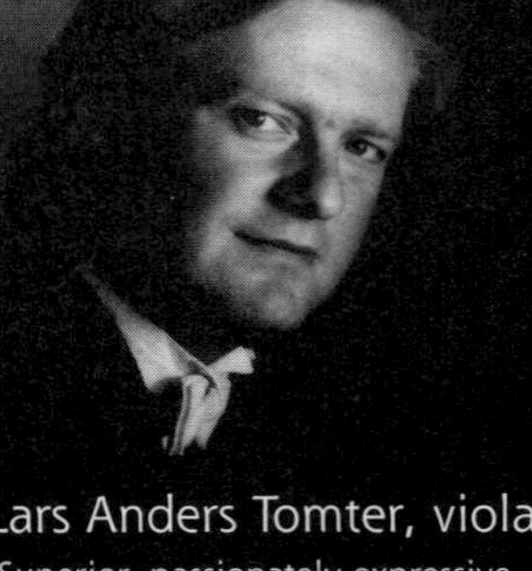

Lars Anders Tomter, viola
"Superior, passionately expressive viola playing"
Der Tagesspiegel, Berlin

Michael Roll, piano
"Playing of the top class from Roll"
Classic CD

Gerhard Markson, conductor
"This was an inspiring performance"
Irish Times

Ab Koster, horn
"A virtuoso performance"
BBC Music Magazine

Peter Gülke, conductor
"With a highly developed sense of tonal range"
Berliner Morgenpost

Grieg Trio
"A historical moment of chamber music"
Hamburger Morgenpost

Rachel Elena Schettmann, violin
"A masterly combination of technique and musicality"
Rhein-Zeitung

PROJECTS WE HAVE ARRANGED IN THE PAST

NORSK MUSIKK
9th November 1997 – 12th February 1998
11 concerts in Berlin and Hamburg
The festival showed the richness of Norwegian Musical Life with an emphasis on the works of Harald Sæverud, celebrating his 100th birthday.
Artists included Ole Edvard Antonsen, Bodil Arnesen, Berlin Symphony (Lior Shambadal), Ensemble ORIOL Berlin, Håvard Gimse, Grieg Trio, Hamburg Symphony (Othmar Maga), Helge Kjekshus, Maria Kliegel, Henning Kraggerud, neuer chor berlin, Einar Steen-Nøkleberg, Lars Anders Tomter and Vertavo String Quartet.

EUROPÄISCHES MUSIKFEST MÜNSTERLAND 1999
14th – 29th August 1999
With an emphasis on the Musical Life of the Baltic States including compositions of Onute Narbutaite, Erkki-Sven Tüür and Peteris Vasks.
Artists included among others David Geringas, Maria Kliegel, Gidon Kremer, Musica Anitqua Köln, Christoph Prégardien and Sine Nomine Quartet Lausanne.

Mi-Joo Lee, piano
"Pianistically speaking, Mi-Joo Lee is a miracle."
Berliner Zeitung

Marc Andreae, conductor
"High voltage until the last bar"
AZ, Nürnberg

Janis Vakarelis, piano
"A pianist straight from Olympus"
tageblatt Echternach

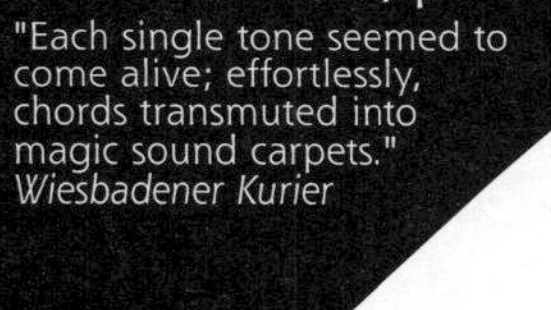

Anna Malikova, piano
"Each single tone seemed to come alive; effortlessly, chords transmuted into magic sound carpets."
Wiesbadener Kurier

Maria Kliegel, cello
"Maria Kliegel is one of the world's leading cellists"
Belfast Telegraph

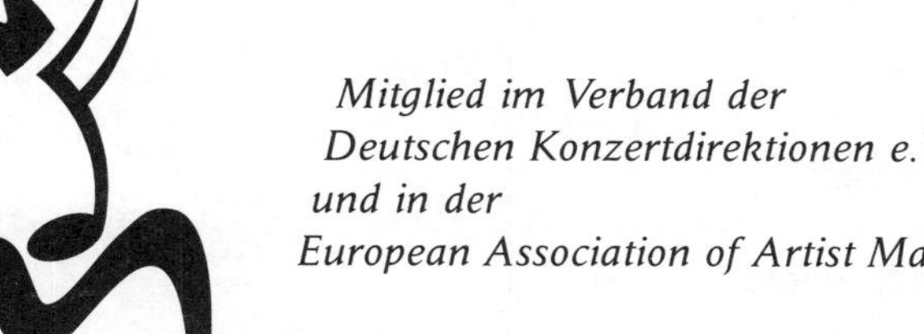

Mitglied im Verband der Deutschen Konzertdirektionen e.V. und in der European Association of Artist Managers

Konzertdirektion Martin Müller

Vintrup 4
D-59320 Ennigerloh-Ostenfelde
Telefon: +49-25 22-96 02 00
Fax: +49-25 22-96 02 01
e-mail: MuellerKD@aol.com

LORE-M. SCHULZ ARTISTS 1999/2000

Conductors	Ivan Anguélov J. David Jackson Daniel Lipton *Europe*
Sopranos	Lucia Aliberti Janice Dixon Hellen Kwon • Petra-Maria Schnitzer • Bridgid Steinberger *Concerts*
Mezzo sopranos	Graciela Alperyn Fredrika Brillembourg Lioba Braun •
Tenors	Peter Galliard Thomas Harper • Robert Lee *Germany* Peter Seiffert • Jorma Sivasti Deon Van der Walt •
Tenor soprano	Arno Raunig
Baritones	Wilhelm Hartmann Siegmund Nimsgern
Basses	Matthias Hölle • Arutjun Kotchinian Attila Jun • Kurt Moll Matti Salminen Hans Sotin • Georg Zeppenfeld

• General Management

Lore-M. Schulz International Artists Management
Zittelstraße 8, D-80796 München
Tel. +49-89-308 70 92, Fax +49-89-308 70 93
email loreschulz.artists@t-online.de

ARTISTS ROSTER
2000/2001

Conductors	Paavo Berglund Luciano Berio Herbert Blomstedt* Leopold Hager* Manfred Honeck* Eiji Oue Marc Piollet* Lothar Zagrosek*

KünstlerSekretariat
am Gasteig

Elisabeth Söling
Lothar Schacke

Piano	Bella Davidovich**
Accompanist	Irwin Gage*, Eric Schneider*
Violin	Viktoria Mullova Peter Zazofsky Frank Peter Zimmermann Nicolaj Znaider
Viola	Tabea Zimmermann
Cello	Truls Mørk
Soprano	Juliane Banse* Sibylla Rubens* Ruth Ziesak
Mezzo	Cornelia Kallisch*
Alto	Ingeborg Danz*
Tenor	Christian Elsner* Michael Schade James R. Taylor*
Baritone	Matthias Goerne* Tom Krause
Bass	Franz-Josef Selig*

* *General Management*
** *Europe*

Chamber music (incl. Klezmer group Kol Simcha), orchestra projects as well as lieder recitals (also with other singers e.g. Cheryl Studer, Stella Doufexis, Dietrich Henschel) available on request.

KünstlerSekretariat am Gasteig
Rosenheimer Straße 52
D-81669 München
Tel. 0049 89 48 20 86 · Fax 0049 89 448 95 22
Internet: www.ks-gasteig.de · e-mail: team@ks-gasteig.de

Krüger Tourneemanagement
Landsberger Altee 144, 10369 **Berlin**
Tel: 30-972 6717 Fax: 30-9760 9900
E-Mail: Krueger.konzertmanagement@t-online.de
director Gisela Krüger
Artforms: classical music (ensembles, orchestras)
Comments: tour and project management

Kulturbüro Köln – Konzeption, Koordination, Koproduktion von Kulturveranstaltungen
Engelbertstr. 32, 50674 **Köln**
Tel: 221-240 3133 Fax: 221-240 3247
E-Mail: Kulturbk@aol.com
Inhaber Jürgen Ruppert (konzeption, produktion u. organisation von festivals, veranstaltungsreihen u. kulturprojekten); künstlerische Sondor- Projekte Nicole Behmeleit; Management für Internationale Tanz- u. Theatergruppen Bettina Wohlfarth
Artforms: management for international dance and repertoire companies *Comments:* organisation of festivals, tours and presenting series of conferences; member of I.E.T.M. and La Federation (f); International Street Theatre Festival Holzminden, Expo 2000 Hannover

Kulturmanagement Sabine Linneweber
Limonenstraße 15a, 12203 **Berlin**
Tel: 30-831 3111 Fax: 30-831 3101
Inhaberin Sabine Linneweber
Artforms: contemporary dance, dance theatre, music theatre *Comments:* management, production, public relation and mediation for international artists

Künstleragentur Helge Rudolf Augstein
Sebastiansplatz 3, 80331 **München**
Tel: 89-2602 4333 Fax: 89-2602 4344
E-Mail: AgenturHRA@aol.com
director Helge Rudolf Augstein; associate Stefan Hahn
Artforms: conductors, singers, instrumentalists

Künstleragentur Markow
Turmstr. 18, 73728 **Esslingen**
Tel: 711-352 001 Fax: 711-350 9770
E-Mail: markow@t-online.de
managing director Ursula Markow
Artforms: instrumentalists

Künstleragentur Stoy
Eschbachweg 5, 79117 **Freiburg/Breisgau**
Tel: 761-60526 Fax: 761-60546
E-Mail: kstoy@privat.toplink.de
contact Klaus Stoy
Artforms: classical and contemporary music *Comments:* management and agency service for chamber music ensembles and solo instrumentalists; see also Orchestras (Ensemble Aventure)

Künstlerdienst Berlin – Landesarbeitsamt Berlin – Brandenburg
Kurfürstendamm 210, 10719 **Berlin**
Tel: 30-884 3050 Fax: 30-8843 0513
Internet: www.arbeitsamt.de
E-Mail: kdberlin@t-online.de
Leiterin des Künstlerdienstes Barbara Kasper; responsible for orchestral musicians Christoph Czakai (30-8843 0552), Hartmut Wettges (30-8843 0551)
Artforms: artists for shows, entertainment, fashion and advertising, instrumentalists for orchestras, soloists, bands, composers

Künstlermanagement Dieter Mauritz
Postfach 140136, 46131 **Oberhausen**
Tel: 208-631 907 Fax: 208-664 577
Inhaber Dieter Mauritz
Artforms: classical and light music soloists *Comments:* visiting address: Wilhelmstr. 54, 46145 Oberhausen

Künstlermanagement Marlies Köchy
Am Dielesken 17, 32351 **Stemwede**
Tel: 5773-1515 Fax: 5773-8451
Internet: www.koechy.de
E-Mail: koechy@t-online.de
Inhaberin Marlies Köchy
Artforms: light music only *Comments:* management of solo artists and groups

Künstlermanagement Viktor Haschke
Franzosengraben 7, 97631 **Bad Königshofen**
Tel: 9761-799 Fax: 9761-6886
E-Mail: v.haschke@t-online.de
Inhaber Victor Haschke
Artforms: rock and pop *Comments:* personal management

Künstlermanagement Wolfgang Kaminski
Untever Ahlenbergweg 47A, 58313 **Herdecke**
Tel: 2330-13344/171-540 3515 (mobile) Fax: 2330-13343
Inhaber Wolfgang Kaminski
Artforms: light entertainment
Comments: personal management

KünstlerSekretariat am Gasteig – Elisabeth Söling/Lothar Schacke
Rosenheimer Str. 52, 81669 **München**
Tel: 89-482 086 Fax: 89-448 9522
Internet: www.ks-gasteig.de
E-Mail: team@ks-gasteig.de
Inhaber Elisabeth Ehlers, Lothar Schacke
Artforms: classical music, singers, opera and oratorios, orchestras, soloists, conductors *Comments:* orchestral tours, personal management

Künstlersekretariat Astrid Schoerke
Mönckebergallee 41, 30453 **Hannover**
Tel: 511-401 048/9 Fax: 511-407 435
Inhaberin Astrid Schoerke
Artforms: soloists, conductors

Künstlersekretariat Rolf Sudbrack
Gösselkoppel 54a, 22339 **Hamburg**
Tel: 40-538 2165/2049 Fax: 40-538 7220
Internet: home.t-online.de/home/Rolf.Sudbrack
E-Mail: Rolf.Sudbrack@t-online.de
Inhaber Rolf Sudbrack
Artforms: chamber music, symphony, composers, conductors, solo instrumentalists *Comments:* worldwide personal management

Künstlersekretariat Stefan Trhal
Waldstr. 36, 30163 **Hannover**
Tel: 511-669 277 Fax: 511-669 200
Inhaber Stefan Trhal
Artforms: solo instrumentalists, orchestras *Comments:* orchestra tours

La Gala – Internationale Kulturprojekte
Postfach 300808, 50778 **Köln**
Tel: 221-550 4315 Fax: 221-955 3508
E-Mail: lagalaint@aol.com
manager Annette Meisl
Artforms: street theatre, music groups from Spain, Latin America and Turkey *Comments:* see also Promoters

Lore-M. Schulz – International Artists Management
Zittelstraße 8, 80796 **München**
Tel: 89-308 7092 Fax: 89-308 7093
E-Mail: loreschulz.artists@t-online.de
director Lore-M. Schulz
Artforms: opera & concert singers, conductors, instrumentalists *Comments:* worldwide

Lothar Stein Management
Am Rothenbüsch 3, 66113 **Saarbrücken**
Tel: 681-73854 Fax: 681-730 165
Inhaber Lothar Stein
Artforms: soloists, choirs and presenters, show programmes, personal management

MamaConcerts & Rau GmbH
Rosenheimer Str. 145E, 81671 **München**
Tel: 89-992 9220 Fax: 89-9929 2222
Internet: www.mamaconcerts.de
E-Mail: mcr@websale.de
Geschäftsführer Marcel Avram, Mario M. Mendrzycki
Artforms: mainly rock, pop, jazz, singer-songwriters
Comments: concert management, tour organiser; see also Promoters

Management Erika Goldschmidt
Zähringer Str. 33, 10707 **Berlin**
Tel: 30-323 6294 Fax: 30-323 9399
Inhaberin Renate Landkammer
Artforms: drama – actors/actresses for film, TV and stage *Comments:* worldwide

Mannheimer Concert Direktion
Postfach 121241, 68063 **Mannheim**
Tel: 621-26908 Fax: 621-26909
künstlerische Leitung Klaus Hoffmeister
Artforms: classical concerts *Comments:* alternative address: N3. 10, 6816 Mannheim

Margaretha Jansen
Hans Schulten Str. 14, 51109 **Köln**
Tel: 221-844 290 Fax: 221-844 290
Inhaberin Magaretha Jansen; Ansprechpartner Kurt Jansen
Artforms: jazz and swing artists *Comments:* personal management

Marguerite Kollo Bühnenvermittlung
Rüsternallee 19, 14050 **Berlin**
Tel: 30-3010 0014 Fax: 30-3010 0015
Inhaberin Marguerite Kollo
Artforms: opera and operetta singers, music theatre, concerts *Comments:* international stage arrangements/negotiator

Media Management March
Hochstadenstr 23, 50674 **Köln**
Tel: 221-239 346 Fax: 221-9212 3625
director Karl-Heinz March
Artforms: cabaret, Kleinkunst, theatre

MediArte Musik – und Medienkonzepte GmbH
Theodorstraße 100, 40472 **Düsseldorf**
Tel: 211-942 710 Fax: 211-942 7122
Internet: www.mediarte.com
E-Mail: info@mediarte.de
contact Markus Hintz
Artforms: music productions, concert management
Comments: hire of video-systems; production of recorded media; music & media production, DVD consulting

Münchner Konzertdirektion Hörtnagel GmbH
Postfach 860520, 81632 **München**
Tel: 89-982 9280 Fax: 89-9829 2833
E-Mail: konzert@hoertnagel.de
Geschäftsführer Georg Hörtnagel
Artforms: conductors, solo instrumentalists, quartets, ensembles, orchestras, chamber orchestras *Comments:* visiting address: Neufahrnerstr. 23, 81679 München; see also Promoters

Music Concept
Brunnerstr. 4a, 85540 **Haar**
Tel: 89-4620 0676 Fax: 89-4620 0677
E-Mail: cvmutius@compuserve.com
contact Catherine von Mutius, Anne de Wael (chamber music), Monika Rebuschat
Artforms: management services for artists and organisations, early music, instrumental and vocal ensembles, orchestras, chamber music
Comments: 2nd address: Monika Rebuschat, Grünstrasse 75, 51063 Köln, Tel/Fax: 221-620 1882; 3rd address: Anne de Waël, Kunzweg 21, 81243 München, tel: 89-834 6294, fax: 89-834 2550

Music Contact Rainer Zellner
Saarstr 8, 72070 **Tübingen**
Tel: 7073-2250 Fax: 7073-2134
Internet: www.musiccontact.com
E-Mail: zellner@musiccontact.com
contact Rainer Zellner
Artforms: folk, blues, gospel, world music, roots music
Comments: production, tours, publishing

Norddeutsche Konzertdirektion Melsine Grevesmühl
Postfach 310265, 27538 **Bremerhaven**
Tel: 471-88068 Fax: 471-88060
Internet: www.grevesmuehl.de
E-Mail: grevesmuehl@t-online.de
Inhaber Melsine and Wolgang Grevesmühl
Artforms: solo instrumentalists, conductors, music and orchestras, choirs, ballet, pantomime, etc.
Comments: visiting address-Triftstrasse 11, 27580 Bremerhaven; concert management; concerts and ballet events; see also Promoters

Odeon Concertagentur Reinhard Söll
Schenkendorfstr. 9, 93049 **Regensburg**
Tel: 941-296 000 Fax: 941-296 0019
Internet: members.aol.com/odeonrgbg/homepage.htm
E-Mail: odeonrgbg@aol.com
Inhaber Reinhard Söll; Mitarbeiterin Kerstin Katz
Artforms: chamber music, solo recitals, orchestras
Comments: 26 concerts; concert management; see also Promoters

Opern- und Konzertagentur Monika Bundschu
Tal 15, 80331 **München**
Tel: 89-2916 1663 Fax: 89-2916 1667
Inhaberin Monika Bundschu
Artforms: singers, conductors, directors
Comments: personal management

Opernagentur Inge Tennigkeit
Kempener Str. 4, 40474 **Düsseldorf**
Tel: 211-516 0060 Fax: 211-5160 0616
Artforms: soloist singers for opera
Comments: represents singers for music theatres and concerts

Opernagentur Lore Blümel
Postfach 1725, 82159 **Gräfelfing**
Tel: 89-859 3864 Fax: 89-859 3759
E-Mail: opkoag-bluemel@t-online.de
Inhaberin Lore Blümel
Artforms: singers, conductors, stage and costume designers, directors *Comments:* visiting address: Pasinger Str. 28, 82152 Planegg; artistic advisor of Schloßkonzerte Neuschwanstein

outsider music consulting
Taunusstr. 5i, 65396 **Walluf**
Tel: 6123-990 990 Fax: 6123-990 991
Internet: www.outsider-music.de
E-Mail: outsider-music@t-online.de
Inhaber Raimund Werner
Artforms: instrumentalists, chamber music, symphony orchestra, all types of music
Comments: classical and jazz music, chanson

Paradise Media
PO Box 112140, 86046 **Augsburg**
Tel: 821-33336 Fax: 821-33309
Internet: www.paradise.de
E-Mail: info@paradise.de
managing director Hubert G Feil
Artforms: performing arts (musical, music, theatre)
Comments: also works as arts management consultancy

PARR – Art Consulting
Guerickestr. 49, 23566 **Lübeck**
Tel: 451-609 2121 Fax: 451-609 2121
Geschäftsführer Dr Thomas Parr
Artforms: orchestras, ballet, theatre, dance *Comments:* art consultancy and management/marketing for theatres, orchestras, dance and ballet

all-stars
Bang on a Can
"radical...
demands to be heard"
The Guardian, London
Contact: Kenny Savelson, Bang on a Can, 222 East 5th Street #12, New York, NY 10003.
Phone 212.777.8442. Fax 212.388.1727. E-Mail Bangcan@aol.com

Persona Musica Karin Wylach
Johann-Michael-Fischer Str. 27a, 86911 **Dießen**
Tel: 8807-929 610/11 Fax: 8807-929 617
E-Mail: kwylach@t-online.de
Inhaber Karin Wylach; orchestral tours, sales Britta Meissner, Konstanze Wunderlich
Artforms: orchestras, soloists

Personal Artists Management Gudrun Rohrbach
Sierichstrasse 99, 22299 **Hamburg**
Tel: 40-488 147 Fax: 40-480 1247
E-Mail: pamhamburg@compuserve.com
Inhaberin Gudrun Rohrbach
Artforms: soloist singers for operas and concerts
Comments: national, international

Peter Seyfferth Artists Management
Walsroder Straße 148,
30853 **Langenhagen/Hannover**
Tel: 511-739 330 Fax: 511-739 332
Internet: www.seyfferth.de
E-Mail: PSeyfferth@gmx.net
director Peter Seyfferth
Artforms: singers, conductors, management for opera and concerts worldwide, personal management of a small number of artists

Philippe Rives
Weisetrasse 46, 12049 **Berlin**
Tel: 30-6270 5136 Fax: 30-6270 5136
contact Philippe Rives
Artforms: physical street and stage performances, festivals, events, indoor-outdoor
Comments: management for Philippe Rives and artists or companies colloaborting on the same projects; international tours

PMI Paradise Management International
Nachtigallenstr. 36, 63263 **Neu-Isenburg**
Tel: 6102-52696 Fax: 6102-52696
director R Klug
Artforms: all types of classical (soloists, ensembles and orchestras) and pop music

PODIUM KONZERT
Ahrensfelder Weg 32A, 22927 **Großhansdorf**
Tel: 4102-61781 Fax: 4102-61997
director Horst Phillipp Langeloh
Artforms: jazz, (swing) orchestras *Comments:* member of Verband der Deutschen Konzertdirektionen

PR2 classic
Kreuznacher Str. 63, 50968 **Köln**
Tel: 221-381 063 Fax: 221-383 955
E-Mail: PR2classic@aol.com
Inhaberin Gabriele Schiller; Mitarbeiter Eva Luise Roth, Ulrike Jessel
Comments: management and PR service for orchestras, artists and projects

Praeger & Meier GmbH
Schnoor 15, 28195 **Bremen**
Tel: 421-336 870 Fax: 421-336 8710
Geschäftsführer Hermann J. Pölking-Eiken
Artforms: classical music
Comments: see also Promoters

Privatsekretariat Cornelia Rothkegel-Hartke
Dinklager Str. 33, 49393 **Lohne**
Tel: 4442-73367 Fax: 4442-73174
Inhaberin Cornelia Rothkegel-Hartke
Artforms: management for soloists and chamber music ensembles

Pro Arte Frankfurter Konzertdirektion GmbH & CoKG
Staufenstraße 4, 60323 **Frankfurt am Main**
Tel: 69-971 2400 Fax: 69-9712 4040
E-Mail: fed-proarte@t-online.de
Geschäftsführer Gerd Reul; Künstlermanagement Melanie von Finckenstein
Artforms: symphony & chamber orchestras, instrumental soloists,
Comments: personal management and organisation of orchestral tours in Germany; see also Promoters

Raddatz Concerts
Burgunder Strasse 4, 79104 **Freiburg/Breisgau**
Tel: 761-23380 Fax: 761-554 862
contact Therese Raddatz
Artforms: instrumentalists, ensembles and orchestras
Comments: organise competitions including Internationaler Violinwettbewerb Ludwig Spohr (triennial 2000); Internationaler Max Reger Wettbewerb für Kammermusik (triennial 2002) and Festival Wolfgang Marschner (annual); annual master classes in Sondershausen/Weimar in cooperation with the Loh-Orchester Sondershausen;
see also Competitions and Promoters

Rafael Concerts GmbH
Frauenberg 4, 97980 **Bad Mergentheim**
Tel: 7931-9790-0 Fax: 7931-979 020
E-Mail: Rafael.Concerts@t-online.de
director Rafael Brown
Artforms: international productions of opera

Reinald Heissler – Remy Theateragentur
Drakestrasse 2, 40545 **Düsseldorf**
Tel: 211-578 051 Fax: 211-553 498
E-Mail: remyagent@t-online.de
Korrektur Neill Thornborrow
Artforms: opera, concerts

Rita Kurzbach – Agentur für Bühne und Literatur
Reinickendorfer Str. 121, 13347 **Berlin**
Tel: 30-465 7326 Fax: 30-465 6550
Inhaberin Rita Kurzbach
Artforms: theatre, dance-theatre *Comments:* negotiation of complete productions; some individual artists; national and international

Salten Gastspiele
Postfach 90, 67114 **Limburgerhof**
Tel: 6236-67811 Fax: 6236-8731
Inhaberin Lilo Salten
Artforms: theatre, soloists, instrumentalists *Comments:* visiting address- Beuthener Strasse 5, 67117 Limburgerhof; see also Promoters

Shaksfin & Company GmbH
Torgauer Strase 27, 28215 **Bremen**
Tel: 421-375 507 Fax: 421-375 508
E-Mail: shaksfin@ibm.net
manging directors Hannes Nimpuno, Michael Dremler
Artforms: classical music, jazz, world music, dance, theatre *Comments:* arts producer and marketing team, arts consultancy; see also Promoters

Shooter Promotions & Classics GmbH
Gartenstr. 6, 60594 **Frankfurt am Main**
Tel: 69-610 9390 Fax: 69-6109 3988
E-Mail: 101565.2526@compuserve.com
Geschaftsführer Willi Engelhorn;
coordinator Christa Wenzl
Artforms: various types of performing arts *Comments:* international tour organiser; alternative E-mail: shooterPromotions@t-online.de

Show Tops
Osterstrasse 26, 30159 **Hannover**
Tel: 511-301 8560 Fax: 511-3018 5630
Inhaber Klaus Ritgen
Artforms: classical music, rock, pop, ballet, techno, events *Comments:* see also Promoters

Siegfried König – Musik u. Showmanagement
Von-Eltz-Str. 4, 56072 **Koblenz**
Tel: 261-24705/24787 Fax: 261-23304
E-Mail: siegfriedkoenig@redseven.de
Inhaber Siegfried König
Artforms: soloists/musicians for gala concerts
Comments: PR agency

Sigrid Rostock Bühnen- und Konzertagentur
Eugen-Schönhaar-Str. 1, 10407 **Berlin**
Tel: 30-425 7514 Fax: 30-423 9136
Artforms: singers for opera, operetta and concerts

Silvana Sintow-Behrens International Promotions
Düsseldorfer Strasse 54A, 10707 **Berlin**
Tel: 30-881 2026/883 6169 Fax: 30-882 5119
Internet: www.classicalia.com
E-Mail: silvana@classicalia.com
artists promotion manager Silvana Sintow-Behrens
Artforms: singers, conductors and instrumentalists

Simane Musikmanagement
Fritz-Frey-Straße 6, 69121 **Heidelberg**
Tel: 6221-408 062 Fax: 6221-408 063
Internet: www.simane.de
E-Mail: musikmanagement@simane.de
director Michaela Simane
Artforms: soloists, chamber orchestras, symphony orchestras, opera, ballet

Solisten Agentur Berlin Werner Blanke
Mierendorffplatz 13, 10589 **Berlin**
Tel: 30-344 1010 Fax: 30-344 6660
Inhaber Werner Blanke
Artforms: classical music soloists

Südwestdeutsche Konzertdirektion Stuttgart Erwin Russ GmbH
Postfach 104262, 70037 **Stuttgart**
Tel: 711-163 5311 Fax: 711-163 5330
E-Mail: sksruss@t-online.de
Inhaber Michael Russ
Artforms: all arts types (from classical to pop)
Comments: visiting address: Charlottenplatz 17, 70173 Stuttgart

Tercetto Artists Management
Rosenheimer Str. 52, 81669 **München**
Tel: 89-482 086 Fax: 89-448 9522
E-Mail: tercetto@t-online.de
contact Elisabeth Ehlers, Lothar Schacke (Germany). Per Boye Hansen (Norway)
Artforms: singers, conductors, stage directors *Comments:* a cooperation between Oslo Arts Management (Per Boye Hansen) and Künstler Sekretariat am Gasteig (Elisabeth Ehlers and Lothar Schacke) – see also separate entries

Theater- & Konzertagentur Hermann & Astrid G. Winkler
Grillparzerstr. 46, 81675 **München**
Tel: 89-470 5857 Fax: 89-470 7123
Inhaber Hermann and Astrid G. Winkler
Artforms: singers, conductors, operas, concerts, directors *Comments:* worldwide

Theateragentur Dr Carl F Jickeli
Nymphenburgerstr. 62, 80335 **München**
Tel: 89-1239 2626 Fax: 89-1239 2627
director Dr Carl F Jickeli
Artforms: artist representation of singers & conductors

Theateragentur Dr Germinal Hilbert
Maximilianstrasse 22, 80539 **München**
Tel: 89-290 747-0 Fax: 89-2907 4790
E-Mail: agentur@hilbert.de
contact Rudolf Meindl, Ingrid Krause, Frank Behrendt, Stefanie Brooks de Semlyen, Christina Sienel
Artforms: opera, concert singers, conductors, producers
Comments: worldwide

Theateragentur Glado von May
Hermann Str. 32, 60318 **Frankfurt am Main**
Tel: 69-283 347 Fax: 69-295 513
Inhaber Glado von May; Mitarbeiterin Heidi Schäfer
Artforms: opera, operetta, concerts; represents singers, conductors *Comments:* worldwide

Theateragentur Luisa Petrov
Glauburgstr. 95, 60318 **Frankfurt am Main**
Tel: 69-5970 3778 Fax: 69-597 4808
Inhaberin Luisa Petrov
Comments: represents singers & conductors for concerts and opera worldwide

Theateragentur Wolfgang Stoll
Martiusstrasse 3, 80802 **München**
Tel: 89-333 162/394 190 Fax: 89-342 674
Inhaber Wolfgang Stoll; Mitarbeiter Karl-Erich Haase
Artforms: represents opera singers for concerts and music-theatres worldwide

Timeless Music Promotion GmbH
Vredener Straße, 48703 **Stadtlohn**
Tel: 2563-4355 Fax: 2563-4356
Internet: www.wwmusic.com/timeless
Geschäftsführer W. Wigt, M. M. Wigt
Artforms: jazz, classical, etc *Comments:* see also Wim Wigt Jazz Production, Netherlands and Wim Wigt Productions, UK

Toger Media & Veranstaltungs GmbH
Otto-Heilmann-Str. 24B, 82031 **Grünwald**
Tel: 89-6491 4053 Fax: 89-6491 4055
E-Mail: info@toger.de
Inhaber Jerry Toger
Artforms: personal management for singers (pop & classic) *Comments:* also concert management and public relations

Tourneemanagement Berlin
Immanuelkirchstr. 5, 10405 **Berlin**
Tel: 30-441 5299 Fax: 30-441 5299
contact Lutz-Rainer Seidel
Artforms: classical music, soloists, chamber music ensembles, orchestras, choirs, operas, ballet, swing, jazz, big bands
Comments: emphasis on Eastern Europe

V.K.S arts promotion
Toepfergasse 6, 53489 **Sinzig**
Tel: 2636-800 380 Fax: 2636-800 380
Inhaber Thomas Rohde
Artforms: presentation of orchestra tours; touring and co-production of opera, theatre & ballet; development and direction of media campaigns; CD label 'd-trax'; consulting services

Voges Bonger Produktion
Domagkstr. 33, Haus 33c, 80807 **München**
Tel: 89-322 7685/30-862 2051
Fax: 89-322 7685/30-862 2060
Internet: www.a-zur.de/orakelplatz
E-Mail: kunstwelt.medien@a-zur.de
Leitung Bonger Voges; Assistenz der Leitung Kristijana Penava, Claudia Perera
Artforms: concept art, dance-theatre, experimental theatre, festival organisation
Comments: second address: Das Orakel von Berlin, Friedrichstraße 245-246, 10969 Berlin :

Walter Fröhlich Agentur für Neue Musik
Kirchstraße 35, 53604 **Bad Honnef**
Tel: 2224-10532/170-858 0600 (mobile)
Fax: 2224-969 821
Internet: www.neuemusik.com
E-Mail: wfroehlich@t-online.de
contact Walter Fröhlich
Artforms: contemporary music, soloists, conductors, ensembles
Comments: personal managment & promotion; also promoter of Kurhaus-Konzerte Bad Honnef

KONZERTDIREKTION HANS ULRICH SCHMID

PIANO
Leif Ove Andsnes
Emanuel Ax
Yefim Bronfman □
Richard Goode
Hélène Grimaud
Jan Gottlieb Jiracek •
Eldar Nebolsin •
Murray Perahia □
Mikhail Pletnev □
Peter Rösel
Peter Serkin
Grigory Sokolov
Mitsuko Uchida □
Mihaela Ursuleasa •
Lars Vogt □

PIANO DUO
Anthony and Joseph Paratore

VIOLIN
Joshua Bell □
Pamela Frank □
Mila Georgieva
Hilary Hahn □
Daishin Kashimoto •
Anne Akiko Meyers ••
Christian Tetzlaff •
Antje Weithaas ■
Pinchas Zukerman □

VIOLIN/PIANO
Pinchas Zukerman/Marc Neikrug □

CELLO
Clemens Hagen •
Lynn Harrell □
Yo-Yo Ma ■
Michael Sanderling •
Tanja Tetzlaff •

HARP
Jana Boušková

FLUTE
James Galway
Aurèle Nicolet •

CLARINET
Sabine Meyer •

HORN
Bruno Schneider

TRUMPET
Håkan Hardenberger •

TROMBONE
Christian Lindberg

RECORDER
Michala Petri ••

PERCUSSION
Evelyn Glennie ■

VOCAL ENSEMBLE
Singer Pur Vocal Sextet •

CHORUS
Knabenchor Hannover,
Leitung: Heinz Hennig
Wiener Sängerknaben

CHAMBER MUSIC
Academy of St. Martin in the Fields Chamber Ensemble
Berliner Barock Solisten •
Bläserensemble Sabine Meyer •
Boston Symphony Chamber Players ••
Houston Symphony Chamber Players ••
Karol Szymanowski String Quartet •
Piano Trio Jean Paul •
Menuhin Festival Piano Quartet □
Nomos String Quartet
Orion String Quartet ••
Trio di Clarone •
Trio ex aequo
Turtle Island String Quartet (Jazz) ••
Wiener Streichsextett •

CHAMBER ORCHESTRAS
Academy of St. Martin in the Fields
Concentus Musicus Wien
Freiburger Barockorchester
Guildhall Strings
Moskauer Solisten, Leitung: Yuri Bashmet
Philharmonia Prag
Saint Paul Chamber Orchestra ••
Scottish Chamber Orchestra
Sinfonia of England
Tafelmusik Baroque Orchestra Toronto
Wiener Kammerorchester
Württembergisches Kammerorchester Heilbronn*
Leitung: Jörg Faerber

CONDUCTORS
George Alexander Albrecht •
Marc Albrecht •
Tetsuro Ban •
Myung-Whun Chung
Thomas Dausgaard
Andrew Davis
Sir Colin Davis
Andreas Delfs ••
Hans Drewanz •
Vladimir Fedosseyev
Michael Gielen
Jahja Ling ••
Shao-Chia Lü ○
Sir Neville Marriner
George Pehlivanian ••
Gennady Roshdestvensky
Kurt Sanderling □
Stefan Sanderling •
Gerard Schwarz
Leonard Slatkin □
Bruno Weil
Massimo Zanetti •
David Zinman

ORCHESTRAS

Academy of St. Martin in the Fields
Atlanta Symphony Orchestra ••
BBC Philharmonic Orchestra
BBC Symphony Orchestra
BBC National Orchestra of Wales
Boston Symphony Orchestra ••
Bournemouth Symphony Orchestra
Budapest Festival Orchestra
Cleveland Orchestra *
Danish National Radio Symphony Orchestra
Detroit Symphony Orchestra ••
Frankfurt Radio Sinfonieorchester
Helsinki Philharmonic
Houston Symphony Orchestra ••
Indianapolis Symphony Orchestra ••
Japan Philharmonic Orchestra ••
London Philharmonic Orchestra
London Symphony Orchestra
Los Angeles Philharmonic *
Minnesota Orchestra ••
National Arts Centre Orchestra of Canada ••
National Symphony Washington ••
NDR Sinfonieorchester Hamburg
New York Philharmonic Orchestra ••
NHK Symphony Orchestra Tokyo ••
Orchester der Beethovenhalle Bonn
Orchestre Nationale du Capitole de Toulouse
Orchestre de Paris
Orchestre Symphonique de Montréal ••
Orquesta Ciudad de Granada
Orquesta Sinfonica de Galicia
Osaka Philharmonic Orchestra ••
Philadelphia Orchestra ••
Pittsburgh Symphony Orchestra ••
Residentie Orkest Den Haag
Royal Philharmonic Orchestra London
Saint Louis Symphony Orchestra ••
San Francisco Symphony ••
Schwedisches Rundfunk Symphonieorchester
Slowenische Philharmonie
Sydney Symphony Orchestra ••
Tonhalle-Orchester Zürich
Wiener Symphoniker

WORLD-WIDE GENERAL MANAGEMENT

in cooperation with Van Walsum Management London

Göteborger Symphoniker
Toronto Symphony Orchestra

SOPRANO

Susan Anthony *
Karine Babajanyan •
Carole FitzPatrick *
Olga Guriakowa ○
Linda Hohenfeld ••
Camilla Nylund *
Marlis Petersen *
Elisabeth Scholl •
Hanna Dóra Sturludóttir ○

MEZZO / ALTO

Annette Elster ○
Maria Ferencik *
Carola Guber *
Barbara Hölzl *
Christiane Iven ○
Gerhild Romberger *
Nathalie Stutzmann ○
Marianna Tarasova *

Altus

Henning Voss *

TENOR

Andreas Karasiak *
Jan Kobow •
Michael Nowak ○
Lothar Odinius •
Marcus Ullmann *

BARITON

Wilhelm Hartmann *
Hanno Müller-Brachmann •
Sebastian Noack •
Thomas Quasthoff •
Andreas Scheibner *
Wolfgang Schöne ○
Yaron Windmüller •

BASS

Marek Gasztecki •
Hans Griepentrog •

DIRECTORS

Thomas Kiemle •
Anthony Pilavachi •

- • General Management
- •• Europe
- □ Germany, Austria
- ■ Germany, Austria, Switzerland
- ○ Germany and other countries
- * special projects
- △ in cooperation with Van Walsum Management London

Except where indicated artists and ensembles are represen-ted in Germany only.

ARTISTS LIST SEASON 1999/2000

Konzertdirektion Hans Ulrich Schmid
P.O. Box 16 67 · D-30016 Hannover · Schmiedestraße 8
30159 Hannover/Germany · Phone +49 511 366 07 - 27/60
Fax +49 511 366 07 - 34 · E-Mail: Mail@KDSchmid.de

UK Office: 4 Addison Bridge Place · London W14 8XP
Phone +44 (0) 20 7602 3648 · Fax +44 (0) 20 7602 3780
E-Mail: kds_uk@vanwalsum.co.uk

4 Addison Bridge Place London W14 8XP England
Telephone +44 (0) 20 7371 4343
Fax +44 (0) 20 7371 4344
E-Mail vwm@vanwalsum.co.uk

The Company, now in its 25th year, was established with the sole aim of achieving excellence in **the international management of artists.** From modest beginnings, we now have 23 staff whilst maintaining a relatively small list of 39 artists, including an increasingly significant number of singers (see opposite page). In addition to our artist management work we are active worldwide as follows:

- We have started to represent **composers** including Mark-Anthony Turnage and Marc-André Dalbavie, promoting their work in collaboration with their publishers
- We have a thriving **Orchestral Touring Department** which lists over 80 orchestras in its client portfolio (past and present) including Czech Philharmonic, Finnish Radio, London Philharmonic, Los Angeles Philharmonic, Les Musiciens du Louvre, NDR Hamburg, The Philharmonia, Royal Concertgebouw, Russian National, Vienna Philharmonic and many others
- We represent **worldwide** Gothenburg Symphony*, Stockholm Chamber, Swedish Radio, Toronto Symphony*, and in Europe, Orpheus*
- Together with Konzertdirektion Hans Ulrich Schmid we present **concert series** with partners in Berlin, Lucerne and Paris
- We are active in **Sponsorship** and **Public Relations**
- We create, develop and organise **Special Projects** such as the recent *Clocks and Clouds* which ran for two years and celebrated the life and work of György Ligeti. The project, presented in conjunction with Sony Classical and the Philharmonia Orchestra, conducted by one of our artists Esa-Pekka Salonen, won major awards. *Clocks and Clouds* encompassed a huge number of symphonic and operatic performances, in London, Brussels, Paris, Frankfurt, Madrid, Salzburg Festival and Tokyo with a host of ancillary events such as chamber music, films, education projects and an exhibition.

* in co-operation with Konzertdirektion Hans Ulrich Schmid

Visit our website

www.vanwalsum.co.uk

Artist Management

Orchestral Tours

Project Management

Composers

Marc-André Dalbavie*	*Worldwide*
Matthias Pintscher*	*Worldwide*
Mark-Anthony Turnage*	*Worldwide*

Conductors

Kristjan Järvi	*Worldwide*
David Jones	*Worldwide*
Stefan Karpe	*Worldwide*
Stephen Kovacevich	*Worldwide*
Marc Minkowski	*Worldwide*
Kent Nagano	*Worldwide*
Matthias Pintscher	*Worldwide*
Esa-Pekka Salonen	*Worldwide*
Jukka-Pekka Saraste	*Worldwide*
Joseph Swensen	*Worldwide*
Michael Tilson Thomas	*Europe*
Ilan Volkov	*Worldwide*
Hugh Wolff	*Europe*

Piano

Imogen Cooper	*Worldwide*
François-Frédéric Guy	*Worldwide*
Stephen Kovacevich	*Worldwide*
Ivan Moravec**	*Europe*
Mitsuko Uchida	*Worldwide*

Violin

Salvatore Accardo	*Worldwide*
Karen Gomyo	*Europe*
Raphael Oleg	*Worldwide*
Mark Steinberg	*Worldwide*
Matthew Trusler	*Worldwide*

Viola

Yuri Bashmet	*Worldwide*

String Quartet

Borodin String Quartet	*Worldwide*
Brentano String Quartet	*Europe*

Soprano

Adele Eikenes	*Worldwide*
Sally Matthews	*Worldwide*
Linda Richardson	*Worldwide*
Vivian Tierney	*Worldwide*

Mezzo Soprano

Imelda Drumm	*Worldwide*

Tenor

Pär Lindskog	*Worldwide*
Mark Padmore	*Worldwide*

Baritone/Bass-Baritone

Andrew Collis	*Worldwide*
Wolfgang Holzmair	*Worldwide*
Stephan Loges	*Worldwide*
Roderick Williams	*Worldwide*

Pianist/Broadcaster

Iain Burnside	*Worldwide*

* *Represented worldwide jointly with* ***Konzertdirektion Hans Ulrich Schmid***

** *Represented in association with* ***Cramer/Marder Artists***

We believe that the management role should be highly active, innovative and imaginative.

Our Address

Van Walsum Management Limited
4 Addison Bridge Place London W14 8XP England
Telephone +44 (0) 20 7371 4343 **Fax** +44 (0) 20 7371 4344
E-Mail vwm@vanwalsum.co.uk
Website www.vanwalsum.co.uk

Collaboration

Konzertdirektion Hans Ulrich Schmid and **Van Walsum Management,** having worked together very successfully on concert promotions and concert series throughout Europe and on orchestral tours worldwide, concluded that a pooling of resources and expertise within artist management is the way forward.

Konzertdirektion Hans Ulrich Schmid

UNITED KINGDOM

KONZERTDIREKTION
HANS ULRICH SCHMID

**Karen McDonald was employed by Konzertdirektion Hans Ulrich Schmid to open an office within Van Walsum Management. From September 1998 Karen McDonald has very successfully represented their general management artists in the UK and other territories such as Australia and Scandinavia.

Konzertdirektion Hans Ulrich Schmid (UK)
4 Addison Bridge Place, London W14 8XP
tel: +44 (0)20 7602 3648
fax: +44 (0)20 7602 3780
email: kds_uk@vanwalsum.co.uk

Karen McDonald

Van Walsum Management

DEUTSCHLAND

In September 1999 Van Walsum Management opened an office within Konzertdirektion Hans Ulrich Schmid. Bettina Mehne, the manager in charge, represents Van Walsum Management's artists in Germany.

Van Walsum Management (Deutschland)
Schmiedestrasse 8, 30159 Hannover
tel: +49 (0) 511 366 0723
fax: +44 (0) 511 366 0724
email: vwm@kdschmid.de

Bettina Mehne

Both managers are in a position to draw on the wide base of contacts and experience of the respective Artist Management Departments. The offices are now technologically linked which means there is instant access to information including artist's availability.

VISIT OUR WEBSITES
www.vanwalsum.co.uk
www.kdschmid.de

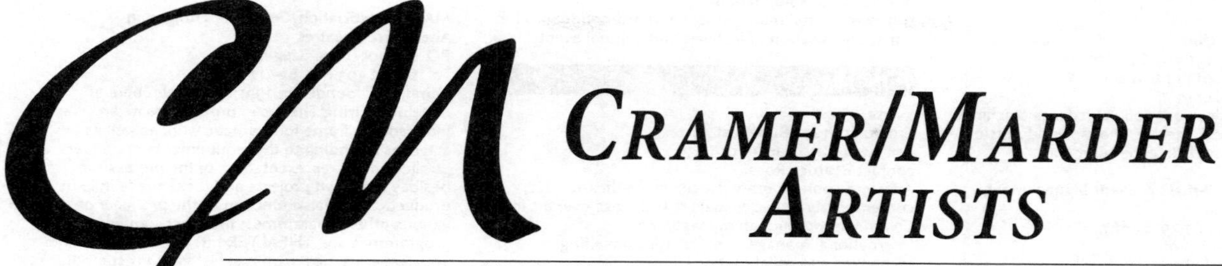

Representing

JEAN-PHILIPPE COLLARD, PIANIST[2]

ALAN FEINBERG, PIANIST[1]

HORACIO GUTIÉRREZ, PIANIST[1]

DANIEL HEGE, CONDUCTOR[1]

ANGELA HEWITT, PIANIST[1]

STEPHEN KOVACEVICH, PIANIST[2,3]

DAVID LOCKINGTON, CONDUCTOR[1]

LOUIS LORTIE, PIANIST[1]

IVAN MORAVEC, PIANIST[1]

ELMAR OLIVEIRA, VIOLINIST[1]

AWADAGIN PRATT, PIANIST[1]

THOMAS QUASTHOFF, BASS-BARITONE[2,4]

THE TAKÁCS QUARTET[2]

MAXIMIANO VALDÉS, CONDUCTOR[1]

ANDRÉ WATTS, PIANIST[1]

[1]WORLDWIDE
[2]NORTH AMERICA
[3]IN COOPERATION WITH VAN WALSUM MANAGEMENT
[4]IN COOPERATION WITH KONZERTDIREKTION HANS ULRICH SCHMID

SELDY CRAMER
3436 Springhill Road
Lafayette, CA 94549
(across the bay from San Francisco)
TEL (925) 299-0623
FAX (925) 299-0624
E-Mail seldy@aol.com

Kari Peters
E-Mail karipeters@aol.com

LINDA MARDER
127 West 96th St., #13B
New York, NY 10025
TEL (212) 864-1005
FAX (212) 864-1066
E-Mail lymarder@aol.com

Charles Cumella
E-Mail ccumella@aol.com

www.cramermarderartists.com

Werner Kühnly Theateragentur
Wörthstrasse 31, 70563 **Stuttgart**
Tel: 711-780 2764 Fax: 711-780 4403
contact Werner Kühnly, Herta Kühnly
Artforms: classical music, vocal soloists, conductors, concert management, personal management

WiV Promotion
Frauenstr. 47, 89073 **Ulm**
Tel: 731-967 640 Fax: 731-967 6417/20
Internet: www.wiventertainment.com
E-Mail: WiVulm@aol.com
director Winfried Völklein; promotion Frederica Machinek
Artforms: jazz, classical, theatre, choirs, world music, musicals, gospel, pop, rock, entertainment

Zenaida des Aubris – Artists & Event Management
Tal 15, 80331 **München**
Tel: 89-2199 8212 Fax: 89-2916 1667
E-Mail: desaubris@aol.com
Direktor Zenaida des Aubris
Artforms: opera singers, conductors, producers, also opera productions

Zentrale Bühnen-Fernseh – und Filmvermittlung (ZBF)
Agent of State Employment Agency
Generalagentur Bonn, Villemomblerstr. 76, 53123 **Bonn**
Tel: 228-713-0
Abteilungsleiterin Ursula Geller
Artforms: actors, singers, dancers and other artists on stage, television and film in Germany and abroad *Comments:* branches: Agentur Berlin, Ordensmeisterstr. 15, 12099 Berlin, Tel: 30-757 600, Fax: 30-7576 0249; Agentur Hamburg, Kreuzweg 7, 20099 Hamburg, Tel:40-284 0150, Fax: 40-2840 1599; Agentur Hamburg (Film/Fernsehen), Jenfelder Allee 80, 22045 Hamburg, 40-6688 5400/01, Fax: 40-6688 5408; Agentur München, Leopoldstraße 19, 80802 München, 89-381 707/0, Fax: 89-381 707/38; Agentur Leipzig, Georg-Schumann-Str. 173, 04159 Leipzig, Tel: 341-580 880, Fax: 341-580 8850

GREECE (+30)

Art and Music Centre
Varvaki 10, 11474 **Athens**
Tel: 1-643 7392/0485 Fax: 1-644 2716
managing director Nicos Diamandis
Artforms: opera, jazz, modern, contemporary, classical and popular music *Comments:* concert promotion and tour arrangement

Formigx Concert Agency
Erechthiou 29A, 11742 **Athens**
Tel: 1-924 5323/303 Fax: 1-921 2568
director Christos Tsenes; promotion Catherine Foskolou
Artforms: classical music, concerts, Nafpliou Festival, Greek opera production, Samou Festival

Hellas Arts Club
2 Promitheos Street, Ekali, 14565 **Athens**
Tel: 1-801 2855 Fax: 1-801 9995
contact Alexandros Sofianos
Artforms: classical music, concerts, festivals

Inter Action Arts Promotion
13, Ellanikou Str., 11635 **Athens**
Tel: 1-725 9054/5 Fax: 1-725 9056
E-Mail: interart@compulink.gr
managing director Lambros K. Dinos; production manager K. Thomopoulou; assistant director Antonis Triantafilopoulos; touring division manager Maria Wienner; publicity director Orpheas Ioannou
Artforms: singers, conductors, orchestras, composers

International Music Amphictyony
Kantouni 16, 11524 **Athens**
Tel: 1-699 4521 Fax: 1-699 4520
E-Mail: nikaps@mail.otenet.gr
managing director Despina Kapsokefalou
Artforms: instrumentalists, singers,conductor, composers, chamber ensembles, orchestras, dance ensembles *Comments:* also project management (festivals, seminars), CD-production, sometimes in collaboration with others

Kritas Productions
9 Anthimou Gazi Street, 10561 **Athens**
Tel: 1-323 5295/721 3046 Fax: 1-323 7159
E-Mail: leonto@ath.forthnet.gr
public relations manager Leonidas Antonopoulos (tel/fax: 1-902 4385); president Theodore Kritas; managing director Alina Kritas

Lavris Ltd – Cultural Events Agency
3, Marasli Str., 10676 **Athens**
Tel: 1-725 8510/2 Fax: 1-725 8513
E-Mail: lavris@hol.gr
managing director Goergia Iliopoulou; artistic director Elizabeth Spyridou; production director Thomi Tsioptsia
Artforms: dance, theatre, choirs, chamber music, symphonic orchestra, ballet, music theatre, jazz, contemporary Greek music, ethnic music and blues

PrimeArt Cultural Productions Ltd
3 Hadjiyanni Mexi & Vass. Sofias Ave., 11528 **Athens**
Tel: 1-721 1414/729 3820/21 Fax: 1-729 3822
E-Mail: primeart@primeart.gr
managing director Natasha Pavlopoulou; artistic director Olga Kalogriadou
Artforms: artists' management and promotion, productions, organisation of festivals and cultural events

HUNGARY (+36)

4 Arts
Eröd u 20, 1027 **Budapest**
Tel: 1-201 6430 Fax: 1-201 6430
contact Beatrice Rossi
Artforms: contemporary dance, dance-theatre, jazz, contemporary music, visual art and cross-over art forms *Comments:* production management, International management, artistic consulting, exchanges and collaborations

Ars-in-Kom Arts and Communications Ltd
Ars-in-Kom Müvészeti és Kommunikációs Kft
Postafiók 222, 5001 **Szolnok**
Tel: 56-424 262/565 Fax: 56-424 262
director Lajos Vass
Artforms: promotes concerts, ballet and opera performances, exhibitions and festivals *Comments:* visiting address: Kossuth Lajos tér 7, 5000 Szolnok

Art Contact
Petőfi S. u. 6 1/2 m, 1053 **Budapest**
Tel: 1-118 3114/5402 Fax: 1-117 590
Kàstner Làslzó
Artforms: dancers, singers (folk, poprock, opera, jazz), music groups, orchestras

Arts and Artists
Pajtas 22, 1131 **Budapest**
Tel: 1-340 0081 Fax: 1-340 0081
director Katalin Kiricsi
Artforms: artist agency, tour arranger, concert promoter, represents soloists, ensembles

Budapest Artists Management
Somloi u. 39, 1118 **Budapest**
Tel: 1-386 6790 Fax: 1-386 6790
managing director Ildiko Gedenyi
Artforms: artists agency, concert promotion, represent soloists, orchestras, chamber groups, arramge tours

Gergely Arts Ltd.
Gergely Müvészeti Ügynökség Kft.
Hollan u 25. I/1., 1136 **Budapest**
Tel: 1-329 4064/350 0846 Fax: 1-350 0846
director Mária Gergely
Artforms: artists agency, concert promoter, tour arranger; represent soloists, chamber groups, orchestras

Hungarian Dance Art Media Centre, The
Magyar Táncmüvészeti Média Kozpont
PF 160, Ráday u. 37, 1092 **Budapest**
Tel: 1-216 8185/217 0795/120-951 2308 (mobile)
Fax: 1-217 0795
E-Mail: camddamc@hotmail.com
contact Kekési Miklos, Brigetta Funalka
Artforms: dance, theatre, opera, music *Comments:* ticketing services; see also Promoters

Hungarokoncert OSZK International Artists Agency
Hungarokoncert OSZK Országos Szorakoztatózenei Központ
Városligeti fasor 38, 1068 **Budapest**
Tel: 1-322 0641 Fax: 1-322 5669/5412
director László Szirmai; deputy director József Huszár
Artforms: artist agency, concert promotion, arranging tours; represent soloists, chamber groups, folklore, pop-rock, jazz, entertainment groups

IAG Europe
Becsi kapu ter 8, 1014 **Budapest**
Tel: 1-356 1866 Fax: 1-356 1866
director Andras Mikle
Artforms: soloists, chamber groups, orchestras, dance ensembles *Comments:* artists agency, arranging tours

Interart Festival Centre
PO Box 80, 1366 **Budapest**
Tel: 1-266 3108 Fax: 1-317 9910
E-Mail: beata@schanda.zpok.hu
director Beata Schanda
Comments: training and promotion of young musicians in the international area; visiting address: Vörösmarty tér 1, 1051 Budapest, producers of International Bartok Festival, see also Festivals

Interconcert Hungary Ltd
Vörösmarty ter 1, Room 422, 1051 **Budapest**
Tel: 1-318 4724/4664/395 5219 Fax: 1-317 9621/318 4416
directors Margit Jasper, Sandor Sallai
Artforms: representing ensembles, folklore, entertainment groups *Comments:* artist agency, arranging tours, festivals

K + P Management
Also Zoldmali 4, 1025 **Budapest**
Tel: 1-335 2367 Fax: 1-335 0969
directors Clara Kuti, Laszlo Pete
Artforms: artist agency, tour arranger, represents soloists, ensembles

MASZK Association/Center for Hungarian Alternative Theatres
PO Box 905, 6701 **Szeged**
Tel: 62-312 303 Fax: 62-312 303
Comments: founded in 1991 by the members of Anselmus Flying Theatre in order to create an independent frame for dramatic work as well as activities attending to the requirements of a wider public and the representatives of the profession; besides their own projects and those made in joint production they also function as the producer of various other programmes; the most significant programmes are: THEALTER Intern. Meeting of Free Theaters – a series of annual festivals; Prospero Books and Ariel Booklets – a project of publishing special books; see also Promoters

Ostermann Ltd.
Ostermann Kft.
Vaci 11B, 1052 **Budapest**
Tel: 1-319 2651 Fax: 1-319 2676
CEO Tamas Frank
Comments: concert promotion

Pentaton Artists & Concert Management Ltd
Pentaton Müvészeti és Koncert Ügynökség Kft
Rákóczi út 65, 1081 **Budapest**
Tel: 1-210 1249 Fax: 1-210 2792
managing director György Lórinczy
Artforms: artist agency, representing singers, soloists, opera/dance ensembles, orchestras, also concert promoters and tour arrangers *Comments:* arrange Budapesti Buscu Festival, June, annual

Sotto Voce International Artists' Management
József A. sgt. 67/A, 6720 **Szeged**
Tel: 20-583 660 Fax: 1-222 4064
Artforms: instrumentalists

Strém Concert Agency
Strém Kulturális Szolgáltató Bt
Bimbó út 75, 1022 **Budapest** II
Tel: 1-326 6152 Fax: 1-326 6152
director Kálmán Strém
Artforms: organises some 70 activities every year, including concerts and festivals *Comments:* see also Promoters

VIP Arts Management
Postafiók 447, 1537 **Budapest**
Tel: 1-302 4290/332 4816 Fax: 1-332 4816
director Teodóra Bán
Comments: promotional agency based at the State Opera House which organises the BudaFest Summer Opera and Ballet Festival; visiting address: Hajós utca 13-15, II/3, 1061 Budapest VI; see also Promoters

IRELAND Republic of (+353)

International Concert Management – ICM Artists and Tours
23 Farmleigh Avenue, **Stillorgan (Co. Dublin)**
Tel: 1-288 6251 Fax: 1-288 6251
E-Mail: icmtours@esatclear.ie
director Ashley Pringle
Artforms: singers, musicians, dance, conductors, etc *Comments:* artists represented worldwide; local and international touring arrangements for choirs, orchestras, ensembles & musicians; personal management; incoming tours, specialists in performing arts

ITALY (+39)

A.C.O.M. organizzazione conertistica internazionale
P.zza Michelangelo Buonarroti 29, 20149 **Milano**
Tel: 02-4800 1924/460 636
Fax: 02-4800 1924
Internet: tin.it/musical/luigilap
E-Mail: llpegna@tin.it
contact Luigi La Pegna
Artforms: represent 90 artists/companies including: conductors, soloists, symphony and chamber orchestras, choirs, ballets (classic, modern, folklorist), chamber music, early music, sacred music, spirituals, gospels, attractions
Comments: local manager for Italy; general manager for many soloists and ensembles (in Europe or world)

A.G.S. – Augusto Grilli Spettacoli
Via Casalborgone 16/I, 10132 **Torino**
Tel: 011-819 5803/3529
Fax: 011-819 3529/5803
Internet: www.alfateatro.it
E-Mail: grilli@alfateatro
Artforms: opera, puppets, variety, musical, operetta
Comments: see also Opera, Puppetry and Venues

Accademia Musicale Italiana – AMIT
Via G. Pezzana 21, 00197 **Roma**
Tel: 06-807 8141 Fax: 06-808 8919
E-Mail: amit@interbusiness.it
artistic director Michele Torassa;
president Federico Amati
Artforms: artists management (soloists, orchestras, choirs) *Comments:* also consultancy and event management; see also Services

Agorà
Via Friuli 51, 20135 **Milano**
Tel: 02-5518 7465/5990 1578 Fax: 02-5518 7465
artistic director Milla Sannoner; legal representative Italia Ulivieri; press officer Paola Felice
Artforms: drama *Comments:* non-profit cultural association

AGR Associati
Viale Monte Grappa 11, 20124 **Milano**
Tel: 02-2901 3282 Fax: 02-2901 9192
E-Mail: agrass@net2000.it
managing director Antonio Gnecchi Ruscone; touring department Alessandra Radice
Artforms: theatre, dance, concerts, opera
Comments: international management for performing arts, management for ballet companies, choreographers; special projects department; organise Milano Festival (q.v.)

Aldo Grompone
Via Giulia 195, 00186 **Roma**
Tel: 06-687 6495 Fax: 06-686 4605
E-Mail: aldo.grompone@agora.stm.it
titolare Aldo Grompone; assistente
Alessandra Ferrando
Artforms: dance, theatre, prose, music, visual arts
Comments: international performing arts management, productions and tours

ali / opera (agenzia lirica internazionale)
Via Piranesi 22, 20137 **Milano**
Tel: 02-718 537 Fax: 02-738 6680
Internet: www.aliopera.com
E-Mail: alipera@aliopera.com
director Italy Beatrice Ferraro; director foreign countries Günther Obwexer; office manager Laura Fassi
Artforms: opera singers, conductors and stage directors

AMC – Artists Mangement Company
Via Valverde 32, 37122 **Verona**
Tel: 045-801 4041 Fax: 045-801 4980
Internet: www.amcmusic.com
E-Mail: amc@amcmusic.com
contact Massimiliano Gugole
Artforms: music: including pianists, conductors, harpsichordists, organists, chamber orchestras, symphony orchestras, early music orchestras

AMP – Artists' Mangement & Productions
Corso di Porta Ticinese 89, 20123 **Milano**
Tel: 02-8942 0788 Fax: 02-8942 0724
E-Mail: amp@netitalia.it
managing director Ettore F. Volontieri; assistant Marianna Costantino
Artforms: singers, conductors, soloists, orchestras
Comments: also office in USA: 310 East St, #3J, New York NY 10021; Tel/Fax: +1 212-861 5603, see also MOD

Andres Neumann International s.r.l.
Via dei Cerchi N.75, 00186 **Roma**
Tel: 06-6992 3004 Fax: 06-6992 3006
E-Mail: neumann@mclink.it
titolare Andres Neumann
Artforms: drama, dance *Comments:* independent producer, management, international touring

ARIA'S
Via Josef Weingartner 4, 39012 **Merano**
Tel: 0473-200 200 Fax: 0473-222 424
E-Mail: arias@rolmail.net
titolari Novella Partacini, Alexandra Plaickner; collaboratore Davide Corghi
Artforms: opera singers, conductors, soloists, choirs

Arts Academy
Via G. A. Guattani 17, 00161 **Roma**
Tel: 06-4425 2208/2303 Fax: 06-4426 5224
Internet: www.artsacademy.com
E-Mail: artsacademy@mclink.it
direttore amministrativo Gianna Battisti; direttore artistico Francesco La Vecchia
Artforms: classical music: chamber, symphonic and choir *Comments:* concert seasons and festivals in Rome and Brazil; manage Festival del Lago; organise Musicorum Tempora in Villa Adriana – Tivoli (Roma), see Festivals

ARTSCENA
Via San Vitale n. 87, 40125 **Bologna**
Tel: 051-267 546 Fax: 051-267 546
Internet: www.geocities.com/broadway/stage/5433
E-Mail: van4573@iperbole.bologna.it
director Anna Antini La Valle
Artforms: contemporary dance and theatre, physical, visual *Comments:* management and promoter

Associazione Arena Sferisterio – Teatro di Tradizione
Via Santa Maria Della Porta, 62100 **Macerata**
Tel: 0733-261 335 Fax: 0733-261 499
Internet: www.macerataopera.org
E-Mail: macerataopera@mercurio.it
sovrintendente Claudio Orazi; direttore tecnico organizzativo Bruno Carletti
Artforms: opera, ballet, classical & symphonic concert
Comments: see also Venues

Associazione Armunia
Castello Pasquini, P.zza Della Vittoria N. 1, 57012 **Castiglioncello (LI)**
Tel: 0586-754 202/759 021 Fax: 0586-754 198
Internet: www.luda.it/Armunia
E-Mail: armunia@luda.it
presidente Massimo Marini; direttore artistico Massimo Paganelli; ufficio organizzazione Fabio Masi, Maria Grazia Ganzerli; direttore amministrativo Simone Morfini; artistic director, dance Stefania Bertolino; artistic director, theatre Francesco Niccolini
Artforms: contemporary dance and theatre, concerts, classical music

Associazione Culturale Mondoteatro
Sede Sociale, Via Montefalco n. 40, Scala B, Office N. 3, 00100 **Roma**
Tel: 06-3362 5210/335-607 8408
Fax: 06-3362 8330
E-Mail: luitan@libero.it
president & artistic director Luigi Tani
Artforms: drama
Comments: see also Drama

Associazione Teatrale Emilia Romagna
Via Giardini 466/G, 41100 **Modena**
Tel: 059-340 221 Fax: 059-342 802
Internet: www.regione.emilia-romagna.it/ater
E-Mail: rer3@nettuno.it
president Maurizio Roi; direttore Roberto Giovannardi
Artforms: dance and music, tours in Italy and abroad; courses for professionals, communication and consultancy *Comments:* see also Festivals, Promoters and Courses

Associazione Teatro di Roma
Via dei Barbieri 21, 00186 **Roma**
Tel: 06-6840 0008/687 5445 Fax: 06-8768 77396
Internet: www.teatro.roma.it
E-Mail: teatrodiroma@mail.nexus.it
presidente Walter Pedullà; direttore Mario Martone; amministrazione Filippo Vacca; produzione Antonietta Rame; attività culturali e progetti speciali Miriam Tassi; promozione Sandro Piccioni; responsabile tecnico Gino Pontini; ufficio stampa Roberta Rem
Artforms: drama *Comments:* also run two theatres; see also Venues and Promoters

Atelier Della Costa Ovest
Via Umberto I, 63, 57014 **Collesalvetti (LI)**
Tel: 0586-962 006/463 Fax: 0586-962 049
direttore artistico Paolo Pierazzini
Artforms: drama *Comments:* also organise workshops and drama courses

Atlantide Entertainment s.r.l.
Lungotevere Flaminio 62, 00196 **Roma**
Tel: 06-320 1532 Fax: 06-320 1425
administrative director Francesco Bellomo; artistic director Michele Placido; technical director
Paolo Fortini
Artforms: drama, TV
Comments: see also Promoters

Change Performing Arts
Via V. Monti 12, 20123 **Milano**
Tel: 02-4819 4494 Fax: 02-4819 5178
E-Mail: change@tin.it
directors Franco Laera, Yasunori Gunji
Artforms: theatre, dance, music *Comments:* producer of international theatre, dance and music events with – among others: Robert Wilson, Philip Glass, Peter Greenaway, Lev Dodin, Robert Lepage, Kodo, Diamanda Galas, Paco De Lucia, Maureen Fleeming, Cesc Gelabert

Christopher Axworthy
via delle Fornaci 37, 00165 **Roma**
Tel: 06-637 2294 Fax: 06-639 0578

Club il Diapason
via Parigi 16, 40121 **Bologna**
Tel: 051-237 651 Fax: 051-237 651
E-Mail: diapason@iperbole.bologna.it
contact Aldo Jani
Artforms: classical and contemporary music *Comments:* special season dedicated to guitar (concerts, recording label, musical edition), opera and lyrical

Club Senza Frontiere
via Loreta 1, 40138 **Bologna**
Tel: 051-307 883/237 661 Fax: 051-237 651
E-Mail: geo0280@iperbole.bologna.it
contact Aldo Jani, Gigi Pavani
Artforms: classical music, folk, Italian music, theatre

Compagnia Della Rancia
Via Filelfo 97, 62029 **Tolentino (MC)**
Tel: 0733-968 460/960 059 Fax: 0733-973 844
Internet: www.musical.it
E-Mail: rancia@musical.it
artistic director Saverio Marconi; administrator Bruno Borraccini; production & organisation director Michele Renzullo; marketing & communication Massimo Zenobi
Artforms: musical productions for the Italian market
Comments: see also Drama and Venues

Concerto Management
Via Roma 107, 84084 **Fisciano (SA)**
Tel: 089-958 565 Fax: 089-891 819
E-Mail: conceman@tin.it
artistic director Domenico Spetrini; assistant Lucy Stefanelli
Artforms: orchestral tours, orchestras, chamber ensembles, soloists, ballet

Coop A/Herostrato
Via Abbrescia N.97, 70100 **Bari**
Tel: 080-553 8319 Fax: 080-558 1564
Internet: www.pangeanet.it/timezones
E-Mail: timezones@pangeanet.it
president Michele Tota
Artforms: cultural events, orchestral touring, concerts
Comments: see also Festival Time Zones

CRT Artificio, Centro Ricerche Teatrali
Via Vincenzo Monti 25, 20123 **Milano**
Tel: 02-4801 7050/54 Fax: 02-4801 7077
E-Mail: artifici@tin.it
direttore Franco Laera
Artforms: national and international theatre productions

Dancers & Co – artist and company management and promotion
Alzaia Naviglio Grande 46, 20144 **Milano**
Tel: 02-5810 0501 Fax: 02-5811 1238
Internet: www.daeco.com
E-Mail: info@daeco.com
coordinator Massimo Nebuloni
Artforms: ballet and dance soloists and groups

Dell'Amore Management
Via Zeffirino Re, 2c, 47023 **Cesena**
Tel: 0547-611 690 Fax: 0547-25895
Internet: www.ejn.it/amor
E-Mail: amor@linknet.it
amministratore Carla Dell'Amore; direzione artistica Franco Dell'Amore; relazioni pubbliche Lorenza Rossi; ufficio stampa Daniela Montanari
Artforms: early music, world music, folk music, jazz, contemporary music
Comments: organise world & ethnic music festivals, management for ensembles

Duetto 2000 Srl
via Lorenzo Magalotti 6, 00197 **Roma**
Tel: 06-808 4237/4956 Fax: 06-808 4342
E-Mail: duetto@pronet.it
legale rappresentante Giuliana Gratton
Artforms: classic, modern and contemporary dance and special events for music, international theatre-dance companies *Comments:* represent among others Momix, Cullberg Ballet, Pilobolus, Compagnie Philippe Genty, Nederland Dans Theatre, Compañia Tango x2, Andaluza de danza

Edipo Management SRL
Viale Piave 37, 42100 **Reggio Emilia**
Tel: 0522-452 518 Fax: 0522-452 277
administrative & technical director Francesco Pulvirenti; public relations Monica Conti
Artforms: produce and promote opera
Comments: see also Opera

Elisa Girard
via Luciano Manara 57, 00153 **Roma**
Tel: 06-589 9479 Fax: 06-581 0245
E-Mail: v.girard@uni.net
titolare Elisa Girard; assistente Paola Federici
Artforms: classical music, symphonic, chamber, ensembles, quartets, ballet

Essevuteatro
Largo Fratelli Alinari 15, 50123 **Firenze**
Tel: 055-238 1611/289 194/230 2799
Fax: 055-238 1611
E-Mail: essevu@lam.it
director Barbara & Giovanni Vernassa
Artforms: theatre *Comments:* distribute, organise and supervise the interest of theatre companies in Toscana, E. Romagna, Veneto

Fascino – Produzione, gestione Teatro srl
Via Pietro Borsieri 20, 00195 **Roma**
Tel: 06-808 6097 Fax: 06-808 0391
E-Mail: parioli@tiscalinet.it
artistic director Maurizio Costanzo; press office Paola Rotunno
Artforms: comedy, contemporary theatre, The Maurizio Costanzo Show *Comments:* produce TV shows

Colwell Arts Management

R.R. 1, New Hamburg, Ontario, Canada N0B 2G0 Tel: (519) 662-3499 Fax: (519) 662-2777
e-mail: jcolwell@golden.net

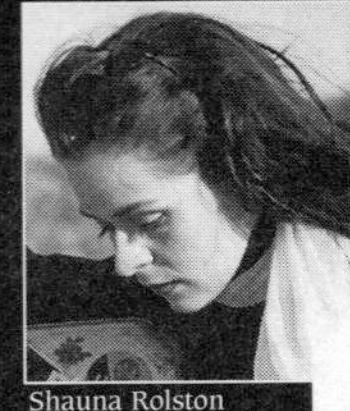
Shauna Rolston
Cello

Patrick Gallois
Gallois Quintet

SOPRANOS
Donna Brown, Karina Gauvin, Sherri Karam, Sharla Nafziger, Linda Perillo, Henriette Schellenberg, Jennie Such

MEZZO-SOPRANOS
Laura Pudwell, Paula Rockwell, Vicki St. Pierre

TENORS
Colin Ainsworth, Robert Breault, Darryl Edwards, Scot Weir

BASS/BARITONES
Marc Boucher, Simon Kirkbride

ENSEMBLES
Baroque Players of Hamilton, Blaha/Fitz-Gerald, *Piano Four Hands;*
Gallois Quintet, Laughton and O'Meara, *Trumpet and Organ;*
True North Brass, *Brass Quintet*

CABARET AND POPS
Andrew Lloyd Webber, *The man and his music;* Bernstein on Broadway;
Love Under the Lights; Masterpieces of Cabaret, *Hamelin and Applebaum;*
Naughty Ladies of the Night, Two on the Aisle

INSTRUMENTALISTS
Bernadene Blaha, *piano;* Patrick Gallois, *flute;*
Susan Hoeppner, *flute;* Stuart Laughton, *trumpet;*
Stéphane Lemelin, *piano;* Shauna Rolston, *cello;*
Piano Six

Stéphane Lemelin
Piano

Bernadene Blaha
Piano

Karina Gauvin
Soprano

Susan Hoeppner
Flute

Laughton & O'Meara
Trumpet and Organ

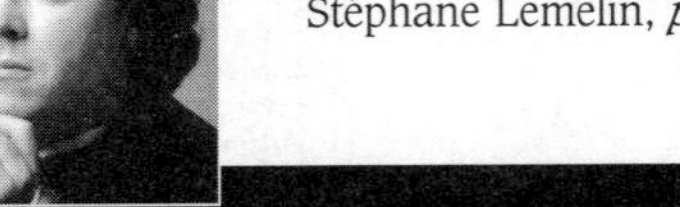
Robert Breault
Tenor

Donna Brown
Soprano

True North Brass
Brass Quintet

Member of IAMA, NAPAMA, ACO, RCCC, ASOL, ACDA, CMA, EMA, ISPA

Von Barock über Jazz...

...bis zur Moderne, wir organisieren die passende Musik zu Ihrem Anlass.

Für eine individuelle Beratung stehen wir Ihnen gerne zur Verfügung.

MiDi Music
Management GmbH

Schönbüel 11-13, CH-6072 Sachseln
Tel. +41 41 662 00 20/22, Fax + 41 41 662 00 21
http://www.swissonline.ch/midimusic e-mail: midimusic@swissonline.ch

GRAFIK IDEEAL, SACHSELN

KONZERT-DIREKTION HANS ADLER

Gegründet 1918 · Inh. Witiko Adler · Mit Erlaubnis der Bundesanstalt für Arbeit

AUGUSTE-VIKTORIA-STRASSE 64 · D-14199 BERLIN
TELEFON: (+49 30) 89 59 92-0 · TELEFAX: (+49 30) 826 35 20
e-mail: info@musikadler.de • Internet: www.musikadler.de

Dirigenten:

Claudio ABBADO
Jonas ALBER
○ Gerd ALBRECHT
Pedro ALCALDE
Takashi ASAHINA
Nikos ATHINÄOS
Daniel BARENBOIM
Piero BELLUGI
Roberto BENZI
Charles Zacharie BORNSTEIN
Alun FRANCIS
Rafael FRÜHBECK DE BURGOS
• Michail JUROWSKI
○ Ken-Ichiro KOBAYASHI
○ Jiri KOUT
Jan KRENZ
Gustav KUHN
Zubin MEHTA
Seiji OZAWA
Tommaso PLACIDI
Michel PLASSON
Donato RENZETTI
Peter SCHNEIDER
+ Wolfgang SAWALLISCH
Jerzy SEMKOW
○ Muhai TANG
Antoni WIT
• Udo ZIMMERMANN

Klavier:

Joacquin ACHUCARRO
Ken ARA
Daniel BARENBOIM
○ Elena BASHKIROWA
Horacio GUTIERREZ
* Babette HIERHOLZER
Cyprien KATSARIS
Alicia de LARROCHA
Jeremy MENUHIN
Menahem PRESSLER
Georg-Friedrich SCHENCK
• Siiri SCHÜTZ
Einar STEEN-NÖKLEBERG

Violine:

David GARRETT
Viviane HAGNER
Daniel HOPE
Martin MUMELTER
Gottfried SCHNEIDER

Viola:

Wolfram CHRIST
Barbara WESTPHAL

Cello:

Antonio MENESES

Gitarre:

Christopher PARKENING

Harfe:

Margit-Anna SÜSS

Klarinette:

Sharon KAM
Karl LEISTER

Duo:

Viviane HAGNER/Nicole HAGNER
Antonio MENESES/Nelson FREIRE
(in Zusammenarbeit mit Konzertdirektion Goette)

Kammermusik:

• ABEGG TRIO
* AMERICAN STRING QUARTET
* BEAUX ARTS TRIO
BERLINER POSAUNEN-ENSEMBLE
(Four in Hand)
• BRANDIS QUARTETT
• DRESDNER KLAVIERTRIO
KATSARIS-KLAVIERQUINTETT
• METROPOLIS-ENSEMBLE
(Bashkirowa / Carruzzo / Fuchs / Schwalke)
TRIO CHRIST / SCHULZ / SÜSS

Sopran:

Ilaria GALGANI
Celina LINDSLEY
Julia VARADY
Stella ZAMBALIS

Mezzosopran / Alt:

Regine GEBHARDT
Renée MORLOC
○ Gabriele SCHRECKENBACH

Tenor:

Reinhart GINZEL
Ernst HAEFLIGER
Werner HOLLWEG
Wieslaw OCHMAN
Kenneth RIEGEL
Endrik WOTTRICH

Bariton / Baß:

Boris CARMELI
George FORTUNE

Kammerorchester:

○ I FIAMMINGHI
(Dirigent: Rudolf Werthen)

Orchester:

DEUTSCHES SYMPHONIE-ORCHESTER BERLIN (RSO)

DRESDNER PHILHARMONIE

ISRAEL PHILHARMONIC ORCHESTRA
(Dirigent: Zubin Mehta)

NATIONAL-SINFONIE-ORCHESTER DES POLNISCHEN RUNDFUNKS KATOWICE
(Dirigent: Antoni Wit)

• RUNDFUNK-SINFONIE-ORCHESTER BERLIN
(Dirigent: Rafael Frühbeck de Burgos)

Chöre:

BERLINER KONZERT-CHOR
(Dirigent: Matthias Elger)

○ KARL-FORSTER-CHOR BERLIN
(Dirigentin: Barbara Rucha)

• PHILHARMONISCHER CHOR BERLIN
(Dirigent: Uwe Gronostay)

• Generalmanagement * Europa ○ verschiedene Länder + nur in Berlin

FirenzeMusica
via Maggio 35, 50125 **Firenze**
Tel: 055-214 705 Fax: 055-282 631
E-Mail: rcoletti@dada.it
titolari Raffaella Coletti, Silvia Ponzanelli
Artforms: classical music singers, lyric singers, orchestra conductors and directors *Comments:* alternative E-mails: ponzanel@dada.it or lberni@dada.it

Florilegio srl
Viale Africa 28, 00144 **Roma**
Tel: 348-581 7288
Internet: www.florilegio.com
E-Mail: flori@ibm.net
direttore generale Livio Togni; resp. distribuzione Italy Max Togni (tel: +33 607-642 225, email: maxo029@ibm.net); resp. distribuzione Europe Jacques Gallissaires (tel: +33 680-013 679); resp. communicazione Catherine de Bellefroid (tel: 0348-420 0757, email: mao@ibm.net)
Artforms: organise touring circus productions

Fontemaggiore soc. coop. a.r.l.
Strada delle Fratte, 06071 **Castel del Piano (PG)**
Tel: 075-528 9555/7487 Fax: 075-528 7487
Internet: www.edisons.it/homepages/fontemaggiore
E-Mail: fontemaggiore@edisons.it
direttore organizzativo Stefano Cipiciani; direttore artistico Giampiero Frondini
Artforms: drama, children's theatre *Comments:* works closely with ministries and local authorities in the production of theatrical events

Future Music
Via Federico Patetta 79, 00167 **Roma**
Tel: 06-662 1973 Fax: 06-6601 3730
Internet: www.timcompetition.org
E-Mail: info@timcompetition.org
legal representative Federico Fait; artistic director Luigi Fait
Artforms: music *Comments:* offers a number of services including artist management, co-production, festivals and competitions organisation; see also Promoters and Competitions

Gianna e Roberto Nicoletti
vicolo Monviso 1, 20010 **Canegrate (MI)**
Tel: 0331-411 142 Fax: 0331-401 515
E-Mail: studnico@box.tin.it
titolare Gianna Nicoletti
Artforms: chamber and symphonic orchestras, soloists
Comments: see also Choirs

Giordano Gabriella s.a.s.
via Settembrini 24, 20124 **Milano**
Tel: 02-2952 1391/2940 4559 Fax: 02-2940 4286
titolare Gabriella Giordano
Artforms: classical music: soloists and ensembles, chamber music *Comments:* agent for Christian Zacharias (pianist) in Italy; exclusive agent for Benedetto Lupo, Simone Pedroni, Filippo Faes and Domenico Nordio

Giuseppe Pastorello
viale Trieste 308, 93100 **Caltanissetta**
Tel: 0934-592 025/554 688 Fax: 0934-592 025
titolare dott. Giuseppe Pastorello
Artforms: symphonic, chamber, recitals, ballet, lyric, operetta, folk music *Comments:* organise Concorso Internazionale 'V. Bellini'-Caltanisetta

Innocentiis artists' management srl, de
via Frattini 18, 37121 **Verona**
Tel: 045-803 1052 Fax: 045-803 1052
E-Mail: d.i.am@iol.it
artistic director Dr. Mag. Corrado de Innocentiis
Artforms: Italian tours by national and international orchestras, choirs and soloists

Islet
via Levanna 35, 00141 **Roma**
Tel: 06-963 5572 Fax: 06-963 5664
titolare Aldo Fasano
Artforms: lyric

Italconcert s.a.s.
Via XX Settembre 20/44, 16121 **Genova**
Tel: 010-553 0574 Fax: 010-553 0574
E-Mail: italconc@tin.it
direzione artistica Giancarlo Carena; segreteria artistica e amministrazione Piergiorgio Carena, Luca Corsi
Artforms: symphony orchestras, chamber orchestras, soloists, conductors, choirs, singers, ballets (classical, modern and folk) *Comments:* organisation of music master classes and ballet stages

Laifer Artists Management
European Office, Via Madalena 45/C, 37138 **Verona**
Tel: 045-562 950 Fax: 045-562 950
director Matthew Laifer
Artforms: lyrical singers
Comments: the Italian office is going to be closed for a while, for any information contact the New York office: Tel: (+1 212) 929 7429, Fax: (+1 212) 633 2628

Link ProPoP
Via Fioravanti N.14, 40129 **Bologna**
Tel: 051-370 855 Fax: 051-370 855
Internet: www.linkproject.org
E-Mail: linkpropop@linkproject.org
coordinators Mauro Boris Borella, Enrico Croci
Artforms: electronic music, post-rock, hip-hop, drum 'n base *Comments:* see also Festivals, Venues and Promoters

Luigi Pignotti – Eventi Culturali
Via ponte Seveso 39, 20125 **Milano**
Tel: 02-6707 5207/04 Fax: 02-6707 4310
E-Mail: pignotti@tiscalinet.it
titolare Luigi Pignotti
Artforms: ballet, dance, folk, musicals, opera, flamenco

Lyric Opera Roma di A.M.Mirri
Via della Pietà 10, int. 6, 00184 **Roma**
Tel: 06-687 8894 Fax: 06-6813 6324
titolare Alberto Mirri
Artforms: opera singers

M.A.S. Juvarra (Multimedia Arte Spettacolo)
c/o Teatro Juvarra, Via Juvarra 15, 10122 **Torino**
Tel: 011-540 675 Fax: 011-517 5084
Internet: www.quiaffari.it/juvarra
E-Mail: multiteatro@tin.it
artistic director Sergio Martin; organisation director Cesare Perotti; president Luciano Capriolo; consultant Giovanna Franco
Artforms: theatre *Comments:* production team at Teatro Juvarra; see also Venues and Drama (formerly known as Cooperativa il Granserragllo)

Mario Giovanni Ingrassia
Via San Zanobi 7, 50018 **Scandicci (FI)**
Tel: 055-730 9131 Fax: 055-730 9127
E-Mail: mamusic@ats.it
director Mario Giovanni Ingrassia
Artforms: instrumental, soloists, ensembles, mainly early and contemporary music

Melodramma s.a.s.
Viale Augusto 119, 80125 **Napoli**
Tel: 081-593 2553 Fax: 081-593 3705
E-Mail: gianbisi@tin.it
titolare Giandomenico Bisi
Artforms: opera singers

Melos Art
Via Divisione Torino 139, 00143 **Roma**
Tel: 06-5051 0007 Fax: 06-501 7400
direttore Dante Mariti
Artforms: opera and classical music, productions of shows

Modena International Music
via Carlo Zucchi, 31 Scala A, 41100 **Modena**
Tel: 059-821 128 Fax: 059-821 132
Internet: www.mimsrl.it
E-Mail: mim@sirnet.it
presidente Francesco Cattini; sezione musica Antonio Convertini, Rita Zappador; sezione danza Roberta Righi; sezione lirica Nicoletta Olivieri
Artforms: classical and jazz music, soloists, ensembles, orchestras, ballet, lyric

Music Center S.n.c. di Oldani Giuseppe & Co
Viale Legioni Romane 26, 20147 **Milano**
Tel: 02-4870 2828/0258 Fax: 02-4870 0692
E-Mail: mcenter@planet.it
titolare e direttore amministrativo Giuseppe Oldani
Artforms: opera singers, orchestras, conductors

Music Promotion s.r.l.
Via Crea 59/A, 10095 **Grugliasco (TO)**
Tel: 011-309 9570 Fax: 011-309 7046
titolare Enrico Canessa
Artforms: classical music, choirs, orchestras, chamber ensembles, soloists

Musical Dorica
Frazione Massignano 66, 60021 **Camerano (AN)**
Tel: 071-801 181/336-429 164 (mobile) Fax: 071-801 235
contact Silvano Frontalini
Artforms: opera lyric, ballet, orchestras, discographic productions *Comments:* 2nd address: Musical Dorica , casella postale nr. 29, 60021 Camerano (AN); Teatro Lirico Europeo tour in Italy, United Kingdom, Germany, France, Spain

Neumann Productions S.r.l.
Via dei Cerchi, N. 75, 00186 **Roma**
Tel: 06-6992 3004 Fax: 06-6992 3006
E-Mail: neumann@mclink.it
titolare Andres Neumann
Artforms: dance, drama

O.R.I.A. Denise Petriccione
via Savoia Cavalleria 10, 20145 **Milano**
Tel: 02-466 216/239 Fax: 02-466 238
E-Mail: oriape@tin.it
titolare Denise Petriccione
Artforms: artists (classical music), orchestras, ensembles

O.R.I.A. Maria Bruzzese
Corso Sempione 40, 20154 **Milano**
Tel: 02-331 1122 Fax: 02-331 1140
E-Mail: oriabru@tin.it
titolare Maria Bruzzese
Artforms: artists (classical music), orchestras, ensembles

Opera Art s.r.l.
Via Isolalta Forette 11, 37068 **Vigasio (VR)**
Tel: 045-664 9911 Fax: 045-664 9912
E-Mail: madradi@tin.it
amministratore unico Mario Dradi; collaboratore Irene Gall, Giorgio Benati
Artforms: lyric – singers and conductors *Comments:* often have special projects

Ornella Cogliolo
via del Babuino 76, 00187 **Roma**
Tel: 06-320 7627 Fax: 06-320 7628
E-Mail: cogliolo@iol.it
titolare Ornella Cogliolo
Artforms: soloists, conductors, orchestras, choirs, singers, ensembles, chamber music, orchestra tours in Italy, contemporary music interpreters

Ouverture di Orta Leonardo & C. s.a.s.
via Claudia Braccianese 44, km 20, 00062 **Roma**
Tel: 06-998 6602 Fax: 06-998 6603
Internet: www.ouverture.net
E-Mail: info@ouverture.net
titolare Dott. Leonardo Orta; assistente Marzia Maramici; estero Franziska Kurth
Artforms: opera singers and conductors

P. Destro – Musica & Musica International Management A.S.C. sezione di Padova
Via A. Marangon 34, 35129 **Padova**
Tel: 049-628 326 Fax: 049-628 326
E-Mail: p.destro@pd.nettuno.it
direttore Pierluigi Destro
Artforms: international tours with chamber and symphonic orchestras mostly from Eastern Europe

Paola Tiberii
Via F. Carota, 5, 65125 **Pescara**
Tel: 085-417 1502 Fax: 085-415 5956
E-Mail: paola.tiberii@ntt.it
titolare Paola Tiberii
Artforms: soloists, ensembles, chamber orchestras

Plexus T. srl
Via di Vigna Murata 1, 00143 **Roma**
Tel: 06-591 9933/9867 Fax: 06-592 5522
artistic/administrative director Lucio Minunni Ardenzi; press officer Cristina Rastelli
Artforms: drama *Comments:* see also Drama

Preludio
Viale Carducci N. 18, 40125 **Bologna**
Tel: 051-342 167 Fax: 051-342 167
E-Mail: alscheda@tin.it
director Alessandra Scheda
Artforms: soloists, chamber music

Prima International Artists Management Srl
Palazzo Zambeccari, Piazza de' Calderini 2/2, 40124 **Bologna**
Tel: 051-264 056 Fax: 051-230 766
Internet: www.primartists.com
E-Mail: prima@primartists.com
direzione Angelo Gabrielli, Virginio Fedeli, Cinzia Salvioli, Elisabetta Longardi; artistic representatives Cinzia Salvioli, Elisabetta Longardi, Serena Marchi, Elis Marchi, Daniela Barbieri, Armando Nuzzo, Marco Marchesi Morselli, Giorgio Bruno, Roberto Gherardi, Valerio Tuka, David Jay
Artforms: lyric singers, soloists, conductors, stage directors, costume, set designers, chamber ensemble *Comments:* represent and promote; 200 artists represented

Pro Music srl
Via Po 43, 00198 **Roma**
Tel: 06-884 2221/18 Fax: 06-884 2222
E-Mail: promus@tin.it
titolari Sonia Quercia, Maurizio Manfrini, Auvelio Cannizzo
Artforms: dance, classical and modern music, jazz, blues

Progetti Dadaumpa srl
Via Milazzo N.5, 40121 **Bologna**
Tel: 051-252 718 Fax: 051-252 854
direttore generale Claudio Corticelli, Emanuela Frassinella; direttore organizzativo e pr Terry Cheggia
Artforms: comedy theatre, musical theatre

Progetti Toscani Associati
Borgo Albizi 15, 50122 **Firenze**
Tel: 055-248 0515/242 650 Fax: 055-247 9757
Internet: www.fabbricaeuropa.net
E-Mail: fabbrica.europa@firenze.net
responsabile settore teatro/danza/musica Maurizia Settembri, Andrés Morte
Comments: management and distribution of own productions; organisation of dance workshops and a course for cultural managers; see also Festivals and Courses

Promo Music
Via di Bertalia 21, 40131 **Bologna**
Tel: 051-634 3467 Fax: 051-634 3467
Internet: www.promomusic.com
E-Mail: promomus@tin.it
administration Marcello Maria Corvino; tour project Chiara Sirk
Artforms: early music, baroque opera, period dance with period musical instruments

Proposte Musicali
via Paolo Erizzo 5/a, 30126 **Venezia-Lido**
Tel: 041-526 3050/8868 Fax: 041-526 3050
direttore artistico Maestro Claudio Gasparoni; segretaria artistica e amministrazione d.ssa Cristina Trivelli
Artforms: chamber ensembles, singers, jazz, dance, early music ensembles, chamber orchestras with soloists *Comments:* organise concerts

Ravenna Manifestazioni
Dante Alighieri 1, 48100 **Ravenna**
Tel: 0544-249 211 Fax: 0544-36303
E-Mail: info@ravennafestival.org
president Christina Muti; artistic direction Franco Masotti
Artforms: opera, ballet, theatre, jazz, ethnic music
Comments: season of opera & ballet Nov-April; Ravenna Festival June/July

Renato Musmeci – Rappresentanze Artistiche Internazionali
Via Bongiovanni, 9b, 98039 **Taormina**
Tel: 0942-625 363/768 Fax: 0942-23751
E-Mail: remrai@tao.it
managing director Renato Musmeci
Artforms: classical music (symphonic and opera), major international orchestras, ballet, modern dance, special theatrical projects & choral groups

Resia s.r.l. – Rappresentanze e Segreterie Int. Artistiche
via Manzoni 31, 20121 **Milano**
Tel: 02-654 161/4/2/3 Fax: 02-659 7851
Internet: www.micheli.org
E-Mail: resiasrl@tin.it
titolari Patrizia Garrasi, Luisa Panarello; sezione concorsi Patrizia Garrasi, Laura Colombo, Gabriella Tabarrini
Artforms: instrumental soloists, chamber groups, conductors *Comments:* organise the Umberto Micheli International Piano Competition, and the Roberto Caruana Premio Stradivari International Cello Competition; alternative E-mails: pgarrasi@tin.it or lpanarel@tin.it

Ricercare – Progetti Artistici Internazionali
Via E. Filiberto 4, 20052 **Monza**
Tel: 039-744 703 Fax: 039-744 797
Internet: www.askesis.it/ricmus
E-Mail: ricercar@askesis.it
titolari Kim Sommerschield, Gabriella Castelli
Artforms: early/classical music, soloists, chamber ensembles, orchestras

Segnali – culture engineering
Via S. Francesco a Ripa 139, 00153 **Roma**
Tel: 06-534 3777 Fax: 06-5820 3574
E-Mail: segnali@uni.net
directors Nestor Saied, Renato Fontana
Artforms: theatre, dance *Comments:* international performing arts management, productions, tours

Solti s.n.c. di Fasano Ermanno & C
via Castagnoli, 00049 **Velletri (RM)**
Tel: 06-963 5083/6015/962 5163
Fax: 06-963 5664
administrator Ermanno Fasano; assistant administrator Rosanna Fasano; settore tecnico Manrico Fasano
Artforms: lyric impresarios

Studio Art – Performing & Fine Arts
Viale Europa 64, 06080 **Bastia Umbra (Perugia)**
Tel: 075-801 0933/348-334 9013 (mobile)
Fax: 075-801 0933
E-Mail: studioart@iol.it
contact Raniero Tazzi, Paola Castellano (mobile: 338-610 1652)
Artforms: piano, violin, string quartet, percussion, singer, vocal ensembles, early music with period instruments, chamber and symphonic orchestras, special projects *Comments:* alternative E-mails: ranierotazzi@iol.it or paolacastellano@iol.it

Torino Spettacoli
P.za Solferino 4, 10121 **Torino**
Tel: 011-562 3800 Fax: 011-562 3435
direzione artistica Germana Erba
Artforms: musical comedy, plays, classical and pop concerts, revues, operetta, cinema *Comments:* see also Venues and Promoters

Ventaglio Artists Management, Il
Via Androna 9, 37013 **Caprino Veronosa (Verona)**
Tel: 045-623 0297/348-384 2334 (mobile)
Fax: 045-623 0297
general manager Clara Corsi Ventaglio

Verona Musica of Vicia Artist Concert Management
Riva S. Lorenzo 19, 37121 **Verona**
Tel: 045-803 2085
Fax: 045-803 2085
president Dr. Giannantonio Bresciani; artistic director Dr. Giovanni Pirani
Artforms: solo instrumentalists (piano etc.), ensembles, orchestras, organises concerts and tours abroad
Comments: provide promotional materials for artists represented

Walter Beloch Artists Management Srl
via Melzi d'Eril 26, 20154 **Milano**
Tel: 02-3310 1922 Fax: 02-331 3643
E-Mail: belochartists@iol.it
director & artists managers (opera) Walter Beloch; artists manager (concerts) Daniela Rodriguez; artists managers (special events/tours) Elena Rossi, Luis Polon
Artforms: opera, concerts, ballet, conductors, special events, tours
Comments: performance production

LATVIA (+371)

Agency Riga 800
Torna 4, IB-103, 1050 **Riga**
Tel: 7-320 550 Fax: 7-320 609
Internet: www.riga800.lv
E-Mail: riga800@rcc.lv
director general Inguna Ribena
Comments: responsible for 2001 European Cultural Month in Riga (August 2001)

Latvian Concert Agency
Latvijas Koncertdirekcija
11a Kalku, 1050 **Riga**
Tel: 7-223 618/213 426 Fax: 7-213 497
artistic director Gints Karklins
Artforms: management of conductors, solo instrumentalists, singers, chamber ensembles, orchestras, touring etc.

Producer Group Remix
Remix producentu grupa
6 Stabu, 1001 **Riga**
Tel: 7-332 325 Fax: 7-821 127
director Aivars Hermanis
Artforms: pop, rock, jazz
Comments: CD, CC producing

Radio SWH
13 Skantes, 1013 **Riga**
Tel: 2-360 929 Fax: 2-782 283
program director Janis Sipkevics
Artforms: pop, rock, jazz

Service Centre Divi
Servisa centrs Divi
26/28 Peldu, PO Box 464, 1047 **Riga**
Tel: 7-227 512 Fax: 7-224 815
director Vladimirs Ikusovs
Comments: concert and show management

LIECHTENSTEIN (+423)

Artists Management Company Est
Postfach 1131, 9490 **Vaduz**
Tel: 75-232 1444 Fax: 75-232 2085
E-Mail: amc@artistsmanagement.com
directors Andreas von Bennigsen, Daniel Zulauf
Artforms: instrumental soloists, chamber music, symphony, special productions/concert management, orchestra tours

LITHUANIA (+370)

Concert Agency Litart
Koncertine Agentura Litart
Laisves al. 51a, 3000 **Kaunas**
Tel: 7-203 261 Fax: 7-706 642

Concert Agency Lithill
Koncertine agentura Lithill
Ankstoji 3, 2001 **Vilnius**
Tel: 2-220 304 Fax: 2-220 309
Internet: www.lithil.lt/
E-Mail: public@lithill.lt
director Algimantas Karaliunas

Concert Agency Partitúra
Koncertine Agentúra Partitúra
Asigalio 21-10, 3043 **Kaunas**
Tel: 7-227 500/722 726
Fax: 7-706 642
Internet: www.ultra.lt/kaunas.jazz
E-Mail: jazz@ultura.lt
director Audra Juciene

Lithuanian Concert Promoters' Association
Zemaitijos 8/11 – 222, 2001 **Vilnius**
Tel: 2-628 503 Fax: 2-220 966
contact E Zalpys
Comments: see also National Organisations and Promoters

Lithuanian National Philharmonic Society
Lietuvos nacionaline filharmonija
Ausros Vartu St. 5, 2001 **Vilnius**
Tel: 2-626 802 Fax: 2-622 859
E-Mail: info@filharmonija.lt
general director Gintautas Kevisas

Touring-Concert Company Arks
Turistine-Koncertine Firma Arks
PO Box 1272, 2056 **Vilnius**
Tel: 2-769 660 Fax: 2-221 456

LUXEMBOURG (+352)

artevents Ltd
129 Mühlenweg, 2155 **Luxembourg**
Tel: 492 924 Fax: 492 884
E-Mail: rfranck@pt.lu
directeur Rémy Franck
Artforms: classical music

Bureau de Concerts Jacques Mauroy s.a. r. l.
19 rue des Primevères, 2351 **Luxembourg**
Comments: see entry in Belgium

MACEDONIA (+389)

Koncertna agencija Mak-Art – Skopje
Nikola Grceto 6/15, **Skopje**
Tel: 1-611 051 Fax: 1-117 867

MONACO (+377)

Bureau de Concerts Pierre-Edouard Ornella
49 rue Plati, 98000 **Monte Carlo**
Tel: 9315 0444 Fax: 9315 9484
directeur Pierre-Edouard Ornella
Artforms: symphony orchestra, opera, chamber orchestra, baroque music *Comments:* works in France, Italy, Spain, Portugal

Old and New Monte Carlo
Villa Amphion, 18, Rue Suffren Reymond, 98000 **Monaco**
Tel: 9350 2499 Fax: 9350 3185
E-Mail: oldandnew@meditnet.com
managing director Valentin Proczynski
Artforms: new productions, tour orchestras, other ensembles

Vivienne H. Taylor
Le Soleil D'Or, 20, Boulevard Prince Rainier III, 98000 **Monaco**
Tel: 9315 0381/680-862 410 Fax: 9216 0245
E-Mail: vtaylor@monaco.mc
Comments: secretariat and other services for a small group of internationally based artists

NETHERLANDS (+31)

Accolade Theaterproducties
Amstel 57, 1018 EJ **Amsterdam**
Tel: 20-622 6094 Fax: 20-622 6094
director Luisa Treves; manager Felix Guttmann
Artforms: theatre
Comments: producing British & American plays, promoting Dutch plays

Amstel Artists Muziekprodukties
Ruysdaelkade 155, 1072 AS **Amsterdam**
Tel: 20-670 9953 Fax: 20-670 9953
E-Mail: amartists@capitolonline.nl
director Jelle Kikkert
Artforms: classical musicians, soloists and ensembles, special projects, cultural travel

Ariëtte Drost Artists Representative
Prins Bernhardweg 18, 6862 ZH **Oosterbeek**
Tel: 26-339 0187 Fax: 26-334 1349
director Ariëtte Drost
Artforms: soloists (instrumental and vocal), chamber music groups, conductors

ARMA Artists Management
Amstel 272, 1017 AM **Amsterdam**
Tel: 20-622 3227 Fax: 20-622 3228
director Johan Jongerbloed
Artforms: conductors, some instrumentalists

Artists & Events Stef Arntz
Oostenburgervoorstraat 88, 1018 MR **Amsterdam**
Tel: 20-625 2198 Fax: 20-639 2758
directors Stef Arntz, Wouter de Boer
Artforms: variety, circus and music events, street theatre, comedy shows, music, dance-theatre

Artists Management Pieter G Alferink Amsterdam BV
Apollolaan 181, 1077 AT **Amsterdam**
Tel: 20-664 3151 Fax: 20-675 2426
E-Mail: alferink@worldonline.nl
director/manager Pieter G. Alferink; artists manager Helga Blaimschein
Artforms: singers, conductors
Comments: see also National Organisations (Netherlands Federation of Concert Agents)

Bureau Berbee, Culturele Affaires
Karle Leidsedwasstraat 12, 1017 RC **Amsterdam**
Tel: 20-627 0455 Fax: 20-625 0616
director Inke Berbee
Artforms: mime, dance *Comments:* see also Promoters, Dance, Drama (Karina Holla)

Charles Aerts Theatre Productions Int bv
Valeriusplein 20, 1075 BH **Amsterdam**
Tel: 20-673 2285 Fax: 20-671 1215
managing director Raymond Aerts
Artforms: singers, ballet companies, theatre companies, contemporary music, business events

Concertdirectie Samama & Co bv
Weteringschans 130, 1017 XV **Amsterdam**
Tel: 20-421 1611 Fax: 20-421 1747
E-Mail: concertdirectie@samama.nl
managing director Niels Veenhuijzen; artists manager Liesbeth Kok; assistant director Esther van Helvoort
Artforms: conductors, soloists and chamber music ensembles, orchestral touring, sponsored series, festival management *Comments:* world wide operations, orchestral touring, special projects, recordings, management, organisation and artistic consultancy for festivals, recording companies, radio, orchestras

Concertmanagement Rob Groen
W G Plein 206, 1054 SE **Amsterdam**
Tel: 20-616 8096 Fax: 20-616 9652
managing director Rob Groen
Artforms: classical music soloists, conductors, orchestras *Comments:* organise tours, concerts and series in Het Concertgebouw (q.v.)

Egmond Film and Television
Potgierenstraat 38, 1053 XX **Amsterdam**
Tel: 20-589 0909 Fax: 20-589 0901
E-Mail: egmondnl@xs4all.nl
sales/marketing Gerard Cornelisse; producer Hans de Weers; develop. Hans de Wolf; legal/finance Bert Nijdam
Artforms: film & television

Euro Stage – promotion production consultancy
Enterpôtdok 78-78a, 1018 AD **Amsterdam**
Tel: 20-620 6556 Fax: 20-623 7951
E-Mail: info@eurostage.nl
managing director Peter Ultee; production manager Carina Heynens
Artforms: opera, ballet, African shows and musicals
Comments: Euro Stage is one of the biggest opera producers in Europe and specialist in African shows

Grunfeld Theaterproducties
Prins Hendrikkade 169-170, 2nd level, 1011 TC **Amsterdam**
Tel: 20-626 0350 Fax: 20-638 3266
E-Mail: info@grunfeld.a2000.nl
senior administration Robert-Jan Grünfeld; pr & publicity Barbara Ennik; finance Lorena Bernardi
Artforms: theatre, cabaret, dance, soloists and ensembles, musicals

Harry Kies Theaterprodukties
Steenschur 17, 2311 ES **Leiden**
Tel: 71-513 3985 Fax: 71-512 6790
Internet: www.harrykies.nl
E-Mail: kies@harrykies.nl
director Harry Kies
Artforms: theatre office
Comments: booking agency; organise cabaret festivals, TV productions

Herzberger Artists
t Woud 1, 3860 PM **Nijkerk**
Tel: 342-472 255 Fax: 342-475 275
director Marianne Herzberger
Artforms: classical musicians, conductors, soloists, singers

Hummelinck Stuurman Theaterbureau
Da Costakade 190A, 1053 XG **Amsterdam**
Tel: 20-616 4004 Fax: 20-612 4341
Internet: www.xs4all.nl/~humstu
E-Mail: Humstu@xs4all.nl
contact Diederick Hummelinck, Arjen Stuurman
Artforms: theatre, drama, cabaret, children's theatre

Impresariaat Frans van Bronkhorst
PO Box 1024, 1200 BA **Hilversum**
Tel: 35-621 7248 Fax: 35-623 1768
E-Mail: impresariaat@speed.a2000.nl
director Frans van Bronkhorst
Comments: produce plays, manage singers, ballet companies, opera

Impresariaat Gislebert Thierens bv
Jan Luykenstraat 21, 1071 CJ **Amsterdam**
Tel: 20-675 0966 Fax: 20-679 8000
director G Thierens
Artforms: mainly theatre productions, some actors management
Comments: produce drama, theatre, musicals, cabaret, organise tours for foreign dance companies

Impresariaat Jacques Senf en Partners
Postbus 42, 3155 ZG **Maasland**
Tel: 10-592 3155 Fax: 10-591 5159
E-Mail: mbongertman@senf.nl
general director Jacques Senf; managing director M. Bongertman
Artforms: drama, theatre, musicals, cabaret

Impresariaat Van Baasbank en Baggerman
Keizersgracht 258, 1016 EV **Amsterdam**
Tel: 20-624 2631/627 6818
Fax: 20-622 7850
E-Mail: baasbank.baggerman@wxs.nl
contact Jaap van Baasbank, J G Baggerman
Artforms: dance, theatre, music-theatre, music
Comments: agents and impressarios for Dutch and foreign contemporary theatre, modern dance, music theatre, organise the 'JuliDans'Festival – see also Festivals and Puppetry

Impresariaat Wim Visser
Kloveniersburgwal 47, 1011 JX **Amsterdam**
Tel: 20-623 3700 Fax: 20-620 8212
E-Mail: iwv@xs4all.nl
manager Wim Visser; assistant Hans Nass
Artforms: international theatre groups, mainly drama, mime-comedy, cabaret, flamenco music, ballet
Comments: general international management Paco Peña, Paco Peña Flamenco Dance Company

Impulse Art Management
Willemsparkweg 114, 1071 HN **Amsterdam**
Tel: 20-675 4061 Fax: 20-675 4771
E-Mail: klimpart@xs4all.nl
managing director Martijn Jacobus
Artforms: orchestras, ensembles, conductors, instrumental and vocal soloists *Comments:* concert promotions; organiser of the International Competition Early Music Ensembles, 'Van Wassenaer Competition'; merged with Marijke Klinkhamer Artists Management – see separate entry

Interartists BV
Postbus 38, 1251 ZZ **Laren**
Tel: 35-533 5835/73-612 2348
Fax: 35-533 5836/73-612 2362
E-Mail: salomons@interartists.nl
director Jeannine Salomons
Artforms: general management, local management of conductors, instrumentalists, orchestral touring
Comments: alternative E-mail: cousine@interartists.nl

International Music Management
PO Box 1498, 3430 BL **Nieuwegein**
Tel: 30-280 2330 Fax: 30-280 3331/5326
E-Mail: immgroap@immgroap.com
managing director Ruud De Graaf
Artforms: classical and pop music, theatre *Comments:* see also Promoters

International Music Productions
Paviljoensgracht 76, 2512 BR **Den Haag**
Tel: 70-363 8778 Fax: 70-360 8114
Internet: home.wxs.nl/~musicimp
E-Mail: musicimp@wxs.nl
directors Michael Hanekroot
Artforms: classical music, dance, tango

International Performing Arts Desk
Lutmastraat 184b, 1073 HG **Amsterdam**
Tel: 20-420 7863 Fax: 20-420 7863
E-Mail: hubscher@worldonline.nl
Marion Hübscher
Artforms: contemporary dance and music agency
Comments: also involved in projects and residencies

Interpresario/Nederlands Theaterbureau
Zeekant 102c, 2586 JH **Den Haag**
Tel: 70-354 3411 Fax: 70-355 7265
managing directors Wout van Liempt, Kees van Liempt, Lucien Dufais; publicity Jackie van der Vlis
Artforms: artists management (singers, musicians, actors) and production (plays, musicals, circus)

Irene Witmer Management
97 Kerkstraat, 1017 GD **Amsterdam**
Tel: 20-524 4040 Fax: 20-524 4044
E-Mail: witmeric@euronet.nl
directors Irene Witmer, Erin Headley
Artforms: classical music *Comments:* international management of classical musicians, concert management and special projects

Ivy Artists b.v.
Postbus 592, 1200 AN **Hilversum**
Tel: 35-628 2270/623 3133 Fax: 35-623 6619
E-Mail: music@ivyartists.com
Artforms: concert, opera, chamber music, orchestral tours, pr/corporate incentives *Comments:* artist management and consultancy

KIK Productions
Postbus 13120, 3507 LC **Utrecht**
Tel: 30-231 3416 Fax: 30-236 7416
director Hans Kik
Comments: production of cabaret, theatre and music performances, personal management of several Dutch stage artists and actors/actresses

Kleine Spui Produkties
Kleine Spui 26, 3811 BE **Amersfoort**
Tel: 33-465 2660 Fax: 33-465 2618
Internet: www.kleinespui.demon.nl
E-Mail: ksp@kleinespui.demon.nl
managing directos Carla Kogelman, Prisca Maas
Artforms: dance, theatre, puppet theatre, object theatre, visual theatre, street theatre, music theatre

Lapwing Music Management
Molenbolt 87, 7241 JK **Lochern**
Tel: 573-252 564 Fax: 573-258 107
director Francine Kampman

Maestro Music Management
Leuvensestraat 44, 2587 GH **Den Haag**
Tel: 70-354 3746 Fax: 70-350 9395
director Michiel de Ligt
Artforms: chamber music

Marianne Brinks Artists Management
Graaf Willemlaan 52, 1181 EH **Amstelveen**
Tel: 20-643 2043 Fax: 20-640 3961
E-Mail: mbrinks@xs4all.nl
director Marianne Brinks
Comments: personal management, concert management, orchestral tours; also managing director of the Delft Chamber Music Festival

Marijke Klinkhamer Artists Management
Willemsparkweg 114, 1071 HN **Amsterdam**
Tel: 20-675 4061 Fax: 20-675 4771
E-Mail: klimpart@xs4all.nl
managing director Marijke Klinkhamer
Artforms: conductors, soloists, chamber music, orchestras

Mexicaanse Hond en Orkater, De
Postbus 57145, 1040 BA **Amsterdam**
Tel: 20-606 0600 (switchboard)/606 0601 (pr)
Fax: 20-606 0616
Internet: www.orkater.nl
E-Mail: info@orkater.nl
financial director Ton Schippers; art director Marc van Warmerdam
Artforms: produces contemporary music theatre, musical theatre *Comments:* visiting address: Westergasfabriek, Haarlemmerweg 8-10, 1040 BE Amsterdam; see also Opera and Drama

Mojo Theater BV
POB 3121, 2601 DC **Delft**
Tel: 15-215 9415 Fax: 15-213 0920
Internet: www.mojotheater.nl
E-Mail: info@mojotheater.nl
contact G Visser
Artforms: produce theatre, drama, cabaret, music, dance/ballet

Naranti Productions
Vendelstraat 2, 1012 XX **Amsterdam**
Tel: 20-638 4505 Fax: 20-421 6853
E-Mail: naranti@naranti.nl
director Bregetta Gadella
Artforms: production company of modern dance

Nederlands Impresariaat
Paulus Potterstraat 12, 1071 CZ **Amsterdam**
Tel: 20-573 0300 Fax: 20-675 1206
E-Mail: info@ned-impresariaat.nl
contact Marijke Jansen; director Andres Mulder
Artforms: chamber music, jazz, children's concerts, soloists, conductors, world music, orchestras

Offshore International Cultural Projects
Madelievenstraat 10, 1015 **Amsterdam**
Tel: 20-422 6006 Fax: 20-422 6007
E-Mail: 106041.3125@compuserve.com
director Neil Wallace; project coordinator Sarah Slootweg; assistant project coordinator Florence Ho
Comments: independent organisation for production, touring and training in the international performing arts

Olé Productions
Wassenaarseweg 45, PO Box 95347, 2509 CH **Den Haag**
Tel: 70-324 5040 Fax: 70-324 5041
Internet: www.ole.nl
E-Mail: mail@ole.nl
managing directors Lucy Ebeli-Herrera, Otto R Selis
Artforms: Latinamerican music, performances, musicians and artists

ON STAGE – Artists and Concert Management
Krugerlaan 17, 2806 EB **Gouda**
Tel: 182-521 498 Fax: 182-521 498
Internet: www.wxs.nl/~onstage
E-Mail: onstage@wxs.nl
contact Iris van der Goot
Artforms: string players, wind players, conductor, pianists, small chamber orchestra, composers, personal management, concert management, specialised in new and contemporary music
Comments: also produces projects including performances in combination with dance, theatre or the arts of design; see also Stiching Podium Kamermuziek (National Organisations)

Pepijn bv
Smidswater 21, 2514 BW **Den Haag**
Tel: 70-364 3846 Fax: 70-356 3745
E-Mail: PePijnbv@xs4all.net
contact Inge van den Werf
Artforms: cabaret theatre *Comments:* theatre address: Lange Zoorhout 5, 2514 EA Den Haag

Riaskoff Concert Management
Concertgebouwplein 15, 1071 LL **Amsterdam**
Tel: 20-664 5353 Fax: 20-671 5106
managing director Marco Riaskoff; artists manager Jeroen Tersteeg; series coordinator & artists manager Jaap Breukel
Artforms: artists management of conductors, instrumentalists and ensembles, orchestral touring
Comments: Promoter of internationally renowned pianorecital series at the Concertgebouw in Amsterdam

Schamlé
Oostelijke Handelskaade 12-0, 1019 BM **Amsterdam**
Tel: 20-418 3034 Fax: 20-418 3948
E-Mail: inurt@xs4all.nl
contact Hans Schamlé, Hedwig Boor
Artforms: producer of modern dance, theatre, mime
Comments: also produce children's plays; work with artists worldwide

Stichting Nieuwe Huizen
Nieuwe Huizen 41, 4811 TL **Breda**
Tel: 76-522 8575 Fax: 76-541 5440
E-Mail: mstrog@inn.nl
manager Anneke Huilmand
Artforms: dance, theatre, performances *Comments:* see also Dance (Montazstroj, Stichting Zuil van Volta)

Strada / arts distribution, La
PO Box 1499, 3800 BL **Amersfoort**
Tel: 33-472 8899 Fax: 33-472 8884
Internet: www.artsdistr.com\lastrada
E-Mail: lastrada@artsdistr.com
administrator/general coordinator Leejo van Putten; artistic director/programmer Riekje Hoffman; producer Eric Bljleveld; technical coordinator Bart Linders
Artforms: outdoor theatre, dance, music, art projects
Comments: agency, producer, festival programmer, producer; visiting address: Van't Eindstraat 22, 3815 NW Amersfoort

Streetwise
Oostenburgervoorstraat 88, 1018 MR **Amsterdam**
Tel: 20-627 7466 Fax: 20-639 2758
managing directors Stef Arntz, Wouter de Boer
Artforms: produce street events, outdoor performances and festivals, corporate entertainment

Styx
PO Box 42024, 2504 EA **Den Haag**
Tel: 70-353 8104 Fax: 70-353 8333
Internet: www.styx.nl
E-Mail: info@styx.nl
director Wim Kuipers
Artforms: music, theatre

Supierz Artist Management
Linnaeus-serre 17, 3823 DL **Amersfoort**
Tel: 33-455 5656 Fax: 33-455 5433
Internet: www.supierz.nl
E-Mail: supierz@planet.nl
general director Z. Supierz; project manager Mariuz Skowronek; public relations Marcel van Zÿl
Artforms: opera, operetta, ballet, folklore, chorus, orchestra, chamber orchestra, soloists, conductors, opera touring, music theatre *Comments:* tours of large-scale opera productions in Benelux, co-produce musicals

The Office, Performing Arts Management
Keizersgracht 261, 1016 EC **Amsterdam**
Tel: 20-622 6979 Fax: 20-622 9081
E-Mail: kantoor@euronet.nl
director Lucine Schipper
Artforms: festivals, ensembles, concert management and large projects *Comments:* concert series, contemporary music; organises International Percussion Festival – see also Festivals; produces large cultural events

Theaterbureau Prima Rima
Nieuwe Herengracht 143, 1011 SG **Amsterdam**
Tel: 20-622 1257/620 4827 Fax: 20-622 1257
E-Mail: primarim@xs4all.nl
managers Els Wijmans, Dymph Verdiesen
Artforms: dance, theatre, music, puppets, esp. for young people *Comments:* see also Puppetry (St Illusie/Ella Snoep)

Theaterbureau Slot
Plantage Muidergracht 155, 1018 TT **Amsterdam**
Tel: 20-422 7899 Fax: 20-624 0470
E-Mail: slot.theater@tref.nl
sales & marketing Gerda Slot Theaterbureau
Artforms: theatre, drama and puppets for children
Comments: see also Drama and Puppetry

Theaterzaken Via Rudolphi
Korte Leidsedwarsstraat 12, 1017 RC **Amsterdam**
Tel: 20-627 7555 Fax: 20-627 8541
E-Mail: info@viarudolphi.nl
managing director Marie Anne Rudolphi
Artforms: contemporary dance, physical theatre, touring, producing, personal management *Comments:* represent Saver Nuver-physical theatre, Carver-physical theatre, Hussaarts & Van Lohuizen, children's theatre; see also Drama and Promoters

Ton Art – Rupert Fäustler
Faes Eliaslaan 39, 3742 AS **Baarn**
Tel: 35-543 0202 Fax: 35-543 0442
general manager Robert Fäustler
Comments: music production, A & R consultancy, orchestra tours

Vision Dance & Theatre Productions
Holzmüller Teengsstraat 46, 1827 PK **Alkmaar**
Tel: 72-515 1756 Fax: 72-515 4991
E-Mail: rscott@wxs.nl
director Randall Scott; assistant director Elly Scott
Artforms: dancers, singers, actors, choreographers-foreign contemporary theatre, modern dance, international theatre group, ballet, flamenco *Comments:* organisation of auditions for theatres/production companies/dance companies; management for companies; casting agency

Wim Wigt Jazz Productions
PO Box 201, 6700 AE **Wageningen**
Tel: 317-413 440 Fax: 317-421 548
Internet: www.wwmusic.com/timeless
E-Mail: riwire@antenna.nl
president W Wigt; vice-president R Wigt
Artforms: jazz groups and musicians *Comments:* organise and promote jazz concerts and tours; see also Timeless Music Promotion in Germany and Wim Wigt Productions in the UK

NORWAY (+47)

Artist Company
Artistcompaniet
Postboks 169, 3320 **Vestfossen**
Tel: 3275 2895/90-506 270 (mobile) Fax: 3275 6477
E-Mail: bbook@online.no
managers Bjarke Book, Roar Stengrimsen
Comments: commerical agency which promotes artists within every genre; visiting address: Storgata 32, 3320 Vestfossen

BLH Artists Management
Strindvegen 38, 7052 **Trondheim**
Tel: 7394 2575/5269 Fax: 7394 2788
E-Mail: blh.artists.management@hf.ntnu.no
director Bea Levine-Humm (mobile: 9321 0079)
Artforms: chamber music, concert management, personal management *Comments:* alternative E-mail: blh@c2i.net

d8 Concerts AS
Karl Johanagt. 8, 0154 **Oslo**
Tel: 2233 6939 Fax: 2242 6705

DA Concert Bureau
Konsertbyrået DA
Postboks 11 Nordstrand, 1112 **Oslo**
Tel: 2203 0220 Fax: 2274 4913
Internet: www.konsertby.no
E-Mail: ekonsert@online.no
administrative director Jan Einar Johnsen
Artforms: musicians within a variety of genres

Debut Management
Postboks 9415, Vålerenga, 0610 **Oslo**
Tel: 2217 6215 Fax: 2217 6225
E-Mail: pepedbut@oslonet.no
administrative director Per Platou
Comments: promoter of young Norwegian artists; visiting address: Brugata. 17, 0610 Oslo

Giant Step AS
Music Production, PO Box 312, 6401 **Molde**
Tel: 7125 5267/7121 6000/90-827 762 (mobile)
Fax: 7125 6665
manger/producer Rolf Bugge

Gunnar Eide AS
Sonja Henles plass 2, 0185 **Oslo**
Tel: 2217 4070 Fax: 2217 4075

Impresario A/S
Tollbugaten 3, 0152 **Oslo** 1
Tel: 2242 6379/3191 Fax: 2233 2238
directors Elsa-Mai Gottschalk, Vibeke Gottschalk
Artforms: represent several classical artists, import ballet, orchestras, musicals and jazz bands *Comments:* approximately 30 concerts a year; see also Promoters

Impressario Terje Gulbrandsen
Postboks 3188 Elisenberg, 0208 **Oslo**
Tel: 2243 4646/94-482 038 (mobile)
Fax: 2243 8387
director Terje Gulbrandsen
Comments: personal representation and direction, advertising, show productions and tour management; visiting address: Lovenskioldsgate 8b, 0208 Oslo

Jo Vestly Production Impresario Ltd
Jo Vestly produksjon impressario A/S
Bjerkelundsveien 5b, 1342 **Jar**
Tel: 6714 5900 Fax: 6714 7707
chairperson Berit Finne Vestly; administrative director Jan Einar Johnsen; producer Jo Vestly; artist promoter Kjell-Ove Torkildsen
Comments: commerical management which also represents individual artists

Jørg-Fr. Ellertsen AS
PO Box 449 Økern, 0513 **Oslo**
Tel: 2222 8070 Fax: 2222 9153

Kjell Kalleklev
Kulturhuset, Georgernes Verft nr. 3, 5011 **Bergen**
Tel: 5555 7630 Fax: 5555 7631
Internet: www.kalleklev.no
E-Mail: kjell@kalleklev.no
director Kjell Kalleklev
Artforms: jazz, roots, rock, contemporary music

Kulturarrangement Lillehammer AS
PO Box 696, 2601 **Lillehammer**
Tel: 6127 9700 Fax: 6127 9701
Internet: www.kalas.no/
E-Mail: jorgen@kalas.no
Comments: total event production/planning, development and organising of large scale events, concert productions, conventions, industrials and special events; organiser of the annual Winter Festival and Lillehammer International Snow Festival

MBS – Music Brokers Scaninavia AS
PO Box 337, 1301 **Sandvika**
Tel: 6754 0201/9051 1055 Fax: 6756 5531
E-Mail: remo.mbs@riksneil.no
managing director Remo Reder

Musiker- og Artistformidlingen
PO Box 360 Sentrum, 0101 **Oslo**
Tel: 2242 0808 Fax: 2242 1008

NAMA Management & Entertainment
Karl Johansgate 2, 0154 **Oslo**
Tel: 2242 0000 Fax: 2241 7952
E-Mail: entertainment@nama.no
administrative director Tore Hansen

Comments: promoter of verbal entertainment and music which works to establish a direct contact between artists and promoters

Oslo Arts Management A/S
Brenneriveien 11, 0182 **Oslo**
Tel: 2220 6307 Fax: 2220 6312
E-Mail: oam@osloarts.no
managing director Per Boye Hansen (email: pbh@osloarts.no); managers Anita Dahlström (email: ad@osloarts.no), Elisabeth Quarré (email: eq@osloarts.no); administrative director Sverre Gunnar Haga
Artforms: orchestras, singers, conductors and instrumentalists, classical music, opera, chamber and early music *Comments:* promote concerts and recitals, general management and representation for Scandinavia; see also Promoters

Oslo Konsertdireksjon
Bjerkebakken 1, 0756 **Oslo**
Tel: 2252 2546 Fax: 2273 0103
director Ruth Klungsøyr
Artforms: classical: conductors, soloists, ballet, orchestras *Comments:* predominantly artists from Russia; see also Promoters

Pan Jazz Production A/S – PJP A/S
PO Box 176, 5701 **Voss**
Tel: 5651 6700/0175 Fax: 5651 6701
E-Mail: pjpaal@online.no
manager Pål Gjersum
Artforms: represent several of Norway's best known artists in jazz, rock and folk music: Mari Boine, Kari Bremmes, Susanne Lundeng, Arild Andersen, Bendik Hofseth, Knut Reiersrud, Terje Rypdal

Petter Sandberg AS
Cort Adelersgt. 2, 0254 **Oslo**
Tel: 2243 1700 Fax: 2244 6640
Internet: www.pettersandberg.no/
E-Mail: ps-as@online.no
Comments: concert management, impresario and event firm; represent Norway's most popular artists

Pro-Arte International Management
John Lunds Plass 1, 5007 **Bergen**
Tel: 5531 9435/95-140 074 (mobile) Fax: 5596 0765
Internet: home.sol.no/~prinmana/
E-Mail: proarte@online.no
managing director Kjell Wernøe
Artforms: instrumentalists, conductors, chamber ensembles and singers

Rikskonsertene- Norwegian Concert Institute
PO Box 2835 Solli, 0204 **Oslo**
Tel: 2283 8350 Fax: 2283 1610
Internet: www.rikskonsertene.no
E-Mail: post@rikskonsertene.no
executive director Einar Solbu
Comments: Norway's largest producer and distributor of live music (approx. 10000 concerts annually); strives towards an overall artistic vision; public concerts, concerts for children, projects, multicultural music; see also National Organisations

ScanArts Management AS
PO Box 5366 Majorstua, 0304 **Oslo**
Tel: 2214 8799/9201 6208 Fax: 2246 3630
director Lars H. Fløeten

Sirkus Management A/S
Cort Adelersgate 2, 0254 **Oslo**
Tel: 2243 1700 Fax: 2244 6640
director Petter Sandberg
Comments: artist promoter; focus on revues, concerts, musical theatre tours and individual artist management; available for consultancy on artists' legal rights; also office in Trondheim: see also Promoters and Services

Stageway A/S
Skuteviksboder 11, 5035 **Bergen – Sandviken**
Tel: 5555 9696 Fax: 5531 2046
E-Mail: stageway@stageway.no
managing director Arne Svare; contact Jan Solles
Artforms: classical, pop, entertainment *Comments:* artists management and representation

Starbeat Entertainment
PO Box 4305, 7002 **Trondheim**
Tel: 7351 7600 Fax: 7351 7800

Tjøme Kulturformidling
c/o Mariann Siern, Eikelivn 25, 3145 **Tjøme**
Tel: 3339 1569/9178 0205 Fax: 3339 1317
Comments: concert and tour management

Trond and Trond
Trond og Trond
Oscarsgate 30, 0352 **Oslo**
Tel: 2269 8010 Fax: 2269 5011
E-Mail: trondogtrond@online.no
administrative director Trond Myhre
Artforms: various kinds of music, individual artist management *Comments:* see also Promoters

Vice-Versa
Ebbelsgate 1, 0183 **Oslo**
Tel: 2211 6416 Fax: 2211 6416
administrative director Guillaume Lacanal; label manager Wilfred Vuillaume
Artforms: specialises in French artists and tours to France

Viggo Lund Management
Akersgata 7, 0158 **Oslo**
Tel: 2241 2400/94-265 672 (mobile) Fax: 2241 5552
administrative director Viggo Lund
Comments: a member of the Norwegian Impresarios' Association (DENIF); represents a number of Norway's most established artists and lecturers; arranges concerts and shows and undertakes tour planning, promotion, seminars and management

Wigen Partners AS
Skippergt. 8-10, 0152 **Oslo**
Tel: 2241 4650/9437 1382 Fax: 2241 4654
E-Mail: wigpart@online.no
Comments: High Times Records

ZONE Productions AS
Tollbugt. 28, 0157 **Olso**
Tel: 2242 4818 Fax: 2242 4819
E-Mail: zoneprod@online.no
Artforms: promoting raves, concert & tours, folk & revere

POLAND (+48)

Agencja Filharmonia
83 Jasna nffl 7, 00-007 **Warszawa**
Tel: 22-827 3723/828 5651 Fax: 22-827 3723
managers Izabella Dargiel, Jerzy Salzman
Comments: classical music, artists' and concert promotion in Poland and worldwide

Andrzej Szwed Artists Management
8-33 Szpitalna Street, 00-031 **Warszawa**
Tel: 22-828 2162 Fax: 22-828 2161
chief officer Andrzej Szwed
Artforms: artist management, concert promotion, orchestral tours, festivals

Artistic Agency Sobiecki
Aleja Solidarnosci 82, ap.126, 00-145 **Warszawa**
Tel: 22-831 1335 Fax: 22-831 1335
director Tadeusz Sobiecki

Classic Management Marek Strasz
Kobielska 32/6, 04-359 **Warszawa**
president Marek Strasz

Classical Recordings and Concerts
ul. Szpitalna 8/33, 00-031 **Warszawa**
Tel: 22-828 3495 Fax: 22-828 2161
E-Mail: musicprod@supermedia.pl
chief officer Maria Kmicik Lejman
Artforms: artists management, concert management, classical recordings

Espo Artists Management
ul. Pogodna 21a, k Warszawy, 05-077 **Wesola**
Tel: 22-773 1559 Fax: 22-773 1559
manager Igor Pogorzelski
Artforms: promotes Polish music abroad, especially classical music; organises concerts, marketing, artists promotion etc.; specializes in chamber & symphony orchestras

Heritage Promotion of Art & Music
Ul. Marszalkowska 2, App 4, 00-581 **Warszawa**
Tel: 22-625 1506/1604/1647 Fax: 22-625 1697
executive director Janusz Pietkievicz; president Renato Musmeci; honorary president Elzbieta Penderecka
Artforms: whole sphere of classical music, drama, personal management, thematic projects, audio & visual recordings; new activity: promotion of European music & theatre productions throughout Europe

Impresariat Inter Art
ul. Narutowicza 15/45, 33-110 **Tarnow** 2
Tel: 14-217 267 Fax: 14-217 267
artistic directors Teresa Kaban, Henryk Blazej
Artforms: festivals, concerts

Jacek Nedzynski Artists Management
Os. Jagiellonskie 12/71, 61-227 **Poznan**
Tel: 61-876 5801 Fax: 61-876 5801/536 947
owner/director Jacek Nedzynski
Artforms: chamber music, choirs, dance, soloists

KiA – Krakowski Impresariat Artystyczny
Os Teatralne 9A, 31-946 **Kraków**
Tel: 12-644 3350 Fax: 12-644 3386
contact Adriana Zolnierczyk, Leszek Kablak
Artforms: serious theatre and theatre-television production; concert and event management

Music Art Agencja Koncertowa
Music Art Concert Agency
ul. Jagielska 29 B, 02-886 **Warszawa** 93
Tel: 22-643 9137 Fax: 22-643 9137
contact Slawomir Sowula

Music Productions
ul. Cynamonowa 2/37, 02-777 **Warszawa**
Tel: 22-648 3938 Fax: 22-648 3950
E-Mail: wojnowak@aol.com
director Wojciech Nowak
Artforms: classical music recordings, concert productions

National Concert Agency, The
Krajowe Biuro Koncertowe
ul. Koszykowa 27 m 7, 00-553 **Warszawa**
Tel: 22-621 6580 Fax: 22-621 6580
E-Mail: kbk@free.art.pl
director Malgorzata Bloch-Wisniewska
Artforms: concerts, festivals, records

Nona Artists Management
ul. Poniatowskiego 14/2, 20-060 **Lublin**
Tel: 81-533 0909
E-Mail: nona@kki.net.pl
general manager Katarzyna P. Osinska; executive manager Artur Andrzejewski
Artforms: soloists (violin, cello, piano, guitar), conductors, composers, ensembles, chamber orchestra

Polish Artists Agency PAGART
Plac Pilsudskiego 9, 00-078 **Warszawa**
Tel: 22-826 0145 (president) Fax: 22-827 5397
president Andrzej Sowinski; opera, ballet, classical music, folk ensembles Maria Gudaniec, Krystyna Karpiuk, Franciszek Redzimski; theatre t.b.a.; entertainment, concert tours, variety Dorota Bernat, Wojciech Bójski, Miroslaw Rossowski; secretary Krystyna Sztuczynske
Artforms: instrumentalists, ensembles
Comments: worldwide

Polish Jazz Society
Chmielna 20, 00-020 **Warszawa**
Tel: 22-827 8371/3926 Fax: 22-827 3926
president Mr Sadowsky

Studio Artists Management
Palac Kultury i Nauki, 00-901 **Warszawa**
Tel: 22-820 4369
director Wladyslaw Serwatowski
Artforms: all kinds of performing and visual arts
Comments: impresarios for international artists; arrange festivals, exhibitions and other artistic events

PORTUGAL (+351)

Artistas Unidos – Produção de Cinema e Teatro
Rua Coelho da Rocha 78, 3°, 1350 **Lisboa**
Tel: 1-395 8982 Fax: 1-395 8983
E-Mail: artistas.unidos@mail.telepac.pt
director Jorge Silva Melo
Artforms: theatre, cinema

BAIRES, Lda
Rua Antonio Enes 313, 4200 **Porto**
Tel: 2-830 1878 Fax: 2-817 148
contact Laura Tallone

Cassefaz Espectáculos – Teatro, Dança, Gestao
Est. Benfica, 400, 1°E, 1500-101 **Lisboa**
Tel: 21-774 0892/343 0746/342 0127 Fax: 21-774 0892/343 0746
E-Mail: cassefaz@mail.telefac.pt
director Miguel Abreu
Artforms: theatre/dance (all types) *Comments:* publish: Guia das Artes do Espectáculo (all information about Portuguese theatre and Portuguese dance); manage Grupo Cassefaz Theatre Company and Transformers Cabaret, cabaret company

Interartes – Agência Artística e Representações Lda.
Av. Oscar Monteiro Torres, 16 r.c.esq., 1000-219 **Lisboa**
Tel: 21-796 8738 Fax: 21-793 5251
E-Mail: interartes@ip.pt
general manager Carlos Pires; chief officer Dr. Graça Conceição; financial manager Pilar Gol
Artforms: music, dance, theatre, shows

Prestissimo
Rua Vasco Santana N°1 – 8° Dto, 2685-246 **Portela-Lrs**
Tel: 1-945 7077 Fax: 1-945 7078
manager Sebastião Ribeiro
Artforms: classical music, soloists
Comments: see also Promoters

ROMANIA (+40)

Artexim
Calea Victoriei 155, bl D 1, Sc. 8, Et. 2, 71012 **Bucharest**
Tel: 1-650 1806/7/9443 4805 (mobile) Fax: 1-311 0200
E-Mail: artexim@dial.rocknet.ro
general manager Mihai Constantinescu; accountant Gabriella Stoidan
Artforms: classical music, opera, jazz, ballet, dance

JMR Art Production
CP 13-53, **Bucharest** 13
Tel: 1-230 3205/92-383 542 Fax: 1-230 3205
president Luigi Gageos

RUSSIA (+7)

All the World – International Theatre Centre
Arbat 35, Office 354, 121002 **Moscow**
Tel: 095-248 0857/1967 Fax: 095-248 0857
general & artistic director Olga Garibova; international project manager Elena Ivanova (tel: 095-269 3882)
Artforms: drama (including co-productions), ballet (tours, gala-concerts etc.), opera, musical festivals, students performances' exchange (Russia – USA)
Comments: partners in Switzerland, USA, France, Norway, Philippines

Art Time Corporation Vremia
3-1 Serebrianichesky per, 109028 **Moscow**
Tel: 095-916 1111 Fax: 095-917 4202
E-Mail: arttime@online.ru
president Svetlana Antikhina
Artforms: soloists, instrumentalists, folk dance/music,classical ballet/music, circus on stage, choirs, festivals

BOGIS Theatre Agency
Merzliakovski Per. 3-1, 103009 **Moscow**
Tel: 095-290 3239 Fax: 095-257 5006
artistic director Galina Bogoliubova

Firebird
Maly Kislovsky 3, Office 304, 103009 **Moscow**
Tel: 095-290 0268 Fax: 095-290 0268
general director Igor Belyaev
Artforms: conductors, vocal soloists
Comments: see also Promoters

Gosconcert
Neglinnaya 15, 103051 **Moscow**
Tel: 095-928 7191/923 9732/925 7264 Fax: 095-921 3578
director Vladimir Panchenko

Gosko
Ul. Radischeva, 191014 **St Petersburg**
Tel: 812-279 6486 Fax: 812-279 6486
director Valdimir Logutenko

Impressariat
V.O. Sredny pr. 55, **St Petersburg**
Tel: 812-218 7356 Fax: 812-218 7356
director Vadim Palmov

Kannon-Dance
St Petersburg
Tel: 812-114 1221/311 7866 (home) Fax: 812-114 1221
Internet: www.chance.spb.su/kannon/
E-Mail: kannon@infopro.spb.su
Comments: promotion agency for dance and show groups

Katerina Novikova
Chekhova 1 apt 33, 191104 **St Petersburg**
Tel: 812-275 5666 Fax: 812-275 5666
E-Mail: alex@kris.spb.su
Artforms: theatre, clownade, singers, music *Comments:* performing art consultant; see also Services

Moscow Concert Organisation SADKO
Gasheka 12-6, 125047 **Moscow**
Tel: 095-250 9832
Comments: see also Promoters

Music art Co
st. Siromolotova 14-320, 620072 **Ekaterinburg**
Tel: 3432-537 204 Fax: 3432-537 204
manager Vadim Egorov; director Leonid Brezgin
Artforms: dance, music, drama

Music Guest-room of Shuvalov's House
Povarskaya 30, 121069 **Moscow**
Tel: 095-290 2422
Comments: see also Promoters

New Artistic Management
PO Box 26, 123557 **Moscow**
Tel: 095-252 4201 Fax: 095-252 4201
board chairman Serguei Voltkovsky
Comments: organises touring and concerts of new, talented musicians

Romans-Salon of Natalia Pavlova
Academica Anokhina 26-3-395, 117602 **Moscow**
Tel: 095-112 0688
Comments: see also Promoters

Russian Centre of the International Theatre Institute
Theatre of Nations, Petrovsky per. 3, 103031 **Moscow**
Tel: 095-229 5672/3865 Fax: 095-229 5672/6033
director Valery Khasanov

Sovinart
Murmansky proezd 18, 129075 **Moscow**
Tel: 095-215 7571 Fax: 095-215 2274
E-Mail: Sovinart.MOS@g23.relcom.ru
managing director Eilina Tikhomirova; senior manager Lydia Satyukova
Artforms: symphony orchestras, ballet, folk dance, solo instrumentalists, conductors, singers (opera and concert), chamber groups, on a worldwide basis
Comments: full member of IAMA and ISPA organisations

Starlet Classical Music Promotions Agency
Tchekhovskogo 75, apt 9, 191123 **St Petersburg**
Tel: 812-275 4831 Fax: 812-275 4831
E-Mail: Starlet@email.convey.ru
artistic director Vladimir Mischuk; general manager Inga Kutianskaya; art manager Denis Leonov
Artforms: mainly classical music, some drama, folk and dance *Comments:* production of celebration events: release of classical LP records and CD

State Moscow Organisation MOSKONTSERT
Leningradski prosp. 30, building 2, 125040 **Moscow**
Tel: 095-212 2101
Comments: see also Promoters

State Theatre of Nations
Petrovsky pereulok 3, 103031 **Moscow**
Tel: 095-229 7777/5672 Fax: 095-229 5672
Comments: produces theatre productions, organises foreign theatre tours and festivals in Russia, Russian theatre tours abroad (drama, ballet, music theatre, opera, pantomime, etc.); see also Promoters and Russian Centre of the ITI

Theater-Concert Agency
Rodchelskaya 11/5, 123100 **Moscow**
Tel: 095-205 2496
Comments: see also Promoters

Tour-Concert Fund RUSKONTSERT
B. Polyanka 2/10, 109180 **Moscow**
Tel: 095-230 0875
Comments: see also Promoters

Vizit
24 Moika Emb., 191186 **St Petersburg**
Tel: 812-314 0644/3162 Fax: 812-314 3162
E-Mail: visit-ie@inforo.spb.ru
director Irina Tshistopashina
Artforms: ballet

SLOVAKIA (+421)

Many telephone and fax numbers in Slovakia are in the process of being changed. We have included all new numbers known at the time of going to print.

Akord – Art Agency
Gessayova 15, 815 03 **Bratislava**
Tel: 7-6573 0080/905-612 621 (mobile)
Fax: 7-6573 0080
director Emil Culinka
Artforms: ensembles, soloists

ART Agency Ltd
Zupné námestie 7, 811 03 **Bratislava**
Tel: 7-5443 4662/63 Fax: 7-5441 3424
E-Mail: artagen@zutom.sk
contact Marta Jedlicková
Artforms: singers, conductors, orchestras (classical music only)

Art Agency MBM, Milan Babjak – MANA
Kalinciakova 18, PO Box 93, 974 05 **Banská Bystrica**
Tel: 88-412 4407 Fax: 88-412 4407
E-Mail: mbabiak@ivko.sk
contact M. Babjak
Artforms: music, dance, theatre, puppets *Comments:* agency for domestic and foreign soloists and ensembles at home and abroad

Interartists Bratislava
Bajzova 4, 821 08 **Bratislava**
Tel: 7-5557 7170 Fax: 7-5557 7170
E-Mail: interart@netax.sk
director Jana Kováciková
Artforms: chamber music, vocal and instrumental soloists, choirs, orchestras

Musa
Postová 4, 811 06 **Bratislava**
Tel: 7-5413 1257 Fax: 7-5413 1257
managing director Elena Kratochvílová

Scriptorium Musicum Ltd
Svetla 3, 811 02 **Bratislava**
Tel: 7-6280 2450/5557 7873
Internet: www.scriptorium.sk
E-Mail: bartovic@tatrahome.sk
director Stanley Bartovic
Artforms: art agency, music publishing house, notesetting, MIDI music, internet music

Slovkoncert – Music Centre
Slovkoncert – Hudobné centrum
Michalská 10, 815 36 **Bratislava**
Tel: 7-5443 4003/4561 Fax: 7-5443 2652
Internet: www.slovkoncert.sk
E-Mail: slovkoncert@netlab.sk
general director of the Music Centre
MA Olga Smetanová
Comments: due to the new organisational structure of the Music Centre, changes may have occurred since going to print; see also National Organisations

ALFONSO AIJÓN, S. A.

Costa Rica, 32 bajo B
28016 MADRID
Tels.: (34) 91 359 52 96 / 09 64
Fax: (34) 91 345 24 89
E-mail: ibermusica@mad.servicom.es

30th ANNIVERSARY

1999 - 2000 SEASON

October 1999

BBC SYMPHONY
Sir Andrew Davis
Truls Mørk

ROYAL CONCERTGEBOUW ORCHESTRA
Nikolaus Harnoncourt
Rudolf Buchbinder

ACADEMY OF ST. MARTIN IN THE FIELDS
Kenneth Sillito
Murray Perahia

ROSA TORRES PARDO

November 1999

DANIEL BARENBOIM

CURTIS INSTITUTE SYMPHONY
André Previn
Anne-Sophie Mutter

MAHLER CHAMBER ORCHESTRA
Daniel Harding

December 1999

PAMELA & CLAUDE FRANK

January 2000

GÜRZENICH ORCHESTER KÖLN
James Conlon
Sarah Chang

MIDORI & ROBERT McDONALD

NEW YORK PHILHARMONIC
ORFEÓN DONOSTIARRA
Kurt Masur &
José Antonio Sáinz Alfaro
Christine Goerke
Annette Markert
Stanford Olsen
Reinhard Hagen
Cynthia Phelps
Rebecca Young

February 2000

ORQUESTA CIUDAD DE GRANADA
Josep Pons

ANDRAS SCHIFF

March 2000

WIENER PHILHARMONIKER
Giuseppe Sinopoli

SÄCHSISCHE STAATSKAPELLE DRESDEN
Sir Colin Davis

FILARMÓNICA CHECA
Vladimir Ashkenazy

FINNISH RADIO SYMPHONY
Jukka-Pekka Saraste

ISRAEL PHILHARMONIC
Zubin Mehta

SINFÓNICA DE EUSKADI
ORFEÓN DONOSTIARRA
Gilbert Varga &
José Antonio Sáinz Alfaro

LONDON SYMPHONY ORCHESTRA
Riccardo Chailly

April 2000

GUSTAV MAHLER JUGENDORCHESTER
Seiji Ozawa
Christian Tetzlaff

May 2000

CHICAGO SYMPHONY
Daniel Barenboim
Elisabete Matos

GEWANDHAUSORCHESTER LEIPZIG
Herbert Blomstedt
Elisabeth Leonskaja

PITTSBURGH SYMPHONY
Mariss Jansons

MURRAY PERAHIA

MARIA JOÃO PIRES

SLOVENIA (+386)

Ars Ramovs – Institute for Art, Marketing, Promotion and Investment
Ars Ramovs – Zavod za Umetnost, Marketing, Promocijo in Investiranje
Slovenska cesta 1, 1101 **Ljubljana**
Tel: 61-125 3366 Fax: 61-174 1541
E-Mail: info@k-ramovs.si
director Klemen Ramovs
Artforms: festivals, concerts, masterclasses *Comments:* agent for domestic and foreign soloists and ensembles at home and abroad; recording; agent for instrument sales; organise festivals, concerts and masterclasses

Brina Jez-Brezavscek
Rutarjeva 5, 1000 **Ljubljana**
Tel: 61-213 972
president Brina Jez-Brezavscek; secretary Mirjam Zgavec
Artforms: soloists and chamber groups

Cankarjev dom Agency
c/o Cankarjev dom Cultural and Congress Centre, Presernova 10, 1000 **Ljubljana**
Tel: 61-176 7100 Fax: 61-224 279
Internet: www.cd-cc.si
E-Mail: natasa-kelhar@cd-cc.si
director general Mitja Rotovnik; head of agency Natasa Kelhar
Artforms: all arts *Comments:* see also Venues

Drustvo za vzpodbujanje in napredek nove glasbe
Muzina Association for the Stimulation and Development of New Music
Rutarjeva 5, 1000 **Ljubljana**
Tel: 61-218 657
president Brina Jez-Brezavscek; secretary Mirjam Zgavec
Comments: association works for the promotion of Slovenian composers born after 1950 in Slovenia and abroad; organises concerts of new music written by Slovenian and non-Slovenian composers.

JHP Artist & Concert Management
Krakovski nasip 6, 1000 **Ljubljana**
Tel: 61-125 7008 Fax: 61-125 7194
E-Mail: jeff013@hotmail.com
director Jeff H. Pivac
Artforms: classical music (soloists, conductors, chamber orchestras, orchestras), early music, jazz, world music, tours
Comments: artist and concert management; management (both artistic and business) to the Radenci XXth Century Chamber Music Festival in Slovenia

Ljubljana Festival
Trg francoske revolucije 1-2, 1000 **Ljubljana**
Tel: 61-126 4340/2011 Fax: 61-221 288
Internet: www.festival-lj.si/
E-Mail: info@festival-lj.si
general manager Darko Brlek; secretary Sonja Vrhovec
Comments: member of the EFA

SPAIN (+34)

23 Arts – Brothers Projections
Apartat Postal 47, 08460 **Palautordera (Barcelona)**
Tel: 93-848 0499 Fax: 93-848 0499
E-Mail: arts@abaforum.es
general manager Roser Vilá
Artforms: street theatre, puppets, clowns & visual theatre

A Priori Gestión Teatral s.l.
c/ Cardenal González de Mendoza, 27 bajo izq., 19004 **Guadalajara**
Tel: 949-210 866/610-290 366 (mobile)
Fax: 949-210 866
director Joseba Garcia
Artforms: all types of theatre *Comments:* produces, promotes and distributes theatre shows

Acteón
c/ Girona 97, 1° 1ª, 08009 **Barcelona**
Tel: 93-207 5773 Fax: 93-207 5773
Internet: www.cccbxaman.org/acteon
E-Mail: acteon@arrakis.es
director Claudio Zulian; production & communication Montse Herrera
Artforms: contemporary opera, multimedia performances, contemporary theatre, installation art
Comments: second address: Apdo. Correos 23349, 08080 Barcelona; own opera and theatre company, see also Opera and Drama

Adela Sanchez Producciones
Residencial Monsacro, Edificio C – nº 1, 1° B, 33162 **Santa Eulalia de Morcín (Asturias)**
Tel: 98-578 3400/629-869 212 (mobile) Fax: 98-578 3417
Internet: www.adelasanchez.com
E-Mail: producciones@adelasanchez.com
directoria Adela G. Sánchez
Artforms: national and international early and classical music, tour organiser and management

Agencia de Conciertos Vitoria
Calle Sagasta 3, 5° Ext izq, 28004 **Madrid**
Tel: 91-594 3773 Fax: 91-594 4337
Internet: empresas.mundivia.es/conciertos_vitoria
E-Mail: conciertos_vitoria@mundivia.es
directoras Felicitas Teller, Beatrice Altobelli
Artforms: classical music: conductors, opera singers, other soloists, orchestras, chamber music *Comments:* alternative E-mail: b.altobelli@mundivia.es

Alfonso G Leoz
Magdalena 7, 3° 1ª, 28012 **Madrid**
Tel: 91-369 2341 Fax: 91-369 2552
management Alfonso G Leoz; assistant Rosa Mª Garcia
Artforms: young singers, opera singers *Comments:* vocal assesors, agents

Altair, Teatre i Cultura
Avda de Jijona 30, 03012 **Alicante**
Tel: 96-525 7690
E-Mail: altair@iponet.es
director Antoni Cuti, Oscar Rodriguez
Artforms: children's theatre

Andréas Claus Management
Sepúlveda, 147-149 Pral. 1ª, 08011 **Barcelona**
Tel: 93-454 5005/6 Fax: 93-454 5873
E-Mail: andreasclaus@readysoft.net
manager Mr. Andréas Claus; produccion Nuria Peiro
Artforms: international management of singers in Europe

Anexa Espectacles S.A. (Anexa)
Diputación 185 ppal. 1ª, 08011 **Barcelona**
Tel: 93-452 5900 Fax: 93-452 5901
E-Mail: info@anexa.nu
director area teatro Toni Albaladejo; director area musica Pedro Saboya
Artforms: theatre, venues, music *Comments:* management and promoters; manages Teatro Victoria with Dagoll Dagom and El Tricicle (drama), La Cubana and Teatre Poliorama; see also Venues

Artcelona/Odas Africa
Plaça Regomir 3, 08002 **Barcelona**
Tel: 93-315 2698 Fax: 93-315 2050
E-Mail: agnesblot@teleline.es
directora general Agnes Blot; secretaria general Mary Pi de la Serra; presidente Odas Africa, Vincent Koala
Artforms: export & import contemporary shows, international coproductions especially African/Australian, artistic consultant for festivals, international meetings, import and export of flamenco *Comments:* self-financing

ARTE 4, T4 s.a.
c/ Real 19, 28250 **Torrelodones (Madrid)**
Tel: 91-859 3962/607-745 423 (mobile) Fax: 91-859 4637
Internet: www.greencom.net/arte4
E-Mail: arte4@greencom.net
director Germán Torrellas; producers Antonia Sánchez, Mocarena Torrellas, Macarena Fueyo
Artforms: classical music, especially Spanish 18th century opera *Comments:* manages and produces Neocantes (q.v.), B Quadro Opera (q.v.) and Concento Musical (q.v.)

Arte Musica
Gran Via 80, Oficina 215-216, 28013 **Madrid**
Tel: 91-541 9642 Fax: 91-541 8470
Internet: www.artemusica.com
E-Mail: concerts@artemusica.com
director general Eduardo Brenlla; asesor musical Raúl Mallavibarrena
Artforms: classical and early music *Comments:* see also Choirs and Early Music

Artistas Internationales
Av. Portugal 1, 28011 **Madrid**
Tel: 91-479 0871 Fax: 91-464 5357
E-Mail: danbert@nova.es
director of production Sergio Conte
Artforms: instrumentalists, soloist and chamber music
Comments: diffusion contemporary music

Baença SL Espectacle
Avda Mediterranea 15, bajos,
08214 **Badia del Valles (Barcelona)**
Tel: 93-729 1015 Fax: 93-729 1015
director Jose Baena Arrebola
Artforms: dance orchestras, Spanish dance music, modern ballet *Comments:* tours in Spain with Spanish music, ballet orchestras and brass bands, mariachis and dance orchestras

Bis Producciones
Federico Sánchez Bedoya nº 20, 3º izq., 41001 **Sevilla**
Tel: 95-422 5699 Fax: 95-422 9356
E-Mail: losulen@zoom.es
contact José Luis Diaz Duero
Artforms: producers of comedy, musical theatre
Comments: see also Drama (Los Ulen)

Bito Produccions
Plaça Sant Jaume, 9, 17190 **Salt (Girona)**
Tel: 972-402 004 Fax: 972-400 019
E-Mail: bitoteatre@arquired.es
directors Josep Demènech, Joaquim Masó
Artforms: Catalan, Spanish and international theatre
Comments: see also Festivals

Bofarull-Torres s.l. – Empresa Cultural
c/ Cerro Carrasqueta nº 63 C – 4º B, 28035 **Madrid**
Tel: 91-376 3384/609-057 742 (mobile) Fax: 91-376 5455
directora de producción Carmen Bofarull; director de distribución Normando Torres
Artforms: performing arts *Comments:* production, distribution and organisation of artistic and cultural activities

Caliopea
c/ Marcelino Fernández nº 5, 1º C, 33010 **Oviedo**
Tel: 985-114 958 Fax: 985-212 884
E-Mail: lbmendez@muniellos.incar.csic.es
director Sebastién Lauro Lillo
Artforms: contemporary dance

Cimbalo Producciones – Javier Estrella
Apodaca 9, bajo dcha, 28004 **Madrid**
Tel: 91-447 6400 Fax: 91-447 9699
E-Mail: cimbalo@mad.servicom.es
director Javier Estrella
Artforms: jazz, world music and early music ensembles, festivals *Comments:* organisers of tours (jazz, world music and early music ensembles); organisers of Festival de Jazz de Madrid (Oct-Nov, annual) and Festival de Musica Antigua de Aranjuez (Nov, annual); see also Festivals

Circuitos Internacionales de Música S.L.
c/ Agen, local 20, 45005 **Toledo**
Tel: 925-254 298 Fax: 925-251 920
E-Mail: rafacim@teleline.es
director Rafael Jimenéz Herranz
Artforms: chamber orchestras, soloists, ensembles, concerts, festivals, conferences, courses

Colorado Producciones S.L.
c/ 29 de Abril 39, 3º izq., 35007 **Las Palmas de Gran Canaria**
Tel: 928-220 407/473 Fax: 928-220 407
Internet: www.coloradoproducciones.com
E-Mail: info@coloradoproducciones.com
director Miguel Ramírez
Artforms: comedy, music (jazz, pop, rock, salsa)
Comments: producers of Festival Int. de Jazz de Canarias; see also Festivals

Conciertos Augusto S.L.
Calle Viento No. 15, 2º B, Majadahonda, 28220 **Madrid**
Tel: 91-634 0205 Fax: 91-634 0250
E-Mail: conciertosaugusto@eipoint.com
director gerente Gonzalo Augusto; organización, contratación Monica Royuela; coordinación Alicia Idigoras
Artforms: classical music: international soloists, ensembles and orchestras *Comments:* music adviser for summer festivals

Conciertos del Norte / Asturias
c/ Sacramento 2, 2º izqda, 33008 **Oviedo**
Tel: 985-233 025 Fax: 985-252 563
Internet: www.clar.net/cm/norte
E-Mail: arlanzon@arrakis.es
director general y productor Luis Manjarrés; director adjunto Isabel Corral
Artforms: mainly gospel, blues, jazz, some chamber music, funk *Comments:* represents artists all over Spain and also Portugal

Conciertos Int. Amadeus
Capitán Haya 22, 2º C, 28020 **Madrid**
Tel: 91-556 9756 Fax: 91-556 9887
director Ricardo de Quesada
Artforms: classical music *Comments:* representation of orchestras, chamber ensembles, soloist; tour organisation

Contrataciones Artísticas Pepa Medìavìlla
c/ Lope de Hoyo 142, 3º, 36º, 28002 **Madrid**
Tel: 91-415 7846 Fax: 91-413 8564
director Pepa Medìavìlla; admin. Mª Eugenìa Tova
Artforms: dance: classical, Spanish

CPF Cultural Projects Factory
c/ Santa Brígida 19, entresuelo C, 28004 **Madrid**
Tel: 91-531 6633 Fax: 91-531 9472
E-Mail: cpfmadrid@mx3.redestb.es
cultural advisor Blas Fernández Gallego; coordinator Teresa Sánchez; executive director Pedro Cheng
Artforms: music, dance, theatre, visual arts, films and conferences *Comments:* produces and programmes cultural projects between Spain and Asia; see also Services and MOD

Crin Artis S.L.
General Pardillas 91, 1º izda, 28006 **Madrid**
Tel: 91-564 0958 Fax: 91-411 4351
E-Mail: sandra@crin.cempresarial.com
director Maida Bustamante
Artforms: salsa, Latin American music, theatre, dance

Donald Scrimgeour
Apartado 905, 41080 **Sevilla**
Tel: 95-434 3802 Fax: 95-434 3807
E-Mail: scrimgeour@facilnet.es
director Donald Scrimgeour
Artforms: dance and ballet companies, dancers, choreographers, producers, conductors, directors, designers
Comments: overseas office at 49 Springcroft Ave, London N2 9JH, tel: +44 20-8444 6248, fax: +44 20-8883 9751

El Buho Servicios Teatrales
c/ Recoletos 12 – 3 izq., 28001 **Madrid**
Tel: 91-576 7219/7181 Fax: 91-576 7219
directora Paula Paz Poveda
Artforms: theatre *Comments:* promotion and distribution of theatre companies

El Foro Espectaculos
c/ Minas 9, 1º ext. A, 28004 **Madrid**
Tel: 91-532 0884 Fax: 91-532 1056
Internet: www.ctv.es/remesal
E-Mail: remesal@ctv.es
director David Remesal
Artforms: theatre, dance *Comments:* distributes, produces and manages

EMJ Art et Musique S.L.
Playa de Sitges 27, Punta Galea,
28290 **Las Rozas (Madrid)**
Tel: 91-630 3070/609-154 122 (mobile) Fax: 91-630 2198
E-Mail: emusique@mad.servicom.es
managing director Elisabeth Michot de Jowers; production manager Fabian Jowers
Artforms: classical chamber music, soloists, ensembles, early music *Comments:* working in Spain, France and Portugal

EuroArte Management, S.L.
c/ Felipe III, nº 4, 28012 **Madrid**
Tel: 91-365 8404/05 Fax: 91-364 0018
director Luis Vivó
Artforms: international ballet companies, dance groups, opera, flamenco and Spanish dance *Comments:* specialise in flamenco companies; organise tours for ballet and dance companies

Euroarts
San Nicolás 5, bajo, 28013 **Madrid**
Tel: 91-542 1655/2441/2117 Fax: 91-542 0533
Internet: www.informet.es/blancadelrei
E-Mail: blancadelrei@imformet.es
director Juan Manuel R Ávila; jefe de administración Antonio C Contreras
Artforms: mainly flamenco but also dance, music, drama *Comments:* specialised in flamenco productions

Euroconcert
Rambla de Catalunya 10, 2º 4ª, 08007 **Barcelona**
Tel: 93-318 5158 Fax: 93-412 4114
E-Mail: euroconcert@bcn.servicom.es
director general Antoni Sàbat
Artforms: classical music, national and international; other arts types on request *Comments:* concert season in Barcelona from October to May

Fermata Arts Management SL
Apartado 463, 45080 **Toledo**
Tel: 925-216 003 Fax: 925-256 265
E-Mail: FERMATA@teleline.es
general manager Dessislava Mincheva
Artforms: classical music, folk (ethnic choirs)
Comments: management of the International Music Festival of Toledo, see also Festivals

Fila 7
Balmes 18-1ª 2º, 08007 **Barcelona**
Tel: 93-412 0434 Fax: 93-412 5221
Internet: www.redestb.com/fila7
E-Mail: fila7@mx3.redestb.es
director artistico Toni Coll; gerente Sergio Danti; jefa prensa Laura Freijo; ventas Anna Garcia, Gema Roura; depart. producción y contratos Vanessa Bartomeu; danza Eulalia Rodrigo; contabilidad Natividad Riera
Artforms: theatre, dance

Francisco Bermúdez, Espectáculos Internacionales
c/ Miloca B 69, Urb. Molìno de la Hoz, 28230 **Las Rozas (Madrid)**
Tel: 91-373 2454/630 3632 Fax: 91-373 2454/630 3632
director Dolores Lane Grant; secretaria Carmen del Pozo
Artforms: classical music and all sorts of shows worldwide

Free Art
Ap. 127, 08950 **Esplugues (Barcelona)**
Tel: 93-473 8669 Fax: 93-372 5948
Internet: www.free-art.com
director Carles Treviño (carlos@free-art.com); direction assistant Marina Espasa (email: marina@free-art.com); international department Pilar Gutiérrez (email: pilar@free-art.com); communication department Lídia Gilabert (email: lidia@free-art.com)
Artforms: street theatre, puppets, comedy & visual theatre *Comments:* see also Puppets

G.E.S Management
López Abadia 3, 50002 **Zaragoza**
Tel: 976-291 646 Fax: 976-298 137
director gerente Jesús Baselga; directora comercial Gloria Serón; promoción y marketing Patricia Perez; asesora juridica Carmen Rodrigo
Artforms: classical music, contemporary dance, ballet, theatre, jazz, new music, comedy *Comments:* tour and concert management; organises tours in Spain and Latin America

Gi M- Gestió i Management
Rambla Catalunya 66, 6º F, 08007 **Barcelona**
Tel: 93-487 8282 Fax: 93-487 7422
E-Mail: gesmanag@maptel.es
director Ignacio Teixidó; manager Mónica García
Artforms: classical music and jazz *Comments:* represents and manages artists and groups, produces and organises festivals and events, produces records for own artists

Harmonía Catalunya
c/ Montserrat 7, 08292 **Esparreguera (Barcelona)**
Tel: 93-777 6060 Fax: 93-777 2165
E-Mail: harcat@intercom.es
contact Montserrat Sitja
Artforms: classical music, orchestras, soloists, chamber music *Comments:* concert promotion and artists management

Hispania Clasica
Calle Los Madrazos 16, 28014 **Madrid**
Tel: 91-429 2625 Fax: 91-429 3530
E-Mail: rdequesada@intermail.es
director general Ricardo de Quesada; Sonsoles Gonzalez de Vega, Maria Fernanda Caballero
Artforms: classical music, gospel *Comments:* classical music promotion and artists management

Ibercámera
Gran Via 636, 1º 2ª, 08007 **Barcelona**
Tel: 93-317 9050 Fax: 93-302 6189
E-Mail: ibercamera@ibercamera.es
director y administrador Jose María Prat; director artístico adjunto Montserrat Crespo
Artforms: classical music and flamenco *Comments:* concert promoters and managers

Iberkoncert
Alameda de Urquijo 34, 48010 **Bilbao**
Tel: 94-410 4746/609-427 207 (mobile)
Fax: 94-421 8582
E-Mail: iberkonzert@clientes.eskaltel.es
director Juan Carlos Sancho
Artforms: musicians (classical), singers, orchestras, directors

Ibermúsica Alfonso Aijón S.A.
Costa Rica 32, bajo B, 28016 **Madrid**
Tel: 91-359 0964/5296 Fax: 91-345 2489
E-Mail: ibermusica@mad.servicom.es
director general Alfonso Aijón
Artforms: classical music (symphonic): major international orchestras

Intercambio de Cultura y Arte
c/ Carretas 14, 5°-1-5, 28012 **Madrid**
Tel: 91-531 2440/1321 Fax: 91-531 5936
Internet: www.icarl.es
E-Mail: icart@mad.servicom.es
director Juan Blanco Noriega; director asistente Trini Gutiérrez
Artforms: flamenco music, song and dance, popular music from Brazil, Portugal and Cuba *Comments:* artists from Spain, Brazil, Portugal, Cuba, Africa; tours and festival organisers

Intermúsica Produccions 2000 s.l.
Santaló 10, 08021 **Barcelona**
Tel: 93-414 1988 (ext 341) Fax: 93-200 9220
director Elena Pokasanieva de Peña
Artforms: classical music: soloists, duos, quartets, quintets, chamber orchestras, orchestras and chorus
Comments: management and promotion of young talents; concert organisation

International Ballet Productions S.L.
Santaló 10, 08021 **Barcelona**
Tel: 93-414 1988 ext 341 Fax: 93-200 9220
director Elena Pokasanieva de Peña
Artforms: classical, modern and traditional ballet
Comments: management and promotion of young talents

Isabel Gonzalez
Duque de Sesto 40, 8°, 28009 **Madrid**
Tel: 91-575 8916 Fax: 91-576 8283
directora Isabel Gonzalez
Artforms: dance: flamenco, classical, contemporary, eastern music

J C Arderius Artist Mangement
Calle de las Cruces, 6 bajo G, 28210 **Las Rozas (Madrid)**
Tel: 91-636 1502/1493 Fax: 91-637 6504
E-Mail: j.c.arderius@jet.es
director Juan Carlos Arderius; pr Ángela Junco; administration Mari Carmen Granados
Artforms: musicians (classical), directors, orchestras
Comments: exchange with Eastern European musicians

Jordi de Ramon Management
Sepúlveda, 147-149 Pral. 1a, 08011 **Barcelona**
Tel: 93-454 5010/07 Fax: 93-454 5873
manager Jordi de Ramon
Artforms: singers *Comments:* international management of singers in Spain; management of the Mallorcan singer Maria del Mar Bonet

Klink Producciones
c/ Alustante 22 – 1° B, 28002 **Madrid**
Tel: 91-510 0397 Fax: 91-510 0399
Internet: www.afra.com/klink
E-Mail: klink@mad.servicom.es
director Mariano Gutierrez
Artforms: blues, rock, new music *Comments:* concert producers

Lateral
Aptdo. Correos 4.132, 30157 **Murcia**
Tel: 968-847 609 Fax: 968-840 789
general manager Miguel R Martinez Molina; tour organiser Benito Rubio; dance manager Adoracion Izquierdo
Artforms: ballet, flamenco, music, theatre, tour organisation, classical music and opera *Comments:* manages Compañía de Danza Española de Murcia; see also Dance

Laura Kumin
c/ Imperial 3, 2° izq., 28012 **Madrid**
Tel: 91-365 7037 Fax: 91-365 7037
contact Laura Kumin
Artforms: dance *Comments:* produces, writing; co-organises Certamen Coreográfico de Madrid with the Agency Paso a Dos; direct A Pedir de Boca, choreographed dinner part featuring Spanish choreographer and cusine; programme dance at Teatro Pradillo; see also Competitions

Lesley Postle
Apto de Correos 43, 08319 **Canyamars (Barcelona)**
Tel: 93-795 5183 Fax: 93-795 5183
director Lesley Postle
Comments: manages British Choral Academy (qv); personal management of Laszlo Heltay (conductor)

LICANUS
Apto. de correos 115, 46450 **Benisaió (Valencia)**
Tel: 96-178 0015/629-618 411 (mobile)
Fax: 96-178 0015
Internet: www.dkey.es/licanus/
E-Mail: sincopa@ciberia.com
Artforms: early music, baroque, contemporary, flamenco, jazz and ethnic music
Comments: international management

Macandé
Av. Repúblíca Argentína 24 2° A modulo 3, Torre Los Remedios, 41011 **Sevilla**
Tel: 95-427 1700 Fax: 95-427 8508
Internet: www.macande.zoom.es
E-Mail: macande@zoom.es
director Manuel Fernandéz; admininstration Debora Garber
Artforms: flamenco, song, music & dance

Magerit Musical Foundation
c/ Castelar 7, 28028 **Madrid**
Tel: 91-355 0075 Fax: 91-355 0075
E-Mail: magerit@magerit.com
gerente Angeles Chamorro; director artistico Sydney d'Agvilo
Artforms: early music, classical music, soloists, conductors, chamber music, choirs, orchestras, jazz, new age music *Comments:* artists management; see also Services

Mamá Mulata Productions
Carmen 39 entlo., 08001 **Barcelona**
Tel: 93-412 3545 Fax: 93-301 0980
E-Mail: lacubana@ctv.es
director Jordi Milán
Artforms: theatre, comedy
Comments: main activity is the production of La Cubana Accions Teatrals; see also Drama

Management i Disseny d'Espectacles
management and event's design
Via Laietana 21, 1° C, 08003 **Barcelona**
Tel: 93-310 5362 Fax: 93-310 4037
E-Mail: mde@ctv.es
director Jaume Martínez; contratación Sonia Isidro
Artforms: blues, rock/pop music, jazz

MapaMusicx
Luis Antunez 6, 2°, 08006 **Barcelona**
Tel: 93-218 6548 Fax: 93-218 6548
E-Mail: acts@hostiatnet.es
director Elisendo Belda

Marta Oliveres
Pistó 38, 08026 **Barcelona**
Tel: 93-435 0300 Fax: 93-450 4246
E-Mail: querala.lucas@mx3.redestb.es
management Marta Oliveres; assistant Aïda Farré
Artforms: theatre, music, electronic art and contemporary dance *Comments:* produce, promote and distribute theatre companies, music and dance; international management; organises tours in Spain

Miguel Lerin-Vilardell
La Rambla n° 54, 2° 1ª, 08002 **Barcelona**
Tel: 93-301 7548 Fax: 93-301 7486
director Miguel Lerin-Vilardell
Artforms: opera singers and orchestra conductors

Mirarte Producciones
c/ Portugal 12, 29017 **Málaga**
Tel: 95-229 4909 Fax: 95-229 4909
contact Maite Serrano, Nuria Fernandez, Jose Antonio Triguero
Artforms: puppets & small format theatre

Música Clasica – Mercedes Sánchez del Río
c/ Cafeto n° 5, 28007 **Madrid**
Tel: 91-501 9150 Fax: 91-551 6153
director Mercedes Sánchez del Río
Artforms: individual artists, ensembles and symphonic and chamber orchestras, conductor, instrumentalist, singer *Comments:* member of the European Association of Artist Managers

Música Gyr Santiago Gyr
Carretera la Bisbal 5,
43712 **Llorenc del Penedés (Tarragona)**
Tel: 977-678 610 Fax: 977-678 313
E-Mail: mgyr@ctv.es
gerente Santiago Gyr
Artforms: instrumental soloists and ensembles, classical music *Comments:* organises Musica Als Patis Festival of Classical Music in Tarragona, Festival Grec de Barcelona; see also Festivals

Musicales Santi
c/ Saclosa 22, 2° 2ª, 08240 **Manresa (Barcelona)**
Tel: 93-872 8507 Fax: 93-872 8507
director Roger Santistere Prat
Artforms: classical music, dance music

MusiEspaña, SL
c/ Zurbano 34, 4° Derecha, 28010 **Madrid**
Tel: 91-308 4724/5786 Fax: 91-310 1065
Internet: www.onfeoed.com/musiespana
E-Mail: h.oran@musiespana.com
director Humberto Orán; administración Paloma Martín
Artforms: personal representation of conductors, instrumentalists, chamber ensembles, orchestras, singers; general management (concert series, opera production, thematic festivals); orchestral touring, sponsorship consultancy

Nacho Sánchez s.l.
c/ Barquillo 32, 1° izquierda, 28004 **Madrid**
Tel: 91-522 2494/531 2129 Fax: 91-522 2440
E-Mail: nachosanchez@ctv.es
director Nacho Sánchez
Artforms: dance (especially ballet), some theatre

Nelson Music Spain
c/ Beneficio 30 1°-1, 28260 **Galapagar (Madrid)**
Tel: 91-858 6802 Fax: 91-858 4715
Internet: www.cempresarial.com/nelsonmusicspain
E-Mail: nelsonmusic@cempresarial.com
director Nelson Hernan Muñoz
Artforms: Spanish jazz, new flamenco: music and dance, folk fusion, flamenco conferences and workshops

Noria, La
c/ González Adalid 12, 30001 **Murcia**
Tel: 968-223 720 Fax: 968-223 721
E-Mail: lanoria@arrakis.es
director Nicolás Torrano Fernández
Artforms: street theatre, physical theatre, community and educational work

NR Contrataciones y Espectáculos
c/ Angel Guimera, 12 bj.,
08100 **Mollet del Valles (Barcelona)**
Tel: 93-570 4496/629-369 689 (mobile) Fax: 93-579 3346
director/manager Manuel Rodriguez Rodriguez
Artforms: Spanish music, flamenco

OKAPI Producciones
Gran Via 56, 4° Izda, 28013 **Madrid**
Tel: 91-559 6143 Fax: 91-542 5728
E-Mail: okapi@intercom.es
director & press Enrique Calabuch (email: enrique@intercom.es); contratación Kike Nieto
Artforms: world music, flamenco, jazz, folk *Comments:* represents, organises festivals, concerts and tours

Oniria International SL
c/ Alzines n° 3, Sant Quirze Parc,
08192 **Sant Quirze del Valles (Barcelona)**
Tel: 93-721 4247 Fax: 93-721 4610
Internet: www.neuronium.com
E-Mail: oniria@neuronium.com
director Michel Huygen; manager Antoni Brunet
Artforms: new age music, pop, rock, dance, audiovisual shows, soundtracks for TV and cinema, multimedia
Comments: websites interactive designs (internet); see also Services

P.M. Osuna S.L.
Pasaje Rogelio Muñoz s/n, Hortaleza, 28043 **Madrid**
Tel: 91-381 2361 Fax: 91-381 9810
E-Mail: osuna@mx3.redestb.es
producer manager Pepe Osuna
Artforms: dance, music, theatre *Comments:* manages and produces; production of a variety of performances

Pentación S.L. Espectáculos
Marquès Viudo. de Pontejos 2, 2ª Pta 13, 28012 **Madrid**
Tel: 91-523 1069/522 8145/523 1766 Fax: 91-523 2560
E-Mail: pentacion@mx4.redestb.es
director general Jesús F Cimarro; secretaria Elena Gómez; ventas Kathleen Lòpez, Graciela Huesca
Artforms: classical and modern theatre and comedy
Comments: produce, promote and distribute theatre shows

Pere Porta Concerts
c/ La Granada del Penedés 18-20, 4° 2ª,
08006 **Barcelona**
Tel: 93-217 5228/5077 Fax: 93-237 0694
E-Mail: pereporta@mail.sendanet.es
directors Pere Porta; adjuntos Cristina Lluis, Patrick Alfaya Mc Shane; contabilidad Carmen Bouer; administración Susana Formells
Artforms: classical music *Comments:* management of classical musicians; conductors, instrumentalists, singers, chamber ensembles

Pigmalión – Productora de Espectáculos
Gran Vía 61, 8ª, 28013 **Madrid**
Tel: 91-584 4000 Fax: 91-541 2199
E-Mail: pigmalion@retemail.es
director Luis Ramírez
Artforms: music, theatre, dance
Comments: produces and presents a variety of art forms at own managed venues, Teatro Lara (q.v.) and Teatro Lope de Vega (q.v.)

Primusic
Juan de la Cueva n° 5, 28007 **Madrid**
Tel: 91-434 8086/7
E-Mail: primusic@teleline.es
directora Carmen Prieto
Artforms: classical music, especially baroque ensembles with original instruments *Comments:* represents orchestras, groups and musicians for tours in Spain

Producción General de Espectáculos S.A.
Av. San Luis 97, 3° B, 28033 **Madrid**
Tel: 91-766 0000 Fax: 91-767 2835
director y programador Francisco Marsó
Artforms: all types of music and theatre

Producciones La Frasca
c/ Cisterniga 9 bajo, 47005 **Valladolid**
Tel: 983-210 881/607-898 047 (mobile) Fax: 983-201 191
director Tomás Martín
Artforms: drama, puppets *Comments:* manage La Quimera de Plástico theatre company, (q.v.); organise tours abroad, mainly in Latin America

Producciones La Zarzuela s.l.
Marques de Casa Riera nº 2, 28014 **Madrid**
Tel: 91-522 3403 Fax: 91-522 1926
director Jose Tamayo; director ejecutivo Manuel Ganchegui
Artforms: zarzuela *Comments:* Antología de la Zarzuela, see also Dance and Opera

Producciones Yllana
C/ Jesus Nº 20, 4º A, 07003 **Palma de Mallorca**
Tel: 971-207 410/609-604 923 (mobile) Fax: 971-202 157
director Marcos Ottone
Artforms: comedy, visual theatre
Comments: they also organise festivals; see also Drama, Festivals and Venues

Programaciones Musicales
c/ Cristobal Colon nº 7, pral 3ª,
08100 **Mollet del Valles (Barcelona)**
Tel: 93-593 9945/639-557 190 (mobile) Fax: 93-309 2371
Internet: www.ejn.it/ag/ibanez.htm
E-Mail: franciba@adam.es
director general Francesc Ibáñez; administración Ella Mogler; productor musical Ramón Escalé
Artforms: blues, jazz, gospel, folk

Promotora
c/o Isabel Castellet, Collserola 59, 08035 **Barcelona**
Tel: 93-211 5005 Fax: 93-211 5005
E-Mail: isoria-castellet@infomail.lacaixa.es
management Isabel Castellet
Artforms: theatre, music, music-flamenco *Comments:* produce, promote and distribute theatre companies, music and dance; international management

Ramón Bielsa
c/ Rodrigo Rebolledo 39, 2º D, 50002 **Zaragoza**
Tel: 976-593 868
director Ramón Bielsa
Artforms: music, cabaret

Real Music Productions, The
Aptdo de Correos 188, 46177 **Bétera (Valencia)**
Tel: 96-168 7341 Fax: 96-168 7342
Internet: www.ctv.es/USERS/trm
E-Mail: trm@ctv.es
director Joaquin Martínez; co-ordinador y administración Aranzazu Alcañíz
Artforms: jazz, new age, flamenco, classical music, blues, salsa, dance
Comments: see also Tebar Asociados

Rial y Eshelman
Molino de Viento 6, 1º B, 28004 **Madrid**
Tel: 91-531 0959 Fax: 91-531 8391
director Jose Rial
Artforms: mainly classical dance groups (international)

Sanzkonzert
c/ Pau Claris 113 1º 2, 08009 **Barcelona**
Tel: 93-487 3833 Fax: 93-487 7892
Internet: www.sanzkonzert.es
E-Mail: sanz@sanzkonzert.es
gerente director Alfonso Sanz López; adjunta dirección Kueta Sanzova
Artforms: chamber ensembles, philharmonic and symphonic orchestras, opera, ballet *Comments:* present their own concert season, see also Promoters

Sauma & Tumbao
c/ Carretas 14, 4º E, 28012 **Madrid**
Tel: 91-532 4320/521 3847 Fax: 91-532 4797
E-Mail: saumatum@teleline.es
director of salsa & folk dept Saúl Rodriguez; director of flamenco dept Francisco Sánchez
Artforms: flamenco, salsa, celtic folk
Comments: managers of Campanas Flamencas (q.v.); see also Dance

Servei d'Espectacles Jesús Herrera
Carrer Estret de Sant Cristòfol 1, 2ª,
08500 **Vic (Barcelona)**
Tel: 93-889 3020 Fax: 93-886 3232
E-Mail: ausamusic@mx2.redestb.es
director Jesús Herrera
Artforms: international music, theatre and dance, street theatre

Serveis de l'Espectacle Focus S.A.
Passatge Trullat 10, 08005 **Barcelona**
Tel: 93-309 7538 Fax: 93-485 1512
E-Mail: focus@mail.cinet.es
director Daniel Martinez; subdirector Jordi Gonzalez; production manager Amparo Martinez; administración Pilar Soldevila; programacion Javier Urbasos
Artforms: theatre productions and exhibitions: drama, classics and musicals
Comments: provides services for theatre productions

Sociedad Musical Armonía, S.L.
Pl. del Príncipe 2, entlo., 39003 **Santander**
Tel: 942-361 880 Fax: 942-361 969
Internet: empresas.mundivia.es/armonia
E-Mail: armonia@mundivia.es
managing director Belen Alonso; president Sorín Melinte; officer Ana Fernandez
Artforms: orchestra tours, opera, soloists and chamber groups *Comments:* worldwide agents of Byzantium spectacle and of Kontakion choir

Sona Espectaculos
Actividades Culturales Unidas, El Palmaret, 7 Bajo,
46120 **Alboraya (Valencia)**
Tel: 96-186 0411/617-972 911 (mobile)
Fax: 96-186 0412
contact José Soriano
Artforms: opera, ballet, classical music *Comments:* organise opera, ballet and concert tours around Spain and Portugal

Syntorama
Barrio Castaño 19, bajo, 20100 **Rentería (Guipuzkoa)**
Tel: 943-529 171 Fax: 943-516 292
Internet: www.noed-rekords.com
E-Mail: syntorama@clientes.euskaltel.es
director Cruz Gorostegui, Mikel Camino;
press Idoia Luzuriaga
Artforms: new music *Comments:* distributing and promoting concerts of new music in Spain; also organise Festival Nuevas Musicas de San Sebastián; at the present time represent exclusively in Spain, artists such as Madredeus, Dulce Pontes, Alasbair Fraiser, Soweto String Quartet, Wim Mertens, Liam O'Flynn, Paul Winter, Rodrigo Leao; own recording company NO – CD Records; see also Festivals and Recorded Media

Takuara
La Bola 4, 4º ext., 28013 **Madrid**
Tel: 91-542 5748 Fax: 91-542 5748
Internet: www.arrakis.es/takuara
E-Mail: takuara@arrakis.es
productora Elena Delgado-Corral; coordinador Cheick Diouk
Artforms: ethnic music from Africa and South America

Tebar Asociados
Apto de Correos 188, 46117 **Bétera (Valencia)**
Tel: 96-168 7341 Fax: 96-168 7342
E-Mail: tebar@apdo.es
directora Amparo Tebar
Artforms: jazz, salsa, blues, classical music *Comments:* produces and presents a variety of international jazz; see also Real Music Productions

TP Teruel Producciones SL
c/ Marroquina 51, 1º A, 28030 **Madrid**
Tel: 91-430 9024/439 9284 Fax: 91-430 5363
director Pepe Teruel; jefe de contratacion Manuel Teruel
Artforms: pop, theatre, classical music, opera, zarzuela, flamenco *Comments:* touring Latin America

Trajana Producciones
c/ Betis 14, ACC, 41010 **Sevilla**
Tel: 95-434 0311 Fax: 95-434 0364
Internet: www.trajana.com
E-Mail: trajana@arrakis.es
general manager Tina Panadero; administrator Rafael Diaz
Artforms: mostly Flamenco companies, dancers, singers and guitarists; artistic consultants for festivals, international meetings
Comments: welcome foreign artists – management of Flamenco dancer Cristina Hoyos; see also Dance

Truke Distribucion
c/ San Nicolás 76, 4º, 31001 **Pamplona**
Tel: 948-225 032/610-883 075 (mobile)
Fax: 948-225 032
agents Belén Alvarez, Helena Amontarain
Artforms: theatre, contemporary dance

SWEDEN (+46)

Almanova Artist
Anekdotgatan 17, 422 41 **Hisings Backa (Gothenburg)**
Tel: 31-744 1419 Fax: 31-222 565
Internet: www.almanova.com
E-Mail: info@almanova.com
contact Sirpa-Leena Kuussaari
Artforms: classical music

Artistsekretariat Ulf Törnqvist
Sankt Eriksgatan 100, 113 31 **Stockholm**
Tel: 8-338 323/333 365/398 325 Fax: 8-338 300
director Ulf Törnqvist
Artforms: singers, conductors, composers

Double Agent artist management
Aprikosgatan 29, 165 60 **Hässelby**
Tel: 8-471 9604 Fax: 8-471 9604
E-Mail: ann-charlotte.hell@swipnet.se
contact Ann-Charlotte Hell
Artforms: classical music, specialises in early music

DPS (Danceproductionservice)
Wallingatan 21, 111 24 **Stockholm**
Tel: 8-676 9620 Fax: 8-676 9624
Internet: www.dansklotet.se
E-Mail: dps@dansklotet.se
general manager Veronica Bedecs; production assistant Lotta Roos
Comments: agency for 7 choreographers and 1 performing group: Örjan Andersson, Philippe Blanchard, Cristina Caprioli, Björn Elisson, Kenneth Kvarnström, Virpi Pahkinen, Jens Östberg and Bogdan Szyber & Carina Reich

Hans Hiort Opera AB
Tegnérgatan 9, 111 40 **Stockholm**
Tel: 8-791 9055/54-140 840 Fax: 8-791 9055/54-100 934
director Hans Hiort
Comments: produces the Stockholm Opera Festival and other operatic events in Sweden and the rest of Scandinavia

Helena Friberg Artists Management (hfam)
Nibblevägen 25, 2 tr, 177 36 **Järfälla**
Tel: 8-5801 2770 Fax: 8-5801 2770
Internet: www.hfam.nu
E-Mail: hfam@swipnet.se
contact Helena Friberg
Artforms: classical music (soloists, singers, conductors and ensembles)

Intercult
Nytorgsgatan 15, 116 22 **Stockholm**
Tel: 8-644 1023 Fax: 8-643 9676
Internet: www.intercult.se
E-Mail: info@intercult.se
artistic director Chris Torch; producer Ida Burén; audience development Rani Sukhia
Artforms: community work, festivals, multicultural and intercultural projects *Comments:* see also Promoters

Konsertbolaget Scandinavian Artists Management AB
Vasagatan 52, 111 20 **Stockholm**
Tel: 8-245 815 Fax: 8-245 595
director Thomas Boltenstern; artist managers Katarina Boltenstern, Michael Ljung
Artforms: classical music

More Promotions
Norragatan, 810 65 **Skärplinge**
Tel: 294-31119 Fax: 294-31119
E-Mail: moreprom@aol.com
Monica Danielsson, Reinhard Bichsel
Artforms: circus, dance, theatre *Comments:* tours with companies from overseas, especially Oceania, Africa (Circus Oz, Circus Ethiopia); organises festivals

Nöjes Kontoret
Sibyllegatan 18, 114 42 **Stockholm**
Tel: 8-5630 5400 Fax: 8-661 2212
Internet: www.nojeskontoret.com
E-Mail: marie@vicky-nojesproduktion.se
managing director Vicky von der Lancken; production coordinators Marie Schroeder, My Stroebaek; financial manager Birgitta Roennhedh
Artforms: event management, theatre & musical productions, FTT Agency (actors, script-writers and director's agency), TV productions

Nordic Artist AB
Box 12881, 112 98 **Stockholm**
Tel: 8-5626 2050 Fax: 8-5626 2060
Internet: www.nordicartist.se
E-Mail: info@nordicartist.se
impresario Johan Englund; marketing director Anna Byström
Artforms: concert promotion, event production/promotion *Comments:* local and international touring arrangements for orchestras, ensembles and choirs; production of television, radio and gramophone recordings; visiting address: Industrigatan 4A; see also Promoters

Scenit Produktion AB
Näkesgatan 1, 116 40 **Stockholm**
Tel: 8-714 0430/31 Fax: 8-714 0432
Internet: www.scenit.se
E-Mail: info@scenit.se
owner and producer Ulrika Skoog; producers Lena Uhlander, Cais-Marie Björnlod
Comments: theatre production company; visiting address: Närkesgatan 1

Scherzo Stockholm Management AB
Hogbergsgatan 66a, 118 54 **Stockholm**
Tel: 8-615 0667 Fax: 8-615 0669
director Kristina Hennel Lee

Svensk Konsertdirektion AB
Box 5076, 402 22 **Göteborg**
Tel: 31-830 095 Fax: 31-408 011
E-Mail: info@loddingkonsert.se
directors Henrik F Lodding, Gunilla Lodding Ruijsenaars
Artforms: soloists, ensembles, orchestras, conductors
Comments: international and national concert and artist management

Svenska Konsertbyrån AB
Jungfrugatan 45, 114 44 **Stockholm**
Tel: 8-665 8088 Fax: 8-665 8066
Internet: www.svenskakonsertbyran.se
E-Mail: info@svenskakonsertbyran.se
managing director Kerstin Hammarström; artist manager Ann Braathen; assistant Christina Svalfors; accountant Arne Rydén
Artforms: classical soloists, singers, conductors and ensembles

Tyndale-Biscoe Promotions
Klubbacken 34, 129 39 **Hägersten**
Tel: 8-464 7624 Fax: 8-464 7624
E-Mail: PhilipTB@aol.com
director Vendela Tyndale-Biscoe

SWITZERLAND (+41)

4 Arts
Münchhaldenstr 11, 8008 **Zürich**
Tel: 1-381 3758 Fax: 1-381 3758
contact Beatrice Rossi
Artforms: dance and contemporary music *Comments:* please see separate entry in Hungary

Agence Artistique Toth
rue Fléclés 14, 2800 **Delémont**
Tel: 32-422 3135 Fax: 32-423 1193
directeur Antal Toth
Artforms: orchestra, variety, ballet, theatre

Agence de Concerts et Spectacles Caecilia
29, rue de la Coulouvreniére, 1204 **Genève**
Tel: 22-809 1520 Fax: 22-809 1528
Internet: www.caecilia.ch
E-Mail: caecilia@caecilia.ch
directeurs Louise-Antoinette Lombard, Pedro Kranz
Artforms: conductors, pianists, instrumentalists, ensembles, chamber orchestras, orchestras, singers *Comments:* promote 26 recitals, chamber music and orchestra concerts in Geneva and Zürich; lyric department: Rennweg 15, 8001 Zürich, Tel: 1-221 3388, Fax: 1-211 7182

Agence Jack Yfar
rue Plantamaur 18-20, case postale 67, 1211 **Genève** 21
Tel: 22-741 4147 Fax: 22-741 4148
director Jack Yfar

Agency Inter Media Maria Zehnder
Zwinglistr 35, 8004 **Zürich**
Tel: 1-241 1739 Fax: 1-242 3297
E-Mail: ZEHNDER_Maria@compuserve.com
Inhaberin Maria Zehnder
Artforms: organisation and production of culture & arts projects, emphasis on music & rhythm *Comments:* culture management /Kulturmanagement

Anne Petkov Artists Management
6 rue du Conseil-Général, 1205 **Genève**
Tel: 22-321 3226 Fax: 22-321 3227
director Anne Petkov
Artforms: small group of singers, conductors and instrumentalists worldwide

Artists Management Zürich
Rütistrasse 52, 8044 **Zürich-Gockhausen**
Tel: 1-821 8957 Fax: 1-821 0127
E-Mail: artistsman@duebinet.ch
Direktorin Rita Schütz
Artforms: opera and concerts; personal management of conductors, singers, producers and designers

Aruno
Hornbachstrasse 50, 8034 **Zürich**
Tel: 1-389 8450 Fax: 1-389 8400
Internet: www.operissimo.com
E-Mail: opera@operissimo.com
manager Bruno Franzen
Artforms: opera

Balmer & Dixon Management AG
Granitweg 2, 8006 **Zürich**
Tel: 1-363 6280 Fax: 1-361 9355
E-Mail: badix@compuserve.com
directors Rudolf Balmer, Ritha Dixon
Artforms: singers, conductors, a few instrumentalists
Comments: personal management mainly on a world wide basis

Bureau de Concerts Wismer-Casetti
Case postale 63, 1222 **Vésenaz**
Tel: 22-752 5439 Fax: 22-752 5372
E-Mail: wismer@infomaniak.ch
directeur Monique Wismer
Artforms: classic music, ballet

Caecilia Lyric Department
Rennweg 15, 8001 **Zürich**
Tel: 1-221 3388 Fax: 1-211 7182
E-Mail: caecilia@caecilia-lyric.ch
Inhaber Mariano Horak; Mitarbeiterin Stephanie Ammann
Artforms: opera and concert singers
Comments: second office in Genève

Circolo Musicale Rappresentanza Artisti
Vignon, 6558 **Lostallo**
Tel: 91-830 1288 Fax: 91-830 1555
Internet: www.ticino.com/usr/musica
E-Mail: etonolla@ticino.com
director Emilia Tonolla-Rosa
Artforms: classical music, special attractions, workshops – instrumental soloists and ensembles *Comments:* artist representation and associated concert promotion

Claudia Bloechlinger Artists Representative
Gatterstr. 1b, 9010 **St Gallen**
Tel: 71-222 3980 Fax: 71-222 3889
contact Frau Schneider
Artforms: classical music ensembles, conductors, singers

Columbia Artists Management AG
Kapuzinerweg 7, 6006 **Luzern**
Tel: 41-420 7758 Fax: 41-420 7759
E-Mail: cami_ch@compuserve.com
Geschäftsführerin Beatrice Vesper; artist manager Michael Eriskat
Artforms: conductors, solo instrumentalists, vocal artists, ensembles, orchestra tours *Comments:* limited list of international artists, presentation of concerts

Denise Conta Personal Artists' Management
1 Chemin de la Mairie, 1294 **Genthod (Genève)**
Tel: 22-774 1229 Fax: 22-774 3138
E-Mail: contartist@bluewin.ch
director Denise Conta
Artforms: personal management *Comments:* representation of Mikhail Pletnev (pianist and conductor)

gerstel & cahn international opera management
Stockerstrasse 10, 8002 **Zürich**
Tel: 76-391 8801 (T Gerstel)/419 4882 (A Cahn)
Fax: 1-391 8759
directors Teddy Gerstel, Aviel Cahn
Artforms: mainly opera singers and conductors, also instrumentalists and the Zürich Chamber Orchestra

Good News Productions AG
Postfach, 8065 **Zürich**
Tel: 1-809 6666 Fax: 1-809 6600
Internet: www.ticketcorner.ch
E-Mail: promotions@email.ch
director André Béchir
Artforms: rock, pop and classical concerts
Comments: concert management; see also Promoters

IBA International Booking Agency
3 avenue Florimont, 1820 **Montreux**
Tel: 21-963 5031 Fax: 21-963 8895
director Willy Leiser; assistant coordination Christiane de Dompierre
Artforms: spiritual, gospel song, jazz, blues, folklore

international cultural exchange (ICE)
15 ch de la Rochette, 1202 **Genève**
Tel: 22-733 2222 Fax: 22-733 4400
Internet: mypage.bluewin.ch/ktice/
E-Mail: ktice@bluewin.ch
impresario Kazuma Tomisawa
Artforms: opera and classical instrumentalists, singers and orchestras, overseas tour, festival and artist promotion *Comments:* find and coordinate sponsorship for major promotions; theatre consultancy (stage and architecture); see also Promoters

Internationale Konzertagentur Pio Chesini
Aeschenvorstadt 24, Postfach, 4010 **Basel**
Tel: 61-272 2229 Fax: 61-272 2291
Artforms: classical musicians only

Konzert und Theater AG Basel
Burgunder Strasse 42, Postfach, 4002 **Basel**
Tel: 61-272 2902 Fax: 61-272 2902
président Hans Rudolf Fuog
Artforms: concerts (classic, jazz etc.)

Konzert-Agentur Suzanne Gfeller
Homelstr. 34, 4114 **Hofstetten**
Tel: 61-733 0373 Fax: 61-733 0374
Internet: www.koncert.ch
E-Mail: gfeller@konzert.ch
Inhaber Susanne Gfeller
Artforms: chamber music, instrumentalist ensembles
Comments: international chamber orchestra – tours

Künstlerkontakt Marlies Düsterhaus
Postfach 7306, 7306 **Fläsch**
Tel: 81-330 1290 Fax: 81-330 1291
Internet: www.kuenstlerkontakt.ch
E-Mail: m.duesterhaus@kuenstlerkontakt.ch
Direktorin Marlies Düsterhaus
Artforms: international clowns, pantomime, cabaret, small theatre, music

media arts productions
Postfach 60, 8034 **Zürich**
Tel: 1-383 4704 Fax: 1-383 4704
director Pamela Hunter
Artforms: music, theatre and opera productions, direction, lighting and presentation

MiDi Music Management GmbH
Schönbüel 11-13, 6072 **Sachseln**
Tel: 41-662 0020/22 Fax: 41-662 0021/23
Internet: www.midimusic.ch
E-Mail: info@midimusic.ch
managing director, PR & customer services Markus Michel (michel@midimusic.ch); manager, finance & administration Walter Dillier (dillier@midimusic.ch)
Artforms: percussion, chamber orchestras, soloists, instrumentalists
Comments: also tour management

Montreux Jazz Festival
Case Postale 126, 1820 **Territet – Montreux**
Tel: 21-966 4444 Fax: 21-966 4441
Internet: www.montreuxjazz.com
E-Mail: info@mgs.ch
artistic director Claude Nobs; artistic coordination Michaela Maithert, Lori Immi; marketing/sponsoring Cyril Zammit; public relations Ingrid Walther; infrastructure/f&b Míchel Muller
Artforms: soloists, bands, choirs; all musical styles, emphasis on concerts, acoustic music
Comments: see also Festivals

More Promotions
Rainweg 2, 4126 **Bettingen**
Tel: 61-601 9068 Fax: 61-601 9068
E-Mail: moreprom@aol.com
Monica Danielsson, Reinhard Bichsel
Artforms: circus, dance, theatre
Comments: tours with companies from overseas, especially Oceania, Africa (Circus Oz, Circus Ethiopia); organises festivals

Musa Promotion, Künstleragentur
Thormannstrasse 64, 3005 **Bern**
Tel: 31-351 4245 Fax: 31-351 4246
manager (Inhaber) Alexandru Lucianu; director Ileana Lucianu
Artforms: opera, instrumental soloists, chamber, symphony orchestras, choirs, ballet, choreography, conductors

Music Management
Untere Zelg 30, 3145 **Bern-Oberscherli**
Tel: 31-849 2323 Fax: 31-849 1719
E-Mail: dtc.thoma@bluewin.ch
director Dina Thoma-Tennenbaum
Artforms: ensembles, orchestras

Music Masters Management
Riedstr. 1, 6343 **Rotkreuz (Zug)**
Tel: 41-799 5929 Fax: 41-799 5931
Internet: www.MMMint.com
E-Mail: mmm@pobox.ch
president Claudius Hirt; new media Marcus Hirt
Artforms: conductors, instrumentalists and ensembles worldwide *Comments:* personal, concert and tour management, concerts & master classes; Music Master Management is part of the FAME group

Music Promotion Manfred Gerber
Platz 11, 8200 **Schaffhausen**
Tel: 52-624 7117 Fax: 52-624 7111
E-Mail: MusicPromotion@datacomm.ch
Inhaber Manfred Gerber; Mitarbeiter Oliver Golloch
Artforms: symphony music, classical ballet, opera – orchestral touring *Comments:* no artists' management

Musica Piú AG
Bantigerstraße 20, 3006 **Bern**
Tel: 31-352 1400 Fax: 31-352 1400
contact Barbara Nyffeler
Artforms: international representation of instrumentalists and opera singers

Paleo Arts et Spectacles
rte de St-Cergue 312, Case Postale 177, 1260 **Nyon**
Tel: 22-361 0101 Fax: 22-365 1020
Internet: www.paleo.ch
E-Mail: paleo@paleo.ch
directeur Daniel Rossellat; responsable de la programmation Jacques Monnier, Isabelle Primault; presse Vincent Sager
Artforms: annual Paleo festival in July – rock, chanson, blues, classical, worldmusic, street performances, rap, electronic *Comments:* see also Festivals

Prestige Artists
16 rue Du-Roveray, 1207 **Genève**
Tel: 22-786 4521 Fax: 22-786 5221
E-Mail: prestigeart@datacomm.ch
managing director Elisabeth Christeler
Artforms: classique, jazz, organise tours

Pro Musicis
Rütistrasse 38, 8032 **Zürich**
Tel: 1-251 6533 Fax: 1-252 2914
Direktorin Silvia Ackermann; assistant Andrea Frehner
Artforms: soloists, chamber music, chamber orchestras

Rent-A-Show AG
Carmenstrasse 12, Postfach, 8030 **Zürich**
Tel: 1-265 5601 Fax: 1-265 5699
E-Mail: info@rentashow.ch
direktor Freddy Burger
Artforms: international artists management, festivals, events, agency

Sardis Artists' Management
Via Generale Guisan 7, 6900 **Lugano-Massagno**
Tel: 91-966 5034 Fax: 91-967 2256
presidente Dr. Yvonne Brodetti
Artforms: classical music only *Comments:* represents artists and concert organisers

Scala-Theater Arlesheim
Schorenweg 10, 4144 **Arlesheim**
Tel: 61-417 9200 Fax: 61-417 9209
E-Mail: scalatheater@bluewin.ch
director Vincent Grabowsky
Artforms: musicals, drama, ballet, operetta, opera, concerts, classical *Comments:* tours, own productions

Schlaepfer und Partner, ASAM
Hottingerstrasse 44, Postfach, 8030 **Zürich**
Tel: 1-261 0000 Fax: 1-251 4342
director Ulrich Schlaepfer
Artforms: orchestras, instrumentalists, night club entertainment for hotels, restaurants, cruises, international booking, circus, TV, variety

Special Diffusion Spectacles
Case Postale 5, 1000 **Lausanne** 24
Tel: 21-841 1783 Fax: 21-841 1700
directeur Jean-Marc Genier
Artforms: production & tours, variétés, comedy, classical theatre, world music *Comments:* work in the Théâtre de Beausobre in Morges – see also Venues

Susanna Wipf
Bahnhofstr. 99, 9240 **Uzwil**
Tel: 71-951 9201 Fax: 71-951 9202
E-Mail: ahagentur@bluewin.ch
Direktion und künstlerische Leitung Susanna Wipf; Sekretariat Lea Tribelhorn (71-951 9202)
Artforms: modern classical music, literature, theatre
Comments: see also Orchestras: Strings of Zurich

Swiss Musictour
Moosstrasse 2, 6003 **Luzern**
Tel: 41-240 5477 Fax: 41-240 2672
directeur Franz Bachmann
Artforms: rock, pop, jazz
Comments: tour and concert organiser

Interclassica
4 Rue Jean Jacques Rousseau, 1800 **Vevey**
Tel: 21-922 4016 Fax: 21-922 4018
president Jean Jacques Indermühle; director Martin Tison Engstroem
Comments: artist representation and concert promotion

TURKEY (+90)

Pozitif Productions
Havyar Sok. No. 54, Cihangir, 80060 **Istanbul**
Tel: 212-252 5167/244 3394 Fax: 212-252 5167
managing directors Mehmet Ulug, Cem Yegul, Ahmet Ulug
Artforms: opera, music, dance

UKRAINE (+380)

Independent Artistic agency
PO Box 2862, 320128 **Dnipropetrovsk**
Tel: 562-352 763 Fax: 562-352 763
E-Mail: agency@ljub.dp.ua
contact Valery Ljubchenko
Artforms: ensembles, singers, pianists, visual art

Kievconcert
Richna St. 4, 252135 **Kiev (Kyiv)**
Tel: 44-216 5015
director Vyacheslav Stratienko

Tiko Agency
Vetrova ulitea 5/2, 252032 **Kiev (Kyiv)**
Tel: 44-268 6240/244 7811 Fax: 44-268 6240/244 7811
manager Leonid Tischenko; vice-chairman Valentina Stepanova
Artforms: large and chamber ensembles, ballet, opera singers, choirs *Comments:* charitable events for children

UNITED KINGDOM (+44)

1st Framework
44-46 Nelson Square, **London** SE1 0QA
Tel: 20-7803 0530 Fax: 20-7803 0531
directors Maxine Webster, Peter Avery
Artforms: stage designers

Acker's International Jazz Agency
53 Cambridge Mansions, Cambridge Road, **London** SW11 4RX
Tel: 20-7978 5885/6 Fax: 20-7978 5882
contact Pamela Frances Sutton, Leslie S Squires
Artforms: personal management; agent for jazz bands, orchestras, big bands and sixties groups

Albemarle of London
74 Mortimer Street, **London** W1N 8HL
Tel: 20-7631 0135 Fax: 20-7323 3074
Internet: www.demon.co.uk/albermarlelondon2
E-Mail: sales@albermarlelondon.demon.co.uk
productions administrator Kim Chritchley
Artforms: theatrical producers; scenic constructors and hire; costume hire

Alexander European Management
38 Lytton Grove, Putney, **London** SW15 2HB
Tel: 20-8780 9377 Fax: 20-8788 1481
director David Bartleet
Artforms: represents Europe-based singers, conductors and directors in the fields of opera, music-theatre and concert

Allied Artists Agency
42 Montpelier Square, **London** SW7 1JZ
Tel: 20-7589 6243 Fax: 20-7581 5269
Internet: www.alliedartists.co.uk
E-Mail: info@alliedartists.co.uk
partners Andrew Rosner, Robert Slotover
Artforms: classical music *Comments:* international management of a wide range of opera and concert artists

Alpha Arts Management
55 Merrit Road, Crofton Park, **London** SE4 1DT
Tel: 20-8692 2700/973-539 562 Fax: 20-8692 0669
contact Alpha Hopkins
Artforms: lighting designers

Anglo-Swiss Artists' Management Ltd
Suite 35-37, Morley Hse, 320 Regent St, **London** W1R 5AD
Tel: 20-7323 2147 Fax: 20-7323 1760
directors Leor Segal, Susanne Baumgartner
Artforms: personal management of conductors, instrumentalists and chamber music ensembles; concert management

Antony Pristavec Artist & Concert Management
3 Plough Way, Surrey Quays, **London** SE16 2LS
Tel: 20-7231 5235 Fax: 20-7231 0535
Internet: members.aol.com/Pristavec/index.html
E-Mail: Pristavec@aol.com
contact Antony Pristavec
Artforms: classical music, personal management (singers, instrumentalists, conductors); concert and tour management *Comments:* specialises in artistic exchange and links between UK and Slovenia; event management of World Piano Competition, London

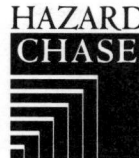

AOR Management Ltd.
Westwood, Lorraine Park,
Harrow Weald HA3 6BX
Tel: 20-8954 7646 Fax: 20-8420 7499
E-Mail: aormanagementUK@compuserve.com
director Jenny Rose
Comments: international management for opera singers

Armada Productions Ltd.
Room 6, 12 Northgate, **Chichester** PO19 1BA
Tel: 1243-790 611 Fax: 1243-790 580
E-Mail: armada@globalnet.co.uk
senior executive Andrew Welch; assistant producer Clelia Mountford
Artforms: theatre and radio production

Artists Management Productions Ltd.
26 Baker Street, **London** W1M 1DF
Tel: 20-7224 1992
Fax: 20-7224 0111
managing director Harvey Goldsmith CBE
Artforms: music, artists management, tours, production, concert promoters

Arts Worldwide Ltd
309A Aberdeen House, 22 Highbury Grove,
London N5 2DQ
Tel: 20-7354 3030
Fax: 20-7354 8404
artistic director Anne Hunt; artist's & touring manager Victoria Burns; general manager Adam Jeanes
Artforms: specialises in presentation of non-western European arts festivals and cultural events together with touring by musicians, dancers and other performing artists

Artsadmin
Toynbee Studios, 28 Commercial St.,
London E1 6LS
Tel: 20-7247 5102 Fax: 20-7247 5103
Internet: www.artsadmin.co.uk
E-Mail: all@artsadmin.co.uk
director Judith Knight; administrators Nicky Childs, Leonie Gombrich, Nicky Molloy, Eduardo Bonito; associate director Gill Lloyd; office manager Helen Ugwu; artist adviser Manick Govinda
Artforms: dance, music, theatre, visual theatre, live art *Comments:* promote and develop new theatre, dance, live art and music by providing companies with a continuous and comprehensive management service

Artsfusion Ltd
74 Mortimer Street, **London** W1N 7DF
Tel: 20-7637 7088 Fax: 20-7636 4822
E-Mail: admin@artsfusion.demon.co.uk
contact Tricia Murray-Bett, Tony Barlow
Artforms: mainly ballet and opera
Comments: see also Opera (Warclaw Opera) and Promoters

ASH Personal Management
8 Valley Road, **London** SW16 2XN
Tel: 20-8677 6171 Fax: 20-8677 6171
artistic director Anthony S. Hyland
Artforms: touring theatre productions
Comments: musicals, comedies, one-act drama, Greek classics, small and large scale touring; representation of theatre, TV and film

Askonas Holt Limited
Lonsdale Chambers, 27 Chancery Lane,
WC2E 1PF
Tel: 20-7400 1700 Fax: 20-7400 1799
Internet: www.askonasholt.co.uk
E-Mail: info@askonasholt.co.uk
president Sir Ian Hunter; chairman Sir Claus Moser; joint chief executives Martin Campbell-White, Robert Rattray; directors Peter Bloor, Mark Hildrew, Peter Martin; consultant Jenifer Eddy; artist managers Nicola-Fee Bahl, Jane Balmer, Rachel Bowron, Jan Burnett, Jilly Clarke, Robert Clarke, Rona Eastwood, Suzanne Spence, Joel Thomas, Celia Willis; travel June Mangan, Tim Mehah, Alison Charles, Jane Nicolson; tours & projects Huw Humphreys, Pip Pirie, Constanze Vageler; marketing Jonathan Fleming, sponsorship Nick Wilson; accounts Claire Mudge, John Wise
Artforms: conductors, instrumentalists, singers, orchestral & dance touring, festivals, arts consultancy, concert management

Associated Arts
8 Shrewsbury Lane, Shooters Hill, **London** SE18 3JF
Tel: 20-8856 4958 Fax: 20-8856 8189
proprietor Karen Baker
Artforms: set and costume designers, directors and lighting designers

Athole Still International Management Ltd
Foresters Hall, 25-27 Westow Street,
London SE19 3RY
Tel: 20-8771 5271 Fax: 20-8771 8172
E-Mail: athole@dial.pipex.com
managing director Athole Still
Artforms: opera, popular music, rock, personal management
Comments: international management of conductors, singers (concert and opera), directors and designers, increasingly active in company touring; management of popular music bands

Back Row Productions
1st Floor, Garrick Theatre, 2 Charing Cross Road,
London WC2
Tel: 20-7240 4282 Fax: 20-7240 7195
Internet: www.backrow.com
E-Mail: brp@backrow.co.uk
managing directors UK Elisabeth Koops, Garry McQuinn; creative director Wayne Harrison; booking agents Philippe Mongay, Elisabet Casanova; producer film & tv Andrew Higgie
Artforms: theatre, musical theatre, dance, film
Comments: producers of TAP DOGS; booking agents; European and Australasian touring; also offices in New York: 185 Franklin Street, New York NY 10013, USA, Tel: +1 212-334 0201, Fax: +1 212-334 2140, and Australia: Suite 2, Level 2, 66 Oxford Street, East Sydney NSW 2011, Australia, Tel: +61 2-9360 0459, Fax: +61 2-9360 0459; new UK branch: New World Booking Service Ltd (q.v.)

Baillie Music Management International
8 Bristol Gardens, **London** W9 2JG
Tel: 20-7286 7526/385-267 700 (mobile)
Fax: 20-7266 2687
E-Mail: alexander_baillie@t-online.de
general manager and president Alexander Baillie
Artforms: classical music (recitals, chamber music)
Comments: own productions, tours and festivals; German address: Marterburg 55-58, Apt. n° 3, 28195 Bremen, Tel/Fax: +49 421-336 5432

Bhathena-Jancovich
Lauderdale House, Waterlow Park, Highgate Hill,
London N6 5HG
Tel: 20-8348 0203 Fax: 20-8348 0206
E-Mail: b-j@dircon.co.uk
co-directors Chenine Bhathena, Leila Jancovich
Artforms: promotion of: physical/visual theatre, dance, mime, circus, drama and new writing
Comments: consultants; tour bookers for performances by British and international companies; festival & arts event coordinators; main interests lie in the development of new work; tour management fundraising; financial management; business planning

Bill Kenwright Ltd
Warwick House, 106 Harrow Road,
London W2 1XD
Tel: 20-7446 6200 Fax: 20-7446 6222
managing director Bill Kenwright; chief executive Brat Finnegan
Artforms: theatre production

Calan Communications – classical music media relations
35 St George's Wharf, 6 Shad Thames,
London SE1 2YS
Tel: 20-7357 7604 Fax: 20-7234 0173
Internet: www.intune.co.uk/calan
E-Mail: jej@dircon.co.uk
director John Jones
Artforms: UK and international media representation for artists, promoters, festivals and record companies

Cambrian Productions Ltd
Fourth Floor, 17 Waterloo Place, **London** SW1Y 4AR
Tel: 20-7930 5930 Fax: 20-7930 5932
E-Mail: hq@cambrian-music.com
contact Nigel Nicholson
Artforms: music, opera, ballet
Comments: organises commercial, sponsored and charitable events internationally; strong links with Far East, Russia and other Republics of the former Soviet Union

Cameron Mackintosh Ltd
No. 1 Bedford Square, **London** WC1B 3RA
Tel: 20-7637 8866 Fax: 20-7436 2683
E-Mail: cmlmail.mhs@compuserve.com
managing director Martin McCallum; chairman Cameron Mackintosh; executive producer Nick Allott
Comments: theatre producers

Caroline Baird Artists
9 Onslow Gardens, **London** N10 3JT
Tel: 20-8444 9003 Fax: 20-8444 9003
E-Mail: caroline@cbartists.com
contact Caroline Baird
Comments: represents Howard Shelley

Caroline Ireland Management
Uwchlaw'r Coed, **Llanbedr (Wales)** LL45 2NA
Tel: 1341-241 532 Fax: 1341-241 532
E-Mail: caroline.ireland@virgin.net
director Caroline Ireland
Comments: personal management for soloists and small ensembles, concert management

Caroline Phillips Management
Tailor House, 63-65 High Street,
Whitwell SG4 8AH
Tel: 1438-871 828 Fax: 1438-871 838
Internet: www.caroline-phillips.co.uk
E-Mail: cphillips@caroline-phillips.co.uk
artists managers Caroline Phillips, Sylvia Carrasco-Oñate
Artforms: conductors, singers

Casarotto Ramsay & Associated
National House, 60-66 Wardour Street,
London W1V 4ND
Tel: 20-7287 4450 Fax: 20-7287 9128
E-Mail: agents@casarotto.uk.com
managing director Giorgio Casarotto
Artforms: various

Centreline Productions
26 Mortimer Street, **London** W1N 7RA
Tel: 20-7323 3976 Fax: 20-7323 6518
managing director Jenny King; associate Janet Powell
Artforms: theatre producer, theatre management and tour bookings agency

Chameleon Arts Management
32 St. Michael's Road,
Sandhurst GU47 8HE
Tel: 1252-873 313 Fax: 1252-871 517
Internet: www.chameleon-arts.co.uk
E-Mail: CamArts@dial.pipex.com
contact Andrew Phillips
Artforms: management of classical artists, singers, soloists, orchestras and choirs; also corporate entertainment

Charles McFinch
23 Farm Road, **Morden** SM4 6RA
Tel: 20-8648 8852 Fax: 20-8687 1741
director Charles McFinch
Artforms: management of conductors, solo instrumentalists, singers and chamber ensembles

Clare Vidal-Hall
28 Perrers Road, **London** W6 0EZ
Tel: 20-8741 7647 Fax: 20-8741 9459
contact Clare Vidal-Hall
Artforms: theatre, television, stage, opera
Comments: representing stage & TV designers, stage & TV directors & choreographers, lighting designers; theatre and television composers

Clarion/Seven Muses
47 Whitehall Park, **London** N19 3TW
Tel: 20-7272 4413/5125/8448 Fax: 20-7281 9687
Internet: www.c7m.dircon.co.uk
E-Mail: c7m@dircon.co.uk
partners Nicholas Curry, Caroline Oakes; senior artists manager Alan Coates; assistant Costas Peristianis
Artforms: personal management of international artists and ensembles excluding solo singers

CMB Music International
Merchant's House, 95 West St, **Faversham** ME13 7JQ
Tel: 1795-536 085/533 822 Fax: 1795-536 085/533 822
E-Mail: vhc@cmbmusic.freeserve.co.uk
directors Vanessa Campion, Guy Bebb,
Artforms: events/concerts: orchestral, open-air, chamber music, jazz
Comments: specialises in new concert productions; organising festivals, country house & open-air concerts and charity events; promotional CDs

Codron Michael, Plays Ltd
Aldwych Theatre offices, Aldwych, **London** WC2B 4DF
Tel: 20-7240 8291 Fax: 20-7240 8467
general manager/productions Paul O'Leary
Artforms: theatre production

Columbia Artists Management Ltd
28 Cheverton Road, **London** N19 3AY
Tel: 20-7272 8020 Fax: 20-7272 8991
director Judith Salpeter; touring director Sergei Selivanov
Artforms: management of international artists; touring of orchestras and dance companies

Como No
34 Osnaburgh Street, **London** NW1 3ND
Tel: 20-7916 5479 Fax: 20-7916 5480
E-Mail: comono@btinternet.com
director Andy Wood; production executive Pablo Farba
Artforms: Latin American performing arts *Comments:* mainly international concert producer

Concert Directory International (CDI)
Lyndhurst, Denton Road, Ben Rhydding,
Ilkley LS29 8QR
Tel: 1943-607 821 Fax: 1943-817 063
E-Mail: pca@ndirect.co.uk
director Catherine Scott
Artforms: singers, early music ensembles, choirs and conductors *Comments:* personal management, concert management

Ingpen & Williams Limited

International Artists' Management

26 Wadham Road, London SW15 2LR, England
Telephone: +44 (0)20 8 874 3222 - Fax: +44 (0)20 8 877 3113
E-mail: info@ingpen.co.uk

Jonathan Groves · David Sigall · Thomas Hull · William Goffe
Lulu Chivers · Helen Hogh · Lucy Jonas · Fiona Wells

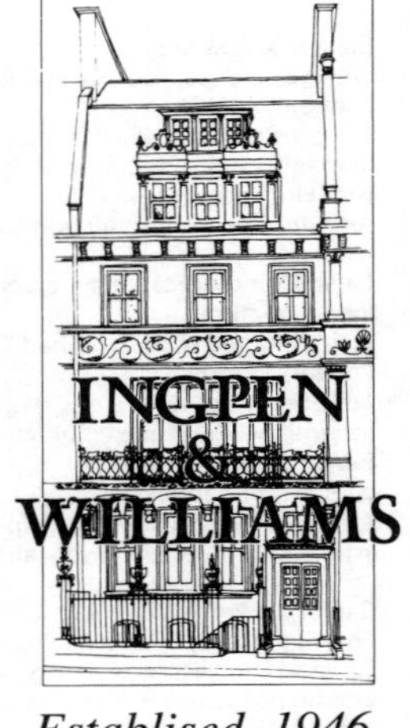

Established. 1946

PLEASE NOTE NEW UK AREA DIALLING CODES

1999-2000 ARTIST LIST

• *Conductors*

Martin André	W
Richard Armstrong CBE	W
Ivor Bolton	W
Richard Bonynge	E
Pierre Boulez	UK
Paul Daniel	W
Sir Edward Downes CBE	W
Sian Edwards	W
Mark Elder CBE	W
Richard Farnes	W
Michael Gielen	W
Heinz Holliger	UK
Diego Masson	W
Alexander Polianichko	W
Antoní Ros Marbá	UK
Michael Schønwandt	W
Markus Stenz	W
Bruno Weil	UK
Garry Walker	W

• *Sopranos*

Laura Aikin	W
Valdine Anderson	W
Susan Chilcott	W
Anne Evans	W
Christine Goerke	E
Sylvia Hamvasi	UK
Kathryn Harries	W
Barbara Hendricks	UK
Alwyn Mellor	W
Kathryn McCusker	W
Suzanne Murphy	W
Joan Rodgers	W
Amanda Roocroft	W
Nadine Secunde	UK
Christine Whittlesey	UK
Sandra Zeltzer	W

• *Mezzo-Sopranos*

Patricia Bardon	W
Jane Irwin	W
Katarina Karnéus	W
Marianne Rørholm	W
Hilary Summers	W
Ann Taylor	W

• *Counter Tenor*

Michael Chance	W

• *Tenors*

Peter Auty	W
Ian Caley	W
Graham Clark	W
Poul Elming	W
John Hudson	W
Paul Nilon	W
Dennis O'Neill	W
Nigel Robson	W

• *Baritones & Basses*

Victor Braun	UK
Nathan Gunn	E
Robert Hayward	W
Robert Holl	UK
Gwynne Howell CBE	W
Monte Jaffe	UK
Franz Mazura	UK
Sherrill Milnes	UK
Sir Donald McIntyre	W
Jan-Hendrik Rootering	UK
Matti Salminen	UK
Wolfgang Schöne	UK
Andrew Shore	W
Henry Waddington	W

• *Opera Directors*

Jonathan Moore	W
Graham Vick	W

• *Piano*

Alfred Brendel	W
Gianluca Cascioli	UK
Till Fellner	UK
Janina Fialkowska	E
Valentina Igoshina	W
Paul Lewis	W
Joanna MacGregor	W
Peter Serkin	UK

• *Accompanist*

Roger Vignoles	W

• *Classical Accordion*

James Crabb	W

• *Violin*

Priya Mitchell	W

• *Cello*

Ralph Kirshbaum	W

• *Oboe*

Maurice Bourgue	UK
Heinz Holliger	UK

• *Clarinet*

Andrew Marriner	W

• *French Horn*

Radovan Vlatkovic	UK

• *Piano Trio*

Peter Frankl, Gyorgy Pauk, Ralph Kirshbaum	W

• *String Trio*

Leopold String Trio	W

• *String Quartets*

Guarneri Quartet	UK
The Lindsays	W
Melos Quartet	UK
Quatuor Sine Nomine Lausanne	UK

• *Orchestras*

Chicago Symphony Orchestra	UK
Tafelmusik	UK

• *Masterclasses*

Phyllis Bryn-Julson	E
Sherrill Milnes	UK
Yvonne Minton	W
Elisabeth Söderström	W
Dame Joan Sutherland	E
Roger Vignoles	W

KEY:

General Management	**W**
European Representation	**E**
UK Representation	**UK**

Connaught Artists Management Ltd.
2 Molasses Row, Plantation Wharf,
London SW11 3UX
Tel: 20-7738 0017 Fax: 20-7738 1179
Internet: www.connaughtartists.com
E-Mail: classicalmusic@connaughtartists.com
directors Jill Segal, Patrick Allen
Artforms: instrumentalists, conductors, singers
Comments: secures sponsorship for selected arts projects and manages the entire sponsorship package

Conway Van Gelder Ltd
3rd Floor, 18-21 Jermyn Street, **London** SW1Y 6HP
Tel: 20-7287 0077 Fax: 20-7287 1940
contact Nicola Van Gelder
Artforms: actors/directors

Cruickshank Cazenove Ltd
97 Old South Lambeth Road, **London** SW8 1XU
Tel: 20-7735 2933 Fax: 20-7820 1081
contact Harriet Cruickshank
Artforms: stage designers/directors

Cryptic Productions
Partick Burgh Halls, 9 Burgh Hall Street,
Glasgow (Scotland) G11 5LW
Tel: 141-338 6929 Fax: 141-357 6924
Internet: www.theatrecryptic.demon.co.uk
E-Mail: theatrecryptic@compuserve.com
general manager Claire Findlay; artistic director Cathie Boyd
Artforms: music theatre, multi-cultural, cross-disciplined, experimental *Comments:* aims to support high calibre artists both nationally and internationally; keen to establish links with companies/countries with a view to producing work

Cultural Co-operation
Toynbee Studios, 28 Commercial Street,
London E1 6LS
Tel: 20-7456 0400 Fax: 20-7456 0401
E-Mail: musicvil@dircon.uk
director Prakash Daswani
Artforms: specialise in the living musical traditions of non-Western societies; organisers of annual festival: The Music Village (London, Berlin and other European cities)

Cultural Industry
36 St John's Lane, **London** EC1M 4BJ
Tel: 20-7336 6781 Fax: 20-7336 6782
E-Mail: 100600.3215@compuserve.com
director Michael Morris; associate producer Christine Gettins
Artforms: contemporary performing arts/international co-production

Curtis Brown
4th Floor, Haymarket House, 28/29 Haymarket,
London SW1Y 4SP
Tel: 20-7396 6600 Fax: 20-7396 0110
Internet: www.curtisbrown.com.uk
E-Mail: curtisbrown@curtisbrown.com.uk
contact Peter Murphy
Artforms: writers for theatre

Dennis Lyne Agency
108 Leonard Street, **London** EC2A 4RH
Tel: 20-7739 6200 Fax: 20-7739 4101
contact Dennis Lyne
Artforms: set and costume designers, lighting designers

Denny Lyster Artists' Management
25 Courthope Road, **London** NW3 2LE
Tel: 20-7485 5932 Fax: 20-7267 0179
director Denny Lyster
Artforms: conductors, instrumentalists, choirs
Comments: member of IAMA

Designers Formation, The
20 Gorsey Road, **Nottingham** NG3 4JL
Tel: 115-969 2633 Fax: 115-969 2633
contact Jill Westby
Artforms: set and costume designers, lighting designers

Donald Scrimgeour Artists' Agent
49 Springcroft Avenue, **London** N2 9JH
Tel: 20-8444 6248 Fax: 20-8883 9751
E-Mail: vwest@dircon.co.uk
contact Valerie West
Artforms: dance and ballet companies, principal dancers, choreographers, teachers, producers, conductors, directors, designers
Comments: overseas office of Donald Scrimgeour Artists' Agent, Apartado 905, 41080 Seville, Spain (qv) tel: +34 95-434 3802 fax: +34 95-434 3807

Dual Control/Opera & Ballet International
The Historic Dockyard, **Chatham** ME4 4TE
Tel: 1634-819 141 Fax: 1634-819 149
E-Mail: Opera.International@btinternet.com
managing director Ellen Kent
Artforms: opera & ballet touring

Duncan C Weldon Productions Ltd
Triumph Proscenium Productions Ltd, Suite 4, Waldorf Chambers, 11 Aldwych, **London** WC2B 4DA
Tel: 20-7343 8800 Fax: 20-7343 8801/7341 8802
director Duncan Weldon
Artforms: theatre

Edward Snape Ltd
22-24 Torrington Place, **London** WC1E 7HF
Tel: 20-7580 6792 Fax: 20-7580 6652
director Edward Snape
Artforms: tour and production management for producers, promoters and repertory companies
Comments: see also Promoters

Elspeth Cochrane Agency
11-13 Orlando Road, **London** SW4 0LE
Tel: 20-7622 0314 Fax: 20-7622 5815
director Elspeth Cochrane
Artforms: choreographers, directors, writers and designers

Encore Concerts in association with CHL Artists, Los Angeles U.S.A.
Bibury House, 2 The Paddocks, Baunton,
Cirencester GL7 7DL
Tel: 1285-640 266 Fax: 1285-640 267
director UK and Europe Elizabeth Goldfinch; managing director USA Christopher Ling
Artforms: chamber groups, conductors, ensembles, soloists, personal management, concert management
Comments: assists in the administration of engagements for own exclusively represented artists in the UK, Europe and worldwide; associated concert management and publicity services; works in close association with CHL Artists (USA)

Felix de Wolfe
Garden Offices, 51 Maida Vale, **London** W9 1SD
Tel: 20-7289 5770 Fax: 20-7289 5731
contact Felix de Wolfe
Artforms: actors, directors, set designers, lighting designers

Flamenco Dance (Juan Martín)
54 Windsor Road, **London** N3 3SS
Tel: 20-8346 4500 Fax: 20-8346 2488
Internet: www.flamencovision.com
E-Mail: hvmartin@dircon.co.uk
managing director Helen Martín
Artforms: Flamenco dance *Comments:* manage Juan Martín and his dance co; produce CDs and cassettes, and videos on flamenco guitar

Gamma
1 Carriage Hall, 29 Floral Street, **London** WC2E 9DP
Tel: 20-7483 3383/USA: +1 800-747 0409
Fax: 20-7483 3353
E-Mail: gamma.london@dial.pipex.com
Artforms: dance, classical music, jazz and world music
Comments: also marketing, graphic design and sponsorship consultancy, tour and production management

Garricks
7 Garricks Street, **London** WC2E 9AR
Tel: 20-7240 0660/7379 7476 Fax: 20-7497 9242
E-Mail: garriks@mcmal.com
contact Megan Willis
Artforms: actors and designers

GBZ Management
PO Box 11845, **London** SE21 8ZS
Tel: 20-8761 6565 Fax: 20-8670 3195
E-Mail: gbz_mgmt@compuserve.com
director Gwenneth Bransby-Zachary
Artforms: instrumentalists, ensembles, composers, dancers (historical) *Comments:* pr, personal and concert management; management of the Parkhouse Award for piano-based string ensembles

Georgina Ivor Associates
28 Old Devonshire Road, **London** SW12 9RB
Tel: 20-8673 7179 Fax: 20-8675 8058
Internet: members.aol.com/GIvor/givor
E-Mail: GIvor@aol.com
director Georgina Ivor; assistant Melanie Harding
Artforms: solo instrumentalists, quartet ensemble
Comments: international artist management & promotion of concert series

Glynis Henderson Management & Production
69 Charlotte Street, **London** W1P 1LA
Tel: 20-7580 9644 Fax: 20-7436 1489
E-Mail: info@ghmp.co.uk
producer Glynis Henderson
Artforms: theatre, comedy, dance
Comments: production, promotion, touring and personal management worldwide

Grant Rogers Musical Artists' Management
64 Watling Street, **Radlett** WD7 7NP
Tel: 1923-855 753 Fax: 1923-855 753/584
E-Mail: nigel.rogers1@virgin.net
Artforms: personal management of singers, instrumentalists and conductors, concert promotion

Guy Masterson Productions
Studio 7, The Bull Theatre, 68 High Street,
Barnet EN5 5SJ
Tel: 20-8449 7800 Fax: 20-8449 5252
Internet: www.guymasterson.com
E-Mail: admin@guymasterson.co.uk
director Guy Masterson (email: guy.m@guymasterson.com); associate director Jenny Sutherland (email: jen.s@guymasterson.com)
Artforms: drama, small scale touring theatre, national and international
Comments: see also Drama

Harlequin Agency Ltd
203 Fidlas Rd., **Cardiff (Wales)** CF14 5NA
Tel: 29-2075 0821 Fax: 29-2075 5971
Internet: www.harlequin-agency
E-Mail: admin@harlequin-agency
artist manager, managing director Doreen O'Neill; artist manager Colin Ure; administration and promotions Peter Tansom
Artforms: personal international management of opera and concert singers and conductors

Harrison/Parrott Ltd
12 Penzance Place, **London** W11 4PA
Tel: 20-7229 9166 Fax: 20-7221 5042
E-Mail: info@harrisonparrott.co.uk
chairman & managing director Jasper Parrott; joint managing director Linda Marks; director Lydia Connolly; associate directors Kaarina Meyer (tours & projects), Trudy Wright (tours & projects), Debra Boraston (director of Birdsong PR); consultant Joe Earle (arts & exhibitions); artists' managers Jane Piper, Ian Stones, Jennifer Spencer, Isabel Yeats;
business manger Ian Giddons
Artforms: international management for conductors, instrumentalists, singers (including opera); international and national orchestral touring; arts sponsorship; festival management; exhibitions and fine arts projects; concerts promotion; public relations, television and video co-productions; has a subsidiary agency specialised in PR services: Birdsong Public Relations, see also Services

Haydn Rawstron (UK) Ltd
36 Station Road, **London** SE20 7BQ
Tel: 20-8659 2659 Fax: 20-8676 9119
E-Mail: haydnraw@aol.com
contact Haydn Rawstron, Ms Chris Gray
Comments: for opera: singers, conductors, producers and designers; for concert work: singers and conductors

Hazard Chase Artists' Management
Richmond House, 16-20 Regent Street,
Cambridge CB2 1DB
Tel: 1223-312 400 Fax: 1223-460 827
Internet: www.hazardchase.co.uk
E-Mail: info@hazardchase.co.uk
managing director James Brown; directors John Bickley, Elizabeth Jones; events & marketing manager Helen Poole
Artforms: fully comprehensive international management service, including sponsorship, concert management, public relations and recordings for a select list of soloists and chamber ensembles

Heather Knight Associates
23 Wolftencroft Close, **London** SW11 2LB
Tel: 20-7223 4034 Fax: 20-7223 8636
director Heather Knight
Artforms: specialises in the organisation of UK and overseas tours for dance companies

Helen Jennings Concert Agency
2 Hereford House, Links Road, **London** W3 0HX
Tel: 20-8992 8502
contact Helen Jennings
Comments: management of concerts and representative

Helen Sykes Artists' Management
First Floor, Parkway House, Sheen Lane,
London SW14 8 LS
Tel: 20-8876 8276 Fax: 20-8876 8277
E-Mail: helen@hsam.u-net.com
proprietor Helen Sykes; administrator Sarah Mahon; artistic manager James Black
Comments: personal management of conductors, solo singers and instrumentalists, and early music ensembles; member of IAMA

Hiss & Boo
Nyes Hill, Wineham Lane, **Bolney** RH17 5SD
Tel: 1444-881 707 Fax: 1444-882 057
Internet: www.hissboo.co.uk
E-Mail: hissboo@msn.com
executive director Ian Liston
Artforms: drama and light entertainment, musical theatre
Comments: produce West End plays; UK tours; co-productions (national and international) member of Theatrical Management Association;
does not accept unsolicited scripts

Conductors

John Adams

Stefan Asbury
Co-ordinator of New Music Activities: Tanglewood Music Center
Artistic Director: Oxford Contemporary Music Festival

Vladimir Ashkenazy
Chief Conductor: Czech Philharmonic Orchestra
Chief Conductor: Deutsches Symphonie-Orchester Berlin

Steuart Bedford

Paolo Carignani
Music Director: Frankfurt Opera
Chief Conductor: Frankfurt Museumsgesellscaft Orchestra

Harry Christophers
Music Director: The Sixteen and The Symphony of Harmony and Invention

Christoph von Dohnányi
Music Director: The Cleveland Orchestra
Principal Conductor and Artistic Adviser: Philharmonia Orchestra

Ivan Fischer
Artistic Director and Principal Conductor: Budapest Festival Orchestra

Lawrence Foster
Music Director and Principal Conductor: Barcelona Symphony Orchestra
Artistic Director: George Enescu Festival

Mikko Franck
Music Director: Orchestra Vivo, Finland

Rumon Gamba
Lloyds Bank Assistant Conductor: BBC Philharmonic Orchestra

Rolf Gupta

Paavo Järvi

Robert King
Artistic Director: The King's Consort

Oliver Knussen
Music Director: London Sinfonietta

Yakov Kreizberg
Chief Conductor and General Music Director: Komische Oper Berlin
Principal Conductor and Artistic Adviser: Bournemouth Symphony Orchestra

Alexander Liebreich
Assistant Conductor: Netherlands Radio Philharmonic Orchestra

Susanna Mälkki

Paul Mann
Assistant Conductor: London Symphony Orchestra

Olli Mustonen

Sakari Oramo
Musical Director: City of Birmingham Symphony Orchestra
Co-Principal Conductor: Finnish Radio Symphony Orchestra

Lawrence Renes
Chief Conductor and Artistic Adviser: Gelders Orchestra
Principal Guest Conductor: Netherlands Radio Philharmonic Orchestra

Ulf Schirmer

Christopher Seaman
Music Director: Rochester Philharmonic Orchestra
Music Director: Naples Philharmonic Orchestra Florida

David Shallon
Principal Conductor and Music Director: Jerusalem Symphony Orchestra
Chief Conductor and Music Director: Orchestre Philharmonique du Luxembourg

Robert Spano
Music Director: Brooklyn Philharmonic Orchestra

Maximiano Valdes
Music Director: Buffalo Philharmonic Orchestra
Principal Conductor: Orquesta Sinfonica del Principado Asturias

Osmo Vänskä
Music Director: Lahti Symphony Orchestra
Chief Conductor: BBC Scottish Symphony Orchestra

Edo de Waart
Chief Conductor and Artistic Director: Sydney Symphony Orchestra
Artistic Director: Netherlands Radio Muzikcentrum
Chief Conductor: Netherlands Radio Philharmonic Orchestra
Chief Conductor: Netherlands Opera

Walter Weller
Conductor Emeritus: Royal Scottish National Orchestra
Principal Guest Conductor and Artistic Adviser: National Orchestra of Spain

David Zinman
Chief Conductor: Tonhalle Orchestra Zurich
Music Director: Tonhalle Gesellschaft
Artistic Director: Aspen Music Festival

Instrumentalists

PIANO

Pierre-Laurent Aimard
Anya Alexeyev
Vladimir Ashkenazy
Stephen Hough
Peter Jablonski
Julian Joseph
Joseph Kalichstein
Aleksandar Madžar
Olli Mustonen
Cristina Ortiz
Jon Kimura Parker
Maurizio Pollini
Mikhaïl Rudy
Krystian Zimerman

STRING QUARTET

The Jerusalem Quartet

VIOLIN

Elisabeth Batiashvili
Pekka Kuusisto
Kurt Nikkanen
Gil Shaham
Christian Tetzlaff
Antje Weithaas

VIOLA

Tabea Zimmermann

CELLO

Steven Isserlis
Daniel Müller-Schott
Truls Mørk

CLARINET

Dimitri Ashkenazy

GUITAR

Manuel Barrueco

Singers

SOPRANO
Orla Boylan
Susan Bullock
Inger Dam-Jensen
Juanita Lascarro
Catrin Wyn-Davies

MEZZO - SOPRANO
Sara Fulgoni
Dolora Zajick

COUNTER-TENOR
Andreas Scholl
Daniel Taylor

TENOR
Barry Banks
Mark Tucker

BARITONE
Peter Coleman-Wright
Garry Magee

BASS
Stephen Richardson

Touring Projects

American Symphony Orchestra
ASKO Ensemble
Australian Youth Orchestra
BBC Symphony Orchestra
BBC Scottish Symphony Orchestra
Bournemouth Symphony Orchestra
Budapest Festival Orchestra
City of Birmingham Symphony Orchestra
The Cleveland Orchestra
Czech Philharmonic Orchestra
Deutsches Symphonie-Orchester Berlin
Deutsche Kammerphilharmonie
Estonian Philharmonic Chamber Choir
Helsinki Philharmonic Orchestra
Julian Joseph Big Band
KODO
Lahti Symphony Orchestra
London Sinfonietta
NDR Symphony Orchestra Hamburg
New Berlin Chamber Orchestra
New York Baroque Dance Company
Norwegian National Theatre
Orchestre de Paris
Orchestre Philharmonique du Luxembourg
Philharmonia Orchestra
Royal Opera House Covent Garden
Royal Philharmonic Orchestra
Royal Philharmonic Concert Orchestra
Russian National Orchestra
Schoenberg Ensemble
Secret Garden
The Swingle Singers
Tallinn Chamber Orchestra
Tapiola Sinfonietta
Tonhalle Orchestra Zürich

Special Project: Hans Werne Henze

Birdsong
Public Relations

Clients include:
Belfast Festival at Queens
The BOC Covent Garden Festival
Rambert Dance Company
Ryuichi Sakamoto
San Francisco Ballet
Visions of Norway

HarrisonParrott
Artist and Project Management

Harrison/Parrott Ltd.
12 Penzance Place
London W11 4PA, UK

T: +44 (0)20 7229 9166
F: +44 (0)20 7221 5042
E: info@harrisonparrott.co.uk

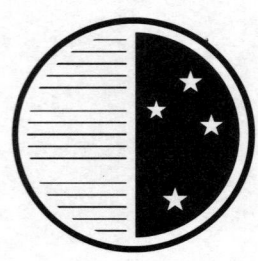

ICM Artists (London) Ltd
Suite 3B, West Point, 39-40 Warple Way, **London** W3 0RG
Tel: 20-8743 0558 Fax: 20-8743 6598
E-Mail: info@icmartists.demon.co.uk
contact David Baldwin
Artforms: instrumentalists, conductors, concert management

Imagination Entertainments Ltd.
25 Store Street, South Crescent, **London** WC1E 7BL
Tel: 20-7323 3300 Fax: 20-7462 2837
E-Mail: bob.eady@imagination.co.uk
contact Bob Eady; director Gary Withers
Artforms: musicals, plays, concerts

IMG Artists
Media House, 3 Burlington Lane, Chiswick, **London** W4 2TH
Tel: 20-8233 5800/41 Fax: 20-8233 5801
E-Mail: artistseurope@imgworld.com
managing director IMG Artists Stephen Wright; joint managing directors IMG arts & entertainment division Michael Storrs, Stephen Flint Wood; director vocal division Tom Graham; director artist management Nicholas Mathias; director orchestral touring Anthony Howard; associate director artist management Kathryn Enticott; associate director orchestral touring Joan Cruickshank; associate director dance division Gillian Newson; press & publicity manager Janie Garnon
Artforms: artist management, orchestral touring, special events and promotions *Comments:* see also IMG Arts Projects (q.v.) and Recorded Media

independance (London Independent Dance Management Agency)
The Ground Floor, 130 Brixton Hill, **London** SW2 1RS
Tel: 20-8678 6664 Fax: 20-8678 6641
E-Mail: farooq.independance@virgin.net
contact Farooq Chaudhry
Artforms: dance

Ingpen and Williams Ltd
26 Wadham Road, **London** SW15 2LR
Tel: 20-8874 3222 Fax: 20-8877 3113
E-Mail: info@ingpen.co.uk
contact David Sigall, Jonathan Groves, William Goffe, Thomas Hull
Comments: 50 year history in the personal worldwide management of conductors, singers, instrumentalists, string quartets and opera producers

Intermusica Artists' Management Ltd
16 Duncan Terrace, **London** N1 8BZ
Tel: 20-7278 5455 Fax: 20-7278 8434
E-Mail: mail@intermusica.co.uk
managing director Stephen Lumsden; director, artists management Susie McLeod; director, tours & projects Peter Savory; artist managers Kathy Schuman, Rachel Champion MacPherson
Comments: personal worldwide representation of distinguished conductors, instrumentalists and chamber ensembles, orchestral touring and special projects, promoter of International Chamber Music Season at South Bank Centre etc.

Invisible Pilots Ltd
The Barony, 16 Sandringham Road, **Petersfield** GU32 2AA
Tel: 1730-267 341 Fax: 1730-267 341
Internet: www.classical-artists.com/invisiblepilots
E-Mail: invisiblepilots@classical-artists.com
director Peter Thompson
Artforms: pianists, instrumentalists, ensemble
Comments: concert promotion

J Audrey Ellison International Artists' Management
135 Stevenage Road, Fulham, **London** SW6 6PB
Tel: 20-7381 9751 Fax: 20-7381 2406
E-Mail: Audrey@Ellison.Intl.freeserve.co.uk
director J Audrey Ellison
Artforms: composers, conductors, instrumentalists, ensembles, orchestras, singers, lecturers *Comments:* personal management of artists and ensembles, concert management

Jeffrey Cambell Management
11A Greystone Court, South Street, **Eastbourne** BN21 4LP
Tel: 1323-411 444 Fax: 1323-411 373
Internet: www.theatricaldesigners.co.uk
E-Mail: cambell@theatricaldesigners.co.uk
director Jeffrey Cambell
Artforms: set and costume designers, lighting designers, sound designers, directors

Jennie Blythe Artists Management
Sunnyside, **Lower Swell** GL54 1LG
Tel: 1451-830 059 Fax: 1451-832 357
E-Mail: jennie.blythe@virgin.net
director Jennie Blythe; assistant Liz Stephens
Artforms: chamber musicians and choirs, personal management, concert management
Comments: general management of the Huddersfield Choral Society, London Choral Society and concert management in major concert halls

John Kehoe Music Production
201 River Meads, Stanstead Abbotts, **Ware** SG12 8EU
Tel: 1920-872 822 Fax: 1920-872 822
E-Mail: jkehoe@globalnet.co.uk
director John Kehoe
Artforms: recording production service in every genre of classical music; project management, session planning and supervision, post-production, manufacturing

John Wallbank
60 Barclay Road, **London** E11 3DG
Tel: 20-8530 7386 Fax: 20-8928 0339
managing director John Wallbank
Comments: producer, consultant and general management

Judy Daish Associates
2 St Charles Place, **London** W10 6EG
Tel: 20-8964 8811 Fax: 20-8964 8966
contact Judy Daish, Deborah Harwood
Artforms: directors, writers, designers

Karen Durant Management
298 Nelson Road, Whitton, **Twickenham** TW2 7BW
Tel: 20-8893 3172 Fax: 20-8893 8090
Internet: www.karen-durant.co.uk
E-Mail: kdm@karen-durant.co.uk
director Karen Durant; administrator Sharon Laviv
Artforms: personal representation of international opera & concert, singers, conductors, ensembles and soloists

Kenneth Cleveland Personal Management Ltd (KCPM)
6 Ganton Street, **London** W1V 1LY
Tel: 20-7734 7304 Fax: 20-7734 7318
E-Mail: kcpmail@kcp.co.uk
director Sally Shutter
Artforms: set and costume designers and lighting designers

Konzertdirektion Hans Ulrich Schmid (UK office)
4 Addison Bridge Place, **London** W14 8XP
Tel: 20-7602 3648 Fax: 20-7602 3780
E-Mail: kds_uk@vanwalsum.demon.co.uk
manager Karen McDonald
Artforms: conductors, instrumentalists, ensembles, singers *Comments:* main office in Hannover, Germany (please see separate entry)

Loesje Sanders
Pound Square, 1 North Hill, **Woodbridge** IP12 1HH
Tel: 1394-385 260 Fax: 1394-388 734
E-Mail: loesje@globalnet.co.uk
contact Loesje Sanders
Artforms: set and costume designers, lighting designers, directors, choreographers

London Artists
3 Wheelers Court, Scholars Lane, **Stratford-upon-Avon** CV37 6HE
Tel: 1789-296 247 Fax: 1789-269 843
E-Mail: londartist@aol.com
managing director Michael Emmerson; pa to managing director Isabel Jackson
Artforms: international manager, consultant and festival director

London Musicians Ltd
Cedar House, Vine Lane, **Hillingdon** UB10 0BX
Tel: 1895-252 555 Fax: 1895-252 556
E-Mail: mail@lonmus.demon.co.uk
managing director David White; orchestral manager Sylvia Addison; artists' manager Catherine le Bris
Comments: orchestral contracting and management for recording, theatre and concerts; artist management

Maestoso Musicmakers Ltd
Milestone, St Nicholas Avenue, **Great Bookham** KT23 4AY
Tel: 1372-457 755 Fax: 1372-450 525
E-Mail: maestoso@btinternet.com
director Elizabeth Pryde
Artforms: classical musicians and ensembles; personal international and national management of artists, small chamber groups, concert promotion and management, British and overseas tours *Comments:* sponsorship consultancy, management and liaison for business and art organisations

Manygate Management
13 Cotswold Mews, 30 Battersea Square, **London** SW11 3RA
Tel: 20-7223 7265 Fax: 20-7585 2830
E-Mail: manygate@easynet.co.uk
contact John Boyden, James Thomson
Comments: international management for conductors, instrumentalists and composers; concert and tour promotion; sponsorship; recording; PR; television and radio production

Mark Riches Personal Management
59 Kendall Avenue South, **Sanderstead** CR2 0QR
Tel: 20-8660 2443 Fax: 20-8660 2443
contact Mark Riches
Artforms: opera singers

Martin Randall Music Management
c/o Martin Randall Travel Ltd, 10 Barley Mow Passage, Chiswick, **London** W4 4PH
Tel: 20-8742 3355 Fax: 20-8742 7766
E-Mail: info@martinrandall.co.uk
managing director Martin Randall; festival organisers Sheila Taylor, Emma Duffield
Artforms: music and cultural tours (opera, chamber music etc.) accompanied by specialist lectures; music festivals – private concerts in historical palaces, churches, country houses and theatres *Comments:* see also Festivals and Services

Mary Craig – C & M Craig Services Ltd.
3 Kersley Street, **London** SW11 4PR
Tel: 20-7228 4855 Fax: 20-7223 2189
E-Mail: mary.craig@mcmail.com
director Mary Craig
Comments: personal international management of opera and concert singers, conductors and directors

Matthew Tullah Management
301 Firs Lane, **London** N13 5QH
Tel: 20-8807 0343 Fax: 20-8807 3800
Internet: ourworld.compuserve.com/homepages/matttullah
E-Mail: 100734.3461@compuserve.com
contact Matthew Tullah
Artforms: singers, vocal ensembles, solo instrumentalists and chamber groups represented; also concert management, promotion and touring management
Comments: artist management, administration, PR and marketing services to music/theatre industry

Mayer & Eden Ltd
34 Kingley Court, **London** W1R 5LE
Tel: 20-7434 1242 Fax: 20-7287 5834
contact Cassie Mayer, Karen Beesley
Artforms: set designers

Melanie Turner
52 Goldsmith Avenue, **London** W3 6HN
Tel: 20-8896 2741 Fax: 20-8896 2741
manager Melanie Turner
Comments: artist management, concert management and special projects

Michael Brewer Artists' Management
8 Edward Court, 317 Hagley Road, **Birmingham** B16 9LQ
Tel: 121-454 3160 Fax: 121-454 0225
Internet: www.mb-artists.ndirect.co.uk
E-Mail: mbrewer@mb-artists.ndirect.co.uk
director Michael Brewer
Artforms: solo instrumentalists, classical ensembles, personal management

Michael Harrold Artist Management
223 Kingston Road, **Leatherhead** KT22 7PE
Tel: 1372-375 728 Fax: 1372-375 728
Internet: www.michaelharrold.co.uk
E-Mail: angelus.organo@pmail.net
director Michael Harrold
Artforms: vocal and instrumental ensembles, soloists, conductors, composers, emphasis on early music
Comments: personal management, tour management, special project management; see also Services

Michael Ladkin Personal Management
Suite One, Ground Floor, 1 Duchess Street, **London** W1N 3DE
Tel: 20-7436 4626 Fax: 20-7436 4627
contact Michael Ladkin
Artforms: actors

Michael Rose Ltd
The Old Dairy, Throop Road, Holdenhurst, **Bournemouth** BH8 0DL
Tel: 1202-522 711 Fax: 1202-522 311
E-Mail: mrl@mrltheatre.u-net.com
contact Michael Rose, David Morgan
Artforms: drama and musicals (UK touring, seasonal productions, West End productions), general management

Michele McLusky
16 Winchester Walk, **London** SE1 9AQ
Tel: 20-7403 7474 Fax: 20-7403 7474
director Michele McLusky
Artforms: festival management, concert promotions and sponsorship

Michelle Braidman Associates
3rd Floor Suite, 10/11 Lower John Street, **London** W1R 3PE
Tel: 20-7437 0817 Fax: 20-7439 3660
E-Mail: michelle@braidman.com
contact Michelle Braidman
Artforms: actors, directors, set designers

MLR Ltd
Douglas House, 16/18 Douglas Street, **London** SW1P 4PB
Tel: 20-7834 4646 Fax: 20-7834 4949
E-Mail: catherine@mlrltd.co.uk
contact Patricia MacNaughton, Catherine Anderson
Artforms: writers, composers, lyricist, set designers

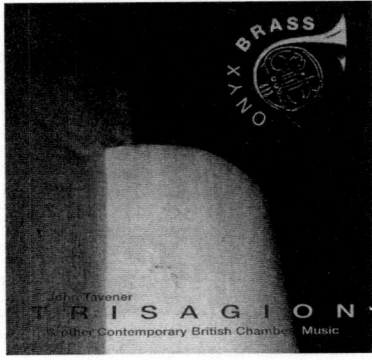

Modrana Music Promotions
41 Parklands Way, **Poynton** SK12 1AL
Tel: 1625-875 389 Fax: 1625-875 389
Internet: members.aol.com/dwsolomons/nwca.htm
E-Mail: David.F.Golightly@btinternet.com
agent and management David Golightly
Artforms: classical, choral music; film orchestration; Russian performers *Comments:* composer; specialises in contacts with central European groups; commercial work of orchestration for films, televisions, etc.

Morgenstern's
34 Thistlewaite Road, **London** E5 0QQ
Tel: 20-8533 1372 Fax: 20-8533 1367
Internet: www.morgensterns.co.uk
E-Mail: morgensterns@dial.pipex.com
contact Julian Morgenstern
Artforms: personal management of freelance orchestral and session musicians

Music International
13 Ardilaun Road, **London** N5 2QR
Tel: 20-7359 5183 Fax: 20-7226 9792
E-Mail: music@musicint.demon.co.uk
managing director Neil Dalrymple
Artforms: singers and conductors (concert and opera) and directors

Music Management (UK) Ltd.
PO Box 1105, **London** SW1V 2DE
Tel: 20-7823 1111 Fax: 20-7823 1001
E-Mail: mm@musicmanagement.demon.co.uk
Artforms: all types of live music *Comments:* concert promotion; corporate music consultants; specialise in private corporate concerts

Musicmakers
Tailor House, 63-65 High Street, **Whitwell** SG4 8AH
Tel: 1438-871 708 Fax: 1438-871 777
E-Mail: musicmakers@compuserve.com
director Christopher Knowles
Comments: international representation of singers and conductors in opera and concerts

Neil Chaffey Concert Promotions
9 Munts Meadow, **Weston** SG4 7AE
Tel: 1462-790 919 Fax: 1462-790 920
director Neil Chaffey
Comments: wind, string and keyboard players, chamber ensembles and small groups, mainly on a worldwide basis, associated concert promotion/management and publicity services

New World Booking Service Ltd
1st Floor, Garrick Theatre, 2 Charing Cross Road, **London** WC2H 0HH
Tel: 20-7240 4282 Fax: 20-7240 7195
Internet: www.backrow.com
E-Mail: brp@backrow.co.uk
managing directors UK Elisabeth Koops, Garry McQuinn; creative director Wayne Harrison; booking agents Philippe Mongay, Elisabet Casanova; producer film & tv Andrew Higgie
Artforms: theatre, musical theatre, dance, film
Comments: producers of TAP DOGS; booking agents; European and Australasian touring; see also Back Row Productions

Newpalm Productions
26 Cavendish Avenue, **London** N3 3QN
Tel: 20-8349 0802/8346 8011
Fax: 20-8346 8257
managing director John Newman
Artforms: drama – West End productions, provincial touring, summer seasons, repertory seasons in major UK theatres and internationally

No Strings Attached (1997) Ltd
1 Grange House, 229 Stoke Newington Church Street, **London** N16 9HL
Tel: 20-7690 7449 Fax: 20-7241 6459
E-Mail: nostring@dircon.co.uk
director John Field
Artforms: puppetry, animatronics
Comments: produces, co-produces and promotes puppetry, puppeteers and animatronicists in UK and internationally; also books shows in Hong Kong and Asia; the UK's only agent for puppetry

Noel Gay Organisation/Noel Gay Artists
19 Denmark Street, **London** WC2H 8NA
Tel: 20-7836 3941 Fax: 20-7287 1816
chief executive Alex Armitage; managing director Nick Ranceford-Hadley
Comments: theatrical agency looking after actors and television personalities; presenters & writers

Okai Collier Company Ltd
103 Lexington Building, Fairfield Row, **London** E3 2UH
Tel: 20-8983 4858 Fax: 20-8983 0858
producer Simon James Collier; artistic director Omar F Okai
Artforms: new and original productions of musicals, drama

Oldham Theatre Workshop
Royton Assembly Hall, Market Square, Royton, **Oldham** OL2 5QS
Tel: 161-911 3240 Fax: 161-911 3244
E-Mail: els.otw@oldham.gov.uk
director Victoria Munnich
Comments: specialise in Theatre workshops, large and small scale productions (evenings and weekends only) for young people aged 8 and above; due to its national reputation, many of the young people are offered work in TV, Films and Theatre

Olivia Ma Artists' Management
65 Campden Street, **London** W8 7EL
Tel: 20-7221 3606 Fax: 20-7221 3607
E-Mail: olivia@omam.u-net.com
director Olivia Ma
Artforms: personal worldwide representation for a small number of musicians and international orchestral touring

Opera and Concert Artists
75 Aberdare Gardens, **London** NW6 3AN
Tel: 20-7328 3097 Fax: 20-7372 3537
contacts Judith Newton, Andrew Dugdale
Comments: international management, mainly singers

Opera Box Ltd
Rhydyberi Cottages, Merthyr Cynog, **Brecon (Wales)** LD3 9SA
Tel: 1874-690 339 Fax: 1874-690 254
Internet: www.operabox.freeuk.com
E-Mail: opera-box@international.freeserve.co.uk
artistic directors Brendan Wheatley, Bridgett Gill; musical director Fraser Goulding; administrator Gayle Parsons
Artforms: performances in theatres and open-air performances at castles in association with English Heritage, National Trust, Borough Councils and Private owners

Out of Joint
20-24 Eden Grove, **London** N7 8EA
Tel: 20-7609 0207 Fax: 20-7609 0203
E-Mail: ojo@outofjoint.demon.co.uk
director Max Stafford-Clark;
producer Graham Cowley
Artforms: drama
Comments: new writing company specialising in touring new plays in UK and internationally; occassionally also tours classics in repertoire

Patrick Garvey Management

INTERNATIONAL ARTIST MANAGEMENT
59 LANSDOWNE PLACE
HOVE, EAST SUSSEX BN3 1FL, UNITED KINGDOM
TEL: +44 (0)1273 206623 FAX: +44 (0)1273 208484
Email: patrick@patrickgarvey.demon.co.uk
www: patrickgarvey.com

Conductors

David Angus	World
Moshe Atzmon	World
Tomasz Bugaj	World
Andrew Constantine	World
Anthony Halstead	World
Dirk Joeres	World
Hannu Koivula	World
Cem Mansur	World
Tuomas Ollila	UK & Sun Terr
David Porcelijn	World exc. Australasia
Ole Schmidt	World exc. Denmark
Leif Segerstam	UK & Sun Terr
Michel Tabachnik	World
Jan Wagner	World
Niklas Willén	World exc. Scan
Takuo Yuasa	World

Composer

Jonathan Harvey — *World*

Organist

Thomas Trotter — *World exc. N. America*

Pianists

John Browning — *Europe*
Philip Fowke — *World*
Piers Lane — *World exc. Recitals*

Violinist

Nicola Loud — *World*

Cellist

Arto Noras — *UK & Sun Terr*

Horn

Michael Thompson — *World*

Ensemble

Michael Thompson Wind Quintet — *World*

Patrick Garvey Management Ltd is a Member of the International Artist Managers' Association (IAMA) and of the Association Européene des Agents Artistiques

Owen/White Management
Top Floor, 59 Lansdowne Place, **Hove** BN3 1FL
Tel: 1273-727 127 Fax: 1273-328 128
E-Mail: owenwhite@compuserve.com
Trudy White, John Owen
Artforms: artist management for singers, conductors and instrumentalists

PAG Concert Promotions
138 Sandy Hill Road, **London** SE18 7BA
Tel: 20-8854 2558 Fax: 20-8854 2558
director Ken Spencer
Artforms: personal management (singers), concert management and promotion

Palava Productions
43 Kingsway Avenue, Kingswood,
Bristol BS15 8AN
Tel: 117-947 7042 Fax: 117-947 7042
E-Mail: sam@palava.demon.co.uk
directors Sam Welbourne, Jacqueline Welbourne
Artforms: musicians, circus performers, actors/actresses, dancers, etc
Comments: multi-arts productions with an original music score may be commissioned; music production and recording; studio facilities available

Pan African Arts Management
12, The Chase, **Edgware** HA8 5DJ
Tel: 20-8381 2517 Fax: 20-8381 2519
Internet: www.arc.co.uk/paam/
E-Mail: rikkistein@compuserve.com
director Rikki Stein
Artforms: international management of traditional and popular African performing arts, ie. Les Ballets Africans (Guinea), the Pan African Orchestra (Ghana), Femi Anikulapo Kuti (Nigeria), Kaloum Star (Guinea), etc.

Patricia Greenan and Penelope Marland Associates
7 Whitehorse Close, Royal Mile,
Edinburgh (Scotland) EH8 8BU
Tel: 131-557 5872 Fax: 131-556 5825
directors Patricia Greenan, Penelope Marland (tel: 20-7223 7319, fax: 20-7771 0675)
Artforms: personal management of opera singers and conductors worldwide
Comments: see also Penelope Marland and Patricia Greenan Associates

Patrick Garvey Management
Top Floor, 59 Lansdowne Place, **Hove** BN3 1FL
Tel: 1273-206 623 Fax: 1273-208 484
Internet: www.patrickgarvey.com
E-Mail: patrick/andrea@patrickgarvey.demon.co.uk
director Patrick Garvey; partner Una Marchetti; administrator Andrea McDermott
Artforms: conductors, composers, instrumental soloists, ensembles & project management
Comments: management of artists, principally conductors and projects, worldwide

Patrick Voullaire
Park Offices, 121 Dora Road, **London** SW19 7JT
Tel: 20-8946 8848 Fax: 20-8944 1317
E-Mail: patrick@voullaire.demon.co.uk
contact Patrick Voullaire
Artforms: singers, conductors, instrumentalists, personal management
Comments: personal management; agent for various other artists

Penelope Marland and Patricia Greenan Associates
10 Roseneath Road, **London** SW11 6AH
Tel: 20-7223 7319 Fax: 20-7771 0675
directors Penelope Marland, Patricia Greenan (tel: 131-557 5872, fax: 131-556 5825)
Artforms: personal management of opera singers and conductors worldwide *Comments:* see also Patricia Greenan and Penelope Marland Associates

Performing Arts
6 Windmill Street, **London** W1P 1HF
Tel: 20-7255 1362 Fax: 20-7631 4631
E-Mail: rhaigh@compuserve.com
directors Richard Haigh, Ruth Harris
Artforms: conductors; directors and designers; lighting designers and choreographers, operates in fields of opera, concerts, musicals, theatre, dance, film, television and radio

Performing Arts Management Ltd.
Canal 7, Clarence Mill, Bollington,
Macclesfield SK10 5JZ
Tel: 1625-575 681 Fax: 1625-572 839
Internet: www.performingarts.co.uk
E-Mail: fifi.butler@performingarts.co.uk
director Nicholas Smith; co-director Sally Smith; marketing manager Judy Weeks; general office manager Clare Scott; events manager Lisa Charlwood; box office manager Chris Kettles; public relations, sampling & sponsorship Fifi Butler
Artforms: outdoor classical concerts with fireworks, concert, promotion & production *Comments:* have own orchestra (freelance); promote about 40 concerts (outdoor only) and tour nationally

Peter Hall Co.
The Penthouse, 7 Leicester Place, **London** WC2H 7BP
Tel: 20-7287 7122 Fax: 20-7287 7123
contact Sir Peter Hall
Artforms: theatre

Peters Fraser & Dunlop
Drury House, 34/43 Russel Street, **London** WC2B 5HA
Tel: 20-7344 1000 Fax: 20-7836 9539
E-Mail: postmaster@psd.co.uk
contact Vanessa Jones, Antony Jones
Artforms: actors, set and costume designers

POEM (Performers of Early Music)
Lyndhurst, Denton Road, Ben Rhydding, **Ilkley** LS29 8QR
Tel: 1943-607 821/860-948 770 (mobile)
Fax: 1943-817 063
Internet: www.ndirect.co.uk/~jgriffett/
directors Annabelle Rose, James Griffett, David Willington
Artforms: authentic performers of early music – instrumentalists, singers, ensembles, orchestras and choirs
Comments: personal management

Pola Jones Associates Ltd.
14 Dean Street, **London** W1V 5AH
Tel: 20-7439 1165 Fax: 20-7437 3994
contact Rebecca Quigley
Artforms: theatre, film and television producers

Portland Wallis Artists' Management
50 Great Portland Street, **London** W1N 5AH
Tel: 20-7636 6785 Fax: 20-7636 6786
general manager Allan Beavis; artists manager Daniel Stinson
Artforms: worldwide personal management of singers and conductors (opera and concert)

Positive Cultural Promotions Ltd
441 New Cross Road, **London** SE14 6TA
Tel: 20-8305 6912 Fax: 20-8694 1327
contact Al Handwicke

ppARTnerships
PO Box 2772, **Brighton** BN1 6FW
Tel: 1273-330 464 Fax: 1273-330 533
E-Mail: pparts@easynet.co.uk
director Peter Luxton
Artforms: contemporary music and new media
Comments: event promotion and production; international touring management and production; festivals production; new media publishing inc audio, CD ROM, television ettc; also artist management for creative contemporary musicians and new media artistis; work in the UK, Europe, USA/Canada, Australia, Japan, South America etc; see also Services

Really Useful Group
22 Tower Street, **London** WC2H 9NS
Tel: 20-7240 0880 Fax: 20-7240 1204
director Andrew Lloyd Webber; chief executive William Taylor; managing director (Really Useful Theatre Group) Kevin Wallace
Artforms: theatre production

Redondo Beach International
43 Greecroft Gardens, **London** NW6 3LN
Tel: 7970-835 473 Fax: 7970-507 153
E-Mail: donrbi@netscapeonline.co.uk
contact Don Mousseau
Artforms: composers

Robert Fox Ltd.
6 Beauchamp Place, **London** SW3 1NG
Tel: 20-7584 6855 Fax: 20-7225 1638
E-Mail: robertfox@rfoxltd.demon.co.uk
managing director Robert Fox
Artforms: theatre and film production company

Robert Gilder & Company
Enterprise House, 59-65 Upper Ground,
London SE1 9PQ
Tel: 20-7928 9008 Fax: 20-7928 9755
director Robert Gilder; artist managers Catrin Ley, Derek Warby, Marcus Spreitzer, Alexandre Mercer
Artforms: opera singers, conductors, instrumental soloists, chamber music groups, stage directors
Comments: worldwide

Robert White Artist Management
182 Moselle Avenue, **London** N22 6EX
Tel: 20-8881 6914 Fax: 20-8888 9662
E-Mail: rwhiteam@aol.com
contact Robert White
Artforms: early music, new music, soloists and small groups *Comments:* member of IAMA; personal management of soloists and small groups specialising in early and new music

Roger Carey Associates
7 St Georges Square, **London** SW1V 2HX
Tel: 20-7630 6301 Fax: 20-7630 0029
E-Mail: bedford@dircon.co.uk
contact Roger Carey
Artforms: actors, director, writers

Rosemary Rogers PR
29 Clifton Street, **St Albans** AL1 3RY
Tel: 1727-848 420 Fax: 1727-845 640
E-Mail: rosemary.rogers@LineOne.net
director Rosemary Rogers
Artforms: public relations for orchestras, individual artists and festivals

Rostrum Promotions
4 Ferniebank Brae,
Bridge of Allan (Scotland) FK9 4PJ
Tel: 1786-834 449 Fax: 1786-833 949
E-Mail: rostrum@compuserve.com
director Fiona Paterson
Artforms: management of classical musicians, arts administration, tour and festival coordination
Comments: see also Promoters

Sally Hope Associates
108 Leonard Street, **London** EC2A 4XF
Tel: 20-7613 5353 Fax: 20-7613 4848
E-Mail: s-hope@dircon.co.uk
contact Sally Hope
Artforms: directors, actors, designers, composers

Sarah Gordon Concert Management
110 Gloucester Avenue, **London** NW1 8HX
Tel: 20-7483 2681 Fax: 20-7586 5343
E-Mail: sarah.gordon@easynet.co.uk
director Sarah Gordon
Artforms: concert and recital management plus music festival administration

Seaview Music
28 Mawson Road, **Cambridge** CB1 2EA
Tel: 1223-508 431 Fax: 1223-508 449
E-Mail: seaview@dial.pipex.com
manager Alison Page; assistant manager Sarah Bruce
Artforms: personal management of artists who perform classical music with a difference

Seifert Dench Associates
24 D'Arblay Street, **London** W1V 3FH
Tel: 20-7437 4551 Fax: 20-7439 1355
E-Mail: seifertden@msn.com
contact Michelle Arnold
Artforms: set designers, composers, directors

Senior Management
32 Wolverton Gardens, **London** W6 7DY
Tel: 20-8563 0618 Fax: 20-8741 5233
Internet: www.schubertensemble.com
E-Mail: senior.mgt@dial.pipex.com
director Ann Senior
Comments: managers of the Schubert Ensemble of London; consultants in orchestral and chamber ensemble touring

Serious
Chapel House, 18 Hatton Place, **London** EC1N 8RU
Tel: 20-7405 9900 Fax: 20-7405 9911
directors David Jones, John Cumming, Claire Whittaker
Artforms: concentrate on new and innovative music
Comments: concert producers, with a strong interest in international cooperation; producers of London Jazz Festival

Sharon Kivity Arts Consultant
19B Albert Road, **Teddington** TW11 0BD
Tel: 20-8977 2961 Fax: 20-8977 6281
E-Mail: sharonarts@btinternet.com
senior consultant Sharon Kivity
Artforms: events and festival direction and management; arts marketing/administration; consultancy and training; editorial and magazine production
Comments: see also Services

Shepherd and Ford Associates
13 Radnor Walk, **London** SW3 4BP
Tel: 20-7352 2200 Fax: 20-7352 2277
E-Mail: info@shepherdford.co.uk
contact Suzanne Ford, Christina Shepherd
Artforms: actors, directors, set designers

Simply Singers
23 Freke Road, **London** SW11 5PU
Tel: 20-7223 7327 Fax: 20-7924 5730
contact Rosemary Grundy, Fiona Sutherland
Artforms: singers (concerts and opera)

Simpson Fox Associates
52 Shaftesbury Avenue, **London** W1V 7DE
Tel: 20-7434 9167 Fax: 20-7494 2887
contact David Watson
Artforms: set and costume designers, lighting designers

Sonata
11 North Park Road, **Glasgow (Scotland)** G20 7AA
Tel: 141-945 3553 Fax: 141-946 7034
Internet: www.sonata.freeserve.co.uk
E-Mail: gtassie@sonata.freeserve.co.uk
managing director Gregor Tassie
Artforms: choirs, opera and soloists; primarily European artists *Comments:* also promote; arrange tours and recording projects; see also Promoters

Stafford Law
6 Barham Close, **Weybridge** KT13 9PR
Tel: 1932-854 489
Fax: 1932-858 521
Margherita Stafford, David Law
Comments: international management of conductors, singers (concert and opera) and producers

Stella Richards Management
42 Hazlebury Road, **London** SW6 2ND
Tel: 20-7736 7786
Fax: 20-7731 5082
contact Stella Richards
Artforms: directors, set designers

Stephannie Williams Artists
9 Central Chambers, Wood Street,
Stratford-upon-Avon CV37 6JQ
Tel: 1789-266 272
Fax: 1789-266 467
Internet: www.swartists.co.uk
E-Mail: enquiries@swartists.co.uk
general manager Stephannie Williams; concerts managers Martin Denny, Jayne Rollason
Artforms: personal management, narrators, instrumentalists, lecture recitals, project management

Stoll Moss Theatres
Manor House, 21 Soho Square,
London W1V 5FD
Tel: 20-7494 5200
Fax: 20-7434 1217
E-Mail: info@stoll/moss.com
chief executive Richard Johnston
Artforms: theatre productions, mainly West End

Sue Lubbock Artist Management
25 Courthope Road, **London** NW3 2LE
Tel: 20-7485 5932 Fax: 20-7267 0179
managing director Sue Lubbock
Comments: personal management for a number of solo instrumentalists, conductors and chamber ensembles (UK/internationally)

Susumu Productions (UK) Ltd
56 Brewer Street, **London** W1R 3FA
Tel: 20-7494 0575
Fax: 20-7494 0577
Internet: susumu.u-net.com
E-Mail: spuk@susumu.u-net.com
director Susumu Matahira; general manager Nick Earle; development manager Richard Porter
Artforms: theatre

Tennant Artists
Unit 2, 39 Tadema Road, **London** SW10 0PZ
Tel: 20-7376 3758
Fax: 20-7351 0679
E-Mail: info@tennantartists.demon.co.uk
directors Christopher Tennant, Angela Sulivan
Comments: international management of conductors, instrumentalists and chamber ensembles with associated concert promotion and public relations

Terry Harrison Artists Management
The Orchard, Market Street,
Charlbury OX7 3PJ
Tel: 1608-810 330
Fax: 1608-811 331
managing director Terry Harrison;
artists' manager Helen Turner
Comments: management of classical musicians, conductors, soloists

Theater Impresariaat Internationaal
35 Summerhouse Avenue,
Heston TW5 9DJ
Tel: 20-8570 6478
director Andrew Leigh; executive producer Donald Sartain; consultant and founder Dr Jan de Blieck OBE
Artforms: theatre productions, recitals, one-man shows
Comments: has since 1948 specialised in presenting English language theatre companies at festivals and on tour in Europe and beyond; its current priority is the promotion of cultural exchanges throughout Europe

Theatre of Comedy Company
Shaftesbury Theatre, 210 Shaftesbury Avenue,
London WC2H 8DP
Tel: 20-7379 3345
Fax: 20-7836 8181
chief executive Andrew Leigh
Artforms: modern and classical comedy; new plays for West End and UK touring

Thelma Holt Ltd.
Waldorf Chambers, 11 Aldwych,
London WC2B 4DA
Tel: 20-7379 0438
Fax: 20-7836 9832
E-Mail: thelma@dircon.co.uk
managing director Thelma Holt
Artforms: theatrical producers

Theobald-Dickson Productions Ltd
The Coach House, Swinhope Hall, Market Rasen,
Swinhope, **Market Rasen** LN8 6HT
Tel: 1472-399 011
Fax: 1472-399 025
Internet: www.barbaradickson.com
contact Bernard Theobald
Artforms: managment for Barbara Dickson
Comments: arts management and record production

TransArt (UK) Ltd
8 Bristol Gardens, **London** W9 2JG
Tel: 20-7286 7526 Fax: 20-7266 2687
Internet: www.transartuk.com
E-Mail: transart@transartuk.com
director Hervé Corre de Valmalète; artists managers Bruno Ceccaldi, Rachel Smith; company secretary Sarah Trice
Artforms: worldwide representation of conductors and instrumentalists *Comments:* works in conjunction with Le Bureau de Concerts de Valmalète, Paris

UK Arts International
2nd Floor, 6 Shaw Street, **Worcester** WR1 3QQ
Tel: 1905-26424
Fax: 1905-22868
Internet: www.ukarts.com
E-Mail: janryan@amendmnt.demon.co.uk
director Jan Ryan; tour coordinating manager Joanna Carr; tour coordinators Meg Morriss, Mark Makin
Artforms: theatre, dance, physical theatre, musicals
Comments: tour mangement; contact: tour booker

Upbeat Management
Sutton Business Centre, Restmor Way,
Wallington SM6 7AH
Tel: 20-8647 5275/8773 1223
Fax: 20-8669 6752
Internet: www.upbeat.co.uk
E-Mail: classic@upbeat.co.uk
Maureen Phillips, Liz Biddle
Artforms: personal management, representation and agency service for solo instrumentalists, chamber music ensembles and jazz groups; concert management *Comments:* see also Recorded Media

Val Fancourt Music Management
16 Ranelagh Avenue, Barnes Common,
London SW13 0BW
Tel: 20-8876 6509 Fax: 20-8876 2551
E-Mail: ValFancourt@compuserve.com
contact Val Fancourt

Valerie Barber PR & Personal Management
Suite 300, Mappin House, 4 Winsley Street,
London W1N 7AR
Tel: 20-7436 1115/6 Fax: 20-7436 5090
E-Mail: vbpr@compuserve.com
director Valerie Barber
Comments: publicity and concert management; woldwide management of Melvyn Tan; UK, France & Australian management of the Skampa Quartet

Van Walsum Management
4 Addison Bridge Place, **London** W14 8XP
Tel: 20-7371 4343 Fax: 20-7371 4344
Internet: www.vanwalsum.co.uk
E-Mail: vwm@vanwalsum.co.uk
managing director Joeske van Walsum; deputy managing director Victoria Rowsell; directors Roderick Thomson, Geoffrey Owen, Rachel Bostock
Comments: international management of conductors, instrumentalists, singers, composers and orchestras; international orchestra tours, promotion of concert series; project management and public relations

Victor Hochhauser
4 Oak Hill Way, **London** NW3 7LR
Tel: 20-7794 0987 Fax: 20-7431 2531
E-Mail: admin@hhauser.sonnet.co.uk
directors Victor Hochhauser, Lilian Hochhauser
Comments: promoters of popular concerts, ballet and dance seasons, concert management for prestigious visiting artists

Vincent Shaw Associates Ltd
20 Jay Mews, Kensington Gore, **London** SW7 2EP
Tel: 20-7581 8215 Fax: 20-7225 1079
Internet: home.clara.net/vincentshaw
E-Mail: vincentshaw@clara.net
director Vincent Shaw; assistant Gavin Humphreys
Artforms: general casting agents for English-speaking theatres in Europe; commercials

Vivyan Ellacott Productions
Kenneth More Theatre, Oakfield Road,
Ilford IG1 1BT
Tel: 20-8553 4464 Fax: 20-8553 5476
Internet: www.kenneth-more.theatre.co.uk
E-Mail: VivyanE@aol.com
director Vivyan Ellacott
Artforms: mainly young opera singers; produce four annual operatic productions at Kenneth More Theatre; also some plays, rock musicals

West End International Ltd
15 Mount Pleasant, **London** WC1X 0AA
Tel: 20-7833 0884 Fax: 20-7833 9883
E-Mail: weint2@aol.com
directors Gary Brown, Martin Yates; production manager Peggy Riley; finance director Ronald Fuss
Artforms: producers of international concert performances, opera gala concerts, celebrity concerts; also producers of 'The Concert' (West End, Broadway, Hollywood) and full musicals

Wim Wigt Production Ltd
22 Upper Brook Street, **London** W1Y 1PD
Tel: 20-8662 1235
Fax: 20-8654 2120
directors W. Wigt, M Wigt
Artforms: jazz, classical, etc.
Comments: see also Netherlands and Germany (Timeless music promotions)

Women's Playhouse Trust
Studio 2: 35, 75 Whitechapel Road,
London E1 1DU
Tel: 20-7377 2110 Fax: 20-7377 2112
E-Mail: igj@wpt.org.uk
artistic director Jules Wright; project director Ian James
Comments: The WPT is a theatre/opera/ music/ visual arts and film production company; all its work is commissioned by the directors or created in co-productions with international partners

Wren Music
8 Park Lane, **Selsey** PO20 OHD
Tel: 1243-604 281
Fax: 1243-604 387
Internet: php.indiana.edu/~elliottp/Wren
E-Mail: m.elliott@chiche.ac.uk
director Martin Elliott
Artforms: responsible for: Wren Baroque Soloists and Orchestra, Wren Singers of London, Wren Consort; present a variety of educational projects in the UK, Canada, Australia and New Zealand
Comments: management solely for the above artists and presentations; alternative Internet: www.musiciansgallery.com

Young Concert Artists Trust
23 Garrick Street, **London** WC2E 9AX
Tel: 20-7379 8477
Fax: 20-7379 8467
chief executive Rosemary Pickering;
artists manager Sue Hudson
Artforms: singers, instrumentalists
Comments: a unique charity representing outstanding young musicians; auditions annually

Zap Productions
Zap Office, 7A Middle Street,
Brighton BN1 1AL
Tel: 1273-821 588 Fax: 1273-206 960
Internet: www.zapuk.com
E-Mail: office@zapuk.com
administrator Pat Butler; programme directors D. Reeves, R. Morley
Artforms: arts festival and event managers
Comments: the leading creator of challenging arts and entertainments programmes in the UK, supporting all types of events including theatre, street theatre, music, circus, dance, comedy and cabaret, in particular producing experimental performances, celebrations and street theatre festivals; developed the National Street Arts Festival with funding from National Lottery; engaged in creative exchanges and collaborations with European festivals with support from the European Union; see also Festivals

YUGOSLAVIA (+381)

Due to the war in Kosovo we have been unable to update the following entries for Yugoslavia

Concert Agency Art Plus
Umetnicka agencija Art Plus
Ljuba Vuckovica 20/15, 11000 **Belgrade**
Tel: 11-476 063 Fax: 11-762 494
director Zeljko Draganic

Concert Agency Beokoncept
Koncertna agencija Beokoncept
Draze Pavlovica 29, 11000 **Belgrade**
Tel: 11-766 883 Fax: 11-766 883
director Ivan Tasovac

Concert Hall Agency Sava Centre
Koncertna agencija Sava centra
Milentija Popovicá 23, 11070 **Novi Beograd**
Tel: 11-609 335/222 Fax: 11-222 1156
director Djodje Milovanovic

Jugokoncert – Yugoslav Concert Management
Koncertna agencija Jugokoncert
Terazije 41, 11000 **Belgrade**
Tel: 11-339 916 Fax: 11-340 478
director Eduard Ille

Radio

Radio
This section is divided into Radio at a national/regional level. It comprises broadcasting stations which initiate productions of interest to arts organisations. For that reason, many commercial radio stations, including classical music radio stations, are not included. **Within country the organisations are ordered alphabetically.**

Radio
Cette rubrique englobe les stations de radio à un niveau national et régional. Elle fait apparaître les stations qui assurent la promotion de productions directement liées à des organisations artistiques. Pour cette raison, de nombreuses stations commerciales, ainsi que des stations qui diffusent de la musique classique, ne sont pas répertoriées ici. **Pour chaque pays les organisations sont classés par ordre alphabétique.**

Rundfunk
Dieses Kapitel umfaßt nationale und regionale Rundfunkanstalten. Andere Rundfunkanstalten, die sich mit Produktionsaufträgen, Eigenproduktionen usw. befassen werden auch aufgeführt. Ausgeschlossen sind kommerzielle Rundfunkanstalten, einschließlich solcher mit vorwiegend klassischer Musik, die einen geringen oder überhaupt keinen Etat für Eigenproduktionen haben. **Die Organisationen sind innerhalb aller Staaten alphabetisch geordnet.**

Radio
Questa sezione riguarda le radio nazionali e regionali. Comprende tutte quelle stazioni che si occupano di produzioni nel campo artistico. Abbiamo escluso molte radio commerciali oltre a quelle che si occupano di musica classica. **All'interno di ogni nazione sono organizzate in ordine alfabetico a seconda della cittá.**

Radiodifusión
Esta sección está dividida en radio estatal a nivel nacional y regional. Incluye emisoras que emiten producciones de interés para organizaciones relacionadas con las artes. Hemos excluido emisoras comerciales de radio incluso emisoras de música clásica que tienen un pequeño o inexistente presupuesto para su propia producción. **Dentro del país, las organizaciones están ordenadas alfabéticamente.**

라디오
이 부문에는 라디오를 전국적/지역적 차원으로 나누었다. 예술 단체들에게 관심이 있을 작품을 만드는 방송국들이 기재되었다. 그런 이유로 많은 상업 방송국들이 포함되지 않았다. **리스트는 국가별로 알파벳순으로 기재되었다.**

无线电
此部分被分为全国性或地区性的无线电。它由制作与艺术团体有关的广播电台组成。出于此因，许多商业广播电台不包括在内。**在各国内，各机构是按字母顺序排列的。**

ラジオ
このリストでは全国局と地方局を掲載しています。ここでは芸術、芸能団体の活動を支援する番組作成を行うラジオ局を扱っているため、多くの商業ラジオ局が除外されています。**リストは国別で、一国内ではアルファベット順に記載されています。**

ALBANIA (+355)

Albanian Radio Television – RTSH Tirana
Tel: 42-28310
Fax: 42-28310
general director Albert Minga (tel/fax: 42-27745/28310); assistant general director Sefedin Cela (tel: 42-28302); radio director Martin Leka (tel: 42-28444)
Orchestras: RTSH Orchestra (director: Dhimiter Gjoka)

Radio IME
RR. F Rada, P 9/1,
AP 8, **Tirana**
Tel: 42-27955
Fax: 42-27955
director Eni Alimerko

Radio Koha
RR. Sami Frasheri P.26/1, **Tirana**
Tel: 42-28781
Fax: 42-28781
director Enkel Demi

Radio Stinet
Rr/Andon Zako Cajupi 34/4, **Tirana**
Tel: 42-25260
Fax: 42-25260
director Arqile Ndini

RTV Klan
RR. Myslym Shyri P. 8/1, **Tirana**
Tel: 42-34424
Fax: 42-34424
director Aleksander Franga

ARMENIA (+374)

Ardzagank Radio FM 103.5
Sport and Concert Hall,
Tsitsernakaberd,
375028 **Yerevan**
Tel: 2-399 911/223 463/398 125
Fax: 2-390 001
editor in chief Artavazd Bayatian

Hay FM
1/3 Pavstos Byuzand Street,
375001 **Yerevan**
Tel: 2-529 868/560 000
Fax: ITN07156
general director Gor Martirosian

Radio Company of Armenia
5 Alek Manookian Street,
375025 **Yerevan**
Tel: 2-522 344 Fax: 2-151 947
director Armen Amirian (tel: 2-553 750)

AUSTRIA (+43)

Österreichischer Rundfunk (ORF)
Argentinierstraße 30a,
1040 **Wien**
Tel: 1-50101-0
Internet: www.orf.at
E-Mail: radio.tr@orf.at
director general Gerhard Weis;
radio drama and literature Dr Konrad Zobel (tel: 1-50101 18467, fax: 1-50101 18929);
radio music Maximilian Blumencron (tel: 1-50101 18241, fax: 1-50101 18340);
head of Radio Österreich 1 Alfred Treiber (tel: 1-50101 18804);
RSO-Wien (Radio Symphonieorchester Wien:)
Dr Andrea Seebohm (tel: 1-50101 18420, fax: 1-50101 18358)
Format, Policy: independent Austrian productions in all the performing arts
Orchestras: RSO-Wien [Radio Symphonie Orchester (q.v.)] *Comments:* see also Orchestras, Television

AZERBAIDZHAN (+994)

Azerbaidzhan State Radio and Television Company
M Guseyn St. 1,
370011 **Baku**
Tel: 12-927 253/385 480
chairman Khudiyev Nizamy Manaf Ogly

BELARUS (+375)

BA Internaitonal
Radio Bi-Ei
ul. Chapaeva 5, 220034 **Minsk**
Tel: 172-364 103
Fax: 172-364 103
director Jevgjenij V Shjerjeshjevskij

Belarusian Radio
Bjelaruskaje Radyjo
ul. Krasnaya 4,
220807 **Minsk**
Tel: 172-332 424/395 810
Fax: 172-366 643
director Wjachjeslav W Kharitonov;
vice-director Vladimir I Jadrjencjev

BELGIUM (+32)

RTBF – Radio-Télévision Belge de la Communauté Française
Boulevard A. Reyers 52, 1044 **Brussels**
Tel: 2-737 2111/2717 (communication)/2175
Fax: 2-737 3012
Internet: www.rtbf.be/radio
E-Mail: info@rtbf.be
director of radio Claude Delacroix;
head of music, Radio 3 Philippe Gaufriez (tel: 2-737 4492/28/74);
chargé de communication de la direction de la radio Gérard Weissenstein
Format, Policy: 5 channels: La Première (info)/Fréquence Wallonie (regional)/Musique 3 (classical/jazz)/'21' (youth)/Bruxelles Capital (regional)/RTBF International *Comments:* see also TV

Vlaamse Radio- en Televisieomroep – VRT
Flemish Radio & Television Company
Auguste Reyerslaan 52, 1043 **Brussels**
Tel: 2-741 3111
Fax: 2-735 3704 (press)
Internet: www.vrt.be
E-Mail: info@vrt.be
chairman of the board Prof Dr Bart de Schutter;
managing director Bert de Graeve; head of internal & external relations Luc van der Borght; director radio Chris Cleeren; press relations (radio) Paul de Meulder; marketing (radio) Isabelle Baele
Format, Policy: 6 radio services: Radio 1 (news and current affairs), Radio 2 (regional stations), Radio 3 (cultural network, mainly classical music), RVI (world service), Studio Brussel (youth emphasis), Donna (entertainment) *Comments:* see also TV

BOSNIA & HERZEGOVINA (+387)

ZID
H. Redëlca 7,
71000 **Sarajevo**
Tel: 71-443 771
Fax: 71-443 771
head of music Jadranka Crnogorac;
director of music production Peter Lukac
Comments: organises concert of alternative rock music (Rock Under Siege)

BULGARIA (+359)

Bulgarian National Radio
4 Dragan Tsankov Blvd, 1040 **Sofia**
Tel: 2-985 241 Fax: 2-657 298
general director Alexander Velev;
secretary general Danail Danev;
head of music department Yordan Rouptchev
Format, Policy: 3 programmes: 'Horizont' (director: Dimiter Dimitrov), 'Hristo Botev' (director: Ada Tchalakova) and 'Bulgaria' (director: Rayna Konstantinova)

Radio 99
113 Tzarigradsko shose Blvd, fl. 8,
1184 **Sofia**
Tel: 2-746 013/716 668
Fax: 2-746 013
director Emil Ivanov

Radio Channel Kom
Hotel 'Sankt Peterburg', Floor 21,
4000 **Plovdiv**
Tel: 32-559 088 Fax: 32-559 088
managing director Jivko Jelev;
music director Valentin Poochkov
Format, Policy: classical and popular music

Radio Classic FM
23 Oborishte Str, 1504 **Sofia**
Tel: 2-943 4587
Fax: 2-943 4587
director Vassil Dimitrov
Format, Policy: classicl music

Radio Darik
82 Dondukov Blvd, 1000 **Sofia**
Tel: 2-984 983 Fax: 2-9849 8522
president Radosvet Radev
Format, Policy: music

Radio Express
1 Bulgaria sq, National Palace of Culture, fl. 17,
1414 **Sofia**
Tel: 2-951 6962/5900
Fax: 2-954 9342
managing director Dessislava Todorova
Format, Policy: music

Radio FM Plus
215 Blvd Tzar Boris III,
1618 **Sofia**
Tel: 2-955 9060
Fax: 2-955 9974
director Peter Puntchev; head of music Vladimir Dinov
Format, Policy: contemporary music

Radio Signal Plus
43 Blvd Tzarigradsko shosse,
1124 **Sofia**
Tel: 2-445 567
Fax: 2-466 718
director Kevork Kevorkian

Radio Tangra
13 Aksakov Str., 1000 **Sofia**
Tel: 2-988 1410 Fax: 2-981 4897
director Kiril Marechkov
Format, Policy: music

Radio Vitosha
1 Fr Nansen Blvd, 1000 **Sofia**
Tel: 2-91000
Fax: 2-91000
director Rumen Dimitrov

CROATIA (+385)

Croatian Radio Rijeka
Hrvatski Radio Rijeka
Korzo 24, **Rijeka**
Tel: 51-657 777 Fax: 51-657 745
director Davor Travas

Croatian Radio Vukovar
Hrvatski radio Vukovar
Hotel za samce,
32223 **Borovo naselje**
Tel: 32-66154/441 541
Fax: 32-65576
director Zeljko Fekete

Radio Dalmacija
Kralja Zvonimira 14/9, 21000 **Split**
Tel: 21-342 910/919
Fax: 21-551 092
director Davor Maric

Radio Opatija
Grand hotel Adriatic, M.Tita 256,
51410 **Opatija**
Tel: 51-719 373/372/215 100
Fax: 51-272 800
director Denis Blaskovic

Radio Pula
Obala 10, 52000 **Pula**
Tel: 52-214 440
Fax: 52-211 170

Radio Varazdin
Ursulinska 5, 42000 **Varazdin**
Tel: 42-211 504/111 Fax: 42-211 160
director Miroslav Hreljuc;
general producer Branko Ostricki

CYPRUS (+357)

Cyprus Broadcasting Corporation
Broadcasting House,
PO Box 4824, 1397 **Nicosia**
Tel: 2-862 081/422 231 Fax: 2-331 172
Internet: www.cybc.com.cy
E-Mail: rik@cybc.com.cy
chairman Antonis Drakos;
director general Pavlos Soteriadis;
head of news and current affairs Evangalos Louca;
head of radio programmes G. Nicolaou;
head of music programmes Elli Korai-Gerolemou

CZECH REPUBLIC (+420)

Cesky rozhlas
Czech Radio
Vinohradská 12, 120 99 **Praha** 2
Tel: 2-2409 4111 (switchboard)
Fax: 2-2421 8084/6 (international dept)
Internet: www.radio.cz
E-Mail: intrel@cro.cz (international dept)
general director Ing. Václav Kasík (tel: 2-2409 4590, fax: 2422 2223); programme director Dr. Josef Havel (tel: 2-2409 4692, fax: 2-2409 4245)
Orchestras: Czech Radio Symphony Orchestra, Big Band Radio Praha, childrens choir and recitation ensemble
Comments: has 5 central stations; CRO 1-Radiojournal-fast information, CRO 2-Praha-all types of programmes, CRO 3-Vltava-cultural programmes (Tel: 2-2409 4364, Fax: 2-2422 2163), CR) CRO 6-Radio Free Europe-Radio Liberty (Tel: 2-2112 1111, Internet: www.rfwrl.org, Email: pechacekp@rferl.org), CRO 7 Radio Praha-sending abroad (Tel: 2-242 8076, Fax: 2-2421 8239) and 8 regional stations: Regina Praha, Brno, Ceské Budejovice, Hradec Králové, Olomouc, Ostrava, Plzen and Ustí nad Labem

Radio Bonton
Zeleny pruh 99, 140 50 **Praha** 4
Tel: 2-6121 8274/643 1974/2564
Fax: 2-6121 8274/3
Internet: radio.bonton.cz
E-Mail: jan.zilvar@bonton.cz
general director Jan Zilvar

Radio Classic FM
Matousova 9,
150 00 **Praha** 5
Tel: 2-540 651/2/3/4
Fax: 2-540 655
director ing. Renata Figerová-Skronská
Format, Policy: classical music and cultural information

Radio Free Europe – Radio Liberty
Vinohradská 1,
110 00 **Praha** 1
Tel: 2-2423 3738/4006
Fax: 2-2112 3313
Internet: www.rferl.org
E-Mail: fendrychovaa@rferl.org

Radio Vox
Zenklova 195,
182 00 **Praha** 8
Tel: 2-688 9277/9738/9739/689 8645/33/51
Fax: 2-689 8635
Internet: www.vox.cz
E-Mail: redakce@vox.cz

DENMARK (+45)

DR Radio – Danish Broadcasting Corporation
Radiohuset, 22 Rosenørns Allé,
1999 **Frederiksberg** C
Tel: 3520 6310/6371 (orchestras dept)
Fax: 3520 6120
Internet: www.dr.dk
E-Mail: ras@dr.dk
head of music department, controller-Channel 2 Birgit Bergholt; artistic director, Radio Symphony Orchestra (DNRSO) and choir Per Erik Veng; conductor DNRSO Gerd Albrecht; conductor choir Stefan Parkman; artistic director, Danish Radio Sinfonietta (DRS) Kim Bohr-Christensen; conductor DSR Adam Fischer; artistic director, Danish Radio Big Band (DRBB) Peter H. Larsen; controller-Channel 1 Peter Johannes Schjødt; controller-Channel 3 t.b.a.; deputy head of music Bent-Erik Rasmussen; pr (radio, tv) Gerda Kristensen
Format, Policy: Channel 1: radio drama, culture (all-language channel with low music output); Channel 2: (incl. satellite and cablechannel DR Klassisk): classical music, jazz; Channel 3: rock, popular music, news, other services; Channel 4: regional programmes *Orchestras:* Danish National Radio Symphony Orchestra, Danish Radio Sinfonietta (light music), Danish Radio Big Band *Choirs:* Danish National Radio Choir *Comments:* Danish Radio organises more than 200 concerts annually, partly with its own orchestras, partly with guest soloists and ensembles from Denmark and abroad

ESTONIA (+372)

Eesti Raadio
Estonian Broadcasting Company
Gonsiori 21, 10147 **Tallinn**
Tel: 6-114 110
Fax: 6-114 457
Internet: www.er.ee
E-Mail: webmaster@er.ee
general director Peeter Sookruus;
Klaasikaraadio's programme director Tiia Teder
Format, Policy: 4 channels broadcast, 55% music, light music, orchestra, big band; one channel is exclusively for classical music *Orchestras:* Estonian Radio Orchestra *Choirs:* Estonian Radio Mixed Choir *Comments:* alternative website: http://er.ee/klassik/klara_en.html

FINLAND (+358)

Classic FM
Postbox 800, 00101 **Helsinki**
Tel: 9-476 7800 Fax: 9-4767 8767
Internet: www.classicfm.fi
E-Mail: henrik.resman@classicfm.fi
managing director Henrik Resman;
programme director Arto Vilkko
Format, Policy: classical music, 24 hours, 6am-12pm presenters

YLE Radio
YLE, Finnish Public Broadcasting Company, PL 90, 00024 **Yleisradio**
Tel: 9-14801
Fax: 9-1480 3216
Internet: www.yle.fi/fbc
director general Arne Wessberg;
director of programmes,
YLE R1 (Radio Ylen Ykkönen) Olli Alho;
producer YLEN Klassinen (digital channel) Ainomaija Pennanen;
manager RSO (Radio Symphony Orchestra) Helena Hiilivirta
Format, Policy: YLE R1: classical music, arts and culture; YLEN Klassinen: classical music *Orchestras:* radio symphony orchestra (q.v.) *Comments:* situated in Helsinki; YLE owns the national radio and television broadcasting distribution technology; YLE broadcasts on 7 radio channels; see also TV

FRANCE (+33)

Radio Classique
12 bis, place Henri Bergson, 75008 **Paris**
Tel: 1-4008 5000
Fax: 1-4008 5080 (administration)/5045 (rédaction)
président directeur général Mario Colaia-Covo
Format, Policy: classical music (from early to contemporary) and business and finance news and in-depth programmes; 24 hours a day

Radio France
Maison de Radio France,
116 avenue du President Kennedy,
75220 **Paris** Cedex 16
Tel: 1-4230 2222/3757 Fax: 1-4230 1488
Internet: www.radio-france.fr
directeur générales J. Marie Cavada;
directeur de la musique à Radio France Pascal Dumay;
délégué du directeur de la musique pour les programmes Jean Pierre Rousseau;
délégué aux activités lyrique et choral Alain Moene;
relations publiques Laurence Laveau;
new music Yves Prin; directeur du Festival de Radio France et de Montpellier René Koering;
responsable du programme 'Hector' Gilles Chauvé
Format, Policy: France Musique (music programmes – mostly classical), France Culture (cultural programmes), France Inter and all the French regional radios, France Info (news), Radio Bleue (3rd age), FIP (music channel) and Radio Auto Routières), and satellite programme 'Hector' *Orchestras:* Orchestre Philharmonique de Radio France (q.v), Orchestre National de France (q.v) *Choirs:* Les Chœurs de Radio France

GEORGIA (+995)

Georgian Tele Radio Corporation Informational Agency
Saqteleradio korporaciis sainformacio saagento
68 Kostava st., 380071 **Tbilisi**
Tel: 32-330 479/368 558 Fax: 32-221 845
director Dimitri Kikvadze; editor Nino Nijaradze
Comments: see also TV

State Tele Radio Company Channel 2
Saxelmwifo telekompania meore arxi
68 Kostava st.,
380071 **Tbilisi**
Tel: 32-368 441/650/590
general director Mikheil Jangirashvili;
assistant Sergo Bitsadze
Comments: see also TV

Television and Radio State Corporation of Georgia
saqar Tvelos televiziisa da radiomauwyeblobis saxelmwifo korporacia
68 Kostava st.,
380071 **Tbilisi**
Tel: 32-332 460/368 331
chairman Archil Gogelia; assistant Ednar Giorgobiani

GERMANY (+49)

Bayerischer Rundfunk
Rundfunkplatz 1, 80300 **München**
Tel: 89-590 001
Fax: 89-5900 2375
Internet: www.br-online.de
head of arts Christoph Lindenmeyer;
Hörspiel und Medienkunst Herbert Kapfer;
head of music Axel Linstädt;
E-musik Dr. Norbert Kristen;
light musik Maximilian Herbstmeier
Format, Policy: approx. 1290 hours a year dedicated to cultural programmes
Orchestras: Symphonieorchester (q.v.), Rundfunkorchester (q.v) *Choirs:* Rundfunkchor
Comments: see also TV

DEUTSCHE WELLE (DW)
Raderberggürtel 50, 50968 **Köln**
Tel: 221-389-0
Fax: 221-389 3000
Internet: www.dwelle.de
E-Mail: info@dwelle.de
Intendant Dieter Weirich;
Kultur/Deutsches Programm/Zentralredaktion Hanno Murena; Kultur Aktuell Stefan Dege, Gaby Reucher, Bernd Wegmeyer, Jochen Kürten; Literatur Dr Erhard Kluge; Wissenschaft/Technik Dr Ute Hänsler; Religion/Ethike Dr Gerhard Appeltauer, Klaus Krämer; Kulturthema Gabriela Schaaf; Hörspiel/Mosaik Carola Hoßfeld; Kulturelles Reisen Winfried Kurrath; Musik/Deutsches Programm Dr Gero Schließ; Konzerte/CD-Productionen Conny Paul; E-Musik Dr Gudrun Stegen, Inge Ivanovic, Dr Dieter Glave; Schlager, Volks- u. Tanzmusik Rolf Peters; Pop u. Rock Jürgen Brendel, Klaus Ulrich, Silke Wünsch; TS-Musik Rick Fülker, Elke Rößler; Außereuropäische Musik Matthias Klaus; Chefredakteur Deutsches Programm (DW-Radio) Joachim Lenz; Chefredakteur Fremdsprachenprogramme (DW-Radio), Kultur Dietrich Schlegel
Format, Policy: short-wave overseas service

Deutschlandfunk
Funkhaus Köln, Raderberggürtel 40, 50968 **Köln**
Tel: 221-345-0 Fax: 221-380 766
Internet: www.dradio.de
Intendant Ernst Elitz;
Vorsitzender des Verwaltungsrats Prof. Dr. Dieter Stolte;
Vorsitzender des Hörfunkrates Hinrich Enderlein;
Verwaltungsdirektor Dr Thomas Gross;
technischer Direktor Helmut Haunreiter;
Programmdirektorin Deutschlandfunk Berlin Gerda Hollunder; Programmdirektor Deutschlandfunk Köln Dr Günter Müchler
Format, Policy: no advertisements; 75% talks (information on politics, economies and culture

DeutschlandRadio Berlin
Hans-Rosenthal Platz, 10825 **Berlin**
Tel: 30-8503-0
Fax: 30-8503-9009
Internet: www.dradio.de
Leiter der Hauptabteilung Musik Gideon Rosengarten (tel: 8503 5600); Abteilungsleiter Musikprogramm Hanni Bode (tel: 8503 5620)
Format, Policy: 46% of programmes are dedicated to music; no advertisements *Orchestras:* Rias Jugendorchester e.V. (30-8503 5655) *Choirs:* 35-strong chamber choir *Comments:* the orchestra and choir are owned and run by the private company Rundfunk Orchester Choir (ROC), GmbH (30-203 090)

Hessischer Rundfunk
Bertramstrasse 8, 60320 **Frankfurt am Main**
Tel: 69-1551/2482(press)
Fax: 69-155 2900/3005(press)
Internet: www.hr-online.gmd.de
E-Mail: pressestelle-fs@hr-online.de
head of cultural department Hans Sarkovicz; radio plays Dr Christoph Buggert; head of music Carsten Dufner; new music and chamber music Dr Bernd Leukert; choir and folk music Gerhard Meier; light music Werner Klein
Orchestras: Radio-Sinfonie-Orchester, Big Band

Klassik Radio GmbH & Co. KG
Brandstwiete 4, 20457 **Hamburg**
Tel: 40-300 5050 Fax: 40-3005 0511
Internet: www.klassikradio.de
E-Mail: info@klassikradio.de
Geschäftsführer Henry C. Brinker;
Programmdirektion Felix Kovac
Format, Policy: classical music (75-80%), 24 hours a day
Comments: private, commercial radio

Mitteldeutscher Rundfunk (MDR)
Postfach 67, 04251 **Leipzig**
Tel: 341-300-0 Fax: 341-300 6789
Internet: www.mdr.de
E-Mail: kommunikation@mdr.de
Intendant Prof Dr Udo Reiter; Hörfunkdirektorin Barbara Molsen; Chefredakteur und Wellenchef MDR info Christian Schneider; Wellenchef MDR Kultur Dr. Detlef Rentsch; manager for the choir and orchestra Holger Kruppe; communication & marketing Susan E. Knoll (Tel: 341-300 6400, Fax: 341 300 6453)
Orchestras: MDR Sinfonieorchester, MDR Kammer Philharmonie *Choirs:* MDR Chor und MDR Kinderchor
Comments: MDR has broadcasting studios in: Dresden (Landesfunkhaus Sachsen), Erfurt (Landesfunkhaus Thüringen) and Magdeburg (Landesfunkhaus Sachsen-Anhalt); visiting address: Hörfunk, Gerberstraße 2, 06108 Halle/Saale; see also TV

Norddeutscher Rundfunk (NDR)
Rothenbaumchaussee 132, 20149 **Hamburg**
Tel: 40-4156-0
Fax: 40-447 602
director of radio programmes Gernot Romann;
head of NDR Radio 3 (classic channel) Wolfgang Knauer;
Hauptredaktion Kulturelles Wort Hanjo Kesting;
head of department orchestra and choir Rolf Beck;
symphonic music Paul Müller;
philharmonic music Hansjoachim Reiser;
Bigband Wolfgang Kunert; choir Angela Piront
Format, Policy: NDR Radio 3 is dominated by classical music, performing arts and drama *Orchestras:* NDR-Sinfonieorchester, Radio Philharmonie Hannover des NDR, NDR Big Band *Choirs:* NDR Chor

Norddeutscher Rundfunk (NDR)
NDR Landesfunkhaus Niedersachsen,
Postfach 4560, 30045 **Hannover**
Tel: 511-988-0 Fax: 511-988 1010
Hauptredaktion Kultur Hanjo Kesting (Tel: 988 2300);
Head of the Orchestral Department Richard Wackeldehne (Tel: 988 2350),
Hans-Joachim Reiser (Tel: 988 2340)
Orchestras: Radio Philharmonie Hannover
Comments: visiting address:
Rudolf-von-Bennigsen-Ufer 22, 30045 Hannover

Norddeutscher Rundfunk (NDR)
Landesfunkhaus Schleswig-Holstein,
Eggerstedtstr. 16, 24033 **Kiel**
Tel: 431-9876-0 Fax: 431-987 6113
Redaktion Heim, Kultur, Niederdeutsch und Wissenschaft Ernst Christ

Norddeutscher Rundfunk (NDR)
Postfach 110144,
19001 **Schwerin**
Tel: 385-59590
Fax: 385-595 9514
E-Mail: info@ndrmv.de
Direktor Gerd Schneider
Format, Policy: a large proportion of radio time is dedicated to the arts including a daily show Das Kultur Journal (19:00 – 20:00) *Comments:* visiting address: NDR Landesfunkhaus Mecklenburg-Vorpommern, Schloßgartenallee 61, 19061 Schwerin

Ostdeutscher Rundfunk Brandenburg (ORB)
August-Bebel-Straße 26-53,
14482 **Potsdam**
Tel: 331-731-0 Fax: 331-731 3571
Internet: www.orb.de
E-Mail: fritz@orb.de
Intendant Prof. Dr Hansjürgen Rosenbauer;
Hörfunkdirektorin Hannelore Steer;
Fernsehdirektor Volker von der Heyd;
Betriebs- und Produktionsdirektor Nawid Goudarzi
Format, Policy: 3 radio stations, 1 TV station
Comments: also have studios in Cottbus, Frankfurt/Oder, Perleberg and Prenzlau; alternative E-mails: radio1@orb.de or studiopotsdam@antennebrandenburg.de

Radio Bremen
Postfach, 28323 **Bremen**
Tel: 421-246-0
Fax: 421-246 1010
Internet: www.radiobremen.de
head of serious music (E-Musik) Peter Schulze; early, sacred music Helmut Schaarschmidt; new music Marita Emigholz; PR/Öffentlichkeitsarbeit Michael Glöckner; head of radio drama Rüdiger Kremer; head of wave band RWZ Dr Jochen Schütt
Format, Policy: emphasis on cultural programmes
Comments: visiting address: Funkhaus, Bürgermeister-Spitta-Allee 45, 28329 Bremen

Saarländischer Rundfunk
Funkhaus Halberg, 66100 **Saarbrücken**
Tel: 681-602-0 Fax: 681-602 3874
Internet: sr-online.de
E-Mail: info@sr-online.de
head of SR1 Europawelle Andreas Weber; head of SR2 Kulturradio Frank Johannsen; head of SR3 Saarlandwelle Elisabeth Sossong; radio drama Dr Robert Karge; head of music Dr Sabine Tomeck; producers, serious music Dr Friedrich Spangemacher, Dr Beate Früh, Josef Weiland, Wolfgang Korb
Format, Policy: SR2 KulturRadio has cultural output
Orchestras: Rundfunk-Sinfonieorchester Saarbrücken (q.v.) *Comments:* see also TV

Sender Freies Berlin
Masurenallee 8-14, 14057 **Berlin**
Tel: 30-3031 3200 Fax: 30-3031 3208
Internet: www.sfb_berlin.de
Hauptabteilungleiterl E-Musik und Koordinator für SFB und ORB 3 Dr Wilhelm Matejka
Format, Policy: Radio 3 has high cultural content and classical music

Südwestrundfunk
Neckarstraße 230, Postfach 70150, 70190 **Stuttgart**
Tel: 7221-929-0 Fax: 7221-929 2600
Internet: www.swr-online.de
Intendant Prof Dr Peter Voß; Geschäftsleitung Prof Peter Voß, Dr Willi Steul, Peter Boudgoust, Dr Heinjo Schröder, Dr Uwe Rosenbaum, Dr Hermann Eicher, Dr Christof Schmid, Bernhard Hermann, Helmut Ochs
Format, Policy: talking programmes include political,cultural and social reports, artistic productions and radio drama, features, essays, discussions, educational programmes, classical music *Orchestras:* SWR Sinfonieorchester Baden-Baden und Freiburg, manager Mathias Weigmann; SWR Rundfunkorchester Kaiserslautern, manager Werner Meyers; SWR Radiosinfonieorchester Stuttgart, manager Felix Fischer; SWR Big Band manager Ulrich de Veer *Choirs:* SWR Vokalensemble Stuttgart; manager Hans-Peter Jahn *Comments:* SWR is located in Stuttgart: Neckarstr. 230, 70190 Stuttgart, Tel: +49 711-929-0, Fax: +49 711-929-2600 and Baden-Baden but as SWR2 (the culture channel) is located in Baden-Baden, we chose to give this address; see also TV

Westdeutscher Rundfunk Köln
50600 **Köln**
Tel: 221-220-1 Fax: 221-220 4800
Internet: www.wdr.de
head of music department Monika Piel;
management symphony orchestra Hans-Martin Höpner;
management big band Wolfgang Hirschmann;
management radio orchestra Dirk Schortemeier (Kölner Rundfunkorchester);
management radio choir Patricia Just
Orchestras: Kölner Rundfunk-Sinfonie-Orchester, Kölner Rundfunkorchester, WDR Big Band
Choirs: Kölner Rundfunkchor *Comments:* visiting address: Appellhofplatz 1, 50667 Köln

GIBRALTAR (+350)

Gibraltar Broadcasting Corporation
Broadcasting House,
18 South Barracks Road, **Gibraltar**
Tel: 79760 Fax: 78673
E-Mail: gbc@gibnet.gi
general manager of TV and Radio George Valarino;
senior presenter Richard Cartwright;
head of production Joseph Adamberry;
senior engineer John Tewkesbury;
news editor Stephen Nesh
Format, Policy: from-7am to 8pm, afterwards links up with world service

GREECE (+30)

Antenna Radio
Kifissias 10-12,
15125 **Marousi (Athens)**
Tel: 1-684 2220/688 6362/634 (pr)
Fax: 1-683 4349
general director Spilios Haramis;
programming director Alkistis Maragoudaki;
head of news Yiannis Papoutchanis;
pr director Olga Pavlatou;
director Christos Kipouropoulos
Format, Policy: news and commentaries during the day, music (classical, jazz and popular) and art programmes in the evening; 24-hour programming

ERT 3 (Hellenic Radio)
2 Angelaki, 54621 **Thessaloniki**
Tel: 31-299 400/611 (international relations)
Fax: 31-299 655 (international relations)
E-Mail: ert3pl@compulink.gr (international relations)
head of international relations Lefty Kongalides
Format, Policy: three stations: two on AM/FM and one on short wave for the Greeks living abroad; one station 9.58 FM/ 1179 AM mostly covers arts and culture and use the logo: the cultural radio for Thessaloniki, head of this station is Vana Haralambidou,
Tel: 31-299 600, Fax: 31-299 651 *Comments:* part of Hellenike Radiofonea-Teleorase SA (ERT), see separate entry

Hellenike Radiofonea-Teleorase SA (ERT)
Greek Broadcasting Corporation
Messoghion Avenue 432, PO Box 60019,
15432 **Aghia Paraskevi (Athens)**
Tel: 1-606 6000
Fax: 1-606 6269/6259/6109
general director, Greek Radio John Tzanetakos;
music programming director George Tsangaris;
musical ensembles director Alchis Baltas
Format, Policy: state radio, under coordination by the Ministry of the Presidency of Government, 24-hour programming: Programme 1 & Programme 2: news, current affairs & commentary, light music;
Programme 3: art and music
Orchestras: National Symphonic Orchestra, National Light Music Orchestra
Choirs: Athens Broadcasting Choir

KLIK-FM Epe
Fragoklissias 7, Paradisos Amarousiou, **Athens**
Tel: 1-689 9144/41/47
Fax: 1-689 9145
E-Mail: Klikfm@compulink.gr
general director Fotis Georgeles;
head of programming John Nenes;
advertising managers Nicos Barlas,
Theodoris Tzouanatos
Format, Policy: current affairs and lifestyle programmes as well as jazz, soul and popular music

HUNGARY (+36)

Magyar Rádió
Hungarian Radio
Bródy Sándor u. 5-7,
1800 **Budapest**
Tel: 1-328 7161
Fax: 1-338 8739
president István Hajdu; artistic director & head of music department (and director of the Budapest Symphony Orchestra, Hungarian Radio's Mixed Choir and Children's Choir) Istvan Alföldi-Boruss; senior manager music department (and manager of the Budapest Symphony Orchestra, Hungarian Radio's Mixed Choir and Children's Choir) Tamás Kelen

ICELAND (+354)

Ríkisútvarp
Icelandic National Broadcasting Service
Efstaleiti 1, 150 **Reykjavik**
Tel: 515 3000
Fax: 515 3010
Internet: www.ruv.is
director general (radio & tv) Markús Örn Antonsson;
head of music Oskar Ingólfsson
Format, Policy: 2 state radio stations: Radio 1 classical music, culture, news; Radio 2 more popular content & current affairs; 18 hours of broacasting

IRELAND Republic of (+353)

Radio Telefis Eireann (RTE)
Donnybrook, **Dublin** 4
Tel: 1-208 3111 Fax: 1-208 3080
director of radio Helen Shaw; assistant editor Radio One Michael Littleton; director of music Niall Doyle; head of radio drama Laurence Foster; general manager, orchestras and performing groups Simon Taylor; public affairs Kevin Healy; general manager National Symphony Orchestra Martyn Westeman;
orchestra manager Sam Ellis
Format, Policy: Lyric FM, FM3 (classical music, cultural programmes), 2FM, RT radio Cork; 24 hours a day
Orchestras: National Symphony Orchestra (q.v.), RTE Chamber Orchestra, RTE Concert Orchestra; RTE Vanbrugh String Quartet *Choirs:* RTE Philharmonic Choir; Cor Na Nog *Comments:* to E-mail: <name of programme>@rte.ie

ITALY (+39)

RAI – Radiotelevisione Italiana
Viale Mazzini 14, 00195 **Roma**
Tel: 06-3686 4501/4313 (programming) 5420 (secretary)
Fax: 06-322 7061 (press)
Internet: www.rai.it
E-Mail: radiorai@rai.it
direttore Giancarlo Santalmassi;
dir. giornale radio Paolo Ruffini;
vice direttore Roberta Carlotto, Angiolino Lonardi, Franco Scaglia, Sergio Valzania
Format, Policy: state radio

LATVIA (+371)

Latvian Radio
Latvijas Radio
8 Doma laukums, 1505 **Riga**
Tel: 7-206 747/722 Fax: 7-206 707
director Dzintris Kolats
Format, Policy: news, local news, current affairs, culture, classical music, popular music, light music, radio plays, education programmes, minority language programmes, programmes for youth, entertainment

National Broadcasting Council of Latvia
Nacionala Radio un Televizijas Padome
Smilsu 1/3, 1934 **Riga**
Tel: 7-220 564
Fax: 7-220 448
E-Mail: tvcounc@melbox.riga.lv
chairman Ojars Rubenis
Format, Policy: central body supervising radio and tv station

Radio SWH
Skantes 13, 1013 **Riga**
Tel: 2-360 929 Fax: 2-782 283
programme director Janis Sipkevics
Format, Policy: private radio, broadcast 24 hours, entertainment, news, current affairs, advertisements, music, world music, modern music, pop, rock

LITHUANIA (+370)

Laisvoji Banga
Naugarduko street 91, 2006 **Vilnius**
Tel: 2-263 836
Fax: 2-263 836

Laisvoji Banga
Naugarduko st. 91, 2006 **Vilnius**
Tel: 2-263 836 Fax: 2-263 836
E-Mail: radio@lbanga.lt

Lietus
Laisves pr. 60, 2056 **Vilnius**
Tel: 2-705 555
Fax: 2-429 152
director general Hubertas Grusnys

Lietuvos Radijas ir Televizija
Lithuanian Radio and Television
Konarskio 49, 2674 **Vilnius**
Tel: 2-263 383 Fax: 2-263 282
director Arvydas Ilginis
Comments: Radio production is distinct from Broadcasting Company: Lithuanian Radio and Broadcasting Centre, tel: 2-459 397, fax: 2-451 738

Lithuanian Radio and Television
Lietuvos radijas ir televizija
Konarskio 49, 2674 **Vilnius**
Tel: 2-263 383 Fax: 2-263 282
deputy director general Algirdas Trakimavieius

M-1 Plius
Laisves pr. 60, 2056 **Vilnius**
Tel: 2-705 555 Fax: 2-429 152

M1
Laisves pr. 60, 2056 **Vilnius**
Tel: 2-705 555 Fax: 2-429 152
director general Hubertas Grusnys

M1 Plius
Laisves pr. 60, 2056 **Vilnius**
Tel: 2-705 555
Fax: 2-429 152
director general Hubertas Grusnys

Radiocentras
Laisvès pr 60, 2019 **Vilnius**
Tel: 2-429 463
Fax: 2-429 073

Radiocentras
Laisves pr. 60, 2056 **Vilnius**
Tel: 2-429 463
Fax: 2-429 073
director Gintautas Babravicius

Ultra Vires
Savanoriy pr. 192,
3005 **Kaunas**
Tel: 4-734 734

Znad Wilii
Laisves pr. 60, 2056 **Vilnius**
Tel: 2-228 264
Fax: 2-429 465

Znad Wilii
Laisves pr. 60, 2056 **Vilnius**
Tel: 2-228 264
Fax: 2-429 465

LUXEMBOURG (+352)

CLT-UFA
45 Boulevard Pierre Frieden,
2850 **Luxembourg**
Tel: 421 421 Fax: 4214 22760
Internet: www.clt-ufa.com
chairman, Board of Directors Gaston Thorn; presidents, chief executive officers Rémy Sautter, Rolf Schmidt-Holtz; executive vice president Jean-Michel Kerdraon; executive vice president and chief financial officer Dominik Belloin; executive vice president general affairs Dan Arendt; pr Mme. Rey (tel: 421 2172)
Comments: CLT-UFA, resulting from the merger on January 13, 1997 of CLT (Compagnie Luxembourgeoise de Télédiffusion) and UFA Film- und Fernseh-GmbH & Co KG of Germany, is Europe's largest TV and radio Group; present in 12 European countries through 22 TV channes, 22 radio stations and a host of subsidiaries in production, rights acquisition and media services, with revenues up to LUF 14 billion

MACEDONIA (+389)

Macedonian Radio and Television
Makedonska Radio-Televizija
Goce Delcev bb, 91000 **Skopje**
Tel: 91-112 200/235 305
Fax: 91-112 156/111 821
director general Melpomeni Korneti; director of radio Gjorgi Varoslija
Format, Policy: 3 broadcasts in Macedonian, Albanian and Turkish

MOLDOVA (+373)

National Company Radio Moldova
1, Miorita str, 2072 **Chisinau**
Tel: 2-723 369
Fax: 2-723 329
chairman Constantin Rotaru

MONACO (+377)

Radio Monte Carlo (RMC)
Quai Antoine 1ffi, 98000 **Monte Carlo**
Tel: 9315 1617 Fax: 9315 1630
president Jean Pastorelli; director general Etienne Combet; administrateur délègué Pierre Yves Revol; directeur général adjoint Alexis Monnier; secretaire de direction Yvonne Romero (tel: 9315 1714)
Format, Policy: programmes in French (5.00am – 12 pm) *Comments:* at time of going to print, RMC had just been privatised – changes are likely but we were unable to incorporate any

NETHERLANDS (+31)

AVRO
PO Box 2, 1200 JA **Hilversum**
Tel: 35-671 7911
Fax: 35-671 7439
Internet: www.avro.nl
E-Mail: webmaster@avro.nl
managing director, radio and tv B. K. Klap; general director F. Maréchal; manager, entertainment/culture/drama M. Benda; manager, radio A. Krijnen; marketing manager C. van Vlissingen; manager, information E. Eljan
Format, Policy: as with the other 8 stations, AVRO is allocated approx 18 hours airtime a week on television
Comments: see also TV

Classic FM VOF
PO Box 1088, 1400 BB **Bussum**
Tel: 35-699 7999
Fax: 35-699 7990
Internet: www.classicfm.nl
E-Mail: sales@classicfm.nl
managing director Ab Trek; music director & head of programming Pieter Buijs; PR and promotions Charlotte Van Ooff
Format, Policy: light classical music, 24 hrs a day
Comments: visiting address: Naarderpoort 2, 1411 MA Naarden

ConcertZender, de
Postbus 275, 1200 AG **Hilversum**
Tel: 35-677 3102
Fax: 35-677 3104
Internet: www.concertzender.nl
E-Mail: concert.post@concertzender.nl
director Marian van Dijk
Format, Policy: classic, contemporary, jazz and world music (24 hrs a day) *Comments:* subsidised by Dutch Ministry of Culture under direction of NOS

Evangelische Omroep
Postbus 21000, 1202 BB **Hilversum**
Tel: 35-647 4747 Fax: 35-647 4227
Internet: www.omroep.nl/eo
E-Mail: eo@omroep.nl
directors A.G. Knevel, A.P. De Boer
Format, Policy: EO is allocated approximately 65 hours weekly; classical music, pop music, news, documentaries, emphasis on evangelic programmes
Comments: see also TV

KRO
Postbus 23000, 1201 EA **Hilversum**
Tel: 35-671 3911 Fax: 35-671 3119
Internet: www.omroep.nl/kro
head of cultural programmes (inc drama) Jos Leussink; head of radio Ceciel Ten Tusscher; president Frans Slangen
Format, Policy: cultural, educational, religious programming; 72 hours a week *Comments:* public broadcasting station, founded 1925; see also TV

NCRV Nederlandse Christelijk Radio Vereniging
Postbus 25000, 1202 HB **Hilversum**
Tel: 35-671 9911 Fax: 35-761 9285
Internet: www.ncrv.nl
E-Mail: webmaster@ncrv.nl
president H Hemink; manager radio G. Oonk
Format, Policy: classical music, cultural programmes, evangelic programmes; 4000 hrs per year
Comments: see also TV

NPS
Postbus 29000, 1202 MA **Hilversum**
Tel: 35-677 3026/4130
Fax: 35-677 4959
Internet: www.nps.nl
E-Mail: nps@omroep.nl
head of press/communication Mrs W.L. Broekhuijsen
Format, Policy: broadcast every night on the classical radio station; broadcast weekly – classical music, world music, modern music, pop, jazz *Comments:* see also TV

TROS
Postbus 28450, 1202 LL **Hilversum**
Tel: 35-671 5715
Fax: 35-671 5236 (general)
Internet: www.omroep.nl/tros
E-Mail: tros@tros.nl
head of classical music and producer, classical music Ankelien van Hoytema; director K. Samplonius
Format, Policy: TROS is allocated 14 hours a week airtime: culture, music, entertainment
Comments: see also Television

VARA
Postbus 175, 1200 AD **Hilversum**
Tel: 35-671 1318
Fax: 35-671 1309
Internet: www.omroep.nl/vara/
E-Mail: vara@vara.nl
director, radio and tv Vera Keur; director of classical music G. Zekveld; casting executive Mauricio Fernandez
Format, Policy: broadcast 15 hours a week; all types of music *Comments:* see also TV

Veronica FM
Postbus 22222,
1202 CT **Hilversum**
Tel: 35-671 8300
Fax: 35-623 1437
Internet: www.veronica.nl
E-Mail: veronicafm@veronica.nl
director radio & television Unico Glorie; programmes director Kees Gerritsen; head of communication department Hans van der Veen
Format, Policy: programmes for people young of mind
Comments: advertising address: I.P., Postbus 74747, 1070 DA Amsterdam, Tel: 20-656 3838, Fax: 20-645 0265; see also TV

VPRO
Postbus 6, 1200 AA **Hilversum**
Tel: 35-671 2525
Fax: 35-671 2240
Internet: www.vpro.nl
E-Mail: pers@vpro.nl
director of radio A.G. Huurma Van Vos; head of classical music A. Van Nyeuwkerk; head of drama Wim Noordhoek
Format, Policy: classical music, cultural programmes, broadcasts 70 hours a week *Comments:* see also Television

NORWAY (+47)

Norsk Rikskringkasting (NRK)
Norwegian Broadcasting Corporation (NBC)
0340 **Oslo**
Tel: 2304 7000
Fax: 2304 8624/8077
Internet: www.nrk.no
radio director Tor Fuglevik; deputy radio director and head of Channel 1 Kari Wener Øfsti; head of Channel 2 Kari Storsletten; head of Channel 3 Nils Heldal; head of music, Channel 1 Per Ole Hagen; head of music, Channel 2 Synne Skouen; head of music, Channel 3 Marius Lillelien; head of culture, Channel 2 Yngvil Kiran; head of drama, Channel 2 Nils Heyerdahl; head of orchestra section, Channel 2 Reidun Berg (Norwegian Radio Orchestra)
Format, Policy: Channel 1: light music, entertainment; Channel 2: serious music, folk music, jazz, drama, theatre; Channel 3: pop, rock *Orchestras:* Norwegian Radio Orchestra (q.v.) *Comments:* see also Television

POLAND (+48)

Polskie Radio SA
Polish Radio SA
Aleje Niepodleglosci 77/85, 00-977 **Warszawa**
Tel: 22-645 9110
Fax: 22-645 5905
chairman Stanislaw Popiolek;
director of Programme I Andrzej Turski (Tel: 22-645 9115, Fax: 22-645 5915);
director of Programme II Elzbieta Markowska (Tel: 22-645 9804, Fax: 22-843 3732);
director of Programme III Piotr Kaczkowski (Tel: 22-645 5547, Fax: 22-645 5947);
director of Programme IV/Radio BIS Krystyna Kepska (Tel: 22-645 9944, Fax: 22-645 5908);
director of Programme V Maciej Tetowski (Tel: 22-645 9305, Fax: 22-645 5917);
director of Polish Radio Theatre Janusz Kukula (Tel & Fax: 645 5461)
Format, Policy: Programme 1: current affairs; Programme II: classical music & literature, Programme III: rock/pop; Programme IV/Radio BIS: educational; Programme V: for Poles abroad *Comments:* direction of classical music recordings: S-1 concert hall, Woronicza 17, 00-999 Warszawa, director: Jolanta Bilinska, Tel: 2-645 5252, Fax: 22-843 4462

Radio ESKA
Zielna 37, 00-108 **Warszawa**
Tel: 22-627 1711 Fax: 22-627 1712
Comments: private radio

Radio KOLOR
Narbutta 41/43, 02-536 **Warszawa**
Tel: 22-622 8585 Fax: 22-622 5405
Comments: private radio

Radio ZET
Piekna 66a, 00-672 **Warszawa**
Tel: 22-622 7575 Fax: 22-622 7900
Comments: created in 1990; first private radio station in Warsaw; since 1994 programme: news, interviews, music; broadcast all over Poland, 24 hours a day, aimed at people aged 20-40

RMF FM
Twarda 30, 00-831 **Warszawa**
Tel: 22-630 6140
Fax: 22-630 6141
Comments: created in 1990; private radio station, programme: music and information; is broadcast in 95% of Poland 24 hours a day, aimed at people aged 15-45

PORTUGAL (+351)

Radio Renascença
Rua Capelo 5, 1294-108 **Lisboa**
Tel: 21-323 9200
Fax: 21-323 9273
Canal 1 director programmes António Sala; information director José Ramos Pinheiro; public relations Dr Henrique Tavares e Castro; RFM director Pedro Tojal
Format, Policy: 2 channels: Canal 1 (private catholic radio) aimed at the general public, news every hour (every half hour in the mornings), mass every Sunday, chat shows, documentaries, performing arts; RFM (pop music) aimed at people aged 20-40; broadcast 24 hours *Comments:* 50 journalists

Radiodifusão Portuguesa EP (RDP)
Av. Eng. Duarte Pacheco 26, 1070-110 **Lisboa**
Tel: 21-387 1109/382 0000
Fax: 21-387 3968/3972/5038
director of Antena 2 (radio 2) João Pereira Bastos
Format, Policy: 3 channels: Antenna 1 (commercial), Antenna 2: 24 hours classical music a day, Antenna 3: youth channel (music, youth programmes); broadcast 24 hours a day

ROMANIA (+40)

Romanian Broadcasting Corporation
General Berthelot 60-62,
Sector 1, **Bucharest**
Tel: 1-222 5647/312 1055/615 9350
Fax: 1-312 1057/222 5641(general director)
general director Tudor Catineanu
Format, Policy: Channel 2 – cultural channel *Orchestras:* National Radio Orchestra

RUSSIA (+7)

Radio Cerebriany Dozhd
Ul. Demiana Bednogo 24, 123308 **Moscow**
Tel: 095-753 8677/78/79
Fax: 095-191 9787

Radio Ekho Moskvy
Ul. New Arbat 11, 121803 **Moscow**
Tel: 095-202 9229
Fax: 095-202 9102

Radio Orpheus
Malaya Nikitskaya 24, 121810 **Moscow**
Tel: 095-222 0193/0083
Fax: 095-290 1916
Format, Policy: all-classical

Russian Public Television and Radio Company – ORT
Ul. Akademika Koroleva 12, 127000 **Moscow**
Tel: 095-217 7210
Fax: 095-217 1162/215 1324
general director Mikhail Shvydkoi (tel: 095-214 5127)
Comments: foreign relations office tel: 095- 217 7898

Russian State Music Centre of Television and Radio
M. Nikitskaya 24, 121069 **Moscow**
Tel: 095-222 0022

Russian State Television and Broadcasting Company (RTR)
5th Street Yamskogo Polya 19/21, 125124 **Moscow**
Tel: 095-214 4978/251 1235
Fax: 095-250 0506

SLOVAKIA (+421)

Many telephone and fax numbers in Slovakia are in the process of being changed. We have included all new numbers known at the time of going to print.

Fun Radio
Leskova 5, PO Box 525, 815 25 **Bratislava**
Tel: 7-5249 7200 Fax: 7-5249 7200
E-Mail: funradio@funradio.sk
contact Milan Králik

Radio Forte
Okruzná 5, PO Box 85, 917 01 **Trnava**
Tel: 805-550 1378 Fax: 805-550 1414
E-Mail: forte@radio-forte.sk
contact Jozef Sustek

Radio Koliba
Brectanová 1, PO Box 54, 830 07 **Bratislava** 37
Tel: 7-5477 1865/5478 8526
Fax: 7-5477 5759
E-Mail: koliba@radio-koliba.sk
contact Monika Benová

Radio Ragtime
Stúrova 9, 811 02 **Bratislava**
Tel: 7-5293 1891/1892 Fax: 7-5292 3776
E-Mail: ragtime@ragtime.sk

Radio Rebeca
Sklabinská 14, 036 01 **Martin**
Tel: 842-220 401/402 Fax: 842-220 403
E-Mail: rebeca@rebeca.sk
contact Vlastimil Baca

Radio Twist
Salviová 1, PO Box 77, 830 00 **Bratislava** 3
Tel: 7-4342 4909
Fax: 7-4342 4908
contact Andrej Hryc

Slovensky rozhlas
Slovak Radio
Mytná 1, PO Box 55, 817 55 **Bratislava**
Tel: 7-5727 3501
Fax: 7-5727 3559
E-Mail: reznik@slovakradio.sk
director Dr. Jaroslav Rezník

SLOVENIA (+386)

Radio Koper Capodistra
Ulica OF 15,
6000 **Koper**
Tel: 66-48505/485 488
Fax: 66-21011
editor Slovenia programme Leon Horvatic;
editor Italian programme Bruno Fonda;
director Italian programme Antonio Rocco
Format, Policy: public service, regional RTV centre; live broadcast of concerts, recorded music, art information service, original radio plays (mostly in Italian); bilingual programmes *Comments:* information, culture, education, entertainment

Radio Maribor
Ilichova 33, 2000 **Maribor**
Tel: 62-101 333
Fax: 62-101 555
editor Ivanka Mulec-Ploj

Radio Slovenija
Radio Slovenia
Tavcarjeva 17, 1000 **Ljubljana**
Tel: 61-175 211
Internet: www.rtvslo.si
editor in charge of cultural programmes Vlado Senica;
editor in charge of music programmes Franc Kriznar;
head of drama Ales Jan;
head of serious music Marjana Mrak
Format, Policy: live broadcasts of concerts and operas, recorded music; arts information service, original radio plays (60 new plays a year), mostly by Slovenian authors *Orchestras:* Symphony Orchestra, Big Band *Choirs:* Chamber choir, Youth choir *Comments:* activities: information, culture, education, entertainment

Radio Student
Cesta 27, Aprila 31, 1000 **Ljubljana**
Tel: 61-123 1431
Fax: 61-123 5176

SPAIN (+34)

Cadena Ser – Sinforadio A3
Gran Via 32-8ffi, 28013 **Madrid**
Tel: 91-347 0700
Fax: 91-522 8693
Internet: www.sinforadio.com
director Jorge de Antón; red. jefe Miguel A Sanchez
Format, Policy: classical music, 24 hours

Cataluña Música
Diagonal 614, 08021 **Barcelona**
Tel: 93-306 9200
Fax: 93-306 9201
Internet: www.catradio.com
E-Mail: correu@catradio.com
head of classical music Pere Burés
Format, Policy: 24 hours classical music, live from 7am to 12.30pm

Radio Clasica de Radio Nacional de España SA
Prado del Rey, 28223 **Madrid**
Tel: 91-346 2129(director Radio)/1386 (producción)
Fax: 91-346 1237
Internet: www.rtve.es
E-Mail: baclas.rne@rtve.es
director radio clasica Adolfo Gross;
jefe producciones musicales Carlos Cruz de Castro;
efe secretaría programes Ricardo Bellés
Format, Policy: all types of classical music 24 hours a day *Orchestras:* Orquesta Sinfónica de Radiotelevisión Española (q.v.), c/ Joaquin Costa 43, 28002 Madrid, Tel: 91-581 7210/7201; Fax: 91-581 7219 *Choirs:* Coro y Orquesta Sinfonica de Radiotelevisión Española (see also Orchestras)
Comments: orchestra also performs independently

SWEDEN (+46)

Sveriges Radio AB
Swedish Broadcasting Corporation
Oxenstiernsgatan 20, 105 10 **Stockholm**
Tel: 8-784 5000
Fax: 8-784 1500
E-Mail: sven.ake.landstrom@stab.sr.se
managing director Lisa Söderberg;
controller, channel 1 Eva Blomqvist; controller, channel 2 Christer Eklund; controller, channel 3 Mats Åkarlund; controller, channel 4 Kjerstin Oscarson; controller, channel 6 Finn Norgren;
controller, channel 7 Jukks Häyrinen;
head of international relations dept. Sven Ake Landström
Format, Policy: channel 1: news, current affairs, culture, drama, documentaries; channel 2: classical music, education and minority language programmes; channel 3: music and programmes for young people; channel 4: light music and entertainment, local news, current affairs and culture; channel 5: radio Stockholm; channel 6: international; channel 7: Finnish language programmes *Orchestras:* Radio Symphony Orchestra (q.v.) *Choirs:* Swedish Radio Choir (q.v.)

SWITZERLAND (+41)

DRS – Radio der Deutschen und Rätoromanischen Schweiz
Radiodirektion DRS, Postfach 4024, **Basel**
Tel: 61-365 3411 Fax: 61-365 3250
Internet: www.schweizerradiodrs.ch
E-Mail: pd-@schweizerradiodrs.ch
director Walter Rügg;
radio 1: programming Heinrich von Grünigen;
head of music Dr. Martin Simon Weber;
radio 2: programming Dr Arthur Godel;
radio 3: programming Andreas Schefer;
head of music Robi Gassmann
Format, Policy: Radio 1: information and light music; Radio 2- classical music and radio plays; Radio 3: modern, popular music, youth programmes
Comments: visiting address: Novarastr. 2, 4059 Basel

RSR – Radio Suisse Romande
Av du Temple 40, 1010 **Lausanne**
Tel: 21-318 1111 Fax: 21-652 9961
Internet: www.rsr.ch
direction Gérard Tchopp; directeur des programmes Isabelle Biruggeli; direction Espace 2 (programme culturel et musical) François Page; direction Couleur 3 (programme pour jeune public) Vincent Steudler; direction Info (rédaction et news) Patrick Mussbaun; la première Isabelle Binggeli;
option musique Vladimir Louvrier
Format, Policy: La premiére (chaîne généraliste), Couleur 3 (chaîne musicale jeune), Espace 2 (Espace 2 carries classical music, drama, cultural transmissions), option musique (chaîne musicale 35-60 ans) *Orchestras:* contract Orchestre de la Suisse Romande (q.v), Orchestre de Chambre de Lausanne (q.v) *Comments:* to E-mail write the persons first name.surname@rsr.ch

RTSI – Radiotelevisione Svizzera di lingua Italiana (Radio Svizzera di Lingua Italiana)
casella postale, 6903 **Lugano**
Tel: 91-803 5111 Fax: 91-803 5355
Internet: www.rtsi.ch
E-Mail: comunicazioneRP@rtsi.ch
head of Rete 1 Jacky Marti;
head of Rete 2 Carlo Piccardi;
head of Rete 3 Angelo Fassora;
direttore regionale (DR) Marco Blaser;
direttore escercizio Fernando Bianchi;
direttore programmi TV Dino Balestra
Format, Policy: radio 2 is cultural channel, radio 3 is for 15-35 year old age range, radio 1 is information, news and entertainment *Orchestras:* Fondazione Orchestra Svizzera Italiana (q.v.) *Choirs:* Coro della Radio Svizzera – conductor: Diego Fasolis *Comments:* radio address: Casella Postale, 6903 Lugano

Schweizer Radio DRS 1
Studio Zürich, Postfach, 8042 **Zürich**
Tel: 1-366 1111 Fax: 1-366 1481
Internet: www.drs1.ch
E-Mail: radio@drs1.ch
Programmleitung Heinrich von Grünigen;
Leiter Musik Dr. Martin Simon Weber;
Information Collette Gradwohl; Leiter Moderation Walter Kälin; Leiter Wort Bernhard Schneider; Leiter Hörspiel & Unterhaltung Franziskus Abgottspon; Programmwirtschaft Ursula Rehmann
Format, Policy: information and light music (24 hours)
Comments: visiting address: Brunnenhofstrasse 22, 8057 Zürich; Schweizer Radio DRS1, Studio Bern, Schwarztorstr. 21, 3007 Bern, Tel: 31-388 9111, Fax: 31-388 9520 (Pressestelle)

Schweizer Radio DRS 2
Studio Basel, Novarastrasse 2, Postfach, 4024 **Basel**
Tel: 61-365 3411 Fax: 61-365 3262
Internet: www.drs2.ch
E-Mail: service@drs2.ch
Programmleitung Dr. Arthur Godel (Studio Basel); Leitung Musik Morgen & Leitung Nachmittag/Musikproduktion Rolf Grolimund; Leitung Wort Abend/Wochenende & Leitung Moderation Martin Bopp; Leitung Wort Morgen Sylvia Scalabrino; Leitung Musik Abend/Wochenende Roland Wächter (Studio Zürich); DRS2-Kulturclub Programmreferat Thomas Weibel (Studio Basel)

Schweizer Radio DRS 3
Studio Zürich, Postfach, 8042 **Zürich**
Tel: 1-366 1111 Fax: 1-366 1131
Internet: www.drs3.ch
Programmleitung Andreas Schefer
Format, Policy: popular music; 140 hours per week
Comments: visiting address: Studio Zürich, Brunnenhofstrasse 22, 8057 Zürich

Swiss Broadcasting Corporation (SBC)
SRG SSR Idée suisse/Schweizerische Radio- und Fernsehgesellschaft (SRG)
Giacomettistr 3, 3000 **Bern** 15
Tel: 31-350 9111 Fax: 31-350 9256
Internet: www.srg-ssr.ch
general director Armin Walpen
Comments: see also TV

TURKEY (+90)

Açik Radyo
Cumhuriyet Cad. Üftade Sok,
ERN Han. No. 1 Kat 4-5-6 Elmadag, **Istanbul**
Tel: 212-296 2389/4 Fax: 212-232 3219

Classic FM
Basin Ekspres Yolu Star Sok. No. 2 ,
Ikitelli, **Istanbul**
Tel: 212-698 4901
Fax: 212-698 4970
director of information service Padre Ignazio Arregni (212-6988 3674)
Format, Policy: classical, opera etc

Radyo Cumhuriyet
Istanbul
Tel: 212-513 8006
Fax: 212-513 7719
coordination Kenan Yalm

Radyo Foreks
Ortaklar Cad. No. 17, 80290 **Mecidiyeköy (Istanbul)**
Tel: 212-215 5336 Fax: 212-215 5350

Turkish State Radio and Television Corporation
Turkiye Radyo Televizyon Kurumu
TRT Sitesi, **Oran-Ankara**
Tel: 312-490 1058 Fax: 312-490 1109
secretary general Ziya Arikan;
deputy secretary general Halid Ertugrul;
director of international relations department Güleser Güler
Format, Policy: 4 channels: radio 3 is classical, pop, jazz, rock

UKRAINE (+380)

National Radio Company of Ukraine
Khreshchatyk St 26,
252001 **Kiev (Kyiv)**
Tel: 44-226 2253
director Volodymyr Reznikov

UNITED KINGDOM (+44)

BBC Bristol
Broadcasting House, Whiteladies Road,
Bristol BS8 2LR
Tel: 117-973 2211
head of features Jeremy Gibson;
head of natural history unit Keith Scholey
Format, Policy: BBC Bristol is the home of the BBC's Natural History Unit; the features department produces a wide range of television and radio programmes

BBC (General Enquiries)
aa
Tel: 8700-100 222
E-Mail: info@bbc.co.uk
Comments: general enquiries about the BBC

BBC Manchester
New Broadcasting House, Oxford Road,
Manchester M60 1SJ
Tel: 161-200 2020
Fax: 161-244 4688
Format, Policy: BBC Manchester is responsible for music policy in North of England, inc. BBC Philharmonic, broadcast concerts, festivals, chamber music, brass bands, choirs *Orchestras:* BBC Philharmonic (q.v.) *Comments:* see also Television

BBC Northern Ireland
Broadcasting House,
Belfast (Northern Ireland) BT2 8HQ
Tel: 28-9033 8000
Fax: 28-9033 8800
controller, BBC Northern Ireland Pat Loughrey; head of broadcasting Anna Carragher; head of production Paul Evans; head of public affairs Rosemary Kelly; head of finance Crawford McLean; head of personnel Liz Torrans; head of research strategy Peter Johnston; head of news & current affairs Andrew Colman: head of resources Stephen Beckett; head of radio drama Robert Cooper, chief producer, music & arts David Byers; senior press officer Austin Hunter; marketing manager Kathy McAllister
Orchestras: Ulster Orchestra

BBC Radio 3 – British Broadcasting Corporation
Broadcasting House, **London** W1A 1AA
Tel: 20-7765 2523
Fax: 20-7765 2511
controller, radio 3 Roger Wright; head of music policy Gwen Hughes; managing editor, radio 3 Brian Barfield; head of presentation Cathy Wearing; commissioning editors Hilary Boulding, Martyn Westerman; finance manager Ben Woolland; head of classical music Dr John Evans; editor specialist music Andrew Kurowski; executive producer sequences and talks Andrew Lyle; editor EBU/World service/Multimedia Graham Dixon; marketing manager James Pestell;
publicity officer Leonora Thomson;
director BBC Proms Nicholas Kenyon
Format, Policy: Radio 3 is the BBC's classical music and cultural network which broadcasts 8760 hours in a year; the programme content is 90% serious music and 10% drama, features, arts programmes and poetry; over 50% of the total music broadcast is either live or specially recorded; the daytime schedule offers regular sequence programmes; each weekday at 1pm there is a lunchtime recital often broadcast live from venues in London and around the country; the evening schedule features relays of concerts and operas, often by the BBC's own orchestras complemented by the most important ensembles and orchestras in the country and around the world *Orchestras:* 5 symphony orchestras provide around 800 hours of output to the network; the BBC Concert Orchestra works principally for Radio 3, but contributes 30% of its output to Radio 3; others are: BBC Symphony Orchestra; BBC Philharmonic (serves venues throughout the North of England from Manchester); BBC Scottish Symphony; BBC National Orchestra of Wales (concerts throughout Wales from its base in Cardiff) *Choirs:* The BBC Singers celebrate their 75th anniversary in 1999; they are Britain's only fulltime professional chamber choir; the BBC Symphony Orchestra appears at the Proms and in their own Winter Season *Comments:* The BBC promotes the Henry Wood Promenade Concerts each summer in the Royal Albert Hall

BBC (Radio) Birmingham
Broadcasting Centre, Pebble Mill Road,
Birmingham B5 7QQ
Tel: 121-432 8888 Fax: 121-432 0939
executive editor, Radio Christopher Marshall;
editor The Archers/Drama Vanessa Whitburn

BBC Scotland
Broadcasting House, Queen Margaret Drive,
Glasgow (Scotland) G12 8DG
Tel: 141-338 2000 Fax: 141-334 0614
controller, Scotland John McCormick; director of BBC SSO Hugh Macdonald; head of arts & entertainment Mike Bolland
Orchestras: BBC Scottish Symphony Orchestra (q.v.)

BBC South East (Elstree)
Elstree Centre, Clarendon Road, **Borehamwood** WD6 1JF
Tel: 20-8953 6100 Fax: 20-8228 8092
head of regional & local programmes (BBC South East, Radio Kent, Thames Valley FM & GLR) Jane Mote; editor, news, current affairs Rodney Davies; editor, First Sight Alison Rooper

BBC South (Southampton)
Broadcasting House, Havelock Road,
Southampton SO14 7PU
Tel: 23-8022 6201 Fax: 23-8033 9931
head of regional & local programmes Craig Henderson; news gathering editors Lee Desty, Mia Costello; editor, Radio Solent Chris van Schaick

BBC South West (Plymouth)
Broadcasting House, Seymour Road, Mannamead,
Plymouth PL3 5BD
Tel: 1752-229 201 Fax: 1752-234 597
E-Mail: rogerclark@bbc.co.uk
head of regional & local programmes (BBC South West, Radio Devon, Radio Cornwall, Radio Guernsey & Radio Jersey) Leo Devine; news editor Roger Clark; editor, current affairs Simon Willis

BBC Wales
Broadcasting House, Llandaff, **Cardiff (Wales)** CF5 2YQ
Tel: 29-2032 2000/8700-100 222 (BBC info centre)
Fax: 29-2055 2973
E-Mail: feedbackwales@bbc.co.uk
controller, BBC Wales Geraint Talfan Davies; administrator, Cardiff Singer of the World Anna Williams; head of broadcast, English language Dai Smith; head of broadcast, Welsh language Gwynn Pritchard; head of production John Geraint; head of arts, music and features Phil George; head of entertainment Geraint Evans; head of drama Pedr James; head of marketing & promotions Catrin Howkins; secretary Wyn Mears; head of strategy & channel management Keith Jones, head of resources Keith Dewhurst
Orchestras: BBC National Orchestra of Wales *Choirs:* BBC Welsh Chorus

BBC West (Bristol)
Broadcasting House, Whiteladies Road, **Bristol** BS8 2LR
Tel: 117-973 2211 Fax: 117-974 4114
head of regional & local programmes (BBC West, Radio Bristol, Somerset Sound, Radio Gloucestershire & BBC Wiltshire Sound) John Conway; editor, news Leo Devine; series producer: Close Up West James Macalpine
Comments: see also TV

Classic FM
PO Box 2834, **London** W1R 7AA
Tel: 20-7343 9000 Fax: 20-7344 2700
Internet: www.classicfm.co.uk
E-Mail: enquiries@classicfm.co.uk
chairman Henry Meakin; chief executive Ralph Bernard; managing director & programme controller Roger Lewis
Format, Policy: 100% classical music *Comments:* visiting address: 7 Swallow Place, London W1R 7AA

Digital One
7 Swallow Place, **London** W1R 7AA
Tel: 20-7518 2620 Fax: 20-7518 2605
E-Mail: digitalone@musicradio.com
cheif executive Quentin Howard;
press officer Alison Halstead (tel: 20-7937 6242)
Format, policy: Digital One is a consortium formed by the GWR Group and NTL to run the national commercial digital radio multiplex; the consortium planned to have launched ten brand new digital only national radio stations from 15 Nov 1999, along with simulcasts of Classic FM, Talk Radio and Virgin; 24 hours

VATICAN CITY (+39)

Radio Vaticana
00120 **Città del Vaticano**
Tel: 06-6988 3551 Fax: 06-6988 3237
Internet: www.vatican.va
E-Mail: promo@vatiradio.va
head of music section Marco Guadagnini; director of programming Padre Federico Lombardi (06-6988 3996); responsible international relations Signora Solange de Maillardoz; director of information service Padre Ignazio Arregui (06-6988 3674)
Format, Policy: musical, documentary, linguistic and informative programmes *Comments:* production and programming, Piazza Pia 3, 00193 Roma

YUGOSLAVIA (+381)

Due to the war in Kosovo we have been unable to update the following entries for Yugoslavia

Association of Yugoslav Radio and TV
Udruzenje jugoslovenskih radio-televizija
General Zdanova 28, BP 284, 11000 **Belgrade**
Tel: 11-333 126/434 910 Fax: 11-434 023
director Vjera Nikolic
Format, Policy: central body linking department heads (including drama and music) both within the country and abroad; does not itself produce programmes

Radio and Television Politika
RTV Politika
Makedonska 29, 11000 **Belgrade**
Tel: 11-322 6983/7427 Fax: 11-322 3421
general manager Dragan Hadzi Antic; deputy directors Bogdan Tirnanic, Radmila Visic; head of cultural programme Ljiljana Lucic; head of music, Radio Aleksandar Novakovic

Radio B-92
Makedonska 22/V, 11000 **Belgrade**
Tel: 11-324 9292/8075 Fax: 11-330 946
general manager Veran Matic; editor-in-chief Sasa Mirkovic; head of music Gordan Paunovic
Comments: independent radio station

Radio Belgrade
Radio Beograd
Krunska (Prol. brigada) 52/II, 11000 **Belgrade**
Tel: 11-324 8888 Fax: 11-322 6768
E-Mail: pvox@eunet.yu
director Milivoje Pavlovic; head of international relations department Marina Matic (tel & fax: 322 4057); head of drama Zoran Popovic; head of music Donata Premeru; director of music production Radivoje Spasic; head of Symphony Orchestra Stanko Marusic; head of Radio Choir Miomir Gacic; head of Big Band Franja Jenc; head of folk orchestra Slobodan Nikolic

Radio Novi Sad
Zarka Zrenjanina 3, 21000 **Novi Sad**
Tel: 21-611 588 Fax: 21-22490
director Kosta Sevarlic; head of music Bosko Buta; director of music production Jovan Adamov

Radio Pristina
Vidovanska bb, 38000 **Pristina**
Tel: 38-22273 Fax: 38-25355
general director, Radio & TV Pristina Petar Jaksic; assistant director Milorad Vujovic; editor-in-chief Milivoje Mihailovic; head of music Blagoje Kosanin; head of drama & music production Gordana Simic
Comments: bilingual in Serbian and Albanian

Radio Yugoslavia
Hilandarska 2, 11000 **Belgrade**
Tel: 11-324 4455 Fax: 11-323 2014
director Nikola Ivanovic;
head of music department Danica Djokic
Format, Policy: external service, programme in 10 languages and special programme in Serbian

RTCG – Radio and TV Montenegro
RTCG – Radio i Televizija Crne Gore
Cetinjski put bb, 81000 **Podgorica**
Tel: 81-25999
general manager Zoran Jocovic

RTS – Radio and TV Serbia
Takovska 10, 11000 **Belgrade**
Tel: 11-324 9000 Fax: 11-341 630
general director Dragoljub Milanovic

Customer Service Page

Dear colleague

All the staff here at Arts Publishing International are continually working to ensure that the PAYE is the most valuable and easy-to-use reference book for the European performing arts market. With your individual requirements you are in the best position to tell us if the PAYE meets your needs. We would therefore be most grateful if you could send us your suggestions and comments on the book.

As well as your suggestions we would appreciate your help in keeping our records as accurate as possible. Please use this page to request information, amend your editorial entry for the next edition or send us new editorial entries. Please direct your mail to: **Editorial Department, Arts Publishing International Ltd., Lime Wharf, Vyner Street, London E2 9DJ, England** or contact us by telephone **(+44) 20 8709 9050**, by fax **(+44) 20 8709 9080** or by e-mail on **paye@api.co.uk**

Amendments

1 Amendments to existing entries in the Performing Arts Yearbook for Europe 2000

Please note: You will receive our formal entry correction letter to update your entry for the PAYE 2001 in May 2000. This space should be used if your information changes after you have returned our request for correct information next May.

Section (eg opera, dance, services and suppliers)

Original company name

New company name (if applicable)

New address

New telephone numbers

New fax numbers

New e-mail address/web site

Changes to personnel

Comments

New Entries

2 New entries for Performing Arts Yearbook for Europe 2001

Please note: All entries are free of charge, but are included at the Editor's discretion

Section

Company name

Address

Telephone numbers

Fax numbers

E-mail address/web site

Personnel

Comments

Mailing

3 Please complete the following section if you want information on our other publications, conferences or special events*

Organisation

Name

Job Title

Address

Tel Fax

E-mail

- The information you have provided may be stored and used under the provisions of the Data Protection Act. If you prefer not to receive mail from third parties please tick this box ☐

Television

Television
This section is divided into Television at a national/regional level. It comprises channels which initiate productions of interest to arts organisations. For that reason, many commercial television stations are not included. **Within country the organisations are ordered alphabetically.**

Télévision
Cette rubrique englobe les stations de télévision à un niveau national et régional. Elle fait apparaîatre les chaînes qui assurent la promotion de production liées à des organisations artistiques. Pour cette raison de nombreuses chaînes commerciales ne sont pas répertoriées ici. **Pour chaque pays les organisations sont classées par ordre alphabétique.**

Fernsehanstalten
Dieses Kapitel umfaßt nationale und regionale Fernsehanstalten. Andere Fernsehanstalten, die sich mit Produktionsaufträgen, Eigenproduktionen usw. befassen, werden auch aufgeführt. Ausgeschlossen sind kommerzielle Fernsehanstalten, die einen geringen oder überhaupt keinen Etat für Eigenproduktionen haben. **Die Organisationen sind innerhalb aller Staaten alphabetisch geordnet.**

Televisione
Questa sezione riguarda le televisioni nazionali e regionali. Comprende tutte quelle stazioni che si occupano di produzioni nel campo artistico. Abbiamo escluso tutte le televisioni commerciali oltre a quelle che si occupano di musica classica. **All'interno di ogni nazione sono organizzate in ordine alfabetico a seconda della cittá.**

Teledifusión
Esta sección está dividida en televisión estatal a nivel nacional y regional. Incluye emisoras y cualquier canal que emita producciones de interés para organizaciones relacionadas con las artes. Hemos excluido emisoras comerciales de TV que tienen un pequeño o inexistente presupuesto para su propia producción. **Dentro de cada país, las organizaciones están ordenadas alfabéticamente.**

텔레비전
이 부문에는 텔레비전을 전국적/지역적 차원으로 나누었다. 예술 단체들에게 관심이 있을 작품을 만드는 텔레비전 방송국들이 기재되었다. 그런 이유로 많은 상업 텔레비전 방송국들이 포함되지 않았다. **리스트는 국가별로 알파벳순으로 기재되었다.**

电视
本部分被分为全国性和地区汜电视。它由制作与艺术团体有关的节目的频道组成。出于此因，许多商业电视台不包括在内。**在各国内，各机构是按字母顺序排列的。**

テレビ
このリストでは全国局と地方局を掲載しています。ここでは芸術、芸能団体の活動を支援する番組作成を行うテレビ局を扱っているため、多くの商業テレビ局が除外されています。**リストは国別で、一国内ではアルファベット順に記載されています。**

ALBANIA (+355)

Alba TV
International Cultural Centre, **Tirana**
Tel: 42-34141/2/3/4 Fax: 42-34144
director Artur Peci
Comments: private television

Albanian Radio Television – RTSH Tirana
Tel: 42-27745 Fax: 42-27745
general director Albert Minga (tel & fax: 42-28310); assistant general director Sefedin Cela (tel: 42-27512); television director Eduart Mazi (tel & fax: 42-27512); television artistic leader Dhimiter Gjoka (tel & fax: 42-26288)

Neser TV
RR. Tefta Tashko Nr. 7, **Tirana**
Tel: 42-40655
general director Gianfranco Liuzzi
Comments: private television

TV Klan
RR. Myslym Shyri P. 8/1, **Tirana**
Tel: 42-34424 Fax: 42-34424
director Aleksander Franga
Comments: private television

TV5 Koha Jonë
Rr/Sami Frashri P./26/1, **Tirana**
Tel: 42-28781
president Nikoll Lesi

TVA
Rruga Kavajes 34/1, **Tirana**
Tel: 42-43932 Fax: 42-27575
director Ardian Taka
Comments: private station

ARMENIA (+374)

AR TV Company
5a Tumanian Street, 375010 **Yerevan**
Tel: 2-523 886/564 149/563 564/587 397 Fax: 2-151 666
president Merujan Ter-Gulanian; vp Vahram Martirosyan

ICN Business TV
1 Saralandji Street, 375025 **Yerevan**
Tel: 2-530 302 Fax: 2-530 302
director Bagrat Sarkisian

Nork TV Company
TV Tower, Nork, 375047 **Yerevan**
Tel: 2-653 090
director Seiran Shakhsuvarian

TV State Company of Armenia
TV Tower, Nork, 375047 **Yerevan**
Tel: 2-558 505/562 460 Fax: 2-506 524
E-Mail: root@tv2arminco.com
general director Tigran Nagdalian

AUSTRIA (+43)

Österreichischer Rundfunk (ORF)
Würzburggasse 30, 1136 **Wien**
Tel: 1-87878-0
Internet: www.orf.at/home.htm
E-Mail: anfrage@orf.at
head of ORF – Kultur Dr. Haide Tenner (1-87878 14300); general director Gerhard Weis
Comments: see also Orchestras and Radio

AZERBAIDZHAN (+994)

Azerbaidzhan State Radio and Television Company
M. Guseyn St. 1, 370011 **Baku**
Tel: 12-927 253/385 480
chairman Khudiyev Nizamy Manaf Ogly

BELARUS (+375)

Belarus National State Television Company
Bjelaruskaja Nacionalnaja Gosudarstvjennaja Tjeljevizionnaja Kompanija
ul. Makajonka 9, 220807 **Minsk**
Tel: 172-634 331 Fax: 172-648 182
president Grigorij L Kisjel

BELGIUM (+32)

Radio-Télévision Belge de la Communauté Française (RTBF)
Boulevard A. Reyers 52, 1044 **Brussels**
Tel: 2-737 2111 Fax: 2-737 4646
Internet: www.rtbf.be/television
E-Mail: fdt@rtbf.be
musique – danse Benoît Jacques de Dixmude (737 2190); directeur, direction de la télévision Gérard Loverius; documentaires Claire Colart; varietes – jeux Pierre Meyer; directeur, direction de l'information Jean-Pierre Gallet; service presse central & coordination Arte-RTBF Marianne De Muylder; responsable ARTE Belgique Carine Bratzlavsky; responsable service médiatíon Francoise de Thier
Format, policy: 2 channels: RTBF 1 (12.00-24.00): general news, entertainment and culture: Eurosport 21: sports channel; RTBF 2 general and culture
Comments: see also Radio

Vlaamse Radio- en Televisieomroep – VRT
Flemish Radio & Television Company
Auguste Reyerslaan 52, 1043 **Brussels**
Tel: 2-741 3111 Fax: 2-734 9351
Internet: www.vrt.be
E-Mail: TV1@vrt.be
chairman of the board Prof Dr Bart de Schutter; managing director Bert de Graeve; head of internal & external relations Luc van der Borght; director television Christina von Wackerbarth; press relations (television) Reinhilde Weyns; marketing (television) Sylvain Peeters
Format, Policy: 3 TV services: TV1, Canvas, KetNet (youth programmes) *Comments:* see also Radio

BOSNIA & HERZEGOVINA (+387)

Radiotelevizija Sarajevo
VI Proleterske Brigade 4, 71000 **Sarajevo**
Tel: 71-652 333 Fax: 71-461 569
general manager Nedjeljko Miljanovic; director Besim Ceric

BULGARIA (+359)

7 Days TV
Television Sedem Dni
26, 170 Str. Compl. Izgrev, 1113 **Sofia**
Tel: 2-971 3255
Fax: 2-971 2002
director Petko Todorov

Bulgarian National Television
29 San Stefano Str., 1504 **Sofia**
Tel: 2-43481
general director Liliana Popova; programme director Svetla Petrova
Format, policy: two channels broadcasting news, music, films etc.

New Television
16 Sveta Nedelia Str, 1000 **Sofia**
Tel: 2-860 3206
Fax: 2-980 7706
director Stefan Dimitrov

CROATIA (+385)

Croatian Radio and TV
Hrvatska Radio Televizija
Prisavlje 3, 10000 **Zagreb**
Tel: 1-616 3366 Fax: 1-615 6301
director Ivica Vrkic

RI TV
Uzarska 17, 51000 **Rijeka**
director Boris Vuckovic

TV Nett
TV Mreza
Preradoviceva 44, 10000 **Zagreb**
Tel: 1-485 6424
Fax: 1-485 6424
director Zvonimir Repac

CYPRUS (+357)

Cyprus Broadcasting Corporation
Broadcasting House, PO Box 24824, 1397 **Nicosia**
Tel: 2-862 417
Fax: 2-330 241
Internet: www.cybc.com.cy
E-Mail: rik@cybc.com.cy
chairman Antonis Draskos; director general Pavlos Soteriades; head of news & current affairs Evangelos Louca; head of tv programmes Andreas Papayiannis; 1st programme officer Michalakis Tofarides

CZECH REPUBLIC (+420)

Czech Television
Ceská televize
Kavcí hory, 140 70 **Praha** 4
Tel: 2-6113 1111 (switchboard)
Internet: www.czech.tv.cz
director Jakub Puchalsky (tel: 2-6121 1602, fax: 2-421 562, email: puchalsky@czech-tv.cz); programme director Gordon Levitt (Tel: 2-6113 4632, Fax: 2-425 484); music producers Radim Smetana, Vítezslav Sykora (Tel: 2-6113 704-7, Fax: 2-6113 7149); drama producers Helena Slavíková (2-6113 7057), Alice Nemanská (tel: 2-6113 7170, fax: 6113 7189); head of public relations Renata Elhenicka
Comments: broadcasts on 2 channels – CT 1 and CT 2

Nova TV
Vladislavova 20, 113 13 **Praha** 1
Tel: 2-2110 0111/3
Fax: 2-2110 0112
Internet: www.nova-tv.cz

DENMARK (+45)

Danmarks Radio-TV
Olaf Palmes Alle 10-12, 8200 **Århus** N
Tel: 8739 7080/3520 3040 Fax: 8739 7244
Internet: www.dr.dk
Comments: main office is in Søborg

Danmarks Radio-TV
TV-Byen, Mørkhøjvej 500, 2860 **Søborg**
Tel: 3520 3040 Fax: 3520 2644
Internet: www.dr.dk
Comments: head-office; non-producing

Opera Channel Aps, The
90 Vester Voldgade, 1552 **Copenhagen**
Tel: 3315 1563 Fax: 3313 0707
general manager Anthony J Whitehouse
Comments: postal address: PO Box 5132, 1211 Geneva 11, Switzerland, Tel: +41 22-328 8390, Fax: +41 22-328 6485

TV2/Danmark (TV2-DK)
Rugaardsvej 25, 5100 **Odense** C
Tel: 6591 1244 Fax: 6591 3322
Internet: www.tv2.dk
E-Mail: tv2@tv2.dk
chief executive and managing director t.b.a.; head of programming Lars Grarup; editor, light entertainment & rock music Anette Rømer; editor of culture and performing art Lone Bastholm (based in Copenhagen); producer, drama Mogens Kløvedal; head of programming, acquisition & co-production Bo Damgaard; film editor Ole Steen Nelsson
Format, policy: all kind of programmes; 17-19 hours a day *Comments:* also have an office in Copenhagen

TV2/Danmark (TV2-DK)
Sortedam Dossering 55a, 2100 **Copenhagen** Ø
Tel: 3537 2200
Fax: 3537 5622 (news)/2227 (programming)
E-Mail: tv2@tv2.dk
head of culture and performing arts Lone Bastholm (email:loba@tv2.dk)
Comments: editorial office with limited production; main office is in Odense (q.v.)

ESTONIA (+372)

Estonian Television
Eesti Televisioon
Faehlmanni 12, 10125 **Tallinn**
Tel: 6-284 100 Fax: 6-284 155
Internet: www.etv.ee
E-Mail: etv@etv.ee
director Toomas Lepp
Format, policy: 1 channel – state owned TV channel

FINLAND (+358)

YLE TV
YLE, Finnish Public Broadcasting Company, PL 90, 00024 **Yleisradio**
Tel: 9-14801 Fax: 9-1480 3216
Internet: www.yle.fi/fbc
director general Arne Wessberg; director of programmes, YLE TV 1 Astrid Gartz; director of programmes, YLE TV 2 Jyrki Pakarinen; head of export Päivi Moore; director of programme, FST (Swedish-language programmes) Leif Jakobsson
Format, policy: TV1: news & current affairs, sport, culture, drama, documentaries, education; TV2: drama, documentaries, children's programmes, regional programmes *Comments:* YLE owns the national radio and television broadcasting distribution technology; see also Radio

FRANCE (+33)

ARTE GEiE – European Culture Channel
2a rue de la Fonderie,
67080 **Strasbourg** Cedex
Tel: 3-8814 2222 Fax: 3-8814 2200
Internet: www.arte-tv.com
president Jobst Plog; vice-president Jérôme Clément; administrative director Wolfgang Bernhard; programme director Victor Rocaries
Format, policy: programming: topical programmes, documentaries, feature films, live & performing arts, news *Comments:* involves the following two organisations: ARTE Deutschland TV GmbH and La Sept ARTE (q.v.); also cooperates with ARD and ZDF in Germany, RTBF in Belgium, SBC in Switzerland and TVE in Spain (see separate entries)

France 2
7 Esplanade Henri de France,
75907 **Paris** Cedex 15
Tel: 1-5622 4358 Fax: 1-5622 5527
Internet: www.france2.fr
théâtre Françoise Roy; responsable, musique classique Eve Rugieri; musique variété Sophie Lapidus; directeur artistique Marc de Florès; administrateur Geneviéve Broust; musique Michel Monpontet
Format, policy: 24 hours

France 3
7 Esplanade Henri de France,
75907 **Paris** Cedex 15
Tel: 1-5622 3030
Fax: 1-5622 7502
Internet: www.france3.fr
directeur artistique and jeux, varietes divertissements Alain Vautier; responsable musique and theatre Martin Even; responsable cinema Patrick Brion; directeur général chargé de l'antenne Jean Reveillon; secrétaire général Didier Hespel; directeur de la communication Jean-Marie Dupont
Format, policy: music, spectacles 170 hrs, cinema 360 hrs, variety, entertainment 580 hrs (1997)

La Sept ARTE
8 rue Marceau,
92785 **Issy-les-Moulineaux**
Tel: 1-5500 7777 Fax: 1-5500 7700
Internet: www.arte-tv.com
president Jérôme Clément;
director,programming Metropolis (cultural magazine) Pierrre Boutang;
responsable de l'unité spectacle Gabrielle Babin;
documentaries Thierry Garrel;
responsable de l'unité jour titre Alain Wieder
Comments: French division of ARTE GEIE (see separate entry)

Muzzik
109 rue du Faubourg St Honoré, 75008 **Paris**
Tel: 1-5389 0660
Fax: 1-5389 0667
E-Mail: cedric@muzzik.fr
president Bruno Deloye; communication Hélène Thiebault (1-5389 0673); promotion Béatrice Loubet
Format, policy: private satellite channel (also cable), broadcasting 24 hrs: classical music 60%, jazz 30% and world music 10% (incl opera, ballet, symphonies, concerts, documentaries, magazines)

GEORGIA (+995)

Georgian Tele Radio Corporation Informational Agency
Saqteleradio korporaciis sainformacio saagento
68 Kostava st.,
380071 **Tbilisi**
Tel: 32-330 479/368 558
Fax: 32-221 845
director Dimitri Kikvadze; editor Nino Nijaradze
Comments: see also Radio

State Tele Radio Company Channel 2
saxelmwifo telekompania meore arxi
68 Kostava st.,
380071 **Tbilisi**
Tel: 32-368 441/650/590
general director Mikheil Jangirashvili;
assistant Sergo Bitsadze
Comments: see also Radio

Television and Radio State Corporation of Georgia
Saqar Tvelos televiziisa da radiomauwyeblobis saxelmwifo korporacia
68 Kostava st., 380071 **Tbilisi**
Tel: 32-332 460/368 331
chairman Archil Gogelia;
assistant Ednar Giorgobiani

GERMANY (+49)

3sat
3sat / ZDF, 55100 **Mainz**
Tel: 6131-706 400
Fax: 6131-706 805
Internet: www.zdf.de
E-Mail: 3sat@zdf.de
Direktor europäische Satellitenprogramme (3sat/Arte) Dr Gottfried Langenstein;
Vice-Director Dr Christof Schmid (3sat/ARD);
Head of 3sat /ORF Peter Zurek;
Head of 3sat /SF DRS Luis Bolliger
Format, policy: broadcasts culture-oriented programme focusing on literature, theatre performances, art, music, films, documentaries and political talk-shows. 3sat presents overall news coverage and background information from three countries – Germany, Austria and Switzerland. The programme is broadcast 24 hours daily.

ARTE Deutschland TV GmbH
Postfach 100213, 76483 **Baden-Baden**
Tel: 7221-93690
Fax: 7221-936 950
Internet: www.arte-tv.com
general managers Dr Klaus Wenger, Dr. Hans-Günther Brüske; head of programming dance, drama, music Thomas Neuhauser; programme coordination & development Peter Wien; Programmverwaltung und Recht Dr. Thomas Sertl; Programm- Marketing und Presse Thomas P. Schmid; Verwaltung Armin Breger; president Peter Voß (director general SWR)
Format, policy: nearly 100% art programmes, documentaries, topical evenings with political, social, lyrical and general items *Comments:* German division of ARTE GEIE (see separate entry in France)

Bayerischer Rundfunk
Floriansmühlstr.60,
80939 **München**
Tel: 89-380 602
Fax: 89-3806 7679
Internet: www.br-online.de
E-Mail: info@br-online.de
Musik- und Fernsehspiel Dr Gabriela Sperl; E-musik Franz Korbinian Meyer; Unterhaltung Thomas Jansing
Format, policy: about 30% of the programme time is dedicated to cultural programmes *Orchestras:* Sinfonie Orchester, Rundfunkorchester *Choirs:* BR Choir
Comments: see also Radio

CLASSICA
c/o Kirch Group,
Robert-Bürkle Straße 2,
85737 **Ismaning**
Tel: 89-9956-0 Fax: 89-9956 2778
managing director Michael S. Fuehr;
editor 20th C music and documentation Arthur Intelmann; editor concerts and performances Dr Thomas Salb; editor ballet, jazz, opera Gabriele Eichinger; editor chamber music Christoph Engel; organisation, administration, production Moritz Petersen
Format, policy: TV channel devoted exclusively to high-quality productions of fine music, from classical music to jazz; every day, on a 24-hour basis, CLASSICA is available on the new German digital satellite package, Premiere World; Mon: ballet, jazz, Tues: 20th-century music, Wed: composers and performers, Thurs: documents and documentaries, Fri: chamber music, Sat: opera, Sun: concerts

Deutsche Welle TV
Voltastr. 6, 13355 **Berlin**
Tel: 30-4646-0
Fax: 30-469 9391
Internet: www.dwelle.de
E-Mail: online@dwelle.de
Fernsehdirektor Dr. Wolfgang Krüger (30-4646 5000); Chefredakteur Christoph Lanz (30-4646 6000); Gesellschaft und Kultur Rolf Rische (30-4646 6500), Axel Radler, Klaus-Dieter Seelig, Anne Preun-Specht, Stefan Tschirner

Hessischer Rundfunk
Bertramstrasse 8,
Postfach 101001,
60222 **Frankfurt am Main**
Tel: 69-1551 Fax: 69-155 3005
Internet: www.hr-online.de
Fernsehspiel u Spielfilm Liane Jessen;
Leiter, Kultur u. Musik Jürgen Kritz;
Film u. Theater Hans-Georg Dickmann;
Musik u. Ballett Frau Dr Swantje Kachur-Ehrentreich
Orchestras: Radio Sinfonie Orchester, HR Big Band

Mitteldeutscher Rundfunk (MDR)
Postfach 67, 04251 **Leipzig**
Tel: 341-300-0
Fax: 341-300 7255
Internet: www.mdr.de
E-Mail: kommunikation@mdr.de
Intendant Prof. Dr Udo Reiter;
Fernsehdirektor Henning Röhl;
Leiter des Programmbereichs Kultur und Wissenschaft Helfrid Spitra; Kommunication und Marketing (PR) Susan E. Knoll (Tel: 341-300 6400, Fax: 341-300 6453)
Orchestras: MDR Sinfonieorchester
Comments: MDR has broadcasting studios in Dresden (Landesfunkhaus Sachsen), Magdeburg (Landesfunkhaus Sachsen-Anhalt) and Erfurt (Landesfunkhaus Thüringen); also MDR Chor, MDR Kinderchor, MDR Deutsches Fernsehballett GmbH

Norddeutscher Rundfunk
Fernsehstudio Lokstedt, Gazellenkamp 57,
22504 **Hamburg**
Tel: 40-4156-0/2300 (press office)
Fax: 40-447 602
Internet: www.ndr.de
Programmbereich Kultur Thomas Schreiber;
Programmgruppe Familie Wolfgang Buresch;
Programmgruppe Kunst und Wissenschaft Dr Christoph Bungartz; Programmgruppe Gesellschaft und Bildung Volker Zielke; Programmbereich Fernsehfilm, Unterhaltung und Serien Verena Kulenkampff; Redaktion Film und Theater Doris J. Heinze; Programmgruppe ARTE Prof Dr Peter von Rüden
Comments: for further NDR addresses see also Radio

Ostdeutscher Rundfunk Brandenburg (ORB)
August-Bebel-Straße 26-53,
14482 **Potsdam**
Tel: 331-731-0
Fax: 331-731 3571
Internet: www.orb.de
E-Mail: kom@orb.de
Intendant Prof. Dr Hansjürgen Rosenbauer;
Kommunikation und Marketing Pia Stein;
Fernsehdirektor Volker von der Heydt;
Hörfunkdirektin Hannelore Steer;
Betriebs- und Produktionsdirektor Nawid Goudarzi

Radio Bremen
28323 **Bremen**
Tel: 421-2460 Fax: 421-246 2010
Internet: www.radiobremen.de
Fernsehfilm u. Unterhaltung Jürgen Breest;
Fernsehfilm Dr. Jutta Boehe-Selle;
Unterhaltung Birgitt Reckmeyer, Rolf Tiesler;
PR Michael Glöckner; Series Dr. Bernhard Gleim
Format, policy: great emphasis is put on cultural programmes *Comments:* visiting address: TV-Studios, Haus-Bredow-Straße 10, 28307 Bremen

Saarländischer Rundfunk
Funkhaus Halberg,
66100 **Saarbrücken**
Tel: 681-6020 Fax: 681-602 3874
Internet: www.sr-online.de
E-Mail: info@sr-online.de
Hauptabteilung Kultur und Bildung Dr Peter Brugger; Hauptabteilung Spiel u. Unterhaltung Dr. Michael Beckert; Fernsehspiel und Serie Martin Buchhorn; Musik FS Helmut Fackler
Format, policy: SR Fernsehen Südwest (joint production with Südwestrundfunk/SWR): 1.5% spots, 28.5% politics, 12.9% culture, 1.4% religion, 3.8% sports, 1.2% games, 10% entertainment, 1.3% music, 6.6% family, 32.8% education *Comments:* see also Radio

Sender Freies Berlin
Masurenallee 8-14, 14057 **Berlin**
Tel: 30-30310 Fax: 30-301 5062
Internet: www.sfb-berlin.de
Intendant Horst Schättle; Fernsehdirektorin Barbara Groth; E-Musik und Radio 3 Dr Wilhelm Matejka; Radio Kultur Dr. Ina Götz; Kulturfernsehdokumentation Dr Hannelore Wolff; Kultur aktuell Dr Wilfried Rott

Südwestrundfunk (SWR)
Neckarstraße 230, Postfach 70150,
70190 **Stuttgart**
Tel: 711-9290 Fax: 711-929 2600
Internet: www.swr-online.de
Intendant Prof. Peter Voß; Geschäftsleitung Prof. Peter Voß, Dr. Willi Steul, Peter Boudgoust, Dr. Heinjo Schröder, Dr. Uwe Rosenbaum, Dr. Hermann Eicher, Dr. Christof Schmid, Bernhard Hermann, Helmut Ochs
Comments: result of the merger between Süddeutscher Rundfunk and Südwestfunk; office address in Baden-Baden: 76522 Baden-Baden; see also Radio

Westdeutscher Rundfunk
Appellhofplatz 1, 50667 **Köln**
Tel: 221-2200 Fax: 221-220 4800
Internet: www.wdr.de
Leiter Programmbereich Fernsehfilm/-spiel Dr Winfried Bonk (220 3290), Gebhard Henke (220 3292); Leiter Unterhaltung Hugo Göke (220 3220); Leiter Programmbereich Kultur-und Wissenschaft Michael Schmid-Ospach (220 3100)

ZDF – Zweites Deutsches Fernsehen
ZDF-Straße 1, Postfach 4040,
55100 **Mainz-Lerchenberg**
Tel: 6131-701 Fax: 6131-702 157
E-Mail: info@zdf.de
Hauptredaktion Kultur Dr. Hans H. Hillrichs;
Hauptredaktion Fernsehspiel Hans Janke;
Hauptredaktion Unterhaltung Wort Dr Claus Beling;
Hauptredaktion Show Viktor Worms;
Programmbereich Musik Evelyn Paulmann

GIBRALTAR (+350)

Gibraltar Broadcasting Corporation
Broadcasting House, 18 South Barracks Road, **Gibraltar**
Tel: 79760 Fax: 78673
E-Mail: gbc@gibnet.gi
general manager of TV and radio George Valarino;
senior producer Joseph Adamberry;
senior presenter Richard Cartwright;
senior engineer John Tewkesbury;
news editor Stephen Nesh

GREECE (+30)

Antenna TV
Kifissias 10-12,
15125 **Marousi (Athens)**
Tel: 1-684 2220/688 6362/634 (pr)
Fax: 1-683 4349/689 0304
general director Spelios Charamis;
programming director Alcestis Maragoudake;
head of news Yiannis Papoutchanis; pr Olga Pavlatou

ET 3 (Hellenic Television 3)
ERT 3, 2 Angelaki,
54621 **Thessaloniki**
Tel: 31-299 400/611 (international relations)
Fax: 31-299 655 (international relations)
E-Mail: ert3pl@compulink.gr (international relations)
cultural section director Nikos Volonakis;
head of international relations Lefty Kongalides
Format, policy: ET 3: performing arts programmes 9%
Comments: ERT 3 has a 20 member orchestra that plays modern and classical music

Mega Channel
Messogeion 117,
11526 **Athens**
Tel: 1-690 3000/698 3000
Fax: 1-698 3600
Internet: www.megatv.com
general director Elias Tsigas;
programming director Iris Zachmnidis;
news & current affairs director Giorgos Leventoyiannis;
planning director Dimitris Fillis; public relations Nadia Georgiou; international sales Ghisela Petropolou

New Hellenic Television
Nea Elliniki Teleorasi (NET)
Messoghion Avenue 432, PO Box 60019,
15432 **Aghia Paraskevi (Athens)**
Tel: 1-606 6000
Fax: 1-600 9611 (director)/9325 (chairman)
chairman of the board Panagiotis Panagiotou;
general director of NET Nikiforos Antonopoulos
Format, policy: NET concentrates on news (former ET-1), ET-2 is renamed 'ET-1' and concentrates on entertaiment

HUNGARY (+36)

Duna Television
Duna Televizió
Meszaros 48, 1016 **Budapest**
Fax: 1-375 1591
president Sandor Sara;
head of music department Ilona Bartalus

Hungarian RTL
Magyar RTL
Kunigunda 41, 1037 **Budapest**
Tel: 1-437 3737
Fax: 1-437 3709
general manager Jean Charles de Keyser

Hungarian Television
Magyar Televízió
Szabadság tér 17, 1054 **Budapest**
Tel: 1-373 5120
Fax: 1-373 5120 (music dept)
president Laszlo Zsolt Szabo;
vice president Ferenc Székely;
head of music department Gergely Koltay
Comments: music department: Szabadsag ter 5-6, 1054 Budapest

TV2 MTM-SBS Communications
Rona 174,
1145 **Budapest**
Tel: 1-467 6400
Fax: 1-220 5921
president Dezsö Pinter

TV3 Budapest Communications Ltd
Budakeszi 51, 1021 **Budapest**
Tel: 1-275 1800
Fax: 1-275 1801
managing director Luc Tomasino

ICELAND (+354)

Icelandic Broadcasting Corp – Channel 2
Lynghalsi 5, 110 **Reykjavík**
Tel: 515 6000
Fax: 515 6851
Internet: www.fjolnet.is
E-Mail: promo@iu.is
head of programming Páll Baldvin Baldvinnsson;
head of news Páll Magnusson;
promotional manager Hildur Halldórsdóttir
Format, policy: performing arts, mainly foreign programmes; interviews with artists, profiles etc

Icelandic National Broadcasting Service – Television
Ríkisútvarpid-Sjónvarp
Laugavegur 176, 105 **Reykjavík**
Tel: 515 3900
Fax: 515 3988/3008
Internet: www.ruv.is
E-Mail: istv@ruv.is
director, television Bjarni Gudmundsson;
head of acquisition Hinrik Bjarnason;
head of Icelandic production Sigurdur Valgeirsson;
head of news Bogi Agustsson
Format, policy: large amount of original televised productions of drama, music etc.; about 40% own programming (approx. 6-7 hours per day)

IRELAND Republic of (+353)

Radio Telefis Eireann (RTE)
Donnybrook, **Dublin** 4
Tel: 1-208 3111
Fax: 1-208 3080
E-Mail: press@RTE.ie
managing director Bob Collins;
director of television production Jo Mulholland;
managing editors Helen O'Rahilly;
press office Kevin Healy
Format, policy: RTE 1, Network 2

RAI – Radiotelevisione Italiana
Segreteria Centrale,
14 Viale Mazzini, 00195 **Roma**
Tel: 06-38781/3686 5420 (secretary)
Fax: 06-372 5680/321 6234(press)
Internet: www.rai.it
E-Mail: rai-tv@rai.it
presidente Roberto Zaccaria;
direttore generale Pier Luigi Celli;
direttore RAI 1 Raiuno Agostino Saccà;
direttore RAI 2 Carlo Freccero;
direttore RAI 3 Francesco Pinto;
direttore Rai International Giancarlo Leone;
direttore RAI News24 Roberto Morrione
Format, policy: RAI has three different channels: RAI 1, RAI 2, RAI 3 and a sky digital channel RAI News24
Orchestras: Orchestra Sinfonica Nazionale della RAI, direttore Andrea Sablich,
responsable Cesare Paolo Dapino

LATVIA (+371)

Latvian Independent TV, LNT
Latvijas Neatkarigia televizija – LNT
Elijas iela 17, 1050 **Riga**
Tel: 7-222 310 Fax: 7-821 128
E-Mail: lnt@lnt.lv
director Andrejs Ekis
Format, policy: independent producer, 1 channel (7.00am-1.00am), all kinds of programmes including news, entertainment, drama, music, culture, film, videoart; draw upon exisiting productions from home and foreign sources

Latvian Television
Latvijas Televizija
3 Zakusalas krastmala, 1509 **Riga**
Tel: 7-200 314 Fax: 7-200 025
E-Mail: ltv@ltv.lv
director Rolands Tjarve
Format, Policy: state TV, 2 programmes: news, all kinds of programmes including drama, entertainment, education, cultural, music, features, documentaries and current affairs, sports and children

National Broadcasting Council of Latvia
Nacionala Radio un Televizijas Padome
Smilsu 1/3, 1934 **Riga**
Tel: 7-220 564 Fax: 7-220 448
E-Mail: tvcounc@melbox.riga.lv
chairman Ojars Rubenis

LITHUANIA (+370)

Baltijos TV
Laisvės pr 60, 2056 **Vilnius**
Tel: 2-41734/419 742/428 917
Fax: 2-428 907

Baltijos TV
Laisves pr. 60, 2056 **Vilnius**
Tel: 2-419 742/428 917
Fax: 2-428 907
director general Gintaras Songaila

Lietuvos Radijas ir Televizija
Lithuanian Radio and Television
S Konarskio 49, 2674 **Vilnius**
Tel: 2-263 292(director general)/2-637 961 (TV director)/2-661 333(director of programmes)/2-661 970 (senior editor of cultural TV programming)
Fax: 2-263 282
TV director Arvydas Ilginis

Lithuanian Radio and Television
Lietuvos radijas ir televizija
Konarskio 49, 2674 **Vilnius**
Tel: 2-263 292/637 961/661 333/970
Fax: 2-263 282
deputy director general Algirdas Trakimavicius

LNK TV
A Merkio street 1, 4303 **Lapés**
Tel: 7-531 269

LNK TV
Pylimo 12, 2001 **Vilnius**
Tel: 2-614 627 Fax: 2-614 618
director general Jonas O. Eriksson

TELE-3
Nemencines pl. 4,
2016 **Vilnius**
Tel: 2-764 290

TV 3
Nemencines pl. 4,
2016 **Vilnius**
Tel: 2-316 129/30/31/32/33
director general Vilma Marciuleviciute

Vilniaus Televizija
A. Vivulskio g. 23
2600 **Vilnius**
Tel: 2-235 560

LUXEMBOURG (+352)

CLT-UFA
45 Boulevard Pierre Frieden, 2850 **Luxembourg**
Tel: 421 421 Fax: 4214 22760
Internet: www.clt-ufa.com
chairman, board of directors Gaston Thorn; presidents, chief executive officers Rémy Sautter, Rolf Schmidt-Holtz; executive vice president TV, production and rights, deputy to CEO Dr Ewald Walgenbach; executive vice president TV Pascal Farcouli; executive vice president general affairs Dan Arendt; pr Mme Rey (421 2172)
Comments: CLT-UFA, resulting from the merger on January 13, 1997 of CLT (Compagnie Luxembourgeoise de Télédiffusion) and UFA Film- und Fernseh-GmbH & Co KG of Germany, is Europe's largest TV and radio group; present in 12 European countries through 22 TV channes, 22 radio stations and a host of subsidiaries in production, rights acquisition and media services, with revenues up to LUF 14 billion

MACEDONIA (+389)

Macedonian Radio and Television
Makedonska Radio-Televizija
Goce Delcev bb, 91000 **Skopje**
Tel: 91-112 200/235 305 Fax: 91-113 156/111 821
director general Melpomeni Korneti;
director of TV Saso Ordanovski
Format, policy: 3 programmes – broadcast in Macedonain, Albanian and Turkish

MOLDOVA (+373)

Telecompania Moldova
1, Miorita str, 2072 **Chisinau**
Tel: 2-233 446 Fax: 2-233 446
chairman Tudor Olaru

MONACO (+377)

Télé Monte-Carlo (TMC)
6 bis Quai Antoine 1ffi, 98000 **Monte Carlo** Cedex
Tel: 9315 1450 Fax: 9216 5481
président Jean Pastorelli;
relations extérieures et communication Michèle Frassa;
journaliste de l'art Maguelone Seguin-Hedon
Format, policy: 1 channel (9.00am – 1.00am)

NETHERLANDS (+31)

Arts Channel
Kunstkanaal
c/o Felix Meritis Foundation, Keizergracht 324,
1016 EZ **Amsterdam**
Tel: 20-627 1496 Fax: 20-624 9368
Internet: www.kunstkanaal.nl
E-Mail: kk@kunstkanaal.nl
financial management Masja Austen; general manager/programme director Linda Bouws;
production/editor Ruth de Liever;
public relations Christine Vroom;
research & aquisitions Petra Vermeulen
Format, policy: the weekly broadcaster of arts and cultural programmes on local cable networks in the Netherlands; Arts Channel-C-Programmes cover the whole gamut of the arts, visual arts, theatre, drama, literature, dance, music, design, video art, film, architecture, etc; they draw upon existing productions from foreign and home sources; Arts Channel also initiates new projects on a small scale; Kunstkanaal currently broadcasts in 3 major cities in the Netherlands: Amsterdam, Rotterdam and The Hague *Comments:* the Arts Channel is structurally subsidised by the Ministry of Education, Culture & Science and the local governments of Rotterdam, Amsterdam and The Hague

AVRO
Postbus 2, 1200 JA **Hilversum**
Tel: 35-671 7911
Fax: 35-671 7439
Internet: www.avro.nl
E-Mail: webmaster@avro.nl
managing director radio & tv B. K. Klap; general director F. Maréchal; manager, entertainment/culture/drama M Benda; manager, radio A. Krijnen; manager, marketing C. van Vlissingen; manager, information E. Eljan
Format, policy: all kinds of programmes including drama, music, culture (18 hours a week – 27% of programme for cultural issues)
Comments: see also Radio

Evangelische Omroep
Postbus 21000, 1202 BB **Hilversum**
Tel: 35-647 4747
Fax: 35-647 4227
Internet: www.omroep.nl/eo
E-Mail: eo@omroep.nl
directors A.P. de Boer, A.G. Knevel; head of planning and production department TV – EO international P. F. van der Wolf; head of children's department H. van Dalen; head of informative department H. Hagoort; head of music department H. le Poole
Format, policy: 19 hours a week *Comments:* independent producer; share channel with TROS; see also Radio

KRO
Postbus 23000, 1201 EA **Hilversum**
Tel: 35-671 3911 Fax: 35-671 3119
Internet: www.omroep.nl/kro
president Frans Slangen; head of radio & television Ton Verlind; head of drama Frank Jansen; head of information Anton Fasel; head of religion Bart Verreijt; head of amusement Bart Römer
Format, policy: information, education and religious broadcasting, 21 hours weekly *Comments:* founded 1925; share channel 1 with NCRV & AVRO; public service broadcasting station; see also Radio

Music Centre of The Netherlands Radio and TV
Postbus 125, 1200 AC **Hilversum**
Tel: 35-671 4100 Fax: 35-671 4171
E-Mail: b.janssen@mco.nl
managing director B H M Janssen;
deputy director M. Damen
Comments: provide equipment and personnel; this includes the 4 orchestras and a choir whose services are available to the various broadcasting organisations

NCRV
Postbus 25000, 1202 HB **Hilversum**
Tel: 35-671 9911 Fax: 35-761 9285
Internet: www.ncrv.nl
E-Mail: webmaster@ncrv.nl
president Harry Hemink; programme manager entertainment section Jan van Dalen;
programme manager information R. Lips
Format, policy: all kinds of programmes, 1200 hours per year *Comments:* see also Radio

NOS
Postbus 26600, 1202 JT **Hilversum**
Tel: 35-677 9222 Fax: 35-677 5158
Internet: www.nos.nl
director Ruurd Bierman
Format, policy: sports, news (every hour) and special events; 24 hours teletex *Comments:* NOS produces sport, news, special events programmes; most of the programmes are shown on Channel 1

NPS
Postbus 29000, 1202 MA **Hilversum**
Tel: 35-677 3026/4130
Fax: 35-677 4959
Internet: www.nps.nl
E-Mail: nps@omroep.nl
head of press/communication Mrs W. L. Broekhuijsen; head of arts and music programming
H. van der Meulen
Format, policy: broadcast weekly – classical music, world music, modern music, opera, modern and classical ballet, pop, jazz and dance on television

TROS
Postbus 28450, 1202 LL **Hilversum**
Tel: 35-671 5715/5364/5373
Fax: 35-671 5236
managing director RTV Huib Boermans; head of programming G. Baars; head of drama and cultural programmes Ted Mooren; chairman Karel van Doodewaerd; financial director Peter Kramer
Comments: TROS produces all kinds of programmes including drama, entertainment, education, cultural; see also Radio

VARA
Postbus 175, 1200 AD **Hilversum**
Tel: 35-671 1318 Fax: 35-671 1309
Internet: www.omroep.nl/vara/
E-Mail: vara@vara.nl
head of drama Robert Kievit, Jan Rutger Achterberg; head of drama & cultural programmes Ham Henbakker
Comments: VARA produce all kinds of programmes including comedy, short dramas, single play dramas; see also Radio

Veronica FM
Postbus 22222, 1202 CT **Hilversum**
Tel: 35-671 8300
Fax: 35-623 1437
Internet: www.veronica.nl
E-Mail: veronicafm@veronica.nl
director radio & television Unico Glorie; programmes director Kees Gerritsen; head of communication department Hans van der Veen
Format, policy: programmes for young people, 7.00am – 1.00am *Comments:* advertising address: I.P., Postbus 74747, 1070 DA, Amsterdam, Tel: 20-656 3838, Fax: 20-645 0265; see also Radio

VPRO
Postbus 11, 1200 JC **Hilversum**
Tel: 35-671 2911
Fax: 35-671 2541
Internet: www.vpro.nl
E-Mail: pers@vpro.nl
director, tv programmes Hans Marten van den Brink
Format, policy: broadcast 19 hours a week
Comments: VPRO produces many programmes including information, drama, cultural, documentary and youth programmes; see also Radio

NORWAY (+47)

Norsk Rikskringkasting (NRK)
Norwegian Broadcasting Corporation (NBC)
0340 **Oslo**
Tel: 2304 7000 Fax: 2304 9541
Internet: www.nrk.no
television director Hans Tore Bjerkaas; deputy television director & head of entertainment Tordis Aavatsmark; head of news and current affairs Tom Berntzen; head of general affairs Oddbjørg Aasen Bjørdal; head of drama Oddvar Bull Tuhus; director of resources Trond Viggo Torgersen; head of visuals Petter Moshus; advisor to director Arild Hellgren;
project leaders Arild Erikstad, Hanne Hoel;
head of cultural affairs Bjorn Hunnederg
Format, policy: all kind of cultural programmes, entertainment, etc. *Comments:* see also Radio

POLAND (+48)

Polsat S.A.
al. Stanów Zjednoczonych 53, 03-965 **Warszawa**
Tel: 22-8104 001 Fax: 22-8134 295
Comments: created in 1993; first private commerical television in Poland; broadcasts 23 hours a day; also satellite channel Polsat 27

Telewizja Polska SA
Polish Television SA
ul. Woronicza 17, 00-999 **Warszawa**
Tel: 22-547 8100 (president) Fax: 22-547 4320
president Robert Kwiatkowski; director TVP1 Slawomir Zielinski (tel: 22-547 6105, fax: 22-547 4235); director TVP2 Nina Terentiew (tel: 22-547 6210, fax: 22-547 4223); director TV Polonia Grzegorz Gajewski (tel: 22-547 6211, fax: 22-547 4250); director TV Theatre Jacek Weksler (tel: 22-547 8110, fax: 22-547 4228)
Format, Policy: channel TVP1 aimed at broad audience, broadcasts about 20 hours a day; channel TVP2 programme art, history, film, theatre and classical music, broadcasts about 17 hours a day; TV Polonia (satellite channel) aimed mainly at Poles living all over the world, promotes Polish culture and science, broadcasts 24 hours a day; TV Theatre every Monday since 1953; also 12 regional channels located in the largest cities in Poland: Bialystok, Bydgoszcz, Gdansk, Katowice, Kraków, Lublin, Lódz, Poznan, Rzeszów, Szczecin, Warszawa and Wroclaw
Comments: public television

TVN
ul. Augustowka 3, 02-981 **Warszawa**
Tel: 22-856 666 Fax: 22-856 666
Comments: private commercial television, broadcasts about 15 hours a day

PORTUGAL (+351)

Radiotelevisão Portuguesa SA (RTP)
Avenida 5 de Outubro 197, 1050 **Lisboa**
Tel: 21-793 1774/794 7000
Fax: 21-797 1045 (public relations)
Internet: www.rtp.pt
E-Mail: rtp@rtp.pt
president Prof. José Maria Brandaõ de Brito; director, public & communication relations Manuel Rocha
Format, policy: 24 hours a day

ROMANIA (+40)

Romanian Television
Calea Dorobanlor 191, Sector 1, 71281 **Bucharest**
Tel: 1-212 0710/0290 Fax: 1-212 1427

RUSSIA (+7)

Channel 5
Zoubovsky blv.4 (RIA Novosti), 119021 **Moscow**
Tel: 095-201 8587 Fax: 095-201 5413/2675
Format, policy: culture channel

NTV Television (Channel 4)
Ul. Akademika Koroleva 12, 127000 **Moscow**
Tel: 095-217 5103/7335/5277/8428 Fax: 095-290 9559

Russian Public Television and Radio Company – ORT
Ul. Akademika Koroleva 12, 127000 **Moscow**
Tel: 095-217 7210/215 7387 Fax: 095-217 1162/215 1324
general director Mikhail Shvydkoi (tel: 095-214 5127)
Comments: foriegn relations office: Tel: 095-217 7898

Russian State Music Centre of Television and Radio
M. Nikitskaya 24, 121069 **Moscow**
Tel: 095-222 0022

Russian State Television and Broadcasting Company (RTR)
5th Street Yamskogo Polya 19/21, 125124 **Moscow**
Tel: 095-214 4978/251 1235 Fax: 095-250 0506
general manager Shvydkoi (tel: 095-214 5127)

Russian-American Corporation of Culture
ul. Mariny Raskovoy 13, floor 1, 125124 **Moscow**
Tel: 095-214 3580

TV-6
Ilyinka st. 15 bld.1, **Moscow**
Tel: 095-217 5156 Fax: 095-217 5127

TV-Center (Channel 3)
Ul. Akademika Koroleva 12, 127000 **Moscow**
Tel: 095-217 5156 Fax: 095-217 5127

SLOVAKIA (+421)

Many telephone and fax numbers in Slovakia are in the process of being changed. We have included all new numbers known at the time of going to print.

MARKÍZA – Slovak TV Company
MARKÍZA – Slovenská televízna spolocnostr
Bratislavská 1/A, PO Box 7, 843 56 **Bratislava**
Tel: 7-6827 4111/6827 4121/4122 Fax: 7-6595 6800
E-Mail: markiza@markiza.sk
director Pavol Rusko

Slovak Television
Slovenská televízia
Mlynská dolina 28, 845 45 **Bratislava**
Tel: 7-6542 3948/5948 Fax: 7-6542 2828/5443 2460
director Milan Materák

Systémová káblová televízia
Stromová 9, 831 01 **Bratislava** 37
Tel: 7-5968 3111/3410/6224 1520 Fax: 7-5968 5300/6224 2001

VTV Television
Stará Prievozská 2, PO Box 37, 824 83 **Bratislava**
Tel: 7-5823 0606/0111 Fax: 7-5823 0607/5821 3730

SLOVENIA (+386)

Televizija Slovenija
TV Slovenia
Kolodvorska 2, 1000 **Ljubljana**
Tel: 61-175 211 Fax: 61-175 2160
acting editor-inochief Janez Lomberger

SPAIN (+34)

Antena 3 de Televisión SA (A3TV)
c/ Isla Graciosa, s/n,
28700 **San Sebastián de los Reyes (Madrid)**
Tel: 91-623 0500 Fax: 91-623 0469
Internet: www.antena3tv.es
E-Mail: antena3tv@antena3tv.es
presidente Jose María Mas; consejero delegado Juan José Nieto; director general en funciones Juan José Díaz; director de programas de producción ajena Francisco Ramos; director de programación Francisco Díaz Ujados
Format, policy: 24 hours

Canal 33 and TV3
Calle de la TV3, 08970 **Saint Joan Despi (Barcelona)**
Tel: 93-499 9333 Fax: 93-473 0671
Internet: www.tvcatalunya.com
director Lluis Olivia; head of music programmes Francesc Fábregas; head of programming Albert Rubio; head of drama programmes Jordi Roure; head of press Xavier Janer
Format, policy: Canal 33- cultural and sports station; theatre, opera, classical and folk music; own productions: TV3- popular and entertainment television (21 hours per week music) Temporada Opera (once a week for 3 months), Temporada Teatro (once a week for 3 months), Temporada Dance (once a week for 3 months)

Televisión Española SA (TVE)
Prado del Rey, 28223 **Madrid**
Tel: 91-346 4000/9780 (prensa) Fax: 91-346 3044/9693
E-Mail: direccion.comunicacion@rtve.es
director tv Ramon Díez; director edición y emisión Juan Menor; dirección gerencia grupo RTVE Candido Perez
Format, policy: all types of classical music, jazz, flamenco, popular music, dance and theatre (classical music 3 hours a week; all others are variable – broadcast festivals, seasons and special events; 24 hours
Orchestras: Orquesta de Radiotelevision Española
Choirs: Coro de Radiotelevision Española *Comments:* 60% own production; also radio (Radio Nacional de España) and discographic label (RTVE Music); see also Radio, Orchestra, Choir and Recorded Media

SWEDEN (+46)

Sveriges Television AB
Swedish Television Company 105 10 **Stockholm**
Tel: 8-784 0000/7811 (press office) Fax: 8-784 1500
E-Mail: pressinfo@svt.se
head of culture and music department Anneli Rogeman; project leader, music Camilla Lundberg; director of drama department Maria Curman; director of Malmö region Bengt Linné; director of Göteborg region Jan Åke Åkesson; director of sales Katarina af Klintberg; head of acquisition Kewe Zahr; press officer BrittMarie Gustafsson
Format, policy: all kinds of programmes, starts 6.00am (with news) stops shortly after 12.00am *Comments:* both channels are coordinated together, scheduled by central planning; there is no difference between both channels

SWITZERLAND (+41)

Opera Channel Aps, The
PO Box 5132, 1211 **Genève** 11
Tel: 22-328 8390 Fax: 22-328 6485
general manager Anthony J Whitehouse
Comments: visiting address: 90 Vester Voldgade, 1552 Copenhagen, Denmark, Tel: +45 3315 1563, Fax: +45 3313 0707

RTSI – Radiotelevisione Svizzera di Lingua Italiana
Casella Postale, 6903 **Lugano**
Tel: 91-803 5111 Fax: 91-803 5355
Internet: www.rtsi.ch
E-Mail: centralino@rtsi.ch
direttore regionale (DR) Ratti Remigio; direttore radio Jackie Marti; direttore programmi TV Dino Balestra; informazione Michele Fazioli; sport Maurizio Canetta; approfondimento e cultura Willy Baggi; cinema Fiction Enzo Pelli; intrattenimento Augusto Chollet
Orchestras: Orchestra della Svizzera Italiana; direttore artistico/amministrativo: Maestro Pietro Antonini
Choirs: Coro delle RTS1

SF DRS -Schweizer Fernsehen DRS
Fernsehstr. 1-4, 8052 **Zürich**
Tel: 1-305 6611 Fax: 1-305 5660
Internet: www.sfdrs.ch
E-Mail: sfdrs@sfdrs.ch
Fernsehdirektor Peter Schellenberg; Abteilungsleiter Info u. Kultur Dr. Peter Studer
Format, Policy: SF1: entertainment; SF2: sport, film; 140 hours per station per week

SRG – Schweizerische Radio- und Fernsehgesellschaft
SBC Swiss Broadcasting Corporation
Giacomettistrasse 3, Postfach, 3015 **Bern**
Tel: 31-350 9111 Fax: 31-350 9256
Internet: www.srg-ssr.ch
E-Mail: arminwalpen@srg-ssr-idee-suisse.ch
director Armin Walpen; general TV affairs Tiziana Mona
Format, Policy: 22 programmes: 6 tv, 18 radio
Comments: head office for Swiss Broadcasting Corporation; see also Radio

TSR – Télévision Suisse Romande
20 quai Ernest Ansermet, Case Postale 234, 1211 **Genève** 8
Tel: 22-708 9911 Fax: 22-708 9804/1908 (press-office)
Internet: www.tsr.ch
head of the department Découvertes Catherine Noyer; responsible, music, opera, ballet, dance, theatre Flavia Matea; responsible rock, divertissement Patrick Allenbach; head of department entertainment fiction Yves Ménestrier; news Philippe Mottaz; general director Guillaume Cheneviere; programme planner Raymond Vauillamoz; head of production and general matters Jean Claude Chanel
Comments: to E-mail write the person's first name.surname@tsr.ch

TURKEY (+90)

9 Kanal
Eski Maslak Yolu No 25 Maslak, **Istanbul**
Tel: 212-285 4300/236/498 Fax: 212-285 4378/79

Ankara Radyosu
Atatürk Bulvari 39, **Sihhiye (Ankara)**
Tel: 312-310 3940 Fax: 312-309 7090

ATV
Medya Plaza Sabah Tesisleri, Ikitelli, 34540 **Istanbul**
Tel: 212-655 0000/502 8446 Fax: 212-502 8802/8295

BRT
Cumhuriyet Cad. No 223 6. Kat Harbiye, **Istanbul**
Tel: 212-296 3960 Fax: 212-296 3951

CTV
Seher Yildizi Sok. Yildiz Apt. No 20 / 4 Etiler, **Istanbul**
Tel: 212-263 1106/0702 Fax: 212-263 0702

Cumhuriyet TV
Istanbul
Tel: 212-623 3040 Fax: 212-623 0457

Discovery Channel
Istanbul
Tel: 212-288 7575/196 Fax: 212-288 9675

ETV
Istanbul
Tel: 216-414 8402/07 Fax: 216-347 2329

Flash TV
Tepebasi Cad. Çatmamescit Mah. Elektrik Sok. No 11 Tepebasi, **Istanbul**
Tel: 212-256 8100 Fax: 212-256 8111

HBB TV
Büyükdere Cad, No.187, 80720 **Levent (Istanbul)**
Tel: 212-281 4800 Fax: 212-281 4814/13

Interstar
Basin Ekspres Yolu Star Sok. No 2 Günesli, **Istanbul**
Tel: 212-448 9000/8000 Fax: 212-448 9365

Istanbul TV
Bulgurlu Cad. Koru Sok. Küçük Çamlica, **Istanbul**
Tel: 216-428 0850/51/52 Fax: 216-428 0861

Kanal 6
Istanbul
Tel: 212-283 0080 Fax: 212-283 0080

Kanal D
Ortaklar Cad. Avni Sözen Fuar Binasi No 17 Mecidiyeköy, **Istanbul**
Tel: 212-215 5111 Fax: 212-215 5305

Kanal E
Büyükdere Cad. 31/1 4 Levent, **Istanbul**
Tel: 212-282 5100 Fax: 212-270 3657

Kent TV
Talatpasa Mah. Emirgazi Cad. Dereyolu No 4 Okmeydani, **Istanbul**
Tel: 212-222 1836 Fax: 212-221 4433

MNG TV
Ihlamurdere Cad. Yesilçimen Sok. No 5 OTIM is Merkezi Fulya / Besiktas, **Istanbul**
Tel: 212-288 5152 Fax: 212-275 8559

NTV
Eski Büyükdere Cad.
USO Centre nffl 61 Maslak, **Istanbul**
Tel: 212-286 3636/335 0020 Fax: 212-286 7135

Prima TV
ATV 2000 Binasi Medya Plaza, 34540 **Ikitelli (Istanbul)**
Tel: 212-502 9802 Fax: 212-656 7330

Show TV
Eski Büyükdere Cad. No 77 Maslak, **Istanbul**
Tel: 212-286 3535 Fax: 212-276 9648

Turkish Radio and Television Corporation
Türkiye Radyo Televizyon Kurumu
TRT Sitesi Oran, **Ankara**
Tel: 312-490 1058 Fax: 312-490 1109
secretary general Ziya Arikan; deputy secretary general Halid Ertugrul; director of international relations Güleser Güler (Tel: 312-490 0379)

UKRAINE (+380)

National Telecompany of Ukraine
Khreshchatyk St. 26, 252001 **Kiev (Kyiv)**
Tel: 44-226 3144
director Oleksander Savenko

UNITED KINGDOM (+44)

Anglia Television
Anglia House, **Norwich** NR1 3JG
Tel: 1603-615 151
Fax: 1603-631 032
E-Mail: angliatv@angliatv.co.uk
chairman David McCall CBE DL; managing director Graham Creelman

BBC
Television Centre, Wood Lane,
London W12 7RJ
Tel: 20-8743 8000
chief executive, broadcast Will Wyatt; director of television Alan Yentob; controller, BBC-1 Peter Salmon; controller, publicity & public relations Sally Osman; controller, BBC-2 Mark Thompson; chief executive, production Matthew Bannister; head, classical music/television Peter Maniura; controller, drama production Colin Adams; head of independents, drama Tessa Ross; head of independents, entertainment Bill Hilary; head of BBC arts Kim Evans; head of music entertainment Trevor Dann; head of programme acquisition Alan Howden; controller, broadcast & presentation Pam Masters
Format, policy: the BBC's two domestic channels – BBC-1 and BBC-2 – serve the UK public with almost 14000 hours of programmes per year *Comments:* BBC-1 is the channel of broad appeal including features, documentaries and current affairs programmes, drama and entertainment, sport and children's programmes; BBC-2 is the channel of innovation and flexibility, special interests are catered for, with a variety of programmes including documentaries, late-night comedy and leisure and lifestyle shows

BBC Birmingham
Pebble Mill Road, **Birmingham** B5 7QQ
Tel: 121-432 8888
Fax: 121-432 8634
Comments: films, series; biggest BBC drama centre outside London; contact: Manager Press & Publicity, Rm 199, Press Office, BBC Birmingham

BBC Bristol
Broadcasting House, Whiteladies Road, **Bristol** BS8 2LR
Tel: 117-973 2211 Fax: 117-974 4114
head of features Jeremy Gibson;
head of natural history unit Keith Scholey
Format, policy: BBC Bristol is the home of the BBC's Natural History Unit; the features department produces a wide range of television programmes, in addition to radio programmes specialising in history, travel, literature and human interest features for Radio 4
Comments: see also Radio

BBC (General Enquiries)
aa
Tel: 8700-100 222
E-Mail: info@bbc.co.uk
Comments: general enquiries about the BBC

BBC Manchester
New Broadcasting House, Oxford Rd, **Manchester** M60 1SJ
Tel: 161-200 2020 Fax: 161-244 4688
head of entertainment Wayne Garvie
Comments: see also Radio

BBC Northern Ireland
Broadcasting House, **Belfast (Northern Ireland)** BT2 8HQ
Tel: 28-9033 8000 Fax: 28-9033 8800
controller, BBC Northern Ireland Pat Loughrey; head of broadcasting Anna Carragher; head of production Paul Evans; head of public affairs Rosemary Kelly; head of finance Crawford McLean; head of personnel Liz Torrans; head of research strategy Peter Johnston; head of news & current affairs Andrew Colman; head of resources Stephen Beckett; chief producer, music & arts David Byers; head of drama Robert Cooper; senior press officer Austin Hunter

BBC Scotland
Broadcasting House, Queen Margaret Drive,
Glasgow (Scotland) G12 8DG
Tel: 141-338 2000 Fax: 141-334 0614
head of drama Barbara McKissak; head of arts and entertainment Mike Bolas; head of production Colin Cameron; head of broadcasting Ken MacQuarrie

BBC South East (Elstree)
Elstree Centre, Clarendon Road, **Borehamwood** WD6 1JF
Tel: 20-9953 6100 Fax: 20-8228 8092
head of local & regional programming Jane Mote; editor news & current affairs Rodney Davies;
editor First Sight Tom Samson
Format, policy: nightly news magazine programmes, as well as regualar 30-minute local current affairs programmes
Comments: the region operates a comprehensive local radio service; they have a bi-media approach – which means that both radio and television share their resources – as well as a range of correspondents specialising in health, education, business, local government and the environment

BBC South (Southampton)
Broadcasting House, Havelock Road,
Southampton SO14 7PU
Tel: 23-8022 6201 Fax: 23-8033 9931
Internet: www.bbc.co.uk/south_today
E-Mail: south.today@bbc.co.uk
acting head of regional & local programmes Craig Henderson; news gathering editors Lee Desty, Mia Costello
Format, policy: nightly news magazine programmes, as well as regular 30-minute local current affairs programmes and parliamentary programmes
Comments: the region operates a comprehensive local radio service; they have a bi-media approach – which means that both radio and television share their resources – as well as a range of correspondents specialising in health, education, business, local government and the environment

BBC South West (Plymouth)
Broadcasting House, Seymour Road, Mannamead,
Plymouth PL3 5BD
Tel: 1752-229 201 Fax: 1752-234 597
E-Mail: roger.clark@bbc.co.uk
head of regional & local programmes Leo Devine; news editor Roger Clark; editor, current affairs Simon Willis
Format, policy: nightly news magazine programmes, as well as regular 30-minute local current affairs programmes and parliamentary programmes
Comments: the region operates a comprehensive local radio service; they have a bi-media approach – which means that both radio and television share their resources – as well as a range of correspondents specialising in health, education, business, local government and the environment

BBC Wales
Broadcasting House, Llandaff, **Cardiff (Wales)** CF5 2YQ
Tel: 29-2032 2000 Fax: 29-2055 2973
E-Mail: feedback.wales@bbc.co.uk
administrator, Cardiff Singer of the World Anna Williams; controller, BBC Wales Geraint Taltan Davies; head of broadcasting, English language Dai Smith; head of broadcasting, Welsh language Gwynn Pritchard; head of production John Geraint; head of arts, music and features Phil George; head of entertainment Geraint Evans; head of drama Pedr James; head of marketing & promotions Catrin Howkins; secretary Wyn Mears; head of strategy & channel management Keith Jones; head of resources Keith Dewhurst

Format, policy: 520 hours English, 520 hours Welsh each year *Orchestras:* BBC National Orchestra in Wales *Choirs:* BBC Welsh Chorus *Comments:* see also Radio

BBC West (Bristol)
Broadcasting House, Whiteladies Road,
Bristol BS8 2LR
Tel: 117-973 2211
Fax: 117-974 114
head of regional & local programmes John Conway; editor news Leo Devine; series producer – Close up West: James Macalpine
Format, policy: nightly news magazine programmes, as well as regular 30-minute local current affairs programmes and parliamentary programmes
Comments: the region operates a comprehensive local radio service; they have a bi-media approach – which means that both radio and television share their resources – as well as a range of correspondents specialising in health, education, business, local government and the environment

Border Television
Television Centre, **Carlisle** CA1 3NT
Tel: 1228-525 101
Fax: 1228-541 384/559 4229 (newsroom)
E-Mail: 10157.677@compuserve.com
controller of programmes Neil Robinson

Carlton Television – Head office
101 St Martin's Lane, **London** WC2N 4AZ
Tel: 20-7240 4000
Fax: 20-7240 4171
Internet: www.carltontv.co.uk
E-Mail: dutyoffice@carltontv.co.uk
chairman Nigel Walmsley; chief executive Clive Jones; director of programmes Steve Hewlett; chief executive, Carlton sales Martin Bowley; finance director Mike Green; commercial director Tom Betts; controller, public affairs Hardeep Kalsi
Format, Policy: ITV covers 15 regional licence holders including Carlton Television; Carlton Television comprises of Carlton Broadcasting, Central Broadcasting and Westcountry; Carlton Broadcasting is responsible for the ITV regional licence for London and the South East and Central Broadcasting is responsible for the ITV regional licence for East, West and South Midlands; Carlton Productions produces Network and Regional programmes for both companies and for other national and international markets; Carlton Sales sells airtime and sponsorship for all three broadcasters; Carlton Television also operates two facilities operations – Carlton Studios in Nottingham supplying studios and related services and Carlton 021 the largest commerical operator of Outside Broadcast services in Europe

Central Broadcasting
Central Court, Gas Street, **Birmingham** B1 2JT
Tel: 121-643 9898 Fax: 121-634 4740
Internet: www.centraltv.co.uk
managing director Ian Squires
Format, policy: 24 hours, 7 days a week *Comments:* Central Broadcasting is the ITV station for the east, west and south midlands

Channel Four Television (C4)
124 Horseferry Rd.,
London SW1P 2TX
Tel: 20-7396 4444
Fax: please phone for relevant dept. fax nos.
Internet: www.channelfour.com
director of programmes Tim Gardan; commissioning editor Art & Music Janey Walker
Format, policy: 24 hrs, 7 days a week

Channel Television
Television Centre, La Pouquelaye,
St Helier, **Jersey (Channel Islands)** JE1 3ZD
Tel: 1534-816 816
Fax: 1534-816 817
Internet: www.channeltv.co.uk
E-Mail: ctvnews@channeltv.co.uk
managing director Michael Lucas; head of productions Tim Ringstore; controller of programme production and development Karen Rankine; director, sales and marketing Gordon de St Cruix; group chief executive John Henwood; group financial director Charles Day; head of local programming Karen Rankine
Format, Policy: local news and features; 8 hours

Grampian Television
Queen's Cross, **Aberdeen (Scotland)** AB15 4XJ
Tel: 1224-846 846
Fax: 1224-846 800
E-Mail: gtv@grampian.tv.co.uk
chairman Calum A. MacLeod, CBE, LLD; controller Derrick Thomson; head of news Bert Ovenstone; head of current affairs Alan Cowie; production services executive Brian Clark; head of public relations Hilary I Buchan
Format, policy: franchise holder of ITV serving the north, north east, Tayside, Fife and the Orkney and Shetland Islands, serving a population of 1.15 million (8 hours of local broadcasting per week)

Granada Media International
The London Television Centre, Upper Ground,
London SE1 9LT
Tel: 20-7737 8603 Fax: 20-7261 8162
Internet: www.int.granadamedia.com
E-Mail: int.info@granadamedia.com
managing director Nadine Nohr; director of sales Suzie Giblin; press and pr manager Sue Affleck; publicity manger Clare Vincent
Comments: Brite is the largest independent distributor in Britain, representing the production powerhouses of Granada TV, LWT and Yorkshire Tyne-Tees TV who together supply the majority of programming to the UK's most successful commerical network, ITV; Brite has programming in all categories including tv-movies, drama, music and arts, entertainment, documentaries and children's programmes

Granada Television
Granada TV Centre, Quay Street, **Manchester** M60 9EA
Tel: 161-832 7211 Fax: 161-832 5805
Internet: www.itv.co.uk
controller of entertainment & comedy Andy Harris; head of sport Don Jones; head of regional affairs Susan Woodward; controller factual programmes Charles Tremayne; head of drama Simon Lewis; head of music Ian Rousham

GWR Group PLC
PO Box 2345, 3B2 Westlea, **Swindon** SN5 7HS
Tel: 20-7344 2744 Fax: 20-7344 2704
E-Mail: jessica.alder@musicradio.com
chief executive Ralph Bernard
Format, policy: 35 radio stations: Classic FM, AM Network-Classic Gold, FM-local radio stations; 24 hours

HTV Wales
Television Centre, Culverhouse Cross, **Cardiff (Wales)** CF5 6XJ
Tel: 29-2059 0590 Fax: 29-2059 7183
Internet: www.htv.co.uk
E-Mail: htv@htv-wales.co.uk
controller, programming (inc. performing arts) Elis Owen; controller, children's & family entertainment Dan Maddicott; managing director, HTV Wales Menna Richards; head of press & pr Mansel Jones; head of drama development Peter Edwards

London Weekend Television
London Television Centre, Upper Ground,
London SE1 9LT
Tel: 20-7620 1620 Fax: 20-7261 3307
E-Mail: holly.morris@granadamedia.co.uk
executive producer Nigel Wattis; deputy executive producer Gilly Greenwood; executive producer of South Bank Show and arts department David Thomas; head of production Richard Thomson; controller of arts Melvyn Bragg; arts press officer Holly Morris (tel: 20-7261 3393)

Meridian Broadcasting Ltd
Television Centre, Northam, **Southampton** SO14 0PZ
Tel: 23-8022 2555 Fax: 23-8033 5050
Internet: www.meridian.tv.co.uk
managing director Mary McNally; head of arts Clare Lewis; controller of drama Michele Buck; director of programmes Richard Simons
Format, policy: approx. 177 hours broadcast in South and South East

Pearson Television
1 Stephen Street, **London** W1P 1PJ
Tel: 20-7691 6000 Fax: 20-7691 6100
director of communications Roy Addison (email: roy.addison@pearsontv.com); chief executive, UK prods. Alan Boyd (email: alan.boyd@pearsontv.com); head of comedy Tony Charles (email: tony.charles@pearsontv.com); executive producer John Fisher (email: john.fisher@pearsontv.com); head of drama Chris Parr (email: chris.parr@pearsontv.com); head of features John Longley (email: john.longley@pearsontv.com)
Comments: independent production and distribution company

S4C – Sianel Pedwar Cymru
Parc Ty Glas, Llanishen, **Cardiff (Wales)** CF4 5DU
Tel: 29-2074 7444 Fax: 29-2075 4444
Internet: www.s4c.co.uk
music advisor Dr Richard Elfyn Jones; director of programmes Huw Eirug
Format, policy: wide range of programmes, transmitting to the whole of Wales; broadcast from 6.00am – 1.00am, 7 days a week (32-34hrs a week are just in Welsh) *Comments:* programmes include: drama, news, documentaries, entertainment, sport, soaps & children's programmes

Scottish Television
Cowcaddens, **Glasgow (Scotland)** G2 3PR
Tel: 141-300 3000 Fax: 141-300 3030
Internet: www.scottishmediagroup.com
chief executive, Scottish Television Enterprises Darrel James; chief executive Andrew Flanagan; controller regional programmes Sandy Ross; controller of drama Phillip Hinchcliffe; programme sales executive Anita Cox

Tyne Tees Television
Television Centre, City Road,
Newcastle upon Tyne NE1 2AL
Tel: 191-261 0181 Fax: 191-261 2302
chairman Charles Allen; director of broadcasting Graeme Thompson; managing director Margaret Fay; head of network features Malcolm Wright; head of youth programmes Lesley Oakden;

Ulster Television
Havelock House, Ormeau Road,
Belfast (Northern Ireland) BT7 1EB
Tel: 28-9032 8122 Fax: 28-9024 6695
Internet: www.utvlive.com
controller of programming Alan Bremner

West Country Television Ltd
Western Wood Way, Langage Science Park,
Plymouth PL7 5BQ
Tel: 1752-333 333 Fax: 1752-333 444
chairman Clive Jones; deputy chairman Barbara Hosking; managing director Mark Haskell; controller public affairs Mark Clare; director of programmes Jane McCloskey; controller news and sport Brad Higgins

Yorkshire Television
Television Centre, **Leeds** LS3 1JS
Tel: 113-243 8283 Fax: 113-244 5107
Internet: www.drci.co.uk/drci/ytti/
E-Mail: info@ytti.co.uk
managing director Richard Gregory; controller of drama Caroline Reynolds; controller of comedy drama and drama features David Reynolds; controller of factual programmes Chris Bryer

YUGOSLAVIA (+381)

Due to the war in Kosovo we have been unable to update the following entries for Yugoslavia

Association of Yugoslav Radio and TV (YRT)
Generala Zdanova 28, 11000 **Belgrade**
Tel: 11-333 126/434 910 Fax: 11-434 023
executive director Vjera Nikolic
Comments: central body linking department heads (including drama and music) both within the country and abroad; does not itself produce programmes

NTV Studio B
Television Studio B
Masarikova 5, 11000 **Belgrade**
Tel: 11-685 374/171 Fax: 11-684 798/659 135
director Zoran Ostojic; head of movie dept Jugoslav Pantelic; head of music Asim Sarvan

Radio and Television Politika
Makedonska 29, 11000 **Belgrade**
Tel: 11-322 6983/7427 Fax: 11-322 3421
general manager Dragan Hadzi Antic; deputy directors Bogdan Tirnanic, Radmila Visic; head of music, TV Zoran Dasic; head of cultural programme Ljiljana Lucic

Radio and TV Novi Sad
Zarka Zrenjanina 3, 21000 **Novi Sad**
Tel: 21-611 588 Fax: 21-22490
general manager Milan Todorov

RTCG – Radio and TV Montenegro
RTCG – Radio i televizija Crne Gore
Cetinjski put bb, 81000 **Podgorica**
Tel: 81-25999
general manager Zoran Jocovic

RTS – Radio and TV Serbia
RTS – Radio televizija Srbije
Takovska 10, 11000 **Belgrade**
Tel: 11-324 9000 Fax: 11-341 630
general director Dragoljub Milanovic

Television Novi Sad
Kamenicki put 45, 21000 **Novi Sad**
Tel: 21-56855 Fax: 21-613 959
director Dragan Jokic; chief editor of programmes Milorad Crnjanin
Comments: multi-lingual productions: Serbian, Hungarian, Romanian, Ruthenian and Slovak

Television Pristina
Ivana Kosancica 12, 38000 **Pristina**
Tel: 38-30501 Fax: 38-21816
general manager, Radio & TV Pristina Petar Jaksic; assistant director Nikola Saric; editor-in-chief Miladin Jovic; head of music Vesna Mulic
Comments: bilingual in Serbian and Albanian

TV Belgrade
Televizija Beograd
Takovska 10, 11000 **Belgrade**
Tel: 11-342 001/324 9000/322 9755 (programme director) Fax: 11-341 630
programme director Jovan Ristic; chief editor of arts programmes Milovan Vitezovic; chief editor of educational programmes Petar Savkovic; chief edior of cultural programmes Predrag Perisic
Format, policy: 3 channels

Recorded Media

Recorded Media
This section comprises producers of compact discs/cassettes/vinyl discs/CDV, with a particular emphasis on offices where A & R decisions are taken. It also includes producers of videos/films of performances and of performing arts documentaries. **Within country the organisations are ordered alphabetically.**

Les Media Diffusés
Cette rubrique englobe les producteurs de disques compacts, cassettes, disques, vidéo-disques. Nous avons mis l'accent sur les bureaux ou des décisions A&R sont prises. Les producteurs de vidéos ou de films sur des représentations ainsi que de documentaires sur les Arts Vivants sont également inclus. **Pour chaque pays les organisations sont classées par ordre alphabétique.**

Tonträgerindustrie
Dieses Kapitel umfaßt CD-, Kassetten-, Vinyl-Disc-, CDV- und Schallplattenproduzenten. Besonders betont werden die Abteilungen, die für A & R, Künstler- u. Repertoire-Entscheidungen verantwortlich sind. Eingeschlossen sind auch Produzenten von Videos, Aufführungs- und Dokumentarfilmen über darstellende Kunst. **Die Einträge sind innerhalb aller Staaten alphabetisch geordnet.**

Produttori Discografici
La sezione comprende produttori di compact discs/cassette/dischi in vinile/video discs con particolare risalto a quelle aziende dove si decide dell'intero svolgimento delle registrazioni, dalle scelte artistiche al repertorio. Sono inclusi inoltre produttori di video e films di spettacoli o documentari d'arte. **Seguono l'ordine alfabeticamente.**

Grabación
Esta sección lista productores de compact discs, cassettes, LPs, CVD, con énfasis en las oficinas donde se toman decisiones sobre A & R (artistas y repertorio). También incluye productores de vídeo/películas de espectáculos y documentales acerca de las artes escénicas. **Dentro de cada país las organizaciones están listadas alfabéticamente.**

Recorded Media (기록 미디어)
이 부문은 CD/카세트/vinyl discs/CDV 등의 제작자들로 구성되었으며, A & R 결정을 내리는 사무실들이 특별히 강조되었다. 또한 공연 비디오/필름 그리고 공연 도큐멘터리 등의 프로듀서들도 포함되었다. **리스트는 국가별로 알파벳순으로 기재되었다.**

录制媒介
本部分包括激光唱盘、卡式磁带、唱片和CDV制作公司，特别重点在于作出艺术家及曲目决定的办事处。它还包括演出录像或电影及表演艺术纪录片的制作公司。**在各国内，各机构是按字母顺序排列的。**

録音メディア
この章には、A&Rを考慮する事務所を中心に、CD、カセット、レコード／CDVを制作する会社が掲載されています。また、舞台芸術や舞台芸術に関するドキュメンタリーを制作するビデオ／映画プロデューサーも含まれます。**リストは国別で、一国内ではアルファベット順に記載されています。**

ALBANIA (+355)

Albafilm Animation
Aleksander Moisiu Nffl 76, **Tirana**
Tel: 42-63669 Fax: 42-63669
director Boris Ikonomi

Albafilm Studio
Kinostudio, **Tirana**
Tel: 42-62732
director Villasova Musa
Arts type: film *Comments:* 250 artistic films, 1500 documentary films, also animation films

La Boheme
Rruga Haxhi Dalliu, P8, 8h 1, Ap. 7,
PO Box 2951, **Tirana**
Tel: 42-29914 Fax: 42-29914

National Film Centre (NFC)
c/o National Cultural Centre,
Deshmoret e Kombit, **Tirana**
Tel: 42-40254
director Petrit Beci

State Central Archive of Film
Tirana
Tel: 42-64970
director Natasha Lako

ARMENIA (+374)

Ardzagank Company
c/o Sport & Concert Hall, Tsitsernakaberd,
375028 **Yerevan**
Tel: 2-399 911/398 125 Fax: 2-390 001
general director Yeghishe Petrossian

Asparez Studio
22 Saryan Street, 375002 **Yerevan**
Tel: 2-537 902
director David Ohanjanian

Cadence Chamber Music Centre Studio
c/o Yerevan Chamber Music Hall, 1 Isahakian Street,
375025 **Yerevan**
Tel: 2-562 839 Fax: 2-151 431 (AT&T)
Internet: www.arminco.com/homepages/nab
E-Mail: nbart@arminco.com
manager Aram Toptchian

OCTA Records Ltd
PO 405, 375010 **Yerevan**
Tel: 2-530 482 Fax: 2-530 482
manager Ruben Tonikian

Studio 9A
1a, Sayat-Nova Street, 375009 **Yerevan**
Tel: 2-285 176 Fax: 2-390 7223
manager Gevorg Hovhannissian

Studio of Radio Company of Armenia
2 Terian Street, 375001 **Yerevan**
Tel: 2-563 532/561 852 Fax: 2-151 947
manager t.b.a.

AUSTRIA (+43)

Annegret Lange Handelsagentur
Auerspergstr. 7/44, 1080 **Wien**
Tel: 1-408 1314
Fax: 1-406 7892
contact Annegret Lange
Format: CD *Own and distributed labels:* distributed: Pierre Verany, Four Hands Music, Dutton Laboratories, Memoir, Cala Records, NMC, Albany, Querstand, Upbeat Records, Canterino, Archiphon, Etcetera, Matous, Cypres, Melisma *Art type:* contemporary, early music *Comments:* European representative for double CD with compositions by Friedrich Nietzsche, produced by the Canadian Concordia University

Extraplatte Musikproduktions- und Verlags GmbH
Währingerstraße 46/11/12, 1090 **Wien**
Tel: 1-310 1084
Fax: 1-310 0324
Internet: www.extraplatte.at/homepage
E-Mail: info@extraplatte.at
A & R manager Eugen Novak
Format: CD – production and distribution *Own and distributed labels:* own labels: Extraplatte, Extra-edition, Extra-special; distributors of 450+ labels worldwide *Art type:* classical, jazz, world, contemporary

Koch International GmbH
Postbox 24, 6600 **Höfen Gewerbegebiet**
Tel: 5672-606 Fax: 5672-65580
Internet: www.kochmusic.com
E-Mail: kochmusic@kochmusic.com
president Franz Koch; A & R Franz Wolf;
publishing manager Rudi Schädler
Format: CDi, CD, CDV, cassette
Own and distributed labels: Koch music publishing international: Verlag (Komponisten, Musik)
Art type: classical and folklore, jazz, rock, pop

Lotus Records Salzburg
Ernsting 31-32, 5121 **Ostermiething**
Tel: 6278-7900 Fax: 6278-7476
Internet: www.lotusrecords.at/
E-Mail: htautscher@lotusrecord.at
managers Harald Tautscher, Elsbeth Elsinger;
press Hildegard Kiel; bookkeeping Annett Auer;
office Bernhard Hötzel
Format: CD, CD-Rom, LP *Own and distributed labels:* own: Lotus Records; distribute: All Saints, AMI Int. Music, Amiata, Celestial Harmonies, Channel Classics, Dorian, ECM, Ellipsis Arts, Phono Music, Stern's, Sattva, Tumi, World Circuit, Waterlily Acoustics, Wergo, Collegno, Ondine, Hannibal, Rykolatino & others *Art type:* classical music, world music, contemporary meditative music, jazz, contemporary classic

MCP-RECORDS Produktions-Vertriebs-Ges.m.b.H.
Industriestraße 5, 6430 **Ötztal**
Tel: 5266-8950-0 Fax: 5266-8950-20
E-Mail: mcprecords@netway.at
managing director Karl Krajic; export manager Louis Bischof; publishing manager Veronika Joechler; repertoire consultant Volker Spielberg;
special product manager Sabine Holdorf
Format: CD, cassette *Own and distributed labels:* MCP, Europrint, ACD, Junior (label for children) *Art type:* classical, new age, pop, German schlager, folk music

Michael Pilz Filmproduktion
Teschnergasse 37, 1180 **Wien**
Tel: 1-402 3392 Fax: 1-408 2649
E-Mail: pilz.film@magnet.at
artist, writer, film-maker, lecturer Michael Pilz
Own and distributed labels: own label: Michael Pilz *Art type:* film production

PAO Records
Froschau 4, 4775 **Diersbach**
Tel: 7719-8060 Fax: 7719-806 012
Internet: www.pao-records.at
E-Mail: Paul.Zauner@telecom.at
director Paul Zauner; artist manager Franz Hackl; A & R manager Ken Vangel; product manager Franz Schindlauer
Format: CD *Art type:* classical, jazz

pepperland music productions
Koelblgasse 13/1, 1030 **Wien**
Tel: 1-798 4262 Fax: 1-799 7305
E-Mail: pepperland@ins.at
contact Gerhard Gutschik
Format: CD *Own and distributed labels:* pepperland *Art type:* classical (from chamber to symphonic), jazz, rock
Comments: sales through Extraplatte (q.v.)

Polyglobe Music
PB. 844, 6023 **Innsbruck**
Tel: 512-370 077 Fax: 512-370 077/33
Internet: www.polyglobemusic.at
E-Mail: office@polyglobemusic.at
contact Stefan Ackermann, Astrid Ackermann-Rassi
Format: CD, MC; production, publishing and distribution *Own and distributed labels:* own: Ethnic; distributed: Aquamarin (Germany) *Art type:* classical, new age, worldmusic, traditional

Preiser & Co GmbH
Fischerstiege 9, 1010 **Wien**
Tel: 1-533 6228 Fax: 1-533 4405
contact Dr. Verena Probst, Michael Preiser
Format: CD production, publishing and distribution
Own and distributed labels: own: Preiser Records, Lebendige Vergangenheit; distribute: Nimbus, Pavilion Records, Bongiovanni, Bis, Biddulph, Dante, MVTO, Testament *Art type:* classical

Re Nova Classics
c/o Andreas Zadeyan, Herzgasse 92/17, 1100 **Wien**
Tel: 1-602 4770/664 141 2707(mobile) Fax: 1-602 4770
E-Mail: abet.rnc@a-topmail.at
contact Andreas Zadeyan
Format: CD *Own and distributed labels:* Re Nova Classics
Art type: classical, jazz *Comments:* see also Agents & Producers (Andreas Zadeyan)

SBF Records
Kirchenplatz 10, 4591 **Molln**
Tel: 7584-4000 Fax: 7584-4000/15
Internet: www.stn.at/sbf/
E-Mail: sbf@stn.at
managing director Manfred Prentner;
secretary Sonya Windhager
Format: CD, CD-Rom *Own and distributed labels:* SBF, Beat Bull, Traunstein, First Classic, Nightingale, K-Tel
Art type: pop, rock, jazz, trip pop, dance, worldmusic, etc. *Comments:* recording studios, music publisher, music distributer, record company

Shamrock Records
Altwaidhofen 37, 3830 **Waidhofen/Thaya**
Tel: 2842-53986 Fax: 2842-52826
E-Mail: shamrock@wvnet.at
contact Uwe Kranner
Format: CD *Own and distributed labels:* Shamrock Records *Art type:* classical, jazz

Sounddesign Austria
Dauphine Strasse 89, PF 109, 4030 **Linz**
Tel: 732-663 586 Fax: 732-663 587
contact Peter Guschelbauer, Sibylle Roithner
Format: CD *Own and distributed labels:* PG Records, Erdenklang, K-617, Going for a Song, Bellevue, Alsur, Ample, Atolt, Arts and Music, Beverly, Connoisseur, CTI, NCA, Mariposa, Pastell, Blue Sun, Timeless, Gallo, Sundance, Pierre Verani, Rivo Alto, Steeple Chase, WPME, Ricer Car, Aria, Trubach, Phoenix, Ducale, Sono, Evasion, Masters of Jazz, Jive Music, Jammin *Art type:* pop, rock, jazz, classical, world music etc

Trans-World Music
Korneuburgerstraße 86,
2103 **Langenzersdorf**
Tel: 2244-4580-0 Fax: 2244-4580-20
E-Mail: indra@magnet.at
contact Robert Indra
Format: CD, songbooks, note books for pop music, musicals for children *Own and distributed labels:* Music Pool Austria, Edition Premiere
Art type: classical and other

Vienna Modern Masters
Margaretenstrasse 125/15, 1050 **Wien**
Tel: 1-545 1778
Fax: 1-544 0785
E-Mail: vmm@teleweb.at
president Clyde A Smith;
vice president and artistic director Nancy Van de Vate
Format: CDs (production) *Art type:* concentrate predominantly but not exclusively on contemporary orchestral classical music *Comments:* non-profit record company devoted to producing compact discs for international distribution; sponsors an annual International Festival for new music in Olomouc, Czech Republic; see also Festivals

Warner Music Austria GmbH
Postfach 285, Erlachgasse 134-140, 1101 **Wien**
Tel: 1-601 590
Fax: 1-602 3623
Geschäftsführer Manfred Lappe;
Financial Director Wolfgang Laimer;
Sales Managers Kurt Dolezal, Günter Unger;
Promotion Irene Gehrsitz, Alexander Moropulo;
Stv Geschäftsführer Manfred Wodara; Marketing Director Klaus Hoffmann; Label Manager Rene Wastler, NN; Warner Classics Carin Munczninski

Zulus Records Vienna
Plattlgasse 8, 1238 **Wien**
Tel: 1-888 1271/544 2427/6991-470 0457 (mobile)
Fax: 1-544 2427/889 3747
contact Mag. Christian Zulus
Format: CDs *Own and distributed labels:* Zulus Records Vienna *Art type:* classical piano *Comments:* emphasis on recordings of pianist Natasa Veljkovic

AZERBAIDZHAN (+994)

Azerbaidzhan House of Sound Recording
A. Alizade St. 12, 370000 **Baku**
director Tagiyev Mubariz Huseyn ogly

BELGIUM (+32)

Accent Record Company
Eikstraat 31, 1673 **Beert**
Tel: 2-356 1878
Fax: 2-360 2718
Internet: www.accent-records.be
E-Mail: andreas.glatt@accent-records.be
managing director Andreas Glatt
Format: CDs *Own and distributed labels:* Accent
Art type: early and classical music

Argos
Rue du Chantier 13, 1000 **Brussels**
Tel: 2-229 0003
Fax: 2-223 7331
Internet: www.magic.be/argos
E-Mail: argos@glo.be
président Frie Depraetere; sales and acquisitions Margo Van Eusden; artistic director Paul Villemsem
Format: all video & film formats *Art type:* focus: contemporary arts *Comments:* policy: distribution of arts programmes for TV, home video and non-commercial market

Baltic NV
Rederijkersstraat 82,
2610 **Wilrijk (Antwerp)**
Tel: 3-828 4084
Fax: 3-829 1068
managing director Ben Gyselinck;
administrator Maria Wuyts
Format: CD, video, cassette *Own and distributed labels:* Supraphon, REM, D. I. Music, Elisar, Steeple Chase, Kontrapunkt, CPO, Music & Arts, Panton, Multisonic, Tudor, Pan. Testament, Concord, Arcodia Entertainment *Art type:* mostly classical (90%), jazz, original film soundtracks *Comments:* music library; distributes more than 200 labels

BMG
Square François Riga, Boite 8, 1030 **Brussels**
Tel: 2-240 2811 Fax: 2-240 2899
Internet: www.click2music.be
E-Mail: claudine.mortier@bmgariola.be
PR & advertising Claudine Mortier;
marketing director Marc De Keyzer;
rock, dance Els Vandenbulcke; MOR Inge Brinkman
Format: CD, cassette, vinyl *Own and distributed labels:* RCA, Ariola, Mushroom, Private, Giant, MEG, American, Arista, Vogue, Deconstruction, News, Bonzai records, Revolution *Art type:* classical music, MOR, dance, rock

Carbon 7
23 Av. Général Eisenhower, 1030 **Brussels**
Tel: 2-242 9703
Fax: 2-245 3885
Internet: www.netbeat.com/carbon7
E-Mail: 100257.214@compuserve.com
contact Muriel D'Archalau; directeur Guy Segers
Format: CD *Own and distributed labels:* Carbon 7 *Art type:* crossover music *Comments:* disc company; distributes for Belgium and Luxembourg

Disques Duchesne
Rue des Guillemins 41, 4000 **Liège**
Tel: 4-252 0701
Fax: 4-252 0701
PDG Jean Duchesne; artistic director Emmanuel Koch
Format: CD, cassette *Own and distributed labels:* Duchesne *Art type:* classical music, folk music

Fonti Musicali
33 rue Jean d'Ardenne, 1050 **Brussels**
Tel: 2-511 6772
Fax: 2-511 4186
E-Mail: fonti.musicali@skynet.be
directeur Claude Flagel
Format: CD *Art type:* historical, early and ethnic dance music

G.H.A records
101 rue Alexandre Markelbach, 1030 **Brussels**
Tel: 2-242 5921 Fax: 2-241 3885
Internet: www.gha.be
E-Mail: info@gha.be
production manager Françoise Emmanuelle Denis
Format: CD *Art type:* classical and jazz (exclusively guitar) *Comments:* see also Agents & Producers

Lavial Sprl
Rue Tenbroek 25A, 1640 **Rhode St Genèse**
Tel: 2-380 3737 Fax: 2-380 4964
E-Mail: lavial@online.be
director Raoul Jakou; administrator Alice Jakou; marketing manager Laurent Jakou (4-9551 7228)
Format: CD, cassette, video (distribution only) *Own and distributed labels:* Hyperion, Clarinet Classics, Stil, Chamade, Dynamic, Stradivarius, Fonè, Ermitage, Donemus, Hänssler, Ondine, Propius, Arts, Collins Classique, Ligiadigital, Gala, Blaricom, Matouch, Nuovara, Hortus, Tring, Arcoballeno, Sounds True *Art type:* classical and other (folk)

Pavane Records
17 rue Ravenstein, 1000 **Brussels**
Tel: 2-513 0965
Fax: 2-514 2194
Internet: www.pavane.com
E-Mail: dewouters.bam@skynet.be
president Antoine de Wouters d'Oplinter; managing director Bertrand de Wouters d'Oplinter
Format: CD only *Own and distributed labels:* Pavane *Art type:* classical music

René Gailly Production – Art & Music Consultants
rue Oscar Maesschalk 12, 1083 **Brussels**
Tel: 2-465 9870
Fax: 2-465 6955
Internet: www.users.skynet.be/Renegailly
E-Mail: rene.gailly@skynet.be
président et administrateur René Gailly; responsable artistique & programmation Véronique Wintgens
Format: CD *Own and distributed labels:* own: René Gailly (Vox Temporis, Terpsychore), SMI + others; distributed: French, English & Belgian labels
Art type: early & classical music

Ricercar
73 rue Burnaumont, 6890 **Anloy Libin**
Tel: 61-656 144 Fax: 61-656 246
Internet: www.ricercararon.be
administrateur Jérôme Lejeune
Format: CD *Art type:* classical music *Comments:* edited/distributed by Musidisc (France)

Syrinx Record
Vogelenstraat 32, 3070 **Kortenberg**
Tel: 2-502 7379
Fax: 2-502 8064
E-Mail: pwattercamps@arcadis.be
administration Marc Grauwels, Pierre Wattercamps
Format: CD *Own and distributed labels:* own label Syrinx
Art type: classical music

TLP Productions
309, Chaussée de Tongres, 4540 **Amay**
Tel: 85-312 235 Fax: 85-312 000
director Jean Stasse; secretary Claudine Landureau
Format: CD, records *Own and distributed labels:* TLP records, Delta Productions (Laserlight) Germany *Art type:* classical music, mainly operettas & musicals, opera *Comments:* see also Agents & Producer and Opera: Théâtre Musical Europées

Vox Temporis Productions
Koninginlaan 22, 9820 **Merelbeke (Gent)**
Tel: 9-231 9712 Fax: 9-231 9712
E-Mail: florian.heyerick@merelbeke.be
producer-director Florian Heyerick
Format: CDs *Own and distributed labels:* own: Vox Temporis *Art type:* unknown or unedited classical music (1500-2000), historical instruments, first recordings, Belgium, international music *Comments:* marketed and distributed by Art & Music Consultants, Oscar Maesschalckstraat 12, 1083 Brussels,
Tel: 2-465 9870, Fax: 2-465 6955

Warner Music Benelux
468 Chausée Romaine, 1853 **Grimbergen**
Tel: 2-263 0300
Fax: 2-263 0330
managing director Benelux Albert Slendebroek; marketing manager Belgium Anne Baugnée; product manager Belgium Peter Van De Velde; sales manager Michel Guillet; head of radio Christel Dequinnemaere; general manager Erik Vink; product Eastwest Eric Lahey
Format: CD, video, laser discs *Own and distributed labels:* Warner Bros, Electra, Eastwest, WEA, Errato, Teldec, Atlantic *Comments:* second address: Noorderweg 68, 1221 AB Hilversum, Netherlands,
Tel: 35-688 2211

BULGARIA (+359)

Balkanton Trading
6 Haidoushka pollana Str., 1612 **Sofia**
Tel: 2-517 247 Fax: 2-542 744
director George Vachev

Gega-New Ltd
5B Akatsia Str., **Sofia**
Tel: 2-669 103/653 179 Fax: 2-669 082
director Juliana Marinova

Mega Music
2 Trapezitsa Str., 1000 **Sofia**
Tel: 2-464 176
director Teherneva

Riva Sound
3rd Floor, 103 Knyaginya Maria Luiza Blvd., 1202 **Sofia**
Tel: 2-317 128/310 060 Fax: 2-317 128
director Vassil Serafimov
Format: licence *Art type:* Bulgarian artists: folk, jazz, modern music

CROATIA (+385)

Croatia Records
Medugorska 61, 10000 **Zagreb**
Tel: 1-290 2100
Fax: 1-290 2121
director Miroslav Lilic

Jazzette Reocrds
Teslina 7, 10000 **Zagreb**
Tel: 1-611 0610/425 520 Fax: 1-611 9619
Own and distributed labels: own: Jazzette records
Art type: jazz *Comments:*
main promoter of jazz events in Zagreb

Orfey of the Croatian Radio and TV
Orfey Hrvatske Radio Televizije
Gruska 10, 10000 **Zagreb**
Tel: 1-615 7955 Fax: 1-615 8353
production Stanislav Mlinar; director Miroslav Skoro

Suzy d.d
Gruska 10, 10000 **Zagreb**
Tel: 1-615 8354 Fax: 1-615 8364
director Milan Skrnjug

CZECH REPUBLIC (+420)

Arco Diva / Ultraphon
Konviktská 5, 110 00 **Praha** 1
Tel: 2-2209 2331/8387 2305
Fax: 2-2209 2330
Internet: www.arcodiva.cz
E-Mail: arcodiva@login.cz
director PhDr. Jirí Stilec

Arta 2HP Production
Lublanská 57, 120 00 **Praha** 1
Tel: 2-298 823/2491 4743 ext 214-15
Fax: 2-298 823
Internet: www.arta.cz
E-Mail: 2hp@arta.cz
Format: CD, mc *Art type:* jazz, rock, classic

Best I.A.
Prístavní 31, 170 00 **Praha** 7
Tel: 2-806 802/6671 3018 Fax: 2-6671 3018
Internet: www.bestia.cz
E-Mail: bestia@mbox.vol.cz
manager Dagmar Durecová
Art type: pop music

BMG (Bertelsman Music Group)
International Ariola CR/SR
Trojanova 18, 120 00 **Praha** 2
Tel: 2-290 859/294 827/2491 7218 Fax: 2-2491 7214
Internet: bmg.cz
E-Mail: bmg@bmg.cz

Edit Ltd
Edit s.r.o.
Zárubova 493, Lhotka, 142 00 **Praha** 4
Tel: 2-471 4540/2091 Fax: 2-471 4540
director Ing. Miroslav Sik
Arts type: folklore, folk & country, pop *Comments:* also edit sheet music and books on music

Globus International
Jaromírova 61, 128 00 **Praha** 2
Tel: 2-439 596/436 536/692 7384 Fax: 2-692 6255
Internet: www.multimedia.cz/globus
E-Mail: globusin@bohem-net.cz
manager Daniel Petrík
Art type: rock music

ICN Polyart Prague v.o.s.
Pod Vincí 21/794, 143 00 **Praha** 4
Tel: 2-6131 3903 Fax: 2-6131 3902
manager Jan Hasenöhrl

Lotos Records Ltd
Vydavatelství Lotos s.r.o.
Plzenská 113, 150 00 **Praha** 5
Tel: 2-5721 1478/536 846/602-363 592 (mobile)
Fax: 2-5721 1478
Internet: web.telecom.cz/cdlotos
E-Mail: cd.lotos@iol.cz
director Ing. Alena Stepánková
Art type: jazz, classical, world music and other genres

Milan Oliverius Art & Recording Production
Italská 27, 120 00 **Praha** 2
Tel: 2-2225 0718/603-460 0283 (mobile)
Fax: 2-2225 0718
Internet: www.oliverius.cz
E-Mail: agency@oliverius.cz
director Milan Oliverius
Art type: classical, folklore
Comments: see also Agents & Producers

Monitor EMI Ltd.
Kovárova 39, 155 00 **Praha** 5
Tel: 2-651 6452/5711 5111 Fax: 2-651 8331/8349
Internet: www.monitor-emi.cz
director Vladimir Kocandrle; manager Josef Prib

Multisonic, a.s.
Zirovnická 2389, POB 32, 106 00 **Praha** 10
Tel: 2-7276 0409 Fax: 2-7276 0417
E-Mail: multisonic@mbox.vol.cz
director Mgr. Renata Severová
Art type: classical music

Popron Music
Jeremiásova 947, 155 00 **Praha** 5
Tel: 2-569 2316/9 Fax: 2-5721 5327
Internet: www.popron.cz
president Peter Schier
Comments: branch: Popron Trading GmbH, Im Gewerbepark A 47, D-93059 Regensburg,
Tel: +49 941-448 662, Fax: +49 941-448 663

Sony Music Bonton
Palackého 1, 112 99 **Praha** 1
Tel: 2-9624 5451/2/3/4/5/6 Fax: 2-2494 9162
E-Mail: czech_reception@cz.sonymusic.com
Art type: popular music genres

Studio Matous
Ronkova 8, 180 00 **Praha** 8
Tel: 2-684 2744/683 6468/6516 Fax: 2-684 3799
Internet: www.matous.cz
E-Mail: s.matous@iol.cz
director Simon Matousek
Art type: classical

Supraphon Records, a.s.
Palackého 1, 112 99 **Praha** 1
Tel: 2-2494 8722/19
Fax: 2-2494 8728
E-Mail: supraphon@bonton.cz
manager Jana Gondová
Format: CD, audio, video, LP

Video Audio Unisa (VAU)
Radlická 99, 150 00 **Praha** 5
Tel: 2-538 400/370/439/602-291 850 (mobile)
Fax: 2-5732 0306
director Jan Kobr

DENMARK (+45)

BMG Denmark A/S
Overgaden neden Vandet 17.2,
1414 **Copenhagen** K
Tel: 3269 9700 Fax: 3269 9799
E-Mail: bmg@bmg.dk
managing director Freddie de Wall;
A & R managers Anders Hansen, Jeppe Bisgaard;
manager finance & administration Nils Trier;
head of marketing/promotion Henrik Daldorph
Format: CD, tape *Own and distributed labels:* own: Ariola, Arista, Bluebird, DDD, Genlyd, Novus, RCA, deconstruction, Catalyst, Conifer, Deutsche Harmonia Mundi, Eurodisc, Jade, Milan, Royal Operahouse, Russian Melodiya, Arte Nova; distribute: Diesel, Giant, Revolution, Mushroom
Art type: classical, jazz, rock, pop, etc.

dacapo
Christianshavns Torv 2, 1410 **Copenhagen** K
Tel: 3296 0602 Fax: 3296 2602
Internet: www.dacapo-records.dk
E-Mail: dacapo@image.dk
director Henrik Rødam;
sales & marketing manager Anna Bremner
Format: CD *Art type:* classical, jazz

Danacord
Norregade 22, 1165 **Copenhagen** K
Tel: 3315 1716 Fax: 3312 1514
Internet: www.danacord.dk
E-Mail: daco@danacord.dk
managing director Jasper Buhl
Format: CD *Art type:* classical

EMI / Medley
Vognmagergade 10, 1120 **Copenhagen** K
Tel: 3393 5222 Fax: 3393 5221
Internet: www.emi/medley.dk
managing director Michael Ritto; A & R Nick Fross;
marketing manager Mik Christinsen;
promotion Marlene Mathiesen (national),
Salli Mortensen (international)
Format: CD, tape *Own and distributed labels:* own: EMI, Medley; distribute: Capitol, IRS, Chrysalis, EMI USA, Blue Note, EMI Classics, CFP, Reflexe, Eminence, Virgin Classics, Angel, Flex (Danish label), AGM (Danish label), Capitol Nashville, Apple, Parlephone
Art type: various/all

Exlibris & Monoland
Klareboderne 3, 1001 **Copenhagen** K
Tel: 3311 0775 Fax: 3311 4051
E-Mail: Jim_Holm@Gyldendal.dk
manager Jim Holm
Format: CD *Own and distributed labels:* Exlibris & Monoland *Art type:* rock, alternative *Comments:* home of Mew, Speaker Bite Me, Sophia

Fona
Gungevej 17, 2650 **Hvidovre**
Tel: 3639 0600 Fax: 3649 3425
Internet: www.fona.dk
E-Mail: pbf@thretail.dk
managing director Frank Henriksen
Format: video, CD, MC *Art type:* all kinds of music

Fønix Musik
Sønder Allé 12, 8000 **Aarhus** C
Tel: 8619 5811 Fax: 8619 5101
Internet: www.fonix.dk
managing director Ole Kjaer; A & R Leila Johansen
Format: CD, cassette, video *Art type:* instrumental & new-age music, meditation, relaxing music

HELIKON Records
Holtug Mosevey 12, 4660 **St Heddinge**
Tel: 5656 7005 Fax: 5656 7006
Internet: www.helikonrecords.dk
E-Mail: jesper@helikonrecords.dk
managing director Jesper Jørgensen
Format: CD *Own and distributed labels:* own: Helikon
Art type: classical music

OH Musik Aps
Postbox 49, Jersie Strandvej 5, 2680 **Solrød**
Tel: 5614 6644 Fax: 5614 6667
E-Mail: oh@ohmusik.dk
managing director Ole Høglund
Format: CD, cassettes *Own and distributed labels:* own: Rondo, Danica, Point; distribute: numerous including: ASV, FMS, Koch, Laserlight, Motette Ursina, MusicMasters, Hänssler, Novalis, Nimbus Records, Say Disc *Art type:* classical

Olga Musik
Boeletvej 4, 8680 **Ry**
Tel: 8689 2428
Fax: 8689 0033
E-Mail: olgamusik@vip.cybercd.dk
managing director Birger Hansen
Format: import CDs and cassettes *Own and distributed labels:* Naxos, Marco Polo, DeCapo, Opus I & II, Bis Harmonia Mundi *Art type:* classical and world music

Storyville
Dortheavej 39, 2400 **Copenhagen** NV
Tel: 3819 8590 Fax: 3819 0110
E-Mail: storyvil@post8.tele.dk
managing director Karl Emil Knudsen; administration Mona Granager; promotion Allan Stephensen
Format: CD, video *Own and distributed labels:* own: Storyville Records; distribute: Jazz Unlimited, Collectors Classics (Jazz), Nostalgia, Jubelee *Art type:* jazz, blues

Universal Music
Amaliegade 45, 1256 **Copenhagen** K
Tel: 3391 2110 Fax: 3391 3110
managing director Jens-Otto Paludan;
marketing manager Michael Boier
Format: CD, tape, video *Art type:* all kinds of music

ESTONIA (+372)

Edition 49
Lauteri 7, 10145 **Tallinn**
Tel: 2-455 472
Internet: www.zzz.ee/edition49/
E-Mail: e49@zzz.ee

Eesti Video
Parnu mnt. 232, 11314 **Tallinn**
Tel: 6-544 968 Fax: 6-544 968
Format: culture videos and documentaries

Forte Records
Kuninga 4, 10146 **Tallinn**
Tel: 6-700 093
Format: LP, MC, CD

Orbital Vox Stuudiod
Jakobsoni 14, 4 K, 10128 **Tallinn**
Tel: 6-419 066 Fax: 6-312 540
Internet: www.online.ee/~orbital_vox/
Format: CD, CD-ROM

Tallinfilm
Harju 9, 10146 **Tallinn**
Tel: 6-442 088/2-443 172
Format: TV and video

Tartu Laululava helistuudio
Laulupeo pst.25, 51007 **Tartu**
Tel: 7-422 952/2506 8694 Fax: 7-422 283
E-Mail: sax@arena.ee
Format: CD, CD-ROM

FINLAND (+358)

Alba Records Oy
PO Box 549, 33101 **Tampere**
Tel: 3-345 1387 Fax: 3-345 1384
E-Mail: timo@alba-records.fi
contact Timo Ruottinen
Art type: classical

FG-Naxos
Kamreerintie 10, 2. krs, 02770 **Espoo**
Tel: 9-615 3615 Fax: 9-6153 6299
Internet: www.hnh.com
contact Jan-Erik Lindqvist
Art type: mainly classical, also religious, jazz & world music

Finlandia Records
PO Box 169, 02101 **Espoo**
Tel: 9-435 011/615 3308 Fax: 9-455 2352
Internet: www.finlandia-records.com
head of Finlandia Records Jari Tiessalo (tel: 435 01335, email: jari.tiessalo@warnermusic.com);
marketing manager Kristiina Nuotio (email: kristiina.nuotio@warnermusic.com);
manager press & promotion Brita Toivonen (tel: 435 01311, email: brita.toivonen@warnermusic.com)
Format: CD, cassette *Art type:* classical music, world music

Ondine Inc.
Fredrikinkatu 77A2, 00100 **Helsinki**
Tel: 9-434 2210 Fax: 9-493 956
Internet: www.ondine.net
E-Mail: ondine@ondine.fi
managing director Reijo Kiilunen; producer Seppo Siirala; marketing director Anu Lindqvist
Format: CD producer *Own and distributed labels:* Ondine, Octopus (own) *Art type:* only classical music

Warner / Chappel Music
Ratapihantie 11, PL 126, 00521 **Helsinki**
Tel: 9-229 560 Fax: 9-2295 6602
E-Mail: ari.nieminen@warnerchappell.com

FRANCE (+33)

2e2m Collection
4, rue Proudhon, 94500 **Champigny**
Tel: 1-4706 1776 Fax: 1-4882 2645
Internet: www.multimusic.com/2e2m
E-Mail: ens2e2m@imaginet.fr
manager Christine Nollier; artistic director Paul Méfano
Format: CD *Own and distributed labels:* own: 2e2m Collection *Art type:* contemporary and classical music

AGAT FILMS et Cie
52 rue Jean-Pierre Timbaud, 75011 **Paris**
Tel: 1-5336 3232 Fax: 1-4357 0022
E-Mail: agatex@imaginet.fr
président, directeur général Maurice Prost; producers Nicolas Blanc, Yvon Davis, Robert Guediguian, Alain Guesnier, Gilles Sandoz, Blanche Guichou; directeur financier et administratif Marc Bordure
Format: documentaries, short films, feature films and TV productions of plays and live performances
Art type: dance, painting, theatre *Comments:* distribution company: Doc & Co, 13, rue Portefouin 75003 Paris, Tel: 1-4277 5687

Album Productions
57 rue des Trois Frères, 75018 **Paris**
Tel: 1-4606 0690 Fax: 1-4606 3634
directeurs Sylvie Faguer, Jean-Luc Léon
Format: videos *Art type:* production of TV documentaries and of feature films for the cinema

Arion
36 Avenue Hoche, 75008 **Paris**
Tel: 1-4563 7670 Fax: 1-4563 7954
E-Mail: info@arion-music.com
présidente directrice générale Manuela Ostrolenk;
attaché de presse et production Stéphane Perreau;
attaché de production Pierre Berani
Format: CD *Own and distributed labels:* Arion, Pierre Verany *Art type:* classical, traditional music

BBC Worldwide France
5 Rue de Ponthieu, 75008 **Paris**
Tel: 1-4495 8400 Fax: 1-4495 8409
Internet: www.bbcworldwide.fr
contact Tim Muff
Format: video, cassette, CD *Art type:* drama, music, documentary *Comments:* BBC Worldwide TV and Publishing operate on a fully commercial basis; BBC Worldwide TV market BBC programmes and develop BBC channel activity around French speaking countries, whilst BBC Worldwide Publishing is active across all areas of publishing media

Bell Air Media
15 Rue du Louvre, 75001 **Paris**
Tel: 1-4488 28181
Fax: 1-4488 2814
manager Francois Duplat;
financial director Zavier Dubois
Format: video, CD's, HDTV *Art type:* productions
Comments: see also Agents & Producers

Bleu Krystal Media
28 rue des Petites Ècuries, 75010 **Paris**
Tel: 1-5334 1590 Fax: 1-4479 0676
E-Mail: bkm@imaginet.fr
director of production Suzanne Masson;
director Phillipe Muller
Format: cinema, videos (on arts & culture)

Dante
7 rue Gaudray, 92170 **Vanves**
Tel: 1-4133 9933
Fax: 1-4638 3703
Internet: www.pl-music.com
E-Mail: dantecd@aol.com
gérant Bruno Saint Germain
Format: production, edition and distribution of CDs-classical music, recording studio *Art type:* specialised in historical releases *Comments:* multi-media realisation

Editing Productions
6 rue des Marronniers, 75016 **Paris**
Tel: 1-4525 2131/2
Fax: 1-4525 1854
Internet: www.editingproductions.fr
E-Mail: editingp@cybercable.fr
président André Halimi
Format: video for TV channels *Art type:* TV documentaries, international entertainment, politics and humour

EMI Music France SA
43 rue Camille Desmoulins, BP 49,
92133 **Issy-les-Moulineaux** Cédex
Tel: 1-4629 2020
Fax: 1-4629 2121
Internet: www.emi.fr
secrétaire général Pierre Darmon; président Marc Lumbroso; directeur artistique et répertoire classique Alain Lanceron; directeur de la production et de la création française Michel Liberman
Format: CD, CDV, cassettes, records, video *Art type:* music, video *Comments:* produce & co-produce

EMI Music, Virgin Classics
43 rue Camille Desmoulin, 92130 **Issy-les-Moulineaux**
Tel: 1-4629 2020 Fax: 1-4629 2155
Internet: www.emi.fr
president Alain Lanceron; A & R administrator Remi Jacobs; international marketing & promotions Bertrand Schmitt; iconographie & texte Bruno Gilardoni
Format: CD, cassette *Own and distributed labels:* Virgin Classics *Comments:* series: Veritas, Veritas Edition, Ultra Violet

Erato Disques SA
50 rue des Tournelles, 75003 **Paris**
Tel: 1-4027 7000
Fax: 1-4804 9543
Internet: www.erato.com
directeur général Didier Durand-Bancel; directeur international promotion et développement artistique Christian Hellwig
Format: CD, cassette *Art type:* classical music *Comments:* part of the Warner Group

Europe Images International
25 rue François 1er, 75008 **Paris**
Tel: 1-4723 2860 Fax: 1-4723 2810
E-Mail: europe_image@europenet.ccmail.compuserve.com
general director Jean Rouilly; director of operations Peter Worsley
Format: TV and video distributor *Art type:* classical music concerts, opera, dance, drama, jazz, world music; portraits, performance, with emphasis on documentary

Gédéon
44/50 av du Capitaine Glarner, 93585 **Saint Ouen** Cédex
Tel: 1-4948 6500 Fax: 1-4948 6503
Internet: www.gedeon.com
films Pierre-François Decouflé; communication Gilles Galud; programmes Stéphane Millière
Format: audio-visual, communication programmes, design, advertising, film, video, video clip

Harmonia Mundi
BP 150, 13631 **Arles** Cédex
Tel: 4-9049 9049 Fax: 4-9049 9614
Internet: www.harmoniamundi.com
E-Mail: info.arles@harmoniamundi.com
président directeur général Bernard Coutaz; directrice de la production Eva Coutaz; directeur administratif & financier Gérard Cointot; coordination internationale Charles Malnuia; directeur commercial disque Patrick Lemanski; directeur commercial livre Frédéric Salbans; responsable des relations presse Jean-Marc Berns; directeur commercial groupe René Goiffon; label manager, classique et jazz Alain Raemackers
Format: produce CD, cassettes; also distribute CD & books *Art type:* classical & early, jazz, traditional and contemporary music

Hodie TM Production
3 chemin des Fausses – Reposes, 78000 **Versailles**
Tel: 1-3953 0428/6-6074 7249
Fax: 1-4257 3310
Internet: perso.libertysurf.fr/hodie
E-Mail: hodie@libertysurf.fr
chairman & aristic director Dr. Maximianno Cobra; chief executive Katarzyna Le-Fé
Format: DVD, documentaries, opera-films, research including publishing and sight, and sound and education

Idéale Audience
6 rue de l'Agent Bailly, 75009 **Paris**
Tel: 1-5320 1400
Fax: 1-5320 1401
E-Mail: ideale@ideale-audience.fr
responsable de distribution et co-production Susanna Scott; producers Olivier Charvel, Hélène Lecoeur; président Pierre-Olivier Bardet
Format: documentaries (music, social) *Own and distributed labels:* Idéale Audience *Art type:* music *Comments:* production of films for TV and cinema

IMG Records
54 Avenue Marceau, 75008 **Paris**
Tel: 1-4431 4431
Fax: 1-4431 4445
E-Mail: artistsparis@imgworld.com
director, artist management Philippe Etourneau; director, orchestral tours Gilles Demonet; director, vocal division Peter Wiggins; consultant, artist management Véronique Jourdain
Format: CDs, TV programmes and video, laser discs *Comments:* see also Agents & Producers

Les Films du Village
24-26 rue des Prairies, 75020 **Paris**
Tel: 1-4462 8877
Fax: 1-4462 7242
Internet: www.films-du-village.com
E-Mail: village@cybercable.fr
directeur général Yves Billon; responsable des projets Jean-Pierre Beaurenaut; responsable de la distribution Victoria Texeira
Format: video cassette (editing, production, distribution) *Own and distributed labels:* Les Films du Village, small independent labels *Art type:* production and distribution of TV documentaries

Musidisc
3 & 5 rue Albert de Vatimesnil, 92300 **Levallois** Cédex
Tel: 1-4149 4249 Fax: 1-4149 4200
E-Mail: musidisc@calvanet.calvacom.fr
président François Grandchamp des Raux; secrétaire général Jean Grandchamp des Raux; directeur général Eric Lemarié; chef de produit rock, variete françaises Valérie Leroux; chef de produit music world Eric Léost; chef de produit rapp, reggae/chef de produit international, blues Serge Bouratchiak
Format: CD, cassette, book cassette *Own and distributed labels:* Accord, Musicdisc, Festival, Una Corda, Jazz Anthologie, le Petit Menestrel, Adès, ADDA BIGDEAL, Disc Ambiance, Disc Az, Font, Musicali, Harp's, Revolun, Studio Davont, Victorie Music, Zip Dog and many more *Art type:* classical music, variety, rock, jazz, world music, children's music, music production for children

Telmondis
18 rue Troyon, 75017 **Paris**
Tel: 1-4574 2200 Fax: 1-4574 2202
E-Mail: telmondi@club-internet.fr
president and managing director Josette Affergan; director of sales and co-productions Josiane Mekies
Format: video *Art type:* produce and distribute performing arts performances (variety, ballet, circus, concerts etc) and documentaries

Warner Classics
14 Ave. Albert Einstein, Zone Industrielle du Coudray, 93151 **Blanc-Mesnil**
Tel: 1-4814 5000 Fax: 1-4814 5050
E-Mail: carole_labbe@wmg.com
director Gilles Desangles
Format: CD, cassette *Own and distributed labels:* distribute: Erato, Teldec, None Such, Finlanda, Warner Music *Art type:* classical, world music and jazz

GEORGIA (+995)

SIMI Studio
125 Agmeshenebeli Ave., 380002 **Tbilisi**
Tel: 32-950 590 Fax: 32-958 996
general manager Vato Kakhidze
Format: DAT, CD *Own and distributed labels:* SONY, Excelsior, Records Digest *Art type:* classical music

Sound Recording Studio Melodia
71 Vaja-Pshavela Ave., 380086 **Tbilisi**
Tel: 32-321 099
general manager Djumber Beradze
Format: cassettes, DAT *Art type:* folk, classical, jazz, rock, pop music

GERMANY (+49)

ARTE NOVA Musikproduktion GmbH
Kastenbauerstraße 2, 81677 **München**
Tel: 89-4136-0 Fax: 89-413 6125
Internet: www.artenova.de
Geschäftsführung Dieter Oehms
Format: exclusively CDs *Art type:* classical music, concerts, opera *Comments:* ARTE NOVA is a unit of BMG Entertainment; planning to move in August 2000, please contact for further details

Bella Musica / Edition Jürgen Rinschler
Eisenbahnstr. 30, 77815 **Bühl/Baden**
Tel: 7223-98550 Fax: 7223-985 566
direktor Jürgen Rinschler
Format: CD, MC, video *Own and distributed labels:* own: Antes Edition *Art type:* all types of music *Comments:* distribution in Italy: Antes Concerto, Via F. Bocconi 1, 20136 Milano Italy, Tel: +39 02-5832 1153, Fax: +39 02-5830 5166

BMG Classics, European Office-Munich
Kastenbauerstrasse 2, 81677 **München**
Tel: 89-4136-0 Fax: 89-4136 9163
managing director Lars Toft; manager, product development Niels Höirup; A & R vice-president Stefan Mikorey; European marketing directors Richard Wenn, Stefan Schmerbeck; administrator, A & R Europe Ortrud Varenholz; director, UK A & R Dolly Williamson; manager, business affairs Dr. Herbert Koch; press manager, non-classical Tanya Koschade; classical manager David Eyer
Format: CD, CDV, cassette, DVD *Own and distributed labels:* Red Seal, Melodia, DHM, Arte Nova, Victor Jazz, Wicklog, Catalyst, Eurodisc *Art type:* classical, crossover, jazz, world music

Cantate / musicaphon
Heinrich-Schütz-Allee 35, 34131 **Kassel**
Tel: 561-937 5412 Fax: 561-937 5425
Internet: www.cantate.de
E-Mail: info@cantate.de
director Dr. Rainer Kahleyss
Format: CD *Own and distributed labels:* Cantate, Musicaphone *Art type:* classical

Claudia Willke Filmproduktion
Arnoldstr. 74, 22763 **Hamburg**
Tel: 40-397 281 Fax: 40-390 0713
E-Mail: 101561.2256@compuserve.com
Format: director & producer of films *Comments:* documentaries and biographies for art and culture focussing on the socio-political aspects

Comma records and tapes
Nachtigallenstr. 36, 63263 **Neu-Isenburg**
Tel: 6102-52696 Fax: 6102-52696
president Roland Bauer
Format: CD, records, tapes

Deutsche Grammophon Gesellschaft GmbH
PO Box 130266, 20102 **Hamburg**
Tel: 40-44181-0 Fax: 40-44181-184
Internet: www.dgclassics.com
Geschäftsführung Christopher Roberts, Wolf D. Gramatke
Format: CD, cassettes and video cassettes *Own and distributed labels:* Deutsche Grammophon, Archiv Produktion *Art type:* only classical *Comments:* visiting address: Alte Rabenstraße 2, 20148 Hamburg

DMB – International Detlef Michael Behrens
Pommersche Straße 9, 10707 **Berlin**
Tel: 30-873 7431/7131 Fax: 30-861 3798
managing director Detlef Michael Behrens; head of buying Ursula Koch; representation Barbara Kyndt
Format: film, video *Own and distributed labels:* DMB – International *Art type:* feature films, entertainment, music etc.

ECM Records
Postfach 600331, 81203 **München**
Tel: 89-851 048 Fax: 89-854 5652
Internet: www.ecmrecords.com
E-Mail: ecm@ecmrecords.com
contact Heike Lies
Format: CD, LP, cassette *Own and distributed labels:* ECM, Carmo, Watt *Art type:* jazz and improvised music, early music, 20th C composers, also classical

Elisar Records
Hauptstrasse 66, 77652 **Offenburg**
Tel: 781-72041
Fax: 781-23406
Internet: www.ivan-rebroff.de
E-Mail: konzertbuero.weber@baden-online.de
Geschäftsführerin Irma Weber; Prokurist Ursula Juncker
Format: classical CDs and cassettes *Own and distributed labels:* Elisar Records *Art type:* classic, sacred, Russian folk music *Comments:* see also Agents & Producers (Konzertbüro Richard Weber)

EMI Electrola GmbH
Postfach 30329, 50773 **Köln**
Tel: 221-49020 Fax: 221-490 2100
Internet: www.emimusic.de
president EMI Music Germany, Switzerland, Austria Heinz Canibol; MD EMI Classics Dr. von Imhoff; GM Germany Rüdiger Fleige
Format: CD, LP, MC *Own and distributed labels:* EMI *Art type:* distribution and marketing *Comments:* visiting address: Maarweg 149, 50825 Köln

ERES EDITION
Postfach 1220, 28859 **Lilienthal (Bremen)**
Tel: 4298-1676
Fax: 4298-5312
director Horst Schubert
Format: CD, MC *Own and distributed labels:* own: Eres *Art type:* Estonian music: sacred, early, choral, instrumental, choir *Comments:* see also Services

EuroArts International
Teckstrasse 64, 70190 **Stuttgart**
Tel: 711-268 7610 Fax: 711-268 7676
Internet: www.euroarts.com
E-Mail: 101644.2613@compuserve.com
managing director Bernd Hellthaler; general manager sales & distribution Elmar Kruse; head of classical music & documentaries Paul Smaczny (Leipzig); head of film dubbing Marina Müller (Berlin); head of postproduction Günter Zorn
Format: CD-ROM, CD, DVD, production for TV, distribution *Art type:* music, opera, dance productions and documentaries, music programmes *Comments:* subdivision: EuroArtes Entertainment GmbH; Berlin Office (synchronisation and fiction): Wilmersdorferstr. 79, 10629 Berlin, tel: 30-3278 3911; Leipzig Office (classical music and documentaries): Mendelssohnhaus, Goldschmidtstr. 12, 04103 Leipzig, Tel: 341-140 840

Fermate Musikproduktion
Hülsenweg 7, 32760 **Detmold**
Tel: 5231-870 320
Fax: 5231-870 321
Internet: www.fermate.de
E-Mail: LB@fermate.de
contact Dipl.-Tonmeister Ludger Böckenhoff
Format: CD *Own and distributed labels:* Fermate, Corona *Art type:* classical, contemporary

Forum Media GmbH
Stahlgruber Ring 11a, 81829 **München**
Tel: 89-427 1065/1066
Fax: 89-427 1246
Geschäftsführer Dr. Eberhard Scheele
Format: film & TV productions *Own and distributed labels:* own: Forum Media *Art type:* classical and children's programming

Freiburger Musik Forum GmbH
Schwarzwaldstr. 298a, Schlosspark Ebnet,
79117 **Freiburg**
Tel: 761-62205 Fax: 761-62229
E-Mail: fmf@fmf.notes-net.de
managing director Rudolf Ruby;
sales & marketing Lutz Volker Scherer
Format: CD *Own and distributed labels:* own: ars musici, Primavera *Art type:* music production, classical only

German Dance Film Institute
Deutsches Tanzfilminstitut
Universität Bremen FB10, Postfach 330 440,
28334 **Bremen**
Tel: 421-218 3828 Fax: 421-218 4297
E-Mail: haertel@uni-bremen.de
artistic director Heide-Marie Härtel
Format: video documentaries (650 titles) *Art type:* dance and ballet *Comments:* Film and Video Archive offers an almost complete overview of dance and ballet productions by German ensembles and soloists form the last ten years, also some European ensembles and soloists; production of documentary features for television

GLM – Georg Löffler Musikverlag
Kaiser-Ludwig-Platz 1, 80336 **München**
Tel: 89-5440 4534 Fax: 89-5440 4535
Internet: www.glm.de
E-Mail: glm@glm.de
Inhaber Georg Löffler; Label Manager Michele Claveau
Format: CD *Own and distributed labels:* Edition Collage, Liffi Records, Musik für Babys *Art type:* Edition Collage jazz artists only, also rock – pop music

hänssler CLASSIC
Max-Eyth-Str. 41, 71088 **Holzgerlingen**
Tel: 7031-7414-0
Fax: 7031-741 4119
Internet: www.haenssler.de/classic
E-Mail: info@haenssler.de
director Günter Hänssler; press & promotion Kerstin Hänssler; international sales & marketing Matthias Lutzweiler (email: sales@haenssler.de)
Format: CD, video *Own and distributed labels:* own: hänssler CLASSIC *Art type:* classical, folk, gospel

KirchGruppe
Robert-Bürkle-Str. 2, 85737 **Ismaning**
Tel: 89-9956-0 Fax: 89-9956 2123
Internet: www.kirchgruppe.de
president, chairman & sole owner Leo Kirch; vice chairman of the board of managing directors & MD, corporate communications Dr. Dieter Hahn; MD, programme production & distribution Jan Mojto; MD, corporate finance Herbert Schroder; MD, sports programming Dr. Stefan Ziffzer; digital projects, MD DFI Markus Tellenbach; MD, technical operations & facilities Dr. Karl Mauthe;
MD, legal affairs & personnel Dr. Klaus Piette
Comments: a multi-media enterprise active in all areas of the entertainment industry, and a leading private European company in film and television; see Beta Film, Unitel

Koch Classics GmbH
Lochhamerstr. 9, 82152 **Planegg**
Tel: 89-857 950 Fax: 89-8579 5290
Internet: www.kochmusic.com
Geschäftsführer Norbert Gubo (email: norbert.gubo@kochmusic.com); marketing & sales promotion Marike Datschewert (email: marike.datschewert@kochmusic.com); producer Koch Classics Dieter Heuler (email: dieter.heuler@kochmusic.com); product and promotion Ulrike Wilckens (email: ulrike.wilckens@kochmusic.com); manager Fremd labels Klaus Schepke (email: klaus.schepke@kochmusic.com)
Format: CD, CDV, MD, cassette, DCC *Own and distributed labels:* own: Koch – Schwann, Koch Classics, Koch International Classics, Koch Jazz; distributed: Chandos, Hyperion, ASV, Supraphon, Cali, Nightingale Classics *Art type:* classical music, new music, music from Russia, England, Germany

kunstvereint – ein Label schafft Kontakt
Bismarckstraße 260, 45889 **Gelsenkirchen**
Tel: 209-988 2282
Fax: 209-988 2362
E-Mail: forumkunstvereint@t-online.de
artistic director Michael Gees
Format: CD *Comments:* see also Agents & Producers (Forum kunstvereint eV)

LAIKA Records
Stavendamm 16, 28195 **Bremen**
Tel: 421-323 811
Fax: 421-337 8163
Internet: www.Laika-Records.com
E-Mail: laika@t-online.de
Format: CD *Art type:* jazz, world music
Comments: distributed by Rough Trade; USA office: 43 Crow Hill Road, Mount Kisco, New York NY 10549, Tel/Fax: +1 914-242 8619

LOFT music
Wessobrunner Str. 4, 82131 **Gauting**
Tel: 89-850 6632/8934 0894
Fax: 89-8934 0860
managing director Dr Manfred Frei
Format: film and video for television, LP, CD, cassette
Art type: jazz and classical music

Medias Res München
Auenstraße 25, 80469 **München**
Tel: 89-201 5901 Fax: 89-202 1041
managing director Roland Zag
Format: Betacam-SP *Comments:* producer and distributor of programmes/series and films on performing arts subjects for cinema and TV; main area of activity – classical music documentaries and literature

Metropolitan
Widenmayerstrasse 5, 80538 **München**
Tel: 89-224 024
Fax: 89-228 3863
E-Mail: productions@metropolitanclassic.de
president Michael S. Fuehr
Format: production *Own and distributed labels:* Teldec Video *Art type:* films of classical concert and studio music performances for TV and home-video

Orfeo International Music GmbH
Augustenstraße 79, 80333 **München**
Tel: 89-542 1360 Fax: 89-5421 3621
E-Mail: Orfeo-International@t-online.de
managing directors Bruno Hailer, Christiane Delank; responsible for A & R Christiane Delank
Format: CD, LP, cassette *Own and distributed labels:* own: Orfeo, Orfeo D'Or *Arts type:* classical

PARS Media GmbH
Leopoldstr. 43, 80802 **München**
Tel: 89-396 511
Fax: 89-397 302
Internet: www.parsmedia.com
E-Mail: jsg@parsmedia.com
managing director Jan Schmidt-Garre;
director/producer Marieke Schroeder
Format: films on & as art *Comments:* alternative E-mail: ms@parsmedia.com

Real-Film
Brückweg 1, 67067 **Ludwigshafen**
Tel: 621-542 789 Fax: 621-542 742
E-Mail: realfilm@t-online.de
Geschäftsinhaber Joachim Petri
Format: video *Art type:* industry and advertising films, dance and theatre

RM Arts
Steinsdorfstr. 14, 80538 **München**
Tel: 89-211 2140
Fax: 89-2112 1433
E-Mail: rmarts@rmarts.ccn.de
managing director Dr. Reiner Moritz
Format: production mainly for TV broadcast and for home video *Comments:* national distribution RM Arts München, international distribution is handled by RM Associates, 46 Great Marlborough Street, London W1V 1DB, Tel: +44 171-439 2637, Fax: +44 171-439 2316 – Neil Mundy, director of programmes, head of sales and co-production Julie Moore

S.U.M.O. Film, Hubertus Siegert
Platz vor dem neuen Tor 1B, 10115 **Berlin**
Tel: 30-2859 9296 Fax: 30-2859 9297
E-Mail: s.u.m.o.film@dtmb.de
Produzent Hubertus Siegert
Format: 35mm films *Art type:* produce documentary films on architecture and social documentation

Sony Music Entertainment (Germany GmbH)
Sony Classical, Stephanstr. 15, 60313 **Frankfurt am Main**
Tel: 69-1388 8239 (press)/8313 (secretariat)
Fax: 69-1388 8113
Internet: www.sonymusic.de
E-Mail: christiane_ritscher@sonymusic.com
managing director (classical marketing) Michael Brüggemann; manager classical for press, promotion & artists Christiane Ritscher
Format: CD, cassette, laser disc, video, CV, MD *Own and distributed labels:* own: Sony Classical, Sony Masterworks; distributed: Collegno *Comments:* also oversee Sony Classical Austria (E-mail: harry_gruber@sonymusic.com) and Switzerland (E-mail: daniel_r.goodwin@sonymusic.com)

Speakers Corner Records
Kronsberg 13, 24161 **Altenholz**
Tel: 431-322 130 Fax: 431-322 158
Internet: www.speakerscorner.de
E-Mail: info@speakerscorner.de
director Kai Seemann;
sales & marketing Christiane Waldmann
Format: manufacturer and distributor of audiophile vinyl-LP's *Own and distributed labels:* own: DECCA, Deutsche Grammophon, Philips, Mercury, Verve, L'Oiseau Lyre, MPS, A&M, Fontana Polydor; distributor: Verve, Mercury *Art type:* classical, jazz, pop (50's-70's)

Teldec Classics International GmbH
Schubertstraße 5-9, 22083 **Hamburg**
Tel: 40-22932-0
Fax: 40-2293 2230
Internet: www.Teldec.com
E-Mail: aimee_paret@wmg.com
managing director Martin Sauer; marketing director Tim Kotowich; director of business and legal affairs Michael Regorz; financial controller Rudolf Ratjen
Format: production and marketing of CD, DVD, cassette *Own and distributed labels:* own: Teldec
Art type: classical

THOROFON Schallplatten KG
Eichhornweg 11, 30900 **Wedemark**
Tel: 5130-79360
Fax: 5130-79829
E-Mail: thorofon@t-online.de
Geschäftsführender Direktor Helmut König
Format: CD *Art type:* classical, folk

TV 2000 KG
Unter den Eichen 5, 65195 **Wiesbaden**
Tel: 611-951 680 Fax: 611-951 6820
Geschäftsführung Günter Herbertz;
producer Hans Günter Herbertz
Format: videos, documentaries, TV productions *Art type:* dance, theatre, music films

Unitel Film- und Fernseh-Produktiongesellschaft mbH & Co
Robert-Bürkle-Str. 2, 85737 **Ismaning**
Tel: 89-9956-0 Fax: 89-9956 2388
managing directors Herbert Schmidt, Dr. Leo Kirch; president, chairman and sole owner Dr Leo Kirch; chief producer Horant H. Hohlfeld
Format: production for film, TV, HDTV *Art type:* operas, ballet, classical music concerts, TV specials, live broadcasts, artist documentaries *Comments:* music production company of the KirchGruppe (q.v.)

VTTV Videothek Electronic TV-Production
Havelchaussee 161, 14055 **Berlin**
Tel: 30-300 953
Fax: 30-3009 5500
E-Mail: PBvttv@t-online.de
Geschäftsführer Paul Bielicki
Format: video, film production for TV, HDTV

WERGO / Schott Music & Media GmbH
Weihergarten 5, 55116 **Mainz**
Tel: 6131-246 890
Fax: 6131-246 216
Internet: www.schott-music.com/
E-Mail: wergo@schott-musik.de
general manager Angelika Servatius;
president Dr Peter Hanser-Strecker
Format: CD, CD-ROM *Own and distributed labels:* own: Wergo, Weltmusik, Ginkgo, Spectrum, Natural Sound, Alcra, MusicAVision, organ
Art type: contemporary music

Werner Kimmig GmbH
Haupstr. 20, 77704 **Oberkirch**
Tel: 7802-92345 Fax: 7802-6661
E-Mail: werner_kimmig@t-online.de
Inhaber Werner Kimmig
Format: TV and video productions *Art type:* shows, series, events, documentaries

GREECE (+30)

BMG Ariola SA
Messoghion 230, 15561 **Holargos (Athens)**
Tel: 1-652 8401
Fax: 1-653 6880
director P. Theofanelis
Format: CD, cassette, video

F-64 Production Co.
Alkiviadou 30, 10439 **Athens**
Tel: 1-823 3117/883 9509 Fax: 1-883 3185
E-Mail: f64tvpro@otenet.gr
managing director Chronis Pechlivanides
Format: video & short film, documentaries
Comments: producers for the advertising industry; underwater film productions

FM Records
7 Knossou str., 11146 **Athens**
Tel: 1-222 301/3/213 0600/6
Fax: 1-222 1603
E-Mail: fmrecord@acci.gr
president Nicos Courtis; general manager Dina Courtis; label manager/import manager Dionisis Tsonopoulos; international exportation manager Kostas Alayannis; press Areti Boyaiyis; marketing Yiannis Ioannou
Format: CD *Own and distributed labels:* own: Stand Up, Atlas; distributed: Edel, 2YX, CNR, Kickin, Distance, Irma, Studio K7, Media, Stress, Colosseum, E.D.M, Basic Beat, MCI, Platipus, Big Time *Art type:* music from Ancient Greece, from the Byzantine and post-Byzantine era, traditional songs and music of the Greeks and their Diaspora and
other Hellenic-influenced regions

General Publishing Company SA
Zalokosta 4, 10671 **Athens**
Tel: 1-363 3603
Fax: 1-364 5168
Internet: www.lyra.lyra.gr
E-Mail: lyra@otenet.gr
managing director P. Maravelias
Format: CD, cassette *Own and distributed labels:* Lyra (own) *Comments:* Greek popular, classical & contemporary music

Minos-EMI
Messoghion 245-247, 15451 **Neo Psychico**
Tel: 1-671 1811
Fax: 1-674 8968
managing director K. Bourmas
Format: CD, cassette, distribution
Art type: popular music, Greek folk music

Musurgia Graeca
c/o General Publishing Company S.A. – Record Division, 4 Zalokosta str., 10600 **Athens**
Tel: 1-363 4648/361 6343/03 Fax: 1-364 5168
Internet: www.lyra.lyra.gr
E-Mail: lyra@otenet.gr
Format: CD *Art type:* producing & distributing on a worldwide basis, audio-visual products spanning from the 5th century B.C. to the newest trends in contemporary Greek music *Comments:* a co-operation amongst three independent music companies in Greece (Orata, General Publishing Company (Lyra) and Kinesis)

Orama Films
104 Themistokleous Street, 10681 **Athens**
Tel: 1-380 2056/9 Fax: 1-382 6185
general manager Lucia Rikaki
Art type: arts and entertainment TV and film production (especially drama and documentaries) *Comments:* production of the only stand-up comedy show in town, daily performances

Sony Music Entertainment (Greece) SA
Messoghion Ave. 311, 15231 **Halandri (Athens)**
Tel: 1-674 6491 Fax: 1-672 2150
managing director D. Giarmenitis
Format: CD, cassette, mini-discs

Universal Music SA
Messoghion Ave. 296, 15561 **Holargos (Athens)**
Tel: 1-652 4213 Fax: 1-652 5797/3586
managing director Tony Ioannou
Format: CD, cassette, LP

Virgin Records Ltd
Messoghion Ave. 557, 15344 **Agia Paraskevi (Athens)**
Tel: 1-608 1324 Fax: 1-601 6401
E-Mail: virgingr@otenet.gr
managing director Yiannis Petrides; marketing manager Kostas Zougvis; press & promotion Chris Kariotis; international manager Tassos Marougos
Format: CD, LP, cassette, Mini Disc *Own and distributed labels:* Virgin Greece labels: CIAD, Beggars Banquet, Mute, XL, Silva Screen, Tommy Boy, Higher Octave, Rhino

Warner Music
Messoghion Ave. 319, 15231 **Halandri (Athens)**
Tel: 1-674 5881 Fax: 1-672 5401
managing director I. Stamboulis; finance director Panos Samartzopoulos; sales manager Stefanos Kotatis
Format: CD, laser disc, cassette

HUNGARY (+36)

BMG Ariola Hungary
Level utca 4, 1023 **Budapest**
Tel: 1-316 0316 Fax: 1-316 0336
managing director Margit Geszti; marketing manager Janos Kallus; A&R manager Zoltan Földes
Format: CD, cassette, VHS *Art type:* classical, pop, jazz

EMI-Quint Records Ltd
EMI-Quint Hanglemezkiadó Kft
Koztelek 6, 1092 **Budapest**
Tel: 1-216 9630 Fax: 1-216 9633
managing director Edina Lekacs;
finance director Zoltan Banga;
marketing director Katalin Benedek;
art director Gabor Kisszabó
Format: CD, cassette, VHS *Art type:* classical, opera, operetta, gypsy & folk, pop, jazz

FONÓ Records
ADYTON
Sztregova u. 3, 1116 **Budapest**
Tel: 1-206 5300 Fax: 1-206 1480/5300
managing directors Tibor Balogh, József Lukács
Format: CD, cassette *Art type:* Hungarian Etno jazz, Hungarian folk music

Hungaroton Records Ltd
Nagy Jeno 12, 1126 **Budapest**
Tel: 1-202 3188 Fax: 1-202 3794
managing director Balint Laczko
Format: CD, MC *Art type:* classical, jazz, folklore

Sony Music Entertainment (Hungary)
Tusnadi u 5/a, 1125 **Budapest**
Tel: 1-355 5591/5688 Fax: 1-355 0213
managing director Laszlo Szüts
Format: CD, MC, VHS *Art type:* classical, pop, rock, opera, operetta, gypsy, folk, jazz

Universal Music
Steindl Imre u.12., 1054 **Budapest**
Tel: 1-269 1142 Fax: 1-269 1140
managing director Laszlo Hegedüs; classical label manager Peter Nadori; sales Tibor Rigo; products manager Istvan Olah; A & R Laszlo Gajda
Own and distributed labels: Universal, Geffen, MCA, Decca, Philips, Deutsche Grammophon, Polydor, Island, Motown

Warner Music Hungary Ltd
Hüvösvölgyi ut 54.III., 1021 **Budapest**
Tel: 1-394 0014/46 Fax: 1-394 0043
managing director Laszlo Pasztor;
marketing director Ferenc Kaszas
Format: CD, cassette *Art type:* classical, pop, jazz

ICELAND (+354)

Iceland Music Information Centre
Sídumúli 34, 108 **Reykjavík**
Tel: 568 3122 Fax: 568 3124
E-Mail: icemic@vortex.is
director Bergthora Jonsdottir
Format: CDs *Own and distributed labels:* label ITM
Art type: Icelandic contemporary, classical, folk and jazz music *Comments:* see also National Organisations

Japis Ltd
PO Box 396, Brautarholt 2, 105 **Reykjavík**
Tel: 580 0800 Fax: 580 0888
E-Mail: japis@japis.is
managing director Ásmundur Jónsson
Own and distributed labels: distribute: UK: Ace, Chandos, Charly, Nimbus, Hyperion, Pearl, XL records, Warp, BMG Ariola *Comments:* Icelandic distributor for Sony and Panasonic

Skifan
PO Box 8120, 128 **Reykjavík**
Tel: 525 5000 Fax: 525 5001
Internet: www.skifan.com
E-Mail: info@skifan.com
chairman Jón Olafsson; financial director Magnus Orriharaldsson; marketing manager Adalsteinn Magnusson; managing director Ragnar Birgisson; head of music division Steinar Berg Isleifsson
Format: publishing, import and distribution of CD, cassette, music video, computer software, feature films & home video distribution *Own and distributed labels:* own: Skifan, Geimsteinn, Spor, Dennis, Sproti; distributed: EMI, Universal, Warner, Sony *Art type:* record company for Icelandic artists, all musical styles, also distributor for major foreign labels

IRELAND Republic of (+353)

Gael Linn Records
26 Merrion Square, **Dublin 2**
Tel: 1-676 7283 Fax: 1-676 9731/7030 (press office)
E-Mail: gaellinn@eircom.net
distribution manager Seamus O'Neil;
press director Martin O'Siadhail
Format: CD, cassette, vinyl *Art type:* Irish language traditional music, world music

Orpheus Productions
33 St.Thomas Road, **Mount Merrion (Co Dublin)**
Tel: 1-288 0461 Fax: 1-283 4548
managing director Ted Dolan
Format: video, film *Art type:* music documentary films, particularly writer profiles

ITALY (+39)

Bèrben
Via Redipuglia 65, 60122 **Ancona**
Tel: 071-204 428
Fax: 071-57414
Internet: www.berben.it
E-Mail: info@berben.it
president Bio Boccosi; administrator Fabio Boccosi
Format: books, CD, tapes, videotapes

BMG Ricordi s.p.a.
Via Sant' Alessandro 7, 00131 **Roma**
Tel: 06-419 951 Fax: 06-4199 5474
Internet: www.bmgricordi.it
E-Mail: alessandra.papa@bertelsmann.de
president Franco Reali; administrative director Paolo Vannini; sales director Giuseppe Dominici; general manager & matrix exploitation Birgit Adels; corporate communications Alessandra Papa; general director Adrian Berwick; manager for the Italian productions Sabrina Gallone
Format: production and distribution of LP/cassettes/CD, home video, books and scores
Art type: classical, pop, jazz

Ducale s.n.c.
Via Per Cadrezzate 6, 21020 **Brebbia (VA)**
Tel: 0332-771 771/770 189 Fax: 0332-771 047
E-Mail: ducale@skylink.it
administrators Tarcisia Barboni, Marco Matalon, Flavia Matalon
Format: CD, tapes *Own and distributed labels:* exclusively for Italy: Naxos, Dejavu, Synfonia, Stradivarius, Marco Polo, Supraphone, Panton; worldwide distribution: Ducale, Rivo Alto, Phoenix, Rainbow, Esperia
Art type: classical and jazz *Comments:* distribution and production

Dynamic – Edizioni Discografiche e Musicali s.r.l.
Via Mura delle Chiappe 39, 16136 **Genova**
Tel: 010-272 2884 Fax: 010-213 937
Internet: www.dynamic.it
E-Mail: info@dynamic.it
administrator & general director
Pietro Mosetti Casaretto
Format: CD *Art type:* classical music

Edizioni Musicali Edipan
Viale Mazzini N. 6, 00195 **Roma**
Tel: 06-322 3474 Fax: 06-322 3471
Internet: www.edipan.com
E-Mail: edipan@edipan.com
Format: CD *Own and distributed labels:* Edipan
Art type: classical and contemporary music

Florence International srl
Via Cavour 60, 50129 **Firenze**
Tel: 055-216 645
Fax: 055-284 058
Internet: www.florenceint.it
E-Mail: info@florenceint.it
sole administrator Roberto Bartoli;
sales manager Adriano Sebastiani
Format: CD *Own and distributed labels:* international labels of classical music, folklore, new age, traditional, lyric

Foné
Via Carlo Goldoni 50/54, 57125 **Livorno**
Tel: 0586-884 069 Fax: 0586-889 687
Internet: www.fone.it
E-Mail: fone@mclink.it
general manager Giulio Cesare Ricci
Format: CD Silver, CD Gold (24kt), LP 180 gr. Virgin Vinyl *Own and distributed labels:* Foné *Art type:* opera, baroque music, classical and romantic music, early and sacred music, jazz

Francesco Bongiovanni s.a.s.
via Rizzoli 28, 40125 **Bologna**
Tel: 051-225 722 Fax: 051-226 128
Internet: www.bongiovanni70.com
E-Mail: giancarlo@bongiovanni70.com
presidente Giancarlo Bongiovanni;
direttore marketing Andrea Bongiovanni
Format: CD, videos (VHS) *Own and distributed labels:* Bongiovanni, Mito Dell' Opera *Art type:* classical music and opera *Comments:* established in 1905

Iktiús s.a.s.
Via Varazze 10, 20149 **Milano**
Tel: 02-4871 2330 Fax: 02-4871 6786
Internet: www.iktius.com
E-Mail: iktius@planet.it
managing director Carlo Tedeschi
Format: CD classic and jazz productions-editions, recording and mastering digital, duplicating CD, tape, video *Own and distributed labels:* Iktiús
Comments: distributed by ERGA & I.R.D. Jazz and independent distribution

Il Melograno
Via Stamira 31, 00162 **Roma**
Tel: 06-4429 1202 Fax: 06-4429 1202
artistic director Ezio Monti
Format: CD, tapes, scores, books, learning materials
Own and distributed labels: Thesaurus Armonicus *Art type:* classical, early, contemporary

La Bottega Discantica
Via Nirone 5, 20123 **Milano**
Tel: 02-862 966 Fax: 02-7200 0642
Internet: www.biblia.it/discantica
E-Mail: discantica@biblia.it
chief editor Luigi Grazioli
Format: CD, scores *Own and distributed labels:* La Bottega Discantica plus other labels *Art type:* classical music and folklore

Materiali Sonori
Via 3 Novembre, 2, 52027 **San Giovanni Valdarno (AR)**
Tel: 055-912 0363/943 888/912 2700
Fax: 055-912 0370
Internet: www.matson.it
E-Mail: matinfo@matson.it
artistic production Arlo Bigazzi, Giampiero Bigazzi; commercial director Lucia Baldini; management & production Francesca Pieraccini; distribution Riccardo Bernini, Stefano Cesari, Paola Rizzo
Format: CD *Own and distributed labels:* Materiali Sonori
Art type: contemporary music

Milano Dischi srl
Via Fantoli 7, 20138 **Milano**
Tel: 02-5540 0332/382
Fax: 02-5540 0385
Internet: www.stradivarius.it
E-Mail: stradiva@tin.it
titolare Roberto Elli; marketing dott. Alessandra Presutti
Format: CD *Own and distributed labels:* Stradivarius, Datum (IT) Olimpia, Unicorn, Priory (UK), SMP (G); Tara, REM (F), Music and Arts (USA), FSM (D), Myto, Urania, Dutton (GB) *Art type:* classical

musicaimmagine records
Via del Corso 494 (Basilica di San Giacomo), 00186 **Roma**
Tel: 06-3600 4667 Fax: 06-3600 4667
E-Mail: musicaimmagine@iol.it
presidente e direttore artistico Flavio Colusso; direttore di produzione Silvia De Palma; consulente artistico Guido Galterio; consulente organizzativo Renato Glulianl; consulente aziendale Guido Allegrezza; coordinatore editoriale Paolo Maria Vitiello; ufficio stampa Lorenza Somogyi-Blanchi; relazioni esterne Thomas Radigk
Format: CD *Own and distributed labels:* own: musicaimmagine *Art type:* early, classical and contemporary music, jazz, ethnic

Musikstrasse
Via Romeo Romei 15, 00136 **Roma**
Tel: 06-3972 8185/4 Fax: 06-3972 8215
Internet: www.talenti.it/bixio
E-Mail: bixioita@tin.it
president & administrator Franco Bixio; general manager Isabella Longo
Format: CD *Own and distributed labels:* Musikstrasse *Art type:* classical music *Comments:* specialize in rarities

Nuova Era Records s.r.l.
C.rso Marconi 37, 10125 **Torino**
Tel: 011-669 8903 Fax: 011-650 5613
E-Mail: nuoera@tin.it
managing director Fulvio Sola; consulente artistico Giannandrea Lodovici; commercial director Gerry Basso; coordinamento produzione Alberto Palmulli
Format: CD *Own and distributed labels:* Nuova Era, Phonographe *Art type:* classical

Panarecord Dischi Palladium
Alzaia Naviglio Grande 72, 20144 **Milano**
Tel: 02-8940 7819 Fax: 02-8941 0411
E-Mail: panareco@tin.it
president & solo administrator Carlo Nasi; general manager Salvatore Occhipinti
Art type: syncronization, music for advertising, editing
Comments: production house for TV, cinema and advertising

Pongo Classica
Via Leonardo da Vinci 11, 22070 **Locate Varesino (CO)**
Tel: 0331-833 019 Fax: 0331-833 645
Internet: www.pongo.it
E-Mail: pongo@dido.net
artistic director & sole administrator Fabio Bertin
Format: CD, tapes, records (vinyl)
Own and distributed labels: Pongo Classica *Art type:* classical

Santabarbara Edizioni, sas
P.za Rosselli 10, 81041 **Bellona (CE)**
Tel: 0823-965 008
Fax: 0823-965 008
Internet: www.santabarbara.it
E-Mail: info@santabarbara.it
artistic & administrative director Luigi Vinciguerra
Format: CD, books and scores
Own and distributed labels: Santabarbara

Semar Publishers srl
Via di Torre Argentina 47, 00186 **Roma**
Tel: 06-687 6523/9333
Fax: 06-6830 8601
Internet: www.semarweb.com
E-Mail: semarpublishers@altavista.net
artistic director & president Sahlan Momo
Format: CD, video, tapes, DAT *Own and distributed labels:* Semar, RZ (D) *Art type:* classical, ethnic
Comments: also organises concerts, contemporary classic; see also Promoters

Sinfonica Jazz
Via Volturno 80 / Cigni, 20047 **Brugherio (MI)**
Tel: 039-287 1615/884 360
Fax: 039-287 1615
artistic director & administrator Pino Amendola
Format: CD, tapes *Own and distributed labels:* Sinfonica Jazz-SJ-America *Art type:* classical & light music

Warner Fonit
Via Milano 10, 20090 **Redecesio di Segrate (MI)**
Tel: 02-216 8700
Fax: 02-216 8710
E-Mail: paolo.noseda@warnermusic.com
marketing manager (classical sector) Paolo Noseda; general director Romano Razzini; promotions Luca Stante; marketing manager (special project sector) Umberto Candiolo
Format: CD, tapes, videotapes, laser disc, DVD *Own and distributed labels:* distribute Teldec (Germany), Erato (France), Nonesuch (USA, contemporary classical, musicals, alternative jazz and ethnic music), Finlandia, Warner Music Vision (classical, ballet, opera), NVC arts, Fonit, Warner Fonit *Art type:* classical music, opera, jazz and world music

LATVIA (+371)

Balss IU, Publishing office of Music
Balss IU, muzikas izdevniecíba
K. Barona 88/2, 1015 **Riga**
Tel: 2-270 329
Fax: 2-272 482
managing director Rainis Upmalis

Microphone Records
Mikrofona ieraksti
Muitas iela 1, 1010 **Riga**
Tel: 7-027 407
Fax: 7-027 215
E-Mail: micrec@micrec.lv
manager Elita Milgrave
Comments: producing all kinds of music records

Platforma Records
Platforma rekords
Elijas 17, 1050 **Riga**
Tel: 7-204 225 Fax: 7-204 391
E-Mail: platformarec@parks.lv
managing director Rimants Liepins
Format: CD, MD, cassettes
Art type: classical music, pop, rock, jazz

Riga Recording Studio Ltd
Rigas skanu ierakstu studija
1 Alksnaja, 1050 **Riga**
Tel: 7-225 725 Fax: 7-226 407
managing director Aldis Ermanbriks
Format: CD, LP, cassettes
Art type: classical music, pop, rock, folk

LITHUANIA (+370)

Bomba Record
UAB Bombos irasai
Zygimantu 6, 2600 **Vilnius**
Tel: 2-312 836/223 558 (distribution) Fax: 2-225 715
E-Mail: headq@bomba.lt
director Vytautas Juozapavicius; director distribution Rimantas Alisauskas
Format: records *Art type:* rock, pop, alternative, modern, Lithuanian music

Koja Records Group
UAB Koja
Tilto 27-9, 2001 **Vilnius**
Tel: 2-313 734 Fax: 2-313 735
E-Mail: headq@koja.lt
contact Saulius Sventickas

Lithuanian Film Studio
Lietuvos Kino Studija
Nemencines pl. 4, 2016 **Vilnius**
Tel: 2-763 444 Fax: 2-764 254
director Robertas Urbonas

Music Company Zona
Muzikos Firma Zona
Seskinės 79, 2010 **Vilnius**
Tel: 2-428 019 Fax: 2-229 991

Recording Studio Arka
Muzikos salonas Arka
Ausros vartu 7, 2024 **Vilnius**
Tel: 2-221 185 Fax: 2-262 423

Recording Studio Bonifa
Irasu studija Bonifa
Asmenos 4, 2001 **Vilnius**
Tel: 2-624 815 Fax: 2-221 358
E-Mail: bonifa@is.lt

Recording Studio Tembras
Garso irasu studija UAB Tembras
A. Mickeviciaus 29, 2004 **Vilnius**
Tel: 2-220 902
Fax: 2-220 902
E-Mail: tembras@taide.lt
director Valdemaras Kirsys

Vilnius Recording Studio
Vilnius Ploksteliu Studija
Barboros Radvilaites 8, 2600 **Vilnius**
Tel: 2-610 419
Fax: 2-610 491
director Rimantas Pupeikis

MACEDONIA (+389)

Production Department of Macedonian Radio
Goce Delcev bb, 91000 **Skopje**
Tel: 91-112 200/235 305
Fax: 91-112 156

MONACO (+377)

Telemondial S.A.M.
7 Avenue de Grande-Bretagne, 98000 **Monaco**
Tel: 9325 7366 Fax: 9325 1334
general manager Uli Maerkle; president Werner Kupper
Format: video tapes, disc laser, cassettes, video; producer *Art type:* the legacy of Herbert von Karajan for home video

NETHERLANDS (+31)

ALLEGRI Film
Keizersgracht 169, 1016 DP **Amsterdam**
Tel: 20-625 4451 Fax: 20-639 0130
E-Mail: delta123@xs4all.nl
general manager Rudolf Evenhuis; producer Frank Scheffer
Format: feature films & documentaries about art & music, also 16 mm films about contemporary composers; mainly for TV & cinemas

BVHAAST Records
99 Prinseneiland, 1013 LN **Amsterdam**
Tel: 20-623 9799 Fax: 20-624 3534
Internet: www.xs4all.nl/~wbk/
E-Mail: wbk@xs4all.nl
manager Susanna von Canon; artistic director Willem Breuker
Format: CD, LP *Own and distributed labels:* own: BVHAAST; distribute: ICP, RAMBOY, Geestgronden, Attacca Babel *Art type:* producing; contemporary classical and jazz music

C-Sales
Postbus 15981, 1001 NL **Amsterdam**
Tel: 20-620 2586 Fax: 20-638 8319
E-Mail: csales@worldonline.nl
managing director Marc Noyons
Format: art and culture videos, feature films *Own and distributed labels:* owns video label 'Editions à Voir', publish & distribute programmes on art and culture in cooperation with European producers and distributors; also owns C-Sales Arthouse Films (feature films)
Comments: releases on VHS and DVD

Daniel Television Productions BV
Croddendyk 8, 7434 PN **Lettele**
Tel: 570-544 544 Fax: 570-544 570
E-Mail: danieltv@wxs.nl
president Bous de Jong
Format: TV *Comments:* independent producer of arts programmes and coproducer with several international TV organisations in the fields of classical and pop music, drama and documentary

Erasmus Muziek Producties
PO Box 25220, 3001 HE **Rotterdam**
Tel: 181-404 272 Fax: 181-404 271
contact W. van Hooff
Format: CD *Art type:* classical repertoire

ID & Dtv
Eekhoat 2, 1112 XH **Diemen**
Tel: 20-314 3314 Fax: 20-690 8528
Internet: www.iddtv.nl
E-Mail: info@iddtv.nl
commerical director R H T Koornstra; programming director Frank de Jonge; business director F M Barfod
Format: film and video *Art type:* all aspects of TV & film production, documentary, children, drama, music, entertainment, events etc. *Comments:* an independent production company

Joan Records
PO Box 577, 8901 BJ **Leeuwarden**
Tel: 58-294 8948 Fax: 58-212 1375
E-Mail: pieter@joan-records.com
managing director Tjarda Faber
Format: production of CD, TV programmes (classical concerts in beautiful surroundings), CD-Rom, Video
Own and distributed labels: Columns Classics *Art type:* classical music *Comments:* visiting address: Tuinen 40, 8911 KE Leeuwarden; in preparation: series of DVD (digital video discs)

NM Classics
c/o Centre Netherlands Music, Havenstraat 31, PO Box 1634, 1200 BP **Hilversum**
Tel: 35-624 0957
Fax: 35-621 0570
Internet: www.cnm.nl
E-Mail: info@cnm.nl
contact G Börger
Format: CD *Art type:* ranging from the authentic performance practice of early music all the way through to the new demands set by the performance of today's music
Comments: exclusively dedicated to repertoire from the Netherlands

Philips Music Group
Amsterdam
Comments: merged with Decca Record Company Limited (see entry United Kingdom) and closed down office in Amersterdam

Vanguard Classics
PO Box 227, 1200 AE **Hilversum**
Tel: 35-689 8800 Fax: 35-689 8897
E-Mail: vanguardclassics@silverminds.nl
managing director and director A&R International Marcel Schopman; assistant A&R international and product manager (Vanguard Classics) Marijke van der Harst; product manager (Naxos) Arjan van Dijk; product manager (Hyperion, BIS, Telarc) Willemijn Mooij
Format: classical CDs and cassettes *Own and distributed labels:* own: Vanguard Classics, WLS, Everyman; distributed: Naxos, BIS, Telarc, Hyperion *Comments:* producer and distributor national and international; division of Silver Minds Music b.v.; visiting address: Noorderweg 68, 1221 AB Hilversum

NORWAY (+47)

Grappa Musikkforlag AS
Akersgt. 7, 0158 **Oslo**
Tel: 2241 2400
Fax: 2241 5552
Internet: www.grappa.no
E-Mail: info@grappa.no
managing director Helge Westbye; producers Arne Akselberg, Tore Simonsen
Comments: established in 1983; one of the oldest independent record companies in Norway

Kirkelig Kulturverksted AS
PO Box 3204 Elisenberg, 0208 **Oslo**
Tel: 2243 0060
Fax: 2243 6140
Internet: www.kkv.no
E-Mail: kkv@kkv.no
export manager Inger Dirdal
Art type: mostly folk music, church music, rock and jazz and especially around the border line between these different kinds of music, classical, world music
Comments: placing traditional music into a contemporary context is one of the most dominant ideas behind the company

Warner Music Norway A/S
Maridals vn. 87B, PO Box 4494, Torshov, 0403 **Oslo**
Tel: 2237 4520 Fax: 2237 0761
E-Mail: fred.engh@warnermusic.com
managing director Mats Nilsson;
marketing manager Fred Engh;
promotions Christer Jacobsen;
record promotion manager Ingvar Aarholt
Format: CD, cassette, vinyl, video *Own and distributed labels:* Warner, Electra, Atlantic, etc.
Art type: rock, pop, classical

POLAND (+48)

CD Accord Music Edition
ul. Jasna 5, 00-950 **Warszawa**
Tel: 22-827 7561 Fax: 22-827 7561
director Andrzej Sasin
Format: CD, records and tapes *Art type:* classical music

DUX Recording Producers
Morskie oko 2, 02-511 **Warszawa**
Tel: 22-849 1131 Fax: 22-849 1131
directors Mazgorzata Polanska, Lech Tozwinski
Format: CD, records, tapes *Art type:* classical music, early music

KOS RECORDS
Hoøa 50, 00-689 **Warszawa**
Tel: 22-625 5810 Fax: 22-625 5810
Format: CD *Art type:* classical, early music

MUSICON Recording Producers
Szodowiec 8/2, 01-708 **Warszawa**
director Krzysztof Kuraszkiewicz
Format: CD, records *Art type:* early music

POLSKIE NAGRANIA
Okaryny 1, 02-787 **Warszawa**
Tel: 22-644 1194
Fax: 22-644 9487
Format: CD, cassettes *Art type:* all types classical

Polstar Records
ul. Jagiellonska 78, 03-301 **Warszawa**
Tel: 22-811 0001/9188
Fax: 22-811 6561
E-Mail: cdn@it.com.pl
president Gary Firth; label manager Graham Hatch; assistant label manager Daryl Fidelak; administration specialist Janusz Biernacki; head of promotion Monika Szadkovska

Polton Warner Music Poland
Odolanska 60, 02-562 **Warszawa**
Tel: 22-845 0968/0352/3892
Fax: 22-845 5474
managing director Helmar Escher
Art type: ethnic, blues, rock, pop *Comments:* part of Warner Music International

PORTUGAL (+351)

Produçoés Multimedias Numérica Lda.
Rua do Barroso 673, 4535 **Paços de Brandão**
Tel: 22-745 9061/9063 Fax: 22-745 9062
E-Mail: aurastudio@mail.teleweb.pt
director A&R Fernando Rocha; secretary of the board of directors Isabel Reis Soares
Format: CD, CD Rom *Own and distributed labels:* own: Numérica *Art type:* all types of music (only Portuguese groups) *Comments:* also have recording studio Aura Studio (address & telephone numbers as above)

RUSSIA (+7)

Alphabeta Records Ltd
PO Box 44, 115446 **Moscow**
Tel: 095-112 4188 Fax: 095-251 6546
managing director Sergei Kropachyov
Format: CDs, LPs *Own and distributed labels:* import and distribution of foreign labels (labels distributed; Collins Classics UK, Tring International UK, Pickwick UK, Connoisseur UK) *Art type:* wholesale export of various Russian recorded music products including classical, sacred, folk and ethnic

Aprelevka Records (Aprelevla Sound Inc)
Avgustovskaya ul. 1, 143360 **Aprelevka**
Tel: 095-436 5194 Fax: 095-436 5203/5194
general manager Igor Tarasov

Melodiya – Tvorchesko-proizvodstvennoje objedineniye
Melodia – Creative-Production Organisation
Tverskoi Boulevard 24, 103009 **Moscow**
Tel: 095-229 9248/6751 Fax: 095-200 2249
general director Valerie Sukhorado
Format: CD, cassette, records

Russian Compact Disc
Leningradsky Prospect 80,
PO Box 83, 125178 **Moscow**
Tel: 095-158 1921 Fax: 095-943 9231
Internet: rcdcorbina.ru
E-Mail: rcd@corbina.ru
director Igor Kabanov, Sergei Libiriov
Format: CD *Own and distributed labels:* Classical Assembly, Czech Historical Recordings, Facsimile, Memory of the Heart, Russian Sacred Music, Talents of Russia *Art type:* classical music

Russian disc
Russki Disk
Voznesensky per. 12, 103009 **Moscow**
Tel: 095-292 1589/2545 Fax: 095-254 6280

SLOVAKIA (+421)

Many telephone and fax numbers in Slovakia are in the process of being changed. We have included all new numbers known at the time of going to print.

Music Video Express
Mlynské nivy 73, 827 99 **Bratislava**
Tel: 7-5824 7478/428
Fax: 7-5824 7329
director Alexander Grman
Own and distributed labels: exclusive distributor of classical label OPUS

Musica Ltd – Records and Publishing
Zelena Str. 8, 816 42 **Bratislava**
Tel: 7-5441 1986
Fax: 7-5441 2939
managing director Jela Kersenbaum

OPUS records and publishing house
Mlynské nivy 73, 827 99 **Bratislava**
Tel: 7-5341 2447/5824 7560
Fax: 7-5824 7560/7550
E-Mail: opus@ba.profinet.sk
Own and distributed labels: OPUS *Art type:* classical, folk
Comments: exculsively distributed by:
Music Video Express (q.v.)

SOLID-STUDIO Ltd
Mlynské nivy 73, 827 99 **Bratislava**
Tel: 7-5824 7527
Fax: 7-5824 7567
director Peter Miklás

SLOVENIA (+386)

Forum Ljubljana
Kersnikova 4, 1000 **Ljubljana**
Tel: 61-319 662/132 7306/3186/131 4254
Art type: producing independent theatre, film, music

Prodko Theatre TV & Catsrecords
Petkovskovo Nabrezje 67, 1000 **Ljubljana**
Tel: 61-139 4580
Fax: 61-139 4585
director & producer Tone Stojko
Format: beta & digital filming, digital editing, photo CDs, music CDs & cassettes *Art type:* theatre, music for children, jazz, pop

Radio Television Slovenia – Records and Tapes
RTV Slovenija -Zalozba kaset in plosc
Dalmatinova 10, 1000 **Ljubljana**
Tel: 61-131 1333 Fax: 61-302 858
director Ivek Krpac; assistant director Ivo Umek
Format: CD, mc, records, video cassettes *Comments:* production, manufacturing and publishing; selling and retail trading of cds, mcs, records and video cassettes; music publishing

Sanje
Cesta 24, junija 23, 1231 **Ljubljana**
Tel: 61-161 2303
Fax: 61-161 2303
directors Rok Zavrtanik, Zalka Drglin
Format: CD, cassettes, audiobooks, video *Art type:* chanson, poetry, radio plays

SPAIN (+34)

Alia Vox – Sonjade – s.l.
Sonjade s.l., Trav. de Gracìa 18, 08021 **Barcelona**
Tel: 93-594 4761
Fax: 93-580 5606
E-Mail: aliavox@compuserve.com
director artísco (Alia Vox) Jordi Savall; administration (Sonjade) Agnés Prunes, Irene Bloc
Format: CDs, DVD *Own and distributed labels:* Alia Vox *Art type:* early music *Comments:* export manager (Alia Vox) Olivier Vannieu: Tel: +32 2-648 7950, Fax: +32 2-648 0449, E-mail: aliavox@skynet.be

Antar Producciones
c/ Costa Rica 13, 1ffl A3, 28016 **Madrid**
Tel: 91-350 2518 Fax: 91-350 2518
Internet: www.escaparates.com/mmusica
E-Mail: antar@sp-editores.es
director Fernando Hernández;
commercial director Mìguel Angel Nuñez
Format: CDs *Own and distributed labels:* Antar *Art type:* jazz, world music, classical

Auvidis Ibérica s.a.
Bertrán 72, 08023 **Barcleona**
Tel: 93-418 8080
Fax: 93-211 0815
Internet: www.auvidis.com
E-Mail: auvidis@mx3.redestb.es
director Claudi Martí; commerical director Jordi Padrol
Format: CDs *Own and distributed labels:* Auvidis, Melodie, Fontalis and others
Art type: ethnic, classical, flamenco

Cambaya Records
Poligono la Azucarera 37 'La Calera',
29200 **Antequera (Malaga)**
Tel: 95-270 2233/284 5720 Fax: 95-270 2233
E-Mail: arecord@arrakis.es
director Antonio Blanco; gerente Antonio Navarro
Format: CD, cassettes
Own and distributed labels: Cambaya

Canal Dansa S.L
Apartat de Correus 2584, 08080 **Barcelona**
Tel: 93-319 8105/416 0957 Fax: 93-319 8105/416 0957
E-Mail: cdansa@arrakis.es
directors Nuria Font, Elisa Huertas
Format: dance videos *Art type:* produce and promote dance video *Comments:* private company supported by the Catalan Department of Culture; organise biennial dance video festival – see also Festivals

Com 4 HD
Gran via, 88 (Edificio España), 28013 **Madrid**
Tel: 91-542 6190 Fax: 91-547 0638
Internet: www.com4hd.com
E-Mail: com4hd@com4hd.com
managing director Manuela Gutiérrez;
president Luis Sanz
Format: high definition programmes of all types; advance television, multimedia, producers, distributor
Art type: performance video and documentaries
Comments: Montreaux prize winner for dance & music video

FERYSA SA de Promociones y Distribuciones Musicales
c/ Isabel Colbrand 10, 28050 **Madrid**
Tel: 91-358 8937/8814
Fax: 91-358 8914
Internet: www.ferysa.es
E-Mail: correo@ferysa.es
director gerente Fernando Rodríguez Polo
Format: CD *Own and distributed labels:* Naxos, Laser Light, Marco Polo, Capriccio *Art type:* distribution of recorded classical music of independent companies

Gaudisc
c/ Historiador Maians 7, 08026 **Barcelona**
Tel: 93-435 5441
Fax: 93-433 0506
E-Mail: gaudisc@ctv.es
co-directors Francesc Canela, Isabel Bech
Format: CDs, video *Own and distributed labels:* distribute: Vanguard, Hungaroton, Orlane and Spanish labels *Art type:* classical, jazz

Harmonia Mundi Iberica s.l.
Av. Pla del Vent 24, Sant Joan Despi, 08970 **Barcelona**
Tel: 93-373 1058 Fax: 93-373 6764
Internet: www.harmoniamundi.com
E-Mail: info.iberica@harmoniamundi.com
director general François Pelaut
Own and distributed labels: Amiata, Arion, Chandos, Dorian, Hyperion, L'Empreinte Digitale, Unicorn, Russian Season, Winter & Winter, etc. *Art type:* classical, early music, world music, jazz, folk

Hispavox
Ciudad de la Imagen, Carretera de Boadilla del Monte Km 2-200, c/ Jose Isbert nffl 6,
28223 **Pozuelo de Alarcón (Madrid)**
Tel: 91-512 9000 Fax: 91-518 6181
Internet: www.emimusic-spain.com
E-Mail: vaxemi@mad.servicom.es
director commercial Aitor Martiarena; director marketing Domingo Garcia; president Miguel Ángel Gomez; promotion Roberto Carballo; artistic director Manuel Illán; director general Jose Luis Rodriguez
Format: CD, cassette, compact disc video, mini disc, singles *Own and distributed labels:* Virgin, EMI, Hispavox, Chrisalys *Art type:* classic, pop, national and international music

NO – CD Rekords
Barrio Castaño 19, Bajo, 20100 **Rentería (Guipuzkoa)**
Tel: 43-529 171 Fax: 43-516 292
E-Mail: nocd@euskalnet.net
directors Cruz Gorostegi, Mikel Camino; press Idoia Luzuriaga
Format: CD *Own and distributed labels:* Cuniform, New Albion *Comments:* recording company of Syntorama; see also Festivals and Agents & Producers

Radio Television Española Música
Casa de la Radio – Prado del Rey, 28223 **Madrid**
Tel: 91-346 1762 Fax: 91-346 1232
Internet: www.rtvemusica.rne.es
E-Mail: rtve_musica.rne@rtve.es
responsable sello discográfico José Luis Ramos
Format: all formats *Own and distributed labels:* own: RTVE Música *Art type:* classical music, Spanish music, jazz, flamenco, opera, folk *Comments:* see also Orchestras, Choirs, Radio and TV

Tritó Edicions
Arcs 8, 1ffl-2ffl, 08002 **Barcelona**
Tel: 93-302 2564
Fax: 93-3022 6700
E-Mail: trito@bcn.servicom.es
director Josep Dolcet
Format: Cds *Own and distributed labels:* Tritós
Art type: Spanish classical music

UM – Unió Musics
Son Bieli, 07311 **Búger (Mallorca)**
Tel: 71-516 501
Fax: 71-516 502
E-Mail: fundacioaca@new-ton.com
president Antonio Caimari Alomar; coordinatora general fundació aca Beatriz Florit Rigo
Format: CD, LP, tape *Own and distributed labels:* UM (Unió Music) distributed in Europe, Japan, USA *Art type:* poetry, contemporary (electro-acustic, classic), image *Comments:* forms part of Fundació ACA – Area Creación Acústica; recording of annual edition of Encontre de Compositors; organise 1ffl Muestia de Cine Alternativo del Mediterraneo (17-24 July); see also Festivals and Promoters

SWEDEN (+46)

AB Frank Hedman
Ankdammsgatan 13, 171 43 **Solna**
Tel: 8-838 445 Fax: 8-839 983
president Hanna Hedman
Format: CDs *Own and distributed labels:* Bluebell Record
Art type: classical music

Caprice Records
Nybrokajen 11, 111 48 **Stockholm**
Tel: 8-407 1600 Fax: 8-407 1648
Internet: www.srk.se
E-Mail: lars.silen@srk.se
general manager, artists & repertoire Kjell Soederqvist; producer Lars Silén; publicity & marketing Anita Tapper; financial department Roland Olsson
Format: CD *Own and distributed labels:* own: Caprice Records *Art type:* classical, jazz, folk, children's & world music

Dreamtime Media
Högbergsgatan 85, 118 54 **Stockholm**
Tel: 8-5701 0124 Fax: 8-640 6023
E-Mail: post@dreamtime.se
managing director Andrew Bowden; press Katja Norbäck
Format: film and video projects, books and magazines, cultural events *Own and distributed labels:* Adeptus film (dance programmes for TV) *Comments:* experimentation with dance video, publish arts magazine for parents, travel literature, advertising, screenplays

Grammofon AB BIS
Bragevägen 2, 182 64 **Djursholm**
Tel: 8-755 4100 Fax: 8-755 7676
Internet: www.bis.se
E-Mail: bis@algonet.se
president Robert von Bahr
Format: CD *Own and distributed labels:* own: BIS *Art type:* contemporary Scandinavian and international classical music; also world premiere recordings

Hans Edler Musik AB
Gökholmsbacken 21, 124 74 **Bandhagen**
Tel: 8-647 5104 Fax: 8-993 939
managing director Hans Edler
Format: CD, cassette *Own and distributed labels:* own: GFO *Comments:* also sheet music publishers; see also Promoters

LCM Production & Records AB
Maria Prästgårdsgatan 14, 118 52 **Stockholm**
Tel: 8-5981 5177
Fax: 8-59815177
Internet: www.lcm.se
E-Mail: kerstin@lcm.se
contact Kerstin Tungården; producer Leif Carlquist
Format: CD, cassettes, video, arts programmes, sound design, dubbing, recordings *Own and distributed labels:* LCM, Locomotion *Art type:* specialist in classical and instrumental music *Comments:* also production company LCM production AB of radio and TV jingles and original scores for features, commercials, documentaries, produce nationwide TV

Prophone Records AB
Botvidsgatan 7, 126 49 **Hagerften**
Tel: 8-685 6360
Fax: 8-685 6370
Internet: www.prophonerecords.se
E-Mail: prophone@com.itv.se
managing director Erland Boëthius; marketing manager Stefan Növermyr
Format: CD, video cassettes *Own and distributed labels:* own: Prophone, Swedish Society Discofil
Art type: classical, jazz, folk

Proprius Musik AB
Box 10251, 100 55 **Stockholm**
Tel: 8-660 9602/213 357
Fax: 8-660 9749
E-Mail: info@proprius.se
managing director/producer Jacob Boëthius
Format: CD, cassette, special editions on vinyl, books *Own and distributed labels:* own: Proprius *Art type:* classical and some jazz

SWITZERLAND (+41)

Claves Records
Trüelweg 14, 3600 **Thun**
Tel: 33-223 1649 Fax: 33-222 8003
Internet: www.claves.ch
E-Mail: claves@tcnet.ch
owner & producer classic Marguerite Dütschler-Huber; graphik computer Christoph Dütschler; musikologe & layout Mark Manion; Sekretariat Ruth Lucas
Format: CD production and distribution; world music library from the King Record Label (Japan) for Switzerland only *Own and distributed labels:* Claves Records, Claves Jazz, King Record
Art type: classical, jazz

Disques VDE-GALLO/Editions Lausanne-Musique
Rue de l'Ale 31, PO Box 945, 1000 **Lausanne** 9
Tel: 21-312 1154 Fax: 21-312 1134
Internet: www.vdegallo.ch
E-Mail: vdegallo@span.ch
proprietor and director Olivier Buttex; production manager Sabine Landerer
Format: CD, mc *Own and distributed labels:* VDE, Gallo, Paroles, Peoples *Art type:* mostly classical and ethnic but other musical directions too
Comments: music library

Hat Hut Records Ltd
PO Box 521, 4020 **Basel**
Tel: 61-373 0773 Fax: 61-373 0774
Internet: www.hathut.com
owner & producer Werner X. Uehlinger
Format: CDs *Own and distributed labels:* hatOLOGY (jazz), hat (now) ART (contemporary/new music), hatNOIR (music crossing boarders) *Art type:* avant-garde, jazz, classical *Comments:* business office: Grelingerstrasse 84, 4052 Basel

Jecklin & Company AG
Rämistrasse 42, 8024 **Zürich** 1
Tel: 1-253 7777 Fax: 1-253 7667
Internet: www.jecklin.com
E-Mail: jecklin.musicalien@ch
president and director Hans Jecklin; assistant label manager Barbara Honegger
Format: CD, LP, mc *Own and distributed labels:* Jecklin Edition, Szene Schweiz, Sounds of Silence, Music of Man Archive, Red Note *Art type:* classical, ethnic music, outer European meditative music, pop, rock, jazz, folk

Musikhaus Pan AG
PO Box 176, Schaffhauserstr. 280,
8057 **Zürich**
Tel: 1-311 2221
Fax: 1-311 4108
E-Mail: pan@pingnet.ch
Geschäftsführer Myrta Keller
Format: CDs and cassettes *Own and distributed labels:* Swiss Pan, Pan Extra *Art type:* jazz, classical, educational *Comments:* also production of notes and books

Musikszene Schweiz – Grammont Portrait
Limmatstrasse 152, 8005 **Zürich**
Tel: 1-227 2040
Fax: 1-277 2335
marketing manager Grégoire Schnegg
Format: CD *Own and distributed labels:* Musikszene Schweiz – Grammont Portrait
Art type: classical, rock, jazz, ethno

Musikvertrieb AG
Badener Str. 555-557, 8048 **Zürich**
Tel: 1-497 1700
Fax: 1-497 1710
E-Mail: mv.sawi@swissonline.ch
classical marketing manager t.b.a.;
managing director,
record division Christoph Lehmann
Format: production of CD, music cassettes; marketing of audio/video devices; also distribution *Own and distributed labels:* distributed: Harmonia Mundi France, Auvidis, BIs, Supraphon, Telarc, Denon, Marco Polo, Arts, Divox, Accent *Art type:* all types

Plainisphare S.A.
1267 **Vich**
Tel: 22-364 3290/3339
Fax: 22-364 3584
directeur des ventes Rolf Knüsel; directeur administratif Jet Duplain; promotion Khiem Nguyen; informatique Christine Turin
Format: CD, LP, video *Own and distributed labels:* own: Plainisphare; distributed: hundreds of labels *Art type:* jazz, classical music, world music

Productions Cascavelle SA
CP 102, Route de la Glane 31, 1709 **Fribourg**
Tel: 26-425 8550
Fax: 26-424 3763 (CD)/1986
manager CDs Pierre Andre Crausaz; press Serge Chowez
Format: CD *Own and distributed labels:* Cascavelle
Comments: only distribution

Tudor Recording
Badenerstraße 531, 8048 **Zürich**
Tel: 1-491 7250 Fax: 1-493 4574
Internet: www.tudor.ch
E-Mail: info@tudor.ch
Owner Wadek Glowacz
Format: CD, cassettes, vinyl, video *Own and distributed labels:* own: Tudor, Glow Music; distribute: numerous including: Wergo, Christophorus, Phono Music, Ars Musici, Motette, Stil, Moment, Bielefelder, Winter & Winter, Kitty-Yo Int. *Comments:* independent distributor and production

TURKEY (+90)

Balet Plak Ve Müzikaset Ticaret
Keresteciler Sitesi Fidan Sokak No. 2/2,
34010 **Merter (Istanbul)**
Tel: 212-507 8672/7576 Fax: 212-507 8870
president A. Yesil Giresunlu; manager, sales & distribution Kadir Mertbasoglu; manager, finance & royalties Haluk Atinç; A&R, marketing, promotion Nazli Onatkut
Own and distributed labels: Turkish licensees for Warner Music and Delphine France

BMG
Istanbul
Tel: 212-274 2724

Kent Plakçilik (EMI)
Istanbul
Tel: 212-514 1621

Polygram
Gümüssuyu Is Merkezi Zefer Turay Sok. No 14, **Istanbul**
Tel: 212-249 7570 Fax: 212-251 2450

Sony Music Turkey
Istanbul
Tel: 212-251 2744/45

UNITED KINGDOM (+44)

Antelope
29B Montague Street, **London** WC1B 5BH
Tel: 20-7209 0099
Fax: 20-7209 0098
E-Mail: antelope@antelope.co.uk
chief executive Mick Csaky
Format: video *Art type:* drama and (arts) documentary series

ASV Records
1 Lochaline Street, **London** W6 9SJ
Tel: 20-8741 2807 Fax: 20-8741 8477
managing director Hywel Davies; production manager Jason Jones; marketing manager Ray Crick; A&R manager Pawlina Bednarczyk; press & promotions manager Jo Nicholson; sales manager Richard Harrison; financial controller Richard Partington
Format: CD, cassettes *Own and distributed labels:* ASV, Quicksilva, Gaudeamus, Living Era, White Line *Art type:* classical music, nostalgia and vintage jazz *Comments:* distributed by Select Music and Video Distribution Ltd (UK)

BBC Worldwide Ltd
Woodlands, 80 Wood Lane, **London** W12 0TT
Tel: 20-8576 2000 Fax: 20-8749 0538
Internet: www.bbcworldwide.com
chief executive Rupert Gavin; managing director, UK region & deputy chief executive Peter Teague; managing director, EMEIA Mark Young; director of finance David King; director, rights of international tv Mike Phillips; director, new media Jeremy Mayhew; managing director, BBC World Patrick Cross; director, human resources Bob McCall; director, global brand development Jeff Taylor; director of strategy Carolyn Fairbairn; director of communications Janie Ironside Wood; director, joint ventures Olga Edridge; director, technology Gary Richards; managing director, Asia Pacific David Vine; president & chief executive officer of BBC Worldwide Americas Peter Phippen;
Comments: BBC Worldwide was formed in May 1994 to coordinate the BBC's international and commerical activities; it encompasses cable and satellite channels and international programme distribution and publishing, led by magazines, new media and books, videos, audio cassettes, CD Roms and a commerical internet site;

Blue Snow
20 Downs View, **Isleworth** TW7 5HS
Tel: 467-810 560
Internet: easyweb.easynet.co.uk/~bluesnow
E-Mail: bluesnow@easynet.co.uk
director Philip Sheppard
Format: CD *Own and distributed labels:* own: Blue Snow
Art type: contemporary jazz, ambience music
Comments: see also Promoters

BMG Conifer
Bedford House, 69-79 Fulham High Street, **London** SW6 3JW
Tel: 20-7384 7500 Fax: 20-7384 7922
Internet: www.bmgclassics.com.uk
director Richard Dinnadge; marketing manager (classical) Rachel Agnew; marketing manager (jazz and cross-over) Grainne Devine
Format: CD, casettes *Own and distributed labels:* own: Conifer Classics, RCA Red Seal, RCA Gold Seal, RCA Victor, Melodiya, Catalyst, DHM, Royal Opera House, Arte Nova, Classic FM; distribute: Telarc, Classic FM Compilations

British Film Institute
21 Stephen Street, **London** W1P 2LN
Tel: 20-7255 1444 Fax: 20-7436 7950
Internet: www.bfi.org.uk
E-Mail: BFI@BFI.org.uk
chairman Alan Parker; director John Woodward; deputy dir Jon Teckman; head of marketing & press Mark Batey
Format: produce 6-8 shorts per year *Comments:* exists to encourage development of film, television & video in the UK

Cala Records
17 Shakespeare Gardens, **London** N2 9LJ
Tel: 20-8883 7306 Fax: 20-8365 3388
Internet: www.calarecords.com
E-Mail: music@calarecords.com
chairman artistic director Geoffrey Simon; manager Matt Hall
Format: CD *Own and distributed labels:* own: The London Sound, Cala, Cala Artists, Cala-The Edge, Cala Cascade, Cala United *Art type:* orchestral, large scale; solo artists; contemporary; cross-over, chamber music, jazz; from gregorian chants to new music

Carlton Video Ltd
TheWaterfront, Elstree Road, **Elstree** WD6 3BS
Tel: 20-8207 6207 Fax: 20-8207 5789
E-Mail: lorenzo@carltonvideo.co.uk
managing director Gerry Donohoe; marketing video Claire Warnford-Davis; legal affairs Lara Massey
Format: video, DVD; distributor *Art type:* all types

Chandos Records Ltd
Chandos House, Commerce Way, **Colchester** CO2 8HQ
Tel: 1206-225 200 Fax: 1206-225 201
Internet: www.chandos-records.com
E-Mail: enquiries@chandos-records.com
managing director Brian Couzens; operations director Ralph Couzens; marketing manager Jeff Coventry; sales manager Ginny Cooper
Format: CD, cassette, recording company and distributor *Own and distributed labels:* own: Chandos, Chaconne, Collect, Chandos Brass, Chandos Opera in English, Enchant; distributed: Musikproduktion Dabring Haus und Grimm, SIMAX, Orfeo, Tactus
Art type: classical

Christopher Swann Associates
89 Wendell Road, **London** W12 9SB
Tel: 20-8749 9056 Fax: 20-8740 9306
director and producer Christopher Swann; assistant producer and production manager Frances Peters
Art type: art and music documentaries, music performances

Classical Recording Company, The
16-17 Wolsey Mews, **London** NW5 2DX
Tel: 20-7482 2303 Fax: 20-7482 2302
Internet: www.classicalrecording.com
E-Mail: info@classicalrecording.com
producer/engineer Simon Weir; engineer Campbell Hughes; production manager Beth Hammond
Format: CD, cassettes, radio *Own and distributed labels:* own: Classical Recording *Art type:* broadcast & radio productions; digital location recording and post production of classical music, spoken word *Comments:* APRS associate members

Collins Classics
Electron House, Croy Avenue, St Mary Croy, **Orpington** BR5 3RJ
Tel: 1869-899 062 Fax: 1869-899 030
E-Mail: richard.ruck@windsong.co.uk
contact Richard Ruck
Format: CD *Own and distributed labels:* Collins Classics
Art type: classical music *Comments:* owned by distributor Pinnacle Records, Tel: 1689-870 622

Complete Record Company, The
22 Prescott Place, **London** SW4 6BT
Tel: 20-7498 9666 Fax: 20-7498 1828
E-Mail: info@complete-record.co.uk
contact Helen Elliott
Format: CDs, LPs, cassettes *Own and distributed labels:* distributors for Vanguard, CRD, Dutton *Art type:* classical music, jazz *Comments:* distributors and marketing

Decca Record Company Limited
347-353 Chiswick High Road, **London** W4 4HS
Tel: 20-8747 8787 Fax: 20-8994 2834
president Costa Pilavachi; senior vice president Evans Mirageas (Head of A&R); lawyer Nicola Levy; head of marketing Didier de Cottignies; executive producer Andrew Cornall; directors of A & R Michael Woodcock, Andrew Cornall, Michael Haas;
director of marketing Paul Mosely
Format: CD, CDV, cassettes, records, VHS, laser discs

EMI Classics
64 Baker Street, **London** W1M 1DJ
Tel: 20-7467 2000 Fax: 20-7467 2200
Internet: www.emiclassics.com
president Richard Lyttelton; senior vice-president A & R Peter Alward; vice-president, international marketing Theo Lap; vice-president, finance John King; interational press & promotion manager Simon Millward; director contracts & business affairs Charles Rodier
Format: CD, cassette, laser disc, video, multimedia

EMI Records Ltd
EMI House, 43 Brook Green, **London** W6 7EF
Tel: 20-7605 5000 Fax: 20-7605 5050
president & chief executive Tony Wadsworth
Format: CD, cassette, LP *Own and distributed labels:* Cooltempo, EMI Gold, Music for Pleasure, EMI Classics, EMI UK, Parlophone, Chrysalis, Capitol, Bluenote, Positiva

EuroArts-Primetime
45-49 Mortimer Street, **London** W1N 7TD
Tel: 20-7636 9421 Fax: 20-7436 7426
general manager Richard Price;
assistant Marie Thompson
Comments: production and distribution of music and arts programmes

Floating Earth Limited
Unit 14, 21 Wadsworth Road, **Perivale** UB6 7JD
Tel: 20-8997 4000 Fax: 20-8998 5767
Internet: www.floatingearth.demon.co.uk
E-Mail: record@floatingearth.com
company secretary Steve Long;
administrator Rachel Haining
Format: CD *Art type:* classical music, some jazz
Comments: classical music production company, including location recording, production, post-production and executive production

Gimell Records Limited
4 Newtec Place, Magdalen Road, **Oxford** OX4 1RE
Tel: 1865-358 282 Fax: 870-056 8880
Internet: www.gimell.com
E-Mail: info@gimell.com
managing director Steve Smith
Format: CD, cassettes

Harcourt Films Ltd
58 Camden Square, **London** NW1 9XE
Tel: 20-7267 0882 Fax: 20-7267 1064
director Jeremy Marre;
production secretary Nellie Medina
Art type: produce TV documentaries about music, adventure, anthropology and wildlife

Harmonia Mundi UK
19-21 Nile Street, **London** N1 7LL
Tel: 20-7253 0865 Fax: 20-7253 3237
Internet: harmoniamundi.com
E-Mail: info.uk@harmoniamundi.com
managing director Serge Rousset (20-7250 1784); commercial manager – classical Ian Lambert (20-7596 5411 ext 211); jazz & traditional music manager Trevor Manwaring (20-7608 2787);
press officer Celia Ballantyne
Format: CD, cassette *Own and distributed labels:* over 40 classical, jazz & world music labels *Comments:* the Harmonia Mundi label specialises in early, baroque and classical music as do several of its distributed labels; other distributed labels include several prestigious contemporary music labels, most of the best historic recordings labels and is very willing to send out free catalogues or label-listings on request

Hazard Chase Productions
Richmond House, 16-20 Regent Street, **Cambridge** CB2 1DB
Tel: 1223-312 400 Fax: 1223-460 827
E-Mail: info@hazardchase.co.uk
executive producers Patrick Allen, John Bickley, James Brown, John Willan
Format: CD, radio, CD-ROM, CD-Extra – programme maker *Art type:* broadcast and radio productions, TV and film soundtracks, demonstration recordings, CDs for commercial release and samplers *Comments:* location recording, editing and mastering

Hyperion Records Ltd
PO Box 25, **London** SE9 1AX
Tel: 20-8294 1166 Fax: 20-8294 1161
Internet: www.hyperion-records.co.uk
E-Mail: info@hyperion-records.co.uk
managing director Ted Perry; sales & advertising manager Mike Spring; press & promotions manager Jenny Wegg; production manager Richard Howard; recording manager Simon Perry
Format: CD, cassette *Own and distributed labels:* own: Hyperion, Helios

Iambic Productions
89 White Ladies Road, **Bristol** BS8 2NT
Tel: 117-923 7222 Fax: 117-923 8343
managing director Chris Hunt;
production manager-London Judy Chesterman;
production manager-Bristol Angela Hall
Art type: TV documentaries, drama, rock and classical concerts – 5 in production *Comments:* also have office in London, please contact the Bristol office for details

IMG Records
Media House, 3 Burlington Lane, **London** W4 2TH
Tel: 20-8233 5800
Fax: 20-8233 5801
managing director Stephen Wright
Format: CDs, television programmes, video and laser discs

KOCH Discover International
Charlotte House, 87 Little Lane, **London** W5 4EH
Tel: 20-8832 1800
Fax: 20-8832 1813
managing director KOCH Rashmi Patani;
classical label manager Tom Norden
Format: CD production/ license *Own and distributed labels:* KOCH International Classics, KOCH Shwann, KOCH Discover, Supraphon, Ondine, Collegium

Landseer Film and TV Productions Ltd
140 Royal College Street, **London** NW1 0TA
Tel: 20-7485 7333
Fax: 20-7485 7573
E-Mail: landseerfilms@msn.com
producer/directors Derek Bailey, Ken Howard, Ross MacGibbon; office manager Claire Mills
Format: arts programme maker *Art type:* film & TV, music & arts, documentaries & performance, current affairs, children and drama
Comments: Avid off-line editing suites

Liam White Productions
36 Westminster Mansions, Great Smith Street, **London** SW1P 3BP
Tel: 20-7799 4280
Fax: 20-7222 6926
managing director Liam White
Art type: art films, documentaries

Linn Records
257 Drakemire Drive, Castlemilk, **Glasgow (Scotland)** G45 9SZ
Tel: 141-307 7777
Fax: 141-631 1485
Internet: www.linn.co.uk
E-Mail: records@linn.co.uk
label manager Philip Hobbs; sales & distribution Yvonne Tipping; press officer Claire Logue
Format: CD, cassette *Own and distributed labels:* Linn Records *Art type:* high quality classical, jazz and folk label *Comments:* parent company: Linn Products Ltd. – manufacturer of top quality Hi-Fi

Lorelt (Lontano Records Ltd)
Toynbee Studios, 28 Commercial Street, **London** E1 6LS
Tel: 20-7247 2950 Fax: 20-7247 2956
administrator Jan Hart;
musical director Odaline de la Martinez
Format: CD *Own and distributed labels:* Lorelt
Comments: music by contemporary British composers and by women and Latin-American composers from all periods

Malachite Ltd
East Kirkby House, **Spilsby** PE23 4BX
Tel: 1790-763 538 Fax: 1790-763 409
E-Mail: info@malachite.co.uk
director and producer Charles Mapleston; executive producer Nancy Thomas; producer Nikki Crane
Art type: design, environmental issues, arts & dance, music and entertainment, and are developing micro-budget fiction

Mayron (UK) Ltd
7-10 Sovereign Park, Coronation Road, Park Royal, **London** NW10 7QP
Tel: 20-8961 8898
Fax: 20-8961 8688
manager T. C. Ho
Format: CD *Art type:* classical

Meridian Records
PO Box 317, Eltham, **London** SE9 4SF
Tel: 20-8857 3213 Fax: 20-8857 0731
E-Mail: lasmara@dircon.co.uk
managing director John Shuttleworth; sound engineer Richard Hughes; producer Gary Skyrme
Format: CD *Own and distributed labels:* own: Meridian, Duo *Art type:* classical

Metronome Recordings Ltd
Carrick Business Centre, Beacon House, Commercial Road, Penryn, **Cornwall** TR10 8AR
Tel: 1326-377 738 Fax: 1326-378 643
E-Mail: 106504.2417@compuserve.com
managing director Tim Smithies
Format: CD, cassette *Own and distributed labels:* Metronome, Soundalive *Comments:* classical music recording and concert tour promotions; classial music label, classical music promotor

Mike Mansfield TV Ltd
5th Floor, 41-42 Berners Street, **London** W1P 3AA
Tel: 20-7580 2581 Fax: 20-7580 2582
director and producer Mike Mansfield;
director Hilary McLaren
Format: film, video *Art type:* music, light entertainment, arts documentary *Comments:* independent production company

MJW Productions
5 Warner House, 43-49 Warner Street, **London** EC1R 5ER
Tel: 20-7713 0400 Fax: 20-7713 0500
producer Anne Beresford; director Margaret Williams
Format: production company *Art type:* film production company specialising in music, dance and arts productions *Comments:* recent commissions from the BBC, Channel 4 and Arts Council of England such as sound on film and dance for the camera

Monsieur X Production
11 South Black Lion Lane, **London** W6 9TJ
Tel: 20-8748 0719
Fax: 20-8748 0719
E-Mail: miranda@doublehappy.demon.co.uk
artistic director Miranda Pennell
Format: 16mm film, video *Art type:* short, innovative films on dance; interdisciplinary dance work *Comments:* distribution through The Lux Centre (20-7684 2782)

Nimbus Records
Wyastone Leys, **Monmouth** NP25 3SR
Tel: 1600-890 682
Fax: 1600-890 779/137
Internet: www.nimbus.ltd.uk
E-Mail: alf.goodrich@nimbus.ltd.uk
chairman/director Gerald Reynolds; deputy chairman Adrian Farmer; head of worldwide sales & marketing Carl Wade; head of press & public relations Alf Goodrich; head of A & R Dominic Fyfe
Format: DVD, CD, cassette, distributor, recording, concerts/live music *Own and distributed labels:* Nimbus Records, Music Masters (classical and jazz), Meridian, Lyrita, Delos *Arts type:* classical music, opera, jazz, world music

NMC Recordings Ltd
Francis House, Francis Street, **London** SW1P 1DE
Tel: 20-7828 3432
Fax: 20-7828 3432
Internet: www.nmcrec.co.uk
E-Mail: nmc@nmcrec.co.uk
administrator Hannah Vlcek; executive producer Colin Matthews; consultant Jennifer Goodwin
Format: CD *Own and distributed labels:* NMC *Art type:* contemporary classical music by British composers
Comments: registered charity

NVC Arts
The Forum, 74-80 Camden Street, **London** NW1 0EG
Tel: 20-7388 3833 Fax: 20-7383 5332
managing director John Kelleher;
director of sales & co-production Kim Thomas;
marketing & video manager Clive Sugars
Format: TV, videocassette, laserdisc *Own and distributed labels:* own: NVC Arts *Art type:* producers and distributorsof live performance programmes of opera, ballet and the performing arts, documentaries

Opera Rara
134-146, Curtain Road, **London** EC2A 3AR
Tel: 20-7613 2858 Fax: 20-7613 2261
Internet: www.opera-rara.com/
E-Mail: operarara@amity.co.uk
musicologist Robert Roberts; artistic director Patric Schmid; managing director Stephen Revell
Format: CDs *Own and distributed labels:* own: Opera Rara *Art type:* predominantly work with Philharmonia (q.v.); 19th Century Italian and French opera (also working with Academy of St Martin in the Fields)
Comments: see also Opera

Pavilion Records Ltd
Sparrows Green, **Wadhurst** TN5 6SJ
Tel: 1892-783 591
Fax: 1892-784 156
managing director John Waite; chairman Philip Leask
Format: CD, cassette *Own and distributed labels:* own: Pearl, Flapper, Opal, Topaz

Portobello Pictures
14-15 D' Arblay Street, **London** W1V 3FP
Tel: 20-7379 5566 Fax: 20-7379 5599
managing director and executive producer Eric Abraham
Format: film *Art type:* features

Priory Records
9B Upper Wingbury Courtyard, **Wingrave** HP22 4LW
Tel: 1296-682 255 Fax: 1296-682 275
Internet: www.priory.org.uk
E-Mail: sales@priory.org.uk
managing director Neil Collier;
A & R manager/senior producer Caroline Paschalides;
manager – finance & sales Callum Ross
Format: CD, cassette *Own and distributed labels:* Amphion, Athene, Audite, Beulah, British Music Society, Calig, Datum, Donemus, Dynamic, Festivo, Guild, Ikon, Isis, Kevin Mayhew, Metier, Motette, Multisonic, Olympia, Ottavo, Priory, Signum (English & German), Somm, Sterling, Stradivarius, Tahra, Tower Hill, Vox *Art type:* classical music distributors

Public Production Co. Ltd., The
117 Praed Street, **London** WC2 1RL
Tel: 20-7402 2789 Fax: 20-7706 9348
E-Mail: aston@mailbox.co.uk
directors Laurence Aston, John L.Walters
Art type: music consultancy, specialist record marketing, record production *Comments:* co-founder and publisher of Unknown Public (creative music journal); see also Publications and Products & Services

Real World Records
Mill Lane, Box, **Corsham** SN13 8PL
Tel: 1225-743 188 Fax: 1225-743 787
Internet: realworld.on.net/rwr
E-Mail: AmandaJones@realworld.co.uk
managing director Mike Large;
A & R director Amanda Jones
Format: CD, cassettes *Own and distributed labels:* label is distributed by EMI Virgin *Art type:* produces world music

Rosetta Pictures
5-7 Sedley Place, **London** W1R 1HH
Tel: 20-7647 5900 Fax: 20-7495 6109
E-Mail: rosetta@globalnet.co.uk
directors Chris Rawlence, Emma Crichton-Miller
Art type: independent production company supplying cultural documentaries and drama programmes to Channel 4 and the BBC *Comments:* formerly called Hauer Rawlence Productions Ltd

Sargasso
PO Box 10565, **London** N1 8SR
Tel: 20-7359 7825 Fax: 20-7359 7825
Internet: www.sargasso.com
E-Mail: info@sargasso.com
label manager Veronique Joly;
artistic director Daniel Biro
Format: CD, record label *Own and distributed labels:* Sargasso Records *Art type:* contemporary classical, electronic, experimental songwriting, new jazz/improvisation *Comments:* visiting address: Almeida Street, London N1 8SR

Sony Music Entertainment (UK) Ltd
10 Great Marlborough Street, **London** W1V 2LP
Tel: 20-7911 8200
Fax: 20-7911 8600
chairman Paul Burger
Format: CD, records, video, cassettes *Art type:* all

Sound Circus
PO Box 354, **Reading** RG1 5TX
Tel: 118-931 2580 Fax: 118-931 2582
Internet: www.soundcircus.com
E-Mail: aston@mailbox.co.uk
record producer Joanna MacGregor
Format: CD *Comments:* mail order, not otherwise available

Streetwise TV
11-15 Betterton Street, **London** WC2H 9PB
Tel: 20-7470 8825 Fax: 20-7470 8826
E-Mail: development@streetwisetv.com
creative & development producer Ian Whittingham
Comments: at present in development of a number of ideas for the BBC, ITV and Channel 5: dramas, documentaries, youth tv, late night tv & music programmes

Swamp Music
PO Box 94, **Derby** DE22 1XA
Tel: 1332-332 336/402-564 804 (mobile) Fax: 1332-332 336
E-Mail: chrishall@swampmusic.demon.co.uk
contact Chris Hall

Testament
PO Box 361, **Bromley** BR2 0QQ
Tel: 20-8464 5947 Fax: 20-8464 5352
director Stewart Brown
Art type: classical music *Comments:* re-releases under licence from EMI records and own productions

Unicorn-Kanchana Records
PO Box 339, **London** W8 7SJ
managing director Nigel Brandt
Format: CD *Own and distributed labels:* own: Unicorn-Kanchana Records

Universal International
8 St James Square, **London** SW1Y 4GU
Tel: 20-7747 4000 Fax: 20-7747 4499
Internet: www.universalstudios.com
chairman Jorgen Larsen;
communications department Amanda Conroy
Format: CDs *Art type:* all kinds of music

Upbeat Recordings Ltd
Sutton Business Centre, Restmor Way, **Wallington** SM6 7AH
Tel: 20-8647 5275/8773 1223 Fax: 20-8669 6752
Internet: www.upbeat.co.uk
E-Mail: info@upbeat.co.uk
managing director Liz Biddle; director Maureen Phillips; director press & pr Beryl Korman
Format: CD, cassettes *Own and distributed labels:* Upbeat Classics, Upbeat Jazz, Upbeat Showbiz, Ossia Classics, Upbeat Recordings; distribution: BMG via Target UK *Art type:* recordings: classical, jazz and showbiz *Comments:* see also Agents and Producers

Warner Classics International
83 Baker Street, **London** W1M 2LA
Tel: 20-7535 9000 Fax: 20-7535 9251
president Marco Bignotti; director A&R development Michael Letchford; director international marketing Naill O'Rourke
Format: CD, CDV, cassette, laserdisc *Own and distributed labels:* Erato Disques, Finlandia, National Video Corporation, Nonesuch, Teldec Classics International

Woolfson Entertainment Group Ltd
Little Manor, Milspit Hill, **London** NW7 2RS
Tel: 20-8906 8898 Fax: 20-8906 0550
Internet: www.woolfson.co.uk
E-Mail: wentg@aol.com
contact Barry Hilton
Comments: the Company represents the theatrical and recorded works of songwriter Eric Woolfson

World Circuit
106 Cleveland Street, **London** W1P 5DP
Tel: 20-7383 4907 Fax: 20-7383 4908
Internet: www.worldcircuit.co.uk
E-Mail: post@worldcircuit.co.uk
contact Jenny Adlington
Format: CD *Own and distributed labels:* World Circuit *Art type:* Latin American and West African music

YUGOSLAVIA (+381)

Due to the war in Kosovo we have been unable to update the following entries for Yugoslavia

Jugodisk
Ljubicka 15, 11000 **Belgrade**
Tel: 11-471 152/473 009 Fax: 11-471 327
director Milena Radosavljevic

RTS PGP – Radiotelevision Serbia Production of Gramophone records
RTS PGP – produkcija ploca RTS
Makedonska 21, 11000 **Belgrade**
Tel: 11-322 0277 Fax: 11-322 7528
managing director Stanko Terzic; classical music & video-film producer Aleksandar Pilipenko; pop-rock producer Dragan Ilic; children music producer Lidija Habic; folk music producer Miroljub Arandelovic Kemis

Competitions

Competitions
Major international music competitions are included, along with the substantially fewer international dance and drama competitions that exist. Competitions intended specifically for children and young people have been excluded. **Within country the venues are ordered by city, and alphabetically within city.**

Concours
Les concours internationaux de musique les plus importants sont répertoriés ainsi que ceux de danse et de théâtre (qui sont toutefois beaucoup moins nombreux). Il est à noter que les concours pour les jeunes ne figurent pas ici.**Pour chaque pays les salles sont classés dans l'ordre des villes et par ordre alphabétique.**

Wettbewerbe
Eingeschlossen sind die wichtigsten internationalen Musikwettbewerbe, sowie die weniger häufig stattfindenden internationalen Tanz- und Schauspielwettbewerbe. Ausgeschlossen sind Kinder-, u. Jugendwettbewerbe.**Die Einträge sind innerhalb aller Staaten alphabetisch nach Stadt und innerhalb der Stadt alphabetisch nach Namen geordnet.**

Concorsi
Sono inclusi tutti i maggiori concorsi internazionali di musica e canto, e soltanto alcuni concorsi internazionali di danza e teatro. Sono stati esclusi i concorsi per bambini e giovanissimi. **Le cittá sono in ordine alfabetico e cosí anche i luoghi all'interno di esse.**

Concursos
Los principales concursos internacionales de música están incluidos junto con los de, en menor número, danza y teatro. Los concursos de interés específico para niños y jóvenes han sido excluidos. **Los concursos están ordenadas por ciudades y en orden alfabético dentro de cada ciudad.**

Competition (대회)
주요 국제 음악 대회들이 기재되었다. 음악대회보다 훨씬 적은 국제 무용 및 연극 대회 또한 기재되었다. 어린이나 청소년들만을 위한 대회는 제외되었다. **리스트는 국가별로 알파벳순으로 기재되었다.**

比賽
包括主要国际音乐比赛，同时还有少数几个尚存的国际舞蹈和戏剧比赛。专为儿童和青年举办的比赛被排除在外。**在各国内，比赛是按字母顺序排列的。**

コンクール
この章には、大型の国際音楽コンクールとともに、数は少ないですが、国際舞踏、演劇コンクールが掲載されています。児童、青少年を対象としたコンクールは除外してあります。**リストは国別で、一国内ではアルファベット順に記載されています。**

CLIBURN 2001 · MOVE THE WORLD

Eleventh Van Cliburn International Piano Competition · May 25 – June 10

Applications due October 1, 2000

2525 Ridgmar Boulevard · Suite 307 · Fort Worth, Texas 76116 U.S.A.

Phone 1/817-738-6536 · Fax 1/817-738-6534

www.cliburn.org

ALBANIA (+355)

Konkursi i muzikes se re
The New Albanian Music Academy of Arts,
Nene Tereza Street, **Tirana**
Tel: 42-62899
Date: May *Frequency:* annual *Eligibility:* for Albanian composers up to 30 yrs *Type:* contemporary music

ARMENIA (+374)

Edward Mirzoyan International Competition for String Ensembles and Orchestras
4-4 Azatoutian Street, 375037 **Yerevan**
Tel: 2-254 493 Fax: 2-151 431 (AT&T)
Internet: www.arminco.com/homepages/nab
E-Mail: nbart@arminco.com
general manager Nika Babaian; president Edward Mirzoyan
Dates: May *Frequency:* biennial (2000)
Eligibility: no age limit
Comments: deadline for applications: 1 December 1999
Type: string ensembles and orchestras

AUSTRIA (+43)

Internationaler Gesangswettbewerb – Ferruccio Tagliavini
c/o Ruefa Reisen, Frauenthalerstr. 8,
8530 **Deutschlandsberg**
Tel: 3462-3130 Fax: 3462-31309
E-Mail: eschubert@ruefa.at
contact Dr. Elisabeth Schubert; art director Vittorio Terranova; assistant Dr. Christina Schubert
Dates: 11-18 April 2000 *Frequency:* annual *Eligibility:* 1st section professionals (>35 years), 2nd section non-professionals (>24 years) *Awards:* professionals: 5k, 4k, and 3k Aus. Schilling; non-professionals: 10k, 6k and 3k Aus. Schilling *Comments:* submissions by 21 March 2000; 1 section several concerts at Milano, Graz, Bad Radkersburg, Therme Loiperdorf *Type:* vocal opera

Internationaler Wettbewerb Franz Schubert u. die Musik der Moderne
International Competition Franz Schubert and the Music of Modernity
c/o Universität für Musik und darstellende Kunst Graz, Leonhardstrasse 15, 8010 **Graz**
Tel: 316-389 1900/1210 Fax: 316-389 1710/1901
Internet: www.mhsg.ac.at
E-Mail: franz.schubert@mhsg.ac.at
contact Mag. Susanne Kogler
Dates: 23 Feb – 3 March 2000 *Frequency:* irregular
Eligibility: singers: 32 (women), 34 (men); pianists: 34; string quartet: 120 (total age), the single participant should not be older than 34; piano solo: 32 *Awards:* duo for voice and piano – prizes: 1st 120k ATS, 2nd 90k ATS, 3rd 60k ATS; piano solo – prizes: 1st 90k ATS, 2nd 60k ATS, 3rd 40k ATS; string quartet – prizes: 1st 240k ATS, 2nd 180k ATS, 3rd 120k ATS; additional prizes for outstanding interpretations of works by Franz Schubert and works of the Music of Modernity, also scholarships, concert engagements and radio broadcast recordings
Comments: application deadline: Nov 15, 1999 *Type:* 3 categories – duo for voice and piano (Lied) and String Quartet are the given categories; the 3rd category alternates every three year; for 2000 it is piano solo

Orgelwettbewerb um den Paul-Hofhaimer Preis der Landeshauptstadt Innsbruck
Städtisches Konzertbüro, Stiftgasse 16, 3. Stock,
6020 **Innsbruck**
Tel: 512-536 0650 Fax: 512-536 0649
contact Dr.Walter Frenzel
Dates: Sept 2001 *Frequency:* triennial *Eligibility:* open to everyone *Awards:* prizes from 30k to 70k Aus. Schillings
Comments: entries to be submitted from September 2000 to February 2001 *Type:* instrumental (organ)

City of Klagenfurt Gustav Mahler Composition Prize
Internationaler Kompositionspreis der Stadt Klagenfurt
c/o Musikforum Viktring, Stift-Viktring-Straße 25,
9073 **Klagenfurt-Viktring**
Tel: 463-282 241 Fax: 463-281 626
Internet: www.happynet.at/musikforum
E-Mail: musikforum@happynet.at
jury members Prof. Siegfried Palm, Wolfang Muthspiel, Christoph Cech, Gerhard Rühm, Dieter Kaufmann
Dates: April 2000 *Frequency:* annual *Eligibility:* compositions entered must not have been published or performed at any time prior to application *Awards:* 1st prize: ATS 50k; 2nd prize: ATS 40k; 3rd prize: ATS 30k
Comments: see also Festivals (Musikforum Viktring – Klagenfurt); for more information please contact Musikforum directly
Type: composition for ensemble and cello solo

Internationaler Wettbewerb für Violoncello
Kommittee des internationalen Wettbewerbes für Violoncello Liezen, Salberweg 24, 8940 **Liezen**
Tel: 3612-22242/664-500 3092 Fax: 3612-22242
artistic director John R. Hauer; management Ute Kruse-Pitte
Dates: 25-30 April 2000 *Frequency:* biennial
Eligibility: 6 age groups from under 9 to over 19 y. old
Awards: diplomas for all winners; cash prizes and concert *Comments:* deadline for entries: Feb 10, 2000
Type: instrumental (violoncello)

Prix Ars Electronica
c/o ORF, Europaplatz 3, 4010 **Linz**
Tel: 732-6900 24267 Fax: 732-6900 24270
Internet: prixars.orf.at
E-Mail: info@prixars.orf.at
chief officer Dr Christine Schöpf (Österreichischer Rundfunk (ORF)/Landesstudio Oberösterreich)
Dates: 2000 *Frequency:* annual *Eligibility:* individual groups, institutions and companies *Awards:* in each category: one Golden Nica, two money awards and up to 12 honorary mentions; 4 categories: computer animation, visual effects, net, interactive art, digital music *Comments:* deadline for entries – end of March 2000; see also Festivals *Type:* international competition for the computer arts: animation, graphics, music, interactive arts and WWW categories

Chorolympiade Linz 2000
Landeskulturzentrum Chorolympiade 2000,
Landstrasse 31, 4021 **Linz**
Tel: 732-782 380 Fax: 732-782 3803
Internet: www.musiker-mundi.com
E-Mail: linz@musiker-mundi.com
Sekretariat Herr Hinterdorfer; Präsident des OSB Rey. R. Herbert Wild
Date: 7-16 July 2000 *Eligibility:* open to delegates from all countries *Type:* 28 different music categories (incl. jazz, classical, etc)

Internationaler Mozartwettbewerb
Universitat Mozarteum Salzburg, Alpenstraße 48,
5020 **Salzburg**
Tel: 662-6198 2200 Fax: 662-6198 2209
Internet: www.moz.ac.at
E-Mail: ulrike.baciu@moz.ac.at
Rektor O.H.Prof. Klaus Ager; Wettbewerbsbüro Dr. Ulrike Baciu
Dates: 2002 or 2003 (not decided yet) *Frequency:* irregular *Comments:* further details were not available at time of going to print

Internationaler Chorwettbewerb Stimmen der Welt auf Schloß Porcia
Tourismusbüro und Kulturamt der Stadtgemeinde Spittal/Drau, Burgplatz 1, 9800 **Spittal/Drau**
Tel: 4762-3420 Fax: 4762-3237
Internet: partner.fh-kaernten.ac.at
E-Mail: c.uggowitzer@spital-drau.at
contact Frau Obernosterer
Dates: 6-9 July 2000 *Frequency:* annual *Eligibility:* choirs from all over the world with between 16 and 50 members *Awards:* prizes between 6k and 12k Aus. Schillings *Comments:* entries by 31 January 2000
Type: choral (mixed)

Dance Screen
IMZ/Dance Screen, Speisinger Strasse 121-127,
1230 **Wien**
Tel: 1-889 0315 Fax: 1-8890 31577
Internet: www.imz.magnet.at/imz/
E-Mail: office@imz.at
coordination Barbara Neundlinger
Dates: 11-17 December 2000 (Monaco) *Frequency:* annual *Eligibility:* dance films, videos produced after June 1999 *Awards:* Dance Screen Award 30k DM + trophies awarded in four categories: 1) stage recording/studio adaptation 2) camera rework 3) screen choreography 4) documentary *Comments:* entry deadline date had not been decided at time of going to print, please contact for further details
Type: films/video on dance

International Beethoven Piano Competition
Internationaler Beethoven Klavierwettbewerb
Anton-von-Webern Platz 1, 1030 **Wien**
Tel: 1-7115 56050 Fax: 1-7115 56059
Internet: www.mhsw.ac.at/beethoven-competition/
E-Mail: beethoven-comp@mhsw.ac.at
general secretary Elga Ponzer
Dates: June 2001 *Frequency:* quadrennial
Eligibility: pianists between 17-32 years old from all nationalities, per CV, good musical background, graduation certificate; strict criteria apply
Awards: cash prizes, concerts, Bösendorfer piano for first prize winners – prizes: 1st 98k, 2nd 70k, 3rd 56k Aus Schilling *Comments:* entry fee ATS 1000; entry examinations will be held worldwide and are expected to be in February 2001; deadline for applications is 30 September 2000 *Type:* piano

Internationaler Fritz Kreisler Violinwettbewerb
PO Box 76, 1031 **Wien**
Tel: 1-7115 56021 Fax: 1-7115 56029
Internet: www.fritz-kreisler.music.at
E-Mail: office@fritz-kreisler.music.at
Präsident Prof Michael Frischenschlager
Dates: 22-30 September 2000
Frequency: quadrennial (2004) *Eligibility:* up to 30 yrs
Awards: cash, concerts, CD production
Comments: deadline for applications: 30 June 2000
Type: violin

Internationaler Hans Gabor Belvedere Gesangswettbewerb
Wiener Kammeroper, Fleischmarkt 24, 1010 **Wien**
Tel: 1-512 0100 Fax: 1-5120 10020
Internet: members.magnet.at/wienerkammeroper
E-Mail: wienerkammeroper@magnet.at
contact Isabella Gabor
Dates: 11-16 July 2000 *Frequency:* annual *Eligibility:* young singers of any nationality, aged under 32 years (male) or under 30 years (female) *Awards:* cash, possible engagements; 1st prize ATS 50k *Comments:* opera, participants may also want to enter operetta competition *Type:* vocal

Reinl-Preis 2000
Franz Josef Reinl-Stiftung, Dr Ernst Grossmann, Singerstr 27, 1010 **Wien**
Tel: 1-512 7555 Fax: 1-513 7588
E-Mail: masser-partner@rip.rdb.at
contact Dr. Ernst Grossmann
Dates: March 2000 (in Vienna) *Frequency:* annual
Eligibility: female composition: female composers born after 1.1.1960, the piece may not have been composed before 1992 and may not have been published or performed; harp: female harpists born after 1.1.1973 who have not completed their studies *Awards:* cash prizes and diplomas *Comments:* closing date: 15 Feb 2000 *Type:* baroque, contemporary

Wiener Internationaler Kompositionswettbewerb
c/o Casinos Austria, Dr-Karl-Lueger-Ring 14,
1015 **Wien**
Tel: 1-5344 0326 Fax: 1-5344 0319
künstlerische Leitung Claudio Abbado; Gesamtorganisation Gerhard Skoff; Jury-Koordination Prof. Lothar Knessl
Dates: performance during the festival Wien modern (world premiere) *Frequency:* annual *Eligibility:* composers under the age of forty *Awards:* 2000: 400k AS (children's chamber opera); 2001: AS 100k (ensemble – max 24 instr., 10-30 min. duration); 2002: AS 100k (for 3-9 instruments, also with live electronic and/or vocal soloist, 10-30 min. duration); 2003: AS 100k (chamber choir a cappella – max 32 voices or with instruments, 10-30 min. duration); 2004: AS 50k (instrument solo incl. organ, 10-30 min. duration); 2005: AS 75k (string quartet, 10-30 min. duration)
Comments: deadline for submissions: 2000: 15 Sept 1999, 2001: 15 Sept 2000, 2002: 15 Sept 2001, 2003: 15 Sept 2002, 2004: 15 Sept 2003, 2005: 15 Sept 2004 ; work submitted for the competitions should have been written no earlier than four years before the deadline; see Festivals *Type:* composition

BELARUS (+375)

Music of Hope International Competition, Gomell, The
Mjezhdunarodnyj Konkurs Muzyka Nadzjei, Gomjell
Ministjerstvo kultury (Ministry of Culture), pr. Mashjerova 11, 220004 **Minsk**
Tel: 172-235 825 Fax: 172-235 825

Minsk 2000 Pianists International Competition, The
Mjezhdunarodnyj Konkurs Pianistov Minsk 2000
Ministjerstvo kultury (Ministry of Culture), pr. Mashjerova 11, 220004 **Minsk**
Tel: 172-235 825 Fax: 172-235 825

M.Oginskij International Competition of Chamber Groups, Smorgonn, The
Mjezhdunarodnyj Konkurs Kamernych Ansambljej imjeni M.Oginskogo, Smorgonn
Ministjerstvo kultury (Ministry of Culture), pr. Mashjerova 11, 220004 **Minsk**
Tel: 172-235 825 Fax: 172-235 825

I. Cvjetajeva International Competition of Youth Pianists, The
Mjezhdunarodnyj Konkurs Junych Pianistov imjeni I. Cvjetajevoj
Ministjerstvo kultury (Ministry of Culture), pr. Mashjerova 11, 220004 **Minsk**
Tel: 172-235 825 Fax: 172-235 825

Ju. Sjemjenjaka International Competition of Young Composers, Grodno, The
Mjezhdunarodnyj Konkurs Junych Kompozitorov imjeni Ju. Sjemjenjaki, Grodno
Ministjerstvo kultury (Ministry of Culture), pr. Mashjerova 11, 220004 **Minsk**
Tel: 172-235 825 Fax: 172-235 825

BELGIUM (+32)

Musica Antiqua International Competition
Festival van Vlaanderen-Brugge, Musica Antiqua Competition, Collaert Mansionstraat 30, 8000 **Bruges**
Tel: 50-332 283 Fax: 50-345 204
Internet: www.musica-antiqua.com
E-Mail: musica-antiqua@unicall.be
director Robrecht Dewitte MBE
Dates: 2-9 Aug 2000 *Frequency:* annual
Eligibility: up to 32 yrs, ensembles average age 32 yrs
Awards: cash (1m BF) *Comments:* see also Festivals
Type: early music: 2000: organ and ensembles

Concours d'Auteurs
c/o Union des Artistes, Rue Marché-Aux-Herbes 105, BP 33, Bureau 310, 1000 **Brussels**
Tel: 2-513 5780 Fax: 2-513 5780
vice présidentes Arianne Masure, Jacques Monseu, Jean-Paul Landresse
Dates: March-April 2001; awards in Feb 2002 *Frequency:* biennial *Eligibility:* the work has to be recieved by mid-Sept *Comments:* office opening hrs: Monday, Tuesday & Thursday 10.00 – 12.00 *Type:* french-speaking playwrights, all theatre genres; the 3 performing arts, singing, drama and choreography can be combined; 2000: playwrights

Concours Musical International Reine Elisabeth de Belgique
Secrétariat, 20 rue aux Laines, 1000 **Brussels**
Tel: 2-513 0099 Fax: 2-514 3297
Internet: www.concours-reine-elisabeth.be
E-Mail: info@concours-reine-elisabeth.be
secretary general Cécile Ferrière
Dates: May *Frequency:* annual
Eligibility: composition competition: no age limit; piano and violin: up to 31 years at enrolment date (15 Jan); singing: up to 32 years at enrolment date
Awards: cash awards: 3.2m BF; recordings, concerts
Comments: free accommodation in host families – special arrangements for flight tickets, accompaniment available *Type:* May 2000: singing

Queen Elisabeth International Music Competition, The
Rue aux Laines 20, 1000 **Brussels**
Tel: 2-513 0099 Fax: 2-514 3297
Internet: www.concours-reine-elisabeth.be
E-Mail: info@concours-reine-elisabeth.be
Date: 5-27 May 2000 *Eligibility:* age limit 31 years
Comments: deadline for application: 15 January 2000
Type: music

Concours International Printemps de la Guitare
Place du Chef-Lieu 9, 6040 **Charleroi-Jumet**
Tel: 71-350 448 Fax: 71-355 320
Internet: www.printempsguitare.be
E-Mail: printemps.guitare@imageweb.be
president Dr André Tobie
Dates: 25 Sept- 07 Oct 2000 *Frequency:* biennial
Eligibility: up to 32 yrs *Awards:* 10 laureates awards: total amount of prize money -1m FB *Type:* classical solo guitarists

Concours International de Chant de Verviers
Opéra Royal de Wallonie, Rue des Dominicains 1, 4000 **Liège**
Tel: 4-221 4720 Fax: 4-221 0201
director Jean Louis Grinda; secretary Cécile Duvivier
Dates: September (opera) *Frequency:* biennial (2001)
Eligibility: women 18-30 yrs, men 18-35 yrs *Awards:* 12 finalist awards from 25k FB to 250k FB *Comments:* competition venue: Grand-Théâtre de Verviers, 2 rue des Artistes, B-4800 Verviers *Type:* lyric artists (opera)

BULGARIA (+359)

Boris Christoff International Competition for Young Opera Singers
7/A Aksakov Str., 1000 **Sofia**
Tel: 2-987 1772 Fax: 2-874 821
E-Mail: sfoper@geobiz.net
president Simeon Pironkov
Dates: June-July *Frequency:* quadrennial (2000)
Eligibility: all nationalities: women up to 33 years, men born up to 35 years *Awards:* cash prizes *Comments:* deadline for applications: 1 March 2000; application fee US$100; member of the World Federation of International Music Competitions; based at Sofia National Opera *Type:* opera singers

Varna International Ballet Competition
6B Hristo Botev Str., 1463 **Sofia**
Tel: 2-808 020/801 802/833 377/52-241 060
Fax: 2-803 791
director Emil Dimitrov
Dates: July *Frequency:* biennial (2000)
Eligibility: 13-27 yrs *Awards:* cash, medals, diplomas
Type: solo (male and female)

CROATIA (+385)

International Choir Competition Zadar
Medunarodno natjecanje zborova Zadar
Trg Petra Zoranica 1, 23000 **Zadar**
Tel: 23-315 807 Fax: 23-315 807
art director Antun Dolicki
Dates: May

International Competition for Young Conductors Lovro Matacic
Medunarodno Natjecanje Mladih Dirigenata Lovro Matacic
Lisinski Concert Hall, c/o Koncertna Dvorana Vatroslava Lisinskog, Trg Stjepana Radica 4, 10000 **Zagreb**
Tel: 1-612 1111 Fax: 1-539 889
general secretary Lovro Lisicic
Dates: September *Frequency:* quadrennial (2003)
Eligibility: conductors of all nationalities, age limit: 35 years *Awards:* concerts with the Zagreb Philharmonic Orchestra, Croation National Opera Company, Dubrovinik Festival and others *Comments:* in collaboration with the Zagreb Philharmonic Orchestra *Type:* conducting

Vaclav Huml International Violin Competition
Vaclav Huml Concours International De Violin
c/o Hrvatski glazbeni zavod, Gunduliceva 6, 10000 **Zagreb**
Tel: 1-430 544
director Andre Mohorovicic
Dates: January *Frequency:* quadrennial (2001)
Type: violin

CZECH REPUBLIC (+420)

Brno International Music Competition
Ars Koncert Ltd, Uvoz 39, 602 00 **Brno**
Tel: 5-4323 3116 Fax: 5-432 3358
E-Mail: ars@arskoncert.cz
secretary Katerina Baranova
Date: 18-23 Sept 2000 *Frequency:* annual
Eligibility: age limit 30 years *Awards:* 1st prize: CZK 100k, 2nd prize: CZK 70k, 3rd prize: CZK 30k
Comments: deadline for entries: 30 April 2000
Type: 2000: tuba, 2001: horn

Emmy Destinn International Voice Competition
Kancelár Emy Destinnové, H.Kvapilové 36, 370 10 **Ceské Budejovice**
Tel: 603-720 300 Fax: 38-34526
Dates: 22-25 April 2000 *Frequency:* annual
Eligibility: categories: I: up to 25 years, II: up to 35 years
Comments: deadline: 31 March 2000
Type: voice

Interpretation Competition
Masarykovo nám, 430 01 **Chomutov**
director Hanousková Jaroslava
Frequency: quadriennial (2003)
Eligibility: aged 18-30 yrs *Type:* woodwind

International Smetana Piano Competition
Hradecká kulturní a vzdelávací spolecnost, tr.Cs.armády 300, 500 02 **Hradec Králové**
Tel: 49-551 4722/4723/4724/4725/3966
Fax: 49-551 3966
E-Mail: hkvs@hk.czcom.cz
Date: 13-18 Nov 2000 *Frequency:* biennial *Eligibility:* age limit 1st category 28 yrs, 2nd category 18 yrs *Comments:* deadline for entries: 30 June 2000 *Type:* piano

Musical Competition of Beethoven's Prize
Správa zámku, Hradce n/Mor. a Radune, 747 41 **Hradec nad Moravicí**
Tel: 653-911 185/186 Fax: 653-911 485
director Ing. Radomír Pribyla; manager Petr Hanousek (tel: 653-626 489)
Dates: 9-16 June 2000 *Frequency:* annual *Eligibility:* violin: categories: I up to 19yrs, II up to 30yrs; piano trio total ages 90 yrs *Comments:* deadline for entries: 11 Feb 2000; the competition is held in the castle Hradec nad Moravicí (North Moravia) *Type:* 2000: violin, violoncello; 2001: piano, string quartet

Schubert International Interpretation Competition for Piano Duos Jeseník
Mèstská kulturní zarízení, ul. 28. ríjna 880, 790 01 **Jeseník**
Tel: 645-411 254 Fax: 645-411 505
Internet: info-jesenik.cz/mkz/schubert
E-Mail: mkz@info-jesenik.cz
Dates: 25-28 April 2001 *Frequency:* biennial
Eligibility: categories: I up to 21yrs, II age addition up to 70yrs *Comments:* deadline for applications: 28 Feb 2001
Type: piano duos

Antonín Dvorák International Vocal Competition
Karlovarsky symfonicky orchestr, I.P. Pavlova 14, 360 01 **Karlovy Vary**
Tel: 17-28707/28708/23310 Fax: 17-23753
manager Marie Dufková
Dates: 3-10 November 2000 *Frequency:* annual
Eligibility: categories: 1st women up to 23 years, men up to 24 years; 2nd women up to 30 years, men up to 32 years *Comments:* deadline for entries: 30 June 2000
Type: vocal

Mezinárodní Sborová Soutez Bedricha Smetany
Informacní Centrum Litomysl, Smetanovo nám 72, 570 01 **Litomysl**
Tel: 464-4150 Fax: 464-612 161
artistic director & conductor Vlastislav Novák

International Fryderyk Chopin Piano Competition
Spolecnost F. Chopina, Hlavni tr. 47, 353 01 **Marianské Lázne**
Tel: 165-622 617 Fax: 165-622 617
president Ivan Klánsky
Dates: June 2001 *Frequency:* biennial
Eligibility: categories: 1st: under 18 years, 2nd: under 28 years *Comments:* deadline for entry: March 31, 2001 *Type:* piano

Iuventus Mundi Cantat
Svatky Písní, Slovenská 5, 772 00 **Olomouc**
Tel: 68-522 7878 Fax: 68-522 7878
Dates: 7-11 June 2000 *Frequency:* annual
Comments: deadline for entry: 31 Jan 2000 *Type:* choir competition for children, youth and adults in the categories of profane, sacred and church

8th International Competition of Blind and Partially Sighted Performers 2000
Spolecenství organizací nevidomych a slabozrakych CR, Karlínské nám 10, 186 03 **Praha** 8
Tel: 2-2481 7393 Fax: 2-2481 8398
E-Mail: sons_zahr@braillnet.cz
chief officer Václav Polásek
Dates: 6-13 Feb 2000 *Frequency:* triennial
Eligibility: age limit 16-36yrs
Comments: deadline for applications: 30 Oct 1999; the competition is held in Marianské Lázne
Type: flute, clarinet, trumpet, horn, trombone, violin, viola, violoncello, double-bass, piano, accordion, guitar, singing

International Broadcasting Competition for Young Musicians Concertino Praga
Cesky rozhlas, Vinohradská 12, 120 99 **Praha** 2
Tel: 2-2409 4492/4288 Fax: 2-2421 8089
E-Mail: jhlinkov@cro.cz
secretary Jana Hlinkova
Frequency: annual
Eligibility: age limit up to 16yrs (piano and string instruments) or 18yrs (woodwinds and chamber ensembles)
Awards: the winners will be introduced in recitals during the next year in Prague and Jindrichuv Hradec on the festival Concertino Praga (June)
Comments: deadline for entries: 30 April every year
Type: 2000: piano, violin, violoncello; 2001: flute, oboe, clarinet, horn, trumpet; 2002: chamber ensembles (2-5 members);

International Television Festival 'Golden Prague'
Ceská televize, Kavci Hory, 140 70 **Praha** 4
Tel: 2-613 4029/4036 Fax: 2-6121 2891
Internet: www.czech-tv.cz/festival/golden_prague
E-Mail: renata.elhenicka@czech-tv.cz
director Renata Elhenická
Dates: 16-20 May 2000 *Frequency:* annual
Comments: deadline for entries: 31 January 2000
Type: serious music programmes, dance, jazz and world music

Prague Spring International Music Competition
Hellichova 18, 118 00 **Praha** 1
Tel: 2-533 474/530 293 Fax: 2-536 040
Internet: www.festival.cz
E-Mail: festival@login.cz
competition secretary Jarmila Nedvedová
Dates: 6-15 May 2000
Frequency: annual *Eligibility:* open to musicians of all nationalities who have not previously won 1st prize in the respective category in the Prague Spring International Music Competition
Awards: cash, engagements *Type:* 2000: conducting, cello (under the age of 30); 2001: flute, oboe

International Competition of the Blind and Partially Sighted Music Composers
c/o Czech Association of the Blind and Partially Sighted, Karlínské nám 10, 186 03 **Praha 8**
Tel: 2-2481 7393 Fax: 2-2481 8398
E-Mail: sons-dolezahr@braillnet.cz
chief officer Václav Polásek
Frequency: triennial (2002) *Eligibility:* no age limit
Type: composers

Heran Violoncello Competition (International)
Klubcentrum, Havlickova 621, 562 01 **Ústí n. Orlicí**
Tel: 465-525 790/245 Fax: 465-525 245
Dates: April 2001 *Frequency:* biennial (2001)
Eligibility: age limit 16 years
Comments: deadline for entries: January 10, 2001
Type: violoncello

Kocian Violin Competition (International)
Klubcentrum, Havlíckova 621, 562 01 **Ústí n. Orlicí**
Tel: 465-525 790/245 Fax: 465-525 245
Dates: 2-7 May 2000 *Frequency:* annual
Eligibility: age limit 16 years
Comments: deadline for entries: January 31, 2000
Type: violin

DENMARK (+45)

Nicolai Malko International Competition for Young Conductors, The
Danmarks Radio, Radiohuset, Rosenørns Allé 22, 1999 **Frederiksberg** C
Tel: 3520 6371 Fax: 3520 6121
secretary general Gert Herzberg; secretary Jette Bay
Dates: June 2001 *Frequency:* triennial (2001)
Eligibility: conductors aged 20-31
Awards: cash, engagements
Comments: deadline for application: Feb 1 2001 (application form available May 2000)
Type: conducting

Carl Nielsen International Music Competitions
Odense Symphony Orchestra, Claus Bergs Gade 9, 5000 **Odense** C
Tel: 6612 0057 Fax: 6591 0047
E-Mail: carlnielsencompetition@odensesymfoni.dk
secretary general Marianne Granvig
Dates: 1-9 June 2000 (violin)
Eligibility: up to 30 yrs
Awards: cash prizes totalling DKK 350000, concerts and recitals *Comments:* last application date for 2000: January 15 *Type:* 2000: violin

International Organ Competition Odense
Læssøegade 74, 5230 **Odense** M
Tel: 6613 6363 Fax: 6613 6363
E-Mail: organcomp@post.tele.dk
secretary Henning Nielsen
Dates: 17-25 August 2000 *Frequency:* biennial
Eligibility: under 35 yrs
Awards: cash *Type:* organ

ESTONIA (+372)

Con brio Singing Competition for Young Singers
Noorte konkurss-festival Con brio
c/o Eesti Kontsert, Estonia pst.4, 10148 **Tallinn**
Tel: 6-446 255 Fax: 6-443 198
Internet: www.concert.ee/
E-Mail: eesti.kontsert@concert.ee
director Enno Mattiesen; artistic director Madis Kolk
Frequency: biennial *Type:* vocal

International Choral Festival Tallinn
Rahvusvaheline koorfestival Tallinn
c/o Estonian Choral Society, Suur-Karja 23, 10140 **Tallinn**
Tel: 2-449 147 Fax: 2-449 147
Internet: www.kul.ee/koor
director Aivar Mäe
Dates: June *Frequency:* triennial
Eligibility: for all types of choirs
Type: choral

FINLAND (+358)

Helsinki International Ballet Competition
Teatterikulma, Meritullinkatu 33, 00170 **Helsinki**
Tel: 9-135 7887 Fax: 9-135 5522
Internet: www.teatteri.org/balletcomp
E-Mail: tinfo@teatteri.org
director Riitta Seppälä; artistic director Jorma Uotinen
Dates: 25 May – 5 June 2001
Eligibility: juniors 15-18 yrs, seniors 19-25 yrs; separate male/female categories
Awards: cash *Comments:* choreography section in competition *Type:* ballet

International Jean Sibelius Violin Competition
BP 31, 00101 **Helsinki**
Tel: 9-4114 3443 Fax: 9-2200 2680
Internet: www.siba.fi/sibeliuscompetition
E-Mail: violincompetition@kolumbus.fi
chairman Tuomas Haapanen; chairman of the jury Auts Sallinen; competition secretary Harri Pohpolainen
Dates: 18 November-2 December 2000 *Frequency:* quinquennial (2000) *Eligibility:* violinists born in 1970 or later *Awards:* cash: I 16k E, II 12.5k E, III 9k E, IV-VIII 1.8k E *Comments:* deadline for applications: August 18, 2000 *Type:* violin

International Sibelius Conductors' Competition
Finlandia Hall, 00100 **Helsinki**
Tel: 40-503 0997 Fax: 40-803 0997
E-Mail: elina.siltanen@icenet.fi
secretary general Elina Siltanen; artistic director Esa-Pekka-Salonen
Dates: 14-18 May 2000 *Frequency:* quinquennial (2000)
Eligibility: up to 35 yrs *Awards:* cash *Comments:* repertoire from Mozart to contemporary Finnish composers
Type: conducting

Mirjam Helin International Singing Competition
Finnish Cultural Foundation, PO Box 203, 00121 **Helsinki**
Tel: 9-602 144 Fax: 9-640 474
Internet: www.skr.fi/mh
E-Mail: mh@skr.fi
executive secretary of the Finnish Cultural Foundation Timo Arjas
Dates: August 2004 *Frequency:* quinquennial (2004)
Eligibility: two categories: women born in 1973 or later, men born in 1971 or later
Awards: four prizes for both categories
Comments: street address: Bulevardi 5 A, 00120 Helsinki *Type:* singing competition – separate female and male categories

International Paulo Cello Competition
BP 7802, 00101 **Helsinki**
Tel: 9-405 441 Fax: 9-2200 2680
competition secretary Minna Pitkänen
Date: November 2001 *Frequency:* quintennial
Awards: cash, total of prizes FIM 165k
Comments: deadline for applications: June 2001
Type: cello

Kuhmo International Chamber Music Competition
Torikatu 39, 88900 **Kuhmo**
Tel: 8-652 0936 Fax: 8-652 1961
Internet: www.kuhmofestival.fi
E-Mail: Kuhmo.festival@kajak.fi
artistic director Seppo Kimanen
Date: July 2000 *Frequency:* annual
Eligibility: musicians under 30 years, any nationality
Awards: cash and engagements in Kuhmo and Helsinki
Comments: appliction deadline: end of April 2000; organised by Kuhmo Chamber Music Festival/Kuhmo Music Society; second address: Fredrikinkatu 77 A 2-4, 00100 Helsinki, Tel: 9-493 902/867, Fax: 9-493 956; see also Festivals *Type:* 2000: quartets; 2001: duos; 2002: piano string trios

Lahti International Organ Competition
Kirkkokatu 5, 15110 **Lahti**
Tel: 3-782 3184 Fax: 3-783 2190
E-Mail: lot@pp.phnet.fi
secretary Petri Vähätalo
Dates: 2001 *Frequency:* quadriennial
Eligibility: under 30 years old *Awards:* cash
Comments: entry fee *Type:* organ

Tampere Choir Festival
Tamperen Säval-Tamperen Choir Festival, Tullikamarinaukio 2, 33100 **Tampere**
Tel: 3-3146 6136 Fax: 3-223 0121
Internet: www.tampere.fi/festival/music/choir.htm
E-Mail: music@tampere.fi
contact Aila Marrinen
Date: June 2001 *Eligibility:* participation fee FIM 500
Comments: deadline for entries: chorus: 9 March 2001, vocal ensembles: 23 March 2001; new details on how to enter will be published in April 2000; please contact office or website *Type:* chorus, vocal ensembles

FRANCE (+33)

Rencontres Chorégraphiques Internationales de Seine-Saint-Denis
96 bis rue Sodi Carnot, 93177 **Bagnolet** Cedex 1
Tel: 1-5582 0808 Fax: 1-4363 8171
E-Mail: ciboc@wanadoo.fr
directrice générale Lorrina Niclas; directrice des Rencontres Anita Mathieu
Dates: 23-28 May 2000
Frequency: biennial (2000)
Awards: the winners will be helped with the creation and diffusion of their work
Comments: the companies are chosen for their work and experience; application from October 1999 for June 2000; 500 participants, 180 will present their work on the international platforms, and 15 among them will be awarded and programmed in May 2000
Type: contemporary choreography

Concours de Composition Musicale
Secrétariat, 3 Bis, rue L'eonel de Moustier, 25000 **Besançon**
Tel: 3-8125 0585 Fax: 3-8181 5215
Internet: www.besancon.com
administrateur Olivier Laval; président, maître Yves-Marie Lehmann; directeur Michel des Borderies
Dates: September *Frequency:* biennial (2000) *Eligibility:* professional composers under 40 yrs – symphonic works *Comments:* member of World Federation of International Music Competitions *Type:* composition

Concours International de Jeunes Chefs d'Orchestre
Secrétariat, 3 Bis, rue L'eonel de Moustier, 25000 **Besançon**
Tel: 3-8125 0585 Fax: 3-8181 5215
administration Olivier Laval; président, maître Yves-Marie Lehmann; directeur Michel des Borderies
Dates: September 2001
Frequency: biennial (2001) *Eligibility:* professional conductors under 35 yrs – symphonic works *Awards:* FF 70k and conducting some French national orchestras and other international orchestras *Comments:* member of World Federation of International Music Competitions *Type:* conducting

Concours International de la Musique Française
28 Rue de la Paix, 78390 **Bois D'Arcy**
Tel: 1-3460 3096 Fax: 1-3460 0853
président Désiré N'Kaoua
Date: October-November *Frequency:* annual *Eligibility:* no age limit *Awards:* 1st prize: FF 25k, 2nd prize: FF 10k, 3rd prize: FF 5k, special prize Désiré N'Kaoua: FF 10k accumalative with other prizes, a recital in Paris is offered & advertising in 137 countries *Comments:* entry fee FF 350 per applicant *Type:* chamber music or piano solo

Bordeaux International String Quartet Competition
Cour Mably, 3 rue Mably, 33000 **Bordeaux**
Tel: 5-5644 0158 Fax: 5-5648 8610
contact Bernard Lummeaux
Date: Sept 2001 *Frequency:* biennial *Awards:* total of FF 500k *Comments:* contact for applications: Isabella Bensa, International Consultant, Keizergracht 294 B, 1016 EW Amersterdam, Netherlands, Tel: +31 20-639 0323, Fax: +31 20-627 7587; deadline for applications: May 2001 *Type:* string quartet

Concours International de Musique Electroacoustique de Bourges
Institut Inter'l de Musique Electroacoustic de Bourges, Place André Malraux, BP 39, 18001 **Bourges** Cedex
Tel: 2-4820 4187 Fax: 2-4820 4551
Internet: www.gmeb.fr
E-Mail: ime-bourges@gmeb.fr
directeurs Christian Clozier, Françoise Barrière
Dates: June *Frequency:* annual
Eligibility: 3 age groups: category 1: under 25 yrs and students, category 2: 25 yrs and over, category 3: composers with at least 20 yrs experience in electroacoustic music *Awards:* cash, recordings, residencies
Comments: see also Festivals
Type: electroacoustic music

Douai International Music Competition – Georges Prêtre Competition
Secrétariat du Orchestre Symphonique, 87 rue de la Fonderie F, 59500 **Douai**
Tel: 3-2771 7777 Fax: 3-2771 7778
Internet: perso.wanadoo.fr/orchestre.douai/
E-Mail: orchestre.symphonique.de.douai@wanadoo.fr
director Henri Vachey; artistic director Emmanuelle Raës
Dates: February *Frequency:* annual *Eligibility:* female singers up to 32 yrs, male singers up to 35yrs; application fee 500 FF *Awards:* 84k FF total prize, remunerated tour of concerts with the Orchestre Symphonique
Comments: accomponist; see also Orchestras *Type:* 2000: opera; 2001: violin; 2002: cello

Concours International de Piano Epinal
BP 428, 88011 **Epinal**
Tel: 3-2982 5332/2931 4545 Fax: 3-2935 2616
executive director Pierre Jeandidier; president Jacques Grasser; secretaire Lucienne Gaspard
Dates: 16-25 March 2001 *Frequency:* biennial (2001)
Eligibility: up to 30 yrs *Awards:* cash, recital for 1st prize, medals *Comments:* deadline 15/01/2001 *Type:* classical piano and contemporary repertoire

Concours Jeunes Compositeurs
c/o GRAME, Centre National de Création Musicale, 9 rue du Garet, BP 1185, 69202 **Lyon** Cedex 1
Tel: 4-7207 3700 Fax: 4-7207 3701
Internet: www.grame.fr
E-Mail: grame@rd-france.fr
Date: January 2001 *Frequency:* biennial *Eligibility:* compsers up to 40 years of age *Awards:* residency at Grame studios for shortlisted composers, winning compositions presented by l'Ensemble Orchestral Contemporain during Grame season *Comments:* deadline for application: April 2000; see also Venues and Promoters (GRAME) *Type:* composition

Concours International de Chant de Marmande (Lot et Garonne et de la région acquitaine)
12 rue du General Brun, 47200 **Marmande**
Tel: 5-5389 6875 Fax: 5-5389 6875
président Philippe Mestres; communication Michel Philippon; conseiller artistique Michel Herbé
Dates: 27-30 August *Frequency:* annual *Eligibility:* under 38 years old *Awards:* FF 125k (9 awards), engagements
Comments: see also Festivals *Type:* opera, voice operetta, French melody, operetta

Concours International d' Opéra
Parc des Cédres Bâliment 4, 77 Boulevard du Redon, 13009 **Marseille**
Tel: 4-9141 2826 Fax: 4-9126 6515
secrétaire général Pierre Duges; président Régis Mathoron
Date: September *Frequency:* biennial (2001) *Eligibility:* niveau conservatoire, age limit: 34 years *Awards:* 6 awards: 1st prize (for men & women): FF 50k, 2nd prize: FF 25k, 3rd prize: FF 15k *Comments:* the competitors have to present 7 opera songs *Type:* opera songs

Concours International Piano 20e Siècle
46 ter, rue Ste Catherine, 45000 **Orléans**
Tel: 1-4245 5681/2-3862 8922 Fax: 1-4245 5681/2-3862 8922
president Association OCI Françoise Thinat; vice president Catherine Mounier; treasurer Joan Gauthier
Dates: 21-29 Feb 2000 *Frequency:* biennial *Eligibility:* pianists under 40 years old *Awards:* total prize money FF 300k *Comments:* deadline for enrolment: 15 January 2000; winners participate in a prestigious concert and also record a CD; registration fee 600F (payable simultaneously with the application) *Type:* piano – repertoire: work from 1900 to the present

Concours International d'Orgue Grand Prix de Chartres
Secrétariat du Grand Prix de Chartres, 75 rue de Grenelle, 75007 **Paris**
Tel: 1-4548 3174/2-3721 5000 (office du tourisme de chartres) Fax: 1-4549 1434
directeur Colette Morillon; president-fondateur du Concours Pierre Firmin-Didot
Dates: September 2000 *Frequency:* biennial *Eligibility:* organists of all nationalities born after 1 June 1963 (under 35 years old) *Awards:* 1st prizes for interpretation:30k FF, 2nd prizes for interpretation:10k FF, and 50 engagements in France and abroad *Comments:* see also Festivals *Type:* organ, interpretation

Concours International de Chant et Musique de Chambre de Paris
8 rue du Dôme, 75116 **Paris**
Tel: 1-4704 7638 Fax: 1-4727 3503
Internet: www.infoservie.fr/ufam
E-Mail: ufam@wanadoo.fr
president Christiane de Bayser
Dates: 25 June-3 July 2000 (voice); Oct-Nov 2000 (chamber music) *Frequency:* biennial *Eligibility:* singers: women up to 32 yrs, men 34 yrs; average age of ensembles 34 yrs *Awards:* cash (FF 150k), engagements *Comments:* closing dates: voice-May 2000; chamber music-September 2000 *Type:* singing (July), chamber music (Oct-Nov)

Concours International de Danse de Paris
36 rue de Laborde, 75008 **Paris**
Tel: 1-4522 2874 Fax: 1-4522 6024
administrateur général Cyril Lafaurie
Dates: Nov 2000 *Frequency:* biennial (2000) *Eligibility:* 15-26 yrs: classical and contemporary professional dancers who have been with a professional dance company for at least an entire season, or are presented by an official dance school (soloists and couples)
Awards: cash prizes & medals
Comments: competition takes place within the frame of Nouveau Festival International de Danse de Paris; every two years also present important classical companies
Type: dance – competiton divided into classical and contemporary sections

Concours International de Flute Jean-Pierre Rampal
c/o Concours Internationaux de la Ville de Paris, Acanthes, 3 rue des Couronnes, 75020 **Paris**
Tel: 1-4033 4535 Fax: 1-4033 4538
general manager Claude Samuel
Dates: autumn 2001 *Frequency:* triennial *Eligibility:* up to 30 years old *Awards:* 1st prize 70k FF *Type:* flute

Concours International de Piano et de Violon Marguerite Long – Jacques Thibaud
32 av Matignon, 75008 **Paris**
Tel: 1-4266 6680 Fax: 1-4266 0643
president M Penin
Dates: 2001 *Frequency:* triennial for each instrument *Eligibility:* 30 yrs *Awards:* cash, one year engagements; for the violin competition: prizes – 1st 150k FF, 2nd 60k FF, 3rd 40k FF, 4th 25k FF, 5th 15k FF, 6th 10k FF, also 1 tour in Asia, South America *Comments:* deadline: 1st September 1999 *Type:* 2001: piano, violin

Concours International de Violoncelle Rostropovitch
c/o Concours Internationaux de la Ville de Paris, Acanthes, 3 rue des Couronnes, 75020 **Paris**
Tel: 1-4033 4535 Fax: 1-4033 4538
general manager Claude Samuel
Dates: 1-14 Oct 2001 *Frequency:* quadrennial (2001) *Eligibility:* up to 33 yrs; application fee *Awards:* 1st prize 70k FF *Type:* instrumental (violoncello)

Concours Maurice André
c/o Concours Internationaux de la Ville de Paris, Acanthes, 3, rue des Couronnes, 75020 **Paris**
Tel: 1-4033 4535 Fax: 1-4033 4538
general manager Claude Samuel
Dates: Autumn 2001 *Frequency:* triennial *Eligibility:* up to 30 years old *Awards:* 1st: 70k FF *Type:* trumpet

International Competition of Classical Choreography
36 rue de Laborde, 75008 **Paris**
Tel: 1-4522 2874 Fax: 1-4522 6024
general administrator Cyril Lafaurie; president Jacques Chirac
Date: Jan 2001 *Frequency:* biennial (2001) *Eligibility:* choreographers under 40 years of age, work for 15-20 minute duration, for 5-10 dancers *Awards:* cash prizes for semi-finals and finals *Comments:* application deadline for 2001: Nov 2000
Type: neo-classical choreography

International Organ Competition
Concours International d'Orgue de la Ville de Paris Acanthes, 3 rue des Couronnes, 75020 **Paris**
Tel: 1-4033 4535 Fax: 1-4033 4538
general manager Claude Samuel
Dates: Oct 2000 *Frequency:* biennial (2000) *Eligibility:* up to 35 years old *Awards:* 2 1st prizes for interpretation and improvisation: 50k FF each *Type:* organ

International Violin and Bow Making Competition
c/o Acanthes, 3 rue des Couronnes, 75020 **Paris**
Tel: 1-4033 4535 Fax: 1-4033 4538
general manager Claude Samuel
Date: Nov-Dec 2000 *Eligibility:* no age limit *Awards:* 1st prizes: Violin Making Competition – 25k FF for each category (violin, viola, cello, contrabass), Bow Making Competition – 10k FF each category (violin, viola, cello, contrabass) *Type:* violin and bow making (violin, viola, cello, contrabass)

Martial Solal Piano Jazz Competition
c/o Acanthes, 3 rue des Couronnes, 75020 **Paris**
Tel: 1-4033 4535 Fax: 1-4033 4538
general manager Claude Samuel
Date: Sept *Frequency:* quadrennial (2002)

Monte-Carlo Piano Masters
Salle Gaveau (J.M. Fournier Productions), 45-47 rue de la Boétie, 75008 **Paris**
Tel: 1-4562 6971 Fax: 1-4225 9780
président Jean-Marie Fournier
Dates: June *Frequency:* annual
Eligibility: exclusively finalists of other international competitions *Awards:* cash, one award: US$30k
Comments: venue: Opéra de Monte-Carlo *Type:* piano

Olivier Messiaen International Competition
c/o Acanthes, 3 rue des Couronnes, 75020 **Paris**
Tel: 1-4033 4535 Fax: 1-4033 4538
general manager Claude Samuel
Date: autumn 2000 *Eligibility:* 30 years old
Awards: 1st prize: 70k FF *Type:* piano

Prix International de Composition Musicale Arthur Honneger
Fondation de France, 40 av Hoche, 75008 **Paris**
Tel: 1-4421 3100 Fax: 1-4421 3101/3154
general secretary (culture) Catia Riccaboni; president Hubert Curein; general secretary of the Fondation de France Patrice Gonon
Dates: 2000 (dates are announced end of the previous year) *Frequency:* biennial (2000)
Eligibility: open to all nationalities and ages
Awards: FF 50k *Comments:* for information contact the General Secretary at the above address *Type:* composition, can also be interpretation

Reading Panel of IRCAM and Ensemble Intercontemporain
c/o IRCAM – Institut de Recherche et Coordination Acoustique/Musique, 1, Place Igor Stravinsky, 75004 **Paris**
Tel: 1-4478 1233/4834 Fax: 1-4277 2947/4478 4806
Internet: www.ircam.fr
E-Mail: berthy@ircam.fr
directeur Laurent Bayle; directeur artistique Eric De Visscher; directeur honoraire Pierre Boulez; directeur pedagogie Marie-Hélène Serra; directeur de la production Alain Jacquinot; directeur scientifique Hugues Vinet; chef du personnel Bertrand Pêrisson; communication Madame Manceau (tel: 1-4478 4808)
Dates: Feb 2000 *Frequency:* annual
Awards: commissioning of works for chamber ensemble or works using the latest technologies, places on 4 week workshops, places on one year course in composition and musical computing
Comments: deadline for applications: Sept-October 1999 for 2000 competition
Type: young composers

Concours International Sinfonia
PO Box 1012, 24001 **Périgueux** Cedex
Tel: 5-5353 3295 Fax: 5-5303 7877
Internet: www.perigord.tm.fr/sinfonia.htm
E-Mail: sinfonia@perigord.tm.fr
direction générale David Théodoridès; administrateur Michel Théodoridès
Dates: 4 days in Sept during the Festival Sinfonia en Pèrigord *Frequency:* biennial (2001)
Eligibility: young ensemble of baroque music
Awards: 1st prize: 40k FF, 2nd prize: 20k FF, 3rd prize: 10k FF, a concert at the next festival Sinfonia, the recording of a radio programme on France Musique, and an opportunity to record a CD with a big distributor
Comments: see also Festivals
Type: baroque music played with old or copied instruments (vocal: cantates, sacred, hymns)

Pro Musicis International Award
Association d'Echanges Artistiques Internationaux, Pro Musicis International Centre, Château de Valesne, 37190 **Saché**
Tel: 2-4773 2121 Fax: 2-4773 2090
contact Carole Lemarié
Frequency: 2 years out of 3 (2001-2002, 2004, etc)
Eligibility: solo classical artists of all types for the following instruments: 2001: harp, harpsichord, string, voice; 2002: guitar, piano, winds; 2003: none and back to the cycle *Awards:* the opportunity to perform in concert halls for the promotion of your career (public concerts) and to repeat twice the programme of the public concert for underprivileged audiences (community service concerts) in each city, specifically in Paris, Rome, Boston, New York, Los Angeles and Hong Kong *Comments:* next competitions 2001; artists receive fees for each public performance *Type:* classical soloists of all types – different instruments each year

Prix Volinine
c/o Chorea Diffusion, 25 Rue Ampère, 78100 **Saint-Germain-en-Laye**
Tel: 1-3973 0924 Fax: 1-3061 2672
director Claudie Jacquelin
Dates: Oct 2001 *Frequency:* biennial (2001) *Eligibility:* minimum 3 dancers, maximum 15 minutes; application fee: 450 FF *Awards:* 80k FF attributed, and performances in prestigious festivals
Comments: enrolment deadline: 15 March 2001, selection in February 2001; the purpose of the competition is to promote the choreographic creation in all its forms of expression *Type:* dance

Grand Prix International Vidéo Danse
UFIP – Vidéo Danse, Village d'Enterprise Cap Var, D2 – 148 Av. Georges Guynemer, 06700 **St-Laurent-du-Var**
Tel: 4-9259 2424 Fax: 4-9259 2425
E-Mail: info@french-riviera.fr
director Jacques Menet
Date: December 2000 *Frequency:* annual *Comments:* deadline for entries: 5 November *Type:* contemp. dance

Concours International d'Instruments à Vent de Toulon
117, Av. Lazard Carnot, 83000 **Toulon**
Tel: 4-9493 5545 Fax: 4-9424 1610
président Henri Tiscornia; directeur Claude-Henry Bonnet; secrétaire générale Mme Tiscornia; pr Charlotte Hamel
Dates: 19-26 May 2000 *Frequency:* annual
Eligibility: all nationalities, under 31 years at the date of the competition *Awards:* 1st 22k FF, 2nd 13k FF, 3rd 9k FF *Comments:* deadline always 1 March *Type:* 2000: trumpet; 2001: trombone; 2002: oboe; 2003: clarinet

Concours International de Chant de la Ville de Toulouse
Théâtre du Capitole, 31000 **Toulouse**
Tel: 5-6162 1351 Fax: 5-6162 9690
general secretary Georges Canet
Dates: last week of September 2000
Frequency: biennial *Eligibility:* 18-33 yrs *Awards:* FF 147500 total, engagements *Comments:* deadline for 2000: mid July 2000; application fee: 100FF, every day the candidate receives 200FF *Type:* vocal

Concours Européan de Duos Lyriques
MISCOM, Berges Catalanes 502, 6 Impasses du Ramier, 31200 **Toulouse**
Tel: 5-6129 8001 Fax: 5-6129 8001
présidente Marie-Héléne Mayeux-Bouchard
Date: July *Frequency:* annual *Eligibility:* no age restrictions
Awards: prizes: FF 10k *Type:* singing, solo, duo, trio

Flori Lege Vocal de Tours
Rue des Minimes, BP 1452, 37014 **Tours** Cedex 1
Tel: 2-4721 6526 Fax: 2-4721 6771
directeur Christain Balandras
Date: March *Frequency:* annual *Awards:* special awards of 2000: Euro 1k *Type:* singing

Concours International de Guitare de Trédrez-Locquémeau
Mairie, 22300 **Trédrez-Locquémeau**
Tel: 2-9635 7452 Fax: 2-9635 7591
responsable Roger Eon
Dates: July 2000 *Frequency:* annual *Eligibility:* guitarists up to 21 years; 3 sections: international, national high and power level *Awards:* 1st: 30k FF; 2nd: 10k FF; 3rd: 5k FF *Comments:* deadline for applications end of May 2000 *Type:* guitar

GEORGIA (+995)

Tbilisi International Piano Competition
8 Griboedov st., 380008 **Tbilisi**
Tel: 32-982 446/987 184 Fax: 32-942 447
director Manana Doidjashvili
Date: 5-18 October *Frequency:* quadriennial *Eligibility:* pianists up to 33 years *Awards:* cash, 6 prizes
Comments: application deadline: 1 April of the same year *Type:* classical and contemporary piano

International Tenor Competition
D.Andguladze Foundation of Vocal Culture, 63 Kostava st., 380015 **Tbilisi**
Tel: 32-330 751
director Guri Zakareishvili
Date: September *Frequency:* every 5 years *Eligibility:* up to 35 years *Awards:* cash, 3 prizes *Comments:* application deadline: 1 March of the same year *Type:* opera

GERMANY (+49)

Internationaler Violinwettbewerb Leopold Mozart
Konservatorium der Stadt Augsburg, Maximilianstr. 59, 86150 **Augsburg**
Tel: 821-324 4892 Fax: 821-313 088
Internet: www.leopold-mozart-competition.de
E-Mail: l.mozart.comp@augsburg.de
competition officer Angelika Kranz
Dates: November 2003 *Frequency:* quadriennial
Eligibility: 15-30 years *Awards:* cash approx. 65k DM, young musicians awards, CD production and concert engagements, audience prize, Mozart prize, extra prizes
Comments: final concert broadcast on Bayerischer Rundfunk; accomodation free; member of the World Federation of International Music Competitions; application deadline: June 2003 *Type:* violin

Prix Europa, SFB
Masurenallee 8-14, 14046 **Berlin**
Tel: 30-3031 1610 Fax: 30-3031 1619
Internet: www.prix-europa.de
E-Mail: prix-europa@t-online.de
Leitung Peter Leonhard Braun, Suanne Hoffmann
Dates: mid-end October *Frequency:* annual *Awards:* 9 different prizes and the Willy Brandt Viewers Prize
Comments: entries must be registered by July; participants must be registered by September *Type:* international TV and radio competition

Fritz-Wortelmann-Preis der Stadt Bochum
Hattinger Str. 467, 44795 **Bochum**
Tel: 234-47720/47729 Fax: 234-47735
Internet: www.dfp-fidena.de
E-Mail: info@dfp-fidena.de
Leitung Annette Dabs-Baucks; Wissenschaftliche Mitarbeit Anke Meyer; Sekretariat Elke Citrich
Date: Nov 2001 *Frequency:* biennial
Eligibility: amateur *Awards:* cash 7.5k DM
Comments: see also National Organisations and Festivals *Type:* amateur puppetry; school theatre and adult theatre

Stadt Coburg International Singers' Contest Alexander Girardi
Internationalier Gesangswettbewerb Alexander Girardi
Stadt Coburg-Kulturabteilung, Steingasse 18, 96450 **Coburg**
Tel: 9561-891 402/411/412
Fax: 9561-891 029
Internet: www.johann-strauss.coburg.de
E-Mail: info@coburg-tourist.de
Leitung und Organisation Albrecht Tauer (Kulturabteilung); Vorsitzender der Jury Prof. Hartmut Hein
Dates: 25 June- 4 July 2001
Frequency: biennial *Eligibility:* female singers 18-30 years, male singers 18-32 years; repertoire: 7 aria opera (incl. 2 set pieces), 5 aria operetta (incl. 1 set piece)
Awards: prizes: 1st 15k DM, 2nd 12k DM, 3rd 9k DM, and special prizes of 3k DM each
Comments: application deadline: 10 April 2001

European Chopin Piano Competition
Chopin-Gesellschaft, Kasinostraße 3, 64293 **Darmstadt**
Tel: 6151-25957/55897/57271 Fax: 6151-25957
Präsident der Chopin Gesellschaft Prof. Lukaszczyk; Vorstandsmitglieder Dr. Helmut Kelleter, Irmgard Hörl, Erna Weitzel
Dates: Oct *Frequency:* triennial (2002)
Eligibility: pianists who are studying or who have studied for at least two semesters or one year in Europe, and who are not older than 30 years
Awards: 1st: DM 9k; 2nd: DM 6k; 3rd: DM 4k
Comments: deadline for applications: May 2002
Type: piano

Blaue Brücke
c/o Dresdner Zentrum für zeitgenössische Musik, Schevenstr. 17, 01326 **Dresden**
Tel: 351-264 620 Fax: 351-264 6223
Internet: www.zeitmusik.de
E-Mail: erkesti@zeitmusik.de
Direktor Prof. Udo Zimmermann; Verwaltungsleiterin Heike Höfer; Leiter der künstl. Produktion MD Jürgen Wirrmann; Musikwissenschaftler Frank Geißler
Frequency: biennial (2000)
Eligibility: composers and interpreters with a new work (i.e. not yet performed or produced)
Awards: 1st prize (one of 3 selected projects): 30k DM
Comments: deadline for entries: 15 Feb 2000; see also National Organisations, Orchestras, Festivals and Venues *Type:* composers and interpreters

International Concours Clara Schumann für Klavier
Robert-Schumann-Gesellschaft, Bilkerstr. 4-6, 40213 **Düsseldorf**
Tel: 211-133 240 Fax: 211-327 083
Internet: members.aol.com/schumannga/gesell.htm
E-Mail: SchumannGA@aol.com
direktorin Dr. Gisela Schäfer
Dates: 1-9 June 2000 *Frequency:* triennial (2000)
Eligibility: up to 30 years of age
Awards: 1st prize: 25k DM, 2nd prize: 10k DM, 3rd prize: 5k DM *Comments:* the competition takes place within the Robert Schumann Festival (q.v.); venue: Tonhalle Düsseldorf *Type:* piano

Internationaler Wettbewerb für junge Pianisten Ettlingen
Sekretariat Musikschule der Stadt Ettlingen, Pforzheimer Str. 25a, 76275 **Ettlingen**
Tel: 7243-101 448/311 Fax: 7243-101 436
Internet: www.ettlingen.de/freizeit
E-Mail: piano.ettlingen@t-online.de
general organisation Frank Reich; artistic director Naoyuki Taneda
Dates: August 2000 *Frequency:* biennial (2000)
Eligibility: category A: pianists born after 11.8.84, category B: pianists born after 11.8.79
Awards: cash, concerts
Comments: deadline for applications: 8 May 2000
Type: piano

International Max Reger Competition for chamber music
c/o Raddatz Concerts, Burgunder Strasse 4, 79104 **Freiburg**
Tel: 761-23380 Fax: 761-554 862
president Wolfgang Marschner
Dates: mid-July 2002 *Frequency:* triennial
Awards: the overall prize money totals DM 30k
Comments: see also Promoters (Raddatz Concerts)
Type: chamber music (string)

International Violin Competition Ludwig Spohr
Internationaler Violinwettbewerb Ludwig Spohr
c/o Raddatz Concerts, Burgunderstrasse 4, 79104 **Freiburg**
Tel: 761-23380 Fax: 761-554 862
president Wolfgang Marschner; administrator Theresa Raddatz
Dates: August 2000
Frequency: triennial (2000) *Eligibility:* up to 32 yrs
Awards: total: 45k DM *Comments:* see also Agents (Raddatz Concerts) *Type:* violin

Internationaler Koloratur-Gesangswettbewerb Sylvia Geszty
Postfach 1163, 75390 **Gechingen**
Tel: 7056-8024 Fax: 7056-4256
Kammersängerin Prof. Sylvia Geszty; Sekretariat Egbert Gross
Dates: 1st round – March 2000, final round – 8-13 May 2000 *Frequency:* biennial (2000)
Eligibility: singers up to 32 yrs
Awards: 57000DM *Comments:* Competition takes place in Luxembourg: Théâtre Municipal Luxembourg with the Orchestre Philharmonique du Luxembourg
Type: vocal

Internationaler Gesangswettbewerb Neue Stimmen
Postfach 103, 33311 **Gütersloh**
Tel: 5241-817 372 Fax: 5241-819 513
E-Mail: nadine.lindemann@bertelsmann.de
programme manager Nadine Lindemann; member of the advisory board of the Bertelsmann Foundation Liz Mohn
Frequency: biennial (2001)
Eligibility: male singers 32 yrs, female singers 30 yrs
Awards: prizes – 1st: 15k DM, 2nd: 10k DM, 3rd: 5k DM
Comments: visiting address: Carl-Bertelsmann-Strasse 256, 33311 Gütersloh *Type:* vocal

Internationaler Robert Stolz Gesangswettbewerb
c/o Sekretariat des Wettbewerbs, Landesverband der Tonkünstler & Musiklehrer eV, Steilshooperstr. 42, 22305 **Hamburg**
Tel: 40-690 1091 Fax: 40-690 1092
contact Erika Menzel
Dates: 9-12 March 2000 *Frequency:* annual *Eligibility:* male & female up to 35 years old *Awards:* cash prizes: 1st: 8000 DM, 2nd: 5000 DM, 3rd: 3000 DM
Comments: deadline for application: 3 Feb 2000; registration fee 50 DM *Type:* Viennese operetta

Johannes-Brahms-Gesellschaft – Internationale Vereinigung e.V.
Peterstr. 39, 20355 **Hamburg**
Tel: 40-452 158 Fax: 40-410 2888
contact Ekart Besch
Dates: Aug-Sept 2001
Frequency: approx. every 2nd year
Eligibility: age limit about 32 years *Awards:* total up to DM 50k *Comments:* the type of instrument varies for each years competition; there is no competition in 2000, the next one should be in 2001, instrument not yet decided *Type:* music of Brahms

NDR Musikpreis 2000
NDR Radio 3, Alte Musik, Rothenbaumchaussee 132, 20149 **Hamburg**
Tel: 40-4156 2701 Fax: 40-4156 7567
Internet: www.ndr.de
E-Mail: g.hertz-eichenrode@ndr.de
organisation Gabriele Hertz-Eichenrode
Date: 28-31 August (in Cappel), 2-3 Sept (in Lübeck), 5 Sept (in Hamburg)
Frequency: annual *Eligibility:* up to 31 years old
Awards: cash: 1st prize: DM 15k, 2nd prize: DM 10k, 3rd prize: DM 5k; concerts, radio appearances, CD recordings *Type:* organ

Internationaler Violin-Wettbewerb Hannover
Stiftung Niedersachsen, Ferdinandstraße 4, 30175 **Hannover**
Tel: 511-990 5413 Fax: 511-314 499
Internet: www.stiftungniedersachsen.de/violin
E-Mail: sn.kultur@t-online.de
executive director Linda Anne Engelhardt; artistic director Krzysztof Wegrzyn
Dates: 5-18 November 2000
Frequency: triennial (2000)
Eligibility: violinists between 16 and 30 yrs of age
Awards: total cash awards of DM 140k, CD production, concert debuts, contact guidence agency *Comments:* dedicated to Joseph Joachim *Type:* violin

International Competition of Composing – Biennale Neue Musik Hannover
Hannoversche Gesellschaft für Neue Musik e.V., z. H. Herrn Hinrich Bergmeier, Warmbüchenstr. 16, 30159 **Hannover**
Tel: 511-306 8531 Fax: 511-306 8533
E-Mail: Bergmeier-HGNM@t-online.de
Frequency: biennial (2001)
Eligibility: composers of any nationality up to the age of 40 yrs; only works that have neither been performed or published to date
Type: composing

Orfeo 2000
Niedersächsische Staatstheater Hannover GmbH, c/o Sabine Sonntag, Opernplatz 1, 30159 **Hannover**
Tel: 511-9999 1002 Fax: 511-9999 1901
E-Mail: sabine_sonntag@oper-hannover.de
Date: preselections: 27 March-1 April 2000, final: 2 April 2000 *Eligibility:* open to women up to 30 years and men up to 32 years of age, and who have been finalists in an international singing competition *Awards:* total prize money: DM 100k (approx. US $52k) *Comments:* submit application including recording and a curriculum vitae to the Staatsper Hannover by 15 January 2000; a jury will then select the competitors; competition organised by Vereins- und Westbank AG in cooperation with the Staatsoper Hannover *Type:* singing (opera)

International Music Competitions Cologne
Dagobertstraße 38, 50668 **Köln**
Tel: 221-9128 18112 Fax: 221-131 204
Internet: www.mhs-koeln.de
president Prof. Dr. Werner Lohmann; secretary general t.b.a.; competition office Barbara Schmidt (e-mail: barbara.schmidt@uni-koeln.de); public relations Dr. Heike Sauer (e-mail: heike.sauer@uni-koeln.de)
Eligibility: cash: 1st prize DM 15k, 2nd prize DM 10k, 3rd prize DM 5k; audience award DM 5k; premium for each contestant of the last stage who does not attain a prize: DM 1k; final concert in Kölner Philharmonie for first three prize winners, further concert engagements or auditions; diplomas and daily allowance for competitors from 2nd stage on; expenses for travel, accomodation and meals have to be paid for by competitors themselves *Comments:* please see the following entries: International Piano Competition Cologne – Foundation Tomassoni; International Singing Competition Cologne – Foundation Hohnen and International Violinwettbewerb Köln – Stiftung Georg Kulenkampff; deadline for applications: 15 June of the year of the competitions; application fee: DM 150; all three competitions are member of the Fédération Mondiale des Concours Internationaux de Musique

International Piano Competition Cologne – The Tomassoni Foundation
Internationaler Klavierwettbewerb Köln – Stiftung Tomassoni
International Music Competitions Cologne, Dagobertstraße 38, 50668 **Köln**
Tel: 221-9128 18112 Fax: 221-131 204
Internet: www.mhs-koeln.de
E-Mail: barbara.schmidt@uni-koeln.de
president Prof. Dr. Werner Lohmann; secretary general t.b.a.; competition office Barbara Schmidt (e-mail: barbara.schmidt@uni-koeln.de); public relations Dr. Heike Sauer (e-mail: heike.sauer@uni-koeln.de)
Dates: Sept/Oct 2001 *Frequency:* quadriennial *Eligibility:* open to all pianists not older than 30 years *Awards:* cash: 1st prize DM 15k, 2nd prize DM 10k, 3rd prize DM 5k; audience award DM 5k; premium for each contestant of the last stage who does not attain a prize: DM 1k; final concert in Kölner Philharmonie for first three prize winners, further concert engagements or auditions; diplomas and daily allowance for competitors from 2nd stage on; expenses for travel, accomodation and meals have to be paid for by competitors themselves *Comments:* founded 1980, final concert in Kölner Philharmonie; member of the Fédération Mondiale des Concours Internationaux de Musique; deadline for applications 15 June with application fee of DM 150; see also International Singing Competition Cologne – Foundation Hohnen and International Violinwettbewerb Köln – Stiftung Georg Kulenkampff
Type: piano

International Singing Competition Cologne – The Helga and Paul Hohnen Foundation
Internationaler Gesangswettbewerb Köln – Stiftung Helga und Paul Hohnen
International Music Competitions Cologne, Dagobertstraße 38, 50668 **Köln**
Tel: 221-9128 18112 Fax: 221-131 204
Internet: www.mhs-koeln.de
E-Mail: barbara.schmidt@uni-koeln.de
president Prof. Dr. Werner Lohmann; secretary general t.b.a.; competition office Barbara Schmidt (e-mail: barbara.schmidt@uni-koeln.de); public relations Dr. Heike Sauer (e-mail: heike.sauer@uni-koeln.de)
Dates: Sept/Oct 2002
Frequency: quadriennial *Eligibility:* open to singers not older than 30 years *Awards:* cash: 1st prize DM 15k, 2nd prize DM 10k, 3rd prize DM 5k; audience award DM 5k; premium for each contestant of the last stage who does not attain a prize: DM 1k; final concert in Kölner Philharmonie for first three prize winners, further concert engagements or auditions; diplomas and daily allowance for competitors from 2nd stage on; expenses for travel, accomodation and meals have to be paid for by competitors themselves *Comments:* founded 1998; final concert in Kölner Philharmonie; member of the Fédération Mondiale des Concours Internationaux de Musique; deadline for application: 15 June; application fee of DM 150; see also International Piano Competition Cologne – Foundation Tomassoni and International Violinwettbewerb Köln – Stiftung Georg Kulenkampff *Type:* singing

International Violin Competition Cologne – The Georg Kulenkampff Foundation
International Violinwettbewerb Köln – Stiftung Georg Kulenkampff
Foundation Georg Kulenkampff, Dagobertstrasse 38, 50668 **Köln**
Tel: 221-912 818-0 Fax: 221-131 204
Internet: www.mhs-koeln.de
E-Mail: barbara.schmidt@uni-koeln.de
president Prof. Dr. Werner Lohmann; secretary general t.b.a.; competition office Barbara Schmidt (e-mail: barbara.schmidt@uni-koeln.de); public relations Dr. Heike Sauer (e-mail: heike.sauer@uni-koeln.de)
Dates: 21 Sept-2 Oct 2003 *Frequency:* quadriennial *Eligibility:* open to violinists not older than 30 years *Awards:* cash: 1st prize DM 15k, 2nd prize DM 10k, 3rd prize DM 5k; audience award DM 5k; premium for each contestant of the last stage who does not attain a prize: DM 1k; final concert in Kölner Philharmonie for first three prize winners, further concert engagements or auditions; diplomas and daily allowance for competitors from 2nd stage on; expenses for travel, accomodation and meals have to be paid for by competitors themselves *Comments:* founded 1988; final concert in Kölner Philharmonie; member of the Fédération Mondiale des Concours Internationaux de Musique; deadline for application: 15 June; application fee of DM 150; see also International Piano Competition Cologne – Foundation Tomassoni and International Singing Competition Cologne – Foundation Hohnen *Type:* violin

International Street Theatre Competition Holzminden
Kulturbüro Köln, Engelbertstr. 32, 50674 **Köln**
Tel: 221-241 3133 Fax: 221-240 3247
E-Mail: kulturbk@aol.com
contact Jürgen Ruppert
Date: 8-14 June 2000 *Frequency:* biennial *Eligibility:* applications by video *Awards:* cash *Comments:* competition held during the International Street Theatre Festival Holzminden; see also Festivals and Agents & Producers *Type:* street theatre

International Pablo Casals Cello Competition
c/o Kronberg Academy, Königsteiner Strasse 5, 61476 **Kronberg**
Tel: 6173-950 085 Fax: 6173-950 086
E-Mail: IKACello@aol.com
director Raimund Trenkler
Date: July 2000 *Frequency:* quadriennial *Eligibility:* open to cellists of all nationalities up to the age of 30 years *Awards:* 1st prize: 30k DM, 2nd prize: 20k DM, 3rd to 6th prizes: total value 28k DM and special prizes (concerts, radio recordings, CD production) *Comments:* registration fee: 150 DM; deadline for registration: 28 Feb 2000; contact for registration criteria *Type:* cello

Internationaler Johann-Sebastian-Bach-Wettbewerb
c/o Bach-Archiv Leipzig, Abt. Veranstaltungen, Postfach 101349, 04013 **Leipzig**
Tel: 341-9644 1669 Fax: 341-96441-95
E-Mail: jsbach@rzaix530.rz.uni-leipzig.de
Generalsekretär Sabine Martin; Präsident Prof. Dr. Hans-Joachim Schulze
Dates: 9-19 July 2000 *Frequency:* biennial *Eligibility:* soloists from 16yrs to 34yrs *Awards:* prizes – 1st: 12k DM, 2nd: 9k DM, 3rd: 6k DM, 4th: 2k DM, 5th/6th: 1k DM; other prizes: concert engagements with orchestras, solo recitals and CD production
Type: 2000: organ, harpsichord

International Instrumental Competition Markneukirchen
Am Rathaus 2, 08258 **Markneukirchen**
Tel: 37422-2010 Fax: 37422-2010/41169
Internet: www.markneukirchen.de
E-Mail: stadt.mkn@t-online.de
Date: 16-27 May 2000 *Frequency:* annual *Eligibility:* horn: up to 30 yrs, tuba: up to 32 yrs *Awards:* total prizes 44k DM, special prizes, engagements *Comments:* deadline for application: 31 January 2000 *Type:* 2000: horn, tuba; 2001: viola, violoncello (15-26 May 2001)

International Chamber-Choir Competition Marktoberdorf
c/o Bayerische Musikakademie, Kurfürstenstr.19, 87616 **Marktoberdorf**
Tel: 8342-961 825 Fax: 8342-40370
Internet: www.modmusik.de
E-Mail: 100530.317@compuserve.com
directors G. A. Rabus, A. Gross; manager J. Schrijner
Dates: week around Whitsun *Frequency:* biennial (2001) *Eligibility:* mixed and female choirs: minimum number of singers: 16, maximum: 36 *Comments:* deadline for applications: mid-October of the year before; special interest: international choir-studios in which 3 to 4 choirs from different countries work together on significant choral pieces for two days *Type:* chamber choirs

Kompositionswettbewerb
c/o Neue Akademie Braunschweig e.V., Reiherweg 3, 38527 **Meine**
Tel: 5304-3578 Fax: 5304-3578
Internet: www.kulturserver.de/home/nab
E-Mail: nab@kulturserver.de
contact Prof. Dr. Dieter Salbert (Komponist), Hans Peter Schier (Musikpädagoge)
Date: Oct-Nov as part of media night *Frequency:* annual *Eligibility:* open to everyone *Awards:* cash *Comments:* deadline for entry: 31 July 2000; see also Promoters (Braunschweigische Musikgesellschaft e.V., Neue Akademie Braunschweig e.V.) *Type:* 2000: synthesizer and computer music

International Carl Orff Singing Competition
Carl Orff-Stiftung, Herzogstraße 57, 80803 **München**
Tel: 89-335 033 Fax: 89-335 937
E-Mail: CarlOrffSt@aol.com
director (Carl Orff Foundation) Gabriele Weiner
Dates: June 2001 *Frequency:* biennial *Eligibility:* male & female singers of all nationalities; performing work by Carl Orff and others *Awards:* 1st prize: 10k DM, 2nd prize: 8k DM, 3rd prize: 6k DM *Comments:* particularly Carl Orff's pieces for the stage and written for soprano, tenor and baritone will be considered; presented by the Carl Orff Foundation in association with the Bavarian Academy of Fine Arts *Type:* singing

International Music Competition of the ARD
International Musikwettbewerb der ARD
Bayerischer Rundfunk, 80300 **München**
Tel: 89-5900 2471 Fax: 89-5900 3573
Internet: www.ard-musikwettbewerb.de
E-Mail: ard.conc@br-mail.de
general secretary Renate Ronnefeld; secretary Gisela Mauss
Dates: 5-22 Sept 2000 *Frequency:* annual *Eligibility:* solo (instrumental) 17-30 yrs, singers: female 20-30yrs, male 20-32yrs, duos 17-32yrs, quartet 17-35yrs (but all together not more than 120yrs) *Awards:* soloists: 1st: 20k DM, 2nd: 14k DM, 3rd: 10k DM; duo: 1st: 25k DM, 2nd: 19.5k DM, 3rd: 13k DM; quartet: 1st: 32k DM, 2nd: 25k DM, 3rd: 19k DM
Comments: deadline for entry 2000: flute/viola 20 April, voice/piano duo/quartet 1 July *Type:* 2000: voice, viola, flute, piano duo, string quartet

musica viva Preis der ARD und BMW AG
musica viva / Bayerischer Rundfunk, Rundfunkplatz 1, 80300 **München**
Tel: 89-5900 2232 Fax: 89-5900 3827
Künstlerischer Leiter der musica viva
Prof. Udo Zimmermann
Date: premier May 2001 *Frequency:* biennial *Awards:* 1st, 2nd and 3rd prizes 50k DM each *Comments:* deadline for entries: October 2000; cooperation in 2000 with ARD *Type:* composition

International Friedrich Kuhlau Flute Competition
Internationaler Flöten-Wettbewerb Friedrich Kuhlau
Herzogenplatz 2, PO Box 2061, 29510 **Uelzen**
Tel: 581-800 240 Fax: 581-800 220
Internet: www.uelzen.de/index50.htm
organiser Hans Rudolf Mentasti
Dates: Nov 2001 *Frequency:* triennial *Eligibility:* up to 32 years *Awards:* cash *Comments:* entry fee-DM 100 *Type:* 1-4 flutes, 2 flutes and piano, 1 flute and piano

Internationaler Robert-Schumann-Wettbewerb
Münzstrasse 12, 08056 **Zwickau**
Tel: 375-212 636/834 130 Fax: 375-834 130
Internet: www.zwickau.de/zw-6.htm
E-Mail: kulturbuero@zwickau.de
Vorsitzender des Wettbewerbs Dr. Gerd Nauhaus; Leiterin des Pressebüros Angelika Michaelis; Leiterin des Organisationsbüros Hannelore Heil
Dates: 15-25 June 2000 *Frequency:* quadriennial *Eligibility:* pianists up to 30, vocalists up to 32 *Awards:* piano -3 prizes (total DM 30k); song – female voices 3 prizes (total DM 30k), male voices 3 prizes (DM 30k); special prize *Comments:* deadline for applications: 1 April 2000 *Type:* piano, singing

GREECE (+30)

International Competition for Composing Dimitris Mitropoulos
18 Alex Soutsou str., 10671 **Athens**
Tel: 1-362 7412 Fax: 1-362 1477
administrator Traute Lutz
Dates: Nov 2000 (conducting), 2001 (composing) *Frequency:* annual *Eligibility:* open to conductors born after April 30, 1965 *Awards:* 1st prize: 4m Drachmas, 2nd prize: 2m Drachmas, 3rd prize: 1m Drachmas, The Orchestra's Preference Award: 1m Drachmas *Comments:* finals take place at the Athens Concert Hall; for each year's theme and details request information from Traute Lutz; closing date for entries: April 30, 2000 *Type:* 2000: conducting, 2001: composition

Maria Callas Grand Prix
3 Adrianou Street, 10555 **Athens**
Tel: 1-321 1987/1955/1949 Fax: 1-321 1196
Internet: www.athenaeum.ids.gr
E-Mail: athenm@ibm.net
president Louly Psychouli; general secretary Anna Koukouraki; executive secretary Michel Bichsel
Dates: 24 March-3 April 2000 (piano); spring 2001 (opera, oratorio-lied) *Frequency:* biennial (alternating between each type) *Eligibility:* all nationalities; piano: up to 32 years of age, voice: women up to 30 years, men up to 32 years *Awards:* piano: one Grand Prix (gold medal, 3m Drs cash award, engagements), all finalists diploma and 300k Drs cash award; voice: one Grand Prix for each section (gold medal, 2m Drs cash award, engagements), sections: opera female singer, opera male singer and oratorio lied *Comments:* registration fee US$100; application deadline: mid Dec (piano), begin Dec (voice); accompanist provided; member of the World Federation of International Music Competitions; see also Venues and Promoters *Type:* 2000: piano; 2001: opera, oratorio-lied

Onassis International Prize – Music for Dance and Original Choreography
c/o Secretariat of the International Onassis Prizes, Eschinou Street 7, 10558 **Plaka (Athens)**
Tel: 1-331 0900 Fax: 1-323 6044
Internet: www.onassis.gr
E-Mail: pubrel@onassis.gr
administrative secretary Barbara Charamis
Date: autumn 2001 *Awards:* cash; 3 prizes for music, 3 for choreography: 1st prize 100k US$, 2nd prize 75k US$, 3rd prize 50k US$ *Comments:* deadline for application: 31 Dec 1999; can be any length, written in Greek, English, French, Spanish, Italian or German, with translations in Greek or English if written in another language than the approved six *Type:* original music composition for dance and original choreography for said music composition

Onassis International Prize – Theatre Plays
c/o Secretariat of the International Onassis Prizes, Eschinou Street 7, 10558 **Plaka (Athens)**
Tel: 1-331 0900 Fax: 1-323 6044
Internet: www.onassis.gr
E-Mail: pubrel@onassis.gr
administrative secretary Barbara Charamis
Dates: autumn 2001 *Eligibility:* playwrights with at least one play staged by a professional company, unpublished *Awards:* cash: 1st prize 150k US$, 2nd prize 100k US$, 3rd prize 75k US$, publishing of play and staging by a company designated by the Foundation *Comments:* can be any length, written in Greek, English, French, Spanish, Italian or German, with translations in Greek or English if written in another language than the approved six; deadline for application: 31 Dec 1999 *Type:* theatre plays (not music or visual theatre)

HUNGARY (+36)

Budapest International Music Competition
PO box 80, 1366 **Budapest**
Tel: 1-266 3108 Fax: 1-317 9910
director Beata Schanda
Dates: Sept *Frequency:* annual *Eligibility:* up to 32 years *Awards:* cash, engagements *Comments:* visiting address: Interart Festivalcenter, Vörösmarty tér 1, 1051 Budapest *Type:* 2000: harp; 2001: Ferenc Liszt Piano Competition; 2002: Jozsef Szigeti Violin Competition

International Conductors Competition of the Hungarian Television (MTV)
Magyar Televizio Nemzetközi Karmesterverseny
PO Box 80, 1366 **Budapest**
Tel: 1-266 3108/373 5246 Fax: 1-317 9910/373 5123
Internet: www.mtv.hu/
E-Mail: webmaster@mtv.hu
director Beata Schanda; producer Judit Várbíró (Hungarian Television)
Dates: May 2001 *Frequency:* triennial (2001) *Eligibility:* up to 35 yrs *Awards:* cash, engagements *Comments:* visiting address: MTV, Szabadság tér 17, 1054 Budapest V *Type:* conducting

International Singing Competition
Budapesti Nemzetközi Énekverseny
Andrássy út 3, II/16, 1061 **Budapest** VI
Tel: 1-317 4186 Fax: 1-317 4186
Internet: www.bmc.hu/operart/index2_en.htm
chairperson, Operart Veronika Gonzalez Horváth
Date: early September *Frequency:* annual *Awards:* cash and opportunity to make their debut in the Hungarian State Opera *Type:* singing

IRELAND Republic of (+353)

John McCormack Golden Voice of Athlone
Athlone Chamber of Commerce,
Jolly Mariner Marina, **Athlone**
Tel: 902-73173 Fax: 902-73326
E-Mail: athcci@iol.ie
executive director (Athlone Chamber of Commerce & Industry) Siobhan Bigley
Dates: spring *Frequency:* biennial (2000) *Eligibility:* non-professional singers of all nationalities aged 17-30 yrs, participants must be born after 1st June 1961 *Awards:* study grant, broadcasts *Type:* singing

Guardian Dublin International Piano Competition
Liffey House, Tara Street, **Dublin** 2
Tel: 1-677 3066 Fax: 1-671 1385
E-Mail: pianos@iol.ie
administrator Ann Fuller; artistic director John O'Conor
Dates: 5-18 May 2000 *Frequency:* triennial (2000) *Eligibility:* 17-30 yrs *Awards:* cash, Kawai Grand, recitals in NYC, London and Paris, engagements with major international orchestras *Comments:* deadline for applications: 30 Nov 1999 *Type:* piano (Steinway/Kawai)

ITALY (+39)

Concorso Internazionale di Chitarra Classica Michele Pittaluga premio Città di Alessandria
Piazza Garibaldi 16, 15100 **Alessandria**
Tel: 0131-251 207 Fax: 0131-235 507
Internet: www.alessandria.alpcom.it/pittaluga
E-Mail: pittalug@e.mail.alessandria.alpcom.it
secretary Dott. Marcello Pittaluga; president of the competition Dott. Arch. Micaela Pittaluga; vice president Dott. ssa Maria Luisa Pittaluga; artistic director (composition) Federico Ermirio; artistic director (performance) Alirio Diaz
Dates: 25-29 Sept 2000 *Frequency:* annual *Eligibility:* composition: no limits; guitar performance: born after 1.1.1970 *Awards:* guitar performance: 1st prize: L 12 million, tour & CD, 2nd prize: L 6 million, 3rd prize: L 3 million, plus L 4.30 million to share among all finalists; composition: 1st prize: L 5 million, 2nd prize: L 2 million, 3rd prize: L 1 million, plus publication *Comments:* deadlines: composition (guitar & orchestra) 15 July 2000, performance: 31 August 2000; is a member of the World Federation of International Music Competitions, Geneve (Switzerland) *Type:* 2000: classic guitar performance and guitar and orchestra composition

International Organist Competition
Associazione Musicale S. Sofia, Casella Postale 324, Via Nuova del Faro, 59, 80071 **Anacapri (NA)**
Tel: 081-837 3514 Fax: 081-837 3514
artistic director Maestro Stefano Giordano
Dates: April 2001 *Frequency:* biennial
Eligibility: max. 35 years old *Awards:* 1st prize: 8m L plus 10 concerts in Italy and abroad, 2nd prize: 3m L, 3rd prize: 2m L, plus 1 concert in Italy *Comments:* the candidates who enter the final test will be Associazione Musicale S. Sofia's guests *Type:* organ

Concorso Musicale Internazionale Riviera del Conero
Via Goito 4, 60121 **Ancona**
Tel: 071-889 625/0348-335 2683 (mobile)
Fax: 071-200 646
Internet: www.musica.it
E-Mail: d.vico@musica.it
direttore responsabile Deborah Vico
Dates: October *Frequency:* annual *Eligibility:* aged under 35 *Awards:* money, a series of concerts in Europe and America and a diploma *Comments:* application deadline: 30 September; international agents are present during the final
Type: all types of music and singing

Concorso Internazionale di Composizione Guido d'Arezzo
Corso Italia 102, 52100 **Arezzo**
Tel: 0575-356 203 Fax: 0575-324 735
E-Mail: fondguid@nots.it
temporary commissioner Paolo Nicchi
Dates: June *Frequency:* annual *Eligibility:* deadline for applications in mid March – no age limit or entry fee *Awards:* 1st prize: 10m L, 2nd prize: 5m L *Comments:* compositions required for coro "a capella" or choir with instruments; see also Promoters *Type:* composition

Concorso Polifonico Internazionale Guido d'Arezzo
Corso Italia 102, 52100 **Arezzo**
Tel: 0575-356 203
Fax: 0575-324 735
E-Mail: fondguid@nots.it
temporary commissioner Paolo Nicchi
Dates: August *Frequency:* annual *Eligibility:* competition exclusively for non-professional choirs *Awards:* 1st prize: L4m, 2nd prize: L2m, 3rd prize: L1m *Comments:* application fee L150k; deadline end of February; see also Promoters *Type:* amateur choirs: mixed, male/female, childrens, Gregorian Chant, Folk-song Festival

International Competition of Composition 2 Agosto
c/o Teatro Testoni,
Via Matteotti 16, 40129 **Bologna**
Tel: 051-371 348 (from 10am to 1pm)
Type: composition

Concorso Internazionale di Composizione 2 Agosto
c/o Teatro Testoni, Via Matteotti N. 16, 40129 **Bolognia**
Tel: 051-371 348
Fax: 051-415 3777
direzione artistica Fabrizio Festa;
segreteria Chiara Monetti
Date: August *Frequency:* annual *Eligibility:* age limit up to 40 yrs *Awards:* 1st prize: 10m L (5k Euro), 2nd prize: 5m L (2.5k Euro), 3rd prize: 3m L (1.5k Euro) *Type:* contemporary composition

International Piano Competition F. Busoni
Conservatorio C Monteverdi,
Piazza Domenicani 19, 39100 **Bolzano**
Tel: 0471-973 579/976 568
Fax: 0471-973 579
E-Mail: busonibz@tin.it
director Prof.ssa Vea Carpi
Dates: Aug-Sept *Frequency:* annual *Eligibility:* 16-32 yrs *Awards:* cash, concert engagements, diplomas, certificates *Type:* piano

Concorso Internazionale di Violino Città di Brescia
Fondazione Romano Romanini,
Via E. Capriolo 48, 25122 **Brescia**
Tel: 030-280 188 Fax: 030-375 0602
contact Mffl. Dr. Mario Conter
Dates: October *Frequency:* biennial (2001) *Eligibility:* up to 32 years *Awards:* money and concerts *Comments:* the Fondazione Romano Romanini also organises international masterclasses for interpreters and composers; see also Orchestras *Type:* instrumental (violin)

Concorso Internazionale per Voci Verdiane città di Busseto
International Contest for Verdian Voices
Piazza Giuseppe Verdi 10, 43011 **Busseto (Parma)**
Tel: 0524-92487/92603 (Teatro Verdi)/931711 (Comune di Busseto)
Fax: 0524-92487
presidente Luigi Mazzetta;
presidente onorario Carlo Bergonzi
Dates: first week of July *Frequency:* annual *Eligibility:* sopranos, tenors and baritones must be under 32yrs, mezzosopranos, contraltos, and bass voices under 35yrs *Awards:* 1st prize 8m L, 2nd prize 5m L, 3rd prize 2m L and many more special prizes in cash, scholarships, tours and concerts *Comments:* collaboration with Orchestra Sinfonica Emilia Romagna "Arturo Toscanini' di Parma *Type:* vocal only on Verdian repertory

Concorso Internazionale V. Bellini per Pianisti e Cantanti Lirici
V.le Trieste 308, 93100 **Caltanissetta**
Tel: 0934-592 025/554 688 Fax: 0934-592 025
segretario Massimo Pastorello;
presidente Maestro Giuseppe Pastorello
Dates: December *Frequency:* annual *Eligibility:* under 32 for piano players, under 35 for singers *Awards:* for each category: 1st prize: L 10m, 2nd prize: L 7m, 3rd prize: L 5m and Premio Maria Callas L 10m for women singers
Type: piano and vocal

Carlo Soliva International Music Competition
Instituto Musicale 'Carlo Soliva', Via Facino Cane 35, 15033 **Casale Monferrato (AL)**
Tel: 0142-55760 Fax: 0142-55760
secretary Maddalena Musso, Adelaide Bobba;
president Pier Narciso Masi
Dates: 26 March-1 April 2000 *Frequency:* biennial (2000) *Eligibility:* A – piano soloist (17/20 years), B – piano soloist 35 years, C – piano duo 35 years, D – chamber music no age limit; payment by cheque: soloist L 90k or L 120k, duo L 160k, for each member over duo L 40k *Awards:* cash, concerts *Comments:* closing date for applications: February 2000; admission fees not known at time of going to print, please contact Instituto Musicale 'Carlo Soliva' for details *Type:* piano soloists, piano duo, chamber music

Concorso Internazionale di Canto Lirico Rocca delle Marie
c/o Rocca delle Macie S.P.A., Loc. Le Macie, 53011 **Castellina in Chianti (SI)**
Tel: 0577-7321 Fax: 0577-743 150
Internet: www.roccamarie.it
E-Mail: rocca@roccamarie.it
presidente Sergio Zingarelli; direttore artistico Domenico Sanna; coordinatori Marco Mucciarelli; presidente della guria Roberto Gabbiani; vicepresidente Renato Bruson
Dates: July *Frequency:* annual *Eligibility:* max. age is 35 yrs; soprano and tenors: 35 yrs *Awards:* 1st prize – Lit. 3m: 2nd prize – Lit. 2m: 3rd prize – Lit. 1m: runners up – Lit. 300k and concerts *Comments:* accommodation is free *Type:* vocal

Stagione Concertistica Concerti Déstate 2000 – 6 Edizione Città di Pietra Ligure
c/o Associazione F. Geminiani,
Via Prae 2, 17023 **Ceriale (SV)**
Tel: 0182-990 717/932 492 Fax: 0182-932 492
E-Mail: mauborri@yahoo.it
president Mauro Borri; vice-president Loredana Cardona; art director Luigi Giachino
Date: May *Frequency:* annual *Eligibility:* under 35yrs *Awards:* scholarships, concerts *Type:* piano, vocal, chamber music, orchestra, lyrical, choirs

Concorso Lirico Angelica Catalani
Via Sesta Strada 27, 60012 **Cesano di Senigallia (AN)**
Tel: 071-660 034/792 2646
Fax: 071-660 194
Internet: yepa.com/artivarie
E-Mail: ange.catalani@fastnet.it
presidente Anna Maria Ferrone;
direttori artistici Anna Maria Ferrone, Stefano Olivi;
direttore organizzativo Marcello Camerlengo
Dates: July *Frequency:* annual *Eligibility:* A – experienced singers; B – Italian students; C – Lieder and chamber singers; D – open category for singers of 600th and 700th opera; E – Andrews Prize, contemporary opera; F – musical and operetta; age limit for A, B and D is 35 years, for C, E and F it is 40 years *Awards:* cash totalling L 12m, concerts *Comments:* president of the jury is Maestro Leone Magiera who usually works with Luciano Pavarotti *Type:* vocal

Concorso Internazionale di Musica da Camera di Chieti – Premio Abruzzi
Societa Italiana della Musica e del Teatro, Via L. Colazilli 5, 66100 **Chieti**
Tel: 0871-401 373 Fax: 0871-401 373
Internet: www.alicom.com/simt
E-Mail: simt@ch.alicom.com
president Antonello Pellegrini (tel: 0360-618 035); artistic director Maurizio Colasanti; press officer Stanislao Liberatore (tel: 0338-612 6507)
Date: April *Frequency:* annual *Awards:* cash, Regione Abruzzo plate, medal, diploma *Comments:* deadline for applications: 15 March; see also Orchestras, Festivals and Promoters *Type:* chamber music ensembles

Concorso Internazionale di Interpretazione Chitarristica De Bonis
c/o Teatro A. Rendano P.za XV Marzo,
87100 **Cosenza**
Tel: 0984-813 220
Fax: 0984-813 220
president Antonello Dieni
Date: September *Frequency:* annual *Eligibility:* no age limit *Awards:* 1st prize: 7m L & 1.5m L for purchasing music and subscription to guitar magazine; 2nd prize: 4.5m L & 1m L voucher music purchasing & subscription to guitar magazine & premio del pubblico 1.5m L; 3rd prize: 2.5m L & 500k L & subscription to guitar magazine *Type:* guitar

Concorso Internazionale per Esecuzione Violinistica Antonio Stradivari
c/o Ente Triennale Internazionale degli Strumenti ad Arco, Corso Matteoti 17, 26100 **Cremona**
Tel: 0372-21454/463 165
Fax: 0372-21454
Internet: www.graffiti.it/triennale
E-Mail: triennale@graffiti.it
president Giancarlo Corada;
president of jury Mffl. Salvatore Accardo
Dates: 10-20 May 2001 *Frequency:* triennial *Eligibility:* under 30 years old on 10 April 2001 *Awards:* cash: 1st prize – 40m L, 2nd prize – 20m L, 3rd – 10m L
Type: violin

Concorso Internazionale per Quartetto D'Archi
c/o Ente Triennale Internazionale Degli Strumenti ad Arco, Corso Matteoti 17, 26100 **Cremona**
Tel: 0372-21454/463 165
Fax: 0372-21454
Internet: www.graffiti.it/triennale
E-Mail: triennale@graffiti.it
presidente Giancarlo Corada
Dates: June 2001 *Frequency:* triennial *Eligibility:* the total age of the 4 musicians should not be more than 135 years *Comments:* the competition is organized with Rotary International 2050 Distretto, Rotary Club Cremona and Cremona PO *Type:* string quartets

Concorso Internazionale Voci Nuove della Lirica G.B. Velluti
c/o Consorzio Interprovinciale per le Mostre e Manifestazioni dell'Artigianato,
Via Marconi, 1,
30031 **Dolo (VE)**
Tel: 041-410 333
Fax: 041-413 520
E-Mail: concorsoliricopresidenza@artigiani-dolo.ve.it
Dates: Sept *Frequency:* annual *Awards:* 1st prize: 5m Lit, 2nd prize: 3m Lit, 3rd prize: 2m Lit *Type:* vocal

Premio Trio di Trieste – The International Competition for Chamber Music Ensembles
Associazione Chamber Music –
Trio di Trieste, via Trieste 29,
34013 **Duino (TR)**
Tel: 040-373 9280
Fax: 040-373 9285
Internet: www.dicamp.univ.trieste.it/cm
secretary Anna Bonicìolli; artistic director Fedra Florit
Dates: last week of May *Frequency:* annual
Eligibility: average age of ensemble members must not exceed 32 years *Awards:* 1st prize: 15m L & 10 concerts in Italy and abroad & CD-contract, 2nd prize: 8m L, 3rd prize: 6m L *Comments:* entry fee 200k lit per ensemble; finalists receive a rebate of 50% of travel expenses; several other special prizes *Type:* piano and strings from duet to quintet

Concorso Internazionale di Musica da Camera Palma d'Oro
International Chamber Music Competition
c/o Associazione di Cultura Musicale,
Via Brunenghi 21,
17024 **Finale Ligure**
Tel: 019-692 135/680 277
Fax: 019-680 404/052
artistic director Prof. Aloise Vecchiato
Dates: August *Frequency:* annual *Eligibility:* pianoforte under 36 yrs; duo pianoforte-violin, pianoforte-violoncello and lieder-under 45 yrs *Awards:* cash
Comments: press: Germany: Tel: +49 2171-42663, Fax: +49 2171-43981, Japan: Tel: +81 3-3704 1368, Fax: +81 3-3704 1368 *Type:* piano, violin and piano, chamber musicians, cello

Concorso Internazionale per Complessi da Camera Città di Firenze Premio Vittorio Gui
Associazione Concorsi e Rassegne Musicali, Via Solferino 15, 50123 **Firenze**
Tel: 055-277 9446 Fax: 055-277 9446
Internet: www.firenze.net/premiogui
E-Mail: acerm@firenze.net
president Massimo Bogianckino
Dates: 9-15 October 2000 *Frequency:* annual *Eligibility:* up to 32 yrs except for the trio, quartet and quintet where the average age of the players must be under 32 yrs *Awards:* 1st prize: 15m L, 2nd prize: 6m L, 3rd prize: 4m L *Comments:* deadline for application: 5 September 2000 *Type:* chamber music, for violin, viola, violoncello, piano duos; string trio and quartet; piano and strings trio, quartet or quintet

Dancing Florence – Concorso Coreografico Internazionale
Florence Dance Center,
Borgo Della Stella 23 R, 50124 **Firenze**
Tel: 055-289 276 Fax: 055-217 810
Internet: www.Florencedance.org
E-Mail: info@Florencedance.org
directors Marga Nativo, Keith Ferrone; coordinator Rosanna Brocanello; press office Alessandro Benedetti; secretaries Francesca Tavassi
Dates: July *Frequency:* annual *Eligibility:* A: soloists – jazz, modern jazz, funky/hip hop; B: soloists – contemporary; C: groups – jazz, modern jazz, funky/hip hop; D: groups – contemporary *Awards:* A: 500k L, B: 50k L, C: 1.5m L, D: 1.5m L; and the chance of showing a new production at the next festival edtition *Comments:* a unique chance for young choreographer; edition of Florence Dance Festival (q.v.) *Type:* choreographic

Incontri Chitarristici di Gargnano – Concorso Internazionale
Via Roma, 25084 **Gargnano (BS)**
Tel: 0365-71931/72625 Fax: 0365-71354
artistic director Gianluigi Fia;
docenti Oscar Ghiglia, Massimo Lonardi
Dates: Aug-Sept *Frequency:* annual *Eligibility:* under 35 years old *Awards:* 1st prize: Lit. 8m + 3 concerts; 2nd prize – Lit. 4m; 3rd prize – Lit. 2m *Type:* instrumental (guitar)

Concorso Internazionale di Violino Premio N. Paganini
Comune di Genova, Casella Postale 586,
c/o Ufficio Postale, 16100 **Genova**
Tel: 010-557 111 Fax: 010-246 9272
E-Mail: prcomuge@pn.itnet.it
artistic director Giorgio Ferrari; president Prof. Vittorio Sirotti; secretary Maria Sanfilippo
Dates: September/October *Frequency:* annual *Eligibility:* between 16-33 years *Awards:* 6 cash prizes, concert engagement for the winner; 1st prize Lit. 20m, 2nd prize Lit. 12m, 3rd prize Lit 8m, 4th prize Lit. 5m, 5th prize Lit 4m, 6th prize Lit. 3m plus 4 special prizes (Lit 4m, Lit 3m, Lit 2m, Lit 2m) *Comments:* application fee: 190kLit, Venue: Teatro Carlo Felice 2000 *Type:* violin

Concorso Internazionale di Violino Premio Rodolfo Lipizer
Via Don Giovanni Bosco 91, 34170 **Gorizia**
Tel: 0481-34775/532 551/533 264 Fax: 0481-536 710
Internet: www.seta.it/lipizer/
E-Mail: lipizer@mail.seta.it
president Lorenzo Qualli; art dir Prof. Elena Lipizer
Dates: 9-17 September 2000 *Frequency:* annual *Eligibility:* under 35 yrs *Awards:* cash, concerts for three seasons *Comments:* see also Promoters (Associazione Culturate Mffl Rodolfo Lipizer) *Type:* violin

Concorso Internazionale Pianistico A.M.A. Calabria
Via P. Celli 23 I, 88046 **Lamezia Terme (CZ)**
Tel: 0968-24580/453 090 Fax: 0968-201 005
Internet: www.infoline.it/amacalabria
E-Mail: amacalabria@infoline.it
art dir Prof. Francescantonio Pollice; press Felicía Di Salvo
Date: 24-28 May 2000 *Frequency:* annual *Eligibility:* soloists under 35 years *Awards:* 1st prize 4m L + 10 concerts, 2nd prize 2m L, 3rd prize 1m L
Comments: see also Promoters *Type:* piano

Concorso Internazionale di Esecuzione Strumentale e Canto Lirico – Premio Citta di Lodi
c/o Accademia Gerundia – Scuola Discipline Artistiche, V.le Piacenza 10, 26900 **Lodi**
Tel: 0371-31840 Fax: 0371-31840
presidente Pietro Farina
Frequency: biennial (2001) *Awards:* cash, scholarships, medals *Comments:* for further details please contact the academy *Type:* instrumental and vocal

Concorso Internazionale per Cantanti Lirici 'Re Manfredi'
Largo dei Baroni Cessa 2, 71043 **Manfredonia (FG)**
Tel: 0884-513 127 Fax: 0884-513 127
presidente e direttore artistico Maestro Nicola Calabrese; vice presidente Sonia Giordano
Dates: December *Frequency:* annual *Eligibility:* all voices under 43 years *Awards:* cash, concerts in Italy, Hamburg and South Korea *Comments:* masterclasses for piano, singing, guitar, violin and jazz organised in the summer *Type:* vocal

Concorso Internazionale Rosetum – G.Puccini
c/o Centro Culturale Rosetum, Via Pisanello 1, 20146 **Milano**
Tel: 02-4870 7203 Fax: 02-4009 2195
Internet: www.rosetum.it
E-Mail: info@rosetum.it
segretario generale Rodolfo Rota;
presidente Padre Demetrio Carlo Patrini
Dates: January *Frequency:* biennial (2001) *Eligibility:* opera singers under 32 yrs *Awards:* cash & concerts; 1st prize 4m Lit., 2nd prize 2m Lit., 3rd prize 1m Lit. + special prizes and concerts *Comments:* venue: Teatro Rosetum 400 *Type:* vocal

International Cello Competition Roberto Caruana Premio Stradivari
Competition's Secretariat, Via Manzoni 31, 20121 **Milano**
Tel: 02-654 161 Fax: 02-659 7851
director Patrizia Garrasi; secretaries Laura Colombo, Gabriella Tabarrini
Dates: April 2002 *Frequency:* triennial *Eligibility:* open to cellists of all nationalities with no age limits *Award:* 1 prize: cash, medal, diploma, concerts *Comments:* application deadline: February 2002; a new composition will be commissioned especially for the final *Type:* cello

International Piano Competition Umberto Micheli
Via Manzoni 31, 20121 **Milano**
Tel: 02-654 161 Fax: 02-659 7851
Internet: www.micheli.org
E-Mail: resiasrl@tin.it
general director (organisation) Patrizia Garrasi; presidents (artistic committee) Luciano Berio, Bruno Canino, Maurizio Pollini; secretariat Laura Colombo
Dates: October 2001 *Frequency:* triennial *Eligibility:* admission is at discretion of the jury, maximum 32 years old *Awards:* 1st prize: cash, engagements, diploma *Comments:* alternative E-mail: info@micheli.org; a new composition will be commissioned for the final *Type:* piano

Premio Dino Ciani
Dino Ciani Prize
c/o Teatro alla Scala, Via Filodrammatici 2, 20121 **Milano**
Tel: 02-88791 Fax: 02-887 9424
Internet: www.lascala.milano.it
segretaria Laura Colombo (887 9280);
president of the jury Maestro Riccardo Muti
Dates: Oct *Frequency:* triennial (2002) *Eligibility:* under 30 yrs; entrance fee L 200k *Awards:* cash, concerts in Italy and abroad *Comments:* founded 1975; alternative Internet: www.lascala.milano.it; deadline: 31 August 2002; part of the World Federation of International Music Competition – FMCIM, Geneva; travel expenses paid for winners of other competitions of the same federation *Type:* piano

Young European Opera Singers Competition
Concorso per Giovani Cantanti Lirici della Comunitá Europea
c/o As.Li.Co., Corso di Porta Nuova 46, 20121 **Milano**
Tel: 02-655 1501 Fax: 02-655 5963
Internet: www.aslico.org
E-Mail: info@aslico.org
presidente Bruno dal Bon; ufficio stampa e comunicazione Barbara Minghetti; organizzazione Paola Moumtzis; amministrazione Giovanni Vegeto; produzione Bruno Carletti
Dates: January-February *Frequency:* annual
Comments: founded in 1949 *Type:* vocal

European Music Competition Città di Moncalieri
Via Carlo Alberto 3/b,
10024 **Moncalieri (TO)**
Tel: 011-640 8597
Fax: 011-640 3060
Date: Oct-Nov *Comments:* applications by: 30 Sept
Type: piano and four hand piano

Rina Sala Gallo Piano Competition
Comune di Monza, 20052 **Monza (MI)**
Tel: 039-382 278 (Asso. musicale di Monza)
Fax: 039-388 608 (comune)
president Gianna Garbagnati;
artistic director Franco Acquati
Dates: 23 September-1 October 2000 *Frequency:* biennial (2000) *Eligibility:* pianists between 15-30 yrs of age *Awards:* cash: 1st prize: L 25m, 2nd prize: L 10m, 3rd prize: L 7m *Type:* piano

Concorso Internazionale di Esecuzione Pianistica
c/o Associazione Musicale Le Muse,
Via Pontirossi 258, 80141 **Napoli**
Tel: 081-751 3218/0974-838 010/6524
Fax: 081-751 3218
E-Mail: flogallo@tin.it
artistic director & president Paola Volpe
Dates: October *Frequency:* annual *Eligibility:* 2 categories: a) max age 23, b) ages 21- max 35 *Awards:* cash, concerts and diplomas *Comments:* deadline for application: September 2000; discount system for accommodation and food *Type:* piano

Concorso Pianistico Internazionale Alfredo Casella
c/o Teatro Augusteo, Via Toledo 264, 80132 **Napoli**
Tel: 081-401 313 Fax: 081-401 313
presidente onorario Aldo Ciccolini;
consulenti artistici Massimo Fargnoli
Dates: December 2000 *Frequency:* biennial *Eligibility:* age limit 32 yrs *Awards:* cash, concerts; 1st prize 15m Lit., 2nd prize 10m Lit., 3rd prize 5m Lit. *Type:* piano

Coreografo Elettronico, Il
c/o Ass. Napolidanza, Via Fornelli 8, 80132 **Napoli**
Tel: 081-422 118 Fax: 081-404 722
direzione artistica Marilena Riccio;
direzione organizzativa Maurizio Genera;
segreteria organizzativa Donatella Saccani
Date: June *Frequency:* annual (2000) *Awards:* cash and promotional activities *Type:* videodance

Arturo Toscanini International Competition for Conductors
c/o Fondazione Arturo Toscanini, Ufficio Concorsi Internazionali, Via G. Tartini 13, 43100 **Parma**
Tel: 0521-274 421 Fax: 0521-272 134
Internet: www.fondazione-toscanini.it
E-Mail: fondazione@toscanini.dsnet.it
general manager Prof. Gianni Baratta; presidente Piero Manganoni; presidente dell giuria Patrick Fournillier
Frequency: triennial (2001) *Eligibility:* under 35 yrs; open to all conductors from all nationalities *Awards:* cash, contracts and diplomas *Comments:* organises by Fondazione Arturo Toscanini *Type:* conducting

Concorso Internazionale di Composizione G. Petrassi
c/oFondazione Arturo Toscanini, Ufficio Concorsi Internazionali, Via G. Tartini 13, 43100 **Parma**
Tel: 0521-274 421 Fax: 0521-272 134
Internet: www.fondazione-toscanini.it
E-Mail: fondazione@toscanini.dsnet.it
president Piero Manganoni; general manager Prof. Gianni Baratta; presidente della giuria George Benjamin; presidente onororio Mffl Goffredo Petrassi
Dates: September *Frequency:* triennial (2001) *Eligibility:* no age limit; for unpublished symphony composition only (no concertos); duration time: 12-30 min; orchestral staff 25-80 *Awards:* cash and publishing of the winner-composition *Comments:* application deadline: May 31, 2000; organises by Fondazione Arturo Toscanini *Type:* compositions for orchestras with 25-80 players

Perugia Classico-Concorso Internazionale di Musica da Camera
Comune di Perugia – Ripartizione XVI economia e lavoro, Via Eburnea 9, 06100 **Perugia**
Tel: 075-577 2253/2256 Fax: 075-577 2255
Internet: www.perugia.it/classico.htm
E-Mail: caronte@numerica.it
organizzazione Elena Trovato
Dates: last week of September *Frequency:* annual *Eligibility:* under 35 years *Awards:* 1st prize: production of 1 CD, 1 concert and cash *Type:* chamber ensembles

International Conducting Competition Mario Gusella
c/o Accademia Musicale Pescarese,
Via dei Peligni 152, 65127 **Pescara**
Tel: 085-451 0504 Fax: 085-451 4575
Internet: www.amp-it.com
E-Mail: amp@amp-it.com
presidente Elio Santangelo; art dir Bruno Mezzena
Dates: September *Frequency:* biennial (2001) *Eligibility:* no age limit; entrance fee 200k lire *Awards:* 1st prize: 5m L + concerts; 2nd prize: 2m L + 2 concerts; 3rd prize: 1.5m L and concert; certificates *Comments:* application form available from the Internet *Type:* conducting

2nd International Competition of Electronic Music Composition Pierre Schaeffer
Accademia Musicale Pescarese,
Via dei Peligni 152, 65127 **Pescara**
Tel: 085-451 0504/2110 Fax: 085-451 4575
Internet: www.amp-it.com
E-Mail: amp@amp-it.com
artistic director of competition M° Riccardo Santoboni; secretary of competition Anna Rita Ticari
Eligibility: no age limit; two categories: a) solo tape, b) tape and instrument(s) *Awards:* 3 prizes and a special mention will be awarded for each category; the winning works will be recorded on a not commerical CD audio; the best piece will be performed during the Festival Varianti, 2000 concert season *Comments:* no more than one composition may be presented in each category (for a maximum of two pieces); each competitor must send a written assent; maximum duration of each piece: 10 minutes *Type:* composition

Concorso Internazionale di Musica – Pinerolo Città della Cavalleria
c/o Accademia di Musica, viale Giolitti 7, 10064 **Pinerolo (TO)**
Tel: 0121-321 040 Fax: 0121-321 040
artistic directors Laura Richaud, Giorgio Pugliaro; press office Paola Giunti, Paolo Cozzo
Dates: 7-14 Nov *Frequency:* annual *Eligibility:* section A: piano – age limit is 32, section B: chamber music with piano (piano duo, piano trio, piano quartet, piano quintet and clarinet) for groups whose average age of the members should not exceed 32 years *Awards:* cash and concerts *Type:* piano; trio (piano, violin, violoncello)

Premio Paolo Borciani Concorso Internazionale per Quartetto d'Archi
International String Quartet Competition
Premio Paolo Borciani
c/o Teatro Municipale Valli, Piazza Martiri del 7 Luglio, 42100 **Reggio Emilia**
Tel: 0522-458 811/908 Fax: 0522-458 822
E-Mail: direzione@i-teatri.re.it
president Elio Canova; executive director Bruno Borghi; artistic director Guido A. Borciani; secretary general Francesca Zini
Dates: 11-18 June 2000 *Frequency:* irregular (next: June 2002; June 2005) *Eligibility:* age limit: global age of the ensemble: 120 yrs; single member 35 yrs; application fee: Lit. 150k (for those notified of admission) *Awards:* prizes – 1st: Lit. 36m + tour in Europe and USA, 2nd: Lit. 26m, 3rd: Lit. 12m, special prize for the best performance of the commissioned quartet: Lit. 4m *Comments:* board and lodging offered to all admitted quartets; travel expenses refunded to quartets awarded the two top prizes in another important competition; member of WFIMC; deadline 31 January 2000 *Type:* string quartets

Settimana Internazionale della Danza – Cittá di Perugia
Piazza San Rufo N. 6, 02100 **Rieti**
Tel: 0746-271 010 Fax: 0746-727 0610
E-Mail: segecov@tiscalinet.it
artistic director Alberto Testa; secretary Nicoletta Balduzzi
Date: 30 April-6 May *Frequency:* annual *Eligibility:* for classical & contemporary dance, age ranges: 12-14 yrs, 15-18 yrs, 19-24 yrs; no age limit for choreographic compositions *Awards:* prize for dance costumes for 12-14 yrs; 15-18 yrs 1st prize: 2m L, 2nd prize: 1m L, 3rd prize: summer stage; 19-24 yrs 1st prize: 2.5m L, 2nd prize: 1.25m L, 3rd prize: summer stage; choreographic composition: 4m L *Type:* classical and contemporary dance and choreographic compositions

International Choir Competition of Riva del Garda
Associazione Concorso Chorale, Via Concordia 25, 38066 **Riva del Garda (TN)**
Tel: 0464-554 073 Fax: 0464-520 900
Type: choir

Concorso Internazionale di Flauto – Syrinx
Via Macchiavelli 50, 00185 **Roma**
Tel: 06-4470 3055 Fax: 06-4470 3059
E-Mail: aifla@nexus.it
directors Gian Luca Morseletto, Stefano Cioffi; uff. stampa Susanna Persichilli
Dates: November *Frequency:* biennial *Eligibility:* under 34 years old; registration fee L 100k *Awards:* cash, musical instruments offered by various manufacturers, concerts *Comments:* organisers of the 'Simposio Flautistico Italiano, Flautissimo'; see also Festivals, Promoters and Publications *Type:* flauto traverso

International Piano Competition for Young Pianists/International Piano Competition Roma
Via P. Bonetti 88-90 scala E/11, 00128 **Roma**
Tel: 06-507 3889 Fax: 06-507 3889
Internet: www.webeco.it/chopinroma
artistic director Marcella Crudeli; secretary Paolo Masotti
Date: October *Frequency:* annual *Eligibility:* catogries for Int. Piano Comp. for Young Pianists: A – born after 1980, B – born after 1974, C & D – born after 1963; Int. Piano Comp: born after 1962 *Awards:* Int. Piano Comp: a piano worth Lit. 45m, Lit. 2m & 30 concerts during the year; special award: FF 15k; a silver trophy from the President of the Republic *Comments:* many other awards according to categories; enrolment deadline: Sept; the competition is supported by ministries governmental organizations, French embassy, Vatican Radio, EPTA Italy, the Mayor of Rome and many others *Type:* piano

Premio Internationale Valentino Bucchi
c/o Fondazione Valentino Bucchi, Via U Peruzzi 20, 00139 **Roma**
Tel: 06-8720 0121/8713 1074 Fax: 06-8713 1527
E-Mail: premio.bucchi@agora.it
president Liliana Pannella
Dates: November *Frequency:* annual (rotate categories) *Eligibility:* performance 32-35 yrs, composition 40 yrs *Awards:* cash, publication of winning compositions *Comments:* different deadlines for different sections; contact above for further information

Torneo Internazionale di Musica
Via Federico Patetta 79, 00167 **Roma**
Tel: 06-662 1973 Fax: 06-6601 3730
Internet: www.timcompetition.org
E-Mail: info@timcompetition.org
presidente Federico Fait; direttore artistico Luigi Fait; coordinatori Dominique Sanges
Dates: Jan-July *Frequency:* annual *Awards:* cash, concerts, CD contract *Comments:* artists can start performing in any country but final phases are in Bari; takes place in several European cities; see also Promoters and Agents & Producers *Type:* vocal, piano, guitar, strings, winds, chamber music, choral music, jazz, pop, music critics

International Verdi Requiem Vocal Competition
IUMA Worldwide Productions,
Via E Filiberto 125, 00185 **Rome**
Tel: 06-7045 2328/7720 1524
Fax: 06-7720 5607
E-Mail: cfcatena@pelagus.it
Date: Nov *Eligibility:* open to singers from Europe, USA, Canada, Japan and Korea, aged 39 and under *Awards:* prizes include concert opportunities in New York *Type:* vocal

Concorso Internazionale per Giovani Cantanti Lirici Riccardo Zandonai
c/o Comune di Rovereto – Assessorato alla Cultura, Via Canestrini N.1, 38068 **Rovereto (TN)**
Tel: 0464-452 159/198 Fax: 0464-436 127
Internet: www.comune.rovereto.tn.it
E-Mail: cultura@comune.rovereto.tn.it
direzione artistica Mietta Sighele
Date: 29 May-3 June 2000 *Frequency:* annual *Eligibility:* age limit 35 yrs *Awards:* 1st prize: 12m L, 2nd prize: 8m L, 3rd prize: 4m L and special prizes *Type:* opera singing

International Musical Competition of Instrumental and Vocal Execution
Concorso Internazionale di esecuzione strumentale e vocale Premio Rovere d'Oro
Via Aurelia 139,
18016 **San Bartolomeo al Mare (IM)**
Tel: 0183-400 967/888/200 Fax: 0183-403 050
E-Mail: roveredoro@hotmail.com
direttore organizzativo Carla Brun; presidente Gina Lagorio Garzanti; direttore & tesoriere operativo Rita Romani Arimondo; direttore artistico Luciano Lanfranchi
Dates: July *Frequency:* annual *Eligibility:* born between 1962-1990 (birth certificate required); application fee *Awards:* golden statue (Rovere d'oro), concerts, scholarships *Comments:* application deadline: 15th June; supported by the Ca.Ri.ge. Foundation; see also Promoters *Type:* 5 sections: chamber, string, wind, harp accordion, piano

Gaetano Zinetti International Chamber Music Competition
Sanguinetto
Tel: 0442-81066 Fax: 0442-365 150
Internet: www.zinetticompetition.org
E-Mail: info@zinetticompetition.org
Eligibility: instrumental ensembles from duo to sextet *Type:* chamber music

Concorso Internazionale di Composizione e Arrangiamento per Orchestra Jazz
PO Box 505, 07100 **Sassari**
Tel: 079-239 465 Fax: 079-239 465
Internet: www.abno.com
E-Mail: scrivereinjazzo@abno.com
responsabile organizzativo Gavino Mele
Date: June *Frequency:* biennial (2000) *Eligibility:* all jazz musicians *Awards:* cash prize for 1st place for each section, prize money 7.5k Euro *Comments:* application deadline: April; contact organisation: the Blue Note Orchestra *Type:* compositions and arrangements for jazz orchestras

Concorso Internazionale di Interpretazione Musicale Citta di Racconigi
Via Novellis N. 21, 12038 **Savigliano (CN)**
Tel: 0172-712 665/0338-700 7149/0347-796 8814
Fax: 0143-89327
Internet: web.tin.it/nhfede/camt/
E-Mail: nhbors@tin.it
direzione artistica Luigi Dominici
Date: May *Frequency:* annual *Awards:* 10m L & concerts *Comments:* also includes Il Premio Speciale Internazionale F. Chopin (Piano) *Type:* piano, lyrical singing, young violinists, pianoforte duos, chamber groups

Concorso Pianistico Internazionale Città di Senigallia
Via Gherardi N. 3,
60019 **Senigallia (AN)**
Tel: 071-65568/60942 Fax: 071-60942
Internet: www.nettuno.it/senigallia/
E-Mail: senigallia@an.nettuno.it
director Domenico Pergolesi
Dates: September *Frequency:* annual *Eligibility:* age limit, 15-36; need proof of attendance of an educational institute *Awards:* 1st prize: 20m L + 3 concerts in America & 10 in Europe; 2nd prize: 7,5m L; 3rd prize: 3m L; 4th prize: 2m L; 5th prize: 1m L; premio musica da camera 1m L; premio accompagnamento del canto 700k L *Comments:* application fee: 200k lire; also organise International Competition for Young Pianists – 28-31 August; age limit – section A: 16 years, 1st prize is a piano; 2nd prize 800 Lit., 3rd prize 700k Lit., 4th prize 600k Lit, 5th prize 500k Lit. *Type:* piano

Concorso Pianistico Internazionale Ettore Pozzoli
Via Paradiso 6, 20038 **Seregno (MI)**
Tel: 0362-222 914 Fax: 0362-222 914
Internet: www.concorsopozzoli.it
E-Mail: pozzoli@concorsopozzoli.it
secretary Diotti Lia
Dates: Sept 2001 *Frequency:* biennial (2001) *Awards:* 1st prize: L 20m + recording and printing of CD with the winner's concert; 2nd prize: L 10m; 3rd prize L 5m; and 2 precial prizes of L 2m for the youngest Italian finalist and the youngest semi-finalist; special prize L 1m for the best performed of the Pozzoli Studies *Type:* piano *Comments:* application deadline: May 2001

Concorso per Giovani Cantanti Lirici della Comunità Europea
European Community Competition for young opera singers
c/o Teatro Lirico Sperimentale di Spoleto – A. Belli, Piazza G. Bovio No. 1, 06049 **Spoleto (PG)**
Tel: 0743-220 440/221 645 Fax: 0743-222 930
Internet: www.caribusiness.it/lirico
E-Mail: teatrolrico@mail.caribusiness.it
president Carlo Belli; artistic director Michelangelo Zurletti; direttore organizzativo Claudio Lepore; assistants Nadia Nigis, Adele Capone; public relations Andrea Penna
Dates: March 2000 *Frequency:* annual *Eligibility:* sopranos and tenors not older than 30, all others not older than 32; applicants must be attending regular study at a Conservatory, music school etc. *Awards:* winners are admitted onto a five month Preparation Course during which scholarship will be awarded.; they will then make their debut in the Opera Season 2000 *Comments:* application deadline is 23 February 2000; see also Festivals and Promoters *Type:* vocal

International New Chamber Opera Competition Orpheus 1999/2000
Concorso Internazionale per Nuove Opere di Teatro Musicale Orphesu 1999/2000
c/o Teatro Lirico Sperimentale di Spolcto 'A Belli', Piazza Bovio 1, 06049 **Spoleto (PG)**
Tel: 0743-220 440/221 645
Fax: 0743-222 930
Internet: www.caribusiness.it/lirico
E-Mail: teatrolirico@mail.caribusiness.it
president Carlo Belli; artistic director Michelangelo Zurletti; direttore organizzativo Claudio Lepore; assistants Nadia Nigis, Adele Capone
Date: March *Frequency:* biennal (2001) *Eligibility:* the competition is open to composers of any nationality, who are under 35 years of age on 31 December 1999 *Awards:* the winning opera will be published by casa Ricordi; the world premiere of the winning opera will take place at the Teatro Caio Melisso during the 2000 season of Teatro Lirico Sperimentale de Spoleto 'A. Belli' and 10m Lira *Comments:* application deadline 31 December 1999; see also Promoters and Festivals *Type:* chamber opera

Concorso Internazionale di Canto Maria Caniglia
c/o Associazione Musicale "Maria Caniglia", Vico dei Sardi 9, 67039 **Sulmona**
Tel: 0864-212 207 Fax: 0864-208 668
presidente e direttore artistico associazione Dott. Filippo Tella; presidente giuria Giorgio Vidusso
Dates: October *Frequency:* annual *Eligibility:* 8-35 yrs; application fee L 100k *Awards:* 1st prize: 8m L + 3 concerts, 2nd prize: 4m L + 3 concerts, 3rd prize: 2m L + 3 concerts; special prizes: 3 scholarships with course fee and accommodation paid *Comments:* deadline for application: 30 Sept 2000; see also Promoters *Type:* vocal

Concorso Internazionale di Pianoforte e Orchestra Citta di Sulmona
Via Della Cona 20, 67039 **Sulmona (AQ)**
Tel: 0864-53733
Fax: 0864-208 668
presidente Tonino Tanturri; vice-presidente Prof.sa Noemi Zurlo; organizzatore Maestro Concezio Barcone; presidente della giuria Maestro Rodolfo Caporali
Dates: 28 Sept-3 Oct 2000 *Frequency:* annual *Eligibility:* up to 32 years *Awards:* cash, concerts and diplomas *Comments:* gala concert performed by the winners in the Teatro Comunale di Sulmona 800 *Type:* piano and orchestra

Concorso Internazionale di Interpretazione Organistica
Via Ovada N. 13, 15070 **Tagliolo Monferrato (AL)**
Tel: 0143-89327/89171
Fax: 0143-89327
Internet: web.tin.it/nhfede/camt/
E-Mail: nhbors@tin.it
direzione artistica Maurizio Barboro
Date: July *Frequency:* annual *Awards:* cash & concerts *Type:* organ

Concorso Internazionale di Esecuzione Musicale Franz Schubert
Via Ovada N. 13, 15070 **Tagliolo Monferrato (AL)**
Tel: 0143-89327/89171
Fax: 0143-89327
Internet: web.tin.it/nhfede/camt/
E-Mail: nhbors@tin.it
direzione artistica Maurizio Barboro
Date: July *Frequency:* annual *Awards:* scholarship of 15m L, 18 concerts, CD recording *Type:* piano duo & four hand piano, lyrical singing, guitar, harp, pianoforte duo, chamber groups, piano & orchestra, flute & orchestra

Concorso Pianistico Internazionale Alessandro Casagrande
Alessandro Casagrande International Piano Competition
Vico S.Lorenzo, 1, 05100 **Terni**
Tel: 0744-549 713/714 Fax: 0744-549 713/426 760
Internet: www.concorsocasagrande.org/
E-Mail: concaseg@tin.it
competition secretary Loredana Riceputi; art director Adriana Casagrande; president Sindaco di Terni
Dates: 31 May-11 June 2000 *Frequency:* biennial (2000) *Eligibility:* up to 28 years *Awards:* 1st prize: L 15m + 14 concerts, 2nd prize: L 8m, 3rd prize: L 5m, all finalists receive a diploma *Comments:* Premio Speciale 'Alessandro Casagrande', Maurice Ravel *Type:* piano

Concorso Internazionale di Composizione Torino
c/o ICONS, Via Cernaia 38, 10122 **Torino**
Tel: 011-542 936 Fax: 011-542 936
Internet: www.arpnet.it/~icon
E-Mail: ecorreg@tin.it
Frequency: annual *Eligibility:* no age limit *Awards:* 1st prize: Lit 4m and engagement in Festival Settembre Musica Turin *Type:* compositions – from 1 to 11 instruments (no voice)

International Chamber Contest
Concorso di Musica da Camera
c/o Assessorato al Turismo – Provincial Regionale, Piazze Vittorio Veneto 1, 91100 **Trapani**
Tel: 0923-23692/22604 Fax: 0923-873 663
Eligibility: 35 years for trios, quartets, quintets the average age of the group as a whole must not exceed 35 years *Awards:* prizes: 35.5m L, concerts *Comments:* reimbursement of travel expenses and lodging for semi-finalists and finalists; second address: c/o Conservatorio di Musica A. Scontrino, via F. Sceusa 1, 91100 Trapani, Tel: 0923-556 124/25/26, Fax: 0923-551 465, E-mail: leasal@tin.it *Type:* string instruments: duo, trio, quartet, quintet with or without piano; wind instruments: duo, trio, quartet, quintet with or without piano

Concorso Internazionale per Direttori d'orchestra Antonio Pedrotti
International Competition for Orchestra Conductors Antonio Pedrotti
Piazza Mostra, 19, 38100 **Trento**
Tel: 0461-231 223 Fax: 0461-232 592
Internet: www.ishost.net/concorsopedrotti
E-Mail: a.pedrotti.competition@tn.nettuno.it
secretary Lorenza Mascagni; direttore artistico Maurizio Dini Ciacci; presidente Mauro Pedrotti
Dates: September 2001 *Frequency:* biennial *Eligibility:* orchestral conductors between 18-35 yrs of age *Awards:* 30m Lit. and engagements with 12 orchestras (Italian & international) *Comments:* see also Promoters *Type:* conducting

Bottega International Competition for Conducting
Corporation for the Civic Theatre of Treviso, Corso del Popolo 31, 31100 **Treviso**
Tel: 0422-410 130 Fax: 0422-52285
Type: conducting

Toti dal Monte International Singing Competition
Ente Teatro Comunale, Corso del Popolo 31, Via Diaz 7, 31100 **Treviso**
Tel: 0422-410 130 Fax: 0422-582 285
press officer Lucio De Piccoli
Date: July *Frequency:* annual *Awards:* prizes: 2.5-3.5m L *Type:* singing

Premio Candoni Arta Terme
c/o Centro Servizi e Spettacoli di Udine, Via Grazzano 6, 33100 **Udine**
Tel: 0432-504 765 Fax: 0432-504 448
E-Mail: cssudine@tin.it
organizers Paolo Pattui, Alberto Bevilacqua; direttore artistico Franco Quadri; ufficio stampa Luisa Schiratti, Fabrizia Maggi
Frequency: annual *Awards:* Mise-en-Space *Type:* playwriting

Concorso Internazionale Valsesia-Musica
c/o Associazione Culturale Valsesia Musica, Corso Roma N. 35, 13019 **Varallo (VC)**
Tel: 0163-560 020 Fax: 0163-52405
E-Mail: valsesiamusica@laproxima.it
Date: June (violin & orchestra), Sept (pianoforte, lyrical singing) *Frequency:* annual *Eligibility:* maximum age 35 yrs *Awards:* violin & orchestra: 1st prize: 5m L & 3 concerts with orchestra, 2nd prize: 3m L & 1 concert, 3rd prize: 2m L & 1 concert; pianoforte & lyrical singing: 1st prize: 10m L & 3 concerts with orchestra, 2nd prize: 4m L & 1 concert, 3rd prize: 2m L & 1 concert, 4th prize: 1m L & 1 concert *Type:* June: violin and orchestra; September: pianoforte, lyrical singing

Concorso Internazionale di Musica Viotti-Valsesia
Associazione Valsesia Musica, Sezione canto lirico, Corso Roma 38, 13019 **Varallos**
Tel: 0163-51280
Date: Aug-Sept *Frequency:* annual *Eligibility:* open to all singers, age limit 34 years (sopranos & tenors) and 35 years (mezzo-sopranos and counter-tenors, basses & baritones) *Comments:* candidates must perform 6 arias chosen from the Italian and foreign lyric repertory from 1750-1950; there are three rounds to complete *Type:* singing

Concorso di Composizione per Organo & per Strumenti, Voce e Organo
c/o A.Gi.Mus, Via IV Novembre, 9, 23829 **Varenna (LC)**
Tel: 0341-815 160
Fax: 0341-815 160
presidente Gabriella Vai; directtore artistico Ennio Cominetti
Dates: deadline 31 Oct, results in December *Frequency:* biennial (2000) *Eligibility:* no age limit *Awards:* cash and publication *Type:* 3 sections – A: only organ, B: organ and one or more instruments, C: organ compositions of easy performance for the young

Concorso di Musica Per Giovani Interpreti
c/o A. GI. Mus, Via IV Novembre, 9, 23829 **Varenna (LC)**
Tel: 0341-815 160
Fax: 0341-815 160
direttore artistico Ennio Cominetti; presidente Gabriella Vai
Dates: May *Frequency:* annual *Eligibility:* no age limit *Awards:* cash, concert engagements, diplomas *Comments:* there is also a section for non-professionals *Type:* piano and guitar soloists, piano duo, chamber music, lyrical, choir

Concorso Internazionale di Musica G.B. Viotti
Società del Quartetto, Casella postale 127, 13100 **Vercelli**
Tel: 0161-255 575/252 667
Fax: 0161-255 575
Internet: www.net4u.it/gbviotti
E-Mail: gbviotti@net4u.it
segreteria amministrativa Rossella Tavano; presidente Maria Arsieni Robbone; direttore artistico Giuseppe Pugliese; segretaria artistica Claudia Tarchetti; ufficio stampa Pier M. Robbone
Dates: October (opera singing, piano, chamber music) *Frequency:* singing, piano and chamber music annual; cello biennial *Eligibility:* up to 35 yrs for singing; up to 30 yrs for piano and for cello (biennial); up to 32 yrs for chamber music *Awards:* prizes: total amount 84m L, 1st prize for section: 25m L; engagements *Comments:* entrance fee: L 70k for each member of a chamber ensemble, L 120k for all others *Type:* singing, piano, cello, chamber ensembles

LATVIA (+371)

Jazeps Vitols International Competition of Pianists
J. Vitola Starptautiskais Pianistu Konkurss
Ministry of Culture of Latvia, 11a K.Valdemara, 1364 **Riga**
Tel: 7-331 587 Fax: 7-227 916
E-Mail: kpol@km.gov.lv
Frequency: quadriennial *Type:* piano

Jazeps Vitols International Competition of Vocalists
Vitola Starptautiskais Vokalistu Konkurss
Ministry of Culture of Latvia, 11a K.Valdemara, 1364 **Riga**
Tel: 7-331 587
Fax: 7-227 916
E-Mail: kpol@km.gov.lv
Frequency: quadriennial *Type:* vocal

Augusts Dombrovski International Competition
Augusta Dombrovska Starptautiskais Konkurss
Ziemeeblazmas 38, 1015 **Riga**
Tel: 7-341 483/879
Fax: 7-341 829
organiser Imants Kalni; director M. Pence
Frequency: annual *Eligibility:* open to young violinists and cellists up to the age of 19 yrs *Type:* violin, cello

LITHUANIA (+370)

Balys Dvarionas' Competition of Young Pianists and Violinists
Tarptautinis Balio Dvariono Jaunuju Pianistu ir Smuikininku Konkursas
Ausros vartu 5, 2001 **Vilnius**
Tel: 2-629 460
Fax: 2-626 989
E-Mail: ciurlionis@post.omnitel.net
competition director Romualdas Kondrotas
Comments: organisers: Lithuanian National Philharmonic Society *Type:* piano and violin

M K Ciurlionis International Piano and Organ Competition
Tarptautinis M K Ciurlionio Pianistu ir Vargonininku Konkursas
Ausros vartu 5, 2001 **Vilnius**
Tel: 2-629 460
Fax: 2-626 989
E-Mail: ciurlionis@post.omnitel.net
director Romualdas Kondrotas
Comments: organisers: Lithuanian National Philharmonic Society *Type:* piano and organ

LUXEMBOURG (+352)

Concours International de Danse de Luxembourg
c/o Jacques Heinen, Rue A Useldinger 41, 4351 **Esch-Sur-Alzette**
Tel: 547 264/555 455 Fax: 547 494
Internet: vebplaza.pt.lu/public/ballet
president Jacques Heinen; direction du concours Irène Heinen
Dates: April *Frequency:* biennial (2001) *Eligibility:* have been professional dancers (for at least one season) A – soloists, B – couples, age range15-27 years old *Awards:* cash – soloists: 1st prize BEF 150k, 2nd prize: BEF 70k; couples: 1st prize: BEF 300k, 2nd prize: BEF 150k, 3rd prize: BEF 70k; juniors: 1st prize: BEF 50k, 2nd prize: BEF 20k, 3rd prize: BEF 10k *Comments:* organised by International Ballet Association Luxembourg
Type: dance

Tendances
c/o Christiane Eiffes, 1 rue du Fort Elisabeth, 1463 **Luxembourg**
Tel: 404 569 Fax: 404 569
chair of jury Christiane Eiffes
Dates: July *Frequency:* annual *Eligibility:* young choreographers with professional training *Awards:* contract for the Festival Cour du Capucins *Comments:* choreography workshop complements the festival/competition
Type: choreography

MALTA (+356)

International Band Contest
c/o CEFIT, Nazju Falzon Street, **Birkirkara** BKR 11
Tel: 491 610/441 157 Fax: 491 598
E-Mail: conceuro@dream.vol.net.mt
managing director Mr Pullicino
Date: June *Eligibility:* any nationality; bands with 50-70 members; only 10% professional musicians *Awards:* cash: 1st prize 2.5k US$, 2nd prize 1.250 US$, 3rd prize 750 US$, 1 prize 750 US$ for best director *Comments:* bands will perform 3 times; all expenses (travel, accomodation) paid by the participants; participation fee: 30 US$ per musician; organised by Concert Europe Incentive Tours; see also Promoters *Type:* wind, brass and symphonic bands (only amateurs)

Malta International Choir Festival
Actel Malta Gorup, 316 Rue d'Argens, **Gzira** GZR 04
Tel: 320 554/556 Fax: 320 557
Internet: www.tourism.org.mt
E-Mail: jims@tourism.org.mt
festival administrator/chairman organising committe Alexander Bonello; artistic & technical director Tanya Bayona; musical advisor John Galea; logistics manager Herbert Brincat; marketing manager Steve Cassar
Dates: November *Frequency:* annual *Eligibility:* amateur choir, adults *Awards:* 1st prize: US$3k & gold trophy, 2nd prize: US$1k & silver trophy, 3rd prize: US$500 & bronze trophy *Type:* choir

MOLDOVA (+373)

International Choirs Competition
24, Puskin str., 2012 **Chisinau**
Tel: 2-243 443 Fax: 2-212 390
manager Maria Biesu
Dates: June *Comments:* only choirs of artistic Institutions (education) *Type:* choirs

International Competition of Young Instrumentalists
87, A.Mateevici str, 2012 **Chisinau**
Tel: 2-242 036/224 344
organiser Constantin Rusnac
Frequency: quadriennial (2001) *Type:* violin, cello, piano

MONACO (+377)

Prix de Composition Musicale Prince Pierre de Monaco
Fondation Prince Pierre de Monaco, 4 Boulevard des Moulins, 98000 **Monte Carlo**
Tel: 9315 8303 Fax: 9350 6694
general secretary Rainier Rocchi
Dates: May *Frequency:* annual *Eligibility:* internationally known composers; no candidatures admitted *Awards:* 100k FF *Comments:* also Prix Litteraire and Prix d'Art Contemporain; this is an award rather than an actual competition *Type:* contemporary music created during the last year

NETHERLANDS (+31)

International Gaudeamus Composers' Competition
Gaudeamus Foundation, Swammerdamstraat 38, 1091 RV **Amsterdam**
Tel: 20-694 7349
Fax: 20-694 7258
Internet: www.xs4all.nl/~gaud
E-Mail: gaud@xs4all.nl
director Henk Heuvelmans
Dates: 31 August-10 September 2000 *Frequency:* annual *Eligibility:* composers up to 30 yrs *Awards:* cash prize for best composer *Comments:* application deadline: 31 Jan 2000, see also National Orgainsations and Festivals
Type: composers (contemporary music)

International Gaudeamus Performers' Competition
Gaudeamus Foundation, Swammerdamstraat 38, 1091 RV **Amsterdam**
Tel: 20-694 7349 Fax: 20-694 7258
Internet: www.xs4all.nl/~gaud
E-Mail: gaud@xs4all.nl
director Henk Heuvelmans
Dates: October 2001 *Frequency:* biennial *Eligibility:* soloists up to 35 yrs, vocalists up to 40 yrs, average age of ensembles no more than 35 yrs, ensembles up to 12 performers *Awards:* cash, concert for winner, special cash prize for best violin/viola player *Comments:* application deadline: 31 Jan 2001 *Type:* performance of contemporary music (soloists, vocalists, ensembles)

Van Wassenaer Concours
Stichting Oude Muziek Nederland, Willemsparkweg 114, 1071 HN **Amsterdam**
Tel: 20-626 6944 Fax: 20-622 7118
E-Mail: klimpart@xs4all.nl
director (Impulse Arts Management) Martyn Jacobus
Dates: 15-18 Nov 2000 *Frequency:* biennial (2000) *Eligibility:* international early music ensembles of not more than 8 members, playing music of the 17th-18th century only, on period or reproduction instruments *Awards:* prizes to be announced *Comments:* deadline for applications: 1 May 2000; application fee: 150 Dfl; competition organised by Impulse Arts Management in collaboration with Early Music Ensembles Association *Type:* early music ensembles (not more than 8 members)

International Competition for Choreographers of Contemporary Dance
Stichting Groningen Dansstad, PO Box 7020, 9701 JA **Groningen**
Tel: 50-313 4965 Fax: 50-311 9279
E-Mail: iccdance@hnn.nl
coordination Annemieke Keurentjes
Frequency: biennial (2000) *Eligibility:* professional choreographers, duration of choreography 8-12 minutes; no solos, first performed after 1 January 1998 *Awards:* 1st prize: a commission by St. Groningen Dansstad to develop a production, a registration or a study; 2nd prize: 5k Dfl; audience prize: 2500 Dfl *Comments:* deadline for applications: 1 September *Type:* contemporary dance choreography

César Franck Organ Competition
Santpoorterstraal 10, 2023 DC **Haarlem**
Tel: 23-525 2766 Fax: 23-525 2766
E-Mail: lhermans@euronet.nl
secretary Louk Hermans
Dates: October 2001 *Frequency:* triennial (one year postponed, to coincide with the centennial of the cathedral in 2001) *Eligibility:* open to professional organists *Awards:* 1st prize: 3000 Dfl, concert engagements, radio recording; 2nd prize: 2000 Dfl; 3rd prize: 1000 Dfl *Comments:* deadline for application forms: 1 June 2001 *Type:* organ (repertory: works by French and romantic and modern French composers)

International Competition for Organ Improvisation Haarlem
Postbus 3333, 2001 DH **Haarlem**
Tel: 23-516 0574 Fax: 23-516 0576
secretary E L S Hendrikse
Dates: July *Frequency:* biennial (2000) *Eligibility:* open *Awards:* cash: DFL 10k *Comments:* visiting address: Klein Heiligland 84, 2001 EJ Haarlem *Type:* organ

International Chamber Music Competition for Strings in Heerlen
P/a Muziekschool Heerlen, Wilhelminaplein 24, 6411 KW **Heerlen**
Tel: 45-571 5277 Fax: 45-571 7218
Internet: www.msh.nl
E-Mail: info@msh.nl
organiser P. W. Weinstock, J. B. P. Essers
Dates: 6-7 May 2000 *Frequency:* annual *Eligibility:* A: ensembles of an average age up to 16 yrs, individual musicians up to 22 yrs; B: ensembles of an average age up to 22 yrs, individual musicians up to 28 yrs; C: ensembles of an average age up to 26 yrs, individual musicians up to 33 yrs *Awards:* cash *Comments:* the competition final will take place in the Municipal Theatre Heerlen; deadline for applications: 29 January 2000; postal address: Postbus 33, 6400 AA Heerlen; promoter: Foundation Charles Hennen Concours *Type:* ensembles (trios, quartetts and quintetts) with or without piano accompaniment

Kirill Kondrashin International Competition for Young Conductors
c/o NOS, PO Box 26444, 1202 JJ **Hilversum**
Tel: 35-677 5453 Fax: 35-677 4311
E-Mail: kondrashin@gsd.nos.nl
manager Max Snijder
Dates: September 2002 *Frequency:* quadriennial *Eligibility:* max age: up to 36 *Awards:* Kirill Kondrashin Prize (fl 75k), EBU Prize for the best performance of the commissioned piece (recommendations to all EBU Orchestras) *Comments:* also masterclasses (next in 2000); venues: Concertgebouw (Amsterdam), Music Centre (MCO) (Hilversum); deadline for applications: April 2002 *Type:* conducting

Concours l'Europe & l'Orgue Maastricht
Jekerschans 75, 6212 GH **Maastricht**
Tel: 43-321 0890 Fax: 43-321 0890
organiser Jean Wolfs
Dates: 2000 *Frequency:* quadriennial (2000) *Eligibility:* organists of all nationalities; no age limit *Awards:* 1st prize: DFL 20k and a concert in Maastricht in 2001, 2nd prize: DFL 10k and a concert in Maastricht in 2001 *Comments:* deadline for applications will be 3 months before the competition; the competition will be held in Liège (Belgium), Aachen (Germany) & Maastricht (finals) *Type:* organ

International Locatelli Concours Amsterdam
Prins Willem van Oranjelaan 4, 1412 GK **Naarden**
Tel: 35-678 1790 Fax: 35-678 1791
director Max Snijder
Dates: October 2001 *Frequency:* biennial *Eligibility:* age limit up to and including 32 years *Awards:* total Dfl 50k + CD recordings *Comments:* competition is held at Concertgebouw Amsterdam; see also Festivals (Muziek Festival Naarden) *Type:* modern violin, baroque violin

Dutch International Vocal Competition s-Hertogenbosch
PO Box 1225, 5200 BG **s-Hertogenbosch**
Tel: 73-690 0999 Fax: 73-690 1166
Internet: www.ivc.nl
E-Mail: info@ivc.nl
general manager Arthur Oostvogel; office manager Bert Van Der Horst (contact for future competitions)
Dates: 22 Sept-1 Oct 2000 *Frequency:* biennial *Eligibility:* up to 30 yrs *Awards:* 1st prize: Euro 20k; public prize & music press prize; Arleen Auger award *Comments:* contact Bert Van Der Horst for deadline for live auditions; entry fee: Euro 150 *Type:* singing

International Franz Liszt Piano Competition
Muziekcentrum Vredenburg, PO Box 550, 3500 AN **Utrecht**
Tel: 30-286 2229 Fax: 30-231 6522
Internet: www.vredenburg.nl/liszt
E-Mail: liszt@vredenburg.nl
secretary K. Groen;
chairman/treasurer Eug. J. R. M. de By;
vice-chairman Peter Smids;
office manager Q. A. Peclen
Dates: 2002 *Frequency:* every three or four years *Eligibility:* 15-30 yrs *Awards:* cash, engagements *Type:* piano

NORWAY (+47)

Fourth International Edvard Grieg Memorial Competition for Composers, The
c/o The Oslo Grieg Society, Gaustadveien 4 b 0372 **Oslo**
Tel: 2249 3630
Fax: 2249 2311
Internet: www.nymusikk.no
pianist, professor Einar Steen-Nøkleberg (president); managing director Per Buer
Eligibility: open to all composers; string quartet duration 12-18 mins *Comments:* deadline for scores: 1 March 2000; the Music in Edvard Munch's Paintings, competition; the task is to give a musical interpretation of the 3 painting of Edvard Munch; information with pictures on request from The Oslo Grieg Society

Queen Sonja International Music Competition
PO Box 5190, Majorstuen, 0302 **Oslo**
Tel: 2336 7067 Fax: 2246 3630
Internet: www.nmh.no/sonja.html
E-Mail: sonja@nmh.no
executive director Lars H Flæten;
president Bjørn F. Boysen
Dates: October *Frequency:* biennial (2001) *Eligibility:* singers of all voices and nationalities: born after 1 Jan 1967; registration fee: US$50 *Awards:* 1st prize: US$ 17k, 2nd prize: US$ 10k, 3rd prize: US$ 7k, 4th -6th prize: US$ 1500; an extra prize will be awarded for the most outstanding interpretation of Edvard Grieg; the winner of the 1st prize will be offered several engagements with Norwegian orchestras and concert institutions *Comments:* please address all correspondence to Lars H. Flaeten; contact for application deadline *Type:* vocal

1st Trondheim International Chamber Music Competition
PO Box 2666 Sentrum, 415 **Trondheim**
Tel: 7394 5269
Fax: 7394 2788
Internet: www.kamfest.no
E-Mail: blh@c2i.net
artistic director Sigmund Tvete Vik;
chairman of the jury Levon Chilingirian
Date: 6-10 September 2000 *Eligibility:* two age ranges for each type: trios total 54 yrs and quartets 72 yrs, trios total 90 yrs and quartets 120 yrs *Awards:* four cash prizes in each type *Comments:* arranged by: Trondheim Chamber Music Festival; administration: BLH Artists Management; deadline for applications: 1 April 2000; entrance fee: NOK 500 per trio, NOK 650 per quartet *Type:* string quartets and piano trios

POLAND (+48)

Grzegorz Fitelberg International Conductors' Competition
Silesian Philharmonic, ul. Sokolska 2, 40-084 **Katowice**
Tel: 32-596 074/589 885 Fax: 32-596 074/589 885
Dates: December *Frequency:* quadriennial (2003) *Eligibility:* up to 30 yrs *Awards:* cash *Type:* conducting

International Krzysztof Penderecki Competition of Contemporary Chamber Music
Stowarzyszenie Kultury Studenckiej, Rakowicka 27, 31-510 **Kraków**
Tel: 12-412 7540 Fax: 12-412 7540
Internet: friko.3.onet.pl./kr/sks
E-Mail: sks@friko3.onet.pl
Eligibility: must be 18-29 yrs *Comments:* contact for more information and application *Type:* soloist, duo, trio, quartet

Wieniawski Violin Competition, The
Henryk Wieniawski Society, ul. Swietoslawska 7, 61-840 **Poznan**
Tel: 61-852 2642 Fax: 61-852 2642
director t.b.a.
Dates: November *Frequency:* quinquennial (2001) *Eligibility:* up to 30 yrs *Awards:* cash, medals, engagements *Type:* violin

Komeda Composers' Competition
Youth Culture Centre, 3 Maja 22, 76-200 **Slupsk**
Tel: 59-431 130 Fax: 59-435 434
Date: 5 November-12 December in Katowice
Comments: see also Festivals (Krzysztof Komeda Jazz Festival) *Type:* composers

Fryderyk Chopin International Piano Competition
F. Chopin Society Poland, ul. Okolnik 1, 00-368 **Warszawa**
Tel: 22-827 9589 Fax: 22-827 9599
director Albert Grudzinski
Dates: October *Frequency:* quinquennial (2000) *Eligibility:* up to 28 yrs *Awards:* cash, medals, engagements *Type:* piano

International Witold Lutoslawski Composers Competition
Teatr Narodowy, Plac Teatralny, 00-950 **Warszawa**
Tel: 22-826 5713 Fax: 22-826 5617
Internet: phil.pol.pl/rules.html
E-Mail: phil@pol.pl
secretary Katarzyna Andrzejowska
Frequency: biennial (2000) *Awards:* cash, medals, performances of winning works *Type:* compositions

Stanislaw Moniuszko International Vocal Competition
Teatr Wielki-Opera Narodowa, Plac Teatralny 1, Box 59, 00-950 **Warszawa**
Tel: 22-692 0441/0642 Fax: 22-692 0548/826 0423/5012
artistic & managing director Maria Foltyn
Dates: 20-29 April 2001 *Frequency:* triennial (2001)
Comments: deadline for applications: 1 Oct 2000

Kazimierz Serocki 7th International Composer's Competition
Polish Society for Contemporary Music (ISCM Polish Section), ISCM Polish Section, Mazowiecka 11, 00-052 **Warszawa**
Tel: 22-827 6981 Fax: 22-827 7804
E-Mail: iscm_pl@ddg.art.pl
Date: June 2000 *Eligibility:* for string quartet with one solo instrument or with solo voice *Comments:* deadline: 5 February 2000; use of tape and live electronics in a composition is permitted *Type:* composition

Concours Musiki Dawnaj
c/o Early Music Society – Warsaw Branch, ul. Zakroczymska 2, 00-225 **Warszawa**
Tel: 22-831 2482 Fax: 22-831 2482
E-Mail: jurbi@friko7.onet.pl
contact Jacek Urbaniak
Date: November 2000 *Frequency:* biennial *Eligibility:* open to amateur and professional ensembles of 2-15 members *Awards:* Category 1 (amateurs): 3 cash prizes; Category 2 (professionals): 3 cash prizes *Comments:* deadline of applications: 1 October 2000
Type: early music

PORTUGAL (+351)

Concurso Internacional de Musica da Cidade do Porto
Av. Boavista 1681 -2°, S2, 10, 4150 **Porto**
Tel: 22-609 5099/5789/606 7258
Fax: 22-600 4307/606 7471
secretary general Elzira Calem; president Fernanda Wandschneider; vice-president Antonio Calem
Dates: 26 Sept-7 Oct *Frequency:* annual *Eligibility:* candidates born between 1 Jan 1968 and 1 Oct 1983; only first 90 applications accepted *Awards:* 1st prize: 1500k escudos, 2nd prize: 500k escudos, 3rd prize: 350k escudos, 4th prize: 150k escudos, concerts, recitals + 3 special cash prizes for different performances
Type: piano

CLEVELAND
INTERNATIONAL
PIANO COMPETITION

ivc
Dutch International
Vocal Competition
's-Hertogenbosch

ROMANIA (+40)

George Enescu International Competition
ARTEXIM, Calea Victoriei 155 Bl.
D1, Et. 2, sector 1, 71012 **Bucharest**
Tel: 1-650 1806 Fax: 1-311 0200
Internet: www.pcnet.ro/enescu
E-Mail: artexim@com.pcnet.ro
contact Mihai Constantinescu
Dates: October *Frequency:* annual
Awards: prizes awarded in all categories: 1st prize US$ 10k, 2nd prize US$ 3k, 3rd prize US$ 2k *Comments:* see also Festivals *Type:* piano, violin and singing

International Music Competition Jeunesses Musicales
C.P. 13-53, **Bucharest**
Tel: 1-323 6600/92-383 542 Fax: 1-323 6600
E-Mail: jmrluigi@dial.kappa.ro
president Luigi Marean Gageos;
artistic director Petru Stoianov
Dates: 9-15 May 2000 *Frequency:* annual *Eligibility:* four different age categories: ages up to 10, 14, 18, 30
Awards: total of US$ 15k; in cash 4.5k, the rest in instruments and scholarships *Comments:* registration fee – $60 US (or 55 Euro); closing date for applications: March 15, 2000 *Type:* instrumental (varies each year); 2000: piano, clarinet, trumpet

Nicolae Bretan International Competition for Vocal Interpretation, The
Gheorghe Dima Music Academy, Str.
IC Bratianu 25, **Cluj-Napoca**
Tel: 64-193 879 Fax: 64-193 879
chief officer Alexandru Farcas (rector Gheorghe Dima Music Academy);
chief officer, USA Dr Judit Bretan Le Bovit
Dates: 24 Sept-1 Oct 2000 *Frequency:* biennial *Eligibility:* age limit: males – 35, females – 30; singers of all nationalities; entrance fee: US$25 *Awards:* 1 Grand prize, 1 Bretan prize and money prizes for 1st to 5th *Comments:* 2nd address: Nicole Bretan Music Foundation, Dr Judit Bretan Le Bovit, 8542 Georgetown Pike, McLean VA 22102 USA Tel/Fax: (+1) 703 893 5871 during the entire competition candidates and their accompanists receive free board and meals; application deadline: 15 July 2000; repertory: entrants must perform several obligatory and candidate's choice Bretan lieder and arias in Romanian, Hungarian or German, plus obligatory lieder from Schubert, Schumann and Wolf, a Mozart opera aria, an opera aria from the international repertory and from 20th century composers of opera and oratorio will be at the candidate's choice; purpose: to showcase the lieder and operas of Romanian composer Nicolae Bretan, to encourage international cultural exchange worldwide, to discover and develop outstanding talent; see also Festivals and Promoters; see also entry in MOD *Type:* opera, sacred songs

RUSSIA (+7)

International Tchaïkovsky Senior Competition
ul Neglinnaya 15, 103051 **Moscow**
Tel: 095-925 9649 Fax: 095-925 9649
director Oleg Skorodoumov
Dates: June *Frequency:* annual *Eligibility:* pianists, violinists, cellists 17-32 yrs, singers 18-34 yrs *Awards:* cash, medals, certificates *Comments:* piano, violin, cello, voice in turn; also organise piano, violin and cello competition for young musicans (up to 16 yrs)
Type: instrumental and vocal

International Ballet Competition Maya
Room 95, Nevsky pr. 85, 191025 **St Petersburg**
Tel: 812-275 4220/3710 Fax: 812-275 3709
E-Mail: Maya@mail.wplus.net
general director Inga Kutianskaya
Eligibility: open to all male and female professional dancers aged no younger than 17 and no older than 26 years on the day of the competition *Comments:* the selection committee will make the choice of candidates from applications and other documents; not more than 60 will be admitted to the 1st elimination round, 40 to the 2nd (semi-final) round, and 20 to the 3rd (final) round; dancers selected to participate in the competition must send the acknowledgement of their participation and participation fee of 50 USD; competitors failing to do so will not be admitted to the competition; please contact the general director Inga Kutianskaya for details of the next competition, as no future details were known at time of going to print *Type:* ballet

International Competition for Young Musicians
c/o St Petersburg Union of Composers, Bolchaya Movskaya ul. 45, 190000 **St Petersburg**
Tel: 812-311 3548
Fax: 812-314 5818
director Grigory Korchmav

International Prokofiev Competition
c/o Directorate of Russian and International Competitions, 3 Radisher St, 101014 **St Petersburg**
Tel: 812-279 6486
Fax: 812-279 6486/542 2635
director Vladimir Lagutenko
Type: piano and symphony conducting

International Shostakovitch Competition
c/o Directorate of Russian and International Competitions, 3 Radisher St, 101014 **St Petersburg**
Tel: 812-279 6486
Fax: 812-279 6486/542 2635
director Vladimir Logutenko
Type: string quartets

SLOVAKIA (+421)

Many telephone and fax numbers in Slovakia are in the process of being changed. We have included all new numbers known at the time of going to print.

J. N. Hummel International Piano Competition
Klavírna súť'az Johanna Nepomuka Hummela
Music Centre, Michalská 10,
815 36 **Bratislava**
Tel: 7-5443 4003/4544/5441 9060
Fax: 7-5443 0379/1373/5441 9016
E-Mail: slovkoncert@netlab.sk
artistic director Marián Lapsansky
Frequency: biennial (2001) *Comments:* member of The World Federation of International Music Competitions
Type: piano

Lucia Popp Singing Competition
Spevácka súť'az Lucie Poppovej
c/o Music Centre – Hudobné centrum,
Michalská 10, 851 36 **Bratislava**
Tel: 7-5443 4003
Fax: 7-5443 2652
Frequency: triennial (2002) *Type:* singing

SLOVENIA (+386)

European Organist Competition for Youth in Ljubljana
Tekmovanja mladih slovenkih glasbenikov – TEMSIG
Tekmovanja Mladih Slovenskih Glasbenikov,
Emonska 20, 1000 **Ljubljana**
Tel: 61-125 1121
Fax: 61-125 1121
E-Mail: nives.fras@cd-cc.si
president Prof. Lovro Sodja
Dates: September 2001 *Frequency:* triennial *Eligibility:* 2 categories: 1) up to 19 yrs, 2) 20-25 years *Awards:* cash and concerts *Comments:* address during competition: Cankarjev dom, Cultural and Congress Centre, Presernova 10, 61000 Ljubljana, tel: 61-1258 121, fax: 61-224 279; organ excursion in Slovenia; tape recording concert of prizewinners *Type:* organ

SPAIN (+34)

Premio de Composición Ciutat d'Alcoi Para Música de Cámara
Centre Cultural, Avda País Valencia N° 1,
03801 **Alcoi**
Tel: 96-554 4122 Fax: 96-554 4425
director artistico Javier Darias;
director del centro Jordi Botella
Dates: November *Frequency:* annual *Eligibility:* international; no age limit *Awards:* cash: 1500000 Pesetas
Comments: organised by Centro Cultural d'Alcoi; see also Venues *Type:* original unpublished scores for chamber groups – composition

Cadaques International Conducting Competition
Concurs Internacional de Cadaqués de Directors d'Orquestra
c/Arcs 8, 1er 2°, 08002 **Barcelona**
Tel: 93-301 9555 Fax: 93-302 2670
Internet: www.trito.es
E-Mail: trito@bcn.servicom.es
general secretary Llorenç Caballero;
coordinator Maria Pau Roca
Dates: end of July 2000 *Frequency:* biennial (2000)
Eligibility: up to 35 yrs old *Awards:* 1 cash prize, engagements with 15 orchestras in Spain
Comments: see also Festivals and Orchestras *Type:* conducting (18th to 20th century music)

Francisco Vinas International Singing Contest
Concours International de Chant Francisco Viñas
Calle Bruc 125, 08037 **Barcelona**
Tel: 93-215 4227/457 8646
president of the organising committee Maria Vilardell
Dates: 11-23 January 2000 *Frequency:* annual *Eligibility:* women 18-32 yrs, men 20-35 yrs *Awards:* cash, engagements, medals, (separate female/male prizes), scholarships *Comments:* deadline for entries: early December of previous year *Type:* vocal (opera, oratorio-lied)

Premio Frederic Mompou
Joventuts Musicals de Barcelona,
c/ Pau Claris 139, 4° 1a, **Barcelona**
Tel: 93-215 2918/3657 Fax: 93-487 2970
Internet: www.teleline.es/personal/jmb.bcn
E-Mail: jmb.bcn@suport.org
presidente Juan Milla
Dates: Oct *Frequency:* annual *Eligibility:* Spanish or resident under 35 years old; unpublished scores – duration 8-15 minutes *Awards:* 1st prize: 350k pts; the winning score will be edited ; 2nd prize: 150k pts
Type: composition

Concurs Internacional de Interpret, Maria Canals
Ars Nova, Gran Via de les Cortscatalanes 654 ppal., 08010 **Barcelona**
Tel: 93-318 7731/4095 Fax: 93-318 7731/4095
secretary general Elisabet Martinez
Date: April 2000 *Frequency:* annual *Eligibility:* age ranges: 18-32 yrs (piano), 18-35 yrs (singers) *Awards:* prizes: 3.5m Ptas & special prizes *Comments:* deadline for applications: 2 Feb 2000 *Type:* piano, singing

Concurso Internacional de Guitarra Francisco Tárrega
Ayuntamiento de Benicasim, c/ Médico Segarra 4, 12560 **Benicasim (Castellón)**
Tel: 964-300 962/303 851 Fax: 964-303 432
Internet: www.gva.es/benicasim
E-Mail: benicasim@gva.es
presidente Alejandro Garcia Guinot;
coordinator Domingo Tarrega Queral
Dates: end Aug-beginning Sept *Frequency:* annual
Eligibility: international, up to 32 yrs by the date of the final trial *Awards:* cash, concerts for winner, special prize for interpretation of Francisco Tárraga, CD recording *Comments:* member of Fédératíon Mondiale de Concours Internationaux de Musique
Type: instrumental (guitar)

International Voice Competition of Bilbao
Concurso Internacional de Canto de Bilbao
c/o Ms Irantzu Elexpe,
Ap de Correos 1532, 48080 **Bilbao**
Tel: 94-424 6533
Fax: 94-424 6454
director of competition José Antonio Amann;
secretary of competition Irantzu Elexpe;
treasurer of competition Jesús Mª Busturia;
secretary of executive committee Pabló Vélez
Dates: 24 Nov-2 Dec 2000 *Frequency:* biennial (2000, 2002) *Eligibility:* born after 3rd December 1966 and no later than 23 November 1982 *Awards:* female voices: 1st prize 1m ptas, 2nd prize 600k ptas, 3rd prize 400k ptas; male voices: 1st prize 1m ptas, 2nd prize 600k ptas, 3rd prize 400k ptas; first two prize winners will be awarded a contract to perform in an opera with 2 recitals in the 2001 season in Bilbao; scholarship of 1.200k ptas; audience prize of 200k ptas; critics prize of 200k ptas; finest interpretation of a lied, song or oratorio aria 500k ptas *Comments:* in interim year present 2 operas with previous year's winner; deadline for applications: 16 Oct; 2nd address: Ibañez de Bilbao, 2-2° izq, 48001 Bilbao *Type:* vocal (Lieder, opera)

Concurso Internacional de Clarinete Ciudad de Dos Hermanas
Ayuntamiento de Dos Hermanas,
41700 **Dos Hermanas (Sevilla)**
Tel: 95-491 9500 Fax: 95-491 9525
Internet: www.doshermanas.es
E-Mail: doshermanas@dipusevilla.es
managing director Juan Rodriguez Romero (Sevilla);
president of the Executive Committee
Marcel Anción (Bruxelles);
secretario del concurso Pedro Sánchez Núñez
(Dos Hermanas – Sevilla)
Dates: Sept-Oct *Frequency:* annual *Eligibility:* any nationality up to 30 yrs *Awards:* 1st prize: 1million ptas, 2nd prize: 500k ptas, 3rd prize: 250k ptas; clarinets and engagements; special prize Manuel Castillo, 200000 ptas *Comments:* registered with the World Federation of International Music Competitions *Type:* clarinet

Concurso Internacional de Piano Cidade de Ferrol
Concello de Ferrol, Cultura, Plaza de Armas s/n,
15402 **Ferrol (La Coruña)**
Tel: 981-336 72
Fax: 981-336 730
Internet: www.ferrol-concello.es/piano99
presidente Xaime Bello Costa; concejal de cultura t.b.a.;
director tecnico del concurso t.b.a.;
secretario Santiago Quintilla
Dates: April 2000 *Frequency:* annual *Eligibility:* pianists, any nationality under 30 years *Awards:* 1st prize: 1.300k pestetas & 2 concerts with the Orquesta Sinfónica de Galícia & 2 concerts with the Orquesta Clásica de Porto; many other prizes including: 2nd prize: 650k pesetas; 3rd prize: 300k pesetas; Premio Gregorio Baudot: 2 awards of 300k pesetas (for best musicians born after 1 Jan 1979); Premio Fundacion Hazen: 300k pesetas for best musician of Spanish music; Premio Especial del Publico: a silver trophy *Comments:* application deadline: March 2000 *Type:* piano

Concurs Internacional de Cant Jaume Aragall
Centre Cultural La Mercè,
Pujada de la Mercè 12,
17004 **Girona**
Tel: 972-760 605/200
Fax: 972-760 648
E-Mail: ccm@ajgirona.org
presidente Josep Nadal; secretaria Silvia Gasset
(tel: 93-487 9896, fax: 93-488 0943)
Dates: June-July 2001 *Frequency:* biennial *Eligibility:* female and male singers under 33, open to all nationalities *Awards:* cash prizes, scholarships, recitals
Comments: deadline for application: 31 April 1999; see also Festivals *Type:* vocal (opera)

Concurso Internacional de Composición Musical Luis de Narváez para Cuarteto de Cuerda
Caja de Granada, c/ Reyes Católicos 51, 2°, 18001 **Granada**
Tel: 958-225 459 Fax: 958-244 621
dirección técnica José García Román
Dates: April *Frequency:* annual *Eligibility:* all nationalities, no restriction on number of compositions; scores should be original, unpublished and never before been played for a public audience *Awards:* cash: 1250k Pts *Comments:* deadline for applications: 31 January 2000; see also Festivals; funded and organized by Caja General de Ahorros de Granada – Obra Social 1 Cultural; see also Festivals *Type:* composition for string quartet (two violins, viola and violoncello)

Concurso Internacional de Canto Luis Mariano
Fundacion Municipal de Música de Irún, Villa Mª Luisa, Mendíbil, Ap. 41, 20302 **Irun**
Tel: 943-617 731 Fax: 943-614 364
E-Mail: conservatorio.irun@udal.gipuzkoa.net
Date: July *Frequency:* annual *Awards:* 4 prizes: 2m Ptas *Comments:* deadline for application: May-June *Type:* singing

Concurso Internacional de Piano Premio 'JAÉN'
Diputación Provincial de Jaén, Plaza S. Francisco s/n, 23071 **Jaén**
Tel: 953-248 000 Fax: 953-248 012
Internet: www.promojaen.es/dipujaen/piano99
E-Mail: cultura@promojaen.es
director del premio Don Manuel Urbano Perez Ortega; presidente del jurado Guillermo Gonzalez
Dates: a week before Easter *Frequency:* annual *Eligibility:* under 36 years *Awards:* 1st prize: 3m Ptas and gold medal, 2nd prize: 1.5m Ptas, 3rd prize: 700k Ptas; premio Rosa Sabater 500k Ptas, music prize for the best interpretation of the compulsory piece 500k Ptas, best interpretation of Spanish music 500k Ptas *Comments:* funded by Diputacion Provincial de Jaén, Inaem *Type:* piano

Alfredo Kraus International Singing Competition
Concurso Internacional de Canto Alfredo Kraus
Fundacion Orquestra Filarmonica de Gran Canaria, C/ Bravo Murillo 21-23, 35003 **Las Palmas de Gran Canarias**
Tel: 928-320 513/321 747 Fax: 928-314 747
E-Mail: orfigc@orfigc.com
gerente Juan Antonio Gonzalez Ojellón; presidente jurado D. Alfredo Kraus
Dates: November *Frequency:* biennial (2001) *Eligibility:* all nationalities: women 18-32 yrs, men 20-35 yrs; 2 categories: male voices and female voices *Awards:* cash, 1st prize: 2m Pesetas, 2nd prize: 1m Pesetas, 3rd prize: 750k Pesetas; engagements *Comments:* organised by Fundación Orquesta Filarmónica de Gran Canaria; see also Promoters *Type:* vocal (two categories: opera and lieder)

Certamen Coreográfico de Madrid
c/o Paso a 2, Calle Tutor, 18 2° Dcha. Ext., 28008 **Madrid**
Tel: 91-365 7037/547 6979 Fax: 91-365 7037/547 6979
directors Laura Kumin, Margaret Jova
Dates: end of October *Frequency:* annual *Eligibility:* all Spanish choreographers, as well as international choreographers who live and work in Spain *Awards:* 1st prize: 600k ptas, plus 150k ptas for touring expenses in Spain, a residency at a prestigious international dance centre and 500k ptas to cover travel and living expenses, also programming abroad via collaborative agreements with international festivals; 2nd prize: 400k ptas; 3rd prize: 300k ptas; prize for outstanding dancer: scholarship for the American Dance Festival plus 300k ptas prize for an original musical composition, 300k ptas (1997 figures) *Comments:* founded in 1987; competition for new work in contemporary dance and contemporary ballet, min. 3 performers, max. 15, max. length of choreography: 15 minutes; application forms and rules mailed out in June; deadline for sending videos of the work: September; see also Certamen de Coreografia de Danza Española y Flamenco *Type:* choreography of contemporary dance, contemporary ballet

Certamen de Coreografía de Danza Española y Flamenco
c/o Producciones Maga, Calle Tutor, 18 2° Dcha. Ext., 28008 **Madrid**
Tel: 91-547 6979 Fax: 91-547 6979
director Margaret Jova
Dates: beginning of July *Frequency:* annual *Eligibility:* Spanish and international choreographers working in Spanish Dance and Flamenco genres *Awards:* cash prizes; prize for an outstanding dancer; prize for an original musical composition; three cash prizes for choreography *Comments:* founded in 1992 and held in Madrid; the choreography must be for min. of two dancers, max. length of the choreography is 15 minutes; the work must either be premièred during the same year as the current edition of the Certamen or at the Certamen itself; regulations are normally mailed out in Februrary or March; deadline for presenting videos of the work is at the end of May; see also Certamen Coreografico de Madrid *Type:* choreography

Concurso Iberoamericano de Coreografía
c/o Fundación Autor Área Teatro, Danza y Audiovisuales, c/ Bárbara de Braganza 7, 28004 **Madrid**
Tel: 91-503 6836
Fax: 91-503 6819
Internet: www.sgae.es
E-Mail: jcuadros@sgae.es
Date: Oct-Nov *Frequency:* annual *Eligibility:* nationals or residents in any Latin American country *Awards:* 6.5k US$ and staging of choreography by Ballet Nacional de Cuba during the International Ballet Festival of La Habana, diploma and commemorative gift *Comments:* deadline: June; contact in Cuba: c/o Ballet Nacional de Cuba, c/ Calzada nº 510 entre calles D y E, El Vedado 10400 Ciudad de La Habana, Cuba, Tel: +537 322 829, Fax: +537 333 117 *Type:* choreography for any Latin American composer's musical score

IX Concurso Internacional de Canto Acisclo Fernandez Carriedo
Fundacion Jacinto e Incocencio Guerrero, Gran Via 78 1°, 28013 **Madrid**
Tel: 91-547 6618
Fax: 91-548 3493
Internet: www.adenle.es/fundaciones/guerrero/
E-Mail: jeig@adenle.es
presidente Lorenzo Lopez Sancho; directora Rose María Garcia Castellanos
Dates: 4-11 April 2000 (1st & 2nd rounds with piano accompaniment 5-7 April, final round with orchestral accompaniment 11 April) *Frequency:* biennial (2000) *Eligibility:* all nationalities, any type of voice, up to 33 yrs *Awards:* cash, 1st prize: 2m Pesetas plus a contract to perform during one of the next two seasons at the Zarzuela Theatre, Jacinto Guerrero Prize for the best singer of Zarzuela (Spanish operetta) 1m Pesetas plus a contract to perform during one of the next two seasons at the Zarzuela Theatre, 2nd prize: 1m Pesetas, prize for the best interpretation of Spanish music 250k Pesetas, prize for the best piano accompanist 150k Pesetas; prize winner will also be offered the chance of appearing in concert
Comments: organised by Fundacion Jacinto e Inocencio Guerrero; deadline for registration: 25 Feb 2000; venue for 1st & 2nd round: Madrid Senior Conservatory of Music (Real Conservatorio Superior de Música de Madrid), calle de Santa Isabel 53; venue for final round: Madrid Zarzuela Theatre, calle de Jovellanos 4 (Stage door: Los Madrazo, 11); see also Promoters
Type: vocal (all types)

Concurso Internacional de Guitarra S A R La Infanta Doña Cristina
Fundacion Jacinto e Incocencio Guerrero, Gran Via 78, 28013 **Madrid**
Tel: 91-547 6618
Fax: 91-548 3493
E-Mail: jeig@adenle.es
presidente Lorenzo López Sancho; directora Rosa Mº Garcia Castellanos
Dates: 6-9 November 2000 *Frequency:* biennial (2000) *Eligibility:* any nationality up to 35 yrs *Awards:* cash, 1st prize: 2500k Pesetas, 2nd prize: 1250k Pesetas, 3rd prize: 600k Pesetas, and a special prize: 250k Pesetas; also concerts in Spain, Europe and USA
Comments: organised by Fundación Jacinto e Inocencio Guerrero; deadline: 28 Sept 2000 ; see also Promoters
Type: guitar

Premio Internacional de Piano Fundación Guerrero
Fundación Jacinto e Inocencio Guerrero, Gran Via 78, 28013 **Madrid**
Tel: 91-547 6618
Fax: 91-548 3493
E-Mail: jeig@adenle.es
presidente Lorenzo López Sancho; directora Rosa Maria García Castellanos
Dates: 12 April 2001 *Frequency:* biennial (2001) *Eligibility:* any nationality; 30 years or under at the start of the competition *Awards:* cash, 1st prize: 2500k Pesetas, 2nd: 1250k Pesetas, 3rd prize: 600k Pesetas, special prize: 250k Pesetas; engagements; special prize (for shortlisted candidates with no prize) 100k Pesetas *Comments:* deadline for applications: 5 March 1999; organised by Fundación Jacinto e Inocencio Guerrero; see also Promoters *Type:* piano

Julián Gayarre International Singing Competition
Santo Domingo 6-3°, 31001 **Pamplona**
Tel: 948-426 072
Fax: 948-223 906
Internet: www.cfnavarra.es/cultura
E-Mail: canto@cfnavarra.es
coordinador Ignacio Aranaz; director artístico Piero Rattalino; presidente José Carreras
Dates: September 2000 *Frequency:* biennial (2000) *Eligibility:* women aged 18-32 yrs, men aged 20-35 yrs *Awards:* cash, engagements, grants and participation in an opera production *Comments:* deadline for applications: 30 June 2000; help with travel expenses and accommodation available; organised by: Gobierno de Navarra; see also Pablo Sarabate International Violin Competition *Type:* vocal

Pablo Sarasate International Violin Competition
Concurso Internacional de Violín Pablo Sarasate
Santo Domingo 6-3°, 31001 **Pamplona**
Tel: 948-426 072 Fax: 948-223 906
Internet: www.cfnavarra.es/cultura
E-Mail: violin@cfnavarra.es
coordinador Ignacio Aranaz
Dates: September *Frequency:* biennial (2001) *Eligibility:* maximum age 27 yrs *Awards:* cash, grants, engagements *Comments:* help with travel and/or accommodation expenses available; organised by: Gobierno de Navarra; see also Julián Gayarre International Singing Competition *Type:* violin

Concurso Nacional Eugenio Marco para Cantantes de Opera
Associacio D'Amics de L'Opera de Sabadell, Plaça Sant Roc 22, 2° 1ª, 08201 **Sabadell**
Tel: 93-725 6734/726 5470 Fax: 93-727 5321
Internet: www.amics-opera-sabadell.es
E-Mail: aaos@sumi.es
presidenta y directora artística Mirna Lacambra Domenéch; vicepresidente y prensa Xavier Gondolbeu; tesorsro y delegado del concurso Jordi Torrents Ponce
Dates: 2000 *Eligibility:* Spanish or foreign residents in Spain under 32 years old, with official qualifications in singing and no professional debut in main roles *Awards:* scholarship for professional singing course and engagement for opera prodcution *Comments:* deadline for appliction: Jan 2000; organised by Associació D'Amics de L'Opera de Sabadell; funded by Generalitat de Catalunya, Banco de Sabadell, Ayuntamiento de Sabadell; see also Opera, Choirs, Festivals and Courses *Type:* opera singing

Paloma O'Shea Santander International Piano Competition
Calle Hernán Cortés 3, Entlo, 39003 **Santander**
Tel: 942-311 451/311 266
Fax: 942-311 266
E-Mail: ccpianoak@mundivia.es
general secretariat Annelies Kaufmann; founder & director Paloma O'Shea; representative in America Brookes McIntyre
Dates: 27 July-7 Aug 2002 *Frequency:* triennial (as an exception, the next competition is not triennial 2002, therefore next but one is in 2004) *Eligibility:* up to 29 yrs *Awards:* first prize and gold medal: approx. 36k euros (46k US$), concerts and recitals all over the world with presentations in the great musical cities (120 engagements in the 1998 edition), a CD-recording; second prize and silver medal: approx. 15k euros (19k US$), concerts in Spain and abroad; third prize and bronze medal: approx. 6k Euros and concerts in Spain; laureates' prize approx. 3k euros (3.8k US$) *Comments:* all participants receive full travel, accomodation and living expenses and count with the collaboration of a renowned Quartet (for the chamber music in the first phase), as well as of outstanding orchestras (for the chamber concert in the Semifinals and for the finalist symphony concert); alternative E-mail: ccpianomar@mundivia.es; representation in the USA: Mrs Brookes McIntyre, 1401 Brickell Avenue, Miami, FL 33131, USA, tel:+1 305-530 2910, fax: +1 305-530 2905 *Type:* piano

Concurso Internacional De Composicion Para Piano Pedro Valcárcel
Fundacion Marcelino Botín, Pedrueca 1, 39003 **Santander**
Tel: 942-226 072 (fundacion)/217 817 (conservatory)
Frequency: annual *Eligibility:* open to any nationality *Awards:* 2 prizes totaling 2m Ptas *Comments:* deadline for applications: Jan 2000; organised by: Fundacion Marcelino Botín and Conservatorio Jesus de Monasterio, Calle Menendez Pelayo 6, 39006 Santander *Type:* piano composition

International Piano Competition José Iturbi
Concurso Internacional de Piano José Iturbi
Diputación Provincial de Valencia, Plaza de Manises 4, 46003 **Valencia**
Tel: 96-388 2783/74
Fax: 96-388 2775
secretaria jurado Marta Conesa Llansola; presidente Joaquín Soriano
Dates: September 2000 *Frequency:* biennial *Eligibility:* under 32 years by the date of the final trial *Awards:* cash, engagements with Spanish and international orchestras *Comments:* deadline for application: 30 June 2000 *Type:* piano

Premio Caja España de Teatro Breve
Obra Cultural de Caja España, Plaza de España 13, 47001 **Valladolid**
Tel: 983-425 500/535
Fax: 983-425 546
Internet: www.cajaespana.es
head of cultral department Maria Calleja
Dates: April-July *Frequency:* annual *Eligibility:* any nationality; no age limits; short plays (35 pages maximum) written in Spanish and unpublished *Awards:* cash: one prize 2m Pesetas *Comments:* organised by Obra Cultural de Caja España. see also Promoters *Type:* short theatre plays

Concurso Internacional de Piano Pilar Bayona
Auditorio, Palacio de Congresos de Zaragoza, c/ Eduardo Ibarra Nº 3, 50009 **Zaragoza**
Tel: 976-721 300 Fax: 976-350 514
Internet: www.auditoriozaragoza.com
E-Mail: auditorio.zaz@sendanet.es
organizador Miguel Angel Tapia
Dates: December *Frequency:* triennial (2001) *Eligibility:* pianists from all countries, minimum age 16, max age 32 at application deadline *Awards:* cash: 1st prize: 2m Pesetas, 2nd prize: 1m Pesetas, 3rd 750k Pesetas *Comments:* deadline for applications: usually 30 September of the year of the competition *Type:* piano

SWEDEN (+46)

Stockholm Electronic Arts Award
EMS, Söder Mälarstrand 61, 118 25 **Stockholm**
Tel: 8-658 1990 Fax: 8-658 6909
Internet: www.srk.se/ems
E-Mail: ems@ems.srk.se
contact, studio head Ulf Stenberg; competition producer Paul Pignon (email: pignon@oden.se)
Dates: November 2000 *Frequency:* annual *Awards:* US$2k *Comments:* this competition is part of the Stockholm Electronic Music Festival, the festival will be changing its concept but details were not known at time of going to print *Type:* new music

SWITZERLAND (+41)

International Competition in Composition of\ Sacred Music
Concours International de Composition de Musique Sacrée
7, Rue des Alpes, case postale 292, 1701 **Fribourg**
Tel: 26-322 4800 Fax: 26-322 8331
E-Mail: sacredmusicfr@pingnet.ch
contact Nicole Renevey
Dates: 2001 *Frequency:* biennial (2001) (a new theme each time) *Eligibility:* composers of all ages and nationalities *Awards:* cash, first performance during the following festival de musiques sacrées (July 2002 for 2001 winners) *Comments:* 2001 rules will be issued around January 2001; deadline for entries: end of July 2001; scores only are requested (no recordings); international jury *Type:* composition

Concours International d' Exécution Musicale
Secrétariat CIEM, 2 Rue Bovy-Lysperg, 1205 **Genève**
Tel: 22-328 6208 Fax: 22-320 4366
Internet: www.geneve.ch/ciem
E-Mail: ciem@ge.maxess.ch
secretary general Didier Schnorhk;
president Richard A. Jeandin
Dates: Nov/Dec *Frequency:* annual *Eligibility:* instrumental: up to 30 years (by 1st Sept of the year of the competition); vocal: up to 35 years for men, up to 32 years for women *Awards:* global: SFr 130000 (1st prize: 15000) *Type:* instrumental & vocal
(1999: voice, violoncelle, flute)

Biennial of Moving Images
Saint-Gervais Genève,
5 rue du Temple, 1201 **Genève**
Tel: 22-908 2000 Fax: 22-908 2001
Internet: www.centreimage.ch
E-Mail: sgg@sgg.ch
director of the Biennial of Moving Images André Iten; assistant Simon Lamuniere; secretary Isabelle Aeby Papabïzas; public relations & press Lysianne Léchot Hirt
Frequency: biennial (2001) *Eligibility:* video and computer art, films by artists *Awards:* City of Geneva SFr 10k & 3 other prizes *Comments:* international jury *Type:* recorded media

Queen Marie José International Prize for Musical Composition 2000
Radio Suisse Romande, Studio de Genève, 66 boulevard Carl-Vogt, 1211 **Genève** 8
Tel: 22-708 7711 Fax: 22-781 5218
Internet: mus.unige.ch/prixrmj
contact Jean Remy Berthoud
Date: November 2000 *Eligibility:* open to composers of all nationalities without age limit; work for string quartet (2 violins, viola and cello) and chromatic concert accordion or string quartet and bandoneon *Comments:* deadline for application: 31 May 2000; duration of performance: minimum 12 mins, maximum 25 mins *Type:* composition

Prix de Lausanne International Ballet Competition
Palais de Beaulieu, Av. Bergières 6,
1004 **Lausanne**
Tel: 21-643 2405
Fax: 21-643 2409
Internet: www.fastnet.ch/PDL
E-Mail: prix.lausanne@fastnet.ch
president Franz Blankart; vice-présidents Charles Gebhard, Antoine Hoefliger; directeur artistique Jan Nuyts; secrétaire générale Patricia Leroy
Dates: 23-30 Jan 2000 *Frequency:* annual
Eligibility: female and male 15-18 yrs *Awards:* scholarships
Type: ballet

Swiss Organ Competition
Concours Suisse de l'orgue
Place du Prieur, 1323 **Romainmotier**
Tel: 24-453 1718/1446
Fax: 24-453 1150
administrative director Bernard Heiniger;
artistic director Guy Bovet;
secretary Marisa Aubert
Dates: 30 Oct-4 Nov in Porrentruy (Jura) *Frequency:* annual *Eligibility:* no age limit *Awards:* 1st prize: 4k SFR, 2nd prize: 2k SFR, 3rd prize: 1k SFR *Comments:* also organises Festival Suisse de l'Orgue,takes place before the competition; deadline: 1 May 2000 *Type:* organ

Concours Cantonal de Danse – Jeunes Danseurs
Concours Cantonal-Jeunes Dansem,
Case postale 284, 1951 **Sion**
Tel: 79-417 0931 Fax: 27-934 3858
Internet: www.regart.ch/bruns-verdi
E-Mail: cie.brunoverdi@bluewin.ch
président fondateur Bruno Verdi
Dates: December 2000 *Frequency:* triennial *Eligibility:* 10-20 years old *Awards:* SFr 500
Comments: 3 categories: classical, jazz, contemporary; deadline for applications is two months before the competition is held *Type:* dance

Tibor Varga International Violin Competition
Case postale 1429, 1951 **Sion**
Tel: 27-323 4317 Fax: 27-323 4662
Internet: www.nouvellis.te.ch/varga/tvarga.htm
E-Mail: festivargasion@vtx.ch
president Pierre Yves Tribolet
Dates: 8-18 August 2000 *Frequency:* annual
Eligibility: 15-32 yrs *Awards:* Grand Prix: CHF 10k; other prizes CHF 25k *Type:* violin

Clara Haskil Piano Competition
Rue du Conseil 31, Case postale 234, 1800 **Vevey** 1
Tel: 21-922 6704
Fax: 21-922 6734
Internet: www.regart.ch/clara-haskil
E-Mail: clara.haskil@smile.ch
director Patrick Peikert; president Olivier Verrey; secretariat Christiane Susset
Dates: Aug 2001 *Frequency:* biennial (2001) *Eligibility:* under 27 yrs *Awards:* 1st prize: SFr 20k plus concert *Type:* piano

Concours Géza Anda
Bleicherweg 18, 8002 **Zürich**
Tel: 1-205 1423 Fax: 1-205 1429
Internet: www.gezaanda.org
E-Mail: gezaanda@bluewin.ch
general secretary Ruth Bossart;
president Hortense Anda-Bührle
Dates: 24 June-6 July 2000 *Frequency:* triennial (2000)
Eligibility: up to 32 yrs *Awards:* cash, engagements in major international music centres, free concert management, several special prizes
Comments: alternative E-mail: info@gezaanda.org
Type: piano

TURKEY (+90)

Yapi Kredi International Leyla Gencer Voice Competition
c/o Yapi Kredi Kültür Sanat Yayincilik A.S., Yapi Kredi Plaza E. Blok Manolya Sokak 1,
Levent, 80620 **Istanbul**
Tel: 212-282 5682/280 6555/1651 Fax: 212-279 5964
organisation Aydin Gün;
general secretary Georges Canet
Frequency: biennial (2001) *Eligibility:* open to singers of all nationalities and voice categories (soprano, mezzo-soprano, contralto, tenor, baritone and bass), aged between 18 yrs and 32 yrs on the date of the competition *Awards:* 1st prize: US $5k, 2nd prize: US $3k, 3rd prize: US $2k; 3 special prizes US $1k each *Comments:* venue: Central Resit Rey Concert Hall, Istanbul *Type:* vocal

UKRAINE (+380)

International Vladimir Krainev's Young Pianists Competition
c/o Kharkov Special Music Boarding School,
Karl Marx Street 19, 310052 **Kharkov**
Tel: 572-122 684 Fax: 572-123 474
president Vladimir Krainev; director Valeri Altukov
Dates: 19-29 March 2000 *Frequency:* biennial (2000)
Eligibility: junior group (before 13 inclusive), senior group (from 14 to 17 inclusive) *Awards:* cash, concerts
Comments: international representation: Agence Artistique Catherine Petit, 26 rue de la Libération, 92210 Saint-Cloud, France, Tel: +33 1-4602 3336, Fax: +33 1-4602 2725, E-mail: aacp@wanadoo.fr; deadline for applications for 2000: Nov 1, 1999 (always the Nov of the previous year) *Type:* piano

Mykola Lyssenko International Competition
Centre of Cultural Initiatives, B-ohdana Khmelnytskoho St 31, 252031 **Kiev (Kyiv)**
Tel: 44-224 0663 Fax: 44-224 0663
director M Burak
Frequency: quadriennial (2000)
Type: voice, violin, violoncello and piano

Serge Lifar International Ballet Competition
City of Kiev Dept of Culture, Shevchenko Blvd 3,
252004 **Kiev (Kyiv)**
Tel: 44-229 7230
director Evdokia Konoz
Dates: June *Frequency:* biennial (2000) *Type:* ballet

Solomiya Krushelnytska International Operatic Singers' Competition
Centre of Cultural Initiatives, B-ohdana Khmelnytskoho St 31, 252031 **Kiev (Kyiv)**
Tel: 44-224 0663 Fax: 44-224 0663
director M Burak
Dates: November-December (in Lviv) *Frequency:* quadrennial (2000) *Comments:* alternately festival (uneven years) and competition *Type:* vocal

Stepan Turchak International Conductors' Competition
Centre of Cultural Initiatives, B-ohdana Khmelnytskoho St 31, 252031 **Kiev (Kyiv)**
Tel: 44-224 0663 Fax: 44-224 0663
director M Burak
Frequency: quadrennial (2002) *Type:* conducting

International Competition for Young Pianists in Memory of Vladimir Horowitz
31 Tolstoy str., 252032 **Kiev (Kyiv)**
Tel: 44-244 3238 Fax: 44-244 3268
E-Mail: kdmu@naverex.kiev.ua
general director Yuri Zilberman;
participant director Lidia Kovtukh
Date: 4-10 Nov 2000 (junior age group), 18 April-4 May 2001 (middle & senior age groups) *Frequency:* biennial
Eligibility: 9-14 yrs (junior age group), 14-19 yrs (middle age group), 19-33 yrs (senior age group) *Awards:* junior: 1st prize: $2k, 2nd prize: $1.2k, 3rd prize: $600, three diplomas of $150 each; middle: 1st prize: $4k, 2nd prize: $2.4k, 3rd prize: $1.5k, three diplomas of $600 each; senior: 1st prize: $7k, 2nd prize: $5k, 3rd prize: $3k, three diplomas of $700 each; the winners will be taped on CD and will participate in various concert tours *Comments:* 4 rounds: 1st, 2nd and 3rd rounds – solo, 4th round – with orchestra;
entrance fee: $70; deadline for applications: 10 Sept 2000 (junior age group), 1 Jan 2001 (middle & senior age groups) *Type:* piano

UNITED KINGDOM (+44)

MASTERPRIZE International Competition for the Composition of Music for Symphony Orchestra
PO Box 248, **Barnet** EN4 9ZU
Tel: 20-8447 1677 Fax: 20-8447 1677
E-Mail: masterpriz@aol.com
competition manager Louise Price;
chairman John McLaren
Dates: registration by 31 March 2000; final 6 May 2001
Frequency: triennial (2001, 2004) *Eligibility:* no restrictions, no works which have won other competitions are accepted *Awards:* 1st prize: 50k; multiple broadcasts from semi-finalist stage; CD of 5 finalist pieces recorded by the LSO; live Gala final with LSO at Avery Fischer Hall, Lincoln Centre, New York with worldwide broadcast *Comments:* MASTERPRIZE partners as follows: BBC Radio 3, BBC World Service, EMI, London Symphony Orchestra and BBC Music Magazine; registration deadline: 31 March 2000; completed manuscripts to be sent by 31 July 2000; winner announced 6 May 2001 *Type:* composition

Cardiff Singer of the World Competition
BBC Wales, Broadcasting House,
Cardiff (Wales) CF5 2YQ
Tel: 1437-563 834/29-2032 2000
Fax: 1437-563 834/29-2055 2973
adminstrator Anna Williams
Dates: 17-23 June 2001 *Frequency:* biennial (2001)
Eligibility: unestablished singers, minimum age 18 yrs, no maximum; selection by audition *Awards:* cash, London recitals, BBC engagements and trophy
Comments: restricted to 25 singers, broadcast by BBC-2/Radio-3 *Type:* vocal

Welsh Singers Competition
Live Music Now! Wales, 1 Miles Court,
Gwaelod y Garth, **Cardiff (Wales)** CF4 8SR
Tel: 29-2081 3398 Fax: 29-2081 3380
director Roy Bohana MBE
Dates: October 2000 *Frequency:* biennial (2000)
Eligibility: age 18 and over; for singers born in Wales or who have received a significant portion of their education in Wales *Awards:* cash prize £2k; specially commissioned trophy; other finalists receive cash prize of £750
Comments: closing date: April 2000; final will take place at St. David's Hall Cardiff 30 October 2000; sponsored by HSBC Bank Plc *Type:* vocal

London International String Quartet Competition
62 High Street, **Fareham** PO16 7BG
Tel: 1329-283 603
Fax: 1329-281 969
Internet: ourworld.compuserve.com/homepage/lsqf
E-Mail: lsqf@compuserve.com
administrator Dennis Sayer;
art director Yfrah Neaman

Dates: 10-16 April (2000) *Frequency:* triennial (2000) *Eligibility:* combined ages of ensemble not to excede 120 yrs on 17 April 2000 *Awards:* cash, UK and European tour for winners *Comments:* deadline for applications: December 1999 *Type:* string quartets

Leeds Conductors' Competition
Music Department, Leeds Leisure Services, Leeds Town Hall, The Headrow, **Leeds** LS1 3AD
Tel: 113-247 8336
Fax: 113-247 8397
E-Mail: matthew.sims@leeds.gov.uk
competition director Matthew Sims
Dates: 2002 *Frequency:* triennial *Eligibility:* British-born conductors under 35 yrs *Awards:* 3 cash prizes and engagements *Comments:* application deadline: mid February 2002 *Type:* conductors

Leeds International Pianoforte Competition
Piano Competition Office,
The University of Leeds, **Leeds** LS2 9JT
Tel: 113-244 6586 Fax: 113-244 6586
Internet: www.leedspiano.com
E-Mail: info@leedspiano.bdx.co.uk
chairman and artistic director Fanny Waterman; administrator Paul Holloway
Dates: September 2000 *Frequency:* triennial (2000) *Eligibility:* under 32 yrs on 1st September 2000 *Awards:* cash total £57k, performance engagements worldwide *Comments:* deadline for applications: 15 March 2000 *Type:* piano

Llangollen International Singer
Llangollen International Musical Eisteddfod, Music Office, Royal International Pavilion, Abbey Road, **Llangollen** LL20 8SW
Tel: 1978-860 236 Fax: 1978-861 300
Internet: www.lime.uk.com
E-Mail: music@lime.uk.com
marketing director Maureen A Jones
Date: July 2000: semi-finals 3 July 2000, finals 7 July 2000 *Frequency:* biennial *Eligibility:* singers in the early stages of professional career; aged between 18 yrs and 26 yrs on day of the final competition; require a letter of recommendation specifically for the competition from a national opera company, the principal of a conservatory of music or the person responsible for classical music at the national broadcasting organisation of the competitor's country *Awards:* 1st prize: £15k *Comments:* only twenty singers can be accommodated in the competition; deadline for applications: 1 Feb 2000; will take place at the Royal International Pavilion *Type:* singing

Donatella Flick Conducting Competition
47 Brunswick Gardens, **London** W8 4AW
Tel: 20-7792 2885
Fax: 20-7792 2574
administrator Judy Strang
Dates: 21-24 Oct 2000 *Frequency:* biennial (2000/2002) *Eligibility:* EC nationals under 35 *Awards:* award of £15k to subsidise for period of up to one year as Assistant Conductor with the London Symphony Orchestra, specialist study and concert engagements *Comments:* application fee: £35, closing date for applications 16 May 2000, final at the Barbican with the LSO *Type:* conducting

International Early Music Network Young Artists' Competition
Early Music Network,
31 Abdale Road, **London** W12 7ER
Tel: 20-8743 0302 Fax: 20-8743 0996
Internet: www.earlymusic.org.uk
E-Mail: glyn@earlymusicnet.demon.co.uk
administrator Glyn Russ
Dates: 2001 *Frequency:* biennial (2001) *Eligibility:* all nationalities; instrumentalists aged 17-30; singers aged 17-35; min. 3 performers ensembles performing repertoire from middle ages to 19th century using appropriate historically-informed playing techniques, instruments and stylistic conventions *Awards:* the winner(s) will receive The Frederik Martin Award, a series of 3-5 concerts as part of the Early Music Network and a concert as part of the 2002 York Early Music Festival; the runners-up may be offered concerts as part of the Young Artists' Series organised by the Early Music Network in London; possibilities of broadcasting/recording with BBC Radio 3 *Comments:* applications available from The Early Music Network *Type:* medieval renaissance, baroque and classical ensembles of 2-8 players

Julius Isserlis Scholarship
The Royal Philharmonic Society,
10 Stratford Place, **London** W1N 9AE
Tel: 20-7491 8110
Fax: 20-7493 7463
E-Mail: admin@rps-uk.demon.co.uk
general administrator Rosemary Johnson
Dates: May 2001 *Frequency:* biennial (2001) *Eligibility:* aged 15-25 yrs of any nationality domiciled (i.e. permanent resident) in United Kingdom *Awards:* scholarship valued at £20k (£10k per annum for two years) *Comments:* specifically a scholarship for UK permanent residents to study abroad

Kathleen Ferrier Awards
The Kathleen Ferrier Memorial Scholarship Fund, 52 Rosebank, Holyport Rd., **London** SW6 6LY
Tel: 20-7381 0985 Fax: 20-7381 0985
administrator Shirley Barr
Dates: 10-14 April 2000 *Frequency:* annual *Eligibility:* British singers (and those from the British Commonwealth and the Republic of Ireland) aged 21-28 yrs *Awards:* prizes totalling £17500 and London recital; deadline for applications: 1 February 2000 *Type:* vocal

Linbury Prize for Stage Design, The
Kallaway Ltd, 2 Portland Road, **London** W11 4LA
Tel: 20-7221 7883 Fax: 20-7229 4595
contact Liz Martell, Alice McQuillin
Dates: 2001 *Frequency:* biennial *Eligibility:* final year graduate & post graduate theatre design students only *Awards:* £500 for each of 12 designers selected for the Linbury Prize Exhibition; for the overall winner: £1.75k prize money and a £2k design commission with a further allocation of £500 towards expenses; for three runners-up: £1.25k prize money and a £2k design commission with £500 towards expenses *Type:* stage design

Parkhouse Award
c/o GBZ Mangement, PO Box 11845, **London** SE21 8ZS
Tel: 20-8761 6565 Fax: 20-8670 3195
E-Mail: gbz_mgmt@compuserve.com
administrator Gwenneth Bransby-Zachary
Dates: spring 2001 *Frequency:* biennial (2001) *Eligibility:* Max age 32 yrs, aggregate of 60 yrs for duo, 90 yrs for trio; 120 yrs for quartet *Awards:* 2 concerts at major halls in London *Comments:* deadline for applications 1st Dec 2000; info Sept 2000 *Type:* piano based ensembles, duo to piano quartet

Richard Tauber Prize 2000
c/o The Anglo-Austrian Music Society, 46 Queen Anne's Gate, **London** SW1H 9AU
Tel: 20-7222 0366 Fax: 20-7233 0293
Internet: www.angloaustrian.org.uk
contacts Mrs Swan, Mr Fessler
Dates: 2000 (1st auditions March, finals June) *Frequency:* biennial (2000) *Eligibility:* female singers over 21 and under 31, male singers over 21 and under 32; if not UK or Austrian citizen, they have to be resident in the UK or Austria *Awards:* cash prize and recital in the Wigmore Hall *Type:* vocal

Royal Over-Seas League Music Competition
Royal Over-Seas League, Park Place, St James's St, **London** SW1A 1LR
Tel: 20-7408 0214 ext 219 Fax: 20-7499 6738
E-Mail: culture@rosl.org.uk
director of cultural affairs Roderick Lakin
Dates: auditions Feb-April 2000 *Frequency:* annual *Eligibility:* instrumentalists up to 28 yrs, singers up to 30 years; open to commonwealth or former commonwealth citizens, including UK *Awards:* 1st prize gold medal and £4k; 4 finalists each get £1500 *Comments:* deadline for applications: 14 January 2000; auditions: February-April 2000; Final: 5 June 2000 at the Queen Elizabeth Hall *Type:* instrumental, vocal

Shell LSO Music Scholarship
London Symphony Orchestra, Barbican Centre, **London** EC2Y 8DS
Tel: 20-7588 1116 Fax: 20-7374 0127
Internet: www.lso.co.uk
E-Mail: shell@lso.co.uk
administrator Helen Smith
Dates: Spring 2000 *Frequency:* annual *Eligibility:* 14-22 yrs; if 22 yrs, must still be a student.; Nationality: British or resident in UK for at least three years *Awards:* Finalists perform with the London Symphony Orchestra competing for:
1st prize: scholarship of £6k and gold medal, 2nd prize: £3k and silver medal, joint 3rd prizes: £1500 and bronze medal each, Gerald McDonald Award £750 *Comments:* application forms available from October of previous year *Type:* instrumental (2000: timpani & percussion)

World Piano Competition
28 Wallace Road, **London** N1 2PG
Tel: 20-7354 1087 Fax: 20-7704 1053
Internet: www.ldn-ipc.dircon.co.uk
E-Mail: ldn-ipc@dircon.co.uk
event co-ordinator Antony Pristavec; chairman and artistic controller Sulamita Aronovsky
Dates: April 2000 *Frequency:* triennial *Eligibility:* up to 29 yrs *Awards:* cash, concert engagements, scholarships, recordings; special educational awards are available to pianists aged 22 yrs and under *Type:* piano

Yehudi Menuhin International Competition for Young Violinists
8 St George's Terrace, **London** NW1 8XJ
Tel: 20-7911 0901 Fax: 20-7911 0903
E-Mail: kgaynor@msn.com
administrator Kim Gaynor
Dates: 14-22 April 2000 in Folkestone *Frequency:* biennial *Eligibility:* 2 sections: junior – under 16 years, senior – under 22 years *Awards:* prizes total more than £14k; winners of both sections will perform with orchestra at Gala Concert *Comments:* details for 2000 competition available by sending SAE to office *Type:* violin

RNCM Broadwood Piano Trio Competition
Royal Northern College of Music,
24 Oxford Road, **Manchester** M13 9RD
Tel: 161-907 5278/5279 Fax: 161-907 5367
E-Mail: info@rncm.ac.uk
contact, festival administrator Carolyn Howlett
Date: November *Frequency:* biennial *Eligibility:* piano trio: open to students currently studying at a conservatory or to ex-students who have left a conservatory within the last 2 years, whose combined ages do not exceed 80 years *Awards:* 1st prize: £6k & recital opportunities, 2nd prize: £3k, 3rd prize: 1.5k *Comments:* part of the RCNM Broadwood International Festival: Glories of the Keyboard; is organised by the Royal Northern College of Music; see also Festivals, Promoters and Venues *Type:* piano trio (chamber music)

Newport International Competition for Young Pianists
Civic Centre, **Newport (Wales)** NP20 4UR
Tel: 1633-232 824 Fax: 1633-232 808
E-Mail: arts.development@newport.gov.uk
honorary secretary Iain Varah;
arts development officer Adrian Ross
Dates: October *Frequency:* triennial (2000) *Eligibility:* pianists under 25 yrs (born on or after 1 September 1975) *Awards:* 1st prize: £5k plus series of engagements around Wales (if dates can be arranged), 2nd prize: £2.5k, 3rd prize: £1k, other prizes £500 *Comments:* entry fee £50 *Type:* piano

Lionel Tertis International Viola Competition
Secretariat, Erin Arts Centre, Victoria Square, **Port Erin (Isle of Man)** IM9 6LD
Tel: 1624-835 858 Fax: 1624-836 658
Internet: homepages.enterprise.net/erinartscentre
E-Mail: erinartscentre@enterprise.net
director John Bethell; administrator Martin Norbury; president Yuri Bashmet; patron Mrs Lionel Tertis
Dates: 19-26 Aug 2000 *Frequency:* triennial (2000) *Eligibility:* any nationality, under 30 years *Awards:* £6k+ *Comments:* have a workshop running concurrently *Type:* viola

St Albans International Organ Festival Competition
PO Box 80, **St Albans** AL3 4HR
Tel: 1727-844 765 Fax: 1727-844 765
E-Mail: iofs@aol.com
general manager Ken Charponiere;
artistic director Andrew Lucas
Dates: 5-15 July 2001 *Frequency:* biennial (2001) *Eligibility:* open to organists of all nationalities born after 7 July 1970 for interpretation competition, open to organists of all nationalities born after 7 July 1966 for improvisation prize *Awards:* interpretation competition: 1st prize £5.5k – plus recitals, 2nd prize £3000 – plus recitals, 3rd prize £1500; improvisation competition: £4000 – plus recitals, audience prize £500 *Comments:* deadline for applications March 2001
Type: organ; two competitions: interpretation competition, improvisation prize

Tunbridge Wells, International Young Concert Artists' Competition
TWIYC Competition Office, PO Box 10,
Tunbridge Wells TN2 5ZQ
Tel: 1892-616 844 Fax: 1892-616 844
E-Mail: twiyca@aol.com
chairman Arthus Boyd
Dates: July 2000 *Frequency:* biennial (2000) *Eligibility:* born after 5th July 1976 *Awards:* £12.250 total in cash for class winners, accompanist and other prizes plus crystal goblet and 'Composition' prize to overall winner *Comments:* entry forms available autumn 1999; entry fee £50; classes: piano, strings (excluding harps and guitars), wind *Type:* instrumental

YUGOSLAVIA (+381)

Due to the war in Kosovo we have been unable to update the following entries for Yugoslavia

International Competition for Young Musicians Petar Konjovic
Medunarodno takmicenje mladih muzicara Petar Konjovic
Jugokoncert, Terazije 41, 11000 **Belgrade**
Tel: 11-339 916 Fax: 11-340 478
Dates: May *Frequency:* annual *Eligibility:* up to 25 years

International Jeunesses Musicales Competition Belgrade
Medunarodno takmicenje Muzicke omladine
Terazije 26/II, 11000 **Belgrade**
Tel: 11-686 380
Fax: 11-235 1517
Internet: www.music-competition.co.yu
E-Mail: ijmcbyu@music-competition.co.yu
executive secretary Bilijana Zdravkovic;
director Miodrag Pavlovic
Dates: March-April *Frequency:* annual *Type:* piano and piano duo

Memorijal Emil Hajek
c/o Fakultet Muzickih umetnosit, Srpskih vladara 50, 11000 **Belgrade**
Tel: 11-642 414 Fax: 11-643 598

Publications

Publications

Journals and directories selected for inclusion are those that it was considered would be of particular interest to PAYE readers. They cover management issues, financing, product, performances or contain contact addresses In general, periodicals concerned primarily with the theory or study of art forms have been excluded, as have those aimed principally at the amateur enthusiast or layman. **Within country the publication are ordered alphabetically.**

Publications.

Les périodiques et guide-annuaires qui figurent ici sont ceux que nous estimons être intéressants pour les lecteurs du PAYE. Ils englobent des probèmes de direction, finance, produit, présentation etc... ou contiennent des adresses de contacts. En général les journaux qui s'occupent principalement de l'étude ou de la théorie des arts sont exclus ainsi que ceux qui s'adressent à l'amateur ou l'enthousiaste. **Pour chaque pays les publications sont classées par ordre alphabétique.**

Veröffentlichungen

Die aufgeführten Veröffentlichungen und Jahrbücher sind diejenigen, die unserer Meinung nach für den Benutzer des PAYE am nützlichsten sind. Sie befassen sich mit Managementfragen, Finanzierung, Produktion, Aufführungen oder nennen Kontaktadressen. Ausgeschlossen sind Veröffentlichungen, die sich vor allem mit der Theorie oder dem Studium von Kunstformen befassen sowie solche, die sich an Amateure wenden. **Die Einträge sind innerhalb aller Staaten alphabetisch geordnet.**

Pubblicazioni specializzate

Le pubblicazioni (giornali, riviste ed annuari) selezionate per l'inclusione in questa sezione sono quelle che abbiamo pensato essere piu' utili ai lettori del PAYE.Includono pubblicazioni di vario genere: management, finanza, produzioni,recensioni, oppure contengono indirizzi utili a chi opera in questo settore. In generale i periodici riguardanti semplicemente la teoria o gli studi sulle varie forme artistiche sono stati esclusi essendo pubblicazioni per lo piu' rivolte ad amatori o a profani. **L'ordine e' naturalmente alfabetico.**

Publicaciones

Esta sección que incluye periódicos y directorios es la que consideramos de mayor interés para los lectores de PAYE. Las publicaciones cubren temas de dirección, financiación, productos, interpretaciones o direcciones de contacto. En general, periódicos y revistas sobre la teoria y el estudio de las artes han sido excluidos, asi como los dirigidos a aficionados. **Dentro de cada país las publicaciones están listadas alfabéticamente.**

Publications (간행물)

PAYE 독자들에게 특별히 관심이 있을 만한 간행물들이 선택 기재되었다. 이 간행물들은 경영 문제, 재정, 제작, 공연 등의 부문을 커버하며 연락주소가 나와 있다. 일반적으로, 예술 이론이나 예술 형태 연구 등을 주로 다루는 잡지는 원칙적으로 아마추어 팬이나 일반인들을 상대로 하는 것이기 때문에 제외되었다. **리스트는 국가별로 알파벳순으로 기재되었다.**

刊物

所选入的期刊和指南是那些据认为PAYE所得税预扣法读者极为感兴趣的期刊和指南。它们包括管理事务、金融、产品、演出或某些联系地址。总体上，主要与艺术形式的理论或研究有关的期刊被排除在外，主要以业余爱好者或外行为对象的期刊也一样。**在各国内，各刊物以字母顺序来排列。**

刊行物

ここでは源泉徴収の対象となっている読者に特に関心が高いと思われる刊行物やディレクトリーを主に選択しました。これらにはマネージメント、財務、製品、パフォーマンスに関わるもの、連絡先等が掲載されたものが含まれます。芸術形態に関する理論や研究を主眼とした定期刊行物やアマチュアやファンを対象とした刊行物は原則として除外されています。**リストは国別で、一国内ではアルファベット順に記載されています。**

ALBANIA (+355)

DRITA
Tirana
Tel: 42-29609
director Xhevahir Spahiu
Comments: Culture-Newspaper

AUSTRIA (+43)

Deutsches Bühnen-Jahrbuch
German Stage Yearbook
Comments: see entry in Germany

Die Bühne – Orac Verlag
The Stage
Alfred Feierfeilstr. 3, 2380 **Perchtoldsdorf**
Tel: 1-86331-0
Fax: 1-86331-590
E-Mail: peter.blaha@orac-zeitschriften.at
Herausgeber Wiener Bühnenverein; Editor Peter Blaha
Focus & policy: German language monthly magazine covering all cultural sections; theatre, opera, concerts, drama *Comments:* published 11 times per year

Konzert Almanach
Comments: see entry in Germany

Kulturrisse
IG Kultur Österreich,
Viktorgasse 22/8, 1040 **Wien**
Tel: 1-503 7120 Fax: 1-5037 12015
Internet: www.igkultur.at/
E-Mail: ig.kultur@thing.at
editorial board Gabriele Gerbasits, Gerald Raunig
Focus & policy: magazine in the field of cultural studies, is published 5 times a year discussing issues such as work and culture, cultural administration, autonomy of art and culture, globalization, loss of culture, interculturalism, ethnopluralism and homogenisation, art and society, the media, censorship
and the freedom of expression

Music Manual
VIVO Zeitschriftenverlag GmbH, Servitenhof, Hauptstr 36, 3400 **Klosterneuburg-Weidling**
Tel: 2243-34940-0
Fax: 2243-349 4012
Internet: www.musicmanual.co.at/mm/
E-Mail: vivo@telecom.at
Chefredakteur Jens-Peter Launert
Focus & policy: published six times a year covering cross-over arts in Europe, with emphasis on German speaking countries; includes regular special supplement Overture (European Festivals Magazine)

Musikhandbuch für Österreich
Music Handbook for Austria
c/o Musikverlag Ludwig Doblinger,
Dorotheergasse 10, 1010 **Wien**
Tel: 1-515 030 Fax: 1-515 0351
E-Mail: music@doblinger.co.at
editor Prof Harald Goertz
Focus & policy: directory in German of the Austrian music scene, listing orchestras, ensembles, choirs, ballet companies, festivals, impresarios, training schools, record companies, broadcasting, music resources and documentation, agents, promoters, cultural and research institutions etc *Comments:* most recent edition was published in 1993

Musikverlag Doblinger KG
Dorotheergasse 10, 1010 **Wien**
Tel: 1-51503-0
Fax: 1-515 0351
E-Mail: music@doblinger.co.at
managing director Helmuth Pany;
promotion manager Dr. Christian Heindl
Focus & policy: music publishers

Österreichische Musikzeitschrift
Austrian Music Magazine
Hegelgasse 13/22, 1010 **Wien**
Tel: 1-512 6869
Fax: 1-5126 8699
E-Mail: oemz@yahoo.com
publisher Dr Marion Diederichs-Lafite;
editor Dr Joachim Diederichs;
advertising Christine Goldenberg
Focus & policy: monthly magazine concentrating on classical and modern music in Austria, Central Europe and internationally, covering all aspects of theory and practice (incl CD & book reviews, information of composers union and music science) *Comments:* a German-English edition is published once a year

tanz Affiche
Eggerthgasse 10/7, 1060 **Wien**
Tel: 1-586 8026
Fax: 1-5868 02610
Internet: www.tanz.at
E-Mail: affiche@tanz.at
Redaktionsleitung Edith M. Wolf Perez, M.A.
Focus & policy: dance and culture
Comments: published 10 times a year

Theaterstatistik
Comments: see entry in Germany

Universal Edition AG (UE)
Bösendorferstrasse 12, 1010 **Wien**
Tel: 1-5058 6950
Fax: 1-505 2720
Internet: www.uemusic.at
E-Mail: uemusic@uemusic.at
managing director Marion von Hartlieb;
promotion manager Balint Andras Varga;
marketing Eric Marinitsch (emarin@uemusic.at);
marketing assistant Angelika Dworak
(dworak@uemusic.at)
Focus & policy: music publishers

Werkstatistik
Comments: see entry in Germany

BELARUS (+375)

Magazin Maladoscc
ul. B. Khmjellnickogo 10a, 220013 **Minsk**
Tel: 172-682 754/761
editor-in-chief Hjenrikh Dalidovich
Focus & policy: youth magazine

Magazin Mastactva
ul. Chichjerina 1, 220029 **Minsk**
Tel: 172-893 467/468
editor-in-chief Aljeksjej Dudarjev
Focus & policy: art magazine

Magazin Polymja
ul. Zakharova 19, 220005 **Minsk**
Tel: 172-848 012/844 991
editor-in-chief Sjergjej Zakonnikov

Newspaper Kultyra
ul. Chichjerina 1, 220029 **Minsk**
Tel: 172-893 466 Fax: 192-893 466
editor-in-chief Ljudmilla Krushinskaja
Focus & policy: newspaper on culture

Newspaper Litaratura i mastactva
ul. Zakharova 19, 220005 **Minsk**
Tel: 172-332 461/525
editor-in-chief Aljess Pissmjenkov
Focus & policy: newspaper on fiction and art

BELGIUM (+32)

Alternatives Théâtrales (Belgium)
44 rue d' Arenberg boite 27, 1000 **Brussels**
Tel: 2-511 7858 Fax: 2-502 7025
E-Mail: alternativestheatrales@arcadis.be
directeur Bernard de Broux
Focus & policy: periodical published four times per year in French on the international theatre scene

Annuaire du Spectacle de la Communauté Française de Belgique
Theatre Yearbook of the French Community of Belgium
c/o Archives & Musée de la Litérature, Blvd de l'Empereur 4, 1000 **Brussels**
Tel: 2-519 5578 Fax: 2-519 5583
responsable scientifique Martine Gilmont;
diffusion Yves De Bruyn
Focus & policy: annual directory in French of drama, dance, opera, mime and puppet companies and productions primarily in the French Community of Belgium *Comments:* supported by the Ministère de la Culture et des Affaires Sociales and the Commissariat Général aux Relations Internationales de la Communauté Francaise de Belgique: Diffusion Belgium – Lansman, 63 rue Royale, 7141 Carnieres (Morlanwlez) tel: +32 64-447 511 fax:+32 64-443 102: Diffusion France – Librairie du Centre Wallonie-Bruxelles, 46 rue Quincampoix 75004 Paris tel: +33-1-4271 5803 fax:+33 1-4804 9085: Diffusion International – Altera Diffusion, rue Emile Feron 168, 1060 Brussels Tel: +32 2-543 0600 Fax: +32 2-543 0609; see also National Organisations

Art et Culture
Palais des Beaux-Arts,
10 rue Royale, 1000 **Brussels**
Tel: 2-507 8212
Fax: 2-514 3044
chief editor Claude Lorent; assistants to chief editor Alain Delaunois, Anne Hustache
Focus & policy: monthly magazine in French covering all the arts in Belgium and abroad, especially within the French community
Comments: monthly subscription price: BF 225 ; annual subscription price (10 issues): BF 2550 (in Europe)

Carnet
Vlaams Theater Instituut (VTI), Sainctelettesquare 19, 1000 **Brussels**
Tel: 2-201 0906 Fax: 2-203 0205
Internet: www.vti.be
E-Mail: info@vti.be
editorial board Klaas Tindemans (director of Vlaams Theater Instituut Brussels), Dragan Klaic (director of Theater Instituut Nederland Amsterdam)
Focus & policy: quarterly journal in English and French and dedicates several articles in each issue to one specific topic, focusing on the Dutch and Flemish theatre world and of interest to a wider international circle of professionals; each issue also presents a number of condensed news items and a selection of forthcoming premieres, tours and festivals
Comments: other address: Theater Instituut Nederland , Herengracht 168, 1016 BP Amsterdam, Netherlands, Tel: 20-623 5104, Fax: 20-620 0051;
see also other publications and National Organisations: Flemish Theatre Institute

Crescendo
111 Rue du Château d'Eau, 1180 **Brussels**
Tel: 2-375 1744
Fax: 2-374 2446
E-Mail: crescendo.mus@skynet.be
director-editor Bernadette Beyne;
public relations Michelle Debra
Focus & policy: bi-monthly music magazine in French covering all aspects of classical music in Europe; distributed in Belgium, France, Luxembourg, Switzerland and worldwide *Comments:* subscriptions 890 BF (6 issues a year), one issue 150 BF

Cultural Funding in Europe
c/o European Foundation Centre (EFC),
51 rue de la Concorde, 1050 **Brussels**
Tel: 2-512 8938
Fax: 2-512 3265
Internet: www.efc.be
E-Mail: efc@efc.be
EFC director John Richardson;
Orpheus programme coordinator/managing editor Miles Heggadon; information systems Neil Burnett;
EFC documentalist André Deridder
Focus & policy: to provide foundations, corporate funders and governmental bodies with a practical work of reference which reflects the disparate cultural programme interests of independent funders; a second key objective is to help stimulate increased cooperation with respect to foundation and corporate funding in the cultural sector *Comments:* profiles 152 foundations and corporate funders with programme interests in the arts, humanities and culture in Europe. Includes subject and geographic indexes and a bibliography

De Scene
The Stage
Lakborslei 114, 2100 **Deurne**
Tel: 3-360 7800
Fax: 3-360 7801
E-Mail: cpub@cp.be
editor Ward Jacobs
Focus & policy: magazine in Flemish on theatre, opera, dance and music in Flanders *Comments:* 10 editions a year; subscription price 950 BF (Belgium), 1300 BF (overseas); published by Continental Publishing

Etcetera
Sainctelettesquare 19, 1000 **Brussels**
Tel: 2-201 0918
Fax: 2-203 0502
editors Marleen Baeten, Marianne Van Kerkhoven, Peter Anthonissen, Clara van den Broek,
Katrien d'Arras, Dries Moreds
Focus & policy: journal in Dutch with reviews, interviews and articles on drama, dance, opera and other arts in Belgium and the Netherlands, published quarterly (4 times a year) *Comments:* see also National Organisations: Flemish Theatre Institute

European Venue Guide
European Network of Information Centres for the Performing Arts, Sainctelettesquare 19, 1000 **Brussels**
Tel: 2-201 0906
Fax: 2-203 0205
Internet: www.enicpa.org
E-Mail: enicpa@ecna.org
coordinator Caroline Derycke
Focus & policy: searchable database about venues in Europe (music excluded), available on-line at http://www.enicpa.org *Comments:* see also International Festival Guide

Guide de la Danse de la Communauté Française de Belgique
Dance Guide of the French Community of Belgium
ASBL Contredanse,
46 rue de Flandre, 1000 **Brussels**
Tel: 2-502 0327
Fax: 2-513 8739
Internet: www.users.skynet.be/contredanse
E-Mail: contredanse@skynet.be
directeur Michel Cheval; coordinatrices Claire Destrée, Béatrice Menet
Focus & policy: directory of dance companies, choreographers, dance schools, studios, festivals etc with a review of the dance profession and support for dance in the French community of Belgium; guide of dance training for this year *Comments:* the Guide is published in 2 volumes: one in October, the other in January every second year; see also Nouvelle De Danses and National Organisations (ContreDanse)

Guide de la Musique de la Communauté Française Conseil Supérieur de la Musique
Music Guide of the French Community of Belgium and Brussels
c/o RTBF, 52 Boulevard Auguste Reyers, 1044 **Brussels**
Tel: 2-736 3145/735 3815 Fax: 2-736 3145
Internet: www.datanet.be/conseildelamusique
contact Isabelle Van Kerrebroeck
Focus & policy: directory of orchestras, classical music ensembles, choirs, jazz, rock, folk ensembles, composers, broadcasting stations, conservatoires, festivals, music publishers, libraries and resourse centres; the directory has a second section containing arts contacts for the French-speaking community; compiled by the Conseil de la Musique de la Communauté Française de Belgique *Comments:* currently preparing 5th edition out in 1999; see also National Organisations

Guide des Stages et Ateliers Musicaux
Communaute Française de Belgique, Conseil Supérieur de la Musique, 52 boulevard Auguste Reyers, 1044 **Brussells**
Tel: 2-736 3145 Fax: 2-736 3145
contact Isabelle Van Kerrebroeck
Focus & policy: published annually; propose lots of activities (100) in Brussels and Wallonie; all types of music

International Festival Guide
European Network of Information Centres for the Performing Arts, Vlaams Theatre Instituut, Saincteletteesquare 19, 1000 **Brussels**
Tel: 2-201 0906 Fax: 2-203 0205
Internet: www.enicpa.org
E-Mail: enicpa@ecna.org
co-ordinator Caroline Derycke
Focus & policy: European listings of performing arts festivals (music excluded) available on-line at: www.enicpa.org *Comments:* see also European Venue Guide

Nouvelles de Danse
ASBL Contredanse, 46 rue de Flandre, 1000 **Brussels**
Tel: 2-502 0327 Fax: 2-513 8739
Internet: www.best.be/bellone
E-Mail: contredanse@skynet.be
publisher Florence Corin;
coordination Claire Destrée; agenda NDD info Béatrice Menet; abonnements Michel Cheval
Focus & policy: every two months publish a magazine about contemporary dance; each issue develops a specific topic (on dance and music, kinesiology, dance and theatre etc) information on performances, auditions, workshops; twice yearly is also published: 'ND info' giving information on dance companies in the French community of Belgium *Comments:* published twice a year, and also have NDD info newspaper which is free; see also Guide de la Danse de la Communante Française de Belgique and National Organisations (ContreDanse)

Petit Cyrano, Le
Chambre des Théâtres pour l'Enfance et la Jeunesse (CTEJ), 321 Avenue de la Courone, 1050 **Brussels**
Tel: 2-648 3458 Fax: 2-640 9712
E-Mail: ctej@skynet.be
responsables de la publication Thierry Oosterbosch; account & publication assistant Isabella Paelinck
Focus & policy: French-speaking Belgian theatre for young people; also publishes Les Carnets de la CTEJ (contact for more information) *Comments:* bi-monthly; compiled by CTEJ (ASSITEJ Belgium) – La Chambre des Théâtre pour l'Enfance et la Jeunesse – see also National Organisations

Vlaams Theaterjaarboek
VTI Sainctelettesquare 19, 1000 **Brussels**
Tel: 2-201 0906
Fax: 2-203 0205
Internet: www.vti.be
E-Mail: info@vti.be
director Klaas Tindemans; pr Trees Dewever; international work Wouter van Looy; documentation Lies van Roey; publications Kristel Marcoen; research Els Baeten
Focus & policy: annual directory of drama, dance and opera companies in Flanders and their productions.
Comments: see also other publications by Flemish Theatre Institute and National Organisations

BOSNIA & HERZEGOVINA (+387)

Muzika
Music
c/o Music Academy, Josipa Stadlera 1, 71000 **Sarajevo**
Tel: 200 299 Fax: 444 896
editor-in-chief Ivan Cavlovic

BULGARIA (+359)

Magazine Gestus
c/o Foundation 'Idea for Theatre', 12 Narodno sabaranie Square, 1000 **Sofia**
Tel: 2-881 760
chief editor Veselina Guleva
Focus & policy: monthly publication for theatre professionals

Magazine Theatre
52 Doundokov Blvd., 1000 **Sofia**
Tel: 2-880 347/881 763
chief editor Keva Apostolova
Focus & policy: monthly publication for theatre professionals

CROATIA (+385)

Frakcija
Centre for Drama Art (CDU),
Hebrangova 21, 10000 **Zagreb**
Tel: 1-485 6455 Fax: 1-485 6459
E-Mail: iod-frakcija@iod.tel.hr
Focus & policy: devoted to reflection, research and contemplation of various practices of performing arts

VIJENAC – art and culture magazine
VIJENAC – novine za kulturu
Ulica Matice Hrvatske 2, 10000 **Zagreb**
Tel: 1-4819 3312 Fax: 1-4819 3312
Focus & policy: art and culture magazine

CYPRUS (+357)

Tone
Tón
Thákurova 3/676, 160 00 **Praha** 6
Tel: 2-2431 0259/9000 1208 Fax: 2-2431 4149
Internet: www.rosamusic.cz
E-Mail: rosa@mbox.vol.cz
editor-in-chief Petr Wagner
Focus & policy: christian music and video

CZECH REPUBLIC (+420)

Amaterska scena
ARTAMA, Kresomyslova 7, PO Box 2, 140 16 **Praha** 4
Tel: 2-6121 5684/7 Fax: 2-6121 5688
editor-in-chief Lenka Laznovsk

Cantus
UCPS – M. Slechtová, Mezibranská 11, 110 00 **Praha** 1
Tel: 2-2221 1755/531 344 Fax: 2-2221 1755
editor-in-chief PhDr Stanislav Pechacek
Focus & policy: vocal music; 4 issues per year

Czech Music
Hudební informacní stredisko CHF, Besední 3, 118 00 **Praha** 1
Tel: 2-5732 0008 ext 533 Fax: 2-539 720
Internet: www.musica.cz
E-Mail: his@vol.cz
editor Adam Klemens
Focus & policy: published every two months, in English
Comments: alternative E-mail: ozmic@login.cz

Czech Theatre
Divadelní ústav, Celetná 17, 110 00 **Praha** 1
Tel: 2-2480 9124 Fax: 2-2481 1452
E-Mail: edicni@divadlo.cz
editor-in-chief Ondrej Cerny
Focus & policy: review of Czech and Slovak contemporary theatre in English and French, published twice a year

Dance Season
Tanecní sezóna
Polská 14, 120 00 **Praha** 2
Tel: 2-2225 0007 Fax: 2-4446 2354
E-Mail: tanecni@post.cz
editor-in-chief Anna Irmanovová
Focus & policy: published monthly

Decibel
Red. Rock & Pop, Novákovych 8, 180 00 **Praha** 8
Tel: 2-6631 1702
Fax: 2-683 3948
Internet: www.decibel.cz
E-Mail: infor@muzikus.cz
Focus & policy: internet music weekly

Divadelní noviny
Theatre Newspaper
Divadelní ústav, Celetná 17, 110 00 **Praha** 1
Tel: 2-2480 9114/231 5912
Fax: 2-2481 1452
Internet: www.divadlo.cz/noviny
E-Mail: divadelni.noviny@czech-theatre.cz
editor-in-chief Jan Kolár
Focus & policy: magazine of theatre makers and theatre goers, reviews, essays, documents modern Czech and world theatre; pubished every two weeks

Divadelní revue
Theatre review
Divadelní ústav, Kabinet pro studium ceského divadla, Celetná 17, 110 00 **Praha** 1
Tel: 2-2480 9133
Fax: 2-2481 1452
E-Mail: divadelni.revue@divadlo.cz
editor-in-chief Dr. Vladimír Just
Focus & policy: theoretical-historical theatre quarterly specialising in Czech theatre history and theory; published every three months

Face to Pop
Ústav hudební vedy MU, Nováka 1,
660 88 **Brno**
Internet: www.phil.muni.cz/music/iaspm
E-Mail: iaspm@phil.muni.cz
editor-in-chief Prof PhDr. Jirí Fukac
Comments: only in English

Harmonie
Novákovych 8, 180 00 **Praha** 8
Tel: 2-6631 1700 Fax: 2-683 0237
Internet: www.muzikus.cz
E-Mail: infoh@muzikus.cz
editor in chief PhDr. Lubos Stehlik
Focus & policy: published monthly;
Tanecní listy is a dance review

Hudební rozhledy
Music Spectator
Radlická 99, 150 00 **Praha** 5
Tel: 2-531 344/5731 2620 Fax: 2-531 343
editor-in-chief Jan Smolík (tel: 5731 2620)
Focus & policy: monthly

Hudební veda
Musicology
Puskinovo nám. 9, 160 00 **Praha** 6
Tel: 2-2431 1212/312 1740
Fax: 2-2432 4728
E-Mail: uhv@imus.cas.cz
editor-in-chief Dr. Milan Kuna
Focus & policy: published 4 times a year

Hudební vychova
Music Education
Pedagogická fakulta Univerzity Karlovy v Praze, M.D. Rettigové 4, 116 39 **Praha** 1
Tel: 2-2190 0134 Fax: 2-9624 2420
E-Mail: jitka.bilkova@pedf.cuni.cz
editor-in-chief Jirí Kolár
Focus & policy: quarterly

Information Bulletin of Theatre Institute
Divadelnì stav, Celetna 17, 110 00 **Praha** 1
Tel: 2-2480 9164/9148
Internet: www.czech-theatre.cz
E-Mail: web@divadlo.cz
editor Ondrej Svoboda
Focus & policy: bulletin with all theatre information from Czech Republic and abroad; published ten times a year

Loutkár
The Puppeteer
Divadelní ústav, Celetná 17, 110 00 **Praha** 1
Tel: 2-2480 9131/232 6028
Fax: 2-2481 1452
E-Mail: loutkar@divadlo.cz
editor-in-chief Pavel Vasícek
Focus & policy: review for puppet playing, published every two months

Melody
Melodie
Pod prusekem 3, 102 00 **Praha** 10
Tel: 2-756 643
Fax: 2-758 067
editor-in-chief PhDr Milos Skalka
Focus & policy: music and society

Music Instruments
Hudební nástroje
Vydavatelství Georgius Smetanovo nábr. 1188,
500 02 **Hradec Králové**
Tel: 49-614 600
Fax: 49-614 600
editor-in-chief Mgr. Frantisek Kusy
Focus & policy: quarterly magazine for organology; some articles also published in German and English

Muzikus
Novákovych 8, 180 00 **Praha** 8
Tel: 2-6631 1701/1703 Fax: 2-683 0237
Internet: www.muzikus.cz
E-Mail: ng@muzikus.cz
editor-in-chief Daniel Andel
Focus & policy: monthly *Comments:* alternative E-mail: honza@muzikus.cz

Opus Musicum
Radnická 10, 602 00 **Brno**
Tel: 5-4221 3567/4121 1597 Fax: 5-4221 3567
Internet: www.com/opusmusicum
E-Mail: opus.musicum@post.cz
editorial office Monika Holá, Nora Zlámalová, Luká Mrovìc
Focus & policy: music review, published 10 times a year

Rocenka
Year Book
Divadelni ústav, Celetná 17, 110 00 **Praha** 1
Tel: 2-2480 9139 Fax: 2-2481 1452
E-Mail: dokumentace.du@czech-theatre.cz
editor Zuzana Jindrová
Focus & policy: list of the theatre artistes and theatre first performances during the season – with indexes

Rock and Pop
Novákovych 8, 180 00 **Praha** 7
Tel: 2-6631 1702/1703 Fax: 2-683 3948
Internet: www.decibel.cz
E-Mail: infor@muzikus.cz
editor Vojtech Lindour
Focus & policy: monthly *Comments:* alternative Internet: www.muzikus.cz

Svet a divadlo
World and Theatre
Celetná 17, 110 00 **Praha** 1
Tel: 2-2481 7180 Fax: 2-2481 8184
E-Mail: svet@divadlo.cz
editor-in-chief Karel Král
Focus & policy: magazine about a world of theatre and the theatre of the world, published every 2 months

Theatre
Divadlo
Sdruzeni 2, 140 00 **Praha** 4
Tel: 2-6122 5187 Fax: 2-6122 5187
editor-in-chief Jirì Bednár
Focus & policy: quarterly

Video tip
Senovázné nám. 23, 112 82 **Praha** 1
Tel: 2-2114 2364
editor-in-chief Jan Jurka
Focus & policy: monthly; on video, film, TV

DENMARK (+45)

Børneteateravisen
c/o Teatercentrum, Suomisvej 2, 2nd Floor, 1927 **Frederiksberg** C
Tel: 3530 4400 Fax: 3530 4401
Internet: www.Teatercentrum.dk
E-Mail: info@teatercentrum.dk
editor Carsten Jensen
Focus & policy: focuses on children's theatre in Denmark; reviews, portraits, interviews, listings *Comments:* quarterly; once a year with a pullout listings catalogue called 'Theater for Boern ug Unge' (Theatre for Children and Young People)

Dansk Musik Årbog Aps
Skt Hans Torv 26, 2200 **Copenhagen** N
Tel: 3524 0262 Fax: 3534 9313
Internet: www.musikinfo.dk
E-Mail: musikinfo@musikinfo.dk
editor in chief Nils Harbo; secretary Majken Edvardsen; advertising Torben Kruse
Focus & policy: music directory for Denmark; published in Danish with English subtitles and table of contents *Comments:* published annually (on December 8); circulation 10 000

Dansk Musiktidsskrift (DMT)
Christian Winthers Vej 14, 1860 **Frederiksberg**
Tel: 3324 4248 Fax: 3324 4246
E-Mail: anders_beyer@information.dk
editor in chief Anders Beyer;
manager, co-editor Hans Mathiasen
Focus & policy: contemporary Danish music as well as foreign composers; debates, reviews and composers' portraits; focus on contemporary music does not exclude features on older composers *Comments:* published 8 times a year; subscriptions and also sale of single copies; circulation 1100

High Fidelity
High Fidelity ApS, Blegdansvej 112 A, 2100 **Copenhagen** Ø
Tel: 7023 7001 Fax: 7023 7002
Internet: www.hifi.dk
E-Mail: hifired@hifi.dk
editor Michael Madsen
Focus & policy: Danish language publication; concentrating on a wide range of audio/hi-fi equipment and developments; also well reviews of recordings, including 74 min. CD *Comments:* subscription price for 1 year DKK 485 (postage not incl.), 8 issues per year

Kvinder I Musik
c/o Musikvidenskabeligt Institut, ved Københavns Universitet, Klerkegade 2, 1308 **Copenhagen** K
Tel: 3532 3759 Fax: 3532 3738
E-Mail: bruland@coco.ihi.ku.dk
editor Inge Bruland
Focus & policy: women in music-composers and performers; focus on classical and contemporary music *Comments:* published biannually; in Danish; circulation of 400

Musical Denmark
c/o The Danish Music Information Centre (MIC), Gråbrødre Torv 16, 1154 **Copenhagen** K
Tel: 3311 2066 Fax: 3332 2016
E-Mail: mic@mic.dk
editor Bendt Viinholt Nielsen
Focus & policy: yearly magazine in English on the Danish music scene *Comments:* published in collaboration with the The Danish Cultural Institute; subscription address – 16 Graabroedre Torv, 1154 Copenhagen K

Organist-bladet
c/o DOKS , Nøvegade 28C, 1, 7100 **Vejle**
Tel: 7572 0933
Fax: 7583 3058
editor in chief Helge Gramstrup
Focus & policy: journal of the Danish Organ Player Society (Dansk Organist og Kantor Samfund); in Danish only; reflecting the mainstream musical life in the Church of Denmark
Comments: published monthly; circulation 1500

Rampelyset
Nygade 15, 6300 **Graasten**
Tel: 7465 1103
Fax: 7465 2093
Internet: www.dats.dk
E-Mail: dats@dats.dk
secretary general Thomas Hauger
Focus & policy: focuses mainly on amateur theatres and theatre groups, also on courses *Comments:* published 5 times a year

RAP
c/o Film- og TV-arbejderforeningen, Kongens Nytorv 21, 1050 **Copenhagen** K
Tel: 3314 3355 Fax: 3314 3303
Internet: www.filmtv.dk
E-Mail: faf@film.tv
editor Peter Bloch
Focus & policy: film, theatre and TV; newsletter of the Danish Film and TV-workers' Union *Comments:* 10 editions a year (not January and July)

Teater i Danmark
Danish Theatre Yearbook
Dansk ITI/TU, Vesterbrogade 26, 3rd Floor, 1620 **Copenhagen** V
Tel: 3386 1210 Fax: 3324 0152
Internet: www.image.dk/~dititu
E-Mail: dititu@image.dk
manager Jan G. Christiansen
Focus & policy: directory of Danish productions and venues

TurneTeater
Touring Theatre
Danmarks Teaterforeninger, Suomisvej 2, 2. sal, 1927 **Frederiksberg** C
Tel: 3535 4846
Fax: 3530 4401
Internet: www.dk-teaterforeninger.dk
E-Mail: date@image.dk
Focus & policy: annual directory of drama, dance and opera productions available for touring

ESTONIA (+372)

Muusikaleht
PO Box 996, **Tallinn**
Tel: 2-423 205
editor-in-chief Mart Vainu
Focus & policy: music newspaper

Sirp
Pärnu mnt. 8, 10148 **Tallinn**
Tel: 2-448 868 Fax: 2-449 247
Internet: www.sirp.ee
E-Mail: sirp@sirp.ee
editor-in-chief Mihkel Mutt
Focus & policy: cultural weekly

Teater, Muusika, Kino
Theatre, Music, Cinema
Narva mnt. 5, 10117 **Tallinn**
Tel: 6-445 468/2-444 787 Fax: 2-444 787
Internet: www.use.ee/tmk
E-Mail: tmk@estpak.ee
editor-in-chief Jüri Aarma
Focus & policy: monthly magazine on the Estonian and international music, theatre and cinema scene

FINLAND (+358)

Arsis
Taiteen keskustoimikunta (Arts Council of Finland), Maneesikatu 7, 00171 **Helsinki**
Tel: 9-1341 7063 Fax: 9-1341 7069
Internet: www.minedu.fi/artcoun/
E-Mail: eija.ristimaki@minedu.fi
editor Eija Ristimäki
Focus & policy: quarterly journal on cultural policy in general; in Finnish with some Swedish text and an English and Swedish abstract

Finnish Music Quarterly
Pieni Roobertinkatu 16, 00120 **Helsinki**
Tel: 9-6803 4048 Fax: 9-6803 4010
Internet: www.musicfinland.com/fmq
E-Mail: anu.karlson@musicfinland.com
editor-in-chief Mr Kai Amberla; editor Ms Anu Karlson
Focus & policy: quarterly magazine in English on the Finnish music scene, with occasional articles also on opera and dance; of particular interest to performers, composers, critics; 1 year's subscription – Finland and Scandinavia FiM 120, Europe and overseas FiM 150

Suomen Sinfoniaorkesterit Konserttikalenteri
Association of Finnish Symphony Orchestras Concert Calendar
Uudenmaankatu 36 D 21, 00120 **Helsinki**
Tel: 9-2709 1411 Fax: 9-621 4414
Internet: www.sinfoniaorkesterit.fi
E-Mail: kai.amberla@sinfoniaorkesterit.fi
senior administrator/executive director Kai Amberla
Focus & policy: seasonal book in Finnish and English detailing information on all Finnish orchestras and advance orchestral programmes published twice a year
Comments: subscription free

Tanssi / Dance magazine
Alexander Theatre, Bulevardi 23-27, 00180 **Helsinki**
Tel: 9-612 1642 Fax: 9-612 1824
Internet: www.kaapeli.fi/~tanssi/lehti
E-Mail: jyrkka@kaapeli.fi
acting editor in chief Hannele Jyrkkä
Focus & policy: quarterly magazine in Finnish specialising in the contemporary and historical phenomena of Finnish and international dance, on dancers and research

Teatteri
Kustannus Oy Teatteri, Meritullinkatu 33, 00170 **Helsinki**
Tel: 9-135 2207 Fax: 9-135 5522
E-Mail: Teatterilehti@kaapeli.fi
editor-in-chief Annukka Ruuskanen
Focus & policy: theatre and dance in Finland; published 8 times a year

Teatterialan Avain/ Osoite – Ja Puhelinnumerohakemisto
Teatterin Tiedotuskeskus Ry (Finnish Theatre Information Centre), Teatterikulma, Meritullinkatu 33, 00170 **Helsinki**
Tel: 9-135 5550 Fax: 9-135 5522
Internet: www.teatteri.org
E-Mail: riitta.seppala@teatteri.org
Focus & policy: theatre contact addresses in Finnish, produced yearly by the Finnish Theatre Information Centre, listing theatre and dance companies and their principal staff and service organisations

Theatre
Finnish Theatre/Theatre Finlandais
Finnish Theatre Information Centre, Meritullinkatu 33, 00170 **Helsinki**
Tel: 9-135 7887 Fax: 9-135 5522
Internet: www.teatteri.org
E-Mail: anneli.kurki@teatteri.org
editor Anneli Kurki
Focus & policy: English and French language magazine on theatre & dance in Finland;
comes out 1-2 times a year

FRANCE (+33)

Actualité de la Scénographie
58 rue Servan, 75011 **Paris**
Tel: 1-4700 1952 Fax: 1-4355 8194
rédacteur Michel Glarydsky;
responsable diffusion Pascale Toussaint
Focus & policy: technical journal in French on theatre set design, lighting and all equipment and services for venues *Comments:* 10 issues a year, subscription for 1 year: FF 385 (France), FF 500 (abroad)

Annuaire du Spectacle
Publications Mandel, BP 1219, 78202 **Mantes-la-Jolie** Cedex
Tel: 1-3098 3210 Fax: 1-3098 3200
Internet: www.mandelnet.com
directeur de la publication Charles Mandel;
responsable de l'annuaire Sylvie Mandel
Focus & policy: comprehensive listing of showbusiness professionals and organisations (cinema, theatre, opera, TV, radio, music, venues) *Comments:* edited every year in November

Ballet 2000
37 Bd. Dubouchage, 06000 **Nice**
Tel: 4-9313 1754 (secretary)/+39 0258-111 192 Fax: 4-9362 0439/+39 0258-111 238 (Italy)
Internet: www.ballet2000.com
E-Mail: info@ballet2000.com
directeur Alfio Agostini
Focus & policy: bi-monthly magazine on the international dance scene in French, Spanish, Italian
Comments: subscriptions: 150FF a year

Cahiers de la Guitare
BP 83, 94472 **Boissy-St-Leger** Cedex
Tel: 1-4598 1291 Fax: 1-4599 1649
Internet: www.cahiers-de-la-guitare.org
E-Mail: ribavillault@cahiers-de-la-guitare.org
rédactrice en chef Danièlle Ribavillault
Focus & policy: magazine about classical guitar, jazz, flamenco, published 4 times a year in French; each issue contains original articles written by specialists; practical information on festivals, competitions, books and record reviews, interview and portrait of composers, performers

Concerts du Melomane, Les
Maison de Radio France, 116 avenue du President Kennedy, 75220 **Paris** Cedex 16
Tel: 1-4230 2580
Fax: 1-4230 4633
Internet: www.lasemaine@radiofrance.fr
E-Mail: etchemendy@radiofrance.francenet.fr
contact Christian Wasselin
Focus & policy: every two months; magazine of the concerts of Radio France *Comments:* alternative E-mail: lasemaine@radiofrance.fr

Danser
129 Bd. Malesherbes, 75017 **Paris**
Tel: 1-5679 3636 Fax: 1-5679 3660
editor-in-chief Jean-Claude Dienis (1-5679 3619);
assistante Dominique Pillette (1-5679 3616);
directeur Joël Cassard;
chef de publicité Marie-Pierre Bastard;
directeur delegue Philippe Ostermann
Focus & policy: journal on the French dance scene; published 11 times a year
Comments: published since 1983

DIAPASON
43, rue du Colonel Pierre-Avia, 75754 **Paris** Cedex 15
Tel: 1-4133 5000
Fax: 1-4133 5718
editor in chief Jean-Marie Piel; editor Jannick Nausette-Fleung; director marketing Christine David
Focus & policy: monthly, classical music

Ecouter Voir
Médiathèque Musicale de Paris, 8,
Porte St. Eustache, 75001 **Paris**
Tel: 1-4233 2050 Fax: 1-4026 6516
rédacteur en chef Michel Sineux; abonnements Simone Cabanes; directeur de la publication Christian Massault
Focus & policy: information on and by professionals working in music *Comments:* 10 issues annually; subscription 450 FF in France, 550 FF in Europe and rest of the world

Festivals et Expositions/Saison Culturelle
Festivals & Exhibitions/Cultural Season
Ministère de la Culture et de la Communication, 3 rue de Valois, 75042 **Paris** Cedex 01
Tel: 1-4015 8390 Fax: 1-4015 8552
Internet: www.culture.fr/
E-Mail: olivierb@culture.fr
Focus & policy: annual directory with addresses, dates and main attractions of festivals and exhibitions in France; published in French by the French Ministry of Culture *Comments:* 2 volumes: Festivals et Expositions – Le Guide Culturel de l'Ete (appears end May), La Saison Culturel – Le Guide Culturel de l'Hiver (appears end Oct), includes main performances of theatre, music, dance and cinema as well as festivals and exhibitions; on sale: Office Central de Partenariat, 149 rue Saint Honoré, 75001 Paris, Tel: 1-4703 4848, price 60FF

Goliath
c/o Hors les Murs, 68 rue de la Folie Méricourt, 75011 **Paris**
Tel: 1-5528 1010 Fax: 1-5528 1011
Internet: www.horslesmurs.asso.fr
E-Mail: info@horslesmurs.asso.fr
realisation Catherine Charpin;
directeur de la publication J. L. Baillet
Focus & policy: published every two years – a directory of listing names and addresses of artists, agents, organisations, suppliers etc working in street theatre in France and all over the world *Comments:* available in France and Europe; also publish a magazine in French about urban performances: Rue de la Folie

Gotha, Le
3 rue Le Goff, 75005 **Paris**
Tel: 1-4326 0737 Fax: 1-4326 9903
E-Mail: public.et.co@wanadoo.fr
chairman Anne Marie Thibaut
Focus & policy: professional guide to art and culture in France

IDEA – International Directory of Electronic Arts
CHAOS, 57, rue Falguière, 75015 **Paris**
Tel: 1-4320 9223 Fax: 1-4322 1124
Internet: nunc.com
E-Mail: bureaud@altern.org
editor Annick Bureaud
Focus & policy: online directory of electronic arts in French and English; lists c.4000 addresses around the world covering computer art and animation, video, interactive art, computer music, holography etc.; lists institutions, artists, theoreticians, critics and curators
Comments: online publication only (http://nunc.com)

In Situ
Office de la Culture 42, 13001 **Marseille**
Tel: 4-9133 3379
Fax: 4-9154 2884
president Berhard Jaquier; directeur Jean-Robert Cain
Focus & policy: theatre, dance, music, cinema, folk, exhibitions *Comments:* 26th century of the town; publication of an diary

International Directory of Circus Arts
c/o Horslesmurs,
68 rue de la Folie Méricourt, 75011 **Paris**
Tel: 1-5528 1010 Fax: 1-5528 1011
Internet: www.horslesmurs.asso.fr
E-Mail: info@horslesmurs.asso.fr
directeur de publication Jean-Luc Baillet; réalisation Céline Boduing
Focus & policy: published every two years (next 2001); directory listing names and addresses of artists, agents, organisations working in circus arts in the world
Comments: also publish a magazine in French: Arts de la piste

L'Avant-Scène Opéra
Editions Premieres Loges,
15, rue Tiquetonne, 75002 **Paris**
Tel: 1-4233 5151
Fax: 1-4233 8091
E-Mail: Premieres.loges@wanadoo.fr
directeur de la publication Michel Pazdro

La Lettre du Musicien
BP 64, 75722 **Paris** Cedex 15
Tel: 1-5677 0400
Fax: 1-5677 0409
Internet: www.lettre.musicien.fr/
E-Mail: info@lettre-musicien.fr
directrice Michèle Worms;
communication et publicité Denise Marinier
Focus & policy: magazine covering all aspects of the classical music scene in France and other countries (published 15 times annually) *Comments:* see also Piano

Le Monde de la Musique
The World of Music
12 bis Place Henri Bergson,
BP 443, 75366 **Paris** Cedex 08
Tel: 1-4008 5050 Fax: 1-4008 5060
redactrice en chef Nathalie Krafft; équipe de rédaction Georges Gad, François Lafon
Focus & policy: more than a monthly record review magazine, as it covers the French classical music and opera scene and policies in general; a list of all the festivals in France and abroad is also published with the July edition: also publishes some special editions every September *Comments:* published 11 times a year

Movement
83 rue Léon Frot, 75011 **Paris**
Tel: 1-4370 0305 Fax: 1-4493 9240

Music and Opera around the World 1999/2000
Musique et Opéra autour du monde,
Editions le fil d'Ariane
17 rue Cler, 75007 **Paris**
Tel: 1-5359 3929
Fax: 1-4705 7461
Internet: www.music-opera.com
E-Mail: contact@music-opera.com
editor Marie-Laure de Bello-Portu; editorial assistant Violaine Thielen; managing editor & administration Armand Cohen, Cecile Temime
Focus & policy: annual publication (July) listing all opera & orchestra performances worldwide, including a presentation of the most important operas and orchestras with seating plan, booking information and 3 idexes: performances, opera and venues

MUSIQZAG
26 ave. Charles Garcia, 94120 **Fontenay-sur-Bois**
Tel: 1-4394 9409 Fax: 1-4394 9392
E-Mail: musiqzag@wanadoo.fr
directeur de la publication Dominique Chantaraud; directeurs de la rédaction Laurent Ronzon, Edwige Renaud; secretaire de la rédaction Patricia Daffy; responsable publicité Isabelle Biscaye-Pierre
Focus & policy: classical music, jazz, ballet: 10 issues annually

Opera International
122 Champs Elysées, 75008 **Paris**
Tel: 1-4289 0919
Fax: 1-4561 1829
rédacteur en chef Sergio Segalini
Focus & policy: monthly magazine on opera, news, record reviews, listings etc.

Piano
c/o La Lettre du Musicien, BP 64, 75722 **Paris** Cedex 15
Tel: 1-5677 0400 Fax: 1-5677 0409
Internet: www.lettre.musicien.fr/
E-Mail: info@lettre-musicien.fr
directrice Michèle Worms; publicité Denise Marinier
Focus & policy: published annually in August; covers all aspects of the piano world
(classical and jazz, worldwide)

PUCK – La Marionnette et les autres arts
Institut International de la Maionnette, 7 Place Winston Churchill, 08000 **Charleville-Mézières**
Tel: 3-2433 7250 Fax: 3-2433 7269
Internet: www.ardennes.com/asso/iim
E-Mail: inst.marionette@ardennes.com
président Jacques Felix; directrice Margareta Niculescu
Focus & policy: scientific research applied to puppetry; annual; in 1998 Puck n° 10 will be published in French
Comments: it is published also in Spanish up to Puck n° 5 and in German up to Puck n° 4; sponsored by the DRAC Champagne – Ardenne, Office Régionale Culturelle de Champagne – Ardenne, Centre National des Lettres – conseil general des Ardennes

Théâtre/Public
Public Theatre
41 avenue des Grésillons, 92230 **Gennevilliers**
Tel: 1-4132 2610
Fax: 1-4086 1744
directeur de la publication Bernard Rothstein;
rédacteur en chef Alain Girault;
administrateur Philippe Grimm;
diffusion Angela de Vincenzo;
secrétariat Catherine Ferval
Focus & policy: bi-monthly magazine on different aspects of French and international drama (aesthetic, social, institutional) and its relationships with other arts, culture and politics; a revue not primarily for information or criticism, but for debate: the revue is in French *Comments:* subscriptions: FF350 (France), FF380 (Europe), FF410 (rest of world), 5 issues a year in France, Belgium, Spain

UBU Scènes d'Europe
European Stages
c/o Association pour l'information théâtrale en Europe,
217 boulevard Péreire, 75017 **Paris**
Tel: 1-4574 7396
Fax: 1-4574 7396
président Gilles Costaz; rédactrice en chef Chantal Boiron; trésorier Patrick Verschuren
Focus & policy: about the theatre in Europe, mainly contemporary theatre and writers; 4 issues a year
Comments: bilingual: in French and in English

World Theatre Directory
Annuaire Mondial du Théâtre – ITI Publication
1 rue Miollis, 75732 **Paris** Cedex 15
Tel: 1-4568 2650
Fax: 1-4566 5040
Internet: iti-worldwide.org
E-Mail: iti@unesco.org
general editor Nicole Leclercq (ITI Communication Committee); internet editor Jennifer Walpole (ITI General Secretariat)
Focus & policy: published on the occassion of Bach ITI World Congress; details country by country the activities of the national centres of the ITI, lists national organisations, theatres, schools, documentation centres, publications etc. *Comments:* information on ITI National Centres' role, services and activities will be available on the Internet site in 2000

GEORGIA (+995)

Khelovneba
18 Uznadze st.,
380002 **Tbilisi**
Tel: 32-951 024/324
editor Nodar Gurabanidze

Teatraluri dziebani
19 Rustaveli ave.,
38008 **Tbilisi**
Tel: 32-931 199
Comments: published by Scientific Board of the Rustaveli Theatre and Film Art Institute

Teatri de tskhovreba
11a G. Leonidze st.,
380007 **Tbilisi**
Tel: 32-999 096
editor Guram Batiashvili

GERMANY (+49)

Acustica – united with acta acustica
S. Hirzel Verlag GmbH & Co,
PO Box 101061, 70009 **Stuttgart**
Tel: 711-2582-0 (publisher)
Fax: 711-2582-294 (publisher)
E-Mail: a.aa@aku.physik.uni-oldenburg.de
editor in chief Dr. Jean-Dominique Polack (Paris); vice editors in chief Prof. Dr. Volker Mellert (Oldenburg)
Focus & policy: bi-monthly journal on venue acoustics etc in English; member journal of the European Acoustics Association EAA (serving 23 European national acoustical societies)

Alte Musik Aktuell
Pro Musica Antiqua,
Postfach 100830, 93008 **Regensburg**
Tel: 941-52687
Fax: 941-53094
E-Mail: pro.musica.antiqua@t-online.de
Herausgeber Pro Musica Antiqua;
Leiter Stephan Schmid
Focus & policy: early music in Germany, Europe and USA
Comments: published 11 times a year; visiting address: Luitpoldstr. 3, 93047 Regensburg; see also Festivals

ballett international / tanz aktuell
Lützowplatz 7, 10785 **Berlin**
Tel: 30-2544 9521
Fax: 30-2544 9524
Internet: www.ballet-tanz.de
E-Mail: redaktion@ballet-tanz.de
managing editors Claudia Assmann, Hartmut Regitz, Arnd Wesemann
Focus & policy: monthly publication in German and English about international developments of classical and contemporary dance; one double issue/yearbook in August/September *Comments:* published by Friedrich Berlin Verlagsgesellschaft, Lützowplatz 7, 12047 Belin

Ballett-Journal/Das Tanzarchiv
Obersteinbach 5a, 51429 **Bergisch-Gladbach**
Tel: 2207-910 074
Fax: 2207-910 075
Internet: www.tanzmedien.de
E-Mail: usteiner@tanzmedien.de
contact Ulrich Steiner
Focus & policy: magazine in German on all aspects of ballet and dance in Germany and internationally, with lists of schools, vacancies, all ballet companies in the German speaking countries and videos available on ballet, dance and aspects of training. Published five times a year (February, April, June, October, December) *Comments:* contact-London: Hans-Theodor Wohlfahrt, Tel : +44 181-891 0733, Fax: +44 181-891 0733

Bühnengenossenschaft
Bühnenschriften-Vertriebsgesellschaft mbH., Postfach 130270, 20102 **Hamburg**
Tel: 40-443 870
Fax: 40-456 002
editor-in-chief Hans Herdlein
Focus & policy: trade paper of Genossenschaft Deutscher Bühnen-Angehöriger, published 10 times a year *Comments:* visiting address: Feldbrunnenstraße 74, 20148 Hamburg; see also National Organisations

Bühnentechnische Rundschau
Markelstr. 9, 12163 **Berlin**
Tel: 30-2147 4970
Fax: 30-2147 4970
E-Mail: winckelsesser@btr-friedrich.de
editorial officer Karin Winckelsesser
Focus & policy: technical journal on all aspects of theatre, film, tv and event technology, main focus on stage designs and theatre architecture
Comments: sold in 32 countries; published 6 times a year + one special issue; Journal of DTHG, Oistat and FNTh; see also Services (Gerling Arendt und Partner)

Deutsches Bühnen-Jahrbuch
German Stage Yearbook
Genossenschaft Deutscher Bühnen-Angehöriger im Verlag der Bühnenschriften-Vetriebs-Gesellschaft mbH, Postfach 130270, 20102 **Hamburg**
Tel: 40-445 185/443 870
Fax: 40-456 002
Redaktion und Anzeigenleitung Gerhard Dräger
Focus & policy: annual directory of German-speaking theatres (including opera and dance companies, orchestras and festivals), with personnel and technical data, in Germany, Austria and Switzerland *Comments:* visiting address: Feldbrunnenstr. 74, 20148 Hamburg; see also National Organisations

Die Deutsche Bühne Theatermagazin
The German Stage Theatre Magazine
Deutscher Bühnenverein,
St. Apern Straße 17-21,
50667 **Köln**
Tel: 221-208 1218 Fax: 221-208 1229
E-Mail: info@die-deutsche-buehne.de
contact, editor-in-chief Herr Brandenburg;
editors Silke Blankemeyer, Knut Lennartz
Focus & policy: monthly theatre magazine covering the German speaking drama, music theatre and dance scene (i.e including Austria and Switzerland), with regular reports on international theatre; published in German

Figurentheater Jahrbuch
c/o Deutsches Forum für Figurentheater und Puppenspielkunst,
Hattingerstr. 467, 44795 **Bochum**
Tel: 234-47729
Fax: 234-47735
Leiterin des dfp Annette Dabs-Baucks
Focus & policy: published by Deutsches Forum für Figurentheater & Puppenspielkunst; published every 2-3 years; latest edition 1997; new edition in preparation

Fono Forum – Klassik, Jazz, HiFi
c/o Reiner H. Nitschke Verlags- GmbH,
Burg Veynau, 53881 **Euskirchen**
Tel: 2256-943 04
Fax: 2256-943 049
E-Mail: fono.forum@nitschke-verlag.de
Geschäftsführer Reiner H. Nitschke;
Chefredakteur Thomas Voigt
Focus & policy: monthly magazine; classical music, jazz, also hifi tests

Forum Modernes Theater
Contemporary Theatre Forum
Gunter Narr Verlag,
Dischingerweg. 5, 72070 **Tübingen**
Tel: 7071-97970
Fax: 7071-75288
E-Mail: narr-franeke@t-online.de
editor Prof. Günter Ahrends;
co-editors Hans-Peter Bayerdörfer, Wilfried Floeck, Herta Schmid, Karlheinz Stierle
Focus & policy: journal published twice a year in German, English and French on theatre theory & practice *Comments:* postal address: Postfach 2567, 72015 Tübingen; address Prof. Ahrends: Ruhr-Universität Bochum, Englisches Seminar, Universitätsstraße 150, 44780 Bochum, tel: 234-700 5051

Handbook of Cultural Affairs in Europe
Europäisches Kulturhandbuch
c/o Zentrum für Kulturforschung/ERICArts,
Am Hofgarten 17, 53113 **Bonn**
Tel: 228-211 058
Fax: 228-217 493
E-Mail: wiesand@ericarts.org
contacts Dr. Andreas Joh. Wiesand, Danielle Cliche
Focus & policy: handbook prepared by experts of different institutes (CIRCLE, ERICArts etc.) networks detailing the organisational structures of cultural policy and key organisations involved in cultural support in 50 European countries *Comments:* order from: Nomos Verlag, 76484 Baden-Baden, fax: 7221-210 427; the latest edition is Autumn 1999, new editions every 3-4 years

impulse
c/o ITI-Zentrum, Postfach 411128, 12121 **Berlin**
Tel: 30-791 1777
Fax: 30-791 1874
Internet: users.aol.com/itigermany/
E-Mail: itigermany@aol.com
editor Martin Roeder-Zerndt;
associate editor Thomas Engel
Focus & policy: newsletter of the German Centre of the I.T.I. in English and German; published 3 times a year

Jahrbuch der Städte mit Theatergastspielen
c/o Dr. Dieter Hadamczik,
Holzhofallee 35,
64295 **Darmstadt**
Tel: 6151-316 061/171-583 3814 (mobile)
Fax: 6151-367 271
E-Mail: dr.hadamczik@t-online.de
contact Dr. Dieter Hadamczik
Focus & policy: yearbook of theatre promoters in German speaking countries *Comments:* editorial office/subscriptions: INTHEGA (Interessengemeinschaft der Städte mit Theatergastspielen e.V.) – Geschäftsstelle im Bürgerhaus Bergischer Löwe, Postfach 200199, 51431 Bergisch Gladbach,
Tel: 2202-459 280, Fax: 2202-459 281

Jazzeitung
Postfach 100245, 93002 **Regensburg**
Tel: 941-945 930
Fax: 941-945 9350
Internet: www.nmz.de
E-Mail: nmz@nmz.de
Leitender Redakteur Andreas Kurt
Focus & policy: annual publication

KLASSIK heute
Fürstenrieder Str. 275, 81377 **München**
Tel: 89-710 500-0 Fax: 89-710 500-50
E-Mail: klassikheute@keller-verlag.de
Chefredakteur Dr. Sören Meyer-Eller,
Hrsg. Josef Keller Verlag
Focus & policy: contents: interviews, reviews and the latest concert and broadcasting programmes re: classical music; reviews of opera premieres in German speaking countries *Comments:* montly magazine; special rates for students; alternative address: Josef Keller GmbH & Co, Verlags KG, Postfach 1455, 82317 Starnberg, Tel: 8151-771-0, Fax: 8151-771 152

Konzert Almanach
Heel Verlag GmbH, Gut Pottscheidt,
53639 **Königswinter**
Tel: 2223-9230-0 Fax: 2223-9230-13
E-Mail: corinna.tandonnet@t-online.de
contact Corinna Tandonnet
Focus & policy: annual concert calendar with seat plans of concert halls in the Federal Republic of Germany; programme information is also given for concerts in major cities in Austria and Switzerland

Lied & Chor
Verlags und Vertriebs GmbH für Chorbedarf,
Postfach 51 10 01, 50946 **Köln**
Tel: 221-371 033
Fax: 221-340 4211
Verlagsleitung Wolfgang Steffen;
Redaktion Peter Lamprecht
Focus & policy: monthly publication for choral singers

Musik Almanach
German Music Council Music Directory
Bärenreiter-Verlag, Heinrich-Schütz-Allee 35-37, 34131 **Kassel-Wilhelmshöhe**
Tel: 561-31050 Fax: 561-3105 240
Internet: www.baerenreiter.com
E-Mail: info@baerenreiter.com
Focus & policy: triennial directory in German (latest edition March 1999, also available on CD-Rom) containing addresses of German orchestras, music ensembles, opera companies, festivals, concert halls, agents, music schools, music societies, publishers, prizes and national/regional/local government responsibilities for music etc
Comments: Gustav-Bosse-Verlag: Heinrich-Schütz-Allee 35-37, 34131 Kassel-Wilhelmshöhe, Internet: www.bosse-verlag.de, E-mail: info@bosse-verlag.de; Deutscher Musikrat (Publisher), Weberstr 59, 53113 Bonn, Tel: 228-2091-0, Fax: 228-2091-200

MusikTexte – Zeitschrift für neue Musik
Postfach 10 24 61, 50464 **Köln**
Tel: 221-952 0215
Fax: 221-952 0216
Internet: www.musiktexte.de
E-Mail: musiktexte@musiktexte.de
Redaktion Gisela Gronemeyer, Reinhard Oehlschlägel
Focus & policy: 5 issues per year; reports, news, interviews, listings on the international new music scene (published in German) *Comments:* visiting address: Gladbacher Str 23, 50672 Köln;
see also World New Music Magazine

Neue Musikzeitung – nmz
Postfach 100245, 93002 **Regensburg**
Tel: 941-945 930 Fax: 941-945 9350
Internet: www.nmz.de
E-Mail: nmz@nmz.de
Herausgeber Theo Geißler; Chefredaktion Theo Geißler (Regensburg), Gerhard Rohde (Frankfurt/Main); Redaktion Dr. Reinhard Schulz, Felix Maria Roehl, Dr Eckart Rohlfs, Andreas Kolb
Focus & policy: monthly publication (double issues Dec/Jan, Jul/Aug): classical, jazz, new music, educational aspects of music

Neue Zeitschrift für Musik
New Magazine for Music
Postfach 3640, 55026 **Mainz**
Tel: 6131-246 850 Fax: 6131-246 212
Internet: www.schott-music.com/zeitschriften/index/htm
E-Mail: NZfM.Redaktion@schott-musik.de
Redaktion Rolf W Stoll
Focus & policy: bi-monthly German-language music journal *Comments:* publishers: Verlag Schott Musik International, Postfach 3640, 55026 Mainz, Tel: 6131-246 857 (subscriptions)/246 852 (advertising)

Oper und Tanz
Postfach 100245, 93002 **Regensburg**
Tel: 941-945 930 Fax: 941-945 9350
Internet: www.nmz.de
E-Mail: nmz@nmz.de
Publisher VdO Stefan Meuschel; Editor-in-chief Walter Kane; 2. Herausgeber Theo Geißler
Focus & policy: bi-monthly magazine for opera, choirs and dance

Opernglas, Das
Opernglas Verlagsgesellschaft mbH,
Grelckstr.36, 22529 **Hamburg**
Tel: 40-585 501 Fax: 40-585 505
Internet: www.opernglas.de
editor Ralf Tiedemann
Focus & policy: magazine published in German 11 times per year on opera productions and related issues; it concentrates on the scene in Germany, but also has international coverage including record reviews, information, opera schedules etc.

Opernwelt
Opera World
Friedrich Berlin Verlags GmbH, Lützowplatz 7, 10785 **Berlin**
Tel: 30-254 4950 Fax: 30-2544 9512
E-Mail: redaktion@opernwelt.de
Redakteure Stephan Mösch, Bernd Feuchtner
Focus & policy: monthly international opera magazine published since 1960

Orchester, Das
The Orchestra
Schott Musik International,
Postfach 3640, 55026 **Mainz**
Tel: 6131-246 853 (editor)/246 857 (subscriptions)
Fax: 6131-246 212 (editor)/246 483 (subscriptions)
Internet: www.schott-music.com/zeitschriften/index.htm
E-Mail: orchester.redaktion@schott-musik.de
editor Andrea Raab, M.A.;
advertisement dept. Dieter Schwarz
Focus & policy: journal of the Deutsche Orchestervereinigung (German Orchestras Association) published 11 times per year in German

Orpheus Opera Magazine
Ritterstr. 11, 10696 **Berlin**
Tel: 30-614 6840 Fax: 30-614 6865
editor Dr. Geerd Heinsen;
founder & publisher Clauspeter Koscielny
Focus & policy: journal published 13 times per year containing information in German on opera, concerts, dance and records in Berlin and elsewhere in Germany, and in the international Opera Scene, being distributed in Germany, Europe and overseas *Comments:* focus especially on opera singers

RONDO
Lucile-Grahn Str. 37, 81675 **München**
Tel: 89-457 2610 Fax: 89-457 26150
Internet: www.rondomagazin.de
E-Mail: post@rondomagazin.de
Geschäftsführer Günter F Bereiter;
Chefredakteur Wolfgang Halder
Focus & policy: bi-monthly journal on classical and jazz music; interviews, features, reviews, concert previews

Tanzdrama
Dance drama
Flemingstr. 10, 22299 **Hamburg**
Tel: 40-480 2644
Fax: 40-480 2644
E-Mail: stoeckeman@aol.com
Chefredakteurin Dr. Patricia Stöckemann
Focus & policy: bi-monthly magazine in German focussing on modern dance forms and events and the history of modern dance and Tanztheater
Comments: published by K. Kieser Verlag, Munich

Tanzplattform Deutschland
c/o Joint Adventures, Emil-Geis-Str 21,
81379 **München**
Tel: 89-724 2515
Fax: 89-723 7782
contact Walter Heun, Ingrid Kalka, Stephanie Thersch
Focus & policy: published to accompany the festival Tanzplattform Deutschland (q.v.) *Comments:* a brochure giving an overview on current artistic and culture-political development in contemporary dance; it provides a database on dance professionals in Germany

Theater der Zeit
im Podewil, Klosterstr 68-70, 10179 **Berlin**
Tel: 30-242 3626/2472 2414 Fax: 30-2472 2415
Internet: www.theaterderzeit.de
E-Mail: tdz@mail.blinx.de
editors Barbara Engelhardt, Thomas Irmer;
manager Harald Müller
Focus & policy: monthly publication on all forms of German speaking theatre, international reviews and reports *Comments:* published in German

Theater heute
Friedrich Berlin Verlag GmbH, Lützowplatz 7,
10785 **Berlin**
Tel: 30-254 495-0 Fax: 30-254 495-12
E-Mail: redaktion@theaterheute.de
editors Dr Michael Merschmeier, Dr Franz Wille, Barbara Burckhardt; publisher Friedrich Berlin Verlag
Focus & policy: monthly review of international and German speaking drama theatre
Comments: subscription: DM 196.30 for one year including the annual yearbook

Theater Rundschau
Theater-Rundschau-Verlag, Bonner Talweg 10,
53113 **Bonn**
Tel: 228-915 031
Fax: 228-915 0345
Internet: www.theatergemeinden.de
E-Mail: bund_tg@t-online.de
editor Heinz-Dieter Terschüren; Geschäftsführer Roswitha Kleinwächter, Norbert Reiche
Focus & policy: articles on theatre, music, literature, news of premieres, competitions in German-speaking countries *Comments:* monthly publication

Theateralmanach
edition Smidt, Wolfratshauser Str. 55,
82049 **Pullach im Isartal**
Tel: 89-793 8180 Fax: 89-793 8180
E-Mail: 100257.1640@compuserve.com
Focus & policy: theatre-directory of all professional German speaking theatres in Austria, Germany, Switzerland; annual, each August *Comments:* gives an over-view of all details and comments of German speaking theatres and venues

TheaterManagement – aktuell
c/o J. P. Marketing & Kommunikation, Postfach 420508, 50899 **Köln**
Tel: 221-420 0494 Fax: 221-941 7898
E-Mail: juergenpreiss@gmx.net
editor Dipl.-Kfm. Jürgen Preiß (marketing consultant)
Focus & policy: infoletter focusing economic aspects of arts management addressing to management directors and leading employees of theatres, musical houses, arenas, festival- and concert organisations, consultant- and the municipal arts offices in German speaking countries

Theaterschrift
Künstlerhaus Bethanien, Mariannenplatz 2,
10997 **Berlin**
Tel: 30-6169 0321 Fax: 30-6169 0330
E-Mail: 100530.2613@compuserve.com
Redaktion Sabine Pochhammer; project manager Ewa Strózczynska-Wille; layout Katrin Schoof; distribution Ewald Bormann
Focus & policy: multi-lingual publication (German, English, French & Dutch); features & interviews with and by international artists and academics from various disciplines; each issue deals with a specific theme; 3 times a year *Comments:* publishers: Hebbel-Theater (Berlin), Felix Meritis Foundation (Amsterdam), EXPO 2000 (Hannover), and Künstlerhaus Bethanien (Berlin)

Theaterstatistik
Deutscher Bühnenverein, Bundesverband Deutscher Theater, St-Apern-Straße 17-21, 50667 **Köln**
Tel: 221-208 120 Fax: 221-208 1228
Internet: www.buehnenverein.de
E-Mail: debut@buehnenverein.de
editor Hartmut Thielen
Focus & policy: annual statistical data on major theatres, orchestras and festivals in the Federal Republic of Germany, Austria and Switzerland; covers box office income, ticket prices, subsidies, numbers of productions, attendances, personnel etc *Comments:* see also National Organisations

TV Produktions Handbuch
Müller adress + Neue Mediengesellschaft Ulm mbH & Co. OHG, Pretzfelder Strasse 15, 90425 **Nürnberg**
Tel: 911-340 9915 Fax: 911-340 9944
E-Mail: service@mueller-address.de
Projektleiter Herr Schöpplein
Focus & policy: annual directory on the media in German-speaking countries; information on services & technical data *Comments:* includes production firms, computer animation companies, broadcasting organisations, publications and media organisations; the latest edition was published in November 99

Werkstatistik
Performance Statistics
Deutscher Bühnenverein, Bundesverband deutscher Theater, St Apern Straße 17-21, 50667 **Köln**
Tel: 221-208 1218 Fax: 221-208 1228
Internet: www.buehnenverein.de
E-Mail: debut@buehnenverein.de
Focus & policy: annual statistics of opera, operetta, musicals, drama, childrens' and youth theatre, dance productions in Germany, Austria and Switzerland; covers production titles, theatres, authors *Comments:* see also National Organisations

World Guide to Foundations
K. G. Saur Verlag, Postfach 70 16 20, 81316 **München**
Tel: 89-7690 2232 Fax: 89-7690 2150
Internet: www.saur.de
E-Mail: CustomerService_Saur@csi.com
Focus & policy: approx. 19000 entries of Foundations worldwide *Comments:* 2nd edition: June 2000

World New Music Magazine
c/o MusikTexte, Postfach 10 24 61, 50464 **Köln**
Tel: 221-952 0215 Fax: 221-952 0216
Internet: www.musiktexte.de
E-Mail: wnmm@musiktexte.de
Herausgeber Graciela Paraskevaides, Reinhard Oehlschlägel, Anders Beyer, Richard Tsang;
Redaktion Gisela Gronemeyer
Focus & policy: ISCM publication (in English); international contemporary music *Comments:* visiting address: Gladbacher Straße 23, 50672 Köln; see also MusikTexte-Zeitschrift für neue Musik

Zeitschrift für Kulturaustausch
Institut für Auslandsbeziehungen,
Postfach 10 24 63, 70020 **Stuttgart**
Tel: 711-222 5112 Fax: 711-222 5131
E-Mail: koerber@ifa.de
Chefredakteur Sebastian Körber
Focus & policy: foreign cultural politics and international cultural relations *Comments:* the only German language magazine covering this area,
also available on-line, via www.ifa.de

GREECE (+30)

Choros
Dragatsaniou 6, 10559 **Athens**
Tel: 1-821 0410 Fax: 1-325 5391
chairman Artemis Ignatiou-Tsezane;
contact Elena Zapoura
Focus & policy: quarterly publication about dance; news update, articles about classical and contemporary dance from Greek and European writers

THESPIS
Hellenic Centre of the International Theatre Institute (UNESCO), Lyciou 9, 10556 **Athens**
public relations officer Vasiliki Manteli;
library officer Anna Lazou
Focus & policy: quarterly publication about theatre

HUNGARY (+36)

évkönyv
Yearbook
Krisztina krt. 57, 1013 **Budapest**
Tel: 1-375 1184 Fax: 1-375 1184
editor Klára Molnár; bibliography Erzsébet Csalló
Focus & policy: published annually by the Hungarian Theatre Institute and Museum; lists Hungarian theatres in Hungary and abroad, staff, repertoire, new productions, theatre events, theatre organisations with bibliography, English and German introduction

Criticai Lapok
Critical Reviews
Arany János u. 27 IV. 2., 1051 **Budapest**
Tel: 1-331 4419/269 3023 Fax: 1-269 3023
editor-in-chief Katalin Szücs
Focus & policy: monthly, theatre reviews & essays

Ellenfény
Back-light
Szentkirályi u. 29-31, 1088 **Budapest**
Tel: 1-138 0774
E-Mail: ellfeny@elender.hu
editors Lívia Fuchs, István Sándor L.
Focus & policy: dance, theatre, contemporary art

Gramophon
Mandula 31, 1025 **Budapest**
Tel: 1-212 4782
Fax: 1-212 4782
editor Attila Retkes
Focus & policy: the Hungarian CD review; published 12 times a year *Comments:* publisher: Amfis Ltd

Hungarian Music Quarterly
Zenemükiadó Vállalat – Editio Musica Budapest ,
Meszaros 15-17, 1016 **Budapest**
Tel: 1-212 1553
Fax: 1-212 1593
editor Antal Boronkay; assistant editor Judit Péteri
Focus & policy: quarterly magazine reporting on the Hungarian music scene
Comments: postal address: POB 322, 1370 Budapest

Muzsika
PO Box 638, 1243 **Budapest**
Tel: 1-352 0722
Fax: 1-352 0722
publisher/editor Maria Feuer
Focus & policy: music publication; published 12 times a year *Comments:* visiting address: Karoly 7, 1075 Budapest

Operaélet
Opera Life
c/o Szomory György, Hajós u. 9., 1065 **Budapest**
Tel: 1-332 9544
Fax: 1-332 9544
editor Berta Székely
Focus & policy: magazine of the Budapest Opera Friends, published 5 times a year

Pesti Est Súgó
POB 914, 1535 **Budapest**
Tel: 1-212 6300 Fax: 1-212 6303
editor in chief Máté Gáspár
Focus & policy: monthly theatre programme magazine
Comments: visiting address address:
Bíró u. 7, 1122 Budapest

Pesti Müsor
Program Magazine of Budapest
Kölcsey u. 2, 1085 **Budapest**
Tel: 1-318 8465
Fax: 1-266 1690
editor-in-chief Dr Péter Kende
Focus & policy: weekly with theatre and cinema program

Színház
Theatre
Báthori u. 10, 1054 **Budapest**
Tel: 1-331 6308 Fax: 1-331 6308
editor-in-chief Tamás Koltai
Focus & policy: monthly, devoted to contemporary theatrical art and dramaturgy; with English summary

Táncmüvészet
Art of Dance
Kerék u. 34, 1035 **Budapest**
Tel: 1-368 5470
editor Zsuzsa Kaán

ICELAND (+354)

Bjartur og Frú Emilía
Theatre and Literature Magazine
POBox 447, 121 **Reykjavík**
Tel: 562 1826 Fax: 562 8360
E-Mail: snar@itn.is
editors Snœbjörn Arngrimsson, Gudjón Pedersen, Halfidi Arngrimsson
Focus & policy: quarterly magazine on Icelandic and international literature and theatre

Leiklistarbladid
Laugavegur 96, 101 **Reykjavík**
Tel: 551 6974/562 2944 Fax: 562 2984
Internet: www.tv.is/bil/
E-Mail: bil@tv.is
editor Sigridur Lara Sigurjonsdottir; contact Vilborg Valgardsdóttir
Focus & policy: amateur theatre in Iceland *Comments:* the publishers are also an organisation for Icelandic amateur theatre; published twice a year

IRELAND Republic of (+353)

Directory of Musicians in Ireland
Music Network, Coach House, Dublin Castle, **Dublin** 2
Tel: 1-671 9429/30 Fax: 1-671 9430
E-Mail: info@musicnetwork.ie
pr manager Assumpta Lawless

ITALY (+39)

Agenda Amatoriale – Guida al Teatro Amatoriale Italiano
Via G. Marcora 18-20, 00153 **Roma**
Tel: 06-584 0581 Fax: 06-584 0425
E-Mail: guideteatro@acli.it
capo redattore Maximilian La Monica
Focus & policy: yearbook about Italian amateur theatre
Comments: published by Editoriale Aesse

Agenda Teatrale
Via G. Marcora 18-20, 00153 **Roma**
Tel: 06-584 0581/2 Fax: 06-584 0425
E-Mail: guideteatro@acli.it
capo redattore Maximilian La Monica
Focus & policy: yearbook about Italian professional theatre *Comments:* published by Editoriale Aesse

Annuario EDT dell'Opera Lirica in Italia
EDT Yearbook of Lyric Opera in Italy
E.D.T. s.r.l., Via Alfieri n. 19, 10121 **Torino**
Tel: 011-559 1811 Fax: 011-559 1824
E-Mail: edt@edt-torino.com
editorial director Enzo Peruccio; marketing manager Cristina Savio; foreign rights Claudia Peruccio; redattore Gabriella Zecchinato
Focus & policy: yearbook listing theatres, opera companies, Italian opera festivals, productions, artistic directors, orchestra and chorus directors, choreographers, interpreters,economic data, press reviews; opera season in Italy *Comments:* the yearbook is published in collaboration with CIDIM – Comitato Nazionale Italiano Musica (q.v.); advertising: Antonietta Sortino, c/o Edt s.r.l., Via Alfieri 19, 10121 Torino, Tel: 011-559 1828

Annuario Musicale Italiano
Italian Musical Yearbook
Largo di Torre Argentina n. 11, 00186 **Roma**
Tel: 06-681 9061
Fax: 06-6819 0651
Internet: www.inrete.it/classica/cidim/cidim.html
E-Mail: cidim.it@flashnet.it
president of CIDIM Francesco Agnello
Focus & policy: comprehensive directory of Italian lyric theatres, orchestras, music ensembles, music festivals, societies, conservatoires, performers, critics, musicologists, music publishers, libraries, archives, national organisations and government cultural and leisure departments at national and regional level *Comments:* published every two years; also on floppy disk and CD-ROM; alternative Internet: www.cidim.it

Balletto Oggi
Ballet Today
Alzaia Naviglio Grande 46, 20144 **Milano**
Tel: 02-5811 1192 Fax: 02-5811 1238
Internet: www.ballet2000.com
E-Mail: info@ballet2000.com
direttore responsabile Alfio Agostini; advertising officer Giovanna Pianigiani
Focus & policy: magazine published 6 times a year in Italian on the international classical dance scene

Bollettino di Informazione A.I.S MT
c/o Associazione Italiana Studi di Musicoterapia, Via Brignole de Ferrari 6/2, 16125 **Genova**
Tel: 010-251 2393 Fax: 010-251 2393
president Giovanna Mutti; chairman Ing Giulio Ravasi; secretary Prof Anselmo Susca; press officer t.b.a.
Focus & policy: studies and contributes to scientific problems related to music therapy; informs the reader about the activities of the association, and about conferences and seminars in Italy and abroad
Comments: members of the World Federation of Music Therapy and ECARTE

Corriere del Teatro – Rivista di Lirica, Concerti, Balletto
Theatre Courier
Via T. Campanella 31,
20090 **Trezzano sul Naviglio (MI)**
Tel: 02-4840 2085 Fax: 02-4840 3322
director Maurilio De Giorgis
Focus & policy: bi-monthly journal with information in Italian on opera, ballet, concerts worldwide, news, including calendar of events

Danza & Danza
Dance & Dance
Mediapress, Viale Premuda 42, 20129 **Milano**
Tel: 02-7600 6387/7601 5509 Fax: 02-794 158
E-Mail: danpress@tin.it
direttore Mario Bedendo; advertising manager Ele Tamburini; subscriptions Silvana Donola
Focus & policy: information and reports on all kinds of dance; published in Italian 9 times per year

Etinforma mensile di Informazione dello spettacolo
Per la Vostra Pubblicità su Etinforma,
Eti, via in Arcione 98, 00187 **Roma**
Tel: 06-6995 1252 Fax: 06-679 7443
direttore responsabile Renzo Tian; vicedirettore Andrea Porcheddu; coordinamento organizzative redazionale e marketing Angela Cutò
Comments: promotion office: Tel: 06-6995 1297/82

Giornale della Musica
Via Alfieri n. 19, 10121 **Torino**
Tel: 011-559 1803/4 Fax: 011-559 1825
Internet: www.edt-torino.com/gdm
E-Mail: gdm@edt-torino.com
director Enzo Peruccio; capo redattore Daniele Martino; redattrice Susanna Franchi
Focus & policy: monthly offering information on music and dance *Comments:* E.D.T. advertising department: Antonietta Sortino, Tel: 011-559 1828

Giornale Dello Spettacolo
Entertainment Journal
Associazione Generale Italiana Dello Spettacolo,
Via di Villa Patrizi 10, 00161 **Roma**
Tel: 06-884 731 Fax: 06-8847 3213
E-Mail: agiscom@tin.it
director Luigi Pietro Filippi
Focus & policy: information and comment on the Italian performed arts and cinema market and scene; published weekly in Italian, 15,000 copies
Comments: subscription only

I Fiati
Via Macchiavelli 50, 00185 **Roma**
Tel: 06-4470 3055 Fax: 06-4470 3059
E-Mail: aifla@nexus.it
direttore responsabile Gianluca Morseletto; vice direttore Stefano Cioffi; capo redattore Susanna Persichilli
Focus & policy: bi-monthly magazine about wind instruments, jazz and folk music *Comments:* see also Syrinx (q.v.), Festivals and Competitions

Il Saggiatore Musicale – Rivista Semestrale di Musicologia
c/o Dipartimento di Musica e Spettacolo,
via Barberia 4, 40123 **Bologna**
Tel: 051-209 2000 (switchboard) Fax: 051-233 117
Internet: muspe1.civfid.unibo.it
E-Mail: saggmus@muspe1.cirfid.unibo.it
direttore Giuseppina La Face Bianconi;
presidente Pier Carlo Brunelli
Focus & policy: bi-annual publication; musicology, music criticism; reviews, focus on interdisciplinary issues; in Italian, English, French, German, Spanish *Comments:* publisher: Olschki, Casella Postale 66, 50100 Firenze, Tel: 055-653 0684, Fax: 055-653 0214, E-mail: celso@olschki.it

L'Opera
The Opera
Theatron Srl, Via Carlo Botta 4, 20135 **Milano**
Tel: 02-5519 3793 Fax: 02-546 0154
E-Mail: rivopera@tin.it
direttore responsabile Sabino Lenoci
Focus & policy: news, stories, documentation etc on lyric music, opera and operetta; published monthly in Italian

La Danza – rassegna nazionale ed internazionale di danza e spettacolo
Dance
Via Torino 5, 36061 **Bassano del Grappa (VI)**
Tel: 0424-521 938/00338-720 4784 (mobile)
Fax: 0424-521 938
direttore Emmino Bertollo; co-direttore Maurizio Perin
Focus & policy: news, interviews, issues, technical details etc of dance published quarterly in Italian; includes calendar of dance events; specialises in photos of last 25 years of theatrical dance (diapositive archive of about 15000 known internationally) *Comments:* also organises multivision shows about dance

Lo Spettacolo in Italia-Annuario Statistico
The Entertainment in Italy Statistics Annual
c/o SIAE Società Italiana degli Autori ed Editori, Viale della Letteratura 30, 00144 **Roma**
Tel: 06-59901 Fax: 06-5964 7052
Focus & policy: statistical analysis of Italian theatre, opera, orchestral, cinema performances/presentations, ticket sales and prices, box office income etc; usually annual, but covering a period a few years in arrear

M & D – Musica e Dischi
Via de Amicis, 47, 20123 **Milano**
Tel: 02-5810 5737/8940 2837 Fax: 02-832 3843
Internet: www.rockol.it/musicaedischi
E-Mail: musedis@impulse.it
direttore Mario de Luigi; redazione Alfredo Marziano; promozione Emanuela Masserani
Focus & policy: monthly trade magazine for professional music operators; circulation: 25k copies in Italy and abroad *Comments:* features the Chi & Dove (who & where) Music Yearbook for Italy

Musica Meccanica
Massimo J. Monaco, Borgo La Noce 7, 50123 **Firenze**
Tel: 055-917 9089/0335-592 5672 Fax: 055-917 9089
Internet: www.musicameccanica.it
E-Mail: musica.meccanica@val.it
director Massimo J. Monaco; administration Elena Patruno
Focus & policy: spectacles and performance dedicated to mechanic and automatic music contstruction of machines and musical robots; recital of songs and cruel ballad; theatrical spectacles, street art

Seicorde – Trimestrale di chitarra con CD
Viale Lombardia 5, 20131 **Milano**
Tel: 02-7063 2252 Fax: 02-2367 253
direttore responsabile Filippo Michelangeli; ufficio abbonamenti Tiziana Laurenzi
Focus & policy: magazine on the guitar published every three months in Italian *Comments:* CD with notes in Italian and English

Sipario
Curtain
Ed. C.A.M.A. s.a.s. (Centro Attori Manifestazioni Artistiche), Via San Marco 34, 20125 **Milano**
Tel: 02-653 270 Fax: 02-2906 0005
E-Mail: siparios@tin.it
coordinamento editoriale Mattia Sebastiano Giorgetti; direttore responsabile Mario Mattia Giorgetti
Focus & policy: journal published 10 times (Jan-Feb / Jul-Aug, double issues) per year on the Italian arts scene, including reviews of theatre, music, dance, opera, cinema and performing arts in general

SIPARIO Annuario dello Spettacolo
Ruscitto Comunicazione – P.le Loreto 9, 20131 **Milano**
Tel: 02-282 9158 Fax: 02-289 8088

Suonare News – Il mensile dei musicisti
V.le Lombardia, 5, 20131 **Milano**
Tel: 02-7063 2252 Fax: 02-236 7253
direttore responsabile Filippo Michelangeli; redazione Daniela Mazzitelli, Cecilia Rivers
Focus & policy: classical music *Comments:* interviews, prices, books and more

SYRINX
Via Macchiavelli 50, 00185 **Roma**
Tel: 06-4470 3055 Fax: 06-4470 3059
E-Mail: aifla@nexus.it
direttore responsabile Francesco Arturo Saponaro; vice direttori Gianluca Morseletto, Stefano Cioffi; capo redattore Susanna Persichilli
Focus & policy: tri-monthly magazine about flutes
Comments: see also I Fiati (q.v.), Festivals and Competitions

Teatro in Italia – Annuario
Italian Theatre – Yearbook
c/o SIAE Società Italiana degli Autori ed Editori, Viale della Letteratura 30, 00144 **Roma**
Tel: 06-59901/599 0629 (direct) Fax: 06-5964 7052
Focus & policy: annual review of Italian theatre productions with casts and credit lists, numbers of productions, attendances, box office income; produced by SIAE in Italian; includes a panorama of Italian subsidised theatre, with data on public funding received, lists budgets of all Italian theatre companies; published in summer

Tuttodanza
Arteatro, Corso della Vittoria 4, 28100 **Novara**
Tel: 0321-30310 Fax: 0321-31014
Internet: www.arteatro.it
E-Mail: tuttodanza@msoft.it
president/owner/editor/asst. publisher Carlo Pesta; vice-president Agnese Omodei Sale
Focus & policy: information on the international dance scene; published in Italian four times per year in Sept, Dec, March, June *Comments:* also organise festival 'Arteatro Riccione' (July/Aug) and a dance season of the Artro Coccial (Nov)

Journal Maksla
Zurnals Maksla
Akademijas laukums 1, a/k 41, 1027 **Riga**
Tel: 7-220 722 Fax: 7-820 608
E-Mail: makslaplus@hotmail.com
editor-in-chief Maija Augstkalna
Focus & policy: 6 editions a year, covers matters of art and culture in Latvia

LATVIA (+371)

Gramatu apskats
Aspazijas bulv. 24-502, 1050 **Riga**
Tel: 7-224 822 Fax: 7-224 822
editor-in-chief Dainis Berzins
Focus & policy: monthly culture magazine, latest edition reviews in Latvian, summary in English

Journal Karogs
Zurnals Karogs
Kr. Barona 12, 1426 **Riga**
Tel: 7-287 626 Fax: 7-287 626
editor-in-chief Mara Zalite
Focus & policy: monthly publication for Latvian and foreign literature; interviews, cultural events etc.

Journal Studija
Zurnāls Studija
11 Novembra krastmala 35, Äl 103, 1050 **Riga**
Tel: 7-222 647 Fax: 7-277 6066
E-Mail: studija@re-lab.net
editor-in-chief Laima Slava
Focus & policy: visual arts magazine in Latvian and English

Journal Teatra Vestnesis
Zurnals Teatra Vestnesis
Dzirnavu iela 135, 1050 **Riga**
Tel: 7-287 560 Fax: 7-211 602
editor-in-chief Anda Burtniece
Focus & policy: quarterly journal in Latvian covering theatre matters – latest productions, reviews, critical essays, interviews, dedicates several articles in each issue to one specific topic, focussing on the Latvian and Russian theatre world and of interest to a wider international circle of professionals

Literatura un Maksla
Balasta dambis 3, 1081 **Riga**
Tel: 7-062 488 Fax: 7-062 500
E-Mail: ilmars@rb.lv
editor-in-chief Aija Lace
Focus & policy: weekly newspaper on art, literature, culture

LITHUANIA (+370)

7 meno dienos
Bernardinu 10, 2001 **Vilnius**
Tel: 2-613 039/617 247 Fax: 2-611 926
editor Linas Vildziunas
Focus & policy: cultural weekly

Ausis
Teatro 11-4, 2600 **Vilnius**
Tel: 2-616 368 Fax: 2-616 368
E-Mail: ausis@bomba.lt
editor Gediminas Juskys

Dienovidis
Pilies 23a, 2600 **Vilnius**
Tel: 2-221 911 Fax: 2-223 101
E-Mail: postmaster@7799.vno.osf.lt
editor Aldona Zemaityte

Gama
Zygimantu 4, 2600 **Vilnius**
Tel: 2-222 583

Krantai
Magazine of the Lithuanian Artists' Association
Z. Liauksmino g. 8/3, 2600 **Vilnius**
Tel: 2-224 743 Fax: 2-224 844
editor Mr Helmutas Sabasevicius
Focus & policy: published 4 times a year

Kulturos barai
Latako 3, 2001 **Vilnius**
Tel: 2-616 696/623 861 Fax: 2-610 538
editor Bronys Savukynas

Literatura ir menas
Universiteto 4, 2600 **Vilnius**
Tel: 2-612 586/521/550 Fax: 2-610 831

Muzikos Barai
Gedimino 32-2, 2001 **Vilnius**
Tel: 2-623 043/221 615 Fax: 2-220 302
E-Mail: muzbar@lmd.vno.osf.lt

Muzu malunas
Gedimino 12a, 2001 **Vilnius**
Tel: 2-610 038 Fax: 2-227 894
E-Mail: daily@lrytas.lt

Siaures Atenai
Maironio 1, 2600 **Vilnius**
Tel: 2-614 431
E-Mail: siaurat@post.5c.lt
editor Linas Paulauskis

Teatras
Gedimino pr. 1, 2001 **Vilnius**
Tel: 2-623 976
chief editor Audronis Liuga

LUXEMBOURG (+352)

Pizzicato-Classic Highlights
129 Mühlenweg, 2155 **Luxembourg**
Tel: 492 924 Fax: 492 884
E-Mail: rfranck@pt.lu
editor-in-chief Remy Franck
Focus & policy: published monthly; news, features, CD reviews, concerts of classical music

NETHERLANDS (+31)

Carnet
Comments: see entry in Belgium

European Cultural Foundation Newsletter
Information Department, European Cultural Foundation, Jan van Goyenkade 5, 1075 HN **Amsterdam**
Tel: 20-676 0222 Fax: 20-675 2231
Internet: www.eurokult.nl
E-Mail: euro.kult@eurokult.org
editor Louise Bolotin
Format & policy: tri-annual

Jaarboek Cultuur
Statistical Yearbook Culture
Statistics Netherlands,
Prinses Beatrixlaan 428, 2273 XZ **Voorburg**
Tel: 70-337 5609 Fax: 70-337 5980
E-Mail: fhve@cbs.nl
head of department of statistics (culture, recreation, sports) Mr. Visser; manager performing arts Peter Sevat; manager of museums Hans Van Der Giessen
Focus & policy: overall statistical information on performing arts and other forms of culture in the Netherlands; data on number of performances, attendance, people employed and financial data; indications of more detailed material; listing of relevant organisations *Comments:* statistics on performing arts, museums, libraries, monuments, visual arts, artistic education; see also Podiumkunsten

Podiumkunsten
Performing Arts
Statistics Netherlands,
Prinses Beatrixlaan 428, 2273 XZ **Voorburg**
Tel: 70-337 4735 Fax: 70-337 5980
E-Mail: psvt@cbs.nl
manager of performing arts Peter Sevat
Focus & policy: statistics on professional performing arts; data on number of performances and attendance; subdivisions into regional data, categories of performing arts, type of accomodation/venues; data on people employed and financial data, also statistics on production

Theaterjaarboek
Theatre Yearbook
Theater Instituut Nederland,
PO Box 19304, 1000 GH **Amsterdam**
Tel: 20-551 3300 Fax: 20-551 3303
E-Mail: info@tin.nl
contact Divera Stavenuiter
Focus & policy: annual review in Dutch of dance and theatre, with lists of Dutch companies (drama, opera, dance, mime and puppetry, their productions and casts; address lists are included as well as festivals and awards

ZING
Plompetorengracht 3, 3512 CA **Utrecht**
Tel: 30-231 3174 Fax: 30-231 8137
Internet: www.snk.nl
E-Mail: snk@euronet.nl
redactie: hoofdredacteur Peter Korz; redactie: eindredacteur Hilbrand Adema
Focus & policy: magazine for all kinds of choral matters (in Dutch); six times a year *Comments:* published by SNK (q.v.) in coopertion with KBZON, KCZB and GOMZ

NORWAY (+47)

KORBLADET
c/o Norges Korforbund, Tollbugt. 28, 0157 **Oslo**
Tel: 2242 6720/6281 3116 Fax: 2241 5808
E-Mail: lynxkvgr@east.no
Focus & policy: choral magazine *Comments:* published by the Norwegian Choir Association

Listen to Norway
c/o Norwegian Music Information Centre (NMIC), Tollbugata 28, 0157 **Oslo**
Tel: 2242 9090 Fax: 2242 9091
Internet: www.mic.no
editor in chief Mona Levin
Focus & policy: journal published 3 times a year in English about the Norwegian music scene; covers all genres; includes reviews and listings

Musikk Praksis
Lerkevn. 4, 2323 **Ingeberg**
Tel: 6259 6111 Fax: 6259 5333
Internet: www.musikkweb.no/musikkpraksis/
E-Mail: musikkpraksis@online.no
Focus & policy: the only professional magazine for music and sound in Norway; 40000 readers, 128 pages, BBS Tel: 2260 3039

Musikkguiden
c/o FARO Musikk & Media AS, PO Box 123 Sentrum, 0102 **Oslo**
Tel: 2242 4150 Fax: 2242 4107
E-Mail: faro@faro.no
editor Simen Rognerud
Focus & policy: the complete Norwegian music address guide; circulation 6000; published in Norwegian
Comments: ISBN: 82-91-030-07-3

NORSK MUSIKERBLAD
PO Box 8806, Youngstroget, 0028 **Oslo**
Tel: 2203 1050/2150 Fax: 2203 2151
Focus & policy: 4000 copies; 10 issues; read by professional musicians, soloists, artists, music teachers, students, dancers and key personnel within Norway's music administration *Comments:* published by the Norwegian Musicians' Union

POLAND (+48)

Almanach Sceny Polskiej
Almanach of Polish Stage
Institute of Art PAN, PO Box 994, 00-950 **Warszawa**
Tel: 22-831 3149 Fax: 22-831 3149
Focus & policy: an annual publication documenting theatrical life in Poland during successive seasons: group members, premieres, repertoires, festivals, awards *Comments:* visiting address: Institute of Art PAN, ul. Dluga 26/28, Warszawa

Dialog
Pulawska 61, 02-595 **Warszawa**
Tel: 22-845 5475/583 Fax: 22-845 3935
Focus & policy: monthly journal in Polish dedicated to Polish and foreign drama and performing arts
Comments: created in 1956

Didaskalia – Gazeta Teatralna
Didaskalia – Theatrical Paper
Golebia 18, 31-007 **Krakow**
Tel: 12-422 1033 ext.1350 (Mon-Fri 7.30-20.00)
Fax: 12-422 1033
Focus & policy: bimonthly in Polish, affiliated with the Jagiellonian University of Krakow, information, reviews, interviews, essays on Polish and foreign performing arts
Comments: created in 1994

Notatnik Teatralny
Theatrical Notes
Rynek-Ratusz 27, 50-100 **Wroclaw**
Tel: 71-343 4267 Fax: 71-343 4267
Focus & policy: quarterly of the Centre of Studies on Jerzy Grotowski's Work and Cultural and Theatre Research, in Polish; essays, interviews on various aspects of the contemporary Polish and foreign performing arts *Comments:* created in 1991

Pamietnik Teatralny
Theatrical Diary
Institute of Art PAN, PO Box 994, 00-950 **Warszawa**
Tel: 22-831 3149 Fax: 22-831 3149
Focus & policy: quarterly in Polish devoted to the history and criticism of the theatre/disertations, studies and materials on Polish and foreign theatre from its beginnings until 20th C *Comments:* created in 1952; visiting address: Institute of Art PAN, ul. Dluga 26/28, Warszawa

Polskie Wydawnictwo Muzyczne S.A.
Polish Music Publishers
Main Office, al. Krasinskiego 11a, 31-111 **Krakow**
Tel: 12-422 0174 Fax: 12-422 0174
Internet: www.pwm.com.pl
E-Mail: pwm@pwm.com.pl
president & director Leszek Polony
Focus & policy: publishes music notes and books on music *Comments:* Warsaw branch: ul Fredry 8, 00-097 Warszawa Tel: 22-827 8923, Fax: 22-826 9780, E-mail: cbn@pwm.com.pl, director Adam Neuer

Ruch Muzyczny
Music Movement
ul. Hankiewicza 1, skr.poczt.36, 00-973 **Warszawa** 22
Tel: 22-822 4934 Fax: 22-823 2642
E-Mail: ruchmuz@polbox.com
editor Ludwik Erhardt
Focus & policy: biweekly magazine in Polish on classical music *Comments:* created in 1956

Teatr
Theatre
Jakubowska 14, 03-902 **Warszawa**
Tel: 22-617 5594/3546 Fax: 22-617 4298
editors Janusz Majcherek, Barbara Osterloff, Wojciech Majcherek
Focus & policy: monthly journal in Polish on theatre and performing arts in Poland *Comments:* created in 1945

Teatr Lalek
Puppet Theatre
c/o Teatr Lalka, Palac Kultury i Nauki, 00-901 **Warszawa**
Tel: 22-620 4960 Fax: 22-620 4960
Focus & policy: bi-annual journal of POLUNIMA in Polish and English (since 1995) on Polish puppet theatre *Comments:* created in 1950

Théâtre en Pologne, Le
Theatre in Poland
Polish Centre of the International Theatre Institute (ITI), pl. Pilsudskiego 9, 00-078 **Warszawa**
Tel: 22-826 1771 Fax: 22-826 3027
Focus & policy: quarterly publication of the Polish ITI Centre in English and French on all aspects of Polish theatre *Comments:* created in 1958; subscriptions: for details of international availability contact the Polish ITI

PORTUGAL (+351)

BLITZ, music newspaper
Avenida Infante dom Henrique 334, 1800 **Lisboa**
Tel: 21-854 2000
Fax: 21-851 8990
E-Mail: blitz@mail.expresso.pt
director Rui Monteiro; editor António Pires
Focus & policy: weekly journal with focus on music and youth culture *Comments:* started in 1984

Promúsica
Campo Grande 56, 8°, 1749-097 **Lisboa**
Tel: 21-791 2500
Fax: 21-791 2563
E-Mail: audiovisuais@fbento.pt
director João Martins; editor João Botas
Focus & policy: music industry and technology trade magazine; focus on the record industry, music technology and musical instruments *Comments:* published monthly; free CD with magazine

RUSSIA (+7)

Ballet
Prospect Mira 52, 129110 **Moscow**
Tel: 095-232 2347
Fax: 095-232 2347
editor Valeria Uralskaya
Focus & policy: review

Dramaturg
Strastnoj Bulvar 12, building 1, 103031 **Moscow**
Tel: 095-214 6161/229 7065
Fax: 095-229 7065
Focus & policy: magazine

Ekran i Scena
Maly Gnezdnikovsky per-k 7, 103055 **Moscow**
Tel: 095-229 7065 Fax: 095-229 7065
Focus & policy: magazine

Intermedia Information Agency
Arbat 35, 121835 **Moscow**
Tel: 095-248 0153/9147/2833 Fax: 095-248 0153
editor-in-chief Eugene Safronov
Focus & policy: publishers of annual guide: Musical Results of the Year

Kultura
Kostianskij per-k 13, 103811 **Moscow** DSP
Tel: 095-208 8921/9900 Fax: 095-208 6604
Focus & policy: newspaper

Kultura Publishing House
Arbat 35, 121835 **Moscow**
Tel: 095-248 1151/3985 Fax: 095-230 2180
director general Nikolai Anastasiev

Literaturnaya Gazeta
Kostianski per. 13, 103811 **Moscow**
Tel: 095-208 5554 Fax: 095-200 0238
Focus & policy: magazine

Moskovsky Nabliudatel
Arbat 35 CDA, 102121 **Moscow**
Tel: 095-258 2372/248 9261
editor Valery Semenovsky
Focus & policy: review

Musical Life
Sadovo-Triumfalnaya 14-12, 103006 **Moscow**
Tel: 095-209 7524
Fax: 095-209 5498
Focus & policy: magazine

Musical Review
Sadovo-Triumfalnaya 14-12, 103006 **Moscow**
Tel: 095-200 6956/209 2188 Fax: 095-200 6306

Muzykalnaya Akademia
Sadovaya Triumfalnaya 14/12, 103006 **Moscow**
Tel: 095-209 2384/2916
Fax: 095-209 2980
editor Yuri Korev
Focus & policy: review

Muzykalnaya Zhizn
Sadovaya Triumfalnaya 14/12, 103006 **Moscow**
Tel: 095-209 2260/7524
Focus & policy: magazine

Rossijskaya Muzykalnaya Gazeta
Pogodinskaya ul. 2/3 appartament 151, 119121 **Moscow**
Tel: 095-246 1454
Internet: www.book-mekka.ru
Focus & policy: newspaper

Teatr
Strastnoi Bulvar 10, STD, 103031 **Moscow**
Tel: 095-209 2846
editor Valerij Semenovsky
Focus & policy: review

SLOVAKIA (+421)

Many telephone and fax numbers in Slovakia are in the process of being changed. We have included all new numbers known at the time of going to print.

Divadlo v Medzicase
Asociácia súcasného divadla, Dunajská 36, 812 92 **Bratislava**
Tel: 7-5292 2107 Fax: 7-5292 6677
Internet: media.gratex.sk/divadlovmedzicase
E-Mail: medzicas@gratex.sk
editor-in-chief Silvia Hroncová
Focus & policy: theatrical review (summaries of the main articles in English)

Hudobny zivot
Musical Life
Národné hudobné centrum, Michalská 10, 815 36 **Bratislava** 1
Tel: 7-5443 3716/0366 Fax: 7-5443 3716/0366
E-Mail: slovedit@netlab.sk
editor-in-chief Dr. Alzbeta Rajterová

Javisko
Národué osvetové centrum, Nám. SNP 12, 815 85 **Bratislava**
Tel: 7-5921 4235/5296 5222
E-Mail: noc@internet.sk
editor-in-chief Adela Demeková
Focus & policy: magazine for professional & amateur theatre

KULTÚRA
Martinská 49, 821 05 **Bratislava**
Tel: 7-4341 1012/1013 Fax: 7-4341 1012/1013
editor in chief Teodor Krizka
Focus & policy: weekly journal about Slovak cultural life (culture, theatre, music, literature, cinema, fine art)

Slovenská hudba
Slovak Music
Michalská 10, 815 36 **Bratislava** 1
Tel: 7-5443 3716/0366 Fax: 7-5443 3716/0366
E-Mail: slovedit@netlab.sk
editor-in-chief Alzbeta Rajterová
Focus & policy: quarterly journal for music culture/study, profile of personalitites, documentation, topical information, reviews CD, tapes and books

Slovenské divadlo
Slovak Theatre
Kabinet divadla a filmu SAV, Dúbravská cesta 9, 813 64 **Bratislava**
Tel: 7-5477 7193 Fax: 7-5477 3567
E-Mail: kadfsekr@savba.savba.sk
Focus & policy: quarterly journal on the Slovak theatre and cinema scene with summaries in English; includes reviews

TANEC
Nadácia Kroky-Steps-Foundation, Inventa, Karloveská 64, 842 58 **Bratislava**
Tel: 7-5249 7509/6542 3274 Fax: 7-6542 3274
editor-in-chief Eva Gajdosová

TEATRO
Pavla Horova 15, 841 07 **Bratislava**
Tel: 7-6477 8613 Fax: 7-6477 8613
E-Mail: info@rmd.sk
editor-in-chief Dr. Katarína Ducárová

SLOVENIA (+386)

Lutka
Novi trg 5, 8000 **Novo Mesto**
Tel: 68-322 371
E-Mail: klemencicevi.dnevi@guest.arnes.si
editorial board Tina Kosi, Mojca Jan, Jelena Sitar, Jurij Rudolf; executive editor Darka Ceh
Focus & policy: magazine on puppetry in Slovenia and abroad; published twice a year

Maska Casopis za scenske umetnosti
Maska Performing Arts Magazine
Metelkova 6, 1000 **Ljubljana**
Tel: 61-131 3122 Fax: 61-131 3122
editor-in-chief Emil Hrvatin; executive editor Rok Vevar; editorial board Emil Hrvatin, Primoz Jesenko, Jedrt Jez, Amelia Kraigher, Bojana Kunst, Blaz Lukan, Gasper Malej, Aldo Milohnic, Rock Vevar
Focus & policy: to reflect and promote Slovene theatre production; to develop new theatre theory; to mediate information; to follow world trends and phenomenons in the theatre; to provide interactive communication among artists from different fields and areas; quarterly magazine *Comments:* subscription price: $35 per year

Muska
Jeunesses Musicales Slovenia Magazine
Kersnikova 4, 1000 **Ljubljana**
Tel: 61-131 7039 Fax: 61-322 570
Internet: www.gms.drustvo.si
editor-in-chief Ika Prusek
Focus & policy: magazine on musical events in Slovenia and abroad, covering different genres; published ten times a year

Slovenska Matica
Slovene Society
Kongresni trg 8, 1000 **Ljubljana**
Tel: 61-214 227 Fax: 61-214 200
editor in chief Drago Jancar;
assistant to the editor Katja Klendienst
Focus & policy: magazine Glasmik published twice a year and covers history, literature, ethnic studies, philosophy

SPAIN (+34)

Actores (Revista de la Unión de Actores de Madrid)
Gran Vía 50, 3° D, 28013 **Madrid**
Tel: 91-541 5318 Fax: 91-541 6072
Internet: www.guiadeactores.es
E-Mail: uniondeactores@render.es
director Teófilo Calle; consejo de redacción Beatriz Bergamín, Pilar Massa, Gloria Vega, Juan Matute, Manuel de Blas, Juan José Pérez Yuste
Focus & policy: theatre, cinema, professional issues, trade union information for actors *Comments:* see also National Organisations

Ade Teatro
Revista de la Asociación de Directores de Escena de España, Costanilla de los Ángeles 13, Bajo, Izquierda, 28013 **Madrid**
Tel: 91-559 1246 Fax: 91-458 3012
director Juan Antonio Hormigón;
redactor jefe Carlos Rodríguez
Focus & policy: quarterly magazine focusing on theatre research, also all kinds of theatre issues; also lists theatre festivals, alternative venues, books etc.
Comments: subscription: 5 issues 39.06 Euro (US $56)

Agenda Clave
Avenida Gaudi 10, 2° 1ffi, 08025 **Barcelona**
Tel: 93-347 5199 Fax: 93-456 1729
E-Mail: claveprof@mx4.redestb.es
editor Jordi Rueda
Focus & policy: biennial directory of music and showbusiness industry in Spain (next edition in 99/2000) *Comments:* see also Publications, 'Clave Professional'

Anuario de Títeres y Marionetas
Puppet Yearbook
PO Box 5090, 48009 **Bilbao**
Tel: 94-424 5902/0437 Fax: 94-424 2550
publisher Concha de la Casa
Focus & policy: Spanish directory of puppetry, covering companies, festivals, veues, publications, TV programmes, puppets collections and more *Comments:* visiting address: Casa de Cultura, Centro Municipal de las Artes de los Títeres, Barrainkua 5, 48009 Bilbao; see also Festivals and National Organisations

Anuario Teatral
c/ Torregalindo n° 10, 28016 **Madrid**
Tel: 91-350 8600 Fax: 91-359 9705
Internet: www.mcu.es/inaem/teatro01.htm
directora Cristina Santolaria
Focus & policy: publication focused on Spanish drama
Comments: dependent on Instituto Nacional de las Artes Escénicas y de la Música, (Ministerio de Educación y Cultura); also publish a professional drama directory Guía Teatral de España (q.v.)

Catalunya Música/Revista Musical Catalana
c/ Sant Francesc de Paula 2, 08003 **Barcelona**
Tel: 93-268 1000 Fax: 93-268 1000
presidente del consejo editorial Félix Millet ; consejo de dirección Pere Artís (editor), Pere Burés (coordinación con Catalunya Música), Jaume Comellas (director periodístico) Lluís Millet (dictor musical)
Focus & policy: Catalan language monthly magazine covering the classical music scene in Catalonia
Comments: subscription price: Spain: 1 year 4200 ptas, 6 months 2350 ptas; abroad: 1 year 5525 ptas; single copy 500 ptas; published by Palau de la Música Catalana (see Venues)

CD Compact – Hi-Tech Ediciones S.L
Roca i Batlle 5, Entr. 1°, 08023 **Barcelona**
Tel: 93-418 4724 Fax: 93-418 4312
Internet: www.musicspain.com
E-Mail: hitech@musicspain.com
editor Jaime Rosal; advertising manager Birgita Sanberg
Focus & policy: classical music & jazz record reviews, monthly listings of festivals and other musical events, published 11 times a year *Comments:* annual subscription rates: Spain – 6500 ptas, Europe – 12500 ptas, overseas – US$125

Clave Profesional
Avenida Gaudi 10, 2°, 1a, 08025 **Barcelona**
Tel: 93-347 5199
Fax: 93-456 1729
E-Mail: claveprof@mx4.redestb.es
contact Jordi Rueda
Focus & policy: bi-monthly magazine for the live music industry *Comments:* see also Agenda Clave

El Encordado – Revista de Guitarra
Comments: see entry in Sweden

Entreacte
Revista de l'Associació d'Actors i Directors Professionals de Catalunya, Pg. Sant Joan 10 pral. 2ª, 08010 **Barcelona**
Tel: 93-231 1484 Fax: 93-231 2448
Internet: www.bcn.es/tjussana/aadpc
E-Mail: aadpc@mail.cinet.es
presidente Hermann Bonnin; secretario general Ferran Rañé; jefe de redacción Enric Cervera
Focus & policy: monthly magazine of the Professional Association of Actors and Directors of Catalunya; published in Catalan, covers theatre, cinema and TV; comes with a book (theatre scripts unpublished); subscription: 2975 ptas (11 issues + 6 books)
Comments: see also National Organisations

Escena
c/o Associació per la fundació Escena, Martinez de la Rosa 13, 08012 **Barcelona**
Tel: 93-217 9090 Fax: 93-217 2929
E-Mail: escena@intercom.es
director-president Albert de la Torre Fornell; directora general Merce Peralta Duarte
Focus & policy: monthly magazine on theatre, dance and music in Spain and Europe; published ten times a year
Comments: annual subscription rates: 6500 ptas in Spain, 440 FF in France, US$ 75.00 rest of the world

Guía d'Actors i Actrius Professionals de Catalunya
Associàcio d'Actors i Directors Professionals de Catalunya, Pg. St. Joan 10 pral. 2ª, 08010 **Barcelona**
Tel: 93-231 1484 Fax: 93-231 2448
Internet: www.bcn.es/tjussana/aadpc
E-Mail: aadpc@mail.cinet.es
responsable de publicaciones Enric Cervera; presidente Hermann Bonnin; vice-presidente Vicky Peña; secretario general Ferrán Rañé
Focus & policy: published every 2 years as a reference guide to Catalonian actors and listing of theatrical designers (incl. photographs) *Comments:* see also National Organisations

Guía de Actores (de la Unión de Actores de Madrid)
Gran Vía 50, 3ºD, 28013 **Madrid**
Tel: 91-541 5318 Fax: 91-541 6072
Internet: www.guiadeactores.es
E-Mail: uniondeactores@render.es
secretario general Jorge Bosso
Focus & policy: actors' directory with photographs (equivalent of Spotlight)
Comments: see also National Organisations

Guía Teatral de España
Spanish Theatre Guide
c/ Torregalindo nº 10, 28016 **Madrid**
Tel: 91-350 8600 Fax: 91-359 9705
Internet: www.mcu.es/inaem/teatro01.htm
director Cristina Santolaria;
gerente Rafael Fernandez Villaverde
Focus & policy: comprehensive guide to Spanish theatre producing companies, theatres, festivals, organisations, training schools, publications, grants, services, companies, administration etc; published in Spanish, it also lists some Spanish theatre festivals, drama schools and publications *Comments:* it is no longer published on paper, now only on the Internet; see also Dance, Puppets and Anuario Teatral

Music D'Ara
Paseo de Cólon nº 6, Espaclo 4º, 08002 **Barcelona**
Tel: 93-268 3719 Fax: 93-268 1259
Internet: www.accompositors.com
E-Mail: acc@accompositors.com
presidente Agustín Charles Soler;
vice presidente Oriol Graus Ribas
Focus & policy: monthly magazine of contemporary composers and compositions in Spain and Europe; publish in Catalan, Spanish and English
Comments: free magazine published by Catalonian Composers Association (q.v.)

Por La Danza
Asociación Cultural por La Danza, c/ Atocha 105, 1º A, 28012 **Madrid**
Tel: 91-420 3032 Fax: 91-420 3963
presidente y coordinación 'Por la Danza' Ana V Cabo; vicepresidente Jorge López; secretario Ana Rosa Ruiz; vicesecretario William Arroyo; publicidad Ana Rosa Ruíz; suscripciones Esperanza Carqués
Focus & policy: bi-monthly dance publication, information on Spanish Dance, opinions and articles
Comments: subscription price: Spain: 4600 ptas; abroad: 3600 ptas for six issues: published by Asociación de Profesionales de la Danza and Asociación Cultural por la Danza: see also National Organisations

Primer Acto
c/ Ricardo de la Vega 18, 28028 **Madrid**
Tel: 91-725 8085
Fax: 91-726 3711
E-Mail: primer-acto@medialabs.es
dirección José Monleón; administración Elena Cuesta; redacción Margarita Reiz;
suscripción Mª Luisa Cisneros
Focus & policy: bi-monthly journal on the Spanish and international theatre scene, five issues a year
Comments: in collaboration with Instituto Nacional de Artes Escénicas y de la Música-Ministerio de Cultura; subscription price: Spain: 4625 ptas, EEC: 7875 ptas, Latin America 7875 ptas, others 7875 ptas; single issue: 1175 ptas; the oldest theatre magazine, with 43 years of edition

Puck
PO Box 5090, 48009 **Bilbao**
Tel: 94-424 5902/0437 Fax: 94-424 2550
publisher Concha de la Casa; secretary Marian Sánchez; translator Luis Gutiérrez
Focus & policy: publication specialized in puppetry theatre; focus on avant-garde puppetry; exploring new techniques and reflecting about the philosophy of puppetry; each issue is a monographic about a contemporary subject related to puppetry *Comments:* edited by Centro Municipal de las Artes de los Títeres: see also National Organisations; visiting address: Casa de Cultura, Barrainkua nº 5, 48009 Bilbao

Recursos de la Música y la Danza en España
Music Resources in Spain
Centro de Documentación de Musica y Danza, Instituto Nacional de las Artes Escénicas y de la Música, Torregalindo 10, 28016 **Madrid**
Tel: 91-350 8600 ext. 124-130 Fax: 91-359 1579
E-Mail: cdmyd@savenet.es
director Antonio Álvarez Cañibano
Focus & policy: comprehensive directory of the database of the same title of the Spanish musical & Dance life: orchestras, choirs, instrumentalists, foundations, conservatoires, festivals, national, regional and local administration; produced by Instituto National de Artes Escénicas y de la Música, Ministerio de Educación y Cultura (q.v.) *Comments:* published by Centro de Documentacion de Musica y Danza; see also National & Regional Ministries

Ritmo
Lira Editorial, S.A., c/ Isabel Colbrand 10, planta 4ª, oficina 95, 28050 **Madrid**
Tel: 91-358 8774/8945 Fax: 91-358 8944
Internet: www.ritmo.es
E-Mail: correo@ritmo.es
director Antonio Rodríguez Moreno; editor Fernando Rodríguez Polo; redactor jefe Pedro González Mira; coordinadora de redacción Elena Trujillo; administrador Jesús Martín Ortega
Focus & policy: monthly magazine of classical music in Spain and worldwide, covering opera, concerts, dance and recordings *Comments:* founded in 1929; subscription prices: Spain: 10450 ptas, abroad: Europe (airmail) US$160, Europe (surface) US$99, USA (air mail) US$240

Scherzo
Cartagena 10, 1º C, 28028 **Madrid**
Tel: 91-356 7622 Fax: 91-726 1864
director Antonio Moral; director adjunto Javier Alfaya
Focus & policy: monthly magazine in Spanish on current news on Spanish, European and American classical music and recorded media scene; ten issues a year
Comments: subscription price: Spain: 1 year 7.7k ptas; abroad: Europe 1 year 12k ptas, USA & Canada 14k ptas, Central & South America 15k ptas registered post + 1k ptas; see also Festivals

SWEDEN (+46)

Danstidningen
Box 9237, 102 73 **Stockholm**
Tel: 8-849 287 Fax: 8-669 0111
editor Anne-Marie Wrange
Focus & policy: focuses on professional dance/dance groups in Sweden, Scandanavia; book reviews, events listings *Comments:* 6 issues annually

MusikDramatik
Box 4038, 102 61 **Stockholm**
Tel: 8-643 9544 Fax: 8-442 1133
Internet: www.partitur.se/md
E-Mail: torbjorn.eriksson@mbox303.swepnet.se
editor Torbjörn Eriksson; advertising manager & subscriptions Sören Tranberg
Focus & policy: magazine about opera, ballet and music with reports from Sweden and all over the world; published 5 times p.a. *Comments:* only opera magazine in Scandinavia

Musikern
Box 43, 101 20 **Stockholm**
Tel: 8-201 925 Fax: 8-168 020
contact Lotta Westbirg
Focus & policy: magazine for musicians published by Swedish musicians Union *Comments:* 9 issues annually (double issue in summer)

Swedish THEATRE Suedois
Svensk Teaterunion – Svenska ITI (Swedish Centre of the ITI), Box 15035, 10465 **Stockholm**
Tel: 8-462 2530 Fax: 8-462 2535
E-Mail: swedish@iti.a.se
Focus & policy: annual review of the Swedish drama and dance scene with English/French text *Comments:* the publication is distributed free of charge

Teater Tidningen
Box 9237, 102 73 **Stockholm**
Tel: 8-849 287 Fax: 8-849 289
Internet: www. teatertidningen.se
E-Mail: rikardhoogland@teatertidningen.se
editor Rikard Hoogland
Focus & policy: focuses on professional theatre/theatre groups in Sweden, Scandanavia, Europe and the USA
Comments: published 5 times a year

Teaterforum
Amatörteaterns Riksförbund, von Rosens väg 1A, 737 40 **Fagersta**
Tel: 223-17010 Fax: 223-17266
E-Mail: info@atr-riks.se
editor Lena Lindstedt
Focus & policy: newsletter for amateur theatre in Sweden and nordic countries; approx. 42,000 members
Comments: published 8 times a year;
annual cost: SEK 150

SWITZERLAND (+41)

Deutsches Bühnen-Jahrbuch
German Stage Yearbook
Comments: see entry in Germany

HARPA
Harp Journal
Odilia Publishing Ltd, Dorneckstr. 105, 4143 **Dornach**
Tel: 61-701 8866 Fax: 61-701 8858
Internet: www.odilia.ch
E-Mail: info@odilia.ch
editor Rudolf Frick
Focus & policy: published 4 times a year *Comments:* alternative E-mails: info@harpa.net; alternative Internet: www.harpa.net

Musik & Theater
Albisriederstr. 80A, PO Box 1680, 8040 **Zürich**
Tel: 1-491 7188 Fax: 1-493 1176
Internet: musikundtheater.ch
E-Mail: musikundtheater@bluewin.ch
Verlagsleiter/Chefredakteur Andrea Meuli
Focus & policy: published 10 times a year:
covers all performing arts

Passagen/Passages/Passages
Pro Helvetia, Communication, Hirschengraben 22, Postfach 8024, **Zürich**
Tel: 1-267 7171 Fax: 1-267 7106
Internet: www.pro-helvetia.ch
E-Mail: phmail@pro-helvetia.ch
Präsidentin Yvette Jaggi; Direktion Bernard Cathomas; Presse/Informaiton Michael Guggenheimer;
Vize-Direktor Rolf Keller
Focus & policy: magazine published twice yearly in English, French and German and covering Swiss cultural policies and issues *Comments:* free of charge abroad; in Switzerland SFr 12.50

Schweizer Musik-Handbuch/Guide Musical Suisse/Guide Musicale Svizzera
Swiss Music Guide
Atlantis Musik Verlag,
Jungholzstr. 28, 8050 **Zürich**
Tel: 1-305 7068 Fax: 1-305 7069
E-Mail: musikverlage@oeschverlag.ch
director & editor Claude Delley;
assistant director Oliver Raths
Focus & policy: annual directory listing orchestras, music ensembles, choirs, opera and ballet companies, jazz groups, festivals, concert agents, foundations, prizes, music schools, publishers, associations, music libraries, agents and media etc in Switzerland
Comments: published in association with Schweizerisches Musik-Archiv, Zürich; edited by SUISA – Stiftung für Musik, Rue de l'Hôpital 22, 2001 Neuchatel; distrubted by Atlantis Musik Verlag, Jungholzstr. 28, 8050 Zürich

Tanz der Dinge, Der
c/o Tanzdingverlag, 8025 **Zürich**
Tel: 1-262 2660 Fax: 1-251 4050
Internet: www.tanzding.ch
E-Mail: tanzding@hotmail.com
chefredakteur Wolfgang J. Brunner;
news redakteurin Marianne Forster
Focus & policy: bi-monthly magazine on dance with reviews, reports, listings – articles are in German
Comments: subscription: SFR 48 in Switzerland, SFR 58 abroad

Tanz – la danse suisse
c/o ASD/SDT, Dufourstrasse 45, 3005 **Bern**
Tel: 31-351 6050
Fax: 31-352 1502
E-Mail: sdt_messerli@aceers.ch
President Anne-Marie Paukh; vice president Armil Wild
Focus & policy: improve the situtation of dancers in Switzerland, socially *Comments:* published by Association Faitiere Suisse des Professionnels de la Danse; each year organise Tanz, a night of performance; promotion of the art of choreography in Switzerland

Theaterstatistik
Comments: see entry in Germany

Werkstatistik
Comments: see entry in Germany

TURKEY (+90)

Adam Sanat
Küçükparmakkapi Sok. No. 17 Beyoglu, **Istanbul**
Tel: 212-293 4105/06
Focus & policy: monthly art magazine

Agon
Theatre
Menekse Sok 8-B/19 Kizilay, **Ankara**
Tel: 312-252 9550
Fax: 312-245 1864
Focus & policy: monthly theatre magazine

Agos
Saksi Sok. Saksi Ap. 19/7 Pangalti, **Istanbul**
Tel: 212-231 5694 Fax: 212-247 5519
Focus & policy: monthly art magazine

Çalinti
Istiklal Cad. Atlas Pasaji 109-19 – Beyoglu, **Istanbul**
Tel: 212-244 3939 Fax: 212-244 0090
Focus & policy: monthly music magazine

Evrensel Kültür
Istiklal Cad. Aznavur Pasaji 212/6 Galatasaray, **Istanbul**
Tel: 212-243 0803/06 Fax: 212-251 1365
Focus & policy: monthly art magazine

Göige tiyatro
Semih Celenk, sk. no 17/ 11 Boztanli, 1807 **Izmir**
Tel: 232-320 4651 Fax: 232-320 4651
Internet: www.rasknet.com.tr
Focus & policy: a new periodical *Comments:* edited by young journalists from Izmir and Istanbl

Gösteri
Hürriyet Tesisleri Günesli Köy, Bakirköy, **Istanbul**
Tel: 212-677 0000/0384 Fax: 212-677 0327
Focus & policy: monthly art magazine

Guide Istanbul, The
Ali Kaya Sok. n° 7 Levent, **Istanbul**
Tel: 212-283 2061/269 8790 Fax: 212-270 6370
Focus & policy: monthly art news and city guide

Istanbul Kültür ve Sanat Haritasi
Istanbul Culture & Arts Map
Perihan Sokak AEA Ishani 126/1 Sisli, **Istanbul**
Tel: 212-296 8241 Fax: 212-296 6244
Focus & policy: monthly art news and diary

Jazz Magazine
Kaya Sultan Sok. Cemal Bey Ap. No 22/4 Erenköy, 81090 **Istanbul**
Tel: 216-372 7731 Fax: 216-416 9445
Focus & policy: monthly jazz magazine

LIR
State Opera and Ballet Monthly Art Magazine
Devlet Opera ve Balesi Müdürlügü,
Opera Binasi, **Ulus (Ankara)**
Tel: 312-310 4328/311 2430 Fax: 312-310 7248/311 2430
Focus & policy: monthly opera and ballet news

Merdiven Art Magazine
Piyerloti Cad. Dostlukyurdu Sok. Yesil Apt. 1/3
Çemberlitas, **Istanbul**
Tel: 212-638 3291 Fax: 212-516 2336
Focus & policy: monthly art magazine

Milliyet Art Magazine
Dogan Madya Center, Mahmutbey Viyadügü Alti, Ikitelli, 34554 **Bagcilar (Istanbul)**
Tel: 212-505 6111 Fax: 212-505 6348
editor Bülent Berkman
Focus & policy: bi-weekly art magazine

Sanat Çevresi
Babi Ali Cad. Tesvire Han. No. 54 Kat 2, **Istanbul**
Tel: 212-512 4571/349 1596 Fax: 212-527 9389
Focus & policy: monthly art magazine

Sinema Dergisi
Medya 3, **Istanbul**
Tel: 212-624 5210
Fax: 212-624 5265
Focus & policy: monthly movie magazine

Tiyatro Dergisi
Aga Hamami Sok. 5/3 Cihangir, **Istanbul**
Tel: 212-243 0937
Fax: 212-252 9414
Focus & policy: monthly theatre magazine

Varlik
Cagaloglu Yokusu 40/2 Edes Han, 34440 **Istanbul**
Tel: 212-522 6924/516 2004 Fax: 212-512 9528/522 6924
Focus & policy: monthly art magazine

UNITED KINGDOM (+44)

Arts Business
PO Box 358, **Cambridge** CB4 3FP
Tel: 1223-316 179 Fax: 1223-785 859
E-Mail: edit@arts-business.co.uk
Focus & policy: fortnightly magazine for arts professionals invoved in the management, administration and development of the arts; it deals with issues such as marketing, lottery bids, fundraising, training, IT, human resource mangement, programming and contracting
Comments: if is free for UK-based arts professionals involved in arts management and administration, but is £2.50 to others

Arts Funding Guide
Directory of Social Change,
24 Stephenson Way, **London** NW1 2DP
Tel: 20-7209 5151
Fax: 20-7209 5049
Internet: www.dsc.org.uk
E-Mail: info@d-s-c.demon.co.uk
head of publishing Alison Baxter;
director Mike Eastwood;
head of events & training Meena Varma;
marketing manager Sam Evans
Focus & policy: guide to fundraising methods and funding sources for arts organisations, museums and arts projects throughout the UK; new edition available from December 1999 – £18.95 + p&p *Perfs:* numerous other titles concerned with fundraising, charity management, planning, finance and law also available

Arts Networking in Europe
Information Department, Arts Council of England, 14 Great Peter Street, **London** SW1P 3NQ
Tel: 20-7333 0100 Fax: 20-7973 6590
E-Mail: information.ace@artsfb.org.uk
editor Rod Fisher
Focus & Policy: a directory of trans-national cultural networks, associations and international non-governmental organisations in Europe

Arts News
National Campaign for the Arts, Pegasus House, 37-43 Sackville Street, **London** W1X 2LD
Tel: 20-7333 0375 Fax: 20-7333 0660
director Victoria Todd; editor Simon Tait;
accountant George Yates-Mercer
Focus & policy: quarterly journal on arts policy and campaigning issues
Comments: an independent lobbying organisation that represents the arts as a whole

Arts Research Digest
Dept of Historical & Critical Studies, University of Northumbria, Faculty Office, Squires Building,
Newcastle upon Tyne NE1 8ST
Tel: 191-227 3894 Fax: 191-227 4572
Internet: www.arts-research-digest.com
E-Mail: hc.ard@unn.ac.uk
editor Ian Gasse; assistant editor Nina Byrne
Focus & policy: summarising recent and current research into the arts and cultural industries in the UK and abroad, for the benefit of practitioners, policy makers, funders, sponsors, academics and researchers from all over the world; continued aim is to make such research more widely known and available *Comments:* published 3 times a year; broad constituency; sections cover policy, funding, training and education, marketing, health, performing arts; visual and applied arts, film, video and broadcasting, digital arts, literature, museums; details of research projects always welcome (in English or French); free entry; subscription for one year: £40 UK, £43 Europe, £55 airmail elsewhere

ArtsBusiness
PO Box 957, Cottenham, **Cambridge** CB4 8AB
Tel: 1954-250 600
Fax: 1954-252 600
Internet: www.arts-business.co.uk
E-Mail: edit@arts-business.co.uk
co-editors Liz Hill, Brian Whitehead
Comments: annual subscription £60 UK, £72 overseas

BBC Music Magazine
Room A1004, Woodlands,
80 Wood Lane, **London** W12 0TT
Tel: 20-8576 3283
Fax: 20-8576 3292
Internet:
www.bbcworldwide.com/music.
E-Mail: music.magazine@bbc.co.uk
editor Helen Wallace; publisher Jessica Gibson; advertisement director Jonathan Gifford; listings editor Catherine Nelson; reviews editor Barry Millington; special issues editor Cara Chanteau
Focus & policy: magazine covering live, broadcast and recorded classical music and jazz, aimed at music enthusiasts at all levels; exclusive monthly cover-mount CD of complete works *Comments:* subscription address: PO Box 279, Sittingbourne, Kent, ME9 8DF, Tel: 1795-414 719 (order)/749 (enquiries); subscription price for 12 issues £45UK, £79 Europe, £89 rest of the world; world's biggest selling monthly music magazine

Belfast Arts Directory, The
c/o Chris Bailey, Belfast City Council, Linen Hall Street, **Belfast (Northern Ireland)** BT2 8BP
Tel: 28-9032 0202 Fax: 28-9027 0325
E-Mail: cbn@artservicesireland.com
editor Chris Bailey
Focus & policy: a directory of art resources in Belfast including funding advice, crafts, film, music, dance and visual arts; price: £5 for individuals, £10 for institutions
Comments: published 1998,
next edition planned for 2000

British & International Music Yearbook
Rhinegold Publishing Ltd,
241 Shaftesbury Avenue, **London** WC2H 8EH
Tel: 20-7333 1760 Fax: 20-7333 1769
Internet: www.rhinegold.co.uk
E-Mail: bpay@rhinegold.co.uk
editor Henry Watson
Focus & policy: annual directory of the British and international classical music industry

British Performing Arts Yearbook
Rhinegold Publishing Ltd, 241 Shaftesbury Avenue,
London WC2H 8EH
Tel: 20-7333 1700 Fax: 20-7333 1769
Internet: www.rhinegold.co.uk
E-Mail: bpay@rhinegold.co.uk
editor Henry Watson
Focus & policy: annual directory of performing arts in Britain with address information and technical data; includes venues, information on performing arts companies, festivals, support organisations, services and suppliers

Choir & Organ
Orpheus Publications Ltd,
7 St Johns Road, **Harrow** HA1 2EE
Tel: 20-8863 2020 Fax: 20-8863 2444
Internet: www.choirandorgan.com
E-Mail: choirandorgan@orphpl.com
editor Matthew Power;
assistant editor Katinka Welz;
choral editor Shirley Ratcliffe;
publisher Cornelius Bohane
Focus & policy: the international world of choral & organ music, sacred and secular *Comments:* bi-monthly publication; subscriptions: (6 issues) UK £17.70, USA US$33.00

Classical Music
Rhinegold Publishing Ltd, 241 Shaftesbury Avenue,
London WC2H 8EH
Tel: 20-7333 1742 Fax: 20-7333 1769
E-Mail: classical.music@rhinegold.co.uk
editor Keith Clarke; deputy editor Rebecca Agnew;
advertising manager Zoë Riddell
Focus & policy: fortnightly magazine on all aspects of the classical music business in the UK, with a particular emphasis on music administration, the work of concert agents, orchestras, ensembles and performers

Contacts
The Spotlight Office, Charles House,
7 Leicester Place, **London** WC2H 7BP
Tel: 20-7437 7631
Fax: 20-7437 5881
Internet: www.spotlightcd.com
E-Mail: info@spotlightcd.com
Focus & policy: free listings published annually of names and addresses etc of theatres, managements, agents, publications, critics, organisations, broadcasting companies, film companies and studios, record companies, training schools, and related advertising

Dance Current Awareness Bulletin
c/o National Resource Centre for Dance, University of Surrey, **Guildford** GU2 5XH
Tel: 1483-259 316 Fax: 1483-259 500
Focus & policy: publication for dance study, indexing major articles and reviews form UK and foreign periodicals; short summaries of articles/reviews grouped under more than 100 subject headings; additional sections include details of recently published resources (books, films, video, etc); conferences and events; and NRCD news *Comments:* DCAB is produced in March, July and Nov; subscription 98/99: corporate £58, group £35, individual £26.50

Dance Europe
PO Box 12661, **London** E5 9TZ
Tel: 20-8985 7767 (advertising)/8533 7815 (editorial)
Fax: 20-8525 0462
Internet: www.danceeurope.co.uk
E-Mail: edit@danceeurope.co.uk
editor Emma Manning; advertising manager Naresh Kaul; associate photographer Bill Cooper; editorial assistant Mark Pillans; illustrator Alexandra Lazarevic; internet manager Tim Martin
Focus & policy: monthly magazine on the professional dance stage throughout Europe incl performance diary
Comments: Newstand distribution by COMAG, subscriptions: 6 issues £16.50 (UK)/£21 (EU)/ £29 World; 12 issues £33 (UK)/ £42 (EU)/£58 World; ISDN: 20-8985 8195; Paris Office: Tel: +33 1-4453 9021

dance now
Dance Books Ltd, 15 Cecil Court, **London** WC2N 4EZ
Tel: 20-7836 2314 Fax: 20-7497 0473
E-Mail: dances@dircon.co.uk
editors David Leonard, Sanjoy Roy; advertising manager Susan Philo (1367-820 367)
Focus & policy: quarterly magazine dealing with the world of theatrical dance *Comments:* Susan Philo: Manor Farm, The Green, Uffington, Oxon SN7 7SB367; yearly subscription price £12 UK, £15.00 overseas, single copy £3.00; available from specialist art bookshops

Dance Theatre Journal
Laban Centre London, Laurie Grove, **London** SE14 6NH
Tel: 20-8694 9620 Fax: 20-8694 8749
E-Mail: info@laban.co.uk
editor Ian Bramley; listings editor Mary Cox; advertising Brian Shilling (1892-677 740);
marketing & production Giles Robertson
Focus & policy: Dance Theatre Journal investigates the new and contemporary in dance, emphasising cutting edge performance and current issues, and asking questions about historical practices; includes comprehensive listings; published 3 times a year *Comments:* subscription: £10 p.a. individual (UK), £12 institution (UK), £14 p.a. individual (overseas), £17 institution (overseas), $22 p.a. individual (USA), $27 institution (USA)

Dance UK News
Battersea Arts Centre, Lavender Hill, **London** SW11 5TF
Tel: 20-7228 4990 Fax: 20-7223 0074
E-Mail: danceuk@easynet.co.uk
editors Josephine Leask, Jane Attenborough, Suzie Leighton
Focus & policy: newsletter of Dance UK; focus on professional dance companies and artists; includes news items, opportunities (e.g. Awards), reports on conferences, seminars, etc.; listings include courses, publications, festivals, etc. but not performances/tours

Double Bassist
Orpheus Publications, St Johns Road, **Harrow** HA1 2EE
Tel: 20-8863 2020 Fax: 20-8424 9945
Internet: www.doublebassist.com
E-Mail: dbassist@orphpl.com
editor Paul Cutts; advertising sales manager Simon Trewavas; production manager Nikki Easton;
assistant editor Katinka Welz
Focus & policy: double bass, history – contemporary; features jazz – classical, performers, makers, educational issues; all the latest news and reviews form the bass world, plus free bass music in each issue; published quarterly

Early Music
Oxford University Press, 70 Baker Street, **London** W1M 1DJ
Tel: 20-7616 5902 Fax: 20-7616 5901
Internet: www.oup.co.uk/earlyj
E-Mail: jnl.early-music@oup.co.uk
editor Tess Knighton; assistant editor David Roberts; advertising manager Arthur Boyars
Focus & policy: quarterly journal covering all aspects of medieval, renaissance, baroque and pre-classical music with special reference to performance practice; book, music and CD reviews, extensive advertising *Comments:* North American address: Oxford University Press, Journals, 2001 Evans Rd. Cary, NC 27513, Tel: 800-852 7323, Fax: 919-677 1714; cost: institutional rate £72/$124, personal rate £72/$80

Early Music Today
Rhinegold Publishing,
241 Shaftesbury Avenue, **London** WC2H 8EH
Tel: 20-7333 1744 Fax: 20-7333 1769
E-Mail: emt@rhinegold.co.uk
editor Lucien Jenkins;
deputy publishing manager Robert Holmes
Focus & policy: bi-monthly; includes news and features; book reviews, CD reviews, professional and amateur events listings etc

Fono
Miller Freeman UK Ltd, 8 Montague Close, **London** SE1 9UR
Tel: 20-7940 8500 Fax: 20-7407 7087
Internet: www.dotmusic.com
E-Mail: fono@dotmusic.com
editor-in-chief Steve Redmond; editor Martin Talbot; international sales manager Matthew Tyrrell
Focus & policy: weekly music trade magazine for Europe dedicated to highlighting and promoting hit records; includes the most accurate airplay data available from 500 radio stations in 15 markets and sales charts from 14 markets *Comments:* from the publishers of Music Week and MBI

Gramophone
Gramophone Publications Ltd, 135 Greenford Road, Sudbury Hill, **Harrow** HA1 3YD
Tel: 20-8422 4562 Fax: 20-8869 8400
Internet: www.gramophone.co.uk
E-Mail: editor@gramophone.co.uk
editor James Jolly; publishing director Kevin Costello; editorial director Mel Nichols
Focus & policy: classical record review, interviews with artists, record related material, monthly publication includes a free CD featuring the best classical releases every month

International Arts Manager
Arts Publishing International Ltd, Lime Wharf, Vyner Street, **London** E2 9DJ
Tel: 20-8709 9050 Fax: 20-8709 9080
E-Mail: editorial@api.co.uk
publisher & managing editor Martin Huber; editor Paul Cutts; staff writer Nick Stellmacher; advertising director Richard Poole; advertising Peter Lynch;
subscriptions Christine Hoffmann
Focus & policy: magazine including issues, news and features of interest to managers in the performing arts *Comments:* published 10 times a year

International Journal of Cultural Policy, The
IPD Marketing Services Ltd, PO Box 310, St. Helier, **Jersey (Channel Islands)** JE4 0WB
Tel: 118-956 0080 Fax: 118-956 8211
Internet: www.gbhap.com
E-Mail: info@gbhap.com
editor Oliver Bennett
Focus & policy: journal aimed at policy makers, practitioners, academics and students with a professional interest in the subject; it carries research papers, information on research in progress, comparative studies, polemical articles, and book reviews which are likely to be of interest to an international readership; some editions of the journal include a series of articles designed around particular themes, which may relate to a specific set of issues, a geographical region, or a particular cultural form *Comments:* 2 issues per year

Juice Magazine
The Place Dance Services, Mary Ward House, 5 Tavistock Place, **London** WC1H 9SN
Tel: 20-7387 1828 (Juice)/7383 3524 Fax: 20-7388 5407
Internet: www.theplace.org.uk
E-Mail: danceservices@theplace.org.uk
editor Carolyn Deby
Focus & policy: monthly magazine listing professional opportunities for independent dancers/choreographers *Comments:* published by The Place Dance Services; subscription & membership of TPDS costs £15 upwards

Kemps International
Variety Media Publications, 6 Bell Yard, **London** WC2A 2JR
Tel: 20-7520 5233 (info)/1371-810 433 (mail order)
Fax: 20-7520 5233
editor Sara Tylor
Focus & policy: yearbook for film, video and TV industry *Comments:* 45000 entries for 60 countries; offices in UK and USA

MBI – Music Business International
Miller Freeman UK Ltd, 8 Montague Close, **London** SE1 9UR
Tel: 20-7940 8500 Fax: 20-7407 7087
Internet: www.dotmusic.com
E-Mail: mbi@dotmusic.com
editor-in-chief Steve Redmond;
sales manager Matthew Tyrrell; editor Ajax Scott; managing editor Hamish Champ
Focus & policy: bi-monthly magazine covering all aspects of the international music business; read by senior executives of record companies and the industry at large; also publish an international directory and statistical reports

Music Opera Dance & Drama in Asia, The Pacific and North America
Arts Publishing International Ltd, Lime Wharf, Vyner Street, **London** E2 9DJ
Tel: 20-809 9050 Fax: 20-8709 9080
E-Mail: mod@api.co.uk
editor Asia & Pacific Shizuka Yokomizo; editor North America Karin Junker; consulting editor Ana Laura Lopez de la Torre; deputy editor Stefan Braun; editorial administrator Marion Qazi; publisher Martin Huber
Focus & policy: annual; directory of 9500 entries for Asia, The Pacific and North America (including Mexico and Cuba); listing national, state and local funding agencies; support organisations; Pan-Pacific organisations; drama; opera; dance; orchestras; puppetry; festivals; venues; radio; television; competitions; presenters and presenting series; artists managers and recorded media; provides contact names, addresses, phone & fax numbers *Comments:* the book includes a free CD-ROM; alternative E-mail: mod@api.co.uk

Music Week
Miller Freeman UK Ltd, 8 Montague Close, **London** SE1 9UR
Tel: 20-7940 8500 Fax: 20-7407 7087
Internet: www.dotmusic.com
E-Mail: musicweek@dotmusic.com
editor-in-chief Steve Redmond; managing editor Tracey Snell; A & R editor Stephen Jones; editor Ajax Scott; deputy group sales manager Judith Rivers
Focus & policy: weekly trade magazine covering all aspects of the UK music industry, with emphasis on popular music; includes official charts as used by BBC Radio One and Top of The Pops, new releases, reviews and talent pages, etc. *Comments:* also available: Music Week Directory, 8500 contact names, companies, addresses and numbers covering all sectors of UK music industry

Music Week Directory
Miller Freeman UK Ltd.,
8 Montague Close, **London** SE1 9UR
Tel: 20-7940 8500
Fax: 20-7407 7087
Internet: www.dotmusic.com
E-Mail: musicweek@dotmusic.com
editor in chief Steve Redmond;
editor Ajax Scott;
deputy group sales manager Judith Rivers
Focus & policy: annual contact guide to all aspects of the UK music industry in general and popular music in particular

Musical Opinion
2 Princes Rd., **St Leonards on Sea** TN37 6EL
Tel: 1424-715 167
Fax: 1424-712 214
Internet: www.slicc.mcmail.com/musop/.htm
E-Mail: musical_opinion@mcmail.com
editor Denby Richards;
assistant editor Caroline Bendell;
advertising manger Motivated Media (tel: 1299-427 717)
Focus & policy: quarterly magazine with monthly supplement including features, previews and reviews of important events in the musical calendar, in-depth interviews with leading musical personalities, reviews of books, music, videos, CDs, concerts, opera and ballet *Comments:* subscription price: 1 year UK £25, 1 year overseas £37 or US$74; founded in 1877

Opera
1A Mountgrove Road, **London** N5 2LU
Tel: 20-7359 1037
Fax: 20-7354 2700
Internet: www.opera.co.uk
E-Mail: operamag@clara.co.uk
editor Rodney Milnes
Focus & policy: long established monthly magazine in English reviewing UK and international productions and the opera scene; includes calendar of forthcoming productions at major opera houses

Opera Now
Rhinegold Publishing Ltd,
241 Shaftesbury Avenue,
London WC2H 8EH
Tel: 20-7333 1740
Fax: 20-7333 1769
E-Mail: opera.now@rhinegold.co.uk
editor Ashutosh Khandekar; deputy editor Antonia Couling; advertising manager Dominic Sewell; assistant editor Matthew Peacock
Focus & policy: glossy bi-monthly magazine in English, which covers the international opera scene; includes calendar of forthcoming productions at major opera houses and reviews of the latest CDs; also includes retrospective articles on singers, news features; profiles of international opera companies

Performing Arts Yearbook for Europe (PAYE)
Arts Publishing International Ltd, Lime Wharf, Vyner Street, **London** E2 9DJ
Tel: 20-8709 9050
Fax: 20-8709 9080
E-Mail: paye@api.co.uk
publisher Martin Huber; editor Karin Junker; consulting editor Ana Laura Lopez de la Torre; deputy editor Stefan Braun; editorial administrator Marion Qazi; advertising director Richard Poole
Focus & policy: published annually (Dec); directory of over 13500 entries in 22 sections covering the performing arts in 51 European countries; lists ministries of culture & funding agencies; opera & dance companies; early music and vocal ensembles; drama companies; venues; puppets & mime; orchestras; festivals; promoters; agents and producers; publications and recorded media as well as service-providers to the performing arts, provides contact names, addresses, phone, fax and Email-numbers plus a large number of website-addresses *Comments:* the book includes a free CD-Rom; alternative E-mail: paye@api.co.uk

Piano
Rhinegold Publishing Ltd, 241 Shaftesbury Avenue, **London** WC2H 8EH
Tel: 20-7333 1724/33 (advertising)
Fax: 20-7333 1769
E-Mail: piano@rhinegold.co.uk
editor Jeremy Siepmann;
marketing manager Richard Thomas;
publishing manager Sarah Williams;
deputy editor Matthew Peacock
Focus & policy: bi-monthly; includes news and features

Plays International
Performing Arts Trust,
33A Lurline Gardens, **London** SW11 4DD
Tel: 20-7720 1950
Fax: 20-7720 1950
editor Peter Roberts
Focus & policy: monthly magazine on the UK drama scene in particular and international theatre in general *Comments:* publish a complete text of a new play every month

Spotlight, The
7 Leicester Place, **London** WC2H 7BP
Tel: 20-7437 7631 Fax: 20-7437 5881
Internet: www.spotlightcd.com
E-Mail: info@spotlightcd.com
chairman Nigel Seale; editor Christine Barry
Focus & policy: The Spotlight bookshelf carries the complete range of catalogues which has developed from the original Actors & Actresses 1927; actors, actresses, children, students, Afro-Asian, stunt artistes, presenters *Comments:* now producing CD-Rom (Apple/PC), Spotlight Casting on the web (internet)

Stage, The
Stage Newspaper Limited, Stage House, 47 Bermondsey Street, **London** SE1 3XT
Tel: 20-7403 1818 Fax: 20-7403 1418 (administration)/7378 0480 (advertising)/7357 9287 (editorial)
Internet: www.thestage.co.uk
E-Mail: newsdesk@thestage.co.uk
managing director Catherine Comerford; head of advertising Marcus Collingbourne; editor Brian Attwood; head of finance Tim Catherall
Focus & policy: weekly newspaper for the professional involved in British theatre, dance, opera, light entertainment, TV and radio; covers productions, casting, management, technical aspects, reviews of productions etc. *Comments:* other emails: subs@thestage.co.uk

Strad Directory, The
Orpheus Publications Ltd, 7 St Johns Road, **Harrow** HA1 2EE
Tel: 20-8863 2020 Fax: 20-8863 2444
Internet: www.thestrand.com
E-Mail: thestrad@orphpl.com
editor Joanna Pieters; deputy editor Juliette Barber, Naomi Sadler
Focus & policy: annual directory; includes guide to auction prices of string instruments, international listings of violin-makers, dealers, restorers and suppliers; also string associations, competitions, exhibitions etc. *Comments:* to order contact: Strad Library, PO Box 935, Finchingfield, Braintree, Essex CM7 4LN, Tel: 1371-810 433, Fax: 1371-811 065

The Singer
Rhinegold Publishing, 241 Shaftesbury Avenue, **London** WC2 8EH
Tel: 20-7333 1746 Fax: 20-7333 1769
E-Mail: thesinger@rhinegold.co.uk
editor Antonia Couling
Focus & policy: bi-monthly; includes news and features on all aspects of all singing styles

Theatre Record
305 Whitton Dene, **Isleworth** TW7 7NE
Tel: 20-8892 6087 Fax: 20-8893 8677
E-Mail: theatrerecord@hotmail.com (editorial)
editor Ian Herbert
Focus & policy: fortnightly journal reprinting unabridged reviews from the national newspaper drama critics of new productions in London and the regions, with cast lists, technical credits and photographs; extensive future listings; annual name and production index *Comments:* subscriptions E-mail: ruth@theatrerecord.demon.co.uk

Unknown Public Ltd
PO Box 354, **Reading** RG1 5TX
Tel: 118-931 2580/20-7402 2789
Fax: 118-931 2582
E-Mail: aston@mailbox.co.uk
publisher Laurence Aston; editor John L Walters
Focus & policy: international CD-journal of contemporary creative music *Comments:* available by subscription only

Visiting Arts Directories
11 Portland Place, **London** W1N 4EJ
Tel: 20-7389 3019
Fax: 20-7389 3016
Internet: www.britcoun.org/visitingarts/
E-Mail: publications@visitingarts.demon.co.uk
managing editor, regional arts profiles Tim Doling; marketing manager Laura Lang
Focus & policy: directories of art organisations; last directories published: Norway, Israel, Hungary, South Africa, Palestine *Comments:* other directories previously published are available

Visiting Arts Magazine
11 Portland Place, **London** W1N 4EJ
Tel: 20-7389 3019
Fax: 20-7389 3016
Internet: www.britcoun.org/visitingarts/
E-Mail: vamag@visitingarts.demon.co.uk
editor John Kundu
Focus & policy: published three times a year; Visiting Arts provides a point of contact between promoters, venues, artists and organisations listing international arts projects available for touring and other foreign events being presented in the UK; it is distributed to UK venues, promoters, festivals, galleries, art specialists, funding bodies, the press, embassies, cultural representatives, British Council offices overseas and other selected international contacts *Comments:* back issues of Visiting Arts are available on request

White Book, The
Bank House, 23 Warwick Road, **Coventry** CV1 2EW
Tel: 24-7655 9658 Fax: 24-7663 1185
Internet: www.whitebook.co.uk
E-Mail: whitebook@dial.pipex.com
editor Sarah Hutchinson; advertising sales Toby East; associate publisher Nigel Waygood
Focus & policy: annual international production directory of entertainment, concert, record, film, TV, conference & exhibition industries, listing performers, services and facilities, manufacturers *Comments:* published annually in January

YUGOSLAVIA (+381)

Due to the war in Kosovo we have been unable to update the following entries for Yugoslavia

Ludus
c/o Association of Drama Artists of Serbia, Terazije 26/I, 11000 **Belgrade**
Tel: 11-686 879/683 848 Fax: 11-687 264
editor-in-chief Feliks Pasic
Focus & policy: monthly theatre newspaper in Serbian; an annual special edition is published in English

Orchestra
Cirila i Metodija 2, 11000 **Belgrade**
Tel: 11-403 443 Fax: 11-403 443
director Ivan Milovanovic
Focus & policy: quarterly ballet magazine

OVDJE
Novaka Miloseva 12/II, 81000 **Podgorica**
Tel: 81-42069
editor-in-chief Radojica Boskovic
Focus & policy: magazine on culture and arts

Stage
Scena
Sterijino pozorje, Zmaj Jovina 22/I, 21000 **Novi Sad**
Tel: 21-27255 Fax: 21-615 976
Focus & policy: bi-monthly journal in Serbian on Yugoslav drama, dance and opera; a bi-annual special edition is published in English

Yugoslav Theatre Yearbook
Godisnjak jugoslovenskih pozoriste
Sterijino pozorje, Zmaj Jovina 22/1, 21000 **Novi Sad**
Tel: 21-27255 Fax: 21-615 976
Focus & policy: annual directory of theatres, prods with info on festivals, academies, documentation centres, appearances by visiting foreign groups etc; published in Serbian

Arts Administration and Management Courses

Arts Administration and Management Courses
The section lists available courses. Within country the courses are ordered by city and alphabetically within city.

Administration et gestion artistiques
Vous trouverez ci-après la liste des cours proposés. **Pour chaque pays, les cours sont classés par ville et par ordre alphabétique.**

Kulturverwaltungs- und Kulturmanagementkurse
In diesem Kapitel werden Kulturverwaltungs- und Kulturmanagementkurse aufgeführt. **Die Einträge für alle Staaten sind alphabetisch nach Stadtnamen und innerhalb der Stadt alphabetisch nach Namen geordnet.**

Corsi di amministrazione e management nel campo artistico
Questa sezione elenca i corsi disponibili. **All'interno di ogni Paese, i corsi sono elencati alfabeticamente per cittá.**

Cursos de dirección y administración en Artes
Incluimos una lista de los cursos que se ofrecen en la actualidad. **Están listados alfabéticamente por ciudades dentro de cada país, y alfabéticamente dentro de cada ciudad.**

Arts Administration and Management Courses (**예술 행정 및 경영 코스**)
이 부문에는 등록이 가능한 코스들이 기재되었다. **리스트는 국가별, 도시별, 그리고 다시 알파벳순으로 기재되었다.**

艺术行政与管理课程
本部分列出了可选的课程。**在各国内，各门课程是按城市排列的，而在城市内又是按字母顺序排列的。**

芸術管理運営コース
ここでは開講されているコースを掲載しました。**リストは国、都市別で、都市内ではアルファベット順に記載されています。**

AUSTRIA (+43)

International Centre for Culture and Management
Jakob-Haringer-Straße 5A,
5020 **Salzburg**
Tel: 662-459 841
Fax: 662-459 838
Internet: www.iccm.co.at
E-Mail: poeschl@iccm.co.at
geschäftsführender Vorstandsvorsitzender Herwig Pöschl; Marketing im Kultur-und Medienbereich Mag DDr Gerbert Schwaighofer MBA (INSEAD); Kultur-und Medienpolitik, Kulturverwaltung Mag Robert Harave; Kultur-und Medienrecht Dr Michael Bauer; allgemeine Kultur-und Medienbetriebslehre Dr Walter Reicher; Finanz-und Rechnungswesen, Controlling O-Univ Prof Dkfm Dr Walter Sertl
Course aims: ICCM aims to act as a real company for the arts and media, offering 'training on projects'; special focus on international and European frameworks of culture management *Course content:* with exception of a basic programme there are no academic lectures or seminars; arts and management theory are developed through practice *Course structure:* participants join in as "ICCM Associates", and work in small teams (5-7) on international projects, from individual research to the realisation of projects in the public sphere
Award made: Master of Advanced Sudies (Arts and Media Management) *Comments:* joint project: the 'European American Virtual Academy' in collaboration with the College for Arts, Entertainment and Media Management at the University of Chicago, the College of Fine Arts and the H. John Heinz III School of Public Policy and Management at Carnegie Mellon University and the Sibelius Academy in Helsinki

Institut für Kulturwissenschaft
Museumsplatz 1/5/3, 1070 **Wien**
Tel: 1-522 5384
Fax: 1-522 5698
Internet: www.thing.at/ikw
E-Mail: ikw@thing.at
contact Beatrice Jaschke
Course content: museum and gallery management
Course length: 2 years part-time *Award made:* Post Graduate Degrees *Entry requirements:* University Degree and work experience

Universität für Musik und Darstellende Kunst
Institut für Kulturmanagement (IKM),
Karlsplatz 2/2/9, 1010 **Wien**
Tel: 1-505 2061/3075
Fax: 1-505 2061/18
Internet: www.mdw.ac.at/ikm/
E-Mail: ikm@mdw.ac.at
head of the institute Prof. Dr. Werner Hasitschka; personnel Franz-Otto Hofecker, Herbert Szirota, Claudia Preschl, Tasos Zembylas
Course aims: to train managers for performing arts, concert organisations, festivals, museums and galleries, media, etc *Course content:* cultural management, aesthetics, marketing, P.R., cultural policy, cultural business management, AV-media, law, contemporary culture *Course length:* 2 years (4 semesters) *Course structure:* direct teaching, seminars *Award made:* Master of Advanced Studies (Kulturmangement) *Entry requirements:* spoken German; written test on cultural subject ; 1st degree

BELARUS (+375)

Belarusian Cultural Studies Institute
Bjeloruskij Institut Probljem Kultury
ul. Kalinovskogo 12, 220086 **Minsk**

BELGIUM (+32)

Fondation Marcel Hicter
Rue Cornet de Grez, 14, 1210 **Brussels**
Tel: 2-219 9886
Fax: 2-217 3572
E-Mail: fond.hicter@glo.be
contact J. P. Deru
Course aims: the Fondation Marcel Hicter has been running the European Diploma in Cultural Project Management since 1989; this pan-European training programme is a pilote programme for area-based cultural administrators with a European dimension. It was set up as a follow-up to the 'Culture and Region' programme of the Council of Europe; the training programme in which already more than 200 young cultural managers from thirty different countries participated is unique in Europe; it aims to improve the management skills and expertise of professionals working in the cultural and artistic field and seeks to promote European cultural diversity and inter-regional exchanges; the programme is supported by the Commission of the European Union, the Council of Europe and UNESCO *Course content:* is based on the involvement of experts from all over Europe and acitve participation of the trainees in structured cultural development projects; its 4 major orientations are: Europe, culture, regions; territorial development; strategic planning of cultural projects; operational management of cultural projects *Course length:* 1 year part-time *Course structure:* training includes 2 residential phases of two weeks each, both taking place in one or two different countries, a practical phase over two periods of 4 months including a case study visit to another European region and an evaluation phase of one week in Greece; the themes discussed during the residential phases are the following: Europe & Culture; territorial development; strategic planning of cultural projects; and operational management of cultural projects *Comments:* also runs the Oracle Network which assembles present and former participants in the European Diploma: see also Supranational Organisations (European Network of Cultural Administration Training Centres – ENCATC)

BULGARIA (+359)

Institute of Management OKOM
1 Macedonia Square, 1000 **Sofia**
Tel: 2-875 882
Fax: 2-872 084
E-Mail: nely@mbox.cit.bg
contact Dimitar Kamenov, Neviana Viatleva

New Bulgarian University – Arts Mangement Programme
21 Montevideo St., 1309 **Sofia**
Tel: 2-957 1582/204 363
Fax: 2-204 363
Internet: www.nbu.acad.bg
E-Mail: baf@mbox.cit.bg
contact Lidia Varbanova

FINLAND (+358)

Syväst Polytechnic
4 Finnsbacken, 02780 **Espoo**
Tel: 9-819 0050 Fax: 9-819 0021
Internet: www.syvast.fi
E-Mail: christian.blom@solvalla-finns.fi
contact Christian Blom
Course content: cultural production
Course length: 3.5 years *Award made:* BA

Sibelius Academy
Sibelius Academy Continuing Education Centre,
PO Box 86, 00251 **Helsinki**
Tel: 9-405 4633 Fax: 9-405 4678
Internet: www.siba.fi/yksikot/koulutuskeskus/
E-Mail: osmo.palonen@siba.fi
director Osmo Palonen
Course aims: aimed at senior and middle managers in arts organisations; the programme equips students with skills to revitalise organisations by improving the efficency of their operations, management, working practices and product development *Course content:* special features of arts organisation management; arts administration and the culture industry; communications and marketing; the public, the client and the consumer; change in organisations; human resource management; project management; financial planning and monitoring; finance; legal issues in the arts, internationalisation; culture as a part of regional development *Course length:* 2 years (part-time) *Course structure:* 40 credits comprising 20 modules of direct teaching: lectures, workshops, case studies; literature and reports; optional studies; diploma work and a one-week study trip *Award made:* Professional Diploma in Arts Management *Entry requirements:* BA, MA or equivalent first degree and experience in administration/management of the arts *Comments:* the programme is run by the continuing education centres of Finland's art academies namely the Sibelius Academy, the University of Art and Design (Helsinki), and the Theatre Academy; main language of instruction is Finnish; closing date for applications: spring 2000

Sibelius Academy
Sibelius Academy, Degree Programme in Arts Mangement, PO Box 86,
00251 **Helsinki**
Tel: 9-405 4637
Fax: 9-405 4684
Internet: www.siba.fi/Studies/Arts_Management
E-Mail: tuovi.martinsen@siba.fi
planning officer Tuovi Martinsen; contact Leena Aarimaa (tel: 9-405 4728)
Course aims: the Arts Management MA Degree Programme is designed to give students the necessary knowledge and skills to take up a management position in an arts organisation and to become dynamic and innovative arts managers *Course content:* administration, management and leadership in the performing arts (music, theatre, dance) *Course length:* 2 years (full-time) *Course structure:* modular structure (60 credits): lectures, seminars and workshops; literature and reports; research and a thesis; practical assignments and placements *Award made:* MA in Arts Management *Entry requirements:* Bachelor's degree, first hand experience of an arts-related field (such as the performing or visual arts), language skills, and overall suitability for the field of Arts Management *Comments:* the language of instruction is English; the next course is likely to commence in the Autumn 2001; more information available in January 2001

Theatre Academy of Finland
PO Box 148, 00511 **Helsinki**
Tel: 9-431 361 Fax: 9-4313 6238
E-Mail: mhatiko@teak.fi
contact Marjatta Häti-Korkeila
Course content: arts management *Course length:* 3 years part-time *Award made:* Diploma

University of Jyväskylä
PO Box 35, 40351 **Jyväskylä**
Tel: 14-601 330 Fax: 14-601 331
contact: librarian Hanlet Saari

Humanities Polytechnic
Tähtiniementie 26, 41800 **Korpilahti**
Tel: 14-820 1214 Fax: 14-820 1101
Internet: www.humak.edu
E-Mail: hannu.ikonen@humak.edu
contact Hannu Ikonen
Course content: post graduate course in cultural management *Course length:* 3.5 years (140 weeks)

Turku Arts Academy
Linnankatu 54, 20100 **Turku**
Tel: 10-553 5215 Fax: 10-553 5202
Internet: www.turkuamk.fi
E-Mail: ingrid.hollingworth@turkuamk.fi
contact Ingrid Hollingworth
Course content: arts management *Course length:* 4 years
Award made: Bachelors Degree

FRANCE (+33)

IPAG
10 placetle la Fleur, 80027 **Amien** Cedex 01
Tel: 3-2282 7262/7131
contact Mme Scalabre
Course aims: to train regional and local civil servants, public administration *Course content:* law, problems socio-contemporary, general economy, politics-economy *Course length:* 1 year *Course structure:* lectures, workshops *Award made:* Licence d'Administration Publique *Entry requirements:* BAC +2 minimum or +3 years in civil service (category B); you should apply with a student file

Université Lyon II
CP 11, 69676 **Bron** Cedex
Tel: 4-7875 7789/7877 2409 Fax: 4-7875 8267
E-Mail: jacques.bonniel@univ-Lyon2.fr
directeur du DESS gestion de projects culturels Jacques Bonniel
Comments: see ARSEC Agence Rhône-Alpes de Services aux estreprises culturelles; training at Arsec

Association Ecume Mastère Spécialisé Européen
ECUME – Pôle de Gestion, 2 bd Gabriel, 21000 **Dijon**
Tel: 3-8039 5251 Fax: 3-8039 5259
E-Mail: ecume@axnet.fr
contact Melle Christelle Le Neouanic
Course aims: the Master's Programme aims to train managers capable of managing high-level interdisciplinary cultural centres or private foundations, creating and developing cultural tourism projects for prestigious European sites, managing enterprises in the cultural industries sector, or developing interregional or trans-European cultural cooperation projects *Course content:* the course is organised around three major points: the institutional environment of culture and European public policies in the sector, managerial techniques applied to specific sectors, and concepts and utilities for institutional management, strategies of enterprises and international projects; it is taught in the form of theoretical study and practical training (subjects: management, cultural enterprise, marketing, communication, languages, etc.) *Award made:* Diploma: Master *Entry requirements:* graduate of a 5 year university course in economy management, communication, architecture, arts, or 3/4 years higher education & experience *Comments:* in 1995 the Master's Programme opened a sub-branch in Bucharest for the whole of Eastern Europe by launching the EcumEst programme in cultural administration, which unites a number of institutional partners (Institut Français de Bucarest, Soros Foundation, British Council, Goethe Institut, French Ministry of Culture, European Union), who recognize the growing managerial needs of the Eastern European countries in the field of culture; Bureau ECUMEST, Institut Français de Bucarest: 77 Bd Dacia, 70256 Bucharest, Romania, Tel/fax: (401) 211 2853, Tel: (401) 210 0224

ECUME – Pole d'Economie et de Gestion
BP 26611, 21066 **Dijon**
Tel: 3-8039 5251 Fax: 3-8039 5259
E-Mail: ecume@axnet.fr
director Corina Suteu
Course aims: European programme to train future cultural enterprise managers able to create, manage and develop cultural and artistic events *Course content:* product marketing, analytical management of activities, management control, event creation and advertising, law and taxation, data processing tools; cultural institutions, politics, networks and organisations; business strategy, international projects, direction. budget control, finance, marketing, European cultural politics

Course length: 1 year, starting in November *Course structure:* 300 hours in residence including: lectures, case studies and seminars; a trip to another European country with a session in a University on cultural tourism and leisure; field surveys; a three-month placement in Europe; professional dissertation and synthesis *Award made:* Mastère Spécialisé en Management des Enterprises Culturelles (diploma issued on behalf of Grandes Ecoles de Gestion françaises) *Entry requirements:* five years of university study although others considered; written applications followed by interview *Comments:* organised in conjunction with Institute Claude Nicolas Ledoux

Master Culturel de Bourgogne
36, rue Chabot-Charny, 21000 **Dijon**
Tel: 3-8058 9854/64 Fax: 3-8058 9855
E-Mail: cpatriat@u-bourgogne.fr
contact Claude Patriat

Mastère Culturel
Ecume Pôle de Gestion, 2, bd Gabriel,
BP 26611, 21066 **Dijon**
Tel: 3-8039 5251 Fax: 3-8039 5259
E-Mail: ecume@axnet.fr
contact Corina Suteu

Université Bordeaux 3 IUT Michel de Montaigne
rue Naudet – BP 204, 33175 **Gradignan** Cedex
Tel: 5-5684 4430 Fax: 5-5637 4255
Internet: iutb.u-bordeaux.fr
E-Mail: ricome@iutb.u-bordeaux.fr
chef de département Marie-Claire Ricome
Course aims: Formation à la Culture: GAC (gestion d' actions culturelles); COMEC (conception de project et médiation culturelle)

Observatoire des Politiques Culturelles – DESS (Direction de projets culturels)
1 rue du Vieux Temple, 38000 **Grenoble**
Tel: 4-7644 3326 Fax: 4-7644 9500
E-Mail: opc@alpes-net.fr
directeur Réné Rizzardo;
directeur de la formation Jean-Pierre Saez
Course aims: to provide regional and local managers in charge of implementing cultural policies and projects with instruments of theoretical and operational analysis in order to meet new cultural needs better; this training is reserved for professionals of local authorities especially *Course content:* training organised with the University Pierre Mendès France and the Institute of Political Sciences of Grenoble; seminars grouped under the following themes: contemporary artistic and cultural stakes; cultural policy: local, national and international outlook; economy and cultural management; cultural industries and regional strategies; short programmess – internships, seminars, field trips, etc. – on specific themes are also offered periodically *Course length:* 2 years *Course structure:* 12 study weeks (1 study week per two months) *Award made:* DESS 'Direction des projets culturels' *Entry requirements:* arts administrators in local government and local arts instititutions (3 places for civil servants) *Comments:* training supported by the CNFPT and the Department of Culture

Groupe HEC – HEC3C
1, rue de la Libération, 78350 **Jouy-en-Josas**
Tel: 1-3967 7000 Fax: 1-3967 7087
contact Yves Evrard, Alain Busson
Course aims: training for proficiency in executive management of artistic and cultural enterprises; intended for participants who have already received basic instruction in management *Course content:* minor in culture and communications which includes the following modules: artistic products; the firm and the media; transversal problematics; the cultural professions *Course length:* 1 trimester, during the third year of study *Course structure:* workshops, debates, internships *Award made:* HEC certificate of specialised studies in artistic and cultural enterprise management *Entry requirements:* open to applicants holding the equivalent of the French "baccalaureat" + five years of college; selection is based on the application, an aptitude test, and an interview with the admissions committee; intended for HEC students orientated toward cultural management; selection takes place through a qualifying exam

ARSEC – Agence Rhone-Alpes de Services aux Entreprises Culturelles
8 rue du Griffon, 69001 **Lyon**
Tel: 4-7839 0105 Fax: 4-7828 9822
E-Mail: arsec@wanadoo.fr
directeur Francis Esther; directrice des affaires internationales Pascale Bonniel Chalier
Course aims: to promote (the emergence of) specialists in cultural organisation management *Course content:* cultural action policy, culture in the economy, dynamics of cultural development, sociological environment and cultural practices in France and in Europe, major trends in the arts, legal and fiscal framework of cultural organisations, management and financial analysis, human resources management, strategic management, information/computer systems, product marketing techniques and compatability, communication policies, Eruopean financial plan
Course length: 1 year programme, beginning of November to the end of October; tuition fee is charged *Course structure:* 1700 hours of training in 11 months at ARSEC in association with the University of Lyon and at the Lumiére University of Lyon II; students also must participate in 500 hours of practical work in a cultural enterprise or public service *Award made:* DESS développement culturel et gestion de projet culturel; responsible for DESS: Catherine Bardugoni *Entry requirements:* must have MA (or equivalent diploma) and experience in cultural matters

AGECIF – Aide à la Gestion des Entreprises Culturelles Ile de France
22 rue de Picardie, 75003 **Paris**
Tel: 1-4887 5824 Fax: 1-4887 6516
E-Mail: agecif@club-internet.fr
directeur Denis Thevenin
Course aims: seminars for professional managers *Course content:* short courses/seminars in various aspects of management, marketing, law, accountancy, computing, production and policies in the cultural sector *Course length:* few days for each choice *Course structure:* lectures, working groups *Award made:* Certificate of AGECIF *Entry requirements:* professional managers in the cultural field *Comments:* semi-public, French Ministry of Culture and Communiction has the right to examine; see also Services

Centre National de la Fonction Publique Territoriale (CNFPT)
10-12 rue d'Anjou, 75008 **Paris**
Tel: 1-5527 4400 Fax: 1-5527 4401
contact Michel Bourbonnaud
Comments: only for French agents of local communities

Formation Internationale Culture Commission Française pour l' UNESCO
210 rue Saint Martin, 75003 **Paris**
Tel: 1-4271 9019
Fax: 1-4271 9009
E-Mail: form.intern.culture@hol.fr
contact Brigitte Remer
Course aims: to give to the professionals who attend an overall knowledge and the tools necessary for the creation of cultural projects, development of cultural anthropological approach to the artistic fields and policies; the tools and methods of the cultural interventions and a socio-economical framework of the cultural policies *Course length:* 10 months *Entry requirements:* expertise in visual arts, audio visual, dance, music, heritage, theatre, international cultural relations *Comments:* supported by the French Embassy abroad; Foreign Affairs Ministry; Education Ministry; foreign students have to pay 20k FF (£2k) for the course; alternative E-mail: ficultur@club-internet.fr

Institut Supérieur de Management Culturel – ISMC
6, Rue de Braque, 75003 **Paris**
Tel: 1-4276 0274
Fax: 1-4276 0274
E-Mail: ismc_paris.mollard@wanadoo.fr
direction Marie-José Mollard; management Claude Mollard; communication Emmanuelle Camara
Course aims: to train cultural managers and cultural engineers *Course content:* links the economic, sociological and political sciences with immersion in the arts to provide an analysis of the cultural system, specific management strategies for production and dissemination of culture *Course length:* varies depending on degree required, plus final study project and examinations; from October to April; tuition fee is charged *Course structure:* 5 months of intensive training, graduate and post-graduate level; 3 months internship in a firm in the cultural sector; final study project and oral examination *Award made:* Certificate & Diploma in Cultural Engineering *Entry requirements:* undergraduate degree from an accredited four-year university or professional school; some graduate level training or a Master's degree is encouraged; applicants are selected by competitive entrance examination that includes a written test *Comments:* also offer 1 year sandwich course in cultural projects management

Université de Paris – Dauphine
Place du Maréchal de Lattre de Tassigny,
75775 **Paris** Cedex 16
Tel: 1-4405 4215
Fax: 1-4405 4949
E-Mail: Hyacinthe.Lena@dauphine.fr
directeur du D.E.S.S. Hyacinthe Lena; secrétairat Daniela Marcelino (Bureau A 522 poste 4215)
Course aims: post-Master's training programme intended to offer students additional applicable, operational training in the basics, principals, methods and techniques of management, applied to various types of cultural organisations *Course content:* particular emphasis is placed on teaching a group of approaches and practices which are used in many different types of private and public organisation in the cultural field *Course length:* 1 academic year, October-July including 3 month placement *Course structure:* lectures, workshops *Award made:* DESS 234 *Comments:* for details of application conditions contact: UFR 3e cycle – SO, Tel: 1-4405 4272

Université de Reims Champagne-Ardennes DESS
UFR de droit et de Science Politique,
57 bis, rue Pierre Taittinger,
51096 **Reims** Cedex
Tel: 3-2691 3838
Fax: 3-2604 2074
contact Janine Daigremont
Course content: policies of culture & European culture and law of the heritage and administration of cultural enterprises; decentralisation and cultural action, local and cultural development; obligatory subjects: law, decentralisation, politics
Course length: 1 academic year *Course structure:* required curriculum plus four options; obligatory workshops, internship, 3 months placement *Award made:* D.E.S.S. in Decentralised Territorial Administration, Local and Cultural Development *Entry requirements:* Master's Degree; regional or national civil servants employed in the field will also be accepted if qualified

Université Paris 8
Institut d'Etudes Européennes,
2 rue de la Liberté, 93526 **St Denis** Cedex
Tel: 1-4940 6592
Fax: 1-4940 6594
E-Mail: iee@univ-paris8.fr
head of department Mireille Azzoug
Course content: arts management course, including work placement *Course length:* 1 year
Award made: Diploma

GEORGIA (+995)

Stichting Caucasus Foundation (Educational Programmes)
45 Chavchavadze Av., 380062 **Tbilisi**
Tel: 32-294 306
Fax: 32-294 306/231 196
E-Mail: SCF@lingua.edu.ge
contacts Levan Khetaguri, Iuri Mgebrishvili
Course content: different cultural management topics such as: international cooperation in the arts; performing arts management: funding, budget planning etc.; sponsorship: methods, funding strategies, case studies; management for cultural policy; seminar programmes include lectures, workshops and discussions *Course length:* short-term courses
Comments: alternative E-mail: IBCCP@lingua.edu.ge; also organise masterclasses and workshops for directors, actors and playwrights

GERMANY (+49)

bbw Akademie
Alt-Moabit 91C, 10559 **Berlin**
Tel: 30-3909 8912
Fax: 30-3909 8933
E-Mail: hmuss@bbw-akademie.de
contact Heike Muss
Course content: theoretical knowledge of all aspects of arts management, plus work placements
Course length: from weekend seminars to 1 year full-time courses *Award made:* course certificate

Institut für Kultur- und Medienmanagement
c/o Hochschule für Musik 'Hanns Eisler' Berlin,
Charlottenstraße 55, 10117 **Berlin**
Tel: 30-229 9216/2465
Fax: 30-229 9216
E-Mail: pr@htm-berlin.de
director of Institute Prof. Dr. Klaus Siebenhaar; co-ordinator Dagmar Boeck
Course aims: to put the student in the position to work economically, artistically, practically and organisationally in the field of culture and media
Course content: management of cultural/media institutions, project management, cultural/media theory and cultural/media history, cultural politics, cultural administration, Law in the context of cultural and media spheres, economics and finance, communication, marketing and technology in the cultural/media areas
Course length: 4 semesters (2 years); oral and written examination *Course structure:* seminars, examinations, project seminars and practicals
Award made: Diploma in Cultural Management (qualified) *Entry requirements:* for post-graduate students and students of the social sciences and arts faculties; course capacity 25-30 per year; deadline for application: last Friday of June every year

Institute for cultural Infrastructure Sachsen and University of Applied Science Zittau/Goerlitz
Brueckenstr. 1, 02826 **Goerlitz**
Tel: 3581-420 9421
Fax: 3581-420 9428
Internet: www.kultur.org
E-Mail: post@kultur.htw-zittau.de
director Matthias Theodor Vogt
Course aims: education of managers for culture and/or collaborators; art directors for cultural and other institutions (with help of a practice-integrated, interactive economic, culture-scientific culture-political, social- and behavioural-scientific management education, border crossing, including the middle- and east-European cultural areas); directors for cultural policy and management

Course content: General base:- foreign languages: English, Polish, Russian, Czech, German for foreigners; psychology, rhetoric, law, computer science, mathematics, statistics; Economical base: (political) economics, business management, accounting/bookkeeping, cost accounting, marketing, administration economies; Cultural management: management/personnel management, financing of cultural/free time institutions, sponsoring, cultural management, cultural economy, law of art and media, cultural marketing; Cultural studies: cultural philosophy, European history of civilization, aesthetics, music and drama, east-west-lectures, project workshop; Pratical in-company training: 5 practical training within 55 weeks an active and scientific employment (work) in theatres (theatre-manager's office, marketing, technology/technical management), cultural administrations (bureau of culture, orchestra, library, festival) *Course length:* 4 years with 12 study periods (3 per year); 1st until 5th period: Stage I Studies; 6th until 12th period: Stage II Studies (submitted for a diploma thesis) *Course structure:* courses: (divided into 4 years) – 1st, 3rd, 5th, 7th, 9th, 11th, 12th period; practical in-company training: 2nd, 4th, 6th, 8th, 10th *Award made:* Diplomkaufmann/Diplomkauffrau (FH) *Entry requirements:* academic standard for university entrance (A-level), for foreign students: examination (of ascertainment) or certificate of German language; examiniation for university entrance of foreign applicants; artistic experience or experience at a cultural institution; interview/aptitude test *Comments:* other internet: www.htw-zittau.de

Hochschule für Musik und Theater Hamburg
Kulturmanagement (Kultur-und Medienmanagement), Harvestehuder Weg 12,
20148 **Hamburg**
Tel: 40-42848-0/4284 82528
Fax: 40-4284 82649
contact Nina Sinz
Course aims: training in cultural and media management *Course content:* part-time programme is intended for post-graduates in music and/or musical sciences or others *Course length:* part-time programmes, 41/2 semesters *Course structure:* theoretical and practical studies with on-the-job training; modern techniques and equipment are used particularly in the audiovisual, communications and broadcasting areas *Award made:* full-time post-graduate programme leads to a full Diploma degree *Entry requirements:* 1st degree; applications before 1 June every year

Hochschule für Wirtschaft und Politik
Kultur-und Bildungsmanagement (Culture and Education Management),
Rentzelstr. 7, 20146 **Hamburg**
Tel: 40-4283 82179
Fax: 40-4283 86479
Internet: www.hwp.uni-hamburg.de
E-Mail: Budde@hwp.uni-hamburg.de
programme coordinators Peter Wismann, Heike Budde (4123 2179)
Course aims: the course conveys qualifications in all fields of culture, developing a professional management expertise within the arts cultural industries *Course content:* 1. practical work in the field of culture & education; 2. culture and educational development; 3. economic, legal & administrative basics; 4. career areas/prospects *Award made:* certificate after 600 hrs *Entry requirements:* at least one year of work experience in a cultural and educational section

Pädagogische Hochschule Ludwigsburg – Institut für Kulturmanagement
Postfach 220, 71602 **Ludwigsburg**
Tel: 7141-140 411
Fax: 7141-140 434
Internet: www.kulturmangement.ph-ludwigsburg.de
E-Mail: kulturmanagement@ph-ludwigsburg.de
contact Prof. Dr. Werner Heinrichs, Prof. Dr. Armin Klein
Course aims: 1) postgraduate studies for cultural management (full-time, 2 years); 2) course in cultural management (part-time, 7-10 weekends) *Course length:* full time 4 semesters; part time 6 semesters (Kontaktstudium für Berufstätige) *Award made:* Magister Artium *Entry requirements:* successful 1st degree in subjects of performing arts, literature, music, business management, administration, law (for postgraduate course) *Comments:* visiting address: Reuteallee 46, 71634 Ludwigsburg

Institut für Internationales Kulturmanagement, Das
Englschalkinger Strasse 199, 81927 **München**
Tel: 89-9393 2866
Fax: 89-939 3867
contact Dr Eckhard Heinz

Fachhochschule Potsdam
Studiengang KulturArbeit, Pappelallee 8-9,
14469 **Potsdam**
Tel: 331-580 1600/1 Fax: 331-580 1699
E-Mail: kleine@fh-potsdam.de
contact Prof. Dr. Helene Kleine
Course aims: establishment of a new type of culture-mediating careers; combination of East and West German experiences interdisciplinary, multinational and multicultural understanding of theatres/culture; development of technical knowledge and innovative and creative approaches to the arts/culture *Course content:* cultural and social change, culture and project work, culture management and administration, media theory and practise with concentration on new media, aesthetics in theory and practise, preparatory instruction in particular self-management and presentation *Course lenght:* 8 semesters *Course structure:* basic courses (4 semesters), advanced courses (4 semesters) 5th semester is a practical semester *Awards made:* Degree Cultural Worker (FH-Diploma) *Entry requirements:* applicants undergo a process of determining suitability for the course; applications to SG Studienangeliegenbeiter by 1st April every year; applicants must be authorised to enter a university; six month preliminary internship in an area of cultural artistic work

Akademie Remscheid für Musische Bildung und Medienerziehung
Küppelstein 34, 42857 **Remscheid**
Tel: 2191-794-0
Fax: 2191-794 205
Internet: www.ars-online.de
E-Mail: akademiers@aol.com
director Prof. Dr. Max Fuchs;
public relations Dr. Eva-Maria Oehrens, tel: 2191-794 225
Course aims: offers a variety of programmes for further education and training in different fields of culture and arts; is the centre of a far-reaching cultural network, maintaining contracts in many countries; is the only federal institute in cultural youth work in Germany *Course content:* cultural management training for those working in pedagogical institutions and cultural projects; special programmes for artists who start working with young people *Course length:* several weeks full-time *Course structure:* direct teaching, workshops, long term degree programmes, post-graduate studies *Award made:* different certificates and diplomas of the Remscheid Academy *Entry requirements:* no formal requirements, except in special courses carried through in connection with other institutions and organisations

GREECE (+30)

Pantion University
Centre for Professional Training, 136 Syngrou Ave,
17671 **Kallithea (Athens)**
Tel: 1-923 4448/922 0865
Fax: 1-923 2979
E-Mail: ipao1@athena.compulink.gr
professor Dora Konsola
Course aims: to train qualified personnel for initiating and directing activities in cultural centres or other cultural institutions and organisations, both public and private, at national, regional or local level *Course content:* Cultural Development and Cultural Policy, Regional Cultural Development, Greek Cultural Heriatge, Contempoary Greek Culture, Planning and Management of Cultural Projects, Management of Cultural Institutions, Private and Public Funding of the Arts, Cultural Action in Local Communities *Course length:* 3 months full-time *Course structure:* theoretical courses, workshops, practical training and field trips; in addition, written and oral presentation of a report on individual projects *Award made:* Certificate of Attendance *Entry requirements:* university degrees and preferably some working experience in the arts

Institute of Cultural Studies of Europe and the Mediterranean (ICUSEM)
11b Konitsis Street,
15125 **Maroussi (Athens)**
Tel: 1-612 9446/7/8
Fax: 1-612 9445
E-Mail: forcores@hol.gr
director Efi Karpodini-Dimitriadi;
office manager Venetia Moschova;
programme collaborator Louisa Tarapidaki
Course aims: organises training programmes for university graduate and post-graduate students equipping them with in-depth knowledge in the field of cultural heritage *Course content:* cultural management, cultural administration (public & private) *Course length:* annual short-term seminar *Entry requirements:* graduates and post-graduates, professionals from the cultural sector *Comments:* organised in collaboration with the City University of London – Dept of Arts Policies and Management

HUNGARY (+36)

Eötvös József Teachers' Training College, Baja
Eötvös József Föiskola Pedagógiai Fakultás, Baja
Szegedi út 2, 6501 **Baja**
Tel: 79-321 655
Fax: 79-321 819
rector Dr. Mária Albertné Herbszt
Course aims: geared to those who wish to make a career in regional community cultural centres, museums or libraries *Course content:* Arts Management

Casus College of Arts & Arts Management
Körösy u. 17, 1117 **Budapest**
Tel: 1-166 4627 Fax: 1-166 4776
contact Andrea Gáncs
Course aims: to systematically teach concepts like budgeting, promotion and publicity in arts organisations; intends to be more practical and flexible *Course content:* first year: a grounding in the basic skills needed as an international art manager; second year: students take more advanced courses on marketing, accounting and computer systems; third year: includes a placement with an arts organisation as well as the preparation of a thesis for their diploma *Course length:* 3 years *Award made:* completion of CASUS college grants various opportunities: further study at another university, scholarship, work abroad, employment in cultural or arts organisations in Hungary, initiating a new cultural organisation *Entry requirements:* usual age: 18-23; must have completed secondary education and maybe art course or experience in artistic and cultural fields *Comments:* school is in the process of applying for state recognition which would enable CASUS to receive financial grants from the Ministry of Culture and Education, and diplomas would be recognised by the Hungarian State. So far, funding comes from registration fees, local councils and various Hungarian foundations; established in 1990 as a non-profit Hungarian organisation; since its beginning the association has been working as a cultural society organising and arranging specific cultural activities, from visual arts exhibitions to theatre performances, for artists and arts groups which did not have the opportunity to show their work within the former system; 80 students at present; none of subject teachers work solely for CASUS as there is a shortage of expert teachers – they all teach in other institutions or work in various art establishments

ELTE University – Cultural and Arts Management Programme
PO Box 107, 1364 **Budapest**
Tel: 1-317 4984 Fax: 1-317 8521
Internet: www.btk.elte.hu/kultman
E-Mail: bujdoso@isis.elte.hu
contact Dezsö Bujdoso
Course length: 1 year *Award made:* Post Graduate Degree

Eötvös Loránd University, Budapest – Department of Adult Education and Art Management
Eötvös Loránd Tudományegyetem, Budapest – Müvelödésszervezö Tanszéki Szakcsoport
Kazinczy utca 23-37, 1075 **Budapest** VII
Tel: 1-352 8981 ext 133
head Dr. Anna Molnár Szabóne
Course aims: geared to those who wish to make a career in regional community cultural centres, museums or libraries *Course content:* Arts Management
Course length: parallel four-year programmes

University of Debrecen
Department of Cultural Studies and Adult Education, Egyetem Tér 1,
Pf. 25, 4010 **Debrecen**
Tel: 52-316 666
Fax: 52-412 336
E-Mail: RUBOV@tigris.klte.hu
contact Kalman Rubovszky

Károly Eszterházy Teacher Training College
Eszterház Károly Tanárképzö Föiskola
Eszterházy tér 1, 3301 **Eger**
Tel: 36-410 466
Fax: 36-410 119
Internet: www.ektf.hu
E-Mail: to@ektf.hu
director Dr. Éva Zám Palcsóné
Course aims: geared to those who wish to make a career in regional community cultural centres, museums or libraries *Course content:* Arts Management

János Apáczai Csere Primary Teacher Training College, Györ
Apáczai Csere János Tanítóképzö Föiskola, Györ
Liszt Ferenc utca 42, 9022 **Györ**
Tel: 96-313 655/656/676
Fax: 96-329 934
Internet: www.apacai.hu
E-Mail: apacai@atif.hu
director Dr. Sándor Cseh
Course aims: geared to those who wish to make a career in regional community cultural centres, museums or libraries *Course content:* Arts Management

Institute of Adult Education and Human Resource Management
Felnöttképzési és Emberi Eröforrásfejlesztési Intézet
Szántó-Kovács János utca 1/b, 7633 **Pécs**
Tel: 72-251 444
Fax: 72-251 100
Internet: www.jpte.hu
E-Mail: csipak@human.jpte.hu
director Dénes Koltay
Course aims: offers programmes of study in Arts Management on a distance education basis to those who wish to make a career in regional community cultural centres, museums or libraries

Dániel Berzsenyi Teacher Training College Szombathely
Berzsenyi Dániel Tanárképző Főiskola, Szombathely
Károli Gáspár tér 4, 9701 **Szombathely**
Tel: 94-313 892/330 739 Fax: 94-312 248
director Dr. László Gál
Course aims: geared to those who wish to make a career in regional community cultural centres, museums or libraries *Course content:* Arts Management

IRELAND Republic of (+353)

University College Dublin
Arts Administration Studies, 530 Library Building, Belfield, **Dublin** 4
Tel: 1-706 7632 (direct line) Fax: 1-269 1963
Internet: midir.ucd.ie/~mms96-01/artsadmin
E-Mail: anne.kelly@ucd.ie
director Anne Kelly; executive assistant Shirley Redmond (shirley.redmond@ucd.ie)
Course aims: professional management training in the cultural area *Course content:* museums and gallery studies, performing and community arts; within each, sessions on Cultural Studies and Business Studies *Course length:* 1 year, full-time *Course structure:* 3 parts, including 12 weeks internship with an arts organisation; includes lectures, workshops, seminars, field-trips, projects and design and management of an arts related research project *Award made:* Higher Diploma in Arts Administration (post-graduate) issued by the National University of Ireland *Entry requirements:* recognized university degree or equivalent qualification

ITALY (+39)

FORMEZ – Centro di Formazione e Studi
c/o Comprensorio Olivetti, via Campi Flegrei 34, 80072 **Arco Felice (NA)**
Tel: 081-525 0111/06-8489 3205 Fax: 081-804 1348
presidente Prof. Stefano Patriarca;
direttore generale Avv. Umberto Ammassari
Course length: short courses *Comments:* Formez mainly operates in the Public Administration sector, with a special focus on the requirements of local and regional authorities; also for those authorities which operate in the underdeveloped areas of the entire national territory; also have offices in Rome and Cagliari

Fabbrica Europa – Centro di Creazione e di Cultura
Borgo Albizi 15, 50122 **Firenze**
Tel: 055-248 0515/247 8332/242 650 Fax: 055-247 9757
Internet: www.fabbricaeuropa.net
E-Mail: fabbrica.europa@firenze.net
director Andrés Morte; responsible for courses Maurizia Settembri
Course aims: to develop new skills, such as creative interaction, within the arts, and international co-operation with young people who already possess executive skills of production and direction of cultural events
Comments: see also Festivals and Agents & Producers

Osservatorio Culturale – Sviluppo Sistemi Informativi e Informatici de Direzione – Direzione Generale Cultura
Settore Cultura Regione Lombardia, Piazza IV Novembre, 5, 20124 **Milano**
Tel: 02-6765 2672 Fax: 02-6765 2698
Internet: www.regione.lombardia.it
E-Mail: cannadav@regione.lombardia.it
contact Giuliana Marangon
Comments: alternative E-mail: giuliana_marangon@reteculturale.regione.lombardia.it

Associazione Teatri Emilia Romagna – A.T.E.R.
Via Giardini 466/G, 41100 **Modena**
Tel: 059-340 221 Fax: 059-342 802
Internet: www.regioneemiliaromagna.it/ater
E-Mail: rer3@nettuno.it
direttore generale Roberto Giovanardi; presidente Maurizio Roi
Course aims: formation of professionals for the theatre world

ECCOM – European Centre for Cultural Organisation and Management
Via Emilia 81, 00187 **Roma**
Tel: 06-4201 3043
E-Mail: eccom@tin.it
contact Emilio Cabasino
Course content: post graduate course in cultural economy; school of specialisation and protection of cultural activity *Course length:* 3 years
Comments: working on a database of young cultural managers in Italy

ARTLAB
Corso Mediterraneo 94, 10129 **Torino**
Tel: 011-568 3365 Fax: 011-503 361
E-Mail: artlab.train@mbox.nes.it
contact Alessandro Bollo, Alberto Gulli
Course aims: to train cultural management in a European dimension *Course content:* cultural policy, economy of culture, marketing and communication, fund-raising, budgeting, new technologies, research, heritage, cultural industries, project management
Course length: Master: phone for info; Basic: 7 weeks full-time (one each month from Nov to June)
Course structure: 'European Master in Cultural Management': ask for info; 'Basic course: a week each month from November 1999 to June 2000
Award made: Master of Turin University; Basic Course and Seminars: Diploma by ARTLAB *Entry requirements:* Master: ask for info; Basic: 3 years of working experience in the cultural field and/or university degree; Seminars: 3 years of working experience in cultural field; selection starts in September *Comments:* see also Services (Fitzcarraldo)

LATVIA (+371)

Latvian Academy of Arts
Latvijas Mākslas akademija
Kalpaka bulv. 13, 1867 **Riga**
Tel: 7-332 202
Fax: 7-228 963
E-Mail: kampars@latnet.lv
rector Janis Osis
Course content: project management
Course length: four years *Award made:* Bachelor Degree

Latvian Academy of Culture
Latvijas Kulturas akademija
24 Ludzas, 1003 **Riga**
Tel: 7-140 175/172
Fax: 7-141 012
E-Mail: lka@acad.latnet.lv
rector Prof. Peteris Lakis
Course content: culture theory and history, culture sociology and management, theatre and cinema art, foreign languages *Course length:* art bachelor's degree – 8 semesters; art master – 4 semesters

LITHUANIA (+370)

Lithuanian Cultural Administrators Training Centre
Lietuvos kultūros darbuotoju tobulinimosi centras
Saltoniskiu str. 58,
2600 **Vilnius**
Tel: 2-752 777
Fax: 2-790 304
director Lina Baniene

NETHERLANDS (+31)

Amsterdam-Maastricht Summer University
PO Box 53066,
1007 RB **Amsterdam**
Tel: 20-620 0225
Fax: 20-624 9368
Internet: www.amsu.edu
E-Mail: office@amsu.edu
director Joanneke Lootsma
Course aims: European Performing Arts Management- a valuable combination of theory and practice under the guidance of experienced arts managers and consultants intended for performing arts managers who wish to acquire knowledge, develop management skills and exchange ideas.The course will deal extensively with management problems encountered by the participants within their own specific organisations
Course length: 3-5 days in July/August
Course structure: lectures, workshops and case studies
Award made: certificate of the Amsterdam Maastricht Summer University *Entry requirements:* professionals in the field

Interfaculty for Arts Management
Amsterdam School of the Arts, PO Box 15079,
1001 MB **Amsterdam**
Tel: 20-527 7800
Fax: 20-527 7802
E-Mail: info@cbv.ahk.nl
contact Meine Fernhont
Course content: arts management *Course length:* 3 years
Award made: Diploma

Hoogeschool Holland
Postbus 261, 1110 AG **Diemen**
Tel: 20-495 1539/06 Fax: 20-495 1920
Internet: www.hsholland.nl
E-Mail: a.v.leeuwen@hsholland.nl
director Rudi Snippe
Course content: arts policy and management
Course length: 4 years *Award made:* Degree

Rijksuniversiteit Groningen
Dept. of Art and Arts Management, Oude Boteringestraat 34, PO Box 716, 9700 AS **Groningen**
Tel: 50-363 6101 Fax: 50-363 7362
E-Mail: L.d.m.e.van.heteren@let.rug.nl
contact Drs Lucia van Heteren
Course aims: training in arts management with attention not only to the arts themselves but to their social context as well; also training in analysing cultural policy
Course content: the programme is arts policy and management and a main subject in Dutch literature, musicology, drama or art history; each of the arts subjects contains courses which are specifically aimed at the management content of the art in question
Course length: 3 years *Award made:* 'doctorandus' *Entry requirements:* preparatory studies at the Faculty of Arts or the Faculty of Management

Faculty of Arts and Culture University of Maastricht
Faculteit der Cultuurwetenschappen
Universiteit van Maastricht
Postbus 616, 6200 MD **Maastricht**
Tel: 43-388 3486 Fax: 43-321 0498
Internet: www.Unimaas.nl/~studies
contact M. Doorman (tel:43-388 3475), P. De Bruyne (tel: 43-388 3051), J. de Jong (tel: 43-388 3310); administrative coordinator ESST Erik Eestermans (tel: 43-388 3384, fax: 43-388 4900, email: ESST@facburfdcw.unimaas.nl)
Course aims: the issues being generated by modern culture form the background for the Arts and Sciences Program; the focus of the program is on the analysis of various, often conflicting scientific and non-scientific points of view, with a particular emphasis on the arts; special consideration is given to the historical and social contexts and traditions and concrete social problems *Course content:* the Arts and Sciences Programme: Art Philosophy; Art Policy, Art Production; the Realism Debate in Nineteenth Century Art; Analysis of Literature and the Visual Arts; Avantgarde and Mass Culture; Postmodernism; Visual Culture: image and sciences, new media, scientific cultural research; Social sciences *Course length:* 4 years full time *Course structure:* the Arts and Science program is set up according to the structure prescribed by Dutch law; one year for the foundation course (propedeusefase), which is concluded with an examination, and three years for the degree course (doctoraalfase) with a final examination
Award made: Master's Degree in Culture and Science Studies (Doctorandus in de Cultuur-en Wetenschapsstudies) *Entry requirements:* possession of an acknowledged Dutch pre-university certificate; dispensation of this requirement is possible by a dispensation of the university of Maastricht, in which it is stated that your previous education is equivalent to the acknowledged Dutch pre-university certificate
Comments: visiting address:
Kapoenstraat 2, 6211 KW Maastricht

Hogeschool Voor De Kunsten Utrecht
Centrum foor Kunst & Media Management,
Postbus 1520, 3500 BM **Utrecht**
Tel: 30-233 2256 Fax: 30-233 2096
Internet: www.hku.nl
director Giep Hagoort (email: giep.hagoort@central.hku.nl); postgraduate course leader Paul van Amerom (email: paul.vanamerom@central.hku.nl)
Course aims: to promote management development in cultural organisations for professional workers *Course content:* 3 year full time B.A. Management degree or 1 year postgrad. part time course in Arts and Media Management; seminars & workshops about cultural leadership and learning organisations; international programs about Cultural Entrepreneurship
Course length: varies from workshops to 3 years full time
Comments: a media facilities management course is offered on a contract basis to arts or media management employees
(length depends on discretion of employer)

Utrecht University – Institute for Media and Re-/presentation
Studierichting Algemene Letteren/Studiepad Kunstbeleid en Kunstmanagment, Kromme Nieuwe Gracht 29, 3512 HD **Utrecht**
Tel: 30-253 6519/6339 Fax: 30-253 6167
Internet: www.let.uu.nl/kbm
E-Mail: frans.bosboom@let.uu.nl
contacts Frans Bosboom, Clara Overduin
Course content: areas of specialisation include management of cultural institutions; policy of the media; budgeting, cost calculation, marketing, personnel management and law (copyright, media law); and art/cultural policy, art discipline (including scientific research) and art and society *Course length:* 2 years, including 3-5 months in a cultural organisation
Award made: Master's Degree *Entry requirements:* 2 year's study in related subjects, e.g. musicology, drama studies

NORWAY (+47)

Telemark College – Institute of Cultural Studies
H Eikas Plass, 3800 **Bo i Telemark**
Tel: 3595 2500 (switchboard)/2613 (dept of art and finance)/2716
Fax: 3595 0636/2216 3616/3595 2601
leader of institute of cultural studies Øystean Dalland; contact Tonje Nielsen
Course content: modular units: communication & mass media; public sector management; introduction to Norwegian cultural history; introduction to cultural sociology; cultural politics; theory of science and methodology; economics; history of art and ideas; cultural activities for children and youth; cultural planning, cultural analysis *Course length:* 1-4 years
Course structure: students take modular units (between 6-15 credits each), a minimum of 60 per academic year
Award made: Candidate of Cultural Studies (1-2 years); Magisterial Candidate of Cultural Studies (3-4 years)
Entry requirements: standard qualifications to access University studies

Stavanger College
Department of Social and Cultural Studies,
Postboks 2557 Ullandhaug,
4004 **Stavanger**
Tel: 5183 1000/5183 3015(general information)
Fax: 5183 1050
contact Erik Fossåskaret; general information Anne Selnes
Course aims: training in Cultural Administration *Course content:* 1st year: a study in Art history; subjects for the following 2 years are: administration, economics and organisational skills in different parts of cultural settings *Course length:* 3 years full-time; part-time also possible *Course structure:* periods of one or two terms; full-time students take three or four courses each term, while part-time students take one or two courses

POLAND (+48)

International Cultural Centre
Miedzynarodowe Centrum Kultury
Rynek Glówny 25, 31-008 **Kraków**
Tel: 12-421 8601/7700
Fax: 12-421 8571/7844
Internet: www.mck.krakow.pl
E-Mail: sekret@mck.krakow.pl
Course aims: cultural management mainly for Central & Eastern European participants *Course length:* 2 weeks *Course structure:* 2 parts: theoretical and practical *Comments:* alternative Internet: encc.net; at time of going to print it was unclear whether the course will happen in 2000 as they were applying for funding; contact them for further information

Public Affairs Institute of the Jagiellonian University
Instytut Spraw Publicznych
Uniwersytetu Jagiellonskiego
Department of Culture Management, Rynek Glówny 8, 31-042 **Kraków**
Tel: 12-411 4784
Fax: 12-422 5892
contact Dariusz Jachimovicz
Course aims: education of managers for public affairs sector *Comments:* created in 1997

RUSSIA (+7)

Moscow School of Social and Economic Sciences
Faculty of Cultural Management,
Profsojuznaja 8-2-136, 117292 **Moscow**
Tel: 095-124 5507
Fax: 095-124 5507
Internet: www.msses.co.ru
E-Mail: s.zuev@msses.co.ru
contact Sergey Zuev
Course content: Master of sciences in cultural management *Course length:* 1 year full-time or 2 years part-time *Award made:* 2 types: Russian diploma and British MA *Comments:* also summer courses in cultural management

Russian Academy of Theatre Arts
Producer's Department, M. Kiolovsky 6,
103009 **Moscow**
Tel: 095-290 4833 Fax: 095-290 4833
contact Marina Andreikina;
head of department Uriy Orlov
Course content: theatre management course *Course length:* 5 years *Award made:* Specialist Degree

Institute for Cultural Programmes
Rubinstein Street 8, 191025 **St Petersburg**
Tel: 812-312 9572/219 4044
Fax: 812-312 9572/219 6598
Internet: www.travel.spb.ru
E-Mail: zonin@artchain.spb.ru
director Andrei Zonin
Course aims: improvement for art managers
Course content: requalification for managers of arts institutions *Course length:* 2 months, no Degree

SLOVAKIA (+421)

Many telephone and fax numbers in Slovakia are in the process of being changed. We have included all new numbers known at the time of going to print.

Academy of Music and Dramatic Arts, Theatre Faculty, The
Vysoká skola múzickych umení –
cinoherná a bábkarská fakulta
Department of Directing and Dramaturgy, Ventúrska 3, 813 01 **Bratislava**
Tel: 7-5443 2306/5441 9344 Fax: 7-5443 2579
E-Mail: dvvsmu@ba.sanet.sk
contact Peter Mikulík

Faculty of Arts of the Komensky University – Department of Cultural Studies
Filozofická fakulta Univerzity Komenskeho – Kateda kulturológie
Gondova 2, 818 01 **Bratislava** 1
Tel: 7-5292 0219/5933 9357 Fax: 7-5296 6016
E-Mail: kkul@fphil.uniba.sk
contact Katarína Podoláková

Faculty of Arts of the Philosopher-Konstantin University – Culture and Travel-Industry Management
Filozofická fakulta Univerzity Konstantína Filozofa – Manazment kultúry a turizmu
Stefánikova 67, 949 74 **Nitra**
Tel: 87-775 4213/111 Fax: 87-512 570
contact Dr. Jaroslav Cukan

SPAIN (+34)

Centre of Studies and Cultural Resources
CERC Centre d'Estudis i Recursos Culturals
Carrer de Montalegre 7, 08001 **Barcelona**
Tel: 93-402 2565
Fax: 93-402 2577
E-Mail: mirallesve@diba.es
director Eduard Miralles;
director of MA studies Luis Bonet
Course content: 1. Diploma in management and cultural policy; 2. MA in cultural management; 3. MA in projects of international cultural cooperation
Course length: Diploma: 1 year; MA: 2 years
Award made: Diploma and MA

Escola Superior d'Administració y Direcció d'Empreses (ESADE)
c/o Centro del Desarrollo Directivo,
Avda de Esplugas 92-96,
08034 **Barcelona**
Tel: 93-280 4008
Fax: 93-495 2067
Internet: www.esade.es/cdd
E-Mail: cdd@esade.es
administration & information Laura Nualart
Course aims: the course is designed for people working in managing and administration of any kind of artistic or cultural organisation; the programme was designed by ESADE in collaboration with Wagner School of Public Service, University of New York; the course for managers of arts institutions culture & leisure (Managing the Arts Enterprise) has been adapted to the European reality *Course content:* the programme is structured in three units: conceptual presentations, practical examples and managing simulations: Northwood Arts Center *Course length:* 40h/1 week, from 21-25 February 2000 *Course structure:* 3 different areas of study: conceptual, practical, and managing simulation *Award made:* Degree of Business Administration, Master in Business Administration *Entry requirements:* experience in this area of management, having had a responsable management position, being able to take important managerial decisions; course at professional managing level *Comments:* gives courses about enterprises management, business, economy etc; founder member of the Community of European Management School (CEMS); contact: Centro de Desarrollo Directivo, Laura Nvaulart, Tel: 93-280 4008, Fax: 93-204 8105; second address: Esade, Auda Pedralbes 60-62, 08034 Barcelona

Universidad de Barcelona, Departamento de Economía Política, Hacienda Pública y Derecho Financiero y Tributario
Pati Manning, c/ Montalegre 7, 08001 **Barcelona**
Tel: 93-402 2569
Fax: 93-402 2577
Internet: www.ub.es/cultural/GChome.htm
E-Mail: cultura@eco.ub.es
director Lluís Bonet; coordinador académico Albert de Gregorio; secretaria Muntsa Quintillas
Course aims: to provide management training and development support to arts practitioners and managers; also aimed at graduate students wishing to start a career in administration, staff management in the cultural industries sector *Course content:* management training course divided in three: introduction to cultural administration, policies of cultural administration, plus a three month exchange in another European country *Course length:* two years, part-time *Award made:* Master in Cultural Administration; 40 credits
Entry requirements: admission by CV and interview

Universidad de Barcelona, Departamento de Economía Política, Hacienda Pública y Derecho Financiero y Tributario
Pati Manning, c/ Montalegre 7,
08001 **Barcelona**
Tel: 93-402 2569
Fax: 93-402 2577
Internet: www.ub.es/cultural/GChome.htm
E-Mail: cultura@eco.ub.es
director Lluís Bonet; coordinador académico Xavier Santajuliana; secretaria Muntsa Quintillas
Course aims: exchange knowledge and skills in the areas of design and implamentation of cooperation projects for cultural development; generate effective programmes of cultural cooperation between Spanish speaking countries *Course content:* five weeks, full-time, in Spain, plus three months developing a personal project of cultural cooperation *Course length:* one year, full-time *Award made:* MA in Cultural Cooperation with Spanish Speaking Countries; 20 credits
Entry requirements: graduates and professionals working in cultural cooperation with a degree equivalent to a Spanish degree

Universidad de Barcelona, Departamento de Economía Política, Hacienda Pública y Derecho Financiero y Tributario
Pati Manning, c/ Montealegre 7, 08001 **Barcelona**
Tel: 93-402 2569
Fax: 93-402 2577
Internet: www.ub.es/cultural/GChome.htm
E-Mail: cultura@eco.ub.es
director Lluís Bonet;
coordinador académico David Rosello;
secretaria Munisa Quintillas
Course aims: to create a stable area of exchange and training for arts practitioners both in the public and private sectors *Course content:* cultural management: five weeks full-time (throughout the year), one week being spent in Strasbourg
Course length: one year, part-time *Award made:* Diploma in Management and Cultural Policies
Entry requirements: graduate or undergraduate students with proven managierial experience

Universidad de Deusto
Institute of Leisure Studies, 48080 **Bilbao**
Tel: 94-413 9075
Fax: 94-413 9089
Internet: www.deusto.es
E-Mail: agoytia@ocio.deusto.es
contact Roberto San Salvador del Valle, Ana Goytia Prat
Course content: MPhil in Leisure Management; MA programme in European Leisure Studies: culture, tourism and sport; PhD Leisure and Human Potential
Course length: MA 1 year full-time; PhD 2 years research, full-time; also summer courses in leisure management

Universidad Complutense de Madrid, Instituto Complutense de Ciencias Musicales (ICCMU)
c/ Fernando VI, 4, 28004 **Madrid**
Tel: 91-319 2710
Fax: 91-349 9710
E-Mail: nfoseca@sgae.es
sub-director Fátima Anllo; coordinator Nereida Fonseca
Course aims: to give a theoretical but practical grounding in skills relevant to cultural research and management *Course content:* 4 different areas: cultural socio-econonmy; cultural politics; managing of cultural institutions; author's rights, copyright and intellectual property *Course length:* 2 year part-time
Course structure: 45hours (45 credits) theoretical and practical units; 16 hours (16 credits) placements in cultural institutions; 7 hours (7 credits) optional units; 5 hours (5 credits) final project
Award made: Masters in Cultural Management; Music, Theatre & Dance *Entry requirements:* university graduate or equivalent qualifications; also exceptionally they admit people with enough experience in management without a university degree *Comments:* supporting institutions: Universidad Complutense de Madrid, Ministerio de Educacion y Cultura, Sociedad General de Autores Y Editores, Comunidad Autonoma de Madrid; next course will be from 1999-2001; application deadline: 9 July, yearly; fees: US$4000

University of Deusto – San Sebastián
Faculty of Philosophy and Literature,
Mundaiz 50 Apdo. 1359,
20080 **San Sebastián – Donosti**
Tel: 943-273 100 ext 287 Fax: 943-292 635
director of postgraduate course in cultural resources Margarita Otaegi
Course content: postgraduate degree in cultural resources management *Course length:* 1 year

Xabide, Cultural Management and Communication
Xabide, Gestión Cultural y Comunicación
Mondragón 11, 01013 **Vitoria-Gasteiz**
Tel: 945-253 500 Fax: 945-253 874
E-Mail: xabide@jet.es
contact Roberto Gómez de la Iglesia
Course content: 1. forum of cultural management, seminars; 2. course on cultural organisation and companies *Course length:* 1. 88 hrs; 2. 100 hrs *Award made:* Diploma

SWEDEN (+46)

Gothenburg University – Division for Cultural Studies
Box 200, 405 30 **Göteborg**
Tel: 31-773 1000 (switchboard)4135/4134/4566 (cultural science) Fax: 31-773 4140
contact Eva Lilja

University of Uppsala
Trädgardsgatan 14, 753 29 **Uppsala**
Tel: 18-471 2500 (switchboard)/2291/2292 (cultural studies dept) Fax: 18-471 2305 (cultural studies)
Internet: www.babks.uu.se
E-Mail: gorel.tunerlov@babks.uu.se
head of cultural studies Lars-Olof Ahlberg
Course aims: to train professionals to work in cultural administration and arts management *Course content:* cultural sociology; cultural policy; cultural theory *Course length:* 2 years and 1-2 years in a different department
Course structure: four semesters full-time, after this the students complement their education in another department of their choice

Award made: Bachelor of Arts (2 year +1); Master of Arts (2 years +2) *Entry requirements:* average University entry requirements *Comments:* tuition in Swedish language; alternative E-mail: lars-olof.ahlberg@kultvet.uu.se

UNITED KINGDOM (+44)

University of Sussex, Centre for Continuing Education, Education Development Building
Falmer, **Brighton** BN1 9RG
Tel: 1273-678 566 Fax: 1273-678 848
E-Mail: j.summerton@sussex.ac.uk
contact Janet Summerton
Course aims: 1) for people working in the arts who wish to develop their expertise & appraise current principles & practises of arts management; 2) develops a range of skills, knowledge & practical experiences for people currently working in the arts *Course content:* 1) mapping the field, critical studies of practice, new directions in arts management; 2) principles of arts management, arts management in practice, arts management: specialist options *Course length:* 1) post-graduate Diploma in Arts & Cultural Management: 1 year, part-time; 2) Certificate in Arts & Cultural Management: 1 year, part-time *Award made:* 1) Postgraduate Diploma in Arts & Cultural Management; 2) Certificate in Arts & Cultural Management *Entry requirements:* 1) normally a 1st degree & relevant experience; 2) some relevant experience

Anglia Polytechnic University
Anglian Business School, East Road,
Cambridge CB1 1PT
Tel: 1223-363 271 Fax: 1223-352 900
E-Mail: b.mornin@anglia.ac.uk
contact Barbara Mornin (ext: 2366)
Course aims: to equip students with the specialist business skills needed for a career in arts managment; class based tuition provides a toolbox of management techniques to help them understand the key issues facing arts managers today *Course content:* Core modules: The Arts Environment, Marketing Management, Managing Finance in the Arts, Working with Information, Managing People & Relationships at Work, Audience Development, Business Planning & Finance and Strategy in the Arts; two options may be chosen from Access, Equality & the Arts, Creative Managment, Cultural Tourism, Education & Arts Development, Legal Issues in the Arts, Youth Arts Strategy & Delivery or a foreign language; for the Masters stage students may either complete a 60 credit dissertation, or a 30 credit dissertation plus a 30 credit Work Based Learning module *Course length:* 1 year full-time including a work placement period, or two years part-time; the part-time route has a realistic work load for busy managers
Award made: MA in Art Administration *Entry requirements:* either a degree with classification of 2ii or above, or a qualification recognised as equivalent; mature candidates will be considered on the basis of previous experience and personal ability

Cambridge Marketing College & Arts Marketing Association
St John's Innovation Centre, Cowley Road,
Cambridge CB4 0WS
Tel: 1223-421 903 Fax: 1223-421 767
E-Mail: arts@marketincollege.com
course director Kieran Cooper
Course aims: specifically for the Arts Marketing industry; to equip people with practical marketing tools whilst setting those skills within a theoretical framework
Course content: the course will include the elements of the CIM Advanced Certificate in Marketing *Course length:* 6 weekends *Course structure:* will be delivered through intensive weekend sessions, a structured reading programme and work-related assignments
Award made: Diploma in Arts Marketing
Comments: it is planned that, after a pilot period, successful students on the Diploma in Arts Marketing will have their qualification accredited by the CIM to Advanced Certificate Level

Welsh College of Music and Drama
Castle Grounds, Cathays Park, **Cardiff (Wales)** CF10 3ER
Tel: 29-2034 2854 Fax: 29-2023 7639
E-Mail: AllenGL@wcmd.ac.uk
contact Gemma Allen (tel: 29-2037 1440); course leader/course set-up Aidan Plender (tel: 29-2056 4569); course set-up Cathi Marcus (tel: 29-2075 1111); head of marketing Mandy Wix
Course length: full-time for one year or part-time for two years *Course structure:* includes a placement at a professional arts organisation anywhere in the UK *Award made:* Advanced Diploma in Arts Management *Entry requirements:* open to anyone who has experience of, or enthusiasm for, arts events

Centre for Cultural Policy Studies
School of Theatre Studies, University of Warwick,
Coventry CV4 7AL
Tel: 24-7652 3020/7652 4399
Fax: 24-7652 4446/7652 06188
Internet: www.warwick.ac.uk/fac/arts/Theatre_S/cp
E-Mail: o.bennett@warwick.ac.uk
course director Oliver Bennett
Course aims: critical perspective on cultural policy in the public, private and voluntary sectors within selected European countries; skills associated with the practice of cultural administration in a European context *Course content:* core courses: Cultural Theory, Cultural Policy, Cultural Industries; Option courses: Administrative Studies and Comparative Studies *Course length:* 1 year full-time, two years part-time *Course structure:* autumn and spring terms: full-time students attend lectures and seminars two days a week, part-time students one day a week *Award made:* MA in European Cultural Policy and Administration *Entry requirements:* 1. second class honours degree or equivalent qualification; 2. fluency in English in reading, writing, speaking and listening, up to the level of the British Council Test of English or Cambridge Certificate *Comments:* examination by continuous assessment

Durham University Business School
Mill Hill Lane, **Durham** DH1 3LB
Tel: 191-374 2230 Fax: 191-374 1281
Internet: www.dur.ac.uk/dubs/index.html
E-Mail: mso.dubs@durham.ac.uk
Comments: please contact directly for further information

USCA – Unit for the Study of Cultural Administration
University of Edinburgh, Holyrood Road, **Edinburgh (Scotland)** EH8 8AQ
Tel: 131-651 6506 Fax: 131-651 6505
Internet: www.ed.ac.uk
E-Mail: usca@ed.ac.uk
chairman Brian Martin
Course content: management of cultural services *Course length:* 1 year full-time *Award made:* MA

De Montfort University- Department of Media and Cultural Productions: MA in European Cultural Planning
Faculty of Humanities and Social Sciences, The Gateway, **Leicester** LE1 9BH
Tel: 116-257 7391
Fax: 116-250 6130
Internet: www.dmu.ac.uk
E-Mail: lrandall@dmu.ac.uk
programme leader for MA Dr Franco Bianchini; programme administrator Lynda Randall
(tel: 116-250 6470)
Course aims: to enable students to: develop a critical understanding of cultural resources and cultural policy and planning in different European countries; learn about leading edge thinking and best practice in cultural planning strategies in Europe; plan the stragegic use of cultural resources in public policy-making; develop the European dimension of work; improve research skills; explore the possibilities of new initiatives and collaborations *Course content:* students will study six subjects – Cultural Policy and Planning, Cultural Theory, European Identities, Planning for Development in Europe, Political Framework and Language study (French, German or Spanish); these six subjects will be studied primarily in relation to France, Germany, Italy, Spain and the UK *Course length:* MA 2 years part-time distance learning *Course structure:* the course is structured so that students attend three block weeks in each of the two years of study (6 in total); these block weeks normally take place in Leicester, but may also be in other European countries *Award made:* MA in European Cultural Planning; if students successfully complete Year One of the course, but do not proceed to Year Two, they may be awarded a Postgraduate Diploma in European Cultural Planning *Entry requirements:* a Second Class Honours Degree or qualification of equivalent standing in a relevant subject; fluency in English; a profile of language learning experience which demonstrates the potential to make progress in French, German or Spanish *Comments:* fees: £1400 per year for EU students, £2800 non-EU students

De Montfort University, Faculty of Humanities and Social Sciences
Arts Management, Crown Building,
Newarke Street, **Leicester** LE1 9BH
Tel: 116-250 6131
Fax: 116-250 6188
Internet: www.dmu.ac.uk
E-Mail: ccm@dmu.ac.uk
subject leader Christopher Maughan
Course aims: provides opportunity for personal development and increased prospects for a successful career in the cultural sector in Europe *Course content:* the degree offers over 20 modules in cultural theory, finance, law, marketing and people management as well as providing students with several opportunities for applying theory and demonstrating their skills in work placements and practical projects *Course length:* 3 years full-time, 6 years part-time *Course structure:* this course is vocational and provides a comprehensive introduction to both the conceptual and practical nature of the subject from a pan European perspective; the modular nature of the degree means that students can include modules from other subject areas such as Performing Arts, Media Studies, History of Art & Design alongside those selected from Arts Management *Award made:* BA Honours in Arts Management
Entry requirements: for those offering UK qualifications, the standard requirements are 2-3 A levels (16 points or better), or BTEC ND or HND; for those offering other qualifications an equivalent standard is required; for applicants over 21 the requirements may be varied following discussion between the applicant and the course team *Comments:* considerable emphasis is placed upon the understanding and awareness which students develop of the role and nature of artistic and cultural activity in a social context; it is this that distinguishes this degree from mainstream business or management studies

Liverpool Institute for Performing Arts (LIPA), The
Mount Street, **Liverpool** L1 9HF
Tel: 151-330 3000
Fax: 151-330 3131
Internet: ww.lipa.ac.uk
E-Mail: reception@lipa.ac.uk
Course content: route specialism, Enterprise Management, core modules which support route studies whilst being involved in interdisciplinary work *Course length:* 3 years – full time *Award made:* BA Honours Degree – Performing Arts (Enterprise Management) *Entry requirements:* completion of LIPA application form, audition/interview

Positive Solutions
6 Bluecoat Chambers, School Lane, **Liverpool** L1 3BX
Tel: 151-709 6511
Fax: 151-709 2575
Internet: www.powerup.com.au/~positive
E-Mail: david@positive.demon.co.uk
contact David Fishel, Cathy Hunt
Course aims: to develop professional management expertise within the arts cultural industries
Course content: short courses in management and leadership skills, customer care, fundraising and other areas *Course length:* 2-10 days *Course structure:* lectures, demonstrations, practical involvement including simulation, role-playing and management games in order to reinforce the techniques and skills being delivered through the training programme
Award made: no specific certification currently offered
Entry requirements: some courses are aimed at people newly arrived in arts administration; others are aimed at those with many years experience who wish to fill in the gaps in their expertise; all courses are currently provided on an in-service basis for existing arts employees *Comments:* Australian contact details: Tel: +61 7-3358 1077, E-mail: positive@powerup.com.au; see also Services

University of Liverpool – Arts Training North West
2 Abercromby Square, **Liverpool** L69 3BX
Tel: 151-794 2918
Fax: 151-794 2909
E-Mail: vfry@liv.ac.uk
administrator Valerie Fry; coordinator Christina Christou (email: christou@liv.ac.uk)
Course aims: to provide management training and staff development support to arts practitioners and arts organisations *Course content:* people management, finance marketing and legal issues, fundraising, media relations, board development *Course length:* individual and short courses *Course structure:* training sessions, briefings, inhouse training programme, advice & consultancy services *Entry requirements:* the courses are aimed at those involved in the promotion and management of arts activities

City University – Department of Arts Policy and Management
Level 7, Frobisher Crescent, Barbican,
London EC2Y 8HB
Tel: 20-7477 8751/3
Fax: 20-7477 8887
Internet: www.city.ac.uk
E-Mail: m.dines@city.ac.uk
Post Graduate Diploma in Cultural Management Alison Meyric Hughes; M.A. in Arts Management Ana Gaio; M.A in Museum and Gallery Management Prof. Patrick Boylan; M.A. in Arts Criticism and M.A. in Arts Criticism & Managment Dr. Juliet Steyn
Course aims: to promote professional arts management training and education for administrators in the arts and entertainment, educationalists in the arts, gallery/museum curators, artists and other arts related professionals *Course content:* Diploma Course is vocational; subjects covered include finance, law, management, marketing, policy in the arts, and education and the arts *Course length:* MA: 1 year full time, 2 years part time, 4 years modular; PGDip: 1 yr full time, 2 years part-time *Course structure:* PGDiploma: teaching methods include lectures, seminars, tutorials, projects, reading and private study; independent and directed field trips; a one-term internship (secondment) and long study; MA: modular structure, students take four separate one-term modules; assessment is made via essays, exams and long study (15000 words) *Award made:* MA in Arts Management; Museum & Gallery Management; Art Criticism: Post Graduate Diploma in Cultural Management, MA in Arts Criticism and Management (and Post Graduate Diploma and Certificate for those who opt not to complete a long study)

Entry requirements: post graduate: a good first degree, work experience within the arts (although exceptional work experience can substitute for more formal requirements) and for mature students work experience in comparable fields will be considered; students whose mother tongue is not English must have IELTS score 7, and TEOFL score 600 *Comments:* alternative E-mail: u.k.richards@city.ac.uk

Directory of Social Change
24 Stephenson Way, **London** NW1 2DP
Tel: 20-7209 4949
Fax: 20-7209 4130
director Mr Eastwood;
head of events & training Meena Varma;
marketing manager Sam Evans
Course content: wide range of short courses concerned with fund-raising, training, marketing, financial management, public relations etc. especially for smaller organisations *Course length:* courses and seminars lasting 1-2 days *Entry requirements:* those involved in the management and administration of voluntary organisations and charities including the arts *Comments:* contact training department for further information

Independent Theatre Council
12, The Leathermarket,
Weston Street, **London** SE1 3ER
Tel: 20-7403 6698
Fax: 20-7403 1745
Internet: www.itc-arts.org
E-Mail: training@itc-arts.org
director Nicola Thorold; training manager Will Forrest; training administrator Craig Burman
Course aims: to train performing arts companies and venues in management and administration skills
Course content: ITC runs a series of training programmes in all aspects of performing arts management, including starting a performing arts company, booking a tour and touring abroad *Course length:* half day seminars; one and two day courses
Entry requirements: the course is intended for small and middle-scale performing arts companies and venues
Comments: all enquiries to the training department at the above address

Interchange Training
Dalby Street, **London** NW5 3NQ
Tel: 20-7284 0530 Fax: 20-7813 7493
Internet: www.interchange.org.uk/training
training manager Tim Martin;
training officer Rose Blackmore
Course aims: to train those who work or are involved in the arts and voluntary sectors in all aspects of management and in self-development and communication skills; courses are delivered at InterChange or can be tailor-made to be delivered in-house *Course content:* mixture of presentations and participative exercises in management, marketing, finance and fundraising, legal responsibilities, training the trainer and staff development, project management, IT training *Course length:* courses last 1 or 2 days, or flexible for in-house courses *Award made:* none but can provide certificates of attendance and written materials which will contribute to a participant's own record of achievement *Entry requirements:* open to all; participants are advised to contact their local Regional Arts Board for assistance with course fees: 50% discount for all groups funded by London Arts Board and London Borough Grants

Management Centre, The
366 Kennington Road, **London** SE11 4DB
Tel: 20-7820 1100 Fax: 20-7820 3828
Internet: www.managementcentre.co.uk
E-Mail: tmc@managementcentre.co.uk
directors Bernard Ross, Clare Segal
Course aims: to train senior and middle management in arts organisations in management, sponsorship and fund-raising skills; courses geared towards practical application *Course length:* ranges from 2-3 days short course training to a week long course at the National Arts Fundraising School *Course structure:* lectures, workshops, tutor input, practical exercises, case studies; open programmes and in-house training *Entry requirements:* courses are aimed at senior and middle management in arts organisations and administration *Comments:* courses include The Leadership Edge, Business Planning, Managing Multiple Priorities, Presentation Skills, Influencing and Negotiating for Results, Project Management, The Excellence Programme, The Internal Consultants Programme, Breakthrough Thinking, The National Arts Fundraising School, Fundraising, Sponsorship; all programmes are also available in-house

National Arts Fundraising School, The
The Management Centre, 366 Kennington Road, **London** SE11 4DB
Tel: 20-7820 1100
Fax: 20-7820 3828
Internet: www.managementcentre.com
E-Mail: tmc@managementcentre.co.uk
director Management Centre Clare Segal; school director Bernard Ross; joint director Mark Butcher
Course aims: improve strategies of arts fundraising, understand the sources and help develop practical solutions *Course content:* strategy tools, research of sources, legal structure, local authorities, national lottery, promotional material improvement, tax breaks, proposal writing, etc. *Course length:* one week, twice a year *Course structure:* 16 modules *Entry requirements:* to be working in a cultural industry

Roehampton Institute London
Enquiries Office, Whitelands College,
West Hill, **London** SW15 3SN
Tel: 20-8392 3232 Fax: 20-8392 3470
Internet: www.roehampton.ac.uk
E-Mail: h.j.evans@roehampton.ac.uk
programme convener, Diploma in Arts Management Pauline Barrie
Course aims: to teach students the different aspects and methodologies of arts administration and managment; provide detailed study of arts policy, mechanisms of funding and to manage an arts organisation professionally *Course content:* law, finance, book-keeping, marketing, administration, plus a dissertation *Course length:* 1 year – 2 hour sessions 2 evenings a week *Award made:* Diploma in Arts Management *Entry requirements:* first degree or equivalent – exemptions are made to those already working in arts management or who have had experience of voluntary arts activities

Dartington College of Arts
Arts Management Department, **Totnes** TQ9 6EJ
Tel: 1803-861 638 Fax: 1803-866 053
Internet: www.dartington.ac.uk
E-Mail: s.kay@dartington.ac.uk
director of arts management dept Sue Kay
Course length: BA: 3 years full-time; MA: 1 year full-time; PhD: 3 years
Award made: BA in arts management; MA in arts management; PhD research degree in arts management

YUGOSLAVIA (+381)

Due to the war in Kosovo we have been unable to update the following entries for Yugoslavia

Faculty of Drama Arts – Cultural Management Department
Bulevar umetnosti 20, 11070 **Belgrade**
Tel: 11-135 684/687 458 Fax: 11-130 862/688 362
Internet: www.fdu.bg.ac.yu
E-Mail: msesic@opennet.org
contact Milena Dragicevic-Sesic

Products and Services

Products and Services
The following is a list ordered alphabetically by company name of products and services useful to those who work in the performing arts. It is preceded/followed by an index of categories included, together with the names of companies offering the products and services in that category.

In some cases companies with offices outside Europe are listed. These are included because they are known to work in Europe. When the organisation name is that of an individual (e.g. Frank Smith Publicity) the ordering is done by christian name. When the company name is, for example, P.R. Frank Smith, the indexing is done on the first word.

Produits et Services
Cette rubrique englobe des services (classés par ordre alphabétique suivant les noms des sociétés) utiles à ceux qui travaillent dans le monde des Arts Vivants. Elle est précédée par un index des catégories, qui répertorie les noms des sociétés.

Dans certains cas, des sociétés basées hors de l'Europe figurent ici parce qu'elles travaillent en Europe. Lorsque le nom d'une société est celui d'une personne (ex: Frank Smith), le prénom figure en premier. Lorsque le nom de la société est par exemple PR Frank Smith, l'initiale du mot figure en premier.

Produkte und Dienstleistungen
Es folgt eine Liste, alphabetisch nach Firmennamen gelistet, von Produkten und Dienstleistungen, die allen Benutzern des PAYE nützlich sein soll. Am Anfang befindet sich ein Index der verschiedenen Kategorien und der verzeichneten Firmen.

Einige Firmen mit Hauptgeschäftstelle außerhalb Europas sind verzeichnet, da sie in Europa arbeiten. Firmen, die nach Eigennamen benannt sind, werden im Index unter dem Vornamen zu finden zu sein. Daß heißt, P.R. Frank Smith, zum Beispiel, ist unter F zu finden.

Prodotti e Servizi
Quello che segue é un elenco, ordinato alfabeticamente per nome di societá, di prodotti e servizi utili agli operatori del settore artistico. É preceduto/seguito da un indice di categorie, insieme ai nomi delle societá che offrono i prodotti ed i servizi appartenenti a ciascuna categoria.

In alcuni casi sono presenti aziende con uffici al di fuori dell'Europa, ma che lavorano comunque in Europa. Quando il nome della societá é quello di una persona (es. Frank Smith) l'elencazione viene fatta secondo il nome di battesimo. Quando invece il nome é, per esempio, P.R. Frank Smith, l'elencazione viene fatta secondo l'iniziale della prima parola.

Productos y Servicios
La que sigue es una lista que ordena alfabeticamente los nombres de las compañías de productos y servicios, muy útil para aquellos que trabajan en el campo de las artes escénicas. Esta precedida por un índice de las categorias incluidas, junto con los nombres de las compañías que ofrecen productos y servicios en dicha categoría.

En algunas ocasiones se han incluido aquellas compañías establecidas en el extranjero pero que trabajan y mantienen relaciones con Europa. Cuando la denominación de una compañía está bajo un nombre propio (por ejemplo Frank Smith), se sigue el orden alfabético del nombre de pila. Si el nombre de la compañía fuera P R Frank Smith la clasificación se haría de acuerdo con el primer vocablo.

Products and Service (**상품 및 서비스**)
공연 예술 관계인들에게 유용한 상품 및 서비스를 제공하는 회사들의 이름이 알파벳순으로 기재되었다. 카테고리 목록이 그 카테고리에서의 상품 및 서비스를 제공하는 회사명과 함께 리스트의 처음이나/마지막에 기재되어 있다. 어떤 경우에는 유럽 외의 지역에 사무실을 가진 회사들이 기재되었다. 이들은 유럽에서 비지니스를 하는 것으로 알려져 있기 때문에 포함되었다. **조직명칭이 개인의 이름일 경우** (**예**: Frank Smith Publicity), **이름** (christian name)**에 따른 순서로 기재되었다. 회사명칭이 예를 들어** P.R. Frank Smith**일 경우는, 첫 단어에 따른 순서로 기재되었다.**

产品和服务
下列是按字母顺序排列的对表演艺术行业的人士有用的产品和服务的公司名称的名录。它的前后是一个类别索引，还有在该类别中提供产品和服务的公司的名称。在某些情况下，也列入了在欧洲以外设有办事处的公司。这是因为这些公司据知在欧洲有艺术活动。**当机构是以个人姓名命名时（如Frank Smith Publicity），顺序是以名来排列的。假如公司为P.R. Frank Smith这样的名称，则索引是按第一个字排列的.**

製品とサービス
ここでは、舞台芸術の領域に関わる人々に役立つと思われる製品とサービスを提供している会社の名前がアルファベット順に記載されています。ここにはまた、含まれるカテゴリーの索引、それぞれのカテゴリーにおいて製品とサービスを提供している会社名が掲載されています。会社の住所がヨーロッパ以外になっている場合がありますが、これらの会社はヨーロッパで業務を提供していることが知られているためリストに含みました。組織名が個人名である場合（例：Frank Smith Publicity）は、姓ではなく名（SではなくF）で探して下さい。**例えば、P.R.Frank Smithのような場合は最初に来る文字で探します。**

CATEGORY LISTINGS

Acoustic Shells (see Moveable Theatre and Show Tents, and Acoustic Shells)

Acousticians (and see Architects, Project Management and Theatre Consultants)
Acoustic Consultants Ltd, Bristol
Acoustic Dimensions, Coventry
Applied Acoustic Design, Staines
Artec Consultants Inc, New York
Arup Acoustics, London
Arup Acoustics, Winchester
Arup Acoustics, Cambridge
Arup Associates, London
Autograph Sound Recording Ltd, London
BDP Acoustics Ltd, Manchester
Charles M Salter Associates Inc, San Francisco
Commins Acoustics Workshop, Paris
Fleming & Barron, London
GRM (groupes de recherches musicales), Paris
Jaffe Holden Scarbrough Acoustics Inc, Norwalk
Ken Dibble Acoustics, Rugby
Kirkegaard & Associates, Chicago
Klepper Marshall King Associates Ltd, Chappaqua
Müller-BBM GmbH, Planegg
New Acoustics, Clydebank
Oscar Faber Acoustics, St Albans
Peter George Associates Inc., New York
Purcell & Noppe + Assocs. Inc., Chatworth
RG Jones Sound Engineering, London
Sandy Brown Associates, London
SONING, Praha
Sound Design Ltd, Bracknell
Talaske Group, Inc., Oak Park
Tim Smith Acoustics, Bristol
XU - acoustique, Paris

Accounting and Tax Services (and see Computerized Management Systems)
Abaco S.L. Servicios Escénicos, Pozuelo de Alarcón (Madrid)
Baker Tilly, London
BDO Stoy Hayward, London
Bittiner, Whitehouse & Cie SA, Genève
Buzzacott, London
Conroy Tobin, London
CR Thomas & Co, London
Deloitte & Touche - Entertainment, Hospitality and Leisure Division, London
Entertainment Accounting International, London
Ernst & Young, London
Ernst & Young Paris - France, Paris
FR Dixon & Co, London
Gelfand, Rennert, Feldman & Brown, London
Godfrey Allan, London
HW Fisher & Company, London
Ivan Sopher and Co, Borehamwood
KPMG, London
KPMG Belgium, Brussels
KPMG Fidal Peat International, Paris La Défence
KPMG Meijbourg & Co, Amsterdam
Lubbock Fine, London
Martin Greene Ravden, London
Richard Laurence & Rossiter, London
Sedley Richard Laurence Voulters, London

Accounting Systems (see Computerized Management Systems)

Architects, Project Management and Theatre Consultants
ACT Consultant Services, Cambridge
All Clear Designs Limited, London
Arts Team @ RHWL, London
Arup Associates, London
Ash Sakula Architects, London
BDP Acoustics Ltd, Manchester
Beneke, Daberto und Partner, Sehnde
Blonski Heard Architects, London
Buro Happold, Bath
Burrell-Foley-Fischer, London
Carr & Angier, Bath
Charles Cosler Theatre Design, Inc., New York
Fleming & Barron, London
Gerling Arendt und Partner, Berlin
John Wyckham Associates, Shaftesbury
Ken Dibble Acoustics, Rugby
Law & Dunbar-Nasmith Architects, Edinburgh (Scotland)
Leonard Greenwood, Guildford
Levitt Bernstein Assocs - architects/landscape architects, London
Michael Holden Associates, London
Michael Hopkins & Partners, London
Next Stage, Southampton
Onno Greiner Martien van Goor Architekten bv, Amsterdam
Peter George Associates Inc., New York
Philips Projects Centre, Eindhoven
Renton Howard Wood Levin Partnership, London
Sandy Brown Associates, London
Technical Insight Ltd, London
Technical Planning International, Kingston upon Thames
Theatre Projects Consultants Ltd, London
Tim Foster Architects, London
Tim Ronalds Architects, London
Whitfield Partners - Architects, London

Audio and Video Services and Equipment
Autograph Sound Recording Ltd, London
Bose GmbH, Friedrichsdorf
Canford Audio PLC, Washington
Charles M Salter Associates Inc, San Francisco
Citronic Ltd, Melksham
Cloud Electronics Ltd, Sheffield
Coemar Spa, Castel Goffredo (MN)
CTL (Control Technology) Ltd, Aylesford
Event Audio Visual Group Inc, Milford
Formula Sound Ltd, Stockport
Harrison, Berkhamsted
Ken Dibble Acoustics, Rugby
Kirkegaard & Associates, Chicago
MUSICOM srl - Strumenti per comunicare, Milano
New Acoustics, Clydebank
NJD Electronics (NJD Ltd), Nottingham
Northern Light, Edinburgh (Scotland)
Northern Lights, Lancaster
RG Jones Sound Engineering, London
SHOWTEC Beleuchtungs-und Beschallungs GmBH, Köln
Shuttlesound Ltd, Mitcham
SIAP Ltd. (System for Improved Acoustic Performance), London
Stage Electrics, Bristol
SYRINX, Hamburg
Talaske Group, Inc., Oak Park
Technical Planning International, Kingston upon Thames
TeleStage Associates Ltd, Bury St Edmunds
TP Sound Services, Elstree
TSE AG, Berlin
Video-Communication France - VCF, Saint Cloud

Box Office Systems (see Computerized Management Systems)

Box Office Tickets (see Ticketing)

Computerized Management Systems (for Accounting, Box Office, Information, Marketing and Ticketing Systems)
Accademia Musicale Italiana - AMIT, Roma
Advantix, Newport Beach
APT Solutions, London
Artifax Software Ltd, Epsom
BOCS (Box Office Computer System), London
Cambridge Software Products, Inc., Cambridge
Cinema Computer Systems, Erkrath
CTS Computer Ticket Service, München
DPS-Datenverarbeitung & Planung Steuerung GmbH, Neckarsulm
Leoni Daniele SRL, S. Agata (RA)
LVP Reserveringssystemen B.V., Rotterdam
Prologue Systems, Madison
Prompt Data Limited, Hemel Hempstead
RIC Corporation, Fort Wayne
SWH Software GmbH, Berlin
Synchro Systems, Newcastle under Lyme
Ticket.com.Network, De Witt
Ticket.com Systems BV, Amsterdam
Ticket.com Systems Pty, Sydney
Ticket Online Software GmbH, Berlin
Tickets.com Systems GmbH, Berlin
Tickets.com Systems, Inc., Syracuse
Tickets.com Systems Ltd, St Albans
TOR Systems Ltd, Stoke on Trent
WM - Data, Abyhoj
Wölbitsch & Partner KG, Leesten

Computer Software for the Performing Arts
APT Solutions, London
Artifax Software Ltd, Epsom
BOCS (Box Office Computer System), London
DATACULTURE Ltd, Milton Keynes
Galathea Systems, London
IBM UK Ltd, Edinburgh (Scotland)
IEG, Inc, Chicago
Musik-Data GmbH, Langenzersdorf
New Notations London, London
Oniria International SL, Sant Quirze Del Valles (Barcelona)
Prometeo, Parma
RIC Corporation, Fort Wayne
SWH Software GmbH, Berlin
SYRINX, Hamburg
TRIPPE:Beratung/Gesellschaft für betriebswirtschaftliche Strategien und Lösungen, Köln
Virtual Reality, Hitchin
Wölbitsch & Partner KG, Leesten

Consultants
AEA Ltd., London
ArtProfi Centre, Moscow
Arts Consortium, London
Arts Management Consulting, Zürich
ArtServices, Belfast (Northern Ireland)
Audience Business, Edinburgh (Scotland)
Brouhaha International, Liverpool
CAGEC (Centre d'Aide à la Gestion de l'Entreprise Culturelle), Nantes
Christian Henner-Fehr Kulturmanagement, Wien
Christopher Hunt, London
Clive Leyland Consulting Ltd, Bolton
Comedia, Bournes Green - nr Stroud
Euclid, Liverpool
Fitzcarraldo Srl, Torino
Fleischmann Arts, Los Angeles
ICOM (Industrial Common Ownership Movement Ltd), Leeds
IMG Arts Projects, London
Institut für Internationales Kulturmanagement (INK) GmbH, München
Interclassica SA, Vevey
Katerina Novikova, St Petersburg
Kerlin Consulting Pty Ltd, Port Melbourne
Leisure & Arts Research (a division of Travel and Tourism Research Ltd), London
Magerit Musical Foundation, Madrid
Marketing Office (Arts) Limited, London
Marketlink Research, London
McCann Matthews Millman Limited, London
OGACA, Strasbourg
OPERA America, Washington
Pannell Kerr Forster Associates, London
Performance Plus, Glasgow (Scotland)
Price Waterhouse Cooper, London
Ripley-Duggan Partnership, London
Sharon Kivity Arts Consultant, Teddington
Spero Communications Ltd, London
Tom Petzal and Associates, Tunbridge Wells
TRIPPE:Beratung/Gesellschaft für betriebswirtschaftliche Strategien und Lösungen, Köln

Consulting Engineers
Max Fordham & Partners, London
Oscar Faber Acoustics, St Albans

Copyright Service and Research
Carlo Cucchiara SAS. di Giuseppe Cucchiara & C., Enna
Leosong Copyright Service Ltd, London
P.I.N., Zagreb

Cultural Planning Consultants
AEA Ltd., London
Anne Minors Performance Consultants, London
Arts Business Limited (ABL), London
Bureau Menno Heling Cultural Marketing, Amsterdam
Comedia, Bournes Green - nr Stroud
CPF - Cultural Projects Factory, Madrid
Cultural Projects Unlimited, Crawsordjohn (Scotland)
Friedland Group Ltd, London
Gillian Perkins, Cambridge
Hayton Associates, Bradford
Hazel Rennard, Kingston upon Thames
Norma Binnie, Hove
Positive Solutions, Liverpool
ppARTnerships, Brighton
Urban Cultures Limited, London

Event Management (incl Consultants) (and see Computerized Management Systems)
Accademia Musicale Italiana - AMIT, Roma
AKT Productions Ltd, London
Asian Arts Access, Guildford
Bakker & Clients, Amsterdam
Clausecker & Bingel Ereignisse GmbH, Berlin
Edinburgh Festival Fringe, Edinburgh (Scotland)
Elizabeth Anderson Associates, London
Fabtronic Group, Northampton
Hannah Horovitz Associates, London
Hans Werner Lacher - ARTCOM European Art Communication, Bruckmühl
Hazel Rennard, Kingston upon Thames
IMG Arts Projects, London
Kallaway Ltd, London
Kik Veranstaltungsberatung, Weinheim
Kimpton Walker Project Management, London
Konzertkasse Casino, Bern
Lisa Peacock Concert Management, London
Magerit Musical Foundation, Madrid
Martin Randall Travel Ltd, London
Maureen Lunn Management, Hedgerley
MUSICOM srl - Strumenti per comunicare, Milano
Nick Randell Associates, Worcester
Organisation for Arts and Media, London

Pippa Pawlik Public Relations, Pargemon (Var)
Public et Communication, Paris
Public Production Co. Ltd, London
Ripley-Duggan Partnership, London

Floors and Floor Coverings
Harlequin (British Harlequin plc), Tonbridge
Sico Europe Ltd, Ashford

Fundraising and Sponsorship Consultants (and see Computerized Management Systems)
AEA Ltd., London
Andrew de Mille Fundraising Consultants, Cookham
Anthony Fawcett Consultants, London
Arts and Industry Ltd/Sponsorship Consulting Ltd, London
Bakker & Clients, Amsterdam
BDS Sponsorship Ltd, London
Brakeley Europe, London
Bureau Menno Heling Cultural Marketing, Amsterdam
Buzzacott, London
Carole Strachan Associates, Abingdon
Chadwick Jones Associates, London
Craigmyle & Company Limited, Harpenden
Crowcroft & Partners, London
Dr Hochegger Kommunikations GmbH, Wien
Foundation Promethea, Brussels
Friedland Group Ltd, London
Gillian Perkins, Cambridge
Gunilla Axsäter Kultur AB, Djursholm
Identity Creation for Business, Kingston upon Hull
Kathy Battista Consultants, London
Kerlin Consulting Pty Ltd, Port Melbourne
Look and Learn Productions Ltd, London
Maecenata Management GmbH, München
Management Centre, London
PRC Public Relations, Amsterdam
Price Waterhouse Cooper, London
SponsArt s.p.r.l., Brussels
Sponsor Service ASA, Oslo
Stichting voor Kunstpromotie, Brussels
TeleCartaz, Lisboa
The Factary Ltd., Bristol
Van Dishoeck & Jongbloed, Amsterdam
Van Dooren Marketing, Communicatie, Sponsoring, Amsterdam

Insurance Services
Adam Brothers Contingency Ltd, London
AON Entertainment Risk Services Ltd, Iver
Europea Limited, Horsham
Gordon & Co, London
La Playa Limited, Cambridge
Les Amis du Bel Objet, Tours
N W Brown Music Division, Cambridge
Robertson Taylor Insurance Brokers, London
Stafford Knight Entertainment Insurance Brokers, London
Walton & Parkinson Limited Insurance Brokers, London

Legal Services
Abaco S.L. Servicios Escénicos, Pozuelo de Alarcón (Madrid)
Barjon-Société d'Avocats, Paris
Boekel De Nerée, Amsterdam
Boekman Foundation, Amsterdam
Campbell Hooper, London
Caubet Chouchana Meyer, Paris
Clintons, London
Collyer-Bristow, London
Davenport Lyons, London
David Wineman, Solicitors, London
Denander & Grahl AB, Stockholm
Denton Hall, London
Eatons, London
Edmonds Bowen + Company, London
Enrich i Amat Advocats, Barcelona
Ernst & Young Paris - France, Paris
Everfhetf, London
Gentle Jayes, London
Goudsmit & Branbergen, Advocaten, Amsterdam
Hamlins Solicitors, London
Harbottle & Lewis, London
Howell Jones & Partners, London
Irving Spellman & Company, London
Joffre - Société d'Avocats, Paris
Kanaar & Co, London
KPMG Fidal Peat International, Paris La Défence
KPMG Meijbourg & Co, Amsterdam
L'Allemand & Legros, Brussels
Lea & Company, Stockport
Lee & Thompson, London
Lichte & Schramm Rechtsanwälte, Hamburg
Magrath & Co, London
Manches & Co, London
Music Consulting, Planegg
Nabarro Nathanson, London
Nauta Dutilh, Amsterdam
Nicholas Morris - Solicitors, London
Nielsen & Nørger Law Office, Copenhagen
Oppenheimer Wolff & Donnelly, Brussels
P.I.N., Zagreb
Russells, London
Schilling & Lom and Partners, London
Seddons, London
Simkins Partnership, London
Sirkus Management A/S, Oslo
SJ Berwin & Co, London
Studio Legale Mondini & Rusconi, Milano
Studio Legale Pojaghi, Milano
Taylor Joynson Garrett, London
Teacher Stern Selby, Solicitors, London
Thomas et Associés, Paris
Tods Murray WS, Edinburgh (Scotland)
Van der Kroft c.s., Amsterdam

Lighting Designers and Equipment
AC Lighting Limited, High Wycombe
Action Lighting, London
ADB Theatre and TV Lighting, Mühlheim am Main
ADB Theatre and TV Lighting, Montrouge
ADB-TTV Technologies S.A., Zaventem
AJS Theatre Lighting & Stage Supplies Ltd, Ringwood
Arena - Technik, Bremen
ARRI Cine Technik GmbH & Co. KG, München
Avolites Ltd, London
Black Light, Edinburgh (Scotland)
Bühnenbau Schnakenberg GmbH u. Co. KG, Wuppertal
CCT Lighting Ltd, Sutton
CELCO, London
Cerebrum Lighting Ltd, New Malden
Clay Paky S.p.A., Pedrengo (BG)
DeSisti Lighting UK Ltd, Thetford
DESPAR Licht und Bühnentechnik GmbH, Mainz
DEW, Woodford Green
DHA Lighting Ltd., London
Donmar Drama Department, London
Doughty Engineering Ltd, Ringwood
Ecla Lux, Ivry-sur-Seine
Event Audio Visual Group Inc, Milford
Fabtronic Group, Northampton
Flashlight, Utrecht
Freitag Technologies GmbH, Bochum
Gerling Arendt und Partner, Berlin
Glantre Engineering Ltd, Reading
Griven SRL, Castel Goffredo (MN)
Hans Wolff & Partners b.v., Amsterdam
Hardware for Xenon Ltd, Hayes
Hollands Licht, Amsterdam
KOBOLD Licht Beleuchtungstechnik GmbH, Wolfratshausen
Lighting Design Partnership Ltd, London
Lighting Technology Group Ltd, London
LSI Projects - ADB Theatre and TV Lighting, Woking
Ludwig Pani Bühnenbeleuchtung & Projektion, Wien
media arts productions, Zürich
NJD Electronics (NJD Ltd), Nottingham
Northern Light, Edinburgh (Scotland)
Northern Lights, Lancaster
Optikinetics Ltd, Luton
OSRAM GmbH, München
Philips Licht Unternehmensbereich der Philips GmbH, Hamburg
Philips Projects Centre, Eindhoven
Power Light B AG, Aesch (Basel)
Pulsar Light of Cambridge Ltd, Cambridge
Reiche & Vogel B. Deltschaft, Berlin
Roscolab Ltd, London
RVE Technologie, Villemomble
SHOWTEC Beleuchtungs-und Beschallungs GmBH, Köln
Sky-Light, Tremblay-en-France
Societé AVAB Sarl, Saint Denis
Solti snc di Fasano Ermanno & c, Velletri (Roma)
Soundlight, Hannover
Spotlight Srl, San Giuliano Milanese (MI)
Stage Control Ltd., Edgware
starkstrom-elektronik AG, Spreitenbach
Strand Lighting GmbH, Berlin
Strand Lighting Italia srl, Pomezia (RO)
Strand Lighting Ltd, Heston
Sylvania, Tienen
Teatro SRL, Castel Goffredo (MN)
Theatrecraft, Bebington
TMB Associates, Burbank
TMB Associates, Brentford
Transtechnik GmbH, Holzkirchen
Universe Lighting, New York
Vari-Lite Production Services, Greenford
Vmkar Production, Zdár nad Sázavou
White Light (Electrics) Ltd, London

Management and Organisational Consultants
Accademia Musicale Italiana - AMIT, Roma
Armada Production, Chichester
Arts Consortium, London
Asian Arts Access, Guildford
AT Kearney, Inc., New York
Bonnar Keenlyside Ltd., London
Chadwick Jones Associates, London
David Jackson & Associates, Cross in Hand
Denander & Grahl AB, Stockholm
Die Kultur AG, Frankfurt am Main
Ernst & Young, London
Genovese Vanderhoff & Associates, Toronto
Hannah Horovitz Associates, London
Hardsell Ltd, London
Hazel Rennard, Kingston upon Thames
IBM UK Ltd, Edinburgh (Scotland)
ICOM (Industrial Common Ownership Movement Ltd), Leeds
Identity Creation for Business, Kingston upon Hull
InterCachet - Paris, Paris
International Arts Bureau Ltd., London
JM Consulting Ltd, Bristol
Kirkham & Elphick Organisational Development Consultants, Bangor (Wales)
Leisure & Arts Research (a division of Travel and Tourism Research Ltd), London
Look and Learn Productions Ltd, London
Maecenata Management GmbH, München
Millward Brown International, Warwick
Music Concept, München
Patrick Boyd Maunsell, Oxford
Positive Solutions, Liverpool
Smith & Williamson, London

Marketing, Press, Promotion and Public Relations Services
Agence Léz Ards Vivants, Montreuil
Anglo-European Arts, London
Annie Houston Reddick Associates, Glasgow (Scotland)
Arts Connect, London
Bakker & Clients, Amsterdam
Birdsong Public Relations, London
Bolton & Quinn Ltd, London
Burns Research Limited, London
CAGEC (Centre d'Aide à la Gestion de l'Entreprise Culturelle), Nantes
Carole Strachan Associates, Abingdon
Clausecker & Bingel Ereignisse GmbH, Berlin
Da Capo Musikmarketing GmbH, Kufstein
Dewynters plc, London
Dvora Lewis Public Relations, London
EVENT-Production GmbH, Köln
GCI Groups, London
GGC Projects - Performing Arts Studio, Amsterdam
Guy Chapman Associates, London
Hannah Horovitz Associates, London
Hans Werner Lacher - ARTCOM European Art Communication, Bruckmühl
Hardsell Ltd, London
Hill & Knowlton, London
Identity Creation for Business, Kingston upon Hull
Jane Morgan Associates, London
Jazz Services, London
Just Tickets, Henley-on-Thames
Kallaway Ltd, London
Kantor Concert Management & Public Relations, London
Kerlin Consulting Pty Ltd, Port Melbourne
Konzertkasse Casino, Bern
KulturKonzept Verlags & Werbebüro, Heroldstatt
M&C Saatchi Arts, London
Macbeth Media Relations, London
Martin Gabriel Promotions, Darlington
Mary De Camp Carlson Public Relations and Marketing, London
Media Factory, Hamburg
Michael Harrold Artist Management, Leatherhead
Musica Europa, Maidenhead
Musik Komm GmbH & Köln Messe GmbH, Köln
Paul Steinhauer Public Relations & Communications, Wien
Pippa Pawlik Public Relations, Pargemon (Var)
PR2 classic, Köln
PRC Public Relations, Amsterdam
Public et Communication, Paris
Public Production Co. Ltd, London
Quintessenz Artists, München
Seréna Woolf marketing et relations publiques, Saint Germain-en-Laye
Simkins Partnership, London
Sophie Cohen Arts Publicity, London
Spero Communications Ltd, London
SYRINX, Hamburg
Tei Williams Press and Arts Marketing, Oxon
TeleCartaz, Lisboa
Traum & Raum, Berlin
Valerie Barber PR, London
Ylva French Communications, London

Marketing Systems (see Computerized Management Systems)

Moveable Stages, Theatre and Show Tents
Event Audio Visual Group Inc, Milford
NÜSSLI (Deutschland) GmbH, Roth
TOP TENTS Zeitverleih Schifke-Tewes, Oer-Erkenschwick

Music publishers
Boosey & Hawkes Music Publishers Ltd, London
Budde Music International GmbH, Berlin
Carlo Cucchiara SAS. di Giuseppe Cucchiara & C., Enna
CF Peters Musikverlag, Frankfurt am Main

ClassiCulturCentrum, Buchen
Editions Chantraine, Tournai
ERES EDITION, Lilienthal (Bremen)
Faber Music Ltd., London
FURORE-Verlag, Kassel
Music Forum, Bratislava
Musikverlag Doblinger, Wien
NotaBene Records AS, Oslo
Schott Frères, Brussels
Scriptorium Musicum, Bratislava
Verlagsgruppe Hermann, Wien

Performing Arts Services and Products/Materials
A.R.T.S., Cardiff (Wales)
Agence Léz Ards Vivants, Montreuil
American Symphony Orchestra League, New York
Art Base - The International Arts Database, Amsterdam
ArtsLink - NSW office, Crows Nest
Ballet Independents' Group - BIG, London
Boekman Foundation, Amsterdam
Centro di Musicologia Walter Stauffer, Cremona
Charivari, Vattetot-sur-Mer
Comme Il Vous Plaira, Paris
COMPRO, Epping
CPF - Cultural Projects Factory, Madrid
DaSilva Puppet Books, Bicester
Eastern Touring Agency, Cambridge
Ernst Krenek Institut, Wien
Famusic s.a., Barcelona
Ferrer Musical, SA, Barcelona
Foundation for Art and Creative Technology (FACT), Liverpool
Foundation of Arts in Brussels, Brussels
GGC Projects - Performing Arts Studio, Amsterdam
HAZEN, Distribuidora General de Pianos SA, Las Rozas (Madrid)
International Arts Bureau Ltd., London
International Cultural Desk, Edinburgh (Scotland)
Jaques Samuel Pianos Ltd, London
Jazz Services, London
Just Tickets, Henley-on-Thames
Laban Centre London, Library and Resource Collection, London
Magical Mart, Sidcup
Markpoint System AB, Göteborg
Model Box Ltd, London
Moving Academy of Performing Arts, Amsterdam
Musica Europa, Maidenhead
Oniria International SL, Sant Quirze Del Valles (Barcelona)
Schiedmayer Celestabau Gmbh Stuttgart, Stuttgart
shinkansen, London

Production Lighting Contractors (see Stage and Scenic Engineering and Studio Equipment)

Project Management (see Architects, Project Management and Theatre Consultants)

Promotional and Security Printing (see Ticketing)

Recording Venues
RG Jones Recording Studios, London
St Georges Music Trust, Bristol
The Warehouse - Studio II, London

Rehearsal Rooms
Belsize Music Rooms, London
Holabird & Root LLP, Chicago
Wigmore Hall - Rehearsal Rooms, London

Scenery, Curtains, Props, Costume Design Makers and Traders
Brancato Costumi Teatrali, Milano
Gerriets Great Britain Ltd, London
IDEEA Dekorationsbau GmbH, Berlin
Kevin Darby Costumes, Cardiff (Wales)
Magical Mart, Sidcup
Nelson Hall, Edinburgh (Scotland)
Scenografie Mattei snc, Ciampino (Roma)
Solti snc di Fasano Ermanno & c, Velletri (Roma)
Tanz- und Theaterbedarf Klaus Schreck GmbH, Bruchsal
TOP TENTS Zeitverleih Schifke-Tewes, Oer-Erkenschwick
Victor Mara Limited, London
W Beyne & ZN.BV, Bussum
Werning Theatertechnik Theaterbedarf GmbH, Recklinghausen

Scenic Construction (see Stage and Scenic Engineering and Studio Equipment)

Scheduling (see Computerized Management Systems)

Security Printing (see Ticketing)

Shipping (see Transport and Travel Services)

Solicitors (see Legal Services)

Sound and Communications Contractors and Equipment (see Stage and Scenic Engineering and Studio Equipment)

Sound Reinforcement Systems (see Stage and Scenic Engineering and Studio Equipment)

Specialist Training, Workshops, Seminars and Advice
Abaco S.L. Servicios Escénicos, Pozuelo de Alarcón (Madrid)
All Clear Designs Limited, London
American Artists Abroad, Rocca de Giorgi (PV)
ArtProfi Centre, Moscow
Arts Partnership, Cardiff (Wales)
Brouhaha International, Liverpool
CAGEC (Centre d'Aide à la Gestion de l'Entreprise Culturelle), Nantes
Circus Maniacs, Bristol
Circus Space, London
Cité de la Musique, Paris
Die Kultur AG, Frankfurt am Main
Institut für Internationales Kulturmanagement (INK) GmbH, München
International Arts Bureau Ltd., London
Internationaler Arbeitskreis Frau und Musik eV, Kassel
Istituto Addestramento Lavoratori dello Spettacolo, Roma
Management Centre, London
McCann Matthews Millman Limited, London
Metier, Bradford
OGACA, Strasbourg
Patrick Boyd Maunsell, Oxford
Positive Solutions, Liverpool
Prometeo, Parma
Salongo, Bristol
shinkansen, London

Sponsorship Consultants (see Fundraising and Sponsorship Consultants)

Stage and Scenic Engineering, Materials and Studio Equipment
Aearo, Stockport
Ahlers & Lambrecht GmbH, Coesfeld
Allen & Heath, Penryyn
Anytronics Ltd, Horndean
Arts Business Limited (ABL), London
Autograph Sound Recording Ltd, London
BBB-Bayerische Bühnenbau GmbH, Weiden
Beneke, Daberto und Partner, Sehnde
BILCO UK Ltd., Bury St Edmunds
Bose GmbH, Friedrichsdorf
Brilliant Stages Ltd, Hitchin
Bühnenbau Schnakenberg GmbH u. Co. KG, Wuppertal
Canford Audio PLC, Washington
Citronic Ltd, Melksham
Cloud Electronics Ltd, Sheffield
Coemar Spa, Castel Goffredo (MN)
CTL (Control Technology) Ltd, Aylesford
Doughty Engineering Ltd, Ringwood
Effective Theatrical Productions Ltd., London
Euroscene Ltd., Bury St Edmunds
Flint Hire and Supply Limited, London
Formula Sound Ltd, Stockport
Gerling Arendt und Partner, Berlin
Gerriets GmbH, Umkirch
Glantre Engineering Ltd, Reading
Harkness Hall Ltd, Borehamwood
La Bottega Veneziana SRL, Quarto D'Altino (VE)
Mannesmann Demag Fördertechnik AG, Wetter
Mannesmann Rexroth GmbH, Lohr am Main
Max Maier GmbH + Co. KG Metallbau, Karlsruhe
NJD Electronics (NJD Ltd), Nottingham
Outback Rigging Ltd, London
Peroni Spa, Gallarate (VA)
SBS GmbH Dresden, Dresden
Scenografie Mattei snc, Ciampino (Roma)
SHOWTEC Beleuchtungs-und Beschallungs GmBH, Köln
Slick Systems, Leek
Solti snc di Fasano Ermanno & c, Velletri (Roma)
Sound Design Ltd, Bracknell
Stage Electrics, Bristol
Statec Bühnentechnik GmbH, Duisburg
Steeldeck Sales Ltd, London
Theatec, Bad Soden
Theatrecraft, Bebington
Triple E Ltd, London
Unusual Rigging Ltd, Bugbrooke
Vmkar Production, Zdár nad Sázavou
Waagner-Biro Binder AG, Wien
Werning Theatertechnik Theaterbedarf GmbH, Recklinghausen

Stage Lighting and Controls (see Lighting Designers and Manufacturers)

Studio Equipment (see Stage and Scenic Engineering and Studio Equipment)

Sub-Titling and Sur-titling
Eikon, Impruneta (FI)
Erik Borgman, Blanden
Prescott Productions, Firenze

Tax Services (see Accounting and Tax Services)

Theatre Consultants (see Architects, Project Management and Theatre Consultants)

Theatre Design (see Architects and Theatre Consultants)

Theatre Lighting and Supplies (see Stage and Scenic Engineering and Studio Equipment)

Theatre Management Systems (see Computerized Management Systems)

Ticketing (and see Computerized Management Systems)
Advantix, Newport Beach
Aluset Security Printing, Leicester
Beckerbillett GmbH, Hamburg
Bemrose Security Promotional Printing, Derby
Billett Service A/S, Oslo
Boca Systems Inc., Boca Raton
CIEL SA Division TIX, Linkebeek
First Call/The Ticketing Group, Crawley
G Hornberger GmbH, Waldfischbach
Globaltickets (from Edwards & Edwards), London
Haubold GmbH Spezialdruckerei, Eschwege
Henry Booth & Co., Hull
Intermec, Chatou
Start Ticket Vertrieb von Veranstaltungskarten GmbH, Frankfurt am Main
Ticket.com.Network, De Witt
Ticket.com Systems BV, Amsterdam
Ticket.com Systems Pty, Sydney
Ticketmaster, Los Angeles
Ticketmaster (UK) Ltd, London
Tungate Group, Stoke on Trent
WM - Data, Abyhoj

Transport and Travel Services
Aircraft Chartering Services Ltd., Epsom
American Overseas Tours Inc., Genève
Anglo-Pacific International plc, London
Clark Transfer, Inc, Harrisburg
Da Capo Musikmarketing GmbH, Kufstein
DAMI Ltd, Moscow
Dijkstra Transport BV, Hilversum
Dovetail Foks, London
EasyPac oHG, Berlin
Ernst Beissner GmbH & Co. KG - Geschäftsbereich Tourneen-Spedition, Hannover
Fair's Fare, London
Fra Diabolo, Barcelona
G & R Removals - Specialist musical instrument transporters, London
Gebrüder Schmiedekampf GmbH & Co., Heidenau
GH Lucking & Sons, Brentford
JET EXECUTIVE - International Charter GmbH, Düsseldorf
Ken Graham Trucking - The Symphony Orchestra Specialists, Tadworth
Maestro Travel and Touring Company, Liverpool
Martin Gabriel Promotions, Darlington
Martin Randall Travel Ltd, London
NotaBene Records AS, Oslo
Paul Gerstbauer, Wien
Prima Klima Reisen GmbH, Berlin
Promenade Music, Morecambe
Ripley-Duggan Partnership, London
Sparta System AB, Göteborg
Specialised Travel Ltd, London
Symphony Tours, Pozuelo de Alarcón (Madrid)
TNT Express (Austria) Ges. mbH, Wiener Neudorf
TNT Express Worldwide, Berlin
TNT Express Worldwide, Schiphol Ryk
Tour Resources International, Inc, Lakeland
Trans Euro Specialised Movements, London
Travel Art International, Copenhagen
Vmkar Production, Zdár nad Sázavou
VSW Expeditie bv, Enschede
Wilson & Co (UK) Ltd, Hounslow

Venue Consultants (see Architects and Theatre Consultants)

EDITORIAL LISTINGS

A.R.T.S.
8 The Maltings, East Timble Street,
Cardiff (Wales) CF1 5EA, United Kingdom
Tel: 44 29-2066 7989
E-Mail: arts@easynet.co.uk
contact Stephen Stocton
Services: management and marketing agency offering a wide range of specialist skill for both consultancy and training

Abaco S.L. Servicios Escénicos
Avda del Monte Alina 44,
28223 **Pozuelo de Alarcón (Madrid)**, Spain
Tel: 34 91-715 0000 Fax: 34 91-715 4047
director general Manu Aguilar
Services: accountancy, legal and employment advice; also courses on production and management

AC Lighting Limited
Unit 3, Spearmast Industrial Park, Lane End Road,
High Wycombe HP12 4JG, United Kingdom
Tel: 44 1494-446 000
Fax: 44 1494-461 024
Internet: www.aclighting.co.uk
E-Mail: sales@aclighting.co.uk
UK sales Phill Capstick; export director Nic Tolkien
Services: international supplier of lighting products

Accademia Musicale Italiana – AMIT
Via G Pezzana, 21, 00197 **Roma**, Italy
Tel: 39 06-807 8141 Fax: 39 06-808 8919
E-Mail: amit@interbusiness.it
artistic director Michele Torassa;
president Federico Amati
Services: management consultancy, box-office telematic systems, event production
Comments: see also Agents & Producers and Festivals (Umbria Jazz, Barocco in Viterbo)

Acoustic Consultants Ltd
Raleigh House, Wellsway, Keynsham, **Bristol** BS31 1HS, United Kingdom
Tel: 44 117-986 2956
director S Peliza
Services: consultants for noise and acoustic aspects of studios. auditoria and recording studios

Acoustic Dimensions
24 Styvechale Avenue,
Coventry CV5 6DX, United Kingdom
Tel: 44 24-7667 3645 Fax: 44 24-7667 9820
Internet: www.acousticdimensions.com
E-Mail: acoustics@compuserve.com
contact Nicholas Edwards
Services: acoustics, auditorium design
Comments: commissions have included the Royal Shakespear Theatre

ACT Consultant Services
The Old Wood Mill, Church Lane, Madingley,
Cambridge CB3 8AF, United Kingdom
Tel: 44 1954-210 766 Fax: 44 1954-211 466
contact Chris Baldwin, John Coffey
Services: theatre design consultants specialising in new build work as well as conversion & refurbishment of existing premises & equipment for a wide range of arts activities; wide-ranging experience in lottery-funded arts development projects

Action Lighting
2 Tudor Estate, Abbey Road, Park Royal,
London NW10 7UY, United Kingdom
Tel: 44 20-8965 6800 Fax: 44 20-8965 0950
E-Mail: action@lighting-tech.com
chief executive Robert Peach; directors David Morgan, Paul De Ville; sales managers Ron Knell, Graham Basset (44 161-876 0576); technical manager Paul De Ville; marketing/PR David Cartwright
Services: complete sales & service to the entertainment industry, including lamps, lanterns, colour filter, gobos, conmol, truss, sound and scenic materials

Adam Brothers Contingency Ltd
12 Camomile Street,
London EC3A 7PT, United Kingdom
Tel: 44 20-7638 3211
Fax: 44 20-7374 0726
E-Mail: allan@hholman.co.uk
contact Robert Wood
Services: non-appearance and cancellation/abandonment insurance for all types of events

ADB Theatre and TV Lighting
Dieselstr 4, 63165 **Mühlheim am Main**, Germany
Tel: 49 6108-9125-0 Fax: 49 6108-912 525
Internet: www.adb.be
E-Mail: adb.lichtelek@t-online.de
Geschäftsführer Herr Musso; Managing Direktors Herr Fahrtmann, Herr Kerber; Projects & Sales Manager Herr B. Jäger
Services: broad line of spotlights, dimmers, motorised sospensions and control systems for stage and studio lighting

ADB Theatre and TV Lighting
47 rue de la Vanne, 92120 **Montrouge**, France
Tel: 33 1-4117 4850 Fax: 33 1-4253 5476
Internet: www.adb.be
managing director Christian Léonard;
director of sales Jean-Paul Legrand;
marketing manager Thibault Manchon
Services: manufacturer of theatre, TV studio and stage lighting equipment

ADB-TTV Technologies S.A.
Theatre and TV Lighting Division, Leuvensesteenweg 585, 1930 **Zaventem**, Belgium
Tel: 32 2-722 1711 Fax: 32 2-722 1764
Internet: www.adb.be
E-Mail: adb-ttv@adb.be
general manager Mike Musso;
business development manager Raph Janssens
Services: comprehensive range of products and services for stage and studio lighting; development, manufacture, sales, installation, commissioning, maintenance, training *Comments:* ADB is a Siemens company with agents in 50 countries

Advantix
4675 MacArthur Court, Suite 1400,
Newport Beach CA 92660, United States of America
Tel: 1 949-862 5400 Fax: 1 949-862 5410
Internet: www.tickets.com
E-Mail: sales@advantix.com
vice-president of international business development Dan Afrasiabi
Services: ticketing solutions; specialise in the development of city-wide and regional ticketing and event management solutions for theatres, stadia, arenas, auditoria, entertainment complexes and sports organisations

AEA Ltd.
Hatton House, 57D Hatton Garden,
London EC1N 8JD, United Kingdom
Tel: 44 20-7242 3133 Fax: 44 20-7242 3422
E-Mail: office@aeaconsulting.com
director Adrian Ellis; senior consultant David Hall
Services: feasibility studies, business planning, organisational reviews, marketing & development strategies

Aearo
First Avenue, Poynton, Industrial Estate,
Stockport SK12 1FJ, United Kingdom
Tel: 44 1625-878 320 Fax: 44 1625-877 348
Internet: www.aearo.com
marketing director David Forrest;
marketing manager Mike Danton
Services: supply Ultra Tech earplugs, safety glasses and all kinds of safety equipment for the head and shoulders

Agence Léz Ards Vivants
56, bd Jeanne d'Arc, 93100 **Montreuil**, France
Tel: 33 1-4287 6013 Fax: 33 1-4287 3613
E-Mail: lezaviva@club-internet.fr
directeur Pierre Hivernat
Services: production and administration of artistic projects, programmation adviser *Comments:* see also Agents & Producers

Ahlers & Lambrecht GmbH
Dreischkamp 15, 48653 **Coesfeld**, Germany
Tel: 49 2541-94320 Fax: 49 2541-943 232
Internet: www.ahlersundlambrecht.de
E-Mail: info@ahlersundlambrecht.de
Geschäftsführer Karl Ahlers, Christoph Ahlers;
Verkaufsleitung Heinrich Ahlers
Services: stage equipment (stages, concert shells, steps, podiums, stage-floor oil, make-up tables, wardrobes)

Aircraft Chartering Services Ltd.
7 High Street, Ewell, **Epsom** KT17 1SG, United Kingdom
Tel: 44 20-8394 2795
Fax: 44 20-8393 6154
E-Mail: sales@aircraft-chartering.co.uk
managing director Mark Hugo; special projects manager Ian Browne; group charters manager Antony Parsons-Gorham; touring manager Andrew Richley
Services: aircraft charter brokers to the leading touring orchestras in Europe and North America

AJS Theatre Lighting & Stage Supplies Ltd
Hightown Ind Est, Crow Arch Ln,
Ringwood BH24 1ND, United Kingdom
Tel: 44 1425-481 132 (sales)/481 125 (hire)
Fax: 44 1425-471 398
Internet: demon.co.uk/aajs
E-Mail: sales@ajs.co.uk
managing director Adrian Sant (adrians@ajs.co.uk); hire manager Simon Sketchley (simons@ajs.co.uk); projects/IT manager Alan Davis (aland@ajs.co.uk); sales Ian Cross (sales@ajs.co.uk); installation dept manager Chris Coates (chrisc@ajs.co.uk)
Services: consultancy design for theatrical and architectural projects; sales and installation of theatre curtaining, ironmongery, lighting, make-up, pyrotechnics, sound, special-effects, staging, etc. *Comments:* UK distributor for Selecon Luminaires, Ben Nye Makeup

AKT Productions Ltd
18 Grosvenor Street,
London W1X 9FD, United Kingdom
Tel: 44 20-7495 4043 Fax: 44 20-7495 0692
Internet: www.aktproductions.co.uk
E-Mail: conferences@aktproductions.co.uk
conference & production manager Ian Bourker
Services: conference and event management, production, technical support and speaker support for conferences

All Clear Designs Limited
3rd Floor, Cooper House, 2 Michael Road,
London SW6 2ER, United Kingdom
Tel: 44 20-7384 2950/51 Fax: 44 20-7384 2951
Internet: www.allclear.co.uk
E-Mail: allclear@easynet.co.uk
director James Holmes-Siedle
Services: architects and training: specialise in making buildings accessible for disabled people and providing disability equality training; fundraising assistance offered

Allen & Heath
Kernich Industrial Estate,
Penryyn TR10 9LU, United Kingdom
Tel: 44 1326-372 070 Fax: 44 1326-377 097
Internet: www.allen-heath.com
E-Mail: sales@allen-heath.com
sales manager, professional products Bob Goleniowski
Services: manufacturer of professional audio mixing consoles for sound reinforcement, installation and recording for theatres, conference centres and small halls throughout the world

Aluset Security Printing
15 Station St., Whetstone,
Leicester LE8 6JS, United Kingdom
Tel: 44 116-2751 600
Fax: 44 116-2751 573
E-Mail: tracy@aluset.demon.co.uk
sales director Brian Kenworthy
Services: printer of security and thermal entrance tickets

American Artists Abroad
Cascina Elaisa, 27043 **Rocca de Giorgi (PV)**, Italy
Tel: 39 0385-99279
Fax: 39 0385-99279
E-Mail: artdownes@maxidata.it
contact Ruth Downes
Services: non-profit organisation which aids and encourages young American performing artists abroad, particularly Europe

American Overseas Tours Inc.
2 Place du Port, 1204 **Genève**, Switzerland
Tel: 41 1-712 342 (sales office)
Fax: 41 1-713 7125 (sales office)
E-Mail: ctvienna@magnet.at
managing director Michael Ecker
Services: specialise in the organisation of orchestra tours (incoming & outgoing, flight and hotel arrangements, bus transfer, freight service) *Comments:* sales office: Gaertnergasse 1/16, 1030 Wien, Tel: +43 1-712 342, Fax: +43 1-713 7125; also has offices in Germany, UK, Hungary and Switzerland

American Symphony Orchestra League
33 West 60th Street, Fifth Floor, **New York** NY 10023-7905, United States of America
Tel: 1 212-262 5161
Fax: 1 212-262 5198
Internet: www.symphony.org
E-Mail: league@symphony.org
president and chief executive officer Charles S. Olton; vice president & director of orchestra academy project Bruce Coppock; vice president of member services Jack McAuliffe; vice president of management development Jessie Rosen; vice president for government affairs & public policy John Sparks; vice president of professional & artistic services Donald Thulean
Services: OLIS, a database of orchestral works, SYMPHONY, a bi-monthly magazine

Andrew de Mille Fundraising Consultants
Hedsordene, **Cookham** SL6 9HW, United Kingdom
Tel: 44 1628-527 753
Fax: 44 1628-529 938
Internet: www.demille.co.uk
E-Mail: andrew@demille.co.uk
partner Andrew de Mille;
senior consultant Patrick Boggon
Services: capital and revenue fundraising, feasibility and planning studies, organisation development, membership development *Comments:* member of the Association of Fundraising Consultants

Anglo-European Arts
25 Fournier Street, **London** E1 6QE, United Kingdom
Tel: 44 20-7247 7219
Fax: 44 20-7247 6094
director Carolyn Humphreys
Services: public relations consultant; artistic consultant for projects, festivals and concert series; concert management

Anglo-Pacific International plc
Unit 1, Bush Industrial Estate, Standard Road,
London NW10 6DF, United Kingdom
Tel: 44 20-8838 8084
Fax: 44 20-8965 4954
E-Mail: info@anglopacific.co.uk
managing director Steve Perry;
operations manager Chris Jacoby
Services: trucking, ocean freight, air freight, carnet services, forwarders to the performing arts *Comments:* official sponsors of the British Council 'on tour'

Anne Minors Performance Consultants
134 Merton Road, West Hill,
London SW18 5SP, United Kingdom
Tel: 44 20-8874 3640
Fax: 44 20-8870 0996
E-Mail: AMinors@compuserve.com
director Anne Minors
Services: consultancy for performance venues

Annie Houston Reddick Associates
Wellpark Enterprise Centre, 120 Sydney Street,
Glasgow (Scotland) G31 1JF, United Kingdom
Tel: 44 141-550 4994
Fax: 44 141-550 4443
E-Mail: ahrassoc@globalnet.co.uk
contact Annie Houston Reddick
Services: creative marketing, press and pr for theatre, dance, music, comedy, visual arts and festivals in the UK and Europe

Anthony Fawcett Consultants
Flat 3, 63 Ears Court Square,
London SW5 9DG, United Kingdom
Tel: 44 20-7370 1905
Fax: 44 20-7370 1905
contact Anthony Fawcett
Services: arts sponsorship

Anytronics Ltd
Units 5 & 6, Hillside Industrial Estate, London Road,
Horndean PO8 OBL, United Kingdom
Tel: 44 1705-599 410
Fax: 44 1705-598 723
managing director Bob Hall
Services: manufacturers of strobes, strobe controllers, modular lighting control systems, expandable lighting controllers, universal switching and dimming packs

AON Entertainment Risk Services Ltd
Pinewood Studios, Pinewood Road, **Iver** SLo oNH,
United Kingdom
Tel: 44 1753-658 200
Fax: 44 1753-653 152
contact Rosemary Gilmour
Services: insurance brokers for the film and television industry

Applied Acoustic Design
The Green Business Centre, The Causeway, **Staines**
TW18 3AL, United Kingdom
Tel: 44 1784-464404 Fax: 44 1784-465447
Internet: www.aad.co.uk
E-Mail: info@aad.co.uk
contact M Bishop, A V H Holdich, P R J Mansfield
Services: worldwide multi-disciplinary acoustical consultants

APT Solutions
Suite 218, Business Design Centre, Upper Street,
London N1 0QH, United Kingdom
Tel: 44 20-7704 8006 Fax: 44 20-7704 8108
Internet: apt.sol.com
contact Roger Bourdon
Services: Artistfile – an internationally installed, multi-lingual computer system for artist management which integrates all management activities with financial accounts and word processing

Arena – Technik
Osterstrasse 5, 28199 **Bremen**, Germany
Tel: 49 421-555 156 Fax: 49 421-556 868
contacts Heinz Siegel, Gabriele Hellwig
Services: manufacturer specialising in dimmer systems, digital and analog, power current measure

Armada Production
Room C, 12 North Gate,
Chichester PO19 1BA, United Kingdom
Tel: 44 1243-790 611
Fax: 44 1243-790 580
E-Mail: armad1@virgin.net
management Andrew Welch
Services: radio production company

ARRI Cine Technik GmbH & Co. KG
Türkenstraße 89, 80799 **München** , Germany
Tel: 49 89-38090 Fax: 49 89-3809 1244
Internet: www.arri.com
E-Mail: hbergmann@Arri.de
Vertriebsleiter Horst Bergmann
Services: produce film cameras, lights and accessories; laboratory and sound studios; also provide post production facilities

Art Base – The International Arts Database
PO Box 74118, 1070 BC **Amsterdam**, Netherlands
Tel: 31 20-664 6441 Fax: 31 20-662 5951
E-Mail: artbase@wxs.nl
director M.A.Simons; communication officer Carlos Amaral; marketing manager Jan Guus Waldorp
Services: international database on cultural events; lists international events in performing arts, fine arts, applied arts, artfairs and auctions

Artec Consultants Inc
114 West 26th Street, 9th Floor,
New York NY 10001-6812, United States of America
Tel: 1 212-242 0120
Fax: 1 212-645 8635
Internet: www.artec-usa.com
E-Mail: info@artecusa.com
chairman/ceo Willem Brons;
managing director Joel E. Rubin, PhD;
president Damian Doria
Services: sound systems, feasibility studies, acoustics consulting, theatre planning

Artifax Software Ltd
38 Ridgeway, **Epsom** KT19 8LB, United Kingdom
Tel: 44 1372-810 081
Fax: 44 1372-743 390
Internet: www.artifaxsoftware.com
E-Mail: admin@artifaxsoftware.com
directors Timothy Nathan, Nina Kaye; sales manager Bob Chase; software engineer Ben Curthoys, Andrew Dunford; support Tim Coleman, Geoffrey Dallamore
Services: computer programs designed for the performing arts market; Artifax Event for venue management, Artifax Agent for artists managers and agents, Artifax Festival for arts festival management

ArtProfi Centre
Sobinovsky 6, 103009 **Moscow**, Russia
Tel: 7 095-290 0411
Fax: 7 095-290 0597
E-Mail: art.profi@g23.relcom.ru
contact Evgeny Dukov
Services: consultancy;
arts management training courses

Arts and Industry Ltd/Sponsorship Consulting Ltd
70 South Lambeth Road,
London SW8 1RL, United Kingdom
Tel: 44 20-7582 0994 Fax: 44 20-7587 1277
Internet: www.sponsorshipconsulting.co.uk
E-Mail:
wendy.stephenson@sponsorshipconsulting.co.uk
managing director Wendy Stephenson
Services: sponsorship consultants in Europe and internationally

Arts Business Limited (ABL), The
38 St. Martin's Lane,
London WC2N 4ER, United Kingdom
Tel: 44 20-7420 9700 Fax: 44 20-7420 9701
E-Mail: info@artsbusiness.co.uk
directors Richard Crossland, Alan Giddings;
managing consultant Philippa Bird
Services: cultural planning; quantitative and qualitative analysis of provision; operational, marketing and programme reviews; market research and analysis; performance measurements programmes; feasibility studies; project management for buildings and new services; advice on leisure mix for commercial developers; CCT and trust related planning; urban regeneration through cultural interventions; assessment of economic impact and related development; project origination, management and marketing for sponsors; arts education reviews *Comments:* ABL is the largest independent arts management consultancy specialising in arts, heritage, entertainment, media and crafts; aim to build and develop consensu amongst stakeholders and detailed knowledge of the workings of the National Lottery and other funding schemes; offer in-house a combination of detailed sector knowledge, research and consultation expertise and market research; have direct access to related skills in retail, museums, planning, building design and fundraising

Arts Connect
22-24 Worple Road, Wimbledon,
London SW19 4DD, United Kingdom
Tel: 44 20-8944 5800 Fax: 44 20-8947 9042
Internet: www.emc-europa.com
E-Mail: artsco.emc@ad.com
contact Robert Moffat
Services: marketing and public relations services for the arts and entertainment industries

Arts Consortium
16 Louvaine Road, **London** SW11 2AQ, United Kingdom
Tel: 44 20-7585 2909
Fax: 44 20-7585 2909
consultants, arts development Brian Harris,
Pat Abraham, Chris Moore
Services: arts organisations business and development plans; arts building feasibility studies; local authority arts development plans;
advise on National Lottery arts projects

Arts Management Consulting
Postfach 60, 8034 **Zürich**, Switzerland
Tel: 41 1-383 4704 Fax: 41 1-383 4704
director Francis Hunter
Services: management consultancy for artists, ensembles and institutions *Comments:* visiting address: Münchhaldenstraße 15, 8008 Zürich, Switzerland

Arts Partnership, The
8 The Maltings, East Tyndall St.,
Cardiff (Wales) CF1 5EA, United Kingdom
Tel: 44 29-2049 5387 Fax: 44 29-2045 5031
E-Mail: arts@easynet.co.uk
contact Mel Jennings, Stephan Stockton
Services: management, marketing and training agency specialising in customer care development and training, and the use of computerised box office systems for marketing

Arts Team @ RHWL
133 Long Acre, **London** WC2E 9AD, United Kingdom
Tel: 44 20-7379 7900 Fax: 44 20-7836 4881
Internet: www.artsteam.co.uk
E-Mail: ArtsTeam@rhwl.co.uk
partners Nicholas Thompson, Barry Pritchard, Norman Bragg; associates Suzie Bridges, Gordon Forbes, Stewart King, Julian Middleton, David Wright; consultant Clare Ferraby
Services: consultants specialising in building feasibility, management and marketing studies for performing arts venues, leisure and conference centre and educational training facilities; subsequent design development, theatre planning, architecture, interior design through all stages of design and construction for new venues and refurbishment of important existing buildings in the UK and Europe *Comments:* completed new buildings include Sadler's Wells Theatre and Donmar Warehouse in London, Bridgewater Hall in Manchester and refurbishment of many West End Theatres

ArtServices
McAvoy House, 17a Ormeau Avenue,
Belfast (Northern Ireland) BT2 8HD, United Kingdom
Tel: 44 28-9023 7717 Fax: 44 28-9023 7717
Internet: www.artservicesireland.com
E-Mail: sales@artservicesireland.com
managing director Mark Robinson
Services: services to the arts and creative industries in design, print, research, consultancy and project management *Comments:* largest current projects is The Cultural Business Network

ArtsLink – NSW office
PO Box 1480, **Crows Nest** NSW 2065, Australia
Tel: 61 2-9966 8718 Fax: 61 2-9966 8719
Internet: www.artslink.org.au
E-Mail: mail@artslink.org.au
director Dirk Pettigrew
Services: performing arts industry documentation centre & information & advisory service; collects & distributes comprehensive material about most aspects of the performing arts in Australia; maintains extensive overseas connections & sources; distribute the Australian Performing Arts Directory and ArtsLinkNews (monthly magazine) in partnership with Performance Media, trade publisher of national performing arts info; maintenance of a national electronic database *Comments:* visiting address: Suite 3, Level 1, 382 Pacific High Way, Crows Nest NSW 2065

Arup Acoustics
Boston House, 36-38 Fitzroy Square,
London W1P 5LL, United Kingdom
Tel: 44 20-7636 2853 Fax: 44 20-7465 3665
Internet: www.arup.com\acoustics
E-Mail: richard.cowell@arup.com
principal consultant Richard Cowell
Services: acoustic consultants *Comments:* also has offices in Winchester and Cambridge, United Kingdom, New York, Sydney, Hong-Kong, Los Angeles, San Francisco, Melbourne

Arup Acoustics
Parkin House, 8 St Thomas Street,
Winchester SO23 9HE, United Kingdom
Tel: 44 1962-869 111 Fax: 44 1962-867 270
Internet: www.arup.com\acoustics
E-Mail: rob.harris@arup.com
contact Rob Harris
Services: acoustic consultants; audio-visual and sound system design *Comments:* also has offices in London and Winchester, New York, Sydney, Hong-Kong, Los Angeles, San Francisco, Melbourne

Arup Acoustics
St Giles Hall, Pound Hill,
Cambridge CB3 0AE, United Kingdom
Tel: 44 1223-355 033
Fax: 44 1223-361 258
Internet: www.arup.com\acoustics
E-Mail: raf.orlowski@arup.com
contact Raf Orlowski
Services: acoustic consultants *Comments:* also has offices in London and Winchester, New York, Sydney, Hong-Kong, Los Angeles, San Francisco, Melbourne

Arup Associates
37 Fitzroy Square, **London** W1P 6AA, United Kingdom
Tel: 44 20-7465 5555 Fax: 44 20-7465 2561
Internet: www.arup.com
E-Mail: a-a@arup.com
architectural director James Burland; press & research office Helen Allen, Sarah Rawlings; finance director & engineer Anthony Broomhead; structural engineer/director Terry Raggett; director, urban desgin Michael Lowe; diector/architect Mick Brundle; director/engineer Richard Lee; director/M&E engineer Peter Warburton
Services: multi-disciplinary architects, engineers, quantity surveyors and urban designers

Ash Sakula Architects
38 Mount Pleasant,
London WC1X 0AN, United Kingdom
Tel: 44 20-7837 9735 Fax: 44 20-7837 9708
Internet: www.ashsak.demon.co.uk
E-Mail: arts@ashsak.demon.co.uk
contact Kahy Ash
Services: highly creative team of architects with experience in arts projects

Asian Arts Access
1 Great Goodwin Drive, Merrow, **Guildford** GU1 2TX, United Kingdom
Tel: 44 1483-538 265 Fax: 44 1483-306 471
Internet: www.asianartsaccess.org
E-Mail: kalwant.ajimal@which.net
executive director K Ajimal
Services: strategic arts planning and development support for arts organisations, local authorities and sponsors; practical organisational help for artists in presenting events; special programme for Asian Arts networks; arts development and programming
Comments: combined arts production available for programming

AT Kearney, Inc.
153 East 53rd Street, Floor 27, **New York** NY 10022, United States of America
Tel: 1 212-350 3151 Fax: 1 212-350 3150
Internet: www.atkearney.com
E-Mail: james_abruzzo@atkearney.com
managing director James Abruzzo
Services: executive search, management consulting

Audience Business, The
Kings Theatre, 2 Leven Street, **Edinburgh (Scotland)** EH3 9LQ, United Kingdom
Tel: 44 131-622 8100 Fax: 44 131-622 8101
chief executive David Jackson
Services: development agency for 31 arts venues in Scotland – providing advice on developing audiences

Autograph Sound Recording Ltd
2 Spring Place, **London** NW5 3BA, United Kingdom
Tel: 44 20-7916 1066 Fax: 44 20-7284 1233
E-Mail: hire@autograph.co.uk
managing director Andrew Bruce; hire director Terry Saunders; technical & service director Tony Robinson; sound designers Bobby Aitken, Matt McKenzie; studio manager Simon Baker
Services: live sound design, professional audio equipment rental, acoustic consultancy, professional audio equipment sales

Avolites Ltd
184 Park Avenue, **London** NW10 7XL, United Kingdom
Tel: 44 20-8965 8522 Fax: 44 20-8965 0290
Internet: www.avolites.com
E-Mail: may@avolites.com
managing director Richard Salzedo; financial director Meena Varatharajan; software director Shahid Anwar; production director Nuri Waheishi; sales director Steve Warren; hire manager Garry Lodge; sales managers May Yam, Tony Shembish
Services: manufacture, sales and hire of the finest lighting control equipment used for major touring acts worldwide

Baker Tilly
2 Bloomsbury Street,
London WC1B 3ST, United Kingdom
Tel: 44 20-7413 5100 Fax: 44 20-7413 5101
Internet: www.bakertilly.co.uk
contacts David Halpern
Services: chartered accountants and business advisors

Bakker & Clients
Egelantiersgracht 49, 1015 RD **Amsterdam**, Netherlands
Tel: 31 20-638 3264 Fax: 31 20-638 3265
Internet: www.bakker-clients.nl
E-Mail: bakker-clients@hod.e2000.nl
director E.G.Bakker
Services: sponsorship consultants, concept development, events and marketing agency

Ballet Independents' Group – BIG
28 Sainfoin Road, **London** SW17 8EP, United Kingdom
Tel: 44 20-8682 1385/8741 2842 Fax: 44 20-8741 2842
E-Mail: susiecrow@easynet.co.uk
managers Susan Crow, Jennifer Jackson
Services: set up to facilitate activities which address issues concerning the nature and future of ballet with the flexibility inherent in the independent sector; BIG can initiate and direct one-off events or on-going programmes – courses, conferences, debates, choreographic platforms; respond to and collaborate with individuals and institutions; facilitate links within and outside the profession *Comments:* BIG aims to develop practical structures which promote contemporary ballet, and to transform the interior culture of the ballet world

Barjon-Société d'Avocats
6 rue de Lisbone, 75008 **Paris**, France
Tel: 33 1-4470 7373
Fax: 33 1-4470 7374
E-Mail: lisbonne@avocaweb.tm.fr
associé Jean-Christophe Barjon
Services: advice in general and legal matters for the performing arts

BBB-Bayerische Bühnenbau GmbH
Am Forst 17, Postfach 1259, 92602 **Weiden**, Germany
Tel: 49 961-3009-0
Fax: 49 961-3009-29
E-Mail: BBB.Weiden@t-online.de
Geschäftsführer Gerhard Bauer, Wols Dernvacher
Services: theatre and event technology

BDO Stoy Hayward
8 Baker Street, **London** W1M 1DA, United Kingdom
Tel: 44 20-7486 5888 Fax: 44 20-7487 3686
Internet: www.bdo.co.uk
E-Mail: haanm@stoyuk.mhs.compuserve.com
partners Michael Haan, Richard Harvey;
manager Bob Hymas
Services: accountancy
Comments: have extensive experience and knowledge of the special accounting needs of the performing arts and are represented throughout Europe

BDP Acoustics Ltd
Sunlight House, Quay House,
Manchester M60 3JA, United Kingdom
Tel: 44 161-834 8441 Fax: 44 161-832 4280
Internet: www.bdp.com.uk
E-Mail: acoustics-manch@bdp.co.uk
director D. W. Templeton
Services: acousticians specialising in auditorium, architectural, building services, enviromental and electro-acoustics and vibration

BDS Sponsorship Ltd
19 Waterside, 44-48 Warf Road,
London N1 7UX, United Kingdom
Tel: 44 20-7689 3333 Fax: 44 20-7689 3344
Internet: www.sponsorship.co.uk
E-Mail: bds@sponsorship.co.uk
chief executive Richard Busby
Services: tackling the unknown? independent consultancy, highly experienced in many new and established areas of sponsorship; strategic advice combined with creative solutions to maximise the return on a sponsors investment – from audits and feasibility studies to implementation and exploitation

Beckerbillett GmbH
Postfach 50 02 49, 22702 **Hamburg**, Germany
Tel: 49 40-3992 0220
Fax: 49 40-390 7233
Verkaufsleiter Reimer-Jörg Andresen
Services: foremost ticket printers for cinemas, theatres, concerts etc.

Belsize Music Rooms
67 Belsize Lane, **London** NW3 5AX, United Kingdom
Tel: 44 20-7916 0111
Fax: 44 20-7916 0222
Internet: www.impulse-music.co.uk/belsize.htm
E-Mail: belsize.music.rooms@dial.pipex.com
partners David Howells, Clare Howells
Services: rehearsal rooms for classical musicians

Bemrose Security Promotional Printing
PO Box 18, Wayzgoose Drive,
Derby DE21 6XG, United Kingdom
Tel: 44 1332-294 242 Fax: 44 1332-295 848
Internet: www.bemrose.co.uk/security
E-Mail: hsp@bemrose.co.uk
contact Trevor Willis
Services: security ticket printing company *Comments:* high security indoor and outdoor events, watermarked security paper, holograms, foils, books, numbered, block row seating plans, design, gift vouchers

Beneke, Daberto und Partner
Wirringer Str. 28, 31319 **Sehnde**, Germany
Tel: 49 5138-6089-0 Fax: 49 5138-608 989
E-Mail: t.beneke@t-online.de
contact Rüdiger Beneke
Services: architects, project management and theatre consulting; specialise in the complete planning and building of theatres, concert halls and other performing arts facilities including all technical equipment and media technology

BILCO UK Ltd.
3 Park Farm Business Centre, Fornham Saint Genevieve, **Bury St Edmunds** IP28 6TS, United Kingdom
Tel: 44 1284-701 696 Fax: 44 1284-702 531
Internet: www.bilco.com
contact Barbara Williams
Services: manufacturer of ASTM tested, acoustically rated fire vents for use over stage area and a complete line of horizontal access doors

Billett Service A/S
PO Box 645, Sentrum, 0106 **Oslo**, Norway
Tel: 47 2282 8100 Fax: 47 2282 8120
Internet: www.billetservice.no
E-Mail: firmapost@billetservice.no
managing director Björn Kgellim
Services: computerized ticket agency

Birdsong Public Relations
12 Penzance Place, **London** W11 4PA, United Kingdom
Tel: 44 20-7229 9166/7313 3524 Fax: 44 20-7221 5042
E-Mail: db.birdsong@harrisonparrott.co.uk
managing director Debra Boraston; senior account manager Kate Gedge; European account manager Lorna Neil; account director Undine Marshfield
Services: PR for the arts in the UK and Europe: dance, music (classical, jazz, pop, world), visual arts, festivals, cultural travel and leisure *Comments:* subsidiary agency of Harrison/Parrott Ltd, see also Agents & Producers

Bittiner, Whitehouse & Cie SA
PO Box 5132, 1211 **Genève**, Switzerland
Tel: 41 22-328 8390 Fax: 41 22-328 6485
E-Mail: bithouse@iprolink.ch
director Anthony Whitehouse
Services: business managers, accountants and tax advisers *Comments:* visitlng address: 66 boulevard St Georges, 1205 Genève

Black Light
18 West Harbour Road,
Edinburgh (Scotland) EH5 1PN, United Kingdom
Tel: 44 131-551 2337 Fax: 44 131-552 0370
Internet: www.black-light.com
E-Mail: main@black-light.com
managing director Gavin Stewart; hire John Barker; sales Karen Fairlie
Services: lighting theatrical specialists

Blonski Heard Architects
24 Links Yard, 29 Spellman Street,
London E1 5LX, United Kingdom
Tel: 44 20-7247 4999 Fax: 44 20-7247 7999
E-Mail: blonski@dial.pipex.com
architects Andrzej Blonski, Michael Heard
Services: architects with international experience in designing theatres, concert halls and facilities for the performing arts

Boca Systems Inc.
1065 S. Rogers Circle, **Boca Raton** FL 33487-2816, United States of America
Tel: 1 561-998 9600 Fax: 1 561-998 9609
Internet: www.bocasystems.com
E-Mail: bocatix@bocasystems.com
vice president Robert Kohn; general manager of ticket sales Andrew Sharp
Services: manufacturer of ticket printers

BOCS (Box Office Computer System)
68 Long Acre, **London** WC2E 9JQ, United Kingdom
Tel: 44 20-7872 9977 Fax: 44 20-7872 9378
Internet: www.bocs.co.uk
European sales director Jean-Marc Soulas
Services: computerized ticketing and marketing system; provides total solutions, fully integrated ticketing, marketing, membership, fundraising, subscriptions and facilities management; computer software *Comments:* leading ticketing and marketing software employed in more than 300 venues; prestigious client list including Royal National Theatre and Royal Opera House in London, Athens Concert Hall and Sydney Opera House

Boekel De Nerée
Atrium Building, 2nd Floor, Strawinskylaan 3037, 1077 ZX **Amsterdam**, Netherlands
Tel: 31 20-431 3131 Fax: 31 20-431 3143
Internet: www.bdn.nl
E-Mail: boekel.de.neree@bdn.nl
contacts AJ van der Marel, JW Knipscheer, PH Ariëns Kappers, Ms. J.A. Schaap
Services: lawyers for recording, publishing, management in the field of music, film and television contracts, media, trade mark and copyright law

Boekman Foundation
Herengracht 415, 1017 BP **Amsterdam**, Netherlands
Tel: 31 20-624 3736/39 (library) Fax: 31 20-638 5239
Internet: www.boekman.nl
E-Mail: secretariaat@boekman.nl
director C. Smithuijsen; editor Boekmancahier I. van Hamersveld; foreign affairs N. van der Wielen, Cathy Brickwood; PR & communication S. Hoogervorst
Services: study centre for arts, culture and related policy; library management, research, publications, conferences

Bolton & Quinn Ltd
8 Pottery Lane, **London** W11 4LZ, United Kingdom
Tel: 44 20-7221 5000 Fax: 44 20-7221 8100
directors Erica Bolton, Jane Quinn
Services: Press & PR

Bonnar Keenlyside Ltd.
Pall Mall Deposit, 124-128 Barlby Road,
London W10 6BL, United Kingdom
Tel: 44 20-8964 5288 Fax: 44 20-8964 4282
Internet: www.b-k.co.uk
E-Mail: info@b-k.org.uk
directors Anne Bonnar (Scotland),
Hilary Keenlyside (England)
Services: specialises in artistic planning, financial analysis, organisational review and strategy development. Britain's leading management consultants for the arts *Comments:* and at: Distillery House, The Grange, Burntisland, Fife KY3 0AA, Scotland, Tel: 1592-874 478, Fax: 1592-874 565

Boosey & Hawkes Music Publishers Ltd
295 Regent Street, **London** W1R 8JH,
United Kingdom
Tel: 44 20-7580 2060 Fax: 44 20-7637 3490
Internet: www.boosey.com
managing director Trevor Glover; director, composers & repertoire Janis Susskind; director, printed music Stephen Richards; director, media music Andrew Sunnucks
Services: major international music publishers providing classical music on hire; printed classical/educational music; music for media usage

Bose GmbH
Max-Planck-Str. 36, 61381 **Friedrichsdorf**, Germany
Tel: 49 6172-7104-0 Fax: 49 6172-710 419
Internet: www.gerd.becker.bose.com
E-Mail: gerd.becker@bose.com
Verkaufsleiter Pro Fi Ulrich Kremp; Verkaufsleiter Hi Fi Marcus Vogel
Services: distribute HiFi and professional sound equipment for concerts, bands, churches, hotels, the Olympic Games etc.

Brakeley Europe
Paramount House, 162-170 Wardour Street,
London W1V 4AB, United Kingdom
Tel: 44 20-7287 3361 Fax: 44 20-7287 8705
E-Mail: 100144.67@compuserve.com
managing director John Kelly; senior consultants Valerie Pakenham Keady, David Carr Morris; consultant Martin Kaufman
Services: fundraising consultancy: including start up help, fundraising audits, planning and feasibility studies, campaign planning and management and general advice

Brancato Costumi Teatrali
via A. Solari 11, 20144 **Milano**, Italy
Tel: 39 02-832 3902/8940 3792
Fax: 39 02-832 3661
E-Mail: brancato@infuturo.it
director Mario Brancati
Services: supply costume tailoring for all fields of the performing arts

Brilliant Stages Ltd
2 Hillgate, Wilburn Way,
Hitchin S94 0SZ, United Kingdom
Tel: 44 1462-455 366 Fax: 44 1462-436 219
Internet: www.brilliantstages.com
E-Mail: ckail@bstages.com
managing director Charlie Kail
Services: specialist stage set fabrication
Comments: a complete in-house design and fabrication service including welders, carpenters, fitters and workshops; a wide range of purpose built stage structures are available for hire; motion controlled, electro-mechanical and hydraulic structures a speciality; a Tomcat company

Brouhaha International
Gostins Building, 32-36 Hanover Street,
Liverpool L1 4LN, United Kingdom
Tel: 44 151-709 3334 Fax: 44 151-709 4994
Internet: www.brouhaha.demon.co.uk
E-Mail: admin@brouhaha.demon.co.uk
director Francisco Carrasco; administrator Karen Miller
Services: presents annual international street festivals incorporating performances, workshops and seminars, develop arts training and research projects; networking focus for European arts (funding, structures, touring, training, placements, tec.); English antenna for Gulliver Clearing House (European Placements Scheme); provide festival and arts administration consultancy and management *Comments:* see also Festivals

Budde Music International GmbH
Hohenzollerndamm 54 a, 14199 **Berlin**, Germany
Tel: 49 30-823 4015 Fax: 49 30-823 7076
Internet: www.buddemusic.de
E-Mail: budde@buddemusic.de
contact Dr. Rolf Budde
Services: Musikverlag (music publisher)

Bühnenbau Schnakenberg GmbH u. Co. KG
Rosenthalstraße 22-26, Postfach 21 06 25,
42369 **Wuppertal**, Germany
Tel: 49 202-469 080 Fax: 49 202-469 0852
Internet: www.schnakenberg.de
E-Mail: sales@schnakenberg.de
general manager t.b.a.; sales manager, marketing Jan-Peter Röpke
Services: stage planning, building and installation; upper and lower machinery, lighting systems, platforms, curtains, track-systems, grandstands, etc.; full service for stages, theatres and convention halls *Comments:* producer of the NIVOflex platform systems

Bureau Menno Heling Cultural Marketing
Prinsengracht 1087,
1017 JH **Amsterdam**, Netherlands
Tel: 31 20-623 5001 Fax: 31 20-638 2196
E-Mail: bmh@access4all.nl
contact Menno Heling
Services: advises cultural organisations on the development of their marketing and communication policies and with the introduction of a more market focused work method; also feasibility studies, strategies for sponsoring and fundraising *Comments:* other activities are development of new projects in cooperation with cultural organisations whereby (interim) project management might be a possibility

Burns Research Limited
23A Saint Leonards Terrace,
London SW3 4QT, United Kingdom
Tel: 44 20-7730 1641 Fax: 44 20-7330 0177
E-Mail: burns3860@aol.com
contact Chrissie Burns
Services: qualitative market research company

Buro Happold
Camden Mill, Lower Bristol Road, **Bath** BA2 3DQ,
United Kingdom
Tel: 44 1225-320 600 Fax: 44 1225-320 601
Internet: www.burohappold.com
chairman Michael Pickson
Services: consulting engineering practice, construction projects worldwide

Burrell-Foley-Fischer
York Central, 70-78 York Way,
London N1 9AG, United Kingdom
Tel: 44 20-7713 5333 Fax: 44 20-7713 5444
E-Mail: bff@kingsx.demon.co.uk
partner Mark Foley
Services: architects

Buzzacott
12 New Fetter Lane, **London** EC4A 1AP,
United Kingdom
Tel: 44 20-7556 1200 Fax: 44 20-7556 1212
Internet: www.buzzacott.co.uk
E-Mail: postmaster@buzzacott.co.uk
specialist charity and arts team,
contact Amanda Francis
Services: audit, accountancy, strategic advice, fundraising, computer systems, tax planning and advice

CAGEC (Centre d'Aide à la Gestion de l'Entreprise Culturelle)
BP 42206, 44022 **Nantes** Cedex 1, France
Tel: 33 240-482 223 Fax: 33 240-471 797
contact Gaelle Berthelot
Services: pr & administration; consultancy for non-profit arts organisation; also offers training courses in arts management *Comments:* visiting address: 22 rue Kerrégan, 44022 Nantes, Cedex 1

Cambridge Software Products, Inc.
Box 1148, 73 Water Street North,
Cambridge ON N1R 6C9, Canada
Tel: 1 519-622 2830 Fax: 1 519-621 1307
E-Mail: comsoft@IBM.NET
president Frank Jaglowitz
Services: computerized ticketing system

Campbell Hooper
35 Old Queen Street, **London** SW1H 9JD,
United Kingdom
Tel: 44 20-7222 9070
Fax: 44 20-7222 5591
Internet: www.campbell-hooper.co.uk
E-Mail: ch@campbell-hooper.co.uk
partner, head of entertainment department
Carolyn Jennings
Services: solicitors firm

Canford Audio PLC
Crowther Road, **Washington** NE38 0BW,
United Kingdom
Tel: 44 191-418 1000 Fax: 44 191-418 1001
Internet: www.canford.co.uk
E-Mail: sales@canford.co.uk
purchasing manager Steve King; UK sales manager Amanda McCall; managing director Iain Elliott
Services: specialist pro-audio distributors and manufacturers *Comments:* communications/talkback systems and accessories

Carlo Cucchiara SAS. di Giuseppe Cucchiara & C.
Via Liberta 46, Casella Postale 76,
94100 **Enna**, Italy
Tel: 39 0935-32805 Fax: 39 0935-32805
Internet: members.tripod.it/edimus/
E-Mail: edimus@tin.it
contact Carlo Cucchiara
Services: musical editions for any instrument and orchestra, research service of scores on customer request by mail, fax, phone and now e-mail

Carole Strachan Associates
1 Glyme Close, **Abingdon** OX14 3SY,
United Kingdom
Tel: 44 1235--538 190 Fax: 44 1235--538 190
E-Mail: carole@carolestrachan.demon.co.uk
Services: consultancy, in particular fundraising, marketing, campaign direction and strategic planning and development *Comments:* has worked for – among others -Welsh National Opera, The National Trust, Citizens Theatre (Glasgow) and University of Oxford

Carr & Angier
The Old Malthouse, Clarence Street, **Bath** BA1 5NS,
United Kingdom
Tel: 44 1225-446 664 Fax: 44 1225-446 654
E-Mail: mail@carrandangier.co.uk
partners Martin Carr, Peter Angier
Services: theatre consultants *Comments:* specialists in the planning of theatres and concert halls, and the design of their performance installations; feasibility studies undertaken

Caubet Chouchana Meyer
49 Champs Elysées, 75008 **Paris**, France
Tel: 33 1-4075 4075
Fax: 33 1-4075 4040
Internet: www.lexforce.com
E-Mail: lexforce@lexforce.com
partner Mr Caubet
Services: entertainment lawyers, international law

CCT Lighting Ltd
4 Tudor Court, Brighton Road, **Sutton** SM2 5AE,
United Kingdom
Tel: 44 20-8770 3636 Fax: 44 20-8643 9848
E-Mail: office@cctlighting.co.uk
joint managing director Mr. D.P. Manners; sales administrator Richard Lovejoy
Services: manufacturer and distributor of lighting equipment, dimmers, control and colour change; design, installation and project management; servicing of stage machinery

CELCO
Midas House, Willow Way, **London** SE26 4QP,
United Kingdom
Tel: 44 20-8699 6788 Fax: 44 20-8699 5056
Internet: www.celco.co.uk
E-Mail: sales@celco.co.uk
contact Colin Whitaker
Services: designers and manufacturers of lighting control boards and dimmers mainly for stage lighting

Centro di Musicologia Walter Stauffer
Corso Garibaldi 178, 26100 **Cremona**, Italy
Tel: 39 0372-410 322 Fax: 39 0372 410 322
Internet: www.rccr.cremona.it/stauffer
presidente dott Paolo Salvelli; vice presidente dott Raffaele Nuovo
Services: research centre; masterclasses for string instruments
Comments: the centre is also a foundation, located in Palazzo Raimondi together with the International Institute of Lute, the School of Paleography & Philology of Music and School of Musicology, to which they offer scholarships; foundation established in 1970

Cerebrum Lighting Ltd
Units 4 & 5, Shannon Comm Ctr, Beverley Way,
New Malden KT3 4PT, United Kingdom
Tel: 44 20-8949 3171
Fax: 44 20-8949 3649/8395 6111 (sales fax)
Internet: www.cerebrum.com
E-Mail: sales@cerebrum.com
managing director John Lethbridge; general manager Jack Exell; sales manager Andrew Stringer
Services: trade distributor and retail outlet for lighting and special effects equipment; all major UK manufacturers products available; specialists in export orders to all regions
Comments: catalogues available on request

CF Peters Musikverlag
Kennedyallee 101,
60596 **Frankfurt am Main**, Germany
Tel: 49 69-6300 9941 Fax: 49 69-6315 2334
Internet: www.edition-peters.de
E-Mail: kbm@edition-peters.de
director Karl Rarichs
Services: music publishers
Comments: also owners of publising company M P Velailess

Chadwick Jones Associates
2 Kelvedon Road, **London** SW6 5BW,
United Kingdom
Tel: 44 20-7731 6012 Fax: 44 20-7736 7271
Internet: virgin.net/cja.arts/
E-Mail: cja.arts@virgin.net
contacts Ian Jones, Anna Gaio, Siarlys Evans, Tom Owen
Services: feasibility studies; building projects; design brief preparation; facilities management; planning; marketing; management; market research; fundraising; have worked across Europe

Charivari
Les Petites Mouettes, Vaucottes,
76111 **Vattetot-sur-Mer**, France
Tel: 33 2-3527 3143
contact Alain Langlois
Services: Belle Epoque merry-go round for hire; constructed and carved in 1906 by Dangeren in Normandy

Charles Cosler Theatre Design, Inc.
232 Madison Avenue, Suite 600,
New York NY 10016-2564, United States of America
Tel: 1 212-213 5008 Fax: 1 212-213 6153
Internet: www.cosler.com
E-Mail: ccosler@cosler.com
contact Charles Cosler
Services: provides theatre design consulting to theatre owners, developers, architects on new construction, historic restoration and adaptive re-use projects, including space planning, interior design and equipment specifications

Charles M Salter Associates Inc
130 Sutter Street, **San Francisco** CA 94104,
United States of America
Tel: 1 415-397 0442 Fax: 1 415-397 0454
Internet: www.cmsalter.com
E-Mail: cmsalter@cmsalter.com
president Charles Salter; senior vice president Dave Schwind; vice president Anthony Nash
Services: consultants in acoustics & audio/visual system design
Comments: recent project experience includes Warner Pavillion, Aspen Concert Hall, Mendocino Center for the Arts, San Jose Repertory Theatre, Disney Concert Hall

Christian Henner-Fehr Kulturmanagement
Boecklinstrasse 48/9, 1020 **Wien**, Austria
Tel: 43 1-720 3483 Fax: 43 1-729 5490
E-Mail: c.henner-fehr@teleweb.at
contact Christian Henner-Fehr
Services: arts consultancy; offers consulting, coaching, workshops and seminars on project management, financing and the European Union for individuals, organisations or companies working in the arts, the cultural sector or in new media

Christopher Hunt
PO Box 27169, **London** W12 9GS, United Kingdom
Tel: 44 20-8994 1593/788-795 7007 (mobile)
Fax: 44 20-7504 8332
E-Mail: cbmhunt@aol.com
contact Christopher Hunt
Services: performing arts consultancy

CIEL SA Division TIX
Villalaan 26, 1630 **Linkebeek**, Belgium
Tel: 32 2-380 9860 Fax: 32 2-380 8876
E-Mail: mhe@euronet.be
manager Michel Hellawell
Services: computerized ticket agency *Comments:* BOCA printers distributor in Belgium

Cinema Computer Systems
Max-Planck-Str. 15b, 40699 **Erkrath**, Germany
Tel: 49 211-209 020 Fax: 49 211-2090 2111
Internet: www.ccsonline.de
E-Mail: sales@ccsonline.de
general manager Thomas Hillmer; head of sales Gert Pfeffer
Services: manufacturer of box office and administration and management systems for movie theatres

Circus Maniacs
43 Kingsway Avenue, Kingswood, **Bristol** BS15 8AN,
United Kingdom
Tel: 44 117-947 7042 Fax: 44 117-947 7042
E-Mail: circusmaniacs@palava.demon.co.uk
director Jackie Williams
Services: circus training school for adults, provide also performers & workshops for local authorities, festivals, fundays, corporate events and productions
Comments: also have a training school and performance company for young people (8-18 years)

Circus Space, The
Coronet Street, **London** N1 6HD, United Kingdom
Tel: 44 20-7729 9522 Fax: 44 20-7729 9422
contact Andrew Hill; pr & marketing manager Gerry Halliday; chief executive Teo Greenstreet; programme director Charlie Holland
Services: provides facilities for circus training and production, organises also classes
Comments: non-profit organisation, client of the London Arts Board, a member of FEDEC (European Federation of Circus Schools)

Cité de la Musique
221 avenue Jean-Jaurès, 75019 **Paris**, France
Tel: 33 1-4484 4484/4500 Fax: 33 1-4484 4501
Internet: www.cite-musique.fr
E-Mail: comm@cite-musique.fr
general director Brigitte Marger; directeur du centre de ressources musiqueux et dances Caroline Rosoor
Services: documentation, music library, conferences, workshops, music museum *Comments:* see also Venues

Citronic Ltd
Halifax Road, Bowerhill Est, **Melksham** SN12 6UB,
United Kingdom
Tel: 44 1225-705 600/725 Fax: 44 1225-709 639
Internet: www.citronic.com
E-Mail: info@citronic.com
sales & marketing director Mike Gerrish
Services: manufacturer of professional electronic audio equipment, pro audio

Clark Transfer, Inc
800 A Paxton Street, **Harrisburg** PA 17104,
United States of America
Tel: 1 717-238 0801 Fax: 1 717-238 4865
Internet: www.clarktransfer.com
E-Mail: tawna@clarktransfer.com
contact/director of marketing Tawna Woolstenhulme; sales Gail Fishel, Denise Weber; international Dan McClafferty
Services: Clark Transfer is the theatrical and performing arts transportation company; offers air-ride trucking in North America for touring Broadway shows, orchestras, ballet companies, operas and other performing arts groups; also manage and coordinate door-to-door international logistics transport by truck, air and sea

ClassiCulturCentrum
c/o Wolfgang Ellenberger, Iglauer Straße 13,
74722 **Buchen**, Germany
Tel: 49 6281-97914 Fax: 49 6281-97915
Internet: www.CCC-Classic.de
E-Mail: CCC_Wolfgang.Ellenberger@t-online.de
contact Wolfgang Ellenberger
Services: music publisher, piano-rental, pianist, conductor *Comments:* grand piano Bösendorfer Imperial among others, the only one world-wide with pianodisc/symphony sound computer system

Clausecker & Bingel Ereignisse GmbH
Kurfürstendamm 48, 10707 **Berlin**, Germany
Tel: 49 30-8867 9579 Fax: 49 30-8867 9585
E-Mail: sabine-clausecker@clausecker-bingel.de
general managers Sabine Clausecker, Eberhard Bingel
Services: productions only, e.g. MTV European Music Awards, UN Klima Konferenz, Swatch beach party, Mercedes Benz – Introduction of the A-Class (A-Motion); communication consulting, especially public relations and event marketing *Comments:* specialist for large outdoor-events

Clay Paky S.p.A.
Via Pascoli 1, 24066 **Pedrengo (BG)**, Italy
Tel: 39 035-654 311 Fax: 39 035-665 976
Internet: www.claypaky.it
E-Mail: cp.sales@claypaky.it
direttore marketing e commerciale Enrico Caironi
Services: designer and manufacturer of a wide range of high quality products for professional show lighting, including intelligent lighting units, special lighting effects, automated fixtures, stage lightings, projectors and relevant controllers; produces microprocessor driven, fully controllable multifunctional projectors

Clintons
55 Drury Lane, **London** WC2B 5SQ, United Kingdom
Tel: 44 20-7379 6080 Fax: 44 20-7240 9310
E-Mail: info@clintons.co.uk
partners John Cohen, David Landsman, Peter Button
Services: solicitors providing services to entertainment industry

Clive Leyland Consulting Ltd
4 Newmeadow, Lowstock, **Bolton** BL6 4PB,
United Kingdom
Tel: 44 1204-848 838 Fax: 44 1204-496 767
E-Mail: cliveleyland@compuserve.com
contact Clive Leyland
Services: substantial experience with major UK arts organisations; IT strategy definition, requirements specification and implementation managements

Cloud Electronics Ltd
140 Staniforth Road, **Sheffield** S9 3HF,
United Kingdom
Tel: 44 114-244 7051 Fax: 44 114-242 5462
Internet: www.cloud.co.uk
E-Mail: info@cloud.co.uk
director Roy Millington; sales admin Janet Barnes
Services: audio equipment

Coemar Spa
Via Inghilterra/Zona Industriale,
46042 **Castel Goffredo (MN)**, Italy
Tel: 39 0376-77521 Fax: 39 0376-780 657
Internet: www.coemar.com
E-Mail: export@coemar.com
responsabile ufficio estero Carlo Galeazi
Services: producer of professional projectors for theatre, TV, studios (NAT, CF1200 spot, CF1200 HE)

Collyer-Bristow
4 Bedford Row, **London** WC1R 4DF,
United Kingdom
Tel: 44 20-7242 7363 Fax: 44 20-7405 0555
Internet: www.collyer-bristow.co.uk
E-Mail: cblaw@collyerbristow.co.uk
director of administration Pat Trottnow
Services: solicitors

Comedia
The Round, **Bournes Green – nr Stroud** GL6 7NL,
United Kingdom
Tel: 44 1452-770 624 Fax: 44 1452-770 596
E-Mail: charleslandrycomedia@compuserve.com
chairman Charles Landry
Services: consultancy research planning; recent works include cultural planning and quality of life studies for Barcelona, Cracow, Glasgow, Helsinki, Mantua, St. Petersburg, Prague, Swedish Ministry of Cultural Affairs, Adelaide, Bulgaria Ministry of Cultural Affairs

Comme Il Vous Plaira
148 rue de Charanton, 75012 **Paris**, France
Tel: 33 1-4343 5558 Fax: 33 1-4343 5525
E-Mail: civp@cybercable.fr
chargé de production Sophie Lagrange
Services: distribution and production of all kinds of performing arts companies (emphasis on theatre companies)

Commins Acoustics Workshop
15 rue Laurence Sanart, 75020 **Paris**, France
Tel: 33 1-4797 1702/609-114 342 (mobile)
Fax: 33 1-4797 1742
E-Mail: comminsacoustics@compuserve.com
contact Daniel Commins
Services: acousticians, room acoustics, architectural acoustics, concert halls, opera houses, theatres, new contruction of renovations
Comments: address in US: Commins Acoustics Workshop Inc, 350 Fifth Avenue #3304, New York, NY 10118, Tel: +1 212-971 1395, Fax: +1 212-564 1135, Email: comminsacoustics@compuserve.com

COMPRO
63 Charles Street, **Epping** CM16 7AX,
United Kingdom
Tel: 44 1992-572 805 Fax: 44 1992-572 805
director Genevieve Pearson
Services: word processing – laser address labels of concert promoters, UK and abroad; complete mailshots, mail merge

Conroy Tobin
Boundary House, 3rd floor, 91-93 Charterhouse Street, **London** EC1M 6HR, United Kingdom
Tel: 44 20-7608 3633 Fax: 44 20-7608 3201
contacts Arnold Conroy, F. Tobin (S.C.C.A)
Services: accountants

CPF – Cultural Projects Factory
c/ Santa Brígida 19, Entlo. C,
28004 **Madrid**, Spain
Tel: 34 91-531 6633 Fax: 34 91-531 9472
E-Mail: cpfmadrid@mx3.redestb.es
cultural advisor Blas Fernández Gallego; coordinator Teresa Sánchez; executive director Pedro Cheng
Services: CPF organises and carries out any type of cultural project, such as monographic or author exhibitions, concerts, theatre, dance, film, conferences
Comments: produces and programmes cultural projects between Spain and Asia

CR Thomas & Co
1929 Building Merton Abbey Mills, 18 Watermill Way, **London** SW19 2RD, United Kingdom
Tel: 44 20-8542 4262
Fax: 44 20-8545 0662
contact Chris Thomas
Services: accountants, tax, royalties

Craigmyle & Company Limited
The Grove, **Harpenden** AL5 1AH, United Kingdom
Tel: 44 1582-762 441 Fax: 44 1582-461 489
Internet: www.craigmyle.mcmail.com
E-Mail: craigmyle@cwcom.net
contact Geoffrey Howard
Services: fundraising consultants
Comments: the company has been involved in over 1300 appeals and helped clients to raise well over £300 million; initial consultations are without charge, fees are based on amount of service to be provided (and are payable in instalments over the period of service) and the company's practice is to submit detailed proposals before entering into contract

Crowcroft & Partners
62 Britton Street, **London** EC1M 5PJ, United Kingdom
Tel: 44 20-7251 1191 Fax: 44 20-7251 1151
E-Mail: sponsorship@crowcroft.demon.co.uk
contact Chris Crowcroft
Services: specialists in the art of business sponsorship; also media/education, community issues

CTL (Control Technology) Ltd
Unit 2 Britannia Business Park, Quarry Wood, **Aylesford** ME20 7NT, United Kingdom
Tel: 44 1622-719 151
Fax: 44 1622-716 425
Internet: www.ctlab.co.uk
E-Mail: bob.owen@msn.com
contact R J Owen
Services: audio-visual equipment, sales and hire

CTS Computer Ticket Service
Dingolfinger Straße 6,
81673 **München**, Germany
Tel: 49 89-416 0040 Fax: 49 89-4160 0445
Internet: www.cts.de
E-Mail: vertriev@cts.de
head of departments Cornelia Einsiedel-Michaely
Services: computerized ticket service

Cultural Projects Unlimited
Croft Head, **Crawsordjohn (Scotland)** ML12 6SU, United Kingdom
Tel: 44 1864-504 206 Fax: 44 1864-504 206
Internet: www.culturalprojects.co.uk
E-Mail: admin@culturalprojects.co.uk
director Bob Clark
Services: project management, organisational change, project development

Da Capo Musikmarketing GmbH
Oberer Stadtplatz 5, 6330 **Kufstein**, Austria
Tel: 43 5372-66660 Fax: 43 5372-666 6016
Internet: www.dacapo.at
E-Mail: info@dacapo.at
Geschäftsführer Matthias Kendlinger
Services: music marketing, tour producer (concert and opera)

DAMI Ltd
43-1 Kutuzovski Avenue, 121170 **Moscow**, Russia
Tel: 7 095-249 7854/219 8572
Fax: 7 095-142 5918
E-Mail: dami@glas.apc.org
general director David Chichua; deputy director Dasha Nemtsova
Services: travel company – event tourism; directory of events 'Where in the World'

DaSilva Puppet Books
63 Kennedy Road, **Bicester** OX6 8BE, United Kingdom
Tel: 44 1869-245 793
Fax: 44 1869-245 793
contact Ray & Joan Da Silva
Services: major supplier of books relating to puppetry; also producing and publishing books

DATACULTURE Ltd
Midsummer House, 405 Midsummer Boulevard, **Milton Keynes** MK9 3BN, United Kingdom
Tel: 44 1908-232 404 Fax: 44 1908-232 414
Internet: www.dataculture.com
E-Mail: databox@dataculture.com
managing director Jonathan Hyams; sales director Charles Davies; director of business development Roger Tomlinson
Services: DATABOX for Windows Ticketing and Marketing software system, a Windows 9X/NT dedicated system; available also in a fully international version, multilingual, multi-currency, Euro compliant; supporting audience development

Davenport Lyons
1 Old Burlington Street, **London** W1X 2NL, United Kingdom
Tel: 44 20-7468 2600 Fax: 44 20-7437 8216
Internet: www.davenport-lyons.com
E-Mail: dl@davenport-lyons.com
partners Leon Morgan, David Rockberger, James Ware, Anthony Fiducia and others
Services: entertainment solicitors; music publishing, music, television, video, film, broadcasting, satellite

David Jackson & Associates
Crowlin Cottage, Little London Road, **Cross in Hand** TN21 0LT, United Kingdom
Tel: 44 1435-868 808 Fax: 44 1435-868 889
E-Mail: deejaay@compuserve.com
director David Jackson
Services: theatre consultancy; audience facilities; event management; specialising in 'front of house' and customer services; general management, box office and marketing planning and organisation, 'customer care', temporary venues, festivals co-ordination, gala and VIP administration, feasibility studies

David Wineman, Solicitors
Craven House, 121 Kingsway, **London** WC2B 6NX, United Kingdom
Tel: 44 20-7831 0521 Fax: 44 20-7831 0731
Internet: www.davidwineman.co.uk
E-Mail: law@davidwineman.co.uk
partners Irving David, Vivian Wineman, Neil Aspess, Malcolm Brahams, Stuart Killen
Services: solicitors offering a full range of legal services with particular expertise in the entertainment industry including music, film, television and sponsorship

Deloitte & Touche – Entertainment, Hospitality and Leisure Division
Stonecutter Court, 1 Stonecutter Street, **London** EC4A 4TR, United Kingdom
Tel: 44 20-7936 3000
Fax: 44 20-7936 2346
Internet: www.deloitte-touche.co.uk
partners Charles Bradbrook, Gavin Hamilton-Deeley, Piers Gregson, Ann Kennedy
Services: accounting, taxation and associated services; audit, corporate finance, corporate special services, forensic, management consultants, managed services, tax
Comments: USA: Larry Wizel, Deloitte & Touche LLP, 2 World Financial Centre, New York NY10281-1414, Tel: +1 212-436 2000, Fax: +1 212-436 5000; France: Jean-Michel Raingeard, BDA/Deloitte & Touche, 185 avenue Charles de Gaulle, 92200 Neuilly sur Seine, France, Tel: +33 1-4088 2800, Fax: +33 1-4088 2828

Denander & Grahl AB
PO Box 4342, 102 67 **Stockholm**, Sweden
Tel: 46 8-702 1300 Fax: 46 8-702 1640
Internet: www.denandergrahl.se
partners Henry Denander, Stefan Grahl
Services: business & legal consulting

Denton Hall
Five Chancery Lane, Clifford's Inn, **London** EC4A 1BU, United Kingdom
Tel: 44 20-7242 1212
Fax: 44 20-7404 0087
Internet: www.dentonhall.com
E-Mail: info@dentonhall.com
chairman James Dallas; media & technology dept. Kenneth Dearsley; departmental executive partner Alan Williams; partners Robert Allan, Adrian Barr-Smith, Nicholas Higham, Michael Ridley, Nick West; consultants Michael Flint, Jerry Katzman
Services: the whole spectrum of entertainment law; television and film production and financing; music; sports and sponsorship; book and journal publishing; copyright and defamation; live stage (Ballet, theatre, opera and music); also multimedia, technology and telecommunications law including cable and satellite and computer law
Comments: a full-service entertainment, media and technology group dedicated to the service of its clients; queries to Ken Dearsley & Alan Williams

DeSisti Lighting UK Ltd
15 Old Market Street, **Thetford** IP24 2EQ, United Kingdom
Tel: 44 1842-752 909
Fax: 44 1842-753 746
E-Mail: desisti@globalnet.co.uk
managing director Bill Smillie; sales director Jon Reay-Young
Services: lights, grip equipment and stands, studio suspension and lighting control systems, design service to capital projects

DESPAR Licht und Bühnentechnik GmbH
Nikolaus-Otto-Str. 9, 55129 **Mainz**, Germany
Tel: 49 6131-50630
Fax: 49 6131-506 3399
E-Mail: info@despar.de
Geschäftsführer Rüdiger Kreckel
Services: planning, providing and installing light systems for theatres, film and TV studios

DEW
400 Rouding Lane South, **Woodford Green** IG8 1EG, United Kingdom
Tel: 44 20-8551 8383
Fax: 44 20-8550 4308
contact David Easom
Services: manufacturer of standard and custom dimming systems for studio, stage and architectural projects

Dewynters plc
48 Leicester Square, **London** WC2H 7QD, United Kingdom
Tel: 44 20-7321 0488
Fax: 44 20-7321 0104
Internet: www.dewynter.com
managing director Anthony Pye Jeary; general manager Mary Williams; chairman Robert De Wynter
Services: advertising agency specialising in theatre and entertainment, media-buying publishing, design, marketing, merchandising

DHA Lighting Ltd.
284-302 Waterloo Rd, **London** SE1 8RQ, United Kingdom
Tel: 44 20-7771 2900 Fax: 44 20-7771 2901
Internet: www.dhalighting.co.uk
E-Mail: sales@dhalighting.co.uk
general manager Diane Grant; finance manager Nina Harrup; graphics manager Vicky Fairall; sales office manager Louise Robson-Tester; IT manager Sean Wigg; production manager Nigel Baker; PR officer/OEM accounts Nina Harrup
Services: lighting *Comments:* also lighting design consultancy: contact Adam Grater, Peter Fordham, Jonathan Howard (Email: design@dhalighting.co.uk)

Die Kultur AG
Arbeitsgemeinschaft für Kulturmanagement-Beratung GmbH
Sitz Nikolauskapelle, Am Königshof,
60388 **Frankfurt am Main**, Germany
Tel: 49 6109-24466 Fax: 49 6109-24467
director Prof. Peter W. Hübner
Services: cultural management consulting. emphasis on marketing and organisation; cultural management courses

Dijkstra Transport BV
Nieuwe Havenweg 47, 1216 BL **Hilversum**, Netherlands
Tel: 31 35-621 4040 Fax: 31 35-624 7519
director M Dijkstra; manager orchestra transport A.C. van Hage
Services: orchestra transport

Donmar Drama Department
2 Tudor Estate, Abbey Road, Park Royal, **London** NW10 7UY, United Kingdom
Tel: 44 20-8453 6004 Fax: 44 20-8453 6005
Internet: www.lighting-tech.com
E-Mail: sales@domar.co.uk
sales coordinator Jonathan Adkins; installation manager Bruce Tompsett; service manager Eddie Hirad
Services: distributors and service agents for Arri, Pulsar, Zero 88, Hall Stage, Lee Filters, Le Maitre, CCT and Rosco; worldwide export

Doughty Engineering Ltd
Crow Arch Lane, **Ringwood** BH24 1NZ, United Kingdom
Tel: 44 1425-478 961 Fax: 44 1425-474 481
Internet: www.dought-engineering.co.uk
E-Mail: sales@doughty-engineering.co.uk
director Mervyn Lister; sales manager Julian Chiverton
Services: manufacturers of a wide variety of items which include; Club, Shadow and Studio lighting stands, Nebula winch stands, Zenith truss lifts, Bulldog Grip Equipment, Easydeck staging, Doughty Clamps, Music and Conductor stands, Scenery fixings, Scenery pulleys, Scnery braces and weights, Hook clamps, Safety bonds, Boom arms and scaffold fitments of all types. Doughty also undertake the fabrication of 'one off' special products ranging from scenery pieces through to safety bonds

Dovetail Foks
Mount Barrow House, 12 Elizabeth Street, **London** SW1 9RB, United Kingdom
Tel: 44 20-7815 3333 Fax: 44 20-7815 3355
E-Mail: jo.johnson@dovetail.foks.co.uk
directors Dean Borg, John Foks
Services: travel consultancy to the television and music industries

DPS-Datenverarbeitung & Planung Steuerung GmbH
Heiner-Fleischmann-Straße 6,
74172 **Neckarsulm**, Germany
Tel: 49 7132-6066 Fax: 49 7132-37464
Geschäftsführer Alf Böttcher
Services: software for venues and promotions

Dr Hochegger Kommunikations GmbH
Goldeggasse 7/2/13, 1040 **Wien**, Austria
Tel: 43 1-505 4701 Fax: 43 1-5054 7019
E-Mail: pr@hochegger.at
Kommunikationsberatung Dr. Hochegger
Services: sponsorship consultancy

Dvora Lewis Public Relations
12 Pilgrim's Lane, **London** NW3 1SN, United Kingdom
Tel: 44 20-7435 9257 Fax: 44 20-7435 1417
E-Mail: dvoralewis@computer.com
contact Dvora Lewis
Services: public relations consultancy handling UK and international press, radio and television publicity; clients include an orchestra, individual artists & international arts events

Eastern Touring Agency
Bolton's Warehouse, Tenison Road, **Cambridge** CB1 2DG, United Kingdom
Tel: 44 1223-500 202 Fax: 44 1223-576 307
E-Mail: info@eta.eastern-arts.co.uk
touring consultant Lynne Williams; tour managers Emma Borley, Caroline Griffin; managing director John Wroe; education development consultant Catherine Rose; marketing assistant Neil Parker
Services: aims to facilitate the touring of innovative performing arts projects within the East of England
Comments: includes regional marketing agency; seeks sponsorship for specific high-profile tours

EasyPac oHG
Colditz Str. 33, 12099 **Berlin**, Germany
Tel: 49 30-7018 9960
Fax: 49 30-7018 9961
E-Mail: easypac@t-online.de
general manager Peter Mruk; contact Uwe Dobschies
Services: flight cases; studio rates, rates for professional TV, audio and video companies

Eatons
22 Blades Court, Deodar Road, **London** SW15 2NU, United Kingdom
Tel: 44 20-8877 9727 Fax: 44 20-8877 9940
E-Mail: eatonslaw@aol.com
senior partner Michael Eaton; partners Martin Dacre, David Glick, Jeremy Wakefield, Elizabeth Hale, Adam van Stratem, Richard Baskind, James Greensoade
Services: solicitors, entertainment law

Ecla Lux
12 rue Molière, 94200 **Ivry-sur-Seine**, France
Tel: 33 1-4672 7636
Fax: 33 1-4658 6756
Internet: www.eclalux.fr
E-Mail: eclalux@aol.com
general director Benoît Israel
Services: lighting, installation and engineering for theatres, TV studios and cinema; also architectural settings

Edinburgh Festival Fringe
180 High Street, **Edinburgh (Scotland)** EH1 1QS, United Kingdom
Tel: 44 131-226 5257 Fax: 44 131-220 4205
Internet: www.edfringe.com
E-Mail: admin@edfringe.com
directors Hilary Strong, Paul Gudgin; marketing & press manager Charlotte di Corpo; production manager Sarah Steven; administration manager Jade Alison; box office manager Michelle Rodden
Services: the Edinburgh Festival Fringe Office is open year-round to provide invaluable information and advise for performers who may wish to participate; we also provide a definitive programme of events, a central box office and press office
Comments: the Edinburgh Fringe is the largest arts festival in the world: every August sees 600 companies give 17,000 performances in around 200 different venues

Editions Chantraine
7 Avenue Henri Paris, 7500 **Tournai**, Belgium
Tel: 32 69-228 718 Fax: 32 69-228 718
E-Mail: chantraine@mail.dotcom.fr
managing director Paul Chantraine
Services: music publishers (music for organ), musical creations for the media & movies (music for symphony orchestra); publisher of the collection Orchestra at Home: concerti for soloist and orchestra, with the soloist part on score and the orchestral accompaniment on CD

Edmonds Bowen + Company
4 Old Park Lane, **London** W1Y 3LJ, United Kingdom
Tel: 44 20-7629 8000 Fax: 44 20-7221 9334
E-Mail: edbow@easynet.co.uk
partners Simon Bowen, Mark Wilkins, Richard Cruickshank
Services: solicitors: litigation, convayencing, music

Effective Theatrical Productions Ltd.
23 Bridford Mews, **London** W1N 1LQ, United Kingdom
Tel: 44 20-7323 2100 Fax: 44 20-7323 2199
executive producer Barry Stead
Services: theatrical production

Eikon
Via della libertà 38, 50023 **Impruneta (FI)**, Italy
Tel: 39 055-201 1500 Fax: 39 055-231 3882
E-Mail: eikon@dada.it
contact Ferri Nedo
Services: surtitles for opera and theatre, available for all of Europe

Elizabeth Anderson Associates
98 Elmshurst Crescent, **London** N2 0LP, United Kingdom
Tel: 44 20-8883 8723
Fax: 44 20-8883 8723
E-Mail: ea@elizabeth-anderson.com
contact Elizabeth Anderson
Services: international conference production; arts consultancy, specializing in dance

Enrich i Amat Advocats
Josep Tarradellas 155 2° 2ª,
08029 **Barcelona**, Spain
Tel: 34 93-419 3798 Fax: 34 93-419 4844
Internet: www.copyright.com
E-Mail: lawspain@filnet.es
contact Enric Enrich, Carlos Enrich
Services: entertainment lawyers, legal services, business law

Entertainment Accounting International
5th floor, Abford House,
15 Wilton Road, **London** SW1V 1LT, United Kingdom
Tel: 44 20-7931 0808 Fax: 44 20-7931 9100
proprietor Mike Donovan; royalty manager Julie Eyre
Services: specialists in accounting for the music and entertainment industries – tour accounting and tax planning, royalty audit and accounting, business & financial management

ERES EDITION
Postfach 1220,
28859 **Lilienthal (Bremen)**, Germany
Tel: 49 4298-1676 Fax: 49 4298-5312
director Horst Schubert
Services: music publisher specialising in Estonian music (choral and instrumental)
Comments: see also Recorded Media

Erik Borgman
Banhagestraat 75, 3052 **Blanden**, Belgium
Tel: 32 16-406 974/477-338 928 (mobile)
Fax: 32 16-401 268
E-Mail: erikborg@compuserve.com
director Erik Borgman
Services: subtitling and simultaneous translations for international theatre festivals and companies

Ernst Beissner GmbH & Co. KG – Geschäftsbereich Tourneen-Spedition
Bultstraße 9, 30159 **Hannover**, Germany
Tel: 49 511-815 081 Fax: 49 511-855 132
E-Mail: BeissnerD@aol.com
contacts Dirk Beißner, Martina Köster
Services: symphony tours, European instrument transport, air cargo charter

Ernst Krenek Institut
Hanuschgasse 3/8, 1010 **Wien**, Austria
Tel: 43 1-513 9447 Fax: 43 1-512 0811
Internet: www.krenek.com
E-Mail: krenek@krenek.com
Generalsekretärin Doris Flekatsch; Presse/Archiv Perra Preinfalk
Services: information and research on the works of the composer Ernst Krenek

Ernst & Young
Becket House, 1 Lambeth Palace Road,
London SE1 7EU, United Kingdom
Tel: 44 20-7951 2000 Fax: 44 20-7928 1345
Internet: www.eyuk.com
E-Mail: tce@ernsty.co.uk
partners Garth Tweedale, Richard Rees-Pulley
Services: international business and financial advisors to the entertainment industry

Ernst & Young Paris – France
Tour Manhattan, 6 Place de l'Iris,
92095 **Paris** Cedex La Défence 2, France
Tel: 33 1-4693 6000 Fax: 33 1-4776 2033
Internet: www.eyuk.com
E-Mail: BrunoPerrin@ernst-young.fr
contact Bruno Perrin
Services: lawyers and accountants

Euclid
1st Floor, 46-48 Mount Pleasant, **Liverpool** L3 5SD, United Kingdom
Tel: 44 151-709 2564 Fax: 44 151-709 8647
E-Mail: euclid@mcmail.com
director Geoffrey Brown
Services: information, events, counselling, contacts for arts organisations and project
Comments: work internationally; also offices in Cardiff: 1st Floor, 2 Crown Court, 9 Duke Street, Cardiff (Wales) CF1 2AY, Tel: +44 29-2023 5885, Fax: +44 29-2023 5882; and Brussels: 5th Floor, rue d'Arion 39-41, 1000 Brussels, Belgium, Tel: +32 2-230 9492, Fax: +32 2-280 1672

Europea Limited
Provender Mill, Mill Bay Lane, **Horsham** RH12 1TQ, United Kingdom
Tel: 44 1403-263 860 Fax: 44 1403-251 884
E-Mail: sjohn@pmill.com
contact Simon John
Services: insurances for performing artists

Euroscene Ltd.
1 Chase Road, Northern Way, **Bury St Edmunds** IP32 6NL, United Kingdom
Tel: 44 1284-760 377 Fax: 44 1284-750 979
directors David Goult, Alan Hack; design office manager Trevor Golding; installation manager Mike Batley
Services: design, manufacture and installation of stage machinery including flying systems, stage and orchestra lifts, revolves, safety curtains, motorised winches, etc.

Event Audio Visual Group Inc
PO Box 368, **Milford** MI 48381, United States of America
Tel: 1 248-449 6520 Fax: 1 248-449 6504
Internet: www.showsource.com
contact Gary Becker
Services: audio visual, show, event equipment (rent, purchase) and services (staging/lighting, sound systems, video production/display, tents/hospitality, exhibits/displays,communications equipment)
Comments: call tollfree from USA 1 800-383 6828

EVENT-Production GmbH
Auf der Riehler Strasse 8, 50668 **Köln**, Germany
Tel: 49 221-9730 3403
Fax: 49 221-726 0942/9730 34150
Internet: www.livingmedia.de
E-Mail: interact@livingmedia.de
Geschäftsführer Arnd Schäfer, Stefan Koch
Services: promotion management; event marketing, especially in the area of technology

Everfhetf
Senador House, 85 Queen Victoria Street,
London EC4V 4GI, United Kingdom
Tel: 44 20-7919 4500 Fax: 44 20-7919 4919
chairmen Frank Presland, Richard Miller; partners Norman Chapman, Craig Eadie, Patrick Isherwood
Services: solicitors

Faber Music Ltd.
3 Queen Square, **London** WC1 3AU, United Kingdom
Tel: 44 20-7278 7436/1279-828 989 (sales)
Fax: 44 20-7833 7939/1279-828 990 (sales)
Internet: www.fabermusic.co.uk
E-Mail: information@fabermusic.co.uk
chairman Tom Pasteur; managing director Richard King; pa to managing director Katy Burke
Services: classical/educational music publishers; UK representatives for Bärenreiter/Alkor edition; music hire & media/film department *Comments:* distribution and sales: Burnt Mill, Elizabeth Way, Harlow CM20 2HX

Fabtronic Group
Unit 6, William Street, Mounts Business Park,
Northampton NN1 3EW, United Kingdom
Tel: 44 1604-638 100 Fax: 44 1604-638 900
Internet: www.fabtronic.co.uk
E-Mail: fablight@aol.co.uk
sales & marketing Murray Dunkley; event/entertainment coordinator Kerry Hodges
Services: sound & lighting sales, hire and installation; event & party organisers; entertainment agency

Fair's Fare
C.P. House, 3rd Floor Tower, 97-107 Uxbridge Road,
London W5 5TL, United Kingdom
Tel: 44 20-8810 0888 Fax: 44 20-8579 8485
E-Mail: sales@fairsfare.com
chief executive Ranjit Anand
Services: travel consultants – searches for most cost-effective fares to the business traveller

Famusic s.a.
Ribas 19, 08013 **Barcelona**, Spain
Tel: 34 93-247 3477 Fax: 34-93 265 8348
E-Mail: ferrermusical@excelweb.es
director Begoña Gómez Morejón; jefe ventas Eugenio Valdés Segura
Services: makers of guitar strings

Ferrer Musical, SA
Marina 136, 08013 **Barcelona**, Spain
Tel: 34 93-231 2707 Fax: 34 93-231 5523
E-Mail: ferrermusical@excelweb.es
director Begoña Gómez Morejón; jefe ventas Eugenio Valdés Segura
Services: distribution of musical instruments

First Call/The Ticketing Group
Ocean House, Hayswick Avenue, **Crawley** RH10 1BF, United Kingdom
Tel: 44 1293-433 600 Fax: 44 1293-433 704
Internet: www.firstcalltickets.com
Services: Europe's largest ticket agency; includes Keith Prowse and First Call *Comments:* please mark correspondence for attention of relevant section head/team leader

Fitzcarraldo Srl
Corso Mediterraneo 94, 10129 **Torino**, Italy
Tel: 39 011-568 3976 Fax: 39 011-503 361
E-Mail: artlab.fitz@alpcom.it
managing director Ugo Bacchella
Services: strategic consultancy, research and studies, feasibility studies for cultural operators *Comments:* member of EFAH (European Forum for Arts and Heritage) and ENCAT (European Network Cultural Administrations Training); partner agencies in UK, France, Belgium, Netherlands, Germany and Spain; associated consultants in 6 other European countries; EU-Consultant member; see also Courses (ARTLAB)

Flashlight
Tractieweg 190, 3534 AB **Utrecht**, Netherlands
Tel: 31 30-244 4842 Fax: 31 30-244 7606
E-Mail: flashlight@point.nl
managing director Fons de Vreede;
sales manager Ed de Boer
Services: hire and sales service for the entertainment industry

Fleischmann Arts
707 Wilshire Boulevard, Suite 1850, **Los Angeles** CA 90017-3501, United States of America
Tel: 1 213-615 1640 Fax: 1 213-615 1644
director Ernest Fleischmann
Services: international arts consultants

Fleming & Barron
Unit A2, 4th floor, Linton House, 39-51 Highgate Road, **London** NW5 1RT, United Kingdom
Tel: 44 20-7482 4030 Fax: 44 20-7284 1239
E-Mail: fleming@dbf-acoustics.demon.co.uk
partners Dr David Fleming, Dr Michael Barron
Services: acoustic consultants and specialists in auditorium acoustics for the design of buildings for performance and training in performing arts, worldwide; also at Bath (UK) and Athens

Flint Hire and Supply Limited
Queens Row, **London** SE17 2PX, United Kingdom
Tel: 44 20-7703 9786 Fax: 44 20-7708 4189
E-Mail: sales@flintltd.demon.co.uk
general manager Alistair Flint; administrator Ben Lyle
Services: suppliers of scenery fittings, tools, hardware, ironmongery, adhesives, paints and textures; hire and sales of MEGADEK staging, curtain tracks, stage weights and braces; 2 paint frames also for hire

Formula Sound Ltd
Ashton Road, Bredbury, **Stockport** SK6 2SR, United Kingdom
Tel: 44 161-494 5650 Fax: 44 161-494 5651
Internet: www.formula-sound.com
E-Mail: info@formula-sound.com
managing director Tony Cockell; sales director Sandra Cockell
Services: designers and manufacturers of audio equipment for use in discotheques, multi-purpose venues, theatres, recording and audio visual studios *Comments:* also manufacturers of environmental noise control products for use in entertainment venues

Foundation for Art and Creative Technology (FACT)
Bleakot Chambers, School Lane, **Liverpool** L1 3BX, United Kingdom
Tel: 44 151-709 2663 Fax: 44 151-707 2150
Internet: www.fact.co.uk
E-Mail: fact@fact.co.uk
development and comm. manager Alison Edbrury
Services: development agency, project managing, visual arts and new technologies *Comments:* FACT is the UK's leading development agency for artists working with creative technology

Foundation of Arts in Brussels
Anspach Laan 32-36, 1000 **Brussels**, Belgium
Tel: 32 2-218 7807 Fax: 32 2-219 7416
Internet: www.agenda.be
E-Mail: art.foundation@skynet.be
projects directors Guy de Bellefroid, Alain Cornet; pr/press Valerie Vernimme
Services: the foundation is a federative body working on the cultural promotion and marketing aspects for the region of Brussels (Belgium); projects: publication of Cultural Guide of Brussels, which lists theatre, dance, opera, concerts, festivals, exhibitions, cultural places and events; collection of national cultural information for distribution to press and media

Foundation Promethea
rue de la Concorde 60, 1050 **Brussels**, Belgium
Tel: 32 2-513 7827 Fax: 32 2-502 2657
directrice Chantal Pirlot
Services: sponsorship consultancy *Comments:* member of CEREC (q.v.); organises annual CAÏUS award (for companies that have sponsored a cultural event)

FR Dixon & Co
73 Wimpole Street, **London** W1M 8DD, United Kingdom
Tel: 44 20-7486 7002 Fax: 44 20-7486 7004
E-Mail: accounts@frdixon.co.uk
partner Frank Dixon
Services: accountants and auditors; taxation advice; touring and withholding tax settlements *Comments:* specialists in music and film industry

Fra Diabolo
c/ Santaló 75, 2° 4ª, 08021 **Barcelona**, Spain
Tel: 34 93-241 9320 Fax: 34 93-241 9321
Internet: www.fra-diabolo.com
E-Mail: fra-diabolo@ctv.es
director Francesc Xavier Mata
Services: opera tour agency; box office for all European opera festivals, box office of Teatro del Liceo

Freitag Technologies GmbH
Fritz-Reuter-Str 64, 44867 **Bochum**, Germany
Tel: 49 2327-3841 Fax: 49 2327-3844
Internet: www.showlaser.de
E-Mail: info@showlaser.de
contact Frank Freitag; Geschäftsführer Thomas Lottig
Services: showlaser, waterscreen, special effects; showlaser rental, show production, special effects, waterscreens and showlaser components; manufacturer of showlaser systems; fibreoptic illumination systems

Friedland Group Ltd
15 Queens Gate Place, **London** SW7 5NX, United Kingdom
Tel: 44 20-7581 5567
Fax: 44 20-7823 7757
E-Mail: mail@friedland.demon.co.uk
managing director Freda Wooldridge
Services: consulting business specialising in fundraising and management for performing arts organisations, venues, heritage and museums

FURORE-Verlag
Naumburger Str 40,
34127 **Kassel**, Germany
Tel: 49 561-897 352 Fax: 49 561-83472
Internet: www.furore-verlag.de
E-Mail: FuroreVerlag.Kassel@t-online.de
managing director Renate Matthei
Services: mailing and publishing service of all range of music by women composers, CDs, music sheets, books, postcards, calendar
Comments: Furore Verlag has been internationally recognized as a publisher of works related to women composers and to the subject of Women in Music since its foundation in 1986; the publishing house specializes in first editions of works by 17th to 19th century women composers, works by contemporary women composers and book publications

G Hornberger GmbH
In der Schorbach 7,
67714 **Waldfischbach**, Germany
Tel: 49 6333-92620 Fax: 49 6333-926232
Geschäftsführer Volker Wagner, Marlies Hornberger
Services: printing company (e.g. tickets)

G & R Removals – Specialist musical instrument transporters
100 Bollo Lane, **London** W4 5LX, United Kingdom
Tel: 44 20-8994 9733
Fax: 44 20-8995 0855
proprietor Dave Green; transport manager Lance Green
Services: over 100 vehicles with weekly journeys to all east and west European countries on air ride suspension in temperature controlled when required

Galathea Systems
54-62 Regent Street, **London** W1R 5PJ, United Kingdom
Tel: 44 20-7734 2299 Fax: 44 20-7287 6728
Internet: www.galathea.co.uk
E-Mail: bruce@globaltickets.com
general manager Richard Leggatt; sales & marketing manager Suzannah Zody; marketing coordinator Bruce Moore
Services: providers of ENTA, software for event management systems, ticketing and marketing operations

GCI Groups
1 Chelsea Manor Gardens, **London** SW3 5PN, United Kingdom
Tel: 44 20-7351 2400 Fax: 44 20-7352 6244
Internet: www.gcigroups.com
E-Mail: gcilondon@greynet.com
contact Anna Passera
Services: PR, marketing and sponsorship *Comments:* currently managing the Michelob Pioneer Programme

Gebrüder Schmiedekampf GmbH & Co.
Hollenstedterstraße 11,
212158 **Heidenau**, Germany
Tel: 49 4182-40330 Fax: 49 4182-403 321
Geschäftsführer u. Verkaufsleiter Bernd Grüneberg
Services: material handling for stages *Comments:* temporarily based in Heidenan as currently re-building new premises on old site in Hamburg: Harkortstieg 1-5, 22765 Hamburg

Gelfand, Rennert, Feldman & Brown
82 Brook Street, **London** W1Y 2NL, United Kingdom
Tel: 44 20-7629 7169 Fax: 44 20-7491 7454
partners Nicholas Brown, Stephen Marks, Jeff Kaye; associate partner Michael Williams
Services: tax clearance, international business management, tour accountancy, royalty examination *Comments:* associated with Price Waterhouse Coopers USA

Genovese Vanderhoff & Associates
77 Carlton Street, Suite 1103,
Toronto ON M5B 2J7, Canada
Tel: 1 416-340 2762 Fax: 1 416-340 6276
E-Mail: quadorw@aol.com
partners Margaret Genovese, Dory Vanderhoof
Services: income development consultants; executive recruitment, strategic planning
Comments: operate worldwide

Gentle Jayes
26 Grosvenor Street, **London** W1X 0BD, United Kingdom
Tel: 44 20-7629 3304 Fax: 44 20-7493 0246
partners David Gentle, Anthony Jayes, Robert Page
Services: solicitors for artists, record companies, producers and publishing companies

Gerling Arendt und Partner
Nachod Str. 19, 12163 **Berlin**, Germany
Tel: 49 30-219 093-0 Fax: 49 30-2140 9370
E-Mail: gerling.arendt@compuserve.com
contact Werner Arendt, Peter Eickbolt, Achim Sell, Norbert Babilon
Services: architects and engineers specialising in the complete planning and building of theatres including cost control and management; design services include all facilities and technical equipment, consultancy and feasability studies are part of the work
Comments: see also Publications (Bühnentechnische Rundschau)

Gerriets GmbH
Postfach 1154, 79220 **Umkirch**, Germany
Tel: 49 7665-9600 Fax: 49 7665-96025
E-Mail: gerriets@t-online.de
Geschäftsführer Walter Gerriets; Verkaufsleiter Manfred Geyer
Services: theatre and stage equipment
Comments: visiting address: Im Kirchenhürstle 5-7, 79224 Umkirch

Gerriets Great Britain Ltd
J412 Tower Bridge Business Complex, Drummond Road, **London** SE16 4EF, United Kingdom
Tel: 44 20-7232 2262 Fax: 44 20-7237 4916
E-Mail: gerriets_gb@compuserve.com
managing director Stewart Crosbie; general manager Gerald Ashby; administrator Debby Greenhill
Services: manufacture and supply theatrical fabric

GGC Projects – Performing Arts Studio
Theater Zuider Amstelkanaal, Fred. Roeskestraat 84, PO Box 74144, 1070 BC **Amsterdam**, Netherlands
Tel: 31 20-675 0613 Fax: 31 20-675 6316
managing director Joke Hammann; technical director Co van Diepen
Services: opera and drama workshops, production/stage/technical theatre management and lighting design

GH Lucking & Sons
Commerce Road, **Brentford** TW8 8LX, United Kingdom
Tel: 44 20-8569 9030 Fax: 44 20-8569 9847
managing director Keith Evans; customer services manager Mark Dooner
Services: transport (road haulage) in UK and abroad; storage; preferred contractors to BBC

Gillian Perkins
Gurney Way, **Cambridge** CB4 2ED, United Kingdom
Tel: 44 1223-350 544 Fax: 44 1223-350 544
E-Mail: cammusic@enterprise.net
director Gillian Perkins
Services: management for events, festivals, education projects; specialist in music education, planning, fundraising to useful evaluation afterwards

Glantre Engineering Ltd
20 Richfield Avenue, **Reading** RG1 8EQ, United Kingdom
Tel: 44 118-964 0000 Fax: 44 118-964 0064
E-Mail: info@glantre.com
joint managing directors Derek Gilbert, Gareth Davies; technical director Vic Dobbs; financial director Francis Wells
Services: design supply and installation of technical installations such as lighting, sound, communications, rigging, machinery, AV and projection systems for theatres, concert halls, cruise ships, studios, conference and presentation facilities

Globaltickets (from Edwards & Edwards)
54-62 Regent Street, **London** W1R 5PJ, United Kingdom
Tel: 44 20-7734 4500 Fax: 44 20-7734 4449
Internet: www.globaltickets.com
managing director Richard Brundle; director of sales & marketing Carol Stenberg
Services: provides tickets for theatre, arts and entertainment events in most major cities in the UK, Europe and North America *Comments:* a member of Global Ticketing Systems Ltd, a worldwide network of ticket agencies which provides pre-booking facilities with instant confirmations

Godfrey Allan
Unity House, 205 Euston Road, **London** NW1 2AY, United Kingdom
Tel: 44 20-7383 9200 Fax: 44 20-7383 9201
partner Nigel Clay
Services: accountancy *Comments:* specialist taxation and V.A.T advice to artists and entertainers visiting the UK and Europe

Gordon & Co
41-43 London Fruit Exchange, Brushfield Street, **London** E1 6EU, United Kingdom
Tel: 44 20-7247 0841 Fax: 44 20-7375 1286
contact Robert Israel
Services: general insurance for theatrical managements, non-appearance and all types of personal insurance; special amateur theatrical package insurance policy

Goudsmit & Branbergen, Advocaten
J.J. Viottastraat 46, PO Box 75458, 1071 JT **Amsterdam**, Netherlands
Tel: 31 20-305 5700 Fax: 31 20-305 5790
E-Mail: mail@goudsmithlaw.nl
contact for entertainment law E A P Engels
Services: entertainment law, solicitors

Griven SRL
Via Bulgaria 16, 46042 **Castel Goffredo (MN)**, Italy
Tel: 39 0376-779 483 Fax: 39 0376-779 682
Internet: www.griven.com
E-Mail: griven@griven.com
managing director Luigi Pederzani; technical director Silvio Pederzani
Services: lighting and effects for discos and theatre
Comments: specialise in architectural lighting

GRM (groupes de recherches musicales)
Maision Radio France, 116 av. du Président Kennedy, 75016 **Paris**, France
Tel: 33 1-4230 2988 Fax: 33 1-4230 4988
E-Mail: grm@ina.fr
administrateur Bourjes Renard; responsable du GRM Danielle Teruggi
Services: research in electronics and acoustics

Gunilla Axsäter Kultur AB
Agnevägen 15, 182 64 **Djursholm**, Sweden
Tel: 46 8-753 4051 Fax: 46 8-753 4049
E-Mail: gunilla@axater.a.se
contact Gunilla Axsäter
Services: cultural sponsorship consultants

Guy Chapman Associates
1-2 Henrietta Street, Covent Garden, **London** WC2E 8PS, United Kingdom
Tel: 44 20-7379 7474 Fax: 44 20-7379 8484
E-Mail: guy@g-c-a-co.uk
general management/tour booking Matthew Bartlett, Jonathan Russell; marketing director Guy Chapman; press Jenny Eldridge, Sally Ann Lycett; marketing Steven Drew, Michael Parke, Bonnie Royal
Services: offer a comprehensive marketing, press, project, tour and general management ; service across all art forms and charities

Hamlins Solicitors
Roxburghe House, 273/287 Regent Street, **London** W1A 4SQ, United Kingdom
Tel: 44 20-7629 1209 Fax: 44 20-7491 2259
E-Mail: admin@hamlins.co.uk
partner, head of entertainment and intellectual property department Laurence Gilmore
Services: copyright, intellectual property, all aspect of the record industry, commercial entertainment, contracts, EC law and litigation, collecting societies

Hannah Horovitz Associates
24 Montagu Square, **London** W1H 1RE, United Kingdom
Tel: 44 20-7486 3722 Fax: 44 20-7584 0384
E-Mail: HorovitzAssoc@compuserve.com
consultant Hannah Horovitz
Services: international arts consultancy

Hans Werner Lacher – ARTCOM European Art Communication
Wiesenstr. 7, 83052 **Bruckmühl**, Germany
Tel: 49 8062-804 547 Fax: 49 8062-804 544
Internet: www.hwl-p.de/artcom
E-Mail: artcom@hwl-p.de
director Hans Werner Lacher
Services: soloists, concerts, festivals *Comments:* see also Agents & Producers and Promoters

Hans Wolff & Partners b.v.
Herengracht 162, 1016 BP **Amsterdam**, Netherlands
Tel: 31 20-627 2248 Fax: 31 20-620 0296
E-Mail: hans@hwpbb.nl
theatre consultant, lighting designer Hans Wolff; theatre consultant Eric Heidens; audio consultant Frans Ockeloen; architect Eric Heldens
Services: lighting designers, theatre consultants
Comments: work closely with architect during construction and renovation of theatres, music halls, concert halls, opera houses and congress centres

Harbottle & Lewis
Hanover House, 14 Hanover Square, **London** W1R 0BE, United Kingdom
Tel: 44 20-7667 5000 Fax: 44 20-7667 5100
Internet: www.harbottle.co.uk
E-Mail: hal@harbottle.co.uk
partners Bob Storer, Medwyn Jones; senior associate Robert Mitchel; consultants Charles Levison, Laurence Harbottle
Services: international entertainment, solicitors

Hardsell Ltd
The Leathmarket (11.3.1), Weston Street, **London** SE1 3ER, United Kingdom
Tel: 44 20-7403 4037 Fax: 44 20-7403 5381
E-Mail: bigideas@hardsell.co.uk
managing dir. Peter Harlock; media dir. Maria Hampton
Services: arts marketing and media consultancy specialising in sales promotion, marketing, media planning, touring and market research, design and print production, marketing audits and strategies to support ongoing operations, feasibility studies and lottery applications

Hardware for Xenon Ltd
140 Clayton Rd., **Hayes** UB3 1BB, United Kingdom
Tel: 44 20-8848 1387
Fax: 44 20-8848 1135
technical sales engineer Jean-Luc Michaud
Services: designs, manufacturers, commercialises and rents Xenon arc lamp projectors, slide projectors, followspots, skylights and light sources

Harkness Hall Ltd
The Gate Studios, Station Road, **Borehamwood** WD6 1DQ, United Kingdom
Tel: 44 20-8953 3611
Fax: 44 20-8207 3657
Internet: www.harknesshall.com
E-Mail: sales@harknesshall.com
engineering director Colin Clark; sales director Ian Sim; technical sales Doug Heather
Services: curtain tracking, raise/lower systems, stage and scenery fittings, curtains; cinema/auditoria screen systems; AV screens
Comments: supply, design, installation and maintenance of stage equipment and screen systems throughout the world; catalogues available on request

Harlequin (British Harlequin plc)
Bankside House, Vale Road, **Tonbridge** TN9 1SJ, United Kingdom
Tel: 44 1732-367 666 Fax: 44 1732-367 755
managing director Bob Dagger; marketing manager Monica Arnott
Services: stage and studio flooring manufacturer, Harlequin produces quality dance, stage, studio, exhibition and television floorings for portable, semi-permanent and permanent applications; specialist advisers to designers, architects and contractors
Comments: UK office covers UK and Ireland; rest of Europe covered by European office at: 29 Rue Nortre Dame, 2240 Luxembourg, Tel: +352-464 422, Fax: +352-464 440, contact: Brian Richards; also offices in USA (Philadelphia, Fort Worth and Los Angeles)

Harrison
4 Cooper House, Ravens Lane, **Berkhamsted** HP4 2DX, United Kindom
Tel: 44 1442-875 900/973-748 351 (mobile)
Internet: www.glw.com
E-Mail: 101601.1602@compuserve.com
European sales Jamie Gray
Services: manufacturer of audio equipment for film, tv and live productions
Comments: US Headquarters: 7104 Crossroad Blvd, Ste. 118, Brentwood TN 37027, USA, Tel: +1 615-370 9001, Fax: +1 615-370 4906

Haubold GmbH Spezialdruckerei
Postfach 1340, 37253 **Eschwege**, Germany
Tel: 49 5651-3090 Fax: 49 5651-309 199
Internet: www.hauboldeschwege.de
E-Mail: haubold@aol.com
Geschäftsführer Gerd Sperling; Verkauf Holger Mäder
Services: printers – tickets, forms; thermal tickets with hologrammes

Hayton Associates
21 Cardigan Street, **Bradford** BD13 1AQ, United Kingdom
Tel: 44 1274-817 829
Fax: 44 1274-817 829
E-Mail: sue.hayton@haytonco.force9.co.uk
contact Sue Hayton
Services: specialises in arts access and participation; providing consultancy services in arts education, new audiences, strategic/business planning and multi-cultural arts

Hazel Rennard
7 Grange Road, **Kingston upon Thames** KT1 2QU, United Kingdom
Tel: 44 20-8549 3932
Fax: 44 20-8241 4641
contact Joe Aveline, Roger Fox
Services: technical planning; feasibility studies, events management & consultancy, safety audit

HAZEN, Distribuidora General de Pianos SA
Carretera de la Coruña, km. 17200, 28230 **Las Rozas (Madrid)**, Spain
Tel: 34 91-639 5548 Fax: 34 91-639 5495
E-Mail: hazen@hazen.es
president Félix Hazen García; general director Félix Hazen San Juan; commercial director Cristina Hazen San Juan
Services: distribution of pianos
Comments: also collaborate in concerts as sponsors Fundación Hazen-Hosseschrueders; sales address: Arrieta 8, 28013 Madrid

Henry Booth & Co.
Stockholm Road/Sutton Fields, **Hull** HU7 0XY, United Kingdom
Tel: 44 1482-826 343 Fax: 44 1482-839 767
Internet: www.henrybooth.co.uk
E-Mail: contact@henry.booth.co.uk
general sales manager Mark Sneddon
Services: ticket printing company; all continuous tickets for Boca-Tor; UBI printing system, Synchro systems, PASS systems

Hill & Knowlton
35 Red Lion Sq., **London** WC1R 4SG, United Kingdom
Tel: 44 20-7413 3000 Fax: 44 20-7413 3737
Internet: www.hillandknowlton.com
E-Mail: jbayles@hillandknowlton.com
business development director Jason Gallucci
Services: PR consultancy including arts

Holabird & Root LLP
300 West Adams Street, **Chicago** IL 60606, United States of America
Tel: 1 312-726 5960 ext 338
public relations coordinator Deborah Kirsner
Services: provides clients in the arts market with innovative performance, support and studio spaces

Hollands Licht
Anjeliersstraat 177, 1015 NG **Amsterdam**, Netherlands
Tel: 31 20-427 0030 Fax: 31 20-620 1874
E-Mail: rogier@hlnl.com
principal lighting designer Rogier van der Heide; lighting designers Juliette Nielsen, Maaike Duÿzer, Bob van der Klaauw; office manager Joaney Jacobs
Services: lighting design for opera, dance, ballet, theatre and architecture

Howell Jones & Partners
19a Wimbledon Bridge, **London** SW19 7NH, United Kingdom
Tel: 44 20-8947 7991 Fax: 44 20-8947 8725
E-Mail: scottlaw@lineone.net
entertainment partner Peter Scott
Services: solicitors; wide expertise in contract negotiations throughout Europe *Comments:* first meeting free without obligation

HW Fisher & Company
Acre House, 11-15 William Road, **London** NW1 3ER, United Kingdom
Tel: 44 20-7388 7000 Fax: 44 20-7380 4900
Internet: www.hwfisher.co.uk
E-Mail: info@hwfisher.co.uk
senior partner Paul Beer; media partners Leslie Kuelsheimer, Julian Challis, Alan Lester, Martin Taylor, Russell Nathan
Services: a medium-sized firm of chartered accountants with a vigorous media department serving clients in all aspects of the entertainment industry, including classical and rock music, film, broadcasting and stage

IBM UK Ltd
Buchan House, 21 St. Andrew Square, **Edinburgh (Scotland)** EH2 1AY, United Kingdom
Tel: 44-131-558 4000 Fax: 44-131-558 4200
Internet: www.ibm.com
location manager Gordon Smith
Services: purveyors of computer equipment e.g. MusicWriter, NoteStation; consultancy services; sponsorship of the arts, project management

ICOM (Industrial Common Ownership Movement Ltd)
Vassalli House, 20 Central Road, **Leeds** LS1 6DE, United Kingdom
Tel: 44 113-2461 737 Fax: 44 113-2440 002
E-Mail: icom@icom.org.uk
European legal structures Helen Barber, Stephanie Willington; European grants Robert Allan, Neil Skinner
Services: all aspects of legal structures for organisations in the voluntary, co-operative and non-profit sectors; registration service for companies, charities, subsidiaries etc; also able to assist with seeking grants from European Structural Funds

IDEEA Dekorationsbau GmbH
Rudower Chaussee 3, Adlershof, 12489 **Berlin**, Germany
Tel: 49 30-6704 4777 Fax: 49 30-6704 4177
Internet: www.ideea.de
E-Mail: ideea@t-online.de
Geschäftsführer Lutz & Peter Brüggemann
Services: stage design for film,TV, theatre, exhibitions

Identity Creation for Business
Identity House, Baker Street, **Kingston upon Hull** HU2 8HE, United Kingdom
Tel: 44 1482-226 429 Fax: 44 1482-226 641
senior partners Richard Dunn, Janet Dunn
Services: creative marketing consultancy; specialises in presentation skills; design and art direction; consultants in the visual arts and music; sponsorship consultants; public relations consultants, producers of annual reports; newsletters and high quality printed material; advertising agents; particular interest in helping German, Austrian, Scandinavian, Benelux and UK businesses through arts sponsorship

IEG, Inc
640 North LaSalle, Suite 600, **Chicago** IL 60610-3777, United States of America
Tel: 1 312-944 1727 Fax: 1 312-789 6488
Internet: www.sponsorship.com
E-Mail: ieg@sponsorship.com
marketing manager Lowell Cantor
Services: database of potential sponsors

IMG Arts Projects
Media House, 3 Burlington Lane, Chiswick, **London** W4 2TH, United Kingdom
Tel: 44 20-8233 5800 Fax: 44 20-8233 5801
E-Mail: ArtsProects@imgworld.com
managing director IMG Artists Stephen Wright; director IMG Artists Asia Ian Smallbone (tel: +60 3-266 2166, fax: +60 3-262 2234)
Services: to provide arts organisations, corporations, and governments with arts project consulting and support, both from ground-up development and for restructuring or building an existing organisation
Comments: also office in Malaysia: Level 61, Tower 2, Petronas Twin Towers, 50800 Kuala Lumpur, Tel: +60 3-2166 2166, Fax: +60 3-2162 6634; a new consulting division of IMG Artists (q.v.); see also Agents & Producers

Institut für Internationales Kulturmanagement (INK) GmbH
Englschalkinger Str. 199, 81927 **München**, Germany
Tel: 49 89-9393 2866 Fax: 49 89-9393 2867
E-Mail: 101512.534@compuserve.com
managing director Dr Eckard Heintz; project manager Kathrin Hauser-Schmolck
Services: arts management seminars, consultancy for professionals

InterCachet – Paris
c/o AGECIF, 22 Rue de Picardie, 75003 **Paris**, France
Tel: 33 1-4887 1742 Fax: 33 1-4887 6516
E-Mail: intercachet@post.club-internet.fr
contact Pascal Foy, Catherine Facerias
Services: administration and management services
Comments: see also Courses

Interclassica SA
rue J.-J. Rousseau 4, 1800 **Vevey**, Switzerland
Tel: 41 21-922 4016 Fax: 41 21-922 4018
president Jean-Jacques Indermühle; partner Martin T:son Engström
Services: arts consultant agency

Intermec
Immeuble le Newton, 23 Ave. de l'Europe, 78402 **Chatou** Cedex, France
Tel: 33 1-3015 2535 Fax: 33 1-3480 1433
E-Mail: intermec.france@intermec.com
general director Olivier Burah
Services: sales of printers for tickets and labels

International Arts Bureau Ltd.
4 Baden Place, Crosby Row, **London** SE1 1YW, United Kingdom
Tel: 44 20-7403 7001(enquiries)/6454 (administration)/0777 (Cultural Contact Point enquiry line)
Fax: 44 20-7403 2009
E-Mail: iab@mcmail.com
director Rod Fisher; manager Valerie Synmoie; information officer, general enquiries Melita Douthwaite-Hodges
Services: publications: International Arts Navigator, bimonthly journal available on subscription; International Arts Quarterly Digest produced on behalf of Arts Council of England and circulated free to arts organisations, info from Arts Council Press Office; independent agency providing information advice, research, publications, training and consultancy on international arts issue policies, funding and projects *Comments:* free enquiry service for UK arts organisations, individuals, local authorities and funding agencies, giving advice and information on EU and international funding opportunities and much more- contact on +44 171-403 7001 or by letter/fax

International Cultural Desk
3 Bruntsfield Crescent, **Edinburgh (Scotland)** EH10 4HD, United Kingdom
Tel: 44 131-446 3001 Fax: 44 131-446 3048
E-Mail: info@icd.org.uk
development manager Hilde Bollen; information officer Kerry Jardine
Services: aims to assist the Scottish cultural community to operate more effectively in an international context by providing timely and targeted information and advice; The Desk provides and disseminates information on funding sources, international opportunities and cultural policy development in Europe, it also assists with establishing contacts internationally; The Desk is not a funding agency *Comments:* publishes a bimonthly information update about forthcoming international opportunities across the whole range of cultural and artistic activity (Communication); also publishes InFocus, a series of specialised guides with an international focus

Internationaler Arbeitskreis Frau und Musik eV
Naumburger Str 40, 34127 **Kassel**, Germany
Tel: 49 561-890 0061 Fax: 49 561-893 642
Internet: home.t-online.de/home/ArchivFrauMusik.Kassel
E-Mail: ArchivFrauMusik.Kassel@t-online.de
Publisher/Editor Renate Matthei; Singer Renate Brosch; Composer Vivienne Olive; Musician Dietburg Spohr
Services: representation organisation of women in music; main focus on women composers; publisher of the magazine VIVAVOCE; body responsible for Archiv Frau und Musik
Comments: archive contains 14,000 items (notes, literature, recordings, photographs, literature etc)

Irving Spellman & Company
8 Christopher Lodge, 9 Avenue Road, Highgate, **London** N6 5DL, United Kingdom
Tel: 44 20-8347 6350 Fax: 44 20-8347 7704
solicitor Irving Spellman
Services: lawyer for music entertainment

Istituto Addestramento Lavoratori dello Spettacolo
Via Fracassini 60, 00196 **Roma**, Italy
Tel: 39 06-361 1926/323 6396
Fax: 39 06-361 1926/323 6396
Internet: www.ials.org
E-Mail: ialsrome@tin.it
president Domenico del Prete; contact Luciano Brogi
Services: training and research in dance, theatre and music; documentation centre; international exchanges for professional artists

Ivan Sopher and Co
5 Elstree Gate, Elstree Way, **Borehamwood** WD6 1JD, United Kingdom
Tel: 44 20-8207 0602 Fax: 44 20-8207 6758
principal Ivan Sopher
Services: chartered accountants

Jaffe Holden Scarbrough Acoustics Inc
114-A Washington Street, **Norwalk** CT 06854, United States of America
Tel: 1 203-838 4167 Fax: 1 203-838 4168
E-Mail: jhs.acoustics@aol.com
president J Christopher Jaffe; principals Mark Holden, Paul Scarbrough, Irene Jaffe; vice president, marketing Stephanie Snow
Services: acoustics specialising in the performing arts

Jane Morgan Associates
8 Heathville Road, **London** N19 3AG, United Kingdom
Tel: 44 20-7263 9867 Fax: 44 20-7263 9877
E-Mail: morgans@dircon.co.uk
director Jane Morgan
Services: marketing, press and pr

Jaques Samuel Pianos Ltd
142 Edgware Road, **London** W2 2DZ, United Kingdom
Tel: 44 20-7723 8818 Fax: 44 20-7224 8692
managing director, artist liaison Terence Lewis
Services: hire of concert pianos (Bösendorfer, Steinway, Yamaha) and related services; selection of facilities with some practise time available FCC for the artist(s)

Jazz Services
Africa House, 64 Kingsway, **London** WC2B 6BD, United Kingdom
Tel: 44 20-7405 0737/47/57 Fax: 44 20-7405 0828
Internet: www.jazzservices.org.uk
E-Mail: admin@jazzservices.org.uk
director Chris Hodgkins; publication/information manager Celia Wood
Services: Jazz Service provides a voice for jazz, promoting its growth, accesibility and development in the UK by providing services in touring, support, information, communication, marketing and publishing
Comments: major website, interactive with database; jazz education book and CD Rom available summer 2000

JET EXECUTIVE – International Charter GmbH
Niederrheinstrasse 42, 40474 **Düsseldorf**, Germany
Tel: 49 211-458 872-0 Fax: 49 211-453 305
Internet: www.jetexecutive.com
E-Mail: sales@jetexecutive.com
managing director Bernd Ringelmanm; air charter broker (cargo) Jürgen Freytag
Services: international air charter broker; offers a range of aircrafts (from small executive jets to large widebody aircrafts) as well as a range of services connected with Aircraft Management and Aircraft Operations; special expertise in cargo-handling (e.g. musical instruments)

JM Consulting Ltd
Saville Court, Saville Place, **Bristol** BS8 4EJ, United Kingdom
Tel: 44 117-923 7594 Fax: 44 117-923 7598
managing director Dr. Jim Port; director Melanie Burdett
Services: consultancy services in corporate planning, organisation structures, management information, accounting and costing

Joffre – Société d'Avocats
36, rue Washington, 75008 **Paris**, France
Tel: 33 1-4562 3500 Fax: 33 1-4359 5205
associés Jean-François Joffre, Françoise Poujet Courbiere
Services: lawyers specialised in royalties

John Wyckham Associates
7 Willow Way, Motcombe, **Shaftesbury** SP7 9QH, United Kingdom
Tel: 44 174-785 0253 Fax: 44 174-785 0254
principal John Wyckham
Services: international theatre design consultants

Just Tickets
Unit 2, Empstead Works, Greys Road, **Henley-on-Thames** RG9 2EF, United Kingdom
Tel: 44 1491-413 150 Fax: 44 1491-413 152
Internet: www.just-tickets.demon.co.uk
E-Mail: sales@just-tickets.demon.co.uk
managing director Jim Birney; financial director Carolyn Birney; production manager Paul Ham
Services: theatrical, leisure ticket

Kallaway Ltd
2 Portland Road, **London** W11 4LA, United Kingdom
Tel: 44 20-7221 7883 Fax: 44 20-7229 4595
E-Mail: info@kallaway.co.uk
managing director William Kallaway; head of communications Lucinda Roberts
Services: specialises in communications and marketing through sponsored arts and education events and schemes; services include consultancy, event production and management, promotion and media planning

Kanaar & Co
6/8 James Street, **London** W1M 5HN, United Kingdom
Tel: 44 20-7495 6060 Fax: 44 20-7495 3770
E-Mail: kan/do/law@msn.com
entertainment/arts partners Nick Kanaar, John Simmons
Services: solicitors' firm specialising in song-writing and publishing, records and video contracts

Kantor Concert Management & Public Relations
67 Teignmouth Rd, **London** NW2 4EA, United Kingdom
Tel: 44 20-8208 2480 Fax: 44 20-8208 2490
E-Mail: dkantor.kcm@webstar.co.uk
proprietor Denise Kantor
Services: concert management, publicity & PR in the UK, musical secretariat, special projects and other services related to music and musicians

Katerina Novikova
Chekhova 1, apt 33, 191104 **St Petersburg**, Russia
Tel: 7 812-275 5666 Fax: 7 812-275 5666
E-Mail: alex@kris.spb.su
coordinator Katerina Novikova
Services: performing arts consultant: theatre, clown, comedy, singers, music
Comments: see also Agents & Producers

Kathy Battista Consultants
2 Maisonettes, Vestry Road, **London** SE5 8NR, United Kingdom
Tel: 44 20-7277 2541 Fax: 44 20-7277 2541
E-Mail: kathybattista@yahoo.co.uk
director & administrator Kathy Battista; assistant Tracey Ferguson
Services: art education consultancy

Ken Dibble Acoustics
PO Box 541, **Rugby** CV21 3YJ, United Kingdom
Tel: 44 1788-541 133 Fax: 44 1788-541 314
Internet: www.KDAcoustic.co.uk
E-Mail: KDAcoustic@aol.com
principal consultant Ken Dibble; consultant Simon J Webster; office manager Laura Dibble
Services: independent consultancy in architectural acoustics, noise control and audio engineering, specialising in performing/recording arts and leisure activities; acoustic design

Ken Graham Trucking – The Symphony Orchestra Specialists
4 Heathcote, **Tadworth** KT20 5TH, United Kingdom
Tel: 44 1737-373 305/385-330 608/609/070 004 (orchestras) Fax: 44 1737-370 813
Internet: www.kengrahamtrucking.com
E-Mail: info@kengrahamtrucking.com
contact Ken Graham
Services: touring orchestras in UK and Europe – custom built trailers with air-suspension, climate controlled, fully alarmed security systems

Kerlin Consulting Pty Ltd
10 Bridge Street, **Port Melbourne** VIC 3207, Australia
Tel: 61 3-9646 4456/412-615 216 (mobile)
Fax: 61 3-9645 6757
E-Mail: gerryk@hyp.com.au
director Gerardine Kerlin
Services: advice and services: public affairs, stakeholder research, communications, issues management, marketing, public relations, media liaison, corporate governance, government relations, sponsorship management and strategies, international relations, protocol, relationship management

Kevin Darby Costumes
Unit 10, Douglas Buildings, Royal Stuart Lane,
Cardiff (Wales) CF10 5CL, United Kingdom
Tel: 44 29-2045 1646 Fax: 44 29-2045 1628
director Kevin Darby
Services: design, supply and hire theatrical costumes, hats, headdresses, masks, feather backpack; for period, light entertainment, pantomime, international revue, can make complete productions to specification; supply costumes for film, tv, theatre, international revue, summer season, pantomime, commericals, product launches and cruise ships

Kik Veranstaltungsberatung
Hauptstr. 139, 69469 **Weinheim**, Germany
Tel: 49 6201-961 667 Fax: 49 6201-961 755
E-Mail: kik-events@t-online.de
Inhaber Renée Neumann
Services: works worldwide, planning, organisation and running of events

Kimpton Walker Project Management
Unit 10, Ellersie Sq., Lyham Rd., **London** SW2 5DZ, United Kingdom
Tel: 44 20-7738 3222 Fax: 44 20-7738 5517
contact David Park, Alan Walker
Services: television, theatre, exhibitions

Kirkegaard & Associates
801 W. Adams Street, Eighth Floor, **Chicago** IL 60607, United States of America
Tel: 1 312-441 1980 Fax: 1 312-441 1981
Internet: www.kirkegaard.com
E-Mail: acoustics@kirkegaard.com
chief officer R Lawrence Kirkegaard (Hon. AIA, FASA); vice president Gainer B Hall (FAIR); associates Carl Giegold (AIA), Scott Pfeiffer, Edward Duggar (AIA), Dawn Schuette (AIA), Clete Dans, Edward McCue, Richard Laidmain, Joseph Myers
Services: international consultants in architectural acoustics since 1976; 25 professionals approach room acoustics, noise control, audio and video with sensitivity to design, function, construction and time/budget constraints; all building types/sizes with particular emphasis on performance and assembly

Kirkham & Elphick Organisational Development Consultants
302 High Street, **Bangor (Wales)** LL57 1UL, United Kingdom
Tel: 44 1248-372 036 Fax: 44 1248-372 035
E-Mail: consultke@aol.com
partners Hazel Kirkham, Chris Elphick
Services: organisational development consultancy, management development and training; Investors in People consultancy

Klepper Marshall King Associates Ltd
59 South Greeley Avenue, **Chappaqua** NY 10514, United States of America
Tel: 1 914-238 5360 Fax: 1 914-238 5607
E-Mail: mark2acous@aol.com
chief officer L. Gerald Marshall
Services: accoustical consultants

KOBOLD Licht Beleuchtungstechnik GmbH
Hans-Urmiller-Ring 17, 82515 **Wolfratshausen**, Germany
Tel: 49 8171-7081 Fax: 49 8171-20367
Geschäftsführer Axel Frömel
Services: lighting for TV and films

Konzertkasse Casino
Herrengasse 25, 3011 **Bern**, Switzerland
Tel: 41 31-311 8172 Fax: 41 31-311 7333
Leitung Daniel Rossier
Services: concert organisation, ticketing for promoters; publicity and consulting for artists; administration

KPMG
8 Salisbury Square, **London** EC4Y 8BB, United Kingdom
Tel: 44 20-7311 1000 Fax: 44 20-7311 3311
Internet: www.kpmg.com
chairman, UK information, communication and entertainment practice David Murrell; head of music practice Richard Bawden; senior tax manager, media & entertainment practice Robert Taylor; head of media consultancy Paul Styles
Services: accountancy, audit, tax and consultancy

KPMG Belgium
Bourget Laan 40, 1130 **Brussels**, Belgium
Tel: 32 2-708 4300 Fax: 32 2-708 4399
Internet: www.kpmg.com
E-Mail: info@kpmg.be
partner Marc Hoydonckx
Services: tax, management, general consultancy and auditing, accountants, computer audio service

KPMG Fidal Peat International
5 cours Valmy, 92923 **Paris La Défence** Cedex, France
Tel: 33 1-5568 6500 Fax: 33 1-5568 6464
Internet: www.kpmg.com
lawyer Jacques Brouillet
Services: tax and legal services related to media and entertainment practice

KPMG Meijbourg & Co
Postbus 74600, 1070 DE **Amsterdam**, Netherlands
Tel: 31 20-656 1656 Fax: 31 20-656 1100
Internet: www.kpmg.meijbourg.nl
E-Mail: TeSpenke.Gerrit@kpmg.nl
partner, media & entertainment practice
Gerrit Te Spenke
Services: tax lawyers

KulturKonzept Verlags & Werbebüro
Uhlandstraße 1, 72535 **Heroldstatt**, Germany
Tel: 49 7389-90183/172-951 3610 (mobile)
Fax: 49 7389-90184
Internet: www.kulturkonzept-wager.de
E-Mail: kulturkonzept@t-online.de
Inhaber Hartmut Wager
Services: publishers and advertising agency

L'Allemand & Legros
Avenue Emile Dermat 19, 1000 **Brussels**, Belgium
Tel: 32 2-629 8880 Fax: 32 2-648 7841
E-Mail: l.l.law@skynet.be
contact Roger l'Allemand
Services: specialise in intellectual property

La Bottega Veneziana SRL
Via Pascoli 27, 30020 **Quarto D'Altino (VE)**, Italy
Tel: 39 0422-824 865/825 521
Fax: 39 0422-824 449
managing director Giuseppe Ranchetti
Services: provides scenery for theatre, TV and open-air spaces; production and distribution

La Playa Limited
PO Box 992, Waterbeach, **Cambridge** CB5 9SQ, United Kingdom
Tel: 44 1223-522 411 Fax: 44 8700-548 706
Internet: www.laplaya.co.uk
E-Mail: info@laplaya.co.uk
managing director Mark Boon
Services: specialises in insurance services for media, arts and entertainment industries, covers include: cancellation and non-appearance, travel and touring, musical instruments/equipment, property, business interruption, liabilities, intellectual property

Laban Centre London, Library and Resource Collection
Laban Centre, Laurie Grove, **London** SE14 6NH, United Kingdom
Tel: 44 20-8692 4070 Fax: 44 20-8694 8749
Internet: www.laban.co.uk
E-Mail: info@laban.co.uk
director Dr Marion North PhD DArts
Services: information service based on college library holding large resources of printed and audio visual materials on all kinds of dance; publications include a list of periodicals held and a list of theses by students at the Centre; admission by appointment;
Laban Centre London is one of the largest and best equipped dance centres in Europe; it includes a fully-equipped theatre, specialist dance studios and pilates-based body control studio
Comments: publish Arts Theatre Journal; see also Dance, National Organisations & Publications

Law & Dunbar-Nasmith Architects
16 Dublin Street, **Edinburgh (Scotland)** EH1 3RE, United Kingdom
Tel: 44 131-556 8631 Fax: 44 131-556 8945
E-Mail: edinburgh@ldn.co.uk
partners Sir James Dunbar-Nasmith, Colin Ross, Mark Hopton, Mark Sidgwick
Services: architects
Comments: also: St. Leonards Road Forres Scotland IV36 1EN, Tel: 44 1309-673 221, Fax: 44 1309-676 397, Email: forres@ldn.co.uk, Andrew Wright & Sam Russell

Lea & Company
Bank Chambers, Market Place, **Stockport** SK1 1UN, United Kingdom
Tel: 44 161-480 6691
Fax: 44 161-480 0904
E-Mail: lea@century21.prestel.co.uk
partner Stephen Lea; music administration co-ordinator Dax Hopwood
Services: specialist legal entertainment services; rights administration services

Lee & Thompson
Green Garden House, 15-22, St Christopher's Place, **London** W1M 5HE, United Kingdom
Tel: 44 20-7935 4665
Fax: 44 20-7486 2391
E-Mail: leath@globalnet.co.uk
senior partner Robert Lee; partners Andrew Thompson, Robert Horsfall, Jeremy Gawade, Reno Antoniades, Zoe Reynolds; lawyers Richard Lever, Mike Brookes, Sonia Diwan, Lucinda Leo, Philip Daniels
Services: specialist entertainment business practice offering legal services in relation to all areas of the entertainment business including music, film, television, merchandising, sponsorship, theatre, book publishing, sport etc

Leisure & Arts Research (a division of Travel and Tourism Research Ltd)
4 Cochrane House, Admirals Way, **London** E14 9UD, United Kingdom
Tel: 44 20-7538 5300 Fax: 44 20-7538 3299
managing director Peter Hodgson
Services: opera/theatre/tourist attractions:- market research, survey research, audience research

Leonard Greenwood
22 Agraria Road, **Guildford** GU2 5LE, United Kingdom
Tel: 44 1483-503 056
E-Mail: og@ppc-lon.com
contact Leonard Greenwood
Services: theatre consultant

Leoni Daniele SRL
via San Martino 1A, 48020 **S. Agata (RA)**, Italy
Tel: 39 0545-45607 Fax: 39 0545-916 257
Internet: www.leonidaniele.it
E-Mail: leonidaniele@interbusiness.it
managing director Daniele Leoni; sales manager and marketing Elena Verlicchi
Services: designs and supplies software systems, self-service and information points; many Italian theatres use its computerized booking system; launched CHARTA, a network system in 1992

Leosong Copyright Service Ltd
Independent House, 54 Larkshall Road, **London** E4 6PD, United Kingdom
Tel: 44 20-8523 9000
Fax: 44 20-8523 8888
E-Mail: erich@independentmusicgroup.com
managing director Ray Ellis; director Ellis Rich; financial controller David Nicholson
Services: copyright administration service

Les Amis du Bel Objet
24 rue Louis Braille, 37000 **Tours**, France
Tel: 33 2-4705 9779 Fax: 33 2-4766 9465
contact Jean-Francois Faroux; president t.b.a.
Services: evaluation and insurance of musical instruments

Levitt Bernstein Assocs – architects/landscape architects
1 Kingsland Passage, **London** E8 2BB, United Kingdom
Tel: 44 20-7275 7676 Fax: 44 20-7275 9348
E-Mail: lbal@compuserve.com
contact Axel Burrough
Services: architects experienced in new-build design and conversion of theatres, concert halls and performance spaces

Lichte & Schramm Rechtsanwälte
Arnold-Heise-Straße 23, 20249 **Hamburg**, Germany
Tel: 49 40-480 0300 Fax: 49 40-4800 3030
partners Walter Lichte, Dr. jur. Balthasar Schramm, Peer Boris Schade, Dr. jur. Thomas Hörner
Services: legal services *Comments:* also in Berlin, München & Köln: Ubierring 7, 50678 Köln, Tel: +49 221-931 8255, Fax: +49 221-931 8266, contact: Dr. Andreas Scheuermann, Burkhard Westerhoff; Knesebeckstraße 30, 10623 Berlin, Tel: +49 30-8855 2030, Fax: +49 30-8855 2033, contact: Dr. Angelika Strittmatter; Schleißheimerstr. 25, 80333 München, Tel: +49 89-542 7770, Fax: +49 89-5427 7727, contact Julianne Ferenczy

Lighting Design Partnership Ltd
63 Gee Street, **London** ECIV 3RS, United Kingdom
Tel: 44 20-7250 3200 Fax: 44 20-7250 0824
E-Mail: london@ldp.net
directors Douglas Brennan, Andre Tammes, Graham Phoenix, Graham Large
Services: lighting consultancy

Lighting Technology Group Ltd
2 Tudor Estate, Abbey Road, Park Royal, **London** NW10 7UY, United Kingdom
Tel: 44 20-8965 6800 Fax: 44 20-8965 0950
Internet: www.lighting-tech.com
E-Mail: sales@lighting-tech.com
directors David Morgan, Bev Bigham (+44 20-8965 6800); sales (London) Ron Knell (+44 20-8965 6800); sales (Manchester) Graham Bassett (+44 161-876 0576); sales (Paris) Garry Nelsson (Tel/Fax: +33 1-3486 2868); marketing David Cartwright (+44 20-8965 6800)
Services: supply of all consumables and hardware to the entertainment lighting industry with particular emphasis on lamps and filters; in-house design with full CAD facilities so full turnkey projects can be undertaken, and after sales maintenance and repair provided by own qualified personnel

Lisa Peacock Concert Management
23A Holland Rd, **London** W14 8HJ, United Kingdom
Tel: 44 20-7602 1416 Fax: 44 20-7371 2726
E-Mail: lisapeacok@aol.com
contact Lisa Peacock
Services: concert management *Comments:* affiliate member of International Artist Managers Association (IAMA)

Look and Learn Productions Ltd
20 Clifton House, Club Row, **London** E2 7HB, United Kingdom
Tel: 44 20-7739 0759
Fax: 44 20-7739 0759
E-Mail: looklearn@aol.com
managing director Nicholas Morgan
Services: production company and consulting business specialising in fundraising and management for performing arts organisations, venues, heritage and museums

LSI Projects – ADB Theatre and TV Lighting
ADB House, 15 Woking Business Park, Albert Drive, **Woking** GU21 5JY, United Kingdom
Tel: 44 1483-764 646 Fax: 44 1483-769 955
E-Mail: info@LSI-adb.com
general manager Russell Dunsire
Services: ADB design manufacture and market world-wide; a comprehensive range of stage & studio lighting and suspension equipment, for both professional and semi-professional applications; services include design, engineering, installation, commissioning, maintenance and training

Lubbock Fine
Russell Bedford House, City Forum, 250 City Road, **London** EC1V 2QQ, United Kingdom
Tel: 44 20-7490 7766 Fax: 44 20-7490 5102
E-Mail: gitter@lubbockfine.co.uk
partner Jeff Gitter
Services: full-service chartered accountants with specialist arts and media department

Ludwig Pani Bühnenbeleuchtung & Projektion
Kandlgasse 23, 1070 **Wien**, Austria
Tel: 43 1-52108-0 Fax: 43 1-526 4287
Internet: www.pani.com
E-Mail: info@pani.com
Inhaberin Frau Kommerzialrat Sieglinde Staub; Firmenleitung/Prokurist Rainer Staub; Verkaufsleiter Wolf-Dieter Hrasek
Services: manufacturer of a range of lighting equipment, specialised in wide ranged slide projection equipment

LVP Reserveringssystemen B.V.
Heemraadssingel 32, 3012 DB **Rotterdam**, Netherlands
Tel: 31 10-425 5077 Fax: 31 10-425 4600
E-Mail: lvpres@lvpres.nl
managing director Francine Kragt
Services: computerized ticketing system
Comments: Belgian office: Route de Barisart 216, 4900 Spa, Tel: +32 87-773 277; German office: M. Bärthel, Am Leutenhäuser Berg 46, 34376 Immenhausen, Tel: +49 56-736 736

M&C Saatchi Arts
36 Golden Square, **London** W1R 4EE, United Kingdom
Tel: 44 20-7543 4500/4622
Fax: 44 20-7543 4501
E-Mail: judy@mcsaatchi.co.uk
chairman David Kershaw; chief executive Judy Grahame
Services: marketing agency/consultancy: planning research, PR, advertising, print design, sponsorship; provides marketing and PR services to the arts

Macbeth Media Relations
Suite 3, Mountfort House, 15/16 Barnsbury Square, **London** N1 1JL, United Kingdom
Tel: 44 20-7700 5959
Fax: 44 20-7700 1329
E-Mail: macbethg@btinternet.com
contacts Ginny Macbeth, Lisa Knowles, Anne White
Services: UK and international press for classical musicians & related projects

Maecenata Management GmbH
Barer Strasse 44, 80799 **München**, Germany
Tel: 49 89-284 452 Fax: 49 89-283 774
Internet: www.maecenata-management.de
E-Mail: mm@maecenata-management.de
partner Rupert Strachwitz, Robert v. Bennigsen
Services: consulting and management support in the non-profit area; professional backing for communication policies, sponsorship schemes, patronage and charity programmes, research; special focus on creation and management of and consultancy services to foundations/trusts
Comments: Tel. Berlin office: +49 30-2838 7900

Maestro Travel and Touring Company
6th Floor, 32 Hanover Street, **Liverpool** L1 4AA, United Kingdom
Tel: 44 151-707 1234
Fax: 44 151-707 1747
Internet: www.maestrotravel.com
E-Mail: maestro@compuserve.com
principal Ken Grundy; manager Nigel Foo
Services: travel management for individual artists; ensembles, choirs and symphony orchestras; highly personalised service and expert advice to meet your budget

Magerit Musical Foundation
Hermanos Machado, 68, 28017 **Madrid**, Spain
Tel: 34 91-355 0075 Fax: 34 91-355 0075
Internet: www.magerit.com
E-Mail: magerit@magerit.com
general manager Mª Angeles Chamorro; artistic director Sydney d'Agvilo
Services: music consulting, festival programming
Comments: see also Agents & Producers

Magical Mart
42 Christchurch Road, **Sidcup** DA15 7HQ, United Kingdom
Tel: 44 20-8300 3579 Fax: 44 20-8300 3579
contact John Styles
Services: magician's and Punch and Judy equipment, ventriloquists' dummies hire and advice
Comments: callers on appointment

Magrath & Co
52-54 Maddox Street, **London** W1R 9PA, United Kingdom
Tel: 44 20-7495 3003
Fax: 44 20-7409 1745
E-Mail: magrath@magrath.ftech.co.uk
senior partner Chris Magrath
Services: consultants in litigation and entertainment

Management Centre, The
366 Kennington Road, **London** SE11 4DB, United Kingdom
Tel: 44 20-7820 1100 Fax: 44 20-7820 3828
Internet: www.managementcentre.co.uk
E-Mail: tmc@managementcentre.co.uk
directors Bernard Ross, Clare Segal
Services: management training, fundraising and business planning
Comments: see also Courses

Manches & Co
Aldwych House, 81 Aldwych, **London** WC2B 4RP, United Kingdom
Tel: 44 20-7404 4433
Fax: 44 20-7430 1133
Internet: www.manches.com
E-Mail: manchesmedia@manches.co.uk
director Alastair Simpson
Services: solicitors

Mannesmann Demag Fördertechnik AG
Postfach 67, 58286 **Wetter**, Germany
Tel: 49 2335-92-0 Fax: 49 2335-927 676
Vorstandsvorsitzender Prof. Dr. Rüdiger Franke
Services: mechanical engineering, material handling products

Mannesmann Rexroth GmbH
Jahnstraße 3-5, Postfach, 97816 **Lohr am Main**, Germany
Tel: 49 9352-180 Fax: 49 9352-181 000
Abteilungsleiter Bühnentechnik Horst Bittner
Services: Hydraulik und Elektronik für die Bühnentechnik

Marketing Office (Arts) Limited
9 Chiswick High Road, **London** W4 2NO, United Kingdom
Tel: 44 20-8994 0066
Fax: 44 20-8994 4499
managing director William Tayleur
Services: marketing consultancy & services; feasibility studies, strategic planning, research, design, print, advertising, PR, promotions in the fields of theatre, opera, ballet, music, TV

Marketlink Research
37 Warple Way, **London** W3 ORJ, United Kingdom
Tel: 44 20-8740 5550
Fax: 44 20-7749 4450
E-Mail: info@marketlinkresearch.co.uk
managing directors Angela Diakopoulou, Nigel Pinto
Services: research consultancy specialising in the arts, entertainment, sponsorship and youth industries
Comments: undertake both qualitative and quantitative work

Markpoint System AB
Säterigan 20, 417 64 **Göteborg**, Sweden
Tel: 46 31-656 900
Fax: 46 31-224 284
Internet: www.markpoint.se
E-Mail: ardi@markpoint.se
marketing managers Arjen Dijkstra, Paul Cheung
Services: manufacturer of ticket printers

Martin Gabriel Promotions
Art Center, Vane Terrace, **Darlington** DL3 7AX, United Kingdom
Tel: 44 1325-467 272
E-Mail: martin@mgprom.freeserve.co.uk
director Martin Roberts
Services: telemarketing, tour bookings/coordination, follow up calling, representation

Martin Greene Ravden
55 Loudoun Road, **London** NW8 0DL, United Kingdom
Tel: 44 20-7625 4545
Fax: 44 20-7625 5265
E-Mail: mgr@mgr.co.uk
business management and management consultancy Lionel Martin; auditing, taxation and management consultancy David Greene; royalty audits, business management and corporate finance David Ravden; accounting and auditing Robert Braham; accounting and business management Steve Daniel; taxation and accounting Eddie Grossman; accounting, auditing and taxation Harish Shah; accounting, royalty audits and taxation Paul Simnock
Services: chartered accountants and business advisers specialising in music and entertainment

Martin Randall Travel Ltd
10 Barley Mow Passage, Chiswick, **London** W4 4PH, United Kingdom
Tel: 44 20-8742 3355
Fax: 44 20-8742 7766
E-Mail: info@martinrandall.co.uk
managing director Martin Randall; festival organisers Sheila Taylor, Emma Duffield
Services: music and cultural tours (opera, chamber music etc.) accompanied by specialist lecturers; music festivals – private concerts in historical palaces, churches, country houses and theatres *Comments:* see also Festivals (Austro-Hungarian Music Festival) and Agents & Producers

Mary De Camp Carlson Public Relations and Marketing
9 Campden Hill Square, **London** W8 7LB, United Kingdom
Tel: 44 20-7221 6444
Fax: 44 20-7229 1275
E-Mail: mcarlson@cwcom.net
Services: an American with 20 years experience in the classical music business, has been operating a public relations consultancy in Britain for the past 15 years; clients include international orchestras, individual artists, festivals and special projects; primary territory is the UK but wider coverage is available through her two European based associates who cover France, Belgium, Germany, Austria and Switzerland

Maureen Lunn Management
Top Farm, Parish Lane, **Hedgerley** SL2 3JH, United Kingdom
Tel: 44 1753-645 008
Fax: 44 1753-647 431
director Maureen Lunn
Services: concert management

Max Fordham & Partners
42-43 Gloucester Crescent, **London** NW1 7PE, United Kingdom
Tel: 44 20-7267 5161
Fax: 44 20-7482 0329
Internet: www.archinet.co.uk/fordham
E-Mail: post@mfp.co.uk
contact Max Fordham, Lucinda Collinge
Services: consulting building services engineers trained in all aspects of building services, providing practical design and efficient contract administration for theatres and recreational facilities

Max Maier GmbH + Co. KG Metallbau
Ohmstraße 8, 76229 **Karlsruhe**, Germany
Tel: 49 721-62529-0 Fax: 49 721-617 808
Abteilungsleiter Bühnentechnik Herr Scheibel; Abteilung Tribünenbau Herr Maier, Herr Bankowitsch; Abteilung Sportsitzschalen Herr Pfefferle
Services: manufacturer of theatre stages; telescopic grandstands, firmly installed grandstands, mobile grandstands, seating

McCann Matthews Millman Limited
Unit 6, Burghley Yard, 106 Burghley Road, **London** NW5 1AL, United Kingdom
Tel: 44 20-7284 4286 Fax: 44 20-7284 4287
E-Mail: john@mcmatmil.co.uk
directors Roger McCann, John Matthews, Anne Millman
Services: specialising in the management and marketing needs of the arts and cultural industries; services include: marketing planning; market research, both quantitative and qualitative; feasibility studies; skills training; customer care training

media arts productions
Postfach 60, 8034 **Zürich**, Switzerland
Tel: 41 1-383 4704 Fax: 41 1-383 4704
director Pamela Hunter
Services: staging, directing, lighting for classical concerts, opera and music theatre

Media Factory
Falkenried 7, 20251 **Hamburg**, Germany
Tel: 49 40-4231 3142 Fax: 49 40-4231 3140
E-Mail: 106056.1050@compuserve.com
director Peter Nolke
Services: PR agency concerned with classical music

Metier
Glyde House, Glydegate, **Bradford** BD5 0BQ, United Kingdom
Tel: 44 1274-738 800 Fax: 44 1274-391 566
Internet: www.metier.org.uk
E-Mail: admin@metier.org.uk
chief executive Duncan Sones
Services: central information resource to co-ordinate regional and sectoral training information schemes; will work on a national level by exchanging information with non-specialist providers or careers advice in order to maximise the information available on training and careers in arts and entertainment *Comments:* government appointed National Training Organisation for the arts and entertainment sector.NTO's ensure that the views of employers on education and training needs are fed to government

Michael Harrold Artist Management
223 Kingston Road, **Leatherhead** KT22 7PE, United Kingdom
Tel: 44 1372-375 728 Fax: 44 1372-375 728
Internet: www.michaelharrold.co.uk
E-Mail: angelus.organo@pmail.net
director Michael Harrold
Services: special project management (recordings, publications, etc), media/public relations, artist representation and concert management *Comments:* see also Agents and Producers

Michael Holden Associates
17 West Heath Drive, **London** NW11 7QG, United Kingdom
Tel: 44 20-8455 4640 Fax: 44 20-8209 1059
E-Mail: MichaelHoldenAssocs@btinternet.com
senior partner Micheal Holden BA, MSTC, FRSA
Services: consultants on new theatres and restoration; building and services design, management study, formation of trust managements, feasibility studies

Michael Hopkins & Partners
27 Broadley Terrace, **London** NW1 6LG, United Kingdom
Tel: 44 20-7724 1751 Fax: 44 20-7723 0932
Internet: www.hopkins.co.uk
E-Mail: hopkins@dial.pipex.com
partner Sir Michael Hopkins
Services: architects; have worked on Glyndebourne Opera House

Millward Brown International
Olympus Avenue, Tachbrook Park, **Warwick** CV34 6RJ, United Kingdom
Tel: 44 1926-452 233 Fax: 44 1926-833 600/ 452 246
Internet: www.millwardbrown.com
director Peter Walshe
Services: market researcher for the arts: audience surveys, potential audience development, leaflet and advertising evaluation and sponsorship, brand equity

Model Box Ltd
Studio 9, 75 Filmer Road, **London** SW6 7JF, United Kingdom
Tel: 44 20-7371 0110 Fax: 44 20-7371 0506
Internet: www.modelbox.co.uk
E-Mail: modelbox@dial.pipex.com
contact Stephen Wentworth
Services: computer-aided design services for entertainment industries; 3-D rendering and computer graphics

Moving Academy of Performing Arts
Herengracht 174, 1016 BR **Amsterdam**, Netherlands
Tel: 31 20-422 6623 Fax: 31 20-422 6624
Internet: www.mapa.nl
E-Mail: info@mapa.nl
artistic director Ide van Heiningen; manager Yolande Hezemans; office assistant Bettina Lorsheijd
Services: organises vocational training for professional theatre and dance artists in central and eastern European countries; develops seminars and workshops in communication, theatre management, theatre pedagogy, scenography, acting and dance training; supports individual performers to create their own independent theatre *Comments:* MAPA has produced a book on 5 years MAPA activity: Moving Minds, available on request at Euro 16 (excl. P&P)

Müller-BBM GmbH
Robert-Koch-Straße 11, 82152 **Planegg**, Germany
Tel: 49 89-85602-0 Fax: 49 89-8560 2111
E-Mail: mi@mbbm.de
managing directors Dr. G. Müller, Dr. J. Scheuren
Services: room and building acoustics, vibration control, machinery acoustics, training and seminars

Music Concept
c/o Anne de Waël, Kunzweg 21, 81243 **München**, Germany
Tel: 49 89-834 6294 Fax: 49 89-834 2550
Services: management and organisational consultancy
Comments: second address: c/o Catherine von Mutius, Brunnerstrasse 4a, 85540 Haar, Tel: +49 89-4620 0676, Fax: +49 89-4620 0677, E-mail: cvmutius@compuserve.com; see also Agents & Producers

Music Consulting
Heimstättenallee 16, 82152 **Planegg**, Germany
Tel: 49 89-859 8382 Fax: 49 89-859 5677
E-Mail: rosenkind@t-online.de
contact Dr. Harry A. Rosenkind
Services: legal advice, artist management

Music Forum
Palackého 2, 851 01 **Bratislava**, Slovakia
Tel: 421 7-5441 8139 Fax: 421 7-5443 0998
Internet: www.scriptorium.sk
E-Mail: scriptorium@tatrahome.sk
director Igor Valentovic
Services: music publishing, sellers of CDs and sheet music *Comments:* see also Scriptorium Musicum (q.v.)

Musica Europa
7a Farm Road, **Maidenhead** SL6 5HX, United Kingdom
Tel: 44 1628-776 795 Fax: 44 1628-632 112
Internet: www.musica-europa.com
E-Mail: bengunner@musica-europa.com
director Ben Gunner
Services: specialises in organising concert tours, exchanges, music festivals & workshops for all types of orchestras and choirs

MUSICOM srl – Strumenti per comunicare
22 viale San Michele del Carso, 20144 **Milano**, Italy
Tel: 39 02-461 525 Fax: 39 02-461 570
E-Mail: musicom@netiol.it
president Alessandro Orizio
Services: organisation of musical events; audiovisual production and distribution

Musik Komm GmbH & Köln Messe GmbH
Communication & Marketing Department, Kaiser-Wilhelm-Ring 20, 50672 **Köln**, Germany
Tel: 49 221-91655-0 Fax: 49 221-91655-160/110
Internet: www.musikkomm.de
E-Mail: musikkomm@musikkomm.de
contact Heike Rybienski
Services: producers of Pop Komm – annual communication fair for trade visitors – one of the biggest events of this kind
Comments: next Pop Komm: 17 – 20 August 2000

Musik-Data GmbH
Korneuburger Straße 86, 2103 **Langenzersdorf**, Austria
Tel: 43 2244-4580-0 Fax: 43 2244-458 020
E-Mail: indra@magnet.at
general manager Wolfgang Indra
Services: computer software, namely HME (Hire Material Electronic), a unique electronic reference work for material-hire – allowing access to information on editions, versions and arrangements throughout the world

Musikverlag Doblinger
Dorotheergasse 10, 1010 **Wien**, Austria
Tel: 43 1-515 030 Fax: 43 1-515 0351
E-Mail: music@doblinger.co.at
Werbeleiter Dr. Christian Heindl
Services: music publishers
Comments: see also Publications

N W Brown Music Division
Richmond House, 16-20 Regent Street, **Cambridge** CB2 1DB, United Kingdom
Tel: 44 1223-720 225 Fax: 44 1223-353 705
E-Mail: mark.boon@nwbrown.co.uk
managing director Mark Boon
Services: general insurance

Nabarro Nathanson
50 Stratton Street, **London** W1X 6NX, United Kingdom
Tel: 44 20-7493 9933 Fax: 44 20-7629 7900
Internet: www.nabarro.com
E-Mail: d.branson@nabarro.com
director David Branson
Services: entertainment solicitors

Nauta Dutilh
PO Box 7113, 1007 JC **Amsterdam**, Netherlands
Tel: 31 20-541 4646 Fax: 31 20-661 2827
Internet: www.nautadutilh.nl
partners Dick van der Stelt, Richard Ebbink
Services: all fields of intellectual property law and financing arrangements

Nelson Hall, The
5 Spittalfield Crescent, **Edinburgh (Scotland)** EH8 9QZ, United Kingdom
Tel: 44 131-667 1728
contact Robert Walton
Services: theatre scenic and costume workshop

New Acoustics
34 Old Mill Road, Duntocher, **Clydebank** G81 6BX, United Kingdom
Tel: 44 1389-878 891 Fax: 44 1389-890 516
E-Mail: mail@newac.demon.co.uk
contact D Bowdler, C Frier
Services: acoustic consultants for performing arts buildings

New Notations London
40 Campbell Close, **London** SW16 6NG, United Kingdom
Tel: 44 20-8677 8473
Internet: www.gibmusic.freeserve.co.uk/nnlondon
E-Mail: nnlondon@gibmusic.freeserve.co.uk
partners S.B. Gibson, S.G. Ferre; adminstrator/marketing assistant Kathryn McCutcheon; engraving/technical support/finance assistant Moira Purkiss
Services: music typesetters and music software sales for PC and Mac; distributors of Score music notation programme Sibelius Centre for South West London

Next Stage
Judds Farm, Winsor Lane, Winsor, **Southampton** SO40 2HG, United Kingdom
Tel: 44 23-8081 2011 Fax: 44 23-8081 2213
E-Mail: 106177.3466@compuserve.com
contact Ray Carter
Services: theatre consultant

Nicholas Morris – Solicitors
52 Lincoln's Inn Fields, **London** WC2A 3LZ, United Kingdom
Tel: 44 20-7404 2340 Fax: 44 20-7404-4720
Internet: www.nicholasmorris.co.uk
E-Mail: mail@nicholasmorris.co.uk
senior partner Geffrey Davies; partners Leonard Lowy, Martin Smith; consultant John Elford
Services: specialist legal services in the performing arts including copyright, music, records, films, videos, cinema and the stage *Comments:* commercially aware firm experienced in all aspects of the performing arts

Nick Randell Associates
Weston Corner, Station Road, Fladbury, **Worcester** WR10 2QW, United Kingdom
Tel: 44 1386-860 390 Fax: 44 1386-860 390
E-Mail: nick.nra@virgin.net
contact Nick Randell
Services: specialist youth arts consultancy, research and project management

Nielsen & Nørger Law Office
Frederiksberggade 16, 1459 **Copenhagen** K, Denmark
Tel: 45 3311 4545 Fax: 45 3311 8081
E-Mail: nn@nnlaw.dk
contact Per Neumann
Services: media, film & television, music publishing

NJD Electronics (NJD Ltd)
10-11 Ascot Industrial Estate, Lenton Street, **Nottingham** NG10 5DJ, United Kingdom
Tel: 44 115-939 4122 Fax: 44 115-949 0453
Internet: www.njd.co.uk
E-Mail: info@njd-electronics.demon.co.uk
managing director Kevin Hopcroft; service sales Jim Ashby; financial director Jan Benyon; engineering manager Ian Benton; director Heather Hopcroft
Services: manufacture of sound and lighting equipment, audio and lighting installation department, design team; provides a complete 'one stop' service for all professional sound and lighting requirements
Comments: free full 40 page colour catalogue available

Norma Binnie
Rowan Cottage, Stirling Place, **Hove** BN3 3YU, United Kingdom
Tel: 44 1273-733 662 Fax: 44 1273-733 662
director Norma Binnie
Services: programming, budgets, marketing, trouble shooting and one to one consultations
Comments: expertise and advice on all aspects of runnnig an arts venue

Northern Light
Assembly St, Leith, **Edinburgh (Scotland)** EH6 7RG, United Kingdom
Tel: 44 131-553 2383 Fax: 44 131-553 3296
Internet: www.northernlight.co.uk
E-Mail: enquiries@northernlight.co.uk
managing director John Allen
Services: supply, hire and install sound, lighting and staging equipment; installations undertaken throughout the UK and overseas *Comments:* branches in Glasgow and London: 79 Loanbank Quadrant, Govan, Glasgow G51 3HZ, Tel: +44 141-440 1771, Fax: +44 141-445 4406; Business Design Centre, Suite 305, 52 Upper Street, Islington Green, London N1 0QH, Tel: +44 20-7288 6250, Fax: +44 20-7288 6251

Northern Lights
89 Scotforth Road, **Lancaster** LA1 4SD, United Kingdom
Tel: 44 1524-845 584
contact Ray Wilkinson
Services: distributors of sound, lighting and special effects equipment in the UK and overseas

NotaBene Records AS
Wolffsgt. 5, 0358 **Oslo**, Norway
Tel: 47 2269 1169 Fax: 47 2269 6305
Services: record production, music publishing, tour organiser

NÜSSLI (Deutschland) GmbH
Rothgrund 6, 91154 **Roth**, Germany
Tel: 49 9171-97630 Fax: 49 9171-976 350
Internet: www.nussli.de
E-Mail: info@nussli.de
Geschäftsführer Dipl.Ing. (FH) Bernd Helmstadt
Services: construction stages for theatre, concerts and special events such as the Olympic Games

OGACA
13 Rue Martin Bucer,
67000 **Strasbourg**, France
Tel: 33 3-8876 2410 Fax: 33 3-8876 2415
E-Mail: ogaca@iname.com
contact Fritz Fernandez
Services: private, non-profit business consultancy for arts organisations; also offers arts management training courses

Oniria International SL
Alzines 3, Sant Quirze Parc,
08192 **Sant Quirze Del Valles (Barcelona)**, Spain
Tel: 34 93-721 4247 Fax: 34 93-721 4610
Internet: www.neuronium.com
E-Mail: multimedia@neuronium.com
director Michel Huygen; manager Antoni Brunet
Services: Website designs customized for companies, artists, musicians and specially focused on the internet
Comments: alternative Internet: www.cd-music.net; see also Agents & Producers

Onno Greiner Martien van Goor Architekten bv
Jan Willem Brouwersstraat 8, 1071 LJ **Amsterdam**, Netherlands
Tel: 31 20-676 1144 Fax: 31 20-675 2536
Internet: www.gvg.nl
E-Mail: gvg@gvg.nl
architect/director Martien van Goor; consultant Onno Greiner
Services: design and build theatres, accomodation for mental health care, museums and renovation; other activities include development research, feasibility studies

OPERA America
1156 15th Street, Suite 810, **Washington** DC 20005-1704, United States of America
Tel: 1 202-293 4466 Fax: 1 202-393 0735
Internet: www.operaam.org
E-Mail: frontdesk@operaam.org (for general enquiries)
president & chief executive office Marc A Scorca (email: marc@operaam.org); director of finance & administration Harris Povich (email: harris@operaam.org); media & audience relations Sam Smith (email: sam@operaam.org); director of operations Eve Smith (email: eve@operaam.org)
Services: provides a variety of informational, technical, and financial services to its members and serves as a resource to the media, funders, government agencies and the general public
Comments: a not-for-profit service organisation; founded to support the professional opera companies of North America, it since has expanded to include allied international companies; other producing, presenting and educational institutions, and others; seeks to promote opera as an exiciting and accessible art form to all segments of society; see also Supranational Organisations and National Organisations in MOD

Oppenheimer Wolff & Donnelly
Avenue Louise 240, Bte 5, 1050 **Brussels**, Belgium
Tel: 32 2-626 0500 Fax: 32 2-626 0510
Internet: www.owdlaw.com
E-Mail: mvanachter@owdlaw.com
accountant Michael van Achter; managing director Mr Russotto
Services: entertainment lawyers

Optikinetics Ltd
38 Cromwell Road, **Luton** LU3 1DN,
United Kingdom
Tel: 44 1582-411 413 Fax: 44 1582-400 613
Internet: www.optikinetics.com
E-Mail: optiuk@optikinetics.com
director Neil Rice
Services: manufacturer of effects lighting equipment and Trilite Structural Systems

Organisation for Arts and Media
5 Dryden Street, **London** WC2E 9NW, United Kingdom
Tel: 44 20-7240 2430 Fax: 44 20-7240 5600
E-Mail: jackie-artsorg@cwcom.net
director Jackie Elliman
Services: marketing and events administration

Oscar Faber Acoustics
Marlborough House, Upper Marlborough Road,
St Albans AL1 3UT, United Kingdom
Tel: 44 20-8784 5784 Fax: 44 20-8784 5700
Internet: www.oscarfaber.co.uk
E-Mail: enquiries@oscarfaber.co.uk
director Stephen Hodkinson; contact John Lloyd
Services: consulting engineers for building and architectural acoustics and vibration control

OSRAM GmbH
Postfach OSRAM, 81536 **München**, Germany
Tel: 49 89-62130 Fax: 49 89-6213 2020
Internet: www.osram.de
vice-president, sales (Austria) Roman Adametz; sales (Germany) Frank Triebel
Services: production and distribution of lamps
Comments: visiting address: Hellabrunner Str 1, 81543 München

Outback Rigging Ltd
Unit 11, Kendal Court, Kendal Ave., Park Royal,
London W3 0RP, United Kingdom
Tel: 44 20-8993 0066 Fax: 44 20-8752 1753
E-Mail: outback@easynet.co.uk
chairman Mark Surtees; operations director Stuart Cooper
Services: provide rigging services for production companies, direct dry higher; theatre rigging for Grease and West Side Story

P.I.N.
Trnsko 39b, 10000 **Zagreb**, Croatia
Tel: 385 1-652 4457 Fax: 385 1-695 056
E-Mail: lkusan@alf.tel.hr
director Ms Lovorka Kusan; consultant Mr Ozren Kanceljak
Services: consulting foreign & domestic parties in fields of copyright, financial law, taxes and author's and neighboring rights and representing foreign & domestic parties in negotiating, execution, monitoring, controlling and overviewing
Comments: alternative E-mail: okancelj@alf.tel.hr

Pannell Kerr Forster Associates
New Garden House, 78 Hatton Garden,
London EC1N 8JA, United Kingdom
Tel: 44 20-7831 7393
Fax: 44 20-7405 6736
Internet: www.pkf.com.uk
senior partner Richard Pearson; managing partner Martin Goodchild
Services: consulting services to the leisure, arts and entertainment industry

Patrick Boyd Maunsell
Osberton House, 298 Woodstock Road,
Oxford OX2 7NR, United Kingdom
Tel: 44 1865-558 940/559 939
Fax: 44 1865-559 939
E-Mail: boydmaun@aol.com
contact Patrick Boyd Maunsell
Services: arts management consultancy; feasibility, policy & option studies; planning facilitation; organisational management review; operational management support & advice; training in financial administration; board development & training

Paul Gerstbauer
Praterstrasse 48, 1020 **Wien**, Austria
Tel: 43 1-512 3866 Fax: 43 1-5123 8665
Geschäftsführer Paul Gerstbauer
Services: flight cases for instruments for international touring *Comments:* head office: Bäcker str. 7, 1010 Wien, Tel: 43 1-512 3866, Fax: 43 1-5123 8665

Paul Steinhauer Public Relations & Communications
Hermanngasse 3, 1070 **Wien**, Austria
Tel: 43 1-5249 6470 Fax: 43 1-5249 6475
Internet: www.PaulSteinhauer.com
E-Mail: office@PaulSteinhauer.com
managing director Paul Steinhauer
Services: international public relations, project-management, sales support, event-marketing for opera, concert, festival, exhibition, CD-production, web-page design

Performance Plus
PO Box 16551, **Glasgow (Scotland)** G31 2RJ,
United Kingdom
Tel: 44 141-551 8789
Fax: 44 141-551 8789
artistic director Marco Romano
Services: consulting work on behalf of concert promoters, devising programmes, hiring artists for specific projects
Comments: event/concert consultancy, exclusively classical music

Peroni Spa
Via Monteleone 93, 21013 **Gallarate (VA)**, Italy
Tel: 39 0331-756 811 Fax: 39 0331-776 260
managing director Michele Peroni
Service: suppliers of every type of fabric that can be used in a theatre

Peter George Associates Inc.
40 Prince Street, **New York** NY 10012-3431, United States of America
Tel: 1 212-334 9700
Fax: 1 212-334 9759
E-Mail: petergeorgeassoc@compuserve.com
president Peter J. George
Services: acoustical and theatre consulting

Philips Licht Unternehmensbereich der Philips GmbH
Steindamm 94, 20099 **Hamburg**, Germany
Tel: 49 40-2899 2261
Fax: 49 40-2899 2366
Geschäftsführer J. Franke
Services: manufacturer, marketing and sales of lighting equipment and batteries

Philips Projects Centre
PO Box 218, 5600 MD **Eindhoven**, Netherlands
Tel: 31 40-278 4015 Fax: 31 40-278 6906
Internet: www.philips/project.philips.com
E-Mail: gerardmuleers@philips.com
contact Mr Muleers
Service: lighting equipment and batteries

Pippa Pawlik Public Relations
L'Harmonie, Quartier Le Plan 830,
Pargemon (Var), France
Tel: 33 4-9447 8100 Fax: 33 4-9447 8792
director Pippa Pawlik
Services: full consultancy service (international) including press and promotion consultancy

Positive Solutions
Bluecoat Chambers, School Lane, **Liverpool** L1 3BX, United Kingdom
Tel: 44 151-709 6511 Fax: 44 151-709 2575
Internet: www.powerup.com.au/~positive
E-Mail: solutions@positive.demon.co.uk
partners David Fishel, Cathy Hunt
Services: organisational and strategic planning & development, feasibility studies, cultural industries development
Comments: exists to enhance opportunities for cultural activity and so assist in the development of creative management; Australian office: 10 Lechmerle Street, New Farm, QLD 4005, Tel/Fax: +61 7-3358 1077, Email: positive@powerup.com.au; see also Courses

Power Light B AG
Industriestrasse 111, 4147 **Aesch (Basel)**, Switzerland
Tel: 41 61-756 9999
Fax: 41 61-756 9990
E-Mail: Powerlight@bluewin.ch
general manager Felix Riva
Services: lighting rental and sales, production services

ppARTnerships
PO Box 2772, **Brighton** BN1 6FW,
United Kingdom
Tel: 44 1273-330 464 Fax: 44 1273-330 533
E-Mail: pparts@easynet.co.uk
director Peter Luxton
Services: selected work in both capital and revenue areas – feasibility studies and business plans; strategic planning and development plans; cultural quarter development; cultural industries sector analysis, economic impact and development; cultural productions, proposals and feasibility studies including festivals, touring and media production projects
Comments: see also Agents & Producers

PR2 classic
Kreuznacher Str. 63, 50968 **Köln**, Germany
Tel: 49 221-381 063
Fax: 49 221-383 955
E-Mail: PR2classic@aol.com
director Gabriele Schiller; managers Eva Luise Roth, Ulrike Jessel
Services: personal worldwide and local representation of artists and PR/press representation for orchestras, artists and special projects
Comments: see also Agents & Producers

PRC Public Relations
Burg Hogguerstraat 1097,
1064 EH **Amsterdam**, Netherlands
Tel: 31 20-611 1970
Fax: 31 20-613 3714
contact H R Steinvoorte
Services: public relations consultancy, sponsoring

Prescott Productions
Via della Chiesa 97, 50125 **Firenze**, Italy
Tel: 39 055-222 556
Fax: 39 055-222 556
Internet: www.prescott.it
E-Mail: mail@prescott.it
director Mauro Conti
Services: surtitles and subtitles for the performing arts, editing, publishing, database

Price Waterhouse Cooper
1 Embankment Place, **London** WC2N 6NN,
United Kingdom
Tel: 44 20-7583 5000
Fax: 44 20-7822 4652
Internet: www.pwcglobal.com
contact Susan Mackenzie Gray
Services: management consultancy; specialise in commercial/financial issues including raising funds, grants and partners; skills include project appraisal, project and business review, project management, asset management, strategy

Prima Klima Reisen GmbH
Hauptstraße 5, 10827 **Berlin**, Germany
Tel: 49 30-7879 27-77 Fax: 49 30-7879 2720
Internet: www.primaklima.de
E-Mail: pkr@bln.de
contact Christian Löw
Services: touring coaches and travel arrangements including Nightliner buses (4-18 beds)

Prologue Systems
4513 Vernon Boulevard, **Madison** WI 53705, United States of America
Tel: 1 608-231 3358 Fax: 1 608-231 6703
Internet: www.protix.com
president Pete Hanson
Services: computerized ticketing and fundraising systems

Promenade Music
404 Marine Road East, **Morecambe** LA4 5AR, United Kingdom
Tel: 44 1524-410 202 Fax: 44 1524-410 802
E-Mail: info@prom-music.co.uk
director David Wood; designer Keith Harris
Services: design and build quality aluminium flight cases; musical instrument suppliers; musical equipment suppliers and hire, installation and mobile recording

Prometeo
Laboratorio Permanente di Elettroacustica, Strada Ospizi Civili, 3, 43100 **Parma**, Italy
Tel: 39 0521-236 605 Fax: 39 0521-235 971
Internet: www.symbolic.pr.it/ensemble.html
E-Mail: prometeo@symbolic.it
direttore Martino Traversa; presidente onorario Claudio Abbado
Services: research, software, musical productions, conferences & seminars

Prompt Data Limited
8 Chipperfield Road, Bovingdon, **Hemel Hempstead** HP3 0JN, United Kingdom
Tel: 44 1442-834 771 Fax: 44 1442-834 771
Internet: www.prompt-data.com
E-Mail: vlundy@cablenet.ie
general manager Vincent Lundy
Services: computerised booking and management solutions to the arts, leisure and recreation industries

Public et Communication
3 rue Le Goff, 75005 **Paris**, France
Tel: 33 1-4326 0737 Fax: 33 1-4326 9903
E-Mail: public.et.co@wanadoo.fr
managing director Anne-Marie Thibaut
Services: marketing agency for cultural, artistic and touristic private and public organisations; supplies market and feasibility studies, builds communication campaigns, organises events

Public Production Co. Ltd, The
117 Praed Street, **London** WC2 1RL, United Kingdom
Tel: 44 20-7402 2789 Fax: 44 20-7706 9348
E-Mail: aston@mailbox.co.uk
directors Laurence Aston, John L. Walters
Services: music consultancy, specialist record marketing, record production *Comments:* co-founder and publisher of Unknown Public (creative music journal); see also Recorded Media and Publications

Pulsar Light of Cambridge Ltd
Henley Rd, **Cambridge** CB1 3EA, United Kingdom
Tel: 44 1223-366 798 Fax: 44 1223-460 708
Internet: www.pulsarlight.com
E-Mail: sales@cpp.com
managing director Paul Mardon; sales & marketing director D. Saunders; publicity & PR Jane Monk; project support manager Andy Graves
Services: manufacturer of lighting equipment

Purcell & Noppe + Assocs. Inc.
21408 Devonshire Street, **Chatworth** CA 91311, United States of America
Tel: 1 818-882 7820 Fax: 1 818-882 0578
president Jack Purcell; vice president/treasurer Roger Noppe
Services: acoustical consulting

Quintessenz Artists
Ferchenbachstr. 7, 80995 **München**, Germany
Tel: 49 89-150 5099 Fax: 49 89-150 3776
Internet: www.quintessenz-artists.com
E-Mail: QuEssenz@aol.com
director Monika Csampai; manager Dr Angelika Leik
Services: promotion and public relations service, for artists, managements and recording companies

Reiche & Vogel B. Deltschaft
Blumenstraße 10, 13585 **Berlin**, Germany
Tel: 49 30-335 7061 Fax: 49 30-336 2058
Internet: www.revolux.com
E-Mail: office@revolux.com
Geschäftsführer Hans Michael Wörwag
Services: spotlight production and complete lighting equipment for stage, multi-purpose halls, studios

Renton Howard Wood Levin Partnership
77 Endell Street, **London** WC2H 9AJ, United Kingdom
Tel: 44 20-7379 7900
Fax: 44 20-7836 4881
senior partners Nicholas Thompson, Geoffrey Mann, John Tebbutt, Peter Shaw, Barry Pritchard
Services: large international architectural practice specialising in design and construction of theatres, concert halls, TV, radio and performing arts facilities worldwide

RG Jones Recording Studios
Beulah Road, **London** SW19 3SB, United Kingdom
Tel: 44 20-8540 9881 Fax: 44 20-8542 4368
Internet: www.rgjones.co.uk
E-Mail: studio@rgjones.co.uk
studio manager Gerry Kitchingham; director Robin Jones
Services: the recording studio offers an SSL console with total recall, 32 track digital and 24 track analogue recording facilities; the studio has a varied client base from classical to pop

RG Jones Sound Engineering
16 Endeavour Way, **London** SW19 8UH, United Kingdom
Tel: 44 20-8971 3100
Fax: 44 20-8971 3101
Internet: www.rgjones.co.uk
E-Mail: enquiries@rgjones.co.uk
managing director Robin Jones; hire John Carroll; sales Ron Purbrick; telecommunications Paul Slaughter
Services: sound engineering company; design, sell, hire and install a wide range of audio and teleconferencing products; the hire operation undertakes works in a wide variety of areas, including television, conferences, trade shows, classical music concerts and speech announcement systems for large events

RIC Corporation
6215 Constitution Drive, **Fort Wayne** IN 46804, United States of America
Tel: 1 219-432 0799
Fax: 1 219-432 9155
Internet: www.riccorp.com
president Rick Kriscka; co-owner and vice president Joan Tracey
Services: provide software for facility management; have developed Concentrix, the events management system as used by the South Bank Centre and the Barbican, London, and 45 other centres around the world

Richard Laurence & Rossiter
2 Pride Court, 80 White Lion Street, **London** N1 9PF, United Kingdom
Tel: 44 20-7278 6799
Fax: 44 20-7278 6852
partner Vernon Rossiter
Services: royalty auditors

Ripley-Duggan Partnership
52 Tottenham Street, **London** W1P 9PG, United Kingdom
Tel: 44 20-7436 1392
Fax: 44 20-7436 1395
E-Mail: ripleyduggan@compuserve.com
director Greg Ripley-Duggan
Services: tour booking and planning services for producers, promoters and repertory companies

Robertson Taylor Insurance Brokers
33 Harbour Exchange Square, **London** E14 9GG, United Kingdom
Tel: 44 20-7538 9840 Fax: 44 20-7538 9919
E-Mail: enquiries@robertson-taylor.co.uk
joint chairman Willie Robertson; joint chairman, joint managing director Bob Taylor; joint managing director/finance director David Franklin; directors Martin Goebbels, John Silcock
Services: specialist insurance brokers to the entertainment industry

Roscolab Ltd
Blanchard Works, Kangley Bridge Rd, **London** SE26 5AQ, United Kingdom
Tel: 44 20-8659 2300
Fax: 44 20-8659 3153
Internet: www.rosco.com
E-Mail: info-uk@rosco.com
director of sales Anna Western; European business development manager Kees Frijters
Services: manufacturer of range of lighting, filters, artificial fog, stage and studio equipment

Russells
Regency House, 1/4 Warwick Street, **London** W1R 6LJ, United Kingdom
Tel: 44 20-7439 8692
Fax: 44 20-7494 3582
E-Mail: media@russells.co.uk
senior partner Tony Russell; partners Anthony English, Mark Sinnott
Services: music and entertainment law

RVE Technologie
23 rue Beausire, 93250 **Villemomble**, France
Tel: 33 1-4854 3163 Fax: 33 1-4528 6753
E-Mail: rvetec@clubinternet.fr
export sales executives Frank Dujardin, Wilfrid Chenay
Services: manufacturer of stage and architectural lighting equipment, dimmers, lighting consoles, lighting control systems, luminaires *Comments:* offer wide range of dimming system, consoles and luminaires

Salongo
20-22 Hepburn Road, St Pauls, **Bristol** BS2 8UD, United Kingdom
Tel: 44 117-944 5579 Fax: 44 117-944 1478
E-Mail: salongo@salongo.demon.co.uk
director Ruth Grosvenor
Services: resource project for African and Caribbean dance and music; offers training and entertainment through workshops, residencies and performances, utilising tutors on local, national and international levels; aim is to raise awareness and understanding of African peoples' dance, music and related arts

Sandy Brown Associates
1 Coleridge Gardens, **London** NW6 3QH, United Kingdom
Tel: 44 20-7624 6033 Fax: 44 20-7625 6688
E-Mail: post@sandybrown.co.uk
acoustic architect David Binns, David Lamberty; acoustic consultants Richard Galbraith, Kyri Kyriakides, Laurence Haslam
Services: independent partnership specialising in architecture and acoustic & audio-visual consultancy with particular expertise in buildings for the performing arts *Comments:* and at: 16 West Terrace, South Queensferry, West Lothian EH30 9LL, Tel: +44 131-331 2020, Fax: +44 131-331 2187

SBS GmbH Dresden
Bosewitzer Str. 20, Postfach 170760, 01242 **Dresden**, Germany
Tel: 49 351-20410 Fax: 49 351-203 8662
Internet: sbs-dresden.de
E-Mail: sbs@sbs-dresden.de
sales manager Manfred Freimüller
Services: stage machinery, control systems

Scenografie Mattei snc
Via Appia Nuova km. 17, 700, 00043 **Ciampino (Roma)**, Italy
Tel: 39 06-7934 0549/41413 (English line)
Fax: 39 06-7934 0295
Internet: www.mattei-srl.it
E-Mail: info@mattei-srl.it
managing director Fabrizio Mattei
Services: stage workshop specialising in painted theatre and cinema scenery, also copies of historic curtains

Schiedmayer Celestabau Gmbh Stuttgart
Lenbachstrasse 53, 70192 **Stuttgart**, Germany
Tel: 49 711-135 3360 Fax: 49 711-1353 3613
Internet: www.pianos.de
E-Mail: schiedmayerstuttgart@t-online.de
directors Elianne Schiedmayer, Urs Bachmann
Services: manufacturers of keyboard instruments; well-known for celestas and keyboard Glockenspiels, repairs second-hand instruments

Schilling & Lom and Partners
Royalty House, 72-74 Dean St., **London** W1V 6AE, United Kingdom
Tel: 44 20-7453 2500 Fax: 44 20-7453 2600
Internet: www.schillinglom.co.uk
E-Mail: legal@schillinglom.co.uk
partners Keith Schilling, Nicholas Lom, Edward Parladorio, Jonathan Coad, Mark Thomson
Services: all aspects of arts and entertainment including music, film, television, book publishing, libel, fashion, general copyright and contract work and litigation in respect of all matters

Schott Frères
30, Rue St Jean, 1000 **Brussels**, Belgium
Tel: 32 2-512 3980 Fax: 32 2-514 2845
administrateur Jean Jacques Junne
Services: music & instrument distribution in bulk, publishes music scores

Scriptorium Musicum
Svetl. 3, 811 02 **Bratislava**, Slovakia
Tel: 421 7-6280 2450
Internet: www.scriptorium.sk
E-Mail: scriptorium@tatrahome.sk
director Stanley Bartowitz
Services: music publishing, note setting, midi-music, internet, publishing *Comments:* see also Music Forum

Seddons
5 Portman Square, **London** W1H 0NT, United Kingdom
Tel: 44 20-7486 9681 Fax: 44 20-7935 5049
Internet: www.seddons.co.uk
E-Mail: postmaster@seddons.co.uk
head of entertainment & media department David Kent
Services: solicitors

Comments: involved in music, book publishing, film, tv, video and computer games; also office in Czech Republic: Rybna 1, 110 00 Praha 1, Tel: +420 2-231 6522/6532, Fax: +420 2-231 6805, E-mail: seddons@terminal.cz

Sedley Richard Laurence Voulters
Kendal House, 1 Conduit Street, **London** W1R 9TG, United Kingdom
Tel: 44 20-7287 9595 Fax: 44 20-7287 9696
E-Mail: srlv23@aol.com
partners Richard Rosenberg, Laurence Finger, Stephen Jeffery, Luffy Ossman, David Sinaman, Marc Voulters, Alok Verma
Services: chartered accountants for the entertainment business

Seréna Woolf marketing et relations publiques
21 bis, rue d'Hennemont,
78100 **Saint Germain-en-Laye**, France
Tel: 33 1-3973 4051 Fax: 33 1-3973 4062
managing director Seréna Woolf
Services: press, marketing, promotion and pr services for individual artists, orchestras, record companies, distributors and festivals; specialises in classical music

Sharon Kivity Arts Consultant
19B Albert Road, **Teddington** TW11 0BD, United Kingdom
Tel: 44 20-8977 2961 Fax: 44 20-8977 6281
E-Mail: sharonarts@btinternet.com
senior consultant Sharon Kivity
Services: events and festival direction and management; arts marketing/administration; consultancy and training; editorial and magazine production *Comments:* see also Agents & Producers

shinkansen
Bedale Gallery, 4 Bedale Street, **London** SE1 9AL, United Kingdom
Tel: 44 20-7357 0823/4 Fax: 44 20-7357 0825
Internet: www.backspace.org/shinkansen
E-Mail: shinkansen@compuserve.com
executive director/touring Debbi Lander; artistic director Ghislaine Boddington; production manager Estelle Neveux; web design/technology applications Andrew Ward
Services: working group: facilitation/moderation/lectures; web activity/training network; research/publications/well-known and emerging artists, production/distribution *Comments:* partner in the European co-operation initiative 'Butterfly Effect Network' with Dietheater Wien (Austria) and Forum Danca (Lisbon); member of IETM (q.v.); lead organisation in the 'Sound Works Exchange' – British/German sound artists network; promoter of multi-environment club events; key research area: fluid space, fluid presence

SHOWTEC Beleuchtungs-und Beschallungs GmBH
Mathias-Bruggen-Str. 21, 50827 **Köln**, Germany
Tel: 49 221-595 3070 Fax: 49 221-595 4579
E-Mail: mail@showtec.de
managing director Thomas Ickenroth; contact Peter Van Den Hurq
Services: lighting and sound for TV, stage, concert, fairs and industrial events, pre production services; full technical service

Shuttlesound Ltd
4, The Willows Centre, Willow Lane, **Mitcham** CR4 4NX, United Kingdom
Tel: 44 20-8646 7114 Fax: 44 20-8640 7583
Internet: www.shuttlesound.co.uk
managing director Paul Barreta; technical support Nigel Meddemmen
Services: distributor of professional audio equipment

SIAP Ltd. (System for Improved Acoustic Performance)
17, West Heath Drive, **London** NW11 7QG, United Kingdom
Tel: 44 20-8455 4640 Fax: 44 20-8209 1059
managing director Michael Holden BA, MSTC
Services: electro-acoustic improvement of auditoria and specialist sound systems for large scale lyric and classical concerts

Sico Europe Ltd
Henwood Industrial Estate, **Ashford** TN24 8DH, United Kingdom
Tel: 44 1233-643 311 Fax: 44 1233-645 143
E-Mail: sales@sico-europe.com
managing director Brian Crack; UK sales manager Tony Crawford
Services: demountable, mobile folding stage systems, portable dance floors and other theatre products

Simkins Partnership
45-51 Whitfield Street, **London** W1P 6AA, United Kingdom
Tel: 44 20-7631 1050 Fax: 44 20-7436 2744
Internet: www.simkins.com
E-Mail: simkins@simkins.com
advertising, photography Charles Swan; film & video Nigel Bennett; sport Stephen Hornsby; music Julian Turton; theatre David T Franks; multimedia Jonathan Sellors
Services: specialises in all areas of media and entertainment law including film, television, video, theatre, music, advertising, multimedia and photography

Sirkus Management A/S
Cort Adelersgate 2, 0254 **Oslo**, Norway
Tel: 47 2243 1700 Fax: 47 2244 6640
director Petter Sandberg
Services: consultancy on artists' legal rights *Comments:* see also Promoters and Agents & Producers

SJ Berwin & Co
222 Gray's Inn Road, **London** WC1X 8HB, United Kingdom
Tel: 44 20-7533 2222 Fax: 44 20-7533 2000
Internet: www.sjberwin.com
E-Mail: info@sjberwin.com
partners (media section) Nigel Palmer, Peter McInerney, Tim Johnson, Jacqualine Hurt
Services: music publishing, records, film, video, television, book publishing, theatre, merchandising, sponsorhsip, copyright & intellectual property

Sky-Light
Z A Charles de Gaulle, 50 Rue Henri Farman,
93297 **Tremblay-en-France**, France
Tel: 33 1-4963 2369 Fax: 33 1-4963 2390
E-Mail: pqcd@wanadoo.fr
planning Annie Colombatto; manager Francoise Laurent
Services: rent and sell projectors, manufacturer of STX for show business

Slick Systems
Portland St North, **Leek** ST13 6AH, United Kingdom
Tel: 44 1538-372 109 Fax: 44 1538-381 315
Internet: www.slick-systems.com
E-Mail: eu-sales@slick-systems.co.uk
chairman Michael Wood; sales Ian Hall, Jo Rushton
Services: manufactures and distributes a range of trussing and ground support towers

Smith & Williamson
1 Riding House Street, **London** W1A 3AS, United Kingdom
Tel: 44 20-7637 5377 Fax: 44 20-7631 0741
Internet: www.smith.williamson.co.uk
E-Mail: 100546.1111@compuserve.com
partner Robert Empson
Services: strategic planning; marketing strategy/plans; management counselling; emphasis on client ownership and skills transfer; specialise in workshop/team facilitation

Societé AVAB Sarl
62 rue Danielle Casanova, 93207 **Saint Denis**, France
Tel: 33 1-4243 3535 Fax: 33 1-4243 0805
E-Mail: avab.france@insonie.fr
director of marketing Jean-Louis Pernette; technical director Christian Rezgui
Services: manufacturer and supplier of luminaires, lighting controls and lighting equipment for theatres

Solti snc di Fasano Ermanno & c
via Castagnoli, 00049 **Velletri (Roma)**, Italy
Tel: 39 06-963 5083/6015 Fax: 39 06-963 5664
administrator Ermanno Fasano; assistant administrator Rosanna Fasano; settore tecnico Manrico Fasano
Services: supply of stage materials (lights, sounds etc); transports; theatres equipment; theatre tailoring (production and hire), wigs, everything for opera
Comments: see also Agents & Producers

SONING
Podlesínská 5, 169 00 **Praha** 6, Czech Republic
Tel: 420 2-5732 1090/547 585
Fax: 420 2-573 2951/544 589
director Ing Zikovsky
Services: acoustic and electroacoustic services- acoustic adaptation of cultural, educational and sports spaces, closed and open spaces sound system, sound proof adaptation in industry, personal protective sound proof aids, production of accoustic cladding SONIT

Sophie Cohen Arts Publicity
54b Thornhill Square, **London** N1 1BE, United Kingdom
Tel: 44 20-7428 9850 Fax: 44 20-7428 9850
director Sophie Cohen
Services: freelance PR consultant for classical & world music, contemporary dance

Sound Design Ltd
Dundas, Chavey Down Road, Winfield Row, **Bracknell** RG42 7PB, United Kingdom
Tel: 44 1344-883 620 Fax: 44 1344-893 620
director/acoustician Courtenay Nicholas
Services: studios, theatres, auditoria etc. design, measurement and corrective services including acoustics and electro acoustics; manufacturer of acoustic doors, absorbers, reflectors, windows and special acoustic equipment; worldwide

Soundlight
Vahrenwalder Str 205-207,
30165 **Hannover**, Germany
Tel: 49 511-373 0267 Fax: 49 511-373 0423
Internet: www.soundlight.de
E-Mail: info@soundlight.de
director Eckart Steffens
Services: manufacturer of dimmer racks and light control desks; MIDI controlled lighting equipment; DMX-512 interfaces and converters; glass fibre transmission systems

Sparta System AB
Hömånadsgatan 16, 415 15 **Göteborg**, Sweden
Tel: 46 31-484 549/102-091 374 (mobile)
Fax: 46 31-484 549
Internet: www.sparta.se
E-Mail: info@sparta.se
contact Erik Saltin
Services: manufacturers of flight cases for touring orchestras; staging, risers and miscellaneous music equipment

Specialised Travel Ltd
12-15 Hanger Green, **London** W5 3EL, United Kingdom
Tel: 44 20-8799 8300
Fax: 44 20-8998 7965
Internet: www.stlon.com
E-Mail: admin@stlon.com
managing director Richard Savage
Services: founded in 1955, fully licensed (ABTA, IATA, CAA) travel agency specialising in the music business, whether individual and group travel, concert tour programmes, or exchanges for choirs, bands and orchestras

Spero Communications Ltd
Grampian House, Meridian Gate, Marsh Wall, **London** E14 9YT, United Kingdom
Tel: 44 20-7538 9946 Fax: 44 20-7538 4747
E-Mail: spero@spercom.co.uk
managing director Ian Spero; director Connie Brighton
Services: specialise in the design of interactive marketing programmes which combine innovation with sound business objectives

SponsArt s.p.r.l.
8 rue de Buisson, bte 3, 1050 **Brussels**, Belgium
Tel: 32 2-647 5070
Fax: 32 2-648 7009
E-Mail: 100756.155@compuserve.com
managing partner Jackie van Aubel
Services: arts sponsorship consultancy, specialized in pan-European and global sponsorships, with full services including sponsorship audit, research, project management, graphic design and production, media relations, corporate hospitality

Sponsor Service ASA
PB 3036, Elisenberg, 0207 **Oslo**, Norway
Tel: 47 2313 6000 Fax: 47 2313 6001
contact Wiggo Aaberg; senior project leader Keith Woods
Services: sponsorship consultants *Comments:* visiting address: Drammensveien 96 G, 0273 Oslo

Spotlight Srl
Via Sardegna 3,
20098 **San Giuliano Milanese (MI)**, Italy
Tel: 39 02-988 301 Fax: 39 02-988 3022
Internet: www.spotlight.it
E-Mail: spot.sales@spotlight.it
amministratore unico Andraghetti Augusto
Services: manufacturer of lighting equipment for theatre, studio and disco

St Georges Music Trust
St Georges, Brandon Hill, **Bristol** BS1 5PZ, United Kingdom
Tel: 44 117-929 4929
Fax: 44 117-927 6537
administrator Catherine Freda
Services: recording studio
Comments: see also Venues

Stafford Knight Entertainment Insurance Brokers
18 London Street, **London** EC3R 7JP, United Kingdom
Tel: 44 20-7265 1717/7628 3135
Fax: 44 20-7481 2218
contacts David Taylor, Pamela Crosby
Services: Lloyd's brokers, complete insurance service to the music and entertainment business

Stage Control Ltd.
Station Parade, Whitchurch Lane, **Edgware** HA8 6RW, United Kingdom
Tel: 44 20-8952 8982 Fax: 44 20-8951 4178
managing director D Jenkins; technical director I New; manager hire dept. M Savage
Services: theatre lighting stockists, colour filters etc; equipment supplied worldwide; custom built lighting control equipment; lighting rental and installations

Stage Electrics
Victoria Road, Avonmouth, **Bristol** BS11 9DB, United Kingdom
Tel: 44 117-982 7282 Fax: 44 117-982 2180
Internet: www.stage-electrics.demon.co.uk
E-Mail: hire@stage-electrics.co.uk
production services manager Richard Cross; hire manager Adrian Searle; buyer Dave Pearce; sales & marketing Linda Moore; support office Nick Dixon; projects manager Nick Ewins
Services: technical services to the entertainment industry including lighting and staging, sound, audio-visual, rigging *Comments:* other E-mails: sales@stage-electrics.co.uk or export@stage-electrics.co.uk

starkstrom-elektronik AG
Güterstraße 11, 8957 **Spreitenbach**, Switzerland
Tel: 41 56-418 7611 Fax: 41 56-401 4986
Internet: www.se-ag.ch
E-Mail: verkauf@se-ag.ch
Geschäftsführer Herrmann Häfliger; Verkaufsleiter B.Huber
Services: manufacturer of lighting control systems, light management and dimmer equipment

Start Ticket Vertrieb von Veranstaltungskarten GmbH
Mainzer Landstrasse 341,
60326 **Frankfurt am Main**, Germany
Tel: 49 69-7588-0 Fax: 49 69-7588 1089/81
Internet: www.start.de
E-Mail: annerose.mertens@start.de
Geschäftsführerin Ivanka Springer
Services: ticketing software

Statec Bühnentechnik GmbH
Baumstr. 42, 47198 **Duisburg**, Germany
Tel: 49 2066-2000-0 Fax: 49 2066-2000-15
Geschäftsführer Werner Klemps, Dipl-Ing Rainer Puls, Winfried Burda
Services: stage machinery (Power Flying System); upper and under machinery, safety curtains, smoke outlets

Steeldeck Sales Ltd
Barpart House, Kings Cross Freight Depot, York Way, **London** N1 0UZ, United Kingdom
Tel: 44 20-7833 2031 Fax: 44 20-7278 3403
Internet: www.steeldeck.co.uk
contacts Philip Parsons, Michael Passmore, Gail Moorcroft
Services: manufacturers of STEELDECK staging and sales & rentals, scenery makers; sole agents for Nivoflex platforms – a range of light aluminium through to motorised

Stichting voor Kunstpromotie
Handelskaai 14, 1000 **Brussels**, Belgium
Tel: 32 2-219 4080 Fax: 32 2-219 0462
Internet: www.stichting-kunstpromotie.be
E-Mail: info@stichting-kunstpromotie.be
director Luc Delrue; delegate administrator t.b.a.
Services: sponsorship consultancy for non-profit and private companies; prepare cultural plan for companies

Strand Lighting GmbH
Ullsteinstrasse 114/142, 12109 **Berlin**, Germany
Tel: 49 30-707 9510 Fax: 49 30-707 95199
E-Mail: info@strand-lighting.de
director Horst Eickmann
Services: manufacturer of lighting systems used in theatres and TV, film & architectual lighting
Comments: the North European office for Strand Lighting Ltd – see separate entry

Strand Lighting Italia srl
Via delle Gardenie 33, 00040 **Pomezia (RO)**, Italy
Tel: 39 06-919 631
Fax: 39 06-914 7136
contact Raffaella Scaccia
Services: manufacturing and providing of lighting systems

Strand Lighting Ltd
North Hyde House, Hayes Road,
Heston UB2 5NL, United Kingdom
Tel: 44 20-8571 3588 Fax: 44 20-8571 3305
Internet: www.strandlighting.com
E-Mail: sales@stranduk.com
marketing coordinator Bethan Dickson
Services: manufacturer and distributor of a complete range of lighting equipment for stage, studio, film and architectural applications throughout the world; the luminaire range includes fresnels, PCs, profiles and floodlights

Studio Legale Mondini & Rusconi
Via Visconti di Modrone 2,
20122 **Milano**, Italy
Tel: 39 02-7600 4838 Fax: 39 02-7601 4053
E-Mail: mondinirusconi@iol.it
partners Giorgio Mondini, Giuseppe Rusconi
Services: arts lawyers; areas of speciality: film, video, TV, music publishing, radio, book publishing, litigation, commercial and international law, corporate law, copyright and intellectual property, telecommunications

Studio Legale Pojaghi
Via Visconti di Modrone, 2, 20122 **Milano**, Italy
Tel: 39 02-7600 8947 Fax: 39 02-7601 3950
E-Mail: pojaghi@tin.it
contact Alberto Pojaghi
Services: solicitors

SWH Software GmbH
Attilastraße 61-67, 12105 **Berlin**, Germany
Tel: 49 30-754 9170 Fax: 49 30-7549 1744
Internet: www.swh-software.de
E-Mail: swh-software@t-online.de
Geschäftsführer Norbert Herich
Services: manufacturer of software

Sylvania
Industriepark, 3300 **Tienen**, Belgium
Tel: 32 16-800 369/365 Fax: 32 16-800 367/818 945
sales & marketing manager Mark Canherb
Services: manufacture and sell lighting for theatre, concerts etc.

Symphony Tours
Via de las dos Castillas 7, Portal 1, 1°A,
28224 **Pozuelo de Alarcón (Madrid)**, Spain
Tel: 34 91-351 2493 Fax: 34 91-351 3220
E-Mail: symphony@jet.es
director Carlos Schwab; co-director Otto Schwab
Services: collaborates with cultural events specially festivals of classical music as well as classical and contemporary dance; travel agency – organises tours for orchestras and collaborates with cultural events
Comments: the company has 16 years of experience in Latin America and Spain

Synchro Systems
International House, Stubbs Gate,
Newcastle under Lyme ST5 1LU, United Kingdom
Tel: 44 1782-741 999 Fax: 44 1782-742 999
Internet: www.synchro.co.uk
E-Mail: enquiries@synchrosystems.co.uk
sales manager Steve Vernon; account manager (theatres) Steve Pugh
Services: produce Venuemaster (venue management system) and Theatar- a complete box office solution for larger venues, eg. Earl's Court and hebos- a low-price computerised box office system which offers ticket selling, patron database, marketing and financial analysis features; runs on stand-alone or networked PC compatible computers *Comments:* sales literature is available, Email: sales@synchro.co.uk

SYRINX - music & media
Mexikoring 33, 22297 **Hamburg**, Germany
Tel: 49 40-6370 9230 Fax: 49 40-6370 9232
Internet: www.syrinx.de
E-Mail: syrinx@syrinx.de
managing director Toni Fiedler; contacts Joehan Rudelt, Jürgen Klimmeck
Services: DVD – consulting, concepts, production, authoring, premastering; editorial services; audio/video production *Comments:* ISDN +49 40-6370 9238

Talaske Group, Inc., The
105 North Oak Park Avenue, **Oak Park** IL 60301, United States of America
Tel: 1 708-524 2800 Fax: 1 708-524 2818
Internet: www.talaske.com
E-Mail: info@talaske.com
president & principal consultant Richard Talaske
Services: acoustical, audio and video consulting: room acoustics design, acoustic isolation design, building systems noise control design, environmental acoustics design, audio and audio/visual systems design and specification

Tanz- und Theaterbedarf Klaus Schreck GmbH
Bismarckstrasse 20, 76646 **Bruchsal**, Germany
Tel: 49 7251-14921 Fax: 49 7251-14920
Internet: www.schreck.net
E-Mail: Klaus@Schreck.net
contact Klaus Schreck
Services: specialise in dance-wear for stage, theatre costumes of elastic fabrics, tights, all kinds of stretch-materials and middle-age legwear; mainly produce to customer's designs

Taylor Joynson Garrett
Carmelite, 50 Victoria Embankment, Blackfriars,
London EC4Y 0DX, United Kingdom
Tel: 44 20-7353 1234 Fax: 44 20-7936 2666
Internet: www.tjg.co.uk
E-Mail: enquiries@tjg.co.uk
partners Paul Mitchell
Services: legal advisors on copyright and all matters relating to the law and business of arts and entertainment, both live and recorded

Teacher Stern Selby, Solicitors
37-41 Bedford Row, **London** WC1R 4JH, United Kingdom
Tel: 44 20-7242 3191 Fax: 44 20-7242 1156
Internet: www.tsslaw.co.uk
partner Roger Selby; contacts Graham Shear, Martine Nathan
Services: legal services to the music industry

Teatro SRL
Via Ubertini 3, 46042 **Castel Goffredo (MN)**, Italy
Tel: 39 0376-780 702
Fax: 39 0376-780 888
E-Mail: 100723.2733@compuserve.com
amministratore unico e titolare Michael George Lowe
Services: designs, develops and markets a comprehensive range of stage lighting fixtures and accessories

Technical Insight Ltd
Studio 10, 75 Filmer Road, **London** SW6 7JF, United Kingdom
Tel: 44 20-7371 0875 Fax: 44 20-7736 0051
managing director John Simpson; architect David Self
Services: project management and consultancy services for the entertainment industry; theatre consultants; full architectural services for new & existing buildings including building refurbishment, redesign and refitting, installations, surveys and reports

Technical Planning International
The Stagehouse, Palace Road,
Kingston upon Thames KT1 2LG,
United Kingdom
Tel: 44 20-8549 6535 Fax: 44 20-8549 6545
E-Mail: techplan@csi.com
senior consultant Richard Brett BSc. C.Eng. FIEE; management Neil Morton
Services: stage and auditorium planners; rigging, machinery, lighting, sound and audiovisual systems designers and consultants

Tei Williams Press and Arts Marketing
7 Acre End Street, Eynsham, **Oxon** OX8 1PE, United Kingdom
Tel: 44 1865-883 139/884 240
Fax: 44 1865-884 011
E-Mail: tei@artsmarketing.demon.co.uk
director Tei Williams
Services: opera, theatre, literature, personality tours, marketing & press work undertaken

TeleCartaz
Rua D. João V, 13-A, Sala 4,
1250-089 **Lisboa**, Portugal
Tel: 351 21-385 4419/5013 Fax: 351 21-385 4419
E-Mail: j.v.mendes.telecartaz@ip.pt
director José Vieira Mendes
Services: marketing and PR for the performing arts; performing arts consultant & sponsorship; booking and delivering tickets for all arts events in Lisbon; front-of-house services in venues, reception and protocol for events

TeleStage Associates Ltd
14 Bunting Road, Moreton Hall Industrial Estate,
Bury St Edmunds IP32 7BX, United Kingdom
Tel: 44 1284-755 512 Fax: 44 1284-755 516
Internet: www.telestage.com
E-Mail: info@telestage.com
managing director Q.S. Hardy; commercial manager Mike Bacon; technical manager Stuart Wilson
Services: designers, manufacturers and installers of electro-mechanical theatre machinery; designers and installers of audio-visual and presentation equipment; TV studio outfitters

The Factary Ltd.
The Coach House, 2 Upper York St, **Bristol** BS2 8QN, United Kingdom
Tel: 44 117-924 0663 Fax: 44 117-944 6262
E-Mail: TheFactary@compuserve.com
managing director Nicola Ramsden; director, Factary Europe Christopher Carnie; research director Robin Jones; marketing director Angela Hepe
Services: research companies, people, foundations and grant-making trusts for fund raisers; Identify sponsors, donors and new board members; fund-raising consultancy;

The Warehouse – Studio II
13 Theed Street, **London** SE1 8ST, United Kingdom
Tel: 44 20-7928 9251 Fax: 44 20-7928 9252
Internet: www.lfo.co.uk
E-Mail: information@lfo.co.uk
contact Elizabeth Szucs
Services: rehearsal and performance space, recording facilities *Comments:* see also Venues

Theatec
Neue Gasse 4, 65812 **Bad Soden**, Germany
Tel: 49 6196-25704/25717
Fax: 49 6196-25719
director Mr Geiss
Services: stage technology – design, engineer and install motorized stage equipment

Theatre Projects Consultants Ltd
3, Apollo Studios, Charlton King's Road,
London NW5 2SW, United Kingdom
Tel: 44 20-7482 4224 Fax: 44 20-7284 0636
E-Mail: post@tpc-lon.com
directors Richard Pilbrow, David Staples, Alan Russell, Jerry Godden, Iain Mackintosh, Anthony Field, Louis Fleming, Mark Strodmer, Marion Daehms

Services: multi-disciplinary team of planners, designers, technical experts in lighting, sound, and stage engineering alongside management consultants. It specialises in all elements of consultancy as related to performance spaces. This includes feasibility studies, stage and auditorium design and guidance in the planning of an entire performing arts facility, as well as expertise in all aspects of theatre technologies, conference and congress facilities, audio visual design, leisure and tourism planning and other special projects *Comments:* additional branches: Conneticut/USA (Tel: +1 203-431 3949, Fax: +1 203-431 4790), Toronto/Canada (Tel: +1 416-515 1502, Fax: +1 416-515 1483), Singapore (Tel: +65 336 4856, Fax: +65 336 4857)

Theatrecraft
Poulton Hall Farm, Poulton Road,
Bebington CH63 9LN, United Kingdom
Tel: 44 151-334 0831 Fax: 44 151-334 0831
contact Mr. S.R. Green
Services: Eltec drama lighting controls, scenery kits, rostra, curtain track, lights for drama and theatre, communications

Thomas et Associés
43-47 av de la Grande Armée,
75782 **Paris** Cedex 16, France
Tel: 33 1-4417 6800 Fax: 33 1-4417 6868
E-Mail: rbulenzi@geloitte.fr
managing directors Jean Bernard Thomas, François Mirikelam
Services: legal services in the artistic domain in general

Ticket.com.Network
PO Box 504, **De Witt** NY 13214,
United States of America
Tel: 1 315-466 4020 Fax: 1 315-471 2715
Internet: www.ticket.com.network
director of marketing Charles Shazking
Services: online ticketing services, event management software

Ticket.com Systems BV
Gedempt Hamerkanaal 25,
1021 KL **Amsterdam**, Netherlands
Tel: 31 20-435 0400 Fax: 31 20-494 5660
sales manager Leendert Rijnsburger

Ticket.com Systems Pty
Suite 901, 92 Pitt Street,
Sydney NSW 2000, Australia
Tel: 61 2-9235 0222 Fax: 61 2-9235 0303
contact Ian English

Ticket Online Software GmbH
Budapester Straße 40, 10787 **Berlin**, Germany
Tel: 49 30-264 907-0
Fax: 49 30-2649 0777
Internet: www.ticktetonline.de
E-Mail: info@ticketonline.de
Geschäftsführer Dr. Klaus Zemke, Wilhelm Mermi
Services: computerised ticketing system, networks, call-centers, vendors, multilingual; distribution in Germany, Switzerland, Austria, Poland and Luxemburg

Ticketmaster
3701 Wilshire Boulevard 7th Floor,
Los Angeles CA 90010, United States of America
Tel: 1 213-381 2000
Fax: 1 213-386 1244/365 3631 (marketing)
Internet: www.ticketmaster.com
director of marketing Alan Richardson
Services: computerized ticket agency; world HQ

Ticketmaster (UK) Ltd
48 Leicester Square, **London** WC2H 7LR,
United Kingdom
Tel: 44 20-7344 4000 Fax: 44 20-7915 0411
Internet: www.ticketmaster.co.uk
managing director Jules Boardman; sales director Nick Blackburn; director of marketing Kate Hampton; director of operations Steve Riley
Services: computerized ticketing service

Tickets.com Systems GmbH
Heinrich-Heine-Platz 9, 10179 **Berlin**, Germany
Tel: 49 30-390 418-0 Fax: 49 30-3904 1866
E-Mail: gmbh@tickets.com
Geschäftsführer Christopher Goodhart
Services: Computergestützte Systeme für Veranstaltungsmanagement, Abonnement – und Kartenvertrieb *Comments:* alternative E-mail: vertrieb@tickets.com

Tickets.com Systems, Inc.
PO Box 959, **Syracuse** NY 13201,
United States of America
Tel: 1 315-479 6663 Fax: 1 315-471 2715
E-Mail: dcollins@tickets.com
contact Karen Goetz; marketing manager Debra Collins
Services: computerized ticketing, marketing, fund development systems; internet and outlet ticketing solutions *Comments:* also office in Costa Mesa: Corporate Office, 555 Anton Blv., 11th & 12th Floor, Costa Mesa, CA 92626, Tel: +1 714-327 5400, Fax: +1 714-327 5410

Tickets.com Systems Ltd
Citygate, 17 Victoria Street, **St Albans** AL1 3JJ,
United Kingdom
Tel: 44 1727-834 303 Fax: 44 1727-859 515
Internet: www.uk.tickets.com
E-Mail: sales@tickets.com
marketing manager Jo Shinner; sales manager Rob Edwards; managing director Christopher Goodhart
Services: provide computerised ticketing/marketing systems for venues through Ticket Wizard and PASS Gold systems; TicketsLive link allows tickets to be sold over the internet *Comments:* alternative Internet: www.ticketslive.com

Tim Foster Architects
1 Purley Place, **London** N1 1QA, United Kingdom
Tel: 44 20-7354 1315 Fax: 44 20-7226 8005
E-Mail: TFA@dial.pipex.com
principal Tim Foster MA, Dip Arch (Cantab) RIBA
Services: architects specialising in the provision of facilities for the performing arts *Comments:* projects include the Tricycle Theatre, the Gate Theatre, the Cliffs Pavilion, the Salisbury Playhouse, Tricycle Cinema and several theatres for schools and colleges

Tim Ronalds Architects
Cairo Studios, 4 Nior Street, **London** N1 7RF,
United Kingdom
Tel: 44 20-7490 7704 Fax: 44 20-7490 1250
E-Mail: tra@cairostudios.demon.co.uk
contact Tim Ronalds MA dipArch RIBA
Services: specialising in arts projects with the capacity to provide comprehensive architectural and arts consultancy from inception to opening

Tim Smith Acoustics
7 Swancombe, Clapton-in-Gordano,
Bristol BS20 7RR, United Kingdom
Tel: 44 1275-848 229
Fax: 44 1275-843 945
contact Dr T J B Smith
Services: consultancy and survey services in building acoustics, environmental noise and vibration, studio and auditorium design etc.

TMB Associates
2102 W. Kenmere Ave, **Burbank** CA 91504,
United States of America
Tel: 1 818-842 9652 Fax: 1 818-842 1064
Internet: www.tmb.com
E-Mail: tmb/info@tmb.com
Chief Executive Officer Colin Waters; President Marshall Bissett; Sales Manager Tommy Stephenson; Technical Sales Manager Warren Mays; Export Sales Manager Jaime Duarte
Services: production lighting, rigging and power distribution equipment *Comments:* 24-hour emergency number: +1 818-829 6116; see also UK office

TMB Associates
The Old Brick Yard, Eastbourne Road,
Brentford TW8 9PG, United Kingdom
Tel: 44 20-8560 9652 Fax: 44 20-8560 1064
Internet: www.tmb.com
E-Mail: tmb/info@tmb.com
operations manager Valerie Walsh; european sales manager Paul Hartley
Services: distributor of portable lighting, electrical, rigging and production equipment; specializing in cabling, connectors, assemblies, fixtures, control, dimming, trussing and complete, integrated systems; production supplies and services for professional customers worldwide *Comments:* see also US office

TNT Express (Austria) Ges. mbH
Industriezentrum NOE/Süd, Straße 7, Objekt 58b,
2355 **Wiener Neudorf**, Austria
Tel: 43 2236-60883
Fax: 43 2236-608 1920
E-Mail: ewald.steiner@tnt.e-mail.com
contact Ewald Steiner, Doris Vymazal, Mr Kilian
Services: transport for the performing industry
Comments: other email: doris.vymazal@tnt.e-mail.com; 2nd office (of 6): Werschweg 20, 8054 Graz/Seiersberg, Tel: +43 316-290 383, Fax: +43 316-2903 3920, Email: marco.niesen@tnt.e-mail.com; see also entries for Germany and the Netherlands

TNT Express Worldwide
Tempelhofer Weg 8, 12099 **Berlin**, Germany
Tel: 49 30-6288 3172/225/224
Fax: 49 30-6288 3297
Internet: www.2.intra.tnt.de
E-Mail: peter.zepezauer@tnt.e-mail.com
contact Peter Zepezauer
Services: transport for the performing industry
Comments: from Germany call 0180-55088 and you get connected with the office near you; see also entries for Austria and the Netherlands; also have offices in Belgium, Denmark, Greece, Italy, Spain and Sweden

TNT Express Worldwide
Bellsingal 51, 1119 NT **Schiphol Ryk**, Netherlands
Tel: 31 31-2047 4400- Fax: 31 31-2047 44400
Services: transport for the performing industry
Comments: other offices in Duiven: Effect 9, 6921 RG Duiven, Tel: +31 26-319 1650, Fax: +31 26-319 2650; Eindhoven: De Schakel 14, 5657 EA Eindhoven, Tel: +31 40-297 6681, Fax: +31 40-297 6778; Rotterdam: Corkstraat 32, 3047 AC Rotterdam, Tel: +31 10-208 0830, Fax: +31 10-462 3241; see also entries for Germany and Austria

Tods Murray WS
66 Queen Street, **Edinburgh (Scotland)** EH2 4NE,
United Kingdom
Tel: 44 131-226 4771 Fax: 44 131-624 7170
E-Mail: richard.findlay@todsmurray.co.uk
entertainment law partner Richard Findlay; lawyer David Smith
Services: general arts and entertainment law; provides legal services to arts and entertainment organisations including theatre companies, film & television production companies, entertainment organisations, event managers and festivals

Tom Petzal and Associates
Pantiles Chambers, 85 High Street,
Tunbridge Wells TN1 1YG, United Kingdom
Tel: 44 1892-506 900 (switchboard)/968 (direct)
Fax: 44 1892-547 120
E-Mail: pantilesbc@compuserve.com
contact Tom Petzal
Services: consultants in arts, sports and charities

TOP TENTS Zeitverleih Schifke-Tewes
Buschstraße 33,
45739 **Oer-Erkenschwick**, Germany
Tel: 49 2368-54435 Fax: 49 2368-58973
Internet: www.schifke-tewes.de
E-Mail: schifke.tewes@cityweb.de
owner Christiane Tewes
Services: event tents, gala tents, theatre tents, modern and classical circus tents, additional equipments and full service

TOR Systems Ltd
58 Longton Road, Trentham, **Stoke on Trent** ST4 8YZ,
United Kingdom
Tel: 44 1782-644 755 Fax: 44 1782-644 346
Internet: www.torsystems.co.uk
E-Mail: tor@torsystems.co.uk
managing director John Jordan; marketing director Ian Perry
Services: high-speed admissions ticketing systems; Windows NT advance booking systems; TOR Q-Cheetah 4-way bar code reader; turnstiles and access gates

Tour Resources International, Inc
931 South Florida Avenue, **Lakeland** FL 33803,
United States of America
Tel: 1 941-687 9669 Fax: 1 941-682 6604
E-Mail: touresourc@aol.com
president/director Richard Munoz; director Debra Munoz
Services: organise worldwide tours for orchestras and other performing arts groups

TP Sound Services
100 Centennial Park, **Elstree** WD6 3SA, United Kingdom
Tel: 44 870-162 1010 Fax: 44 870-162 1020
E-Mail: lnegrotti@tpser.com
managing director Richard Rogers; production director David Perry; hire desk Lisa Negrotti
Services: sound system design and rental for applications ranging from West End theatrical productions to corporate meetings

Trans Euro Specialised Movements
Drury Way, Brent Park, **London** NW10 0JN,
United Kingdom
Tel: 44 20-8451 5633 Fax: 44 20-8459 7121
Internet: www.transeuro.com
E-Mail: rachel.james@transeuro.com
managing director Paul Evans; sales and logistics manager Paul Bates; day-to-day operations Mike Smith
Services: UK and European road freight to the show and event industries; includes airfreight, seafreight, casemaking and storage; also export packing and forwarding services for household goods, antiques and fine arts and exhibitions, customs brokerage

Transtechnik GmbH
Ohm 1-3, 83607 **Holzkirchen**, Germany
Tel: 49 8024-9900 Fax: 49 8024-990 300
Internet: www.transtechnik.com
E-Mail: info@transtec
marketing Rose Marx, Regine Kreidl
Services: supplies professional lighting systems for theatres, opera houses and TV studios

Traum & Raum
Gasteiner Straße 9, 10717 **Berlin**, Germany
Tel: 49 30-8640 9118 Fax: 49 30-8640 9120
E-Mail: traumuraum@aol.com
directors Karin Kerner, Hille Jan Breiteneicher
Services: complete prepress and publication of theatre, film and music books, leaflets, magazines, programmes and listings publications; organise PR for festivals

Travel Art International
PO Box 9050, 1022 **Copenhagen** K, Denmark
Tel: 45 3313 3770 Fax: 45 3313 3708
Internet: www.travelart.dk
E-Mail: travelart@rejser.dk
director Lone Ricks
Services: travel agency, dealing solely with organising concert tours for orchestras and choirs, also look after the individual artist *Comments:* visiting address: Dr. Tvaergade 57, 1022 Copehagen K

Triple E Ltd
Unit 5, Hyson Industrial Estate, Hyson Road, **London** SE16 3PA, United Kingdom
Tel: 44 20-7237 6354 Fax: 44 20-7237 7650
Internet: www.tabtrack.com
E-Mail: info@tabtrack.com
managing director David Edelstein
Services: manufacturer of wide range of curtains and scenery tracks, automation and hardware for stage and studios

TRIPPE:Beratung/Gesellschaft für betriebswirtschaftliche Strategien und Lösungen
Rennebergstr. 1, 50939 **Köln**, Germany
Tel: 49 221-942 0450 Fax: 49 221-9420 4580
Internet: www.trippeberatung.de
E-Mail: mailbox@trippeberatung.de
consultant Hans Trippe
Services: consultant for box office management, software developers

TSE AG
Invalidenstr. 50-51, 10557 **Berlin**, Germany
Tel: 49 30-390 610 Fax: 49 30-3906 1199
technical equipment & financial Michael Sterw; marketing Peter Weinert; personnel & projects Christoph von Sauberzweig
Services: provision of sound systems for concerts and events

Tungate Group
Brookhouse Way, Cheadle, **Stoke on Trent** ST10 1SR, United Kingdom
Tel: 44 1538-755 755 Fax: 44 1538-756 062
Internet: www.tungategroup.co.uk
E-Mail: tungateforms@webfactory.co.uk
managing director Harvey Ball; chairman Ray Tungate; sales manager – tickets Mike Waller
Services: thermal, non-thermal and computer roll-tickets for theatres and stadiums hroughout the UK and into Europe

Universe Lighting
242 West 27th Street, **New York** NY 10001, United States of America
Tel: 1 212-255 4455 Fax: 1 212-255 5999
Internet: www.universelighting.com
E-Mail: scottthurm@aol.com
president Scott Thurm; export & sales manager Carolyn Long; lighting designer Matthew Tirschwell
Services: supplies theatrical lighting equipment worldwide, architectural lighting design services

Unusual Rigging Ltd
The Wharf, **Bugbrooke** NN7 3QD, United Kingdom
Tel: 44 1604-830 083 Fax: 44 1604-831 144
Internet: www.unusual.co.uk
E-Mail: services@unusual.com
contact Alan Jacobi, Robin Elias
Services: supply of permanent and temporary lifting or tracking systems, automated control, rigging hardware, and specialised engineering fabrication and installation, service and testing work

Urban Cultures Limited
37b New Cavendish Street, **London** W1M 8JR, United Kingdom
Tel: 44 707-122 6573
E-Mail: adc18@dial.pipex.com
managing director John Montgomery
Services: specialise in urban cultural planning, economic development, the cultural industries, town planning & urban design

Valerie Barber PR
Suite 300, Mappin House, 4 Winsley Street, **London** W1N 7AR, United Kingdom
Tel: 44 20-7436 1115/6 Fax: 44 20-7436 5090
E-Mail: VBPR@compuserve.com
contact Valerie Barber, Nicky Tomas, Emy MacLaren
Services: public relations consultancy specialising in UK and European media coverage (including jazz & world music)

Van der Kroft c.s.
Jan Luykenstraat 16, 1017 CN **Amsterdam**, Netherlands
Tel: 31 20-670 6060 Fax: 31 20-670 6061
E-Mail: lawyers@vanderkroft.nl
lawyers R. P. J. Ribbert, M. Leopold, Th. J. Bousie, M. E. Van Praag Sigaar, H. J. Bolte, R. Van Dongen; office manager Dr. M. B. Bousie
Services: entertainments lawyer

Van Dishoeck & Jongbloed
Keizersgracht 616, 1017 ER **Amsterdam**, Netherlands
Tel: 31 20-627 2611 Fax: 31 20-620 5825
E-Mail: vdj@worldonline.nl
partners Pieter Jongbloed, Dania van Dishoeck
Services: fund-raising, sponsorship consulting, marketing and PR

Van Dooren Marketing, Communicatie, Sponsoring
Prinz Hendrikkade 135, 1011 AR **Amsterdam**, Netherlands
Tel: 31 20-530 4030 Fax: 31 20-530 4035
E-Mail: doorenbv@euronet.nl
senior personnel Job R.Q. van Dooren
Services: sponsorship consultants

Vari-Lite Production Services
20-22 Fairway Drive, **Greenford** UB6 8PW, United Kingdom
Tel: 44 20-8575 6666
Fax: 44 20-8575 0424
Internet: www.vlps.com
E-Mail: info@london.vlps.com
general manager David March; director sales & marketing Edward Pagett
Services: lighting rental and production company providing equipment and services to the concert touring, trade show, theatre, corporate, television and events market; Vari-Lite automated lighting system, conventional lighting, rigging and support equipment are backed by the most experienced programmers, operators and technicans

Verlagsgruppe Hermann
Goldschmiedgasse 10/3, 1010 **Wien**, Austria
Tel: 43 1-534 6220/6240/6230
Fax: 43 1-534 6267
contact Alexander Hermann
Services: music publisher specialising in Austrian and contemporary music (Strauss Edition Wien, Edition Contemp Arts and Wiener Notensatz, part of Verlagsgruppe Hermann)

Victor Mara Limited
1/7 Newport Street, **London** SE11 6AJ, United Kingdom
Tel: 44 20-7735 1518 Fax: 44 20-7735 9163
E-Mail: info@vgroup.co.uk
general manager Mark Cosgrove; director of production Iain Gillie
Services: scenic painting and building for stage and television and events

Video-Communication France – VCF
48 quai Carnot, 92210 **Saint Cloud**, France
Tel: 33 1-4112 1212 Fax: 33 1-4112 1200
président Pascal Farcouli
Services: video services company; audio-visual production

Virtual Reality
47 West Hill, **Hitchin** SG5 2HY, United Kingdom
Tel: 44 1462-620 653
Internet: www.mhmvr.co.uk
Services: VR photography, VR projects software creates easily updated pr, bid presentations, CDs, kiosks, websites

Vmkar Production
U malého lesa 10, 591 01 **Zdár nad Sázavou**, Czech Republic
Tel: 420 616-21741 Fax: 420 616-21745
contact Ing Gregorowicz
Services: theatre technology, lighting, transport of sets and decor

VSW Expeditie bv
Transportcentrum 19, PO Box 1333, 7500 BH **Enschede**, Netherlands
Tel: 31 53-432 0220 Fax: 31 53-430 6961
E-Mail: vsw.expeditie@wss.nl
contact Willem van der Struik
Services: operating over 30 special equipped trucks/air suspension/double and triple loading decks/tail lifts/internal hydraulic systems/temperature controlled/up to 105 cubic meters; offering customs facilities such as ATA/TIR Carnet for West and Eastern European concert tours; concert piano handling all over Europe; warehousing in humidity controlled facilities (over 3000 sq. m.)

W Beyne & ZN.BV
PO Box 76, 1400 AB **Bussum**, Netherlands
Tel: 31 35-693 8692 Fax: 31 35-693 8755
E-Mail: beyne@worldonline.nl
contact Rene Beyne
Services: manufacturer and distributor of stage curtains and draperies; supplier of all theatre textiles

Waagner-Biro Binder AG
Stadlauer Str. 54, Postfach 11, 1221 **Wien**, Austria
Tel: 43 1-28844-0 Fax: 43 1-2884 4333
Bereichsleiter Ing. Albert Rainer Haselböck (head of department)

Walton & Parkinson Limited Insurance Brokers
20 St Dunstan's Hill, **London** EC3R 8PP, United Kingdom
Tel: 44 20-7929 4747
Fax: 44 20-7929 4884
E-Mail: gb8bfh3j@ibmmail.com
managing director Richard K. Walton; director Clifford I. Parkinson; manager Emma Chant
Services: Specialist insurance brokers to theatre owners, producers and suppliers with competitive schemes for all aspects of theatre, including non-appearance, cancellation and other contingency risks, hazardous work and theatrical productions themselves

Werning Theatertechnik Theaterbedarf GmbH
Lise-Meitner-Strasse 30, 45659 **Recklinghausen**, Germany
Tel: 49 2361-9213-0 Fax: 49 2361-9213-15
E-Mail: wtt@werning.de
Geschäftsführer Andrea Werning
Services: sales of a wide range of equipment used in theatres eg. lighting, fabrics, wood

White Light (Electrics) Ltd
57 Filmer Rd, **London** SW6 7JF, United Kingdom
Tel: 44 20-7731 3291
Fax: 44 20-7371 0806
Internet: www.whitelight.ltd.uk
E-Mail: 100637.3040@compuserve.com
general manager Bryan Raven; hire manager Mike Crossman; projects manager, architectural division Paul Simson
Services: hire and sales of lighting equipment throughout Europe; also manufacturers of VSFX, the moving effects projection system

Whitfield Partners – Architects
30 Warner Street, **London** EC1R 5EX, United Kingdom
Tel: 44 20-7837 4040 Fax: 44 20-7837 8385
partners Sir William Whitfield, Andrew Lockwood, David Walsh
Services: architects

Wigmore Hall – Rehearsal Rooms
36 Wigmore Street, **London** W1H 0BP, United Kingdom
Tel: 44 20-7486 1907 Fax: 44 20-7224 3800
Internet: www.wigmorehall.org.uk
E-Mail: info@wigmorehall.org.uk
general administrator Marion Friend
Services: rehearsal room for hire between 10.00 am to 6.00 pm Monday to Friday *Comments:* discounts are offered to students, Westminster ResCard holders, senior citizens and the unemployed; see also Venues

Wilson & Co (UK) Ltd
Unit 5/6, Parkway Trading Estate, Cranford Lane, **Hounslow** TW5 9QA, United Kingdom
Tel: 44 20-8814 7000 Fax: 44 20-8814 7077
special projects manager Martin Hayes
Services: a complete worldwide service for passengers and cargo, Wilson & Co have had over thirty years experience in the logistics of overseas tours for theatrical companies, rock and roll bands, symphony orchestras and ballet companies; complete budgets supplied prior to tour

WM – Data
Hermodsveg 22, 8239 **Abyhoj**, Denmark
Tel: 45 8744 4444 Fax: 45 8744 4487
Internet: www.wmdata.dk
E-Mail: humad@wmdata.com
chief consultant Torben Iversen
Services: computerized ticket and booking system and event management system

Wölbitsch & Partner KG
Am Sueablick 4C, 96129 **Leesten**, Germany
Tel: 49 9505-803 434
Fax: 49 9505-803 436
E-Mail: woelbitsch@t-online.de
Geschäftsführer Hubert Wölbitsch
Services: OPAS- orchestra planning and administration system *Comments:* users include Royal Concertgebouw Orchestra, Münchner Philharmoniker, Wiener Philharmoniker, MCO Hilversum, L.A. Philharmonic

XU – acoustique
53 Boulevard St. Martin, 75003 **Paris**, France
Tel: 33 1-4271 5838 Fax: 33 1-4271 7578
E-Mail: xuaam@worldonline.fr
acoustic consultant (freelance) Albert Yaying Xu
Services: acoustic research and design for performing art facilities (architectural acoustics)

Ylva French Communications
Grosvenor Gardens House, 35-37 Grosvenor Gardens, **London** SW1W 0BX, United Kingdom
Tel: 44 20-7233 6789 Fax: 44 20-7233 6770
Internet: www.ylvafrench.co.uk
E-Mail: ylva@ylvafrench.co.uk
director Ylva French
Services: public relations, marketing strategy planning and implementation

Index of Editorial Entries

Index
The index of editorial entries will enable you to:
• identify on which page an entry for an organisation appears (eg. Gmundner Festspiele, Gmunden, p. 2237).
When the organisation name is that of an individual (eg. J X Rylta, Frank Smith) the ordering is done by christian name (J X...., Frank).
When the organisation name is, for example, Künstlersekretariat Frank Smith, the indexing is done on the first word (Künstlersekretariat).

Index
Der Index ermöglicht:
• das schnelle Auffinden von Informationen über eine bestimmte Organisation, (z.B. Gmundner Festspiele, Gmunden, p.237).
Wo Organisationen den Namen eines Individuums tragen (z.B. J X Rylta, Frank Smith), werden sie nach dem Vornamen geordnet (J X..., Frank). Wo Organisationen z.B. Künstlersekretariat Frank Smith heißen, sind sie nach dem ersten Wort des Titels alphabetisch geordnet (K...).

Indice
El índice de información editorial le permitirá a Vd identificar las páginas en donde aparece:
• información para una organización (por ejemplo Gmundner Festspiele, Gmunden, p.237).
Cuando el nombre de la compañía es un nombre propio (por ejemplo J X Rylta, Frank Smith), se ha ordenado por el nombre cristiano (J X..., Frank). Cuando el nombre de la organización es, por ejemplo Künstlersekretariat Frank Smith, es clasificada bajo la primera palabra (K...).

L'Index.
L'Index des parutions vous permettra de:
• Retrouver les pages ou se trouvent les renseignements concernant chaque organisme (eg Gmundner Festspiele, Gmunden, p.237).
Dans le cas ou le nom de l'organisation est ce d'un individu (par exemple J X Rylta, Frank Smith), nous avons commencé avec le prénom (J X..., Frank). Dans le cas ou un organisation se nomme par exemple 'Kunstlersekretariat Frank Smith', nous avons commencé avec le premier mot (K...).

Indice
L'indice delle entrate editoriali vi permetterá di:
• trovare a quale pagina appare l'entrata di una organizzazione (es Gmundner Festspiele, Gmunden, p. 237)
Quando l'organizzazione prende il nome dal titolare (es JX Rylta, Frank Smith) viene inserita alfabeticamente a seconda del nome di battesimo (JX..., Frank Smith). Dove il nome dell'organizzazione é Kunstlersekretariat Frank Smith si elenca seguendo l'iniziale della prima parola (K...).

색인
편집 명단 색인을 이용하면:
* 찾는 조직이 몇 페이지에 기재되어 있는지 알 수 있다 (즉, Gmundner Festspiele, Gmunden, p. 2237).

조직명칭이 개인의 이름일 경우는 (예: J X Rylta, Frank Smith), 이름 (christian name: J X...., Frank)에 따른 순서로 기재되었다. 조직명칭이 예를 들어 "Künstlersekretariat Frank Smith"일 경우는, 첫 단어에 (Künstlersekretariat) 따른 순서로 기재되었다.

索引
编辑条目的索引将使你能够：

● 找到某一机构的条目在哪页出现（例如：Gmunder Festspiele, Gmunden, p. 2237）。

如机构名称为一个人的名字时（例如：J X Rylta, Frank Smith），则顺序按名排列(J X..., Frank）。如果机构名称为Künstlersekretariat Frank Smith等，则索引按第一个字编排(Künstlersekretariat）。

索引
索引を使用することによって：
* エントリー団体、組織に関する情報が掲載されたページが分かります（例：Gmundner Festspiele、Gmunden p.2237）

団体名が個人名である場合（例：J X Rylta、Frank Smith）、姓ではなく名（J X...、Frank ）で引いて下さい。団体名がKünstlersekretariat Frank Smithといった場合は最初の単語（Künstlersekretariat ）で引いて下さい。

Index of Editorial Entries

B

C

E

F

G

H

I

L

O

P

Q

R

S

T

U

V

W

X

Y

Z

Index of Advertisers by Category

ASSOCIATIONS and ORGANISATIONS

ATTRACTIONS

BALLET – see DANCE COMPANIES, DANCERS, MIMES and PRODUCTIONS main heading

BRASS BANDS – see ORCHESTRAS and BANDS main heading

BUSINESS and PROFESSIONAL COMPANIES, SERVICES and SUPPLIERS

COSTUME and SET DESIGNERS – see DESIGNERS main heading

DANCE COMPANIES, DANCERS, MIMES and PRODUCTIONS

DESIGNERS

DIRECTORS and PRODUCERS

DUOS

Cello and piano

Flute and piano (harp)

Two pianos/piano duets

Violin and piano

Miscellaneous

EARLY MUSIC

Orchestra, opera, ensembles, dance and productions

Soloists

EDUCATION

Conservatories

Colleges of Further and Higher Education

Educational Concerts

Other Advanced training

Residential schools and courses

Universities

ENSEMBLES and GROUPS

Ensembles

Quintets

Quartets

Trios

Contemporary Music

Early Music – see EARLY MUSIC main heading

Folk – see Folk main heading

Jazz – see JAZZ main heading

Vocal

Vocal and instrumental

FACILITIES – see VENUES and PROMOTING BODIES

FESTIVALS

FILM ACCOMPANIMENTS

FOLK

Groups ....

FOLK DANCE – and see DANCE main heading

INSTRUMENT MAKERS & SUPPLIERS

INSTRUMENTALISTS

Accompanists and Continuo

Bassoonists

Cellists

Clarinettists

Double bassists

Flute players

Fortepiano

Guitar and lute

Other instruments

JAZZ, GOSPEL and BLUES

LECTURES, MASTERCLASSES and LECTURERS

LIGHT ENTERTAINMENT – see ATTRACTIONS main heading

MASTERCLASSES – see LECTURES main heading

MIME (and see DANCE COMPANIES, DANCERS, MIMES and PRODUCTIONS main heading)

MUSIC DIRECTORS – see CONDUCTORS and MUSIC DIRECTORS main heading

MUSICALS

NARRATORS

OPERA, MUSIC-THEATRE, CHAMBER OPERA COMPANIES, COACHES and PRODUCTIONS

OPERA PRODUCERS see DIRECTORS and PRODUCERS main heading

ORCHESTRAS and BANDS

Chamber and string orchestras

Light orchestras and bands

Symphony orchestras

Youth orchestras

Brass bands and wind orchestras

POPULAR SONGWRITERS and SINGERS and PERFORMERS

PRODUCERS – see DIRECTORS and PRODUCERS main heading

PUBLICATIONS

PUBLIC RELATIONS

PUBLISHERS

Books, magazines and newspapers

Sheet music

Others

RADIO & TV

RECORDED MEDIA, PRODUCERS and PRODUCTIONS

SINGERS

Sopranos ....

Mezzo-sopranos and contraltos

Boy Sopranos, counter-tenors, falsettists, male altos, and male sopranos

Tenors

Baritones, bass-baritones and basses

Others (Musical, Chanson etc)

SPECIAL EVENTS

SPONSORS & PATRONS OF THE ARTS

STAGE DIRECTORS – see DIRECTORS and PRODUCERS main heading

THEATRE and THEATRE PRODUCTIONS (and see ATTRACTIONS main heading)

TRADE SHOWS

VENUES and PROMOTING BODIES

VIDEO PRODUCTIONS (see RECORDED MEDIA main heading)

VOCAL MASTERCLASSES – see LECTURES main heading

WORLD MUSIC

Alphabetical Index of Advertisers

D

E

F

G

H

I

M

N

O

S

Customer Service Page

Dear colleague

All the staff here at Arts Publishing International are continually working to ensure that the PAYE is the most valuable and easy-to-use reference book for the European performing arts market. With your individual requirements you are in the best position to tell us if the PAYE meets your needs. We would therefore be most grateful if you could send us your suggestions and comments on the book.

As well as your suggestions we would appreciate your help in keeping our records as accurate as possible. Please use this page to request information, amend your editorial entry for the next edition or send us new editorial entries. Please direct your mail to: **Editorial Department, Arts Publishing International Ltd., Lime Wharf, Vyner Street, London E2 9DJ, England** or contact us by telephone **(+44) 20 8709 9050**, by fax **(+44) 20 8709 9080** or by e-mail on **paye@api.co.uk**

Amendments

1 Amendments to existing entries in the Performing Arts Yearbook for Europe 2000

Please note: You will receive our formal entry correction letter to update your entry for the PAYE 2001 in May 2000. This space should be used if your information changes after you have returned our request for correct information next May.

Section (eg opera, dance, services and suppliers)

Original company name

New company name (if applicable)

New address

New telephone numbers

New fax numbers

New e-mail address/web site

Changes to personnel

Comments

New Entries

2 New entries for Performing Arts Yearbook for Europe 2001

Please note: All entries are free of charge, but are included at the Editor's discretion

Section

Company name

Address

Telephone numbers

Fax numbers

E-mail address/web site

Personnel

Comments

Mailing

3 Please complete the following section if you want information on our other publications, conferences or special events*

Organisation

Name

Job Title

Address

Tel Fax

E-mail

- The information you have provided may be stored and used under the provisions of the Data Protection Act. If you prefer not to receive mail from third parties please tick this box ☐